# NON–LEAGUE CLUB DIRECTORY 2014

### (36th Edition)

## EDITORS
## MIKE WILLIAMS & TONY WILLIAMS

# NON-LEAGUE CLUB DIRECTORY 2014
## ISBN 978-1-869833-72-5

Editors
Mike Williams
(Tel: 01548 531 339)
tw.publications@btinternet.com)
Tony Williams
(Tel: 01823 490 684)
Email: t.williams320@btinternet.com

Published by Tony Williams Publications Ltd
(Tel: 01548 531 339)
Email: tw.publications@btinternet.com

Printed by Polestar Wheatons (Exeter, Devon)

Sales & Distribution
T.W. Publications (01548 531 339)

Front Cover: Guernsey's Dave Rihoy sets himself to cross the ball whilst Whyteleafe's Louis Clark
prepares to block his effort during this FA Vase tie.
Photo: Keith Clayton.

# foreword....

I am delighted to write this foreword for The Non League Club Directory which is a true tour de force and has rightly become the Bible of the grass roots game.

As editor in chief of The Non-League Paper I am particularly pleased to be able to praise Tony Williams and his son Michael for their Herculean efforts in producing this impressive yearbook.

Had it not been for Tony's infectious enthusiasm some 15 years ago, there would be no NLP.

Back then I was the launch editor of Sport First, Britain's first all-sport Sunday newspaper. Tony came to see me and suggested, no insisted, that the newspaper should have a dedicated section for Non-League football.

I obliged and when I left some 18 months later I did so with the realisation that Non-League had a huge following who were catered for only by Tony's own impressive monthly Teamtalk magazine.

So, with Tony's considerable help, I launched The Non-League Paper and 13 years, and some 700 editions, later we're still going strong thanks to the kind of enthusiasts who buy this fine book.

I hope you all have as much fun and satisfaction from your Non-League season as I know Tony will...and much deserved.

David Emery
Editor in chief, The Non-League Paper

# SOCCER BOOKS LIMITED
## 72 ST. PETERS AVENUE (Dept. NLD)
## CLEETHORPES
## N.E. LINCOLNSHIRE
## DN35 8HU
## ENGLAND
### Tel. 01472 696226   Fax 01472 698546
Web site   www.soccer-books.co.uk
e-mail   info@soccer-books.co.uk

Established in 1982, Soccer Books Limited has one of the largest ranges of English-Language soccer books available. We continue to expand our stocks even further to include many more titles including German, French, Spanish and Italian-language books.

With well over 200,000 satisfied customers over the past 30 years, we supply books to virtually every country in the world but have maintained the friendliness and accessibility associated with a small family-run business. The range of titles we sell includes:

YEARBOOKS – All major yearbooks including editions of the Sky Sports Football Yearbook (previously Rothmans), Supporters' Guides, South American Yearbooks, North & Central American Yearbooks, Asian Football Yearbooks, Yearbooks of African Football, Non-League Club Directories, Almanack of World Football.

CLUB HISTORIES – Complete Statistical Records, Official Histories, Definitive Histories plus many more including photographic books.

WORLD FOOTBALL – World Cup books,  European Championships History, Statistical histories for the World Cup, European Championships, South American and European Club Cup competitions and foreign-language Season Preview Magazines for dozens of countries.

BIOGRAPHIES & WHO'S WHOS – of Managers and Players plus Who's Whos etc.

ENCYCLOPEDIAS & GENERAL TITLES – Books on Stadia, Hooligan and Sociological studies, Histories and hundreds of others, including the weird and wonderful!

DVDs – Season reviews for British clubs, histories, European Cup competition finals, World Cup matches and series reviews, player profiles and a selection of almost 60 F.A. Cup Finals with many more titles becoming available all the time.

For a printed listing showing a selection of our titles, contact us using the information at the top of this page. Alternatively, our web site offers a secure ordering system for credit and debit card holders and Paypal users and lists our full range of 2,000 new books and 400 DVDs.

# CONTENTS

# THE EDITORS

**TONY WILLIAMS**
**Editor**

Educated at Malvern College, one of the country's best football schools in the late sixties, he represented England Under 18 against Scotland at Celtic Park before serving as an administrative officer in the Royal Air Force for five years.

He was on Reading's books from the age of 16 to 22, but also represented F.A. Amateur XI's and the R.A.F. while playing mainly in the old Isthmian League for Corinthian Casuals, Dulwich Hamlet and Kingstonian and joining Hereford United and Grantham during R.A.F. postings.

After taking an F.A. Coaching badge he coached at Harrow Borough, Epsom & Ewell and Hungerford Town and was asked to edit Jimmy Hill's Football Weekly after initial experience with the Amateur Footballer. Monthly Soccer and Sportsweek followed before he had the idea for a football Wisden and was helped by The Bagnall Harvey Agency to find a suitable generous sponsor in Rothmans.

After launching the Rothmans Football Yearbook in 1970 as its founder and co-compiler with Roy Peskett, he was asked to join Rothmans (although a non-smoker!) in the company's public relations department and was soon able to persuade the Marketing Director that Rothmans should become the first ever sponsor of a football league.

After a season's trial sponsoring the Hellenic and Isthmian Leagues, it was decided to go national with the Northern and Western Leagues and for four years he looked after the football department at Rothmans, with Jimmy Hill and Doug Insole presenting a brilliant sponsorship package which amongst many other innovations included three points for a win and goal difference.

So Non-League football led the way with league sponsorship and two, now well accepted, innovations.

Sportsmanship and goals were also rewarded in a sponsorship that proved a great success for football and for Rothmans. Indeed the sportsmanship incentives could be of great value to-day in the Football Association's bid to improve the game's image by ridding the game of dissent and cheating.

After the cigarette company pulled out of their sports sponsorship Tony produced the first Non-League Annual and later The Football League Club Directory, launching 'Non-League Football' magazine with "The Mail on Sunday" and then "Team Talk."

After his ten years with Hungerford Town, he moved West and served Yeovil Town as a Director for seven years but was thrilled when David Emery's plans for the exciting Non-League Media emerged and came into reality, thus giving the grass roots of the game the publicity and promotion that he and his team had been attempting to set up since the Annual (now Directory) was launched in 1978.

The aim of the company has always been to promote the non-league 'family,' its spirit and its general development. So a plaque from The Football Association inscribed 'To Tony Williams for his continued promotion of all that's good in football' was greatly appreciated as was the trophy to commemorate the thirtieth edition of the Directory and the recent GLS "Lifetime Award' for promoting non-league football.

## MIKE WILLIAMS
### Editorial Manager

What started out as a holiday job in 1988 helping put together (literally in those days) the Non-League Club Directory and League Club Directory, in the end forged a career which saw him work for Coventry City Football Club, e-comsport in London and finally return to TW Publications in 2003.

During his eight year spell with TW Publications he learned the ropes of all aspects of publishing culminating in the roll of production manager for the Non-League Club Directory, Team Talk Magazine, the League Club Directory and many more publications published by the company.

1995 saw the opportunity to take up the post of Publications Manager at Coventry City Football Club, and the transfer was made in the April of that year. Sky Blue Publications was formed and the League Club Directory became their leading title. Re-branded as the Ultimate Football Guide he was to deal with all aspects of the book, from design to sales and was also put on a steep learning curve into the world of Premiership programme production. The three years spent at the Midland's club gave him a great insight into all departments of a Premiership club, having produced publications for them all.

Leaving Coventry City F.C. in 1998, and after a spell working on a world wide football player database for e-comsport in London, he returned to the West Country in 2001 to set up his own design/publishing company, which incorporated working on the Directory again. 2009 saw the full time switch to TW Publications and the responsibilities of publishing the Directory.

Having gone to a rugby school his football playing career was delayed. However, becoming the youngest player to have played for the First XV and representing Torbay Athletics club at 100 and 200m proved his sporting pedigree. At the age of 20 he begun his football career which, at it's height, saw him playing for Chard Town in the Western League Premier Division.

Now enjoying his time helping run local side Loddiswell Athletic in the South Devon League, with the odd appearance here and there for their Reserve team (when needed), he relishes the challenge of maintaining the club's status as the top club in the South Hams area.

# ACKNOWLEDGMENTS

Well, that was different!

If you've purchased this book very close to this year's publication date, you'll be reading it almost a month earlier than ever before (two months if you remember when the Directory came out in October!) Having listened to you, our readers, the common request was 'Could you bring the book out earlier'.

This year's book may not include many 2013-14 squad photos but it is out as close to the new season's kick-off as possible. Which I hope will help make sense of the new league constitutions a lot sooner than in the past.

The new deadline put the production into uncharted territory as never before have I asked leagues and clubs for assistance so early. I should not have worried, as yet again help was on hand.

There are so many people I'd like to thank personally and most are listed below, but if your name is not there, please don't think your assistance wasn't appreciated, it very much was, it's just at this stage of the production process my mind is a little frazzled!

## 'OUR TEAM' OF PHOTOGRAPHERS

Peter Barnes, Graham Brown, Keith Clayton, Alan Coomes, Jonathan Holloway, 'Uncle Eric' Marsh, Roger Turner, Bill Wheatcroft and Gordon Whittington.

Despite the terrible weather up and down the country 'our' band of photographers managed to capture action from the Conference to local football.

## FA COMPETITIONS DEPARTMENT

Steve Clark, Chris Darnell and Scott Bolton

## CONTRIBUTORS

Alan Allcock. Alan Beecham. Alan Constable. Anthony Golightly. Bryan Freeman. Cyril Windiate. Gary Johnson. Harvey Ackerman. James Baylis. John Gorman. Kellie Disapline. Ken Green. Louise Edwards. Mark Senior. Matthew Panting. Neil Juggins. Philip Gurr. Robert Smale. Robin Flight. Ron Holpin.

Arthur Evans (Photographer & reports).
Dr. Andrew Sarnecki (Pecking Order). James Wright.
Richard Rundle (Football Club History Database).
Mike Simmonds (Schools).

And as always, not forgetting Dad - he still thinks this modern technology is a miracle (daily!) but his support and enthusiasm for the non-League game is second to none.
The huge task of publishing this book each year could not be done without him.

Thank you

*Mike Williams*

# 'TIMES ARE CHANGING'

Thirty six years ago, with the encouragement of Football Association Secretary Ted Croker, we compiled our first Non-League Football Annual. Mr Croker was an ex League and non-League footballer himself. He really loved the game and appreciated his position at the headquarters of our national sport. He was also particularly keen that the non-league levels of the game should have an annual of their own. It was a privilege to work closely with those at Lancaster Gate, the FA's headquarters, where everyone seemed so proud to be part of the team looking after the game they loved so much.

It hasn't been difficult to promote all that we feel is good about the massive non-league world which, after all, is about 95% of football in this country. We have enjoyed producing the books and the magazines which hopefully have helped the image of semi-professional and amateur football.

There is no doubt that the popularity of the game, especially on world television, has brought massive amounts of money into football and the priorities of national associations, leagues, clubs, players and even supporters, have been turned upside down.

We appreciate the introduction of wonderful technology has reduced the attraction of the annual publication, so we are planning to develop our website to give the true non-league supporter a constant up dating of the information that we will also eventually present for you in the format of The Yearbook after the end of the season.

To help our Website to provide a unique coverage of the game outside The Football league, we have included all 270 clubs who play in the top twelve divisions below The Football League Division Two, plus regular additional clubs from steps 5 and 6, that bring the total to well over 300.

These clubs also have a year by year history featuring the senior leagues in which they have competed since our book was first published in 1977. To illustrate these records we have included over 3,000 team pictures, which bring back many memories for players and supporters alike.

Having been involved with a varied selection of publications at all levels of non-league football, we have a massive supply of information, photographs and statistics with which we hope to present you within a 'Modern History of Non-League Football'.

We have started with a review of the decades after the Second World War and then, when we reach the seventies and the launch of our first little yearbook, we will give an in depth review of every season featuring leagues, cups, representative matches, publications and the games characters.

# 'DISTURBING SURVEY'

A recent survey published in the national press, came to the conclusion that numbers involved in all sports throughout England had dropped since The Olympic Games, with Association Football being the sport which had been hit by the biggest percentage drop.

At the top level, the massive television coverage and the increased cost of tickets and travel must discourage many fans, while at our level in non-league football important facets of the game have changed.

Less local players play for senior non-league clubs these days. Supporters no longer have many local lads to watch and get to know socially after the games, when the majority of players need to travel longer distances home and need to avoid socialising as there could be drink and drive problems.

Just as the old dressing room team spirit is difficult to develop in the senior clubs, as highly paid overseas players at the top level probably do not all speak the same language or have the same sense of humour, traditions are also changing at non-league levels.

Growing up within a well run local football club, youngsters could learn to win gracefully and lose bravely, be able to give and accept the 'mickey taking' in the right spirit, accept criticism and learn the real meaning of team spirit and loyalty.

The massive financial rewards have changed the attitude of top players and indeed their supporters, who have very little patience with their team who are being paid hundreds of thousands pounds a week. So it can be understood if non-league supporters sometimes doubt the dedication and loyalty of their well paid stars, travelling to play for a club for which they, the local supporters, have been attached for years. The fun, the spirit, the loyalty and excitement that one grows up with when playing or watching 'your club' is very special and can help greatly in the character building of youngsters. I'm sure thousands of us have built our love of the game on these principles.

I'm also sure that many clubs still do enjoy a wonderful club spirit where players, committee men and supporters all live for their match days, comradeship and exciting results. Sadly the influence and importance of money however, has infiltrated into many more levels of the national game in recent years.

In the last ten years, how many clubs have been disbanded, changed their names to start again or been fined or docked points for financial problems? What did we think of the very highly paid England 'Under 21' players in their European Finals ? Or the treatment The Doncaster Belles Club have received in the reorganising of the English Women's League?

On the other hand, what an uplifting achievement Tunbridge Wells Football Club produced by reaching a Wembley Vase Final and what a fantastic effort by The Guernsey Club who were prepared to travel and often help sponsor their opponents. The Channel Islanders coped with a frightening back log of fixtures and achieved promotion from The Combined Counties League and qualified for a Vase Semi-Final in a wonderful season with a limited choice of players but superb support.

Let's hope the traditional non-league spirit that has been appreciated by so many of us, still lives and can attract many more in the years to come.

*Tony Williams*

# PECKING ORDER 2012-2013  by A J Sarnecki

| 09-10 | 10-11 | 11-12 | 12-13 | Step | League | FA Cup ent 1 | FA Cup xmt | FA Cup won 1 | FA Trophy ent 3 | FA Trophy xmt 2/8 | FA Trophy won 1 | FA Vase ent 1 | FA Vase xmt 4/6 | FA Vase won | C pts | T pts | V pts | Total pts |
|---|---|---|---|---|---|---|---|---|---|---|---|---|---|---|---|---|---|---|
| 1 | 1 | 1 | 1 | 1 | FOOTBALL CONFERENCE Premier | 24 | 240 | 27 | 24 | 192 | 35 | | | | 291 | 299 | 0 | 590 |
| 3 | 2 | 2 | 2 | 1 | FOOTBALL CONFERENCE North | 22 | 132 | 37 | 22 | 132 | 24 | | | | 191 | 220 | 0 | 411 |
| 2 | 3 | 3 | 3 | 1 | FOOTBALL CONFERENCE South | 22 | 132 | 37 | 22 | 132 | 24 | | | | 181 | 222 | 0 | 403 |
| 4 | 4 | 4 | 4 | 2 | ISTHMIAN Premier | 22 | 0 | 41 | 22 | 44 | 28 | | | | 63 | 138 | 0 | 201 |
| 5 | 5 | 5 | 5 | 3 | NORTHERN PREMIER Premier | 22 | 0 | 32 | 22 | 44 | 28 | | | | 54 | 138 | 0 | 192 |
| 6 | 6 | 6 | 6 | 3 | SOUTHERN Premier | 22 | 0 | 30 | 22 | 44 | 14 | | | | 52 | 124 | 0 | 176 |
| 13 | 13 | 13 | 7 | 5 | NORTHERN First | 22 | 0 | 29 | | | | 23 | 48 | 38 | 51 | 0 | 109 | 160 |
| 7 | 8 | 8= | 8= | 4 | NORTHERN PREMIER First North | 22 | 0 | 28 | 22 | 0 | 24 | | | | 50 | 90 | 0 | 140 |
| 9 | 10= | 10= | 8= | 4 | SOUTHERN First South & West | 22 | 0 | 29 | 22 | 0 | 23 | | | | 51 | 89 | 0 | 140 |
| 11 | 9 | 12 | 10 | 4 | NORTHERN PREMIER First South | 22 | 0 | 21 | 22 | 0 | 26 | | | | 43 | 92 | 0 | 135 |
| 12 | 8= | 8= | 11 | 4 | ISTHMIAN First North | 22 | 0 | 26 | 22 | 0 | 14 | | | | 48 | 80 | 0 | 128 |
| 8 | 7 | 7 | 12 | 4 | ISTHMIAN First South | 22 | 0 | 18 | 22 | 0 | 20 | | | | 40 | 86 | 0 | 126 |
| 11 | 13= | 13= | 13= | 4 | SOUTHERN First Central | 22 | 0 | 24 | 22 | 0 | 7 | | | | 46 | 73 | 0 | 119 |
| 14 | 15 | 15= | 13= | 5 | WESSEX Premier | 21 | 0 | 22 | | | | 21 | 18 | 35 | 45 | 0 | 74 | 119 |
| 22 | 22= | 17 | 15= | 5 | MIDLAND ALLIANCE | 21 | 0 | 22 | | | | 22 | 18 | 31 | 43 | 0 | 71 | 114 |
| 23 | 20= | 19 | 15= | 5 | COMBINED COUNTIES Premier | 21 | 0 | 17 | | | | 21 | 18 | 30 | 44 | 0 | 70 | 114 |
| 15 | 14 | 16 | 17 | 5 | UNITED COUNTIES Premier | 20 | 0 | 15 | | | | 21 | 34 | 19 | 37 | 0 | 74 | 111 |
| 16 | 19 | 17= | 18 | 5 | NORTH WEST COUNTIES Premier | 22 | 0 | 22 | | | | 22 | 24 | 25 | 37 | 0 | 71 | 108 |
| 20= | 16 | 20 | 19 | 5 | SPARTAN SOUTH MIDLANDS Premier | 21 | 0 | 16 | | | | 22 | 18 | 23 | 43 | 0 | 63 | 106 |
| 23= | 20= | 16 | 20 | 5 | NORTHERN COUNTIES EAST Premier | 21 | 0 | 11 | | | | 20 | 22 | 28 | 33 | 0 | 72 | 105 |
| 19 | 18 | 21= | 21= | 5 | HELLENIC Premier | 17 | 0 | 11 | | | | 20 | 28 | 28 | 28 | 0 | 76 | 104 |
| 18 | 17 | 21= | 21= | 5 | WESTERN Premier | 20 | 0 | 16 | | | | 18 | 14 | 26 | 36 | 0 | 68 | 104 |
| 17 | 24 | 23 | 23 | 5 | EASTERN COUNTIES Premier | 19 | 0 | 17 | | | | 18 | 28 | 29 | 36 | 0 | 63 | 99 |
| 25 | 22= | 22= | 24 | 5 | ESSEX SENIOR | 18 | 0 | 10 | | | | 22 | 12 | 14 | 28 | 0 | 60 | 88 |
| 20 | 25 | 25 | 25 | 5 | SUSSEX COUNTY First | 19 | 0 | 13 | | | | 15 | 0 | 21 | 32 | 0 | 55 | 87 |
| 24 | 26 | 26 | 26 | 5 | KENT Premier | 13 | 0 | 8 | | | | 20 | 0 | 20 | 21 | 0 | 59 | 80 |
| 28 | 33= | 27 | 27= | 6 | WEST MIDLAND REGIONAL Premier | 15 | 0 | 13 | | | | 17 | 0 | 12 | 28 | 0 | 40 | 68 |
| 35= | 30= | 30= | 27= | 6 | NORTHERN Second | 14 | 0 | 5 | | | | 18 | 0 | 11 | 19 | 0 | 49 | 68 |
| 27= | 27 | 29 | 29 | 6 | NORTH WEST COUNTIES First | 10 | 0 | 11 | | | | 18 | 0 | 15 | 21 | 0 | 30 | 51 |
| 35 | 35 | 35 | 30 | 6 | EAST MIDLAND COUNTIES | 9 | 0 | 3 | | | | 19 | 0 | 14 | 13 | 0 | 36 | 49 |
| 34 | 37 | 37 | 31 | 6 | EASTERN COUNTIES First | 10 | 0 | 3 | | | | 15 | 0 | 8 | 15 | 0 | 33 | 48 |
| 33 | 32 | 32 | 32= | 6 | NORTHERN COUNTIES EAST First | 11 | 0 | 6 | | | | 11 | 0 | 13 | 13 | 0 | 31 | 44 |
| 35= | 38 | 38 | 32= | 6 | WESTERN First | 9 | 0 | 3 | | | | 15 | 0 | 12 | 15 | 0 | 27 | 42 |
| 31 | 36 | 36 | 34 | 6 | SPARTAN SOUTH MIDLANDS First | 9 | 0 | 4 | | | | 15 | 0 | 6 | 11 | 0 | 31 | 42 |
| 39 | 28 | 28 | 35 | 6 | MIDLAND COMBINATION Premier | 7 | 0 | 4 | | | | 11 | 0 | 13 | 11 | 0 | 29 | 40 |
| 37 | 39 | 39 | 36 | 6 | UNITED COUNTIES First | 8 | 0 | 2 | | | | 7 | 0 | 9 | 11 | 0 | 27 | 38 |
| 36 | 40 | 40 | 37 | 6 | WESSEX First | 6 | 0 | 1 | | | | 9 | 0 | 7 | 10 | 0 | 26 | 36 |
| 32 | 41 | 41 | 38 | 6 | SOUTH WEST PENINSULA Premier | 6 | 0 | 3 | | | | 9 | 0 | 6 | 8 | 0 | 22 | 30 |
| 38 | 43 | 43 | 39 | 6 | COMBINED COUNTIES First | 1 | 0 | 0 | | | | 4 | 0 | 5 | 7 | 0 | 22 | 29 |
| 41 | 44 | 44 | 40 | 6 | HELLENIC First West | 1 | 0 | 0 | | | | 4 | 0 | 5 | 6 | 0 | 21 | 27 |
| 39 | 58= | 58= | 41 | 7 | SUSSEX COUNTY Second | 1 | 0 | 1 | | | | 3 | 0 | 2 | 3 | 0 | 17 | 20 |
| 38 | 50= | 51 | 42 | 7 | CENTRAL MIDLANDS South | 1 | 0 | 0 | | | | 2 | 0 | 3 | 3 | 0 | 12 | 15 |
| new | 51 | 45= | 43 | 7 | HELLENIC First East | 0 | 0 | 0 | | | | 3 | 0 | 3 | 0 | 0 | 9 | 9 |
| 43 | 45= | 48= | 44 | 7 | WEST MIDLAND REGIONAL First | 0 | 0 | 0 | | | | 1 | 0 | 3 | 0 | 0 | 7 | 7 |
| 47= | 48= | 45= | 45= | 6 | SOUTH WEST PENINSULA First East | 1 | 0 | 1 | | | | 1 | 0 | 1 | 2 | 0 | 4 | 6 |
| 49 | 45= | 51= | 45= | 7 | KENT INVICTA | 0 | 0 | 0 | | | | 2 | 0 | 1 | 0 | 0 | 5 | 5 |
| 50= | 51= | 51= | 47 | 7 | ESSEX & SUFFOLK BORDER Premier | 0 | 0 | 1 | | | | 2 | 0 | 0 | 0 | 0 | 4 | 4 |
| new | 55= | 55= | 48= | 7 | CENTRAL MIDLANDS North | 0 | 0 | 0 | | | | 1 | 0 | 0 | 2 | 0 | 2 | 4 |
| new | 45= | 45= | 48= | 7 | GLOUCESTERSHIRE SENIOR | 0 | 0 | 0 | | | | 1 | 0 | 0 | 0 | 0 | 3 | 3 |
| 50= | 43 | 43 | 50 | 7 | DORSET PREMIER | 0 | 0 | 0 | | | | 2 | 0 | 1 | 0 | 0 | 3 | 3 |
| 44= | 45= | 45= | 51= | 7 | SOUTH WEST PENINSULA First West | 0 | 0 | 0 | | | | 1 | 0 | 0 | 0 | 0 | 3 | 3 |
| 47= | 57 | 57 | 51= | – | WEARSIDE | 0 | 0 | 0 | | | | 1 | 0 | 0 | 0 | 0 | 2 | 2 |
| 44= | 54= | 54= | 51= | 7 | LEICESTERSHIRE SENIOR Premier | 0 | 0 | 0 | | | | | | | 0 | 0 | 2 | 2 |
| 55= | 58= | 58= | 51= | 7 | SOMERSET SENIOR Premier | 0 | 0 | 0 | | | | 1 | 0 | 0 | 0 | 0 | 2 | 2 |
| | | | 51= | 7 | MIDDLESEX SENIOR | 0 | 0 | 0 | | | | 1 | 0 | 0 | 0 | 0 | 2 | 2 |
| | | | | 7 | DONCASTER SENIOR | 0 | 0 | 0 | | | | | | | 0 | 0 | 2 | 2 |
| 47= | 57= | 57= | 57= | 7 | MIDLAND COMBINATION First | 0 | 0 | 0 | | | | 1 | 0 | 0 | 0 | 0 | 1 | 1 |
| 50= | 50= | 58= | 57= | 7 | HERTS SENIOR COUNTY Premier | 0 | 0 | 0 | | | | 1 | 0 | 0 | 0 | 0 | 1 | 1 |
| | | | | 7 | ESSEX OLYMPIAN Premier | 0 | 0 | 0 | | | | 1 | 0 | 0 | 0 | 0 | 1 | 1 |

Northern League emphatically belies its classification as "Step 5", coming ahead of all the Step 4 Leagues

Points are given for status (acceptance into each of the three competitions), for prestige (exemption from early rounds) and performance (number of wins, however achieved, even by walkover). Entry to the Vase is valued at one point, that to the Trophy at 3. Cup entry gives a further bonus of three points. The number of entries from each league is shown in the appropriate column. Points for exemptions are valued at two for each round missed. The entry in the table is the number of teams given exemptions. Finally, all wins are valued at one point, regardless of opposition: giving extra points for defeating 'stronger' opponents would be too arbitrary. After all, if they lost then they were not stronger on the day!

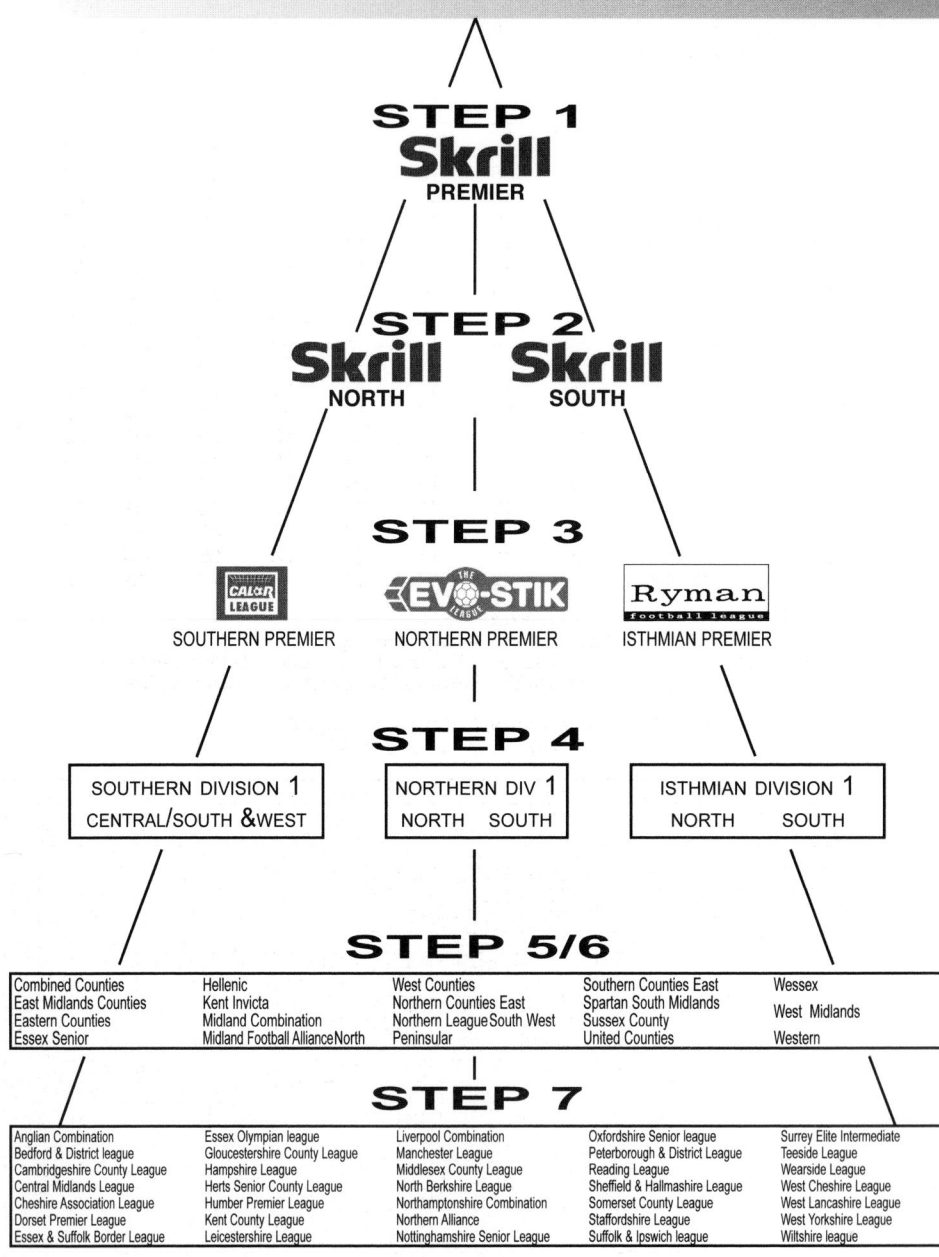

# FOOTBALL LEAGUE

## STEP 1
### Skrill
#### PREMIER

## STEP 2
### Skrill
#### NORTH
### Skrill
#### SOUTH

## STEP 3
CALOR LEAGUE
SOUTHERN PREMIER

EVO-STIK
NORTHERN PREMIER

Ryman football league
ISTHMIAN PREMIER

## STEP 4

| SOUTHERN DIVISION 1 CENTRAL/SOUTH &WEST | NORTHERN DIV 1 NORTH  SOUTH | ISTHMIAN DIVISION 1 NORTH  SOUTH |
|---|---|---|

## STEP 5/6

| | | | | |
|---|---|---|---|---|
| Combined Counties | Hellenic | West Counties | Southern Counties East | Wessex |
| East Midlands Counties | Kent Invicta | Northern Counties East | Spartan South Midlands | West Midlands |
| Eastern Counties | Midland Combination | Northern League South West | Sussex County | |
| Essex Senior | Midland Football Alliance North | Peninsular | United Counties | Western |

## STEP 7

| | | | | |
|---|---|---|---|---|
| Anglian Combination | Essex Olympian league | Liverpool Combination | Oxfordshire Senior league | Surrey Elite Intermediate |
| Bedford & District league | Gloucestershire County League | Manchester League | Peterborough & District League | Teeside League |
| Cambridgeshire County League | Hampshire League | Middlesex County League | Reading League | Wearside League |
| Central Midlands League | Herts Senior County League | North Berkshire League | Sheffield & Hallmashire League | West Cheshire League |
| Cheshire Association League | Humber Premier League | Northamptonshire Combination | Somerset County League | West Lancashire League |
| Dorset Premier League | Kent County League | Northern Alliance | Staffordshire League | West Yorkshire League |
| Essex & Suffolk Border League | Leicestershire League | Nottinghamshire Senior League | Suffolk & Ipswich league | Wiltshire league |

# FOOTBALL CONFERENCE PREMIER DIVISION 2012-13

| | | P | W | D | L | F | A | GD | Pts |
|---|---|---|---|---|---|---|---|---|---|
| 1 | (P) Mansfield Town | 46 | 30 | 5 | 11 | 92 | 52 | 40 | 95 |
| 2 | Kidderminster Harriers | 46 | 28 | 9 | 9 | 82 | 40 | 42 | 93 |
| 3 | (P) Newport County AFC | 46 | 25 | 10 | 11 | 85 | 60 | 25 | 85 |
| 4 | Grimsby Town | 46 | 23 | 14 | 9 | 70 | 38 | 32 | 83 |
| 5 | Wrexham | 46 | 22 | 14 | 10 | 74 | 45 | 29 | 80 |
| 6 | Hereford United | 46 | 19 | 13 | 14 | 73 | 63 | 10 | 70 |
| 7 | Luton Town | 46 | 18 | 13 | 15 | 70 | 62 | 8 | 67 |
| 8 | Dartford | 46 | 19 | 9 | 18 | 67 | 63 | 4 | 66 |
| 9 | Braintree Town | 46 | 19 | 9 | 18 | 63 | 72 | -9 | 66 |
| 10 | Forest Green Rovers | 46 | 18 | 11 | 17 | 63 | 49 | 14 | 65 |
| 11 | Macclesfield Town | 46 | 17 | 12 | 17 | 65 | 70 | -5 | 63 |
| 12 | Woking | 46 | 18 | 8 | 20 | 73 | 81 | -8 | 62 |
| 13 | Alfreton Town | 46 | 16 | 12 | 18 | 69 | 74 | -5 | 60 |
| 14 | Cambridge United | 46 | 15 | 14 | 17 | 68 | 69 | -1 | 59 |
| 15 | Nuneaton | 46 | 14 | 15 | 17 | 55 | 63 | -8 | 57 |
| 16 | Lincoln City | 46 | 15 | 11 | 20 | 66 | 73 | -7 | 56 |
| 17 | Gateshead | 46 | 13 | 16 | 17 | 58 | 61 | -3 | 55 |
| 18 | Hyde FC | 46 | 16 | 7 | 23 | 63 | 75 | -12 | 55 |
| 19 | Tamworth | 46 | 15 | 10 | 21 | 55 | 69 | -14 | 55 |
| 20 | Southport | 46 | 14 | 12 | 20 | 72 | 86 | -14 | 54 |
| 21 | (R) Stockport County | 46 | 13 | 11 | 22 | 57 | 76 | -19 | 50 |
| 22 | (R) Barrow | 46 | 11 | 13 | 22 | 45 | 83 | -38 | 46 |
| 23 | (R) Ebbsfleet United | 46 | 8 | 15 | 23 | 55 | 89 | -34 | 39 |
| 24 | (R) AFC Telford United | 46 | 6 | 17 | 23 | 52 | 79 | -27 | 35 |

## PLAY-OFFS

Semi-Finals 1st Leg / 2nd Leg
Wrexham 2-1 Kidderminster Harriers / Kiddermintser Harriers 1-3 Wrexham
Grimby Town 0-1 Newport County AFC / Newport County AFC 1-0 Grimsby Town

Final (@ Wembley, 05/5/13) - Att: 16,346
Wrexham 0-2 Newport County AFC

| | 1 | 2 | 3 | 4 | 5 | 6 | 7 | 8 | 9 | 10 | 11 | 12 | 13 | 14 | 15 | 16 | 17 | 18 | 19 | 20 | 21 | 22 | 23 | 24 |
|---|---|---|---|---|---|---|---|---|---|---|---|---|---|---|---|---|---|---|---|---|---|---|---|---|
| 1 AFC Telford United | | 0-0 | 1-1 | 3-0 | 1-2 | 0-2 | 2-2 | 1-2 | 0-0 | 1-2 | 0-0 | 1-3 | 0-2 | 1-1 | 0-0 | 0-2 | 2-2 | 2-4 | 0-3 | 1-3 | 2-2 | 3-3 | 1-0 | 0-2 |
| 2 Alfreton Town | 1-1 | | 4-0 | 1-1 | 1-1 | 3-2 | 3-0 | 2-1 | 3-2 | 0-2 | 0-3 | 5-1 | 1-1 | 0-2 | 3-0 | 1-2 | 0-3 | 4-3 | 0-3 | 3-3 | 2-3 | 3-0 | 0-3 | 1-2 |
| 3 Barrow | 0-0 | 1-3 | | 0-1 | 1-4 | 0-0 | 1-1 | 2-2 | 0-2 | 0-2 | 0-2 | 1-1 | 1-1 | 1-2 | 1-0 | 1-0 | 0-4 | 0-3 | 1-2 | 3-2 | 0-2 | 2-0 | 2-0 | 0-1 |
| 4 Braintree Town | 3-2 | 2-1 | 2-3 | | 0-3 | 0-2 | 3-1 | 3-1 | 2-1 | 2-0 | 0-2 | 2-2 | 1-1 | 0-3 | 2-0 | 0-3 | 2-1 | 1-2 | 2-2 | 1-3 | 0-0 | 2-1 | 1-1 | 1-5 |
| 5 Cambridge United | 3-3 | 0-3 | 2-1 | 1-0 | | 1-2 | 1-1 | 0-0 | 3-0 | 0-0 | 1-3 | 0-1 | 1-3 | 2-1 | 2-2 | 2-0 | 4-1 | 0-0 | 1-3 | 2-0 | 4-1 | 1-1 | 1-0 | 1-4 |
| 6 Dartford | 1-4 | 5-1 | 0-1 | 0-0 | 1-1 | | 3-1 | 0-1 | | 3-0 | 1-2 | 4-0 | 2-1 | 1-0 | 2-4 | 1-0 | 2-0 | 2-0 | 0-1 | 2-2 | 1-1 | 2-3 | 4-1 | 2-1 |
| 7 Ebbsfleet United | 1-3 | 0-0 | 2-4 | 0-1 | 2-4 | 2-2 | | | 0-2 | 3-1 | 1-1 | 1-0 | 3-2 | 1-1 | 1-1 | 0-4 | 3-1 | 1-1 | 1-1 | 4-1 | 0-0 | 1-1 | 2-2 | 1-1 |
| 8 Forest Green Rovers | 0-0 | 1-1 | 1-1 | 4-1 | 1-1 | 2-3 | 4-1 | | | 1-0 | 0-1 | 3-1 | 0-1 | 3-0 | 1-2 | 1-1 | 1-2 | 1-2 | 1-0 | 0-1 | 4-1 | 1-2 | 3-1 | 0-0 |
| 9 Gateshead | 1-1 | 2-0 | 0-1 | 1-2 | 0-0 | 2-0 | 2-0 | 1-1 | | 1-1 | 3-2 | 3-0 | 2-0 | 1-1 | 5-1 | 2-2 | 4-1 | 0-0 | 0-2 | 2-2 | 1-1 | 0-2 | 2-1 | 0-1 |
| 10 Grimsby Town | 1-0 | 4-2 | 0-0 | 3-0 | 0-0 | 2-1 | 1-1 | 1-2 | | | 1-1 | 2-0 | 1-3 | 4-1 | 0-1 | 4-1 | 3-0 | 0-0 | 2-2 | 1-2 | 2-0 | 5-1 | 1-0 | |
| 11 Hereford United | 1-1 | 3-3 | 2-1 | 0-0 | 4-2 | 1-0 | 4-2 | 1-2 | 1-1 | 0-2 | | 1-2 | 0-1 | 3-2 | 1-0 | 2-1 | 1-2 | 2-3 | 0-0 | 2-2 | 1-2 | 5-2 | 2-1 | 1-1 |
| 12 Hyde | 2-1 | 1-1 | 0-0 | 1-2 | 2-1 | 3-0 | 1-0 | 0-1 | 1-1 | 3-2 | 5-2 | | 0-4 | 1-5 | 1-2 | 1-1 | 0-1 | 0-1 | 2-2 | 0-2 | 0-1 | 2-1 | 7-0 | 2-0 |
| 13 Kidderminster H. | 1-0 | 3-1 | 2-0 | 2-1 | 3-2 | 5-1 | 3-2 | 0-1 | 1-1 | 0-0 | 0-1 | 3-0 | | 3-0 | 0-2 | 3-0 | 2-3 | 3-2 | 1-0 | 2-2 | 4-0 | 4-1 | 2-2 | 2-0 |
| 14 Lincoln City | 3-2 | 1-2 | 0-0 | 3-0 | 0-0 | 2-1 | 1-1 | 1-4 | 3-2 | 3-2 | 1-0 | 1-2 | 2-3 | | 1-2 | 2-0 | 3-1 | 1-0 | 3-3 | 3-2 | 1-0 | 1-2 | | |
| 15 Luton Town | 0-1 | 3-0 | 6-1 | 2-3 | 3-2 | 0-2 | 2-0 | 1-1 | 2-2 | 1-1 | 1-1 | 1-2 | 1-2 | 3-0 | | 4-1 | 2-3 | 2-2 | 2-0 | 3-1 | 1-0 | 0-0 | 3-1 | 1-0 |
| 16 Macclesfield Town | 2-1 | 1-2 | 2-0 | 2-1 | 2-1 | 2-0 | 1-2 | 1-2 | 0-4 | 1-3 | 0-1 | 3-2 | 1-0 | 2-1 | 1-1 | | 0-3 | 1-1 | 0-0 | 2-2 | 1-1 | 2-0 | 0-0 | 2-0 |
| 17 Mansfield Town | 1-0 | 1-2 | 8-1 | 2-0 | 3-1 | 5-0 | 4-1 | 1-0 | 4-0 | 2-0 | 1-1 | 1-0 | 0-2 | 0-0 | 2-2 | 3-1 | | 3-4 | 1-0 | 1-0 | 4-1 | 2-0 | 3-1 | 1-0 |
| 18 Newport County | 2-1 | 2-0 | 4-2 | 1-0 | 6-2 | 0-0 | 1-0 | 0-5 | 3-1 | 0-0 | 2-0 | 1-3 | 2-1 | 5-2 | 4-1 | 2-0 | | | 4-0 | 2-1 | 0-0 | 2-2 | 2-3 | 1-1 |
| 19 Nuneaton Town | 3-1 | 1-0 | 1-1 | 4-2 | 4-1 | 1-0 | 4-5 | 1-1 | 0-0 | 3-1 | 0-1 | 0-0 | 3-1 | 0-1 | 1-0 | 3-3 | 1-1 | 1-2 | | 0-1 | 2-0 | 2-1 | 0-0 | 0-0 |
| 20 Southport | 0-3 | 0-2 | 5-2 | 0-2 | 2-1 | 2-2 | 1-0 | 1-2 | 2-1 | 1-1 | 2-2 | 0-1 | 1-3 | 4-2 | 1-3 | 3-2 | 1-2 | 0-2 | 3-1 | | 1-1 | 0-3 | 1-2 | 1-4 |
| 21 Stockport County | 2-2 | 1-0 | 3-1 | 1-3 | 1-1 | 0-1 | 3-1 | 2-1 | 1-2 | 1-2 | 2-3 | 0-2 | 1-0 | 2-0 | 0-1 | 3-4 | 1-3 | 1-0 | 3-2 | 3-4 | | 0-1 | 1-2 | 2-3 |
| 22 Tamworth | 0-0 | 1-1 | 1-3 | 1-4 | 1-2 | 3-2 | 0-1 | 2-1 | 2-0 | 0-1 | 2-2 | 2-0 | 0-1 | 1-0 | 1-2 | 0-0 | 0-1 | 1-2 | 2-1 | 1-0 | | | 2-1 | 0-1 |
| 23 Woking | 5-2 | 1-2 | 3-1 | 1-4 | 2-1 | 1-0 | 1-0 | 2-0 | 2-1 | 0-1 | 1-1 | 2-1 | 2-2 | 1-1 | 3-1 | 5-4 | 1-2 | 1-3 | 6-1 | 2-3 | 1-0 | 2-3 | | 2-0 |
| 24 Wrexham | 4-1 | 1-1 | 3-0 | 1-1 | 1-0 | 2-2 | 4-1 | 2-1 | 1-1 | 0-0 | 1-2 | 2-0 | 1-2 | 2-4 | 0-0 | 0-0 | 2-1 | 1-1 | 6-1 | 2-2 | 3-1 | 2-2 | 3-1 | |

# FOOTBALL CONFERENCE NORTH 2012-13

| | | P | W | D | L | F | A | GD | Pts |
|---|---|---|---|---|---|---|---|---|---|
| 1 | (P) Chester FC | 42 | 34 | 5 | 3 | 103 | 32 | 71 | 107 |
| 2 | Guiseley | 42 | 28 | 7 | 7 | 83 | 45 | 38 | 91 |
| 3 | Brackley Town | 42 | 26 | 7 | 9 | 76 | 44 | 32 | 85 |
| 4 | Altrincham | 42 | 24 | 8 | 10 | 100 | 51 | 49 | 80 |
| 5 | (P) FC Halifax | 42 | 21 | 12 | 9 | 86 | 38 | 48 | 75 |
| 6 | Harrogate Town | 42 | 20 | 9 | 13 | 72 | 50 | 22 | 69 |
| 7 | Bradford P A | 42 | 19 | 9 | 14 | 75 | 52 | 23 | 66 |
| 8 | Gainsborough Trinity | 42 | 18 | 12 | 12 | 68 | 45 | 23 | 66 |
| 9 | Solihull Moors | 42 | 17 | 9 | 16 | 58 | 54 | 4 | 60 |
| 10 | Oxford City | 42 | 13 | 16 | 13 | 62 | 57 | 5 | 55 |
| 11 | Gloucester City | 42 | 16 | 6 | 20 | 54 | 63 | -9 | 54 |
| 12 | Vauxhall Motors | 42 | 15 | 8 | 19 | 58 | 64 | -6 | 53 |
| 13 | Stalybridge Celtic | 42 | 13 | 13 | 16 | 55 | 62 | -7 | 52 |
| 14 | Workington (-4pts) | 42 | 16 | 8 | 18 | 60 | 68 | -8 | 52 |
| 15 | Worcester City | 42 | 14 | 8 | 20 | 57 | 62 | -5 | 50 |
| 16 | Boston United | 42 | 14 | 7 | 21 | 68 | 73 | -5 | 49 |
| 17 | Bishops Stortford | 42 | 12 | 13 | 17 | 58 | 74 | -16 | 49 |
| 18 | Colwyn Bay | 42 | 14 | 7 | 21 | 57 | 78 | -21 | 49 |
| 19 | Histon | 42 | 11 | 11 | 20 | 48 | 73 | -25 | 44 |
| 20 | (R) Corby Town | 42 | 12 | 8 | 22 | 66 | 92 | -26 | 44 |
| 21 | (R) Droylsden | 42 | 5 | 7 | 30 | 43 | 124 | -81 | 22 |
| 22 | (R) Hinckley United (-6pts) | 42 | 3 | 4 | 35 | 37 | 143 | -106 | 7 |

## PLAY-OFFS

Semi-Finals 1st Leg / 2nd Leg
FC Halifax 1-1 Guiseley / Guiseley 0-2 FC Halifax
Altrincham 2-1 Brackley Town / Brackley Town 3-0 Altrincham

Final (@ Brackley Town, 12/5/13)
Brackley Town 0-1 FC Halifax

| | 1 | 2 | 3 | 4 | 5 | 6 | 7 | 8 | 9 | 10 | 11 | 12 | 13 | 14 | 15 | 16 | 17 | 18 | 19 | 20 | 21 | 22 |
|---|---|---|---|---|---|---|---|---|---|---|---|---|---|---|---|---|---|---|---|---|---|---|
| 1 Altrincham | | 2-1 | 7-1 | 1-4 | 3-1 | 2-4 | 1-1 | 2-1 | 6-0 | 2-0 | 0-1 | 2-0 | 1-3 | 3-0 | 8-0 | 5-0 | 3-1 | 2-1 | 2-1 | 1-0 | 2-0 | 1-2 |
| 2 Bishop's Stortford | 1-1 | | 1-0 | 1-3 | 2-1 | 1-2 | 2-2 | 2-1 | 2-1 | 1-2 | 1-5 | 1-2 | 2-5 | 0-2 | 1-1 | 3-1 | 0-0 | 4-1 | 0-0 | 2-2 | 0-1 | 0-3 |
| 3 Boston United | 2-3 | 1-1 | | 3-4 | 0-4 | 3-2 | 1-0 | 1-1 | 5-1 | 1-2 | 2-1 | 4-0 | 1-3 | 1-2 | 1-2 | 6-0 | 3-1 | 2-2 | 2-2 | 0-1 | 1-2 | 1-3 |
| 4 Brackley Town | 0-1 | 1-0 | 0-2 | | 3-1 | 2-3 | 1-3 | 2-4 | 3-2 | 0-0 | 2-2 | 0-1 | 1-0 | 2-1 | 5-0 | 2-1 | 0-0 | 2-1 | 4-1 | 1-0 | 2-0 | 3-1 |
| 5 Bradford Park Avenue | 2-2 | 2-1 | 2-1 | 0-1 | | 0-0 | 1-2 | 2-0 | 5-0 | 1-1 | 0-2 | 2-1 | 1-3 | 1-0 | 4-0 | 0-0 | 1-2 | 1-0 | 1-3 | 2-0 | 4-2 | 1-0 |
| 6 Chester | 2-0 | 4-1 | 1-0 | 0-0 | 1-1 | | 2-1 | 2-1 | 5-0 | 2-1 | 3-1 | 2-0 | 4-0 | 2-0 | 3-2 | 2-0 | 0-1 | 4-1 | 2-0 | 4-2 | 1-0 |
| 7 Colwyn Bay | 1-3 | 1-2 | 0-2 | 1-1 | 1-2 | 1-5 | | 1-0 | 1-3 | 0-3 | 1-0 | 1-0 | 0-2 | 1-2 | 3-2 | 3-1 | 3-1 | 3-1 | 2-3 | 2-4 | 0-3 | 1-4 |
| 8 Corby Town | 2-5 | 2-2 | 2-1 | 0-4 | 4-5 | 1-2 | 3-1 | | 5-0 | 1-5 | 0-0 | 3-2 | 2-3 | 0-2 | 5-3 | 0-0 | 1-1 | 2-3 | 1-0 | 0-1 | 1-0 | 1-3 |
| 9 Droylsden | 0-5 | 1-2 | 0-1 | 0-3 | 0-7 | 3-4 | 2-0 | 2-2 | | 0-6 | 1-3 | 1-0 | 0-3 | 1-3 | 3-2 | 2-2 | 1-3 | 2-4 | 1-1 | 5-2 | 0-2 | 0-1 |
| 10 F.C. Halifax Town | 3-4 | 1-1 | 1-2 | 0-0 | 0-1 | 1-1 | 0-1 | 4-1 | | 3-1 | 5-0 | 1-1 | 1-2 | 7-0 | 3-3 | 3-1 | 0-0 | 1-2 | 1-1 | 5-0 | 4-0 | 5-1 |
| 11 Gainsborough Trinity | 2-4 | 2-2 | 2-0 | 1-1 | 1-1 | 0-2 | 3-1 | 2-2 | 3-0 | 3-0 | | 0-1 | 1-2 | 1-1 | 5-0 | 1-0 | 1-2 | 1-1 | 1-2 | 2-1 | 1-0 | 1-1 |
| 12 Gloucester City | 0-0 | 5-1 | 1-0 | 1-4 | 1-0 | 0-1 | 2-2 | 0-1 | 4-0 | 1-2 | 1-2 | | 2-2 | 0-2 | 4-1 | 1-1 | 0-1 | 1-1 | 4-3 | 1-1 | 4-2 | 0-1 |
| 13 Guiseley | 1-1 | 1-2 | 2-1 | 0-2 | 1-0 | 2-1 | 2-2 | 2-1 | 7-1 | 1-1 | 2-0 | 3-1 | | 2-0 | 2-4 | 2-1 | 1-0 | 1-0 | 1-0 | 2-1 | 3-3 | 2-0 |
| 14 Harrogate Town | 1-2 | 2-2 | 4-2 | 6-1 | 1-1 | 1-3 | 1-2 | 6-1 | 1-1 | 1-1 | 1-1 | 0-0 | 1-0 | | 5-0 | 2-0 | 1-3 | 2-4 | 0-0 | 3-1 | 3-1 | 3-1 |
| 15 Hinckley United | 0-6 | 1-5 | 2-4 | 1-3 | 1-4 | 0-6 | 1-3 | 6-3 | 2-2 | 0-2 | 0-2 | 0-3 | 0-3 | 0-2 | | 0-1 | 0-2 | 1-1 | 0-3 | 0-6 | 0-5 | 1-1 |
| 16 Histon | 2-0 | 2-0 | 1-1 | 3-0 | 1-4 | 1-1 | 3-1 | 1-2 | 3-1 | 0-1 | 0-3 | 2-1 | 1-4 | 1-3 | 2-1 | | 1-1 | 0-0 | 0-2 | 0-0 | 0-0 | 3-0 |
| 17 Oxford City | 2-2 | 1-1 | 4-2 | 2-1 | 1-1 | 0-1 | 1-2 | 2-0 | 2-2 | 2-1 | 1-1 | 1-2 | 0-3 | 0-0 | 6-2 | 0-0 | | 1-2 | 0-0 | 1-1 | 2-2 | 5-0 |
| 18 Solihull Moors | 2-1 | 0-1 | 1-0 | 0-1 | 3-1 | 0-3 | 2-0 | 3-0 | 2-1 | 0-3 | 0-2 | 2-3 | 2-0 | 2-0 | 1-0 | 1-1 | 1-2 | | 1-0 | 2-3 | 0-1 | 2-2 |
| 19 Stalybridge Celtic | 2-2 | 3-1 | 0-1 | 0-3 | 2-0 | 2-6 | 3-3 | 1-2 | 0-0 | 1-0 | 1-1 | 4-0 | 1-1 | 1-0 | 4-0 | 2-1 | 2-2 | 0-3 | | 0-1 | 0-2 | 1-4 |
| 20 Vauxhall Motors | 2-1 | 2-2 | 4-0 | 0-2 | 1-3 | 0-3 | 1-1 | 1-1 | 4-0 | 1-3 | 1-2 | 1-2 | 2-0 | 0-1 | 2-1 | 2-0 | 2-1 | 2-1 | 0-0 | | 1-0 | 1-3 |
| 21 Worcester City | 0-0 | 2-0 | 0-3 | 1-2 | 2-0 | 0-1 | 2-0 | 5-1 | 2-1 | 0-1 | 0-3 | 0-1 | 0-1 | 2-2 | 3-1 | 2-3 | 3-2 | 1-3 | 1-2 | 2-2 | | 1-1 |
| 22 Workington | 2-1 | 2-3 | 1-1 | 0-0 | 1-6 | 1-1 | 1-2 | 2-3 | 2-1 | 0-1 | 0-3 | 0-1 | 0-2 | 1-2 | 2-1 | 3-1 | 1-2 | 1-0 | 4-1 | 3-1 | 1-0 | |

# FOOTBALL CONFERENCE SOUTH 2012-13

|    |                          | P  | W  | D  | L  | F  | A  | GD  | Pts |
|----|--------------------------|----|----|----|----|----|----|-----|-----|
| 1  | (P) Welling United       | 42 | 26 | 8  | 8  | 90 | 44 | 46  | 86  |
| 2  | (P) Salisbury City (-1pt)| 42 | 25 | 8  | 9  | 80 | 47 | 33  | 82  |
| 3  | Dover                    | 42 | 22 | 10 | 10 | 69 | 44 | 25  | 76  |
| 4  | Eastleigh                | 42 | 22 | 6  | 14 | 79 | 61 | 18  | 72  |
| 5  | Chelmsford               | 42 | 22 | 6  | 14 | 70 | 56 | 14  | 72  |
| 6  | Sutton United            | 42 | 20 | 10 | 12 | 66 | 49 | 17  | 70  |
| 7  | Weston-S-Mare            | 42 | 19 | 10 | 13 | 61 | 55 | 6   | 67  |
| 8  | Dorchester               | 42 | 19 | 8  | 15 | 59 | 62 | -3  | 65  |
| 9  | Boreham Wood             | 42 | 15 | 17 | 10 | 59 | 46 | 13  | 62  |
| 10 | Havant and Waterlooville | 42 | 14 | 16 | 12 | 68 | 60 | 8   | 58  |
| 11 | Bath City                | 42 | 15 | 10 | 17 | 60 | 58 | 2   | 55  |
| 12 | Eastbourne Borough       | 42 | 14 | 9  | 19 | 42 | 52 | -10 | 51  |
| 13 | Farnborough (-14pts)     | 42 | 19 | 7  | 16 | 76 | 75 | 1   | 50  |
| 14 | Basingstoke Town         | 42 | 12 | 12 | 18 | 63 | 73 | -10 | 48  |
| 15 | Bromley                  | 42 | 14 | 6  | 22 | 54 | 69 | -15 | 48  |
| 16 | Tonbridge Angels         | 42 | 12 | 12 | 18 | 56 | 77 | -21 | 48  |
| 17 | Hayes & Yeading          | 42 | 13 | 9  | 20 | 64 | 89 | -25 | 48  |
| 18 | Staines Town             | 42 | 13 | 8  | 21 | 61 | 78 | -17 | 47  |
| 19 | Maidenhead United        | 42 | 13 | 6  | 23 | 64 | 68 | -4  | 45  |
| 20 | (R) AFC Hornchurch       | 42 | 11 | 11 | 20 | 47 | 64 | -17 | 44  |
| 21 | (R) Billericay Town      | 42 | 11 | 7  | 24 | 62 | 90 | -28 | 40  |
| 22 | (R) Truro City (-10pts)  | 42 | 9  | 8  | 25 | 57 | 90 | -33 | 25  |

## PLAY-OFFS

Semi-Finals 1st Leg / 2nd Leg
Chelmsford City 1-0 Salisbury City / Salisbury City 2-0 Chelmsford City
Eastleigh 1-3 Dover Athletic / Dover Athletic 0-2 Eastleigh (Dover won 4-2 on penalties)

Final (@ Salisbury, 12/5/13)
Salisbury City 3-2 Dover Athletic (AET)

|    |                      | 1   | 2   | 3   | 4   | 5   | 6   | 7   | 8   | 9   | 10  | 11  | 12  | 13  | 14  | 15  | 16  | 17  | 18  | 19  | 20  | 21  | 22  |
|----|----------------------|-----|-----|-----|-----|-----|-----|-----|-----|-----|-----|-----|-----|-----|-----|-----|-----|-----|-----|-----|-----|-----|-----|
| 1  | AFC Hornchurch       |     | 3-0 | 2-1 | 1-0 | 1-1 | 1-0 | 0-2 | 1-0 | 0-1 | 0-1 | 1-0 | 1-1 | 2-2 | 2-0 | 0-2 | 2-2 | 1-1 | 1-1 | 1-1 | 1-2 | 0-3 | 0-0 |
| 2  | Basingstoke Town     | 0-2 |     | 2-1 | 3-3 | 2-3 | 1-1 | 1-2 | 2-1 | 0-1 | 2-2 | 0-3 | 6-2 | 1-2 | 2-2 | 2-0 | 0-4 | 3-1 | 2-1 | 1-0 | 3-2 | 0-1 | 1-3 |
| 3  | Bath City            | 3-1 | 1-1 |     | 2-1 | 0-0 | 0-2 | 2-2 | 2-3 | 1-2 | 2-2 | 1-1 | 3-2 | 2-0 | 2-3 | 3-1 | 0-0 | 0-1 | 0-4 | 3-0 | 1-1 | 1-0 | 1-2 |
| 4  | Billericay Town      | 1-1 | 1-3 | 2-0 |     | 1-1 | 2-3 | 0-1 | 3-1 | 1-2 | 1-2 | 4-0 | 2-1 | 3-1 | 4-1 | 1-0 | 1-2 | 2-3 | 2-4 | 3-3 | 2-1 | 1-2 | 0-0 |
| 5  | Boreham Wood         | 2-1 | 1-1 | 0-0 | 3-0 |     | 1-2 | 0-0 | 1-2 | 1-1 | 2-1 | 3-0 | 3-1 | 1-2 | 3-0 | 2-1 | 1-0 | 1-1 | 3-0 | 4-2 | 0-0 | 1-1 | 0-1 |
| 6  | Bromley              | 4-0 | 1-2 | 1-0 | 0-1 | 1-1 |     | 2-0 | 2-1 | 0-4 | 0-2 | 3-1 | 1-3 | 1-1 | 0-4 | 3-2 | 1-2 | 0-0 | 0-2 | 1-1 | 4-0 | 0-2 | 0-1 |
| 7  | Chelmsford City      | 1-4 | 2-0 | 0-1 | 1-1 | 2-1 | 3-2 |     | 4-0 | 0-3 | 1-0 | 1-1 | 6-0 | 1-1 | 6-2 | 3-1 | 2-1 | 3-2 | 1-0 | 2-1 | 3-2 | 2-3 | 2-1 |
| 8  | Dorchester Town      | 3-1 | 2-2 | 2-1 | 6-1 | 0-0 | 0-4 | 1-0 |     | 1-0 | 2-1 | 1-0 | 2-0 | 0-0 | 2-2 | 4-0 | 2-1 | 0-4 | 0-1 | 1-2 | 2-2 | 2-1 | 2-1 |
| 9  | Dover Athletic       | 1-0 | 0-5 | 2-0 | 4-1 | 0-1 | 1-0 | 0-1 | 0-0 |     | 0-0 | 2-0 | 2-2 | 2-2 | 2-1 | 2-0 | 1-3 | 0-1 | 1-1 | 0-1 | 3-2 | 3-2 | 3-1 |
| 10 | Eastbourne Borough   | 1-1 | 1-0 | 0-3 | 2-1 | 1-1 | 3-0 | 1-2 | 0-0 | 0-3 |     | 1-0 | 0-1 | 0-1 | 2-1 | 0-2 | 1-2 | 2-0 | 0-1 | 1-2 | 1-0 | 0-3 | 0-2 |
| 11 | Eastleigh            | 1-0 | 1-1 | 3-1 | 5-0 | 1-1 | 3-0 | 0-1 | 3-1 | 1-3 | 1-0 |     | 3-1 | 2-2 | 3-1 | 4-2 | 1-0 | 4-3 | 1-1 | 4-1 | 3-1 | 1-3 | 3-0 |
| 12 | Farnborough          | 1-1 | 2-1 | 0-1 | 4-3 | 0-3 | 2-0 | 3-1 | 1-1 | 5-2 | 0-1 | 6-2 |     | 1-1 | 4-1 | 2-1 | 2-1 | 3-1 | 1-3 | 4-1 | 4-1 | 0-3 | 2-1 |
| 13 | Havant & Waterlooville | 5-2 | 4-1 | 2-1 | 5-0 | 1-1 | 1-2 | 1-1 | 4-0 | 1-1 | 2-3 | 0-3 | 0-1 |     | 2-1 | 2-1 | 2-2 | 3-1 | 3-0 | 2-2 | 1-0 | 0-1 | 0-3 |
| 14 | Hayes & Yeading United | 1-3 | 2-1 | 2-2 | 4-2 | 0-1 | 1-1 | 3-0 | 1-3 | 2-4 | 1-1 | 2-1 | 3-2 | 1-4 |     | 1-1 | 2-3 | 4-0 | 0-0 | 3-2 | 1-2 | 2-1 | 2-1 |
| 15 | Maidenhead United    | 2-4 | 2-2 | 0-1 | 3-2 | 2-1 | 4-2 | 2-1 | 1-2 | 1-2 | 1-2 | 0-2 | 3-2 | 2-0 | 0-2 |     | 0-1 | 1-1 | 0-1 | 3-1 | 8-0 | 2-1 | 0-1 |
| 16 | Salisbury City       | 2-1 | 0-2 | 3-2 | 2-0 | 2-1 | 3-1 | 2-1 | 4-0 | 1-1 | 1-0 | 5-3 | 1-0 | 5-1 | 2-0 | 1-1 |     | 3-1 | 1-0 | 2-1 | 4-1 | 3-1 | 1-1 |
| 17 | Staines Town         | 3-1 | 2-0 | 1-3 | 1-2 | 1-1 | 3-1 | 1-3 | 2-1 | 0-2 | 0-2 | 1-3 | 1-2 | 1-1 | 7-1 | 0-6 | 3-2 |     | 1-4 | 1-4 | 1-0 | 2-2 | 1-1 |
| 18 | Sutton United        | 3-1 | 3-2 | 0-2 | 3-0 | 2-1 | 4-3 | 1-0 | 1-2 | 2-2 | 2-0 | 2-1 | 0-1 | 1-1 | 5-1 | 1-1 | 1-0 | 1-2 |     | 2-2 | 0-1 | 2-1 | 1-3 |
| 19 | Tonbridge Angels     | 1-0 | 0-0 | 3-4 | 1-1 | 4-2 | 0-3 | 0-4 | 0-2 | 2-1 | 1-1 | 3-1 | 2-3 | 1-0 | 1-1 | 2-1 | 1-2 | 1-0 | 1-1 |     | 3-2 | 1-1 | 1-1 |
| 20 | Truro City           | 3-2 | 2-2 | 2-1 | 2-4 | 2-0 | 0-1 | 1-2 | 1-2 | 0-3 | 2-2 | 1-3 | 3-3 | 3-3 | 3-1 | 0-1 | 1-1 | 0-3 | 1-2 | 2-0 |     | 0-3 | 1-2 |
| 21 | Welling United       | 4-0 | 1-1 | 1-1 | 5-2 | 4-0 | 3-1 | 3-0 | 3-2 | 1-1 | 2-0 | 1-1 | 2-0 | 1-0 | 3-0 | 3-2 | 1-0 | 3-2 | 2-2 | 4-1 | 4-3 |     | 4-1 |
| 22 | Weston-super-Mare    | 1-0 | 5-2 | 1-4 | 1-0 | 2-4 | 3-0 | 3-0 | 2-0 | 0-3 | 3-2 | 2-4 | 1-1 | 2-2 | 1-1 | 1-1 | 0-3 | 1-0 | 1-1 | 2-0 | 0-2 | 2-0 |     |

# ALDERSHOT TOWN

**Chairman:** TBA once the club comes out of administration.
**Secretary:** Bob Green      **(T)** 01252 320 211      **(E)** admin@theshots.co.uk
**Commercial Manager:** Dan Boardman      **(T)** 01252 320 211
**Programme Editor:** Victoria Rogers      **(T)** 01252 320 211
**Ground Address:** EBB Stadium, High street, Aldershot, GU11 1TW
**(T)** 01252 320 211                  **Manager:** TBA

## Club Factfile

**Founded:** 1992      **Nickname:** Shots
**Previous Names:** None
**Previous Leagues:** Isthmian 1992-2003. Conference 2003-2008. Football League 2008-13.

**Club Colours (change):** red/blue/red (blue/red/blue)

**Ground Capacity:** 7,500   **Seats:** 1,800   **Covered:** 6,850   **Clubhouse:** Yes   **Shop:** Yes

**Directions**
Exit from the M3 at junction 4 and take the A331 to Aldershot , after 3 miles take the 4th exit off the A331 and take the Town Centre route to Aldershot.
1.25 miles from the A331 junction the ground will be on your right hand side. Located on the High Street in Aldershot.

**Previous Grounds:** None

**Record Attendance:** 7,500 v Brighton & Hove Albion, FA Cup 1st Round, 18/11/2000
**Record Victory:** 8-0 v Bishop's Stortford (A) Isthmian Premier 05/09/1998
**Record Defeat:** 0-6 v Worthing (A) Isthmian League Cup 02/03/99
**Record Goalscorer:** Mark Butler - 155 (1992-96)
**Record Appearances:** Jason Chewings - 400
**Additional Records:**

**Senior Honours:**
Isthmian League Premier Division 2002-03. Conference 2007-08.

### 10 YEAR RECORD

| 03-04 | | 04-05 | | 05-06 | | 06-07 | | 07-08 | | 08-09 | | 09-10 | | 10-11 | | 11-12 | | 12-13 | |
|---|---|---|---|---|---|---|---|---|---|---|---|---|---|---|---|---|---|---|---|
| Conf | 5 | Conf | 4 | Conf | 13 | Conf | 9 | Conf | 1 | FL 2 | 15 | FL 2 | 6 | FL 2 | 14 | FL 2 | 11 | FL 2 | 24 |

# MATCH RESULTS 2012-13

| Date | Comp | H/A | Opponents | Att: | Result | Goalscorers | Pos | No. |
|------|------|-----|-----------|------|--------|-------------|-----|-----|
| Aug 11 | LC 1 | A | Wolverhampton Wanderers | 11,555 | D 1-1 | Rankine 62 (lost 6-7 on pens) | | 1 |
| 18 | FL 2 | A | Plymouth Argyle | 7,020 | W 2-0 | Brown 5, Payne 54 (pen) | | 2 |
| 21 | FL 2 | H | Exeter City | 2,678 | L 1-2 | Reid 17 | | 3 |
| 25 | FL 2 | H | Cheltenham Town | 2,166 | L 0-1 | | | 4 |
| Sept 1 | FL 2 | A | Fleetwood Town | 2,510 | L 1-4 | Davies 37 (og) | | 5 |
| 4 | JPT 1 | A | Exeter City | 1,944 | D 0-0 | (Won 4-3 on pens) | | 6 |
| 8 | FL 2 | A | Bristol Rovers | 5,117 | D 2-2 | Reid 18, Rodman 57 | | 7 |
| 15 | FL 2 | H | Morecambe | 1,960 | D 0-0 | | | 8 |
| 18 | FL 2 | H | Barnet | 1,760 | W 1-0 | Reid 68 | | 9 |
| 22 | FL 2 | A | Accrington Stanley | 1,379 | L 0-1 | | | 10 |
| 29 | FL 2 | H | York City | 2,176 | L 0-2 | | | 11 |
| Oct 2 | FL 2 | A | Torquay United | 2,358 | L 3-4 | Reid 3 (28, 37 (pen), 47) | | 12 |
| 6 | FL 2 | H | Chestefield | 2,006 | L 0-1 | | | 13 |
| 9 | JPT 2 | A | Plymouth Argyle | 2,580 | L 1-2 | Reid 12 | | 14 |
| 13 | FL 2 | A | Gillingham | 5,039 | L 0-4 | | | 15 |
| 20 | FL 2 | H | Rotherham United | 1,953 | L 0-3 | | | 16 |
| 23 | FL 2 | A | Southend United | 4,225 | W 2-1 | Hylton 1, Bradley 87 | | 17 |
| 27 | FL 2 | A | Dagenham & Redbridge | 1,771 | D 0-0 | | | 18 |
| Nov 3 | FAC 1 | H | Hendon | 1,822 | W 2-1 | Hylton 57, 85 | | 19 |
| 6 | FL 2 | H | Wycombe Wanderers | 2,042 | D 0-0 | | | 20 |
| 10 | FL 2 | H | Bradford City | 2,143 | L 0-2 | | | 21 |
| 17 | FL 2 | A | AFC Wimbledon | 4,321 | D 1-1 | Lopez 45 | | 22 |
| 20 | FL 2 | A | Burton Albion | 1,712 | W 1-0 | Lopez 4 | | 23 |
| 24 | FL 2 | H | Port Vale | 1,992 | L 1-3 | Lopez 29 | | 24 |
| Dec 1 | FAC 2 | A | Fleetwood Town | 1,757 | W 3-2 | Hylton 19, 75, Vincenti 45 | | 25 |
| 8 | FL 2 | A | Oxford United | 5,721 | D 1-1 | Mekki 84 | | 26 |
| 15 | FL 2 | H | Rochdale | 1,910 | W 4-2 | Lopez 8, Vincenti 39, Rose 45, Reid 90 | | 27 |
| 22 | FL 2 | A | Northampton Town | 4,574 | L 0-2 | | | 28 |
| 26 | FL 2 | H | Bristol Rovers | 2,862 | D 2-2 | Hector 33, Reid 76 (pen) | | 29 |
| Jan 1 | FL 2 | A | Barnet | 2,772 | W 1-0 | Reid 48 (pen) | | 30 |
| 5 | FAC 3 | H | Rotherham United | 2,992 | W 3-1 | Hylton 3 (6, 23, 62) | | 31 |
| 12 | FL 2 | H | Accrington Stanley | 1,912 | W 2-0 | Brown 12, Lopez 81 | | 32 |
| 19 | FL 2 | A | York City | 2,757 | D 0-0 | | | 33 |
| 22 | FL 2 | H | Northampton Town | 1,191 | L 1-2 | Lopez 2 | | 34 |
| 26 | FAC 4 | A | Middlesbrough | 12,684 | L 1-2 | Hylton 89 | | 35 |
| Feb 2 | FL 2 | A | Exeter City | 3,755 | D 0-0 | | | 36 |
| 9 | FL 2 | H | Plymouth Argyle | 3,241 | L 1-2 | Vincenti 11 | | 37 |
| 12 | FL 2 | A | Morecambe | 1,226 | L 1-2 | Hylton 90 | | 38 |
| 16 | FL 2 | A | Cheltenham Town | 3,119 | D 1-1 | Rose 23 | | 39 |
| 19 | FL 2 | H | Torquay United | 2,095 | W 1-0 | Brown 83 | | 40 |
| 23 | FL 2 | H | Fleetwood Town | 2,032 | W 2-0 | Hylton 38, 84 | | 41 |
| 26 | FL 2 | A | Chestefield | 3,968 | D 0-0 | | | 42 |
| Mar 2 | FL 2 | H | Gillingham | 3,267 | D 1-1 | Reid 47 | | 43 |
| 9 | FL 2 | A | Bradford City | 10,397 | D 1-1 | Cadogan 45 | | 44 |
| 12 | FL 2 | A | Burton Albion | 1,568 | L 1-2 | McCallum 3 | | 45 |
| 16 | FL 2 | H | AFC Wimbledon | 3,699 | L 0-1 | | | 46 |
| 29 | FL 2 | H | Rochdale | 2,280 | D 1-1 | Mekki 73 | | 47 |
| Apr 1 | FL 2 | H | Oxford United | 2,927 | W 3-2 | McCallum 13, Reid 49 (pen), Goulding 87 | | 48 |
| 9 | FL 2 | A | Port Vale | 6,197 | D 1-1 | McCallum 74 | | 49 |
| 13 | FL 2 | A | Wycombe Wanderers | 4,290 | L 1-2 | Stanley 68 | | |
| 16 | FL 2 | H | Southend United | 2,568 | L 0-2 | | | |
| 20 | FL 2 | H | Dagenham & Redbridge | 2,861 | W 1-0 | Rankine 56 | | |
| 27 | FL 2 | A | Rotherham United | 11,300 | L 0-2 | | 24 | 50 |

| GOALSCORERS | Lge | FAC | LC/JPT | Total | Pens | Hat-tricks | Cons Run | | Lge | FAC | LC/JPT | Total | Pens | Hat-tricks | Cons Run |
|-------------|-----|-----|--------|-------|------|-----------|----------|---|-----|-----|--------|-------|------|-----------|----------|
| Hylton | 7 | 5 | | 12 | | 1 | | Cadogan | 1 | | | 1 | | | |
| Reid | 11 | 1 | | 12 | 4 | 1 | 2 | Goulding | 1 | | | 1 | | | |
| Lopez | 6 | | | 6 | | | 3 | Hector | 1 | | | 1 | | | |
| Brown | 3 | | | 3 | | | | Payne | 1 | | | 1 | 1 | | |
| McCallum | 3 | | | 3 | | | 2 | Rodman | 1 | | | 1 | | | |
| Vincenti | 2 | 1 | | 3 | | | | Stanley | 1 | | | 1 | | | |
| Mekki | 2 | | | 2 | | | | Opponents | 1 | | | | | | |
| Rankine | 1 | | 1 | 2 | | | | Cons Run - Consecutive scoring games. | | | | | | | |
| Rose | 2 | | | 2 | | | | | | | | | | | |
| Bradley | 1 | | | 1 | | | | | | | | | | | |

# ALFRETON TOWN

**Chairman:** Wayne Bradley
**Secretary:** Bryan Rudkin  **(T)** 07710 444 195  **(E)** bryanrudkin@hotmail.com
**Commercial Manager:** Charlotte Webster  **(T)** 01773 830 277
**Programme Editor:** Image2print Ltd  **(T)**
**Ground Address:** Impact Arena, North Street, Alfreton, Derbyshire DE55 7FZ
**(T)** 01773 830 277  **Manager:** Nicky Law

Alfreton's Tom Shaw challenges for the ball during the Conference Premier's
pre-season friendly against Burton Albion. Photo: Bill Wheatcroft.

## Club Factfile

**Founded:** 1959  **Nickname:** The Reds
**Previous Names:** Formed when Alfreton Miners Welfare and Alfreton United merged.
**Previous Leagues:** Central Alliance (pre reformation 1921-25) 59-61. Midland Combination 1925-27, 61-82. Northern Counties East 1982-87. Northern Premier 1987-99.

**Club Colours (change):** All red (All blue)

**Ground Capacity:** 3,600  **Seats:** 1,500  **Covered:** 2,600  **Clubhouse:** Yes  **Shop:** Yes

**Directions**
From M1 Junction 28 Take A38 towards Derby for 2 miles.
Then take slip road onto B600 Turn right at Tjunction towards town centre.
At pedestrian crossing turn left into North Street and the ground is on the right hand side.

**Previous Grounds:** None

**Record Attendance:** 5,023 v Matlock Town - Central Alliance 1960
**Record Victory:** 15-0 v Loughbrough  Midland League 1969-70
**Record Defeat:** 1-9 v Solihull - FAT 1997. 0-8 v Bridlington - 1992
**Record Goalscorer:** J Harrison - 303
**Record Appearances:** J Harrison - 560+
**Additional Records:** Paid £2,000 to Worksop Town for Mick Goddard
Received £7,000 from Ilkeston Town for Paul Eshelby
**Senior Honours:**
Northern Counties East 1984-85, 2001-02. Northern Premier League Division 1 2002-03.
Conference North 2010-11.
Derbyshire Senior Cup x7

### 10 YEAR RECORD

| 03-04 | 04-05 | 05-06 | 06-07 | 07-08 | 08-09 | 09-10 | 10-11 | 11-12 | 12-13 |
|---|---|---|---|---|---|---|---|---|---|
| NP P  4 | Conf N  14 | Conf N  17 | Conf N  14 | Conf N  16 | Conf N  3 | Conf N  3 | Conf N  1 | Conf  15 | Conf  13 |

# MATCH RESULTS 2012-13

| Date | Comp | H/A | Opponents | Att: | Result | Goalscorers | Pos | No. |
|------|------|-----|-----------|------|--------|-------------|-----|-----|
| Aug 11 | BSP | A | Stockport County | 3448 | L 0-1 | | 22 | 1 |
| 14 | BSP | H | Southport | 562 | D 3-3 | Clayton 6 85 Tomlinson 61 (pen) | 18 | 2 |
| 18 | BSP | H | Hereford United | 690 | L 0-3 | | 21 | 3 |
| 25 | BSP | A | Barrow | 798 | W 3-0 | Clayton 28 71 Tomlinson 51 | 15 | 4 |
| 27 | BSP | H | Nuneaton Town | 680 | L 0-3 | | 21 | 5 |
| Sept 1 | BSP | A | Dartford | 1145 | L 1-5 | Meadows 80 | 21 | 6 |
| 4 | BSP | A | Lincoln City | 1566 | W 2-1 | Wilson 64 Kempson 80 | 21 | 7 |
| 8 | BSP | H | Luton Town | 1392 | W 3-0 | Wilson 2 66 Bradley 23 (pen) | 14 | 8 |
| 15 | BSP | A | Forest Green Rovers | 1072 | D 1-1 | Bradley 90 (pen) | 16 | 9 |
| 22 | BSP | H | Kidderminster Harriers | 659 | D 1-1 | Bradley 29 | 15 | 10 |
| 29 | BSP | H | Braintree Town | 496 | D 1-1 | Bradley 44 (pen) | 17 | 11 |
| Oct 6 | BSP | A | Mansfield Town | 1437 | W 2-1 | Bradley 1 Arnold 87 | 16 | 12 |
| 9 | BSP | H | Grimsby Town | 1192 | L 0-2 | | 18 | 13 |
| 13 | BSP | A | Ebbsfleet United | 804 | D 0-0 | | 18 | 14 |
| 20 | FAC Q4 | H | Gateshead | 338 | W 2-0 | Arnold 55 Tomlinson 64 | | 15 |
| 27 | BSP | H | AFC Telford United | 572 | D 1-1 | Tomlinson 45 | 16 | 16 |
| Nov 3 | FAC 1 | A | Wrexham | 2409 | W 4-2 | Clayton 27 Bradley 60 (pen) Tomlinson 79 90 | | 17 |
| 6 | BSP | A | Gateshead | 475 | L 0-2 | | 16 | 18 |
| 9 | BSP | H | Newport County | 663 | W 4-3 | Arnold 5 Clayton 15 70 Bradley 44 (pen) | 16 | 19 |
| 17 | BSP | A | Woking | 1537 | W 2-1 | Clayton 26 54 | 15 | 20 |
| 20 | BSP | A | Hyde FC | 444 | D 1-1 | Franks 39 | 12 | 21 |
| 24 | FAT 1 | H | Kidderminster Harriers | 361 | L 1-3 | Bradley 18 | | 22 |
| Dec 2 | FAC 2 | H | Leyton Orient | 1104 | L 2-4 | Clayton 3 Tomlinson 51 | | 23 |
| 8 | BSP | A | Luton Town | 5648 | L 0-3 | | 18 | 24 |
| 17 | BSP | H | Cambridge United | 534 | D 1-1 | Law 28 | 18 | 25 |
| 26 | BSP | A | Mansfield Town | 4186 | W 2-1 | Clayton 37 Tomlinson 57 | 15 | 26 |
| Jan 1 | BSP | H | Mansfield Town | 1537 | L 0-3 | | | 27 |
| 5 | BSP | H | Dartford | 522 | W 3-2 | Meadows 45 89 Brown 75 | | 28 |
| 8 | BSP | H | Wrexham | 628 | L 1-2 | Tomlinson 33 | | 29 |
| 12 | BSP | A | Hereford United | 1565 | D 3-3 | Clayton 37 Arnold 57 Franklin 63 | 14 | 30 |
| 19 | BSP | A | AFC Telford United | 1291 | D 0-0 | | 14 | 31 |
| Feb 2 | BSP | H | Grimsby Town | 3868 | L 2-4 | Bradley 27 (pen) Clayton 71 | 17 | 32 |
| 7 | BSP | H | Woking | 606 | L 0-3 | | 18 | 33 |
| 12 | BSP | A | Cambridge United | 1779 | W 3-0 | Franks 52 Arnold 89 Clayton 90 | 15 | 34 |
| 16 | BSP | H | Macclesfield Town | 740 | L 1-2 | Clayton 36 | 16 | 35 |
| 19 | BSP | A | Nuneaton Town | 781 | L 0-1 | | 17 | 36 |
| 23 | BSP | A | Kidderminster Harriers | 2209 | L 1-3 | Tomlinson 29 | 17 | 37 |
| 26 | BSP | H | Hyde FC | 476 | W 5-1 | TOMLINSON 3 (4 14 47) Clayton 69 Boden 89 | 16 | 38 |
| Mar 2 | BSP | A | Wrexham | 3706 | D 1-1 | Boden 57 | 16 | 39 |
| 9 | BSP | A | Tamworth | 703 | D 1-1 | Soares 29 | 16 | 40 |
| 12 | BSP | H | Ebbsfleet United | 459 | W 3-0 | Bradley14 (Pen) Tomlinson 28 Rose 71 | 14 | 41 |
| 16 | BSP | H | Gateshead | 566 | W 3-2 | Tomlinson 77 Hewitt 78 Boden 90 | 13 | 42 |
| 28 | BSP | A | Braintree Town | 409 | L 1-2 | Soares 90 | 15 | 43 |
| 30 | BSP | H | Lincoln City | 1189 | L 0-2 | | 17 | 44 |
| Apr 1 | BSP | A | Southport | 830 | W 2-0 | Brown 2 Meadows 37 | 15 | 45 |
| 6 | BSP | H | Stockport County | 1157 | L 2-3 | Meadows 21 Arnold 90 | 15 | 46 |
| 9 | BSP | H | Barrow | 525 | W 4-0 | Clayton 46 55 Arnold 70 81 | 15 | 47 |
| 11 | BSP | H | Tamworth | 568 | W 3-0 | Bradley 19 Clayton 30  Arnold 62 | 13 | 48 |
| 13 | BSP | A | Newport County | 2138 | L 0-2 | | 14 | 49 |
| 20 | BSP | H | Forest Green Rovers | 759 | W 2-1 | Law 9 Arnold 37 | 13 | 50 |

| GOALSCORERS | Lge | FAC | FAT | Total | Pens | Hat-tricks | Cons Run | | Lge | FAC | FAT | Total | Pens | Hat-tricks | Cons Run |
|-------------|-----|-----|-----|-------|------|------------|----------|---|-----|-----|-----|-------|------|------------|----------|
| Clayton | 17 | 2 | | 19 | | | 2 | Soares | 2 | | | 2 | | | |
| Tomlinson | 10 | 4 | | 15 | 1 | 1 | 2 | Franklin | 1 | | | 1 | | | |
| Bradley | 8 | 1 | 1 | 11 | 7 | | 4 | Hewitt | 1 | | | 1 | | | |
| Arnold | 9 | 1 | | 10 | | | 3 | Kempson | 1 | | | 1 | | | |
| Meadows | 5 | | | 5 | | | | Rose | 1 | | | 1 | | | |
| Boden | 3 | | | 3 | | | | Cons Run - Consecutive scoring games. | | | | | | | |
| Franks | 3 | | | 3 | | | | | | | | | | | |
| Wilson | 3 | | | 3 | | | | | | | | | | | |
| Brown | 2 | | | 2 | | | | | | | | | | | |
| Law | 2 | | | 2 | | | | | | | | | | | |

# BARNET

**Chairman:** Anthony Kleanthous
**Secretary:** Andrew Adie   **(T)** 020 8381 3800   **(E)** aadie@barnetfc.com
**Commercial Manager:** Tony Peck   **(T)** 020 8381 3800
**Programme Editor:** David Bloomfield   **(T)** 020 8381 3800
**Ground Address:** The Hive, Camrose Avenue, Edgware, Middlesex, HA8 6AG
**(T)** 020 8381 3800   **Manager:** Edgar Davids

The brand new West Stand - which can seat 2,684.

## Club Factfile

**Founded:** 1885   **Nickname:** The Bees
**Previous Names:** New Barnet 1885-88. Barnet 1888-1902 (folded). Barnet Alston 1904-19.
**Previous Leagues:** Post 1945 - Athenian 1945-65. Southern 1965-79. Conference 1979-91, 2001-05. Football League 1991-2001, 05-13.

**Club Colours (change):** All black & amber (All purple & white)

**Ground Capacity:** 5,176   **Seats:** 2,684   **Covered:** 5,176   **Clubhouse:** Yes   **Shop:** Yes

**Directions:** Leave M1 at junction 4, take the A41 towards Edgware, at the first roundabout turn right on to the A410 towards Stanmore (London Road), pass the Stanmore Tube Station on your left, at the next set of lights, turn left on the A4140 (Marsh Lane into Honeypot Lane) towards Queensbury/Kingsbury after approx 2 miles turn left at the roundabout by the Tesco petrol station in to Taunton Way, then Camrose Avenue, The Hive is on your left hand side.

**Previous Grounds:** Underhill 1907-2013

**Record Attendance:** 11,026 v Wycombe Wanderers FA Amateur Cup 01/01/1953
**Record Victory:** 7-0 v Blackpool Division 3 11/11/2000
**Record Defeat:** 1-9 v Peterborough Division 3 05/09/1998
**Record Goalscorer:** Arthur Morris - 400
**Record Appearances:**
**Additional Records:**

**Senior Honours:**
Athenian League 1931-32, 32-33, 46-47, 58-59, 63-64, 64-65. Southern League Division One 1965-66, Division One South 1977-78.
Football Conference 1990-91, 2004-05.
Amateur Cup 1945-46.

### 10 YEAR RECORD

| 03-04 | | 04-05 | | 05-06 | | 06-07 | | 07-08 | | 08-09 | | 09-10 | | 10-11 | | 11-12 | | 12-13 | |
|---|---|---|---|---|---|---|---|---|---|---|---|---|---|---|---|---|---|---|---|
| Conf | 4 | Conf | 1 | FL 2 | 18 | FL 2 | 14 | FL 2 | 12 | FL 2 | 17 | FL 2 | 11 | FL 2 | 22 | FL 2 | 22 | FL 2 | 23 |

# MATCH RESULTS 2012-13

| Date | Comp | H/A | Opponents | Att: | Result | Goalscorers | Pos | No. |
|------|------|-----|-----------|------|--------|-------------|-----|-----|
| Aug 14 | LC 1 | A | Birmingham City | 9905 | L 1-5 | Nurse 31 | | 1 |
| 18 | FL 2 | A | Port Vale | 4608 | L 0-3 | | | 2 |
| 21 | FL 2 | H | Bristol Rovers | 1794 | D 1-1 | Holmes 9 | | 3 |
| 25 | FL 2 | H | York City | 1889 | L 1-3 | Nurse 30 | | 4 |
| Sept 1 | FL 2 | A | Rochdale | 2021 | L 0-2 | | | 5 |
| 8 | FL 2 | H | Gillingham | 2835 | L 1-3 | Saville 23 | | 6 |
| 15 | FL 2 | A | Bradford City | 9566 | L 0-3 | | | 7 |
| 18 | FL 2 | A | Aldershot Town | 1760 | L 0-1 | | | 8 |
| 22 | FL 2 | H | Rotherham United | 1821 | D 0-0 | | | 9 |
| 29 | FL 2 | A | Fleetwood Town | 3615 | L 1-2 | Hyde 5 | | 10 |
| Oct 2 | FL 2 | H | Exeter city | 1483 | L 1-2 | Hyde 81 | | 11 |
| 6 | FL 2 | A | Southend United | 5025 | D 2-2 | Holmes 54, Hyde 65 | | 12 |
| 9 | JPT 1 | A | Leyton Orient | 1404 | L 0-1 | | | 13 |
| 13 | FL 2 | H | Plymouth Argyle | 3229 | L 1-4 | Stephens 16 | | 14 |
| 19 | FL 2 | H | Northampton Town | 2721 | W 4-0 | Pearce 56, Yiadom 65, Edgar 90, Oster 90 | | 15 |
| 23 | FL 2 | A | Wycombe Wanderers | 3244 | D 0-0 | | | 16 |
| 27 | FL 2 | A | Chesterfield | 5611 | W 1-0 | Byrne 90 (Pen) | | 17 |
| Nov 3 | FAC 1 | H | Oxford United | 2346 | L 0-2 | | | 18 |
| 6 | FL 2 | H | Torquay United | 1544 | W 1-0 | Kamdjo 79 | | 19 |
| 10 | FL 2 | A | Morecambe | 1653 | L 1-4 | Nurse 90 | | 20 |
| 16 | FL 2 | H | Accrington Stanley | 2238 | D 1-1 | Byrne 71 (Pen) | | 21 |
| 20 | FL 2 | H | Oxford United | 1626 | D 2-2 | Hyde 5, 70 | | 22 |
| 24 | FL 2 | A | Cheltenham Town | 2591 | L 0-1 | | | 23 |
| Dec 8 | FL 2 | H | AFC Wimbledon | 3217 | D 1-1 | Hyde 64 | | 24 |
| 15 | FL 2 | A | Dagenham & Redbridge | 2020 | L 0-1 | | | 25 |
| 21 | FL 2 | H | Burton Albion | 1751 | W 3-2 | HOLMES 3 (42, PEN 53, 66) | | 26 |
| 26 | FL 2 | A | Gillingham | 7448 | W 1-0 | Hyde 19 | | 27 |
| 29 | FL 2 | A | Exeter City | 4085 | D 2-2 | Nurse 76, Iro 90 | | 28 |
| Jan 1 | FL 2 | H | Aldershot Town | 2772 | L 0-1 | | | 29 |
| 5 | FL 2 | H | Bradford City | 2317 | W 2-0 | Atieno 41, Oster 48 | | 30 |
| 12 | FL 2 | A | Rotherham United | 7434 | W 2-0 | Hyde 21, Yiadom 82 | | 31 |
| 26 | FL 2 | A | Burton Albion | 2050 | L 0-1 | | | 32 |
| Feb 1 | FL 2 | A | Bristol Rovers | 8527 | L 1-2 | Crawford 90 | | 33 |
| 9 | FL 2 | H | Port vale | 2398 | D 0-0 | | | 34 |
| 16 | FL 2 | A | York City | 3594 | W 2-1 | Yiadom 25, Hyde 73 | | 35 |
| 23 | FL 2 | H | Rochdale | 1870 | D 0-0 | | | 36 |
| 26 | FL 2 | H | Southend United | 2211 | W 2-0 | Hyde 33, Davids 84 | | 37 |
| Mar 2 | FL 2 | A | Plymouth Argyle | 8210 | L 1-2 | Hyde 21 | | 38 |
| 9 | FL 2 | H | Morecambe | 2012 | W 4-1 | Gambin 52, LOPEZ 3 (65, pen 70, 87) | | 39 |
| 12 | FL 2 | A | Oxford United | 5027 | L 0-1 | | | 40 |
| 16 | FL 2 | A | Accrington Stanley | 1559 | L 2-3 | Johnson 45, Jenkins 63 | | 41 |
| 19 | FL 2 | H | Fleetwood Town | 1731 | W 2-0 | Byrne 23, Gambin 60 | | 42 |
| 23 | FL 2 | H | Cheltenham Town | 2400 | D 0-0 | | | 43 |
| 29 | FL 2 | H | Dagenham & Redbridge | 3680 | D 0-0 | | | 44 |
| Apr 1 | FL 2 | A | AFC Wimbledon | 4696 | W 1-0 | Marsh-Brown 85 | | 45 |
| 6 | FL 2 | H | Chesterfield | 2574 | L 0-2 | | | 46 |
| 16 | FL 2 | A | Torquay United | 2722 | L 2-3 | Hyde 58, 77 | | 47 |
| 20 | FL 2 | H | Wycombe Wanderers | 6001 | W 1-0 | Hyde 81 | | 48 |
| 27 | FL 2 | A | Northampton Town | 7471 | L 0-2 | | 23 | 49 |

| GOALSCORERS | Lge | FAC | LC | Total | Pens | Hat-tricks | Cons Run | | Lge | FAC | LC | Total | Pens | Hat-tricks | Cons Run |
|-------------|-----|-----|-----|-------|------|------------|----------|---|-----|-----|-----|-------|------|------------|----------|
| Hyde | 14 | | | 14 | | | 3 | Davids | 1 | | | 1 | | | |
| Holmes | 5 | | | 5 | 1 | 1 | | Edgar | 1 | | | 1 | | | |
| Nurse | 3 | 1 | | 4 | | | | Iro | 1 | | | 1 | | | |
| Byrne | 3 | | | 3 | 2 | | | Jenkins | 1 | | | 1 | | | |
| Lopez | 3 | | | 3 | 1 | 1 | | Johnson | 1 | | | 1 | | | |
| Yiadom | 3 | | | 3 | | | | Kamdjo | 1 | | | 1 | | | |
| Gambin | 2 | | | 2 | | | | Marsh-Brown | 1 | | | 1 | | | |
| Oster | 2 | | | 2 | | | | Pearce | 1 | | | 1 | | | |
| Antieno | 1 | | | 1 | | | | Saville | 1 | | | 1 | | | |
| Crawford | 1 | | | 1 | | | | Cons Run - Consecutive scoring games. | | | | | | | |

# BRAINTREE TOWN

**Chairman:** Lee Harding
**Secretary:** Tom Woodley    **(T)** 07950 537 179    **(E)** tawoodley@talktalk.net
**Commercial Manager:** Alan Stuckley    **(T)** 07800 885849
**Programme Editor:** Lee Harding    **(T)** 07771 810440
**Ground Address:** The Amlin Stadium, off Clockhouse Way, Braintree CM7 3RD
**(T)** 01376 345 617    **Manager:** Alan Devonshire

## Club Factfile

**Founded:** 1898    **Nickname:** The Iron
**Previous Names:** Crittall Athletic > 1968, Braintree and Crittall Athletic > 1981, Braintree > 1983
**Previous Leagues:** N.Essex 1898-1925, Essex & Suffolk Border 1925-29, 55-64, Spartan 1928-35, Eastern Co. 1935-37, 38-39, 52-55, 70-91, Essex Co. 1937-38, London 1945-52, Gt London 1964-66, Met 1966-70, Southern 1991-96, Isthmian 1996-2006

**Club Colours (change):** Orange/blue/blue (White/orange/orange)

**Ground Capacity:** 4,222    **Seats:** 553    **Covered:** 1,288    **Clubhouse:** Yes    **Shop:** Yes

**Directions** Leave M11 at junction 8A (for Stansted Airport) and follow A120 towards Braintree and Colchester for 17 miles. At Gallows Corner roundabout (with WestDrive Kia on your right) take first exit into Cressing Road. Clockhouse Way and the entrance to the ground are three quarters of a mile on the left and are clearly sign-posted.

**Previous Grounds:** The Fiar Field 1898-1903, Spalding Meadow and Panfield Lane

**Record Attendance:** 4,000 v Tottenham Hotspur - Testimonial May 1952
**Record Victory:** 12-0 v Thetford - Eastern Counties League 1935-36
**Record Defeat:** 0-14 v Chelmsford City (A) - North Essex League 1923
**Record Goalscorer:** Chris Guy - 211 (1963-90)
**Record Appearances:** Paul Young - 524 (1966-77)
**Additional Records:** Gary Bennett scored 57 goals during season 1997-98
**Senior Honours:** Received £10,000 from Brentford for Matt Metcalf and from Colchester United for John Cheesewright
Eastern Counties League 1983-84, 84-85, Essex Senior Cup 1995-96. Isthmian League Premier Division 2005-06.
Conference South Champions 2010-11.
East Anglian Cup x3

| 10 YEAR RECORD | | | | | | | | | |
|---|---|---|---|---|---|---|---|---|---|
| 03-04 | 04-05 | 05-06 | 06-07 | 07-08 | 08-09 | 09-10 | 10-11 | 11-12 | 12-13 |
| Isth P    23 | Isth P    4 | Isth P    1 | Conf S    3 | Conf S    5 | Conf S    14 | Conf S    7 | Conf S    1 | Conf    12 | Conf    9 |

# MATCH RESULTS 2012-13

| Date | Comp | H/A | Opponents | Att: | Result | Goalscorers | Pos | No. |
|---|---|---|---|---|---|---|---|---|
| Aug 11 | BSP | H | Hyde | 596 | D 2-2 | Sheppard 47 Quinton 90 | 8 | 1 |
| 14 | BSP | A | Ebbsfleet United | 857 | W 1-0 | Davis 70 | 7 | 2 |
| 18 | BSP | A | AFC Telford United | 1524 | L 0-3 | | 20 | 3 |
| 25 | BSP | H | Newport County | 611 | L 1-2 | Quinton 53 | 16 | 4 |
| 28 | BSP | A | Woking | 1588 | W 4-1 | Holman 16 64 Cestor (og) 51 Symons 54 | 11 | 5 |
| Sept 1 | BSP | H | Tamworth | 501 | W 2-1 | Gash 21 Holman 60 (pen) | 10 | 6 |
| 4 | BSP | H | Kidderminster Harriers | 579 | D 1-1 | Holman 17 | 11 | 7 |
| 8 | BSP | A | Macclesfield Town | 1509 | L 1-2 | Quinton 21 (pen) | 12 | 8 |
| 15 | BSP | A | Mansfield Town | 2049 | L 0-2 | | 15 | 9 |
| 22 | BSP | H | Stockport County | 653 | D 0-0 | | 14 | 10 |
| 25 | BSP | H | Dartford | 721 | L 0-2 | | 16 | 11 |
| 29 | BSP | A | Alfreton Town | 496 | D 1-1 | Davis 80 (pen) | 16 | 12 |
| Oct 6 | BSP | H | Barrow | 608 | L 2-3 | Marks 8 Holman 12 | 18 | 13 |
| 9 | BSP | A | Luton Town | 5523 | W 3-2 | Holman 6 Marks 32 Paine 67 | 16 | 14 |
| 13 | BSP | A | Hereford United | 1537 | D 0-0 | | 16 | 15 |
| 20 | FAC4Q | H | Lowestoft Town | 634 | W 3-2 | Marks 3 15 O'Connor 50 | | 16 |
| Nov 6 | BSP | A | Lincoln City | 1455 | L 0-3 | | 21 | 17 |
| 10 | BSP | H | Gateshead | 678 | W 2-1 | Marks 6 Wells 55 | 19 | 18 |
| 13 | FAC 1 | H | Tranmere Rovers | 1503 | L 0-3 | | | 19 |
| 17 | BSP | A | Grimsby Town | 3722 | L 0-3 | | 21 | 20 |
| 20 | BSP | H | Wrexham | 508 | L 1-5 | Sheppard 18 | 22 | 21 |
| Dec 4 | FAT 1 | H | Havant & Waterlooville | 192 | L 1-2 | Marks 51 | | 22 |
| 8 | BSP | A | Southport | 803 | W 2-0 | Marks 16 20 | 21 | 23 |
| 18 | BSP | H | Forest Green Rovers | 480 | W 3-1 | Marks 29 Daley 71 Davis 82 (pen) | 17 | 24 |
| 26 | BSP | H | Cambridge United | 1133 | L 0-3 | | 19 | 25 |
| Jan 1 | BSP | A | Cambridge United | 2406 | L 0-1 | | | 26 |
| 5 | BSP | A | Tamworth | 763 | W 4-1 | Holman 17 Paine 20, Daley 61 Davis 88 (pen) | | 27 |
| 8 | BSP | H | Macclesfield Town | 502 | L 0-3 | | | 28 |
| 12 | BSP | H | AFC Telford United | 507 | W 3-2 | Daley 51 Marks Davis 80 (pen) | 17 | 29 |
| 26 | BSP | A | Nuneaton Town | 761 | W 4-2 | Mulley 16 Holman 48 Wells 67 Dack 87 | 13 | 30 |
| Feb 9 | BSP | H | Hereford United | 658 | L 0-2 | | 16 | 31 |
| 12 | BSP | A | Forest Green Rovers | 918 | L 1-4 | Daley 42 | 16 | 32 |
| 19 | BSP | A | Grimsby Town | 880 | W 2-0 | Daley 27 76 | 15 | 33 |
| 26 | BSP | H | Luton Town | 1003 | W 2-0 | Marks 42 Davis 49 | 15 | 34 |
| Mar 2 | BSP | A | Gateshead | 327 | W 2-1 | Wells 10 Marks 86 | 13 | 35 |
| 6 | BSP | A | Stockport County | 3250 | W 3-1 | Holman 47 Davis 53 60 | 14 | 36 |
| 9 | BSP | H | Woking | 506 | D 1-1 | Holman 84 | 14 | 37 |
| 21 | BSP | A | Nuneaton Town | 421 | D 2-2 | Sparks 16 Marks 32 | 14 | 38 |
| 26 | BSP | H | Lincoln City | 447 | L 0-3 | | 13 | 39 |
| 28 | BSP | H | Alfreton Town | 409 | W 2-1 | Marks 1 Davis 85 | 13 | 40 |
| 30 | BSP | A | Kidderminster Harriers | 2266 | L 1-2 | Davis 44 | 13 | 41 |
| Apr 1 | BSP | H | Ebbsfleet United | 822 | W 3-1 | Daley 12 Mulley 41 Davis 65 (pen) | 13 | 42 |
| 3 | BSP | H | Southport | 451 | L 1-3 | Marks 61 | 13 | 43 |
| 6 | BSP | A | Hyde | 509 | W 2-1 | Mulley 42 Wright 45 | 11 | 44 |
| 9 | BSP | A | Newport County | 1864 | L 0-1 | | 12 | 45 |
| 11 | BSP | A | Dartford | 1051 | D 0-0 | | 12 | 46 |
| 13 | BSP | H | Mansfield Town | 1755 | W 2-1 | Paine 60 Sheppard 71 | 10 | 47 |
| 16 | BSP | A | Wrexham | 2312 | D 1-1 | Wright 18 | 9 | 48 |
| 20 | BSP | A | Barrow | 780 | W 1-0 | Holman 88 | 9 | 49 |

| GOALSCORERS | Lge | FAC | FAT | Total | Pens | Hat-tricks | Cons Run | | Lge | FAC | FAT | Total | Pens | Hat-tricks | Cons Run |
|---|---|---|---|---|---|---|---|---|---|---|---|---|---|---|---|
| Marks | 12 | 3 | | 15 | | | 3 | Dack | 1 | | | 1 | | | |
| Davis | 11 | | | 11 | 5 | | 2 | Gash | 1 | | | 1 | | | |
| Holman | 11 | | | 11 | 1 | | 2 | Sparks | 1 | | | 1 | | | |
| Daley | 7 | | | 7 | | | | Symons | 1 | | | 1 | | | |
| Mulley | 3 | | | 3 | | | | Own goals | 1 | | | 1 | | | |
| Paine | 3 | | | 3 | | | | Cons Run - Consecutive scoring games. | | | | | | | |
| Quinton | 3 | | | 3 | 1 | | | | | | | | | | |
| Shepherd | 3 | | | 3 | | | | | | | | | | | |
| Wells | 3 | | | 3 | | | | | | | | | | | |
| Wright | 2 | | | 2 | | | | | | | | | | | |

# CAMBRIDGE UNITED

**Chairman:** Dave Doggett
**Secretary:** Claire Osbourn      **(T)** 01223 566500      **(E)** claire.osbourn@cambridge-united.co.uk
**Commercial Manager:** n/a      **(T)**
**Programme Editor:** Mark Johnson      **(T)** mark.johnson.6@btinternet.com
**Ground Address:** The R Costings Abbey Stadium, Newmarket Road, Cambridge CB5 8LN
**(T)** 01223 566 500      **Manager:** Richard Money

2012-13 Squad - Back row L-R: Michael Wylde, Luke Allen, Ross Jarvis, Jack Eades, Scott Garner, Sam Smith, Billy Gibson, Tom Shaw,
James Jennings, Harrison Dunk, Rory McAuley. Middle row L-R: Greg Reid (physiotherapist), Michael Gash, Ricky Wellard, Josh Coulson, Craig Ross, Jonathan Hedge, Will Norris, Blaine Hudson, Tom Elliott, Liam Hughes, Lance Key (GK coach)
Front row L-R: Luke Berry, Adriano Moke, James Brighton, Andy Pugh, Jez George (Manager), Nolan Keeley (First Team Coach), Adam Marriott, Robbie Willmott, Kevin Roberts, Jonathon Thorpe

## Club Factfile

**Founded:** 1912      **Nickname:** The U's
**Previous Names:** Abbey United 1919-51.
**Previous Leagues:** United Counties. Eastern Counties 1951-58. Southern 1958-70. Football League 1970-2005.

**Club Colours (change):** Amber/black/black (Sky blue/blue/blue)

**Ground Capacity:** 9,217   **Seats:** 2,500   **Covered:** 5,000   **Clubhouse:** Yes   **Shop:** Yes

**Directions**
A14 towards Cambridge and Newmarket, leave A14 at Junction with B1047. Turn right at top of slip road, follow road through Fen Ditton to TJunction and traffic lights. Turn right at lights, and go straight over at roundabout. Ground is on left hand side approximately 1/2 mile from roundabout.

**Previous Grounds:**

**Record Attendance:** 14,000 v Chelsea - Friendly 01/05/1970
**Record Victory:** 5-1 v Bristol City - FA Cup 5th Round 1989-90
**Record Defeat:** 0-7 v Sunderland - League Cup 2nd Round 2002-03
**Record Goalscorer:** John Taylor - 86 (1988-92, 96-2001)
**Record Appearances:** Steve Spriggs - 416 (1975-87)
**Additional Records:** Paid £192,000 to Luton Town for Steve Claridge 11/92. Received £1m from Manchester United for Dion Dublin 08/92 and from Leicester City for Trevor Benjamin 07/2000
**Senior Honours:** Football League Division Division Four 1976-77. Three 1990-91.

| | | | | | 10 YEAR RECORD | | | | | |
|---|---|---|---|---|---|---|---|---|---|---|
| 03-04 | 04-05 | 05-06 | 06-07 | 07-08 | 08-09 | 09-10 | 10-11 | 11-12 | 12-13 |
| FL 3   13 | FL 2   24 | Conf   12 | Conf   17 | Conf   2 | Conf   2 | Conf   10 | Conf   17 | Conf   9 | Conf   14 |

# MATCH RESULTS 2012-13

| Date | Comp | H/A | Opponents | Att: | Result | Goalscorers | Pos | No. |
|------|------|-----|-----------|------|--------|-------------|-----|-----|
| Aug 11 | BSP | A | Forest Green Rovers | 1128 | D 1-1 | Elliott 33 | 12 | 1 |
| 14 | BSP | H | Lincoln City | 2546 | W 2-1 | Elliott 3 Moke 81 | 8 | 2 |
| 18 | BSP | H | Southport | 2004 | W 2-0 | Elliott 52 55 | 4 | 3 |
| 25 | BSP | A | Nuneaton Town | 1175 | D 2-2 | Elliott 52 Jennings 90 | 5 | 4 |
| 27 | BSP | H | Dartford | 2691 | L 1-2 | Jennings 86 (pen) | 9 | 5 |
| Sept 1 | BSP | A | Stockport County | 3060 | D 1-1 | Berry 37 | 13 | 6 |
| 4 | BSP | A | Luton Town | 6592 | L 2-3 | Welland 13 McAuley 88 | 17 | 7 |
| 8 | BSP | H | Wrexham | 3304 | L 1-4 | Coulson 84 | 17 | 8 |
| 15 | BSP | H | AFC Telford United | 1962 | D 3-3 | Pugh 70 Gash 75 Shaw 90 | 17 | 9 |
| 22 | BSP | A | Hereford United | 1677 | L 2-4 | Gash 14 47 | 18 | 10 |
| 25 | BSP | H | Kidderminster Harriers | 1815 | L 1-3 | Coulson 50 | 19 | 11 |
| 29 | BSP | A | Barrow | 904 | W 4-1 | Gash 5 (pen) Flyn 8 (og) Pugh 52 Shaw 72 | 15 | 12 |
| Oct 6 | BSP | H | Mansfield Town | 2545 | W 4-1 | Gash 9 Berry 49 Elliott 51 Jarvis 58 | 14 | 13 |
| 9 | BSP | A | Woking | 1420 | L 1-2 | Willmott 64 | 15 | 14 |
| 13 | BSP | A | Gateshead | 768 | D 0-0 | | 16 | 15 |
| 20 | FAC Q4 | H | Luton Town | 2321 | L 0-2 | | | 16 |
| 27 | BSP | H | Hyde | 1779 | L 0-1 | | 18 | 17 |
| Nov 6 | BSP | A | Newport County | 1787 | L 2-6 | Elliott 29 Berry 69 | 20 | 18 |
| 10 | BSP | H | Macclesfield Town | 1821 | W 2-0 | Willmott 55 Elliott 58 | 18 | 19 |
| 17 | BSP | H | Tamworth | 3003 | D 1-1 | Dunk 76 | 18 | 20 |
| 24 | FAT 1 | A | Billericay Town | 537 | W 3-0 | Gash 39 Pugh 53 Elliott 88 | | 21 |
| Dec 4 | BSP | A | Ebbsfleet United | 842 | W 4-2 | ELLIOTT 3 (1 64 76) Smith 65 | 17 | 22 |
| 8 | BSP | H | Gateshead | 1840 | W 3-0 | Shaw 15 Coulson 47 Jennings 61 | 13 | 23 |
| 15 | FAT 2 | H | Gateshead | 1019 | L 0-1 | | | 24 |
| 18 | BSP | A | Alfreton Town | 534 | D 1-1 | Gash 90 (pen) | 13 | 25 |
| 26 | BSP | A | Braintree Town | 1133 | W 3-0 | Gash 25 Smith 59 Pugh 62 | 10 | 26 |
| 29 | BSP | A | Dartford | 1716 | D 1-1 | Gash 45 | 8 | 27 |
| Jan 1 | BSP | H | Braintree Town | 2406 | W 1-0 | Gash 74 | | 28 |
| 5 | BSP | H | Stockport County | 2305 | W 4-1 | Hughes 19 55 Coulson 42 Elliott 70 | | 29 |
| 16 | BSP | H | Nuneaton Town | 1740 | L 1-3 | Gash 88 | 8 | 30 |
| 26 | BSP | H | Grimsby Town | 2764 | D 0-0 | | 9 | 31 |
| Feb 2 | BSP | A | AFC Telford United | 1788 | W 2-1 | Pugh 17 Gash 74 | 8 | 32 |
| 9 | BSP | A | Kidderminster Harriers | 1949 | L 2-3 | Gowling 43 (og)  Gash 89 | 9 | 33 |
| 12 | BSP | H | Alfreton Town | 1779 | L 0-3 | | 10 | 34 |
| 16 | BSP | A | Mansfeld Town | 2508 | L 1-3 | Hughes 31 | 10 | 35 |
| 23 | BSP | H | Hereford United | 2171 | L 1-3 | Shaw 51 | 13 | 36 |
| 26 | BSP | A | Tamworth | 668 | W 2-1 | Elliott 9 Gash  64 (pen) | 11 | 37 |
| Mar 2 | BSP | H | Forest Green Rovers | 2221 | D 0-0 | | 11 | 38 |
| 5 | BSP | A | Southport | 615 | L 1-2 | Blissett 1 | 12 | 39 |
| 9 | BSP | H | Woking | 2054 | W 1-0 | Shaw 90 | 11 | 40 |
| 16 | BSP | A | Grimsby Town | 3516 | W 1-0 | Naylor 27 (og) | 9 | 41 |
| 19 | BSP | H | Ebbsfleet United | 1737 | D 1-1 | Dunk 80 | 10 | 42 |
| 26 | BSP | A | Hyde | 404 | L 1-2 | Hughes 15 | 11 | 43 |
| 30 | BSP | H | Luton Town | 3217 | D 2-2 | Shaw 20 Blisset 61 | 11 | 44 |
| Apr 1 | BSP | A | Lincoln City | 2721 | D 0-0 | | 12 | 45 |
| 6 | BSP | H | Newport County | 2102 | D 0-0 | | 13 | 46 |
| 9 | BSP | A | Wrexham | 2574 | L 0-1 | | 13 | 47 |
| 13 | BSP | H | Barrow | 2758 | W 2-1 | Smith 26 Elliott 45 | 13 | 48 |
| 20 | BSP | A | Macclesfield Town | 1984 | L 1-2 | Elliott 15 | 14 | 49 |

| GOALSCORERS | Lge | FAC | FAT | Total | Pens | Hat-tricks | Cons Run | | Lge | FAC | FAT | Total | Pens | Hat-tricks | Cons Run |
|-------------|-----|-----|-----|-------|------|------------|----------|---|-----|-----|-----|-------|------|------------|----------|
| Elliott | 15 | 1 | | 16 | | 1 | 4 | Dunk | 2 | | | 2 | | | |
| Gash | 13 | 1 | | 14 | 3 | | 4 | Willmott | 2 | | | 2 | | | |
| Shaw | 6 | | | 6 | | | | Jarvis | 1 | | | 1 | | | |
| Pugh | 4 | 1 | | 5 | | | | Macauley | 1 | | | 1 | | | |
| Coulson | 4 | | | 4 | | | | Moke | 1 | | | 1 | | | |
| Hughes | 4 | | | 4 | | | | Welland | 1 | | | 1 | | | |
| Berry | 3 | | | 3 | | | | Own Goals | 3 | | | 3 | | | |
| Jennings | 3 | | | 3 | 1 | | | Cons Run - Consecutive scoring games. | | | | | | | |
| Smith | 3 | | | 3 | | | | | | | | | | | |
| Blissett | 2 | | | 2 | | | | | | | | | | | |

# CHESTER

**Chairman:** Tony Durkin
**Secretary:** Calvin Hughes    **(T)** 07739 351 711    **(E)** calvin_hughes@o2.co.uk
**Commercial Manager:** Dave Richie        **(T)** 07876 832 857
**Programme Editor:** Rob Ashcroft        **(T)** 07935 218 619
**Ground Address:** Exacta Stadium, Bumpers Lane, Chester. CH1 4LT
**(T)** 01244 371 376                    **Manager:** Neil Young

2012-13 Squad - Back Row: Alex Hay (Chief Scout), Levi Mackin, Michael Powell, Michael Taylor, Paul Linwood, Dave Hankin, Adam Proudlock, Lee Worrall (Goalkeeping Coach)
Middle Row:Jimmy Soul (Kit Man), Dom Collins, Robbie Booth, Martin Fearon, John Danby, George Horan (Captain), Matty McGinn, Will Osbourne (Physio), Calvin Hughes (Football Secretary)
Front Row: Sean Clancy, Antoni Sarcevic, Wes Baynes, Gary Jones (Assistant Manager), Neil Young (Manager), Gary Powell (First Team Coach), Ashley Williams, Iain Howard, Nathan Jarman, Marc Williams

## Club Factfile

**Founded:** 1885      **Nickname:** Blues
**Previous Names:** Chester > 1983, Chester City 1983-2010
**Previous Leagues:** Cheshire 1919-31, Football League 1931-2000, 2004-09, Conference 2000-04, 09-10 (Did not finish the season)

**Club Colours (change):** Blue and white stripes/blue/blue (All purple)

**Ground Capacity:** 6,012    **Seats:** 3,284    **Covered:** Yes    **Clubhouse:** Yes    **Shop:** Yes

**Directions** Stay on the M56 until you reach a roundabout at the end of the motorway. Follow the signs to North Wales & Queensferry A5117. After around one and a half miles you will reach a set of traffic lights where you need to bear left on to the A550 (signposted North Wales & Queensferry). Then from the A550, take the A548 towards Chester. Head straight through the first set of traffic lights and after passing a Vauxhall and then a Renault garage on your left, turn right at the next lights into Sovereign Way. Continue to the end of Sovereign Way and then turn right into Bumpers Lane and the entrance to the Club car park is just down on the right.

**Previous Grounds:** Faulkner Street 1885-98, The Old Showground 98-99, Whipcord Lane 1901-06, Sealand Road 06-90, Macclesfield FC 90-92

**Record Attendance:** 20,378 v Chelsea - FA Cup 3rd Round replay 16/01/1952
**Record Victory:** 12-0 v York City - 01/02/1936
**Record Defeat:** Not known
**Record Goalscorer:** Stuart Rimmer - 135
**Record Appearances:** Ray Gill - 406 (1951-62)
**Additional Records:** Paid £100,000 to Rotherham for Gregg Blundell.
**Senior Honours:** Received £300,000 from Liverpool for Ian Rush.
Conference 2003-04, Conference North 2012-13.
Cheshire Senior Cup 1894-95, 96-97, 1903-04, 07-08, 08-09, 30-31, 31-32, 2012-13. Herefordshire Senior Cup 1991-92 (shared).
Welsh Cup 1907-08, 32-33, 46-47. NPL Division One North 2010-11, Premier Division 2011-12.

## 10 YEAR RECORD

| 03-04 | | 04-05 | | 05-06 | | 06-07 | | 07-08 | | 08-09 | | 09-10 | | 10-11 | | 11-12 | | 12-13 | |
|---|---|---|---|---|---|---|---|---|---|---|---|---|---|---|---|---|---|---|---|
| Conf | 1 | FL 2 | 20 | FL 2 | 15 | FL 2 | 18 | FL 2 | 22 | FL 2 | 23 | Conf | dnf | NP1N | 1 | NP P | 1 | Conf N | 1 |

# MATCH RESULTS 2012-13

| Date | Comp | H/A | Opponents | Att: | Result | Goalscorers | Pos | No. |
|---|---|---|---|---|---|---|---|---|
| Aug 18 | BSN | A | Oxford City | 1025 | W 1-0 | Howard 2 | 8 | 1 |
| 22 | BSN | H | Workington | 3007 | W 1-0 | Mills 62 | 5 | 2 |
| 25 | BSN | H | Colwyn Bay | 2404 | W 2-1 | Jarman 27 Mills 72 | 3 | 3 |
| 27 | BSN | A | Altrincham | 1940 | W 4-2 | Mills 13 20 Powell 80 McGinn 90 | 3 | 4 |
| Sept 1 | BSN | A | Solihull Moors | 566 | W 3-0 | Jarman 8 Mills 44 Howard 88 | 3 | 5 |
| 5 | BSN | H | FC Haifax Town | 3112 | W 2-1 | Mills 10 Hankin 52 | 2 | 6 |
| 8 | BSN | H | Guiseley | 2937 | W 4-0 | MILLS 3 ( 5 25 60) Howard 84 | 2 | 7 |
| 15 | BSN | A | Boston United | 1249 | L 2-3 | Howard 48 49 | 3 | 8 |
| 22 | FAC Q2 | A | Gainsborough T | 756 | D 1-1 | Jarman 30 | | 9 |
| 29 | BSN | A | Stalybridge Celtic | 1193 | W 6-2 | Sarcevic 20 47 Jarman 33 HOWARD 3 (36 43 73) | 3 | 10 |
| Oct 2 | FAC Q2r | H | Gainsborough T | 1492 | W 2-1 | Collins 65 Mackin 106 *aet | | 11 |
| 6 | FAC Q3 | H | FC Halifax | 2613 | D 1-1 | Sarcevic 57 | | 12 |
| 9 | FAC Q3r | A | FC Halifax | 1542 | L 1-3 | Williams M 60 | | 13 |
| 13 | BSN | A | Bishop's Stortford | 812 | W 2-1 | Jarman 76 Sarcevic 84 | 2 | 14 |
| 17 | BSN | H | Bradford PA | 2031 | D 1-1 | Williams D 60 | 1 | 15 |
| 27 | BSN | H | Histon | 2410 | W 2-1 | Jarman 8 Sarcevic 57 | 1 | 16 |
| 30 | BSN | A | Vauxhall Motors | 1752 | W 3-0 | Roberts-Nurse 9 (og) Williams D 65 Clancy 71 | 1 | 17 |
| Nov 10 | FAT Q3 | H | Worksop Town | 1410 | D 2-2 | Jarman 5 15 | | 18 |
| 14 | FAT Q3r | A | Worksop Town | 457 | L 0-2 | | | 19 |
| 18 | BSN | A | Gloucester City | 852 | W 1-0 | Jarman 64 | 2 | 20 |
| 24 | BSN | A | Histon | 428 | W 4-1 | Gray 8 43 Horan 23 Jarman 30 | 1 | 21 |
| 27 | BSN | H | Corby Town | 1853 | W 2-1 | McGinn 16 Hankin 89 | 1 | 22 |
| Dec 1 | BSN | H | Worcester City | 2640 | W 4-2 | Sarcevic 9 Curran 63 Howard 69 McGinn 75 (pen) | 1 | 23 |
| 8 | BSN | A | Brackley Town | 1155 | W 3-2 | Hankin 22 B.Mills 33 Horan 74 | 1 | 24 |
| 15 | BSN | H | Bishop's Stortford | 2058 | W 4-1 | Mills 5 CURRAN 3 ( 62 74 86) | 1 | 25 |
| 19 | BSN | H | Harrogate Town | 1803 | W 2-0 | Sarcevic 56 Williams 71 | 1 | 26 |
| 26 | BSN | H | Droylsden | 2934 | W 5-0 | Baynes 2 Sarcevic 19 Williams M 36 Mills 64 Curran 76 | 1 | 27 |
| 29 | BSN | H | Hinckley United | 2701 | W 3-0 | Sarcevic 35 Howard 58 Williams M 67 | 1 | 28 |
| Jan 1 | BSN | A | Droylsden | 1056 | W 4-3 | Sarcevic 2 Curran 4 Williams M 8 Turner 41 | 1 | 29 |
| 5 | BSN | A | Bradford PA | 957 | D 0-0 | | 1 | 30 |
| 9 | BSN | H | Oxford City | 1905 | W 2-0 | Linwood 9 Jarman 54 | 1 | 31 |
| 12 | BSN | A | Hinckley United | 648 | W 6-0 | Jarman 2 Curran 41 Sarcevic 46 66 Gray 68 Brown 88 | 1 | 32 |
| 19 | BSN | H | Stalybridge Celtic | 2094 | W 4-1 | Jarman 11 Horan 27 Williams M 43 Baynes 88 | 1 | 33 |
| Feb 3 | BSN | H | Brackley Town | 2689 | D 0-0 | | 1 | 34 |
| 16 | BSN | A | Corby Town | 768 | W 2-1 | Hankin 13 Jarman 17 | 1 | 35 |
| 19 | BSN | A | Workington | 531 | D 1-1 | Williams 50 | 1 | 36 |
| 23 | BSN | H | Vauxhall Motors | 2912 | W 2-0 | Daniels 13 Jarman 89 | 1 | 37 |
| 27 | BSN | H | Gainsborough Trinity | 1918 | W 3-1 | Gray 25 McGinn 39 Jarman 56 | 1 | 38 |
| Mar 9 | BSN | A | Harrogate Town | 815 | W 3-1 | Jarman 38 Gray 58 McKinn74 | 1 | 39 |
| 16 | BSN | H | Gloucester City | 2626 | W 2-0 | Gray 8 Hamblin 44 (og) | 1 | 40 |
| 30 | BSN | A | Colwyn Bay | 1463 | W 5-1 | GRAY 3 (30 62 64) McGinn 55 Sarcevic 90 | 1 | 41 |
| Apr 1 | BSN | H | Altrincham | 3089 | W 2-0 | McGinn 24 Collins 85 | 1 | 42 |
| 4 | BSN | A | Gainsborough Trinity | 678 | W 2-0 | Horan 25 Gray 30 | 1 | 43 |
| 6 | BSN | H | Boston United | 3685 | W 1-0 | Turner 47 | 1 | 44 |
| 13 | BSN | A | Guiseley | 1535 | L 1-2 | Gray 46 | 1 | 45 |
| 20 | BSN | H | Solihull Moors | 3414 | L 0-1 | | 1 | 46 |
| 24 | BSN | H | FC Halifax Town | 1262 | D 1-1 | Williams 6 | 1 | 47 |
| 27 | BSN | A | Worcester City | 4075 | W 1-0 | Horan 8 | 1 | 48 |

| GOALSCORERS | Lge | FAC | LC | Total | Pens | Hat-tricks | Cons Run | | Lge | FAC | LC | Total | Pens | Hat-tricks | Cons Run |
|---|---|---|---|---|---|---|---|---|---|---|---|---|---|---|---|
| Jarman | 14 | 1 | 2 | 17 | | | 3 | Collins | 1 | 1 | | 2 | | | |
| Sarcevic | 12 | 1 | | 13 | | | 4 | Turner | 2 | | | 2 | | | |
| Mills | 12 | | | 12 | | | 6 | Williams D | 2 | | | 2 | | | |
| Gray | 11 | | | 11 | 1 | | 4 | Brown | 1 | | | 1 | | | |
| Howard | 10 | | | 10 | | 1 | 2 | Clancy | 1 | | | 1 | | | |
| Williams M | 7 | 1 | | 8 | | | | Daniels | 1 | | | 1 | | | |
| Curran | 7 | | | 7 | | | | Linwood | 1 | | | 1 | | | |
| McGinn | 7 | | | 7 | 1 | | | Mackay | | | 1 | 1 | | | |
| Horan | 5 | | | 5 | | | | Powell | 1 | | | 1 | | | |
| Hankin | 4 | | | 4 | | | | Own Goals | 2 | | | 2 | | | |
| Baynes | 2 | | | 2 | | | | Cons Run - Consecutive scoring games. | | | | | | | |

# DARTFORD

**Chairman:** Bill Archer & David Skinner
**Secretary:** Peter Martin      **(T)** 07976 054 202      **(E)** peter@martinpe.freeserve.co.uk
**Commercial Manager:** Nicolla Collett      **(T)** 01322 299990
**Programme Editor:** Tony Jaglo      **(T)** 07830 816958
**Ground Address:** Princes Park Stadium, Grassbanks, Darenth Road, Dartford DA1 1RT
**(T)** 01322 299 990      **Manager:** Tony Burman

2012-13 Squad - Back Row (L-R): Jay Porter, Mark Arber, Tom Bonner, Ryan Sawyer, Elliot Bradbrook, Tom Champion, George Monger.
Middle Row: Steve Mosely (Coach), Paul Sawyer (Coach), Richard Rose, James Rogers, Louis Wells, Deren Ibrahim, Jacob Erskine, Lee Burns, Dave Phillips (Physio) John Macrae (Goalkeeper Coach).
Front Row: Danny Harris, Ryan Hayes, Adam Green, Tony Burman (Manager), Lee Noble, Jon Wallis, Nathan Collier.

## Club Factfile

**Founded:** 1888      **Nickname:** The Darts
**Previous Names:** None
**Previous Leagues:** Kent League 1894-96, 97-98, 99-1902, 09-14, 21-26, 93-96, Southern 1996-2006

**Club Colours (change):** White/black/white (Pale blue/navy/pale blue)

**Ground Capacity:** 4,097   **Seats:** 640   **Covered:** Yes   **Clubhouse:** Yes   **Shop:** Yes

**Directions** From M25 clockwise leave at Junction 1 B to roundabout controlled by traffic lights. Take third exit onto Princes Road, (A225) then second exit at next roundabout. Continue down hill to traffic lights (ground on your left), turn left into Darenth Road then second turning on your left into Grassbanks leading to car park. From M25 anti-clockwise leave at Junction 2 onto slip road A225 to roundabout, then first exit, second exit at next roundabout then down hill to traffic lights turn left into Darenth Road, then second turning on your left into Grassbanks leading to car park.

**Previous Grounds:** The Brent/Westgate House, Potters Meadow, Engleys Meadow, Summers Meadow, Watling Street

**Record Attendance:** 4,097 v Horsham YMCA - Isthmian Division 1 South 11/11/2006 and v Crystal Palace - Friendly 20/07/2007
**Record Victory:** Not known
**Record Defeat:** Not known
**Record Goalscorer:** Not known
**Record Appearances:** Steve Robinson - 692
**Additional Records:** Paid £6,000 to Chelmsford City for John Bartley
**Senior Honours:** Received £25,000 from Redbridge Forest for Andy Hessenthaler
Southern League Division 2 1896-97, Eastern Section 1930-31, 31-32, Southern Championship 30-31, 31-32, 73-74, 83-84, Southern Division 1980-81, League Cup 1976-77, 87-88, 88-89, Championship Shield 1983-84, 87-88, 88-89.
Isthmian League Division 1 North 2007-08, Premier Division 2009-10. Kent Senior Cup 1929-30, 34-35, 38-39, 69-70.

### 10 YEAR RECORD

| 03-04 | | 04-05 | | 05-06 | | 06-07 | | 07-08 | | 08-09 | | 09-10 | | 10-11 | | 11-12 | | 12-13 | |
|---|---|---|---|---|---|---|---|---|---|---|---|---|---|---|---|---|---|---|---|
| SthE | 16 | SthE | 16 | SthE | 7 | Isth1S | 7 | Isth1N | 1 | Isth P | 8 | Isth P | 1 | Conf S | 10 | Conf S | 2 | Conf | 8 |

# MATCH RESULTS 2012-13

| Date | Comp | H/A | Opponents | Att: | Result | Goalscorers | Pos | No. |
|---|---|---|---|---|---|---|---|---|
| Aug 11 | BSP | H | Tamworth | 1370 | L 2-3 | Bradbrook 45 Crawford 79 | 20 | 1 |
| 14 | BSP | A | Woking | 1846 | L 0-1 | | 21 | 2 |
| 18 | BSP | A | Macclesfield Town | 1420 | L 0-2 | | 23 | 3 |
| 25 | BSP | H | Kidderminster Harriers | 1068 | W 1-0 | Burns 36 | 18 | 4 |
| 27 | BSP | A | Cambridge United | 2691 | W 2-1 | Harris 48 Collier 88 | 14 | 5 |
| Sept 1 | BSP | H | Alfreton Town | 1145 | W 5-1 | CRAWFORD 3 (11 48 82) Erskine 37 Bradbrook 45 | 12 | 6 |
| 4 | BSP | H | Newport County | 1446 | W 2-1 | Crawford 49 Rose 90 | 8 | 7 |
| 8 | BSP | A | Gateshead | 758 | L 0-2 | | 10 | 8 |
| 17 | BSP | H | Hereford United | 1601 | W 4-0 | Hayes 6 Rogers 47 Harris 76 Wallis 89 | 6 | 9 |
| 22 | BSP | A | Wrexham | 3772 | D 2-2 | Harris 4 Noble 90 | 7 | 10 |
| 25 | BSP | A | Braintree Town | 721 | W 2-0 | Bonner 17 Erskine 34 | 6 | 11 |
| 29 | BSP | H | Hyde | 1338 | W 2-1 | Crawford 85 Rose 90 | 5 | 12 |
| Oct 6 | BSP | A | Grimsby Town | 4009 | W 2-0 | Champion 52 Burchall 82 | 5 | 13 |
| 9 | BSP | H | AFC Telford United | 1359 | L 1-4 | Bradbrook 75 | 5 | 14 |
| 13 | BSP | A | Barrow | 1278 | D 0-0 | | 6 | 15 |
| 20 | FAC Q4 | A | Forest Green Rovers | 891 | D 1-1 | Erskine 53 | | 16 |
| 23 | FAC Q4r | H | Forest Green Rovers | 804 | L 1-4 | Crawford 27 | | 17 |
| 27 | BSP | H | Mansfield Town | 1737 | W 2-0 | Bradbrook 45 Hayes 45 | 4 | 18 |
| Nov 6 | BSP | H | Forest Green Rovers | 915 | L 0-1 | | 6 | 19 |
| 10 | BSP | A | Luton Town | 6567 | W 2-0 | Noble 6 Bonner 41 | 5 | 20 |
| 17 | BSP | H | Southport | 1506 | D 2-2 | Bradbrook 17 33 (pen) | 5 | 21 |
| 24 | FAT 1 | A | Kingstonian | 508 | W 4-0 | Erskine 21 Bradbrook 51 Harris 63 Collier 76 | | 22 |
| Dec 1 | BSP | A | Tamworth | 832 | L 2-3 | Ajayi 18 Harris 70 | 5 | 23 |
| 4 | BSP | A | Nuneaton Town | 651 | L 0-1 | | 5 | 24 |
| 8 | BSP | A | Lincoln City | 1466 | L 2-4 | Crawford 48 71 | 6 | 25 |
| 15 | FAT 2 | H | Tonbridge Angels | 937 | W 3-0 | Crawford 6 Bradbrook 51 Wallis 67 | | 26 |
| 22 | BSP | A | Kidderminster Harriers | 1779 | L 1-5 | Erskine 9 | 7 | 27 |
| 26 | BSP | H | Ebbsfleet United | 3116 | W 3-1 | Crawford 52 68 Bradbrook 80 | 7 | 28 |
| 29 | BSP | H | Cambridge United | 1716 | D 1-1 | Crawford 23 | 7 | 29 |
| Jan 1 | BSP | A | Ebbsfleet United | 2242 | D 2-2 | Wallis 12 Crawford 48 | | 30 |
| 5 | BSP | A | Alfreton Town | 522 | L 2-3 | Hayes 3, Collier 59 | | 31 |
| 15 | BSP | H | Macclesfield Town | 821 | W 2-0 | Wallis 14, Noble 82 | 7 | 32 |
| 12 | FAT 3 | H | Bromley | 1305 | W 4-2 | GREEN 3 (6 34 52) Crawford 67 | | 33 |
| 30 | FAT 4 | A | FC Halifax Town | 921 | D 1-1 | Harris 68 | | 34 |
| Feb 2 | BSP | A | Mansfield Town | 2598 | L 0-5 | | 10 | 35 |
| 6 | FAT 4r | H | FC HalifaxTown | 805 | W 3-2 | Noble, Bradbrook Hayes | | 36 |
| 9 | BSP | A | Lincoln City | 1789 | L 1-2 | Noble 76 | 10 | 37 |
| 12 | BSP | H | LutonTown | 1802 | W 1-0 | Hayes 72 | 9 | 38 |
| 16 | FAT S-F 1 | A | Grimsby Town | 3573 | L 0-3 | | 11 | 39 |
| 23 | FAT S-F 2 | H | Grimsby Town | 2153 | D 0-0 | | 11 | 40 |
| Mar 2 | BSP | A | Southport | 823 | D 2-2 | Crawford 29 Bonner 59 | 12 | 41 |
| 5 | BSP | H | Stockport County | 757 | D 1-1 | Harris 70 | 12 | 42 |
| 9 | BSP | H | Wrexham | 815 | W 2-1 | Evans 74 Bradbrook 90 | 12 | 43 |
| 16 | BSP | A | Hyde | 475 | L 0-3 | | 12 | 44 |
| 20 | BSP | H | Barrow | 908 | L 0-1 | | 12 | 45 |
| 23 | BSP | H | Gateshead | 1020 | W 3-0 | Hayes 66 72 Sheringham 86 | 12 | 46 |
| 26 | BSP | A | Hereford United | 662 | L 0-1 | | 12 | 47 |
| 30 | BSP | A | Newport County | 2111 | D 0-0 | | 12 | 48 |
| Apr 1 | BSP | H | Woking | 1407 | W 4-1 | Collier 7 Noble 45 90 Sheringham 60 | 10 | 49 |
| 6 | BSP | A | AFC Telford United | 1375 | W 2-0 | Prioe 11 Sheringham 49 | 9 | 50 |
| 9 | BSP | H | Grimsby Town | 1201 | L 1-2 | Evans 26 | 10 | 51 |
| 11 | BSP | H | Braintree Town | 1051 | D 0-0 | | 8 | 52 |
| 13 | BSP | A | Stockport County | 6113 | W 1-0 | Sheringham 72 | 8 | 53 |
| 16 | BSP | H | Forest Green Rovers | 575 | W 3-2 | Harris 8 Bradbrook 25 (pen) 52 | 7 | 54 |
| 20 | BSP | H | Nuneaton Town | 1844 | L 0-1 | | 8 | 55 |

| GOALSCORERS | Lge | FAC | FAT | Total | Pens | Hat-tricks | Cons Run | | Lge | FAC | FAT | Total | Pens | Hat-tricks | Cons Run |
|---|---|---|---|---|---|---|---|---|---|---|---|---|---|---|---|
| Crawford | 13 | 1 | 2 | 16 | | 1 | 3 | Bonner | 2 | | | 2 | | | |
| Bradbrook | 10 | | 3 | 13 | 1 | | 2 | Evans | 2 | | | 2 | | | |
| Hayes | 7 | | 1 | 8 | | | | Rose | 2 | | | 2 | | | |
| Harris | 6 | | 2 | 8 | | | | Ajayi | 1 | | | 1 | | | |
| Noble | 6 | | 1 | 7 | | | | Birchall | 1 | | | 1 | | | |
| Erskine | 3 | 1 | 1 | 5 | | | | Burns | 1 | | | 1 | | | |
| Collier | 3 | | 1 | 4 | | | | Champion | 1 | | | 1 | | | |
| Sheringham | 4 | | | 4 | | | | Price | 1 | | | 1 | | | |
| Green | | | 3 | 3 | | 1 | | Rogers | 1 | | | 1 | | | |
| Wallis | 3 | | 1 | 3 | | | | Cons Run - Consecutive scoring games. | | | | | | | |

# FC HALIFAX TOWN

**Chairman:** David Bosmworth

**Secretary:** Hayley Horne    **(T)** 01422 341 222    **(E)** hayleyhorne@halifaxafc.co.uk

**Commercial Manager:** Debbie Charlton    **(T)** 07715 372 333

**Programme Editor:** Greg Stainton    **(T)** marketing@sandalbmw.net

**Ground Address:** The Shay Stadium, Shay Syke, Halifax HX1 2YS

**(T)** 01422 341 222      **Manager:** Neil Aspin

## Club Factfile

**Founded:** 1911    **Nickname:** Shaymen

**Previous Names:** Halifax Town 1911-2008 then reformed as F.C. Halifax Town

**Previous Leagues:** Yorkshire Combination 1911-12, Midland 1912-21, Football League 1921-93, 98-2002, Conference 1993-98, 2002-08

**Club Colours (change):** Blue & white/white & blue/white & blue (White/white & blue/white & blue)

**Ground Capacity:** 6,561    **Seats:** 2,330    **Covered:** 4,231    **Clubhouse:** Yes    **Shop:** Yes

**Directions**

M62, junction 24, head towards Halifax on A629 and the Town Centre.
After 3-4 miles, ground is on the right (Shaw Hill) sign posted The Shay.

**Previous Grounds:** Sandhall Lane 1911-15, Exley 1919-20

**Record Attendance:** 36,885 v Tottenham Hotspur - FA Cup 5th Round 14/02/1953

**Record Victory:** 12-0 v West Vale Ramblers - FA Cup 1st Qualifying Road 1913-14

**Record Defeat:** 0-13 v Stockport County - Division 3 North 1933-34

**Record Goalscorer:** Albert Valentine

**Record Appearances:** John Pickering

**Additional Records:**

**Senior Honours:**
Conference 1997-98, Conference North Play-offs 2012-13. Northern Premier League Division 1 North 2009-10, Premier Division 2010-11. West Riding County Cup 2012-13.

### 10 YEAR RECORD

| 03-04 | | 04-05 | | 05-06 | | 06-07 | | 07-08 | | 08-09 | | 09-10 | | 10-11 | | 11-12 | | 12-13 | |
|---|---|---|---|---|---|---|---|---|---|---|---|---|---|---|---|---|---|---|---|
| Conf | 19 | Conf | 9 | Conf | 4 | Conf | 16 | Conf | 20 | NP1N | 8 | NP1N | 1 | NP P | 1 | Conf N | 3 | Conf N | 5 |

# MATCH RESULTS 2012-13

| Date | Comp | H/A | Opponents | Att: | Result | Goalscorers | Pos | No. |
|------|------|-----|-----------|------|--------|-------------|-----|-----|
| Aug 18 | BSN | A | Bishop's Stortford | 622 | W 2-1 | Johnson 53  Francis 57 (og) | 6 | 1 |
| 21 | BSN | H | Colwyn Bay | 1130 | L 0-1 |  | 11 | 2 |
| 25 | BSN | H | Workington | 1167 | W 5-1 | Johnson 25 Seddon 32 41 Rainford 51 Lee Gregory 75 | 6 | 3 |
| 27 | BSN | A | Bradford PA | 1614 | D 1-1 | Seddon 13 | 5 | 4 |
| Sept 1 | BSN | H | Oxford City | 1172 | W 3-1 | Marshall 45 Johnson 5 62 | 5 | 5 |
| 5 | BSN | A | Chester | 3112 | L 1-2 | Worthington 56 | 6 | 6 |
| 8 | BSN | A | Hinckley United | 522 | W 2-0 | Johnson 16 Gregory 68 | 4 | 7 |
| 15 | BSN | H | Gloucester City | 1291 | W 5-0 | Worthington 1 GREGORY 4 ( 9 40 45 54) | 4 | 8 |
| 22 | FAC Q2 | H | Abbey Hey | 936 | W 6-0 | Gregory 43  Worsley 44  Worthington 50 73  Johnson 71 84 |  | 9 |
| 29 | BSN | A | Histon | 478 | W 1-0 | Johnson 48 | 4 | 10 |
| Oct 6 | FAC Q3 | A | Chester | 2813 | D 1-1 | Hockley 82 |  | 11 |
| 9 | FAC Q3r | H | Chester | 1542 | W 3-1 | Worthington 5 Gregory 52 Worsley 66 |  | 12 |
| 13 | BSN | H | Boston United | 1326 | L 1-2 | Seddon 86 | 5 | 13 |
| 20 | FAC Q4 | A | Lincoln City | 1940 | D 0-0 |  |  | 14 |
| 23 | FAC Q4r | H | Lincoln City | 1418 | L 0-2 |  |  | 15 |
| 27 | BSN | A | Brackley Town | 522 | D 0-0 |  | 6 | 16 |
| Nov 6 | BSN | H | Vauxhall Motors | 858 | W 4-0 | Titchener 10 Seddon 12 Worthington 52 Johnson 85 | 6 | 17 |
| 10 | FAT Q3 | A | Cammell Laird | 301 | W 1-0 | Seddon 78 | 5 | 18 |
| 17 | BSN | H | Droylsden | 1332 | W 4-1 | TITCHENER 3 ( 62 71 90) Johnson 81 | 5 | 19 |
| 24 | FAT 1 | H | Altrincham | 885 | W 5-2 | Gregory 31 SEDDON 3 (42 44 45) Johnson 52 | 5 | 20 |
| Dec 8 | BSN | A | Worcester City | 1032 | W 1-0 | Seddon 79 | 5 | 21 |
| 18 | FAT 2 | H | Maidstone United | 747 | W 2-1 | Seddon 5 90 | 4 | 22 |
| 26 | BSN | H | Gainsborough T | 1515 | W 3-1 | Worthington 7 Gregory 45 Toulson 61 | 4 | 23 |
| Jan 1 | BSN | A | Gainsborough T | 906 | L 0-3 |  | 5 | 24 |
| 8 | BSN | H | Solihull Moors | 979 | D 0-0 |  | 5 | 25 |
| 12 | FAT 3 | H | Chelmsford City | 1137 | W 3-0 | Needham 12 60  St Juste 53 | 5 | 26 |
| 29 | FAT4 | H | Dartford | 921 | D 1-1 | Gregory 28 | 7 | 27 |
| Feb 2 | BSN | A | Corby Town | 439 | W 5-1 | Kelly 5 GREGORY 3 (11 24 66) Seddon 46 | 7 | 28 |
| 5 | FAT4r | A | Dartford | 805 | L 2-3 | Gardner 2 89 | 8 | 29 |
| 9 | BSN | H | Histon | 1118 | D 3-3 | Titchener 49 Gardner 59 (pen) Worsley 71 | 8 | 30 |
| 16 | BSN | A | Droylsden | 643 | W 6-0 | Titchener 7 SEDDON 3 (40 53 83) Gardner 43 Worthington 55 | 7 | 31 |
| 19 | BSN | A | Gloucester City | 303 | D 2-2 | Needham 21 Seddon 25 | 7 | 32 |
| 23 | BSN | H | Stalybridge Celtic | 1037 | D 0-0 |  | 6 | 33 |
| 26 | BSN | H | Vauxhall Motors | 251 | W 3-1 | McManus 5 Gardner 64 Lee Gregory 75 | 5 | 34 |
| Mar 2 | BSN | H | Worcester City | 1275 | W 5-0 | GREGORY 4 (13 63 84 88) Titchener 32 | 4 | 35 |
| 5 | BSN | H | Hinckley United | 900 | W 7-0 | Gardner 10 GREGORY 3 (16 44 50), Johnson 70 (pen) 81 Titchenor 75 | 4 | 36 |
| 6 | BSN | H | HarrogateTown | 1133 | L 1-2 | Gardner 12 | 4 | 37 |
| 9 | BSN | A | Solihull Moors | 331 | W 3-0 | Needham 20 Worthington 64 Gardner 90 | 4 | 38 |
| 16 | BSN | H | Brackley Town | 1361 | D 0-0 |  | 4 | 39 |
| 19 | BSN | A | Colwyn Bay | 331 | W 3-0 | Gregory 31 Seddon 46 Worsley 73 | 4 | 40 |
| 30 | BSN | A | Workington | 481 | W 1-0 | Seddon 3 | 4 | 41 |
| Apr 1 | BSN | A | Bradford PA | 1611 | L 0-1 |  | 4 | 42 |
| 3 | BSN | A | Guiseley | 1137 | D 1-1 | Gardner 65 | 4 | 43 |
| 6 | BSN | H | Altrincham | 1435 | L 3-4 | Titchener 24 44 McManus 45 | 5 | 44 |
| 9 | BSN | H | Bishop's Stortfod | 926 | D 1-1 | Needham 40 | 5 | 45 |
| 11 | BSN | H | Corby Town | 838 | W 2-0 | McManus 38 Bolton 85 | 4 | 46 |
| 13 | BSN | A | Boston United | 1069 | W 2-1 | Worsley 42  Titchenor 68 | 4 | 47 |
| 16 | BSN | A | Oxfrd City | 262 | D 2-2 | Bolton 59 Gardner 68 | 4 | 48 |
| 18 | BSN | A | Harrogate Town | 698 | D 1-1 | Bolton 64 | 4 | 49 |
| 20 | BSN | H | Guiseley | 1598 | D 1-1 | Gregory 49 | 4 | 50 |
| 23 | BSN | A | Altrincham | 990 | L 0-2 |  | 5 | 51 |
| 25 | BSN | H | Chester | 1262 | D 1-1 | Johnson 38 | 5 | 52 |
| 27 | BSN | A | Stalybridge Celtic | 744 | L 0-1 |  | 5 | 53 |
| 30 | P-Off S-F 1 | H | Guiseley | 2367 | D 1-1 | Gardner 17 (pen) |  | 54 |
| May 4 | P-Off S-F 2 | A | Guiseley | 2424 | W 2-0 | Johnson 52 Gregory 83 |  | 55 |
| 11 | P-Off Final | A | Brackley Town | 2604 | W 1-0 | Gregory 75 |  | 56 |

| GOALSCORERS | Lge | FAC | LC | Total | Pens | Hat-tricks | Cons Run | | | Lge | FAC | LC | Total | Pens | Hat-tricks | Cons Run |
|-------------|-----|-----|----|-------|------|------------|----------|--|--|-----|-----|----|-------|------|------------|----------|
| Gregory | 22 | 2 | 2 | 26 | 4 |  | 3 | | Hockley |  | 1 |  | 1 |  |  |  |
| Seddon | 13 |  | 6 | 19 | 2 |  | 3 | | Kelly | 1 |  |  | 1 |  |  |  |
| Johnson | 12 | 2 | 1 | 15 | 1 |  | 2 | | Marshall | 1 |  |  | 1 |  |  |  |
| Titchener | 11 |  |  | 11 |  | 1 | 2 | | Rainford | 1 |  |  | 1 |  |  |  |
| Gardner | 9 |  | 2 | 11 | 2 |  | 2 | | St Juste |  |  | 1 | 1 |  |  |  |
| Worthington | 6 | 3 |  | 9 |  |  |  | | Toulson | 1 |  |  | 1 |  |  |  |
| Needham | 3 |  | 2 | 5 |  |  |  | | Own Goals | 1 |  |  | 1 |  |  |  |
| Worsley | 3 | 2 |  | 5 |  |  |  | | Cons Run - Consecutive scoring games. | | | | | | | |
| Bolton | 3 |  |  | 3 |  |  |  | | | | | | | | | |
| McManus | 3 |  |  | 3 |  |  |  | | | | | | | | | |

# FOREST GREEN ROVERS

**Chairman:** Dale Vince OBE

**Secretary:** Michelle McDonald   **(T)** 01453 834 860   **(E)** Michelle.McDonald@fgrfc.com

**Commercial Manager:** Chris Wintle    **(T)** 01453 834 860

**Programme Editor:** Terry Brumpton    **(T)** 07771 802 048

**Ground Address:** The New Lawn, Smiths Way, Nailsworth, Gloucestershire GL6 0FG

**(T)** 01453 834 860            **Manager:** David Hockaday

James Norwood scores for Rovers against Port Vale in the FA Cup First Round.
Photo: Peter Barnes

## Club Factfile

**Founded:** 1890    **Nickname:** Rovers

**Previous Names:** Stround FC 1980s-92.

**Previous Leagues:** Stroud & District 1890-1922, Gloucestershire Northern Senior 1922-67, Gloucestershire Senior 1967-73, Hellenic 1973-82, Southern 1982-89.

**Club Colours (change):** Green/black/black (All white)

**Ground Capacity:** 5,141   **Seats:** 2,000   **Covered:** 1,000   **Clubhouse:** Yes   **Shop:** Yes

**Directions**

Nailsworth is on the A46 between Stroud and Bath. At mini roundabout in town turn up Spring Hill towards Forest Green (signposted) and the stadium is at the top of the hill after the second roundabout.
Satnav users should enter GL6 0ET and not the mail post code. Please note on Matchdays there is a Temporary Traffic Order in place on the highway around the stadium. Car parking is available inside the stadium at £3 per vehicle.

**Previous Grounds:** Moved to the New Lawn in 2006 - 400 meters away from the old Lawn ground.

**Record Attendance:** 4,836 v Derby County - FA Cup 3rd Round 03/01/2009

**Record Victory:** 8-0 v Fareham Town - Southern League Southern Division 1996-97

**Record Defeat:** 0-7 v Moor Green - Southern League Midland Division 1985-86

**Record Goalscorer:** Karl Bayliss

**Record Appearances:** Alex Sykes

**Additional Records:** Paid £20,000 to Salisbury City for Adrian Randall. Received £35,000 from Nuneaton Borough for Marc

**Senior Honours:** McGregor and from Oxford United for Wayne Hatswell.

FA Vase 1981-82. Hellenic League 1981-82. Gloucestershire Senior Cup 1984-85, 85-86, 86-87.
Gloucestershire Senior Professional Cup 1984-85, 86-86, 87-87.

### 10 YEAR RECORD

| 03-04 | | 04-05 | | 05-06 | | 06-07 | | 07-08 | | 08-09 | | 09-10 | | 10-11 | | 11-12 | | 12-13 | |
|---|---|---|---|---|---|---|---|---|---|---|---|---|---|---|---|---|---|---|---|
| Conf | 18 | Conf | 20 | Conf | 19 | Conf | 14 | Conf | 8 | Conf | 18 | Conf | 21 | Conf | 20 | Conf | 10 | Conf | 10 |

# MATCH RESULTS 2012-13

| Date | Comp | H/A | Opponents | Att: | Result | Goalscorers | Pos | No. |
|------|------|-----|-----------|------|--------|-------------|-----|-----|
| Aug11 | BSP | H | Cambridge United | 1128 | D 1-1 | Klukowski 90 (pen) | 13 | 1 |
| 14 | BSP | A | AFC Telford United | 857 | W 2-1 | Racine 5 Blackburn 40 (og) | 9 | 2 |
| 18 | BSP | A | Gateshead | 531 | D 1-1 | Styche 90 (pen) | 10 | 3 |
| 25 | BSP | H | Woking | 979 | W 3-1 | Vieira 62 Taylor 90 90 | 6 | 4 |
| 27 | BSP | A | Kidderminster Harriers | 1742 | W 1-0 | Norwood 81 | 3 | 5 |
| Sept 1 | BSP | H | Hyde | 768 | W 3-1 | Styche 12 Turley 18 Wright 90 | 2 | 6 |
| 4 | BSP | H | Ebbsfleet United | 914 | W 4-1 | Klukowski 18 Wright 26 Taylor 30 Oshodi 41 | 1 | 7 |
| 8 | BSP | A | Grimsby Town | 3270 | L 0-1 | | 2 | 8 |
| 15 | BSP | H | Alfreton Town | 1072 | D 1-1 | Klukowski 10 | 3 | 9 |
| 22 | BSP | A | Macclesfield Town | 1729 | W 2-1 | Taylor 35 Brogan 90 | 2 | 10 |
| 25 | BSP | A | Hereford United | 1656 | W 2-1 | Wright 16 Klukowski 32 | 2 | 11 |
| 29 | BSP | H | Lincoln City | 1395 | W 3-0 | Taylor 16 51 Vieira 63 | 1 | 12 |
| Oct 6 | BSP | A | Wrexham | 4063 | L 1-2 | Norwood 90 | 2 | 13 |
| 9 | BSP | H | Tamworth | 1022 | L 1-2 | Collins J 61 | 2 | 14 |
| 13 | BSP | A | Mansfield Town | 2019 | L 0-1 | | 5 | 15 |
| 20 | FAC Q4 | H | Dartford | 891 | D 1-1 | Norwood 12 | | 16 |
| 23 | FAC Q4r | A | Dartford | 804 | W 4-1 | Klukowski 30 60 Taylor 72 Vieira 90 | | 17 |
| 27 | BSP | A | Luton Town | 2112 | L 1-2 | Klukowski 47 | 6 | 18 |
| Nov 3 | FAC 1 | H | Port Vale | 1753 | L 2-3 | Norwood 34 Oshodi 49 | | 19 |
| 6 | BSP | A | Dartford | 915 | W 1-0 | Klukowski 11 | 5 | 20 |
| 10 | BSP | H | Stockport County | 1176 | W 4-1 | Klukowski 5 Hobson 15 (og) Norwood 25 Styche 87 | 3 | 21 |
| 17 | BSP | A | Barrow | 853 | D 2-2 | Norwood 15 Taylor 88 | 3 | 22 |
| 24 | FAT 1 | H | AFC Totton | 523 | W 2-1 | Brogan 50 Styche 90 | | 23 |
| Dec 1 | BSP | H | Nuneaton Town | 948 | W 1-0 | Norwood 52 | 3 | 24 |
| 8 | BSP | H | Macclesfield Town | 901 | D 1-1 | Stokes 85 | 4 | 25 |
| 15 | FAT 2 | H | Gainsborough Trinity | 496 | L 1-2 | Stokes 79 | | 26 |
| 18 | BSP | A | Braintree Town | 480 | L 1-3 | Stokes 74 | 4 | 27 |
| 26 | BSP | H | Newport County | 2332 | L 1-2 | Brogan 47 | 6 | 28 |
| Jan 1 | BSP | A | Newport County | 2787 | W 5-0 | NORWOOD 3 (38 68 78) Klukowski 45 Styche 74 | | 29 |
| 5 | BSP | A | Hyde | 553 | W 1-0 | Norwood 46 | | 30 |
| 12 | BSP | A | Nuneaton Town | 910 | D 1-1 | Taylor 57 | 4 | 31 |
| 19 | BSP | A | Stockport County | 2802 | L 1-2 | Styche 63 | 4 | 32 |
| 27 | BSP | A | Lincoln City | 1666 | W 2-1 | Klukowski 7 Stokes 45 | 4 | 33 |
| Feb 2 | BSP | H | Wrexham | 1940 | D 0-0 | | 3 | 34 |
| 9 | BSP | A | Luton Town | 6374 | D 1-1 | Taylor 14 | 3 | 35 |
| 12 | BSP | H | Braintree Town | 918 | W 4-1 | NORWOOD 3 ( 19 27 64) Klukowski 53 | 3 | 36 |
| 16 | BSP | H | Gateshead | 1139 | W 1-0 | Vieira 60 | 3 | 37 |
| 19 | BSP | H | Kidderminster Harriers | 1449 | L 0-1 | | | 38 |
| 26 | BSP | A | Woking | 1105 | L 0-2 | | 6 | 39 |
| Mar 2 | BSP | A | Cambridge United | 2221 | D 0-0 | | 6 | 40 |
| 5 | BSP | H | Grimsby Town | 744 | L 0-1 | | 6 | 41 |
| 9 | BSP | H | Barrow | 904 | D 1-1 | Norwood 90 | 6 | 42 |
| 12 | BSP | A | Southport | 632 | W 2-1 | Odubade 87 Burns 90 | 6 | 43 |
| 16 | BSP | H | Mansfield Town | 1109 | L 1-2 | Norwood 87 | 6 | 44 |
| 30 | BSP | A | Ebbsfleet United | 749 | W 2-0 | Norwood 38 Connolly 82 | 6 | 45 |
| Apr 1 | BSP | H | AFC Telford United | 1061 | D 0-0 | | 6 | 46 |
| 6 | BSP | A | Tamworth | 773 | L 1-2 | Klukowski 48 | 6 | 47 |
| 9 | BSP | H | Hererford United | 1142 | L 0-1 | | 7 | 48 |
| 13 | BSP | H | Southport | 1496 | L 0-1 | | 7 | 49 |
| 16 | BSP | H | Dartford | 575 | L 2-3 | Stokes 48 Turley 79 | 8 | 50 |
| 20 | BSP | A | Alfreton Town | 759 | L 1-2 | Turley 55 | 10 | 51 |

| GOALSCORERS | Lge | FAC | FAT | Total | Pens | Hat-tricks | Cons Run | | Lge | FAC | FAT | Total | Pens | Hat-tricks | Cons Run |
|-------------|-----|-----|-----|-------|------|------------|----------|--|-----|-----|-----|-------|------|------------|----------|
| Norwood | 15 | 2 | | 17 | | 2 | 2 | Burns | 1 | | | 1 | | | |
| Klukowski | 11 | 2 | | 13 | 1 | | 2 | Collins | 1 | | | 1 | | | |
| Taylor | 8 | 1 | | 9 | | | | Connolly | 1 | | | 1 | | | |
| Stokes | 5 | | 1 | 6 | | | | Odubade | 1 | | | 1 | | | |
| Styche | 5 | | 1 | 6 | 1 | | | Racine | 1 | | | 1 | | | |
| Vieira | 3 | 1 | | 4 | | | | Own Goals | 2 | | | 2 | | | |
| Brogan | 2 | | 1 | 3 | | | | Cons Run - Consecutive scoring games. | | | | | | | |
| Turley | 3 | | | 3 | | | | | | | | | | | |
| Wright | 3 | | | 3 | | | | | | | | | | | |
| Oshodi | 1 | 1 | | 2 | | | | | | | | | | | |

# GATESHEAD

**Chairman:** Graham Wood

**Secretary:** Mike Coulson    **(T)** 07912 869 943    **(E)** mike.coulson@gateshead-fc.com

**Commercial Manager:** Grahamme McDonald    **(T)** 07917 886 721

**Programme Editor:** Jeff Bowron    **(T)** 07801 847 004

**Ground Address:** International Stadium, Neilson Road, Gateshead NE10 0EF

**(T)** 0191 478 3883    **Manager:** Anthony Smith

*Meta Ltd*
*Demolition / Asbestos Contractors*
*Meta ltd*  Tel: 0191 499 1955 : www.meta.ltd.uk

2013-14 Squad - Back Row (L-R): Ben Clark, Adam Boyes, Joe Tait, James Curtis, Richard Brodie, Liam Hatch, James Brown.
Middle Row: George Spurs (Kitman), Marcus Maddison, Dan Smith, Lewis Galpin, Phil Turnbull, Jordan Nixon, Adam Bartlett,
Dale Connor, Josh Walker, Luke Carr, Callum Patton, Rob Ramshaw, Gary Neasham (Physio).
Front Row: Luke O'Brien, James Marwood, Jamie Chandler, Graham Wood (Chairman), David Rush (Asst. Manager),
Anth Smith (Manager), Tony Norman (Goalkeeper Coach), Brian Waites (Vice -Chairman), Micky Cummins, Craig Baxter, Colin Larkin.

## Club Factfile

**Founded:**  1930    **Nickname:** Tynesiders, The Heed

**Previous Names:** Gateshead Town, Gateshead United.

**Previous Leagues:** Football League 1930-60, Northern Counties east 1960-62, North Regional 1962-68, Northern Premier 1968-70, 73-83, 85-86, 87-90, Wearside 1970-71, Midland 1971-72, Alliance/Conf 1983-85, 86-87, 90-98

**Club Colours (change):**  White/black/black & white (Sky blue with claret/sky blue/sky blue & claret)

**Ground Capacity:** 11,795  **Seats:** 11,795  **Covered:** 3,300    **Clubhouse:** Yes    **Shop:** Yes

**Directions:** Travelling up on the A1, turn off at the junction with the A194 just north of the Washington Services. Follow the A194 until the roundabout junction with the A184, turn left onto this road. The International Stadium is on the right after approximately 3 miles.

**Previous Grounds:** Redheugh Park 1930-71

**Record Attendance:** 11,750 v Newcastle United - Friendly 07/08/95

**Record Victory:** 8-0 v Netherfield - Northern Premier League

**Record Defeat:** 0-9 v Sutton United - Conference 22/09/90

**Record Goalscorer:**  Paul Thompson - 130

**Record Appearances:** Simon Smith - 501 (1985-94)

**Additional Records:** Record transfer fee paid; £9,000 - Paul Cavell, Dagenham & Redbridge 1994

**Senior Honours:**  Record transfer fee received; £150,000 Lee Novak, Huddersfield Town 2009

Northern Premier League 1982-83, 85-86, Northern Premier League play-off 2007-8, Conference North play-off 2008-9, Durham Challenge Cup 2010-11

### 10 YEAR RECORD

| 03-04 | 04-05 | 05-06 | 06-07 | 07-08 | 08-09 | 09-10 | 10-11 | 11-12 | 12-13 |
|---|---|---|---|---|---|---|---|---|---|
| NP P  6 | NP P  17 | NP P  17 | NP P  9 | NP P  3 | Conf N  2 | Conf  20 | Conf  15 | Conf  8 | Conf  17 |

# MATCH RESULTS 2012-13

| Date | Comp | H/A | Opponents | Att: | Result | Goalscorers | Pos | No. |
|------|------|-----|-----------|------|--------|-------------|-----|-----|
| Aug 11 | BSP | A | Luton Town | 6743 | D 2-2 | Hatch 25 Odubade 35 | 9 | 1 |
| 14 | BSP | H | Mansfield Town | 801 | W 4-1 | Hatch 11 Fisher 56 86 Bush 71 | 3 | 2 |
| 18 | BSP | H | Forest Green Rovers | 531 | D 1-1 | Fisher 53 | 9 | 3 |
| 24 | BSP | A | Stockport County | 3213 | W 2-1 | Donaldson 55 Cummins 66 | 2 | 4 |
| 27 | BSP | H | Lincoln City | 803 | D 1-1 | Marwood 45 | 7 | 5 |
| Sept 1 | BSP | A | Nuneaton Town | 835 | W 1-0 | Odubade 63 | 4 | 6 |
| 4 | BSP | A | Southport | 686 | L 1-2 | Gillies 74 | 7 | 7 |
| 8 | BSP | H | Dartford | 758 | W 2-0 | Cummins 40 Gillies 63 | 6 | 8 |
| 16 | BSP | H | Tamworth | 622 | L 0-2 | | 7 | 9 |
| 22 | BSP | A | Woking | 1609 | L 1-2 | Turnbull 68 | 11 | 10 |
| 25 | BSP | A | Grimsby Town | 3202 | L 0-3 | | 12 | 11 |
| 29 | BSP | H | AFC Telford United | 524 | D 1-1 | McGorrigan 31 | 11 | 12 |
| Oct 6 | BSP | A | Hyde | 470 | D 1-1 | Gillies 35 | 11 | 13 |
| 9 | BSP | H | Macclesfield Town | 557 | D 2-2 | Chandler 37 Curtis 63 | 11 | 14 |
| 13 | BSP | H | Cambridge United | 768 | D 0-0 | | 12 | 15 |
| 20 | FAC Q4 | A | **Alfreton Town** | 338 | L 0-2 | | | 16 |
| 27 | BSP | A | Kiddermnster Harriers | 1639 | D 1-1 | Clark 90 | 13 | 17 |
| Nov 3 | BSP | H | Woking | 473 | W 2-1 | Gillies 32 Hatch 45 | 8 | 18 |
| 6 | BSP | H | Alfreton Town | 475 | W 2-0 | Hatch 5 Gillies 36 | 8 | 19 |
| 10 | BSP | A | Braintree Town | 678 | L 1-2 | Donaldson 29 | 8 | 20 |
| 17 | BSP | A | Wrexham | 3011 | D 1-1 | Donaldson 63 | 7 | 21 |
| 23 | FAT 1 | H | **Macclesfield Town** | 312 | **W 2-0** | **Bullock, 1 own goal** | | 22 |
| Dec 1 | BSP | A | Newport County | 1473 | L 1-3 | Odubade 70 | 8 | 23 |
| 8 | BSP | A | Cambridge United | 1840 | L 0-3 | | 14 | 24 |
| 15 | FAT 2 | A | **Cambridge United** | 1019 | **W 1-0** | **Odubade 90** | | 25 |
| 26 | BSP | A | Barrow | 1135 | W 2-0 | Gillies 41 85 | 11 | 26 |
| 29 | BSP | A | Lincoln City | 1906 | D 1-1 | Gillies 61 (pen ) | 12 | 27 |
| Jan 1 | BSP | H | Barrow | 610 | L 0-1 | | 16 | 28 |
| 29 | FAT 3 | H | **Barrow** | 728 | **L 2-3** | **Clark 35 Magnay 61** | | 29 |
| Feb 2 | BSP | A | Tamworth | 618 | L 0-2 | | 20 | 30 |
| 9 | BSP | A | Ebbsfleet United | 636 | L 1-3 | Gillies 74 | 20 | 31 |
| 16 | BSP | A | Forest Green Rovers | 1139 | L 0-1 | | 20 | 32 |
| 19 | BSP | H | Wrexham | 513 | L 0-1 | | 22 | 33 |
| 23 | BSP | A | Macclesfield Town | 1467 | W 4-0 | Chandler 2 45 Brown 18 Donaldson 20 | 20 | 34 |
| Mar 2 | BSP | H | Braintree Town | 327 | L1-2 | Everson 85 | 22 | 35 |
| 5 | BSP | H | Kidderminster Harriers | 273 | W 2-0 | Chandler 71 Hatch 90 | | 36 |
| 9 | BSP | H | Hyde | 371 | W 3-0 | Brown 4 Donaldson 83 (pen) Everson 88 | 17 | 37 |
| 13 | BSP | A | AFC Telford United | 1260 | D 0-0 | | 18 | 38 |
| 16 | BSP | A | Alfreton Town | 566 | L 2-3 | Brown 20 (og) Gillies 40 (pen) | 19 | 39 |
| 19 | BSP | H | Hereford United | 259 | W 3-2 | Donaldson 19 Brown 43 55 | 18 | 40 |
| 23 | BSP | A | Dartford | 1020 | L 0-3 | | 19 | 41 |
| 26 | BSP | H | Grimsby Town | 351 | D 1-1 | Thanoj | 19 | 42 |
| 28 | BSP | H | Newport County | 227 | D 0-0 | | 18 | 43 |
| 30 | BSP | H | Southport | 406 | D 2-2 | Gillies 90 Cummings 90 | 18 | 44 |
| Apr 1 | BSP | A | Mansfield Town | 3472 | L 0-4 | | 19 | 45 |
| 6 | BSP | H | Luton Town | 382 | W 5-1 | Donaldson 12 66 Gillies 15 45 (pen) Hatch 90 | 18 | 46 |
| 9 | BSP | H | Nuneaton Town | 304 | L 0-2 | | 19 | 47 |
| 13 | BSP | A | Hereford United | 1599 | D 1-1 | Magnay 24 | 19 | 48 |
| 16 | BSP | H | Stockport County | 685 | D 1-1 | Gillies 56 | 19 | 49 |
| 20 | BSP | H | Ebbsfleet United | 532 | W 2-0 | Hatch 49 Henderson 90 | 17 | 50 |

| GOALSCORERS | Lge | FAC | FAT | Total | Pens | Hat-tricks | Cons Run | | Lge | FAC | FAT | Total | Pens | Hat-tricks | Cons Run |
|-------------|-----|-----|-----|-------|------|-----------|----------|---|-----|-----|-----|-------|------|-----------|----------|
| Gillies | 14 | | | 14 | 3 | | 2 | Curtis | 1 | | | 1 | | | |
| Hatch | 7 | | | 7 | | | | Magnay | 1 | | 1 | 2 | | | |
| Odubade | 3 | 1 | | 4 | | | | Marwood | 1 | | | 1 | | | |
| Donaldson | 8 | | | 8 | 1 | | | McGorrigan | 1 | | | 1 | | | |
| Fisher | 3 | | | 3 | | | | Turnbull | 1 | | | 1 | | | |
| Clark | 1 | | 1 | 2 | | | | Brown | 4 | | | 4 | | | |
| Cummins | 3 | | | 3 | | | | Everson | 2 | | | 2 | | | |
| Bush | 1 | | | 1 | | | | Thanoj | 1 | | | 1 | | | |
| Bullock | | | 1 | 1 | | | | Henderson | 1 | | | 1 | | | |
| Chandler | 4 | | | 4 | | | | Own Goals | 1 | | 1 | 2 | | | |
| | | | | | | | | Cons Run - Consecutive scoring games. | | | | | | | |

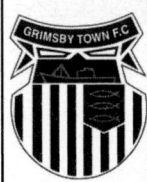

# GRIMSBY TOWN

**Chairman:** John Fenty

**Secretary:** Ian Fleming    **(T)** 07711 188 542    **(E)** ian@gtfc.co.uk

**Commercial Manager:** Dave Smith    **(T)** 07801 081 874

**Programme Editor:** Jack Johnson    **(T)** 07540 126 369

**Ground Address:** Blundell Park, Cleethorpes, North East Lincolnshire DN35 7PY

**(T)** 01472 605 050        **Manager:** Paul Hurst & Rob Scott

Grimsby's McKeown saves well during the FA Trophy Final at Wembley.
Photo: Keith Clayton.

## Club Factfile

**Founded:** 1878    **Nickname:** The Mariners

**Previous Names:** Grimsby Pelham 1878-79

**Previous Leagues:** Football League 1892-2010

**Club Colours (change):** Black & white stripes/black/black (Blue/white/blue)

**Ground Capacity:** 10,033   **Seats:** Yes    **Covered:** Yes    **Clubhouse:** Yes    **Shop:** Yes

**Directions:** From the North/West All routes follow M180 onto the A180 to Grimsby. At first roundabout go straight on then follow signs for Cleethorpes (A180) onto Grimsby Road. Blundell Park is situated behind the Drive Thru' McDonalds. From the South A46 (Lincoln) Follow A46 into Grimsby, go straight on at roundabout after dual carriageway, following signs to Cleethorpes. At the 'Grimsby Institute' get in the right hand lane and keep following signs for Cleethorpes. At Isaac's Hill roundabout turn left onto Grimsby Road, the ground is on the right hand side behind the Drive Thru' at McDonalds.

**Previous Grounds:** Clee Park, Abbey Park

**Record Attendance:** 31,657 v Wolverhampton Wanderers - FA Cup 5th Round 20/02/1937

**Record Victory:** 9-2 v Darwen - Division 2 15/04/1899

**Record Defeat:** 1-9 v Arsenal - Division 1 28/01/1931

**Record Goalscorer:** Pat Glover - 180 (1930-39)

**Record Appearances:** John McDermott - 754 (1987-2007)

**Additional Records:** Paid £500,000 to Preston North End for Lee Ashcroft 11/08/1998

**Senior Honours:** Received £1.5m from Everton for John Oster July 1997

Football League Division 2 1900-01, 33-34, Division 3 North 1925-26, 55-56, Division 3 1979-80, Division 4 1971-72. Division 2 Play-offs 1997-98.

League Group Cup 1982. Auto Windscreen Shield 1998.

### 10 YEAR RECORD

| 03-04 | | 04-05 | | 05-06 | | 06-07 | | 07-08 | | 08-09 | | 09-10 | | 10-11 | | 11-12 | | 12-13 | |
|-------|----|-------|----|-------|----|-------|----|-------|----|-------|----|-------|----|-------|----|-------|----|-------|----|
| FL 2 | 21 | FL 2 | 18 | FL 2 | 4 | FL 2 | 15 | FL 2 | 16 | FL 2 | 22 | FL 2 | 23 | Conf | 11 | Conf | 11 | Conf | 4 |

# MATCH RESULTS 2012-13

| Date | Comp | H/A | Opponents | Att: | Result | Goalscorers | Pos | No. |
|------|------|-----|-----------|------|--------|-------------|-----|-----|
| Aug 11 | BSP | A | Southport | 1743 | D 1-1 | Disley 74 | 14 | 1 |
| 14 | BSP | H | Stockport County | 3670 | L 1-2 | Pond 69 | 19 | 2 |
| 18 | BSP | H | Nuneaton Town | 3095 | D 0-0 | | 18 | 3 |
| 25 | BSP | A | Wrexham | 3127 | D 0-0 | | 17 | 4 |
| 27 | BSP | H | Mansfield Town | 3397 | W 4-1 | Artus 35 G Pearson 45 (pen) 76 Colbeck 61 | 12 | 5 |
| Sept 1 | BSP | A | Hereford United | 2059 | W 2-0 | Southwell 40 S Pearson 44 | 11 | 6 |
| 4 | BSP | A | Barrow | 966 | D 2-2 | Elding 67 83 (Pen) | 12 | 7 |
| 8 | BSP | H | Forest Green Rovers | 3270 | W 1-0 | Pond 63 | 7 | 8 |
| 15 | BSP | A | Kidderminster Harriers | 1811 | D 0-0 | | 9 | 9 |
| 21 | BSP | H | Luton Town | 4074 | W 4-1 | Colbeck 8 Cook 40 Hannah 43 Beckwith 71 (og) | 5 | 10 |
| 25 | BSP | H | Gateshead | 3202 | W 3-0 | Niven 13 Pond 20 Hannah 70 | 4 | 11 |
| 29 | BSP | A | Newport County | 2958 | D 0-0 | | 6 | 12 |
| Oct 6 | BSP | H | Dartford | 4009 | L 0-2 | | 6 | 13 |
| 9 | BSP | A | Alfreton Town | 1192 | W 2-0 | Neilson 40 Hannah 89 | 6 | 14 |
| 13 | BSP | A | AFC Telford United | 2439 | W 2-1 | Pond 12 Mlller 39 | 4 | 15 |
| 20 | FAC Q4 | H | **Kidderminster Harriers** | **2092** | **L 2-4** | **Niven 20 Neilson 45** | | 16 |
| 27 | BSP | H | Macclesfield Town | 3014 | L 0-1 | | 5 | 17 |
| Nov 3 | BSP | A | Tamworth | 1042 | W 1-0 | Cook 63 | 3 | 18 |
| 6 | BSP | A | Hyde | 822 | L 2-3 | Hannah 45 53 | 4 | 19 |
| 10 | BSP | H | Woking | 3518 | W 5-1 | Hatton 11 76 Disley 18 Hannah 34 Cook 90 | 2 | 20 |
| 11 | BSP | H | Braintree Town | 3722 | W 3-0 | Hannah 43 65 Disley 52 | 1 | 21 |
| 24 | FAT 1 | H | **Buxton** | **1389** | **D 0-0** | | | 22 |
| 28 | FAT 1r | A | **Buxton** | **444** | **W 1-0** | **Miller 87** | | 23 |
| Dec 1 | BSP | A | Ebbsfleet United | 1164 | D 1-1 | Marshall 3 | 2 | 24 |
| 8 | BSP | H | Tamworth | 3109 | W 2-0 | Disley 7 Hannah 51 | 1 | 25 |
| 15 | FAT 2 | H | **Havant & Waterlooville** | **1215** | **W 4-0** | **S.Pearson 2 Cook 9 60 G.Pearson 36** | | 26 |
| 22 | BSP | H | Wrexham | 4302 | W 1-0 | Hannah 77 | 1 | 27 |
| 26 | BSP | A | Lincoln City | 5702 | W 4-1 | Cook 37 Boyce 43 (og) Disley 58 Colbeck 66 | 1 | 28 |
| Jan 1 | BSP | H | Lincoln City | 7405 | D 1-1 | Miller 22 | 1 | 29 |
| 5 | BSP | H | Hereford United | 3783 | D 1-1 | Pond 2 | 1 | 30 |
| 12 | FAT 3 | A | **Welling United** | **1037** | **W 2-1** | **Devitt 30 ( pen) Marshall 51** | | 31 |
| 23 | BSP | H | Hyde United | 2755 | W 2-0 | Cook 84 90 | 1 | 32 |
| 26 | BSP | A | Cambridge United | 2764 | D 0-0 | | | 33 |
| 29 | FAT 4 | H | **Luton Town** | **2791** | **W 3-0** | **Devitt 8 Cook 75 Marshall 76** | | 34 |
| Feb 2 | BSP | H | Alfreton Town | 3868 | W 4-2 | Devitt 41 (pen) Brodie 45 Cook 58 Disley 81 | 1 | 35 |
| 9 | BSP | A | AFC Telford United | 4462 | W 1-0 | Brodie 48 | 1 | 36 |
| 16 | FAT S-F 1 | H | **Dartford** | **3573** | **W 3-0** | **Disley 25 85 Cook 87** | 1 | 37 |
| 19 | BSP | A | Braintree Town | 880 | L 0-1 | | 2 | 38 |
| 23 | FAT S-F 2 | A | **Darford** | **2153** | **D 0-0** | | | 39 |
| 26 | BSP | H | Ebbsfleet United | 3129 | W 3-2 | Marshall 1 Cook 38 Disley 87 | 3 | 40 |
| Mar 5 | BSP | A | Forest Green Rovers | 744 | W 1-0 | Naylor 74 | 4 | 41 |
| 9 | BSP | H | Kidderminster Harriers | 4629 | L 1-3 | Miller 50 | 5 | 42 |
| 12 | BSP | A | Mansfield Town | 3896 | L 0-2 | | 5 | 43 |
| 16 | BSP | H | Cambridge United | 3516 | L 0-1 | | 5 | 44 |
| 19 | BSP | A | Nuneaton Town | 964 | L 0-1 | | 5 | 45 |
| 24 | FAT F | N | **Wrexham** | **35266** | **D1-1** | **Cook 71 - Lost 1-4 on pens** | 5 | 46 |
| 26 | BSP | H | Gateshead | 351 | D 1-1 | Thanoj 47 | 5 | 47 |
| 30 | BSP | H | Barrow | 3532 | D 0-0 | | 5 | 48 |
| Apr 1 | BSP | A | Stockport County | 3804 | W 2-1 | Hannah 48 Hatton 57 | 5 | 49 |
| 3 | BSP | A | Macclesfield Town | 1776 | W 3-1 | Cook 13 Pearson 37 Artus 71 | 5 | 50 |
| 6 | BSP | H | Southport | 3780 | D 2-2 | Cook 35 Taylor 90 | 5 | 51 |
| 9 | BSP | A | Dartford | 1201 | W 2-1 | Cook 79 Thomas 88 | 5 | 52 |
| 12 | BSP | A | Luton Town | 5662 | D 1-1 | Southwell 54 | 5 | 53 |
| 16 | BSP | A | Woking | 1570 | W 1-0 | John-Lewis 75 | 5 | 54 |
| 20 | BSP | H | Newport County | 4555 | W 3-0 | Devitt 18 Thanoj 24 Hearn 44 | 4 | 55 |
| 24 | P.Off S-F1 | H | **Newport County** | **5414** | **L 0-1** | | | 56 |
| 28 | P.Off S-F2 | A | **Newport County** | **6615** | **L 0-1** | | | 57 |

| GOALSCORERS | Lge | FAC | FAT | Total | Pens | Hat-tricks | Cons Run | | Lge | FAC | FAT | Total | Pens | Hat-tricks | Cons Run |
|-------------|-----|-----|-----|-------|------|------------|----------|---|-----|-----|-----|-------|------|------------|----------|
| Cook | 11 | | 5 | 16 | | | 2 | Hatton | 3 | | | 3 | | | |
| Hannah | 11 | | | 11 | | | 3 | Neilson | 1 | 1 | | 2 | | | |
| Disley | 7 | | 2 | 9 | | | | Niven | 1 | 1 | | 2 | | | |
| Pond | 5 | | | 5 | | | | S.Pearson | 1 | | 1 | 2 | | | |
| Devitt | 2 | | 2 | 4 | 2 | | | Southwell | 2 | | | 2 | | | |
| Marshall | 2 | | 2 | 4 | | | | Thanoj | 2 | | | 2 | | | |
| Miller | 3 | | 1 | 4 | | | | Hearn | 1 | | | 1 | | | |
| G.Pearson | 3 | | 1 | 4 | 1 | | | John-Lewis | 1 | | | 1 | | | |
| Colbeck | 3 | | | 3 | | | | Naylor | 1 | | | 1 | | | |
| Artus | 2 | | | 2 | | | | Taylor | 1 | | | 1 | | | |
| Brodie | 2 | | | 2 | 1 | | | Thomas | 1 | | | 1 | | | |
| Elding | 2 | | | 2 | | | | Own Goals | 2 | | | 2 | | | |
| | | | | | | | | Cons Run - Consecutive scoring games. | | | | | | | |

# HEREFORD UNITED

**Chairman:** David Keyte

**Secretary:** Lee Symonds    **(T)** 0844 2761 939    **(E)** club@herefordunited.co.uk

**Commercial Manager:** n/a      **(T)**

**Programme Editor:** Jamie Griffiths    **(T)** 0844 2761 939

**Ground Address:** Edgar Street Athletic Ground, Blackfriars Street, Hereford HR4 9JU

**(T)** 0844 2761 939      **Manager:** Martin Foyle

2012-13 Squad

## Club Factfile

**Founded:** 1924      **Nickname:** The Bulls

**Previous Names:** St Martins and RAOC amalgamated in 1924 to form Hereford United.

**Previous Leagues:** Birmingham. Birmingham Combination. Southern 1939-72. Football League 1972-97, 2006-12. Conference 1997-2006.

**Club Colours (change):** White/black/white (Red & black/white/red & black)

**Ground Capacity:** 8,843    **Seats:** 2,761    **Covered:** 6,082    **Clubhouse:** Yes    **Shop:** Yes

**Directions**

Edgar Street is in the heart of the City of Hereford.

The main road, Edgar Street, which lends it's name to the ground is the main A49 which runs directly through Hereford City Centre in a North-South direction.

**Previous Grounds:** None

**Record Attendance:** 18,114 v Sheffield Wednesday - FA Cup 3rd Round 04.01.1958

**Record Victory:** (League ) 6-0 v Burnley (A) - Division Four 24.01.1987

**Record Defeat:** (League) 1-7 v Mansfield Town - Division Three

**Record Goalscorer:** (League) Stewart Phillips - 93, 1980-91. Goals in a Season - Dixie McNeil - 35, 1975-76.

**Record Appearances:** (League) Mel Pejic - 412, 1980-92.

**Additional Records:** Received £440,000 from Queen's Park Rangers for Darren Peacock 1990.

**Senior Honours:**    Paid £80,000 to Walsall for Dean Smith 1994.

Football League Division Three 1974-76. Southern League Division One 1958-59. Welsh Cup 1989-90.

### 10 YEAR RECORD

| 03-04 | | 04-05 | | 05-06 | | 06-07 | | 07-08 | | 08-09 | | 09-10 | | 10-11 | | 11-12 | | 12-13 | |
|---|---|---|---|---|---|---|---|---|---|---|---|---|---|---|---|---|---|---|---|
| Conf | 2 | Conf | 2 | Conf | 2 | FL 2 | 16 | FL 2 | 3 | FL 1 | 21 | FL 2 | 16 | FL 2 | 21 | FL 2 | 23 | Conf | 6 |

# MATCH RESULTS 2012-13

| Date | Comp | H/A | Opponents | Att: | Result | Goalscorers | Pos | No. |
|---|---|---|---|---|---|---|---|---|
| Aug 11 | BSP | H | Macclesfield Town | 2139 | W 2-1 | Canham 15 Jackson 66 | 5 | 1 |
| 14 | BSP | A | Tamworth | 3670 | D 2-2 | Watkins 9 Pell 35 (pen) | 6 | 2 |
| 18 | BSP | A | Alfreton Town | 690 | W 3-0 | Watkins 55 Canham 64 Nichols 68 | 2 | 3 |
| 25 | BSP | H | Ebbsfleet United | 1906 | W 4-2 | Watkins 27 Canham 37 Carruthers 49 Bowman 89 | 2 | 4 |
| 28 | BSP | A | Newport County | 4365 | L 0-2 | | 4 | 5 |
| Sept 1 | BSP | H | Grimsby Town | 2059 | L 0-2 | | 9 | 6 |
| 4 | BSP | H | Woking | 1481 | W 2-1 | Sammons 5 Clucas 44 | 6 | 7 |
| 8 | BSP | A | Hyde United | 688 | L 2-5 | Bowman 5 77 | 8 | 8 |
| 15 | BSP | A | Dartford | 1601 | L 0-4 | | 12 | 9 |
| 22 | BSP | H | Canbridge United | 1677 | W 4-2 | Bowman 35 Clucas 48 Jackson 51 53 | 10 | 10 |
| 25 | BSP | H | Forest Green Rovers | 1656 | L 1-2 | Stam 7 | 11 | 11 |
| 29 | BSP | A | Mansfield Town | 2246 | D 1-1 | Jackson 22 | 10 | 12 |
| Oct 6 | BSP | H | Stockport County | 1889 | L 1-2 | Marsh 77 | 12 | 13 |
| 9 | BSP | A | Nuneaton Town | 969 | D 0-0 | | 12 | 14 |
| 13 | BSP | H | Braintree United | 1537 | D 0-0 | | 14 | 15 |
| 20 | FAC Q4 | A | FC United | 2212 | W 2-0 | Bowman 38 (pen) 81 | | 16 |
| 27 | BSP | A | Southport | 1028 | D 2-2 | Clucas 6 Bowman 14 (pen) | 14 | 17 |
| Nov 3 | FAC 1 | H | Shrewsbury Town | 3251 | W 3-1 | Evans 3 Bowman 12 73 (pen) | | 18 |
| 6 | BSP | H | Luton Town | 2108 | W 1-0 | McQuilkin 55 | 12 | 19 |
| 10 | BSP | A | Wrexham | 3620 | W 2-1 | Todd 8 Graham 90 | 9 | 20 |
| 17 | BSP | A | Lincoln City | 2233 | L 2-3 | Bowman 55 Evans 82 | 10 | 21 |
| 24 | FAT 1 | A | Ebbsfleet United | 651 | W 1-0 | O'Keefe 73 | | 22 |
| Dec 3 | FAC 2 | A | Cheltenham Town | 5070 | D 1-1 | O'Keefe 20 | | 23 |
| 7 | BSP | A | Barrow | 867 | W 2-0 | O'Keefe 45 Bowman 78 | 11 | 24 |
| 12 | FAC 2r | H | Cheltenham Town | 5026 | L 1-2 | Clucas 74 | | 25 |
| 15 | FAT 2 | H | Chelmsford City | 1124 | L 0-3 | | | 26 |
| 26 | BSP | H | Kidderminster Harriers | 2902 | L 0-1 | | 14 | 27 |
| Jan 1 | BSP | A | Kidderminster Harriers | 3674 | W 1-0 | O'Keefe 13 | | 28 |
| 5 | BSP | A | Grimsby Town | 3783 | D 1-1 | Bowman 42 | 10 | 29 |
| 8 | BSP | H | AFC Telford United | 1490 | D 1-1 | Watkins 2 | | 30 |
| 12 | BSP | H | Alfreton Town | 1565 | D 3-3 | Bowman 20 48 Stam 45 | 11 | 31 |
| Feb 2 | BSP | H | Southport | 1513 | D 2-2 | Bowman 75 O'Keefe 84 | 12 | 32 |
| 9 | BSP | A | Braintree Town | 606 | W 2-0 | Sharp 20 Watkins 58 | 12 | 33 |
| 12 | BSP | H | Wrexham | 1781 | L 0-1 | | 12 | 34 |
| 16 | BSP | H | Lincoln City | 1914 | W 3-2 | Stam 13 Sharp 57 61 | 11 | 35 |
| 19 | BSP | A | Ebbsfleet United | 614 | L 0-1 | | 11 | 36 |
| 20 | BSP | A | Cambridge United | 2171 | W 3-1 | Bowman 40 (pen) 75 (pen) Jarvis 71 (og) | 9 | 37 |
| 26 | BSP | A | Stockport County | 2618 | W 3-2 | Graham 29 Bowman 64 (pen) O'Keefe 81 | 7 | 38 |
| Mar 2 | BSP | H | Nuneaton Town | 1908 | D 0-0 | | 7 | 39 |
| 5 | BSP | H | Newport County | 2519 | L 2-3 | O'Keefe 42 (pen)75 (pen) | | 40 |
| 9 | BSP | A | Luton Town | 6001 | D 1-1 | Jackson 23 | 9 | 41 |
| 16 | BSP | H | Barrow | 1273 | W 2-1 | O'Keefe 36 (pen) Smikle 90 | 8 | 42 |
| 19 | BSP | A | Gateshead | 259 | L 2-3 | Sharp 17 Jackson 50 | 9 | 43 |
| 23 | BSP | H | Hyde United | 1152 | L 1-2 | O'Keefe 25 | 10 | 44 |
| 26 | BSP | H | Dartford | 662 | W 1-0 | O'Keefe 38 | 8 | 45 |
| 30 | BSP | A | Woking | 2303 | D 1-1 | McNerney 44 (og) | 8 | 46 |
| Apr 1 | BSP | H | Tamworth | 1424 | W 5-2 | O'Keefe 17 (pen) 45 (pen) McDonald 29, Clucas 50 James 67 | 7 | 47 |
| 6 | BSP | A | Macclesfield Town | 1687 | W 1-0 | Clucas 3 | 7 | 48 |
| 9 | BSP | A | Forest Green Rovers | 1142 | W 1-0 | McDonald 56 | 6 | 49 |
| 13 | BSP | H | Gateshead | 1599 | D 1-1 | Clucas 65 | 6 | 50 |
| 16 | BSP | H | Mansfield Town | 2141 | L 1-2 | Bowman 8 | 6 | 51 |
| 20 | BSP | A | AFC Telford United | 2102 | W 4-0 | Clucas 39 47 Jackson 62 O'Keefe 73 | 6 | 52 |

| GOALSCORERS | Lge | FAC | FAT | Total | Pens | Hat-tricks | Cons Run | | Lge | FAC | FAT | Total | Pens | Hat-tricks | Cons Run |
|---|---|---|---|---|---|---|---|---|---|---|---|---|---|---|---|
| Bowman | 15 | 4 | | 19 | 6 | | 3 | Carruthers | 1 | | | 1 | | | |
| O'Keefe | 12 | 1 | 1 | 14 | 5 | | 3 | James | 1 | | | 1 | | | |
| Clucas | 8 | 1 | | 9 | | | | Marsh | 1 | | | 1 | | | |
| Jackson | 7 | | | 7 | | | | McQuilkin | 1 | | 1 | 1 | | | |
| Watkins | 5 | | | 5 | | | | Nicholas | 1 | | | 1 | | | |
| Sharp | 4 | | | 4 | | | | Pell | 1 | | | 1 | | | |
| Canham | 3 | | | 3 | | | | Sammons | 1 | | | 1 | | | |
| Stam | 3 | | | 3 | | | | Smikle | 1 | | | 1 | | | |
| Evans | 1 | 1 | | 2 | | | | Todd | 1 | | | 1 | | | |
| Graham | 2 | | | 2 | | | | Own Goals | 2 | | | 2 | | | |
| McDonald | 2 | | | 2 | | | | Cons Run - Consecutive scoring games. | | | | | | | |

# HYDE FC

**Chairman:** Tahir Khan

**Secretary:** Andrew McAnulty    **(T)** 07866 165 957    **(E)** secretary@hydefc.co.uk

**Commercial Manager:** Mark Worthington    **(T)** 07515 676 392

**Programme Editor:** Emily Liles    **(T)** 07817 645 151

**Ground Address:** Ewen Fields, Walker Lane, Hyde SK14 5PL

**(T)** 0161 367 7273    **Manager:** Scott McNiven

2012-13 Squad.

## Club Factfile

**Founded:** 1885    **Nickname:** The Tigers

**Previous Names:** Hyde F.C., Hyde United > 2011.

**Previous Leagues:** Lancashire & Cheshire 1919-21, Manchester 1921-30, Cheshire County 1930-68, 1970-82, Northern Premier 1968-70, 1983-2004

**Club Colours (change):** Red/navy/red (All blue)

**Ground Capacity:** 4,073    **Seats:** 550    **Covered:** 4,073    **Clubhouse:** Yes    **Shop:** Yes

**Directions:** M60 (Manchester Orbital Motorway) to Junction 24, take the M67 (towards Sheffield) to junction 3 (Hyde/Dukinfield/Stalybridge). Once on exit slipway, keep to the right-hand lane heading for Hyde town centre. At the traffic lights at end of the slipway turn right, then at the second set of lights turn left (Morrisons on left) onto Mottram Road. Turn right at next lights onto Lumn Road. Left at Give Way sign onto Walker Lane. Ground entrance is on left, just after Hyde Leisure Pool, and is clearly signposted. Please note for Satnav, use SK14 5PL

**Previous Grounds:** None

**Record Attendance:** 7,600 v Nelson - FA Cup 1952

**Record Victory:** 9-1 v South Liverpool 04/1991

**Record Defeat:** 0-26 v Preston North End - FA Cup 1887

**Record Goalscorer:** David Nolan - 117 in 404 appearances (1992-2003). Ged Kimmins - 117 in 274 appearances (1993-98)

**Record Appearances:** Steve Johnson - 623 (1976-1988)

**Additional Records:** Paid £8,000 to Mossley for Jim McCluskie 1989    Received £50,000 from Crewe Alexandra for Colin Little 1995

**Senior Honours:**
Northern Premier League Division 1 2003-04, Premier Division 2004-05, League Cup x3. Conference North 2011-12.
Cheshire Senior Cup x6. Manchester Premier cup x6.

### 10 YEAR RECORD

| 03-04 | | 04-05 | | 05-06 | | 06-07 | | 07-08 | | 08-09 | | 09-10 | | 10-11 | | 11-12 | | 12-13 | |
|---|---|---|---|---|---|---|---|---|---|---|---|---|---|---|---|---|---|---|---|
| NP 1 | 1 | NP P | 1 | Conf N | 11 | Conf N | 8 | Conf N | 9 | Conf N | 20 | Conf N | 15 | Conf N | 19 | Conf N | 1 | Conf | 18 |

# MATCH RESULTS 2012-13

| Date | Comp | H/A | Opponents | Att: | Result | Goalscorers | Pos | No. |
|---|---|---|---|---|---|---|---|---|
| Aug 11 | BSP | A | Braintree Town | 598 | D 2-2 | Spencer 23 36 (pen) | 10 | 1 |
| 18 | BSP | H | Luton Town | 1141 | L 1-2 | Blinkhorn 55 | 17 | 2 |
| 14 | BSP | A | Barrow | 798 | D 0-0 | | 16 | 3 |
| 15 | BSP | A | Lincoln City | 1745 | L 2-3 | Spencer 64 (pen) Jevons 70 | 23 | 4 |
| 25 | BSP | A | Mansfield Town | 2203 | L 0-1 | | 20 | 5 |
| 27 | BSP | H | Southport | 734 | L 0-2 | | 21 | 6 |
| 29 | BSP | A | Dartford | 1338 | D 1-1 | Brown 28 | 24 | 7 |
| 22 | BSP | H | Nuneaton Town | 585 | D 2-2 | Griffin 19 Jevons 65 | 23 | 8 |
| Sept 1 | BSP | A | Forest Green Rovers | 768 | L 1-3 | Crowther 56 | 13 | 9 |
| 4 | BSP | A | Wrexham | 376 | L 0-3 | | 23 | 10 |
| 8 | BSP | H | Hereford United | 688 | W 5-2 | Spencer 39 Brown 52 JEVONS 3 (72 80 84) | 23 | 11 |
| 6 | BSP | H | Gateshead | 470 | L 0-2 | | 24 | 12 |
| Oct 9 | BSP | A | Kidderminster Harriers | 1457 | L 0-3 | | 24 | 13 |
| 13 | BSP | H | Tamworth | 657 | W 2-1 | Jevons 54 75 | 24 | 14 |
| 20 | FAC Q4 | H | Harrogate Town | 395 | D 1-1 | Jevons 8 (pen) | | 15 |
| 27 | BSP | A | Cambridge United | 1779 | W 1-0 | Crowther 83 | 23 | 16 |
| 31 | FAC Q4r | A | Harrogate Town | 247 | L 0-1* | | | 17 |
| Nov 6 | BSP | H | Grimsby Town | 822 | W 3-2 | Brown 4 68 Crowther 17 | 22 | 18 |
| 10 | BSP | A | Ebbsfleet United | 779 | L 2-3 | Crowther 4 Blinkhorn 11 | 22 | 19 |
| 17 | BSP | A | Newport County | 2096 | W 3-1 | Jevons 29 (pen) Ashworth 76 Spencer 90 | 22 | 20 |
| 20 | BSP | H | Alfreton Town | 444 | D 1-1 | Jevons 42 | 21 | 21 |
| 24 | FAT 1 | H | Barrow | 436 | D 1-1 | Brown 11 | | 22 |
| 27 | FAT 1r | A | Barrow | 728 | L 0-1 | | | 23 |
| Dec 1 | BSP | H | Woking | 429 | W 7-0 | JEVONS 4 (44 61 89 90) Spencer 51 M.Harris 79 Poole 86 | 18 | 24 |
| 4 | BSP | A | Macclesfield T | 1124 | L 2-3 | Brown 4 Jevons 45 (pen) | 20 | 25 |
| 8 | BSP | H | AFC Telford United | 523 | W 2-1 | Poole 55 Spencer 66 | 16 | 26 |
| 26 | BSP | A | Stockport County | 3963 | W 2-0 | Griffin 10 Sedgewick 20 | 12 | 27 |
| 29 | BSP | H | Southport | 1068 | W 1-0 | Griffin 21 | 9 | 28 |
| Jan 1 | BSP | H | Stockport County | 2540 | L 0-1 | | 12 | 29 |
| 5 | BSP | H | Forest Green Rovers | 553 | L 0-1 | | 12 | 30 |
| 22 | BSP | A | Grimsby Town | 2755 | L 0-2 | | 16 | 31 |
| Feb 2 | BSP | A | Woking | 1236 | L 1-2 | S. Spencer 20 | 18 | 32 |
| 9 | BSP | H | Macclesfield | 1184 | L 0-1 | Spencer 90 | 19 | 33 |
| 12 | BSP | A | AFC Telford United | 1394 | W 3-1 | Blinkhorn 35 Spencer 60 Jevons 79 (pen) | 18 | 34 |
| 16 | BSP | H | Kidderminster Harriers | 717 | L 0-4 | | 17 | 35 |
| 19 | BSP | H | Mansfield Town | 675 | L 0-1 | | 18 | 36 |
| 23 | BSP | A | Tamworth | 746 | L 0-2 | | 18 | 37 |
| 26 | BSP | A | Alfreton Town | 476 | L 1-5 | Broadbent 85 | 18 | 38 |
| Mar 2 | BSP | H | Newport County | 640 | L 0-1 | | 19 | 39 |
| 9 | BSP | A | Gateshead | 371 | L 0-3 | | 21 | 40 |
| 12 | BSP | A | Luton Town | 4847 | W 2-1 | Almond 19 Milligan 70 (pen) | 20 | 41 |
| 16 | BSP | H | Dartford | 475 | W 3-0 | Hogan 26 Blinkhorn 69 Almond 83 | 18 | 42 |
| 23 | BSP | A | Hereford United | 1152 | W 2-1 | Brown 63 Almond 73 | 17 | 43 |
| 26 | BSP | A | Cambridge United | 404 | W 2-1 | Blinkhorn 3 Brizell 81 | 14 | 44 |
| 30 | BSP | H | Wrexham | 1846 | W 2-0 | Hogan 30 McCartan 90 | 14 | 45 |
| Apr 1 | BSP | A | Barrow | 1001 | D 1-1 | Hogan 2 | 15 | 46 |
| 6 | BSP | H | Braintree Town | 509 | L 1-2 | Milligan 83 | 16 | 47 |
| 9 | BSP | H | Ebbsfleet United | 385 | W 1-0 | Blinkhorn 43 | 15 | 48 |
| 13 | BSP | A | Woking | 1236 | L 1-2 | S. Spencer 20 | 18 | 49 |
| 20 | BSP | H | Lincoln City | 1390 | L 1-5 | Ashworth 50 | 18 | 50 |

| GOALSCORERS | Lge | FAC | FAT | Total | Pens | Hat-tricks | Cons Run | | Lge | FAC | FAT | Total | Pens | Hat-tricks | Cons Run |
|---|---|---|---|---|---|---|---|---|---|---|---|---|---|---|---|
| Jevons | 15 | 1 | | 16 | 4 | 2 | 2 | Spencer | 2 | | | 2 | 2 | | |
| Brown | 8 | | 1 | 9 | | | | Brizell | 1 | | | 1 | | | |
| Spencer | 8 | | | 8 | | | | Harris | 1 | | | 1 | | | |
| Blinkhorn | 6 | | | 6 | | | | McCartan | 1 | | | 1 | | | |
| Crowther | 4 | | | 4 | | | | Poole | 1 | | | 1 | | | |
| Almond | 4 | | | 4 | | | | Sedgewick | 1 | | | 1 | | | |
| Ashworth | 3 | | | 3 | | | | Cons Run - Consecutive scoring games. | | | | | | | |
| Griffin | 3 | | | 3 | | | | | | | | | | | |
| Hogan | 3 | | | 3 | | | | | | | | | | | |
| Milligan | 2 | | | 2 | 1 | | | | | | | | | | |

# KIDDERMINSTER HARRIERS

**Chairman:** Mark Serrell
**Secretary:** Jon Harris  **(T)** 07786 992272  **(E)** info@harriers.co.uk
**Commercial Manager:** Ruth Serrell, John  **(T)** 01562 823 931
**Programme Editor:** Matt Wall  **(T)** 01562 823 931
**Ground Address:** Aggborough Stadium, Hoo Road, Kidderminster DY10 1NB
**(T)** 01562 823 931  **Manager:** Steve Burr

2012-13 Squad - Back Row (L-R): Keith Briggs, Kyle Storer, James Vincent, Callum Gittings, Jamille Matt, Justin Nisbett.
Middle Row: Gavin Crowe, Ade Ganderton, Mickey Demetriou, Ryan Austin, Daniel Lewis, Mike Williams, Danny Pilkington, Andy Fearn, Jerry Gill.
Front Row: Ryan Rowe, Ricky Shakes, Marvin Johnson, Anthony Malbon, Steve Burr, Lee Vaughan, Ricky Shakes, Jack Byrne, Exodus Geohaghon.

## Club Factfile

**Founded:** 1886  **Nickname:** Harriers
**Previous Names:** Kidderminster > 1891
**Previous Leagues:** Birmingham 1889-90, 91-1939, 47-48, 60-62. Midland 1890-91. Southern 1939-45, 48-60, 72-83. Birmingham Comb. 1945-47. West Midlands 1962-72. Conference 1983-2000. Football League 2000-05.
**Club Colours (change):** Red & white/red & white/white & red (Purple & amber/purple & amber/purple)

**Ground Capacity:** 6,419  **Seats:** 3.175  **Covered:** 3,062  **Clubhouse:** Yes  **Shop:** Yes

**Directions:** From North M5 Junc 3 onto A456 to Kidderminster, From South M5 Junc 6 onto A449 to Kidderminster. Alternatively M40/42 Junc 1 onto A38 to Bromsgrove/A448 to Kidderminster. (All routes follow Brown signs to (SVR) Steam Railway then follow signs to Aggborough). Aggborough is signposted at either end of Hoo Road.

**Previous Grounds:** None

**Record Attendance:** 9,155 v Hereford United - 27/11/48
**Record Victory:** 25-0 v Hereford (H) - Birmingham Senior Cup 12/10/1889
**Record Defeat:** 0-13 v Darwen (A) - FA Cup 1st Round 24/01/1891
**Record Goalscorer:** Peter Wassell - 432 (1963-74)
**Record Appearances:** Brendan Wassell - 686 (1962-74)
**Additional Records:** Paid £80,000 to Nuneaton Borough for Andy Ducros July 2000
Recieved £380,000 from W.B.A. for Lee Hughes July 1997
**Senior Honours:**
FA Trophy 1986-87. Conference 1993-94, 1999-2000.

### 10 YEAR RECORD

| 03-04 | 04-05 | 05-06 | 06-07 | 07-08 | 08-09 | 09-10 | 10-11 | 11-12 | 12-13 |
|---|---|---|---|---|---|---|---|---|---|
| FL 3  16 | FL 3  23 | Conf  15 | Conf  10 | Conf  13 | Conf  6 | Conf  13 | Conf  6 | Conf  6 | Conf  2 |

# MATCH RESULTS 2012-13

| Date | Comp | H/A | Opponents | Att: | Result | Goalscorers | Pos | No. |
|---|---|---|---|---|---|---|---|---|
| Aug 11 | BSP | A | Lincoln City | 2112 | L 0-1 | | 23 | 1 |
| 14 | BSP | H | Luton Town | 2275 | L 0-2 | | 22 | 2 |
| 18 | BSP | H | Mansfield Town | 1770 | L 2-3 | Byrne 8 Johnson 52 | 24 | 3 |
| 25 | BSP | A | Dartford | 1068 | L 0-1 | | 24 | 4 |
| 27 | BSP | H | Forest Green Rovers | 1742 | L 0-1 | | 24 | 5 |
| Sept 1 | BSP | A | Barrow | 716 | D 1-1 | Pilkington 8 | 24 | 6 |
| 4 | BSP | A | Braintree Town | 579 | D 1-1 | Demetriou 89 | 24 | 7 |
| 8 | BSP | H | Southport | 1650 | D 2-2 | Storer 17 Malbon 88 | 24 | 8 |
| 15 | BSP | H | Grimsby Town | 1811 | D 0-0 | | 24 | 9 |
| 22 | BSP | A | Alfreton Town | 659 | D 1-1 | Malbon 65 | 24 | 10 |
| 25 | BSP | A | Cambridge United | 1815 | W 3-1 | ROWE 3 ( 60 69 85) | 23 | 11 |
| 29 | BSP | H | Macclesfield Town | 1654 | W 3-0 | Dunckley 43 Rowe 50 Johnson 73 | 20 | 12 |
| Oct 6 | BSP | A | Ebbsfleet United | 728 | D 1-1 | Malbon 28 | 20 | 13 |
| 9 | BSP | H | Hyde United | 1457 | W 3-0 | Vincent 16 Rowe 23 90 | 20 | 14 |
| 13 | BSP | A | Stockport County | 3426 | L 0-1 | | 21 | 15 |
| 20 | FAC Q4 | A | **Grmsby Town** | 2092 | **W 4-2** | **Malbon 9 Dunckley 15 Vaughan 18 Johnson 90** | | 16 |
| 27 | BSP | A | Gateshead | 1639 | D 1-1 | Malbon 46 | 21 | 17 |
| Nov 3 | FAC 1 | H | **Oldham Athletic** | 2888 | **L 0-2** | | | 18 |
| 6 | BSP | A | Woking | 1168 | D 2-2 | Blissett 16 42 | 19 | 19 |
| 10 | BSP | H | Nuneaton Town | 1592 | W 1-0 | Gowling 89 | 17 | 20 |
| 17 | BSP | A | AFC Telford United | 2160 | W 2-0 | Johnson 82 Rowe 90 | 16 | 21 |
| 24 | FAT 1 | A | **Alfreton Town** | 361 | **W 3-1** | **Pilkington 34 Dunkley 76 Rowe 84** | | 22 |
| Dec 1 | BSP | H | Wrexham | 2378 | W 2-0 | Matt 57 Blissett 70 | 11 | 23 |
| 4 | BSP | A | Tamworth | 1031 | W 1-0 | Rowe 90 | 8 | 24 |
| 8 | BSP | H | Newport County | 1951 | W 3-2 | MATT 3 ( 23 58 78) | 8 | 25 |
| 15 | FAT 2 | A | **Bromley** | 432 | **L 0-1** | | | 26 |
| 22 | BSP | H | Dartford | 1779 | W 5-1 | Dunckley 4 Matt 32 69 Williams 76 L.Vaughan 90 | 6 | 27 |
| 26 | BSP | A | Hereford United | 2902 | W 1-0 | Matt 6 | 5 | 28 |
| Jan 1 | BSP | H | Hereford United | 3674 | L 0-1 | | 5 | 29 |
| 5 | BSP | H | Barrow | 1703 | W 2-0 | Rowe 3 Matt 83 | 5 | 30 |
| 12 | BSP | A | Mansfield Town | 2405 | W 2-0 | Demetriou 22 L.Vaughan 25 | 5 | 31 |
| 19 | BSP | A | Macclesfield Town | 1342 | L 0-1 | | 5 | 32 |
| 29 | BSP | H | AFC Telford United | 1785 | W 1-0 | Johnson 37 | 5 | 33 |
| Feb 9 | BSP | H | Cambridge United | 1949 | W 3-2 | Dunckley 27 Johnson 42  Malbon 51 | 4 | 34 |
| 16 | BSP | A | Hyde | 717 | W 4-0 | Malbon 20 58 Johnson 55 Pearson 87 | 5 | 35 |
| 19 | BSP | A | Forest Green Rovers | 1449 | W 1-0 | Malbon 26 | 4 | 36 |
| 23 | BSP | H | Alfreton Town | 2209 | W 3-1 | Morgan-Smith 1 Gowling 38 Malbon 45 | 3 | 37 |
| 26 | BSP | A | Nuneaton Town | 1087 | W 1-0 | Malbon 71 | 2 | 38 |
| Mar 2 | BSP | H | Ebbsfleet United | 2048 | W 3-2 | Vincent 14 Malbon 61 Gittings 88 | 3 | 39 |
| 5 | BSP | A | Gateshead | 273 | L 0-2 | | 3 | 40 |
| 9 | BSP | A | Grimsby Town | 4629 | W 3-1 | Malbon 32 77 Gash 45 | 2 | 41 |
| 16 | BSP | H | Tamworth | 2392 | W 4-1 | Briggs 37 Pilkington 45 Gash 58 84 | 2 | 42 |
| 19 | BSP | A | Newport County | 2652 | W 2-1 | Gash 27 Dunckley 90 | 1 | 43 |
| 23 | BSP | A | Southport | 946 | W 3-1 | Gash 43 Malbon 86 Rowe 90 | 1 | 44 |
| 26 | BSP | H | Woking | 2035 | D 2-2 | Gowling 13 Malbon 55 | 1 | 45 |
| 30 | BSP | H | Braintree Town | 2266 | W 2-1 | Malbon 60  Wells 63 (og) | 1 | 46 |
| Apr 1 | BSP | A | Luton Town | 6108 | W 2 -1 | Gowlng 13 Malbon 35 | 1 | 47 |
| 6 | BSP | A | Lincoln City | 2326 | W 3-0 | Jackman 27 Storer 80 L.Vaughan 89 | 1 | 48 |
| 13 | BSP | A | Wrexham | 4013 | W 2-1 | Vincent 19 Gash 71 | 1 | 49 |
| 20 | BSP | A | Stockport County | 6453 | W 5-0 | Malbon 6 53 Dunckley 57 Devaney 75 | 2 | 50 |
| 23 | P.Offs S-F 1 A | | **Wrexham** | 6315 | **L 1-2** | **Gash 55 (pen)** | | 51 |
| 28 | P.Offs S-F 2 H | | **Wrexham** | 6202 | **L 1-3** | **Dunckley 64** | | 52 |

| GOALSCORERS | Lge | FAC | FAT | Total | Pens | Hat-tricks | Cons Run | | Lge | FAC | FAT | Total | Pens | Hat-tricks | Cons Run |
|---|---|---|---|---|---|---|---|---|---|---|---|---|---|---|---|
| Malbon | 19 | 1 | | 20 | | | 5 | Storer | 2 | | | 2 | | | |
| Rowe | 10 | | 1 | 11 | | 1 | | Briggs | 1 | | | 1 | | | |
| Matt | 8 | | | 8 | | 1 | | Byrne | 1 | | | 1 | | | |
| Dunckley | 6 | 1 | 1 | 7 | | | | Devaney | 1 | | | 1 | | | |
| Johnson | 6 | 1 | | 7 | | | | Gittings | 1 | | | 1 | | | |
| Gash | 7 | | | 7 | | | | Jackman | 1 | | | 1 | | | |
| Gowling | 4 | | | 4 | | | | Morgan-Smith | 1 | | | 1 | | | |
| Vaughan L | 3 | 1 | | 4 | | | | Pearson | 1 | | | 1 | | | |
| Blissett | 3 | | | 3 | | | | Williams | 1 | | | 1 | | | |
| Pilkington | 2 | | 1 | 3 | | | | Own Goal | 1 | | | 1 | | | |
| Vincent | 3 | | | 3 | | | | Cons Run - Consecutive scoring games. | | | | | | | |
| Demetriou | 2 | | | 2 | | | | | | | | | | | |

# LINCOLN CITY

**Chairman:** Bob Dorrian
**Secretary:** Steve Prescott    **(T)** 07818 597 686    **(E)** steve.prescott@redimps.com
**Commercial Manager:** Russell Moore    **(T)** 07971 122234
**Programme Editor:** John Vickers    **(T)** 07881 913 249
**Ground Address:** Sincil Bank Stadium, Lincoln LN5 8LD
**(T)** 01522 880 011      **Manager:** Gary Simpson

## Club Factfile

**Founded:** 1884    **Nickname:** Imps
**Previous Names:** None
**Previous Leagues:** Midland (Founder Member) 1889-91, 1908-09, 1911-12, 1920-21, Football Alliance 1891-92, Football League (Founder Member) 1892-1908, 1909-11, 1912-20, 1921-86, 1988-2011, Conference 1986-88.

**Club Colours (change):** Red & white stripes/black/red (Green & white/white/white)

**Ground Capacity:** 9,800    **Seats:** Yes    **Covered:** Yes    **Clubhouse:**    **Shop:** Yes

**Directions**
**From South:** Exit A1 at s/p 'Lincoln A46, Sleaford A17' onto the A46. At roundabout after 9.4 mile take 3rd exit (s/p Lincoln South A1434). Keep on A1434, following 'Lincoln and City Centre' signs for 4.3 miles. Then get into inside lane (s/p City Centre, Worksop A7) and go straight on (1st exit) at r'about into the High St. After 0.5 miles get in outside lane, and go straight on at lights (s/p City Ctre, Worksop A57). After 0.1 miles turn right into Scorer Street. **From North:** Exit A1(M) at the r'about after the Fina and Shell garages (s/p Lincoln A57, E. Markham) onto the A57. At junc. after 9.9 miles turn right (s/p Lincoln A57), remaining on A57 which here runs alongside the Foss Dyke. At r'about after 5.9 miles turn right (Lincoln South, Newark A46, Grantham A1) onto the A46. Straight on at r'about after 1.8 miles. At next r'about after 1.6 miles (by BP station) turn left (s/p) Lincoln South B1190, Doddington Ind.Est., into Doddington Rd, Sraight on for 2 miles to T-junction. Here, turn left (no signpost) onto Newark Rd A1434. Keep on A1434 following City Centre signs. Go straight on (1st exit) at r'about into the High St. After (0.5 miles get in outside lane, and go straight on at lights (s/p City Ctre, Worksop A57). After 0.1 miles turn right into Scorer St. Tip: Have some change ready for a small toll bridge (Dunham) en route.

**Previous Grounds:** John O'Gaunt's 1883-94.

**Record Attendance:** 23,196 v Derby County, League Cup 4th Round 15/11/1967.
**Record Victory:** 11-1 v Crewe Alexandra, Division Three North 29/09/1951.
**Record Defeat:** 3-11 v Manchester City, Division Two 23/03/1895.
**Record Goalscorer:** (League) Andy Graver - 143, 1950-55, 58-61.
**Record Appearances:** (League) Grant Brown - 407, 1989-2002.
**Additional Records:** Paid, £75,000 for Tony Battersby from Bury, 08/1998.
     Received, £500,000 for Gareth Ainsworth from Port Vale, 09/1997.
**Senior Honours:**
Midland League 1908-09, 20-21. Football League Division Three North 1931-32, 47-48, Division Four 1975-76.
Football Conference 1987-88.

### 10 YEAR RECORD

| 03-04 | | 04-05 | | 05-06 | | 06-07 | | 07-08 | | 08-09 | | 09-10 | | 10-11 | | 11-12 | | 12-13 | |
|---|---|---|---|---|---|---|---|---|---|---|---|---|---|---|---|---|---|---|---|
| FL 3 | 7 | FL 2 | 6 | FL 2 | 7 | FL 2 | 5 | FL 2 | 15 | FL 2 | 13 | FL 2 | 20 | FL 2 | 23 | Conf | 17 | Conf | 16 |

# MATCH RESULTS 2012-13

| Date | Comp | H/A | Opponents | Att: | Result | Goalscorers | Pos | No. |
|---|---|---|---|---|---|---|---|---|
| Aug 11 | BSP | H | Kidderminster Harriers | 2112 | W 1-0 | Taylor 39 | 6 | 1 |
| 14 | BSP | A | Cambridge United | 2546 | L 1-2 | Boyce 39 | 13 | 2 |
| 18 | BSP | A | Newport County | 3024 | L 1-2 | Taylor 51 | 15 | 3 |
| 25 | BSP | H | Macclesfield Town | 2009 | L 2-3 | Taylor 31 Boyce 89 | 17 | 4 |
| 27 | BSP | A | Gateshead | 803 | D 1-1 | Robinson 89 | 18 | 5 |
| Sept 1 | BSP | H | Ebbsfleet United | 1682 | D 1-1 | Nicolau 3 | 17 | 6 |
| 4 | BSP | H | Braintree Town | 1566 | L 1-2 | Nicolau 27 | 17 | 7 |
| 8 | BSP | A | AFC Telford United | 1794 | D 1-1 | Oliver 43 | 22 | 8 |
| 15 | BSP | H | Hyde United | 1745 | W 3-2 | Larkin 43 (pen) 67 (pen) Oliver 88 | 18 | 9 |
| 22 | BSP | A | Tamworth | 1042 | L 0-1 | | 21 | 10 |
| 25 | BSP | H | Nuneaton Town | 1579 | W 2-1 | Nicolau 75 Miller 85 | 15 | 11 |
| 29 | BSP | A | Forest Green Rovers | 1395 | L 0-3 | | 19 | 12 |
| Oct 6 | BSP | H | Luton Town | 2970 | L 1-2 | Taylor 58 | 21 | 13 |
| 9 | BSP | A | Mansfield Town | 2325 | D 0-0 | | 21 | 14 |
| 13 | BSP | A | Wrexham | 3809 | W 4-2 | Nicolau 20 Taylor 56 Robinson 69 Larkin 88 | 20 | 15 |
| 20 | FAC Q4 | H | FC Halifax Town | 1940 | D 0-0 | | | 16 |
| 23 | FAC Q4r | A | FC Halifax Town | 1418 | W 2-0 | Sheridan 11 Taylor 76 | | 17 |
| 27 | BSP | H | Stockport County | 1873 | D 3-3 | Taylor 53 90 Nutter 66 | 19 | 18 |
| Nov 3 | FAC 1 | H | Walsall | 2032 | D 1-1 | Taylor 45 | | 19 |
| 6 | BSP | H | Braintree Town | 1455 | W 3-0 | Massey 5 (og) Boyce 47 Taylor 49 | 15 | 20 |
| 10 | BSP | A | Barrow | 987 | W 2-1 | Power 40 Oliver 64 | 13 | 21 |
| 13 | FAC 1r | A | Walsall | 1762 | W 3-2* | Power 50 Oliver 102 110 | | 22 |
| 17 | BSP | H | Hereford United | 2233 | W 3-2 | Taylor 45 Gallinagh 71 (og) Larkin 81 (pen) | 9 | 23 |
| 24 | FAT 1 | A | Tamworth | 726 | L 1-3 | Power 40 | | 24 |
| Dec 1 | FAC 2 | H | Mansfield Town | 4127 | D 3-3 | Power 45 66 Taylor 47 | | 25 |
| 4 | BSP | H | Woking | 2526 | L 0-2 | | 12 | 26 |
| 8 | BSP | A | Dartford | 1466 | W 4-2 | Gray 7 LARKIN 3 ( 24 32 45) | 10 | 27 |
| 12 | FAC 2r | A | Mansfield Town | 5304 | L 1-2 | Smith | | 28 |
| 26 | BSP | H | Grimsby Town | 5702 | L 1-4 | Power 53 (pen) | 13 | 29 |
| 29 | BSP | H | Gateshead | 1906 | D 1-1 | Robinson 63 | 13 | 30 |
| Jan 1 | BSP | A | Grimsby Town | 7405 | D 1-1 | Power 9 | | 31 |
| 5 | BSP | A | Ebbsfleet United | 889 | D 1-1 | Robinson 90 | 13 | 32 |
| 8 | BSP | A | Southport | 815 | L 2-4 | Taylor 37 Oliver 80 | | 33 |
| 12 | BSP | H | Newport County | 1970 | L 2-4 | Oliver 44 Bush 78 | 15 | 34 |
| 26 | BSP | H | Forest Green Rovers | 1663 | L 1-2 | Smith 86 (pen) | 17 | 35 |
| Feb 9 | BSP | H | Dartford | 1789 | W 2-1 | Oliver 6 Larkin 89 (pen) | 14 | 36 |
| 12 | BSP | A | Stockport County | 2769 | L 0-2 | | 18 | 37 |
| 16 | BSP | A | Hereford United | 1914 | L 2-3 | Musa 9 (og) Power 38 (pen) | 18 | 38 |
| 23 | BSP | H | Barrow | 1830 | D 0-0 | | 19 | 39 |
| 26 | BSP | H | Mansfield Town | 2734 | L 0-1 | | 19 | 40 |
| Mar 2 | BSP | A | Woking | 1766 | D 1-1 | Oliver 25 | 18 | 41 |
| 6 | BSP | A | Macclesfield Town | 1557 | L 1-2 | Power 23 (pen) | 18 | 42 |
| 9 | BSP | H | Southport | 1827 | W 1-0 | Power 14 (pen) | 18 | 43 |
| 12 | BSP | H | Wrexham | 1379 | L 1-2 | Westwood 34 (og) | 19 | 44 |
| 16 | BSP | A | Nuneaton Town | 1122 | L 0-1 | | 20 | 45 |
| 23 | BSP | H | AFC Telford United | 1724 | W 3-2 | Jordan 12 Taylor 77 88 | 20 | 46 |
| 26 | BSP | A | Braintree Town | 447 | W 3-1 | Diagne 26 74 Boyce 79 | 17 | 47 |
| 30 | BSP | A | Alfreton Town | 1189 | W 2-0 | Hobson 41 Oliver 81 | 15 | 48 |
| Apr 1 | BSP | H | Cambridge United | 2721 | D 0-0 | | 16 | 49 |
| 6 | BSP | A | Kidderminster Harriers | 2326 | L 0-3 | | 19 | 50 |
| 9 | BSP | A | Luton Town | 5393 | L 0-3 | | 20 | 51 |
| 13 | BSP | H | Tamworth | 3174 | W 2-1 | Taylor 67 Power 83 (pen) | 18 | 52 |
| 20 | BSP | A | Hyde United | 1390 | W 5-1 | Power 27 (pen) Falana 45 OLIVER 3( 48 62 86) | 16 | 53 |

| GOALSCORERS | Lge | FAC | FAT | Total | Pens | Hat-tricks | Cons Run | | Lge | FAC | FAT | Total | Pens | Hat-tricks | Cons Run |
|---|---|---|---|---|---|---|---|---|---|---|---|---|---|---|---|
| Taylor | 13 | 3 | | 16 | | | 4 | Gray | 1 | | | 1 | | | |
| Oliver | 11 | 2 | | 13 | 1 | | 2 | Miller | 1 | | | 1 | | | |
| Power | 8 | 3 | 1 | 11 | 6 | | 2 | Nutter | 1 | | | 1 | | | |
| Larkin | 8 | | | 8 | 4 | 1 | | Sheridan | | 1 | | 1 | | | |
| Nicolau | 4 | | | 4 | | | | Jordan | 1 | | | 1 | | | |
| Robinson | 4 | | | 4 | | | | Hobson | 1 | | | 1 | | | |
| Boyce | 4 | | | 4 | | | | Falana | 1 | | | 1 | | | |
| Diagne | 2 | | | 2 | | | | Own Goals | 4 | | | | | | |
| Smith | 1 | 1 | | 2 | 1 | | | Cons Run - Consecutive scoring games. | | | | | | | |
| Bush | 1 | | | 1 | | | | | | | | | | | |

# LUTON TOWN

**Chairman:** Nick Owen

**Secretary:** Kevan Platt    **(T)** 01582 411 622    **(E)** kevan.platt@lutontown.co.uk

**Commercial Manager:** Dave Hoskins    **(T)** 01582 411 622

**Programme Editor:** Andrew Barringer    **(T)** 01582 411 622

**Ground Address:** Kenilworth Stadium, 1 Maple Road, Luton LU4 8AW

**(T)** 01582 411 622          **Manager:** John Still

## Club Factfile

**Founded:** 1885     **Nickname:** The Hatters

**Previous Names:** None

**Previous Leagues:** Football League 1897-1900, 1920-2009. Southern 1900-20.

**Club Colours (change):** Orange/navy/white (All white)

**Ground Capacity:** 10,226    **Seats:** 10,226    **Covered:** All     **Clubhouse:** Yes    **Shop:** Yes

**Directions**

From the North: Exit the M1 at Junction 11, and join the A505 towards Luton. Follow the A505 for approximately 1.5 miles and Kenilworth Road is on your right as you leave the one-way system along Dunstable Road. To park, follow the one-way around, turning left, right and right again all in about 100 yards so that you do a complete U-turn and then take the second left into Ash Road. Continue down to the bottom, turn left at the end and the club is in front of you. Continue straight past the club and the road bends immediately over a dual carriageway bridge. Beyond this is plenty of street parking (and a great fish shop) if you are early. From the South: You can join the M1 from the M25 at Junction 21A, which is Junction 6 of the M1. Exit at Junction 11 and follow directions above in From the North. From the East: If you are on the A1, leave at Junction 8 of the A1(M) and take the A602 towards Hitchin, then follow the signs to Luton along the A505. When you come into Luton, head for the City Centre and once you reach the one-way system, follow signs to Dunstable and you will see Kenilworth Road on your left. From the West: Come in on the A505 and follow the directions above in From the North.

**Previous Grounds:** Excelsior, Dallow Lane 1885-97, Dunstable Road 1897-1905

**Record Attendance:** 30,069 v Blackpool - FA Cup 6th Round Replay 04/03/59

**Record Victory:** 12-0 v Bristol Rovers - Division 3 South 13/04/36

**Record Defeat:** 0-9 v Small Heath - Division Two 12/11/1898

**Record Goalscorer:** Gordon Turner - 243 (1949-64)

**Record Appearances:** Bob Morton - 495 (1948-64)

**Additional Records:** Paid £850,000 to Odense for Lars Elstrup

                 Recieved £2,500,000 from Arsenal for John Hartson

**Senior Honours:**

Football League Division 3 South 1936-37, Division 4 1967-68, Division 2 1981-82, Division 1 2004-05. League Cup 1988. League Trophy 2008-09

### 10 YEAR RECORD

| 03-04 | | 04-05 | | 05-06 | | 06-07 | | 07-08 | | 08-09 | | 09-10 | | 10-11 | | 11-12 | | 12-13 | |
|---|---|---|---|---|---|---|---|---|---|---|---|---|---|---|---|---|---|---|---|
| FL 2 | 10 | FL 1 | 1 | FLCh | 10 | FLCh | 23 | FL 1 | 24 | FL 2 | 24 | Conf | 2 | Conf | 3 | Conf | 5 | Conf | 7 |

# MATCH RESULTS 2012-13

| Date | Comp | H/A | Opponents | Att: | Result | Goalscorers | Pos | No. |
|------|------|-----|-----------|------|--------|-------------|-----|-----|
| Aug 11 | BSP | H | Gateshead | 6743 | D 2-2 | Shaw 61 Fleetwood 71 | 11 | 1 |
| 14 | BSP | A | Kidderminster Harriers | 2275 | W 2-0 | Fleetwood 22 30 | 4 | 2 |
| 18 | BSP | A | Hyde | 1141 | W 2-1 | O Donnell 68 Fleetwood 78 | 3 | 3 |
| 25 | BSP | H | AFC Telford United | 5970 | L 0-1 | | 9 | 4 |
| 27 | BSP | A | Ebbsfleet United | 1701 | W 3-1 | Fleetwood 10 73 Rendell 19 | 5 | 5 |
| Sept 1 | BSP | H | Macclesfield United | 5803 | W 4-1 | Howells 1 Gray 17 Rendell 82 Fleetwood 90 | 3 | 6 |
| 4 | BSP | H | Cambridge United | 6592 | W 3-2 | Kovacs 18 Gray 53 Beckwith 61 | 2 | 7 |
| 8 | BSP | A | Alfreton Town | 1392 | L 0-3 | | 5 | 8 |
| 15 | BSP | H | Wrexham | 6675 | D 0-0 | | 5 | 9 |
| 21 | BSP | A | Grimsby Town | 4074 | L 1-4 | Rendell 75 | 6 | 10 |
| 25 | BSP | A | Tamworth | 1137 | W 2-1 | Kasim 63 Fleetwood 66 | 5 | 11 |
| 29 | BSP | H | Southport | 5696 | W 3-1 | Fleetwood 4 Rendell 47 51 (pen) | 4 | 12 |
| Oct 6 | BSP | A | Lincoln City | 2970 | W 2-1 | Farman 28 (og) Shaw 61 | 4 | 13 |
| 9 | BSP | H | Braintree Town | 5523 | L 2-3 | Ainge 37 Walker 58 | 4 | 14 |
| 13 | BSP | H | Nuneaton Town | 6148 | W 2-0 | Lawless 86 90 | 3 | 15 |
| 20 | FAC Q4 | A | Cambridge United | 2321 | W 2-0 | Gray 7 Shaw 70 | | 16 |
| 27 | BSP | A | Forest Green Rovers | 2112 | W 2-1 | Fleetwood 74 Rendell 90 (pen) | 2 | 17 |
| Nov 3 | FAC 1 | H | Nuneaton Town | 1686 | D 1-1 | Rendell 84 | | 18 |
| 6 | BSP | A | Hereford United | 2108 | L 0-1 | | 3 | 19 |
| 10 | BSP | A | Dartford | 8587 | L 0-2 | | 6 | 20 |
| 13 | FAC 1r | A | Nuneaton Town | 1596 | W 2-0 | Rendell 22 72 (pen) | | 21 |
| 18 | BSP | A | Mansfield Town | 2619 | D 2-2 | Gray 26 67 | 6 | 22 |
| 27 | FAT 1 | A | Dorchester Town | 688 | D 2-2 | Martin 1 (og) Fleetwood 78 | | 23 |
| Dec 1 | FAC 2 | H | Dorchester Town | 3287 | W 2-1 | Gray 30 Lawless 68 | | 24 |
| 4 | FAT 1r | H | Dorchester Town | 897 | W 3-1 | O'Donnell 11 Walker 17 70 | | 25 |
| 8 | BSP | H | Alfreton Town | 5648 | W 3-0 | O'Donnell 53 Smith 56 Gray 58 | 4 | 26 |
| 11 | BSP | A | Newport County | 2247 | L 2-5 | Gray 16 Shaw 61 | 4 | 27 |
| 26 | BSP | H | Woking | 6744 | W 3-1 | Kovacs 15 Shaw 37 Rendell 82 (pen) | 4 | 28 |
| Jan 1 | BSP | A | Woking | 2961 | L 1-3 | Gray 8 | 6 | 29 |
| 5 | FAC 3 | H | Wolverhampton W | 9638 | W 1-0 | Lawless 46 | | 30 |
| 8 | BSP | H | Barrow | 5165 | W 6-1 | Neilson 2 Kovacs 27 SHAW 3( 29 59 64) Gray 72 | 6 | 31 |
| 16 | BSP | A | AFC Telford United | 1606 | D 0-0 | | 6 | 32 |
| 26 | FAC 4 | A | Norwich City | 26521 | W 1-0 | Rendell 80 | | 33 |
| 29 | FAT 3 | A | Grimsby Town | 2791 | L 0-3 | | | 34 |
| Feb 2 | BSP | A | Barrow | 1188 | L 0-1 | | 7 | 35 |
| 9 | BSP | H | Forest Green Rovers | 6374 | D 1-1 | Gray 5 | 7 | 36 |
| 12 | BSP | A | Dartford | 1802 | L 0-1 | | 7 | 37 |
| 16 | FAC 5 | H | Millwall | 9768 | L 0-3 | | | 38 |
| 19 | BSP | A | Macclesfield Town | 1981 | D 1-1 | Gray 15 | 8 | 39 |
| 23 | BSP | H | Mansfield Town | 5968 | L 2-5 | Rendell 36 Gray 47 | 8 | 40 |
| 26 | BSP | A | Braintree Town | 1003 | L 0-2 | | 10 | 41 |
| Mar 2 | BSP | A | Stockport County | 4074 | W 1-0 | Howells 45 | 8 | 42 |
| 5 | BSP | A | Nuneaton Town | 1173 | D 0-0 | | 7 | 43 |
| 9 | BSP | H | Hereford United | 6001 | D 1-1 | Martin 87 | 8 | 44 |
| 12 | BSP | H | Hyde | 4847 | L 1-2 | Howells 37 | | 45 |
| 16 | BSP | A | Wrexham | 3907 | D 0-0 | | 11 | 46 |
| 19 | BSP | H | Stockport County | 5106 | W 1-0 | McNulty 44 | 8 | 47 |
| 23 | BSP | A | Tamworth | 5501 | D 0-0 | | 8 | 48 |
| 30 | BSP | A | Cambridge United | 3217 | D 2-2 | Shaw 53 Taiwo 65 (pen) | 9 | 49 |
| Apr 1 | BSP | H | Kidderminster Harriers | 6108 | L 1-2 | Gray 83 | 9 | 50 |
| 6 | BSP | A | Gateshead | 382 | L 1-5 | Walker 35 | 12 | 51 |
| 9 | BSP | H | Lincoln City | 5393 | W 3-0 | Martin 41 72 Gray 43 | 9 | 52 |
| 12 | BSP | H | Grimsby Town | 5662 | D 1-1 | Lawless 76 | 10 | 53 |
| 16 | BSP | H | Newport County | 5125 | D 2-2 | Hall 12 Gray 79 | 11 | 54 |
| 18 | BSP | H | Ebbsfleet United | 5934 | W 2-0 | Wall 4 77 | 9 | 55 |
| 20 | BSP | A | Southport | 1406 | W 3-1 | Robinson 30 Gray 34 82 | 7 | 56 |

| GOALSCORERS | Lge | FAC | FAT | Total | Pens | Hat-tricks | Cons Run | | Lge | FAC | FAT | Total | Pens | Hat-tricks | Cons Run |
|-------------|-----|-----|-----|-------|------|-----------|----------|-----|-----|-----|-----|-------|------|-----------|----------|
| Gray | 14 | 2 | | 16 | | | 2 | Wall | 2 | | | 2 | | | |
| Rendell | 8 | 4 | | 12 | 4 | | | Ainge | 1 | | | 1 | | | |
| Fleetwood | 10 | | 1 | 11 | | | 3 | Beckwith | 1 | | | 1 | | | |
| Shaw | 10 | 1 | | 11 | | 1 | | Hall | 1 | | | 1 | | | |
| Lawless | 3 | 2 | | 5 | | | | Kasim | 1 | | | 1 | | | |
| Walker | 2 | | 2 | 4 | | | | McNulty | 1 | | | 1 | | | |
| Howells | 3 | | | 3 | | | | Neilson | 1 | | | 1 | | | |
| Kovacs | 3 | | | 3 | | | | Robinson | 1 | | | 1 | | | |
| Martin | 3 | | | 3 | | | | Smith | 1 | | | 1 | | | |
| O'Donnell | 2 | | 1 | 3 | | | | Own Goal | 1 | | 1 | 1 | | | |
| | | | | | | | | Cons Run - Consecutive scoring games. | | | | | | | |

# MACCLESFIELD TOWN

**Chairman:** Dave Towns (Chief Exe)

**Secretary:** Julie Briggs     **(T)** 01625 264 686     **(E)** juliebriggs@mtfc.co.uk

**Commercial Manager:** Dave Towns     **(T)** 01625 264 686

**Programme Editor:** Tom Rance     **(T)** 07718 206 953

**Ground Address:** Moss Rose Ground, London Road, Macclesfield SK11 7SP

**(T)** 01625 264 686            **Manager:** John Askey

## Club Factfile

**Founded:** 1874     **Nickname:** The Silkmen

**Previous Names:** None

**Previous Leagues:** Manchester. Cheshire County. Northern Premier. Conference 1987-97. Football League 1997-2012.

**Club Colours (change):** Blue/white/blue (All white)

**Ground Capacity:** 6,335   **Seats:** 2,599   **Covered:** Yes     **Clubhouse:** Yes   **Shop:** Yes

**Directions**
From North (M6), Exit Junction 19, Knutsford. Follow the A537 to Macclesfield. Follow signs for the Town Centre. The follow signs A523 Leek, the ground is a mile out of town. The ground is sign-posted from the Town Centre
From South (M6), Exit Junction 17 Sandbach. Follow A534 to Congleton. Then A536 to Macclesfield. After passing the Rising Sun on the left, less than a mile, turn right into Moss Lane. Follow this around and it will bring you to the rear of the ground.

**Previous Grounds:** Rostron Field 1874-1891.

**Record Attendance:** 9,008 v Winsford United - Cheshire Senior Cup 04.02.1948.
**Record Victory:** 15-0 v Chester St Marys - Cheshire Senior Cup Second Round 16.02.1886.
**Record Defeat:** 1-13 v Tranmere Rovers Reserves - 03.05.1929.
**Record Goalscorer:** Not known
**Record Appearances:** Not known
**Additional Records:**

**Senior Honours:**
Manchester League 1908-09, 10-11. Cheshire County League 1931-32, 32-33, 53-54, 60-61, 63-64, 67-68.
Northern Premier League 1968-69, 69-70, 86-87. Bob Lord Trophy 1993-94. Conference 1994-95, 96-97, Championship Shield 1996, 1997, 1998.
FA Trophy 1969-70, 95-96. Cheshire Senior cup x20 most recently 1999-2000.

### 10 YEAR RECORD

| 03-04 | | 04-05 | | 05-06 | | 06-07 | | 07-08 | | 08-09 | | 09-10 | | 10-11 | | 11-12 | | 12-13 | |
|---|---|---|---|---|---|---|---|---|---|---|---|---|---|---|---|---|---|---|---|
| FL 3 | 20 | FL 2 | 5 | FL 2 | 17 | FL 2 | 22 | FL 2 | 19 | FL 2 | 20 | FL 2 | 19 | FL 2 | 15 | FL 2 | 24 | Conf | 11 |

# MATCH RESULTS 2012-13

| Date | Comp | H/A | Opponents | Att | Result | Goalscorers | Pos | No. |
|------|------|-----|-----------|-----|--------|-------------|-----|-----|
| Aug 11 | BSP | A | Hereford United | 2139 | L 1-2 | Barnes-Homer 59 (pen) | 21 | 1 |
| 14 | BSP | H | Wrexham | 2368 | W 2-0 | Rowe 81 Whitehead 90 | 10 | 2 |
| 18 | BSP | H | Dartford | 1420 | W 2-0 | Champion 34 (og) Henry 89 (pen) | 6 | 3 |
| 25 | BSP | A | Lincoln City | 2009 | W 3-2 | Fairhurst 12 Barnes-Homer 77 Holroyd 87 | 3 | 4 |
| 27 | BSP | H | Barrow | 1711 | W 2-0 | Barnes-Homer 16 90 | 2 | 5 |
| Sept 1 | BSP | A | Luton Town | 5803 | L 1-4 | Brown 51 | 5 | 6 |
| 4 | BSP | A | Stockport County | 4208 | W 4-3 | HOLROYD 3 (27 35 51) Tunicliffe 82 (og) | 4 | 7 |
| 8 | BSP | H | Braintree Town | 1509 | W 2-1 | Kissock 75 Barnes-Homer 85 (pen) | 1 | 8 |
| 15 | BSP | A | Nuneaton Town | 939 | D 3-3 | Murtagh 70 Barnes-Homer 90 Mendy 90 | 2 | 9 |
| 22 | BSP | H | Forest Green Rovers | 1729 | L 1-2 | Barnes-Homer 64 | 4 | 10 |
| 29 | BSP | A | Kidderminster Harriers | 1654 | L 0-3 | | 8 | 11 |
| Oct 6 | BSP | H | Alfreton Town | 1437 | L 1-2 | Barnes-Homer 26 (pen) | 8 | 12 |
| 10 | BSP | A | Gateshead | 557 | D 2-2 | Barnes-Homer 71 Mackreth 84 | 9 | 13 |
| 13 | BSP | H | Newport County | 1544 | D 1-1 | Barnes-Homer 81 | 9 | 14 |
| 20 | FAC Q4 | H | Marine | 1189 | W 3-1 | Barnes-Homer 41 (pen) 82 Morgan-Smith 89 | | 15 |
| 27 | BSP | A | Grimsby Town | 3014 | L 1-3 | Barnes-Homer 83 (pen) | 7 | 16 |
| Nov 3 | FAC 1 | A | Swindon Town | 6408 | W 2-0 | Diagne 63 Thompson 89 (og) | | 17 |
| 6 | BSP | H | Tamworth | 1089 | W 2-0 | Morgan-Smith 14 Jackson 79 | 7 | 18 |
| 10 | BSP | A | Cambridge United | 1821 | L 0-2 | | 7 | 19 |
| 17 | BSP | H | Ebbsfleet United | 1896 | L 1-2 | Holroyd 45 | 8 | 20 |
| 20 | BSP | H | Mansfield Town | 1272 | L 0-3 | | 9 | 21 |
| 24 | FAT 1 | A | Gatehead | 312 | L 0-2 | | | 22 |
| Dec 4 | BSP | H | Hyde | 1124 | W 3-2 | Barnes-Homer 56 Brown 82 Holroyd 90 | 7 | 23 |
| 8 | BSP | A | Forest Green Rovers | 901 | D 1-1 | Fairhurst 24 | 9 | 24 |
| 15 | BSP | H | Nuneaton Town | 1280 | D 0-0 | | 9 | 25 |
| 18 | FAC 2 | A | Barrow | 1179 | D 1-1 | Charnock 19 | | 26 |
| 26 | BSP | A | Southport | 1173 | L 2-3 | Mackreth 55 Barnes-Homer 70 | 9 | 27 |
| 29 | FAC2r | H | Barrow | 1554 | W 4-1 | Kissock 7 Holroyd 16 69 Barnes-Homer 67 | | 28 |
| Jan 1 | BSP | H | Southport | 1481 | D 2-2 | Jackson 42 Barnes-Homer 80 84 | 11 | 29 |
| 5 | FAC 3 | H | Cardiff City | 3165 | W 2-1 | Barnes-Homer 85 88 (pen) | | 30 |
| 12 | BSP | A | Braintree Town | 502 | W 3-0 | Morgan-Smith 12 Fairhust 67 80 | | 31 |
| 16 | BSP | A | Dartford | 821 | L 0-2 | | | 32 |
| 18 | BSP | H | Kidderminster Harriers | 1342 | W 1-0 | Fairhurst 56 | 9 | 33 |
| 26 | FAC 4 | H | Wigan Athletic | 5849 | L 0-1 | | | 34 |
| Feb 2 | BSP | A | Ebbsfleet United | 799 | W 4-0 | Murtagh 2 Fairhurst 58 Mackreth 63 89 | 9 | 35 |
| 9 | BSP | A | Hyde | 1184 | D 1-1 | Fairhurst 22 | 8 | 36 |
| 12 | BSP | A | Tamworth | 670 | D 0-0 | | 8 | 37 |
| 16 | BSP | A | Alfreton Town | 740 | W 2-1 | Audel 31 Fairhurst 58 | 7 | 38 |
| 19 | BSP | H | Luton Town | 1984 | D 1-1 | Fairhurst 76 | 7 | 39 |
| 23 | BSP | H | Gateshead | 1467 | L 0-4 | | 7 | 40 |
| Mar 6 | BSP | H | Lincoln City | 1557 | W 2-1 | Barnes-Homer 55 Garner 47 (og) | 7 | 41 |
| 9 | BSP | A | AFC Telford United | 1567 | W 2-0 | Morgan-Smith 30 54 | 7 | 42 |
| 12 | BSP | H | Woking | 1350 | D 0-0 | | 7 | 43 |
| 19 | BSP | H | AFC Telford United | 1381 | W 2-1 | Fairhurst 3 Barnes-Homer 90 | 7 | 44 |
| 27 | BSP | A | Barrow | 716 | L 0-1 | | 7 | 45 |
| 30 | BSP | H | Stockport County | 4027 | D 1-1 | Barnes-Homer 63 | 7 | 46 |
| Apr 1 | BSP | A | Wrexham | 4351 | D 0-0 | | 7 | 47 |
| 3 | BSP | H | GrimsbyTown | 1776 | L 1-3 | Mills 26 | 8 | 48 |
| 6 | BSP | H | Hereford United | 1687 | L 0-1 | | 8 | 49 |
| 9 | BSP | A | Mansfield Town | 3694 | L 1-3 | Mills 89 | 8 | 50 |
| 11 | BSP | A | Newport County | 1606 | L 1-4 | Burgess 3 | 9 | 51 |
| 13 | BSP | A | Woking | 1543 | L 4-5 | Fairhurst 60 83 Madjo 71 Gnahoua 90 | 11 | 52 |
| 20 | BSP | H | Cambridge United | 1987 | W 2-1 | Mills 39 Madjo 45 | 11 | 53 |

| GOALSCORERS | Lge | FAC | FAT | Total | Pens | Hat-tricks | Cons Run | | Lge | FAC | FAT | Total | Pens | Hat-tricks | Cons Run |
|-------------|-----|-----|-----|-------|------|------------|----------|-----|-----|-----|-----|-------|------|------------|----------|
| Barnes-Homer | 18 | 5 | | 23 | 6 | | 5 | Burgess | 1 | | | | | | |
| Fairhurst | 12 | | | 12 | | 1 | 2 | Charnock | | 1 | | 1 | | | |
| Holroyd | 6 | 2 | | 8 | | | | Diagne | | 1 | | 1 | | | |
| Morgan-Smith | 5 | 1 | | 6 | | | | Gnahoua | 1 | | | 1 | | | |
| Mils | 3 | | | 3 | | | | Henry | 1 | | | 1 | 1 | | |
| Brown | 2 | | | 2 | | | | Kissock | 1 | 1 | | 1 | | | |
| Jackson | 2 | | | 2 | | | | Mendy | 1 | | | 1 | | | |
| Mackreth | 2 | | | 2 | | | | Rowe | 1 | | | 1 | | | |
| Madjo | 2 | | | 2 | | | | Whitehead | 1 | | | 1 | | | |
| Murtagh | 2 | | | 2 | | | | Own Goals | 3 | 1 | | 4 | | | |
| Audel | 1 | | | 1 | | | | Cons Run - Consecutive scoring games. | | | | | | | |

# NUNEATON TOWN

**Chairman:** Ian Neale (Chief Exe)

**Secretary:** Richard Dean     **(T)** 02476 385 738     **(E)** richard.dean1955@o2.co.uk

**Commercial Manager:** Gemma Brown     **(T)** 02476 385 738

**Programme Editor:** Jodie Faries     **(T)** jodie.faries@nuneatontownfc.com

**Ground Address:** Liberty Way, Nuneaton CV11 6RR

**(T)** 02476 385 738        **Manager:** Kevin Wilkin

2012-13 Squad.

## Club Factfile

**Founded:** 2008     **Nickname:** The Boro

**Previous Names:** Nuneaton Borough 1937-2008

**Previous Leagues:** Central Amateur 1937-38, Birmingham Combination 1938-52, West Midlands 1952-58, Southern 1958-79 81-82, 88-90, 2003-04, 08-10, Conference 1979-81, 82-88, 99-03, 04-08

**Club Colours (change):** Blue & white stripes/blue & white/blue (Red & white/red & white/red)

**Ground Capacity:**     **Seats:** Yes     **Covered:** Yes     **Clubhouse:** Yes     **Shop:** Yes

**Directions** From the South, West and North West, exit the M6 at Junction 3 and follow the A444 into Nuneaton. At the Coton Arches roundabout turn right into Avenue Road which is the A4254 signposted for Hinckley. Continue along the A4254 following the road into Garrett Street, then Eastboro Way, then turn left into Townsend Drive. Follow the road round before turning left into Liberty Way for the ground. From the North, exit the M1 at Junction 21 and follow the M69. Exit at Junction 1 and take the 4th exit at roundabout onto A5 (Tamworth, Nuneaton). At Longshoot Junction turn left onto A47, continue to roundabout and take the 1st exit onto A4254, Eastboro Way. Turn right at next roundabout into Townsend Drive, then right again into Liberty Way, CV11 6RR.

**Previous Grounds:** Manor Park

**Record Attendance:** 22,114 v Rotherham United - FA Cup 3rd Round 1967 (At Manor Park)

**Record Victory:** 11-1 - 1945-46 and 1955-56

**Record Defeat:** 1-8 - 1955-56 and 1968-69

**Record Goalscorer:** Paul Culpin - 201 (55 during season 1992-93)

**Record Appearances:** Alan Jones - 545 (1962-74)

**Additional Records:** Paid £35,000 to Forest green Rovers for Marc McGregor 2000

**Senior Honours:** Received £80,000 from Kidderminster Harriers for Andy Ducros 2000

Southern League Midland Division 1981-82, 92-93, Premier Division 1988-99, Premier Division Play-offs 2009-10. Conference North Play-offs 2011-12.

Birmingham Senior Cup x7.

## 10 YEAR RECORD

| 03-04 | | 04-05 | | 05-06 | | 06-07 | | 07-08 | | 08-09 | | 09-10 | | 10-11 | | 11-12 | | 12-13 | |
|---|---|---|---|---|---|---|---|---|---|---|---|---|---|---|---|---|---|---|---|
| SthP | 4 | Conf N | 2 | Conf N | 3 | Conf N | 10 | Conf N | 7 | SthE | 2 | SthP | 2 | Conf N | 6 | Conf N | 5 | Conf | 15 |

# MATCH RESULTS 2012-13

| Date | Comp | H/A | Opponents | Att: | Result | Goalscorers | Pos | No. |
|------|------|-----|-----------|------|--------|-------------|-----|-----|
| Aug 11 | BSP | H | Ebbsfleet United | 1088 | L 4-5 | Brown 8 90  Walker 17 Thompson-Brown 56 | 18 | 1 |
| 14 | BSP | A | Newport County | 2646 | L 0-4 | | 24 | 2 |
| 18 | BSP | A | Grimsby Town | 3095 | D 0-0 | | 22 | 3 |
| 25 | BSP | H | Cambridge United | 1175 | D 2-2 | Walker 53 Armson 90 (pen) | 22 | 4 |
| 27 | BSP | A | Alfreton Town | 680 | W 3-0 | WALKER 3 (54 79 90) | 16 | 5 |
| Sept 1 | BSP | H | Gateshead | 835 | L 0-1 | | 18 | 6 |
| 4 | BSP | H | AFC Telford United | 992 | W 3-1 | Walker 13 Armson 74 (pen)  Brown 87 | 16 | 7 |
| 8 | BSP | A | Woking | 1512 | L 1-6 | Brown 90 | 20 | 8 |
| 15 | BSP | H | Macclesfield Town | 939 | D 3-3 | Brown 6 Armison  13 (pen) Sleathe  77 | 20 | 9 |
| 22 | BSP | A | Hyde | 585 | D 2-2 | York 74 75 | 20 | 10 |
| 25 | BSP | A | Lincoln City | 1579 | L 1-2 | Armson 3 | 20 | 11 |
| 29 | BSP | H | Wrexham | 1543 | D 0-0 | | 21 | 12 |
| Oct 6 | BSP | A | Southport | 1302 | L 1-3 | Walker 75 | 22 | 13 |
| 9 | BSP | H | Hereford United | 969 | D 0-0 | | 22 | 14 |
| 13 | BSP | A | Luton Town | 6148 | L 0-2 | | 22 | 15 |
| 20 | FAC Q4 | A | AFC Telford United | 1251 | D 2-2 | Waite 2 Sleathe 83 | | 16 |
| 23 | FAC Q4r | H | AFC Telford United | 616 | W 1-0* | Armson 108 | | 17 |
| 27 | BSP | A | Barrow | 644 | D 1-1 | Brown 90 | 24 | 18 |
| Nov 3 | FAC 1 | A | Luton Town | 3089 | D 1-1 | Waite 20 | | 19 |
| 6 | BSP | H | Mansfield Town | 338 | D 1-1 | Taylor 50 | 24 | 20 |
| 10 | BSP | A | Kidderminster Harriers | 1592 | L 0-1 | | 24 | 21 |
| 13 | FAC 1r | H | Luton Town | 1596 | L 0-2 | | | 22 |
| 17 | BSP | H | Stockport County | 1221 | W 2-0 | Brown 45 Walker 82 (pen) | 24 | 23 |
| 24 | FAT 1 | A | AFC Telford United | 737 | L 0-1 | | | 24 |
| Dec 1 | BSP | A | Forest Green Rovers | 948 | L 0-1 | | 24 | 25 |
| 4 | BSP | H | Dartford | 651 | W 1-0 | Brown 45 | 22 | 26 |
| 8 | BSP | A | Wrexham | 2739 | L 1-6 | York 89 | 24 | 27 |
| 15 | BSP | A | Macclesfield | 1280 | D 0-0 | | 24 | 28 |
| 26 | BSP | H | Tamworth | 1389 | W 2-1 | Brown 84 Armson 89 (pen) | 22 | 29 |
| Jan 2 | BSP | A | Tamworth | 1516 | L 1-2 | Forsdick 18 | | 30 |
| 12 | BSP | H | Forest Green Rovers | 910 | D 1-1 | Gordon 82 | 22 | 31 |
| 16 | BSP | A | Cambridge United | 1740 | W 3-1 | Armson 14 60  Brown 64 | 22 | 32 |
| 21 | BSP | H | Braintree Town | 761 | L 2-4 | Forsdick 41 Gordon 77 | 22 | 33 |
| Feb 2 | BSP | A | Stockport County | 4133 | L 2-3 | Brown 14 18 | 23 | 34 |
| 9 | BSP | H | Southport | 779 | L 0-1 | | 23 | 35 |
| 16 | BSP | A | Barrow | 998 | W 2-1 | Brown 89 Dance 90 | 21 | 36 |
| 19 | BSP | H | Alfreton Town | 781 | W 1-0 | Dance 90 (pen) | 20 | 37 |
| 26 | BSP | H | Kidderminster Harriers | 1087 | L 0-1 | | 21 | 38 |
| Mar 2 | BSP | A | Hereford United | 1908 | D 0-0 | | 21 | 39 |
| 5 | BSP | H | Luton Town | 1173 | D 0-0 | | 22 | 40 |
| 16 | BSP | H | Lincoln City | 1122 | W 1-0 | York 90 | 21 | 41 |
| 19 | BSP | H | Grimsby Town | 964 | W 1-0 | Brown 17 | 18 | 42 |
| 21 | BSP | A | Braintree Town | 421 | D 2-2 | York 20 Arnison 44 | 18 | 43 |
| 26 | BSP | A | Mansfield Town | 2384 | L 0-1 | | 18 | 44 |
| 28 | BSP | H | Woking | 609 | D 0-0 | | 18 | 45 |
| 30 | BSP | A | AFC Telford United | 1893 | W 3-0 | Phillips 34 Brown 49 73 | 19 | 46 |
| Apr 1 | BSP | H | Newport County | 1068 | L 1-2 | Forsdick 15 | 20 | 47 |
| 6 | BSP | A | Ebbsfleet United | 695 | D 1-1 | Brown 90 | 21 | 48 |
| 9 | BSP | A | Gateshead | 304 | W 2-0 | York 11 Brown 36 | 18 | 49 |
| 13 | BSP | H | Hyde | 1158 | W 3-1 | Brown 34, Forsdick 55 Moult 69 | 16 | 50 |
| 20 | BSP | A | Dartford | 1844 | W 1-0 | York 81 | 15 | 51 |

| GOALSCORERS | Lge | FAC | FAT | Total | Pens | Hat-tricks | Cons Run | | Lge | FAC | FAT | Total | Pens | Hat-tricks | Cons Run |
|-------------|-----|-----|-----|-------|------|-----------|----------|--|-----|-----|-----|-------|------|-----------|----------|
| Brown | 19 | | | 19 | | | 3 | Phillips | 1 | | | 1 | | | |
| Armson | 8 | 1 | | 9 | 4 | | | Taylor | 1 | | | 1 | | | |
| Walker | 8 | | | 8 | 1 | 1 | 2 | Thompson-Brown | 1 | | | 1 | | | |
| York | 7 | | | 7 | | | | Cons Run - Consecutive scoring games. | | | | | | | |
| Forsdick | 4 | | | 4 | 1 | | | | | | | | | | |
| Dance | 2 | | | 2 | | | | | | | | | | | |
| Gordon | 2 | | | 2 | | | | | | | | | | | |
| Sleathe | 1 | 1 | | 2 | | | | | | | | | | | |
| Waite | | | 2 | 2 | | | | | | | | | | | |
| Moult | 1 | | | 1 | | | | | | | | | | | |

# SALISBURY CITY

**Chairman:** William Harrison-Allen
**Secretary:** Peter Matthiae   **(T)** 07784 303 035   **(E)** peter.matthiae@salisburycity-fc.co.uk
**Commercial Manager:** TBA   **(T)**
**Programme Editor:** Paul Osborn   **(T)** 01722 324 733
**Ground Address:** Raymond McEnhill Stadium, Partridge Way, Old Sarum SP4 6PU
**(T)** 01722 776 655            **Manager:** Mikey Harris

## Club Factfile

**Founded:** 1947     **Nickname:** The Whites
**Previous Names:** Salisbury F.C.
**Previous Leagues:** Western 1947-68, Southern 1968-2004, 2010-11, Isthmian 2004-05, Conference 2005-10.

**Club Colours (change):** All white with black trim (Blue with yellow trim/blue with yellow trim/yellow)

**Ground Capacity:** 5,000   **Seats:** 500   **Covered:** 2,247   **Clubhouse:** Yes   **Shop:** Yes

**Directions**
Situated A345 Salisbury/Amesbury Road.
From North/East/West: Leave A303 at Countess roundabout at Amesbury and take A345 towards Salisbury until Park and Ride roundabout from where the ground is signposted.
From South: Proceed to A345 and then follow directions to Amesbury until Park
and Ride roundabout from where the ground is signposted.

**Previous Grounds:** Victoria Park

**Record Attendance:** 3,100 v Nottingham Forest - FA Cup 2nd Round 2006
**Record Victory:** 11-1 v RAF Colerne (H) - Western League Division 2 1948
**Record Defeat:** 0-7 v Minehead (A) - Southern League 1975
**Record Goalscorer:** Royston Watts - 180 (1959-65)
**Record Appearances:** Barry Fitch - 713 (1963-75)
**Additional Records:** Paid £15,000 to Bashley for Craig Davis
**Senior Honours:**   Received £20,000 from Forest Green Rovers for Adrian Randall
Western League 1957-58, 60-61. Southern League Premier Division 1994-95, 2005-06.

### 10 YEAR RECORD

| 03-04 | 04-05 | 05-06 | 06-07 | 07-08 | 08-09 | 09-10 | 10-11 | 11-12 | 12-13 |
|---|---|---|---|---|---|---|---|---|---|
| SthE 6 | Isth P 12 | SthP 1 | Conf S 2 | Conf 12 | Conf 16 | Conf 12 | SthP 3 | Conf S 10 | Conf S 2 |

# MATCH RESULTS 2012-13

| Date | Comp | H/A | Opponents | Att: | Result | Goalscorers | Pos | No. |
|------|------|-----|-----------|------|--------|-------------|-----|-----|
| Aug 17 | BSS | H | AFC Hornchurch | 663 | W 2-1 | White 59 Brett 83 | 6 | 1 |
| 21 | BSS | A | Tonbridge Angels | 520 | W 2-1 | White 70 74 | 1 | 2 |
| 25 | BSS | A | Truro City | 336 | D 1-1 | Brett 67 | 3 | 3 |
| 27 | BSS | H | Farnborough | 776 | W 1-0 | Fitchett 90 | 1 | 4 |
| Sept 1 | BSS | A | Chelmsford City | 716 | L 1-2 | Fitchett 8 | 3 | 5 |
| 4 | BSS | H | Bath City | 752 | W 3-2 | White 6 Fitchett 39 (pen) Brett 57 | 2 | 6 |
| 8 | BSS | H | Eastbourne Borough | 769 | W 1-0 | White 8 | 2 | 7 |
| 15 | BSS | A | Hayes & Yeading | 293 | W 3-2 | White 16 21 Matthews 33 | 1 | 8 |
| 22 | FAC Q2 | A | Newport (I.o.W) | 559 | W 3-0 | McPhee 15 30  White 41 | | 9 |
| 29 | BSS | A | Staines Town | 341 | L 2-3 | Brett 86 89 | 1 | 10 |
| Oct 2 | BSS | A | Dorchester Town | 759 | W 4-0 | Sinclair 9 McPhee 18 80 Matthews 54 | 1 | 11 |
| 6 | FAC Q3 | A | Hayes & Yeading | 210 | L 1-2 | McPhee 7 (pen) | | 12 |
| 13 | BSS | H | Boreham Wood | 742 | D 2-2 | White 46 72 | | 13 |
| 20 | BSS | A | Dover Athletic | 813 | W 3-1 | McPhee 52 81 White 76 | 1 | 14 |
| 27 | BSS | A | Bromley | 495 | W 2-1 | McPhee 33 Dutton 90 | 1 | 15 |
| 30 | BSS | H | Hayes & Yeading  U | 791 | W 2-0 | Fitchett 38 87 (pen) | 1 | 16 |
| Nov 3 | BSS | H | Maidenhead United | 755 | D 1-1 | Fitchett 12 | 1 | 17 |
| 10 | FAT Q3 | H | Weston-s-Mare | 510 | W 3-0 | McPhee 22 24 Fitchett 65 | | 18 |
| 17 | BSS | A | Welling United | 483 | L 0-1 | | 1 | 19 |
| 24 | FAT 1 | A | Maidstone United | 1365 | L 0-2 | | | 20 |
| Dec 1 | BSS | A | Maidenhead United | 320 | W 1-0 | Dutton 54 | 1 | 21 |
| 8 | BSS | H | Chelmsford City | 704 | W 3-2 | White 41 Sinclair 56 Fitchett 68 | 1 | 22 |
| 15 | BSS | H | Eastbourne Borough | 576 | W 2-1 | Wellard 11 McPhee 80 | 1 | 23 |
| Jan 1 | BSS | H | Eastleigh | 887 | W 5-3 | White 1 39  Lewis 12  Fitchett 68 Ademeno 81 | 1 | 24 |
| 5 | BSS | H | Sutton United | 740 | W 1-0 | Kavangh 59 (og) | 1 | 25 |
| 12 | BSS | A | AFC Hornchurch | 270 | D 2-2 | Spencer 31 (og) White 83 | 1 | 26 |
| 15 | BSS | H | Truro City | 533 | W 4-3 | McPhee 7 27 Lewis 66 White 90 | 1 | 27 |
| 19 | BSS | H | Staines Town | 464 | W 3-1 | White 5 Frear 11 McPhee 20 | 1 | 28 |
| 29 | BSS | A | Farnborough | 449 | L 1-2 | White 90 | 1 | 29 |
| Feb 2 | BSS | H | Bromley | 783 | W 3-1 | White 72 Sinclair  82 Frear 84 | 1 | 30 |
| 9 | BSS | A | Dorchester Town | 641 | L 1-2 | White 77 | 1 | 31 |
| 12 | BSS | A | Eastleigh | 872 | L 0-1 | | 1 | 32 |
| 16 | BSS | H | Billericay Town | 764 | W 2-0 | Brett 22 White 52 | 1 | 33 |
| 20 | BSS | A | Boreham Wood | 221 | L 0-1 | | 2 | 34 |
| 23 | BSS | A | Havant & Waterlooville | 837 | D 2-2 | Fitchett 49 61 | 1 | 35 |
| Mar 2 | BSS | H | Weston-s-Mare | 666 | D 1-1 | Fitchett 7 | 2 | 36 |
| 5 | BSS | H | Basingstoke Town | 468 | L 0-2 | | 2 | 37 |
| 9 | BSS | A | Weston-s-Mare | 348 | W 3-0 | FITCHETT 3 ( 39 81 90) | 2 | 38 |
| 30 | BSS | H | Tonbridge Angels | 705 | W 2-0 | White 24 Flitchett 90 | 2 | 39 |
| Apr 1 | BSS | A | Bath City | 731 | D 0-0 | | 2 | 40 |
| 6 | BSS | H | Welling United | 1158 | W 2-1 | White 20 72 | 2 | 41 |
| 9 | BSS | H | Dover Athletic | 670 | D 1-1 | Fitchett 90 | 2 | 42 |
| 13 | BSS | A | Billericay Town | 374 | W 2-1 | McPhee 32 White75 | 2 | 43 |
| 20 | BSS | H | Havant & Waterlooville | 771 | W 5-1 | Dutton 6 McPhee 36 Brett 49 Fitchett 87 90 | 2 | 44 |
| 22 | BSS | A | Sutton United | 456 | L 0-1 | | 2 | 45 |
| 27 | BSS | A | Basingstoke Town | 535 | W 4-0 | Sinclair 22 Ademeno 39 White 75 Frear 77 | 2 | 46 |
| 30 | P-Off S-F 1 | A | Chelmsford City | 1248 | L 0-1 | | | 47 |
| May 4 | P-Off S-F 2 | H | Chelmsford City | 1554 | W 2-0 | Searle 46 (og), Sinclair 91 *aet | | 48 |
| 12 | P-Off F | H | Dover Athletic | 3408 | W 3-2 | White 2, Wellard 50, Sinclair 99 *aet | | 49 |

| GOALSCORERS | Lge | FAC | FAT | Total | Pens | Hat-tricks | Cons Run | | | Lge | FAC | FAT | Total | Pens | Hat-tricks | Cons Run |
|-------------|-----|-----|-----|-------|------|-----------|----------|---|---|-----|-----|-----|-------|------|-----------|----------|
| White | 26 | 1 | | 27 | | | 5 | | Wellard | 2 | | | 2 | | | |
| McPhee | 11 | 3 | 2 | 16 | 1 | | 2 | | Own Goals | 3 | | | 3 | | | |
| Fitchett | 18 | | 1 | 19 | 2 | 1 | 3 | | Cons Run - Consecutive scoring games. | | | | | | | |
| Brett | 7 | | | 7 | | | | | | | | | | | | |
| Sinclair | 6 | | | 6 | | | | | | | | | | | | |
| Dutton | 3 | | | 3 | | | | | | | | | | | | |
| Frear | 3 | | | 3 | | | | | | | | | | | | |
| Lewis | 2 | | | 2 | | | | | | | | | | | | |
| Matthews | 2 | | | 2 | | | | | | | | | | | | |
| Ademeno | 2 | | | 2 | | | | | | | | | | | | |

# SOUTHPORT

**Chairman:** Charles Clapham
**Secretary:** Ken Hilton **(T)** 07802 661 906 **(E)** secretary@southportfc.net
**Commercial Manager:** Haydn Preece **(T)** 07768 000 818
**Programme Editor:** Rob Urwin **(T)** programme@southportfc.net
**Ground Address:** Merseyrail Community Stadium, Haig Avenue, Southport, Merseyside PR8 6JZ
**(T)** 01704 533 422 **Manager:** Alan Wright

## Club Factfile

**Founded:** 1881 **Nickname:** The Sandgrounders
**Previous Names:** Southport Central, Southport Vulcan
**Previous Leagues:** Preston & District, Lancashire 1889-1903, Lancashire comb. 1903-11, Central 1911-21, Football League 1921-78, Northern Premier 1978-93, 2003-04, Conference 1993-2003

**Club Colours (change):** Yellow & black stripes/yellow/yellow (All sky blue)

**Ground Capacity:** 6,008 **Seats:** 1,660 **Covered:** 2,760 **Clubhouse:** Yes **Shop:** Yes

**Directions:** Leave M6 at junction 26. Join M58 to junction 3. Join A570 signposted Southport, follow A570 through Ormskirk Town Centre following signs for Southport. At the big roundabout (McDonalds is on the left) take the fourth exit. Proceed along this road until you reach the 2nd set of pedstrian lights and take the next left into Haig Avenue.

**Previous Grounds:** Sussex Road Sports Ground, Scarisbrick New Road, Ash Lane (later named Haig Avenue)

**Record Attendance:** 20,010 v Newcastle United - FA Cup 1932
**Record Victory:** 8-1 v Nelson - 01/01/31
**Record Defeat:** 0-11 v Oldham Athletic - 26/12/62
**Record Goalscorer:** Alan Spence - 98
**Record Appearances:** Arthur Peat - 401 (1962-72)
**Additional Records:** Paid £20,000 to Macclesfield Town for Martin McDonald

**Senior Honours:**
Lancashire Senior Cup 1904-05. Liverpool Senior Cup 1930-31, 31-32, 43-44, 62-63, 74-75, 90-91, 92-93, 98-99, Shared 57-58, 63-64. Football League Division 4 1972-73. Northern Premier League Challenge Cup 1990-91. Northern Premier League Premier Division 1992-93. Conference North 2004-05, 2009-10.

### 10 YEAR RECORD

| 03-04 | | 04-05 | | 05-06 | | 06-07 | | 07-08 | | 08-09 | | 09-10 | | 10-11 | | 11-12 | | 12-13 | |
|---|---|---|---|---|---|---|---|---|---|---|---|---|---|---|---|---|---|---|---|
| NP P | 6 | Conf N | 10 | Conf | 18 | Conf | 23 | Conf N | 4 | Conf N | 5 | Conf N | 1 | Conf | 21 | Conf | 7 | Conf | 20 |

# MATCH RESULTS 2012-13

| Date | Comp | H/A | Opponents | Att: | Result | Goalscorers | Pos | No. |
|------|------|-----|-----------|------|--------|-------------|-----|-----|
| Aug 11 | BSP | H | Grimsby Town | 598 | D 1-1 | Grand 87 | | 1 |
| 14 | BSP | A | Alfreton Town | 562 | D 3-3 | Whalley 31 Almond 68 Tames 90 | 15 | 2 |
| 18 | BSP | A | Cambridge United | 2004 | L 0-2 | | 19 | 3 |
| 25 | BSP | H | Tamworth | 1014 | L 0-3 | | 23 | 4 |
| 27 | BSP | A | Hyde | 734 | W 2-0 | Almond 12 Tames 50 | 17 | 5 |
| Sept 1 | BSP | H | AFC Telford United | 1005 | L 0-3 | | 20 | 6 |
| 4 | BSP | H | Gateshead | 686 | W 2-1 | Whalley 70 Ledsham 87 | 17 | 7 |
| 8 | BSP | A | Kidderminster Harriers | 1650 | D 2-2 | Ledsham 59 Grand 65 (pen) | 18 | 8 |
| 15 | BSP | H | Ebbsfleet United | 872 | W 1-0 | Lever 90 (pen) | 14 | 9 |
| 22 | BSP | A | Newport County | 2802 | L 1-2 | Lever 18 (pen) | 16 | 10 |
| 25 | BSP | H | Stockport County | 818 | D 1-1 | Willis 85 | 14 | 11 |
| 29 | BSP | A | Luton Town | 5696 | L 1-3 | Parry 45 | 14 | 12 |
| Oct 6 | BSP | H | Nuneaton Town | 1302 | W 3-1 | Lever 19 (pen) Grand 24 Almond 68 | 17 | 13 |
| 9 | BSP | A | Barrow | 924 | L 2-3 | Lynch 28 Anderson 56 (og) | 17 | 14 |
| 13 | BSP | A | Woking | 1739 | W 3-2 | Parry 40 Lynch 56 Lever 82 (pen) | 15 | 15 |
| 20 | FAC Q4 | A | Wrexham | 1911 | L 0-2 | | | 16 |
| 27 | BSP | H | Hereford United | 1028 | D 2-2 | Ledsham 33 Lever 38 (pen) | 15 | 17 |
| Nov 6 | BSP | H | Wrexham | 1324 | L 1-4 | Tames 37 | 16 | 18 |
| 10 | BSP | A | Mansfield Town | 1918 | L 0-1 | | 20 | 19 |
| 17 | BSP | A | Dartford | 1506 | D 2-2 | Akrigg 21 Ledsham 90 | 20 | 20 |
| 24 | FAT 1 | A | Stafford Rangers | 531 | W 4-0 | Almond 5 Tames 46 74 Owens 57 | | 21 |
| Dec 1 | BSP | A | Stockport County | 3445 | W 4-3 | Almond 6 Akrigg 8 Owens 3 Rowe 89 (og) | 17 | 22 |
| 8 | BSP | H | Braintree Town | 803 | L 0-2 | | 19 | 23 |
| 15 | FAT 2 | A | Stockport County | 1328 | D 1-1 | Ledsham 1 | | 24 |
| 18 | FAT 2r | H | Stockport County | 750 | W 3-1 | Ledsham 1 Whalley 68 Almond 90 | | 25 |
| 26 | BSP | H | Macclesfield Town | 1173 | W 3-2 | Willis 24 Almond 29 Whalley 77 | 18 | 26 |
| 29 | BSP | H | Hyde | 1068 | L 0-1 | | 18 | 27 |
| Jan 1 | BSP | A | Macclesfield Town | 1481 | D 2-2 | Lever 8 11 | | 28 |
| 5 | BSP | A | AFC Telford United | 1643 | W 3-1 | Grand 65 69 Almond 77 | 17 | 29 |
| 8 | BSP | H | Lincoln City | 815 | W 4-2 | Grand 18 25 Owens 32 Ledsham 77 | 12 | 30 |
| 12 | FAT 3 | A | Kings Lynn | 1498 | W 2-0 | Parry 17 Tames 85 | | 31 |
| 20 | BSP | H | Mansfield Town | 804 | L 1-2 | Whalley 6 | 13 | 32 |
| 26 | FAT 4 | H | Wrexham | 1473 | L 1-3 | Whalley 74 (pen) | | 33 |
| 29 | BSP | A | Wrexham | 3002 | D 2-2 | Ledsham 13 Owens 81 | 13 | 34 |
| Feb 2 | BSP | A | Hereford United | 1513 | D 2-2 | Whalley 32 68 | 13 | 35 |
| 9 | BSP | A | Nuneaton Town | 779 | W 1-0 | O'Halloran 15 (og) | 13 | 36 |
| 12 | BSP | H | Barrow | 806 | W 5-2 | Willis 49 Ledsham 57 73 Almond 65 Owens 78 | 11 | 37 |
| 23 | BSP | H | Woking | 911 | L 1-2 | Chalmers 61 | 14 | 38 |
| Mar 2 | BSP | H | Dartford | 823 | D 2-2 | Owens 40 Whalley 83 (pen) | 14 | 39 |
| 5 | BSP | H | Cambridge United | 615 | W 2-1 | Byrne 54 Whalley 60 (pen) | 13 | 40 |
| 9 | BSP | A | Lincoln City | 1827 | L 0-1 | | 13 | 41 |
| 12 | BSP | H | Forest Green Rovers | 632 | L 1-2 | Whalley 30 (pen) | 13 | 42 |
| 16 | BSP | A | Ebbsfleet United | 603 | L 1-4 | Almond 48 | 15 | 43 |
| 19 | BSP | A | Tamworth | 565 | L 1-2 | Chalmers 40 | 16 | 44 |
| 23 | BSP | H | Kiddermnster Harries | 946 | L 1-3 | Hattersley 58 | 16 | 45 |
| 26 | BSP | H | Newport County | 606 | L 0-2 | | 18 | 46 |
| 30 | BSP | A | Gateshead | 406 | D 2-2 | Almond 58 Whalley 64 | 20 | 47 |
| Apr 1 | BSP | H | Alfreton Town | 830 | L 0-2 | | 20 | 48 |
| 3 | BSP | A | Braintree Town | 451 | W 3-1 | Almond 9 62 Gand 50 | 18 | 49 |
| 6 | BSP | A | Grimsby Town | 3780 | D 2-2 | Ledsham 19 45 | 17 | 50 |
| 13 | BSP | A | Forest Green Rovers | 1496 | W 1-0 | Stokes 77 (og) | 17 | 51 |
| 20 | BSP | H | Luton Town | 1406 | L 1-3 | Clancy 2 | 20 | 52 |

| GOALSCORERS | Lge | FAC | FAT | Total | Pens | Hat-tricks | Cons Run | | Lge | FAC | FAT | Total | Pens | Hat-tricks | Cons Run |
|-------------|-----|-----|-----|-------|------|-----------|----------|---|-----|-----|-----|-------|------|-----------|----------|
| Almond | 11 | | 2 | 13 | | | 2 | Chalmers | 2 | | | 2 | | | |
| Ledsham | 10 | | 2 | 12 | | | 2 | Lynch | 2 | | | 2 | | | |
| Whalley | 10 | | 2 | 12 | 4 | | 2 | Byrne | 1 | | | 1 | | | |
| Grand | 8 | | | 8 | 1 | | | Clancy | 1 | | | 1 | | | |
| Lever | 7 | | | 7 | 5 | | 2 | Hattersley | 1 | | | 1 | | | |
| Owens | 5 | 1 | | 6 | | | 2 | Own Goals | 4 | | | 4 | | | |
| Tames | 3 | | 3 | 6 | | | | Cons Run - Consecutive scoring games. | | | | | | | |
| Parry | 2 | | 1 | 3 | | | | | | | | | | | |
| Willis | 3 | | | 3 | | | | | | | | | | | |
| Akrigg | 2 | | | 2 | | | | | | | | | | | |

# TAMWORTH

**Chairman:** Bob Andrews

**Secretary:** Rod Hadley    **(T)** 01827 657 98    **(E)** clubsec@thelambs.co.uk

**Commercial Manager:** Elaine Gibson    **(T)** 07795 841 106

**Programme Editor:** Terry Brumpton    **(T)** 07771 802 048

**Ground Address:** The Lamb Ground, Kettlebrook, Tamworth, Staffordshire B77 1AA

**(T)** 01827 657 98 opt. 3      **Manager:** Dale Belford

## Club Factfile

**Founded:** 1933    **Nickname:** The Lambs

**Previous Names:** None

**Previous Leagues:** Birmingham Combination 1933-54, West Midlands (originally Birmingham League) 1954-72, 84-88, Southern 1972-79, 83-84, 89-2003, Northern Premier 1979-83

**Club Colours (change):** All red (All sky blue)

**Ground Capacity:** 4,100    **Seats:** 518    **Covered:** 1,191    **Clubhouse:** Yes    **Shop:** Yes

**Directions**

M42 Junction 10. Take A5/A51 to Town centre, then follow the signs for Kettlebrook and Tamworth FC.

**Previous Grounds:** Jolly Sailor Ground 1933-34

**Record Attendance:** 5,500 v Torquay United - FA Cup 1st Round 15/11/69

**Record Victory:** 14-4 v Holbrook Institue (H) - Bass Vase 1934

**Record Defeat:** 0-11 v Solihull (A) - Birmingham Combination 1940

**Record Goalscorer:** Graham Jessop - 195

**Record Appearances:** Dave Seedhouse - 869

**Additional Records:** Paid £7,500 to Ilkeston Town for David Hemmings December 2000

**Senior Honours:** Received £7,500 from Telford United for Martin Myers 1990

Birmingham Senior Cup 1960-61, 65-66, 68-69. West Midlands League 1964-65, 65-66, 71-72, 87-88. FA Vase 1988-89. Southern League Premier Division 2002-03. Conference North 2008-09.

### 10 YEAR RECORD

| 03-04 | | 04-05 | | 05-06 | | 06-07 | | 07-08 | | 08-09 | | 09-10 | | 10-11 | | 11-12 | | 12-13 | |
|---|---|---|---|---|---|---|---|---|---|---|---|---|---|---|---|---|---|---|---|
| Conf | 17 | Conf | 15 | Conf | 20 | Conf | 22 | Conf N | 15 | Conf N | 1 | Conf | 16 | Conf | 19 | Conf | 18 | Conf | 19 |

# MATCH RESULTS 2012-13

| Date | Comp | H/A | Opponents | Att: | Result | Goalscorers | Pos | No. |
|------|------|-----|-----------|------|--------|-------------|-----|-----|
| Aug 11 | BSP | A | Dartford | 1370 | W 3-2 | Till 27 Cunnington 40 76 | 4 | 1 |
| 14 | BSP | H | Hereford United | 1265 | D 2-2 | Wright 48 Cunnington 88 | 5 | 2 |
| 18 | BSP | H | Stockport County | 1270 | W 1-0 | Oji 45 | 17 | 3 |
| 25 | BSP | A | Southport | 1014 | W 3-0 | Cunnington 36 (pen) Collins 45 Wright 49 | 2 | 4 |
| 27 | BSP | H | Wrexham | 1433 | L 0-1 | | 6 | 5 |
| Sept 1 | BSP | A | Braintree Town | 501 | L 1-2 | Cunnington 35 | 8 | 6 |
| 4 | BSP | A | Mansfield Town | 2105 | L 0-2 | | 10 | 7 |
| 8 | BSP | H | Barrow | 892 | L 1-3 | Cunnington 42 (pen) | 13 | 8 |
| 15 | BSP | A | Gateshead | 622 | W 2-0 | Cunnington 36 (pen) Marshall 51 | 11 | 9 |
| 22 | BSP | H | Lincoln City | 1042 | W 1-0 | Kerry 1 | 8 | 10 |
| 25 | BSP | H | Luton Town | 1137 | W 1-2 | Dempston 22 | 8 | 11 |
| 29 | BSP | A | Woking | 1467 | W 3-2 | Wright 8 Cunnington 23 Baldock 70 | 7 | 12 |
| Oct 6 | BSP | H | Newport County | 1201 | L 1-2 | Cunnington 61 | 7 | 13 |
| 9 | BSP | A | Forest Green Rovers | 1022 | W 2-1 | Cunnington 22 25 (pen) | 7 | 14 |
| 13 | BSP | A | Hyde | 667 | L 1-2 | Kelly 31 | 7 | 15 |
| 20 | FAC Q4 | A | Barrow | 1104 | L 0-2 | | | 16 |
| 27 | BSP | H | Ebbsfleet United | 838 | L 0-1 | | 9 | 17 |
| Nov 3 | BSP | H | Grimsby Town | 1042 | L 0-1 | | 10 | 18 |
| 6 | BSP | A | Macclesfield Town | 1089 | L 0-2 | | 13 | 19 |
| 10 | BSP | H | AFC Telford United | 935 | D 0-0 | | 14 | 20 |
| 17 | BSP | A | Cambridge United | 3003 | D 1-1 | Cunnington 77 | 14 | 21 |
| 24 | FAT 1 | H | Lincoln City | 726 | W 3-1 | KELLY 3 ( 71 86 90) | | 22 |
| Dec 1 | BSP | H | Dartford | 832 | W 3-2 | Barrow 56 (pen) 85 (pen) Hendrie 88 | 9 | 23 |
| 4 | BSP | H | Kidderminster H | 1031 | L 0-1 | | 11 | 24 |
| 8 | BSP | A | Grimsby Town | 3109 | L 0-2 | | 15 | 25 |
| 15 | FAT 2 | H | Corby Town | 683 | D 1-1 | Wright 60 | | 26 |
| 19 | FAT 2r | A | Corby Town | 300 | W 4-2 | Wright 32 Baldock 38 58 Courtney 67 | | 27 |
| 26 | BSP | A | Nuneaton Town | 1389 | L 1-2 | Wright 34 | 17 | 28 |
| 29 | BSP | A | Wrexham | 3703 | D 2-2 | Gudger 29  Barrow 85 | 17 | 29 |
| Jan 2 | BSP | H | Nuneaton Town | 1516 | W 2-1 | Barrow 44 Tait 76 | | 30 |
| 5 | BSP | H | Braintree Town | 763 | L 1-4 | Cunnington 72 | 18 | 31 |
| 12 | FAT 3 | A | Gainsborough Trinity | 756 | L 1-2 | Turner 87 | | 32 |
| Feb 2 | BSP | H | Gateshead | 618 | W 2-0 | Lloyd 80 Cunnington 90 (pen) | 15 | 33 |
| 9 | BSP | A | Newport County | 1712 | D 2-2 | I.Hendrie 74 Cunnington 90 (pen) | 15 | 34 |
| 12 | BSP | H | Macclesfield Town | 670 | D 0-0 | | 17 | 35 |
| 16 | BSP | A | AFC Telford United | 1747 | D 3-3 | WRIGHT 3 ( 18 41 77) | 15 | 36 |
| 19 | BSP | A | Stockport County | 2732 | W 1-0 | Cunnington 16 (pen) | 15 | 37 |
| 23 | BSP | H | Hyde | 746 | W 2-0 | Oji 51 Wright  57 | 12 | 38 |
| 26 | BSP | H | Cambridge United | 668 | L 1-2 | Cunnington 89 | 13 | 39 |
| Mar 2 | BSP | A | Barrow | 896 | L 0-2 | | 15 | 40 |
| 9 | BSP | H | Alfreton Town | 703 | D 1-1 | Byfield 65 | 14 | 41 |
| 16 | BSP | A | Kidderminster Harriers | 2392 | L 1-4 | Cunnington 5 | 16 | 42 |
| 19 | BSP | H | Southport | 2652 | W 2-1 | Lloyd 83 Byfied 90 | 14 | 43 |
| 23 | BSP | A | Luton Town | 5501 | D 0-0 | | 14 | 44 |
| 30 | BSP | H | Mansfield Town | 1968 | L 0-1 | | 16 | 45 |
| Apr 1 | BSP | A | Hereford United | 1424 | L 2-5 | Connor 74 (og) Hendrie 88 | 17 | 46 |
| 6 | BSP | H | Forest Green Rovers | 773 | W 2-1 | Cunnington 6 42 | 16 | 47 |
| 11 | BSP | A | Alfreton Town | 568 | L 0-3 | | 16 | 48 |
| 13 | BSP | A | Lincoln City | 3174 | L 1-2 | Gray 7 (og) | 20 | 49 |
| 16 | BSP | A | Ebbsfleet United | 488 | D 1-1 | Wylde 72 | 20 | 50 |
| 20 | BSP | H | Woking | 1509 | W 2-1 | Marshall 36  Cunnington 60 (pen) | 19 | 51 |

| GOALSCORERS | Lge | FAC | FAT | Total | Pens | Hat-tricks | Cons Run | | Lge | FAC | FAT | Total | Pens | Hat-tricks | Cons Run |
|-------------|-----|-----|-----|-------|------|-----------|----------|--|-----|-----|-----|-------|------|-----------|----------|
| Cunnngton | 21 | | | 21 | 8 | | 3 | Collins | 1 | | | 1 | | | |
| Wright | 8 | | 2 | 10 | | 1 | 3 | Dempster | 1 | | | 1 | | | |
| Barrow | 4 | | | 4 | 2 | | | Gudger | 1 | | | 1 | | | |
| Kelly | 1 | | 3 | 4 | | 1 | | Kerry | 1 | | | 1 | | | |
| Baldock | 1 | | 2 | 3 | | | | Tait | 1 | | | 1 | | | |
| Hendrie | 3 | | | 3 | | | | Till | 1 | | | 1 | | | |
| Byfield | 2 | | | 2 | | | | Turner | | | 1 | 1 | | | |
| Lloyd | 2 | | | 2 | | | | Wylde | 1 | | | 1 | | | |
| Marshall | 2 | | | 2 | | | | Own Goals | 2 | | | 2 | | | |
| Oji | 2 | | | 2 | | | | Cons Run - Consecutive scoring games. | | | | | | | |
| Courtney | | | 1 | 1 | | | | | | | | | | | |

# WELLING UNITED

**Chairman:** Paul Websdale

**Secretary:** Barrie Hobbins     **(T)** 0208 301 1196     **(E)** wellingutdfcsecretary@hotmail.co.uk

**Commercial Manager:** Paul White     **(T)** 0777 556 755

**Programme Editor:** Paul Carter     **(T)** paul_carter40@yahoo.co.uk

**Ground Address:** Park View Road Ground, Welling, Kent DA16 1SY

**(T)** 0208 301 1196        **Manager:** Jamie Day

2013-14 Squad with the Conference South trophy.

## Club Factfile

**Founded:** 1963     **Nickname:** The Wings

**Previous Names:** None

**Previous Leagues:** Eltham & District 1963-71, London Spartan 1971-77, Athenian 1978-81, Southern 1981-86, 2000-04, Conference 1986-2000

**Club Colours (change):** Red/red/white (Yellow & green/green/green)

**Ground Capacity:** 4,000   **Seats:** 1,070   **Covered:** 1,500   **Clubhouse:** Yes   **Shop:** Yes

**Directions**

M25 to Dartford then A2 towards London.
Take Bexleyheath/Blackfen/Sidcup,turn off (six miles along A2) then follow A207 signed welling.
Ground is 1 mile From A2 on main road towards Welling High Street.

**Previous Grounds:** Butterfly Lane, Eltham 1963-78

**Record Attendance:** 4,100 v Gillingham - FA Cup

**Record Victory:** 7-1 v Dorking - 1985-86

**Record Defeat:** 0-7 v Welwyn Garden City - 1972-73

**Record Goalscorer:** Not known

**Record Appearances:** Not known

**Additional Records:** Paid £30,000 to Enfield for Gary Abbott

**Senior Honours:**   Received £95,000 from Birmingham City for Steve Finnan 1995

Southern League 1985-86. Conference South 2012-13.
Kent Senior Cup 1985-86, 98-99, 2008-09. London Senior Cup 1989-90. London Challenge Cup 1991-92.

| 10 YEAR RECORD | | | | | | | | | |
|---|---|---|---|---|---|---|---|---|---|
| 03-04 | 04-05 | 05-06 | 06-07 | 07-08 | 08-09 | 09-10 | 10-11 | 11-12 | 12-13 |
| SthP 9 | Conf S 16 | Conf S 9 | Conf S 8 | Conf S 16 | Conf S 7 | Conf S 9 | Conf S 6 | Conf S 3 | Conf S 1 |

# MATCH RESULTS 2012-13

| Date | Comp | H/A | Opponents | Att: | Result | Goalscorers | Pos | No. |
|------|------|-----|-----------|------|--------|-------------|-----|-----|
| Aug 18 | BSS | H | Bath City | 479 | D 1-1 | Lafayette 57 | 13 | 1 |
| 20 | BSS | A | Chelmsford City | 868 | W 3-2 | Lafayette 26 Chambers 32 Franks 57 | 6 | 2 |
| 25 | BSS | A | Tonbridge Angels | 592 | D 1-1 | Baker 50 | 7 | 3 |
| 27 | BSS | H | Sutton United | 644 | D 2-2 | Healy 51 (pen) Main 71 | 7 | 4 |
| Sept 1 | BSS | A | Hayes & Yeading | 194 | L 1-2 | Lafayette 41 | 15 | 5 |
| 4 | BSS | H | Eastbourne Borough | 471 | W 2-0 | Lafayette 50 Hughes-Mason 75 | 9 | 6 |
| 8 | BSS | H | Staines Town | 518 | W 3--2 | Clarke 15 Jalladeher 82 Main 90 | 5 | 7 |
| 15 | BSS | A | Farnborough | 564 | W 3-0 | Healy 4 65 Hughes -Mason 15 | 3 | 8 |
| 22 | FAC Q2 | A | Concord Rangers | 235 | D 1-1 | Lafayette 25 | | 9 |
| 25 | FAC Q2r | H | Concord Rangers | 267 | W 2-1 | King (og) 24 Healy 75 (pen) | | 10 |
| 29 | BSS | A | Dorchester Town | 550 | L 1-2 | Jermyn 53 (og) | 4 | 11 |
| Oct 2 | BSS | H | Dover Athletic | 543 | D 1-1 | Healy 90 | 5 | 12 |
| 6 | FAC Q2 | H | Thurrock | 402 | D 1-1 | Lafayette 33 | | 13 |
| 9 | FAC Q3r | H | Thurrock | 176 | W 3-1 | Healy 8 72 Clarke 20 | | 14 |
| 13 | BSS | A | Bromley | 1334 | W 2-0 | Fairweather-Johnson 36 Clarke 48 | 16 | 15 |
| 20 | FAC Q4 | H | Bishop's Stortford | 544 | L 1-3 | Main 90 | | 16 |
| 27 | BSS | H | Maidenhead United | 302 | L 1-2 | Lafayette 17 | 6 | 17 |
| Nov 3 | BSS | A | Havant & Waterloobille | 568 | W 1-0 | Lafayette 78 | 5 | 18 |
| 11 | FAT Q3 | A | Cray Wanderers | 262 | W 1-0 | McLaren 71 | | 19 |
| 17 | BSS | A | Salisbury City | 483 | W 1-0 | Lafayette 86 | 4 | 20 |
| 24 | FAT 1 | H | Newport County | 441 | W 2-0 | Healy 36 Martin 58 | | 21 |
| 27 | BSS | H | Billericay Town | 408 | W 5-2 | Martin 11 Healy 37 (pen) Kinch 42 Hughes-Mason 74 Main 76 | 2 | 22 |
| Dec 1 | BSS | A | Eastleigh | 546 | W 3-1 | Kinch 57 Acheampong 68 Hughes-Mason 79 | 2 | 23 |
| 4 | BSS | H | Bromley | 551 | W 3-1 | Healy 13 (pen) Lafayette 67 Fairweather-Johnson 90 | 2 | 24 |
| 8 | BSS | H | Hayes & Yeading | 467 | W 3-1 | Lafayette 41 Hughes-Mason 78 87 | 2 | 25 |
| 15 | FAT 2 | A | Woking | 826 | W 1-0 | Day 7 | | 26 |
| 26 | BSS | A | AFC Hornchurch | 483 | W 3-0 | Hughes-Mason 34 56 Fazackerly 72 | 2 | 27 |
| Jan 1 | BSS | H | AFC Hornchurch | 670 | W 4-0 | Acheampong 12 41 Jalladeher 16 Clarke 67 | 2 | 28 |
| 5 | BSS | H | Truro City | 508 | W 4-3 | Fazackerly 8 Healy 63 (pen) Lafayette 84 Acheampong 90 2 | 2 | 29 |
| 12 | FAT 3 | H | Grimsby Town | 1037 | L 1-2 | Healy 25 (pen) | | 30 |
| 26 | BSS | A | Basingstoke Town | 388 | W 1-0 | Lafayette 34 | 2 | 31 |
| Feb 2 | BSS | H | Dorchester Town | 516 | W 3-2 | Franks 6 Healy 51 Lafayette 79 | 2 | 32 |
| 5 | BSS | H | Boreham Wood | 433 | W 4-0 | Clarke 27 Franks 45 Hughes-Mason 64 Jones 63 (og) | 2 | 33 |
| 9 | BSS | A | Dover Athletic | 1005 | L 2-3 | Healy 5 Clarke 29 | 2 | 34 |
| 12 | BSS | A | Sutton United | 478 | L 1-2 | Lafayette 87 | 2 | 35 |
| 16 | BSS | H | Havant & Waterlooville | 609 | W 1-0 | Martin 61 | 2 | 36 |
| 19 | BSS | H | Farnborough | 457 | W 2-0 | Acheampong 39 Lafayette 64 | 1 | 37 |
| 23 | BSS | A | Weston-s-Mare | 288 | L 0-2 | | 2 | 38 |
| Mar 2 | BSS | H | Maidenhead United | 545 | W 3-2 | Martin 54 Clarke 76 Gallagher 90 | 1 | 39 |
| 9 | BSS | H | Basingstoke Town | 720 | D 1-1 | Gallagher 90 | 1 | 40 |
| 12 | BSS | H | Tonbridge Angels | 447 | W 4-1 | Acheampong 39 81 Lafayette 43 Clarke 62 | 1 | 41 |
| 16 | BSS | H | Billericay Town | 519 | W 2-1 | Franks 17 Beckles 85 (og) | 1 | 42 |
| 19 | BSS | A | Bath City | 367 | L 0-1 | | 1 | 43 |
| 23 | BSS | A | Truro City | 448 | W 3-0 | Fairweather-Johnson 20 Lafayette 42 68 (pen) | 1 | 44 |
| 29 | BSS | H | Chelmsford City | 1065 | W 3-0 | Reid 7 66 Hughes-Mason 75 | 1 | 45 |
| Apr 1 | BSS | A | Eastbourne Borough | 631 | W 3-0 | Kinch 19 Acheampong 56 Hughes-Mason 80 | 1 | 46 |
| 6 | BSS | A | Salisbury City | 1158 | L 1-2 | Healy 86 (pen) | 1 | 47 |
| 9 | BSS | A | Staines Town | 356 | D 2-2 | Lafayette 39 51 | 1 | 48 |
| 13 | BSS | H | Weston-s-Mare | 851 | W 4-1 | GUTHRIE 3 ( 23 27 41) Reid 76 | 1 | 49 |
| 20 | BSS | A | Boreham Wood | 466 | D 1-1 | Clarke 66 | 1 | 50 |
| 27 | BSS | H | Eastleigh | 1522 | D 1-1 | Guthrie 13 | 1 | 51 |

| GOALSCORERS | Lge | FAC | FAT | Total | Pens | Hat-tricks | Cons Run | | Lge | FAC | FAT | Total | Pens | Hat-tricks | Cons Run |
|-------------|-----|-----|-----|-------|------|-----------|----------|---|-----|-----|-----|-------|------|-----------|----------|
| Lafayette | 20 | 2 | | 22 | 1 | | 2 | Main | 2 | 1 | | 3 | | | |
| Healy | 11 | 3 | 2 | 16 | 7 | | 2 | Reid | 3 | | | 3 | | | |
| Hughes-Mason | 11 | | | 11 | | | 2 | Fazackerley | 2 | | | 2 | | | |
| Clarke | 8 | 1 | | 9 | | | | Gallagher | 2 | | | 2 | | 2 | |
| Acheampong | 7 | | | 8 | | | | Lalladeher | 2 | | | 2 | | | |
| Franks | 4 | | | 4 | 2 | | | Baker | 1 | | | 1 | | | |
| Fairweather-Johnson | 3 | | | 3 | | | | Chambers | 1 | | | 1 | | | |
| Guthrie | 4 | | | 4 | | 1 | | Day | | | 1 | 1 | | | |
| Martin | 3 | 1 | | 4 | | | | McLaren | | | 1 | 1 | | | |
| Kinch | 3 | | | 3 | | | 2 | Own Goals | 3 | 1 | | 3 | | | |
| | | | | | | | | Cons Run - Consecutive scoring games. | | | | | | | |

# WOKING

**Chairman:** Mike Smith

**Secretary:** Derek Powell   **(T)** 01483 772 470   **(E)** derek.powell@wokingfc.co.uk

**Commercial Manager:** Elliot Machin   **(T)** 01483 772 470

**Programme Editor:** Tom Eastwood   **(T)** 07786 911 036

**Ground Address:** Kingfield Stadium, Kingfield Road, Woking, Surrey GU22 9AA

**(T)** 01483 772 470   **Manager:** Garry Hill

2013-13 Squad.

## Club Factfile

**Founded:** 1889   **Nickname:** The Cards

**Previous Names:** None

**Previous Leagues:** Isthmian 1911-92.

**Club Colours (change):** Red and white/black/white (Yellow/black/yellow)

**Ground Capacity:** 6,000   **Seats:** 2,500   **Covered:** 3,900   **Clubhouse:** Yes   **Shop:** Yes

**Directions:** Exit M25 Junction 10 and follow A3 towards Guildford. Leave at next junction onto B2215 through Ripley and join A247 to Woking. Alternatively exit M25 junction 11 and follow A320 to Woking Town Centre. The ground is on the outskirts of Woking opposite the Leisure Centre.

**Previous Grounds:** Wheatsheaf, Ive Lane (pre 1923)

**Record Attendance:** 6,000 v Swansea City - FA Cup 1978-79 and v Coventry City - FA Cup 1996-97

**Record Victory:** 17-4 v Farnham - 1912-13

**Record Defeat:** 0-16 v New Crusaders - 1905-06

**Record Goalscorer:** Charlie Mortimore - 331 (1953-65)

**Record Appearances:** Brian Finn - 564 (1962-74)

**Additional Records:** Paid £60,000 to Crystal Palace for Chris Sharpling

**Senior Honours:** Received £150,000 from Bristol Rovers for Steve Foster

Surrey Senior Cup 1912-13, 26-27, 55-56, 56-57, 71-72, 90-91, 93-94, 95-96, 99-2000, 2003-04, 2011-12. FA Amateur Cup 1957-58. Isthmian League Cup 1990-91, Premier Division 1991-92. FA Trophy 1993-94, 94-95, 96-97. Vauxhall Championship Shield 1994-95. GLS Conference Cup 2004-05. Conference South 2011-12.

### 10 YEAR RECORD

| 03-04 | | 04-05 | | 05-06 | | 06-07 | | 07-08 | | 08-09 | | 09-10 | | 10-11 | | 11-12 | | 12-13 | |
|---|---|---|---|---|---|---|---|---|---|---|---|---|---|---|---|---|---|---|---|
| Conf | 9 | Conf | 8 | Conf | 11 | Conf | 15 | Conf | 17 | Conf | 21 | Conf S | 5 | Conf S | 5 | Conf S | 1 | Conf | 12 |

# MATCH RESULTS 2012-13

| Date | Comp | H/A | Opponents | Att: | Result | Goalscorers | Pos | No. |
|---|---|---|---|---|---|---|---|---|
| Aug 11 | BSP | A | Wrexham | 4088 | L 1-3 | Bubb 66 | 24 | 1 |
| 14 | BSP | H | Dartford | 1846 | W 1-0 | Sole 82 (pen) | 14 | 2 |
| 18 | BSP | H | Barrow | 1373 | W 3-1 | McNerney 20 Bubb 57 Pires 79 | 7 | 3 |
| 25 | BSP | A | Forest Green Rovers | 979 | L 1-3 | Betsy 43 (pen) | 11 | 4 |
| 28 | BSP | H | Braintree Town | 1588 | L 1-4 | Williams 45 | 14 | 5 |
| Sept 1 | BSP | A | Mansfield Town | 2061 | L 1-3 | McNerney 84 | 16 | 6 |
| 4 | BSP | A | Hereford United | 1481 | L 1-2 | Betsy 82 | 18 | 7 |
| 8 | BSP | H | Nuneaton Town | 1512 | W 6-1 | McCallum 25 Parkinson 45, BUBB 4 ( 48 55 68 70) | 16 | 8 |
| 15 | BSP | A | Stockport County | 3151 | W 2-1 | McCallum 24 Pires 65 | 13 | 9 |
| 22 | BSP | H | Gateshead | 1609 | W 2-1 | Parkinson 6 McCallum 26 | 12 | 10 |
| 25 | BSP | A | Ebbsfleet United | 738 | D 2-2 | Parkinson 16 Bubb 22 | 9 | 11 |
| 29 | BSP | H | Tamworth | 1467 | L 2-3 | Betsy 69 Cestor 90 | 12 | 12 |
| Oct 6 | BSP | A | AFC Telford United | 1584 | L 0-1 | | 15 | 13 |
| 9 | BSP | H | Cambridge United | 1420 | W 2-1 | Bubb 19 Betsy 60 | 10 | 14 |
| 13 | BSP | A | Southport | 1739 | L 2-3 | Betsy 11 McCallum 73 | 13 | 15 |
| 20 | FAC Q4 | H | Ebbsfleet United | 1272 | L 0-1 | | | 16 |
| 27 | BSP | A | Newport County | 2068 | W 3-2 | Betsy 6 15 Bubb 67 | 10 | 17 |
| Nov 3 | BSP | A | Gateshead | 473 | L 1-2 | Parkinson 6 | 11 | 18 |
| 6 | BSP | H | Kidderminster Harriers | 1168 | D 2-2 | Sawyer 3 Bubb 65 | 11 | 19 |
| 10 | BSP | A | Grimsby Town | 3418 | L 1-5 | Sinclair 2 | 15 | 20 |
| 17 | BSP | H | Alfreton Town | 1537 | L 1-2 | Williams 39 | 17 | 21 |
| 24 | FAT 1 | H | Farnborough | 979 | W 7-0 | Williams 6 34 Stockley 14 53, Knott 32 61 McCallum 77 | | 22 |
| Dec 1 | BSP | A | Hyde | 429 | L 0-7 | | 19 | 23 |
| 4 | BSP | A | Lincoln City | 2526 | L 0-2 | Betsy 6 (pen) Bubb 67 | 14 | 24 |
| 8 | BSP | H | Stockport County | 1520 | W 1-0 | Doyle 85 | 12 | 25 |
| 15 | FAT 2 | H | Welling United | 826 | L 0-1 | | | 26 |
| 26 | BSP | A | Luton Town | 6744 | L 1-3 | McNerney 71 | 16 | 27 |
| Jan 1 | BSP | H | Luton Town | 2961 | W 3-1 | Knott 3 74 Stockley 78 | 15 | 28 |
| 15 | BSP | H | Ebbsfleet United | 1419 | W 1-0 | Stockley 89 | | 29 |
| Feb 2 | BSP | H | Hyde United | 1236 | W 2-1 | Knott 10 47 | 11 | 30 |
| 9 | BSP | A | Alfreton Town | 606 | W 3-0 | Bubb 67 Betsy 72 Knott 83 | 11 | 31 |
| 16 | BSP | H | Newport County | 2116 | L 1-3 | McCallum 90 | 13 | 32 |
| 19 | BSP | A | Barrow | 624 | L 0-2 | | 13 | 33 |
| 23 | BSP | A | Southport | 911 | W 2-1 | Bubb 42 69 | 11 | 34 |
| 26 | BSP | H | Forest Green Rovers | 1105 | W 2-0 | Betsy 51 Parkinson 78 | 9 | 35 |
| Mar 2 | BSP | H | Lincoln City | 1766 | D 1-1 | Johnson 2 | 10 | 36 |
| 6 | BSP | H | Mansfield Town | 1179 | L 1-2 | Bubb 69 (pen) | 10 | 37 |
| 9 | BSP | A | Cambridge United | 2054 | L 0-1 | | 12 | 38 |
| 12 | BSP | A | Macclesfield Town | 1350 | D 0-0 | | 12 | 39 |
| 16 | BSP | H | AFC Telford United | 1320 | W 5-2 | BUBB 3 ( 4 43 89 pen) Stockley 13 Betsy 90 | 10 | 40 |
| 19 | BSP | A | Braintree Town | 506 | D 1-1 | Stockley 22 | 11 | 41 |
| 26 | BSP | A | Kidderminster Harriers | 2035 | D 2-2 | Bubb 22 (pen) Knott 56 | 10 | 42 |
| 28 | BSP | A | Nuneaton Town | 609 | D 0-0 | | 10 | 43 |
| 30 | BSP | H | Hereford United | 2303 | D 1-1 | Betsy 52 | 10 | 44 |
| Apr 1 | BSP | A | Dartford | 1407 | L 1-4 | Stockley 34 | 13 | 45 |
| 6 | BSP | H | Wrexham | 1518 | W 2-0 | Stockley 60 68 | 10 | 46 |
| 13 | BSP | H | Macclesfield Town | 1543 | W 5-4 | Knott 4 33 Betsy 7 Stockley 23 (pen) 28 | 9 | 47 |
| 16 | BSP | H | Grimsby Town | 1570 | L 0-1 | | 10 | 48 |
| 20 | BSP | A | Tamworth | 1509 | L 1-2 | Stockley 21 | 12 | 49 |

| GOALSCORERS | Lge | FAC | FAT | Total | Pens | Hat-tricks | Cons Run | | Lge | FAC | FAT | Total | Pens | Hat-tricks | Cons Run |
|---|---|---|---|---|---|---|---|---|---|---|---|---|---|---|---|
| Bubb | 19 | | | 19 | 3 | 2 | 1 | Doyle | 1 | | | 1 | | | |
| Betsy | 13 | | | 13 | 2 | | 2 | Sawyer | 1 | | | 1 | | | |
| Stockley | 10 | | 2 | 12 | 1 | | | Sinclair | 1 | | | 1 | | | |
| Knott | 8 | | 2 | 10 | | | 2 | Sole | 1 | | | 1 | 1 | | |
| McCallum | 5 | | 1 | 6 | | | 3 | Johnson | 1 | | | 1 | | | |
| Parkinson | 5 | | | 5 | | | | Cons Run - Consecutive scoring games. | | | | | | | |
| Wiliams | 2 | | 2 | 4 | | | | | | | | | | | |
| McNerney | 3 | | | 3 | | | | | | | | | | | |
| Pires | 2 | | | 2 | | | | | | | | | | | |
| Cestor | 1 | | | 1 | | | | | | | | | | | |

# WREXHAM

**Chairman:** Don Bircham (Chief Exe)

**Secretary:** Geraint Parry          **(T)** 07801 749 021          **(E)** geraint.parry@wrexhamfc.tv

**Commercial Manager:** Steven Cook          **(T)** 07921 371 766

**Programme Editor:** Terry Brumpton          **(T)** 07771 802 048

**Ground Address:** Racecourse Ground, Mold road, Wrexham LL11 2AN

**(T)** 01978 262 129                    **Manager:** Andy Morrell

Johnny Hunt scores the winning penalty in the FA Trophy final against Grimsby Town.
Photo: Keith Clayton.

## Club Factfile

**Founded:** 1872          **Nickname:** The Robins

**Previous Names:** Wrexham Athletic for the 1882-83 season only

**Previous Leagues:** The Combination 1890-94, 1896-1906, Welsh League 1894-96, Birmingham & District 1906-21, Football League 1921-2008

**Club Colours (change):** Red/white/red (All green)

**Ground Capacity:** 15,500  **Seats:** 10,100  **Covered:** 15,500  **Clubhouse:** Yes    **Shop:** Yes

**Directions**

From Wrexham by-pass (A483) exit at Mold junction (A451).
Follow signs for Town Centre and football ground is half a mile on the left hand side.

**Previous Grounds:** Rhosddu Recreation Ground during the 1881-82 and 1882-83 seasons.

**Record Attendance:** 34,445 v Manchester United - FA Cup 4th Round 26/01/57

**Record Victory:** 10-1 v Hartlepool United - Division Four 03/03/62

**Record Defeat:** 0-9 v v Brentford - Division Three

**Record Goalscorer:** Tommy Bamford - 201 (1928-34)

**Record Appearances:** Arfon Griffiths - 592 (1959-79)

**Additional Records:** Paid £800,000 to Birmingham City for Bryan Hughes March 1997

**Senior Honours:**     Received £210,000 from Liverpool for Joey Jones October 1978

Welsh FA Cup 1877-78, 81-82, 92-93, 96-97, 1902-03, 04-05, 08-09, 09-10, 10-11, 13-14, 14-15, 20-21, 23-24, 24-25, 30-31, 56-57, 57-58, 59-60, 71-72, 74-75, 77-78, 85-86, 94-95. Welsh Lge 1894-95, 95-96. Combination 1900-01, 01-02, 02-03, 04-05. Football Lge Div. 3 1977-78. FAW Prem. Cup 1997-98, 99-2000, 00-01, 02-03, 03-04. F. Lge Trophy 2004-05. FA Trophy 2012-13.

### 10 YEAR RECORD

| 03-04 | | 04-05 | | 05-06 | | 06-07 | | 07-08 | | 08-09 | | 09-10 | | 10-11 | | 11-12 | | 12-13 | |
|---|---|---|---|---|---|---|---|---|---|---|---|---|---|---|---|---|---|---|---|
| FL 2 | 13 | FL 1 | 22 | FL 2 | 13 | FL 2 | 19 | FL 2 | 24 | Conf | 10 | Conf | 11 | Conf | 4 | Conf | 2 | Conf | 5 |

# MATCH RESULTS 2012-13

| Date | Comp | H/A | Opponents | Att: | Result | Goalscorers | Pos | No. |
|------|------|-----|-----------|------|--------|-------------|-----|-----|
| Aug 11 | BSP | H | Woking | 4088 | W 3-1 | Ogleby 18 Kedes 41 Creighton 74 | 1 | 1 |
| 14 | BSP | A | Macclesfield Town | 2368 | L 0-2 | | 12 | 2 |
| 18 | BSP | A | Ebbfleet United | 843 | D 1-1 | Hunt 49 | 13 | 3 |
| 25 | BSP | H | Grimsby Town | 3127 | D 0-0 | | 13 | 4 |
| 27 | BSP | A | Tamworth | 1433 | W 1-0 | Courtney 8 | 10 | 5 |
| Sept 1 | BSP | H | Newport County | 3820 | W 2-0 | Cieslewicz 24 Wright 82 | 7 | 6 |
| 4 | BSP | H | Hyde | 3176 | W 2-0 | Little 78 Harris 90 | 5 | 7 |
| 8 | BSP | A | Cambridge United | 3304 | W 4-1 | Morrell 34 56 D.Wright 48 86 | 3 | 8 |
| 15 | BSP | A | Luton Town | 6675 | D 0-0 | | 4 | 9 |
| 22 | BSP | H | Dartford | 3772 | D 2-2 | D Wright 16 Bishop 42 | 3 | 10 |
| 25 | BSP | H | Barrow | 2881 | W 3-0 | Harris 18 Bishop 71 Ogleby 83 | 3 | 11 |
| 29 | BSP | A | Nuneaton Town | 1543 | D 0-0 | | 3 | 12 |
| Oct 6 | BSP | H | Forest Green Rovers | 4053 | W 2-1 | Cieslewicz 57 73 | 3 | 13 |
| 10 | BSP | A | Stockport County | 3789 | W 3-2 | Hattersley 25 (og) Ashton 37 (pen) 87 (pen) | 2 | 14 |
| 13 | BSP | H | Lincoln City | 3809 | L 2-4 | Colbeck 79 Clarke 90 | 2 | 15 |
| 20 | FAC Q4 | H | Southport | 1911 | W 2-0 | Keates 42 Ormorod 90 | | 16 |
| Nov 3 | FAC 1 | H | Alfreton Town | 2409 | L 2-4 | Ashton 2 (pen) D.Wright 85 | | 17 |
| 6 | BSP | A | Southport | 1324 | W 4-1 | Harris 56 Lynch 78 (og) Ogleby 81 Westwood 86 | 2 | 18 |
| 10 | BSP | H | Hereford United | 3620 | L 1-2 | Wright 58 | 4 | 19 |
| 17 | BSP | H | Gateshead | 3011 | D 1-1 | Rushton 37 | 4 | 20 |
| 20 | BSP | A | Braintree Town | 508 | W 5-1 | Wright 9 65 Ormorod 16 Rushton 39 Cieslewicz 79 | 2 | 21 |
| 24 | FAT 1 | H | Rushall Olympic | 1085 | W 5-0 | MORRELL 3 ( 15 17 88) Cieslewicz 67 90 | | 22 |
| Dec 1 | BSP | A | Kidderminster Harriers | 2378 | L 0-2 | | 4 | 23 |
| 8 | BSP | H | NuneatonTown | 2739 | W 6-1 | Hunt 20 Morell 31 Ashton 45 90 (pen) Ogleby 73 Cieslewicz 83 | 2 | 24 |
| 15 | FAT 2 | H | Solihull Moors | 1111 | W 3-2 | Ormorod 45 Cieslewicz 60 Keates 65 (pen) | | 25 |
| 22 | BSP | A | Grimsby Town | 4302 | L 0-1 | | 3 | 26 |
| 26 | BSP | H | AFC Telford United | 4330 | W 4-1 | Ormorod 2 71 Rushton 60 Wright 69 | 3 | 27 |
| 29 | BSP | H | Tamworth | 3703 | D 2-2 | Ormorod 24 Wright | 3 | 28 |
| Jan 1 | BSP | A | AFC Telford United | 2931 | W 2-0 | Wright 24 Cieslewicz 85 | 2 | 29 |
| 5 | BSP | A | Newport County | 3627 | D 1-1 | Wright 34 | | 30 |
| 8 | BSP | A | Alfreton Town | 628 | W 3-1 | Ashton 17 Wright 49 Clarke 75 | 1 | 31 |
| 12 | FAT 3 | A | Sutton United | 775 | W 5-0 | Ogleby 32 Rushton 39 Hunt 43 Clarke 45 Thornton 90 | | 32 |
| 26 | FAT 4 | H | Southport | 1473 | W 3-1 | Clarke 28 Westwood 45 Harris 59 | | 33 |
| 29 | BSP | H | Southport | 3002 | D 2-2 | Wright 7 Clarke 70 | | 34 |
| Feb 2 | BSP | A | Forest Green Rovers | 1840 | D 0-0 | | 2 | 35 |
| 9 | BSP | A | Stockport County | 4206 | W 3-1 | Clarke 8 D.Wright 82 Ogleby 88 | 2 | 36 |
| 12 | BSP | A | Hereford United | 1781 | W 1-0 | Harris 32 | 2 | 37 |
| 16 | FAT S-F 1 | H | Gainsborough Trinity | 3409 | W 3-1 | Wright 18 Cieslewicz 65 Ashton 90 | | 38 |
| 19 | BSP | A | Gateshead | 513 | W 1-0 | Ormorod 60 | 1 | 39 |
| 23 | FAT S-F 2 | A | Gainsborough Trinity | 3307 | L 1-2 | Morrell 21 | | 40 |
| 26 | BSP | A | Barrow | 889 | W 1-0 | Thornton 84 | 1 | 41 |
| Mar 2 | BSP | H | Alfreton Town | 3706 | D 1-1 | Thornton 9 | 1 | 42 |
| 5 | BSP | H | Ebbsfleet United | 2390 | W 4-1 | Adebola 3 Ormorod 11 Thornton 29 Ogleby 45 | 1 | 43 |
| 9 | BSP | A | Dartford | 815 | L 1-2 | D.Wright 26 | 1 | 44 |
| 12 | BSP | A | Lincoln City | 1379 | W 2-1 | Ormorod 61 Adebola 66 | 1 | 45 |
| 16 | BSP | H | Luton Town | 3907 | D 0-0 | | 2 | 46 |
| 26 | FAT F | N | Grimsby Town | 35,266 | D1-1 | Thornton 82 (pen) *aet Won 4-1 on pens | | 47 |
| 30 | BSP | A | Hyde | 1846 | L 0-2 | | 3 | 48 |
| Apr 1 | BSP | A | Macclesfield Town | 4351 | D 0-0 | | 4 | 49 |
| 6 | BSP | H | Mansfield Town | 4378 | W 2-1 | Keates 68 Wright 78 | 3 | 50 |
| 6 | BSP | A | Woking | 1518 | L 0-2 | | 3 | 51 |
| 9 | BSP | H | Cambridge United | 2574 | W 1-0 | Colbeck 5 | 3 | 52 |
| 13 | BSP | H | Kidderminster Harriers | 4013 | L 1-2 | D.Wright 62 | 4 | 53 |
| 16 | BSP | H | Braintree Town | 2312 | D 1-1 | Morrell 3 | 4 | 54 |
| 20 | BSP | A | Mansfield Town | 6394 | L 0-1 | | 5 | 55 |
| 24 | P.Offs SF 1 | H | Kidderminster Harriers | 5414 | W 2-1 | Artell 44 Ashton 85 (pen) | | 56 |
| 28 | P.Offs SF 2 | A | Kidderminster H | 6202 | W 3-1 | Ormorod 29 Clarke 69 Ashton 89 (pen) | | 57 |
| May 5 | P.Off F | N | Newport County | 16346 | L 0-2 | | | 58 |

| GOALSCORERS | Lge | FAC | FAT | Total | Pens | Hat-tricks | Cons Run | | Lge | FAC | FAT | Total | Pens | Hat-tricks | Cons Run |
|-------------|-----|-----|-----|-------|------|------------|----------|---|-----|-----|-----|-------|------|------------|----------|
| Wright | 15 | 1 | 1 | 17 | | | 3 | Bishop | 2 | | | 2 | | | |
| Cieslewicz | 6 | 4 | | 10 | | | 2 | Colbeck | 2 | | | 2 | | | |
| Ashton | 7 | 1 | | 8 | 6 | | | Westwood | 1 | | 1 | 2 | | | |
| Morrell | 4 | | 4 | 8 | | 1 | | Wright S | 2 | | | 2 | | | |
| Omerod | 7 | | 1 | 8 | | | | Artell | 1 | | | 1 | | | |
| Ogleby | 6 | | 1 | 7 | | | | Courtney | 1 | | | 1 | | | |
| Clarke | 5 | | 2 | 6 | | | | Creighton | 1 | | | 1 | | | |
| Harris | 4 | | 1 | 5 | | | | Kedes | 1 | | | 1 | | | |
| Thornton | 3 | | 2 | 5 | 1 | | | Little | 1 | | 1 | 1 | | | |
| Rushton | 3 | | 1 | 4 | | | | Own Goals | 2 | | | 2 | | | |
| Hunt | 2 | | 1 | 3 | | | | Cons Run - Consecutive scoring games. | | | | | | | |
| Keates | 1 | 1 | 1 | 3 | 1 | | | | | | | | | | |
| Adebola | 2 | | | 2 | | | | | | | | | | | |

# MANSFIELD TOWN - MATCH RESULTS 2012-13

| Date | Comp | H/A | Opponents | Att: | Result | Goalscorers | Pos | No. |
|------|------|-----|-----------|------|--------|-------------|-----|-----|
| Aug 11 | BSP | H | Newport County | 2924 | L 3-4 | Speight 48 89 Green 50 | 19 | 1 |
| 14 | BSP | A | Gateshead | 801 | L 1-4 | Jones 18 | 23 | 2 |
| 18 | BSP | A | Kidderminster Harriers | 1770 | W 3-2 | Green 45 Meikle 60 78 | 16 | 3 |
| 25 | BSP | H | Hyde | 2203 | W 1-0 | Green 7 | 12 | 4 |
| 27 | BSP | A | Grimsby Town | 3397 | L 1-4 | Rhead 86 | 15 | 5 |
| Sept 1 | BSP | H | Woking | 2061 | W 3-1 | Briscoe 10 Rhead 45 Speight 90 | 14 | 6 |
| 4 | BSP | H | Tamworth | 2105 | W 2-0 | Green 45 (pen) Jones 62 | 9 | 7 |
| 8 | BSP | A | Ebbsfleet United | 828 | L 1-3 | Briscoe 42 (pen) | 11 | 8 |
| 15 | BSP | H | Braintree Town | 2049 | W 2-0 | Stevenson 42 Speight 86 | 8 | 9 |
| 22 | BSP | A | AFC Telford United | 1736 | D 2-2 | Beevers 12 Speight 39 (pen) | 9 | 10 |
| 29 | BSP | H | Hereford United | 2248 | D 1-1 | Geohaghon 45 | 9 | 11 |
| Oct 6 | BSP | A | Cambridge United | 2545 | L 1-4 | Speight 71 | 13 | 12 |
| 9 | BSP | H | Lincoln City | 2325 | D 0-0 | | 12 | 13 |
| 13 | BSP | H | Forest Green Rovers | 2019 | W 1-0 | Rhead 89 | 10 | 14 |
| 20 | FAC Q4 | A | Workington | 721 | W 2-1 | Speight 32 71 | | 15 |
| 27 | BSP | A | Dartford | 1737 | L 0-2 | | 12 | 16 |
| Nov 3 | FAC 1 | H | Slough Town | 1686 | D 0-0 | | | 17 |
| 6 | BSP | A | Nuneaton Town | 338 | D 1-1 | Wright 59 | 14 | 18 |
| 10 | BSP | H | Southport | 1918 | W 1-0 | Hutchinson 2 | 10 | 19 |
| 13 | FAC 1r | A | Slough Town | 1593 | D 1-1 | Woozley 45 (og) *aet Won 4-1 on pens | | 20 |
| 18 | BSP | H | Luton Town | 2619 | D 2-2 | Hutchison 8 Green 85 | 11 | 21 |
| 20 | BSP | A | Macclesfield Town | 1272 | W 3-0 | Green 40 Meikle 66 Jones 88 | 7 | 22 |
| 24 | FAT 1 | H | Matlock Town | 1615 | D 1-1 | Murray 24 | | 23 |
| 27 | FAT 1r | A | Matlock Town | 758 | L 1-2 | Daniel 21 | | 24 |
| Dec 1 | FAC 2 | A | Lincoln City | 4127 | D 3-3 | Green 21 Briscoe 53 Rhead 90 | | 25 |
| 8 | BSP | H | Ebbsfleet United | 1845 | W 4-1 | Hutchinson 15 Stones 37 (og) Howell 70  Green 78 (pen) | 8 | 26 |
| 12 | FAC 2r | H | Lincoln City | 5304 | W 2-1 | Farmer 14 (og) Briscoe 77 | | 27 |
| 26 | BSP | H | Alfreton Town | 4186 | L 1-2 | Dempster 35 | 11 | 28 |
| Jan 1 | BSP | A | Alfreton Town | 1537 | W 3-0 | Geohaghon 43 Daniel 57 Dempster 72 | | 29 |
| 6 | FAC 3 | H | Liverpool | 7574 | L 1-2 | Green 79 | | 30 |
| 12 | BSP | H | Kidderminster Harriers | 2405 | L 0-3 | | 10 | 31 |
| 16 | BSP | A | Stockport County | 2647 | W 3-1 | Daniel 38 Stevenson 40 Green 45 | | 32 |
| 19 | BSP | A | Southport | 804 | W 2-1 | Murray 19 Stevenson 54 | 8 | 33 |
| Feb 2 | BSP | H | Dartford | 2598 | W 5-0 | Murray 5 Howell 54 Jones 66 `Green 79 Stevenson 85 (pen). | 6 | 34 |
| 9 | BSP | H | Barrow | 2226 | W 8-1 | Stevenson 8 68  GREEN 3 ( 23 pen  32 52 pen) | 6 | 35 |
| | | | | | | Daniel 30 Murray 43  Howell 70 Rose 17(pen) | 6 | 36 |
| 12 | BSP | A | Newport County | 1902 | L 0-2 | | 6 | 36 |
| 16 | BSP | A | Cambridge United | 740 | W 3-1 | Stevenson 11 Jones 39 Daniel 71 | 7 | 37 |
| 19 | BSP | A | Hyde FC | 675 | W 1-0 | Briscoe 46 | 6 | 38 |
| 23 | BSP | A | Luton Town | 5968 | W 3-2 | Green 32 (pen) Daniel 44 Meikle 90 | 6 | 39 |
| 26 | BSP | A | Lincoln City | 2734 | W 1-0 | Green 90 | 4 | 40 |
| Mar 2 | BSP | H | AFC Telford United | 2725 | W 1-0 | Green 49 | 3 | 41 |
| 6 | BSP | A | Woking | 1179 | W 2-1 | Briscoe 33 Jones 77 | 3 | 42 |
| 9 | BSP | A | Stockport County | 2628 | W 4-1 | CHAPMAN 3 (13 20 77) Green 57 | 3 | 43 |
| 12 | BSP | A | Grimsby Town | 3896 | W 2-0 | Rhead 64 Chapman 82 | 2 | 44 |
| 16 | BSP | A | Forest Green Rovers | 1109 | W 2-1 | Oshodi 30 (og) Stevenson 47 | 1 | 45 |
| 26 | BSP | H | Nuneaton Borough | 2384 | W 1-0 | Briscoe 67 | 2 | 46 |
| 30 | BSP | A | Tamworth | 1968 | W 1-0 | Jones 61 | 2 | 47 |
| Apr 1 | BSP | H | Gateshead | 3472 | W 4-0 | Howell 21 Briscoe 73 Green 77 Hutchinson 90 (pen) | 2 | 48 |
| 4 | BSP | A | Wrexham | 4378 | L 1-3 | Green 53 | 2 | 49 |
| 6 | BSP | A | Barrow | 1114 | W 4-0 | Green 29 42 (pen) Dempster 60 Stevenson 90 | 2 | 50 |
| 9 | BSP | H | NMacclesfield Town | 3694 | W 3-1 | Green 17 Jones 41 Stevenson 51 | 2 | 51 |
| 13 | BSP | A | Braintree Town | 1755 | L 1-2 | Green 8 | 2 | 52 |
| 16 | BSP | A | Hereford United | 2141 | W 2-1 | Green 37 90 | 1 | 53 |
| 20 | BSP | H | Wrexham | 6394 | W 1-0 | Green 40 (pen) | 1 | 54 |

| GOALSCORERS | Lge | FAC | FAT | Total | Pens | Hat-tricks | Cons Run | | Lge | FAC | FAT | Total | Pens | Hat-tricks | Cons Run |
|-------------|-----|-----|-----|-------|------|------------|----------|-----|-----|-----|-----|-------|------|------------|----------|
| Green | 25 | 2 | | 27 | 7 | 1 | 7 | Meikle | 4 | | | 4 | | | |
| Stevenson | 10 | | | 10 | 1 | | | Murray | 3 | | 1 | 4 | | | |
| Briscoe | 6 | 2 | | 8 | 1 | | | Dempster | 3 | | | 3 | | | |
| Jones | 8 | | | 8 | | | | Geohaghan | 2 | | | 2 | | | |
| Speight | 6 | 2 | | 8 | 1 | | | Beevers | 1 | | | 1 | | | |
| Daniel | 4 | | 1 | 5 | | | | Rose | 1 | | | 1 | 1 | | |
| Rhead | 4 | 1 | | 5 | | | | Wright | 1 | | | 1 | | | |
| Chapman | 4 | | | 4 | | | | Own Goals | 2 | 2 | | 4 | | | |
| Howell | 4 | | | 4 | | | | Cons Run - Consecutive scoring games. | | | | | | | |
| Hutchinson | 4 | | 1 | 4 | | | | | | | | | | | |

# NEWPORT COUNTY - MATCH RESULTS 2012-13

| Date | Comp | H/A | Opponents | Att: | Result | Goalscorers | Pos | No. |
|------|------|-----|-----------|------|--------|-------------|-----|-----|
| Aug 11 | BSP | A | Mansfield Town | 2,924 | W 4-3 | Yakubu 10, James 13, O Connor 56, Louis 66 | 2 | 1 |
| 14 | BSP | H | Nuneaton | 2,646 | W 4-0 | O Connor 13, 52, Louis 20, Evans 86 | 1 | 2 |
| 18 | BSP | H | Dartford | 3024 | W 2-1 | O Connor 7 27 | 1 | 3 |
| 25 | BSP | A | Braintree Town | 611 | W 2-1 | Porter 69 Yakubu 84 | 1 | 4 |
| 28 | BSP | H | Hereford United | 4365 | W 2-0 | Sandell 75 O Connor 90 | 1 | 5 |
| Sept 1 | BSP | A | Wrexhan | 3820 | L 0-2 | | 1 | 6 |
| 4 | BSP | A | Dartford | 1446 | L 1-2 | O Connor 54 | 3 | 7 |
| 8 | BSP | H | Stockport County | 2308 | D 0-0 | | 4 | 8 |
| 15 | BSP | A | Barrow | 802 | W 3-0 | Evans 44 Crow 76 77 | 1 | 9 |
| 22 | BSP | H | Southport | 2802 | W 2-1 | O Connor 76 Swallow 90 | 1 | 10 |
| 25 | BSP | 63 | AFC Telford United | 1503 | W 4-2 | O Connor 45 Preston 49 (og) Yakubu 72, Sandell 78 | 1 | 11 |
| 29 | BSP | H | Grimsby Town | 2968 | D 0-0 | | 2 | 12 |
| Oct 6 | BSP | A | Tamworth | 1201 | W 2-1 | Yakubu 45 O Connor 63 | 1 | 13 |
| 9 | BSP | H | Ebbsfleet United | 2453 | W 1-0 | Yakubu 30 | 1 | 14 |
| 13 | BSP | A | Macclesfield | 1544 | D 1-1 | James 43 | 1 | 15 |
| 20 | FAC Q4 | A | Yate Town | 1190 | D 3-3 | Louis 7 O Connor 89 James 90 | | 16 |
| 23 | FAC Q4r | H | Yate Town | 1483 | L 1-3 | O Connor 43 *aet | | 17 |
| 27 | BSP | H | Woking | 2088 | L 2-3 | Sandell 45 Flynn 89 | 1 | 18 |
| Nov 6 | BSP | A | Cambridge United | 1787 | W 6-2 | Minshull 16 Flynn 17 Sandell 30 O'Connor 62 70 Smith 90 | 1 | 19 |
| 10 | BSP | A | Alfreton Town | 663 | L 3-4 | Smith 34 Evans 60 O'Connor 89 | 1 | 20 |
| 17 | BSP | H | Hyde United | 2096 | L 1-2 | Jolley 55 | 2 | 21 |
| 24 | FAT 1 | A | Welling United | 441 | L 0-2 | | | 22 |
| Dec 1 | BSP | H | Gateshead | 1473 | W 3-1 | Jolley 38 56 Smith 53 | 1 | 23 |
| 8 | BSP | A | Kidderminster Harriers | 1951 | L 2-3 | Smith 31 Evans 37 | 3 | 24 |
| 11 | BSP | H | Luton Town | 2247 | W 5-2 | O'Connor 12 JOLLEY 3 (23 38 67) Sandell 64 | 1 | 25 |
| 26 | BSP | A | Forest Green Rovers | 2332 | W 2-1 | Swallow 70 Charles 74 | 2 | 26 |
| Jan 1 | BSP | H | Forest Green Rovers | 2787 | L 0-5 | | | 27 |
| 5 | BSP | H | Wexham | 3627 | D 1-1 | Porter 56 | 3 | 28 |
| 12 | BSP | A | Lincoln City | 1970 | W 4-2 | O'Connor 22 37 Willmott 40 45 | 2 | 29 |
| 19 | BSP | H | Barrow | 2107 | L 0-2 | | 2 | 30 |
| Feb 9 | BSP | H | Tamworth | 1712 | D 2-2 | Donnelly 1 Anthony 30 | 5 | 31 |
| 12 | BSP | H | Mansfield Town | 1902 | W 2-0 | Sandell 66 Jolley 78 | 4 | 32 |
| 16 | BSP | A | Woking | 2116 | W 3-1 | Minshull 19 34 Anthony 37 | 4 | 33 |
| 23 | BSP | H | AFC Telford United | 1761 | W 2-1 | Jolley 55 `Crow 75 | 3 | 34 |
| Mar 2 | BSP | A | Hyde | 640 | W 1-0 | Jolley 10 | 4 | 35 |
| 5 | BSP | A | Hereford United | 2519 | W 3-2 | Minshull 72 81 Willmott 90 | | 36 |
| 9 | BSP | A | Ebbsfleet United | 808 | D 1-1 | Minshull 44 | 4 | 37 |
| 17 | BSP | A | Gateshead | 227 | D 0-0 | | 4 | 38 |
| 19 | BSP | H | Kidderminster Harries | 2652 | L 1-2 | Sandell 45 | 4 | 39 |
| 23 | BSP | A | Stockport County | 3154 | L 0-1 | | 4 | 40 |
| 26 | BSP | A | Southport | 606 | W 2-0 | O'Connor 10 Jolley 34 | 4 | 41 |
| 30 | BSP | H | Dartford | 2111 | D 0-0 | | 4 | 42 |
| Apr 1 | BSP | A | Nuneaton Town | 1068 | W 2-1 | Willmott 58 Armson 77 (og) | 3 | 43 |
| 6 | BSP | A | Cambridge United | 2012 | D 0-0 | | 4 | 44 |
| 9 | BSP | H | Braintree Town | 1864 | W 1-0 | Washington 48 | 4 | 45 |
| 11 | BSP | H | Macclesfield Town | 1606 | W 4-1 | Jolley 24 Sandell 41 (pen) Willmott 45 65 | 3 | 46 |
| 13 | BSP | H | Alfreton Town | 2138 | W 2-0 | Jolley 45 Anthony 67 | 3 | 47 |
| 16 | BSP | H | Luton Town | 5125 | D 2-2 | Jolley 52 84 | 3 | 48 |
| 20 | BSP | A | Grimsby Town | 4555 | L 0-3 | | 3 | 49 |
| 23 | P.Offs S-F 1 A | | Grimsby Town | 5414 | W 1-0 | Jacubu 89 | | 50 |
| 27 | P.Offs S-F 2 H | | Grimsby Town | 6615 | W 1-0 | Jolley 31 | | 51 |
| May 5 | P.Off Final N | | Wrexham | 16346 | W 2-0 | Jolly 86 O'Connor 90 | | 52 |

| GOALSCORERS | Lge | FAC | FAT | Total | Pens | Hat-tricks | Cons Run | | Lge | FAC | FAT | Total | Pens | Hat-tricks | Cons Run |
|-------------|-----|-----|-----|-------|------|------------|----------|---|-----|-----|-----|-------|------|------------|----------|
| O'Connor | 18 | 2 | | 20 | | | 3 | James | 2 | 1 | | 3 | | | |
| Jolley | 16 | | | 16 | 1 | | 3 | Louis | 2 | 1 | | 3 | | | |
| Sandell | 8 | | | 8 | 1 | | | Flynn | 2 | | | 2 | | | |
| Minshall | 6 | | | 6 | | | | Porter | 2 | | | 2 | | | |
| Willmott | 6 | | | 6 | | | | Swallow | 2 | | | 2 | | | |
| Yakubu | 6 | | | 6 | | | | Clarke | 1 | | | 1 | | | |
| Evans | 4 | | | 4 | | | | Donnelly | 1 | | | 1 | | | |
| Smith | 4 | | | 4 | | | | Washington | 1 | | | 1 | | | |
| Anthony | 3 | | | 3 | | | | Own Goals | 2 | | | 2 | | | |
| Crow | 3 | | | 3 | | | | Cons Run - Consecutive scoring games. | | | | | | | |

# Football Conference Play-off Final 2012-13

Above: Newport's Pipe controls the ball in front of Wrexham's Clarke.
Photo: Keith Clayton.

Above right: Wrexham's Johnny Hunt fires a shot at the Newport goal despite the presence of David Pipie. Photo: Peter Barnes

Right: Jolley opens the scoring for Newport County.
Photo: Keith Clayton.

Tony James, Newport County, attempts to block Wrexham player/manager Andy Morrell.
Photo: Roger Turner.

Let the celebrations begin, Newport County move on to the Football League.
Photo: Peter Barnes.

## Conference Premier Statistics 2012-13

| | MCV | MCD | MCwW | MCwD | MCSG | MCwS | TGS | MCCS | TNCS |
|---|---|---|---|---|---|---|---|---|---|
| AFC Telford United | 2 | 7 | 25 | 3 | 11 | 3 | 14 | 2 | 7 |
| Alfreton Town | 2 | 3 | 5 | 6 | 7 | 2 | 13 | 2 | 10 |
| Barrow | 3 | 5 | 7 | 6 | 10 | 2 | 17 | 3 | 14 |
| Braintree Town | 4 | 4 | 7 | 6 | 7 | 3 | 15 | 2 | 8 |
| Cambridge United | 3 | 4 | 8 | 5 | 14 | 3 | 10 | 2 | 13 |
| Dartford | 4 | 3 | 4 | 5 | 10 | 2 | 15 | 2 | 17 |
| Ebbsfleet United | 2 | 3 | 10 | 5 | 6 | 2 | 12 | 3 | 5 |
| Forest Green Rovers | 4 | 5 | 6 | 7 | 18 | 4 | 10 | 2 | 11 |
| Gateshead | 2 | 6 | 9 | 6 | 8 | 2 | 14 | 3 | 13 |
| Grimsby Town | 4 | 4 | 7 | 18 | 9 | 3 | 14 | 3 | 25 |
| Hereford United | 3 | 3 | 5 | 7 | 13 | 2 | 10 | 3 | 14 |
| Hyde | 5 | 6 | 7 | 6 | 10 | 3 | 16 | 2 | 8 |
| Kiddeminster Harriers | 6 | 5 | 10 | 9 | 8 | 2 | 11 | 2 | 15 |
| Lincoln City | 4 | 3 | 8 | 10 | 10 | 3 | 12 | 2 | 9 |
| Luton Town | 3 | 2 | 8 | 6 | 11 | 2 | 14 | 3 | 16 |
| Macclesfield Town | 4 | 5 | 8 | 6 | 10 | 2 | 13 | 3 | 14 |
| Mansfield Town | 12 | 2 | 4 | 12 | 18 | 2 | 5 | 3 | 19 |
| Newport County | 5 | 3 | 4 | 9 | 9 | 1 | 11 | 2 | 16 |
| Nuneaton Town | 3 | 3 | 9 | 5 | 6 | 3 | 17 | 4 | 17 |
| Southport | 3 | 6 | 8 | 4 | 13 | 2 | 10 | 1 | 6 |
| Stockport County | 2 | 3 | 9 | 4 | 8 | 2 | 13 | 2 | 10 |
| Tamworth | 4 | 5 | 7 | 6 | 9 | 5 | 14 | 2 | 10 |
| Woking | 4 | 4 | 4 | 6 | 12 | 2 | 10 | 1 | 9 |
| Wrexham | 4 | 1 | 4 | 13 | 10 | 2 | 12 | 4 | 18 |

MCV - Most Consecutive Victories
MCD - Most Consecutive Defeats
MCwW - Most Consecutive without a Win
MCwD - Most Consecutive without a defeat
MCSG - Most Consecutive Scoring Games
MCwS - Most Consecutive without Scoring
TGS - Total Games without Scoring
MCCS - Most Consecutive Clean Sheets
TNCS - Total Number of Clean Sheets

## Goalscorers with at least Ten goals in League, FA Cup and FA Trophy in 2012-2013

| | | | | | | | Total Individual Scorers | Hat tricks | Pens | OG scored by opponents |
|---|---|---|---|---|---|---|---|---|---|---|
| AFC Telford United | Jones | 11 | | | | | 16+3 og | 1 | 3 | 3 Mansfield, Newport , Southport |
| Alfreton Town | Clayton | 19 | Tomlinson | 15 | Bradley | 11 | 16+0 | 1 | 8 | 0 |
| Barrow | Boyes | 17 | Baker | 14 | | | 12+2 | 1 | 7 | 2 Ebbsfleet United, Gateshead |
| Braintree Town | Marks | 15 | Davis | 11 | Holman | 11 | 14+1 | 0 | 7 | 1 Woking |
| Cambridge United | Elliott | 16 | Gash | 14 | | | 16+3 | 1 | 4 | 3 Barrow, Grimsby, |
| Kidderminster | | | | | | | | | | |
| Dartford | Crawford | 16 | Bradbrook | 13 | | | 19+0 | 2 | 1 | 0 |
| Ebbsfleet United | Elder | 13 | Enver-Marum | 11 | | | 14+0 | 0 | 4 | 0 |
| Forest Green Rovers | Norwood | 17 | Klukowski | 13 | | | 15+2 | 2 | 2 | 2 AFC Telford, Stockport |
| Gateshead | Gillies | 14 | | | | | 19+2 | 0 | 4 | 2 Macclesfield, Alfreton |
| Grimsby Town | Cook | 16 | Hannah | 11 | | | 23+2 | 0 | 4 | 2 Lincoln, Luton |
| Hereford United | Bowman | 19 | O'Keefe | 14 | | | 20+2 | 0 | 12 | 2 Cambridge United, Woking |
| Hyde | Jevons | 16 | | | | | 16+0 | 2 | 7 | 0 |
| Kiddeminster Harriers | Malbon | 20 | Rowe | 11 | | | 20+1 | 2 | 0 | 1 Braintree |
| Lincoln City | Taylor | 16 | Oliver | 13 | Power | 11 | 17+4 | 2 | 11 | 3 Braintree, Hereford (2) |
| Luton Town | Gray | 16 | Rendell | 12 | Fleetwood | 11 | 18+2 | 1 | 3 | 2 Dorchester , Lincolny |
| | Shaw | 11 | | | | | | | | |
| Macclesfield Town | Barnes-Homer | 23 | Fairhurst | 12 | | | 20+3 | 1 | 7 | 4 Dartford, Lincoln, Stockport, Swindon Town |
| Mansfield Town | Green | 27 | Stevenson 10 | | | | 17+4 | 1 | 12 | 4 Ebbsfleet, Forest Green R. Lincoln, Slough |
| Newport County | O'Connor | 19 | Jolley | 15 | | | 18+2 | 1 | 1 | 2 AFC Telford, Nuneaton |
| Nuneaton Town | Brown | 19 | | | | | 13+0 | 0 | 6 | 0 |
| Southport | Almond | 13 | Ledsham | 12 | Whalley | 12 | 15+4 | 0 | 11 | 4 Barrow, Forest Green R. Nuneaton, Stockport |
| Stockport County | Hattersley | 11 | | | | | 23+1 | 1 | 5 | 1 Newport County |
| Tamworth | Cunnington | 21 | Wright | 10 | | | 18+2 | 2 | 9 | 2 Hereford, Lincoln |
| Woking | Bubb | 19 | Betsy | 13 | Stockley | 12 | 15+0 | 2 | 7 | 0 |
| | Knott | 10 | | | | | | | | |
| Wrexham | Wright D | 17 | Cieslewicz | 10 | | | 22+2 | 1 | 8 | 2 Southport, Stockport |

# A.F.C. TELFORD UNITED

**Chairman:** Ian Dosser
**Secretary:** Mrs Sharon Bowyer **(T)** 07970 040 106 **(E)** sharon.bowyer@telfordutd.co.uk
**Commercial Manager:** Paul Riley **(T)** 07855 776 586
**Programme Editor:** James Baylis **(T)** 07977 481 186
**Ground Address:** New Bucks Head Stadium, Watling Street, Wellington, Telford TF1 2TU
**(T)** 01952 640 064 **Manager:** Liam Watson

Celebrations after the Shropshire Senior Cup win during the 2013-14 pre-season.
Photo: James Baylis.

## Club Factfile

**Founded:** 2004 **Nickname:** The Bucks
**Previous Names:** AFC Telford United was formed when Telford United folded in May 2004
**Previous Leagues:** As AFC Telford United: Northern Premier 2004-06
As Telford United: Southern 1969-79. Alliance/Conference 1979-2004

**Club Colours (change):** All white (Red & blue/blue/blue)

**Ground Capacity:** 6,380 **Seats:** 2,200 **Covered:** 4,800 **Clubhouse:** Yes **Shop:** Yes

**Directions:** (Sat Nav follow TF1 2NW into Haybridge Road) From M54 Junction 6, A5223 towards Wellington, straight over first roundabout (retail park). Straight over second roundabout (B5067). Left at third roundabout (Furrows garage). Continue over railway bridge and follow road round to the right, then turn left into AFC Telford United Car Park.

**Previous Grounds:** None - Renovation of the old Bucks Head started in 2000 and was completed in 2003.

**Record Attendance:** 4,215 v Kendal Town - Northern Premier League play-off final
**Record Victory:** 7-0 v Runcorn (A) - Northern Premier League Division One 2005-06
**Record Defeat:** 3-6 v Bradford P.A. (H) - Northern Premier League Division One 2005-06
**Record Goalscorer:** Kyle Perry - 32 (2004-06)
**Record Appearances:** Stuart Brock - 132 (2004-09)
**Additional Records:** Paid £5,000 to Tamworth for Lee Moore 08/12/06
Received £33,000 from Burnley for Duane Courtney 31/08/05
**Senior Honours:**
Northern Premier League Division 1 Play-off 2004-05, Premier Division Play-off 2006-07. Conference League Cup 2008-09.
Shropshire Senior Cup 2012-13.

### 10 YEAR RECORD

| 03-04 | | 04-05 | | 05-06 | | 06-07 | | 07-08 | | 08-09 | | 09-10 | | 10-11 | | 11-12 | | 12-13 | |
|---|---|---|---|---|---|---|---|---|---|---|---|---|---|---|---|---|---|---|---|
| Conf | 12 | NP 1 | 3 | NP P | 10 | NP P | 3 | Conf N | 2 | Conf N | 4 | Conf N | 11 | Conf N | 2 | Conf | 20 | Conf | 24 |

# MATCH RESULTS 2012-13

| Date | Comp | H/A | Opponents | Att: | Result | Goalscorers | Pos | No. |
|---|---|---|---|---|---|---|---|---|
| Aug 11 | BSP | A | Barrow | 1041 | D 0-0 | | 16 | 1 |
| 14 | BSP | H | Forest Green Rovers | 1582 | L 1-2 | Rooney 60 | 20 | 2 |
| 18 | BSP | H | Braintree Town | 1524 | W 3-0 | Spray 15 St Aimie 18 Rooney 83 (pen) | 11 | 3 |
| 25 | BSP | A | Luton Town | 5970 | W 1-0 | St Aimie 42 | 8 | 4 |
| 27 | BSP | H | Stockport County | 2079 | D 2-2 | St Aimie 56 Valentine 65 | 8 | 5 |
| Sept 1 | BSP | A | Southport | 1005 | W 3-0 | Jones 25 Grand 49 (og)  St Aimie 57 | 6 | 6 |
| 4 | BSP | A | Nuneaton Town | 992 | L 1-3 | Rooney 37 (Pen) | 7 | 7 |
| 8 | BSP | H | Lincoln City | 1794 | D 1-1 | Trainer 87 | 9 | 8 |
| 11 | BSP | A | Cambridge United | 1962 | D 3-3 | Jones 57 Davies 83 Spray 87 | 10 | 9 |
| 15 | BSP | H | Mansfield Town | 1736 | D 2-2 | Tafazolli 15 (og) Davies 34 | 13 | 10 |
| 25 | BSP | H | Newport County | 1503 | L 2-4 | St Aimie 27 Sandell 81 (og) | 13 | 11 |
| 29 | BSP | A | Gateshead | 524 | D 1-1 | Leslie 64 | 13 | 12 |
| Oct 6 | BSP | H | Woking | 1584 | W 1-0 | Byfield 7 (pen) | 9 | 13 |
| 9 | BSP | A | Dartford | 1359 | W 4-1 | Jones 35 37 Hubbins 56 Trainer 69 | 8 | 14 |
| 13 | BSP | H | Grimsby Town | 2349 | L 1-2 | Jones 21 | 8 | 15 |
| 20 | FAC Q4 | H | Nuneaton Town | 1251 | D 2-2 | Jones 8 Valentine 90 | | 16 |
| 23 | FAC Q4r | A | Nuneaton Town | 616 | L 0-1 | *aet | | 17 |
| 27 | BSP | A | Alfreton Town | 572 | D 1-1 | Sharp 69 | 8 | 18 |
| Nov 6 | BSP | H | Ebbsfleet Uited | 1542 | D 2-2 | Jones 6 26 | 10 | 19 |
| 10 | BSP | A | Tamworth | 935 | D 0-0 | | 11 | 20 |
| 17 | BSP | H | Kidderminster Harriers | 2160 | L 0-2 | | 12 | 21 |
| 24 | FAT 1 | H | Nuneaton Town | 737 | W 1-0 | Leslie 18 | | 22 |
| Dec 4 | BSP | H | Barrow | 1333 | D 1-1 | Leslie 44 | 15 | 23 |
| 8 | BSP | A | Hyde | 523 | L 1-2 | Leslie 35 | 17 | 24 |
| 15 | FAT 2 | A | King's Lynn Town | 955 | L 1-3 | Taylor 29 | | 25 |
| 26 | BSP | A | Wrexham | 4330 | L 1-4 | Reid 73 | 20 | 26 |
| 29 | BSP | A | Stockport County | 2791 | D 2-2 | Trainer 68 Hubbins 79 | 19 | 27 |
| Jan 1 | BSP | H | Wrexham | 2931 | L 0-2 | | | 28 |
| 5 | BSP | H | Southport | 1643 | L 1-3 | Reid 88 | | 29 |
| 8 | BSP | A | Hereford United | 1490 | D 1-1 | Kinsella 90+1 | | 30 |
| 12 | BSP | A | Braintree Town | 507 | L 2-3 | Rooney 66, 90+3 | | 31 |
| 15 | BSP | D | Luton Town | 1606 | D 0-0 | | 20 | 32 |
| 19 | BSP | H | Alfreton Town | 1291 | D 0-0 | | 21 | 33 |
| 29 | BSP | A | Kidderminster Harriers | 1785 | L 0-1 | | 21 | 34 |
| Feb 2 | BSP | H | Cambridge United | 1788 | L 1-2 | Reid 26 | 21 | 35 |
| 9 | BSP | A | Grmsby Town | 4462 | L 0-1 | | 21 | 36 |
| 12 | BSP | H | Hyde | 1394 | L 1-3 | Peniket 66 | 21 | 37 |
| 16 | BSP | H | Tamworth | 1747 | D 3-3 | Craney 30 Trainer 73  Reid 85 | 22 | 38 |
| 23 | BSP | A | Newport County | 1761 | L 1-2 | Trainer 90 | 24 | 39 |
| Mar 2 | BSP | A | Mansfield Town | 2725 | L 0-1 | | 24 | 40 |
| 9 | BSP | H | Macclesfield Town | 1567 | L 0-2 | | 24 | 41 |
| 14 | BSP | H | Gateshead | 1260 | D 0-0 | | 24 | 42 |
| 16 | BSP | A | Woking | 1320 | L 2-5 | Jones 54  Williams 81 | 24 | 43 |
| 19 | BSP | A | Macclesfield Town | 1381 | L 1-2 | Jones 34 | 24 | 44 |
| 23 | BSP | A | Lincoln City | 1724 | L 2-3 | Jones 39 Leslie 53 | 24 | 45 |
| 30 | BSP | H | Nuneaton Town | 1893 | L 0-3 | | 23 | 46 |
| Apr 1 | BSP | A | Forest Green Rovers | 1061 | D 0-0 | | 24 | 47 |
| 6 | BSP | H | Dartford | 1375 | L 0-2 | | 24 | 48 |
| 13 | BSP | A | Ebbsfleet United | 686 | W 3-1 | WILLIAMS 3 ( 18 28 35) | 24 | 49 |
| 20 | BSP | H | Hereford United | 2102 | L 0-4 | | 24 | 50 |

## GOALSCORERS

| Name | Lge | FAC | FAT | Total | Pens | Hat-tricks | Cons Run | Name | Lge | FAC | FAT | Total | Pens | Hat-tricks | Cons Run |
|---|---|---|---|---|---|---|---|---|---|---|---|---|---|---|---|
| Jones | 10 | 1 | | 11 | | | 3 | Valentine | 1 | 1 | | 2 | | | |
| Leslie | 4 | | 1 | 5 | | | | Byfield | 1 | | | 1 | 1 | | |
| Rooney | 5 | | | 5 | 2 | | | Crawley | 1 | | | 1 | | | |
| Trainer | 5 | | | 5 | | | | Kinsella | 1 | | | 1 | | | |
| St Aimie | 5 | | | 5 | | | | Peniket | 1 | | | 1 | | | |
| Williams | 4 | | 1 | 5 | 1 | | | Sharp | 1 | | | 1 | | | |
| Reid | 4 | | | 4 | | | | Own Goals | 3 | | | 3 | | | |
| Davies | 2 | | | 2 | | | | | | | | | | | |
| Hubbins | 2 | | | 2 | | | | | | | | | | | |
| Spray | 2 | | | 2 | | | | | | | | | | | |

Cons Run - Consecutive scoring games.

# ALTRINCHAM

**Chairman:** Grahame Rowley
**Secretary:** Derek Wilshaw          **(T)** 07833 636 381          **(E)** dwilshaw@altrinchamfootballclub.co.uk
**Commercial Manager:** Paul Daine          **(T)** 0161 929 3955
**Programme Editor:** Grahame Rowley.          **(T)** 0161 928 1045
**Ground Address:** The J Davidson Stadium, Moss Lane, Altrincham, Cheshire WA15 8AP
**(T)** 0161 928 1045                              **Manager:** Lee Sinnott

2012-13 Squad - Back row (L-R): Gianluca Havern, Danny Mitchley, Stuart Coburn, Simon Richman, Adam Reid, Ryan Brooke, Scott Leather. Middle row: Duncan Watmore, John Skelhorn (kitman), Luke Pickering (kitman), Scott Phelan, Danny Hall, Nicky Clee, Damian Reeves, Ian Senior (coach), Alan Ainsley (physio), Sam Grimshaw. Front row: Patrick Lacey, Carl Rodgers, Grahame Rowley (chairman), Lee Sinnott (manager), Shaun Densmore (captain), Neil Tolson (assistant manager), Paul Daine (director), James Lawrie, Matt Doughty.
Photo: Gavin Rathbone of GR Photography.

## Club Factfile

**Founded:** 1903          **Nickname:** The Robins
**Previous Names:** Broadheath FC 1893-1903.
**Previous Leagues:** Manchester 1903-11. Lancashire C. 1911-19. Cheshire C. 1919-68. Northern Premier 1968-79,97-99. Conference 1979-97, 99-

**Club Colours (change):** Red & white stripes/red/red. (Aqua/grey/aqua)

**Ground Capacity:** 6,085   **Seats:** 1,154   **Covered:** Yes      **Clubhouse:** Yes   **Shop:** Yes

**Directions**
From M6 junction19, turn right towards Altrincham into town centre (approx 15 minutes). Turn down Lloyd Street, past Sainsburys or the right. Tesco Extra on left. Then follow signs for Altrincham F.C.

**Previous Grounds:** Pollitts Field 1903-10.

**Record Attendance:** 10,275 - Altrincham Boys v Sunderland Boys English Schools Shield 1925.
**Record Victory:** 9-2 v Merthyr Tydfil - Conference 1990-91.
**Record Defeat:** 1-13 v Stretford (H) - 04.11.1893.
**Record Goalscorer:** Jack Swindells - 252 (1965-71).
**Record Appearances:** John Davison - 677 (1971-86).
**Additional Records:** Transfer fee paid - £15k to Blackpool for Keith Russell. Received - £50k from Leicester for Kevin Ellison.

**Senior Honours:**
Cheshire Senior Cup Winners 1904-05, 33-34, 66-67, 81-82. F.A. Trophy Winners 1977-78, 85-86.
Football Alliance Champions 1979-80, 80-81. N.P.L. Premier Champions 1998-99.
Conference North & South Play-off Winners 2004-05.

### 10 YEAR RECORD

| 03-04 | | 04-05 | | 05-06 | | 06-07 | | 07-08 | | 08-09 | | 09-10 | | 10-11 | | 11-12 | | 12-13 | |
|---|---|---|---|---|---|---|---|---|---|---|---|---|---|---|---|---|---|---|---|
| NP P | 12 | Conf N | 5 | Conf | 22 | Conf | 21 | Conf | 21 | Conf | 15 | Conf | 14 | Conf | 22 | Conf N | 8 | Conf N | 4 |

# MATCH RESULTS 2012-13

| ate | Comp | H/A | Opponents | Att: | Result | Goalscorers | Pos | No. |
|---|---|---|---|---|---|---|---|---|
| ug 18 | BSN | H | Brackley Town | 716 | L 1-4 | Watmore 26 | 20 | 1 |
| 1 | BSN | A | Harrogate Town | 532 | W 2-1 | Watmore 4 Richman 76 | 15 | 2 |
| 5 | BSN | A | Vauxhall Motors | 300 | L 1-2 | Reeves 90 | 15 | 3 |
| 7 | BSN | H | Chester | 1940 | L 2-4 | Reeves 31 50 | 19 | 4 |
| ep 1 | BSN | H | Histon | 652 | W 5-0 | Rodgers 27 Lawrie 47 Reeves 65 67, Watmore 76 | 10 | 5 |
| | BSN | A | Gainsborough Trinity | 536 | W 4-2 | REEVES 4 ( 3 23 32 36pen) | 9 | 6 |
| | BSN | A | Oxford City | 257 | D 2-2 | Reeves 40 (pen) 58 (pen) | 9 | 7 |
| 5 | BSN | H | Bradford PA | 806 | W 3-1 | Reeves 8 90 Clee 26 | 8 | 8 |
| 2 | FAC Q2 | A | Shildon | 288 | W 3-1 | Reeves 3 11 Lawrie 7 | | 9 |
| 9 | BSN | A | Bishop's Stortford | 481 | D 1-1 | Lawrie 22 | 7 | 10 |
| ct 6 | FAC Q3 | A | Leek Town | 962 | W 2-0 | Reeves 69 Richman 89 | | 11 |
| 3 | BSN | A | Corby Town | 572 | W 5-2 | Doughty 13 (pen) Reeves 28 41, Watmore 31 Moult 40 | 7 | 12 |
| 0 | FAC Q4 | A | Boston United | 1200 | W 3-1 | Lawrie 58 Moult 70 Clee 89 | | 13 |
| 3 | BSN | H | Workington | 638 | L 1-2 | Reeves 69 | 7 | 14 |
| 7 | BSN | A | Solihull Moors | 258 | L 1-2 | Densmore 19 | 9 | 15 |
| 0 | BSN | H | Guiseley | 698 | L 1-3 | Richman 22 | 11 | 16 |
| lov 4 | FAC 1 | A | Burton Albion | 1989 | D 3-3 | Rodgers 29 Stanton 34 (og) McCrory 85 og) | | 17 |
| 0 | FAT Q3 | A | Worcester City | 785 | W 3-0 | Clee 23 Hall 28 Reeves 29 | | 18 |
| 5 | FAC 1r | H | Burton Albion | 2428 | L 0-2 | | | 19 |
| 7 | BSN | H | Hinckley United | 768 | W 8-0 | Lawrie 7 Moult 29 Densmore 45 68, Clee 23 Brooke 88 Watmore 89 90 | 11 | 20 |
| 4 | FAT 1 | A | FC Halifax Town | 885 | L 2-5 | Reeves 5 Clee 53 | | 21 |
| )ec 1 | BSN | A | Boston United | 782 | W 3-2 | Reeves 49 59 Clee 66 | 9 | 22 |
| | BSN | H | Gainsbororugh Trinity | 728 | L 0-1 | | 10 | 23 |
| 5 | BSN | A | Brackley Town | 330 | W 1-0 | Reeves 24 | 10 | 24 |
| '6 | BSN | A | Stalybridge Celtic | 802 | D 2-2 | Watmore 22 52 | 12 | 25 |
| an 1 | BSN | H | Stalybridge Celtic | 889 | W 2-1 | Reeves 38 (pen) Moult 39 | 8 | 26 |
| | BSN | H | Harrogate Town | 707 | W 3-0 | Richman 32 Rodgers 49 Reeves 74 | 5 | 27 |
| 2 | BSN | A | Worcester City | 824 | D 0-0 | | 5 | 28 |
| 9 | BSN | H | Boston United | 561 | W 7-2 | Reeves 12 68 Richman 35 42 , Watmore 39 Leather 49 Brooke 85 | 5 | 29 |
| eb 2 | BSN | H | Gloucester City | 762 | W 2-0 | Densmore 45 Reeves 46 | 5 | 30 |
| ) | BSN | H | Corby Town | 774 | W 2-1 | Reeves 16  Watmore 46 | 4 | 31 |
| 2 | BSN | A | Histon | 240 | L 0-2 | | 4 | 32 |
| 6 | BSN | A | Workington | 374 | L 1-2 | Moult 17 | 4 | 33 |
| 3 | BSN | H | Colwyn Bay | 769 | D 1-1 | Densmore 11 | 6 | 34 |
| 6 | BSN | A | Gloucester City | 205 | D 0-0 | | 8 | 35 |
| Mar 2 | BSN | H | Oxford City | 740 | W 3-1 | Reeves 41 81 Watmore 82 | 7 | 36 |
| 5 | BSN | A | Droylsden | 258 | W 5-0 | Reeves 17 72 Mills 37 Watmore 45 Densmore 84 (pen) | 6 | 37 |
| 3 | BSN | H | Solihull Moors | 558 | W 2-0 | Reeves 60 Lawrie 90 | 5 | 38 |
| 6 | BSN | A | Colwyn Bay | 431 | W 3-1 | Reeves 23 55 Watmore 81 | 5 | 39 |
| 3 | BSN | H | Worcester City | 777 | W 2-0 | Clee 55 Reeves 59 | 5 | 40 |
| 0 | BSN | H | Vauxhall Motors | 930 | W 1-0 | Lawrie 79 | 5 | 41 |
| pr 1 | BSN | A | Chester | 3089 | L 0-2 | | 5 | 42 |
| 5 | BSN | A | FC Halifax Town | 1435 | W 4-3 | Reeves 35 70 Richman 42 57 | 4 | 43 |
| 1 | BSN | A | Guiseley | 459 | D 1-1 | Moult 78 | 5 | 44 |
| 3 | BSN | H | Bishop's Stortford | 807 | W 2-1 | Rodgers 3  Lawrie 67 | 5 | 45 |
| 7 | BSN | A | Bradford PA | 476 | D 2-2 | Lawrie 73 Havern 84 | 5 | 46 |
| 0 | BSN | A | Hinckley United | 534 | W 6-0 | Reeves 40 Havern 53 Rodgers 71, Watmore 75 Brooke 84 90 | 5 | 47 |
| 3 | BSN | H | FC Halifax Town | 990 | W 2-0 | Clee 48 Doughty 68 | 4 | 48 |
| 7 | BSN | H | Droylsden | 1274 | W 6-0 | Clee 16 Moult 19 65 Brooke 29 46 Lawrie 87 | 4 | 49 |
| 0 | P.Off S-F 1 | H | Brackley Town | 1618 | W 2-1 | Richman  79 Moult 90 | | 50 |
| May 4 | P.Off S-F 2 | A | Brackley Town | 1353 | L 0-3 | | | 51 |

| GOALSCORERS | Lge | FAC | LC | Total | Pens | Hat-tricks | Cons Run | | Lge | FAC | LC | Total | Pens | Hat-tricks | Cons Run |
|---|---|---|---|---|---|---|---|---|---|---|---|---|---|---|---|
| Reeves | 36 | 3 | 2 | 41 | 1 | | 7 | Havern | 2 | | | 2 | | | |
| Watmore | 14 | | | 14 | | | 2 | Hall | | 1 | | 1 | | | |
| Lawrie | 8 | 2 | | 10 | | | | Leather | 1 | | | 1 | | | |
| Clee | 6 | 1 | 2 | 9 | | | | Mills | 1 | | | 1 | | | |
| Moult | 8 | 1 | | 8 | | | | Own Goals | | 2 | | 2 | | | |
| Richman | 8 | 1 | | 8 | | | | Cons Run - Consecutive scoring games. | | | | | | | |
| Brooke | 6 | | | 6 | | | | | | | | | | | |
| Densmore | 6 | | | 6 | 1 | | | | | | | | | | |
| Rodgers | 4 | 1 | | 5 | | | | | | | | | | | |
| Doughty | 2 | | | 2 | | | | | | | | | | | |

# BARROW

**Chairman:** Brian Keen
**Secretary:** Russell Dodd     **(T)** 07789 757 639     **(E)** secbafc@aol.com
**Commercial Manager:** n/a     **(T)**
**Programme Editor:** Bob Herbert     **(T)** 01229 829 133
**Ground Address:** Furness Building Society Stadium, Wilkie Road, Barrow-in-Furness LA14 5UW
**(T)** 01299 823 061     **Manager:** Dave Bayliss

## Club Factfile

**Founded:** 1901     **Nickname:** Bluebirds
**Previous Names:** None
**Previous Leagues:** Lancashire Combination 1901-21. Football League 1921-72. Northern Premier 1972-79, 83-84, 86-89, 92-98, 99-04. Conference 1979-83, 84-86, 89-92, 98-99.

**Club Colours (change):** Blue & white/white with blue trim/blue with white trim (All yellow with black trim)

**Ground Capacity:** 4,500     **Seats:** 1,000     **Covered:** 2,200     **Clubhouse:** Yes     **Shop:** Yes

**Directions**
M6 Junction 36, onto A590 signposted Barrow. Follow A590 all the way to the outskirts of Barrow (approx. 27 miles) entering via Industrial route. In a further 2 miles you pass the Fire Station on the right hand side, take next left into Wilkie Road, the ground is on the right.

**Previous Grounds:** Strawberry & Little Park, Roose.

**Record Attendance:** 16,854 v Swansea Town - FA Cup 3rd Round 1954
**Record Victory:** 12-0 v Cleator - FA Cup 1920
**Record Defeat:** 1-10 v Hartlepool United - Football League Division 4 1959
**Record Goalscorer:** Colin Cowperthwaite - 282 (December 1977 - December 1992)
**Record Appearances:** Colin Cowperthwaite - 704
**Additional Records:** Paid £9,000 to Ashton United for Andy Whittaker (07/94)
**Senior Honours:** Received £40,000 from Barnet for Kenny Lowe (01/91)
Lancashire Senior Cup 1954-55. Lancashire Challenge Trophy 1980-81. Northern Premier League 1983-84, 88-89, 97-98. FA Trophy 1989-90, 2009-10.

### 10 YEAR RECORD

| 03-04 | | 04-05 | | 05-06 | | 06-07 | | 07-08 | | 08-09 | | 09-10 | | 10-11 | | 11-12 | | 12-13 | |
|---|---|---|---|---|---|---|---|---|---|---|---|---|---|---|---|---|---|---|---|
| NP P | 3 | Conf N | 16 | Conf N | 14 | Conf N | 16 | Conf N | 5 | Conf | 20 | Conf | 15 | Conf | 18 | Conf | 13 | Conf | 22 |

# MATCH RESULTS 2012-13

| Date | Comp | H/A | Opponents | Att: | Result | Goalscorers | Pos | No. |
|------|------|-----|-----------|------|--------|-------------|-----|-----|
| Aug 11 | BSP | H | AFC Telford United | 1041 | D 0-0 | | 17 | 1 |
| 14 | BSP | A | Forest Green Rovers | 798 | D 0-0 | | 17 | 2 |
| 18 | BSP | A | Woking | 1373 | L 1-3 | Hunter 15 | 20 | 3 |
| 25 | BSP | H | Alfreton Town | 798 | L 1-3 | Boyes 77 | 21 | 4 |
| 27 | BSP | A | Mansfield Town | 1742 | L 0-2 | | 23 | 5 |
| Sept 1 | BSP | H | Kidderminster Harriers | 716 | D 1-1 | Baker 77 | 22 | 6 |
| 4 | BSP | H | Grimsby Town | 966 | D 2-2 | Baker 45 (pen) Jackson 60 | 22 | 7 |
| 8 | BSP | A | Tamworth | 892 | W 3-1 | Jackson 19 Boyes 79 90 | 21 | 8 |
| 15 | BSP | H | Newport County | 802 | L 0-3 | | 22 | 9 |
| 22 | BSP | A | Ebbsfleet United | 780 | W 4-2 | BAKER 3 ( 20 36 pen 63) Walsh 25 (og) | 19 | 10 |
| 25 | BSP | A | Wrexham | 2881 | L 0-3 | | 21 | 11 |
| 29 | BSP | H | Cambridge United | 904 | L 1-4 | Skelton 54 | 22 | 12 |
| Oct 6 | BSP | A | Braintree Town | 608 | W 3-2 | Almond 42 81 Rowe 90 | 19 | 13 |
| 9 | BSP | H | Southport | 924 | W 3-2 | Boyes 73 84 Baker 86 | 19 | 14 |
| 13 | BSP | H | Dartford | 1278 | D 0-0 | | 19 | 15 |
| 20 | FAC Q4 | H | Tamworth | 1104 | W 2-0 | Almond 53 Boyes 83 | | 16 |
| 27 | BSP | A | Nuneaton Town | 844 | D 1-1 | Rowe 64 | 17 | 17 |
| Nov 3 | FAC 1 | A | Guiseley | 1605 | D 2-2 | Boyes 44 Hunter 48 | | 18 |
| 6 | BSP | A | Stockport County | 2805 | L1-3 | Rose 64 | 18 | 19 |
| 10 | BSP | H | Lincoln City | 987 | L 1-2 | Baker 85 (pen) | 22 | 20 |
| 13 | FAC 1r | H | Guiseley | 1371 | W 1-0 | Hunter 90 | | 21 |
| 17 | BSP | H | Forest Green Rovers | 853 | D 2-2 | Boyes 45 Flynn 61 | 23 | 22 |
| 24 | FAT 1 | A | Hyde | 436 | D 1-1 | Flynn 90 | | 23 |
| 27 | FAT 1r | H | Hyde | 728 | W 1-0 | Baker 59 | | 24 |
| Dec 4 | BSP | A | AFC Telford United | 1333 | D 1-1 | Jackson 90 | 21 | 25 |
| 8 | BSP | H | Hereford United | 867 | L 0-2 | | 23 | 26 |
| 15 | FAT 2 | A | Chesham United | 470 | W 5-1 | Boyes 25 64 McConville 26 Baker 71 (pen) Rowe 89 | | 27 |
| 18 | FAC 2 | H | Macclesfield Town | 1179 | D 1-1 | Baker 29 | | 28 |
| 26 | BSP | H | Gateshead | 1135 | L 0-2 | | 24 | 29 |
| 29 | FAC 2r | A | Macclesfield Town | 1592 | L 1-4 | Boyes 16 | | 30 |
| Jan 1 | BSP | A | Gateshead | 610 | W 1-0 | Boyes 1 | 24 | 31 |
| 5 | BSP | A | Kidderminster Harriers | 1703 | L 0-2 | | 24 | 32 |
| 8 | BSP | A | Luton Town | 5165 | L 1-6 | Boyes 68 | 24 | 33 |
| 19 | BSP | A | Newport County | 2107 | W 2-0 | Flynn 41 Rowe 62 | 23 | 34 |
| 29 | FAT 3 | A | Gateshead | 728 | W 3-2 | Baker 30 (pen) Flynn 75 Magnay (og) 88 | | 35 |
| Feb 2 | BSP | H | Luton Town | 1188 | W 1-0 | Boyes 5 | 22 | 36 |
| 5 | FAT 4 | A | Gainsborough Trinity | 785 | L 0-2 | | 22 | 37 |
| 9 | BSP | A | Mansfield Town | 2226 | L 1-8 | Rowe 17 (pen) | 22 | 38 |
| 12 | BSP | A | Southport | 806 | L 2-5 | Flynn 6 Boyes 83 (pen) | 22 | 39 |
| 16 | BSP | H | Nuneaton Town | 998 | L 1-2 | Boyes 48 | 22 | 40 |
| 19 | BSP | H | Woking | 624 | W 2-0 | Rowe 9 53 | 22 | 41 |
| 20 | BSP | A | Lincoln City | 1830 | D 0-0 | | 22 | 42 |
| 26 | BSP | H | Wrexham | 889 | L 0-1 | | 22 | 43 |
| Mar 2 | BSP | A | Tamworth | 896 | W 2-0 | D.Rowe 15 Harvey 90 | 20 | 44 |
| 9 | BSP | A | Forest Green Rovers | 904 | D 1-1 | Baker 63 | 20 | 45 |
| 12 | BSP | H | Stockport County | 803 | L 0-2 | | 21 | 46 |
| 16 | BSP | A | Hereford United | 1273 | L1-2 | Boyes 22 | 22 | 47 |
| 19 | BSP | A | Dartford | 908 | W1-0 | Baker 74 (pen | 21 | 48 |
| 27 | BSP | H | Macclesfield Town | 716 | W1-0 | Harvey 58 | 17 | 49 |
| 30 | BSP | A | Grimsby Town | 3532 | D 0-0 | | 22 | 50 |
| Apr 1 | BSP | H | Hyde | 1001 | D 1-1 | Pearson 22 | 22 | 51 |
| 3 | BSP | H | Ebbsfleet Uniited | 844 | D 1-1 | Boyes 77 | 21 | 52 |
| 6 | BSP | H | Mansfield Town | 1114 | L 0-4 | | 22 | 53 |
| 9 | BSP | A | Alfreton Town | 525 | L 0-4 | | 22 | 54 |
| 13 | BSP | A | Cambridge United | 2758 | L 1-2 | Baker 45 (pen) | 22 | 55 |
| 20 | BSP | H | Braintree Town | 780 | L 0-1 | | 22 | 56 |

| GOALSCORERS | Lge | FAC | FAT | Total | Pens | Hat-tricks | Cons Run | | Lge | FAC | FAT | Total | Pens | Hat-tricks | Cons Run |
|-------------|-----|-----|-----|-------|------|------------|----------|---|-----|-----|-----|-------|------|------------|----------|
| Boyes | 13 | 3 | 2 | 18 | 1 | | 2 | Rose | 1 | | | 1 | | | |
| Baker | 10 | 1 | 3 | 14 | 6 | 1 | 2 | Skelton | 1 | | | 1 | | | |
| Rowe | 7 | | 1 | 8 | 1 | | | Own Goals | 1 | | 1 | 2 | | | |
| Flynn | 3 | | 2 | 5 | | | | Cons Run - Consecutive scoring games. | | | | | | | |
| Almond | 2 | 1 | | 3 | | | | | | | | | | | |
| Hunter | 1 | 2 | | 3 | | | | | | | | | | | |
| Jackson | 3 | | | 3 | | | | | | | | | | | |
| Harvey | 2 | | | 2 | | | | | | | | | | | |
| McConville | | | 1 | 1 | | | | | | | | | | | |
| Pearson | 1 | | | 1 | | | | | | | | | | | |

# BOSTON UNITED

**Chairman:** David Newton
**Secretary:** John Blackwell    **(T)** 07860 663 299    **(E)** admin@bufc.co.uk
**Commercial Manager:** Craig Singleton    **(T)** 07966 952 694
**Programme Editor:** Craig Singleton    **(T)** craig.singleton@bufc.co.uk
**Ground Address:** Jakemans Stadium, York Street, Boston PE21 6JN
**(T)** 01205 364 406    **Manager:** Dennis Greene

## Club Factfile

**Founded:** 1933    **Nickname:** The Pilgrims
**Previous Names:** Reformed as Boston United when Boston Town folded in 1933
**Previous Leagues:** Midland 1933-58, 62-64, Southern 1958-62, 98-2000, United Counties 1965-66, West Midlands 1966-68, Northern Premier 1968-79, 93-98, 2008-10, Alliance/Conference 1979-93, 2000-02, 07-08, Football League 2002-07

**Club Colours (change):** Amber and black halves/black/black (Sky blue/navy blue/sky blue)

**Ground Capacity:** 6,645    **Seats:** 1,323    **Covered:** 6,645    **Clubhouse:** Yes    **Shop:** Yes

**Directions** A1 to A17 Sleaford to Boston-Over Boston Railway Station crossing, bear right at the Eagle Public House-To light over Haven Bridge-straight along John Adams Way(Dual Carriageway) -Turn right at traffic lights into main ridge, then right again into York Street(This is opposite Eagle Fisheries)-Ground is signposted after Railway crossing.

**Previous Grounds:** None

**Record Attendance:** 10,086 v Corby Town - Floodlights inauguration 1955
**Record Victory:** 12-0 v Spilsby Town - Grace Swan Cup 1992-93
**Record Defeat:** Not known.
**Record Goalscorer:** Chris Cook - 181
**Record Appearances:** Billy Howells - 500+
**Additional Records:** Paid £30,000 to Scarborough for Paul Ellender, 08/2001
**Senior Honours:** Received £50,000 from Bolton Wanderers for David Norris 2000
Central Alliance League 1961-62. United Counties League 1965-66. West Midlands League 1966-67, 67-68.
Northern Premier League 1972-73, 73-74, 76-77, 77-78, League Cup 1973-74, 75-76. Southern League 1999-2000. Conference 2001-02.

### 10 YEAR RECORD

| 03-04 | | 04-05 | | 05-06 | | 06-07 | | 07-08 | | 08-09 | | 09-10 | | 10-11 | | 11-12 | | 12-13 | |
|---|---|---|---|---|---|---|---|---|---|---|---|---|---|---|---|---|---|---|---|
| FL 3 | 11 | FL 2 | 16 | FL 2 | 11 | FL 2 | 23 | Conf N | 10 | NP P | 16 | NP P | 3 | Conf N | 3 | Conf N | 11 | Conf N | 16 |

# MATCH RESULTS 2012-13

| Date | Comp | H/A | Opponents | Att: | Result | Goalscorers | Pos | No. |
|---|---|---|---|---|---|---|---|---|
| Aug 18 | BSN | A | Droylsden | 344 | W 1-0 | Newsham 11 | 7 | 1 |
| 21 | BSN | H | Histon | 968 | W 6-0 | M.JONES 3 (28 34 77) Fairclough 45 Marc Newsham 58 89 | 3 | 2 |
| 25 | BSN | H | Hinckley Athletic | 1105 | L 1-2 | Weir-Daley 61 | 5 | 3 |
| 27 | BSN | A | Bishops Stortford | 559 | L 0-1 | | 7 | 4 |
| Sept 1 | BSN | H | Workington | 937 | L 1-3 | Weir-Daley 38 | 9 | 5 |
| 4 | BSN | A | Oxford City | 203 | L 2-4 | Weir-Daley 11 12 | 12 | 6 |
| 8 | BSN | A | Colwyn Bay | 284 | W 2-0 | Weir-Daley 1 Newsham 84 | 10 | 7 |
| 15 | BSN | H | Chester | 1249 | W 3-2 | Fairclough 8 35 Milnes 37 | 9 | 8 |
| 22 | FAC Q2 | H | Kettering Town | 901 | W 1-0 | Fairclough 66 | | 9 |
| 29 | BSN | A | Bradford PA | 399 | L 1-2 | Jones 55 | 10 | 10 |
| Oct 6 | FAC Q3 | A | Tadcaster Albion | 368 | W 2-0 | Jones 47 Newsham 60 (Pen) | | 11 |
| 13 | BSN | H | FC Halifax Town | 326 | W 2-1 | Jones 9 Newsham 71 | 10 | 12 |
| 20 | FAC Q4 | H | Altrincham | 1200 | L 1-3 | Jones 11 | | 13 |
| 27 | BSN | H | Worcester City | 877 | L 1-2 | Newsham 38 | 14 | 14 |
| 30 | BSN | A | Stalybridge Celtic | 363 | W 1-0 | Weir-Daley 57 | 11 | 15 |
| Nov 3 | BSN | H | Gainsborough Trinity | 1079 | W 2-1 | Ross 15 Newsham 15 (pen) | 7 | 16 |
| 10 | FAT Q3 | H | Colwyn Bay | 694 | W 3-1 | Newsham 27 82 Sanders 90 | | 17 |
| 17 | BSN | H | Guiseley | 944 | L 1-3 | Jones 29 | 9 | 18 |
| 20 | BSN | H | Worcester City | 424 | D 2-2 | Ward 2 Newsham 25 | 9 | 19 |
| 24 | FAT 1 | H | Skelmersdale U | 710 | D 1-1 | Weir-Daley 64 | | 20 |
| 27 | FAT 1r | A | Skelmersdale U | 295 | L 1-2 | Newsham 85 | | 21 |
| Dec 1 | BSN | H | Altrincham | 782 | L 2-3 | Newsham 51 Smith 68 | 10 | 22 |
| 5 | BSN | A | Gloucester City | 187 | L 0-1 | | 10 | 23 |
| 8 | BSN | A | Vauxhall Motors | 172 | L 0-4 | | 12 | 24 |
| 15 | BSN | H | Droylsden | 759 | W 5-1 | Weir-Daley 32 Jones 37 Newsham 45 63 Reed 83 | 11 | 25 |
| 26 | BSN | H | Corby Town | 1176 | D 1-1 | Newsham 48 | 11 | 26 |
| 29 | BSN | H | Oxford City | 871 | W 3-1 | Newsham 7 Jones 64 90 | 8 | 27 |
| Jan 1 | BSN | A | Corby Town | 572 | L 1-2 | Weir-Daley 26 | 10 | 28 |
| 5 | BSN | A | Workington | 390 | D 1-1 | Newsham 49 | 11 | 29 |
| 8 | BSN | H | Harrogate Town | 770 | L 1-2 | Newsham 90 | 12 | 30 |
| 12 | BSN | H | Colwyn Bay | 887 | W 1-0 | Jones 32 | 9 | 31 |
| 29 | BSN | A | Altrincham | 561 | L 1-7 | Silk 19 | 10 | 32 |
| Feb 3 | BSN | A | Gainsborough Trinity | 908 | D 2-2 | Milnes 25 Newsham 70 | 12 | 33 |
| 9 | BSN | A | Guiseley | 742 | L 1-2 | Lister 86 | 14 | 34 |
| 16 | BSN | H | Stalybridge Celtic | 905 | D 2-2 | Weir-Daley 40 Newsham 61 | 15 | 35 |
| 23 | BSN | A | Solihull Moors | 245 | L 0-1 | | 15 | 36 |
| 26 | BSN | A | Harrogate Town | 281 | L 2-4 | MIlnes 52 Newsham 63 | 15 | 37 |
| Mar 2 | BSN | H | Vauxhall Motors | 800 | L 0-1 | | 15 | 38 |
| 5 | BSN | H | Gloucester City | 548 | W 4-0 | Weir-Daley 21 71 Fairclough 89 Marshall 90 | 14 | 39 |
| 9 | BSN | A | Brackley Town | 383 | W 2-0 | Fairclough 48 Weir-Daley 85 | 12 | 40 |
| 16 | BSN | A | Worcester City | 669 | W 3-0 | Ross 16 Milnes 54 Newsham 74 | 11 | 41 |
| 23 | BSN | H | Bradford PA | 851 | L 0-4 | | 12 | 42 |
| 30 | BSN | A | Hinckley United | 353 | W 4-2 | Weir-Daley 1 73 Ross 60 Newsham 66 | 10 | 43 |
| Apr 1 | BSN | H | Bishops Stortford | 270 | D 1-1 | Ross 2 | 12 | 44 |
| 6 | BSN | A | Chester | 3685 | L 0-1 | | 12 | 45 |
| 13 | BSN | H | FC Halifax Town | 1069 | L 1-2 | Newsham 65 (pen) | 13 | 46 |
| 20 | BSN | A | Histon | 487 | D 1-1 | Mills 2 | 15 | 47 |
| 27 | BSN | H | Brackley Town | 1108 | L 3-4 | Stainfield 33 Newsham 78 (pen) Foster 85 | 16 | 48 |

| GOALSCORERS | Lge | FAC | LC | Total | Pens | Hat-tricks | Cons Run |
|---|---|---|---|---|---|---|---|
| Newsham | 22 | 1 | 3 | 26 | 4 | | 3 |
| Weir-Daley | 14 | | 1 | 15 | | | 3 |
| Jones | 10 | 2 | | 12 | 1 | | |
| Fairclough | 5 | 1 | | 6 | | | |
| Milnes | 4 | | | 4 | | | |
| Ross | 4 | | | 4 | | | |
| Foster | 1 | | | 1 | | | |
| Lister | 1 | | | 1 | | | |
| Marshall | 1 | | | 1 | | | |
| Mills | 1 | | | 1 | | | |

| | Lge | FAC | LC | Total | Pens | Hat-tricks | Cons Run |
|---|---|---|---|---|---|---|---|
| Reed | 1 | | | 1 | | | |
| Sanders | | | 1 | 1 | | | |
| Silk | 1 | | | 1 | | | |
| Smith | 1 | | | 1 | | | |
| Stainfield | 1 | | | 1 | | | |
| Ward | 1 | | | 1 | | | |

Cons Run - Consecutive scoring games.

SKRILL NORTH - STEP 2

# BRACKLEY TOWN

**Chairman:** Sara Crannage
**Secretary:** Pat Ashby  **(T)** 07969 825 636  **(E)** pat.ashby55@btinternet.com
**Commercial Manager:** Jan Butters  **(T)** 07766 226 655
**Programme Editor:** Brian Martin  **(T)** 07515 477 577
**Ground Address:** St James Park, Churchill Way, Brackley NN13 7EJ
**(T)** 01280 704 077  **Manager:** Jon Brady

2012-13 Squad - Back Row (L-R): Steve Diggin, Will Green, Krystof Zylski, Josh Green, Billy Turley, Michael Corcoran, Wayne Hatswell. Middle Row: Brett Solkhon, Marvin Robinson, Glenn Walker, Gary Mulligan, Elliot Sandy, Curtis McDonald, Tom Winters, Jordan Marshall (Kitman). Front Row: Owen Story, James Clifton, Darren Collins (Asst Manager), Jon Brady (Manager), Karl Ballard (Sports Therapist), Carl Palmer, Eddie Odhiambo, Eddie Nisevic.
Trophies: Southern League Premier Division Champions Shield, Southern League Champions Cup, The Maunsell Cup, The Northamptonshire Hillier Senior Cup
Photo: Brian Martin.

### Club Factfile

**Founded:** 1890  **Nickname:** Saints
**Previous Names:** None
**Previous Leagues:** Banbury & District, North Buckinghamshire, Hellenic 1977-83, 94-97, 99-2004, United Counties 1983-84, Southern 1997-99
**Club Colours (change):** Red and white stripes/red/white (All yellow)

**Ground Capacity:** 3,500  **Seats:** 300  **Covered:** 1,500  **Clubhouse:** Yes  **Shop:** Yes

**Directions:** Take A43 from Northampton or Oxford, or A422 from Banbury to large roundabout south of town. Take exit marked Brackley and follow towards the town (Tesco store on left). Pass the Locomotive public house and take first turning right, signposted Football Club, into Churchill Way - road leads into Club car park.

**Previous Grounds:** Banbury Road, Manor Road, Buckingham Road > 1974

**Record Attendance:** 960 v Banbury United - 2005-06
**Record Victory:** Not known
**Record Defeat:** Not known
**Record Goalscorer:** Paul Warrington - 320
**Record Appearances:** Terry Muckelberg - 350
**Additional Records:** Received £2,000 from Oxford City for Phil Mason 1998

**Senior Honours:**
Hellenic League Premier Division 1996-97, 2003-04, Division 1 Cup 1982-83. Southern League Division 1 Midlands 2006-07. Southern Premier Division 2011-12. Northamptonshire Senior Cup 2011-12.

**10 YEAR RECORD**

| 03-04 | 04-05 | 05-06 | 06-07 | 07-08 | 08-09 | 09-10 | 10-11 | 11-12 | 12-13 |
|---|---|---|---|---|---|---|---|---|---|
| Hel P 1 | SthW 7 | SthW 3 | SthM 1 | SthP 8 | SthP 11 | SthP 5 | SthP 9 | SthP 1 | Conf N 3 |

# MATCH RESULTS 2012-13

| Date | Comp | H/A | Opponents | Att: | Result | Goalscorers | Pos | No. |
|---|---|---|---|---|---|---|---|---|
| Aug 18 | BSN | A | Altrincham | 716 | W 4-1 | Sandy 20 (pen) Mulligan 52 80 Winters 89 | 1 | 1 |
| 21 | BSN | H | Hinckley United | 303 | W 5-0 | Sandy 14 Storey 47 Winters 69 Odihambo 75 Diggin 90 | 1 | 2 |
| 25 | BSN | H | Bishop Stortford | 358 | W 1-0 | Walker 39 | 1 | 3 |
| 27 | BSN | A | Corby Town | 644 | W 4-0 | Walker 8 Green 21 Story 39 Robinson 82 | 1 | 4 |
| Sept 1 | BSN | H | Droylsden | 307 | W 3-2 | Story 45 Sandy 45 (pen) Mulligan 77 | 1 | 5 |
| 4 | BSN | A | Gloucester City | 201 | W 4-1 | Story 1 42 Walker 67 Diggin 90 | 1 | 6 |
| 8 | BSN | A | Bradford PA | 446 | W 1-0 | Mulligan 48 | 1 | 7 |
| 15 | BSN | H | Workington | 476 | W 3-1 | Clifton 45 Sandy 77 Walker 90 | 1 | 8 |
| 22 | FAC Q2 | H | Daventry Town | 332 | W 4-0 | WINTERS 3 (70 76 79) Diggin 72 | | 9 |
| 29 | BSN | A | Colwyn Bay | 284 | D 1-1 | Green 27 | 1 | 10 |
| Oct 2 | BSN | H | Histon | 324 | W 2-1 | Sandy 37 Diggin 58 | 1 | 11 |
| 6 | FAC Q3 | A | Arlesey Town | 227 | L 3-4 | Solkhon 32 Diggin 70 (pen) Robinson 77 | | 12 |
| 13 | BSN | A | Harrogate Town | 487 | L 1-6 | Walker 39 | 1 | 13 |
| 20 | BSN | H | Gainsborough Trinity | 320 | D 2-2 | Walker 18 Story 23 | 1 | 14 |
| 27 | BSN | H | FC Halifax Town | 522 | D 0-0 | | 3 | 15 |
| 29 | BSN | A | Worcester City | 1029 | W 2-1 | Diggin 16 75 | 1 | 16 |
| Nov 3 | BSN | A | Vauxhall Motors | 288 | W 2-0 | Robinson 12 Diggin 73 | 1 | 17 |
| 10 | FAT Q3 | A | Thurrock | 99 | W 2-0 | Robinson 42 Mulligan 84 | | 18 |
| 17 | BSN | H | Stalybridge Celtic | 380 | W 4-1 | Robinson 12 Story 15 Solkorn 52 Walker 85 | 1 | 19 |
| 24 | FAT 1 | A | Guiseley | 524 | L 1-3 | Walker 74 | | 20 |
| Dec 8 | BSN | H | Chester | 1155 | L 2-3 | Diggin 87 90 | 3 | 21 |
| 15 | BSN | H | Altrincham | 330 | L 0-1 | | 3 | 22 |
| 26 | BSN | H | Oxford City | 476 | D 0-0 | | 3 | 23 |
| Jan 1 | BSN | A | Oxford City | 342 | L1-2 | Winters 73 | 3 | 24 |
| 5 | BSN | A | Droylsden | 192 | W 3-0 | Winters 7 22 Johnson 29 | 3 | 25 |
| 12 | BSN | H | Bradford PA | 304 | W 3-1 | Walker 56 Diggin 78 Clayton 82 (og) | 3 | 26 |
| 29 | BSN | A | Hinckley United | 152 | W 3-1 | Diggin 24 70 Winters 60 | 3 | 27 |
| Feb 2 | BSN | A | Chester | 2689 | D 0-0 | | 3 | 28 |
| 5 | BSN | H | Gloucester City | 169 | L 0-1 | | 3 | 29 |
| 9 | BSN | H | Harrogate Town | 232 | W 2-1 | Reid 40 Louis 60 | 3 | 30 |
| 12 | BSN. | A | Stalybridge Celtic | 211 | W 3-0 | Louis 12 Reid 43 70 | 3 | 31 |
| 16 | BSN | H | Solihull Borough | 330 | W 2-1 | Reid 23 75 | 3 | 32 |
| Mar 2 | BSN | A | Guiseley | 608 | W 2-0 | Louis 29 Winters 70 | 3 | 33 |
| 5 | BSN | A | Histon | 158 | L 0-3 | | 3 | 34 |
| 9 | BSN | H | Boston United | 383 | L 0-2 | | 3 | 35 |
| 12 | BSN | A | Workington | 251 | D 0-0 | | 3 | 36 |
| 16 | BSN | A | FC Halifax Town | 1361 | D 0-0 | | 3 | 37 |
| 26 | BSN | A | Gainsborough Trinity | 560 | W1-0 | Diggin 4 (pen) | 3 | 38 |
| 30 | BSN | A | Bishop's Stortford | 349 | W 3-1 | Winters 15 63 Story 19 | 3 | 39 |
| Apr 1 | BSN | H | Corby Town | 391 | L 2-4 | Jellyman 23 (og) Piergianni 59(og) | 3 | 40 |
| 6 | BSN | H | Guiseley | 285 | W 1-0 | Story 84 | 3 | 41 |
| 9 | BSN | H | Vauxhall Motors | 247 | W 1-0 | Walker 9 | 3 | 42 |
| 13 | BSN | A | Solihull Moors | 221 | W 1-0 | Winters 89 | 3 | 43 |
| 16 | BSN | H | Colwyn Bay | 243 | L 1-3 | Smyth 43 (og) | 3 | 44 |
| 20 | BSN | H | Worcester City | 382 | W 2-0 | Winters 22 38 | 3 | 45 |
| 27 | BSN | A | Boston United | 1108 | W 4-3 | Clifton 19 Diggin 25 Louis 31 Robinson 74 | 3 | 46 |
| 30 | P-Off S-F 1 | A | Altrincham | 1618 | L 1-2 | Louis 71 | | 47 |
| 31 | P-Off S-F 2 | H | Altrincham | 1353 | W 3-0 | Louis 4 Reid 26 Walker 54 | | 48 |
| May 12 | P-Off Final | H | FC Halifax Townl | 2604 | L 0-1 | | | 49 |

| GOALSCORERS | Lge | FAC | LC | Total | Pens | Hat-tricks | Cons Run | | Lge | FAC | LC | Total | Pens | Hat-tricks | Cons Run |
|---|---|---|---|---|---|---|---|---|---|---|---|---|---|---|---|
| Diggin | 13 | 2 | | 15 | 2 | | 2 | Solkhon | 1 | 1 | | 2 | | | |
| Winters | 12 | 3 | | 15 | | 1 | 2 | Clifton | 2 | | | 2 | | | |
| Walker | 10 | | 1 | 11 | | | 2 | Johnson | 1 | | | 1 | | | |
| Story | 9 | | | 9 | | | | Odihambo | 1 | | | 1 | | | |
| Louis | 6 | | | 6 | | | | Own Goals | 4 | | | 4 | | | |
| Reid | 6 | | | 6 | | | | Cons Run - Consecutive scoring games. | | | | | | | |
| Robinson | 4 | 1 | 1 | 6 | | | | | | | | | | | |
| Mulligan | 4 | | 1 | 5 | | | | | | | | | | | |
| Sandy | 5 | | | 5 | 2 | | | | | | | | | | |
| Green | 2 | | | 2 | | | | | | | | | | | |

# BRADFORD PARK AVENUE

**Chairman:** Dr. John Dean
**Secretary:** Colin Barker      **(T)** 07863 180 787      **(E)** colin.barker1@tesco.net
**Commercial Manager:** Kevin Hainsworth      **(T)** 07912 271 498
**Programme Editor:** Tim Parker      **(T)** 07738 675 776
**Ground Address:** Horsfall Stadium, Cemetery Road, Bradford, West Yorkshire BD6 2NG
**(T)** 01484 400 007      **Manager:** John Deacey

## Club Factfile

**Founded:** 1907      **Nickname:** Avenue
**Previous Names:** Reformed in 1988
**Previous Leagues:** Southern 1907-08, Football League 1908-70, Northern Premier 1970-74, West Riding Co.Am. 1988-89, Central Midlands 1989-90, North West Counties 1990-95
**Club Colours (change):** All green (White with red, amber & black stripes/white/white)

**Ground Capacity:** 5,000   **Seats:** 1,247   **Covered:** 2,000   **Clubhouse:** Yes   **Shop:** Yes

**Directions**
M62 to junction 26. Join M606 leave at second junction. At the roundabout take 2nd exit (A6036 signposted Halifax) and pass Odsal Stadium on the left hand side. At next roundabout take the 3rd exit (A6036 Halifax, Horsfall Stadium is signposted). After approximately one mile turn left down Cemetery Road immediately before the Kings Head Public House. Ground is 150 yards on the left.

**Previous Grounds:** Park Ave. 1907-73, Valley Parade 1973-74, Manningham Mills 1988-89, McLaren Field 1985-93, Batley 1993-96

**Record Attendance:** 2,100 v Bristol City - FA Cup 1st Round 2003
**Record Victory:** 11-0 v Derby Dale - FA Cup 1908
**Record Defeat:** 0-7 v Barnsley - 1911
**Record Goalscorer:** Len Shackleton - 171 (1940-46)
**Record Appearances:** Tommy Farr - 542 (1934-50)
**Additional Records:** Paid £24,500 to Derby County for Leon Leuty 1950
Received £34,000 from Derby County for Kevin Hector 1966
**Senior Honours:**
Football League Division 3 North 1928. North West Counties League 1994-95.
Northern Premier League Division 1 2000-01, Division 1 North 2007-08. Premier Division Play-offs 2011-12.
West Riding Senior Cup x9. West Riding County Cup x2.

### 10 YEAR RECORD

| 03-04 | 04-05 | 05-06 | 06-07 | 07-08 | 08-09 | 09-10 | 10-11 | 11-12 | 12-13 |
|---|---|---|---|---|---|---|---|---|---|
| NP P   17 | Conf N   22 | NP P   21 | NP 1   4 | NP1N   1 | NP P   7 | NP P   2 | NP P   3 | NP P   4 | Conf N   7 |

# MATCH RESULTS 2012-13

| Date | Comp | H/A | Opponents | Att: | Result | Goalscorers | Pos | No. |
|------|------|-----|-----------|------|--------|-------------|-----|-----|
| Aug 18 | BSN | H | Worcester City | 453 | D 2-2 | Marshall 77 88 | 11 | 1 |
| 21 | BSN | A | Vauxhall Motors | 235 | W 3-1 | Hotte 23 Holland 44 James 53 | 5 | 2 |
| 25 | BSN | A | Harrogate Town | 548 | D 1-1 | Marshall 30 | 10 | 3 |
| 27 | BSN | H | FC Halifax Town | 1614 | D 1-1 | Holland 45 | 8 | 4 |
| Sept 1 | BSN | A | Corby Town | 381 | W 5-4 | Walker 23 (og) Greaves 34 39 Holland 45 48 | 6 | 5 |
| 3 | BSN | H | Stalybridge Celtic | 501 | L 1-3 | Walker 24 | 8 | 6 |
| 8 | BSN | H | Brackley Town | 446 | L 0-1 | | 11 | 7 |
| 15 | BSN | A | Altrincham | 806 | L 1-3 | Marshall 52 | 14 | 8 |
| 22 | FAC Q2 | A | Curzon Ashton | 237 | W 3-1 | Davidson 23 Holland 51 80 | | 9 |
| 29 | BSN | H | Boston United | 399 | W 2-1 | Hotte 35 James 74 | 12 | 10 |
| Oct 6 | FAC Q3 | A | Carlton Town | 151 | W 3 -1 | Walker 27 Greaves 35 Marshall 77 | | 11 |
| 13 | BSN | H | Gloucester City | 405 | W 2-1 | Walker 9 Marshall 73 | 12 | 12 |
| 17 | BSN | A | Chester | 2031 | D 1-1 | Holland 3 | 9 | 13 |
| 20 | FAC Q4 | H | Ossett Albion | 477 | W 4-1 | Knowles 36 Davidson 55 90 Gay 84 (og) | | 14 |
| 27 | BSN | H | Bishop's Stortford | 358 | W 2-1 | Knowles 43 James 90 | 7 | 15 |
| 30 | BSN | A | Colwyn Bay | 457 | W 2-1 | Jones 70 Walker 80 | 6 | 16 |
| Nov 3 | FAC 1 | A | Doncaster Rovers | 4602 | L 1-3 | Marshall 56 | | 17 |
| 10 | FAT Q3 | A | Stafford Rangers | 419 | L 1-3 | Marshall 44 | | 18 |
| 17 | BSN | A | Solihull Moors | 252 | L 1-3 | Greaves 84 | 8 | 19 |
| 19 | BSN | H | Hinckley United | 301 | W 4-0 | Holland 1 22 Greaves 38 56 | 7 | 20 |
| 24 | BSN | A | Workington | 397 | W 6-0 | Deavey 18 Davidson 47 Duckworth 51 | 4 | |
| | | | | | | Holland 68 Marshall 87 Greaves 89 | | 21 |
| Dec 1 | BSN | A | Histon | 264 | W 4-1 | Knowles 6 Duckworth 7 Davidson 19 James 86 | 4 | 22 |
| 15 | BSN | A | Worcester City | 709 | L 0-2 | | 4 | 23 |
| 17 | BSN | H | Gainsborough T | 265 | L 0-2 | | 5 | 24 |
| 26 | BSN | A | Guiseley | 1017 | L 0-1 | | 6 | 25 |
| 29 | BSN | A | Stalybridge Celtic | 514 | L 0-2 | | 6 | 26 |
| Jan 1 | BSN | H | Guiseley | 703 | L 1-3 | Holland 44 | 7 | 27 |
| 5 | BSN | H | Chester | 957 | D 0-0 | | 9 | 28 |
| 12 | BSN | A | Brackley Town | 304 | L 1-3 | Duckworth 83 | 11 | 29 |
| Feb 3 | BSN | H | Solihull Moors | 285 | W 1-0 | Marshall 48 | 9 | 30 |
| 9 | BSN | A | Gloucester City | 303 | L 0-1 | | 10 | 31 |
| 18 | BSN | H | Vauxhall Motors | 272 | W 2-0 | Marshall 36 Corner 44 | 9 | 32 |
| 23 | BSN | H | Corny Town | 285 | W 2-1 | Davidson 18 Corner 32 | 9 | 33 |
| Mar 2 | BSN | A | Droylsden | 254 | W 7-0 | Davidson 11 90 Walker 13 Knowles 15, Marshall 23 39 Savory 82 | 8 | 34 |
| 4 | BSN | H | Workington | 284 | W 1-0 | Clayton 64 | 8 | 35 |
| 12 | BSN | A | Gainsborough Trinity | 414 | D 1-1 | Marshall 59 | 8 | 36 |
| 23 | BSN | A | Boston United | 851 | W 4-0 | DAVIDSON 3 ( 28 70 82) Marshall 84 (Pen) | 8 | 37 |
| April 1 | BSN | A | HalifaxTown | 1611 | W 1-0 | Marshall 67 | 7 | 38 |
| 3 | BSN | H | Harrogate Town | 329 | W 1-0 | Holland 85 | | 39 |
| 6 | BSN | A | Hinckley United | 250 | W 4-1 | Holland 28 Hotte 40 69 Baker 90 | 7 | 40 |
| 8 | BSN | H | Oxford City | 302 | L 1-2 | Corner 79 | 7 | 41 |
| 10 | BSN | A | Oxford City | 180 | D 1-1 | Deacey 42 | 7 | 42 |
| 13 | BSN | H | Droylsden | 350 | W 5-0 | Baker 45 Walker 51 Hotte 55 Marshall 80 Jackson 82 | 6 | 43 |
| 17 | BSN | H | Altrincham | 476 | D 2-2 | Marshall 56 Deacey 83 | 6 | 44 |
| 20 | BSN | A | Bishops Stortford | 402 | L 1-2 | Marshall 36 | 7 | 45 |
| 22 | BSN | H | Colwyn Bay | 275 | L 1-2 | Daly 78 | 7 | 46 |
| 27 | BSN | H | Histon | 360 | D 0-0 | | 7 | 47 |

| GOALSCORERS | Lge | FAC | LC | Total | Pens | Hat-tricks | Cons Run | | Lge | FAC | LC | Total | Pens | Hat-tricks | Cons Run |
|-------------|-----|-----|-----|-------|------|-----------|----------|--|-----|-----|-----|-------|------|-----------|----------|
| Marshall | 16 | 2 | 1 | 19 | 1 | | 2 | Duckworh | 3 | | | 3 | | | |
| Holland | 11 | 2 | | 13 | | | 2 | Baker | 2 | | | 2 | | | |
| Davidson | 8 | 3 | | 11 | 1 | | | Clayton | 1 | | | 1 | | | |
| Greaves | 6 | 1 | | 7 | | | | Daly | 1 | | | 1 | | | |
| Walker | 5 | 1 | | 6 | | | | Jackson | 1 | | | 1 | | | |
| Hotte | 5 | | | 5 | | | | Jones | 1 | | | 1 | | | |
| James | 4 | | | 4 | | | | Savory | 1 | | | 1 | | | |
| Knowles | 3 | 1 | | 4 | | | | Own Goals | 1 | 1 | | 2 | | | |
| Corner | 3 | | | 3 | | | | Cons Run - Consecutive scoring games. | | | | | | | |
| Deacey | 3 | | | 3 | | | | | | | | | | | |

# COLWYN BAY

**Chairman:** Bob Paton
**Secretary:** Carol Beard    **(T)** 07595 894 622    **(E)** carol@colwynbayfc.co.uk
**Commercial Manager:** Carol Beard    **(T)** 07595 894 622
**Programme Editor:** Matt Sampson    **(T)** matt@colwynbayfc.co.uk
**Ground Address:** The Football Stadium, Llanelian Road, Old Colwyn, North Wales LL29 8UN
**(T)** 01492 514 580        **Manager:** Frank Sinclair

### Club Factfile

**Founded:** 1885     **Nickname:** The Bay / Seagulls
**Previous Names:** None
**Previous Leagues:** North Wales Coast 1901-21, 33-35, Welsh National 1921-30, North Wales Combination 1930-31,
               Welsh League (North) 1945-84, North West Counties 1984-91

**Club Colours (change):** Sky blue and maroon/maroon/sky blue (All red)

**Ground Capacity:** 2,500    **Seats:** 250    **Covered:** 700    **Clubhouse:** Yes    **Shop:** Yes

**Directions**
From Queensferry take the A55 and exit at Junction 22 signposted Old Colwyn at end of slip road turn left, up the hill to the mini roundabout, straight across onto Llanelian Road, ground is approx half mile on the right.

**Previous Grounds:** Eirias Park

**Record Attendance:** 5,000 v Borough United at Eirias Park 1964
**Record Victory:** Not known
**Record Defeat:** Not known
**Record Goalscorer:** Peter Donnelly
**Record Appearances:** Bryn A Jones
**Additional Records:**

**Senior Honours:**
Northern League Division 1 1991-92, Division 1 Play-off 2009-10

| 10 YEAR RECORD | | | | | | | | | |
|---|---|---|---|---|---|---|---|---|---|
| 03-04 | 04-05 | 05-06 | 06-07 | 07-08 | 08-09 | 09-10 | 10-11 | 11-12 | 12-13 |
| NP 1   16 | NP 1   13 | NP 1   12 | NP 1   5 | NP1S   7 | NP1N   4 | NP1N   4 | NP P   2 | Conf N   12 | Conf N   18 |

# MATCH RESULTS 2012-13

| Date | Comp | H/A | Opponents | Att: | Result | Goalscorers | Pos | No. |
|------|------|-----|-----------|------|--------|-------------|-----|-----|
| Aug 18 | BSN | H | Solihull Moors | 310 | W 3-1 | Williams 22 Lloyd 31 Holsgrove 71 | 4 | 1 |
| 21 | BSN | A | FC Halifax Town | 1328 | W 1-0 | Holsgrove 74 | 3 | 2 |
| 25 | BSN | A | Chester | 2404 | L 1-2 | Holsgrove 29 | 7 | 3 |
| 27 | BSN | H | Stalybridge Celtic | 365 | L 2-3 | Sinclair 26 Evans 32 | 9 | 4 |
| Sept 1 | BSN | A | Worcester City | 832 | L 0-2 | | 11 | 5 |
| 4 | BSN | H | Guiseley | 254 | L 0-2 | | 9 | 6 |
| 8 | BSN | H | Boston United | 287 | L 0-2 | | | 7 |
| 15 | BSN | A | Corby Town | 411 | L 1-3 | Berkley 23 pen) | 19 | 8 |
| 22 | FAC Q2 | H | Warrington Town | 249 | W 3-2 | Lloyd, Hopley (2) | | 9 |
| 29 | BSN | H | Brackley Town | 284 | D 1-1 | Hopley 37 | 17 | 10 |
| Oct 6 | FAC Q3 | H | Guiseley | 318 | D 1-1 | Hopley 1 | | 11 |
| 9 | FAC Q3r | A | Guiseley | 360 | L 1-3 | Hopley | | 12 |
| 13 | BSN | H | Hinckley United | 318 | W 3-2 | Berkley 50 (pen) Hopley 72 Evans 75 | 17 | 13 |
| 20 | BSN | A | Hinckley United | 315 | W 3-1 | Williams 6 Hopley 20 Breeze 86 | 14 | 14 |
| 27 | BSN | A | Droylsden | 235 | L 0-2 | | 17 | 15 |
| 30 | BSN | H | Bradford PA | 457 | L 1-2 | Hopley 81 | 17 | 16 |
| Nov 3 | BSN | A | Oxford City | 243 | W 2-1 | Evans 42 Rainford 67 (pen) | 13 | 17 |
| 10 | FAT Q3 | A | Boston United | 694 | L 1-3 | Hopley 65 | | 18 |
| Dec 1 | BSN | A | Gainsborough T | 426 | L 1-3 | Sinclair 36 | 17 | 19 |
| 8 | BSN | H | Harrogate Town | 322 | L 1-2 | Lloyd 69 | 19 | 20 |
| 15 | BSN | H | Histon | 325 | W 3-1 | Rainford 27 78 Hopley 32 | 18 | 21 |
| 26 | BSN | A | Vauxhall Motors | 168 | D 1-1 | Holden 7 | 18 | 22 |
| Jan 1 | BSN | H | Vauxhall Motors | 282 | L 2-4 | Hopley 50 Lloyd 56 (pen) | 18 | 23 |
| 5 | BSN | H | Worcester City | 303 | L 0-3 | | 19 | 24 |
| 12 | BSN | A | Boston United | 887 | L 0-1 | | 19 | 25 |
| 29 | BSN | A | Solihull Moors | 102 | L 0-2 | | 20 | 26 |
| Feb 2 | BSN | H | Workington | 268 | L 1-4 | Lampkin 80 | 20 | 27 |
| 9 | BSN | H | Bishop's Stortford | 236 | L 1-2 | Byrne 51 | 20 | 28 |
| 19 | BSN | A | Guiseley | 2189 | D 2-2 | Lea 41 Hopley 65 | 20 | 29 |
| 23 | BSN | A | Altrincham | 769 | D 1-1 | Hopley 58 | 20 | 30 |
| Mar 2 | BSN | H | Corby Town | 278 | W 1-0 | Meechan 17 | 20 | 31 |
| 5 | BSN | A | Harrogate Town | 215 | W 2-1 | Payne 8 Lea 23 | 20 | 32 |
| 9 | BSN | A | Histon | 309 | L 1-2 | Sinclair 90 | 20 | 33 |
| 16 | BSN | H | Altrincham | 431 | L 1-3 | Lampkin 57 | 20 | 34 |
| 19 | BSN | H | Harrogate Town | 331 | L 0-3 | | 20 | 35 |
| 27 | BSN | A | Gloucester City | 602 | D 2-2 | Evans 8 Sinclair 82 | 20 | 36 |
| 30 | BSN | H | Chester | 1463 | L 1-5 | Payne 80 (pen) | 20 | 37 |
| Apr 1 | BSN | A | Stalybridge Celtic | 316 | D 3-3 | Meadowcroft 16 Lea 30 Hopley 89 | 20 | 38 |
| 6 | BSN | A | Bishop's Stortford | 319 | D 2-2 | Ellison 62 83 (pen) | 20 | 39 |
| 9 | BSN | H | Droylsden | 197 | L 1-3 | Payne 26 | 20 | 40 |
| 13 | BSN | H | Gainsborough Trinity | 234 | L 0-1 | | 20 | 41 |
| 16 | BSN | A | Brackley Town | 243 | W 3-1 | Hopley 11 Ellison 17 Payne 55 | 20 | 42 |
| 18 | BSN | H | Oxford City | 303 | W 3-1 | Payne 5 51 Hopley 58 | 19 | 43 |
| 20 | BSN | A | Workington | 412 | W 2-1 | Hopley 9 Payne 40 | 18 | 44 |
| 22 | BSN | A | Bradford PA | 275 | W 2-1 | Hopley 53 Payne 67 | 17 | 45 |
| 27 | BSN | H | Gloucester City | 633 | W 1-0 | McKenna 33 | 18 | 46 |

| GOALSCORERS | Lge | FAC | LC | Total | Pens | Hat-tricks | Cons Run | | Lge | FAC | LC | Total | Pens | Hat-tricks | Cons Run |
|-------------|-----|-----|----|-------|------|------------|----------|--|-----|-----|----|-------|------|------------|----------|
| Hopley | 14 | 4 | 1 | 19 | | | 6 | Lampkin | 2 | | | 2 | | | |
| Payne | 8 | | | 8 | 1 | | | Williams | 2 | | | 2 | | | |
| Evans | 4 | | | 4 | | | | Breeze | 1 | | | 1 | | | |
| Lloyd | 3 | 1 | | 4 | 1 | | | Byrne | 1 | | | 1 | | | |
| Sinclair | 4 | | | 4 | | | | Holden | 1 | | | 1 | | | |
| Ellison | 3 | | | 3 | 1 | | | Meadowcroft | 1 | | | 1 | | | |
| Holsgrove | 3 | | | 3 | | | | Meechan | 1 | | | 1 | | | |
| Lea | 3 | | | 3 | | | | McKenna | 1 | | | 1 | | | |
| Rainford | 3 | | | 3 | 1 | | | Cons Run - Consecutive scoring games. | | | | | | | |
| Berkley | 2 | | | 2 | 2 | | | | | | | | | | |

# GAINSBOROUGH TRINITY

**Chairman:**
**Secretary:** Pete Wallace      **(T)** 07841 163 110      **(E)** petewallace@aol.com
**Commercial Manager:** John Myskiw      **(T)** 07977 751 549
**Programme Editor:** Pete Wallace      **(T)** 07841 163 110
**Ground Address:** The Northolme, Gainsborough, Lincolnshire DN21 2QW
**(T)** 01427 613 295 (office) 613 688 (Social C)      **Manager:** Steve Housham

## Club Factfile

**Founded:** 1873      **Nickname:** The Blues
**Previous Names:** Trinity Recreationists
**Previous Leagues:** Midland Counties 1889-96, 1912-60, 61-68, Football League 1896-1912, Central Alliance 1960-61,
Northern Premier 1968-2004

**Club Colours (change):** All blue (All yellow)

**Ground Capacity:** 4,340      **Seats:** 504      **Covered:** 2,500      **Clubhouse:** Yes      **Shop:** Yes

**Directions**
The Northolme is situated on the A159, Gainsborough to Scunthorpe road, approximately a third of a mile north of the Town Centre. Public Car Park on the right 150 yards before the Ground. Any person parked illegally in the Streets around the Ground will be issued with a ticket from the Police.

**Previous Grounds:** None

**Record Attendance:** 9,760 v Scunthorpe United - Midland League 1948
**Record Victory:** 7-0 v Fleetwood Town and v Great Harwood Town
**Record Defeat:** 1-7 v Stalybridge Celtic - Northern Premier 2000-01 and v Brentford - FA Cup 03-04.
**Record Goalscorer:** Not known
**Record Appearances:** Not known
**Additional Records:** Paid £3,000 to Buxton for Stuart Lowe
**Senior Honours:** Received £30,000 from Lincoln City for Tony James
Midland Counties League 1890-91, 1927-28, 48-49, 66-67
Lincolnshire Senior Cup x18

### 10 YEAR RECORD

| 03-04 | 04-05 | 05-06 | 06-07 | 07-08 | 08-09 | 09-10 | 10-11 | 11-12 | 12-13 |
|---|---|---|---|---|---|---|---|---|---|
| NP P    10 | Conf N   11 | Conf N   16 | Conf N   12 | Conf N   11 | Conf N   13 | Conf N   14 | Conf N   18 | Conf N   4 | Conf N   8 |

# MATCH RESULTS 2012-13

| Date | Comp | H/A | Opponents | Att: | Result | Goalscorers | Pos | No. |
|------|------|-----|-----------|------|--------|-------------|-----|-----|
| Aug 18 | BSN | H | Gloucester City | 538 | L 0-1 | | 16 | 1 |
| 21 | BSN | A | Stalybridge Celtic | 382 | D 1-1 | Yates 79 | 16 | 2 |
| 25 | BSN | A | Guiseley | 462 | L 0-2 | | 19 | 3 |
| 27 | BSN | H | Harrogate Town | 470 | D 1-1 | Hawkridge 20 | 21 | 4 |
| Sep 1 | BSN | A | Vauxhall Motors | 156 | W 2-1 | Noone 4 (og) Connor 63 | 16 | 5 |
| 4 | BSN | H | Altrincham | 536 | L 2-4 | Stamp 60 Clarke 73 | 16 | 6 |
| 8 | BSN | H | Worcester City | 518 | W1-0 | Stamp 84 | 13 | 7 |
| 15 | BSN | A | Solihull Moors | 222 | W 2-0 | Stamp 60 Connor 86 | 11 | 8 |
| 22 | FAC Q2 | H | Chester | 756 | D 1-1 | Connor 10 | | 9 |
| 29 | BSN | H | Corby Town | 516 | D 2-2 | Waterfall 36 Knowles 53 | 13 | 10 |
| Oct 2 | FAC Q2r | A | Chester | 1492 | L 1-2 | Yates 90 *aet | | 11 |
| 13 | BSN | H | Droylsden | 497 | W 3-0 | Knowles 7 Hawkridge 23 Nelthorpe 38 | 11 | 12 |
| 20 | BSN | A | Brackley Town | 320 | D 2-2 | Connor 4 71 | 9 | 13 |
| 27 | BSN | A | Workington | 493 | D 1-1 | Yates 73 | 10 | 14 |
| 30 | BSN | H | Hinckley United | 451 | W 5-0 | KNOWLES 4 (14 20 32 48) Hawkridge 78 | 8 | 15 |
| Nov 3 | BSN | A | Boston United | 1079 | L 1-2 | Clarke 41 | 9 | 16 |
| 10 | FAT Q3 | H | Hinckley United | 357 | D 1-1 | Stamp 27 | | 17 |
| 13 | FAT Q3r | A | Hinckley United | 181 | W 4-1 | Knowles 3 Stamp 21 Leary 51 Connor 83 | | 18 |
| 17 | BSN | A | Bishop's Stortford | 511 | W 5-1 | Knowles 25 28 Leary 57 Stamp 65 Connor 86 | 7 | 19 |
| 24 | FAT 1 | H | Harrogate Town | 386 | W 2-0 | Hawkridge 24 (pen) Connor 90 | | 20 |
| Dec 1 | BSN | H | Colwyn Bay | 426 | W 3-1 | Stamp 7 Hawkridge 55 Knowles 77 | 8 | 21 |
| 8 | BSN | A | Altrincham | 728 | W 1-0 | Barraclough | 6 | 22 |
| 15 | FAT 2 | A | Forest Green Rovers | 496 | W 2-1 | Stamp 15 72 | | 23 |
| 17 | BSN | A | Bradford PA | 265 | W 2-0 | Hawkridge 69 Barraclough 75 | 5 | 24 |
| 22 | BSN | H | Stalybridge Celtic | 506 | L 1-2 | Young 5 | 4 | 25 |
| 26 | BSN | A | FC Halifax Town | 1515 | L 1-3 | Hogan 13 (og) | 5 | 26 |
| Jan 1 | BSN | H | FC Halifax Town | 906 | W 3-0 | Nelthorpe 53 Hawkridge 63 (pen) Stamp 65 | 4 | 27 |
| 5 | BSN | H | Solihull Moors | 515 | D 1-1 | Roma 81 | 4 | 28 |
| 12 | FAT 3 | H | Tamworth | 756 | W 2-1 | Russell 15 Yates 21 | | 29 |
| 29 | BSN | A | Workington | 191 | W 3-0 | Russell 15 Connor 68 Yates 76 | 4 | 30 |
| Feb 2 | BSN | H | Boston United | 908 | D 2-2 | Hone 64 Yates 78 | 5 | 31 |
| 5 | FAT 4 | H | Barrow | 784 | W 2-0 | Leary 22 Waterfall 29 | | 32 |
| 9 | BSN | A | Droylsden | 184 | W 3-1 | Waterfall 12 Jones 28 Hone 41 | 5 | 33 |
| 16 | FAT S-F 1 | A | Wrexham | 3409 | L 1-3 | Stamp 28 | | 34 |
| 19 | BSN | A | Histon | 212 | W 3-0 | Barraclough 18 Nelthorpe 21 58 | 4 | 35 |
| 23 | FAT S-F 2 | H | Wrexham | 2307 | W 2-1 | Hawkridge 26 Leary 79 | | 36 |
| 27 | BSN | A | Chester | 1918 | L 1-3 | Nelthorpe 28 | 6 | 37 |
| Mar 2 | BSN | A | Hinckley United | 333 | W 2-0 | Connor 14 43 | 6 | 38 |
| 12 | BSN | H | Bradford PA | 414 | D 1-1 | Connor 9 | 7 | 39 |
| 16 | BSN | H | Bishop's Stortford | 522 | D 2-2 | Stamp 8 Barraclough 72 | 7 | 40 |
| 18 | BSN | H | Worcester City | 536 | W 3-0 | Waterfall 22 Young 45 Russell 83 (Pen) | 7 | 41 |
| 26 | BSN | H | Brackley Town | 560 | L 0-1 | | 7 | 42 |
| 30 | BSN | H | Guiseley | 600 | L 1-2 | Bower 17 (og) | 8 | 43 |
| Apr 1 | BSN | A | Harrogate Town | 408 | D 0-0 | | 8 | 44 |
| 4 | BSN | H | Chester | 678 | L 0-2 | | 8 | 45 |
| 6 | BSN | H | Oxford City | 446 | L 1-2 | Connor 90 | 8 | 46 |
| 9 | BSN | H | Histon | 346 | W 1-0 | Connor 87 | 8 | 47 |
| 13 | BSN | A | Colwyn Bay | 234 | L 0-1 | | 8 | 48 |
| 16 | BSN | A | Gloucester City | 320 | W 2-1 | Stamp 32 Russell 42 | 8 | 49 |
| 20 | BSN | H | Vauxhall Motors | 431 | W 2-1 | Russell 34 Stamp 51 | 8 | 50 |
| 23 | BSN | A | Oxford City | 180 | D 1-1 | Waterfall 15 | 8 | 51 |
| 27 | BSN | A | Corby Town | 1856 | D 0-0 | | 8 | 52 |

| GOALSCORERS | Lge | FAC | LC | Total | Pens | Hat-tricks | Cons Run | | Lge | FAC | LC | Total | Pens | Hat-tricks | Cons Run |
|-------------|-----|-----|-----|-------|------|------------|----------|---|-----|-----|-----|-------|------|------------|----------|
| Connor | 10 | 1 | 2 | 13 | | 1 | 3 | Clarke | 2 | | | 2 | | | |
| Stamp | 9 | | 3 | 12 | | | 3 | Hone | 2 | | | 2 | | | |
| Knowles | 9 | | 1 | 10 | | | 2 | Young | 2 | | | 2 | | | |
| Hawkridge | 6 | | 2 | 8 | 2 | | | Jones | 1 | | | 1 | | | |
| Yates | 4 | 1 | | 1 | 6 | | | Roma | 1 | | | 1 | | | |
| Leary | 2 | | 3 | 5 | | | | Own Goals | 3 | | | 3 | | | |
| Nelthorpe | 5 | | | 5 | | | | Cons Run - Consecutive scoring games. | | | | | | | |
| Russell | 4 | | 1 | 5 | | | | | | | | | | | |
| Waterfall | 4 | | 1 | 5 | | | | | | | | | | | |
| Barraclough | 4 | | | 4 | | | | | | | | | | | |

# GLOUCESTER CITY

**Chairman:** Nigel Hughes

**Secretary:** Shaun Wetson      **(T)** 07813 931 781      **(E)** swgcfc@gmail.com

**Commercial Manager:** Commercial Office      **(T)** 01452 534 115

**Programme Editor:** Mike Dunstan      **(T)** 07899 743 951

**Ground Address:** Cheltenham Tn FC, The Abbey Business Stad., Whaddon Rd GL52 5NA

**(T)** 01242 573 558 (Cheltenham Town No.)      **Manager:** David Mehew

Action from The Tigers' 2-1 win over Thatcham Town
in the 2nd Qualifying Round of the FA Cup. Photo: Peter Barnes.

## Club Factfile

**Founded:** 1889      **Nickname:** The Tigers

**Previous Names:** Gloucester Y.M.C.A.

**Previous Leagues:** Bristol & District (now Western) 1893-96, Gloucester & Dist. 1897-1907, North Gloucestershire 1907-10, Gloucestershire North Senior 1920-34, Birmingham Combination 1935-39, Southern 1939-2000

**Club Colours (change):** Yellow & black/black/black (All royal blue)

**Ground Capacity:** 7,289  **Seats:** Yes  **Covered:** Yes  **Clubhouse:** Yes  **Shop:** Yes

**Directions:** From the North (M5) leave at Jnctn 10, follow road A4019) towards Cheltenham, keep going straight through traffic lights until you reach a roundabout, PC World will be on your left and McDonalds on your right. Turn left here, after 500 yards you will then come to a double roundabout, go straight over, keep going for another 300 yards then turn right into Swindon Lane, follow the road over the level crossing and 2 mini roundabouts until you come to a large roundabout, go straight over, signposted Prestbury, continue past Racecourse and turn right into Albert Road, follow this to the end then turn left at roundabout into Prestbury Road, 200yards turn into Whaddon Road.

**Previous Grounds:** Longlevens 1935-65, Horton Road 1965-86, Meadow Park 1986-2007, Corinium Stadium Cirencester 2007-10

**Record Attendance:** Longlevens: 10,500 v Tottenham - Friendly 1952. Meadow Park: 4,000 v Dagenham & Red. - FAT 3rd Q Rnd 12/04/97

**Record Victory:** 10-1 v Sudbury Town (H) - FA Cup 3rd Qualifying Round 17/10/98

**Record Defeat:** 1-12 v Gillingham - 09/11/46

**Record Goalscorer:** Reg Weaver - 250 (1930s)

**Record Appearances:** Stan Myers & Frank Tredgett - (1950s)

**Additional Records:** Paid £25,000 to Worcester City for Steve Ferguson 1990-91

**Senior Honours:** Received £25,000 from AFC Bournemouth for Ian Hedges 1990

Southern League Cup 1955-56, Midland Division 1988-89, Premier Division Play-off 2008-09.
Gloucestershire Senior Cup x19

### 10 YEAR RECORD

| 03-04 | 04-05 | 05-06 | 06-07 | 07-08 | 08-09 | 09-10 | 10-11 | 11-12 | 12-13 |
|---|---|---|---|---|---|---|---|---|---|
| SthW 2 | SthP 15 | SthP 13 | SthP 10 | SthP 6 | SthP 3 | Conf N 18 | Conf N 14 | Conf N 14 | Conf N 11 |

# MATCH RESULTS 2012-13

| Date | Comp | H/A | Opponents | Att: | Result | Goalscorers | Pos | No. |
|------|------|-----|-----------|------|--------|-------------|-----|-----|
| Aug 17 | BSN | A | Gainsborough Trinity | 538 | W 1-0 | Mullins 15 | 9 | 1 |
| 21 | BSN | H | Oxford City | 338 | L 0-1 | | 12 | 2 |
| 25 | BSN | A | Histon | 221 | L 1-2 | Edwards 90 | 13 | 3 |
| 27 | BSN | H | Solihull Moors | 323 | D 1-1 | Mullins 25 | 15 | 4 |
| Sept 1 | BSN | A | Guiseley | 541 | L 1-3 | Hogg 26 | 18 | 5 |
| 4 | BSN | H | Brackley Town | 201 | L 1-4 | Harris 90 | 18 | 6 |
| 8 | BSN | H | Stalybridge Celtic | 252 | W 4-3 | Mullins 31 Hamblin 38 90 Davies 78 | 16 | 7 |
| 15 | BSN | A | FC Halifax Town | 1291 | L 0-5 | | 17 | 8 |
| 22 | FAC Q2 | H | Thatcham Town | 231 | W 2-1 | Edwards 21 (pen) Morford 48 | | 9 |
| 29 | BSN | A | Droylsden | 181 | L 0-1 | | 19 | 10 |
| Oct 2 | BSN | H | Bishop's Stortford | 180 | W 5-1 | Harding 2 Holland 8 42  Goddard 6 Hamblin 65 | 16 | 11 |
| 7 | FAC Q3 | H | Eastleigh | 202 | W 1-0 | Hamblin | | 12 |
| 13 | BSN | A | Bradford PA | 405 | L 1-2 | Edwards 30 | 18 | 13 |
| 20 | FAC Q4 | H | Chippenham Town | 675 | W 1-0 | Edwards 90 | | 14 |
| 27 | BSN | A | Hinckley United | 316 | W 3-0 | Edwards 58 (pen) Morford 82 90 | 15 | 15 |
| 31 | BSN | A | Corby Town | 237 | L 2-3 | Webb, Edwards | 16 | 16 |
| Nov 11 | FAT Q3 | H | Maidenhead United | 450 | L 0-1 | | | 17 |
| 14 | FAC 1 | H | Leyton Orient | 1381 | L 0-2 | | | 18 |
| 18 | BSN | H | Chester | 852 | L 0-1 | | 18 | 19 |
| Dec 5 | BSN | H | Boston United | 187 | W 1-0 | Davis 60 | 17 | 20 |
| 8 | BSN | H | Workington | 230 | L 0-1 | | 18 | 21 |
| 15 | BSN | A | Vauxhall Motors | 122 | W 2-1 | Graham 51 Edwards 90 | 17 | 22 |
| 26 | BSN | A | Worcester City | 1290 | W 1-0 | Andrews 38 | 16 | 23 |
| Jan 1 | BSN | H | Worcester City | 640 | W 4-2 | Goddard 45 Edwards 47 Morford 52 Hogg 56 | 16 | 24 |
| Feb 2 | BSN | A | Altrincham | 762 | L 0-2 | | 17 | 25 |
| 5 | BSN | A | Brackley Town | 169 | W 1-0 | Davies 77 | 15 | 26 |
| 9 | BSN | H | Bradford PA | 303 | W1-0 | Hotte 54 (og) | 15 | 27 |
| 12 | BSN | H | Guiseley | 220 | D 2-2 | Webb 34 Edwards 72 (pen) | 15 | 28 |
| 16 | BSN | A | Oxford City | 446 | W 2-1 | Morford 19 85 | 14 | 29 |
| 19 | BSN | H | FC Halifax Town | 303 | L 1-2 | Andrews 84 (pen) | 14 | 30 |
| 23 | BSN | H | Harrogate Town | 446 | L 0-2 | | 14 | 31 |
| 26 | BSN | H | Altrincham | 205 | D 0-0 | | 14 | 32 |
| Mar 2 | BSN | A | Workington | 356 | W 1-0 | | 13 | 33 |
| 5 | BSN | A | Boston United | 548 | L 0-4 | | 13 | 34 |
| 9 | BSN | H | Hinckley United | 293 | W 4-1 | Rawlings 16 Mann 71 Davies 73 Edwards 88 (pen) | 11 | 35 |
| 12 | BSN | H | Droylsden | 349 | W 4-0 | Davies 33 Holland 45 Edwards 77 Liddiard 87 | 9 | 36 |
| 16 | BSN | A | Chester | 2626 | L 0-2 | | 9 | 37 |
| 27 | BSN | H | Colwyn Bay | 602 | D 2-2 | Webb 18  Liddiard 84 | 10 | 38 |
| 30 | BSN | H | Histon | 323 | D 1-1 | Hogg 88 | 11 | 39 |
| Apr 1 | BSN | A | Solihull Moors | 209 | W 3-2 | Andrews 41 (pen) Holland 72 Mann 78 | 10 | 40 |
| 3 | BSN | A | Bishop's Stortford | 270 | W 2-1 | Edwards 18 Morford 64 | 10 | 41 |
| 6 | BSN | H | Vauxhall Motors | 301 | D 1-1 | Morford 79 | 9 | 42 |
| 9 | BSN | A | Harrogate Town | 301 | L 0-1 | | 9 | 43 |
| 13 | BSN | A | Stalybridge Celtic | 344 | L 0-4 | | 9 | 44 |
| 16 | BSN | H | Gainsborough Trinitty | 320 | L 1-2 | Morford 59 | 10 | 45 |
| 20 | BSN | H | Corby Town | 355 | L 0-1 | | 10 | 46 |
| 27 | BSN | A | Colwyn Bay | 633 | L 0-1 | | 11 | 47 |

| GOALSCORERS | Lge | FAC | LC | Total | Pens | Hat-tricks | Cons Run | | Lge | FAC | LC | Total | Pens | Hat-tricks | Cons Run |
|-------------|-----|-----|-----|-------|------|-----------|----------|-----|-----|-----|-----|-------|------|-----------|----------|
| Edwards | 9 | 2 | | 11 | 4 | | 4 | Golland | 2 | | | 2 | | | |
| Morford | 8 | 1 | | 9 | | | | Holland | 2 | | | 2 | | | |
| Davies | 5 | | | 5 | | | | Liddiard | 2 | | | 2 | | | |
| Hamblin | 3 | 1 | | 4 | | | | Mann | 2 | | | 2 | | | |
| Andrews | 3 | | | 3 | 2 | | | Graham | 1 | | | 1 | | | |
| Hogg | 3 | | | 3 | | | | Hardy | 1 | | | 1 | | | |
| Mullins | 3 | | | 3 | | | | Harris | 1 | | | 1 | | | |
| Webb | 3 | | | 3 | | | | Rawlings | 1 | | | 1 | | | |
| Edwards | 2 | | | 2 | | | | Own Goals | 1 | | | 1 | | | |
| Goddard | 2 | | | 2 | | | | Cons Run - Consecutive scoring games. | | | | | | | |

# GUISELEY

**Chairman:** Steve Parkin
**Secretary:** Adrian Towers    **(T)** 07946 388 739    **(E)** admin@guiseleyafc.co.uk
**Commercial Manager:** tbc c/o Secretary    **(T)**
**Programme Editor:** Rachel O'Connor    **(T)** 0113 250 6205
**Ground Address:** Nethermoor Park, Otley Road, Guiseley, Leeds LS20 8BT
**(T)** 01943 873 223 (Office) 872 872 (Club)    **Manager:** Steve Kittrick

## Club Factfile

**Founded:** 1909    **Nickname:** The Lions
**Previous Names:** None
**Previous Leagues:** Wharfedale, Leeds, West Riding Counties, West Yorkshire, Yorkshire 1968-82, Northern Counties East 1982-91, Northern Premier 1991-2010

**Club Colours (change):** White/navy/navy (All yellow)

**Ground Capacity:** 3,000    **Seats:** 427    **Covered:** 1,040    **Clubhouse:** Yes    **Shop:** Yes

**Directions:** From the West M62, M606 then follow signs to A65 through Guiseley to Ground on Right. From South and East M1 and M621 towards Leeds City Centre. Continue on M621 to Junction 2, follow Headingly Stadium signs to A65 towards Ilkley then as above. From North West From Skipton, A65 Ilkley, via Burley By-pass A65 towards Leeds, Ground quarter of a mile on left after Harry Ramsden's roundabout From North/NE A1M, leave at A59, towards Harrogate, then A658 signed Leeds Bradford Airport, at Pool turn right onto A659 Otley, continue towards Bradford/Leeds, to Harry Ramsden roundabout then A65 Leeds ground quarter of a mile on left.

**Previous Grounds:** None

**Record Attendance:** 2,486 v Bridlington Town - FA Vase Semi-final 1st Leg 1989-90
**Record Victory:** Not known
**Record Defeat:** Not known
**Record Goalscorer:** Not known
**Record Appearances:** Not known
**Additional Records:**

**Senior Honours:**
Northern Counties East 1990-91. FA Vase 1990-91.
Northern Premier League Division 1 1993-94, Premier Division 2009-10, Challenge Cup 2008-09.

### 10 YEAR RECORD

| 03-04 | 04-05 | 05-06 | 06-07 | 07-08 | 08-09 | 09-10 | 10-11 | 11-12 | 12-13 |
|---|---|---|---|---|---|---|---|---|---|
| NP 1 9 | NP P 10 | NP P 14 | NP P 6 | NP P 6 | NP P 3 | NP P 1 | Conf N 5 | Conf N 2 | Conf N 2 |

# MATCH RESULTS 2012-13

| Date | Comp | H/A | Opponents | Att: | Result | Goalscorers | Pos | No. |
|------|------|-----|-----------|------|--------|-------------|-----|-----|
| Aug 18 | BSN | A | Histon | 303 | W 4-1 | N.Boshell 41 49 Forrest 87 Rothery 90 | 2 | 1 |
| 21 | BSN | H | Droylsden | 431 | W 7-1 | Wilson 30 81 N.Boshell 7 34 Ellis 40, Rothery 65 (pen) Brogan 89 | 1 | 2 |
| 25 | BSN | H | Gainsborough Trinity | 262 | W 2-0 | Rothery 7 22 | 1 | 3 |
| 27 | BSN | A | Workington | 374 | W 2-0 | Brooksby 62 Rothery 77 | 1 | 4 |
| Sept 1 | BSN | H | Gloucester City | 541 | W 3-1 | N.Boshell 51 69  Wilson 55 | 1 | 5 |
| 4 | BSN | A | Colwyn Bay | 254 | W 2-0 | Wilson 58 Brogan 86 | 1 | 6 |
| 8 | BSN | A | Chester | 2937 | L 0-4 | | 3 | 7 |
| 15 | BSN | H | Bishop's Stortford | 496 | L 1-2 | Walshaw 55 | 3 | 8 |
| 18 | BSN | H | Harrogate Town | 453 | W 2-0 | Walshaw 29 Bower 63 | 2 | 9 |
| 22 | FAC Q2 | A | Bamber Bridge | 249 | W 1-0 | Walshaw 78 | | 10 |
| 29 | BSN | A | Oxford City | 303 | W 3-0 | Brooksby 2 Wilson 75 N.Boshell 90 | 2 | 11 |
| Oct 2 | BSN | A | Stalybridge Celtic | 412 | W 1-0 | Walshaw 8 | 2 | 12 |
| 6 | FAC Q3 | A | Colwyn Bay | 318 | D 1-1 | Walshaw 24 | | 13 |
| 9 | FAC Q3r | H | Colwyn Bay | 360 | W 3-1 | Brooksby (2) Rothery | | 14 |
| 13 | BSN | A | Solihull Moors | 245 | L 0-2 | | 3 | 15 |
| 20 | FAC Q4 | H | Buxton | 847 | W 2-0 | Walshaw 30 N.Boshell 90 | | 16 |
| 27 | BSN | H | Vauxhall Motors | 756 | W 2-1 | Bower 44 88 | 2 | 17 |
| 30 | BSN | A | Altrincham | 698 | W 3-1 | N.Boshell 39 Walshaw 84 88 | 2 | 18 |
| Nov 3 | FAC 1 | H | Barrow | 1605 | D 2-2 | Brooksby 14 D.Boshell 35 | | 19 |
| 10 | FAT Q3 | H | Whitby Town | 506 | W 7-0 | Holsgrove 5 Holdsworth 36  Wilson 51 | | |
| | | | | | | WALSHAW 3 (42 55 88) N. Boshell 88 | | 20 |
| 13 | FAC 1r | A | Barrow | 1372 | L 0-1 | | | 21 |
| 17 | BSN | A | Boston United | 944 | W 3-1 | Brooksby 44 Holsgrove 49 79 | 2 | 22 |
| 20 | BSN | H | Worcester City | 424 | D 3-3 | Wilson 15 Bower 17 N.Boshell 55 | 3 | 23 |
| 24 | FAT 1 | H | Brackley Town | 524 | W 3-1 | N.Boshell 40 (pen) Rothery 77 (pen) Holsgrove 78 | | 24 |
| Dec 1 | BSN | A | Hinckley United | 192 | W 3-0 | Brooksby 1 D Boshell 16 Wilson 61 | 2 | 25 |
| 8 | BSN | H | Histon | 484 | W 2-1 | Rothery  8 Wilson 69 | 2 | 26 |
| 15 | FAT 2 | A | Skelmersdale United | 310 | L 0-2 | | | 27 |
| 26 | BSN | H | Bradford PA | 1017 | W 1-0 | D.Boshell 24 | 2 | 28 |
| Jan 1 | BSN | H | Bradford PA | 703 | W 3-1 | Wilson 35 Holdsworth 74 78 | 2 | 29 |
| 5 | BSN | A | Bishops Stortford | 377 | W 5-2 | Holdsworth 7 Wilson 34 87 McWilliams 73 Brooksby 78 | 2 | 30 |
| 8 | BSN | H | Corby Town | 328 | W 2-1 | Walshaw 63 Wilson 79 | 2 | 31 |
| 12 | BSN | H | Oxford City | 605 | W 1-0 | Walshaw 50 | 2 | 32 |
| Feb 9 | BSN | H | Boston United | 742 | W 2-1 | Pearson 1 Walshaw 66 | 2 | 33 |
| 12 | BSN | A | Gloucester City | 220 | D 2-2 | Wilson 17 19 | 2 | 34 |
| 16 | BSN | A | Vauxhall Motors | 357 | L 0-2 | | 2 | 35 |
| 19 | BSN | H | Colwyn Bay | 2189 | D 2-2 | Walshaw 9 Brooksby 44 | 2 | 36 |
| 23 | BSN | A | Worcester City | 738 | W 1-0 | Walshaw 89 | 2 | 37 |
| Mar 2 | BSN | H | Brackley Town | 608 | L 0-2 | | 2 | 38 |
| 6 | BSN | A | Corby Town | 229 | W 3-2 | Walshaw 3 46 Wilson 82 | 2 | 39 |
| 9 | BSN | A | Droylsden | 211 | W 3-0 | Holdsworth 23 Marsh 27 Walshaw 46 | 2 | 40 |
| 16 | BSN | H | Solihull Moors | 512 | W 1-0 | Wilson 32 | 2 | 41 |
| 30 | BSN | A | Gainsborough Trinity | 600 | W 2-1 | Holsgrove 72 Carole 76 | 2 | 42 |
| Apr 1 | BSN | H | Workington | 513 | W 2-0 | Lawlor 7 Dale 86 | 2 | 43 |
| 3 | BSN | H | FC Halifax Town | 1137 | D 1-1 | Bower 9 | 2 | 44 |
| 6 | BSN | A | Brackley Town | 285 | L 0-1 | | 2 | 45 |
| 9 | BSN | A | Stalybridge Celtic | 263 | D 1-1 | Wilson 2 | 2 | 46 |
| 11 | BSN | H | Altrincham | 459 | D 1-1 | Wilson 37 | 2 | 47 |
| 13 | BSN | H | Chester | 1535 | W 2-1 | Wilson 8 71 | 2 | 48 |
| 20 | BSN | A | FC Halifax Town | 1598 | D 1-1 | Wilson 40 | 2 | 49 |
| 23 | BSN | A | Harrogate Town | 414 | W 2-1 | Walshaw 52 88 | 2 | 50 |
| 27 | BSN | H | Hinckley United | 750 | L 2-4 | Pearson 71  Walshaw 74 | 2 | 51 |
| 30 | P-O S-F 1 | A | FC Halifax Town | 2367 | L 0-2 | | | 52 |
| May 4 | P-O S-F 2 | H | FC Halifax Town | 2424 | L 0-1 | | | 53 |

| GOALSCORERS | Lge | FAC | LC | Total | Pens | Hat-tricks | Cons Run | | Lge | FAC | LC | Total | Pens | Hat-tricks | Cons Run |
|-------------|-----|-----|----|-------|------|-----------|----------|--|-----|-----|----|-------|------|-----------|----------|
| Walshaw | 16 | 3 | 3 | 22 | 1 | | 3 | Pearson | 2 | | | 2 | | | |
| Wilson | 21 | | 1 | 22 | | | 4 | Carole. | 1 | | | 1 | | | |
| Boshell | 9 | 1 | 2 | 12 | 1 | | 2 | Dale. | 1 | | | 1 | | | |
| Brooksby | 6 | 3 | | 9 | | | | Ellis. | 1 | | | 1 | | | |
| Rothery | 6 | 1 | 1 | 8 | 2 | | | Forrest. | 1 | | | 1 | | | |
| Bower | 5 | | | 5 | | | | Lawlor. | 1 | | | 1 | | | |
| Holsgrove | 3 | | 2 | 5 | | | | Marsh. | 1 | | | 1 | | | |
| Holdsworth | 4 | | 1 | 5 | | | | McWilliams. | 1 | | | 1 | | | |
| D.Boshall | 2 | 1 | | 3 | | | | Cons Run - Consecutive scoring games. | | | | | | | |
| Brogan | 2 | | | 2 | | | | | | | | | | | |

# HARROGATE TOWN

**Chairman:** Irving Weaver

**Secretary:** Charlie Lockwood　　**(T)** 07896 828 236　　**(E)** charlielockwood@gharrogatetownafc.com

**Commercial Manager:** Garry Plant　　**(T)** 07740 822 497

**Programme Editor:** Peter Arnett　　**(T)** 07894 401 110

**Ground Address:** The CNG Stadium, Wetherby Road, Harrogate HG2 7SA

**(T)** 01423 880 675　　　　　　　　　　　　**Manager:** Simon Weaver

## Club Factfile

**Founded:** 1935　　**Nickname:** Town

**Previous Names:** Harrogate Hotspurs 1935-48.

**Previous Leagues:** West Riding 1919-20, Yorkshire 1920-21, 22-31, 57-82, Midland 1921-22, Northern 1931-32, Harrogate & Dist. 1935-37, 40-46, W. Riding Co.Am. 1937-40, W. Yorks. 1946-57, N.C.E. 1982-87, N.P.L. 1987-2004

**Club Colours (change):** Yellow & black/black/yellow (All blue)

**Ground Capacity:** 3,291　　**Seats:** 502　　**Covered:** 1,300　　**Clubhouse:** Yes　　**Shop:** Yes

**Directions**

A61 to Harrogate, turn right on to A658, and at roundabout take A661, proceed through second set of lights (Woodlands pub) ground approx. 500 mtrs on the right. From A1 Wetherby. Leave A1 at Wetherby on to A661 to Harrogate. Stay on this road and when reaching Harrogate at Woodland pub lights, ground 500mtrs on the right.

**Previous Grounds:** None

**Record Attendance:** 4,280 v Railway Athletic - Whitworth Cup Final 1950

**Record Victory:** 13-0 v Micklefield

**Record Defeat:** 1-10 v Methley United - 1956

**Record Goalscorer:** Jimmy Hague - 135 (1956-58 and 1961-76)

**Record Appearances:** Paul Williamson - 428 (1980-81, 1982-85, and 1986-93)

**Additional Records:**

**Senior Honours:**
West Riding County Cup 1962-63, 72-73, 85-86. Northern Premier League Division 1 2001-02.
West Riding Challenge Cup x2.

### 10 YEAR RECORD

| 03-04 | | 04-05 | | 05-06 | | 06-07 | | 07-08 | | 08-09 | | 09-10 | | 10-11 | | 11-12 | | 12-13 | |
|---|---|---|---|---|---|---|---|---|---|---|---|---|---|---|---|---|---|---|---|
| NP P | 5 | Conf N | 6 | Conf N | 5 | Conf N | 6 | Conf N | 6 | Conf N | 9 | Conf N | 21 | Conf N | 12 | Conf N | 15 | Conf N | 6 |

# MATCH RESULTS 2012-13

| Date | Comp | H/A | Opponents | Att: | Result | Goalscorers | Pos | No. |
|------|------|-----|-----------|------|--------|-------------|-----|-----|
| Aug 18 | BSN | A | Hinckley United | 301 | W 2-0 | Chilaka 35 Killock 63 | 5 | 1 |
| 21 | BSN | H | Altrincham | 532 | L 1-2 | Chilaka 47 | 9 | 2 |
| 25 | BSN | H | Bradford PA | 548 | D 1-1 | Killock 16 | 11 | 3 |
| 27 | BSN | A | Gainsborough Trinity | 470 | D 1-1 | Beesley 61 | 12 | 4 |
| Sept 4 | BSN | A | Droylsden | 202 | W 3-1 | Kerr 16 (og) Chilaka 59 Deon 84 | 9 | 5 |
| 8 | BSN | A | Histon | 246 | W 3-1 | Chilaka 32 Hawkins 38 (og) Dean 71 (Pen) | 6 | 6 |
| 15 | BSN | H | Oxford City | 444 | L 1-3 | Merris 17 | 10 | 7 |
| 18 | BSN | A | Guiseley | 453 | L 0-2 | | 10 | 8 |
| 22 | FAC Q2 | A | **West Auckland** | 180 | D 2-2 | **Chilaka 25 74** | | 9 |
| 29 | BSN | A | Worcester City | 954 | D 2-2 | Clayton 26 Beesley 90 | 11 | 10 |
| Oct 2 | FAC Q2r | H | **West Auckland** | 151 | W 5-1 | **Dean 40 (pen) Elam 68 Beesley 70 Chilaka 78** | | 11 |
| 6 | FAC Q3 | H | **Frickley Athletic** | 349 | W 3-2 | **Beesley 15 23 Bolder 75** | | 12 |
| 13 | BSN | A | Brackley Town | 487 | W 6-1 | Chilaka 25 Platt 37 Beesley 44 51 White 45 Forrest 66 | 9 | 13 |
| 20 | FAC Q4 | A | **Hyde** | 395 | D 1-1 | **Osbourne 88** | | 14 |
| 31 | FAC Q4r | H | **Hyde** | 247 | W 1-0 | **Clayton 118 *aet** | | 15 |
| Nov 4 | FAC 1 | A | **Torquay United** | 1817 | W 1-0 | **Chilaka 20** | | 16 |
| 10 | FAT Q3 | A | **Vauxhall Motors** | 131 | W 3-1 | **Platt 41 53 Beesley 59** | | 17 |
| 17 | BSN | H | Vauxhall Motors | 393 | W 3-1 | Beesley 19 Elam 23 Dean 39 | 12 | 18 |
| 20 | BSN | A | Stalybridge Celtic | 367 | L 0-1 | | 14 | 19 |
| 24 | FAT 1 | A | **Gainsborough Trinity** | 386 | L 0-2 | | | 20 |
| Dec 1 | FAC 2 | H | **Hastings United** | 2986 | D 1-1 | **Platt 41** | | 21 |
| 8 | BSN | A | Colwyn Bay | 322 | W 2-1 | Platt 13 28 | 14 | 22 |
| 13 | FAC 2r | A | **Hastings United** | 4028 | D-1-1 | **Platt 90 *aet** | | 23 |
| 15 | BSN | H | Hinckley United | 1440 | W 5-0 | Chilaka 2 20 Nowakowski 4 Killock 56 Platt 68 | 12 | 24 |
| 19 | BSN | A | Chester | 1803 | L 0-2 | | 12 | 25 |
| Jan 1 | BSN | A | Workington | 406 | W 2-1 | Elam 7 Baker 85 | 12 | 26 |
| 5 | BSN | A | Altrincham | 707 | L 0-3 | | 13 | 27 |
| 8 | BSN | A | Boston United | 770 | W 2-1 | Chilaka 20 60 | 11 | 28 |
| 29 | BSN | H | Corby Town | 99 | W 6-1 | Chilaka 53 68 Jouhill 49 Knowles 55 79 Baker 87 | 9 | 29 |
| Feb 5 | BSN | H | Workington | 284 | W 3-1 | Elam 65 Knowles 71 76 | 8 | 30 |
| 9 | BSN | A | Brackley Town | 232 | L 1-2 | Woods 90 | 9 | 31 |
| 12 | BSN | H | Worcester city | 49 | W 3-1 | Beesley 26 44 Chilaka 40 | 8 | 32 |
| 19 | BSN | H | Droylsden | 253 | D 1-1 | Killock 17 | 8 | 33 |
| 23 | BSN | A | Gloucester City | 242 | W 2-0 | Platt 9 Knowles 17 (pen) | 7 | 34 |
| 26 | BSN | H | Boston United | 281 | W 4-2 | Platt 7 Woods 26 Knowles 68 Elam 91 | 6 | 35 |
| Mar 2 | BSN | H | Histon | 478 | W 2-0 | Platt 4 Knowles 34 | 6 | 36 |
| 5 | BSN | H | Colwyn Bay | 215 | L 1-2 | Knowles 2 | 5 | 37 |
| 7 | BSN | A | FC Halifax Town | 1133 | W 2-1 | Bloomer 5 Bolland 11 | 5 | 38 |
| 9 | BSN | H | Chester | 815 | L 1-3 | Knowles 76 | 5 | 39 |
| 12 | BSN | H | Bishops Stortford | 184 | D 2-2 | Killock 41 Larkin 52 | 5 | 40 |
| 16 | BSN | A | Corby Town | 273 | W 2-0 | Knowles 53 Bolder 70 | 6 | 41 |
| 19 | BSN | A | Bishop Stortford | 275 | W 2-0 | Forrest 45 Chilaka 85 | 5 | 42 |
| Apr 1 | BSN | H | Gainsborough Trinity | 408 | D 0-0 | | 6 | 43 |
| 4 | BSN | A | Bradford PA | 329 | L 0-1 | | 6 | 44 |
| 6 | BSN | H | Solihull Moors | 371 | L 2-4 | Dean 70 89 | 6 | 45 |
| 9 | BSN | H | Gloucester City | 301 | W 1-0 | Beesley 3 | 6 | 46 |
| 13 | BSN | A | Oxford City | 263 | D 0-0 | | 7 | 47 |
| 16 | BSN | A | Solihull Moors | 419 | L 0-2 | | 7 | 48 |
| 18 | BSN | H | FC Halifax Town | 698 | D 1-1 | Bolder 21 | 7 | 49 |
| 20 | BSN | H | Stalybridge Celtic | 430 | D 0-0 | | 6 | 50 |
| 23 | BSN | H | Guiseley | 414 | L 1-2 | Woods 6 | 6 | 51 |
| 27 | BSN | A | Vauxhall Motors | 162 | W 1-0 | Forest 90 | 6 | 52 |

| GOALSCORERS | Lge | FAC | LC | Total | Pens | Hat-tricks | Cons Run | | Lge | FAC | LC | Total | Pens | Hat-tricks | Cons Run |
|-------------|-----|-----|-----|-------|------|-----------|----------|---|-----|-----|-----|-------|------|-----------|----------|
| Chilaka | 13 | 4 | | 17 | | | 2 | Baker | 2 | | | 2 | | | |
| Beesley | 8 | 3 | 1 | 11 | | | 4 | Blomero | 1 | | | 1 | | | |
| Platt | 7 | 2 | 2 | 11 | | | 4 | Bolland | 1 | | | 1 | | | |
| Knowles | 10 | | | 10 | 1 | | 4 | Jouhill | 1 | | | 1 | | | |
| Dean | 5 | 1 | | 6 | 2 | | | Larkin | 1 | | | 1 | | | |
| Elam | 4 | 1 | | 5 | | | | Merris | 1 | | | 1 | | | |
| Killock | 5 | | | 5 | | | | Nowakowski | 1 | | | 1 | | | |
| Bolder | 2 | 1 | | 3 | | | | Osbourne | | 1 | | 1 | | | |
| Clayton | 1 | 2 | | 3 | | | | White | 1 | | | 1 | | | |
| Forrest | 3 | | | 3 | | | | Own Goals | 2 | | | 2 | | | |
| Woods | 3 | | | 3 | | | | Cons Run - Consecutive scoring games. | | | | | | | |

# HEDNESFORD TOWN

**Chairman:** Stephen Price
**Secretary:** Terry McMahon    **(T)** 07901 822 040    **(E)** mcmahon64@gmail.com
**Commercial Manager:** n/a    **(T)**
**Programme Editor:** Simon Faulkner    **(T)** 07969 373 372
**Ground Address:** Keys Park, Park Road, Hednesford, Cannock WS12 2DZ
**(T)** 01543 422 870      **Manager:** Rob Smith

Promotion winning Squad.

## Club Factfile

**Founded:** 1880    **Nickname:** The Pitmen
**Previous Names:** Hednesford 1938-74
**Previous Leagues:** Walsall & District, Birmingham Combination 1906-15, 45-53, West Midlands 1919-39, 53-72, 74-84, Midland Counties 1972-74, Southern 1984-95, 2001-2005, 2009-11, Conference 1995-2001, 05-06, Northern Premier 2006-09

**Club Colours (change):** White/black/black (All red)

**Ground Capacity:** 6,039    **Seats:** 1,011    **Covered:** 5,335    **Clubhouse:** Yes    **Shop:** Yes

**Directions:** Leave M6 at J11 and follow the signs for Cannock. At the next island take the third exit towards Rugeley (A460). On reaching the A5 at Churchbridge island, rejoin the A460 signposted Rugeley and follow this road over five traffic islands. At the sixth traffic island, by a Texaco petrol station, turn right past a McDonalds restaurant and follow this road to the next island which is 'Cross Keys Island'. Go over this island to the next small island and turn right. Keys Park football ground is on left.

**Previous Grounds:** The Tins 1880-1903. The Cross Keys 1903-95.

**Record Attendance:** 3,169 v York City - FA Cup 3rd Round 13/01/1997
**Record Victory:** 12-1 v Redditch United - Birmingham Combination 1952-53
**Record Defeat:** 0-15 v Burton - Birmingham Combination 1952-53
**Record Goalscorer:** Joe O'Connor - 230 in 430 games
**Record Appearances:** Kevin Foster - 463
**Additional Records:** Paid £12,000 to Macclesfield Town for Steve Burr
**Senior Honours:** Received £50,000 from Blackpool for Kevin Russell
Southern League Premier Division 1994-95. FA Trophy 2004-05.
Staffordshire Senior Cup x3 Most recently 2012-13. Birmingham Senior Cup 1935-36, 2012-13.

### 10 YEAR RECORD

| 03-04 | | 04-05 | | 05-06 | | 06-07 | | 07-08 | | 08-09 | | 09-10 | | 10-11 | | 11-12 | | 12-13 | |
|---|---|---|---|---|---|---|---|---|---|---|---|---|---|---|---|---|---|---|---|
| SthP | 20 | SthP | 4 | Conf N | 22 | NP P | 7 | NP P | 8 | NP P | 8 | SthP | 4 | SthP | 2 | NP P | 5 | NP P | 2 |

# MATCH RESULTS 2012-13

| Date | Comp | H/A | Opponents | Att: | Result | Goalscorers | Pos | No. |
|---|---|---|---|---|---|---|---|---|
| Aug 18 | NPL | H | Frickley Athletic | 418 | W 3-2 | Durrell 36 (pen) Harvey 50 66 | 6 | 1 |
| 21 | NPL | A | Eastwood Town | 195 | W 2-0 | Osbourne 48 Durrell 56 | 3 | 2 |
| 25 | NPL | A | Blyth Spartans | 325 | W 2-1 | Harvey 56 McPherson 67 | 4 | 3 |
| 27 | NPL | H | Stafford Rangers | 920 | D 2-2 | Durrell 50 (pen) Woolfe 90 | 4 | 4 |
| Sept 2 | NPL | A | FC United | 1702 | D 1-1 | Lennon 81 | 5 | 5 |
| 4 | NPL | H | Eastwood Town | 439 | W 2-0 | Woolfe 47 O'Connor 51 | 5 | 6 |
| 8 | FAC Q1 | A | Redditch United | 276 | W 3-0 | Woolfe 41 56 Durrell 63 | | 7 |
| 15 | NPL | A | Chorley | 722 | W 2-1 | Woolfe 43 Melbourne 87 | 3 | 8 |
| 18 | NPL | H | Worksop Town | 406 | L 0-4 | | 3 | 9 |
| 22 | FAC Q2 | A | Nuneaton Griff | 298 | W 3-2 | Macpherson 1 Harvey 51 Rey 59 | | 10 |
| 29 | FAT Q1 | H | Bedworth United | 307 | W 3-1 | Woolfe 3 Bailey 50 Durrell 65 | | 11 |
| Oct 6 | FAC Q3 | H | Buxton | 498 | D 2-2 | Macpherson 30 Woolfe 36 | | 12 |
| 10 | FAC Q3r | A | Buxton | 302 | L 1-2* | Macpherson 74 | | 13 |
| 13 | NPL | H | Ashton United | 489 | L 1-2 | Disney 53 | 9 | 14 |
| 16 | NPL | A | Nantwich Town | 237 | D 1-1 | Durrell 29 | 9 | 15 |
| 20 | NPL | A | Grantham Town | 227 | W 3-2 | Harvey 35 Bailey 76 O'Connor 82 | 8 | 16 |
| 23 | NPL | H | Witton Albion | 371 | W 2-1 | O'Connor 90 Durrell 90 (pen) | 3 | 17 |
| 27 | FAT Q2 | A | Trafford | 188 | W 2-0 | Durrell 59 Osborne 81 | | 18 |
| 30 | NPL | H | Marine | 403 | W 2-0 | Durrell 68 Rey 77 | 2 | 19 |
| Nov 3 | NPL | A | Whitby Town | 292 | W 2-0 | Wells 18 Osborne 63 | 2 | 20 |
| 11 | FAT Q3 | A | Romulus | 224 | W 2-1 | Macpherson 45 Rey 81 | | 21 |
| 17 | NPL | A | Stocksbridge PS | 143 | D 3-3 | Bailey 10 Rey 36 Durrell 64 | 4 | 22 |
| 20 | NPL | A | Matlock Town | 253 | W 3-2 | Rey 13 58 Francis 40 | 3 | 23 |
| 24 | FAT 1 | H | Solihull Moors | 355 | L 1-2 | Macpherson 20 | | 24 |
| 27 | NPL | H | Ilkeston | 319 | W 2-0 | Durrell 46 84 (pen) | 2 | 25 |
| Dec 1 | NPL | A | North Ferriby United | 405 | W 3-2 | Durrell 54 (pen) 84 (pen) Rey 89 | 2 | 26 |
| 8 | NPL | H | FC United | 929 | W 1-0 | Durrell 66 | 2 | 27 |
| 15 | NPL | A | Frickley Athletic | 201 | L 1-2 | Durrell 38 | 2 | 28 |
| 26 | NPL | A | Stafford Rangers | 1124 | W 1-0 | Rey 77 | 2 | 29 |
| Jan 1 | NPL | H | Rushall Olympic | 698 | L 3-4 | Durrell 8 (pen) Harvey 21 Bailey 55 | 2 | 30 |
| 5 | NPL | A | Chorley | 493 | W 3-1 | Harvey 26 67 Rey 61 | 2 | 31 |
| 12 | NPL | A | Worksop Town | 390 | L 0-4 | Woolfe 24 Durell 45 65 Rey 89 | 2 | 32 |
| Feb 2 | NPL | H | Nantwich Town | 403 | W 3-0 | Bailey 1 Durrell 31 Barnes 66 | 2 | 33 |
| 9 | NPL | A | Ashton United | 153 | D 2-2 | Lennon 47 Durrell 75 | 2 | 34 |
| 16 | NPL | H | Grantham Town | 463 | W 3-0 | Bailey 4 Rey 47 Harvey 54 | 2 | 35 |
| Mar 2 | NPL | A | Witton Albion | 507 | D 1-1 | Bailey 88 | 2 | 36 |
| 5 | NPL | H | AFC Hyde | 295 | W 2-0 | Macpherson 42 Lennon 90 | 2 | 37 |
| 9 | NPL | H | Matlock Town | 391 | D 2-2 | Durrell 64 (pen) Melbourne 82 | 2 | 38 |
| 16 | NPL | H | North Ferriby United | 906 | L 2-3 | Harvey 60 Durrell 67 (pen) | 2 | 39 |
| 26 | NPL | A | Kendal Town | 101 | W 3-1 | Harvey 2 Lennon 22 Durrell 67 (pen) | 2 | 40 |
| 30 | NPL | H | Buxton | 459 | W 3-2 | Taylor 7 Harvey 54 76 | 2 | 41 |
| Apr 1 | NPL | A | Rushall Olympic | 602 | D 2-2 | O'Connor 77 Patterson 87 | 2 | 42 |
| 4 | NPL | H | Kendal Town | 344 | W 2-1 | Lennon 40 60 | 2 | 43 |
| 6 | NPL | A | Marine | 323 | D 0-0 | | 2 | 44 |
| 9 | NPL | H | Blyth Sprtans | 501 | W 3-0 | Harvey 3 Taylor 52 Lennon 63 | 2 | 45 |
| 13 | NPL | H | Whitby Town | 504 | W 4-0 | Bailey 7 Lennon 5 Harvey 59 65 | 2 | 46 |
| 17 | NPL | A | Buxton | 298 | W 2-0 | Lennon 15 Taylor 61 | 2 | 47 |
| 20 | NPL | A | Ilkeston | 529 | W 2-0 | Bailey 34 Taylor 84 | 2 | 48 |
| 27 | NPL | H | Stocksbridge PS | 706 | W 4-1 | Durrell 1 87 (pen) Harvey 6 Francis 61 | 2 | 49 |
| May 4 | NPL | A | AFC Fylde | 563 | W 2-1 | Durrell 30 Rey 85 | 2 | 50 |
| 7 | P-Off S-F | H | AFC Fylde | 1360 | D 3-3 | Durrell 56 98 (pen) Macpherson 71 *aet W 3-1 pens | | 51 |
| 11 | P-Off Final | H | FC United | 4412 | W 2-1 | Harvey 32 Osborne 42 | | 52 |

| GOALSCORERS | Lge | FAC | FAT | Total | Pens | Hat-tricks | Cons Run | | Lge | FAC | FAT | Total | Pens | Hat-tricks | Cons Run |
|---|---|---|---|---|---|---|---|---|---|---|---|---|---|---|---|
| Durrell | 26 | 1 | 2 | 29 | 11 | | 4 | Francis | 2 | | | 2 | | | |
| Harvey | 17 | 1 | | 17 | | | 3 | Melbourne | 2 | | | 2 | | | |
| Rey | 10 | 1 | 1 | 12 | | | 3 | Barnes | 1 | | | 1 | | | |
| Bailey | 8 | | 1 | 9 | | | 2 | Disney | 1 | | | 1 | | | |
| Lennon | 8 | | | 8 | | | | Lennon | 1 | | | 1 | | | |
| Woolfe | 4 | 3 | 1 | 8 | | | 3 | Patterson | 1 | | | 1 | | | |
| MacPherson | 3 | 3 | 2 | 7 | | | 2 | Wells | 1 | | | 1 | | | |
| O'Connor | 4 | | | 4 | | | | Cons Run - Consecutive scoring games. | | | | | | | |
| Taylor | 4 | | | 4 | 2 | | | | | | | | | | |
| Osborne | 3 | | 1 | 3 | | | | | | | | | | | |

# HISTON

**Chairman:** Russell Hands
**Secretary:** Howard Wilkins **(T)** 01223 237 373 **(E)** howard.wilkins@histonfc.co.uk
**Commercial Manager:** Bill Parker **(T)** 07801 197 734
**Programme Editor:** Howard Wilkins **(T)** 01223 237 373
**Ground Address:** The Glass World Stadium, Bridge Road, Impington, Cambridge CB24 9PH
**(T)** 01223 237 373 **Manager:** Brian Page

## Club Factfile

**Founded:** 1904 **Nickname:** The Stutes
**Previous Names:** Histon Institute
**Previous Leagues:** Cambridgeshire 1904-48, Spartan 1948-60, Delphian 1960-63, Eastern Counties 1966-2000,
Southern 2000-05.

**Club Colours (change):** Red and black stripes/black/black (Blue & white stripes/blue/blue)

**Ground Capacity:** 3,250 **Seats:** 450 **Covered:** 1,800 **Clubhouse:** Yes **Shop:** Yes

**Directions** From the M11 (Northbound) Junc 14, take the A14 eastbound signed towards Newmarket. Take the first exit off the A14 and at the roundabout, take the first exit onto the B1049. Go straight over the traffic lights, past the Holiday Inn Hotel (on your right) and the entrance to the club is half a mile on your right.

**Previous Grounds:** None

**Record Attendance:** 6,400 v King's Lynn - FA Cup 1956
**Record Victory:** 11-0 v March Town - Cambridgeshire Invitation Cup 15/02/01
**Record Defeat:** 1-8 v Ely City - Eastern Counties Division One 1994
**Record Goalscorer:** Neil Kennedy - 292
**Record Appearances:** Neil Andrews and Neil Kennedy
**Additional Records:** Paid £6,000 to Chelmsford City for Ian Cambridge 2000. Received £30,000 from Manchester United for
**Senior Honours:** Guiliano Maiorana.
Eastern Counties League Cup 1990-91, Eastern Counties League 1999-2000, Southern League Premier 2004-05, Conference South 2006-07.
Cambridgeshire Professional Cup 2012-13.

### 10 YEAR RECORD

| 03-04 | 04-05 | 05-06 | 06-07 | 07-08 | 08-09 | 09-10 | 10-11 | 11-12 | 12-13 |
|---|---|---|---|---|---|---|---|---|---|
| SthE 2 | SthP 1 | Conf S 5 | Conf S 1 | Conf 7 | Conf 3 | Conf 18 | Conf 24 | Conf N 16 | Conf N 19 |

# MATCH RESULTS 2012-13

| Date | Comp | H/A | Opponents | Att: | Result | Goalscorers | Pos | No. |
|---|---|---|---|---|---|---|---|---|
| Aug 18 | BSN | H | Guiseley | 303 | L 1-4 | Holman 40 | 21 | 1 |
| 21 | BSN | A | Boston United | 968 | L 0-6 | | 22 | 2 |
| 25 | BSN | H | Gloucester City | 221 | W 2-1 | Eades 88 (pen) Sheppard 90 (pen) | 17 | 3 |
| 27 | BSN | A | Hinckley United | 363 | W 1-0 | Sear 90 | 11 | 4 |
| Sept 1 | BSN | A | Altrincham | 652 | L 0-5 | | 14 | 5 |
| 4 | BSN | H | Worcester City | 204 | D 0-0 | | | 6 |
| 8 | BSN | H | Harrogate Town | 246 | L 1-3 | Dowie 2 | 18 | 7 |
| 15 | BSN | A | Stalybridge Celtic | 389 | L 1-2 | Stevenson 37 | 18 | 8 |
| 22 | FAC Q2 | A | Eastwood Town | 159 | W 5-3 | OTOBO 3 ( 61 64 79) Stevenson 63 Roberts 83 | | 9 |
| 29 | BSN | H | FC Halifax Town | 478 | L 0-1 | | 21 | 10 |
| Oct 2 | BSN | A | Brackley Town | 324 | L1-2 | Ivy-Ward 22 | 21 | 11 |
| 6 | FAC Q3 | H | Corby Town | 330 | D 1-1 | Ivy-Wood 51 | | 12 |
| 10 | FAC Q3r | A | Corby Town | 510 | L 1-2 | Hoban 84 | | 13 |
| 13 | BSN | H | Vauxhall | 260 | W 2-0 | Dowie 67 Stevenson 80 (pen) | 20 | 14 |
| 20 | BSN | A | Droylsden | 187 | D 2-2 | Stevenson 30 (pen) Sear 68 | 17 | 15 |
| 27 | BSN | A | Chester | 2410 | L 1-2 | Clerima 51 | 20 | 16 |
| 30 | BSN | H | Solihull Moors | 412 | D 0-0 | | 19 | 17 |
| Nov 3 | BSN | H | Corby Town | 305 | L 3-4 | Fitzimmons 28 Clerima 44 Stevenson 86 | 20 | 18 |
| 10 | FAT Q3 | H | Boreham Wood | 177 | L1-2 | Vihete 32 | | 19 |
| 24 | BSN | H | Chester | 428 | L 1-4 | Collins 61 (og) | 20 | 20 |
| Dec 1 | BSN | H | Bradford PA | 264 | L 1-4 | Waters 60 | 21 | 21 |
| 8 | BSN | A | Guiseley | 484 | L 1-2 | Taaffe 82 | 21 | 22 |
| 15 | BSN | A | Colwyn Bay | 326 | L 1-3 | Stevenson 22 | 21 | 23 |
| 26 | BSN | H | Bishops Stortford | 344 | W 2-0 | Taaffe 55 Freeman 90 | 20 | 24 |
| Jan 1 | BSN | A | Bishops Stortford | 505 | L 1-3 | Hoban 10 | 20 | 25 |
| 5 | BSN | A | Corby Town | 410 | D 0-0 | | 20 | 26 |
| 12 | BSN | H | Workington | 218 | W 3-0 | Porter 28 Waters 53 75 | 20 | 27 |
| 26 | BSN | A | Worcester City | 904 | W 3-2 | Stevenson 27 (pen) Taaffe 43 Waters 86 | 19 | 28 |
| Feb 2 | BSN | H | Droylsden | 290 | W 3-1 | Taaffe 13 19 Hawkins 22 | 18 | 29 |
| 5 | BSN | A | Oxford City | 175 | D 0-0 | | 17 | 30 |
| 9 | BSN | A | FC Halifax Town | 1118 | D 3-3 | Hoban 16 Taaffe 46 Fitzimmons 77 | 19 | 31 |
| 12 | BSN | H | Altrincham | 240 | W 2-0 | Sheppard 9 Stevenson 25 (pen) | 18 | 32 |
| 19 | BSN | H | Gainsborough Trinity | 212 | L 0-3 | | 18 | 33 |
| 23 | BSN | H | Oxford City | 247 | D 1-1 | Freeman 55 | 18 | 34 |
| Mar 2 | BSN | A | Harrogate Town | 478 | L 0-2 | | 18 | 35 |
| 5 | BSN | H | Brackley Town | 158 | W 3-0 | Stevenson 37 (pen) Dowie 54 Sheppard 59 | 16 | 36 |
| 9 | BSN | H | Colwyn Bay | 309 | W 2-1 | Sheppard 32 82 | 16 | 37 |
| 16 | BSN | A | Workington | 304 | L 1-3 | Sheppard 54 | 17 | 38 |
| 30 | BSN | A | Gloucester City | 323 | D 1-1 | Taaffe 61 | 18 | 39 |
| Apr 1 | BSN | H | Hinckley United | 318 | W 2-1 | Richens 32 Stevenson 35 | 15 | 40 |
| 6 | BSN | H | Stalybridge Celtic | 321 | L 0-2 | | 18 | 41 |
| 9 | BSN | A | Gainsborough Trinity | 346 | L 0-1 | | 18 | 42 |
| 13 | BSN | A | Vauxhall Motors | 192 | L 0-2 | | 18 | 43 |
| 20 | BSN | H | Boston United | 487 | D 1-1 | Fitzimmons | 20 | 44 |
| 23 | BSN | A | Solihull Moors | 185 | D 1-1 | Richens 39 | 19 | 45 |
| 27 | BSN | A | Bradford PA | 360 | D 0-0 | | 19 | 46 |

| GOALSCORERS | Lge | FAC | LC | Total | Pens | Hat-tricks | Cons Run | | Lge | FAC | LC | Total | Pens | Hat-tricks | Cons Run |
|---|---|---|---|---|---|---|---|---|---|---|---|---|---|---|---|
| Stevenson | 9 | 1 | | 10 | 4 | | 2 | Richens | 2 | | | 2 | | | |
| Taaffe | 7 | | | 7 | | | | Sear | 2 | | | 2 | | | |
| Sheppard | 6 | | | 6 | 1 | | | Eades | 1 | | | 1 | 1 | | |
| Waters | 4 | | | 4 | | | | Hawkins | 1 | | | 1 | | | |
| Dowie | 3 | | | 3 | | | | Holman | 1 | | | 1 | | | |
| Fitzimmons | 3 | | | 3 | | | | Porter | 1 | | | 1 | | | |
| Hoban | 2 | 1 | | 3 | | | | Roberts | | 1 | | 1 | | | |
| Otobo | | 3 | | 3 | | 1 | | Vihete | | | 1 | 1 | | | |
| Clerima | 2 | | | 2 | | | | Own Goals | 1 | | | 1 | | | |
| Freeman | 2 | | | 2 | | | | Cons Run - Consecutive scoring games. | | | | | | | |
| Ivy-Wood | 1 | 1 | | 2 | | | | | | | | | | | |

# LEAMINGTON

**Chairman:** Jim Scott
**Secretary:** Richard Edy    **(T)** 07762 866 123    **(E)** matchsecretary@leamingtonfc.co.uk
**Commercial Manager:** Nic Sproul    **(T)** 07710 112 292
**Programme Editor:** Sally Ellis    **(T)** programme@leamingtonfc.co.uk
**Ground Address:** New Windmill Ground, Harbury Lane, Whitmarsh, Leamington CV33 9QB
**(T)** 01926 430 406    **Manager:** Paul Holleran

Southern League Premier Division Championship winning squad.
Back Row L to R: Andy Jenkins (kitman) James Mace, Craig Owen, Joe Magunda, Michael Quirke, Liam Daly, Kevin Sawyer, Matty Dodd, Richard Batchelor, Mark Davidson (Community Director).
Front Row L to R: Alex Taylor, Dean Perrow, Lee Chilton, James Husband, Liam O'Neill (Coach) Jamie Hood, Paul Holleran (manager), Michael Tuohy, Sam Adkins, Stephan Morley, Tom Berwick.

## Club Factfile

**Founded:** 1892    **Nickname:** The Brakes
**Previous Names:** Leamington Town 1892-1937, Lockheed Borg & Beck 1944-46 , Lockheed Leamington 1946-73, AP Leamington 1973-88
**Previous Leagues:** Birmingham Combination, Birmingham & District, West Midlands Regional, Midland Counties, Southern, Midland Combination, Midland Alliance 2005-07. Southern 2007-13.

**Club Colours (change):** Gold with black trim/black with gold trim/gold with black trim (White with black trim/white/white with black trim)

**Ground Capacity:** 5,000    **Seats:** 120    **Covered:** 720    **Clubhouse:** Yes    **Shop:** Yes

**Directions**
From West and North – M40 Southbound – Exit J14 and take A452 towards Leamington. Ahead at 1st island. Next island take 2nd exit A452 (Europa Way). Next island take 4th exit (Harbury Lane) signposted Harbury and Bishops Tachbrook. Next island take 3rd exit (Harbury Lane). At traffic lights continue straight ahead Harbury Lane. Ground is 1.5 miles on left.
From South – M40 northbound – Exit J13. Turn right onto A452 towards Leamington. At 1st island take 3rd exit A452 (Europa Way) and follow as above (Europa Way onwards).

**Previous Grounds:** Old Windmill Ground

**Record Attendance:** 1,380 v Retford United - 17/02/2007
**Record Victory:** Not known
**Record Defeat:** Not known
**Record Goalscorer:** Josh Blake - 166
**Record Appearances:** Josh Blake - 314
**Additional Records:**

**Senior Honours:**
Birmingham & District 1961-62. West Midlands Regional 1962-63. Midland Counties 1964-65.
Southern League 1982-83, 2012-13, Division 1 Midlands 2008-09.
Midland Combination Division 2 2000-01, Premier Division 2004-05. Midland Alliance 2006-07, League cup 2005-06.

### 10 YEAR RECORD

| 03-04 | | 04-05 | | 05-06 | | 06-07 | | 07-08 | | 08-09 | | 09-10 | | 10-11 | | 11-12 | | 12-13 | |
|---|---|---|---|---|---|---|---|---|---|---|---|---|---|---|---|---|---|---|---|
| MCmP | 2 | MCmP | 1 | MidAl | 5 | MidAl | 1 | SthM | 2 | SthM | 1 | SthP | 10 | SthP | 5 | SthP | 7 | SthP | 1 |

# MATCH RESULTS 2012-13

| Date | Comp | H/A | Opponents | Att: | Result | Goalscorers | Pos | No. |
|---|---|---|---|---|---|---|---|---|
| Aug 18 | SPL | A | Bedford Town | 901 | D 2-2 | Downing 12 Daly 88 | 11 | 1 |
| 21 | SPL | H | Stourbridge | 417 | D 1-1 | Berwick 10 | 13 | 2 |
| 25 | SPL | H | Hitchin Town | 381 | W 3-0 | Dodd 30 (Pen) 86 L.Moore 76 | 8 | 3 |
| 27 | SPL | A | Bedworth United | 447 | W 3-0 | Berwick 22 Chiltern 44 L.Moore 68 | 5 | 4 |
| Sept 1 | SPL | H | Cambridge City | 502 | W 1-0 | Berwick 4 | 2 | 5 |
| 3 | SPL | A | Frome Town | 229 | W 2-0 | Berwick 70 Mace 81 | 1 | 6 |
| **8** | **FAC Q1** | **H** | **Stourbridge** | **602** | **D 2-2** | **Solly 55 Daly 88** | | 7 |
| **11** | **FAC Q1r** | **A** | **Stourbridge** | **440** | **W 2-1** | **Daly 40 Batchelor 91 *aet** | | 8 |
| 15 | SPL | H | Arlesey | 536 | W 4-3 | Berwick 7 Daly 29 85 Magunda 81 (pen) | 1 | 9 |
| 18 | SPL | A | Redditch United | 269 | D 1-1 | Daly 90 | 1 | 10 |
| **22** | **FAC Q2** | **A** | **Corby Town** | **516** | **L 2-3** | **Dodd 3 Adkins 90** | | 11 |
| **29** | **FAT Q1** | **A** | **Belper Town** | **228** | **D 2-2** | **Berwick 36 Morley 43** | | 12 |
| **Oct 2** | **FAT Q1r** | **H** | **Belper Town** | **226** | **D 2-2** | **Batchelor 54 78 *aet L 3-4 pens** | | 13 |
| 13 | SPL | A | Bashley | 229 | W 2-0 | Dodd 27 Taylor 87 | 2 | 14 |
| 27 | SPL | A | Hemel Hempstead | 477 | W 3-1 | Bruce 19 (og) Johnson 34 Chilton 54 | 2 | 15 |
| Nov 3 | SPL | H | Chippenham Town | 621 | W 1-0 | Johnson 7 | 2 | 16 |
| 13 | SPL | H | Kettering Town | 418 | W 2-1 | Johnson 25 Chilton 76 | 2 | 17 |
| 17 | SPL | H | St Neotes Town | 707 | W 3-0 | Daly 3 Morley 14 Chilton 20 | 2 | 18 |
| Dec 1 | SPL | H | AFC Totton | 554 | W 2-1 | Chilton 12 Dodd 66 | 2 | 19 |
| 8 | SPL | A | St Albans City | 356 | L 0-3 | | 2 | 20 |
| 15 | SPL | H | Bideford | 429 | W 2-1 | Dodd 38 (pen) Husband 58 | 2 | 21 |
| 18 | SPL | H | Gosport Borough | 351 | L 1-3 | Berwick 34 | 2 | 22 |
| 26 | SPL | A | Banbury United | 465 | L 0-3 | | 2 | 23 |
| Jan 1 | SPL | H | Bedworth United | 643 | W 6-1 | S.MOORE 3 ( 22 69 70) L.Moore 42 Chilton 59 Mace 90 | 2 | 24 |
| 5 | SPL | A | Stourbridge | 667 | L 1-5 | S.Moore 45 | 2 | 25 |
| 13 | SPL | H | Frome Town | 524 | W 2-0 | Batchelor 12 Daly 17 | 2 | 26 |
| 15 | SPL | A | Weymouth | 422 | W 4-0 | Batchelor 62 L.Moore 64 85 S.Moore 75 | 1 | 27 |
| 26 | SPL | A | Arlesey Town | 290 | W 2-0 | Dodd 15 (pen) Chilton 73 | 1 | 28 |
| 29 | SPL | A | Barwell | 367 | W 3-1 | Johnson 12 Chilton 61 S Moore 90 | 1 | 29 |
| Feb 3 | SPL | A | Kettering Town | 412 | W 3-1 | Chilton 25,50 S.Moore 90 | 1 | 30 |
| 9 | SPL | H | Barwell | 552 | L 0-6 | | 1 | 31 |
| 16 | SPL | A | St Neots Town | 434 | W 1-0 | Batchelor 66 | 1 | 32 |
| 19 | SPL | A | Hitchin Town | 350 | W 1-0 | Johnson 90 | 1 | 33 |
| 23 | SPL | H | Chesham United | 501 | L 0-1 | | 1 | 34 |
| Mar 2 | SPL | A | Gosport Borough | 586 | L 0-3 | | 1 | 35 |
| 5 | SPL | A | Chesham United | 231 | D 1-1 | Adkins 87 | 1 | 36 |
| 9 | SPL | H | Bashley | 462 | W 4-1 | S.Moore 5 Daly 49 Batchelor 87 Johnson 90 | 1 | 37 |
| 12 | SPL | H | Redditch United | 301 | W 2-0 | Hood 64 Johnson 76 | 1 | 38 |
| 19 | SPL | H | Bedford Town | 381 | W 3-0 | Daly 28 Chilton 29 S.Moore 56 | 1 | 39 |
| 30 | SPL | A | Cambridge City | 450 | W 4-1 | DODD 3 (45 75 80 all pens) S. Moore 90 | 1 | 40 |
| Apr 1 | SPL | H | Banbury Uited | 734 | W 4-1 | Daly 3 69 Dodd 83 S.Moore 87 | 1 | 41 |
| 6 | SPL | A | AFC Totton | 368 | W 2-0 | Batchelor 1 S.Moore 20 | 1 | 42 |
| 13 | SPL | H | Weymouth | 891 | D 1-1 | Batchelor 40 | 1 | 43 |
| 16 | SPL | A | Chippenham Town | 588 | W 2-0 | Johnson 20 S.Moore 30 | 1 | 44 |
| 20 | SPL | A | Bideford | 360 | W 1-0 | Batchelor 76 | 1 | 45 |
| 23 | SPL | H | Hemel Hempstead T | 539 | W 3-2 | JOHNSON 3 ( 31 45 50) | 1 | 46 |
| 27 | SPL | H | St Albans City | 1027 | W 2-1* | Dodd 40 (pen) Johnson 44 | 1 | 47 |
| | | | | | | | | 48 |
| | | | | | | | | 49 |
| | | | | | | | | 50 |
| | | | | | | | | 51 |

| GOALSCORERS | Lge | FAC | FAT | Total | Pens | Hat-tricks | Cons Run |
|---|---|---|---|---|---|---|---|
| Dodd | 12 | 1 | | 13 | | 1 | 2 |
| Daly | 10 | 2 | | 12 | | | 4 |
| Johnson | 12 | | | 12 | | 1 | 3 |
| S Moore | 12 | | | 12 | 7 | 1 | 2 |
| Chilton | 11 | | | 11 | | | 3 |
| Batchelor | 7 | 1 | 2 | 10 | | | 2 |
| Berwick | 6 | | 1 | 7 | | | 3 |
| L.Moore | 5 | | | 5 | | | 2 |
| Adkins | 1 | 1 | | 2 | | | |
| Mace | 2 | | | 2 | | | |
| Morley | 1 | | 1 | 2 | | | |
| Downing | 1 | | | 1 | | | |
| Hood | 1 | | | 1 | | | |
| Husband | 1 | | | 1 | | | |
| Magunda | 1 | | | 1 | 1 | | |
| Solly | | 1 | | 1 | | | |
| Taylor | 1 | | | 1 | | | |
| Own Goals | 1 | | | 1 | | | |

Cons Run - Consecutive scoring games.

# NORTH FERRIBY UNITED

**Chairman:** Les Hare

**Secretary:** Steve Tather  **(T)** 07845 378 512  **(E)** tather@tather39.karoo.co.uk

**Commercial Manager:** Les Hare  **(T)** 07813 688 220

**Programme Editor:** Richard Watts  **(T)** 07814 836 504

**Ground Address:** Grange Lane, Church Road, North Ferriby HU14 3AB

**(T)** 01482 634 601  **Manager:** Billy Heath

Northern Premier League Premier Division Championship winning squad.
Back l-r Chris Hall, Neil Stevens, Nathan Peat, Liam King, Ryan Kendal, Jack Maldoon, Russell Fry, Louis Mobbs, Tim Taylor, Ben Hunter. Middle l-r Danny Clark, Lee Morris, Sam Belcher, Gregg Anderson, Antoni Pecora, Adam Nicklin, Paul Foot, Mark Gray, Dene Lisle, Chris Bolder. Front l-r James Williams, Steve Gardner, Martin Woodmansey (Kit Manager), Billy Heath (Manager), Mark Carroll (Coach), Sara Henderson (Physio), Gary Bradshaw, Steve Ridley. Photo: Paul Whiteley.

## Club Factfile

**Founded:** 1934  **Nickname:** United

**Previous Names:** None

**Previous Leagues:** East Riding Church, East Riding Amateur, Yorkshire 1969-82, Northern Counties East 1982-2000. Northern Premier 2000-13.

**Club Colours (change):** White with green trim/green/green (All yellow with green trim)

**Ground Capacity:** 3,000  **Seats:** 250  **Covered:** 1,000  **Clubhouse:** Yes  **Shop:** Yes

**Directions**
Main Leeds to Hull road A63 or M62. North Ferriby is approx. 8 miles west of Hull.
Proceed through village past the Duke of Cumberland Hotel.
Turn right down Church Road. Ground mile down on left.

**Previous Grounds:** Not known

**Record Attendance:** 1,927 v Hull City - Charity game 2005

**Record Victory:** 9-0 v Hatfield Main - Northern Counties East 1997-98

**Record Defeat:** 1-7 v North Shields - Northern Counties East 1991

**Record Goalscorer:** Mark Tennison - 161

**Record Appearances:** Paul Sharp - 497 (1996-2006)

**Additional Records:** Andy Flounders scored 50 during season 1998-99

**Senior Honours:** Received £60,000 from Hull City for Dean Windass

Northern Counties East 1999-2000. Northern Premier League Division 1 2004-05, Premier Division 2012-13.
East Riding Senior Cup 1970-71, 76-77, 77-78, 78-79, 90-91, 96-97, 97-98, 98-99, 99-2000, 00-01, 01-02, 02-03, 06-07, 07-08, 08-09, 09-10, 10-11, 12-13.

### 10 YEAR RECORD

| 03-04 | | 04-05 | | 05-06 | | 06-07 | | 07-08 | | 08-09 | | 09-10 | | 10-11 | | 11-12 | | 12-13 | |
|---|---|---|---|---|---|---|---|---|---|---|---|---|---|---|---|---|---|---|---|
| NP 1 | 17 | NP 1 | 1 | NP P | 5 | NP P | 13 | NP P | 15 | NP P | 10 | NP P | 4 | NP P | 5 | NP P | 9 | NP P | 1 |

# MATCH RESULTS 2012-13

| Date | Comp | H/A | Opponents | Att. | Result | Goalscorers | Pos | No. |
|------|------|-----|-----------|------|--------|-------------|-----|-----|
| Aug 18 | NPL | H | Buxton | 168 | D 1-1 | Anderson 30 | 13 | 1 |
| 22 | NPL | A | Worksop Town | 301 | L 1-2 | Clarke 2 | 16 | 2 |
| 25 | NPL | A | AFC Fylde | 239 | L 0-1 | | 18 | 3 |
| 27 | NPL | H | Frickley Athletic | 207 | W 4-0 | Anderson 22 King 44 Bradshaw 66 Clarke 90 | 12 | 4 |
| Sept 1 | NPL | A | Rushall Olympic | 190 | W 3-0 | Hunter 54 Bradshaw 61 Kendall 76 | 12 | 5 |
| 4 | NPL | H | Worksop Town | 238 | W 2-0 | Kendall 30 Bradshaw 44 | 12 | 6 |
| 8 | FAC Q1 | A | Eccleshill United | 99 | W 2-0 | Bradshaw 41 (pen) 87 | | 7 |
| 15 | NPL | A | Kendal Town | 143 | W 4-2 | KENDALL 3 ( 9 28 58) Muldoon 86 | 6 | 8 |
| 18 | NPL | H | Whitby Town | 223 | D 1-1 | Muldoon 90 | 9 | 9 |
| 22 | FAC Q2 | H | Ossett Albion | 236 | L 1-2 | Bradshaw 5 | | 10 |
| 29 | FAT Q1 | A | Frickley Athletic | 146 | W 4-1 | Williams 38 (pen) Peat 86 Bradshaw 88 Muldoon 90 | | 11 |
| Oct 6 | NPL | H | Matlock Town | 219 | W 2-1 | Bradshaw 32 Kendall 71 (pen) | 5 | 12 |
| 9 | NPL | A | Stocksbridge PS | 98 | W 4-0 | Turner 17 (og) Bradshaw 25 Williams 35 (pen) Kendall 84 | 1 | 13 |
| 13 | NPL | H | Witton Albion | 251 | W 2-0 | Bolder 12 King 25 | 1 | 14 |
| 16 | NPL | A | Grantham Town | 128 | W 3-2 | Bolder 58 Kendall 70 80 | 1 | 15 |
| 20 | NPL | A | Stafford Rangers | 450 | W 2-0 | Fry 22 Kendall 90 | 1 | 16 |
| 23 | NPL | H | FC United | 538 | D 1-1 | Fry 42 | 1 | 17 |
| 27 | FAT Q2 | A | Buxton | 215 | L 1-2 | Bolder 78 | | 18 |
| 30 | NPL | H | Ilkeston | 274 | D 1-1 | Kendall 88 | 1 | 19 |
| Nov 3 | NPL | A | Nantwich Town | 260 | W 3-2 | Wilson 18 45 Kendall 30 | 1 | 20 |
| 10 | NPL | H | Marine | 286 | W 3-1 | Lisles 3 Kendall 19 Clarke 55 | 1 | 21 |
| 17 | NPL | A | Chorley | 620 | W 1-0 | King 90 | 1 | 22 |
| 24 | NPL | A | Ashton United | 176 | W 2-0 | Kendall 19 King 88 | 1 | 23 |
| Dec 1 | NPL | A | Hednesford Town | 405 | L 2-3 | Wilson 48 80 | 1 | 24 |
| 8 | NPL | H | Rushall Olympic | 243 | D 2-2 | Lisles 9 Anderson 40 | 1 | 25 |
| 15 | NPL | A | Buxton | 196 | L 0-2 | | 1 | 26 |
| 26 | NPL | A | Frickley Athletic | 255 | W 3-2 | Kendall 48 88 Wilson 65 | 1 | 27 |
| 29 | NPL | A | Eastwood Town | 141 | W 5-0 | Williams 10 82 Bolder 19 Kendall 63 90 | 1 | 28 |
| Jan 1 | NPL | H | Blyth Spartans | 300 | W 3-2 | Wilson 20 74 Anderson 53 | 1 | 29 |
| 5 | NPL | H | Kendal Town | 237 | W 3-2 | Anderson 19 Kendall 35 Williams 85 (pen) | 1 | 30 |
| Feb 2 | NPL | H | Grantham Town | 301 | W 3-1 | Wilson 29 74 Kendall 51 | 1 | 31 |
| 9 | NPL | A | Witton Albion | 374 | W 4-2 | Wilson 23 Kendall 35 45 Anderson 78 | 1 | 32 |
| 16 | NPL | H | Stafford Ranagers | 232 | D 1-1 | King 34 | 1 | 33 |
| 23 | NPL | H | AFC Fylde | 267 | L 0-1 | | 1 | 34 |
| Mar 3 | NPL | A | FC United | 2465 | D 1-1 | Kendall 14 (pen) | 1 | 35 |
| 6 | NPL | A | Whitby Town | 242 | W 4-1 | Anderson 7 KENDALL 3 (10 36 71) | 1 | 36 |
| 9 | NPL | H | Stocksbridge PS | 219 | W 5-1 | Kendall 7 24 Wilson 32 King 40 Banks 82 | 1 | 37 |
| 16 | NPL | A | Hednesford Town | 906 | W 3-2 | Kendall 8 Wilson 52 79 | 1 | 38 |
| 30 | NPL | H | Eastwood Town | 301 | W 6-1 | Bradshaw 8 13 King 33 42 Kendall 45 77 | 1 | 39 |
| Apr 1 | NPL | A | Blyth Spartans | 326 | W 1-0 | Buchanan 90 | 1 | 40 |
| 6 | NPL | A | Ilkeston | 417 | D 2-2 | Clarke 9 Kendall 75 | 1 | 41 |
| 13 | NPL | H | Nantwich Town | 321 | D 0-0 | | 1 | 42 |
| 16 | NPL | A | Matlock Town | 261 | W 2-0 | King 58 Kendall 71 | 1 | 43 |
| 20 | NPL | A | Marine | 472 | W 3-1 | Kendall 33 (pen) Wilson 36 Bradshaw 90 | 1 | 44 |
| 27 | NPL | H | Chorley | 435 | W 1-0 | Kendal 41 (pen) | 1 | 45 |
| May 4 | NPL | H | Ashton United | 626 | W 2-0 | Kendall 18 Wilson 17 | 1 | 46 |

| GOALSCORERS | Lge | FAC | FAT | Total | Pens | Hat-tricks | Cons Run | | Lge | FAC | FAT | Total | Pens | Hat-tricks | Cons Run |
|-------------|-----|-----|-----|-------|------|-----------|----------|---|-----|-----|-----|-------|------|-----------|----------|
| Kendall | 36 | | | 36 | 4 | 2 | 5 | Muldoon | 2 | | 1 | 3 | | | |
| Wilson | 15 | | | 15 | | | 2 | Peat | | | 1 | 1 | | | |
| Bradshaw | 8 | 3 | 1 | 12 | 1 | | 4 | Hunter | 1 | | | 1 | | | |
| Anderson | 6 | | | 6 | | | 2 | Buchanan | 1 | | | 1 | | | |
| King | 9 | | | 9 | | | | Banks | 1 | | | 1 | | | |
| Williams | 4 | | 1 | 5 | 3 | | | Own Goals | 1 | | | 1 | | | |
| Bolder | 3 | | 1 | 4 | | | 2 | Cons Run - Consecutive scoring games. | | | | | | | |
| Clarke | 4 | | | 4 | | | | | | | | | | | |
| Fry | 2 | | | 2 | | | 2 | | | | | | | | |
| Lisles | 2 | | | 2 | | | | | | | | | | | |

# OXFORD CITY

**Chairman:** Brian Cox
**Secretary:** John Shepperd    **(T)** 07748 628 911    **(E)** shepoxf@tiscali.co.uk
**Commercial Manager:** Colin Taylor    **(T)** 07817 885 396
**Programme Editor:** Colin Taylor    **(T)** ctoxford@btinternet.com
**Ground Address:** Court Place Farm, Marsh Lane, Marston, Oxford OX3 0NQ
**(T)** 01865 744 493      **Manager:** Mike Ford

Back Row (L-R): Mike Ford (Manager), Chris Adams (Fitness Coach), Chris Wilmott, Mark Bell, Andy Ballard, Nick Townsend, Adam Learoyd, Declan Benjamin, Louis Joyce, Callum Mcnish, Steve Basham, Nick Stanley, Ryan Barney, Juan Martin, Stuart Peace (Asst.Manager), Andy Sinnott (Coach).
Front Row: Amy Taylor (Physio), Felipe Barcelos, Liam Malone, Jamie Cook, Paul Stonehouse, Darren Pond, Andy Gunn, Zac Mceachran, Matty Haycocks (Coach).

## Club Factfile

**Founded:** 1882    **Nickname:** City
**Previous Names:** None
**Previous Leagues:** Isthmian 1907-88, 94-2005, South Midlands 1990-93, Spartan South Midlands 2005-06

**Club Colours (change):** Blue and white hoops/blue/blue (All yellow)

**Ground Capacity:** 3,000   **Seats:** 300    **Covered:** 400    **Clubhouse:** Yes    **Shop:** Yes

**Directions:** Ground lies off A40 ring road, northern by-pass.
Follow signs for J.R. Hospital in yellow and small green signs to Court Place Farm Stadium.

**Previous Grounds:** The White House 1882-1988, Cuttleslowe Park 1990-91, Pressed Steel 1991-93

**Record Attendance:** 9,500 v Leytonstone - FA Amateur Cup - 1950
**Record Victory:** Not known
**Record Defeat:** Not known
**Record Goalscorer:** John Woodley
**Record Appearances:** John Woodley
**Additional Records:** Paid £3,000 to Woking for S Adams
**Senior Honours:** Received £15,000 from Yeovil Town for Howard Forinton
FA Amateur Cup 1905-06. Oxford Senior Cup x3
Spartan South Midlands League Premier Division 2005-06. Southern Premier Play-offs 2011-12.

| | | | | | 10 YEAR RECORD | | | | | |
|---|---|---|---|---|---|---|---|---|---|---|
| 03-04 | 04-05 | 05-06 | 06-07 | 07-08 | 08-09 | 09-10 | 10-11 | 11-12 | 12-13 |
| Isth1N   19 | SthW   21 | SSM P   1 | SthW   12 | SthW   4 | SthP   6 | SthP   13 | SthP   14 | SthP   2 | Conf N   10 |

# MATCH RESULTS 2012-13

| Date | Comp | H/A | Opponents | Att: | Result | Goalscorers | Pos | No. |
|------|------|-----|-----------|------|--------|-------------|-----|-----|
| Aug 17 | BSN | H | Chester FC | 1025 | L 0-1 | | 17 | 1 |
| 21 | BSN | A | Gloucester City | 338 | W 1-0 | Mills 65 | 12 | 2 |
| 25 | BSN | A | Solihull Moors | 189 | W 2-1 | Benjamin 45 Cook 82 | 8 | 3 |
| 27 | BSN | H | Worcester City | 365 | D 2-2 | Skendi 89 Benjamin 90 | 6 | 4 |
| Sept 1 | BSN | A | FC Halifax Town | 1172 | L 1-3 | Willmott 3 | 8 | 5 |
| 4 | BSN | H | Boston United | 203 | W 4-2 | Gunn 3 Pond 47 Mills 75 Barcelos 88 | 7 | 6 |
| 8 | BSN | H | Altrincham | 257 | D 2-2 | Benjamin 50 Basham 51 | 8 | 7 |
| 15 | BSN | A | Harrogate Town | 444 | W 3-1 | Pond 9 Benjamin 27 52 | 7 | 8 |
| 18 | BSN | H | Corby Town | 261 | W 2-0 | Basham 8 Pond 48 | 4 | 9 |
| 21 | FAC Q2 | A | Yate Town | 150 | L 1-2 | Gunn | | 10 |
| 28 | BSN | H | Guiseley | 303 | L 0-3 | | 5 | 11 |
| Oct 2 | BSN | A | Hinckley United | 234 | W 2-0 | Benjamin 10 Cook 57 | 4 | 12 |
| 13 | BSN | H | Workington | 427 | W 5-0 | Ballard 28 Shariff 48 Cook 80 Bashem 83 88 | 4 | 13 |
| 20 | BSN | A | Vauxhall | 236 | L 1-2 | Ballard 49 | 4 | 14 |
| 27 | BSN | H | Stalybridge Celtic | 245 | D 0-0 | | 4 | 15 |
| 30 | BSN | A | Bishop's Stortford | 343 | D 0-0 | | 4 | 16 |
| Nov 3 | BSN | H | Colwyn Bay | 243 | L 1-2 | Learoyd 69 | 5 | 17 |
| 10 | FAT Q3 | A | Sholing | 68 | W 1-0 | Barcelos 64 | | 18 |
| 17 | BSN | A | Corby Town | 299 | D 1-1 | Cook 43 | 6 | 19 |
| Dec 1 | BSN | H | Droylsden | 183 | D 2-2 | Learoyd 72 Ballard 87 | 6 | 20 |
| 4 | FAT 1 | H | Bishop's Stortford | 134 | W 1-0 | Stanley 4 | | 21 |
| 15 | FAT 2 | A | Sutton United | 347 | L 0-1 | | | 22 |
| 26 | BSN | A | Brackley Town | 476 | D 0-0 | | 8 | 23 |
| 29 | BSN | A | Boston United | 871 | L 1-3 | Learoyd 32 | 9 | 24 |
| Jan 1 | BSN | A | Brackley Town | 342 | W 2-1 | Barcelos 79 Ballard 81 | 6 | 25 |
| 5 | BSN | H | Vauxhall Motors | 183 | D 1-1 | Barcelos 15 | 8 | 26 |
| 8 | BSN | A | Chester FC | 1905 | L 0-2 | | 8 | 27 |
| 12 | BSN | A | Guiseley | 605 | L 0-1 | | 10 | 28 |
| Feb 2 | BSN | H | Hinckley United | 319 | W 6-2 | Basham 6 BARCELOS 4 ( 27 33 43 46) Ballard 45 | 8 | 29 |
| 5 | BSN | H | Histon | 175 | D 0-0 | | 8 | 30 |
| 9 | BSN | A | Workington | 312 | W 2-1 | Bell 28 Holgate 52 | 7 | 31 |
| 16 | BSN | H | Gloucester City | 446 | L 1-2 | Cook 73 | 9 | 32 |
| 23 | BSN | A | Histon | 247 | D 1-1 | Barcelos 86 | 10 | 33 |
| Mar 2 | BSN | A | Altrincham | 740 | L 1-3 | Barcelos 21 | 12 | 34 |
| 30 | BSN | H | Solihull Moors | 310 | L 1-2 | Pond 53 | 15 | 35 |
| Apr 1 | BSN | A | Worcester City | 597 | L 2-3 | Pond 30 Stanley 78 | 16 | 36 |
| 6 | BSN | A | Gainsborough Trinity | 446 | W 2-1 | Barcelos 13 Cook 37 | 15 | 37 |
| 8 | BSN | A | Bradford PA | 302 | W 2-1 | Stanley 14 Willott 59 | 13 | 38 |
| 10 | BSN | A | Bradford PA | 180 | D 1-1 | Cook 33 | 14 | 39 |
| 13 | BSN | H | Harrogate Town | 263 | D 0-0 | | 12 | 40 |
| 16 | BSN | H | FC Halifax Town | 262 | D 2-2 | Barcelos 11 Learoyd 90 | 14 | 41 |
| 18 | BSN | A | Colwyn Bay | 303 | L 1-3 | Bell 73 | 14 | 42 |
| 20 | BSN | A | Droylsden | 166 | W 3-1 | Cook 34 Basham 38 Barcelos 66 | 12 | 43 |
| 23 | BSN | H | Gainsborough Trinity | 180 | D 1-1 | Cook 37 (pen) | 11 | 44 |
| 25 | BSN | A | Stalybridge Celtic | 204 | D 2-2 | Barcelos 86 Bell 90 | 10 | 45 |
| 27 | BSN | H | Bishop's Stortford | 345 | D 1-1 | Cook 66 | 10 | 46 |

| GOALSCORERS | Lge | FAC | LC | Total | Pens | Hat-tricks | Cons Run | | Lge | FAC | LC | Total | Pens | Hat-tricks | Cons Run |
|-------------|-----|-----|-----|-------|------|-----------|----------|--|-----|-----|-----|-------|------|-----------|----------|
| Barcelos | 13 | | 1 | 14 | | 1 | 2 | Mills | 2 | | | 2 | | | |
| Cook | 10 | | | 10 | 1 | | | Willmott | 2 | | | 2 | | | |
| Basham | 6 | | | 6 | | | | Holgate | 1 | | | 1 | | | |
| Benjamin | 6 | | | 6 | | | | Shariffe | 1 | | | 1 | | | |
| Ballard | 5 | | | 5 | | | | Skendi | 1 | | | 1 | | | |
| Pond | 5 | | | 5 | | | | Cons Run - Consecutive scoring games. | | | | | | | |
| Learoyd | 4 | | | 4 | | | | | | | | | | | |
| Bell | 3 | | | 3 | | | | | | | | | | | |
| Stanley | 2 | | 1 | 3 | | | | | | | | | | | |
| Gunn | 1 | 1 | | 2 | | | | | | | | | | | |

# SOLIHULL MOORS

**Chairman:** Nigel Collins
**Secretary:** Robin Lamb     **(T)** 07976 752 493     **(E)** robin.lamb5@btinternet.com
**Commercial Manager:** Gary Shipway     **(T)** 07766 010 601
**Programme Editor:** John Clothier     **(T)** 07884 481 882
**Ground Address:** Damson Park, Damson Parkway, Solihull B91 2PP
**(T)** 0121 705 6770     **Manager:** Marcus Bignot

## Club Factfile

**Founded:** 2007     **Nickname:** Moors
**Previous Names:** Today's club was formed after the amalgamation of Solihull Borough and Moor Green in 2007
**Previous Leagues:** None

**Club Colours (change):** Blue & yellow hoops/blue/blue & yellow hoops (Red & white hoops/black/red & white hoops)

**Ground Capacity:** 3,050    **Seats:** 280    **Covered:** 1,000    **Clubhouse:** Yes    **Shop:** Yes

**Directions**
M42 junction 6 take the A45 towards Birmingham after approximately 1.5 miles take the left filter lane at the traffic lights onto Damson Parkway. Ground approximately 1 mile on the right.

**Previous Grounds:** None

**Record Attendance:** 1,076 v Rushden & Diamonds - FA Cup 4th Qualifying Round 27/10/2007
**Record Victory:** 4-1 v Southport - Conference South 05/04/2008
**Record Defeat:** 1-6 v Kettering Town - Conference South 01/01/2008
**Record Goalscorer:** Not known
**Record Appearances:** Carl Motteram - 71 (2007-09)
**Additional Records:**

**Senior Honours:**
None

### 10 YEAR RECORD

| 03-04 | 04-05 | 05-06 | 06-07 | 07-08 | 08-09 | 09-10 | 10-11 | 11-12 | 12-13 |
|---|---|---|---|---|---|---|---|---|---|
| | | | | Conf N 17 | Conf N 16 | Conf N 17 | Conf N 7 | Conf N 19 | Conf N 9 |

**CONFERENCE NORTH ACTION:** from the Gloucester City v Chester match. Photo: Peter Barnes.

# MATCH RESULTS 2012-13

| Date | Comp | H/A | Opponents | Att: | Result | Goalscorers | Pos | No. |
|------|------|-----|-----------|------|--------|-------------|-----|-----|
| Aug 17 | BSN | A | Colwyn Bay | 310 | L 1-3 | Knights 83 | 18 | 1 |
| 21 | BSN | H | Corby Town | 195 | W 3-0 | Knights 13 Bogle 27 Birch 44 | 8 | 2 |
| 25 | BSN | H | Oxford City | 189 | L 1-2 | Birch 53 | 12 | 3 |
| 27 | BSN | A | Gloucester City | 323 | D 1-1 | Hurran 80 | 14 | 4 |
| Sept 1 | BSN | H | Chester | 566 | L 0-3 | | 17 | 5 |
| 4 | BSN | A | Bishop's Stortford | 334 | L 1-4 | Bogle 90 (pen) | 17 | 6 |
| 8 | BSN | A | Droylsden | 273 | W 4-2 | English 18 Bogle 40 Clarke 45 Knights 64 | 15 | 7 |
| 12 | BSN | H | Gainsborough Trinity | 222 | L 0-2 | | 16 | 8 |
| 22 | FAC Q2 | H | Westfields | 124 | D 1-1 | Bogle 37 | | 9 |
| 25 | FAC Q2r | A | Westfields | 153 | W 2-1 | Blackwood, Bogle | | 10 |
| 29 | BSN | A | Vauxhall Motors | 105 | L 1-2 | Fleet 65 | 16 | 11 |
| Oct 2 | BSN | H | Worcester City | 207 | L 0-1 | | 18 | 12 |
| 5 | FAC Q3 | A | AFC Fylde | 278 | L 1-4 | Beswick 58 | | 13 |
| 13 | BSN | H | Guiseley | 245 | W 2-0 | Denny 51 Kemp 62 | 16 | 14 |
| 27 | BSN | H | Altrinchham | 258 | W 2-1 | English 88 Angus 90 | 16 | 15 |
| 30 | BSN | A | Histon | 412 | D 0-0 | | 15 | 16 |
| Nov 3 | BSN | A | Workington | 364 | D 1-1 | Bogle 27 (pen) | 17 | 17 |
| 10 | FAT Q3 | H | AFC Fylde | 155 | W 2-1 | Bogle 18 20 | | 18 |
| 17 | BSN | H | Bradford PA | 252 | W 3-1 | Kemp 13 Bogle 81 (pen) Blackwood 90 | 13 | 19 |
| 20 | BSN | A | Boston United | 681 | D 2-2 | Angus 4 Bogle 90 | 13 | 20 |
| 24 | FAT 1 | A | Hednesford Town | 355 | W 2-1 | English 31 Bogle 40 | | 21 |
| Dec 8 | BSN | H | Stalybridge Celtic | 202 | W 1-0 | Longdon 65 | 11 | 22 |
| 15 | FAT 2 | A | Wrexham | 1111 | L 2-3 | English 38 57 | | 23 |
| 26 | BSN | H | Hinckley United | 208 | W 1-0 | Angus 52 | 12 | 24 |
| Jan 1 | BSN | H | Hinckley United | 338 | D 1-1 | Angus 72 | 14 | 25 |
| 5 | BSN | A | Gainsborough Trinity | 515 | D 1-1 | Waterfall 90 (og) | 14 | 26 |
| 8 | BSN | A | FC Halifax Town | 979 | D 0-0 | | 14 | 27 |
| 12 | BSN | H | Droylsden | 191 | W 2-1 | Angus 76 89 | 12 | 28 |
| 29 | BSN | H | Colwyn Bay | 102 | W 2-0 | Bogle 33 52 | 8 | 29 |
| Feb 2 | BSN | A | Bradford PA | 285 | L 0-1 | | 11 | 30 |
| 5 | BSN | H | Bishop's Stortford | 149 | L 0-1 | | 12 | 31 |
| 9 | BSN | H | Vauxhall Motors | 162 | L 2-3 | Langdon 60 Spencer 70 | 13 | 32 |
| 11 | BSN | A | Worcester City | 653 | W 3-1 | Birch 8 English 33 Denny 48 | 9 | 33 |
| 16 | BSN | A | Brackley Town | 330 | L 1-2 | Langdon 90 | 11 | 34 |
| 23 | BSN | H | Boston United | 245 | W 1-0 | Mayo 48 | 11 | 35 |
| Mar 2 | BSN | A | Stalybridge Celtic | 308 | W 3-0 | English 40 Bogle 55 Fleet 68 | 9 | 36 |
| 9 | BSN | H | FC Halifax Town | 331 | L 0-3 | | 10 | 37 |
| 13 | BSN | A | Altrincham | 558 | L 1-2 | Bogle 83 | 11 | 38 |
| 16 | BSN | A | Guiseley | 512 | L 0-1 | | 12 | 39 |
| 20 | BSN | A | Corby Town | 272 | W 3-2 | Birch 22 Beswick 36 Knights 70 | 9 | 40 |
| 30 | BSN | A | Oxford City | 310 | W 2-1 | English 11 Birch 21 | 9 | 41 |
| Apr 1 | BSN | H | Gloucester City | 209 | L 2-3 | Bogle 83 (Pen) Beswick 90 | 10 | 42 |
| 6 | BSN | A | Harrogate Town | 371 | W 4-2 | BOGLE 3 ( 35 44 56) Kemp 59 | 10 | 43 |
| 13 | BSN | H | Brackley Town | 221 | L 0-1 | | 11 | 44 |
| 16 | BSN | H | Harrogate Town | 419 | W 2-0 | G.Birch 60 Angus 63 | 9 | 45 |
| 20 | BSN | A | Chester | 3414 | W 1-0 | Bogle 9 (pen) | 9 | 46 |
| 23 | BSN | H | Histon | 184 | D 1-1 | Pierpoint 87 | 9 | 47 |
| 27 | BSN | H | Workington | 275 | D 2-2 | Beswick 53 73 | 9 | 48 |

| GOALSCORERS | Lge | FAC | LC | Total | Pens | Hat-tricks | Cons Run | | Lge | FAC | LC | Total | Pens | Hat-tricks | Cons Run |
|-------------|-----|-----|----|-------|------|-----------|----------|-----------|-----|-----|----|-------|------|-----------|----------|
| Bogle | 15 | 2 | 3 | 20 | 5 | 1 | 5 | Fleet | 2 | | | 2 | | | |
| English | 5 | | 3 | 8 | | | | Clarke | 1 | | | 1 | | | |
| Angus | 7 | | | 7 | | | | Hurran | 1 | | | 1 | | | |
| Birch | 6 | | | 6 | | | | Mayo | 1 | | | 1 | | | |
| Beswick | 4 | 1 | | 5 | | | | Pierpoint | 1 | | | 1 | | | |
| Knights | 4 | | | 4 | | | | Spencer | 1 | | | 1 | | | |
| Kemp | 3 | | | 3 | | | | Own Goals | 1 | | | 1 | | | |
| Langdon | 3 | | | 3 | | | | Cons Run - Consecutive scoring games. | | | | | | | |
| Blackwood | 1 | 1 | | 2 | | | | | | | | | | | |
| Denny | 2 | | | 2 | | | | | | | | | | | |

# STALYBRIDGE CELTIC

**Chairman:** Rob Gorski

**Secretary:** John Hall      **(T)** 07813 864 492      **(E)** celticblueblood@hotmail.com

**Commercial Manager:** n/a      **(T)**

**Programme Editor:** Nick Shaw      **(T)** 0161 633 1117

**Ground Address:** Bower Fold, Mottram Road, Stalybridge, Cheshire SK15 2RT

**(T)** 0161 338 2828      **Manager:** Jim Harvey

**Back row (L-R):** Kelvin Bleau, Alex Andrews, Joel Bembo-Leta;, Jordan Barrow, Jonny Lyndsay, Jack Laird, Adam Pepper.
**Middle Row:** Julie Dransfield (Sports Therapist), Dave Pover (Sports Therapist), Corey Gregory, Alex Mudimu, Dennis Sheriff, Ashley Woodhouse, Andy Ralph, Kristian Platt, Greg Wilkinson, Sam Egerton, Mark Storah (Kit Manager), Alan Keeling.
**Front Row:** Jamie Mullan, Mark Lees, Rob Gorski (Chairman), Jim Harvey (Manager), Tim Ryan (Assistant Manager), Syd White (Chief Executive), Mitchell Austin, Callum Warburton.

## Club Factfile

**Founded:** 1909      **Nickname:** Celtic

**Previous Names:** None

**Previous Leagues:** Lancashire Combination 1911-12, Central League 1912-21, Southern 1914-15, Football League 1921-23, Cheshire Co. 1923-82, North West Co. 1982-87, N.P.L. 1987-92, 98-2001, Conference 1992-98, 01-02

**Club Colours (change):** Royal blue & white/white/blue (All white)

**Ground Capacity:** 6,108    **Seats:** 1,200    **Covered:** 2,400    **Clubhouse:** Yes    **Shop:** Yes

**Directions:** Leave the M6 at junction 19 (Northwich). At the roundabout at the end of the slip road turn right (exit 3 of 4) to join the A556 towards Altrincham. Stay on the A556 for 5 miles to a roundabout with the M56. Turn right at the roundabout (exit 3 of 4) onto the M56. Stay on the M56 for 6 1/2 miles to junction 3 (M60 signposted Sheffield, M67) Stay on the M60 for 7 miles to junction 24 (M67, Denton) At the roundabout turn right (exit 4 of 5) to join the M67. Stay on the M67 to the very end, Junction 4. At the roundabout turn left (exit 1 of 4) onto the A57 (Hyde Road). After 1/2 a mile you will reach a set of traffic lights (signposted Stalybridge). Turn left onto B6174 (Stalybridge Road). Almost immediately, there is a mini roundabout. Turn left (exit 1 of 5) onto Roe Cross Road (A6018). Follow this road for 1 3/4 miles passing the Roe Cross Inn on the right and through the cutting (the road is now called Mottram Road). When you pass the Dog and Partridge on the right, you will be almost there. Bower Fold is on the left opposite a sharp right turn next to the Hare and Hounds pub. If the car park is full (it usually is), parking can be found on the streets on the right of Mottram Road.

**Previous Grounds:** None

**Record Attendance:** 9,753 v West Bromwich Albion - FA Cup replay 1922-23

**Record Victory:** 16-2 v Manchester NE - 01/05/1926 and v Nantwich - 22/10/1932

**Record Defeat:** 1-10 v Wellington Town - 09/03/1946

**Record Goalscorer:** Harry Dennison - 215

**Record Appearances:** Kevan Keelan - 395

**Additional Records:** Cecil Smith scored 77 goals during the 1931-32 season

**Senior Honours:** Paid £15,000 to Kettering Town for Ian Arnold 1995. Received £16,000 from Southport for Lee Trundle.
Manchester Senior Cup 1922-23.
Northern Premier League Premier Division 1991-92, 2000-01.
Cheshire Senior Cup x2.

### 10 YEAR RECORD

| 03-04 | 04-05 | 05-06 | 06-07 | 07-08 | 08-09 | 09-10 | 10-11 | 11-12 | 12-13 |
|---|---|---|---|---|---|---|---|---|---|
| NP P 11 | Conf N 19 | Conf N 7 | Conf N 18 | Conf N 2 | Conf N 6 | Conf N 9 | Conf N 10 | Conf N 6 | Conf N 13 |

# MATCH RESULTS 2012-13

| Date | Comp | H/A | Opponents | Att: | Result | Goalscorers | Pos | No. |
|------|------|-----|-----------|------|--------|-------------|-----|-----|
| Aug 17 | BSN | A | Workington | 446 | L 1-4 | Austin 36 | 22 | 1 |
| 21 | BSN | H | Gainsborough Trinity | 382 | D 1-1 | Bembo-Leta 66 | 18 | 2 |
| 25 | BSN | H | Droylsden | 548 | D 0-0 | | 18 | 3 |
| 27 | BSN | A | Colwyn Bay | 365 | W 3-2 | Pepper 74 Sheriff 81 Metcalf 89 (og) | 13 | 4 |
| Sept 1 | BSN | H | Hinckley United | 467 | W 4-0 | Wilkinson 28 Pepper 35 Barrow 45 (pen) Laird 80 | 7 | 5 |
| 3 | BSN | A | Bradford PA | 501 | W 3-1 | Laird 17 Wilkinson 71 Warburton 79 | 6 | 6 |
| 8 | BSN | A | Gloucester City | 252 | L 3-4 | Pepper 4 (pen) Laird 22 Austin 68 | 7 | 7 |
| 15 | BSN | H | Histon | 289 | W 2-1 | Laird 14 89 | 6 | 8 |
| 22 | FAC Q2 | H | **Vauxhall Motors** | **420** | **W 1-0** | **Gregory 60** | | 9 |
| 29 | BSN | H | Chester | 1193 | L 2-6 | Laird 60 Barrow 87 | 8 | 10 |
| Oct 2 | BSN | A | Guiseley | 412 | L 0-1 | | 8 | 11 |
| 6 | FAC Q3 | H | **Whitby Town** | **372** | **W 3-1** | **Mullen 16 Barrow 35 Wilkinson 65** | | 12 |
| 13 | BSN | H | Worcester City | 1038 | W 2-1 | Pepper 53 (pen) Platt 88 | 8 | 13 |
| 20 | FAC Q4 | A | **Stockport County** | **2123** | **L 3-5** | **Laird 45 90 Gregory 62** | | 14 |
| 27 | BSN | A | Oxford City | 245 | D 0-0 | | 8 | 15 |
| 30 | BSN | H | Boston United | 363 | L 0-1 | | 10 | 16 |
| Nov 10 | FAT Q3 | A | **Matlock Town** | **402** | **L 1-2** | **Gregory 34** | | 17 |
| 17 | BSN | A | Brackley Town | 380 | L 1-4 | Austin 71 | 14 | 18 |
| 20 | BSN | H | Harrogate Town | 367 | W 1-0 | Laird 2 | 10 | 19 |
| Dec 1 | BSN | H | Vauxhall Motors | 331 | L 0-1 | | 11 | 20 |
| 8 | BSN | A | Solihull Moors | 202 | L 0-1 | | 15 | 21 |
| 15 | BSN | H | Workington | 343 | L 1-4 | Laird 46 | 15 | 22 |
| 22 | BSN | A | Gainsborough Trinity | 506 | W 2-1 | Austin 50 Bleau 67 | 13 | 23 |
| 26 | BSN | H | Altrincham | 802 | D 2-2 | Laird 1 61 | 12 | 24 |
| 29 | BSN | H | Bradford PA | 514 | W 2-0 | Mullan 3 Buckley 61 | 10 | 25 |
| Jan 1 | BSN | A | Altrincham | 889 | L 1-2 | Wilkinson 13 | 11 | 26 |
| 5 | BSN | A | Hinckley United | 306 | W 3-0 | Austin 14 Laird 44 Bembo-Leta 86 | 10 | 27 |
| 8 | BSN | H | Bishops Stortford | 149 | W 3-1 | Mullan 34 Laird 45 Platt 72 | 5 | 28 |
| 12 | BSN | H | Corby Town | 422 | L 1-2 | Platt 66 (pen) | 7 | 29 |
| 19 | BSN | A | Chester | 2095 | L 1-5 | Laird 65 | 7 | 30 |
| Feb 2 | BSN | A | Bishop's Stortford | 328 | D 0-0 | | 10 | 31 |
| 9 | BSN | H | Worcester City | 357 | L 0-2 | | 12 | 32 |
| 12 | BSN | H | Brackley Town | 211 | L 0-3 | | 12 | 33 |
| 16 | BSN | A | Boston United | 905 | D 2-2 | Hall 17 Gregory 51 | 12 | 34 |
| 23 | BSN | A | FC Halifax Town | 1037 | D 0-0 | | 13 | 35 |
| Mar 2 | BSN | H | Solihull Moors | 308 | L 0-3 | | 14 | 36 |
| 9 | BSN | A | Corby Town | 266 | L 0-1 | | 15 | 37 |
| 16 | BSN | A | Vauxhall Motors | 209 | D 0-0 | | 16 | 38 |
| 30 | BSN | A | Droylsden | 356 | D 1-1 | Hall 36 | 16 | 39 |
| Apr 1 | BSN | H | Colwyn Bay | 316 | D 3-3 | Buckley 3 Platt 49 (pen) Hall 79 | 17 | 40 |
| 6 | BSN | A | Histon | 321 | W 2-0 | Buckley 36 Pepper 90 | 16 | 41 |
| 9 | BSN | H | Guiseley | 263 | D 1-1 | Austin 76 | 15 | 42 |
| 13 | BSN | H | Gloucester City | 344 | W 4-0 | Austin 11 623 Buckley 57 Hall 73 | 16 | 43 |
| 20 | BSN | A | Harrogate Town | 430 | D 0-0 | | 16 | 44 |
| 24 | BSN | H | Oxford City | 204 | D 2-2 | Lees 23 Pepper 32 | 16 | 45 |
| 27 | BSN | H | FC Halifax Town | 744 | W 1-0 | Austin 31 | 13 | 46 |

| GOALSCORERS | Lge | FAC | LC | Total | Pens | Hat-tricks | Cons Run | | Lge | FAC | LC | Total | Pens | Hat-tricks | Cons Run |
|-------------|-----|-----|----|----|------|------------|----------|--|-----|-----|----|----|------|------------|----------|
| Laird | 13 | 2 | | 15 | | | 2 | Bembo-Leta | 2 | | | 2 | | | |
| Austin | 9 | | | 9 | | | 2 | Bleau | 1 | | | 1 | | | |
| Pepper | 6 | | | 6 | 2 | | | Lees | 1 | | | 1 | | | |
| Buckley | 4 | | | 4 | | | 2 | Sherriff | 1 | | | 1 | | | |
| Gregory | 1 | 2 | 1 | 4 | | 1 | | Warburton | 1 | | | 1 | | | |
| Hall | 4 | | | 4 | | | | Own Goals | 1 | | | 1 | | | |
| Platt | 4 | | | 4 | 1 | | 2 | Cons Run - Consecutive scoring games. | | | | | | | |
| Wilkinson | 3 | 1 | | 4 | | | | | | | | | | | |
| Barrow | 2 | 1 | | 2 | | | | | | | | | | | |
| Mullen | 2 | 1 | | 3 | | | | | | | | | | | |

# STOCKPORT COUNTY

**Chairman:** Lord Peter Snape
**Secretary:** Tony Whiteside  **(T)** 0161 286 8888 x257  **(E)** tony.whiteside@stockportcounty.com
**Commercial Manager:** Phil Brennan  **(T)** 07538 110 439
**Programme Editor:** Phil Brennan  **(T)** phil.brennan@stockportcounty.com
**Ground Address:** Edgeley Park, Hardcastle Road, Stockport SK3 9DD
**(T)** 0161 286 8903  **Manager:** Ian Bogie

## Club Factfile

**Founded:** 1883  **Nickname:** County or Hatters
**Previous Names:** Heaton Norris Rovers 1883-88, Heaton Norris 1888-90.
**Previous Leagues:** Football League 1900-2011.

**Club Colours (change):** Royal blue/white/ royal white (Sky & white stripe/black/white)

**Ground Capacity:** 10,800 **Seats:** Yes  **Covered:** Yes  **Clubhouse:**  **Shop:** Yes

**Directions**
**From The South** (M6): Exit the M6 at Junction 19 (sign-posted 'Manchester Airport, Stockport A55, M56 East') and at the r'about turn right onto the A556. At the Bowden r'about after 4.2 miles, turn right (sign-posted 'Manchester M56') onto the M56. Exit the M56 after 6.9 miles (sign-posted 'Stockport M60, Sheffield M67') onto the M60. Exit the M60 at Junction 1 ('sign-posted 'Stockport Town Centre and West'). At the r'about turn right and continue through to the second set of lights and turn left (ignoring the sign directing you to Stockport Co.) and follow the road to the left, which is Chestergate. At the lights turn right up King Street, past the fire station on the right to the top of the hill, turn right at the r'about signed Edgeley. Continue down Hardcastle street turning left after the bus stop signed Caroline Street. **From the North** (M62 from Leeds): Follow the M62 onto the M60 and continue south. Exit the M60 at Junction 1 ('sign-posted Stockport Town centre') At the roundabout turn right and continue through to the second set of lights and turn left (ignoring the sign directing you to Stockport Co.) and follow the road to the left, which is Chestergate. At the traffic lights turn right up King Street, past the fire station on the right to the top of the hill, turn right at the roundabout signed Edgeley. Continue down Hardcastle street turning left after the bus stop signed Caroline Street. At the end of Caroline St turn right where you will see the main car park on the left. (not available on Match Days)

**Previous Grounds:** Nursery Inn, Green Lane 1889-1902.

**Record Attendance:** 27,833 v Liverpool, FA Cup 5th Round 11/02/1950.
**Record Victory:** 13-0 v Halifax Town, Division Three North 06/01/1934.
**Record Defeat:** 1-8 v Chesterfield, Division Two 19/04/1902.
**Record Goalscorer:** (League) Jack Connor - 132, 1951-56.
**Record Appearances:** (League) Andy Thorpe - 489, 1978-86, 88-92.
**Additional Records:** Paid, £800,000 for Ian Moore from Nottingham Forest, 07/1998.
**Senior Honours:** Received, £1,600,000 for Alun Armstrong from Middlesbrough, 02/1998.
League Division Three North 1921-22, 36-37, Division Four 1966-67.

| 10 YEAR RECORD | | | | | | | | | |
|---|---|---|---|---|---|---|---|---|---|
| 03-04 | 04-05 | 05-06 | 06-07 | 07-08 | 08-09 | 09-10 | 10-11 | 11-12 | 12-13 |
| FL 2 19 | FL 1 24 | FL 2 22 | FL 2 8 | FL 2 4 | FL 1 18 | FL 1 24 | FL 2 24 | Conf 16 | Conf 21 |

# MATCH RESULTS 2012-13

| Date | Comp | H/A | Opponents | Att: | Result | Goalscorers | Pos | No. |
|------|------|-----|-----------|------|--------|-------------|-----|-----|
| Aug 11 | BSP | H | Alfreton Town | 3448 | W 1-0 | Hattersley 36 | 7 | 1 |
| 14 | BSP | A | Grimsby Town | 3670 | W 2-1 | Rowe 81 Whitehead 90 | 2 | 2 |
| 18 | BSP | A | Tamworth | 1270 | L 0-1 | | 8 | 3 |
| 24 | BSP | H | Gateshead | 3213 | L 1-2 | Connor 34 | 9 | 4 |
| 27 | BSP | A | AFC Telford United | 2079 | D 2-2 | Whitehead 42 61 | 11 | 5 |
| Sept 1 | BSP | H | Cambridge United | 3060 | D 1-1 | Newton 30 (pen) | 15 | 6 |
| | BSP | H | Macclesfield Town | 4208 | L 3-4 | Hattersley 24 Whitehead 29 O.Donnell 61 | 15 | 7 |
| | BSP | A | Newport County | 2306 | D 0-0 | | 15 | 8 |
| 15 | BSP | H | Woking | 3151 | L 1-2 | Kenyon 15 | 19 | 9 |
| 22 | BSP | A | Braintree Town | 653 | D 0-0 | | 17 | 10 |
| 25 | BSP | A | Southport | 818 | D 1-1 | Hattersley 40 | 18 | 11 |
| 29 | BSP | H | Ebbsfleet United | 4641 | W 3-1 | Hobson 51 53 Collins 57 | 14 | 12 |
| Oct 6 | BSP | A | Hyde | 1889 | W 2-1 | Hobson 18 42 | 10 | 13 |
| 20 | BSP | H | Wrexham | 3789 | L 2-3 | Hattersley 23 84 | 14 | 14 |
| 23 | BSP | H | Kidderminster H | 3426 | W 1-0 | Newton 44 (pen) | 11 | 15 |
| 30 | FAC Q4 | H | Stalybridge Celtic | 2123 | W 5-3 | Hobson 39 Whitehead 45 Rowe 45 | | 16 |
| | | | | | | Newton 61 (pen), Sheridon 82 | | 17 |
| 27 | BSP | A | Lincoln City | 1873 | D 3-3 | Fogbola 46 Hobson 62 Turnbull 75 | 11 | 18 |
| Nov 3 | FAC 1 | A | Southend United | 3084 | L 0-3 | | | 19 |
| 6 | BSP | H | Barrow | 2805 | W 3-1 | Hattersley 36 49 Mainwaring 58 | 9 | 20 |
| 10 | BSP | A | Forest Green Rovers | 1176 | L 1-4 | Newton 76 (pen) | 12 | 21 |
| 17 | BSP | A | Nuneaton Town | 1221 | L 0-2 | | 13 | 22 |
| 24 | FAT 1 | H | Ossett Town | 1679 | W 6-0 | JENNINGS 3 (10 39 55) Hattersley 16 79 Rose 75 | | 23 |
| Dec 1 | BSP | A | Southport | 3445 | L 3-4 | Turnbull 42 Hattersley 44 (pen) Halls 58 | 16 | 24 |
| 8 | BSP | A | Woking | 1520 | L 0-1 | | 19 | 25 |
| 15 | FAT 2 | H | Southport | 1328 | D 1-1 | Jennings 89 | | 26 |
| 18 | FAT 2r | A | Southport | 750 | L 1-3 | Collins 13 | | 27 |
| 26 | BSP | H | Hyde | 3963 | L 0-2 | | 21 | 28 |
| 29 | BSP | H | AFC Telford United | 2791 | D 2-2 | Jennings 70 Hobson 90 | 21 | 29 |
| Jan 1 | BSP | A | Hyde United | 2540 | W 1-0 | Jennings 60 | | 30 |
| 5 | BSP | A | Cambridge United | 2305 | L 1-4 | Whitehead 20 | 20 | 31 |
| 16 | BSP | H | Mansfield Town | 2647 | L 1-3 | Meaney 81 | 20 | 32 |
| 19 | BSP | H | Forest Green Rovers | 2802 | W 2-1 | Newton 40 Nolan 49 | 20 | 33 |
| Feb 2 | BSP | H | Nuneaton Town | 4133 | W 3-2 | Jennings 4 Hattersley 10 Nolan 67 | 16 | 34 |
| 9 | BSP | A | Wrexham | 4206 | L 1-3 | Jennings 90 | 17 | 35 |
| 12 | BSP | H | Lincoln City | 2769 | W 2-0 | Hattersley 57 Newton 63 | 14 | 36 |
| 16 | BSP | A | Ebbsfleet United | 912 | D 0-0 | | 14 | 37 |
| 19 | BSP | H | Tamworth | 2732 | L 0-1 | | 15 | 38 |
| 26 | BSP | H | Hereford United | 2618 | L 2-3 | Cirak 17 Tunnicliffe 63 | 17 | 39 |
| Mar 2 | BSP | H | Luton Town | 4074 | L 0-1 | | 17 | 40 |
| 5 | BSP | A | Dartford | 757 | D 1-1 | Cullen 11 | 17 | 41 |
| 9 | BSP | A | Mansfield Town | 2628 | L 1-4 | Marshall 69 | 19 | 42 |
| 12 | BSP | A | Barrow | 803 | W 2-0 | Cullen 76 81 | 17 | 43 |
| 16 | BSP | H | Braintree Town | 3250 | L 1-3 | Kenyon 84 | 18 | 44 |
| 19 | BSP | A | Luton Town | 5106 | L 0-1 | | 19 | 45 |
| 23 | BSP | H | Newport County | 3154 | W 1-0 | Minshull 60 (og) | 18 | 46 |
| 30 | BSP | A | Macclesfield Town | 4027 | D 1-1 | Mocken 75 | 21 | 47 |
| Apr 1 | BSP | A | Grmsby Town | 3804 | L 1-2 | Kenyon 61 | 21 | 48 |
| 6 | BSP | A | Alfreton Town | 1157 | W 3-2 | Tunnicliffe 40 Cullen 49 Nolan 61 | | 49 |
| 13 | BSP | H | Dartford | 6113 | L 0-1 | | 21 | 49 |
| 16 | BSP | A | Gateshead | 685 | D 1-1 | Cirak 90 | 21 | 50 |
| 20 | BSP | H | Kidderminster Harriers | 6453 | L 0-4 | | 21 | 51 |

| GOALSCORERS | Lge | FAC | FAT | Total | Pens | Hat-tricks | Cons Run | | Lge | FAC | FAT | Total | Pens | Hat-tricks | Cons Run |
|-------------|-----|-----|-----|-------|------|-----------|----------|---|-----|-----|-----|-------|------|-----------|----------|
| Hattersley | 10 | | 1 | 11 | 1 | | 2 | Turnbull | 2 | | | 2 | | | |
| Jennings | 4 | | 4 | 8 | | 1 | | Connell | 1 | | | 1 | | | |
| Hobson | 5 | 1 | | 6 | | | | Fogbola | 1 | | | 1 | | | |
| Newton | 5 | 1 | | 6 | 4 | | | Halls | 1 | | | 1 | | | |
| Whitehead | 5 | 1 | | 6 | | | | O'Donnell | 1 | | | 1 | | | |
| Rowe | 1 | 1 | 1 | 3 | | | | Mainwaring | 1 | | | 1 | | | |
| Cullen | 4 | | | 4 | | | | Marshall | 1 | | | 1 | | | |
| Kenyon | 3 | | | 3 | | | | Meaney | 1 | | | 1 | | | |
| Nolan | 3 | | | 3 | | | | Mocken | 1 | | | 1 | | | |
| Cirak | 2 | | | 2 | | | | Sheridan | | 1 | | 1 | | | |
| Colin | 1 | | 1 | 2 | | | | Own Goals | 1 | | | 1 | | | |
| Rose | 1 | | 1 | 2 | | | | Cons Run - Consecutive scoring games. | | | | | | | |
| Tunnicliffe | 2 | | | 2 | | | | | | | | | | | |

# VAUXHALL MOTORS

**Chairman:** Alan Bartlam

**Secretary:** Mike Harper    **(T)** 07817 400 202    **(E)** mike.harper@sky.com

**Commercial Manager:** tbc    **(T)**

**Programme Editor:** Ceri Richards    **(T)** 07946 409 176

**Ground Address:** Rivacre Park, Rivacre Road, Ellesmere Port, South Wirrall CH66 1NJ

**(T)** 0151 328 1114 (Club) 327 2294 (Social)    **Manager:** Carl Macauley

## Club Factfile

**Founded:** 1963    **Nickname:** The Motormen

**Previous Names:** Vauxhall Motors 1963-87, Vauxhall GM 1995-99

**Previous Leagues:** Ellesmere Port, Wirral Combination, West Cheshire 1966-87, 92-95, North West Co. 1987-92, 95-2000, Northern Premier 2000-04

**Club Colours (change):** White/blue/blue (Yellow/green/yellow)

**Ground Capacity:** 3,500    **Seats:** 266    **Covered:** 1,000    **Clubhouse:** Yes    **Shop:** Yes

**Directions:** Leave M53 at junction 5 and take A41 towards North Wales. At first set of traffic lights (Hooton Crossroads) turn left into Hooton Green. At 'T' junction turn left into Hooton Lane. At next 'T' junction turn right into Rivacre Road. Ground is 200 yards on right.

**Previous Grounds:** Hooton Park 1963-87.

**Record Attendance:** 1,500 - FA XI fixture for the opening of Rivacre Park 1987

**Record Victory:** Not known

**Record Defeat:** Not known

**Record Goalscorer:** Terry Fearns - 111

**Record Appearances:** Carl Jesbitt - 509

**Additional Records:**

**Senior Honours:**
North West Counties League Division 2 1988-89, 95-96, Division 1 1999-2000.
Wirral Senior Cup 1987.

### 10 YEAR RECORD

| 03-04 | 04-05 | 05-06 | 06-07 | 07-08 | 08-09 | 09-10 | 10-11 | 11-12 | 12-13 |
|---|---|---|---|---|---|---|---|---|---|
| NP P 9 | Conf N 15 | Conf N 18 | Conf N 15 | Conf N 21 | Conf N 11 | Conf N 20 | Conf N 17 | Conf N 18 | Conf N 12 |

**CONFERENCE NORTH ACTION:** Gloucester City striker, Darren Edwards under pressure from Harrogate Town's Matt Bloomer. Photo: Peter Barnes.

# MATCH RESULTS 2012-13

| Date | Comp | H/A | Opponents | Att: | Result | Goalscorers | Pos | No. |
|---|---|---|---|---|---|---|---|---|
| Aug 17 | BSN | A | Corby Town | 548 | W 1-0 | Hannigan 30 | 10 | 1 |
| 21 | BSN | H | Bradford PA | 235 | L 1-3 | Ellison 65 | 13 | 2 |
| 25 | BSN | H | Altrincham | 300 | W 2-1 | Thompson 24 Parkinson 84 | 9 | 3 |
| 27 | BSN | A | Droylsden | 550 | L 2-5 | Ellison 34 Parkinson 61 | 10 | 4 |
| Sept 1 | BSN | H | Gainsborough Trinity | 158 | L 1-2 | Rutter 10 | 13 | 5 |
| 4 | BSN | A | Workington | 402 | L 1-3 | Hannigan 45 | 15 | 6 |
| 8 | BSN | A | Bishop's Stortford | 375 | D 2-2 | Parkinson 9 Burns 78 (pen) | 17 | 7 |
| 15 | BSN | H | Hinckley Town | 173 | W 2-1 | Rutter 47 Parkinson 56 | 13 | 8 |
| 22 | FAC Q2 | A | Stalybridge Celtic | 460 | L 0-1 | | | 9 |
| 29 | BSN | H | Solihull Moors | 105 | W 2-1 | Hannigan 77 Burns 85 (pen) | 9 | 10 |
| Oct 13 | BSN | A | Histon | 260 | L 0-2 | | 13 | 11 |
| 20 | BSN | H | Oxford City | 238 | W 2-1 | Thompson 22 Rutter 88 | 11 | 12 |
| 27 | BSN | A | Guiseley | 756 | L 1-2 | Rutter 79 | 12 | 13 |
| 30 | BSN | H | Chester | 1752 | L 0-3 | | 13 | 14 |
| Nov 3 | BSN | H | Brackley Town | 288 | L 0-2 | | 15 | 15 |
| 6 | BSN | A | FC Halifax Town | 858 | L 0-4 | | 15 | 16 |
| 10 | FAT 3Q | H | Harrogate Town | 131 | L 1-3 | Rutter 48 | | 17 |
| 17 | BSN | A | Harrogate Town | 393 | L 1-3 | Booth 52 | 17 | 18 |
| Dec 1 | BSN | A | Stalybridge Celtic | 331 | W 1-0 | Moss 90 | 14 | 19 |
| 8 | BSN | H | Boston United | 172 | W 4-0 | Rutter 12 14 Fearnehough 24 Stott 33 | 13 | 20 |
| 15 | BSN | H | Gloucester City | 122 | L 1-2 | Stott 34 | 14 | 21 |
| 26 | BSN | H | Colwyn Bay | 168 | D 1-1 | Stott 90 | 15 | 22 |
| Jan 1 | BSN | A | Colwyn Bay | 282 | W 4-2 | Noone 13 Hannigan 16 Rutter 57 61 | 15 | 23 |
| 5 | BSN | A | Oxford City | 183 | D 1-1 | Nicholas 1 | | 24 |
| 12 | BSN | H | Bishop's Stortfor | 143 | D 2-2 | Rutter 49 Stott 63 (pen) | 16 | 25 |
| Feb 2 | BSN | A | Worcester City | 751 | D 2-2 | Stott 8 66 | 14 | 26 |
| 5 | BSN | A | Hinckley United | 151 | W 6-0 | Anoruo 6 Barnes 7 Stott 18 Fearnehough 48 | 14 | 27 |
| | | | | | | Hannigan 57 Burns 61 (pen) | | |
| 9 | BSN | A | Solihull Moors | 162 | W 3-2 | Anoruo 30 Nicholas 46 Noone 66 | 11 | 28 |
| 12 | BSN | H | Guiseley | 357 | W 2-0 | Noone 56 Anorue 75 | 10 | 29 |
| 18 | BSN | A | Bradford PA | 272 | L 0-2 | | 10 | 30 |
| 23 | BSN | A | Chester | 2912 | L 0-2 | | 12 | 31 |
| 26 | BSN | H | FC Halifax Town | 251 | L 1-3 | Rutter 90 | 11 | 32 |
| Mar 2 | BSN | A | Boston United | 800 | W 1-0 | Stott 40 | 11 | 33 |
| 9 | BSN | H | Worcester City | 220 | W 1-0 | Clair 56 | 9 | 34 |
| 16 | BSN | H | Stalybridge Celtic | 209 | D 0-0 | | 10 | 35 |
| 19 | BSN | H | Workington | 136 | L 1-3 | Stott 32 | 10 | 36 |
| 26 | BSN | H | Corby Town | 106 | D 1-1 | Burns 52 (Pen) | 10 | 37 |
| 30 | BSN | A | Altrincham | 930 | L 0-1 | | 12 | 38 |
| Apr 1 | BSN | H | Droylsden | 148 | W 4-0 | Stott 21 33 Fearnehough 39 Rutter 52 | 11 | 39 |
| 6 | BSN | A | Gloucester City | 301 | D 1-1 | Stott 90 | 11 | 40 |
| 9 | BSN | A | Brackley Town | 247 | L 0-1 | | 11 | 41 |
| 13 | BSN | H | Histon | 192 | W 2-0 | Noone 49 Nicholas 85 | 10 | 42 |
| 20 | BSN | A | Gainsborough Trinity | 431 | L 1-2 | Anoruo 90 | 11 | 43 |
| 27 | BSN | H | Harrogate Town | 162 | L 0-1 | | 12 | 44 |

| GOALSCORERS | Lge | FAC | LC | Total | Pens | Hat-tricks | Cons Run | | Lge | FAC | LC | Total | Pens | Hat-tricks | Cons Run |
|---|---|---|---|---|---|---|---|---|---|---|---|---|---|---|---|
| Stott | 12 | | | 12 | 1 | | 3 | Thompson | 2 | | | 2 | | | |
| Rutter | 11 | 1 | | 10 | | | 1 | Barnes | 1 | | | 1 | | | |
| Hannigan | 5 | | | 5 | | | | Booth | 1 | | | 1 | | | |
| Anoruo | 4 | | | 4 | | | | Clair | 1 | | | 1 | | | |
| Burns | 4 | | | 4 | 4 | | | Moss | 1 | | | 1 | | | |
| Noone | 4 | | | 4 | | | | Noon | 1 | | | 1 | | | |
| Fearnehough | 3 | | | 3 | | | | Cons Run - Consecutive scoring games. | | | | | | | |
| Nicholas | 3 | | | 3 | | | | | | | | | | | |
| Parkinson | 3 | | | 3 | | | | | | | | | | | |
| Ellison | 2 | | | 2 | | | | | | | | | | | |

# WORCESTER CITY

**Chairman:** Anthony Hampson
**Secretary:** Joe Murphy  **(T)** 07837 086 205  **(E)** joemurphy77@yahoo.co.uk
**Commercial Manager:** n/a  **(T)**
**Programme Editor:** Rob Bazley  **(T)** r.bazley@sky.com
**Ground Address:** c/o Kidderminster H., Aggborough Stadium, Hoo Road, Kidderminster, DY10 1NB
**(T)** 01562 823 931  **Manager:** Carl Heeley

2012-13 Squad - Back Row: Shab Khan, Rob Elvins, Mike Symons, Jacob Rowe, Lee Ayres, Danny Edwards.
Middle Row: Joe Murphy (Secretary), Pete O'Connell (Chiropodist), Martyn Obrey (Assistant Physiotherapist), Stuart Whitehead, Danny Glover, Glyn Thompson, Matt Sargeant, Charlie Reece, Jay Denny, Lawson Mayor (Physiotherapist), Ashley Kingdon (Goalkeeper Coach), Kevin Gardiner (Kit Manager).
Front Row: Dan Polan, Matt Breeze, Tyler Weir, Carl Heeley (Manager), Matt Gardiner (Assistant Manager), Greg Mills, Ellis Deeney, Tom Thorley. Photo: Worcester News.

## Club Factfile

**Founded:** 1902  **Nickname:** City
**Previous Names:**
**Previous Leagues:** West Midlands, Birmingham, Southern 1938-79, 85-2004, Alliance 1979-85

**Club Colours (change):** Blue & white stripes/blue/white (Green/white/green)

**Ground Capacity:** 4,004  **Seats:** 1,125  **Covered:** 2,000  **Clubhouse:** Yes  **Shop:** Yes

**Directions:** NORTH - Take the M5 coming off at junction 3, follow signs for Severn Valley Railway, take the A456 to Kidderminster, turn left at traffic lights (opposite the Land Oak pub) onto the A449 to Worcester, at the next set of traffic lights turn right towards the Town Centre, then left onto Hoo Road (just before the roundabout at the bottom of hill), the ground should be 300 yards on the left hand side. SOUTH - Take the M5 to junction 6, follow A440 towards Kidderminster, turn right at the first island near McDonalds Drive Thru, take the first left into Hoo Road (opposite the Viaduct Pub), you should find the ground after half a mile on the right hand side.

**Previous Grounds:** Severn Terrace, Thorneloe, Flagge Meadow. St George's Lane 1905-2013.

**Record Attendance:** 17,042 v Sheffield United - FA Cup 4th Round 24/01/1959
**Record Victory:** 18-1 v Bilston - Birmingham League 21/11/1931
**Record Defeat:** 0-10 v Wellington - Birmingham League 29/08/1920
**Record Goalscorer:** John Inglis - 189 (1970-77)
**Record Appearances:** Bobby McEwan - 596 (1959-75)
**Additional Records:** Paid £8,500 to Telford United for Jim Williams 1981
**Senior Honours:** Received £27,000 from Everton for John Barton
Birmingham League 1913-14, 24-25, 28-29, 29-30.
Southern League Cup 1939-40, 2000-01, Division 1 1967-68, 76-77, Premier 1978-79.
Birmingham Senior Cup 1975-76. Worcestershire Senior Cup x26 (last win 1996-97).

### 10 YEAR RECORD

| 03-04 | | 04-05 | | 05-06 | | 06-07 | | 07-08 | | 08-09 | | 09-10 | | 10-11 | | 11-12 | | 12-13 | |
|---|---|---|---|---|---|---|---|---|---|---|---|---|---|---|---|---|---|---|---|
| SthP | 5 | Conf N | 7 | Conf N | 8 | Conf N | 9 | Conf N | 12 | Conf S | 16 | Conf S | 20 | Conf N | 16 | Conf N | 7 | Conf N | 15 |

# MATCH RESULTS 2012-13

| ate | Comp | H/A | Opponents | Att: | Result | Goalscorers | Pos | No. |
|---|---|---|---|---|---|---|---|---|
| ug 17 | BSN | A | Bradford PA | 453 | D 2-2 | Symons 11 Elvins 59 | 12 | 1 |
| ) | BSN | H | Bishop's Stortford | 768 | W 2-0 | Symons 36 82 | 1 | 2 |
| 5 | BSN | H | Corby Town | 738 | W 5-1 | Khan 21 Glover 49 (pen) 52 Symons 67 Taylor 71 | 4 | 3 |
| 7 | BSN | A | Oxford City | 365 | D 2-2 | Symons 54 Thorley 90 | 4 | 4 |
| ept 1 | BSN | H | Colwyn Bay | 832 | W 2-0 | Thorley 21 Glover 28 (pen) | 4 | 5 |
|  | BSN | A | Histon | 204 | D 0-0 |  | 5 | 6 |
|  | BSN | A | Gainsborough Trinity | 518 | L 0-1 |  | 5 | 7 |
| 5 | BSN | H | Droylsden | 325 | W 2-1 | Taylor 39 Thorley 71 (pen) | 5 | 8 |
| 2 | FAC Q2 | A | Gornal Athletic | 385 | W 4-0 | Taylor Symons Rowe Reece |  | 9 |
| 9 | BSN | H | Harrogate Railway | 954 | D 2-2 | White 11 (og) Glover 80 | 6 | 10 |
| ct 2 | BSN | A | Solihull Moors | 207 | W 1-0 | Thorley 45 | 6 | 11 |
|  | FAC Q3 | A | Weston-s-Mare | 556 | D 1-1 | Breeze 71 |  | 12 |
|  | FAC Q3r | H | Weston-s-Mare | 1013 | W 1-0 | Symons 50 |  | 13 |
| 3 | BSN | H | Stalybridge Celtic | 1038 | L 1-2 | Glover 27 | 6 | 14 |
| 0 | FAC Q4 | A | Bromley | 610 | L 0-1 |  |  | 15 |
| 7 | BSN | A | Boston United | 877 | W 2-1 | Breeze 25 Meecham 86 | 5 | 16 |
| 9 | BSN | H | Brackley Town | 1029 | L 1-2 | Mills 54 |  | 17 |
| lov 3 | BSN | A | Hinckley United | 359 | W 5-0 | Symons 39 Thorley 42 Reece 44 Elvins 84 Edwards 86 | 4 | 18 |
| 0 | FAT Q3 | H | Altrincham | 785 | L 0-3 |  |  | 19 |
| 7 | BSN | H | Workington | 817 | D 1-1 | Weir 21 | 5 | 20 |
| 0 | BSN | A | Guiseley | 424 | D 3-3 | Symons 54 84 Deeney 74 | 3 | 21 |
| ec 1 | BSN | A | Chester | 2640 | L 2-4 | Mills 53 Edwards 86 | 5 | 22 |
|  | BSN | H | FC Halifax Town | 1032 | L 0-1 |  | 7 | 23 |
| 5 | BSN | H | Bradford PA | 709 | W 2-0 | Rowe 11 Mills 74 | 5 | 24 |
| 6 | BSN | H | Gloucester City | 1290 | L 0-1 |  | 7 | 25 |
| an 1 | BSN | A | Gloucester City | 640 | L 2-4 | Elvins 65 Patterson 82 | 9 | 26 |
|  | BSN | A | Colwyn Bay | 303 | W 3-0 | Patterson 38 Hutchinson 84 Taylor 87 | 6 | 27 |
| 2 | BSN | H | Altrincham | 824 | D 0-0 |  | 6 | 28 |
| 6 | BSN | H | Histon | 804 | L 2-3 | Taylor 51 Glover 54 | 6 | 29 |
| 9 | BSN | A | Droylsden | 140 | W 2-0 | Glover 25 Taylor 30 | 6 | 30 |
| eb 2 | BSN | H | Vauxhall Motors | 751 | D 2-2 | Glover 28 80 | 6 | 31 |
|  | BSN | A | Stalybridge Celtic | 357 | W 2-0 | Glover 82 Symons 85 | 6 | 32 |
| 1 | BSN | H | Solihull Moors | 653 | L 1-3 | Taylor 42 | 6 | 33 |
| 6 | BSN | A | Harrogate Town | 49 | L 1-3 | Edwards 87 | 6 | 34 |
| 23 | BSN | H | Gloucester City | 738 | L 0-1 |  | 8 | 35 |
| Mar 2 | BSN | A | FC Halifax Town | 1275 | L 0-5 |  | 10 | 36 |
| ) | BSN | A | Vauxhall Motors | 220 | L 0-1 |  | 12 | 37 |
| 6 | BSN | H | Boston United | 669 | L 0-3 |  | 13 | 38 |
| 8 | BSN | H | Gainsborough Trinity | 536 | L 0-3 |  | 13 | 39 |
| 23 | BSN | A | Altrincham | 777 | L 0-2 |  | 14 | 40 |
| 30 | BSN | A | Corby Town | 275 | L 0-1 |  | 14 | 41 |
| Apr 1 | BSN | H | Oxford City | 597 | W 3-2 | Symons 3 Morris 36 Khan 64 | 13 | 42 |
| 5 | BSN | A | Workington | 373 | L 0-1 |  | 14 | 43 |
| 3 | BSN | H | Hinckley United | 828 | W 3-1 | Moore 26 Symons 37 Breeze 71 | 15 | 44 |
| 6 | BSN | A | Bishops Stortford | 261 | W 1-0 | Thorley 62 | 13 | 45 |
| 0 | BSN | A | Brackley Town | 382 | L 0-2 |  | 14 | 46 |
| 27 | BSN | H | Chester | 4075 | L 0-1 |  | 14 | 47 |

| GOALSCORERS | Lge | FAC | LC | Total | Pens | Hat-tricks | Cons Run | | Lge | FAC | LC | Total | Pens | Hat-tricks | Cons Run |
|---|---|---|---|---|---|---|---|---|---|---|---|---|---|---|---|
| Symons | 11 | 2 |  | 13 |  |  | 4 | Reece | 1 | 1 |  | 2 |  |  |  |
| Glover | 10 |  |  | 10 | 2 |  | 4 | Rowe | 1 | 1 |  | 2 |  |  |  |
| Taylor | 6 | 1 |  | 7 |  |  |  | Deeney | 1 |  |  | 1 |  |  |  |
| Thorley | 6 |  |  | 6 |  | 1 |  | Hutchinson | 1 |  |  | 1 |  |  |  |
| Breeze | 2 | 1 |  | 3 |  |  |  | Meecham | 1 |  |  | 1 |  |  |  |
| Edwards | 3 |  |  | 3 |  |  |  | Weir | 1 |  |  | 1 |  |  |  |
| Elvins | 3 |  |  | 3 |  |  |  | Morris | 1 |  |  | 1 |  |  |  |
| Mills | 3 |  |  | 3 |  |  |  | Moore | 1 |  |  | 1 |  |  |  |
| Khan | 2 |  |  | 2 |  |  |  | Own Goals | 1 |  |  | 1 |  |  |  |
| Patterson | 2 |  |  | 2 |  |  |  | Cons Run - Consecutive scoring games. | | | | | | | |

# WORKINGTON

**Chairman:** Humphrey Dobie
**Secretary:** Alec Graham    **(T)** 07788 537 811    **(E)** alec.graham@workingtonafc.com
**Commercial Manager:** n/a    **(T)**
**Programme Editor:** Paul Armstrong    **(T)** 079512 43717
**Ground Address:** Borough Park, Workington, Cumbria CA14 2DT
**(T)** 01900 602 871      **Manager:** Darren Edmondson

2012-13 Squad - Back row (left to right) Sue Pollock, Kyle May, Jordan Connerton, Gareth Arnison, Niall Cowperthwaite, Aaran Taylor, David Hewson (captain), Shaun Routledge, Jonny Wright, Stefan Scott, Dan Wordsworth, Chris Wraighte, Lee Andrews, Alan Clark. Front row (left to right) Phil McLuckie, Mark Boyd, Jake Simpson, Darren Edmondson (manager), Humphrey Dobie (chairman), Tony Elliott (assistant manager), Gari Rowntree, Anthony Wright, Mark Sloan.

## Club Factfile

**Founded:** 1884    **Nickname:** Reds
**Previous Names:** None
**Previous Leagues:** Cumberland Assoc. 1890-94, Cumberland Senior 1894-1901, 03-04. Lancashire 1901-03, Lancashire Comb. 1904-10, North Eastern 1910-11, 21-51, Football League 1951-77, N.P.L. 1977-2005
**Club Colours (change):** Red/white/red (Green & black stripes/black/green & black stripes)
**Ground Capacity:** 2,500    **Seats:** 500    **Covered:** 1,000    **Clubhouse:** Yes    **Shop:** Yes

**Directions:** A66 into Workington. At traffic lights at bottom of hill (HSBC opposite), turn left towards town centre. Approach traffic lights in centre lane (Washington Central Hotel on your right) and turn right. Continue on this road, passing over a mini roundabout, a pedestrian crossing and a further set of traffic lights. You will come to the Railway Station (facing you), carry on through the junction and bear right, passing the Derwent Park Stadium (Rugby League/speedway), then left and Borough Park becomes visible ahead of you.

**Previous Grounds:** Various 1884-1921, Lonsdale Park 1921-37

**Record Attendance:** 21,000 v Manchester United - FA Cup 3rd round 04/01/1958
**Record Victory:** 17-1 v Cockermouth Crusaders - Cumberland Senior League 19/01/1901
**Record Defeat:** 0-9 v Chorley (A) - Northern Premier League 10/11/1987
**Record Goalscorer:** Billy Charlton - 193
**Record Appearances:** Bobby Brown - 419
**Additional Records:** Paid £6,000 to Sunderland for Ken Chisolm 1956   Received £33,000 from Liverpool for Ian McDonald 1974
**Senior Honours:**
North West Counties League 1998-99
Cumberland County Cup x23

### 10 YEAR RECORD

| 03-04 | | 04-05 | | 05-06 | | 06-07 | | 07-08 | | 08-09 | | 09-10 | | 10-11 | | 11-12 | | 12-13 | |
|---|---|---|---|---|---|---|---|---|---|---|---|---|---|---|---|---|---|---|---|
| NP 1 | 7 | NP P | 2 | Conf N | 13 | Conf N | 3 | Conf N | 14 | Conf N | 12 | Conf N | 4 | Conf N | 11 | Conf N | 13 | Conf N | 14 |

# MATCH RESULTS 2012-13

| ate | Comp | H/A | Opponents | Att: | Result | Goalscorers | Pos | No. |
|---|---|---|---|---|---|---|---|---|
| ug 17 | BSN | H | Stalybridge Celtic | 446 | W 4-1 | Arnison 33 (pen) 68 Wright 34 Scott 85 | 3 | 1 |
| | BSN | A | Chester | 3007 | L 0-1 | | 8 | 2 |
| | BSN | A | FC Halifax Town | 1167 | L 1-5 | Arnison 77 | 14 | 3 |
| | BSN | H | Guiseley | 374 | L 0-2 | | 18 | 4 |
| ept 1 | BSN | A | Boston United | 937 | W 3-1 | Arnison 10 (pen) 86 Wright 79 | 12 | 5 |
| | BSN | H | Vauxhall Motors | 402 | W 3-1 | Connerton 70 84 Arnison 73 | 10 | 6 |
| | BSN | H | Corby Town | 304 | L 2-3 | Wright 34 Connerton 78 | 12 | 7 |
| 5 | BSN | A | Brackley Town | 476 | L 1-3 | Wright 51 | 15 | 8 |
| 2 | FAC Q2 | A | Blyth Spartans | 502 | D 1-1 | Vaulks 26 | | 9 |
| 9 | BSN | H | Hinckley United | 291 | W 2-1 | Bolton 47 Arnison 58 | 14 | 10 |
| ct 1 | FAC 2Q | H | Blyth Spartans | 319 | W 1-0 | May | | 11 |
| | FAC Q3 | A | Barwell | 217 | D 1-1 | Arnison 48 | | 12 |
| | FAC Q3r | H | Barwell | 386 | W 2-0 | Vaulks 77 Simpson 86 | | 13 |
| 3 | BSN | A | Oxford City | 427 | L 0-5 | | 14 | 14 |
| | FAC Q4 | H | Mansfield Town | 721 | L 1-2 | Arnison 87 | | 15 |
| 3 | BSN | A | Altrincham | 638 | W 2-1 | Mwasiles 23 Arnison 45 (pen) | 13 | 16 |
| 7 | BSN | A | Gainsborough T | 493 | D 1-1 | Arnison 30 | 11 | 17 |
| 0 | BSN | H | Droylsden | 363 | W 2-1 | Vaulks 59 Wright 78 | 10 | 18 |
| ov 3 | BSN | H | Solihull Moors | 384 | D 1-1 | Connerton 69 | 10 | 19 |
| 0 | FAT Q3 | A | Ossett Town | 158 | L 1-2 | Wright 13 | | 20 |
| 7 | BSN | A | Worcester City | 817 | D 1-1 | Arnison 60 | 10 | 21 |
| 4 | BSN | H | Bradford PA | 397 | L 1-6 | Wright 21 | 11 | 22 |
| ec 8 | BSN | A | Gloucester City | 230 | W 1-0 | Mwasiles 4 | 9 | 23 |
| 5 | BSN | H | Stalybridge Celtic | 343 | W 4-1 | Mwasiles 40 90 Arnison 53 Hewson 72 | 9 | 24 |
| an 1 | BSN | H | Harrogate Town | 406 | L 1-2 | Hopper 57 | 13 | 25 |
| | BSN | H | Boston United | 390 | D 1-1 | May | 12 | 26 |
| 2 | BSN | A | Histon | 216 | L 0-3 | | 15 | 27 |
| 9 | BSN | H | Gainsborough Trinity | 191 | L 0-3 | | 15 | 28 |
| eb 2 | BSN | A | Colwyn Bay | 268 | W 4-1 | McGee 44 McLuckie 48, St Juste 60 Greenhalgh 74 | 16 | 29 |
| | BSN | A | Harrogate Town | 284 | L 1-3 | McLuckie 22 | 17 | 30 |
| | BSN | H | Oxford City | 312 | L 1-2 | Wright 84 | 18 | 31 |
| 6 | BSN | H | Altrincham | 374 | W 3-1 | Wright 16 89 | 16 | 32 |
| 9 | BSN | H | Chester | 531 | D 1-1 | Rowntree 53 | 16 | 33 |
| 3 | BSN | A | Hinckley United | 239 | D 1-1 | Wright 46 | 17 | 34 |
| Mar 2 | BSN | H | Gloucester City | 356 | L 0-1 | | 17 | 35 |
| | BSN | A | Bradford PA | 284 | L 0-1 | | 17 | 36 |
| | BSN | A | Bishop's Stortford | 377 | W 3-0 | McLuckie 6 Arnison 62 (pen) 65 | 17 | 37 |
| 2 | BSN | H | Brackley Town | 251 | D 0-0 | | 17 | 38 |
| 6 | BSN | H | Histon | 304 | W 3-1 | Arnison 1 26 Wright 14 | 15 | 39 |
| 9 | BSN | A | Vauxhall Motors | 136 | W 3-1 | Wright 10 Baldry 64 Hazel 90 | | 40 |
| 6 | BSN | H | Bishop Stortford | 181 | L 2-3 | Arnison 44 57 | 13 | 41 |
| 0 | BSN | H | FC Halifax Town | 481 | L 0-1 | | 13 | 42 |
| pr 1 | BSN | A | Guiseley | 513 | L 0-2 | | 14 | 43 |
| | BSN | H | Worcester City | 373 | W 1-0 | Arnison 67 | 13 | 44 |
| 3 | BSN | A | Corby Town | 314 | W 3-1 | Piergianni 2 (og) Hazel 20 Arnison 59 | 14 | 45 |
| 6 | BSN | A | Droylsden | 100 | W 1-0 | Hazel 42 | 12 | 46 |
| 0 | BSN | H | Colwyn Bay | 412 | L 1-2 | Wordswort 31 | 13 | 47 |
| 7 | BSN | A | Solihull Moors | 275 | D 2-2 | Wright 25 Connerton 69 | 14 | 48 |

| GOALSCORERS | Lge | FAC | LC | Total | Pens | Hat-tricks | Cons Run |
|---|---|---|---|---|---|---|---|
| Arnison | 19 | 2 | | 21 | 4 | | 3 |
| Wright | 13 | 1 | | 14 | | | 2 |
| Connerton | 5 | | | 5 | | | |
| Mwasiles | 4 | | | 4 | | | |
| Hazel | 3 | | | 3 | | | |
| McLuckie | 3 | | | 3 | | | |
| Vaulks | 1 | 2 | | 3 | | | |
| May | 1 | 1 | | 2 | | | |
| Baldry | 1 | | | 1 | | | |
| Bolton | 1 | | | 1 | | | |
| Greenhalgh | 1 | | | 1 | | | |

| | Lge | FAC | LC | Total | Pens | Hat-tricks | Cons Run |
|---|---|---|---|---|---|---|---|
| Hewson | 1 | | | 1 | | | |
| Hopper | 1 | | | 1 | | | |
| McGhee | 1 | | | 1 | | | |
| Rowntree | 1 | | | 1 | | | |
| St Juste | 1 | | | 1 | | | |
| Scott | 1 | | | 1 | | | |
| Simpson | | 1 | | 1 | | | |
| Wordsworth | 1 | | | 1 | | | |
| Own Goals | 1 | | | 1 | | | |
| Cons Run - Consecutive scoring games. | | | | | | | |

# BASINGSTOKE TOWN

**Chairman:** Rafi Razzak

**Secretary:** Richard Trodd    **(T)** 07887 507 447    **(E)** richard.trodd@ntlworld.com

**Commercial Manager:** John Gaston    **(T)** 07782 379 400

**Programme Editor:** James Holly    **(T)** jamesholly21@gmail.com

**Ground Address:** Camrose Ground, Western Way, Basingstoke RG22 6EZ

**(T)** 01256 327 575      **Manager:** Jason Bristow

2012-13 Squad

Back Row L-R: Alex Charlick, Nathan Campbell, Chris Paterson, Stefan Brown, Delano Sam-Yorke, Shaun McAuley, Joe McDonnell, Ross Adams, Ashley Bayes, Stuart Lake, Jay Gasson, Tim Sills, Rob Rice, Nathan Smart, Matthew Warner.
Front Row L-R: Kieron Maylen, Jordace Holder-Spooner, Wes Daly, Jason Bristow ( Manager ), Kevin Braybrook ( Ass Manager ), Jide Ogunbote, Toby Little, Simon Dunn.

## Club Factfile

**Founded:** 1896     **Nickname:** Dragons

**Previous Names:** None

**Previous Leagues:** Hampshire 1900-40, 45-71, Southern 1971-87, Isthmian 1987-2004

**Club Colours (change):** Blue and yellow/blue/yellow (All red)

**Ground Capacity:** 6,000   **Seats:** 651    **Covered:** 2,000    **Clubhouse:** Yes    **Shop:** Yes

**Directions**

Leave M3 at junction 6 and turn left onto South Ringway which is the A30.
Straight over first roundabout. At second roundabout turn left into Winchester Road.
Proceed past ground on right to roundabout.
Take fifth exit into Western Way. Ground on right.

**Previous Grounds:** Castle Field 1896-1947

**Record Attendance:** 5,085 v Wycombe Wanderers - FA Cup 1st Round replay 1997-98

**Record Victory:** 10-1 v Chichester City (H) - FA Cup 1st Qualifying Round 1976

**Record Defeat:** 0-8 v Aylesbury United - Southern League April 1979

**Record Goalscorer:** Paul Coombs - 159 (1991-99)

**Record Appearances:** Billy Coomb

**Additional Records:** Paid £4,750 to Gosport Borough for Steve Ingham

**Senior Honours:**
Hampshire League 1967-68, 69-70, 70-71. Southern League Southern Division 1984-85.
Hampshire Senior Cup 1970-71, 89-90, 95-96, 2007-08.

### 10 YEAR RECORD

| 03-04 | | 04-05 | | 05-06 | | 06-07 | | 07-08 | | 08-09 | | 09-10 | | 10-11 | | 11-12 | | 12-13 | |
|---|---|---|---|---|---|---|---|---|---|---|---|---|---|---|---|---|---|---|---|
| Isth P | 14 | Conf S | 6 | Conf S | 19 | Conf S | 19 | Conf S | 15 | Conf S | 18 | Conf S | 15 | Conf S | 13 | Conf S | 5 | Conf S | 14 |

# MATCH RESULTS 2012-13

| Date | Comp | H/A | Opponents | Att: | Result | Goalscorers | Pos | No. |
|---|---|---|---|---|---|---|---|---|
| Aug 18 | BSS | H | Sutton United | 424 | W 2-1 | Holder-Spooner 43 Sills 67 | 3 | 1 |
| 21 | BSS | A | Eastleigh | 608 | D 1-1 | Warner 73 | 7 | 2 |
| 27 | BSS | H | Hayes & Yeading | 406 | D 2-2 | Holder-Spooner 5 Sills 30 | 11 | 3 |
| Sept 1 | BSS | A | Tonbridge Angels | 518 | D 0-0 | | 13 | 4 |
| 4 | BSS | H | Truro City | 301 | W 3-2 | Sam-Yorke 7 9 Daley 45 | 10 | 5 |
| 8 | BSS | H | AFC Hornchurch | 359 | L 0-2 | | 10 | 6 |
| 15 | BSS | A | Eastbourne Borough | 531 | L 0-1 | | 14 | 7 |
| 22 | FAC Q2 | H | Weymouth | 324 | W 3-1 | Sills 37 Adams 46 McNish 90 | | 8 |
| 25 | BSS | A | Staines Town | 310 | L 0-2 | | 15 | 9 |
| 29 | BSS | A | Billericay Town | 479 | W 3-1 | SILLS 3 (17 32 43) | 11 | 10 |
| Oct 2 | BSS | H | Bromley | 253 | D 1-1 | Sills 35 | 12 | 11 |
| 6 | FAC Q3 | A | Dorchester Town | 580 | L 0-1 | | | 12 |
| 13 | BSS | H | Havant & Waterlooville | 410 | L 1-2 | Sam-Yorke 26 | 15 | 13 |
| 20 | BSS | A | Weston-s-Mare | 282 | L 2-5 | Brown 74 Sam-Yorke 85 | 20 | 14 |
| 27 | BSS | H | Dover Athletic | 353 | L 0-1 | | 20 | 15 |
| 30 | BSS | H | Eastbourne Borough | 283 | D 2-2 | Sam-Yorke 32 Daly 45 | 19 | 16 |
| Nov 10 | FAT Q3 | A | AFC Totton | 368 | L 0-3 | | | 17 |
| 12 | BSS | A | Boreham Wood | 201 | D 1-1 | Sills 2 | 19 | 18 |
| 17 | BSS | H | Chelmsford City | 377 | L 1-2 | Sills 46 | 21 | 19 |
| Dec 8 | BSS | H | Tonbridge Angels | 320 | W 1-0 | Dunn 85 | 21 | 20 |
| 15 | BSS | A | AFC Hornchurch | 260 | L 0-3 | | 21 | 21 |
| 26 | BSS | A | Farnborough | 572 | L 1-2 | | 21 | 22 |
| Jan 1 | BSS | H | Farnborough | 420 | W 6-2 | Dunn 44 Sills 58 SAM-YORK 4 (51 52 61 64) | 21 | 23 |
| 5 | BSS | H | Bath City | 391 | W 2-1 | Sam-Yorke 25 77 | 19 | 24 |
| 12 | BSS | H | Staines Town | 550 | W 3-1 | McAuley 27 Sills 37 Gasson 54 | 13 | 25 |
| 26 | BSS | H | Welling United | 388 | L 0-1 | | 18 | 26 |
| Feb 1 | BSS | A | Havant & Waterlooville | 635 | L 1-4 | McAuley 28 | 20 | 27 |
| 5 | BSS | A | Dorchester Town | 290 | D 2-2 | Lake 7 Dunn 9 | 20 | 28 |
| 9 | BSS | A | Bromley | 457 | W 2-1 | Dunn 4 46 | 17 | 29 |
| 12 | BSS | A | Hayes & Yeading | 149 | L 1-2 | Sam-Yorke | 18 | 30 |
| 16 | BSS | H | Dorchester Town | 471 | W 2-1 | Williams 50 Warner 56 | 14 | 31 |
| 19 | BSS | A | Sutton United | 402 | L 2-3 | Williams 34 Sam-Yorke 75 | 15 | 32 |
| 23 | BSS | A | Maidenhead United | 267 | D 2-2 | Williams 49 55 | 16 | 33 |
| Mar 2 | BSS | H | Billericay Town | 419 | D 3-3 | Williams 17 90 Luke 41 (og) | 16 | 34 |
| 5 | BSS | A | Salisbury Clty | 468 | W 2-0 | Dunn 28 Sam-Yorke 90 | 16 | 35 |
| 9 | BSS | A | Welling United | 720 | D 1-1 | Williams 45 | 14 | 36 |
| 12 | BSS | H | Maidenhead United | 250 | W 2-0 | Daley 4 Williams 12 | 12 | 37 |
| 23 | BSS | A | Bath City | 560 | D 1-1 | Sills 84 | 14 | 38 |
| 30 | BSS | H | Eastleigh | 532 | L 0-3 | | 14 | 39 |
| Apr 1 | BSS | A | Truro City | 385 | D 2-2 | Daley 35 Sam -Yorke 76 | 14 | 40 |
| 6 | BSS | A | Dover Athletic | 735 | W 5-0 | Williams 13 69 Dunn 23 79 Sam-Yorke 88 | 13 | 41 |
| 9 | BSS | H | Weston-s-Mare | 260 | L 1-3 | Williams 82 | 13 | 42 |
| 13 | BSS | H | Boreham Wood | 270 | L 2-3 | Lake 59 Ray 90 | 13 | 43 |
| 20 | BSS | A | Chelmsford City | 828 | L 0-2 | | 13 | 44 |
| 27 | BSS | A | Salisbury City | 535 | L 0-4 | | 14 | |

| GOALSCORERS | Lge | FAC | LC | Total | Pens | Hat-tricks | Cons Run | | Lge | FAC | LC | Total | Pens | Hat-tricks | Cons Run |
|---|---|---|---|---|---|---|---|---|---|---|---|---|---|---|---|
| Sam-York | 16 | | | 16 | 1 | | 2 | Brown | 1 | | | 1 | | | |
| Sills | 12 | 1 | | 13 | | | 2 | Daley | 1 | | | 1 | | | |
| Williams | 11 | | | 11 | | | 4 | Glasson | 1 | | | 1 | | | |
| Dunn | 8 | | | 8 | | | | McNish | | 1 | | 1 | | | |
| Daley | 3 | | | 3 | | | | Ray | 1 | | | 1 | | | |
| Holder-Spooner | 2 | | | 2 | | | | Own Goals | 1 | | | 1 | | | |
| Lake | 2 | | | 2 | | | | Cons Run - Consecutive scoring games. | | | | | | | |
| McCauley | 2 | | | 2 | | | | | | | | | | | |
| Warner | 2 | | | 2 | | | | | | | | | | | |
| Adams | | 1 | | 1 | | | | | | | | | | | |

# BATH CITY

**Chairman:** Manda Rigby
**Secretary:** Quentin Edwards    **(T)** 07785 795 532    **(E)** qcath@blueyonder.co.uk
**Commercial Manager:** Bob Chester    **(T)** 07786 092 836
**Programme Editor:** Mark Stillman    **(T)** 07929 110 109
**Ground Address:** Twerton Park, Twerton, Bath, Somerset BA2 1DB
**(T)** 01225 423 087      **Manager:** Lee Howells

## Club Factfile

**Founded:** 1889     **Nickname:** The Romans
**Previous Names:** Bath AFC 1889-92. Bath Railway FC 1902-05. Bath Amateurs 1913-23 (Reserve side)
**Previous Leagues:** Western 1908-21. Southern 1921-79, 88-90, 97-2007. Alliance/Conference 1979-88, 90-97.

**Club Colours (change):** Black & white stripes/black/black (Purple/white/purple)

**Ground Capacity:** 8,840   **Seats:** 1,017   **Covered:** 4,800   **Clubhouse:** Yes   **Shop:** Yes

**Directions:** Take Junction 18 off M4. 3rd exit off roundabout and follow A46 (10 miles) to Bath City Centre. Along Pulteney Road then right into Claverton Street and then follow A36 Lower Bristol Road (1.5 miles). Left under Railway bridge (signs Bath City FC) into Twerton High Street and ground is 2nd turning on left.

**Previous Grounds:** The Belvoir Ground 1889-92 & 1902-15. Lambridge Show Ground 1919-32.

**Record Attendance:** 18,020 v Brighton & Hove Albion - FA Cup
**Record Victory:** 8-0 v Boston United - 1998-99
**Record Defeat:** 0-9 v Yeovil Town - 1946-47
**Record Goalscorer:** Paul Randall - 106
**Record Appearances:** David Mogg - 530
**Additional Records:** Paid £15,000 to Bristol City for Micky Tanner. Received £80,000 from Southampton for Jason Dodd.
**Senior Honours:**
Southern Lge Western Div.2 1928-29. Southern Lge Western Division 1933-34. Southern League 1959-60, 77-78, 2006-07.
Southern League Cup 1978-79. Somerset Premier Cup 1951-52, 52-53, 57-58, 59-60, 65-66, 67-68, 69-70, 77-78, 80-81,
81-82, 83-84, 84-85, 85-86, 88-89, 89-90, 93-94, 94-95, 2007-08.

### 10 YEAR RECORD

| 03-04 | | 04-05 | | 05-06 | | 06-07 | | 07-08 | | 08-09 | | 09-10 | | 10-11 | | 11-12 | | 12-13 | |
|---|---|---|---|---|---|---|---|---|---|---|---|---|---|---|---|---|---|---|---|
| SthP | 16 | SthP | 6 | SthP | 2 | SthP | 1 | Conf S | 8 | Conf S | 8 | Conf S | 4 | Conf | 10 | Conf | 23 | Conf S | 11 |

# MATCH RESULTS 2012-13

| Date | Comp | H/A | Opponents | Att: | Result | Goalscorers | Pos | No. |
|------|------|-----|-----------|------|--------|-------------|-----|-----|
| Aug 18 | BSS | A | Welling United | 479 | D 1-1 | Brown 20 | 9 | 1 |
| 21 | BSS | H | Maidenhead United | 587 | W 3-1 | GUTHRIE 3 (3 36 78) | 4 | 2 |
| 25 | BSS | H | Havant & Waterlooville | 535 | W 2-0 | Low 10 Guthrie 72 | 1 | 3 |
| 27 | BSS | A | Dorchester Town | 559 | L 1-2 | Griffin 13 | 3 | 4 |
| Sept 1 | BSS | H | Billericay Town | 616 | W 2-1 | Griffin 39 70 | 1 | 5 |
| 4 | BSS | A | Salisbury City | 857 | L 2-3 | Griffin 16 Keats 76 | 3 | 6 |
| 8 | BSS | A | Bromley | 495 | L 0-1 | | 8 | 7 |
| 15 | BSS | H | Dover Athletic | 614 | L 1-2 | Griffin 50 | 11 | 8 |
| 22 | FAC Q2 | A | Buckland Athletic | 369 | W 2-1 | Brown 57 Guthrie 68 | | 9 |
| 29 | BSS | H | Boreham Wood | 508 | D 0-0 | | 13 | 10 |
| Oct 2 | BSS | A | Truro City | 344 | L 1-2 | Guthrie 40 | 17 | 11 |
| 6 | FAC Q3 | H | Gosport Borough | 586 | D 1-1 | Grifin 86 (pen) | | 12 |
| 9 | FAC Q3r | A | Gosport Borough | 324 | L 1-3 | Canham 27 | | 13 |
| 13 | BSS | H | Hayes & Yeading | 720 | L 2-3 | Allen 14 Canham 43 | 20 | 14 |
| 20 | BSS | A | Tonbridge Angels | 536 | W 4-3 | Canham 11 33 Allen 41 56 | 13 | 15 |
| 27 | BSS | H | AFC Hornchurch | 509 | W 3-1 | Allen 20 Burnell 35 Canham 87 | 12 | 16 |
| 30 | BSS | A | Eastleigh | 525 | L 1-3 | Allen 34 | 13 | 17 |
| Nov 4 | BSS | H | Farnborough Town | 605 | W 3-2 | Griffin 18 85 Canham 80 | 10 | 18 |
| 10 | FAT Q3 | A | Leatherhead | 287 | D 4-4 | Allen 8 Canham 29 70 Brown 30 | | 19 |
| 13 | FAT Q3r | H | Leatherhead | 341 | W 2-0 | Griffin 36 Allen 73 | | 20 |
| 17 | BSS | A | Sutton United | 512 | W 2-0 | Preece 25 Morgan 89 | 6 | 21 |
| 24 | FAT 1 | A | Chesham United | 301 | L 1-2 | Morgan 74 | | 22 |
| Dec 1 | BSS | H | Eastbourne Boro | 540 | D 2-2 | Ball 78 Jones 91 | 8 | 23 |
| 8 | BSS | A | Billericay Town | 388 | L 0-2 | | 8 | 24 |
| 26 | BSS | H | Weston-s-Mare | 683 | L 1-2 | Griffin 45 (pen) | 9 | 25 |
| Jan 5 | BSS | A | Basingstoke Town | 391 | L 1-2 | Low 1 | 17 | 26 |
| 8 | BSS | A | Weston-s-Mare | 218 | W 4-1 | Nichols 10 Griffin 13 Low 72 Mike 90 | 12 | 27 |
| 15 | BSS | H | Bromley | 386 | L 0-2 | | 12 | 28 |
| 26 | BSS | A | Hayes & Yeading | 177 | D 2-2 | Preece 31 Griffin 69 | 14 | 29 |
| Feb 2 | BSS | H | Staines Town | 1073 | L 0-1 | | 18 | 30 |
| 5 | BSS | A | Farnborough | 326 | W 1-0 | Chamberlain 78 | 13 | 31 |
| 9 | BSS | A | Boreham Wood | 207 | D 0-0 | | 12 | 32 |
| 12 | BSS | H | Dorchester Town | 418 | L 2-3 | Griffin 27 43 | 13 | 33 |
| 16 | BSS | H | Tonbridge Angels | 564 | W 3-0 | Keats 46 Morgan 60 Griffin 67 | 12 | 34 |
| 19 | BSS | A | Eastbourne Borough | 406 | W 3-0 | Preece 38 73 Chamberlain 45 | 9 | 35 |
| 23 | BSS | H | Truro City | 574 | D 1-1 | Low 10 | 11 | 36 |
| Mar 2 | BSS | A | Dover Athletic | 873 | L 0-2 | | 13 | 37 |
| 5 | BSS | A | Havant & Waterlooville | 406 | L 1-2 | Keats 9 | 15 | 38 |
| 9 | BSS | A | AFC Hornchurch | 340 | L 1-2 | Griffin 73 | 16 | 39 |
| 16 | BSS | H | Chelmsford City | 512 | D 2-2 | Jones 9 Keats 90 | 15 | 40 |
| 19 | BSS | H | Welling United | 367 | W 1-0 | Simpson 36 | 13 | 41 |
| 23 | BSS | H | Basingstoke Town | 560 | D 1-1 | Chamberlain 32 | 13 | 42 |
| 30 | BSS | A | Maidenhead United | 320 | W 1-0 | Chamberlain 55 | 10 | 43 |
| Apr 1 | BSS | H | Salisbury City | 731 | D 0-0 | | 12 | 44 |
| 6 | BSS | A | Chelmsford City | 656 | W1-0 | Griffin 50 | 12 | 45 |
| 12 | BSS | H | Eastleigh | 545 | D 1-1 | Griffin 64 | 12 | 46 |
| 20 | BSS | A | Staines Town | 484 | W 3-1 | Jones 13 Preece 83 Lennox 87 | 11 | 47 |
| 27 | BSS | H | Sutton United | 613 | L 0-4 | | 11 | 48 |

| GOALSCORERS | Lge | FAC | LC | Total | Pens | Hat-tricks | Cons Run | | Lge | FAC | LC | Total | Pens | Hat-tricks | Cons Run |
|-------------|-----|-----|----|-------|------|------------|----------|----|-----|-----|----|-------|------|------------|----------|
| Griffin | 16 | 1 | 1 | 18 | 2 | | 3 | Morgan | 2 | | 1 | 3 | | | |
| Canham | 5 | 1 | 2 | 8 | | | | Ball | 1 | | | 1 | | | |
| Allen | 5 | | 2 | 7 | | | | Burnell | 1 | | | 1 | | | |
| Guthrie | 5 | 1 | | 6 | | 1 | | Lennox | 1 | | | 1 | | | |
| Preece | 5 | | | 5 | | | | Mike | 1 | | | 1 | | | |
| Chamberlain | 4 | | | 4 | | | | Nicholls | 1 | | | 1 | | | |
| Keats | 4 | | | 4 | | | | Simpson | 1 | | | 1 | | | |
| Low | 4 | | | 4 | | | | Cons Run - Consecutive scoring games. | | | | | | | |
| Brown | 1 | 1 | 1 | 3 | | | | | | | | | | | |
| Jones | 3 | | | 3 | | | | | | | | | | | |

# BISHOP'S STORTFORD

**Chairman:** Luigu Del Basso
**Secretary:** Ian Kettridge    **(T)** 07904 169 017    **(E)** ianket@aol.com
**Commercial Manager:** John Turner    **(T)** 077100 79158
**Programme Editor:** John Allington    **(T)** 01279 306 456
**Ground Address:** Woodside Park, Dunmow Road, Bishop's Stortford, Herts CM23 5RG
**(T)** 01279 306 456          **Manager:** Rod Stringer

## Club Factfile

**Founded:** 1874    **Nickname:** Blues or Bishops
**Previous Names:** None
**Previous Leagues:** East Herts 1896-97, 1902-06, 19-21, Stansted & District 1906-19, Herts County 1921-25, 27-29,
         Herts & Essex Border 1925-27, Spartan 1929-51, Delphian 1951-63, Athenian 1963-73, Isthmian 1974-2004

**Club Colours (change):** All blue (White/black/black)

**Ground Capacity:** 4,000    **Seats:** 298    **Covered:** 700    **Clubhouse:** Yes    **Shop:** Yes

**Directions**
Woodside Park is situated 1/4 mile from Junction 8 of M11.
Follow A1250 towards Bishop's Stortford Town Centre, entrance to the ground is signposted through Woodside Park Industrial Estate.

**Previous Grounds:** Rhodes Avenue 1919-1997.

**Record Attendance:** 6,000 v Peterborough Town - FA Cup 2nd Round 1972-73 and v Middlesbrough - FA Cup 3rd Round replay 1982-83
**Record Victory:** 11-0 v Nettleswell & Buntwill - Herts Junior Cup 1911
**Record Defeat:** 0-13 v Cheshunt (H) - Herts Senior Cup 1926
**Record Goalscorer:** Post 1929 Jimmy Badcock - 123
**Record Appearances:** Phil Hopkins - 543
**Additional Records:**

**Senior Honours:**
Athenian League 1969-70. FA Amateur Cup 1973-74. Isthmian League Division 1 1980-81. FA Trophy 1980-81.
London Senior Cup 1973-74. Premier Inter League Cup 1989-90. Herts Senior Cup x10 Most recently 2011-12.

### 10 YEAR RECORD

| 03-04 | 04-05 | 05-06 | 06-07 | 07-08 | 08-09 | 09-10 | 10-11 | 11-12 | 12-13 |
|---|---|---|---|---|---|---|---|---|---|
| Isth P   11 | Conf S   10 | Conf S   15 | Conf S   5 | Conf S   10 | Conf S   9 | Conf S   18 | Conf S   16 | Conf N   10 | Conf N   17 |

# MATCH RESULTS 2012-13

| Date | Comp | H/A | Opponents | Att: | Result | Goalscorers | Pos | No. |
|------|------|-----|-----------|------|--------|-------------|-----|-----|
| Aug 18 | BSN | H | FC Halifax Town | 622 | L 1-2 | Akurang 39 | 13 | 1 |
| 21 | BSN | A | Worcester City | 768 | L 0-2 | | 18 | 2 |
| 25 | BSN | A | Brackley Town | 358 | L 0-1 | | 21 | 3 |
| 27 | BSN | H | Boston United | 559 | W 1-0 | Obafemi 9 | 17 | 4 |
| Sept 4 | BSN | H | Solihull Moors | 334 | W 4-1 | Marriott 11 Sinclair-Furlong 15 Cawley 65 Sappleton 90 | 15 | 5 |
| 8 | BSN | H | Vauxhall Motors | 375 | D 2-2 | Sinclair-Furlong 51 Marriott 44 | 14 | 6 |
| 15 | BSN | A | Guiseley | 496 | W 2-1 | Spence 30 Johnson 90 | 12 | 7 |
| 22 | FAC Q2 | A | Enfield Town | 460 | W 4-1 | Waller-Lassen 22 SAPPLETON 3 (40 60 86 ) | | 8 |
| 29 | BSN | H | Altrincham | 481 | D 1-1 | Sappleton 85 | 15 | 9 |
| Oct 2 | BSN | A | Gloucester City | 180 | L 1-5 | Sappleton 59 (pen) | 15 | 10 |
| 6 | FAC Q3 | A | Chalfont St Peter | 241 | D 1-1 | Waller-Lassen 38 | | 11 |
| 9 | FAC Q3r | H | Chalfont St Peter | 268 | W 3-1 | Sappleton 22 81 Prestedge 90 | | 12 |
| 13 | BSN | H | Chester | 812 | L 1-2 | Herd 78 | 15 | 13 |
| 20 | FAC Q4 | A | Welling United | 544 | W 3-1 | Sappleton 36 (pen) 67 (pen) Sinclair-Furlong 42 | | 14 |
| 27 | BSN | A | Bradford PA | 358 | L 1-2 | Sturrick 32 | 18 | 15 |
| 30 | BSN | H | Oxford City | 343 | D 0-0 | | 18 | 16 |
| Nov 3 | FAC 1 | H | Hastings United | 1212 | L 1-2 | Johnson 7 | | 17 |
| 10 | FAT Q3 | A | AFC Hornchurch | 304 | W 3-2 | Sappleton 5 27 (pen) Abdullahi 90 | | 18 |
| 17 | BSN | H | Gainsborough Trinity | 511 | L 1-3 | Sappleton 46 | 19 | 19 |
| Dec 1 | BSN | H | Corby Town | 317 | W 2-1 | Prestedge 14 Sturrick 90 | 18 | 20 |
| 4 | FAT 1 | A | Oxford City | 134 | L 0-1 | | | 21 |
| 8 | BSN | A | Droylsden | 195 | W 2-1 | Johnson 76 Bailey-Dennis 90 | 17 | 22 |
| 15 | BSN | A | Chester | 2056 | L 1-4 | Prestedge 29 | 19 | 23 |
| 26 | BSN | A | Histon | 344 | L 0-2 | | 19 | 24 |
| Jan 1 | BSN | H | Histon | 505 | W 3-1 | Sturrick 80 Baker 81 Melaugh 87 | 19 | 25 |
| 5 | BSN | H | Guiseley | 377 | L 2-5 | Johnson 38 Cawley 90 | 18 | 26 |
| 8 | BSN | A | Stalybridge Celtic | 149 | L 1-3 | Sturrick 21 | 18 | 27 |
| 12 | BSN | A | Vauxhall Motors | 143 | W 3-1 | Johnson 30 Chambers 34 Rutter (og) 62 | 18 | 28 |
| Feb 2 | BSN | H | Stalybridge Celtic | 328 | D 0-0 | | 19 | 29 |
| 5 | BSN | A | Solihull Moors | 149 | W 1-0 | Cawley 53 | 18 | 30 |
| 9 | BSN | A | Colwyn Bay | 236 | W 2-1 | Nije 65 82 | 16 | 31 |
| 16 | BSN | H | Hinckley United | 388 | D 1-1 | Bailey-Dennis 38 | | 32 |
| 23 | BSN | A | Droylsden | 298 | W 2-1 | Prestedge 81 (pen) Francis 86 | 16 | 33 |
| 27 | BSN | A | Corby Town | 263 | D 2-2 | Roberts 73 Cawley 74 | | 34 |
| Mar 9 | BSN | H | Workington | 377 | L 0-3 | | 18 | 35 |
| 12 | BSN | A | Harrogate Town | 184 | D 2-2 | Prestedge 59 Woodall 86 | 18 | 36 |
| 16 | BSN | A | Gainsborough Trinity | 522 | D 2-2 | Woodall 2 Webb 90 | | 37 |
| 19 | BSN | H | Harrogate Town | 275 | L 0-2 | | 18 | 38 |
| 26 | BSN | A | Workington | 181 | W 3-2 | Prestedge 3 Woodall 56 (pen) 90 | 16 | 39 |
| 30 | BSN | H | Brackley Town | 349 | L 1-3 | Woodall 13 | 17 | 40 |
| Apr 1 | BSN | H | Boston United | 908 | D 1-1 | Prestedge 35 | 17 | 41 |
| 3 | BSN | H | Gloucester City | 270 | L 1-2 | Lobjoit 44 | 18 | 42 |
| 6 | BSN | H | Colwyn Bay | 319 | D 2-2 | Johnson 25 Lobjoit 56 | 17 | 43 |
| 9 | BSN | A | FC Halifx Town | 926 | D 1-1 | Johnson 32 | 17 | 44 |
| 13 | BSN | A | Altrincham | 807 | L 1-2 | Wodall 84 | 17 | 45 |
| 16 | BSN | H | Worcester City | 261 | L 0-1 | | 17 | 46 |
| 20 | BSN | H | Bradford PA | 402 | W 2-1 | Prestedge 45 Bailey-Dennis 62 | 17 | 47 |
| 23 | BSN | A | Hinckley United | 204 | W 5-1 | Johnson 18 58 Lobjoit 48 Waller-Lassen 53 Sappleton 84 | 17 | 48 |
| 27 | BSN | A | Oxford United | 345 | D 1-1 | Sappleton 57 | 17 | 49 |

| GOALSCORERS | Lge | FAC | LC | Total | Pens | Hat-tricks | Cons Run | | Lge | FAC | LC | Total | Pens | Hat-tricks | Cons Run |
|-------------|-----|-----|-----|-------|------|-----------|----------|--|-----|-----|-----|-------|------|-----------|----------|
| Sappleton | 6 | 7 | 2 | 15 | 4 | 1 | 3 | Akurang | 1 | | | 1 | | | |
| Johnson | 8 | 1 | | 9 | | | | Baker | 1 | | | 1 | | | |
| Prestedge | 7 | 1 | | 8 | 1 | | | Chambers | 1 | | | 1 | | | |
| Woodall | 6 | | | 6 | 1 | | | Francis | 1 | | | 1 | | | |
| Cawley | 4 | | | 4 | | | | Melaugh | 1 | | | 1 | | | |
| Sturrick | 4 | | | 4 | | | | Obafemi | 1 | | | 1 | | | |
| Lobjoit | 3 | | | 3 | | | | Spence | 1 | | | 1 | | | |
| Sinclear-Furlonge | 2 | 1 | | 3 | | | | Roberts | 1 | | | 1 | | | |
| Waller-Lasson | 1 | 2 | | 3 | | | | Webb | 1 | | | 1 | | | |
| Abdullahi | 1 | | 1 | 2 | | | | Own Goals | 1 | | | 1 | | | |
| Bailey-Dennis | 2 | | | 2 | | | | Cons Run - Consecutive scoring games. | | | | | | | |
| Marriott | 2 | | | 2 | | | | | | | | | | | |
| Nije | 2 | | | 2 | | | | | | | | | | | |

# BOREHAM WOOD

**Chairman:** Danny Hunter
**Secretary:** Peter Smith    **(T)** 07711 745 987    **(E)** peter.s.smith@royalmail.com
**Commercial Manager:** Mandee Morris    **(T)** 020 8953 5097
**Programme Editor:** John Gill    **(T)** 07956 275 111
**Ground Address:** Meadow Park, Broughinge Road, Boreham Wood WD6 5AL
**(T)** 0208 953 5097      **Manager:** Ian Allinson

## Club Factfile

**Founded:** 1948     **Nickname:** The Wood
**Previous Names:** Boreham Wood Rovers and Royal Retournez amalgamated in 1948 to form today's club
**Previous Leagues:** Mid Herts 1948-52, Parthenon 1952-57, Spartan 1956-66, Athenian 1966-74, Isthmian 1974-2004, Southern 2004-10

**Club Colours (change):** White/black/white (All sky blue)

**Ground Capacity:** 4,502    **Seats:** 600    **Covered:** 1,568    **Clubhouse:** Yes    **Shop:** Yes

**Directions**
Leave A1 at A5135 and follow A5135 towards Borehamwood.
Cross two mini roundabouts then at large roundabout turn right (second exit) into Brook Road then take first right after car park for Broughinge Road.

**Previous Grounds:** Eldon Avenue 1948-63

**Record Attendance:** 4,030 v Arsenal - Friendly 13/07/2001
**Record Victory:** Not known
**Record Defeat:** Not known
**Record Goalscorer:** Mickey Jackson
**Record Appearances:** Dave Hatchett - 714
**Additional Records:** Received £5,000 from Dagenham & Redbridge for Steve Heffer

**Senior Honours:**
Athenian League 1973-74. Isthmian League Division 2 1976-77, Division 1 1994-95, 2000-01.
Southern League East 2005-06, Premier Division Play-off 2009-10.
Herts Senior cup 1971-72, 98-99, 2001-02. London Challenge Cup 1997-98.

### 10 YEAR RECORD

| 03-04 | | 04-05 | | 05-06 | | 06-07 | | 07-08 | | 08-09 | | 09-10 | | 10-11 | | 11-12 | | 12-13 | |
|---|---|---|---|---|---|---|---|---|---|---|---|---|---|---|---|---|---|---|---|
| Isth1N | 9 | SthE | 7 | SthE | 1 | Isth P | 7 | Isth P | 19 | Isth P | 18 | Isth P | 4 | Conf S | 14 | Conf S | 8 | Conf S | 9 |

# MATCH RESULTS 2012-13

| Date | Comp | H/A | Opponents | Att: | Result | Goalscorers | Pos | No. |
|------|------|-----|-----------|------|--------|-------------|-----|-----|
| Aug 18 | BSS | H | Eastleigh | 204 | W 3-0 | Montgomery 35 Effiong 55 Riza 66 | 1 | 1 |
| 21 | BSS | A | AFC Hornchurch | 270 | D 1-1 | O'Loughlin 57 | 2 | 2 |
| 25 | BSS | A | Hayes & Yeading | 137 | W 1-0 | Riza 30 (pen) | 2 | 3 |
| 27 | BSS | H | Chelmsford City | 372 | D 0-0 | | 2 | 4 |
| Sept 1 | BSS | A | Truro City | 329 | L 0-2 | | 9 | 5 |
| 4 | BSS | H | Sutton United | 265 | W 3-0 | Montgomery 13 Vihete 52 86 | 6 | 6 |
| 8 | BSS | H | Farnborough | 226 | W 3-1 | Riza 19 79 (pen) Montgomery 82 | 4 | 7 |
| 16 | BSS | A | Tonbridge Angels | 451 | L 2-4 | Riza 26 (pen) Hutton 68 | 5 | 8 |
| 22 | FAC Q2 | A | St Neots Town | 432 | W 2-1 | Morgan 38  Riza 57 | | 9 |
| 29 | BSS | A | Bath City | 508 | D 0-0 | | 5 | 10 |
| Oct 1 | BSS | H | Billericay Town | 242 | W 3-0 | EFFIONG 3 ( 34 53 66) | 3 | 11 |
| 6 | FAC Q3 | A | Northwood | 225 | W 4-0 | Akurang 5 Hutton 11 Effiong 63 Hastings 85 | | 12 |
| 13 | BSS | A | Salisbury City | 742 | D 2-2 | Akurang 58 Hutton 77 | 2 | 13 |
| 20 | FAC Q4 | A | Hayes & Yeading United | 350 | W 3-2 | Vilhete 31 Nunn 78 Riza 79 | | 14 |
| 27 | BSS | A | Weston-s-Mare | 231 | W 4-2 | Akurang 45 90 Morgan 70 Reynolds 75 | 2 | 15 |
| Nov 3 | FAC 1 | H | Brentford | 1495 | L 0-2 | | | 16 |
| 10 | FAT Q3 | A | Histon | 177 | W 2-1 | Stevenson 46 Reynolds 89 | | 17 |
| 12 | BSS | H | Basingstoke Town | 201 | D 1-1 | Riza 74 (pen) | 3 | 18 |
| 17 | BSS | A | Dover Athletic | 613 | W 1-0 | Jefford 33 | 3 | 19 |
| 24 | FAT 1 | A | Bromley | 430 | D 1-1 | Riza 25 (pen) | | 20 |
| 26 | FAT 2 | H | Bromley | 188 | L 0-2 | | | 21 |
| Dec 1 | BSS | H | Weston-s Mare | 202 | L 0-1 | | 5 | 22 |
| 8 | BSS | H | Truro City | 200 | D 0-0 | | 4 | 23 |
| 15 | BSS | A | Farnborough Town | 451 | W 3-0 | Riza 6 Morgan 68 Nunn 70 | 4 | 24 |
| 26 | BSS | A | Staines Town | 251 | D 1-1 | O'Loughlin 80 | 4 | 25 |
| 29 | BSS | A | Chelmsford City | 837 | L 1-2 | Riza 55) | 4 | 26 |
| Jan 1 | BSS | H | Staines Town | 204 | D 1-1 | Norris 63 | 5 | 27 |
| 5 | BSS | H | Eastbourne Borough | 205 | W 2-1 | Montgomery 21 Noto 54 (pen) | 4 | 28 |
| 8 | BSS | H | Maidenhead United | 201 | W 2-1 | Norris 38 57 | 4 | 29 |
| 28 | BSS | H | Hayes & Yeading | 203 | W 3-0 | Thalassitis 50 Noto 55 (pen) Montgomery 65 | 3 | 30 |
| Feb 5 | BSS | A | Welling United | 433 | L 0-4 | | 5 | 31 |
| 9 | BSS | H | Bath City | 207 | D 0-0 | | 5 | 32 |
| 16 | BSS | A | Bromley | 348 | D 1-1 | Montgomery 70 | 5 | 33 |
| 20 | BSS | H | Salisbury City | 221 | W 1-0 | Isaac 72 | 5 | 34 |
| 23 | BSS | H | Dover Athletic | 251 | D 1-1 | Thalassitis 25 | 5 | 35 |
| 26 | BSS | A | Maidenhead United | 178 | L 1-2 | Thalassitis 90 | 5 | 36 |
| Mar 2 | BSS | H | Tonbridgw Angels | 206 | W 4-2 | Morgan 15 Thalassitis 37 Pires 53 55 | 5 | 37 |
| 9 | BSS | A | Dorchester Town | 429 | D 0-0 | | | 38 |
| 12 | BSS | A | Eastleigh | 401 | D 1-1 | O'Loughlin 81 | 5 | 39 |
| 27 | BSS | A | Billericay Town | 212 | D 1-1 | Montgomery 22 | 6 | 40 |
| 29 | BSS | H | AFC Hornchurch | 287 | W 2-1 | Montgomery 21 Pires 75 | 6 | 41 |
| Apr 1 | BSS | A | Sutton United | 468 | L 1-2 | Morgan 67 | 6 | 42 |
| 6 | BSS | H | Dorchester Town | 201 | L 1-2 | Moore 64 (og) | 7 | 43 |
| 9 | BSS | H | Havant & Waterlooville | 164 | L 1-2 | Akurang 71 | 8 | 44 |
| 13 | BSS | A | Basingstoke Town | 270 | W 3-2 | O'Loughlin 17 Montgomery 52 Thalassitis  75 | 7 | 45 |
| 16 | BSS | A | Eastbourne Borough | 371 | D 1-1 | Thalassitis 55 | 7 | 46 |
| 20 | BSS | H | Welling United | 466 | D 1-1 | Isaac 72 | 8 | 47 |
| 23 | BSS | H | Bromley | 159 | L 1-2 | Moone 72 | 9 | 48 |
| 27 | BSS | A | Havant & Waterlooville | 828 | D 1-1 | Hastings 88 | 9 | 49 |

| GOALSCORERS | Lge | FAC | LC | Total | Pens | Hat-tricks | Cons Run | | Lge | FAC | LC | Total | Pens | Hat-tricks | Cons Run |
|-------------|-----|-----|----|-------|------|------------|----------|--|-----|-----|----|-------|------|------------|----------|
| Riza | 8 | 2 | 1 | 11 | 5 | | 3 | Pires | 3 | | | 3 | | | |
| Montgomery | 9 | | | 9 | | | | Isaac | 2 | | | 2 | | | |
| Thalassitis | 6 | | | 6 | | | | Noto | 2 | | | 2 | 2 | | |
| Effiong | 4 | 1 | | 5 | | 1 | | Nunn | 1 | 1 | | 2 | | | |
| Morgan | 4 | 1 | | 5 | | | | Reynolds | 1 | | 1 | 2 | | | |
| Akurang | 4 | 1 | | 4 | | | | Stevenson | 1 | | 1 | 2 | | | |
| Hutton | 3 | 1 | | 4 | | | | Jefford | 1 | | | 1 | | | |
| O'Loughlin | 4 | | | 4 | | | | Moone | 1 | | | 1 | | | |
| Hastings | 1 | 1 | | 3 | | | | Own Goals | 1 | | | 1 | | | |
| Norris | 3 | | | 3 | | | | Cons Run - Consecutive scoring games. | | | | | | | |

# BROMLEY

**Chairman:** Ashley Reading

**Secretary:** Colin Russell    **(T)** 07970 031 511    **(E)** colin@bromleyfc.co.uk

**Commercial Manager:** Barry Wickenden    **(T)** 020 8460 5291

**Programme Editor:** Jeff Hutton    **(T)** 020 8460 5291

**Ground Address:** The Stadium, Hayes Lane, Bromley, Kent BR2 9EF

**(T)** 020 8460 5291    **Manager:** Mark Goldberg

Photo: Keith Clayton.

## Club Factfile

**Founded:** 1892    **Nickname:** The Lillywhites

**Previous Names:** None

**Previous Leagues:** South London, Southern, London, West Kent, South Surburban, Kent, Spartan 1907-08, Isthmian 1908-11, 52-2007, Athenian 1919-1952

**Club Colours (change):** White/black/black (All red)

**Ground Capacity:** 5,000    **Seats:** 1,300    **Covered:** 2,500    **Clubhouse:** Yes    **Shop:** Yes

**Directions**

From M25 Motorway: Leaving the M25 at Junction 4, follow the A21 to Bromley and London, for approximately 4 miles and then fork left onto the A232 signposted Croydon/Sutton. At the 2nd set of traffic lights turn right into Baston Road (B265), following it for about 2 miles as it becomes Hayes Street and then Hayes Lane. Bromley FC is on right hand side of road just after a mini roundabout. From the Croydon/Surrey areas use the A232, turn left into Baston Road (B265), following it for about 2 miles as it becomes Hayes Street and then Hayes Lane. From West London use the South Circular Road as far as West Dulwich and then via Crystal Palace, Penge, Beckenham and Bromley South areas. From North and East London use the Blackwall Tunnel and then the A20 road as far as Sidcup. Then use the A232 to Keston Common, turn right into Baston Road (B265), following it for about 2 miles as it becomes Hayes Street and then Hayes Lane.

**Previous Grounds:** White Hart Field. Widmore Road. Plaistow Cricket Ground.

**Record Attendance:** 10,798 v Nigeria - 1950

**Record Victory:** 13-1 v Redhill - Athenian League 1945-46

**Record Defeat:** 1-11 v Barking - Athenian League 1933-34

**Record Goalscorer:** George Brown - 570 (1938-61)

**Record Appearances:** George Brown

**Additional Records:** Received £50,000 from Millwall for John Goodman

**Senior Honours:**

Amateur Cup 1910-11, 37-38, 48-49.
Isthmian League 1908-09, 09-10, 53-54, 60-61. Athenian League 1922-23, 48-49, 50-51.
Kent Senior Cup 1949/50, 76-77, 91-92, 96-97, 2005-06, 06-07. Kent Amateur Cup x12. London Senior Cup x4

### 10 YEAR RECORD

| 03-04 | 04-05 | 05-06 | 06-07 | 07-08 | 08-09 | 09-10 | 10-11 | 11-12 | 12-13 |
|---|---|---|---|---|---|---|---|---|---|
| Isth1S 8 | Isth1 4 | Isth P 11 | Isth P 2 | Conf S 11 | Conf S 13 | Conf S 12 | Conf S 11 | Conf S 17 | Conf S 15 |

# MATCH RESULTS 2012-13

| Date | Comp | H/A | Opponents | Att: | Result | Goalscorers | Pos | No. |
|---|---|---|---|---|---|---|---|---|
| Aug 17 | BSS | H | Staines | 483 | D 0-0 | | 15 | 1 |
| 21 | BSS | A | Eastboune Borough | 655 | L 0-3 | | 21 | 2 |
| 25 | BSS | A | Chelmsford City | 667 | L 2-3 | Pacquette 8 55 | 21 | 3 |
| 27 | BSS | H | Tonbridge Angels | 805 | D 1-1 | Araba 86 | 20 | 4 |
| Sept 1 | BSS | A | Farnborough | 458 | L 0-2 | | 21 | 5 |
| 4 | BSS | H | AFC Hornchurch | 408 | W 4-0 | Joseph-Dubois 4 22 Pacquette 11 52 (pen) | | 6 |
| 8 | BSS | H | Bath City | 495 | W 1-0 | Joseph-Dubois 10 | 13 | 7 |
| 15 | BSS | A | Truro City | 538 | W 1-0 | Joseph-Dubois 38 | 10 | 8 |
| 22 | FAC Q2 | A | Sutton United | 511 | W 1-0 | Joseph-Dubois 74 | 9 | 9 |
| 29 | BSS | H | Havant & Waterlooville | 582 | D 1-1 | Joseph-Dubois 19 | 10 | 10 |
| Oct 2 | BSS | A | Basingstoke Town | 253 | D 1-1 | Buchanan 15 | 11 | 11 |
| 6 | FAC Q3 | A | Dover Athletic | 715 | W 2-1 | Pacquette 28 Finn 75 | | 12 |
| 13 | BSS | H | Welling United | 1334 | L 0-2 | | 16 | 13 |
| 20 | FAC Q4 | H | Worcester City | 610 | W 1-0 | Pacquette 90 | | 14 |
| 27 | BSS | H | Salisbury City | 495 | L 1-2 | Buchanan 38 | 19 | 15 |
| 30 | BSS | H | Maidenhead United | 333 | W 3-2 | Waldren 26 42 Pacquette 57 | 16 | 16 |
| Nov 3 | FAC 1 | A | Fleetwood Town | 1695 | L 0-3 | | | 17 |
| 10 | FAT Q3 | H | Staines Town | 420 | D 1-1 | Buchanan 9 | | 18 |
| 13 | FAT Q3r | H | Staines Town | 360 | W 2-0 | Finn 48 Chaaban 88 | | 19 |
| 17 | BSS | H | Billericay Town | 450 | L 0-1 | | 19 | 20 |
| 26 | FAT 1 | H | Boreham Wood | 430 | D 1-1 | Joseph-Dubois 87 | | 21 |
| Dec 1 | BSS | A | Havant & Waterlooville | 748 | W 2-1 | Pigott 11 68 | 17 | 22 |
| 4 | BSS | A | Welling United | 551 | L 1-3 | Fuseini 76 | 17 | 23 |
| 8 | BSS | H | Farnborough | 378 | L 1-3 | Fuseini 65 | 19 | 24 |
| 15 | FAT 2 | H | Kidderminster H | 432 | W 1-0 | Waldren 44 (pen) | | 25 |
| 29 | BSS | A | Tonbridge Angels | 682 | W 3-0 | Jones 11 Rhule 41 Pigott 57 | 19 | 26 |
| Jan 1 | BSS | H | Sutton United | 556 | L 0-2 | | 20 | 27 |
| 5 | BSS | H | Eastleigh | 315 | W 3-1 | Fussini 28 Joseph-Dubois 46 Theophanous 58 | 16 | 28 |
| 8 | BSS | A | Dorchester Town | 323 | W 4-0 | Theophanous 19 85 Swaine 60 Buchanan 61 | 10 | 29 |
| 12 | FAT 3 | A | Dartford | 1305 | L 2-4 | Joseph-Dubois 14 Buchanan 75 | | 30 |
| 15 | BSS | A | Bath City | 386 | W 2-0 | Theophanous 38 Joseph-Dubois 56 | 10 | 31 |
| 26 | BSS | H | Weston-s-Mare | 390 | L 0-1 | | 10 | 32 |
| Feb 2 | BSS | A | Salisbury City | 783 | L 1-3 | Joseph-Dubois 46 | 10 | 33 |
| 9 | BSS | H | Basingstoke Town | 457 | L 1-2 | Waldren 74 (pen) | 15 | 34 |
| 16 | BSS | H | Boreham Wood | 348 | D 1-1 | Jones 86 | 17 | 35 |
| 19 | BSS | A | Hayes & Yeading | 122 | D 1-1 | Joseph-Dubois 55 | 14 | 36 |
| 23 | BSS | A | Billericay Town | 427 | W 3-2 | Fuseini 35 Joseph-Dubois 54 Theophanus 90 (pen) | 13 | 37 |
| 26 | BSS | H | Chelmsford City | 293 | W 2-0 | Theophanous 10 Finn 80 | 13 | 38 |
| Mar 2 | BSS | H | Dorchester Town | 438 | W 2-1 | Joseph-Dubois 56 Buchanan 86 | 9 | 39 |
| 5 | BSS | A | Sutton United | 442 | L 3-4 | Joseph-Dubois 58 Buchanan 53 Theophanous 68 | 9 | 40 |
| 9 | BSS | H | Truro City | 343 | W 4-0 | Fuseini 1 Theophanous 48 Joseph-Dubois 66 69 | 9 | 41 |
| 19 | BSS | A | Dover Athletic | 715 | L 0-1 | | 10 | 42 |
| 26 | BSS | A | Staines Town | 308 | L 1-3 | Buchanan 1 | 11 | 43 |
| 30 | BSS | H | Eastbourne B | 551 | L 0-2 | | 13 | 44 |
| Apr 1 | BSS | A | AFC Hornchurch | 316 | L 0-1 | | 13 | 45 |
| 6 | BSS | A | Weston-s-Mare | 297 | L 0-3 | | 14 | 46 |
| 13 | BSS | H | Hayes & Yeading | 433 | L 0-4 | | 15 | 47 |
| 16 | BSS | A | Eastleigh | 508 | L 0-3 | | 17 | 48 |
| 20 | BSS | A | Maidenhead United | 420 | L 2-4 | Waldren 22 Joseph-Dubois 82 | 17 | 49 |
| 23 | BSS | A | Boreham Wood | 159 | W 2-1 | Theophanous 83 Joseph-Dubois 90 | 14 | 50 |
| 27 | BSS | H | Dover Athletic | 811 | L 0-4 | | 15 | 51 |

| GOALSCORERS | Lge | FAC | LC | Total | Pens | Hat-tricks | Cons Run | | Lge | FAC | LC | Total | Pens | Hat-tricks | Cons Run |
|---|---|---|---|---|---|---|---|---|---|---|---|---|---|---|---|
| Joseph-Dubois | 16 | 1 | 2 | 19 | | | 5 | Chaaban | | 1 | | 1 | | | |
| Theophanous | 9 | | | 9 | | | | Rhule | 1 | | | 1 | | | |
| Buchanan | 6 | | 2 | 8 | | | | Swaine | 1 | | | 1 | | | |
| Pacquette | 5 | 2 | | 7 | 1 | | | Cons Run - Consecutive scoring games. | | | | | | | |
| Fuseine | 5 | | | 5 | | | | | | | | | | | |
| Waldren | 4 | | 1 | 5 | 2 | | | | | | | | | | |
| Piggott | 3 | | | 3 | | | | | | | | | | | |
| Finn | 1 | 1 | 1 | 3 | | | | | | | | | | | |
| Jones | 2 | | | 2 | | | | | | | | | | | |
| Araba | 1 | | | 1 | | | | | | | | | | | |

# CHELMSFORD CITY

**Chairman:** Mansell Wallace
**Secretary:** Alan Brown **(T)** 07963 626 381 **(E)** algbrown@blueyonder.co.uk
**Commercial Manager:** Mick Hooker **(T)** 01279 771 954
**Programme Editor:** Billy Shaw **(T)** billyontheradio@yahoo.co.uk
**Ground Address:** Melbourne Park Stadium, Salerno Way, Chelmsford CM1 2EH
**(T)** 01245 290 959 **Manager:** Dean Holdsworth

## Club Factfile

**Founded:** 1938 **Nickname:** City or Clarets
**Previous Names:** None
**Previous Leagues:** Southern League 1938-2004. Isthmian 2004-08

**Club Colours (change):** Claret & white/claret & white/white (White & royal blue/royal blue/royal blue)

**Ground Capacity:** 3,000 **Seats:** 1,300 **Covered:** 1,300 **Clubhouse:** Yes **Shop:** Yes

**Directions:** Leave A12 at J15 and head towards Chelmsford. At the roundabout turn left into Westway. Turn left onto the A1060 signposted Sawbridgeworth. At the second set of traffic lights turn right into Chignal Road. Turn right into Melbourne Avenue. Salerno Way is on your left. At the end of the football pitches and immediately before the block of flats, turn left at the mini roundabout in Salerno Way to enter the Stadium car park.

**Previous Grounds:** New Writtle Street 1938-97, Maldon Town 1997-98, Billericay Town 1998-2005

**Record Attendance:** 16,807 v Colchester United - Southern League 10/09/1949. Salerno Way: 2,998 v Billericay Town - Isthmian Jan. 2006
**Record Victory:** 10-1 v Bashley (H) - Southern League 26/04/2000
**Record Defeat:** 1-10 v Barking (A) - FA Trophy 11/11/1978
**Record Goalscorer:** Tony Butcher - 287 (1957-71)
**Record Appearances:** Derek Tiffin - 550 (1950-63)
**Additional Records:** Paid £10,000 to Dover Athletic for Tony Rogers 1992
**Senior Honours:** Received £50,000 from Peterborough United for David Morrison
Southern League 1945-46, 67-68, 71-72, Southern Division 1988-89, League Cup 1945-46, 59-60, 90-91.
Essex Professional Cup 1957-58, 69-70, 70-71, 73-74, 74-75. Non-League Champions Cup 1971-72.
Essex Senior Cup 1985-86, 88-89, 92-93, 2002-03. Isthmian League Premier Division 2007-08.

### 10 YEAR RECORD

| 03-04 | | 04-05 | | 05-06 | | 06-07 | | 07-08 | | 08-09 | | 09-10 | | 10-11 | | 11-12 | | 12-13 | |
|---|---|---|---|---|---|---|---|---|---|---|---|---|---|---|---|---|---|---|---|
| SthP | 18 | Isth P | 8 | Isth P | 10 | Isth P | 3 | Isth P | 1 | Conf S | 5 | Conf S | 3 | Conf S | 4 | Conf S | 6 | Conf S | 5 |

# MATCH RESULTS 2012-13

| Date | Comp | H/A | Opponents | Att: | Result | Goalscorers | Pos | No. |
|---|---|---|---|---|---|---|---|---|
| Aug 17 | BSS | A | Havant & Waterlooville | 273 | D 1-1 | Slabber 47 | 10 | 1 |
| 20 | BSS | H | Welling United | 868 | L 2-3 | Calver 18 Parker 90 | 16 | 2 |
| 25 | BSS | H | Bromley | 667 | W 3-2 | Searle 35 Cook 58 Slabber 75 (pen) | 11 | 3 |
| 27 | BSS | A | Boreham Wood | 372 | D 0-0 | | 13 | 4 |
| Sept 1 | BSS | H | Salisbury City | 716 | W 2-1 | Church 16 Slabber 62 (pen) | 10 | 5 |
| 4 | BSS | A | Dover Athletic | 832 | W 1-0 | Slabber 13 (pen) | 7 | 6 |
| 8 | BSS | A | Dorchester Town | 463 | L 0-1 | | 7 | 7 |
| 15 | BSS | H | Weston-s-Mare | 938 | W 2-1 | Rainford 75 Ledgister 79 | 6 | 8 |
| 22 | FAC Q2 | H | **Leatherhead** | 519 | W 2-1 | **Rainford 30  68** | | 9 |
| 29 | BSS | H | Truro City | 820 | W 3-2 | Slabber 46 Rainford 62 (pen) Calver 90 | 3 | 10 |
| Oct 2 | BSS | A | Sutton United | 487 | L 0-1 | | 4 | 11 |
| 6 | FAC Q3 | A | **Cray Wanderers** | 320 | W 2-1 | **Slabber 50 54** | | 12 |
| 13 | BSS | H | Eastleigh | 919 | D 1-1 | Simmonds 82 | 5 | 13 |
| 20 | FAC Q4 | H | **East Thurrock United** | 902 | D 2-2 | **Bridges 44 Clark 88** | | 14 |
| 23 | FAC Q4r | A | **East Thurrock United** | 595 | D 4-4 | **Edmans 21 48 Slabber 101 Cornhill 115 *aet W 5-3 pens** | | 15 |
| 27 | BSS | A | Staines Town | 966 | W 3-2 | Cook 4 Edmans 36 Slabber 59 | 3 | 16 |
| 30 | BSS | A | AFC Hornchurch | 515 | W 2-0 | Cook 40 52 | 2 | 17 |
| Nov 3 | FAC 1 | H | **Colchester United** | 3016 | W 3-1 | **Simmonds 23 63 Slabber 89** | | 18 |
| 10 | FAT Q3 | A | **Dover Athletic** | 570 | D 1-1 | **Clark 67** | | 19 |
| 13 | FAT Q3r | A | **Dover Athletic** | 720 | W 4-2 | **Simmonds 30 116 Slabber 90 104** | | 20 |
| 17 | BSS | A | Basingstoke Town | 377 | W -1 | Simmonds 49 Smart 81 (og)_ | 2 | 21 |
| 20 | BSS | A | Hates & Yeading | 224 | L 0-3 | | 2 | 22 |
| 24 | FAT 1 | A | **Hampton & Richmond B** | 241 | D 1-1 | **Cornhill 52** | 23 | 23 |
| Dec 1 | FAC 2 | A | **Crawley Town** | 3012 | L 0-3 | | | 24 |
| 8 | BSS | A | Salisbury City | 704 | L 2-3 | Hamilton 19 Cornhill 34 | 6 | 25 |
| 10 | FAT 1r | H | **Hampton & Richmond B** | 301 | W 3-2 | **Brindley 3 Cook 5 (pen) Simmonds 34** | | 26 |
| 15 | FAT 2 | A | **Hereford United** | 1124 | W 3-0 | **Edmans 20 27  Rainford 42** | | 27 |
| 29 | BSS | H | Boreham Wood | 837 | W 2-1 | Cook 63  Vassel 78 | 6 | 28 |
| Jan 1 | BSS | H | Billericay Town | 1211 | W 1-0 | Slabber 82 | 6 | 29 |
| 5 | BSS | A | Maidenhead United | 380 | L 1-2 | Slabber 15 (pen) | 6 | 30 |
| 12 | FAT 3 | A | **FC Halifax Town** | 1137 | L 0-3 | | | 31 |
| 26 | BSS | A | Truro City | 421 | W 2-1 | Slabber 55 Vassel 70 | 5 | 32 |
| 28 | BSS | H | Dorchester Town | 565 | W 4-0 | Cook 1 Riza 28 Vassel 33 Miller 75 | 4 | 33 |
| Feb 2 | BSS | H | Hayes & Yeading | 747 | W 6-2 | SLABBER 3 ( 25 41 pen 71) Vassell 65 81 Riza 83 | 4 | 34 |
| 4 | BSS | H | Billericay Town | 918 | D 1-1 | Slabber 45 (pen) | 4 | 35 |
| 9 | BSS | A | Tonbridge Angels | 625 | W 4-0 | Cook 17 Slabber 49 Edmans 80 Palmer 83 | 3 | 36 |
| 16 | BSS | A | Eastleigh | 676 | L 0-1 | | 4 | 37 |
| 18 | BSS | H | Havant & Waterloovville | 732 | D 1-1 | Edmans 66 | 4 | 38 |
| 23 | BSS | H | Sutton Uited | 702 | W 1-0 | Edmans 26 | 4 | 39 |
| 26 | BSS | A | Bromley | 293 | L 0-2 | | 4 | 40 |
| Mar 2 | BSS | A | Staines Town | 384 | W 3-1 | Rainford 27  Cook  46 Slabber 72 | 4 | 41 |
| 5 | BSS | H | Weston-s-Mare | 200 | L 0-3 | | 4 | 42 |
| 13 | BSS | H | AFC Hornchurch | 428 | L 1-4 | Cook 79 | 4 | 43 |
| 16 | BSS | A | Bath City | 512 | D 2-2 | Miller 34 Bakare 46 | 4 | 44 |
| 18 | BSS | H | Farnborough | 474 | W 6-0 | Miller 13 Bakare 20  54 Clarke 27 Inns 46 Bridges 60 | 4 | 45 |
| 25 | BSS | H | Eastbourne Borough | 406 | W 1-0 | Slabber 73 | 4 | 46 |
| 29 | BSS | A | Welling United | 1065 | L 0-3 | | 4 | 47 |
| Apr 1 | BSS | H | Dover Athletic | 910 | L 0-3 | | 4 | 48 |
| 6 | BSS | H | Bath City | 656 | L 0-1 | | 5 | 49 |
| 13 | BSS | A | Eastbourne Borough | 479 | W 2-1 | Slabber 31 Bakare 83 | 5 | 50 |
| 15 | BSS | H | Tonbridge Angels | 635 | W 2-1 | Slabber 13 31 | 4 | 51 |
| 20 | BSS | H | Basingstoke Town | 828 | W 2-0 | Edmans 33 77 | 4 | 52 |
| 22 | BSS | H | Maidenhead United | 626 | W 3-1 | Simmonds 44  Bakare  75 Cook 90 (pen) | 3 | 53 |
| 27 | BSS | A | Farnborough | 621 | L 1-3 | Slabber 90 | 5 | 54 |
| 28 | P-Off S-F 1 | H | **Salisbury City** | 1248 | W 1-0 | **Cook 90 (pen)** | | 55 |
| May 4 | P-Off S-F 2 | A | **Salisbury City** | 1554 | L 0-2 | | | 56 |

| GOALSCORERS | Lge | FAC | LC | Total | Pens | Hat-tricks | Cons Run | | Lge | FAC | LC | Total | Pens | Hat-tricks | Cons Run |
|---|---|---|---|---|---|---|---|---|---|---|---|---|---|---|---|
| Slabber | 20 | 4 | 2 | 26 | 6 | 1 | 3 | Calver | 2 | | | 2 | | | |
| Cook | 11 | | 1 | 12 | 4 | | 2 | Riza | 2 | | | 2 | | | |
| Edmans | 6 | 2 | 2 | 10 | | | 2 | Brindley | | 1 | | 1 | | | |
| Simmonds | 3 | 2 | 3 | 8 | | | | Church | 1 | | | 1 | | | |
| Rainford | 3 | 2 | 1 | 6 | 1 | | | Hamilton | 1 | | | 1 | | | |
| Bakare | 5 | | | 5 | | | | Inns | 1 | | | 1 | | | |
| Vassell | 5 | | 1 | 5 | | | | Ledgister | 1 | | | 1 | | | |
| Clark | 3 | 1 | | 4 | | | | Parker | 1 | | | 1 | | | |
| Cornhill | 1 | 1 | 1 | 3 | | | | Own Goals | 1 | | | 1 | | | |
| Miller | 3 | | | 3 | | | | Cons Run - Consecutive scoring games. | | | | | | | |
| Bridges | 1 | 1 | | 2 | | | | | | | | | | | |

# CONCORD RANGERS

**Chairman:** Antony Smith
**Secretary:** Chris Crerie     **(T)** 0790 952 8818     **(E)** concordrangers@btinternet.com
**Commercial Manager:** tbc     **(T)**
**Programme Editor:** Phil Crowe     **(T)** 0753 499 7284
**Ground Address:** Aspect Arena, Thames Road, Canvey Island, Essex SS8 0HH
**(T)** 01268 515 750                           **Manager:** Danny Cowley

Promotion winning squad.
Back Row (L-R): Steve Wright (Physiotherapist), Jason Hallett, Danny Glozier, Adam Flanagan, Steve King, Reece Harris,
Michael Jordan, James White, John Easterford, Lee White, Danny Clare (Goalkeeping Coach).
Front Row: Gary Ewers (1st Team Backroom Staff), Chris Bourne, Billy Coyne, Danny Spendlove, Tony Stokes (1st Team Captain),
Danny Cowley (1st Team Manager), Glen Alzapiedi (1st Team Assistant Manager), Nicky Cowley, James Elmes, Tosan Popo,
Jacob Cleaver, Miki Hood (1st Team Backroom Staff).

## Club Factfile

**Founded:** 1967     **Nickname:** Beachboys
**Previous Names:** None
**Previous Leagues:** Southend & District, Southend Alliance, Essex Intermediate 1988-91, Essex Senior 1991-2008.

**Club Colours (change):** Yellow/blue/blue (All blue)

**Ground Capacity:** 1,500   **Seats:** Yes   **Covered:** Yes   **Clubhouse:** Yes   **Shop:**

**Directions**
A130 onto Canvey Island.
Turn right into Thorney Bay Road.
Then right again into Thames Road.

**Previous Grounds:** Waterside

**Record Attendance:** 1,500 v Lee Chapel North - FA Sunday Cup 1989-90
**Record Victory:** Not Known
**Record Defeat:** Not Known
**Record Goalscorer:** Not Known
**Record Appearances:** Not Known
**Additional Records:**

**Senior Honours:**
Essex Intermediate League Division 2 1990-91. Essex Senior League 1997-98, 2003-04, 07-08

### 10 YEAR RECORD

| 03-04 | | 04-05 | | 05-06 | | 06-07 | | 07-08 | | 08-09 | | 09-10 | | 10-11 | | 11-12 | | 12-13 | |
|---|---|---|---|---|---|---|---|---|---|---|---|---|---|---|---|---|---|---|---|
| ESen | 1 | ESen | 9 | ESen | 7 | ESen | 7 | ESen | 1 | Isth1N | 5 | Isth1N | 2 | Isth P | 8 | Isth P | 14 | Isth P | 4 |

# MATCH RESULTS 2012-13

| Date | Comp | H/A | Opponents | Att: | Result | Goalscorers | Pos | No. |
|---|---|---|---|---|---|---|---|---|
| Aug 18 | RPL | H | Bognor Regis Town | 212 | L 1-3 | Stokes 32 | 19 | 1 |
| 21 | RPL | A | Lowestoft Town | 668 | L 1-4 | Hallett 61 | 20 | 2 |
| 25 | RPL | A | Carshalton | 320 | W 2-1 | Hallett 23 Spendlove 76 | 14 | 3 |
| 27 | RPL | H | Kingstonian | 152 | L 0-3 | | 17 | 4 |
| Sept 1 | RPL | A | Hendon | 157 | D 2-2 | White 57 Stokes 67 | 17 | 5 |
| 8 | FAC Q1 | H | Needham Market | 132 | W 1-0 | H.Elmes 18 | | 6 |
| 15 | RPL | A | Wealdstone | 225 | D 2-2 | H.Elmes 29 Stokes 83 | 19 | 7 |
| 22 | FAC Q2 | H | Welling United | 235 | D 1-1 | H,Elmes (pen) | | 8 |
| 26 | FAC Q2r | A | Welling United | 267 | L 1-2 | Stokes 69 | | 9 |
| 29 | FAT Q1 | A | Kettering Town | 215 | W 3-0 | H.Elmes 20 King 47 Hallett 82 | | 10 |
| Oct 9 | RPL | A | Margate | 217 | W 2-0 | Stokes 80 83 | 11 | 11 |
| 13 | RPL | A | Wingate & Finchley | 262 | D 0-0 | | 15 | 12 |
| 20 | RPL | H | Cray Wanderers | 161 | L 0-4 | | 16 | 13 |
| 27 | FAT Q2 | H | Enfield Town | 148 | L 0-2 | | | 14 |
| Nov 3 | RPL | H | Harrow | 104 | W 2-1 | Cowley 53 H Elmes 79 (pen) | 13 | 15 |
| 6 | RPL | H | Hampton & Richmond B | 214 | W 2-1 | H Elmes 5 Harris 60 | 10 | 16 |
| 10 | RPL | H | Carshalton Athletic | 122 | W 6-3 | H.Elmes 4 (pen) 71 Stokes 22 61 Walker 27 Spendlove 80 | 9 | 17 |
| 17 | RPL | H | Met Police | 210 | W 5-1 | STOKES 3 (10 59 64) Walker 45 Spendlove 53 | 7 | 18 |
| 24 | RPL | H | Whitehawk | 226 | D 2-2 | Spendlove 37 Cowley 52 | 7 | 19 |
| Dec 2 | RPL | A | Thurrock | 222 | W 1-0 | Cowley 55 | 5 | 20 |
| 8 | RPL | A | Hastings United | 458 | D 2-2 | Stokes 45 70 | 7 | 21 |
| 15 | RPL | H | Lewes | 108 | L 3-6 | Stokes 33 90 Lampe 69 | 10 | 22 |
| 26 | RPL | H | Canvey Island | 338 | W 3-0 | H.Elmes 8 20 White 88 | 7 | 23 |
| Jan 2 | RPL | A | Cray Wanderers | 155 | W 2-0 | King 18 Stokes 20 | 5 | 24 |
| 5 | RPL | H | Margate | 228 | W 2-1 | Cowley 16 King 83 | 3 | 25 |
| 26 | RPL | A | Bury Town | 375 | W 4-0 | H.ELMES 3 ( 23 61 70) Hallett 29 | 4 | 26 |
| Feb 2 | RPL | H | Hastings United | 238 | W 4-0 | Hallett 45 46 H.Elmes (pen) 40 Gordon 69 | 2 | 27 |
| 9 | RPL | A | Lewes | 442 | W 3-0 | Hallett 47 Gordon 82 Spendlove 90 | 2 | 28 |
| 16 | RPL | A | Whitehawk | 225 | L 0-1 | | 3 | 29 |
| 26 | RPL | H | Lowestoft Town | 65 | D 1-1 | Hallett 45 | 4 | 30 |
| Mar 2 | RPL | A | Bognor Regis Town | 390 | W 1-0 | Stokes 59 | 4 | 31 |
| 5 | RPL | A | Enfield Town | 252 | W 1-0 | Hallett 53 | 3 | 32 |
| 7 | RPL | H | Wingate & Finchley | 164 | W 4-1 | McKENZIE (3) Makofo | 3 | 33 |
| 12 | RPL | A | Hampton & Richmond B | 139 | D 1-1 | Glozier 45 (pen) | 3 | 34 |
| 19 | RPL | H | Bury Town | 218 | W 3-2 | Gordon 60 Hallett 72 Stokes 82 | 3 | 35 |
| 21 | RPL | H | Thurrock | 154 | D 1-1 | Stokes 88 | 3 | 36 |
| 23 | RPL | H | Enfield Town | 282 | W 3-0 | King 37 80 Hallett 90 | 3 | 37 |
| 26 | RPL | H | East Thurrock U | 163 | D 2-2 | Hallett 84 Stokes 89 | 3 | 38 |
| 28 | RPL | A | Wealdstone | 610 | L 1-2 | Grenhalgh 70 | 3 | 39 |
| Apr 1 | RPL | A | Canvey Island | 616 | W 2-0 | Stokes 3 Hallett 43 | 3 | 40 |
| 4 | RPL | H | Hendon | 122 | L 1-2 | Cowley 5 | 3 | 41 |
| 6 | RPL | H | East Thurrock U | 210 | L 1-3 | Spendlove 9 | 4 | 42 |
| 13 | RPL | H | Harrow Borough | 183 | L 1-2 | Cowley 56 | 4 | 43 |
| 16 | RPL | A | Leiston | 150 | W 3-0 | Stokes 7 75 Greenhalgh 18 | 4 | 44 |
| 20 | RPL | A | Metropolitan Police | 120 | W 2-0 | Cowley 1 King 14 | 4 | 45 |
| 22 | RPL | A | Kingstonian | 205 | W1-0 | Easterford 65 | 4 | 46 |
| 27 | RPL | H | Leiston | 243 | D 0-0 | | 4 | 47 |
| May 1 | Play-Off S-F | A | Wealdstone | 1055 | W 2-1 | King 89 Stokes 108 *aet | | 48 |
| 6 | Play-Off F | A | Lowestoft Town | 2490 | W 2-1 | King 13 Gordon 85 | | 49 |

| GOALSCORERS | Lge | FAC | FAT | Total | Pens | Hat-tricks | Cons Run | | Lge | FAC | FAT | Total | Pens | Hat-tricks | Cons Run |
|---|---|---|---|---|---|---|---|---|---|---|---|---|---|---|---|
| Stokes | 23 | 1 | | 24 | | 1 | 2 | White | 2 | | | 1 | | | |
| Elmes | 11 | 2 | 1 | 14 | 4 | 1 | 3 | Easterford | 1 | | | 1 | | | |
| Hallett | 12 | | 1 | 13 | | | 2 | Glazier | 1 | | | 1 | 1 | | |
| King | 7 | | 1 | 8 | | | | Harris | 1 | | | 1 | | | |
| Cowley | 7 | | | 7 | | | | Lampe | 1 | | | 1 | | | |
| Spendlove | 6 | | | 6 | | | | Makofo | 1 | | | 1 | | | |
| Gordon | 4 | | | 4 | | | | Cons Run - Consecutive scoring games. | | | | | | | |
| McKenzie | 3 | | | 3 | | | | | | | | | | | |
| Greenhalgh | 2 | | | 2 | | | | | | | | | | | |
| Walker | 2 | | | 1 | | | | | | | | | | | |

# DORCHESTER TOWN

**Chairman:** Shaun Hearn
**Secretary:** David Martin  **(T)** 07971 172 795  **(E)** dorchdave@gmail.com
**Commercial Manager:** Shaun Hearn  **(T)** 07976 363 699
**Programme Editor:** tbc  **(T)**
**Ground Address:** The Green King Community Stadium, Weymouth Avenue, Dorchester DT1 2RY
**(T)** 01305 262 451  **Manager:** Phil Simkin

## Club Factfile

**Founded:** 1880  **Nickname:** The Magpies
**Previous Names:** None
**Previous Leagues:** Dorset, Western 1947-72

**Club Colours (change):** Black with white stripe/black/black (All yellow & red)

**Ground Capacity:** 5,009  **Seats:** 710  **Covered:** 2,846  **Clubhouse:** Yes  **Shop:** Yes

**Directions:** The stadium is located at the junction of A35 Dorchester Bypass and the A354 to Weymouth, adjacent to Tesco. There is a coach bay for the team coach at the front of the stadium. Any supporters coach should park on the railway embankment side of the stadium.

**Previous Grounds:** Council Recreation Ground, Weymouth Avenue 1908-1929, 1929-90, The Avenue Ground 1929

**Record Attendance:** 4,159 v Weymouth - Southern Premier 1999
**Record Victory:** 7-0 v Canterbury (A) - Southern League Southern Division 1986-87
**Record Defeat:** 0-13 v Welton Rovers (A) - Western League 1966
**Record Goalscorer:** Not known
**Record Appearances:** Derek 'Dinkie' Curtis - 458 (1950-66)
**Additional Records:** Denis Cheney scored 61 goals in one season. Paid £12,000 to Gloucester City for Chris Townsend 1990.
**Senior Honours:** Received £35,000 from Portsmouth for Trevor Sinclair.
Western League 19954-55. Southern League 1985-86, Division 1 East 2002-03. Dorset Senior Cup x8 Most recently 2011-12.

### 10 YEAR RECORD

| 03-04 | | 04-05 | | 05-06 | | 06-07 | | 07-08 | | 08-09 | | 09-10 | | 10-11 | | 11-12 | | 12-13 | |
|---|---|---|---|---|---|---|---|---|---|---|---|---|---|---|---|---|---|---|---|
| SthP | 17 | Conf S | 8 | Conf S | 11 | Conf S | 17 | Conf S | 21 | Conf S | 19 | Conf S | 17 | Conf S | 17 | Conf S | 11 | Conf S | 8 |

# MATCH RESULTS 2012-13

| Date | Comp | H/A | Opponents | Att: | Result | Goalscorers | Pos | No. |
|------|------|-----|-----------|------|--------|-------------|-----|-----|
| Aug 18 | BSS | H | Eastbourne Borough | 447 | W 2-1 | Ward 87 Reid 90 | 5 | 1 |
| 21 | BSS | A | Staines Town | 252 | L 1-2 | Clough 59 | 11 | 2 |
| 25 | BSS | A | Farnborough | 432 | D 1-1 | Ward 30 | 13 | 3 |
| 27 | BSS | H | Bath City | 559 | W 2-1 | Walker 60 Martin 63 | 6 | 4 |
| Sept 1 | BSS | A | Sutton United | 420 | W 2-1 | Nicholls 14 Watson 16 | 2 | 5 |
| 4 | BSS | H | Eastleigh | 404 | W 1-0 | Reid 89 | 2 | 6 |
| 8 | BSS | H | Chelmsford City | 463 | W 1-0 | Reid 64 | 2 | 7 |
| 15 | BSS | A | AFC Hornchurch | 273 | L 0-1 | | 2 | 8 |
| 22 | FAC Q2 | H | Wooton Bassett | 406 | W 4-0 | Watson 12 Reid 20 90 Walker 34 | | 9 |
| 28 | BSS | H | Welling United | 550 | W 2-1 | Gleeson 40 Clough 90 | 2 | 10 |
| Oct 2 | BSS | A | Salisbury City | 759 | L 0-4 | | 2 | 11 |
| 6 | FAC Q3 | H | Basingstoke Town | 580 | W 1-0 | Gleeson 52 | | 12 |
| 13 | BSS | A | Billericay Town | 477 | L 1-3 | Watson 90 | 4 | 13 |
| 20 | FAC Q4 | H | Bury Town | 555 | W 3-1 | Clough 6 Crittenden 86 Watson 90 | | 14 |
| 27 | BSS | H | Tonbridge Angels | 463 | L 1-2 | Garcia 48 | 8 | 15 |
| Nov 4 | FAC 1 | H | Plymouth Argyle | 3196 | W 1-0 | Gosling 49 | | 16 |
| 10 | FAT Q | A | Didcot Town | 179 | W 2-1 | Green 50 90 | | 17 |
| 13 | BSS | A | Havant & Waterlooville | 526 | L 0-4 | | 8 | 18 |
| 17 | BSS | A | Maidenhead United | 303 | W 2-1 | Watson 40 Regis 63 (og) | 9 | 19 |
| 27 | FAT 1 | H | Luton Town | 688 | D 2-2 | Jermyn 58 Clough 90 | | 20 |
| Dec 1 | FAC 2 | A | Luton Town | 3287 | L 0-2 | | | 21 |
| 4 | FAT 1r | A | Luton Town | 897 | L 1-3 | Thomson 86 | | 22 |
| 8 | BSS | H | Sutton United | 456 | L 0-1 | | 14 | 23 |
| Jan 1 | BSS | H | Truro City | 520 | D 2-2 | Thomson 20 Watson 75 | 18 | 24 |
| 5 | BSS | H | Hayes & Yeading | 403 | D 2-2 | Monteiro 27 (og) Watson 77 | 20 | 25 |
| 8 | BSS | H | Bromley | 323 | L 0-4 | | 21 | 26 |
| 15 | BSS | H | Dover Athletic | 305 | W 1-0 | Nicholls 17 | 16 | 27 |
| 26 | BSS | H | Havant & Waterlooville | 455 | D 0-0 | | 15 | 28 |
| 28 | BSS | A | Chelmsford Clty | 565 | L 0-4 | | 15 | 29 |
| Feb 2 | BSS | A | Welling United | 516 | L 2-3 | Nicholls 25 Clough 75 | 19 | 30 |
| 5 | BSS | H | Basingstoke Town | 290 | D 2-2 | Malsom 28 Clough 65 | 19 | 31 |
| 9 | BSS | H | Salisbury City | 641 | W 2-1 | Smeeton 27 Watson 76 | 13 | 32 |
| 12 | BSS | A | Bath City | 418 | W 3-2 | Watson 20 Malsom 38 Pugh 80 | 12 | 33 |
| 16 | BSS | H | Basingstoke Town | 471 | L 1-2 | Moore 59 | 13 | 34 |
| 19 | BSS | A | Truro City | 314 | W 2-1 | Moore 21 89 | 11 | 35 |
| 23 | BSS | A | Tonbridge Angels | 365 | W 2-0 | Clough 27 Watson 89 | 8 | 36 |
| 26 | BSS | H | Billericay Town | 308 | W 6-1 | Clough 4 54 Crittendon 69 Malsom 73 Watson 82 Walker 89 | 8 | 37 |
| Mar 2 | BSS | A | Bromley | 438 | L 1-2 | Watson 7 | 8 | 38 |
| 5 | BSS | A | Eastbourne Borough | 341 | D 0-0 | | 8 | 39 |
| 9 | BSS | H | Boreham Wood | 429 | D 0-0 | | 8 | 40 |
| 19 | BSS | A | Weston-s-Mare | 268 | L 0-2 | | 9 | 41 |
| 26 | BSS | H | Farnborough | 244 | W 2-0 | Nicholls 22 Walker 44 | 8 | 42 |
| 30 | BSS | A | Staines Town | 487 | L 0-4 | | 9 | 43 |
| Apr 1 | BSS | A | Eastleigh | 468 | L 1-3 | Brooks 49 | 11 | 44 |
| 6 | BSS | A | Boreham Wood | 201 | W 2-1 | Moore 22 Watson 87 | 11 | 45 |
| 9 | BSS | H | AFC Hornchurch | 327 | W 3-1 | Clough 9 Moore 61 90 | 9 | 46 |
| 16 | BSS | H | Maidenhead United | 258 | W 4-0 | Clough 17 Moore 20 Malsom 66 Watson 78 | 9 | 47 |
| 20 | BSS | A | Dover Athletic | 823 | D 0-0 | | 9 | 48 |
| 23 | BSS | A | Hayes & Yeading | 168 | W 3-1 | Watson 15 Malsom 58 Clough 76 | 8 | 49 |
| 27 | BSS | H | Weston -s Mare | 623 | W 2-1 | Watson 17 75 | 8 | 50 |

| GOALSCORERS | Lge | FAC | LC | Total | Pens | Hat-tricks | Cons Run | | Lge | FAC | LC | Total | Pens | Hat-tricks | Cons Run |
|-------------|-----|-----|----|-------|------|-----------|----------|---|-----|-----|----|-------|------|-----------|----------|
| Watson | 15 | 2 | | 17 | | | 2 | Ward | 2 | | | 2 | | | |
| Clough | 10 | 1 | 1 | 12 | | | 2 | Brooks. | 1 | | | 1 | | | |
| Moore | 7 | | | 7 | | | 2 | Garca. | 1 | | | 1 | | | |
| Malsom | 5 | | | 5 | | | | Gosling. | | 1 | | 1 | | | |
| Reid | 3 | 2 | | 5 | | | 2 | Jermyn. | | | 1 | 1 | | | |
| Nicholls | 4 | | | 4 | | | | Martin. | 1 | | | 1 | | | |
| Walker | 3 | 1 | | 4 | | | | Pugh. | 1 | | | 1 | | | |
| Crittenden | 1 | | 1 | 2 | | | | Smeeton. | 1 | | | 1 | | | |
| Gleeson | 1 | 1 | | 2 | | | | Own Goals | 2 | | | 2 | | | |
| Green | | | 2 | 2 | | | | Cons Run - Consecutive scoring games. | | | | | | | |
| Thomson | 1 | | 1 | 2 | | | | | | | | | | | |

# DOVER ATHLETIC

**Chairman:** Jim Parmenter
**Secretary:** Franke Clarke    **(T)** 07794 102 664    **(E)** frank.clarke@doverathletic.com
**Commercial Manager:** n/a    **(T)**
**Programme Editor:** Chris Collings    **(T)** 07977 507 273
**Ground Address:** Crabble Athletic Ground, Lewisham, Dover, Kent CT17 0JB
**(T)** 01304 822 373    **Manager:** Chris Kinnear

## Club Factfile

**Founded:** 1983    **Nickname:** The Whites
**Previous Names:** Dover F.C. until club folded in 1983
**Previous Leagues:** Southern 1983-93, 2002-04, Conference 1993-2002, Isthmian 2004-2009

**Club Colours (change):** White/black/black (All pink)

**Ground Capacity:** 6,500    **Seats:** 1,000    **Covered:** 4,900    **Clubhouse:** Yes    **Shop:** Yes

**Directions:** From outside of Kent, find your way to the M25, then take the M2/A2 (following the signs to Canterbury, then from Canterbury follow signs to Dover) as far as the Whitfield roundabout (there is a McDonald's Drive-Thru on the left). Take the fourth exit at this roundabout, down Whitfield Hill. At the bottom of the hill turn left at the roundabout and follow this road until the first set of traffic lights. At the lights turn right (180 degrees down the hill) and follow the road under the railway bridge, the ground is a little further up the road on the left. There is no parking for supporters within the ground, although parking is available in the rugby ground, which is just inside the main entrance - stewards will direct you. If you have to take the M20/A20 leave the A20 in Folkestone (the exit immediately after the tunnel through the hill) and travel through the Alkham Valley (turn left at the roundabout at the end of the slip-road and then left again, following the signs for Alkham) which will eventually take you near Kearsney train station (turn right into Lower Road just before the railway bridge, before you get to the station).

**Previous Grounds:** None.

**Record Attendance:** 4,186 v Oxford United - FA Cup 1st Round November 2002
**Record Victory:** 7-0 v Weymouth - 03/04/1990
**Record Defeat:** 1-7 v Poole Town
**Record Goalscorer:** Lennie Lee - 160
**Record Appearances:** Jason Bartlett - 359
**Additional Records:** Paid £50,000 to Farnborough Town for David Lewworthy August 1993
**Senior Honours:** Received £50,000 from Brentford for Ricky Reina 1997
Southern League Southern Division 1987-88, Premier Division 1989-90, 92-93, Premier Inter League Cup 1990-91.
Kent Senior Cup 1990-91. Isthmian League Division 1 South 2007-08, Premier Division 2008-09.

### 10 YEAR RECORD

| 03-04 | | 04-05 | | 05-06 | | 06-07 | | 07-08 | | 08-09 | | 09-10 | | 10-11 | | 11-12 | | 12-13 | |
|---|---|---|---|---|---|---|---|---|---|---|---|---|---|---|---|---|---|---|---|
| SthP | 19 | Isth P | 21 | Isth1 | 5 | Isth1S | 3 | Isth1S | 1 | Isth P | 1 | Conf S | 2 | Conf S | 7 | Conf S | 7 | Conf S | 3 |

# MATCH RESULTS 2012-13

| Date | Comp | H/A | Opponents | Att: | Result | Goalscorers | Pos | No. |
|---|---|---|---|---|---|---|---|---|
| Aug 18 | BSS | H | Farnborough | 809 | D 2-2 | Sessegnon 22 Cogan 35 | 7 | 1 |
| 21 | BSS | A | Sutton United | 565 | D 2-2 | Bricknell 46 Huke 83 | 13 | 2 |
| 25 | BSS | A | AFC Hornchurch | 355 | W 1-0 | Cogan 82 | 5 | 3 |
| 27 | BSS | H | Eastbourne Borough | 825 | D 0-0 | | 8 | 4 |
| Sept 1 | BSS | A | Eastleigh | 639 | W 3-1 | Willock 33 May 44 Bricknell 87 | 4 | 5 |
| 4 | BSS | H | Chelmsford City | 832 | L 0-1 | | 6 | 6 |
| 8 | BSS | H | Hayes & Yeading | 726 | L 0-1 | | 9 | 7 |
| 15 | BSS | A | Bath City | 614 | W 2-1 | Bricknell 61 Thomson 70 | 7 | 8 |
| 22 | FAC Q2 | H | Tonbridge Angels | 625 | W 2-1 | May 4 Webb 43 | | 9 |
| 29 | BSS | H | Maidenhead United | 721 | W 2-0 | May 65 Bricknell 76 | 6 | 10 |
| Oct 2 | BSS | A | Welling United | 543 | D 1-1 | May | 6 | 11 |
| 6 | FAC Q3 | H | Bromley | 715 | L 1-2 | May | | 12 |
| 20 | BSS | H | Salisbury City | 813 | L 1-3 | May (pen) 90 | 11 | 13 |
| 27 | BSS | A | Basingstoke Town | 353 | W 1-0 | Huke 4 | 7 | 14 |
| Nov 3 | BSS | A | Eastbourne Borough | 664 | W 3-0 | Cogan 18 May 52 (pen) Willock 72 | 6 | 15 |
| 10 | FAT Q3 | A | Chelmsford City | 570 | D 1-1 | Modeste 35 | | 16 |
| 13 | FAT Q3r | H | Chelmsford City | 720 | L 2-4 | Willock 25 McMahon 46 | | 17 |
| 17 | BSS | H | Boreham Wood | 613 | L 0-1 | | 8 | 18 |
| 20 | BSS | H | Billericay Town | 607 | W 4-1 | Cogan 9 Bricknell 17 53 Huke 51 | 2 | 19 |
| 24 | BSS | H | Weston-s-Mare | 502 | W 3-1 | May 6 (pen) Bricknell 81 Modeste 82 | 2 | 20 |
| Dec 1 | BSS | A | Billericay Town | 501 | W 2-1 | Bricknell 13 81 | 3 | 21 |
| 4 | BSS | A | Truro City | 279 | W 3-0 | May 38 Bricknell 75 Willock 82 | 3 | 22 |
| 8 | BSS | H | Eastleigh | 725 | W 2-0 | May 4 (pen) 37 | 3 | 23 |
| 14 | BSS | A | Hayes & Yeading | 284 | W 4-2 | McMahon 47 May 60 66 Monteiro 68 (og) | 2 | 24 |
| 26 | BSS | A | Tonbridge Angels | 710 | L 1-2 | May | 3 | 25 |
| Jan 1 | BSS | H | Tonbridge Angels | 1102 | L 0-1 | | 3 | 26 |
| 5 | BSS | H | Staines Town | 726 | L 0-1 | | 3 | 27 |
| 12 | BSS | A | Farnborough | 541 | L 2-5 | Bricknell 62 May 57 | 3 | 28 |
| 15 | BSS | A | Dorchester Town | 305 | L 0-1 | | 3 | 29 |
| Feb 2 | BSS | H | Truro City | 824 | W 3-2 | Sterling 6 Simpemba 27 Willock 46 | 3 | 30 |
| 9 | BSS | H | Welling United | 1005 | W 3-2 | May 6 Willock 55 Bricknell 86 | 4 | 31 |
| 16 | BSS | A | Weston-s-Mare | 302 | W 3-0 | Modeste 12 56 Simpemba 37 | 3 | 32 |
| 23 | BSS | A | Boreham Wood | 251 | D 1-1 | Thomson 20 | 3 | 33 |
| Mar 2 | BSS | H | Bath City | 873 | W 2-0 | May 24 Jones 71 (og) | 3 | 34 |
| 5 | BSS | A | Maidenhead United | 229 | W 2-1 | May 16 Cogan 70 | 3 | 35 |
| 9 | BSS | H | Havant & Waterloovillle | 821 | D 2-2 | Sterling 37 Cogan 45 | 3 | 36 |
| 19 | BSS | H | Bromley | 715 | W 1-0 | Harrington 62 | 3 | 37 |
| 26 | BSS | H | AFC Hornchurch | 483 | W 1-0 | May-90 | 3 | 38 |
| 30 | BSS | H | Sutton United | 1023 | D 1-1 | May-68 | 3 | 39 |
| Apr 1 | BSS | A | Chelmsford City | 910 | W 3-0 | Modeste 31 May 33 Webb 66 | 3 | 40 |
| 6 | BSS | H | Basingstoke Town | 735 | L 0-5 | | 3 | 41 |
| 9 | BSS | A | Salisbury City | 670 | D 1-1 | Sterling 23 | 3 | 42 |
| 16 | BSS | A | Havant & Waterloville | 594 | D 1-1 | Ottaway 8 | 3 | 43 |
| 20 | BSS | H | Dorchester Town | 823 | D 0-0 | | 3 | 44 |
| 23 | BSS | A | Staines Town | 321 | W 2-0 | May 53 Thomson 90 | 3 | 45 |
| 27 | BSS | A | Bromley | 811 | W 4-0 | Ottaway 13 Ademola 57 McMahon 63 Bricknell 90 | 3 | 46 |
| 30 | P-Off S-F 1 | A | Eastleigh | 915 | W 3-1 | Ademola 1 May 18 McMahon 90 | | 47 |
| May 4 | P-Off S-F 2 | H | Eastleigh | 1662 | L 0-2 | *aet Won 4-2 on penalties | | 48 |
| 10 | P-Off Final | A | Salisbury City | 3408 | L 2-3 | Simpempa 88 Bricknell 118 *aet | | 49 |

| GOALSCORERS | Lge | FAC | LC | Total | Pens | Hat-tricks | Cons Run | | Lge | FAC | LC | Total | Pens | Hat-tricks | Cons Run |
|---|---|---|---|---|---|---|---|---|---|---|---|---|---|---|---|
| May | 21 | 2 | | 23 | 4 | | 5 | Ottaway | 2 | | | 2 | | | |
| Bricknell | 14 | | | 14 | | | | Webb | 1 | 1 | | 2 | | | |
| Willock | 5 | 1 | | 6 | | | | Ademola | 2 | | | 2 | | | |
| Cogan | 6 | | | 6 | | | | Harrington | 1 | | | 1 | | | |
| Modeste | 4 | 1 | | 5 | | | | Sessegnon | 1 | | | 1 | | | |
| McMahon | 3 | 1 | | 4 | | | | Own Goals | 2 | | | 2 | | | |
| Huke | 3 | | | 3 | | | | Cons Run - Consecutive scoring games. | | | | | | | |
| Simpemba | 3 | | | 3 | | | | | | | | | | | |
| Sterling | 3 | | | 3 | | | | | | | | | | | |
| Thomson | 3 | | | 3 | | | | | | | | | | | |

# EASTBOURNE BOROUGH

**Chairman:** Len Smith
**Secretary:** Mrs Jan Field     **(T)** 07749 572 693     **(E)** janfield38@sky.com
**Commercial Manager:** Sharon Hind     **(T)** 07850 582 434
**Programme Editor:** David Bealey     **(T)** programme@ebfc.co.uk
**Ground Address:** Langney Sports Club, Priory Lane, Eastbourne BN23 7QH
**(T)** 01323 766 265     **Manager:** Tommy Widdrington

Copyright © Jane Stokes (DJ Stotty Images)

2012-13 Squad - Back: Nick Redman (Goalkeeper coach), Ethan Strevett, James Walker, Danny Potter, Anwar Uddin, Nick Jordan, Marvin Hamilton, Matt Turpin, H.Silva (Analyst)
Middle: Damian Karchinski (Kitman), Jake McPherson, Darren Baker, Charlie Gorman, Darren Lok, Tim Gilbert, Gary Hart, Sam Cole, Ben Adams, Dave Funnell (Kitman), Ray Tuppen (Sports Therapist).
Front: Chris Morgan, David Knight, Tommy Widdrington (Manager), Ollie Rowe, Alan Kimble (Coach), Simon Johnson, Chris Shepherd.

## Club Factfile

**Founded:** 1966     **Nickname:** Borough
**Previous Names:** Langney Sports > 2001
**Previous Leagues:** Eastbourne & Hastings, Sussex County, Southern

**Club Colours (change):** Red with navy stripe/navy/red (All yellow)

**Ground Capacity:** 4,151     **Seats:** 542     **Covered:** 2,500     **Clubhouse:** Yes     **Shop:** Yes

**Directions:** From M25 take M23/A23 eastbound to A27 Polegate by pass pick up and follow signs for crematorium 50yds past crematorium turn right at mini roundabout into Priory Road Stadium 100yds on left.

**Previous Grounds:** None

**Record Attendance:** 3,770 v Oxford United - FA Cup 1st Round 05/11/05
**Record Victory:** 10-1 v Haywards Heath Town - Sussex County Division One 1991-92
**Record Defeat:** 0-8 v Sheppey United (A) - FA Vase 09/10/93 and v Peachaven & Tels (A) - Sussex Co. Div.1 09/11/93
**Record Goalscorer:** Nigel Hole - 146
**Record Appearances:** Darren Baker - 689
**Additional Records:** Paid £1,800 to Yeovil Town for Yemi Odoubade.
**Senior Honours:**     Received £15,000 from Oxford United for Yemi Odoubade.
Sussex County League 1999-2000, 02-03. Sussex Senior Cup 2001-02.

### 10 YEAR RECORD

| 03-04 | 04-05 | 05-06 | 06-07 | 07-08 | 08-09 | 09-10 | 10-11 | 11-12 | 12-13 |
|---|---|---|---|---|---|---|---|---|---|
| SthP 11 | Conf S 5 | Conf S 17 | Conf S 7 | Conf S 2 | Conf 13 | Conf 19 | Conf 23 | Conf S 18 | Conf S 12 |

# MATCH RESULTS 2012-13

| Date | Comp | H/A | Opponents | Att: | Result | Goalscorers | Pos | No. |
|---|---|---|---|---|---|---|---|---|
| Aug 18 | BSS | A | Dorchester Town | 447 | L 1-2 | Knight 64 | 18 | 1 |
| 21 | BSS | H | Bromley | 655 | W 3-0 | Walker 40 (pen) Ademeno 45 (pen) Shepherd 49 | 9 | 2 |
| 25 | BSS | H | Billericay Town | 705 | W 2-1 | Shephard 28 Hart 76 | 4 | 3 |
| 27 | BSS | A | Dover Athletic | 825 | D 0-0 | | 5 | 4 |
| Sept 1 | BSS | H | Maidenhead United | 627 | L 0-2 | | 12 | 5 |
| 4 | BSS | A | Welling United | 471 | L 0-2 | | 13 | 6 |
| 8 | BSS | A | Salisbury City | 769 | L 0-1 | | 14 | 7 |
| 15 | BSS | H | Basingstoke Town | 531 | W 1-0 | Lok 84 | 12 | 8 |
| 22 | FAC Q2 | A | Waltham Abbey | 223 | W 4-2 | Ademeno 25 Shepherd 75 85 (pen) Lok 78 | | 9 |
| 29 | BSS | A | Weston-s-Mare | 236 | L 2-3 | Johnson 18 Knight 51 | 16 | 10 |
| Oct 2 | BSS | H | Tonbridge Angels | 415 | L 1-2 | Remy 76 | 19 | 11 |
| 6 | FAC Q3 | H | Hendon | 439 | D 2-2 | Shephard 71 85 | | 12 |
| 9 | FAC Q3r | A | Hendon | 150 | L 1-2* | Lok 100 | | 13 |
| 13 | BSS | H | Sutton United | 618 | L 0-1 | | 21 | 14 |
| 20 | BSS | A | AFC Hornchurch | 278 | W 1-0 | Shepherd 69 | 17 | 15 |
| 27 | BSS | H | Eastleigh | 594 | W 1-0 | Raymond 48 | 15 | 16 |
| 30 | BSS | A | Basingstoke Town | 283 | D 2-2 | Remy 68 Rowe 83 | 14 | 17 |
| Nov 3 | BSS | H | Dover Athletic | 664 | L 0-3 | | 16 | 18 |
| 10 | FAT Q3 | A | Kings Lynn Town | 661 | L 0-3 | | 13 | 19 |
| 17 | BSS | H | Truro City | 514 | W 1-0 | Rowe 57 | 15 | 20 |
| Dec 1 | BSS | A | Bath City | 540 | D 2-2 | Ibe 26 Charles 46 | 12 | 21 |
| 8 | BSS | A | Maidenhead United | 251 | W 2-1 | Charles 78 Lok 86 | 11 | 22 |
| 15 | BSS | H | Salisbury City | 576 | L 1-2 | Rowe 90 | 11 | 23 |
| 26 | BSS | H | Havant & Waterlooville | 582 | L 0-1 | | 11 | 24 |
| Jan 1 | BSS | A | Havant & Waterlooville | 727 | W 3-2 | Watts 26 Charles 30 Gorman 62 | 9 | 25 |
| 5 | BSS | A | Boreham Wood | 205 | L 1-2 | Adelsbury 37 | 10 | 26 |
| 26 | BSS | A | Staines Town | 323 | W 2-0 | Charles 46 Walker 70 (pen) | 11 | 27 |
| Feb 2 | BSS | H | AFC Hornchurch | 544 | D 1-1 | Charles 27 | 11 | 28 |
| 9 | BSS | H | Weston-s-Mare | 570 | L 0-2 | | 16 | 29 |
| 16 | BSS | A | Sutton United | 587 | L 0-2 | | 19 | 30 |
| 19 | BSS | H | Bath City | 406 | L 0-3 | | 19 | 31 |
| 23 | BSS | A | Farnborough | 368 | W 1-0 | Lok 90 | 17 | 32 |
| Mar 2 | BSS | A | Eastleigh | 507 | L 0-1 | | 18 | 33 |
| 5 | BSS | H | Dorchester Town | 341 | D 0-0 | | 18 | 34 |
| 9 | BSS | H | Farnborough | 502 | L 0-1 | | 18 | 35 |
| 19 | BSS | H | Hayes & Yeading U | 379 | W 2-1 | Johnson 15 Lok 90 | 16 | 36 |
| 25 | BSS | A | Chelmsford City | 406 | L 0-1 | | 16 | 37 |
| 30 | BSS | A | Bromley | 551 | W 2-0 | Adelsbury 54 Johnson 78 | 15 | 38 |
| Apr 1 | BSS | H | Welling United | 631 | L 0-3 | | 16 | 39 |
| 6 | BSS | A | Truro City | 318 | D 2-2 | Rowe 69 Lok 90 | 17 | 40 |
| 9 | BSS | A | Billericay Town | 317 | W 2-1 | Charles 52 60 | 16 | 41 |
| 13 | BSS | H | Chelmsford City | 479 | L 1-2 | Hart 90 | 16 | 42 |
| 16 | BSS | H | Boreham Wood | 371 | D 1-1 | Charles 54 | 16 | 43 |
| 17 | BSS | A | Hayes & Yeading U | 197 | D 1-1 | Smith 14 | 15 | 44 |
| 23 | BSS | A | Tonbridge Angels | 624 | D 1-1 | Smith 50 | 15 | 45 |
| 27 | BSS | H | Staines Town | 596 | W 2-0 | Charles 59 85 | 12 | 46 |

| GOALSCORERS | Lge | FAC | LC | Total | Pens | Hat-tricks | Cons Run | | Lge | FAC | LC | Total | Pens | Hat-tricks | Cons Run |
|---|---|---|---|---|---|---|---|---|---|---|---|---|---|---|---|
| ECharles | 10 | | | 10 | | | 2 | Smith | 2 | | | 2 | | | |
| Lok | 5 | 2 | | 7 | | | | Walker | 2 | | | 2 | 2 | | |
| Shepherd | 3 | 4 | | 7 | 1 | | | Gorman | 1 | | | 1 | | | |
| Rowe | 4 | | | 4 | | | | Ibe | 1 | | | 1 | | | |
| Johnson | 3 | | | 3 | | | | Raymond | 1 | | | 1 | | | |
| Adelsbury | 2 | | | 2 | | | | Watts | 1 | | | 1 | | | |
| Ademeno | 1 | 1 | | 2 | 1 | | | Cons Run - Consecutive scoring games. | | | | | | | |
| Hart | 2 | | | 2 | | | | | | | | | | | |
| Knight | 2 | | | 2 | | | | | | | | | | | |
| Remy | 2 | | | 2 | | | | | | | | | | | |

# EASTLEIGH

**Chairman:** Stewart Donald
**Secretary:** Ray Murphy        **(T)** 07508 431 451        **(E)** raymurphy@ntlworld.com
**Commercial Manager:** Mark Jewell        **(T)** 07837 665 229
**Programme Editor:** Stewart Donald        **(T)** 07900 337 771
**Ground Address:** Silverlake Stadium 'Ten Acres', Stoneham Lane, Eastleigh SO50 9HT
**(T)** 02380 613 361        **Manager:** Ian Baird

2012-13 Squad
Back Row L to R – Osei Sankofa, Lee Peacock, Craig McAllister, Wayne Shaw, Daryl McMahon, Tom Jordan, Jack Dovey, Gary Elphick, Mitchell Nelson, Michael Green, Andy Forbes.
Front Row L to R – Ken Kudjodji, Glen Southam, Chris Flood, Marvin Williams, Jai Reason, Moses Ademola, Adam Everitt, Damian Scannell.

## Club Factfile

**Founded:** 1946        **Nickname:** The Spitfires
**Previous Names:** Swaythling Athletic 1946-59, Swaythling 1973-80
**Previous Leagues:** Southampton Junior & Senior 1946-59, Hampshire 1950-86, Wessex 1986-2003, Southern 2003-04, Isthmian 2004-05

**Club Colours (change):** Blue with white trim/white/blue (White with blue trim/blue/white)

**Ground Capacity:** 2,300        **Seats:** 175        **Covered:** 385        **Clubhouse:** Yes        **Shop:** Yes

**Directions**
From junction 13 of M3, turn right into Leigh Road, turn right at Holiday Inn, at mini roundabout take second exit, at the next mini roundabout take second exit, then next mini roundabout take first exit. Then take the first turning right (signposted) ground 200 metres on the left.

**Previous Grounds:** Southampton Common. Westfield >1957.

**Record Attendance:** 2,589 v Southampton - Friendly July 2005
**Record Victory:** 12-1 v Hythe & Dibden (H) - 11/12/1948
**Record Defeat:** 0-11 v Austin Sports (A) - 01.01.1947
**Record Goalscorer:** Johnnie Williams - 177
**Record Appearances:** Ian Knight - 611
**Additional Records:** Paid £10,000 to Newport (I.O.W.) for Colin Matthews

**Senior Honours:**
Southampton Senior League (West) 1950.
Wessex League Cup 1992,2003, Division One 2002-03.
Hampshire Senior Cup 2011-12.

### 10 YEAR RECORD

| 03-04 | | 04-05 | | 05-06 | | 06-07 | | 07-08 | | 08-09 | | 09-10 | | 10-11 | | 11-12 | | 12-13 | |
|---|---|---|---|---|---|---|---|---|---|---|---|---|---|---|---|---|---|---|---|
| SthE | 4 | Isth P | 3 | Conf S | 8 | Conf S | 15 | Conf S | 6 | Conf S | 3 | Conf S | 11 | Conf S | 8 | Conf S | 12 | Conf S | 4 |

# MATCH RESULTS 2012-13

| Date | Comp | H/A | Opponents | Att: | Result | Goalscorers | Pos | No. |
|------|------|-----|-----------|------|--------|-------------|-----|-----|
| Aug 17 | BSS | A | Boreham Wood | 204 | L 0-3 | | 22 | 1 |
| 21 | BSS | H | Basingstoke Town | 608 | D 1-1 | McAllister 30 | 20 | 2 |
| 25 | BSS | H | Weston s-Mare | 445 | W 3-0 | Ademola 26 46 McAllister 48 | 14 | 3 |
| 27 | BSS | A | Havant & Waterlooville | 903 | W 3-0 | Ademola 32 Williams 55 McAllister 62 | 4 | 4 |
| Sept 1 | BSS | H | Dover Athletic | 639 | L 1-3 | McAllister 20 | 11 | 5 |
| 4 | BSS | A | Dorchester Town | 404 | L 0-1 | | 13 | 6 |
| 8 | BSS | A | Billericay Town | 503 | L 0-4 | | 16 | 7 |
| 15 | BSS | H | Maidenhead United | 506 | W 4-2 | Ademola 37 Sankofa 56 Jordan 77 Southam 90 | 13 | 8 |
| 22 | FAC Q2 | A | Farnborough | 444 | W 2-1 | McAllister 7 61 (pen) | | 9 |
| 29 | BSS | H | Hayes & Yeading | 577 | W 3-1 | Reason 29 88 Southam 69 | 8 | 10 |
| Oct 2 | BSS | A | Farnborough | 302 | L 2-6 | Ademola 26 Reason 89 | 13 | 11 |
| 7 | FAC Q3 | A | Gloucester City | 202 | L 0-1 | | | 12 |
| 10 | BSS | A | Staines Town | 509 | W 4-3 | Ademola 39 Reason 41 83 Southam 58 | 7 | 13 |
| 13 | BSS | A | Chelmsford City | 919 | D 1-1 | Ademola 55 | 7 | 14 |
| 27 | BSS | A | Eastbourne Borough | 594 | L 0-1 | | 14 | 15 |
| 30 | BSS | H | Bath City | 525 | W 3-1 | Scannell 12 McAllister 16 Reason 39 | 9 | 16 |
| Nov 3 | BSS | H | Sutton United | 636 | W 1-0 | Reason 12 | 3 | 17 |
| 10 | FAT Q3 | H | Hayes & Yeading | 241 | L 1-4 | Peacock 41 | | 18 |
| 17 | BSS | A | AFC Hornchurch | 298 | L 0-1 | | 7 | 19 |
| Dec 1 | BSS | H | Welling United | 546 | L 1-3 | McAllister 9 | 10 | 20 |
| 8 | BSS | A | Dover Athletic | 725 | L 0-2 | | 12 | 21 |
| Jan 1 | BSS | A | Salisbury City | 887 | L 3-5 | Reason 20 Pacquette 40 Clarke 33 (og) | 19 | 22 |
| 5 | BSS | A | Bromley | 315 | L 1-3 | Reason 4 (pen) | 21 | 23 |
| 8 | BSS | H | Billericay Town | 344 | W 5-0 | Beckwith 8 Scannell 32 81 Beasant 67 (og) Hughes 90 | 16 | 24 |
| 26 | BSS | H | Farnborough | 606 | W 3-1 | Southam 14 Todd 71 Binns 90 | 12 | 25 |
| Feb 2 | BSS | A | Sutton United | 471 | L 1-2 | Scannell 90 | 15 | 26 |
| 5 | BSS | A | Weston-s-Mare | 210 | W 4-2 | Scannell (2) Reason Binns | 10 | 27 |
| 9 | BSS | A | Staines Town | 240 | W 3-1 | McAllister 43 Scannell 84 Beckwith 90 | 8 | 28 |
| 12 | BSS | H | Salisbury City | 872 | W 1-0 | McAllister 54 | 8 | 29 |
| 16 | BSS | H | Chelmsford City | 676 | W 1-0 | Reason 44 (pen) | 6 | 30 |
| 23 | BSS | A | Hayes & Yeading | 159 | L 1-2 | Todd 86 | 7 | 31 |
| 26 | BSS | H | Havant & Waterlooville | 579 | D 2-2 | Reason 66 (pen) Hughes 75 | 8 | 32 |
| Mar 2 | BSS | H | Eastbourne Borough | 507 | W 1-0 | Zebroski 48 | 7 | 33 |
| 9 | BSS | A | Maidenhead United | 309 | W 2-0 | Reason 42 (pen) Lacey 90 | 7 | 34 |
| 12 | BSS | H | Boreham Wood | 401 | D 1-1 | Reason 17 | 7 | 35 |
| 26 | BSS | A | Tonbridge Angels | 170 | L 1-3 | Zebroski 80 | 7 | 36 |
| 29 | BSS | A | Basingstoke Town | 532 | W 3-0 | Hughes 41 Watkins 74 79 | 7 | 37 |
| Apr 1 | BSS | H | Dorchester Town | 524 | W 3-1 | Reason 40 Southam 45 Zebroski 51 | 7 | 38 |
| 6 | BSS | H | AFC Hornchurch | 504 | W 1-0 | Watkins 83 | 6 | 39 |
| 9 | BSS | A | Truro City | 201 | W 3-1 | McAllister 65 Reason 9 80 | 5 | 40 |
| 13 | BSS | A | Bath City | 545 | D 1-1 | Watkins 90 | 6 | 41 |
| 16 | BSS | H | Bromley | 508 | W 3-0 | McAllister 75 82 McAuley 86 (pen) | 5 | 42 |
| 20 | BSS | H | Tonbridge Angels | 627 | W 4-1 | McALLISTER 3 ( 46 53 88) Beckwith 70 | 5 | 43 |
| 23 | BSS | H | Truro City | 1320 | W 3-1 | Southam 27 Scannell 69 McAllister 77 | 5 | 44 |
| 27 | BSS | A | Welling United | 1522 | D 1-1 | McAllister 84 | 4 | 45 |
| 30 | P-Off S-F 1 | H | Dover Athletic | 915 | L 1-3 | Zebroski 66 | | 45 |
| May 4 | P-Off S-F 2 | A | Dover Athletic | 1662 | W 2-0 | Southam 51, Zebroski 91 *aet Lost 2-4 on penalties | | 46 |

| GOALSCORERS | Lge | FAC | FAT | Total | Pens | Hat-tricks | Cons Run | | Lge | FAC | FAT | Total | Pens | Hat-tricks | Cons Run |
|-------------|-----|-----|-----|-------|------|-----------|----------|--|-----|-----|-----|-------|------|-----------|----------|
| McAllister | 16 | 2 | | 18 | 1 | 1 | 4 | Lacey | 2 | | | 2 | | | |
| Reason | 15 | | | 15 | 3 | | 2 | Todd | 2 | | | 2 | | | |
| Scannell | 8 | | | 8 | | | 3 | Jordan | 1 | | | 1 | | | |
| Ademola | 7 | | | 7 | | | 2 | McAuley | 1 | | | 1 | 1 | | |
| Southam | 7 | | | 7 | | | | Pacquette | 1 | | | 1 | | | |
| Zebroski | 5 | | | 5 | | | 2 | Peacock | | | 1 | 1 | | | |
| Watkins | 4 | | | 4 | | | | Sankofa | 1 | | | 1 | | | |
| Hughes | 3 | | | 3 | | | | Williams | 1 | | | 1 | | | |
| Beckwith | 3 | | | 2 | | | | Own Goals | 2 | | | 2 | | | |
| Binns | 2 | | | 2 | | | | Cons Run - Consecutive scoring games. | | | | | | | |

# EBBSFLEET UNITED

**Chairman:** Dr Abdulla M.S. Al-Humaidi
**Secretary:** Peter Danzey　　　**(T)** 07403 285 385　　**(E)** peter@eufc.co.uk
**Commercial Manager:** Maria Mucci　　　**(T)** 07584 651 316
**Programme Editor:** Simon Crisford　　　**(T)** 01474 533 796
**Ground Address:** Stonebridge Road, Northfleet, Kent DA11 9EQ
**(T)** 01474 533 796　　　　　　　　　　**Manager:** Steve Brown

## Club Factfile

**Founded:** 1946　　　**Nickname:** The Fleet
**Previous Names:** Gravesend United and Northfleet United merged in 1946 to form Gravesend and Northfleet > 2007
**Previous Leagues:** Southern 1946-79, 80-96. Alliance 1979-80, Isthmian 1997-2001

**Club Colours (change):** Red/white/red (White/red/white)

**Ground Capacity:** 4,184　**Seats:** 500　**Covered:** 3,000　**Clubhouse:** Yes　**Shop:** Yes

**Directions**
A2 to Ebbsfleet/Eurostar International Junction.
Follow Brown signs to 'The Fleet'.

**Previous Grounds:** Gravesend United: Central Avenue

**Record Attendance:** 12,036 v Sunderland - FA Cup 4th Round 12/02/1963
**Record Victory:** 8-1 v Clacton Town - Southern League 1962-63
**Record Defeat:** 0-9 v Trowbridge Town - Southern League Premier Division 1991-92
**Record Goalscorer:** Steve Portway - 152 (1992-94, 97-2001)
**Record Appearances:** Ken Burrett - 537
**Additional Records:** Paid £8,000 to Wokingham Town for Richard Newbery 1996 and to Tonbridge for Craig Williams 1997
**Senior Honours:**　Received £35,000 from West Ham United for Jimmy Bullard 1998
Southern League 1956-57, Division 1 South 1974-75, Southern Division 1994-95. Isthmian League Premier 2001-02.
FA Trophy 2007-08. Kent Senior Cup 1948-49, 52-53, 80-81, 99-00, 00-01, 01-02.

### 10 YEAR RECORD

| 03-04 | | 04-05 | | 05-06 | | 06-07 | | 07-08 | | 08-09 | | 09-10 | | 10-11 | | 11-12 | | 12-13 | |
|---|---|---|---|---|---|---|---|---|---|---|---|---|---|---|---|---|---|---|---|
| Conf | 11 | Conf | 14 | Conf | 16 | Conf | 7 | Conf | 11 | Conf | 14 | Conf | 22 | Conf S | 3 | Conf | 14 | Conf | 23 |

# MATCH RESULTS 2012-13

| Date | Comp | H/A | Opponents | Att: | Result | Goalscorers | Pos | No. |
|------|------|-----|-----------|------|--------|-------------|-----|-----|
| Aug 11 | BSP | A | Nuneaton Town | 1088 | W 5-4 | Phipp 20 88 Elder 23 Ashikodi 31 Enver-Marum 50 | 2 | 1 |
| 14 | BSP | H | Braintree Town | 857 | L 0-1 | | 11 | 2 |
| 18 | BSP | H | Wrexham | 843 | D 1-1 | Enver-Marum 70 | 12 | 3 |
| 25 | BSP | A | Hereford United | 1906 | L 2-4 | Ashikodi 50 Howe 90 | 14 | 4 |
| 27 | BSP | H | Luton Town | 1701 | L 1-3 | Elder 86 | 20 | 5 |
| Sept 1 | BSP | A | Lincoln City | 1682 | D 1-1 | Bellamy 62 | 19 | 6 |
| 4 | BSP | A | Forest Green Rovers | 914 | L 1-4 | Walsh 4 | 19 | 7 |
| 8 | BSP | H | Mansfield Town | 828 | W 3-1 | Elder 58 Walsh 60 Enver-Marum 81 (pen) | 19 | 8 |
| 15 | BSP | A | Southport | 872 | L 0-1 | | 21 | 9 |
| 22 | BSP | H | Barrow | 780 | L 2-4 | Phipp 46 Wlder 49 | 22 | 10 |
| 25 | BSP | H | Woking | 738 | D 2-2 | Howe 8 Walsh 75 | 22 | 11 |
| 29 | BSP | A | Stockport County | 4641 | L 1-3 | Elder 61 (pen) | 23 | 12 |
| Oct 6 | BSP | H | Kidderminster Harriers | 726 | D 1-1 | Elder 35 | 23 | 13 |
| 9 | BSP | A | Newport County | 2453 | L 0-1 | | 23 | 14 |
| 13 | BSP | H | Alfreton Town | 804 | D 0-0 | | 23 | 15 |
| 20 | FAC Q4 | A | Woking | 1272 | W 1-0 | Ashikodi 87 | | 16 |
| 27 | BSP | A | Tamworth | 838 | W 1-0 | Phipp 45 | 22 | 17 |
| Nov 6 | BSP | A | AFC Telford United | 1542 | D 2-2 | Jones 6 26 | 23 | 18 |
| 3 | FAC 1 | A | Carlisle United | 2373 | L 2-4 | Elder 57, Howe 90 | | 19 |
| 10 | BSP | H | Hyde United | 779 | W 3-2 | Barrett 35 Elder 72 Godden 79 | | 20 |
| 17 | BSP | A | Macclesfield | 1896 | W 2-1 | Walsh 57 Elder 86 (pen) | 19 | 21 |
| 24 | FAT 1 | H | Hereford United | 651 | L 0-1 | | | 22 |
| Dec 1 | BSP | H | Grimsby Town | 1164 | D 1-1 | Godden 42 | 20 | 23 |
| 4 | BSP | H | Cambridge United | 842 | L 2-4 | Enver-Marum 13 Godden 49 | 21 | 24 |
| 8 | BSP | A | Mansfield Town | 1845 | L 1-4 | Enver-Marum 23 | 22 | 25 |
| 26 | BSP | A | Dartford | 3116 | L 1-3 | Enver-Marum 48 | 23 | 26 |
| Jan 1 | BSP | H | Dartford | 2242 | D 2-2 | Elder 50 90+4 | 23 | 27 |
| 5 | BSP | H | Lincoln City | 889 | D 1-1 | Phipp 36 | 23 | 28 |
| 15 | BSP | A | Woking | 1419 | L 0-1 | | 23 | 29 |
| Feb 3 | BSP | H | Macclesfield Town | 799 | L 0-4 | | 24 | 30 |
| 9 | BSP | H | Gateshead | 636 | W 3-1 | Scott 3 38 Enver- Marum 67 | 24 | 31 |
| 16 | BSP | H | Stockport County | 912 | D 0-0 | | 24 | 32 |
| 19 | BSP | H | Hereford United | 614 | W 1-0 | Scott 37 | 24 | 33 |
| 26 | BSP | A | Grimsby Town | 3129 | L 1-3 | Enver- Marum 74 | 23 | 34 |
| Mar 2 | BSP | A | Kidderminster Harriers | 2048 | L 2-3 | Shitto 13 Elder 90 (pen) | 23 | 35 |
| 5 | BSP | A | Wrexham | 2390 | L 1-4 | Elder 77 | 23 | 36 |
| 9 | BSP | H | Newport County | 808 | D 1-1 | Enver-Marum 55 | 23 | 37 |
| 12 | BSP | A | Alfreton Town | 459 | L 0-3 | | 23 | 38 |
| 16 | BSP | H | Southport | 603 | W 4-1 | Bellamy 6 Payne 12 Elder 14 Godden 29 | 23 | 39 |
| 19 | BSP | A | Cambridge United | 1737 | D 1-1 | Godden 70 | 23 | 40 |
| 30 | BSP | H | Forest Green Rvers | 749 | L 0-2 | | 23 | 41 |
| Apr 1 | BSP | A | Braintree Town | 822 | L 1-3 | Enver-Marum 36 | 23 | 42 |
| 3 | BSP | A | Barrow | 451 | D 1-1 | Walsh 41 | 23 | 43 |
| 6 | BSP | H | Nuneaton Town | 695 | D 1-1 | Phipp 34 | 23 | 44 |
| 9 | BSP | A | Hyde | 385 | L 0-1 | | 23 | 45 |
| 13 | BSP | H | AFC Telford United | 686 | L 1-3 | Payne 16 | 23 | 46 |
| 16 | BSP | H | Tamworth | 488 | D 1-1 | Enver-Marum 80 | 23 | 47 |
| 18 | BSP | A | Luton Town | 5934 | L 0-2 | | 23 | 48 |
| 20 | BSP | A | Gateshead | 532 | L 0-2 | | 23 | 49 |

| GOALSCORERS | Lge | FAC | FAT | Total | Pens | Hat-tricks | Cons Run | | Lge | FAC | FAT | Total | Pens | Hat-tricks | Cons Run |
|-------------|-----|-----|-----|-------|------|-----------|----------|---|-----|-----|-----|-------|------|-----------|----------|
| Elder | 13 | 1 | | 14 | 3 | | 2 | Bellamy | 2 | | | 2 | | | |
| Enver-Marum | 11 | | | 11 | 1 | | 3 | Wilder | 1 | | | 1 | | | |
| Phipp | 5 | | | 5 | | | | Shitto | 1 | | | 1 | | | |
| Walsh | 5 | | | 5 | | | | Payne | 2 | | | 2 | | | |
| Ashikodi | 2 | 1 | | 3 | | | | Cons Run - Consecutive scoring games. | | | | | | | |
| Godden | 5 | | | 5 | | | | | | | | | | | |
| Howe | 2 | | 1 | 3 | | | | | | | | | | | |
| Jones | 2 | | | 2 | | | | | | | | | | | |
| Scott | 3 | | | 3 | | | | | | | | | | | |
| Barrett | 1 | | | 1 | | | | | | | | | | | |

# FARNBOROUGH

**Chairman:** Steve Duly (Interim)

**Secretary:** Steve Duly      **(T)** 07922 666 621      **(E)** steve.duly@farnboroughfc.co.uk

**Commercial Manager:** Steve Duly      **(T)** 07922 666 621

**Programme Editor:** Steve Duly      **(T)** 07922 666 621

**Ground Address:** Rushmoor Stadium, Cherrywood Road, Farnborough, Hants GU14 8UD

**(T)** 01252 541 469                      **Manager:** Spencer Day

2012-13 Squad.

## Club Factfile

**Founded:** 1967      **Nickname:** Boro

**Previous Names:** Farnborough Town 1967-2007

**Previous Leagues:** Surrey Senior 1968-72, Spartan 1972-76, Athenian 1976-77, Isthmian 1977-89, 99-2001, Alliance/Conference 1989-90, 91-93, 94-99, Southern 1990-91, 93-94, 2007-10

**Club Colours (change):** Yellow/blue/yellow (All purple)

**Ground Capacity:** 4,190      **Seats:** 627      **Covered:** 1,350      **Clubhouse:** Yes      **Shop:** Yes

**Directions**
Leave the M3 at Junction 4 and take the A331 signed to Farnham, after a few hundred yards exit at the second slip road- signed A325 Farnborough, turn right at the roundabout and cross over the dual carriageway and small roundabout, passing the Farnborough Gate shopping centre on your left hand side, at the next roundabout turn left (first exit) onto the A325. Go over a pelican crossing and at the next set of lights take the right filter into Prospect Avenue. At the end of this road turn right at the roundabout into Cherrywood Road, the ground is half a mile on the right hand side.

**Previous Grounds:** None as Farnborough. Queens Road as Farnborough Town

**Record Attendance:** 2,230 v Corby Town - Southern Premier 21/03/2009
**Record Victory:** 7-0 v Newport (I.O.W.) (A) - Southern League Division 1 South & West 01/12/2007
**Record Defeat:** 0-4 v Hednesford Town (A) - Southern League Premier Division 04/03/2010
**Record Goalscorer:** Dean McDonald - 35 (in 53+3 Appearances 2009-10)
**Record Appearances:** Nic Ciardini - 147 (2007-10)
**Additional Records:**

**Senior Honours:**
Southern League Division 1 South & West 2007-08, Premier Division 2009-10.
Farnborough Town: Southern League Premier Division 1990-91, 93-94. Isthmian League Division 1 1984-85, Premier Division 2000-01.
Hampshire Senior Cup 1974-75, 81-82, 83-84, 85-86, 90-91, 2003-04.

### 10 YEAR RECORD

| 03-04 | | 04-05 | | 05-06 | | 06-07 | | 07-08 | | 08-09 | | 09-10 | | 10-11 | | 11-12 | | 12-13 | |
|---|---|---|---|---|---|---|---|---|---|---|---|---|---|---|---|---|---|---|---|
| Conf | 20 | Conf | 21 | Conf S | 3 | Conf S | 11 | SthW | 1 | SthP | 2 | SthP | 1 | Conf S | 2 | Conf S | 16 | Conf S | 13 |

# MATCH RESULTS 2012-13

| Date | Comp | H/A | Opponents | Att: | Result | Goalscorers | Pos | No. |
|------|------|-----|-----------|------|--------|-------------|-----|-----|
| Aug 17 | BSS | A | Dover Athletic | 809 | D 2-2 | Bennett 64 Page 79 (pen) | 8 | 1 |
| 21 | BSS | H | Weston-s Mare | 352 | W 2-1 | Ciardini 60 85 | 5 | 2 |
| 25 | BSS | H | Dorchester Town | 432 | D 1-1 | Page 37 | 6 | 3 |
| 27 | BSS | A | Salisbury City | 776 | L 0-1 | | 15 | 4 |
| Sept 1 | BSS | H | Bromley | 458 | W 2-0 | Ciardini 34 36 | 8 | 5 |
| 4 | BSS | A | Maidenhead United | 359 | L 2-3 | Makofo 57 Ciardini 73 (pen) | 10 | 6 |
| 8 | BSS | A | Boreham Wood | 226 | L 1-3 | Bennett 30 | 12 | 7 |
| 15 | BSS | H | Welling United | 584 | L 0-3 | | 17 | 8 |
| 22 | FAC Q2 | H | Eastleigh | 444 | L 1-2 | **Tarpey 70** | | 9 |
| 29 | BSS | A | AFC Hornchurch | 263 | D 1-1 | Tarpey 10 | 19 | 10 |
| Oct 2 | BSS | H | Eastleigh | 302 | W 6-2 | Bennett 5 Ciardini 22 Connolly 34 62 | 14 | |
| | | | | | | Huggins 64 Nelson 65 (og) | | 11 |
| 13 | BSS | H | Tonbridge | 513 | W 4-1 | Ciardini 4 Bennett 22 Tarpey 50 Connolly 72 | 9 | 12 |
| 20 | BSS | A | Havant & Waterlooville | 755 | W 1-0 | Connolly 17 | 5 | 13 |
| 27 | BSS | A | Hayes & Yeading | 318 | L 2-3 | Tarpey 26 Hammond 90 | 9 | 14 |
| 30 | BSS | H | Truro City | 343 | W 4-1 | Tarpey 14 Connolly 40 Inman 83 Day 90 | 4 | 15 |
| Nov 3 | BSS | A | Bath City | 605 | L 2-3 | Connolly 56 Bennett 78 | 7 | 16 |
| 10 | FAT Q3 | H | **Truro City** | 320 | W 3-2 | **Hammond 22 Bennett 65 Connolly 87** | | 17 |
| 17 | BSS | H | Staines Town | 581 | W 3-1 | Connolly 5 75 Bennett 62 | 5 | 18 |
| 24 | FAT 1 | A | **Woking** | 979 | L 0-7 | | | 19 |
| Dec 8 | BSS | A | Bromley | 378 | W 3-1 | Huggins 12 Ciardini 21 Tarpey 60 | 5 | 20 |
| 15 | BSS | H | Boreham Wood | 451 | L 0-3 | | 5 | 21 |
| 26 | BSS | H | Basingstoke Town | 572 | W 2-1 | Inns 8 Tarpey 11 | 5 | 22 |
| Jan 1 | BSS | A | Basingstoke Town | 440 | L 2-6 | Inns 21 Connolly 76 | 6 | 23 |
| 12 | BSS | H | Dover Athletic | 541 | W 5-2 | Bennett 6 11 Tarpey 25 Connolly 30 41 | 5 | 24 |
| 26 | BSS | A | Eastleigh | 606 | L 1-3 | Bennett 69 | 7 | 25 |
| 29 | BSS | H | Salisbury City | 449 | W 2-1 | Connolly 44 90 | 5 | 26 |
| Feb 2 | BSS | A | Tonbridge Angels | 491 | W 3-2 | Connolly 20 33 Tarpey 56 | 7 | 27 |
| 5 | BSS | H | Bath City | 326 | L 0-1 | | 7 | 28 |
| 9 | BSS | H | Havant & Waterlooville | 483 | D 1-1 | Inman 5 | 7 | 29 |
| 16 | BSS | H | Hayes & Yeading | 519 | W 4-1 | Huggins 9 Bennett 26 Connolly 45 81 | 8 | 30 |
| 19 | BSS | A | Welling United | 457 | L 0-2 | | 9 | 31 |
| 23 | BSS | H | Eastbourne Borough | 368 | L 0-1 | | 10 | 32 |
| Mar 2 | BSS | H | AFC Hornchurch | 386 | D 1-1 | Peniket 79 | 10 | 33 |
| 5 | BSS | A | Billericay Town | 229 | L 1-2 | Peniket50 | 11 | 34 |
| 9 | BSS | A | Eastbourne Borough | 502 | W 1-0 | Ball 15 | 10 | 35 |
| 16 | BSS | A | Sutton United | 840 | W 1-0 | Tarpey 53 | 8 | 36 |
| 18 | BSS | A | Chelmsford CIty | 474 | L 0-6 | | 8 | 37 |
| 26 | BSS | A | Dover Athletic | 244 | L 0-2 | | 10 | 38 |
| 30 | BSS | A | Weston-s-Mare | 635 | D 1-1 | Peniket 63 | 11 | 39 |
| Apr 1 | BSS | H | Maidenhead United | 368 | W 2-1 | Peniket 16 Ciardini 87 | 9 | 40 |
| 6 | BSS | H | Staines Town | 410 | W 2-1 | Peniket 27 Hammond 53 | 9 | 41 |
| 13 | BSS | H | Sutton United | 460 | L 1-3 | Page 53 | 11 | 42 |
| 20 | BSS | A | Truro City | 364 | D 3-3 | Hammond 31 Peniket 39 McGarry 83 | 12 | 43 |
| 23 | BSS | H | Billericay Town | 297 | W 4-3 | McGarry 13 Page 9 56 Bennet 60 | 11 | 44 |
| 27 | BSS | H | Chelmsford City | 621 | W 3-1 | Bennett 46 Laidler 84 Huggins 90 | 13 | 45 |

| GOALSCORERS | Lge | FAC | FAT | Total | Pens | Hat-tricks | Cons Run | | Lge | FAC | FAT | Total | Pens | Hat-tricks | Cons Run |
|-------------|-----|-----|-----|-------|------|------------|----------|--|-----|-----|-----|-------|------|------------|----------|
| Connolly | 17 | 1 | | 18 | | | 4 | McGarry | 2 | | | 2 | | | |
| Bennett | 12 | 1 | | 12 | | | 3 | Ball | 1 | | | 1 | | | |
| Tarpey | 9 | 1 | | 10 | | | 2 | Day | 1 | | | 1 | | | |
| Ciardini | 9 | | | 9 | 1 | | | Laidlaw | 1 | | | 1 | | | |
| Peniket | 6 | | | 6 | | | | Makofo | 1 | | | 1 | | | |
| Hammond | 3 | 1 | | 4 | | | | Own Goal | 1 | | | 1 | | | |
| Huggins | 4 | | | 4 | | | | Cons Run - Consecutive scoring games. | | | | | | | |
| Page | 5 | | | 3 | 1 | | | | | | | | | | |
| Inman | 2 | | | 2 | | | | | | | | | | | |
| Inns | 2 | | | 2 | | | | | | | | | | | |

# GOSPORT BOROUGH

**Chairman:** Mark Hook
**Secretary:** Brian Cosgrave **(T)** 07984 960 537 **(E)** brian.cosgrave@hotmail.co.uk
**Commercial Manager:** Antony Sheehan **(T)** 07847 208 162
**Programme Editor:** Jeremy Fox **(T)** 07877 486 467
**Ground Address:** Privett Park, Privett Road, Gosport, Hampshire PO12 0SX
**(T)** 023 9250 1042 (Match days only) **Manager:** Alex Pike

## Club Factfile

**Founded:** 1944 **Nickname:** The 'Boro'
**Previous Names:** Gosport Borough Athletic
**Previous Leagues:** Portsmouth 1944-45, Hampshire 1945-78, Southern 1978-92, Wessex 1992-2007

**Club Colours (change):** Yellow/navy/navy (Navy/yellow/yellow)

**Ground Capacity:** 4,500 **Seats:** 450 **Covered:** 600 **Clubhouse:** Yes **Shop:** Yes

**Directions**
Exit M27 at J11. Take A32 Fareham to Gosport road.
After 3 miles take the 3rd exit at Brockhurst r/a, into Military Road.
At next r/a take 1st exit into Privett Road. Ground is approx. 400 yards on left.

**Previous Grounds:** None

**Record Attendance:** 4,770 v Pegasus - FA Amateur Cup 1951
**Record Victory:** 14-0 v Cunliffe Owen - Hampshire League 1945-46
**Record Defeat:** 0-9 v Gloucester City - Southern Premier Division 1989-90 and v Lymington & N.M. - Wessex Lge 99-2000
**Record Goalscorer:** Ritchie Coulbert - 192
**Record Appearances:** Tony Mahoney - 765
**Additional Records:**

**Senior Honours:**
Hampshire League 1945-46, 76-77, 77-78. Hampshire Senior Cup 1987-88. Wessex League Cup 1992-93.
Wessex League 2006-07. Southern Division 1 South & West Play-offs 2011-12, Premier Division Play-offs 2012-13.

### 10 YEAR RECORD

| 03-04 | | 04-05 | | 05-06 | | 06-07 | | 07-08 | | 08-09 | | 09-10 | | 10-11 | | 11-12 | | 12-13 | |
|---|---|---|---|---|---|---|---|---|---|---|---|---|---|---|---|---|---|---|---|
| Wex | 3 | Wex1 | 4 | Wex1 | 5 | WexP | 1 | Sthsw | 11 | Sthsw | 12 | Sthsw | 8 | Sthsw | 13 | Sthsw | 3 | SthP | 5 |

# MATCH RESULTS 2012-13

| Date | Comp | H/A | Opponents | Att: | Result | Goalscorers | Pos | No. |
|------|------|-----|-----------|------|--------|-------------|-----|-----|
| Aug 18 | SPL | H | Barwell | 327 | L 1-2 | Wilde 54 (pen) | 17 | 1 |
| 21 | SPL | A | Bideford | 297 | W 2-0 | Brown 20 Bennett 90 | 10 | 2 |
| 25 | SPL | H | Redditch United | 336 | L 2-3 | Holland 3 King 38 | 15 | 3 |
| 27 | SPL | H | Bashley | 307 | D 0-0 | | 15 | 4 |
| Sept 1 | SPL | A | Arlesey Town | 121 | D 1-1 | Cook 80 | 15 | 5 |
| 4 | SPL | A | Chippenham Town | 260 | L 2-3 | Bennett 11 Woodward 57 | 17 | 6 |
| 8 | FAC Q1 | A | Bashley | 205 | D 1-1 | Middleton 90 (og) | | 7 |
| 11 | FAC Q1r | H | Bashley | 182 | W 3-2 | Molineux 47 60 Woodward 105 | | 8 |
| 15 | SPL | A | Chesham United | 270 | W 3-0 | Bennett 63 83 Woodward 78 | 11 | 9 |
| 18 | SPL | H | St Albans City | 242 | L 0-1 | | 15 | 10 |
| 22 | FAC Q2 | H | Bideford | 232 | W 2-0 | Poate 25 King 38 | | 11 |
| 29 | FAT Q1 | A | Slough Town | 190 | W 4-0 | BENNETT 3 (15 64 85) Molineux 48 | | 12 |
| Oct 2 | SPL | A | Weymouth | 413 | D 3-3 | Dunford 26 Smith 65 Bennett 75 | 13 | 13 |
| 6 | FAC Q3 | A | Bath City | 586 | D 1-1 | Wooden 78 | | 14 |
| 9 | FAC Q3r | H | Bath City | 324 | W 3-1 | Bennett 53 Martin 60 Wooden 64 | | 15 |
| 13 | SPL | H | Cambridge City | 340 | L 1-2 | Wooden 53 | 19 | 16 |
| 21 | FAC Q4 | A | Slough Town | 523 | D 0-0 | | | 17 |
| 23 | FAC Q4r | H | Slough Town | 635 | L 1-2 | Brown 30 | | 18 |
| 27 | FAT Q2 | A | AFC Totton | 349 | L 2-3 | Dunford 54 Wilde 72 | | 19 |
| Nov 3 | SPL | H | Bedford Town | 219 | L 0-1 | | 21 | 20 |
| 10 | SPL | H | Hemel Hempstead Town | 298 | D 3-3 | Wilde 67 Bennett 81 Pearce 90 | 21 | 21 |
| 13 | SPL | H | Banbury United | 303 | W 3-2 | Bennett 45 Smith 68 Igoe 90 | 20 | 22 |
| 17 | SPL | A | Bedworth United | 130 | D 1-1 | Bennett 23 | | 23 |
| 14 | SPL | A | Stourbridge | 251 | D 1-1 | Bennett 11 | 19 | 24 |
| Dec 1 | SPL | H | Hitchin Town | 299 | D 0-0 | | 20 | 25 |
| 8 | SPL | A | St Neots Town | 280 | W 3-2 | Dunford 2 Wooden 19 Wilde 34 (Pen) | 16 | 26 |
| 15 | SPL | H | Kettering Town | 283 | W 7-0 | Dunford 29 BENNETT 3 (45 48 59) Wooden 47 Wilson 73 Norton 79 | 15 | 27 |
| 18 | SPL | A | Leamington | 351 | W 3-1 | Igoe 17 Bennett 22 90 | 10 | 28 |
| 26 | SPL | H | AFC Totton | 372 | W 1-0 | Bennett 19 | 10 | 29 |
| Jan 1 | SPL | A | Bashley | 190 | D 1-1 | Bennett 83 | 10 | 30 |
| 5 | SPL | H | Bideford | 279 | W 2-0 | Wilde 33 41 | 8 | 31 |
| 12 | SPL | A | Chippenham Town | 371 | D 0-0 | | 9 | 32 |
| 15 | SPL | H | Frome Town | 179 | D 0-0 | | 9 | 33 |
| 26 | SPL | H | Chesham United | 320 | W 3-1 | Brown 18 Molineux 45 Williams 62 | 6 | 34 |
| Feb 2 | SPL | H | Weymouth | 401 | D 0-0 | | 6 | 35 |
| 5 | SPL | A | Barwell | 84 | W 2-1 | Woodward 48 Smith 72 | 6 | 36 |
| 9 | SPL | A | Banbury United | 223 | W 4-2 | WILLIAMS 3 ( 27pen 48 53) Cook 32 | 6 | 37 |
| 16 | SPL | H | Bedworth United | 374 | W 1-0 | Williams | 6 | 38 |
| 23 | SPL | A | Hemel Hempstead Town | 280 | D 1-1 | Wooden 23 | 6 | 39 |
| 26 | SPL | A | St Albans City | 205 | W 6-1 | Woodward 1 5 Wooden 12 Cook 22 Williams 45 Wilde 87 | 5 | 40 |
| Mar 2 | SPL | H | Leamington | 586 | W 3-0 | Wooden 34 Williams 65 Brown 80 | 5 | 41 |
| 9 | SPL | H | Cambridge City | 228 | W 4-0 | Williams 20 62 Dunford 35 Wilde 84 | 5 | 42 |
| 19 | SPL | A | Redditch United | 101 | W 2-0 | Williams 24 Wooden 70 | 4 | 43 |
| 30 | SPL | H | Arlesey Town | 459 | L 0-1 | | 5 | 44 |
| Apr 1 | SPL | H | Gosport Borough | 426 | L 2-3 | Wooden 49 Williams 84 | 5 | 45 |
| 6 | SPL | A | Hitchin Town | 256 | L 0--1 | | 6 | 46 |
| 9 | SPL | H | Bedford Town | 306 | W 4-0 | Wooden 11 Williams 42 Brown 62 Smith 90 | 6 | 47 |
| 13 | SPL | H | Stourbridge | 403 | L 1-3 | Wooden 83 | 6 | 48 |
| 20 | SPL | A | Kettering Town | 568 | W 3-1 | Wooden 19 Williams 59 Igoe 83 | 6 | 49 |
| 23 | SPL | A | Frome Town | 165 | D 1-1 | Williams 6 | 6 | 50 |
| 27 | SPL | H | St Neots Town | 511 | W 1-0 | Williams 42 | 5 | 51 |
| 30 | P-Off S-F | A | Stourport | 993 | W 2-1 | Williams 57 Wooden 61 | | 52 |
| May 6 | P-Off Final | A | Hemel Hempstead Town | 2254 | D 2-2 | King 2 Wilde 35 *aet W 5-4 pens | | 53 |

| GOALSCORERS | Lge | FAC | FAT | Total | Pens | Hat-tricks | Cons Run | | Lge | FAC | FAT | Total | Pens | Hat-tricks | Cons Run |
|-------------|-----|-----|-----|-------|------|-----------|----------|---|-----|-----|-----|-------|------|-----------|----------|
| Bennett | 16 | 1 | 3 | 20 | | 2 | 4 | Igoe | 3 | | | 3 | | | |
| Williams | 16 | | | 16 | 1 | | 4 | King | 2 | 1 | | 2 | | | |
| Wooden | 13 | 2 | | 15 | | | 3 | Holland | 1 | | | 1 | | | |
| Wilde | 9 | | 1 | 10 | 2 | | 2 | Norton | 1 | | | 1 | | | |
| Dunford | 4 | | 1 | 5 | | | | Poate | | 1 | | 1 | | | |
| Woodward | 5 | 1 | | 5 | | | 2 | Pearce | 1 | | | 1 | | | |
| Brown | 3 | 1 | | 4 | | | | Wilson | 1 | | | 1 | | | |
| Molineux | 1 | 2 | 1 | 4 | | | | Martin | | 1 | | 1 | | | |
| Smith | 4 | | | 4 | | | | Own Goals | | 1 | | 1 | | | |
| Cook | 3 | | | 3 | | | | Cons Run - Consecutive scoring games. | | | | | | | |

# HAVANT AND WATERLOOVILLE

**Chairman:** Derek Pope

**Secretary:** Trevor Brock    **(T)** 07768 271 143    **(E)** trevor.brock52@yahoo.com

**Commercial Manager:** Adrian Aymes    **(T)** 07814 150 032

**Programme Editor:** Adrian Aymes    **(T)** aaymes2125@aol.com

**Ground Address:** Westleigh Park, Martin Road, West Leigh, Havant PO7 8EJ

**(T)** 02392 787 822      **Manager:** Lee Bradbury

## Club Factfile

**Founded:** 1998    **Nickname:** Hawks

**Previous Names:** Havant Town and Waterlooville merged in 1998

**Previous Leagues:** Southern 1998-2004

**Club Colours (change):** White/navy/white (All red)

**Ground Capacity:** 4,800   **Seats:** 562   **Covered:** 3,500   **Clubhouse:** Yes   **Shop:** Yes

**Directions:** Ground is a mile and a half from Havant Town Centre. Take A27 to Havant then turn onto B2149 (Petersfield Road). Turn right at next junction after HERON pub into Bartons Road then take first right into Martin Road.

**Previous Grounds:** None

**Record Attendance:** 4,400 v Swansea City - FA Cup 3rd Round 05/01/2008

**Record Victory:** 9-0 v Moneyfields - Hampshire Senior Cup 23/10/2001

**Record Defeat:** 0-5 v Worcester City - Southern Premier 20/03/2004

**Record Goalscorer:** James Taylor - 138

**Record Appearances:** James Taylor - 297

**Additional Records:** Paid £5,000 to Bashley for John Wilson

**Senior Honours:** Received £15,000 from Peterborough United for Gary McDonald

Southern League Southern Division 1998-99. Russell Cotes Cup 2003-04

### 10 YEAR RECORD

| 03-04 | | 04-05 | | 05-06 | | 06-07 | | 07-08 | | 08-09 | | 09-10 | | 10-11 | | 11-12 | | 12-13 | |
|---|---|---|---|---|---|---|---|---|---|---|---|---|---|---|---|---|---|---|---|
| SthP | 12 | Conf S | 13 | Conf S | 6 | Conf | 4 | Conf S | 7 | Conf S | 15 | Conf S | 6 | Conf S | 9 | Conf S | 19 | Conf S | 10 |

**CONFERENCE SOUTH ACTION:** Mott (Welling) keeper and Michael Malcolm (Bromley) miss the ball whilst Fraser Franks (Welling) bring's it under control. Photo: Keith Clayton.

# MATCH RESULTS 2012-13

| Date | Comp | H/A | Opponents | Att: | Result | Goalscorers | Pos | No. |
|---|---|---|---|---|---|---|---|---|
| Aug 17 | BSS | H | Chelmsford City | 273 | D 1-1 | Palmer 90 | 11 | 1 |
| 21 | BSS | A | Truro City | 390 | D 3-3 | Palmer 63 91 Nanetti 71 | 14 | 2 |
| 25 | BSS | A | Bath City | 535 | L 0-2 | | 18 | 3 |
| 27 | BSS | H | Eastleigh | 903 | L 0-3 | | 21 | 4 |
| Sept 1 | BSS | A | Staines Town | 329 | D 1-1 | Palmer 33 | 20 | 5 |
| 4 | BSS | H | Hayes & Yeading | 475 | W 2-1 | Dawson 50 Ramsey 67 | 16 | 6 |
| 8 | BSS | H | Tonbridge Angels | 805 | D 2-2 | Harris 28 Palmer 65 | 15 | 7 |
| 15 | BSS | A | Sutton United | 826 | D 1-1 | Downer 41 (og) | 18 | 8 |
| 22 | FAC Q2 | A | North Leigh | 194 | L 0-1 | | | 9 |
| 25 | BSS | H | Weston-s -Mare | 460 | L 0-3 | | 20 | 10 |
| 29 | BSS | A | Bromley | 582 | D 1-1 | Jones 82 | 20 | 11 |
| Oct 6 | BSS | A | AFC Hornchurch | 215 | D 2-2 | Palmer 59 64 | 21 | 12 |
| 13 | BSS | A | Basingstoke Town | 410 | W 2-1 | Taggert 51 Palmer 78 | 19 | 13 |
| 20 | BSS | H | Farnborough | 755 | L 0-1 | | 21 | 14 |
| 27 | BSS | A | Billericay Town | 401 | L 1-3 | Taggert 62 | 21 | 15 |
| Nov 3 | BSS | H | Welling United | 568 | L 0-1 | | 21 | 16 |
| 10 | FAT Q3 | A | Bognor Regis Town | 702 | W 4-1 | Ramsey 3 (pen) T.Taggart 24 81 Jones 90 | | 17 |
| 13 | BSS | H | Dorchester Town | 526 | W 4-0 | Ramsey 11 (Pen) Palmer 26 Taggert 64 Harris 76 | 19 | 18 |
| 17 | BSS | A | Weston-s-Mare | 267 | D 2-2 | Moss 51 80 | 17 | 19 |
| Dec 1 | BSS | H | Bromley | 748 | L 1-2 | Palmer 24 | 20 | 20 |
| 4 | FAT 1 | A | Braintree Town | 192 | W 2-1 | Nanetti (pen) Bailey | | 21 |
| 8 | BSS | H | Staines Town | 661 | W 3-1 | Kabba 21 Palmer 28 Jones 79 | 17 | 22 |
| 15 | FAT 2 | A | Grimsby Town | 1215 | L 0-4 | | | 23 |
| 26 | BSS | A | Eastbourne Borough | 582 | W 1-0 | Nanetti 58 (pen) | 17 | 24 |
| Jan 1 | BSS | H | Eastbourne Borough | 727 | L 2-3 | Kabba 88 Strugnell 90 | 17 | 25 |
| 5 | BSS | H | AFC Hornchurch | 641 | W 5-2 | Strugnell 16 Kabba 29 PALMER 3 ( 46 83 90) | 12 | 26 |
| 8 | BSS | A | Tonbridge Angels | 397 | L 0-1 | | 16 | 27 |
| 26 | BSS | A | Dorchester Town | 455 | D 0-0 | | 17 | 28 |
| Feb 2 | BSS | H | Basingstoke Town | 635 | W 4-1 | Kabba 18 90 Palmer 21 Arthur 34 | 12 | 29 |
| 9 | BSS | A | Farnborough | 483 | D 1-1 | Strugnell 60 | 14 | 30 |
| 16 | BSS | A | Welling United | 609 | L 0-1 | | 18 | 31 |
| 18 | BSS | A | Chelmsford City | 732 | D 1-1 | Ryan 65 (pen) | 19 | 32 |
| 23 | BSS | H | Salisbury City | 837 | D 2-2 | Ryan 63 71 | 19 | 33 |
| 26 | BSS | A | Eastleigh | 579 | D 2-2 | Kabba 49 Nanetti 59 (pen) | 17 | 34 |
| Mar 2 | BSS | H | Sutton United | 683 | W 3-0 | Palmer 39 57 Bossman 86 | 15 | 35 |
| 5 | BSS | H | Bath City | 406 | W 2-1 | Palmer 56 Harris 70 | 11 | 36 |
| 9 | BSS | A | Dover Athletic | 821 | D 2-2 | Kabba 59 Nanetti 74 | 12 | 37 |
| 12 | BSS | H | Billericay Town | 355 | W 5-0 | Nanetti 10 (pen) Palmer 25 33 Kabba 52 73 | 10 | 38 |
| 26 | BSS | H | Maidenhead United | 308 | W 2-1 | Arthur 8 Ramsey 41 | 9 | 39 |
| 29 | BSS | H | Truro City | 715 | W 1-0 | Palmer 46 | 8 | 40 |
| Apr 1 | BSS | A | Hayes & Yeading | 167 | W 4-1 | Ramsey 29 PALMER 3 ( 63 76 90) | 8 | 41 |
| 6 | BSS | A | Maidenhead United | 282 | L 0-2 | | 8 | 42 |
| 9 | BSS | A | Boreham Wood | 164 | W 2-1 | Hutchinson 2 Gotta 89 | 8 | 43 |
| 16 | BSS | H | Dover Athletic | 594 | D 1-1 | Grant 38 | 10 | 44 |
| 20 | BSS | A | Salisbury City | 771 | L 1-5 | Ryan 57 | 10 | 45 |
| 27 | BSS | H | Boreham Wood | 828 | D 1-1 | Kabba 46 | 10 | 46 |

| GOALSCORERS | Lge | FAC | FAT | Total | Pens | Hat-tricks | Cons Run | | Lge | FAC | FAT | Total | Pens | Hat-tricks | Cons Run |
|---|---|---|---|---|---|---|---|---|---|---|---|---|---|---|---|
| Palmer | 24 | | | 24 | 2 | | 2 | Moss | 2 | | | 2 | | | |
| Kabba | 10 | | | 10 | | | 2 | Bailey | | | 1 | 1 | | | |
| Nanetti | 5 | 1 | | 6 | 5 | | | Bossman | 1 | | | 1 | | | |
| Ramsey | 4 | | 1 | 5 | 2 | | | Dawson | 1 | | | 1 | | | |
| Taggart | 3 | | 2 | 5 | | | | Gotta | 1 | | | 1 | | | |
| Ryan | 4 | | | 4 | 1 | | | Grant | 1 | | | 1 | | | |
| Harris | 3 | | | 3 | | | | Hutchinson | 1 | | | 1 | | | |
| Lones | 2 | 1 | | 3 | | | | Own Goal | 1 | | | | | | |
| Strugnell | 3 | | | 3 | | | | Cons Run - Consecutive scoring games. | | | | | | | |
| Arthur | 2 | | | 2 | | | | | | | | | | | |

# HAYES & YEADING

**Chairman:** Tony O'Driscoll
**Secretary:** Bill Gritt     **(T)** 07710 102 004     **(E)** secretary@hyufc.com
**Commercial Manager:** Bill Perryman     **(T)** 07780 870 920
**Programme Editor:** Andy Corbett     **(T)** 07540 940 169
**Ground Address:** The Sharda Glass Community Stadium, Beaconsfield Road, Hayes UB4 0SL
**(T)** 0208 573 2075          **Manager:** Phil Babb

The new Sharda Glass Community Stadium under construction. The club hope to move in
early in the 2013-14 campaign. Photo courtesy: www.hyufc.com

## Club Factfile

**Founded:** 2007     **Nickname:**
**Previous Names:** Hayes - Botwell Mission 1909-29. Hayes and Yeading merged to form today's club in 2007
**Previous Leagues:** Isthmian

**Club Colours (change):** Red/black/black & white (Blue/blue/black & white)

**Ground Capacity:** 6,000    **Seats:** 2,500    **Covered:** 3,900    **Clubhouse:** Yes    **Shop:** Yes

**Directions:** From the M40/A40(M) Head eastbound towards London, take the Target Roundabout exit signposted Northolt, Harrow & Hayes. At the top of the slip road take the fourth exit (the first after the exit towards London) onto the A312 towards Hayes. The next roundabout (The White Hart) is about is about 1 mile and a half on. Here ignore signs to Yeading (third exit) instead take the second exit towards Hayes & Heathrow to stay on the A312 (Hayes-By - Pass). At the next roundabout again ignore signs to Yeading and carry straight over. Take the next exit signposted Southall and Uxbridge (A4020 Uxbridge Road). At the top of the slip road take the first exit towards Southall and follow the directions below Head eastbound along the (A4020) Uxbridge Road. Head eastbound along the (A4020) Uxbridge Road signposted towards Southall. Get into the far right hand lane as soon as you can and turn right into Springfield Road at the next set of Traffic Lights (There is a petrol station and a retail development with a Wickes on the corner of Springfield Road). Follow the road to the School, the Road bears left into Beaconsfield Road, and about 100 yards on your right is the entrance to the ground. **NB: First team home fixtures will initially be played at Woking's Kingfield Stadium. (see Woking FC).**
**Previous Grounds:** Kingfield Stadium (Woking FC) 2012-13.

**Record Attendance:** 1,881 v Luton Town - Conference Premier 06/03/2010
**Record Victory:** 8-2 v Hillingdon Borough (A) - Middlesex Senior Cup 11/11/08
**Record Defeat:** 0-8 v Luton Town (A) - Conference Premier 27/03/10
**Record Goalscorer:** Josh Scott - 40 (2007-09)
**Record Appearances:** James Mulley - 137 (2007-10)
**Additional Records:**

**Senior Honours:**
Conference South Play-offs 2008-09

### 10 YEAR RECORD

| 03-04 | 04-05 | 05-06 | 06-07 | 07-08 | 08-09 | 09-10 | 10-11 | 11-12 | 12-13 |
|---|---|---|---|---|---|---|---|---|---|
| | | | | Conf S 13 | Conf S 4 | Conf 17 | Conf 16 | Conf 21 | Conf S 17 |

# MATCH RESULTS 2012-13

| Date | Comp | H/A | Opponents | Att: | Result | Goalscorers | Pos | No. |
|------|------|-----|-----------|------|--------|-------------|-----|-----|
| Aug 18 | BSS | A | Weston-super Mare | 550 | D 1-1 | Oyenuga 38 | 12 | 1 |
| 21 | BSS | H | Billericay Town | 267 | W 4-2 | Oyenuga 28 40 Joseph 50 Anderson 83 | 3 | 2 |
| 25 | BSS | H | Boreham Wood | 137 | L 0-1 | | 8 | 3 |
| 27 | BSS | A | Basingstoke Town | 406 | D 2-2 | Cox 90 Wishart 90 | 9 | 4 |
| Sept 1 | BSS | H | Welling United | 194 | W 2-1 | Anderson 8 Oyenuga 46 | 6 | 5 |
| 4 | BSS | A | Havant & Waterlooville | 475 | L 1-2 | Anderson 11 | 7 | 6 |
| 8 | BSS | A | Dover Athletic | 726 | W 1-0 | Joseph 70 | 6 | 7 |
| 15 | BSS | H | Salisbury City | 293 | L 2-3 | Williams 37 Oyenuga 90 (pen) | 9 | 8 |
| 23 | FAC Q2 | H | Heybridge Swifts | 139 | W 3-2 | Oyenuga 47 (pen) Anderson 82 | | 9 |
| 29 | BSS | A | Eastleigh | 577 | L 1-3 | Joseph 84 | 15 | 10 |
| Oct 2 | BSS | H | Staines Town | 181 | W 4-0 | Oyenuga 13 Anderson 30 Williams 72 81 | 8 | 11 |
| 6 | FAC Q3 | H | Salisbury City | 210 | W 2-1 | Butcher 44 Williams 90 | | 12 |
| 13 | BSS | A | Bath City | 720 | W 3-2 | Williams 7 Anderson 35 Oyenuga 90 (pen) | 6 | 13 |
| 20 | FAC Q4 | H | Boreham Wood | 350 | L 2-3 | Anderson 1 Wright 5 | | 14 |
| 27 | BSS | H | Farnborough | 318 | W 3-2 | Wishart 42 N'Diaye 62 Williams 86 | 5 | 15 |
| 30 | BSS | A | Salisbury City | 791 | L 0-2 | | 6 | 16 |
| Nov 10 | FAT Q3 | A | Eastleigh | 231 | W 4-1 | Goddard 28 Anderson 35 Joseph 50 Wishart 81 | | 17 |
| 17 | BSS | A | Tonbridge Angels | 624 | D 1-1 | Bentley 61 | 10 | 18 |
| 20 | BSS | H | Chelmsford City | 224 | W 3-0 | Wishart 21 Oyenuga 39 (Pen) Moutaouakil 69 | 6 | 19 |
| 24 | FAT 1 | A | Corby Town | 322 | L 2-3 | Bentley 32 Williams 44 | | 20 |
| Dec 1 | BSS | H | AFC Hornchurch | 141 | L 1-3 | Joseph 59 | 7 | 21 |
| 8 | BSS | A | Welling United | 467 | L 0-3 | | 9 | 22 |
| 16 | BSS | H | Dover Athletic | 284 | L 2-4 | Cadmore 30 N'Diaye 77 | 9 | 23 |
| 26 | BSS | H | Maidenhead United | 123 | D 1-1 | Oyenuga 13 (pen) | 8 | 24 |
| Jan 1 | BSS | A | Maidenhead United | 404 | W 2-0 | Ekim 8 Lowe 90 | 8 | 25 |
| 5 | BSS | A | Dorchester Town | 403 | D 2-2 | Lowe 80 90 | 8 | 26 |
| 12 | BSS | H | Weston -s-Mare | 120 | W 2-1 | Bygrave 7 Cadmore 15 | 8 | 27 |
| 26 | BSS | H | Bath City | 177 | D 2-2 | N'Diaye 60 Bygrave 89 | 8 | 28 |
| 28 | BSS | A | Boreham Wood | 203 | L 0-3 | | 8 | 29 |
| Feb 2 | BSS | A | Chelmsford City | 747 | L 2-6 | Hand 31 (pen) Oyenuga 89 | 8 | 30 |
| 9 | BSS | H | Truro City | 495 | L 1-2 | Collins 19 | 9 | 31 |
| 12 | BSS | H | Basingstoke Town | 149 | W 2-1 | N'Diaye 54 Collins 81 | 9 | 32 |
| 16 | BSS | A | Farnborough | 519 | L 1-4 | Collins 14 | 9 | 33 |
| 19 | BSS | H | Bromley | 122 | D 1-1 | Collins 41 | 12 | 34 |
| 23 | BSS | H | Eastleigh | 159 | W 2-1 | N'Diaye 57 Cox 59 | 9 | 35 |
| Mar 2 | BSS | A | Truro City | 378 | L 1-3 | Kendall 66 (og) | 11 | 36 |
| 9 | BSS | H | Sutton United | 233 | D 0-0 | | 13 | 37 |
| 19 | BSS | A | Eastbourne Borough | 379 | L 1-2 | Oyenuga 81 | | 38 |
| 30 | BSS | A | Billericay Town | 424 | L 1-4 | Butcher 75 | 16 | 39 |
| Apr 1 | BSS | H | Havant & Waterlooville | 167 | L 1-4 | Williams 73 | 19 | 40 |
| 4 | BSS | A | Staines Town | 247 | L 1-7 | Williams 7 | 19 | 41 |
| 8 | BSS | H | Tonbridge Angels | 235 | W 3-2 | Corcoran 66 Collins 70 Oyenuga 84 | 15 | 42 |
| 13 | BSS | A | Bromley | 433 | W 4-0 | Cox 11 Wishart 12 Oyenuga 14 Corcoran 64 | 14 | 43 |
| 17 | BSS | A | Sutton United | 416 | L 1-5 | Oyenuga 14 | 14 | 44 |
| 20 | BSS | H | Eastbourne Borough | 197 | D 1-1 | Oyenuga 20 | 14 | 45 |
| 23 | BSS | H | Dorchester Town | 168 | L 1-3 | Collins 14 | 16 | 46 |
| 27 | BSS | A | AFC Hornchurch | 281 | L 0-2 | | 17 | 47 |

| GOALSCORERS | Lge | FAC | FAT | Total | Pens | Hat-tricks | Cons Run | | Lge | FAC | FAT | Total | Pens | Hat-tricks | Cons Run |
|-------------|-----|-----|-----|-------|------|-----------|----------|---|-----|-----|-----|-------|------|-----------|----------|
| Oyenuga | 15 | 2 | | 17 | 5 | | 4 | Bygrave | 2 | | | 2 | | | |
| Williams | 7 | 1 | 1 | 9 | | | | Cadmore | 2 | | | 2 | | | |
| Anderson | 5 | 2 | 1 | 8 | | | | Corcoran | 2 | | | 2 | | | |
| Collins | 5 | | | 5 | | | | Ekim | 1 | | | 1 | | | |
| Joseph | 4 | | 1 | 5 | | | | Goddard | | | 1 | 1 | | | |
| Wishart | 4 | | 1 | 5 | | | | Hand | 1 | | | 1 | 1 | | |
| Cox | 3 | | | 3 | | | | Moutaouakil | 1 | | | 1 | | | |
| Lowe | 3 | | | 3 | | | | Wright (18) | | 1 | | 1 | | | |
| Bentley | 1 | | 1 | 2 | | | | Own Goals | 1 | | | 2 | | | |
| Butcher | 1 | 1 | | 2 | | | | Cons Run - Consecutive scoring games. | | | | | | | |

# MAIDENHEAD UNITED

**Chairman:** Peter Griffin
**Secretary:** Ken Chandler     **(T)** 07863 183 872     **(E)** kenneth.chandler@btinternet.com
**Commercial Manager:** tbc     **(T)**
**Programme Editor:** Mark Roach     **(T)** markroachonline@yahoo.co.uk
**Ground Address:** York Road, Maidenhead, Berkshire SL6 1SF
**(T)** 01628 636 314     **Manager:** Johnson Hippolyte

2012-13 Squad - Back row, left to right: Aryan Tajbakhsh, Devante McKain, Leon Solomon, Alec Wall, Marcus Rose, Leigh Henry.
Middle row, left to right: Jon Urry, Max Bangura, Ashley Watson, Joe Crook, James Regis, Jonathan Hippolyte, Alex Tokarczyk,
Billy Lumley, Michael Pearce, Harry Pritchard, Jamie Connor Martel Powell, Paul Semakula, Stefan Powell, Jordan Chandler.
Front row, left to right: Michael Pook, David Pratt, Lee Barney, Mark Nisbet, Simon Lane, Johnson Hippolyte, Dereck Brown,
Bobby Behzadi, Reece Tison-Lascaris Derek Duncan, Daniel Brown.
Photo: Stefan Baisden.

## Club Factfile

**Founded:** 1870     **Nickname:** Magpies
**Previous Names:** Maidenhead F.C and Maidenhead Norfolkians merged to form today's club
**Previous Leagues:** Southern 1894-1902, 2006-07, West Berkshire 1902-04, Gr. West Suburban 1904-22, Spartan 1922-39,
Gr. West Comb. 1939-45, Corinthian 1945-63, Athenian 1963-73, Isthmian 1973-2004, Conf. 2004-06

**Club Colours (change):** Black & white stripes/black/white (Yellow/blue/yellow)

**Ground Capacity:** 4,500     **Seats:** 400     **Covered:** 2,000     **Clubhouse:** Yes     **Shop:** Yes

**Directions**
The Ground is in the town centre.
200 yards from the station and two minutes walk from the High Street.
Access from M4 Junctions 7 or 8/9.

**Previous Grounds:** Kidwells Park (Norfolkians)

**Record Attendance:** 7,920 v Southall - FA Amateur Cup Quarter final 07/03/1936
**Record Victory:** 14-1 v Buckingham Town - FA Amateur Cup 06/09/1952
**Record Defeat:** 0-14 v Chesham United (A) - Spartan League 31/03/1923
**Record Goalscorer:** George Copas - 270 (1924-35)
**Record Appearances:** Bert Randall - 532 (1950-64)
**Additional Records:** Received £5,000 from Norwich City for Alan Cordice 1979

**Senior Honours:**
Corinthian League 1957-58, 60-61, 61-62.
Berks & Bucks Senior Cup x19.

### 10 YEAR RECORD

| 03-04 | 04-05 | 05-06 | 06-07 | 07-08 | 08-09 | 09-10 | 10-11 | 11-12 | 12-13 |
|---|---|---|---|---|---|---|---|---|---|
| Isth P   12 | Conf S   20 | Conf S   22 | SthP   4 | Conf S   17 | Conf S   6 | Conf S   16 | Conf S   19 | Conf S   20 | Conf S   19 |

# MATCH RESULTS 2012-13

| Date | Comp | H/A | Opponents | Att: | Result | Goalscorers | Pos | No. |
|------|------|-----|-----------|------|--------|-------------|-----|-----|
| Aug 18 | BSS | H | Tonbridge Angels | 550 | W 3-1 | Semakula 38 Behzadi 64 (pen) Pratt 90 | 12 | 1 |
| 21 | BSS | A | Bath City | 587 | L 1-3 | Brown 73 | 10 | 2 |
| 2 | BSS | A | Sutton United | 454 | D 1-1 | Pritchard 27 | 12 | 3 |
| 27 | BSS | H | Staines Town | 386 | D 1-1 | Pratt 38 | 14 | 4 |
| Sept 1 | BSS | A | Eastbourne Borough | 627 | W 2-0 | Pratt 12 30 | 7 | 5 |
| 4 | BSS | H | Farnborough | 359 | W 3-2 | Tilson-Lascaris 3 Pratt 48 Behzadi 67 (pen) | 5 | 6 |
| 8 | BSS | H | Truro City | 274 | W 8-0 | TILSON-LASCARIS 3 (38 48 57) Wall 64 87 | 3 | |
| | | | | | | Semakula 67 Behzadi75 Barney 90 | | 7 |
| 15 | BSS | A | Eastleigh | 506 | L 2-4 | Soloman 19 Tilson-Lascaris 66 | 8 | 8 |
| 22 | FAC Q2 | H | **Bognor Regis Town** | **316** | **W 4-2** | **Pratt 10 23 Soloman 60 Behzadi 88 (pen)** | | 9 |
| 29 | BSS | A | Dover Athletic | 721 | L 0-2 | | 7 | 10 |
| Oct 2 | BSS | H | AFC Hornchurch | 245 | L 2-4 | Pritchard 53 Wall 73 | 7 | 11 |
| 6 | FAC Q3 | A | **Didcot Town** | **301** | **L 0-1** | | | 12 |
| 13 | BSS | H | Weston-s-Mare | 372 | L 0-1 | | 12 | 13 |
| 27 | BSS | H | Welling United | 302 | W 2-1 | Nisbet 59 79 | 11 | 14 |
| 30 | BSS | A | Bromley | 333 | L 2-3 | Semakula 71 Flood 74 | 12 | 15 |
| Nov 3 | BSS | A | Salisbury City | 755 | D 1-1 | Tilson-Lascaris 18 | 14 | 16 |
| 11 | FAT Q3 | A | **Gloucester City** | **450** | **W 1-0** | **Tilson-Lascaris 30** | | 17 |
| 17 | BSS | H | Dorchester Town | 303 | L 1-2 | Brown 3 | 16 | 18 |
| Dec 1 | BSS | H | Salisbury City | 321 | L 0-1 | | 19 | 19 |
| 4 | FAT 1 | A | **Sutton United** | **217** | **L 0-1** | | | 20 |
| 8 | BSS | H | Eastbourne Borough | 251 | L 1-2 | Pritchard 17 | 20 | 21 |
| 15 | BSS | A | Truro City | 365 | W 1-0 | Wall 56 | 17 | 22 |
| 26 | BSS | A | Hayes & Yeading Utd | 123 | D 1-1 | Tilson- Lascaris 89 | 17 | 23 |
| 29 | BSS | A | Staines Town | 303 | W 6-0 | Flood 31 Pritchard 5 39 Pratt 83 86 Wall 90 | 9 | 24 |
| Jan 1 | BSS | H | Hayes & Yeading Utd | 404 | L 0-2 | | 12 | 25 |
| 5 | BSS | H | Chelmsford City | 380 | W 2-1 | Wall 29 90 | 9 | 26 |
| 8 | BSS | A | Boreham Wood | 201 | L 1-2 | Brown 17 | 10 | 27 |
| 12 | BSS | A | Tonbridge Angels | 436 | L 1-2 | Wall 39 | 10 | 28 |
| Feb 2 | BSS | A | Weston-s-Mare | 271 | D 1-1 | Wall 54 | 14 | 29 |
| 9 | BSS | H | Billericay Town | 301 | W 3-2 | Wall 9 77 Tilson-Lascaris 90 | 11 | 30 |
| 16 | BSS | A | AFC Hornchurch | 338 | W 2-0 | Wall 21 Behzadi 51 (pen) | 10 | 31 |
| 23 | BSS | H | Basingstoke Town | 267 | D 2-2 | Behzadi 37 76 (pen) | 13 | 32 |
| 26 | BSS | H | Boreham Wood | 178 | W 2-1 | Wall 2 Brown 26 | 10 | 33 |
| Mar 2 | BSS | A | Welling United | 545 | L 2-3 | Pratt 46 Pritchard 66 | 12 | 34 |
| 5 | BSS | H | Dover Athletic | 229 | L 1-2 | Pratt 79 | 14 | 35 |
| 9 | BSS | H | Eastleigh | 309 | L 0-2 | | 15 | 36 |
| 12 | BSS | A | Basingstoke Town | 250 | L 0-2 | | 15 | 37 |
| 26 | BSS | A | Havant & Waterlooville | 308 | L 1-2 | Pacquette 70 | 16 | 38 |
| 30 | BSS | H | Bath City | 320 | L 0-1 | | 18 | 39 |
| Apr 1 | BSS | A | Farnborough | 368 | L 1-2 | Pook 44 | 20 | 40 |
| 6 | BSS | H | Havant & Waterlooville | 282 | W 2-0 | Pacquette 29 42 | 16 | 41 |
| 9 | BSS | A | Sutton United | 261 | L 0-1 | | 17 | 42 |
| 16 | BSS | A | Dorchester Town | 258 | L 0-4 | | 19 | 43 |
| 20 | BSS | H | Bromley | 422 | W 4-2 | Pratt 17 Tilson-Lascaris 34 Pacquette 63 84 | 17 | 44 |
| 22 | BSS | A | Chelmsford City | 626 | L 1-3 | Powell 39 | 17 | 45 |
| 27 | BSS | A | Billericay Town | 340 | L 0-1 | | 19 | 46 |

| GOALSCORERS | Lge | FAC | FAT | Total | Pens | Hat-tricks | Cons Run | | Lge | FAC | FAT | Total | Pens | Hat-tricks | Cons Run |
|-------------|-----|-----|-----|-------|------|------------|----------|---|-----|-----|-----|-------|------|------------|----------|
| Wall | 13 | | | 13 | | | 4 | Soloman | 1 | 1 | | 2 | | | |
| Pratt | 10 | 2 | | 12 | | | 3 | Barney | 1 | | | 1 | | | |
| Tilson-Lascaris | 9 | | 1 | 10 | 1 | | | Pook | 1 | | | 1 | | | |
| Behzadi | 6 | 1 | | 7 | 5 | | | Powell | 1 | | | 1 | | | |
| Pritchard | 6 | | | 6 | | | | Cons Run - Consecutive scoring games. | | | | | | | |
| Pacquette | 5 | | | 5 | | | | | | | | | | | |
| Brown | 4 | | | 4 | | | | | | | | | | | |
| Semakula | 3 | | | 3 | | | | | | | | | | | |
| Flood | 2 | | | 2 | | | | | | | | | | | |
| Nesbitt | 2 | | | 2 | | | | | | | | | | | |

# STAINES TOWN

**Chairman:** Matthew Boon

**Secretary:** Steven Parsons    **(T)** 07850 794 315    **(E)** steve@stainestownfootballclub.co.uk

**Commercial Manager:** Angie Payne    **(T)** 07825 067 232

**Programme Editor:** Steve Parsons    **(T)** 07850 794 315

**Ground Address:** Wheatsheaf Park, Wheatsheaf Lane, Staines TW18 2PD

**(T)** 01784 225 943    **Manager:** Marcus Gayle

2012-13 Squad - Back row (L-R) - Roy Lewis (team attendant), Martyn Spong (Academy Director / Reserve Team Manager), Hanif Boyle, Louis Hollingsworth, Louis-Rae Beadle, Jordaan Brown, Jack Turner, Kyle Merson, Teddy Ngoy, Tony Garrod, Osa Obamwonyi, Chan Quan, Mark Fabian (Youth Team Manager), Thiago Melo (Physiotherapist).
Front: Reece Hall, Ade Osifuwa, Max Worsfold, Scott Taylor (Player/Coach), Marcus Gayle (Manager), Gus Hurdle (Assistant Manager), David Wheeler, Troy Ferguson, Sam Bates.
Insets: Elliott Godfrey (captain), Dominic Ogun, Emmanuel Shosanya, Bajram Pashaj.

## Club Factfile

**Founded:** 1892    **Nickname:** The Swans

**Previous Names:** Staines Albany & St Peters Institute merged in 1895. Staines 1905-18, Staines Lagonda 1918-25, Staines Vale (WWII)

**Previous Leagues:** Great Western Suburban, Hounslow & District 1919-20, Spartan 1924-35, 58-71, Middlesex Senior 1943-52, Parthenon 1952-53, Hellenic 1953-58, Athenian 1971-73, Isthmian 1973-2009

**Club Colours (change):** Old gold & blue/blue/blue (All white)

**Ground Capacity:** 3,000    **Seats:** 300    **Covered:** 850    **Clubhouse:** Yes    **Shop:** Yes

**Directions**

Leave M25 at Junction 13. If coming from the North (anticlockwise), bear left onto A30 Staines By-Pass; if coming from the South (clockwise), go round the roundabout and back under M25 to join By-Pass. Follow A30 to Billet Bridge roundabout, which you treat like a roundabout, taking last exit, A308, London Road towards Town Centre. At 3rd traffic lights, under iron bridge, turn left into South Street, passing central bus station, as far as Thames Lodge (formerly Packhorse). Turn left here, into Laleham Road, B376, under rail bridge. After 1km, Wheatsheaf Lane is on the right, by the traffic island. Ground is less than 100 yds on left. Please park on the left.

**Previous Grounds:** Groundshared with Walton & Hersham and Egham Town whilst new Wheatsheaf stadium was built 2001-03.

**Record Attendance:** 2,750 v Banco di Roma - Barassi Cup 1975 (70,000 watched the second leg)

**Record Victory:** 14-0 v Croydon (A) - Isthmian Division 1 19/03/1994

**Record Defeat:** 1-18 - Wycombe Wanderers (A) - Great Western Suburban League 27/12/1909

**Record Goalscorer:** Alan Gregory - 122

**Record Appearances:** Dickie Watmore - 840

**Additional Records:**

**Senior Honours:**

Spartan League 1959-60. Athenian League Division 2 1971-72, Division 1 1974-75, 88-89.
Middlesex Senior cup 1975-76, 76-77, 77-78, 88-89, 90-91, 94-95, 97-98, 2009-10, 12-13. Barassi Cup 1975-76.
Isthmian Full Members Cup 1994-95, Premier Division Play-off 2008-09.

### 10 YEAR RECORD

| 03-04 | | 04-05 | | 05-06 | | 06-07 | | 07-08 | | 08-09 | | 09-10 | | 10-11 | | 11-12 | | 12-13 | |
|---|---|---|---|---|---|---|---|---|---|---|---|---|---|---|---|---|---|---|---|
| Isth1S | 6 | Isth P | 9 | Isth P | 6 | Isth P | 12 | Isth P | 2 | Isth P | 2 | Conf S | 8 | Conf S | 15 | Conf S | 15 | Conf S | 18 |

# MATCH RESULTS 2012-13

| Date | Comp | H/A | Opponents | Att: | Result | Goalscorers | Pos | No. |
|---|---|---|---|---|---|---|---|---|
| Aug 17 | BSS | A | Bromley | 483 | D 0-0 | | 16 | 1 |
| 21 | BSS | H | Dorchester Town | 252 | W 2-1 | Garrod 15 Wheeler 22 | 8 | 2 |
| 27 | BSS | A | Maidenhead United | 386 | D 1-1 | Weir 33 | 12 | 3 |
| Sept 1 | BSS | D | Havant & Waterlooville | 329 | D 1-1 | Garrod 43 | 14 | 4 |
| 4 | BSS | A | Weston-s Mare | 181 | L 0-1 | | 15 | 5 |
| 8 | BSS | A | Welling United | 518 | L 2-3 | Beadle 11 Garrod 69 | 17 | 6 |
| 15 | BSS | H | Billericay Town | 363 | L 1-2 | Wheeler 45 | 19 | 7 |
| 22 | FAC Q2 | H | Hastings United | 289 | L 2-3 | Garrod 29 Wheeler 65 | | 8 |
| 25 | BSS | H | Basingstoke Town | 310 | W 2-0 | Taylor 25 Hall 90 | 14 | 9 |
| 29 | BSS | H | Salisbury City | 341 | W 3-2 | Wheeler 14 Garrod 25 (pen) Theophonous 90 | 9 | 10 |
| Oct 2 | BSS | A | Hayes & Yeading | 181 | L 0-4 | | 16 | 11 |
| 6 | BSS | A | Eastleigh | 509 | L 3-4 | Garrod 25 Wheeler 57 Hall 90 | 16 | 12 |
| 13 | BSS | H | AFC Hornchurch | 347 | W 3-1 | THEOPHONOUS 3 ( 8 28 51) | 11 | 13 |
| 20 | BSS | A | Sutton United | 569 | W 2-1 | Theophonous 36 (pen ) Brown 85 | 8 | 14 |
| 23 | BSS | H | Truro City | 271 | W 1-0 | Theophonous 15 | 2 | 15 |
| 27 | BSS | A | Chelmsford City | 966 | L 2-3 | Theophonous 66 68 | 4 | 16 |
| Nov 3 | BSS | H | Tonbridge Angels | 375 | L 1-4 | Theophonous 87 | 8 | 17 |
| 10 | FAT Q3 | A | Bromley | 420 | D 1-1 | Beadle 71 | | 18 |
| 13 | FAT Q3r | H | Bromley | 360 | L 0-2 | | | 19 |
| 17 | BSS | A | Farnborough | 581 | L 1-3 | Godfrey 90 (pen) | 12 | 20 |
| Dec 1 | BSS | H | Sutton United | 316 | L 1-4 | Taylor 50 | 14 | 21 |
| 8 | BSS | A | Havany & Waterloville | 661 | L 1-3 | Langley 40 | 15 | 22 |
| 15 | BSS | H | Weston-s-Mare | 230 | D 1-1 | Beadle 67 | 16 | 23 |
| 26 | BSS | H | Boreham Wood | 251 | D 1-1 | Wheeler 60 | 16 | 24 |
| 29 | BSS | H | Maidenhead United | 303 | L 0-6 | | 17 | 25 |
| Jan 1 | BSS | A | Boreham Wood | 204 | D 1-1 | Page 78 | 16 | 26 |
| 5 | BSS | A | Dover Atheltic | 726 | W 1-0 | Wheeler 38 | 11 | 27 |
| 12 | BSS | A | Basingstokke Town | 550 | L 1-3 | Beadle  12 | 17 | 28 |
| 19 | BSS | A | Salisbury City | 464 | L 1-3 | Wheeler 45 | 17 | 29 |
| 26 | BSS | H | Eastbourne Borough | 323 | L 0-2 | | 20 | 30 |
| Feb 2 | BSS | A | Bath City | 1073 | W1-0 | Marsh 89 | 13 | 31 |
| 9 | BSS | H | Eastleigh | 240 | L 1-3 | Mills 13 | 19 | 32 |
| 16 | BSS | A | Truro City | 478 | W 3-0 | Marsh 35 Wheeler 48 Page 64 | 16 | 33 |
| 23 | BSS | A | AFC Hornchurch | 234 | D 1-1 | Worsfold 6 | 18 | 34 |
| Mar 2 | BSS | H | Chelmsford City | 384 | L 1-3 | Ferguson 11 | 19 | 35 |
| 26 | BSS | H | Bromley | 158 | W 3-1 | Marsh 42 Beadle 62 Wheeler 81 | 20 | 36 |
| 30 | BSS | A | Dorchester Town | 487 | W 4-0 | Marsh 36 Wheeler 45  Beadle 48  Brown 90 | 17 | 37 |
| Apr 4 | BSS | H | Hayes &Yeading | 247 | W 7-1 | Wheeler 16 Marsh 26 52 Page 59 | 15 | 38 |
| 6 | BSS | H | Farnborough | 410 | L 1-2 | Wheeler 69 | 15 | 39 |
| 9 | BSS | H | Welling United | 356 | D 2-2 | Brown 79 Beadle 83 | 15 | 40 |
| 13 | BSS | A | Tonbrdge Angels | 511 | L 0-1 | | 17 | 41 |
| 16 | BSS | A | Billericay Town | 263 | W 3-2 | Wheeler 2 Marsh 24 Brown 90 | 14 | 42 |
| 20 | BSS | H | Bath City | 464 | L 1-3 | Marsh 79 (pen) | 16 | 43 |
| 23 | BSS | H | Dover Athletic | 321 | L 0-2 | | 17 | 44 |
| 27 | BSS | A | Eastbourne Borough | 596 | L 0-2 | | 18 | 45 |

| GOALSCORERS | Lge | FAC | FAT | Total | Pens | Hat-tricks | Cons Run | | Lge | FAC | FAT | Total | Pens | Hat-tricks | Cons Run |
|---|---|---|---|---|---|---|---|---|---|---|---|---|---|---|---|
| Wheeler | 13 | 1 | | 14 | | | 4 | Worsfold | 2 | | | 2 | | | |
| Theophonous | 9 | | | 9 | 1 | 1 | 5 | Godfrey | 1 | | 1 | 1 | 1 | | |
| Marsh | 8 | | | 8 | 1 | | | Langley | 1 | | | 1 | | | |
| Rae-Beadle | 5 | | 1 | 6 | | | | Mills | 1 | | | 1 | | | |
| Garrod | 5 | 1 | | 6 | | | | Weir | 1 | | | 1 | | | |
| Brown | 5 | | | 5 | | | | Cons Run - Consecutive scoring games. | | | | | | | |
| Page | 3 | | | 3 | | | | | | | | | | | |
| Ferguson | 2 | | | 2 | | | | | | | | | | | |
| Hall | 2 | | | 2 | | | | | | | | | | | |
| Taylor | 2 | | | 2 | | | | | | | | | | | |

# SUTTON UNITED

**Chairman:** Bruce Elliott
**Secretary:** Gerard Mills          **(T)** 0793 270 2375          **(E)** honsec@suttonunited.net
**Commercial Manager:** Graham Baker          **(T)** 07816 088 281
**Programme Editor:** Lyall Reynolds          **(T)** 07809 416 866
**Ground Address:** Borough Sports Ground, Gander Green Lane, Sutton, Surrey SM1 2EY
**(T)** 0208 644 4440          **Manager:** Paul Doswell

2012-13 Squad. Photo: Paul Loughlin.

## Club Factfile

**Founded:** 1898          **Nickname:** The U's
**Previous Names:** None
**Previous Leagues:** Sutton Junior, Southern Suburban, Athenian 1921-63, Isthmian 1963-86, 91-99, 2000-04, 2008-11, Conference 1999-2000, 04-08

**Club Colours (change):** All amber (All white)

**Ground Capacity:** 7,032          **Seats:** 765          **Covered:** 1,250          **Clubhouse:** Yes          **Shop:** Yes

**Directions**
Travel along the M25 to junction 8. Then north on the A217 for about 15-20 minutes. Ignoring signs for Sutton itself, stay on the A217 to the traffic lights by the Gander Inn (on the left), turn right into Gander Green Lane. The Borough Sports Ground is about 200 yards up this road on the left hand side, if you reach West Sutton station you have gone too far.

**Previous Grounds:** Western Road, Manor Lane, London Road, The Find

**Record Attendance:** 14,000 v Leeds United - FA Cup 4th Round 24/01/1970
**Record Victory:** 11-1 v Clapton - 1966 and v Leatherhead - 1982-83 both Isthmian League
**Record Defeat:** 0-13 v Barking - Athenian League 1925-26
**Record Goalscorer:** Paul McKinnon - 279
**Record Appearances:** Larry Pritchard - 781 (1965-84)
**Additional Records:** Received £100,000 from AFC Bournemouth for Efan Ekoku 1990

**Senior Honours:**
Anglo Italian Cup 1979. Isthmian League (x4) 2010-11. Athenian League x3.
London Senior Cup x2. Surrey Senior Cup x2.

### 10 YEAR RECORD

| 03-04 | | 04-05 | | 05-06 | | 06-07 | | 07-08 | | 08-09 | | 09-10 | | 10-11 | | 11-12 | | 12-13 | |
|---|---|---|---|---|---|---|---|---|---|---|---|---|---|---|---|---|---|---|---|
| Isth P | 2 | Conf S | 15 | Conf S | 13 | Conf S | 13 | Conf S | 22 | Isth P | 5 | Isth P | 2 | Isth P | 1 | Conf S | 4 | Conf S | 6 |

# MATCH RESULTS 2012-13

| Date | Comp | H/A | Opponents | Att: | Result | Goalscorers | Pos | No. |
|------|------|-----|-----------|------|--------|-------------|-----|-----|
| Aug 17 | BSS | A | Basingstoke Town | 424 | L 1-2 | Dundas 38 | 16 | 1 |
| 21 | BSS | H | Dover Athleric | 565 | D 2-2 | Kavanagh 31 Rents 67 | 17 | 2 |
| 25 | BSS | H | Maidenhead United | 454 | D 1-1 | Rents 10 | 17 | 3 |
| 27 | BSS | A | Welling United | 644 | D 2-2 | Beautyman 5 Vassell 83 | 17 | 4 |
| Sept 1 | BSS | H | Dorchester Town | 420 | L 1-2 | Gwillm 58 (pen) | 17 | 5 |
| 4 | BSS | A | Boreham Wood | 265 | L 0-3 | | 19 | 6 |
| 8 | BSS | A | Weston-s-Mare | 277 | D 1-1 | Beautyman 10 | 21 | 7 |
| 15 | BSS | H | Havant & Waterlooville | 826 | D 1-1 | Dundas 70 | 21 | 8 |
| 22 | FAC Q2 | H | Bromley | 511 | L 0-1 | | | 9 |
| 29 | BSS | A | Tonbridge Angels | 605 | D 1-1 | Vassell 89 | 21 | 10 |
| Oct 2 | BSS | H | Chelmsford City | 467 | W 1-0 | Beautyman 8 | 21 | 11 |
| 6 | BSS | H | Tonbridge Angels | 549 | D 2-2 | Watkins 4 Ottaway 71 | 20 | 12 |
| 13 | BSS | A | Eastbourne Borough | 618 | W 1-0 | Watkins 90 | 18 | 13 |
| 20 | BSS | H | Staines Town | 569 | L 1-2 | Payne 90 | 19 | 14 |
| 27 | BSS | A | Truro City | 613 | W 2-1 | Stuart 16 Payne 86 | 17 | 15 |
| Nov 3 | BSS | A | Eastleigh | 636 | L 0-1 | | 18 | 16 |
| 10 | FAT Q3 | H | Ramsgate | 261 | W 2-0 | Ottaway 14 Vassell 82 | | 17 |
| 17 | BSS | H | Bath City | 512 | L 0-2 | | 20 | 18 |
| Dec 1 | BSS | A | Staines Town | 316 | W 4-1 | Rents 61 (pen) 83 Dundas 64 Kavanagh 89 | 18 | 19 |
| 4 | FAT 1 | A | Maidenhead United | 217 | W 1-0 | Ottaway 29 | | 20 |
| 8 | BSS | A | Dorchester Town | 456 | W 1-0 | Clough 45 (og) | 13 | 21 |
| 15 | FAT 2 | H | Oxford City | 347 | W 1-0 | Watkins 54 | | 22 |
| Jan 1 | BSS | A | Bromley | 556 | W 2-0 | Williams 36 Beautyman 46 | 13 | 23 |
| 5 | BSS | A | Salisbury City | 740 | L 0-1 | | 15 | 24 |
| 12 | FAT 3 | H | Wrexham | 775 | L 0-5 | | | 25 |
| Feb 2 | BSS | H | Eastleigh | 471 | W 2-1 | Rents 43 (pen) Dundas 83 | 17 | 26 |
| 9 | BSS | A | AFC Hornchurch | 352 | D 1-1 | Dundas 86 | 20 | 27 |
| 12 | BSS | H | Welling United | 478 | W 2-1 | Dundas 59 Ottaway 64 | 14 | 28 |
| 16 | BSS | H | Eastbourne B | 587 | W 2-0 | Ottaway 18 Rents 31 (pen) | 11 | 29 |
| 19 | BSS | H | Basingstoke Town | 402 | W 3-2 | Pacquette 2 Williams 15 Dundas 88 | 10 | 30 |
| 23 | BSS | A | Chelmsford City | 702 | L 0-1 | | 12 | 31 |
| Mar 2 | BSS | A | Havant & Waterlooville | 683 | L 0-3 | | 14 | 32 |
| 5 | BSS | H | Bromley | 442 | W 4-3 | Dundas 40 51 Stewart 74 Beautyman 90 | 10 | 33 |
| 9 | BSS | A | Hayes & Yeading | 233 | D 0-0 | | 11 | 34 |
| 12 | BSS | H | Truro City | 360 | L 0-1 | | 13 | 35 |
| 16 | BSS | H | Farnborough | 840 | L 0-1 | | 13 | 36 |
| 19 | BSS | A | Billericay Town | 293 | W 4-2 | Beautyman 34 78 Dundas 68 (pen) Benjamin 71 | 12 | 37 |
| 26 | BSS | H | Weston-s-Mare | 308 | L 1-3 | Sinclair 8 | 12 | 38 |
| 30 | BSS | A | Dover Athletic | 1023 | D 1-1 | Benjamin 90 | 12 | 39 |
| Apr 1 | BSS | H | Boreham Wood | 468 | W 2-1 | Folkes 13 Beautyman 62 | 10 | 40 |
| 6 | BSS | H | Billericay Town | 566 | W 3-0 | Williams 12 Beautyman 62 Sinclair 65 | 10 | 41 |
| 9 | BSS | A | Maidenhead United | 261 | W 1-0 | Dundas 45 (pen) | 10 | 42 |
| 13 | BSS | A | Farnborough | 460 | W 3-1 | Williams 5 66 Rents 54 | 8 | 43 |
| 17 | BSS | H | Hayes & Yeading | 416 | W 5-1 | Williams 17 21 Dundas 32 81 (pen) Downer 53 | 7 | 44 |
| 20 | BSS | H | AFC Hornchurch | 516 | W 3-1 | Beautyman 37 Williams 85 Morrell-Williamson 87 | 7 | 45 |
| 22 | BSS | H | Salisbury City | 456 | W 1-0 | Williams 1 | 6 | 46 |
| 27 | BSS | A | Bath City | 613 | W 4-0 | Williams 34 63 Griffiths 53 Dundas 56 | 6 | 47 |

| GOALSCORERS | Lge | FAC | FAT | Total | Pens | Hat-tricks | Cons Run | | Lge | FAC | FAT | Total | Pens | Hat-tricks | Cons Run |
|-------------|-----|-----|-----|-------|------|------------|----------|---|-----|-----|-----|-------|------|------------|----------|
| Dundas | 14 | | | 14 | 3 | | 3 | Downer | 1 | | | 1 | | | |
| Williams | 12 | | | 12 | | | 5 | Folkes | 1 | | | 1 | | | |
| Beautyman | 10 | | | 10 | | | 2 | Griffiths | 1 | | | 1 | | | |
| Rents | 6 | | | 6 | 3 | | | Gwillm | 1 | | | 1 | | | |
| Ottaway | 3 | | 2 | 5 | | | | Morrell-Williamson | 1 | | | 1 | | | |
| Vassell | 2 | 1 | | 3 | | | | Pacquette | 1 | | | 1 | | | |
| Watkins | 2 | | 1 | 3 | | | | Stewart | 1 | | | 1 | | | |
| Benjamin | 2 | | | 2 | | | | Stuart | 1 | | | 1 | | | |
| Kavanagh | 2 | | | 2 | | | | Own Goals | 1 | | | 1 | | | |
| Payne | 2 | | | 2 | | | | Cons Run - Consecutive scoring games. | | | | | | | |
| Sinclair | 2 | | | 2 | | | | | | | | | | | |

# TONBRIDGE ANGELS

**Chairman:** Steve Churcher
**Secretary:** Charlie Cole      **(T)** 07825 702 412      **(E)** chcole1063@aol.com
**Commercial Manager:** Darren Apps      **(T)** 07952 908 716
**Programme Editor:** Geoff Curtis      **(T)** 07930 868 568
**Ground Address:** Longmead Stadium, Darenth Avenue, Tonbridge, Kent TN10 3LW
**(T)** 01732 352 417      **Manager:** Tommy Warrilow

2012-13 Squad.
Back Row (Left to Right): Melvin Slight (Physio), Rob Churcher (Kit man), Nathan Koranteng, Sonny Miles, Ollie Schulz, Lee Worgan, Mikel Suarez, Ben Judge, George Crimmen, Ryan Waterman, Terry Sedge (Coach), Simon Balsdon (Coach), Tina Jenner (Physio).
Front Row (Left to Right): Robbie Kember, George Purcell, Tom Davis, Alex O'Brien (Coach), Tommy Warrilow (Manager), Frannie Collin, Lee Browning, Rory Hill Chris Piper.
Photo: David Couldridge

## Club Factfile

**Founded:** 1948      **Nickname:** Angels
**Previous Names:** Tonbridge Angels, Tonbridge F.C., Tonbridge A.F.C.
**Previous Leagues:** Southern 1948-80, 93-2004, Kent 1989-93, Isthmian 2004-11.

**Club Colours (change):** Blue/white/blue (White/red/white)

**Ground Capacity:** 2,500    **Seats:** 707    **Covered:** 1,500    **Clubhouse:** Yes    **Shop:** Yes

**Directions:** From M25. Take A21 turning at Junction 5 to junction with A225/b245 (signposted Hildenborough). After passing Langley Hotel on left thake slightly hidden left turn into Dry Hill Park Road. Left again at mini roundabout into Shipbourne Road (A227) and then left again at next roundabout into Darenth Avenue' Longmead stadium can be found at the bottom of the hill at the far end of the car park.

**Previous Grounds:** The Angel 1948-80

**Record Attendance:** 8,236 v Aldershot - FA Cup 1951
**Record Victory:** 11-1 v Worthing - FA Cup 1951
**Record Defeat:** 2-11 v Folkstone - Kent Senior Cup 1949
**Record Goalscorer:** Jon Main scored 44 goals in one season including seven hat-tricks
**Record Appearances:** Mark Giham
**Additional Records:**

**Senior Honours:**
Kent Senior Cup 1964-65, 74-75

### 10 YEAR RECORD

| 03-04 | | 04-05 | | 05-06 | | 06-07 | | 07-08 | | 08-09 | | 09-10 | | 10-11 | | 11-12 | | 12-13 | |
|---|---|---|---|---|---|---|---|---|---|---|---|---|---|---|---|---|---|---|---|
| SthE | 3 | Isth P | 20 | Isth1 | 3 | Isth P | 11 | Isth P | 8 | Isth P | 3 | Isth P | 8 | Isth P | 2 | Conf S | 9 | Conf S | 16 |

# MATCH RESULTS 2012-13

| ate | Comp | H/A | Opponents | Att: | Result | Goalscorers | Pos | No. |
|---|---|---|---|---|---|---|---|---|
| ug 17 | BSS | A | Maidenhead United | 304 | L 1-3 | Collin 48 | 21 | 1 |
| | BSS | H | Salisbury City | 520 | L 1-2 | Collin 34 | 22 | 2 |
| | BSS | H | Welling United | 592 | D 1-1 | Collin 57 (pen) | 20 | 3 |
| | BSS | A | Bromley | 805 | D 1-1 | Suarez 9 | 19 | 4 |
| ept 1 | BSS | H | Basingstoke Town | 518 | D 0-0 | | 19 | 5 |
| | BSS | A | Billericay Town | 369 | D 3-3 | Lovell 2 Collin 85 Judge 90 | 19 | 6 |
| | BSS | A | Havant & Waterlooville | 805 | D 2-2 | Piper 11 Muggeridge 25 | 20 | 7 |
| | BSS | H | Boreham Wood | 451 | W 4-2 | Purcell 4 6 Collin 68 Browning 89 | 16 | 8 |
| 2 | FAC Q2 | A | Dover Athletic | 625 | L 1-2 | Purcell 29 | | 9 |
| | BSS | H | Sutton United | 605 | D 1-1 | Muggeridge 2 | 18 | 10 |
| ct 2 | BSS | A | Eastbourne Borough | 415 | W 2-1 | Piper 37 80 | 17 | 11 |
| | BSS | A | Sutton United | 549 | D 2-2 | Suarez 74 Lovell 85 | 10 | 12 |
| | BSS | A | Farnborough | 513 | L 1-4 | Collin 49 (pen) | 17 | 13 |
| | BSS | H | Bath City | 536 | L 3-4 | Collin 63 (pen) Elphick 89 Schulz 90 | 18 | 14 |
| 7 | BSS | A | Dorchester Town | 463 | W 2-1 | Piper 31 45 | 16 | 15 |
| ov 3 | BSS | A | Staines Town | 375 | W 4-1 | Davis 51 Collin 63 (pen) 67 Browning 85 | 11 | 16 |
| 0 | FAT Q3 | H | Hitchin Town | 513 | W 2-1 | Purcell 4 Piper 35 | | 17 |
| 7 | BSS | H | Hayes & Yeading | 624 | D 1-1 | Hill 74 | 13 | 18 |
| 7 | FAT 1 | A | Merthyr Town | 229 | W 2-1 | Miles 21 Browning 90 | | 19 |
| ec 1 | BSS | A | Truro City | 346 | L 0-2 | | 15 | 20 |
| | BSS | A | Basingstoke Town | 320 | L 0-1 | | 16 | 21 |
| 5 | FAT 2 | A | Dartford | 937 | L 0-3 | | | 22 |
| 5 | BSS | H | Dover Athletc | 710 | W 2-1 | Miles 20 Purcell 64 | 12 | 23 |
| 9 | BSS | H | Bromley | 682 | L 0-3 | | 15 | 24 |
| an 1 | BSS | A | Dover Athletic | 1102 | W 1-0 | Ijaha 90 | 10 | 25 |
| | BSS | A | Weston -s- Mare | 305 | L 0-2 | | 13 | 26 |
| | BSS | H | Havant & Waterlooville | 397 | W 1-0 | Collin 22 (pen) | 9 | 27 |
| | BSS | H | Maidenhead United | 436 | W 2-1 | Lovell 35 Collin 63 | 9 | 28 |
| 6 | BSS | A | AFC Hrnchurch | 362 | D 1-1 | Collin 64 | 9 | 29 |
| eb 2 | BSS | H | Farnborough | 491 | L 2-3 | Collin 37 Lovell 73 | 9 | 30 |
| | BSS | H | Chelmsford City | 625 | L 0-4 | | 10 | 31 |
| 6 | BSS | A | Bath City | 564 | L 0-3 | | 15 | 32 |
| 9 | BSS | H | AFC Hornchurch | 304 | W 1-0 | Piper 45 (pen) | 13 | 33 |
| 3 | BSS | H | Dorchester Town | 365 | L 0-2 | | 15 | 34 |
| Mar 2 | BSS | A | Boreham Wood | 206 | L 2-4 | Suarez  11 79 | 17 | 35 |
| 2 | BSS | A | Welling United | 447 | L 1-4 | Collin 49 | 17 | 36 |
| 6 | BSS | H | Eastleigh | 170 | W 3-1 | Lovell 44 Collin 61 Browning 64 | 17 | 37 |
| 0 | BSS | A | Salisbury City | 705 | L 0-2 | | 19 | 38 |
| pr 1 | BSS | H | Billericay Town | 595 | D 1-1 | Ijaha 90 | 18 | 39 |
| | BSS | H | Weston-s-Mare | 283 | D 1-1 | Lovell 55 | 18 | 40 |
| | BSS | A | Hayes & Yeading | 235 | L 2-3 | Collin  5 Lovell 8 | 20 | 41 |
| 3 | BSS | H | Staines Town | 511 | W 1-0 | Collin 7 | 18 | 42 |
| 5 | BSS | A | Chelmsford City | 635 | L 1-2 | Suarez 88 | 18 | 43 |
| 0 | BSS | A | Eastleigh | 627 | L 1-4 | Suarez 25 | 19 | 44 |
| 3 | BSS | H | Eastbourne Borough | 624 | D 1-1 | Ijaha 73 | 19 | 45 |
| 7 | BSS | H | Truro City | 582 | W 3-2 | Gayle 2 Collin 16 43 | 16 | 46 |

| GOALSCORERS | Lge | FAC | FAT | Total | Pens | Hat-tricks | Cons Run | | Lge | FAC | FAT | Total | Pens | Hat-tricks | Cons Run |
|---|---|---|---|---|---|---|---|---|---|---|---|---|---|---|---|
| Collin | 19 | | | 19 | 5 | | 4 | Gayle | 1 | | | 1 | | | |
| Piper | 6 | | 1 | 8 | 1 | | | Hill | 1 | | | 1 | | | |
| Lovell | 7 | | | 7 | | | | Judge | 1 | | | 1 | | | |
| Suarez | 7 | | | 7 | | | | Schulz | 1 | | | 1 | | | |
| Purcell | 3 | 1 | 1 | 5 | | | | Cons Run - Consecutive scoring games. | | | | | | | |
| Browning | 3 | | 1 | 4 | | | | | | | | | | | |
| Ijaha | 3 | | | 3 | | | | | | | | | | | |
| Muggeridge | 2 | | | 2 | | | | | | | | | | | |
| Davis | 1 | | | 1 | | | | | | | | | | | |
| Elphick | 1 | | | 1 | | | | | | | | | | | |

# WESTON-SUPER-MARE

**Chairman:** Paul Bliss

**Secretary:** Richard Sloane     **(T)** 0771 107 8589     **(E)** wsmsecretary@hotmail.co.uk

**Commercial Manager:** Oli Bliss     **(T)** 01934 621 618

**Programme Editor:** Phil Sheridan     **(T)** 07963 166 031

**Ground Address:** Woodspring Stadium, Winterstoke Road, Weston-super-Mare BS24 9AA

**(T)** 01934 621 618     **Manager:** Craig Laird

2012-13 Squad - Back Row: Martin Slocombe; Dayle Grubb; Kane Ingram; Ashley Kington; Owen Irish; Jamie Price; Callum Laird; Robbie Maggs; Ross Stearn; Nabi Diallo
Middle Row: Jamie Laird; Brett Trowbridge; Chas Hemmings; Nat Pepperell; Lloyd Irish; Matt Villis; Chris Young; Marc McGregor; Pete Monks
Front Row: Dave Callow Physio; Ben Kirk (Captain); Jon Haile Assistant Manager; Richard Sloane Director; Craig Laird Manager; Any Callow Physio; Barrie Neale Kitman

## Club Factfile

**Founded:** 1899     **Nickname:** Seagulls

**Previous Names:** Borough or Weston-super-Mare

**Previous Leagues:** Somerset Senior, Western League

**Club Colours (change):** All white (All royal blue)

**Ground Capacity:** 3,000    **Seats:** 278    **Covered:** 2,000    **Clubhouse:** Yes    **Shop:** Yes

**Directions**

Leave the M5 at Junction 21, take the dual carriageway A370 and continue straight until the 4th roundabout with ASDA on the right. Turn left into Winterstoke Road, bypassing a mini roundabout and continue for 1/2 mile. Woodspring Stadium is on the right.

**Previous Grounds:** Langford Road, Winterstoke Road

**Record Attendance:** 2,623 v Woking - FA Cup 1st Round replay 23/11/1993 (At Winterstoke Road)

**Record Victory:** 11-0 v Paulton Rovers

**Record Defeat:** 1-12 v Yeovil Town Reserves

**Record Goalscorer:** Matt Lazenby - 180

**Record Appearances:** Harry Thomas - 740

**Additional Records:** Received £20,000 from Sheffield Wednesday for Stuart Jones

**Senior Honours:**
Somerset Senior Cup 1923-24, 26-67.
Western League 1991-92.

### 10 YEAR RECORD

| 03-04 | | 04-05 | | 05-06 | | 06-07 | | 07-08 | | 08-09 | | 09-10 | | 10-11 | | 11-12 | | 12-13 | |
|---|---|---|---|---|---|---|---|---|---|---|---|---|---|---|---|---|---|---|---|
| SthP | 10 | Conf S | 11 | Conf S | 14 | Conf S | 21 | Conf S | 20 | Conf S | 17 | Conf S | 21 | Conf S | 12 | Conf S | 13 | Conf S | 7 |

# MATCH RESULTS 2012-13

| Date | Comp | H/A | Opponents | Att: | Result | Goalscorers | Pos | No. |
|---|---|---|---|---|---|---|---|---|
| Aug 17 | BSS | H | Hayes & Yeading | 550 | D 1-1 | Ingram 7 | 14 | 1 |
| 21 | BSS | A | Farnborough | 352 | L 1-2 | Stearn 90 | 19 | 2 |
| 25 | BSS | A | Eastleigh | 445 | L 0-3 | | 22 | 3 |
| 27 | BSS | H | Truro City | 870 | L 0-2 | | 22 | 4 |
| Sept 1 | BSS | A | AFC Hornchurch | 245 | D 0-0 | | 22 | 5 |
| 4 | BSS | H | Staines Town | 181 | W 1-0 | Villis 81 | 19 | 6 |
| 8 | BSS | H | Sutton United | 277 | D 1-1 | Stearn 88 (pen) | 19 | 7 |
| 15 | BSS | A | Chelmsford City | 938 | L 1-2 | Stearn 19 | 20 | 8 |
| 22 | FAC Q2 | A | Frome Town | 256 | W 2-0 | Ingram 40 Stearn 52 | | 9 |
| 25 | BSS | A | Havant & Waterlooville | 460 | W 3-0 | Slocombe 20 Grubb 81 Pepperall 85 | 16 | 10 |
| 29 | BSS | H | Eastbourne Borough | 236 | W 3-2 | Diallo 31 Stearn 55 Kington 90 | 12 | 11 |
| Oct 6 | FAC Q3 | H | Worcester City | 556 | D 1-1 | Ingram 12 | | 12 |
| 8 | FAC Q3r | A | Worcester City | 1013 | L 0-1 | | | 13 |
| 13 | BSS | A | Maidenhead United | 372 | W 1-0 | Ingram 62 | 10 | 14 |
| 20 | BSS | H | Basingstoke Town | 282 | W 5-2 | Diallo 11 Hemmings 16 Ingram 18, Steam 51 Kington 59 | 6 | 15 |
| 27 | BSS | H | Boreham Wood | 231 | L 2-4 | Hemmings 24 Stearn 43 | 10 | 16 |
| Nov 3 | BSS | A | Billericay Town | 395 | D 0-0 | | 12 | 17 |
| 10 | FAT Q3 | A | Salisbury City | 510 | L 0-3 | | | 18 |
| 17 | BSS | H | Havant & Waterlooville | 267 | D 2-2 | Kington 71 Hemmings 88 | 14 | 19 |
| 24 | BSS | A | Dover Athletic | 502 | L 1-3 | Dialio 85 | 14 | 20 |
| Dec 1 | BSS | A | Boreham Wood | 202 | W 1-0 | Monks 45 | 9 | 21 |
| 8 | BSS | H | AFC Hornchurch | 256 | W 1-0 | Trowbridge 41 | 7 | 22 |
| 15 | BSS | A | Staines Town | 230 | D 1-1 | Trowbridge 88 | 7 | 23 |
| 26 | BSS | A | Bath Cty | 683 | W 2-1 | Slocombe 34 Ingram 78 | 6 | 24 |
| Jan 5 | BSS | H | Tonbridge Angels | 305 | W 2-0 | Stearn 44 69 | 5 | 25 |
| 8 | BSS | H | Bath City | 218 | L 1-4 | Stearn 27 (pen) | 6 | 26 |
| 12 | BSS | A | Hayes & Yeading | 120 | L 1-2 | Grubb 38 | 7 | 27 |
| 26 | BSS | A | Bromley | 390 | W 1-0 | Kington 52 | 6 | 28 |
| Feb 2 | BSS | A | Maidenhead United | 271 | D 1-1 | Grubb 16 | 6 | 29 |
| 5 | BSS | H | Eastleigh | 240 | L 2-4 | Stearn (2) | 7 | 30 |
| 9 | BSS | A | Eastbourne Borough | 570 | W 2-0 | Hemmings 16 McClaggon 40 | 6 | 31 |
| 16 | BSS | H | Dover Athletic | 302 | L 0-3 | | 7 | 32 |
| 23 | BSS | H | Welling United | 288 | W 2-0 | Laird 46 Grubb 90 | 6 | 33 |
| 26 | BSS | A | Truro City | 226 | W 2-1 | Diallo 4 Ingram 52 | 6 | 34 |
| Mar 2 | BSS | A | Salisbury City | 666 | D 1-1 | McClaggon 54 | 6 | 35 |
| 5 | BSS | H | Chelmsford Town | 200 | W 3-0 | Grubb 42 Hemmings 48 Trowbridge 75 | 6 | 36 |
| 9 | BSS | H | Salisbury City | 348 | L 0-3 | | 6 | 37 |
| 19 | BSS | H | Dorchester Town | 268 | W 2-0 | Ingram 25 40 | 5 | 38 |
| 26 | BSS | A | Sutton United | 308 | W 3-1 | McCLAGGON 3 ( 5 21 90) | 5 | 39 |
| 30 | BSS | H | Farnborough | 635 | D 1-1 | Grubb 79 | 5 | 40 |
| Apr 1 | BSS | A | Tonbridge Angels | 283 | D 1-1 | Grubb 89 | 5 | 41 |
| 6 | BSS | H | Bromley | 297 | W 3-0 | Kington 2 Stearn 39 Grubb 71 | 4 | 42 |
| 9 | BSS | A | Basingstoke Town | 260 | W 3-1 | Kirk 4 Stearn 21 Price 86 | 4 | 43 |
| 13 | BSS | A | Welling United | 851 | L 1-4 | Monks 90 | 4 | 44 |
| 20 | BSS | H | Billericay Town | 320 | W 1-0 | Ingram 88 | 6 | 45 |
| 27 | BSS | A | Dorchester Town | 623 | L 1-2 | Trowbridge 49 | 7 | 46 |

| GOALSCORERS | Lge | FAC | FAT | Total | Pens | Hat-tricks | Cons Run | | Lge | FAC | FAT | Total | Pens | Hat-tricks | Cons Run |
|---|---|---|---|---|---|---|---|---|---|---|---|---|---|---|---|
| Stearn | 14 | 1 | | 15 | 2 | | 3 | Kirk | 1 | | | 1 | | | |
| Ingram | 8 | 2 | | 10 | | | 2 | Laird | 1 | | | 1 | | | |
| Grubb | 8 | | | 7 | | | | McLaren | 1 | | | 1 | | | |
| Hemmings | 5 | | | 5 | | | | Pepperall | 1 | | | 1 | | | |
| Kington | 5 | | | 5 | | | | Price | 1 | | | 1 | | | |
| Diallo | 4 | | | 4 | | | | Trowbridge | 1 | | | 1 | | | |
| McClaggon | 4 | | | 4 | | | | Villis | 1 | | | 1 | | | |
| Trowbridge | 3 | | | 3 | | | | Cons Run - Consecutive scoring games. | | | | | | | |
| Monks | 2 | | | 2 | | | | | | | | | | | |
| Slocombe | 2 | | | 2 | | | | | | | | | | | |

# WHITEHAWK

**Chairman:** John Summers
**Secretary:** John Rosenblatt      **(T)** 07724 519 370      **(E)** johnrosenblatt@whitehawkfc.com
**Commercial Manager:** Kevin Keehan      **(T)** 07713 062 642
**Programme Editor:** Nathan Jones      **(T)** 07944 298 417
**Ground Address:** Enclosed Ground, East Brighton Park, Wilson Avenue, Brighton BN2 5TS
**(T)** 01273  601 244      **Manager:** Darren Freeman

Isthmian Premier Division Championship winning squad.
Back Row (L-R): Ross Standen, Matt Lawrence, Sam Gargan, Andy Pearson, Ben Godfrey, Chris Winterton, Tommy Fraser, Ryan James, James Fraser, Sami El-Abd, Darren Freeman, Paul Stevenson
Front Row: Joe Keehan, Lee Newman, Jerahl Hughes, Paul Armstrong, Mark Knee, Josh Jones, Scott McGleish, Charlie Walker, Paul Dollner

## Club Factfile

**Founded:** 1945      **Nickname:** Hawks
**Previous Names:** Whitehawk & Manor Farm Old Boys untill 1958.
**Previous Leagues:** Brighton & Hove District, Sussex County > 2010. Isthmian 2010-13.

**Club Colours (change):** All red (All blue)

**Ground Capacity:** 3,000      **Seats:** Yes      **Covered:** 500      **Clubhouse:** Yes      **Shop:** No

**Directions** From N (London) on M23/A23 – after passing Brighton boundary sign & twin pillars join A27 (sp Lewes); immediately after passing Sussex University (on L) leave A27 via slip rd at sp B2123, Falmer, Rottingdean; at roundabout at top of slip rd turn R onto B2123 (sp Falmer, Rottingdean); in 2m at traffic lights in Woodingdean turn R by Downs Hotel into Warren Road; in about 1m at traffic lights turn L into Wilson Ave, crossing racecourse; in 1¼m turn L at foot of hill (last turning before traffic lights) into East Brighton Park; follow lane for the ground.

**Previous Grounds:** None

**Record Attendance:** 2,100 v Bognor Regis Town - FA Cup 1988-89
**Record Victory:** Not known
**Record Defeat:** Not known
**Record Goalscorer:** Billy Ford
**Record Appearances:** Ken Powell - 1,103
**Additional Records:**

**Senior Honours:**
Sussex County League Division 1 1961-62, 63-64, 83-84, 2009-10. Division 2 1967-68, 80-81.
Isthmian League Division 1 South 2011-12, Premier Division 2012-13.
Sussex Senior Cup 1950-51, 61-62, 2011-12. Sussex RUR Charity Cup x3.

### 10 YEAR RECORD

| 03-04 | | 04-05 | | 05-06 | | 06-07 | | 07-08 | | 08-09 | | 09-10 | | 10-11 | | 11-12 | | 12-13 | |
|---|---|---|---|---|---|---|---|---|---|---|---|---|---|---|---|---|---|---|---|
| SxC1 | 8 | SxC1 | 3 | SxC1 | 3 | SxC1 | 2 | SxC1 | 2 | SxC1 | 13 | SxC1 | 1 | Isth1S | 3 | Isth1S | 1 | Isth P | 1 |

# MATCH RESULTS 2012-13

| Date | Comp | H/A | Opponents | Att: | Result | Goalscorers | Pos | No. |
|---|---|---|---|---|---|---|---|---|
| Aug 18 | RPL | H | Lowestoft Town | 135 | L 1-3 | McGleish 8 (pen) | 20 | 1 |
| 21 | RPL | A | Cray WanderersCray Wanderers | | W 2-1 | Lawrence 89 McGleish 90 | 11 | 2 |
| 25 | RPL | A | Enfield Town | 375 | W 3-1 | Jones 44 75 McGleish 45 | 6 | 3 |
| 27 | RPL | H | Hendon | 145 | D 0-0 | | 7 | 4 |
| Sept 1 | RPL | A | Wealdstone | 402 | D 1-1 | Jones 3 | 8 | 5 |
| 8 | FAC Q1 | H | Sittingbourne | 136 | W 5-0 | McGleish (pen) Fraser Gargan (2) Newman | | 6 |
| 15 | RPL | A | Thurrock | 122 | W 5-1 | FRASER 3 ( 31 48 50) Gargan 73 Hughes 90 | 6 | 7 |
| 22 | FAC Q2 | H | Hitchin Town | 144 | D 1-1 | Gargan 12 | | 8 |
| 25 | FAC Q2r | A | Hitchin Town | 185 | L 0-5 | | | 9 |
| 29 | FAT Q1 | A | Bury Town | 301 | D 0-0 | | | 10 |
| Oct 2 | FAT Q1r | H | Bury Town | 50 | W 1-0 | Newman 57 | | 11 |
| 6 | RPL | H | Wingate & Finchley | 73 | W 3-1 | Gargan 25 Wallace 41 McCrea 75 | 2 | 12 |
| 9 | RPL | A | Canvey Island | 212 | W 2-1 | Keehan 21 Wallace 61 | 1 | 13 |
| 13 | RPL | A | Hampton & Richmond B | 616 | L 0-1 | | 3 | 14 |
| 23 | RPL | A | Carshalton Athletic | 121 | W 1-0 | Jones 40 | 2 | 15 |
| 27 | FAT Q2 | H | Grays Athletic | 144 | D 1-1 | Wallace 68 | | 16 |
| Nov 3 | RPL | A | Bury Town | 372 | W 3-1 | Gargon 49 52 Wallace 58 | 2 | 17 |
| 10 | FAT Q3 | A | Maidstone United | 1571 | L 2-3 | Walker 61 63 | | 18 |
| 13 | RPL | H | Metropolitan Police | 145 | D 1-1 | Mills 31 | 2 | 19 |
| 17 | RPL | H | Leiston | 142 | W 5-1 | Fraser 3 WALLACE 3(14 45 74) Mills 76 | 1 | 20 |
| 24 | RPL | A | Concord Rangers | 226 | D 2-2 | Wallace 29 Jones 69 | 1 | 21 |
| Dec 1 | RPL | H | Harrow Borough | 201 | D 0-0 | | 1 | 22 |
| 8 | RPL | A | Lewes | 674 | W 3-2 | Mills 55 Louis 72 Jones 82 | 2 | 23 |
| 14 | RPL | A | East Thurrock United | 141 | D 1-1 | Wallace 90 (pen) | 2 | 24 |
| 26 | RPL | H | Hastings United | 290 | D 2-2 | Walker 27 Keehan 53 | 2 | 25 |
| 29 | RPL | H | Enfield Town | 163 | W 6-0 | Walker 12 Armstrong 27 (pen) 86 LOUIS 3 ( 72 83 88) | 1 | 26 |
| Jan 1 | RPL | A | Bognor Regis Town | 626 | W 3-1 | James 37 Fraser 44 Rossi-Branco 87 | 1 | 27 |
| 5 | RPL | H | Canvey Island | 159 | W 5-4 | Walker 14 Mills 75 90 Jones 78 Malcolm 82 | 1 | 28 |
| 12 | RPL | A | Wingae & Finchley | 133 | W 3-2 | Malcolm 34 37 Fraser 50 | 1 | 29 |
| 26 | RPL | A | Metropolitan Police | 165 | W 5-2 | MALCOLM 3 (14 35 90) Araba 46 Fraser 82 | 1 | 30 |
| Feb 2 | RPL | H | Lewes | 485 | W 3-1 | Malcolm 43 Mills 58 89 | 1 | 31 |
| 5 | RPL | A | Hendon | 136 | D 1-1 | Pearson 14 | 1 | 32 |
| 9 | RPL | A | Margate | 418 | L 1-2 | Malcolm 10 | 1 | 33 |
| 16 | RPL | H | Concord Rangers | 113 | W 1-0 | Fraser 1 | 1 | 34 |
| 19 | RPL | H | Kingstonian | 187 | W 2-0 | Mills 62 90 | 1 | 35 |
| 23 | RPL | A | Harrow Borough | 91 | L 1-3 | Malcolm 13 | 1 | 36 |
| 26 | RPL | H | Cray Wanderers | 90 | W 2-0 | Branco 50 Araba 79 | 1 | 37 |
| Mar 2 | RPL | A | Lowestoft Town | 871 | D 0-0 | | 1 | 38 |
| 9 | RPL | H | Wealdstone | 587 | D 1-1 | Araba 27 | 1 | 39 |
| 16 | RPL | A | Thurrock | 209 | W 3-0 | Losasso 10 Fraser 35 Mills 40 | 1 | 40 |
| 19 | RPL | H | Matgate | 149 | D 1-1 | Henry 41 (pen) | 1 | 41 |
| 23 | RPL | H | Carshalton Athletic | 158 | W 2-0 | J.Fraser 68 Henry 90 | 1 | 42 |
| 26 | RPL | H | Hampton & Richmonmd B | 104 | D 0-0 | | 1 | 43 |
| 29 | RPL | H | Bognor Regis Town | 271 | W 3-0 | Fraser 13 Keehan 34 Henry 67 | 1 | 44 |
| Apr 1 | RPL | A | Hastings United | 496 | W 2-0 | Mils 35 Gargan 80 | 1 | 45 |
| 6 | RPL | A | Kingstonian | 305 | W 3-2 | El-Abd 35 Keehan 68 Malcolm 77 | 1 | 46 |
| 13 | RPL | H | Bury Town | 181 | D 2-2 | Mills 14 Henry 38 | 1 | 47 |
| 21 | RPL | A | Leiston | 365 | W 2-0 | Gargan 71 (pen) 75 | 1 | 48 |
| 27 | RPL | H | East Thurrock United | 438 | W 1-0 | Henry 88 | 1 | 49 |

| GOALSCORERS | Lge | FAC | FAT | Total | Pens | Hat-tricks | Cons Run | | Lge | FAC | FAT | Total | Pens | Hat-tricks | Cons Run |
|---|---|---|---|---|---|---|---|---|---|---|---|---|---|---|---|
| Mills | 12 | | | 12 | | | 2 | J.Fraser | 2 | | | 2 | | | |
| Fraser | 9 | 1 | | 10 | | 1 | 2 | Newman | | 1 | 1 | 2 | | | |
| Gargan | 7 | 3 | | 10 | 1 | | | Branco | 1 | | | 1 | | | |
| Malcolm | 10 | | | 10 | | 1 | | El Abd | 1 | | | 1 | | | |
| Wallace | 8 | | 1 | 9 | 1 | 1 | 2 | Hughes | 1 | | | 1 | | | |
| Jones | 7 | | | 7 | | | | James | 1 | | | 1 | | | |
| Henry | 5 | | | 5 | 1 | | | Lawrence | 1 | | | 1 | | | |
| Walker | 3 | | 2 | 5 | | | 2 | Losasso | 1 | | | 1 | | | |
| Keehan | 4 | | | 4 | | | | Lowe | 1 | | | 1 | | | |
| McGleish | 3 | 1 | | 4 | 2 | | 3 | McCrea | 1 | | | 1 | | | |
| Araba | 3 | | | 3 | | | | Pearson | 1 | | | 1 | | | |
| Louis | 3 | | | 3 | 1 | | | Ross-Branco | 1 | | | 1 | | | |
| Armstrong | 2 | | | 2 | 1 | | | Cons Run - Consecutive scoring games. | | | | | | | |

## Conference North Statistics 2012-13

| | MCV | MCD | MCwW | MCwD | MCSG | MCwS | TGS | MCCS | TNCS |
|---|---|---|---|---|---|---|---|---|---|
| Altrincham | 6 | 3 | 4 | 9 | 18 | 1 | 5 | 3 | 14 |
| Bishop's Stortford | 2 | 3 | 7 | 7 | 12 | 2 | 9 | 2 | 4 |
| Boston United | 3 | 4 | 7 | 3 | 18 | 3 | 10 | 3 | 10 |
| Brackley Town | 9 | 3 | 5 | 11 | 14 | 4 | 9 | 3 | 20 |
| Bradford PA | 4 | 5 | 7 | 9 | 15 | 4 | 7 | 3 | 12 |
| Chester | 10 | 2 | 3 | 25 | 18 | 1 | 4 | 3 | 19 |
| Colwyn Bay | 5 | 6 | 9 | 5 | 8 | 3 | 9 | 1 | 3 |
| Corby Town | 2 | 5 | 8 | 5 | 20 | 2 | 9 | 2 | 6 |
| Droylsden | 1 | 10 | 16 | 2 | 8 | 4 | 16 | 1 | 3 |
| FC Halifax Town | 7 | 1 | 6 | 8 | 11 | 3 | 10 | 4 | 20 |
| Gainsborough Trinity | 7 | 2 | 5 | 8 | 38 | 2 | 7 | 2 | 16 |
| Gloucester City | 3 | 5 | 6 | 4 | 6 | 3 | 15 | 2 | 11 |
| Guiseley | 6 | 2 | 4 | 6 | 7 | 1 | 7 | 4 | 16 |
| Harrogate Town | 4 | 2 | 5 | 10 | 15 | 2 | 10 | 3 | 12 |
| Hinckley United | 1 | 8 | 33 | 2 | 7 | 3 | 22 | 0 | 0 |
| Histon | 3 | 6 | 9 | 6 | 8 | 2 | 12 | 2 | 11 |
| Oxford City | 2 | 3 | 5 | 5 | 9 | 2 | 10 | 2 | 11 |
| Solihull Moors | 2 | 3 | 3 | 9 | 10 | 2 | 10 | 2 | 11 |
| Stalybridge Celtic | 3 | 3 | 12 | 5 | 9 | 4 | 14 | 2 | 14 |
| Vauxhall Motors | 2 | 6 | 6 | 8 | 13 | 3 | 11 | 3 | 10 |
| Worcester City | 2 | 9 | 9 | 6 | 7 | 7 | 17 | 2 | 13 |
| Workington | 2 | 3 | 4 | 5 | 12 | 2 | 10 | 2 | 7 |

MCV - Most Consecutive Victories
MCD - Most Consecutive Defeats
MCwW - Most Consecutive without a Win
MCwD - Most Consecutive without a defeat
MCSG - Most Consecutive Scoring Games
MCwS - Most Consecutive without Scoring
TGS - Total Games without Scoring
MCCS - Most Consecutive Clean Sheets
TNCS - Total Number of Clean Sheets

### Goalscorers with at least Ten goals in League, FA Cup and FA Trophy in 2012-2013

| | | | | | | | Total Individual Scorers | Hat tricks | Pens | OG scored by opponents |
|---|---|---|---|---|---|---|---|---|---|---|
| Altrincham | Damian Reeves | 41 | Duncan Whatmore | 14 | James Lawrie | 10 | 14 +2 ogs | 1 | 5 | 2 Burton Albion |
| Bishop's Stortford | Ricky Sappleton | 15 | | | | | 23 + 1 | 1 | 5 | 1 Vauxhall Moors |
| Boston United | Marc Newsham | 26 | Spencer Weir-Daley | 15 | Mark Jones | 12 | 16 + 0 | | 4 | |
| Brackley Town | Steve Diggin | 15 | Tom Winters | 15 | Glenn Walker | 11 | 14 + 4 | 1 | 3 | 4 Corby 2, Bradford PA, Colwyn Bay |
| Bradford PA | Richard Marshall | 19 | Danny Holland | 13 | Alex Davidson | 11 | 17 + 2 | 1 | 1 | 2 Corby Town, Ossett Albion |
| Chester | Nathan Jarman | 17 | Antoni Sarcevic | 13 | Ben Mills | 12 | | | | |
| | | | Tony Gray | 11 | Iain Howard | 10 | 19 + 2 | 2 | 1 | 2 Gloucester, Vauxhall Motors |
| Colwyn Bay | Rob Hopley | 19 | | | | | 18 + 0 | | 7 | 1 Droylsden |
| Corby Town | Josh Moreman | 17 | Ryan Semple | 12 | | | 17 + 1 | 1 | 4 | |
| Droylsden | | | | | | | 18 + 2 | 1 | 6 | 2 Worcester City, Whitby Town |
| FC Halifax Town | Lee Gregory | 26 | Gareth Seddon | 19 | Dale Johnson | 15 | | 7 | | |
| | | | Dan Gardner | 11 | Alex Titchener | 11 | 16 + 1 | | 3 | 1 Bishop's Stortford |
| Gainsborough Trinity | Paul Connor | 13 | Darryn Stamp | 12 | Dominic Knowles | 10 | 15 + 3 | 1 | 3 | 3 FC Halifax, Guiseley, Vauxhall Motors |
| Gloucester City | Darren Edwards | 11 | | | | | 18 + 1 | | 6 | 1 Bradford PA |
| Guiseley | James Walshaw | 22 | Josh Wilson | 22 | Micky Boshell | 12 | 18 + 0 | 1 | 3 | |
| Harrogate Town | Chibuzor Chilaka | 17 | Paul Beesley | 11 | Tom Platt | 11 | | | | |
| | | | | | Dominic Knowles | 10 | 20 + 2 | | 3 | 2 Droylsden and Histon |
| Hinckley United | | | | | | | 14 + 0 | 2 | | |
| Histon | James Stevenson | 10 | | | | | 19 + 1 | | 7 | 1 Chester |
| Oxford City | Felipe Barcelos | 14 | Jamie Cook | 10 | | | 15 + 0 | 1 | 1 | |
| Solihull Moors | Omar Bogle | 20 | | | | | 16 + 1 | 1 | 5 | 1 Gainsborough Trinity |
| Stalybridge Celtic | Jack Laird | 15 | | | | | 15 + 1 | | 5 | 1 Colwyn Bay |
| Vauxhall Motors | Ashley Stott | 12 | Tom Rutter | 10 | | | 16 + 0 | | 5 | |
| Worcester City | Michael Symon | 13 | Danny Glover | 10 | | | 18 + 1 | | 3 | 1 Harrogate Railway |
| Workington | Gareth Arnison | 21 | Johnnie Wright | 14 | | | 19 + 1 | | 4 | 1 Corby Town |

## Conference South Statistics 2012-13

| | MCV | MCD | MCwW | MCwD | MCSG | MCwS | TGS | MCCS | TNCS |
|---|---|---|---|---|---|---|---|---|---|
| AFC Hornchurch | 2 | 6 | 10 | 4 | 7 | 2 | 10 | 2 | 8 |
| Basingstoke Town | 3 | 4 | 9 | 5 | 12 | 2 | 12 | 1 | 5 |
| Bath City | 2 | 3 | 5 | 8 | 13 | 1 | 9 | 3 | 12 |
| Billericay Town | 3 | 6 | 7 | 5 | 10 | 3 | 10 | 1 | 5 |
| Boreham Wood | 3 | 3 | 4 | 7 | 11 | 3 | 10 | 3 | 14 |
| Bromley | 4 | 5 | 5 | 7 | 9 | 3 | 12 | 4 | 13 |
| Chelmsford City | 4 | 3 | 4 | 10 | 10 | 3 | 12 | 2 | 11 |
| Dorchester Town | 4 | 3 | 7 | 6 | 9 | 3 | 13 | 2 | 13 |
| Dover Athletic | 6 | 5 | 5 | 11 | 11 | 2 | 9 | 3 | 15 |
| Eastbourne Borough | 2 | 3 | 5 | 4 | 7 | 4 | 16 | 2 | 11 |
| Eastleigh | 4 | 6 | 6 | 9 | 25 | 2 | 7 | 2 | 11 |
| Farnborough | 3 | 4 | 5 | 4 | 10 | 2 | 9 | 2 | 4 |
| Havant & Waterlooville | 4 | 3 | 6 | 10 | 10 | 2 | 11 | 1 | 6 |
| Hayes & Yeading | 2 | 4 | 6 | 5 | 12 | 1 | 6 | 1 | 6 |
| Maidenhead United | 3 | 7 | 7 | 5 | 10 | 2 | 12 | 1 | 7 |
| Salisbury City | 5 | 2 | 4 | 8 | 18 | 2 | 7 | 3 | 13 |
| Staines Town | 3 | 4 | 11 | 4 | 10 | 2 | 9 | 1 | 7 |
| Sutton United | 8 | 2 | 10 | 11 | 11 | 3 | 11 | 4 | 13 |
| Tonbridge Angels | 3 | 3 | 7 | 6 | 14 | 3 | 10 | 1 | 5 |
| Truro City | 2 | 5 | 9 | 4 | 7 | 3 | 11 | 2 | 5 |
| Welling United | 12 | 2 | 3 | 12 | 37 | 1 | 2 | 4 | 16 |
| Weston-s Mare | 3 | 3 | 5 | 6 | 13 | 3 | 8 | 2 | 15 |

MCV - Most Consecutive Victories
MCD - Most Consecutive Defeatss
MCwW - Most Consecutive without a Win
MCwD - Most Consecutive without a defeat
MCSG - Most Consecutive Scoring Games
MCwS - Most Consecutive without Scoring
TGS - Total Games without Scoring
MCCS - Most Consecutive Clean Sheets
TNCS - Total Number of Clean Sheets

### Goalscorers with at least Ten goals in League, FA Cup and FA Trophy in 2012-2013

| | | | | | | | | Total Individual Scorers | Hat tricks | Pens | OG scored by opponents |
|---|---|---|---|---|---|---|---|---|---|---|---|
| AFC Hornchurch | Martin Tuohy | 12 | | | | | | 13 + 2 ogs | | 6 | 2 Chelmsford, Maidenhead |
| Basingstoke Town | Delano Sam-Yorke | 16 | Tim Sills | 13 | Manny Williams | 11 | | 15 + 1 | 1 | 0 | 1 Billericay Town |
| Bath City | Charlie Griffin | 18 | | | | | | 17 + 0 | 1 | 2 | 0 |
| Billericay Town | Glenn Poole | 16 | Jay May | 12 | Rob Swaine | 10 | | 15 + 1 | 2 | 6 | 1 Cambridge City |
| Boreham Wood | Omar Riza | 11 | | | | | | 18 + 1 | 1 | 7 | 1 Dorchester Town |
| Bromley | Pierre Joseph-Dubois | 19 | | | | | | 13 + 0 | | 3 | 0 |
| Chelmsford City | Jamie Slabber | 26 | Tony Cook | 12 | Rob Edmans | 10 | | 17 + 1 | 1 | 11 | 1 Basingstoke Town |
| Dorchester Town | Ben Watson | 17 | Charlie Clough | 12 | | | | 19 + 2 | | 0 | 2 Hayes & Yeading, Maidenhead |
| Dover Athletic | Ben May | 23 | Billy Bricknell | 13 | | | | 15 + 2 | | 4 | 2 Bath , Hayes & Yeading |
| Eastbourne Borough | Elliott Charles | 10 | | | | | | 16 + 0 | | 4 | 0 |
| Eastleigh | Craig McAllister | 18 | Jai Reason | 15 | | | | 18 + 2 | 1 | 5 | 2 Billericay Town, Salisbury City |
| Farnborough | Reece Connolly | 18 | Dan Bennett | 12 | David Tarpey | 10 | | 15 + 1 | | 2 | 1 Eastleigh |
| Havant & Waterlooville | Oliver Palmer | 24 | Sahr Kabba | 10 | | | | 17 + 1 | 2 | 8 | 1 Sutton United |
| Hayes & Yeading | Hudos Oyenuga | 17 | | | | | | 18 + 2 | | 6 | 1 Truro City |
| Maidenhead United | Alex Wall | 13 | David Pratt | 12 | Reece Tilson -Lascaris | 10 | | 14 + 0 | 1 | 5 | 0 |
| Salisbury City | Jamie White | 26 | Danny Fitchett | 19 | Chris McPhee | 16 | | 11 + 2 | 1 | 3 | 2 AFC Hornchurch, Sutton |
| Staines Town | David Wheeler | 14 | | | | | | 15 + 0 | 1 | 3 | 0 |
| Sutton United | Craig Dundas | 14 | Marvin Williams | 12 | Harry Beautyman | 10 | | 19 + 1 | | 6 | 1 Dorchester Town |
| Tonbridge Angels | Frannie Collin | 19 | | | | | | 14 + 0 | | 6 | 0 |
| Truro City | Kieffer Moore | 13 | Andy Watkins | 12 | Stuart Yetton | 10 | | 13 + 1 | | 2 | 1 Billericay Town |
| Welling United | Ross Lafayette | 22 | Joe Healy | 16 | Kieron Hughes | 11 | | 19 + 3 | 1 | 8 | 3 Billericay Town, Boreham, Concord Rangers, Dorchester |
| Weston-s Mare | Ross Stearn | 15 | Kane Ingram | 10 | | | | 17+ 0 | | 2 | 0 Chelmsford, Maidenhead |

# Click Back in Time!

Over 36 years of publishing the Non-League Club Directory has filled a room full of information and photographs covering the game we know and love.

What we intend, over time, is to create a website that shares with you everything we have accumulated, which we hope will bring back some fond memories of season's gone by.

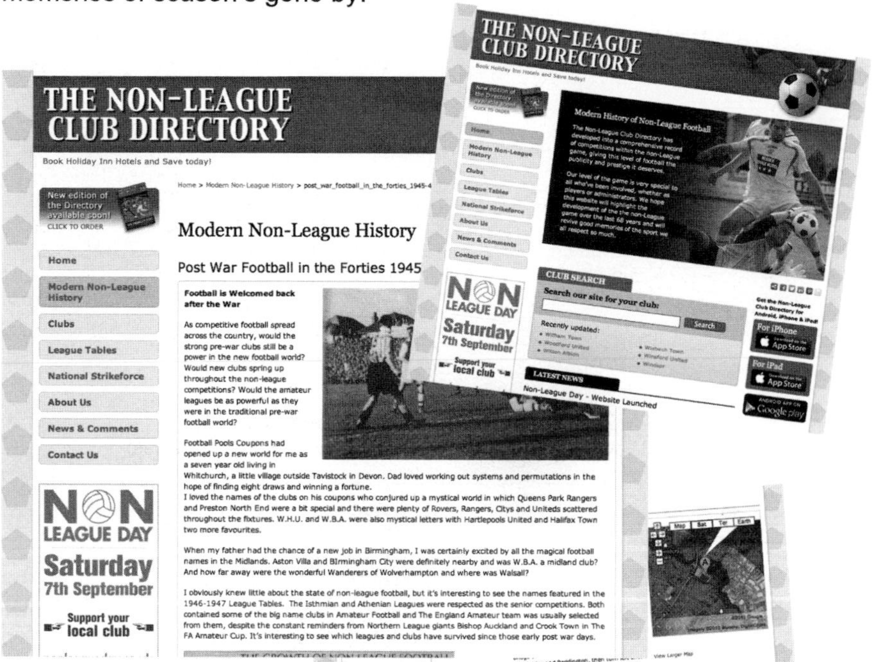

A unique look back at how the game has evolved since the 1940s will also make for interesting reading, including league tables from season's gone by.

Log on to **www.non-leagueclubdirectory.co.uk** today and see how many faces from teams gone by you recognise

# PREMIER DIVISION 2012-13

| | | P | W | D | L | F | A | GD | Pts |
|---|---|---|---|---|---|---|---|---|---|
| 1 | (P) North Ferriby United | 42 | 28 | 9 | 5 | 96 | 43 | 53 | 93 |
| 2 | (P) Hednesford Town | 42 | 28 | 9 | 5 | 91 | 47 | 44 | 93 |
| 3 | FC United of Manchester | 42 | 25 | 8 | 9 | 86 | 48 | 38 | 83 |
| 4 | Witton Albion | 42 | 24 | 8 | 10 | 85 | 57 | 28 | 80 |
| 5 | AFC Fylde | 42 | 23 | 6 | 13 | 93 | 51 | 42 | 75 |
| 6 | Rushall Olympic | 42 | 20 | 10 | 12 | 69 | 55 | 14 | 70 |
| 7 | Buxton | 42 | 18 | 13 | 11 | 72 | 56 | 16 | 67 |
| 8 | Chorley | 42 | 20 | 7 | 15 | 63 | 52 | 11 | 67 |
| 9 | Worksop Town | 42 | 20 | 6 | 16 | 91 | 68 | 23 | 66 |
| 10 | Ashton United | 42 | 15 | 14 | 13 | 71 | 66 | 5 | 59 |
| 11 | Marine | 42 | 16 | 11 | 15 | 61 | 61 | 0 | 59 |
| 12 | Ilkeston FC | 42 | 15 | 13 | 14 | 67 | 55 | 12 | 58 |
| 13 | Whitby Town | 42 | 16 | 9 | 17 | 68 | 72 | -4 | 57 |
| 14 | Nantwich Town | 42 | 15 | 8 | 19 | 63 | 76 | -13 | 53 |
| 15 | Stafford Rangers | 42 | 12 | 15 | 15 | 54 | 60 | -6 | 51 |
| 16 | Blyth Spartans | 42 | 15 | 6 | 21 | 70 | 87 | -17 | 51 |
| 17 | Matlock Town | 42 | 12 | 9 | 21 | 54 | 80 | -26 | 45 |
| 18 | Frickley Athletic | 42 | 10 | 9 | 23 | 58 | 88 | -30 | 39 |
| 19 | Grantham Town | 42 | 9 | 9 | 24 | 56 | 75 | -19 | 36 |
| 20 | Stocksbridge Park Steels | 42 | 9 | 9 | 24 | 67 | 106 | -39 | 36 |
| 21 | (R) Kendal Town | 42 | 9 | 6 | 27 | 65 | 112 | -47 | 33 |
| 22 | (R) Eastwood Town | 42 | 3 | 6 | 33 | 36 | 121 | -85 | 15 |

## PLAY-OFFS

### Semi-Finals

FC United of Manchester 3-1 Witton Albion

Hednesford Town 3-3 AFC Fylde (Hednesford won 3-1 on penalties)

### Final (@ Hednesford Town, 11/5/13)

Hednesford Town 2-1 FC United of Manchester

| | | 1 | 2 | 3 | 4 | 5 | 6 | 7 | 8 | 9 | 10 | 11 | 12 | 13 | 14 | 15 | 16 | 17 | 18 | 19 | 20 | 21 | 22 |
|---|---|---|---|---|---|---|---|---|---|---|---|---|---|---|---|---|---|---|---|---|---|---|---|
| 1 | AFC Fylde | | 1-2 | 1-0 | 5-0 | 0-1 | 5-1 | 4-2 | 3-2 | 5-3 | 1-2 | 2-3 | 4-0 | 2-0 | 3-0 | 3-2 | 1-0 | 1-3 | 0-1 | 4-0 | 4-3 | 1-2 | 2-2 |
| 2 | Ashton United | 2-2 | | 2-0 | 0-1 | 3-2 | 6-0 | 1-2 | 0-0 | 1-1 | 2-2 | 2-1 | 2-4 | 2-0 | 2-1 | 0-2 | 2-3 | 0-0 | 2-3 | 2-2 | 1-3 | 5-3 | |
| 3 | Blyth Spartans | 0-5 | 4-1 | | 2-2 | 1-3 | 1-0 | 1-2 | 4-2 | 1-0 | 1-2 | 3-2 | 1-3 | 3-3 | 2-1 | 1-1 | 0-1 | 1-1 | 1-0 | 5-0 | 2-2 | 0-3 | 3-2 |
| 4 | Buxton | 1-0 | 6-1 | 2-0 | | 1-1 | 6-2 | 0-3 | 1-0 | 1-1 | 0-2 | 0-0 | 1-2 | 1-4 | 1-0 | 3-1 | 2-0 | 2-0 | 2-1 | 7-0 | 2-1 | 2-2 | 0-3 |
| 5 | Chorley | 1-4 | 1-1 | 1-0 | 2-1 | | 2-1 | 1-2 | 5-1 | 2-0 | 1-2 | 1-0 | 5-0 | 1-0 | 1-0 | 3-3 | 0-1 | 1-6 | 2-0 | 1-1 | 2-3 | 1-2 | 1-1 |
| 6 | Eastwood Town | 1-4 | 0-5 | 1-4 | 1-5 | 0-1 | | 2-2 | 0-1 | 2-2 | 0-2 | 1-4 | 2-5 | 1-2 | 3-3 | 1-5 | 0-5 | 2-1 | 2-2 | 1-2 | 0-2 | 3-4 | 0-1 |
| 7 | FC United of Manchester | 2-1 | 3-0 | 1-2 | 1-3 | 4-1 | | | 3-0 | 1-0 | 1-1 | 6-0 | 0-1 | 4-0 | 1-2 | 4-0 | 3-0 | 4-0 | 3-2 | 0-1 | 1-0 | | |
| 8 | Frickley Athletic | 1-1 | 1-1 | 2-1 | 3-3 | 0-1 | 1-0 | 2-4 | | 0-0 | 2-1 | 2-1 | 0-2 | 1-2 | 0-2 | 2-3 | 3-3 | 2-1 | 4-2 | 0-2 | 0-0 | 2-1 | 4-1 |
| 9 | Grantham Town | 1-2 | 0-2 | 2-2 | 0-0 | 0-1 | 4-0 | 2-4 | 2-1 | | 2-3 | 1-1 | 3-4 | 1-4 | 0-3 | 2-3 | 2-1 | 2-2 | 1-2 | 2-3 | 1-3 | 3-0 | |
| 10 | Hednesford Town | 2-0 | 1-2 | 3-0 | 3-2 | 3-1 | 2-0 | 1-0 | 3-2 | 3-0 | | 2-0 | 2-1 | 2-0 | 2-2 | 3-0 | 2-3 | 3-4 | 2-2 | 4-1 | 4-0 | 2-1 | 0-4 |
| 11 | Ilkeston | 1-1 | 2-2 | 3-1 | 1-1 | 1-0 | 2-1 | 1-1 | 4-2 | 2-0 | 0-2 | | 4-4 | 1-0 | 0-2 | 3-0 | 2-2 | 0-1 | 0-2 | 1-0 | 3-1 | 2-3 | 2-1 |
| 12 | Kendal Town | 2-2 | 2-2 | 1-3 | 1-2 | 1-4 | 6-0 | 1-5 | 0-2 | 1-0 | 1-3 | 3-2 | | 2-3 | 4-1 | 0-1 | 2-4 | 0-2 | 2-2 | 0-5 | 2-4 | 1-2 | 3-3 |
| 13 | Marine | 0-4 | 0-0 | 5-1 | 2-0 | 2-0 | 2-0 | 0-3 | 2-2 | 1-0 | 0-3 | 2-2 | 1-0 | | 1-2 | 2-1 | 1-3 | 1-1 | 2-1 | 2-5 | 3-0 | 2-3 | |
| 14 | Matlock Town | 2-1 | 2-2 | 1-3 | 1-1 | 1-0 | 0-1 | 2-2 | 3-1 | 3-2 | 2-3 | 1-1 | 3-0 | 1-0 | | 0-5 | 0-2 | 0-3 | 2-3 | 1-1 | 0-0 | 1-2 | 1-5 |
| 15 | Nantwich Town | 0-3 | 0-2 | 2-1 | 2-2 | 0-1 | 1-0 | 2-3 | 3-2 | 0-2 | 1-1 | 1-0 | 1-1 | 2-3 | 0-1 | | 2-3 | 0-2 | 1-1 | 4-3 | 2-1 | 2-1 | 0-5 |
| 16 | North Ferriby United | 0-1 | 2-0 | 3-2 | 1-1 | 1-0 | 6-1 | 1-1 | 4-0 | 3-1 | 2-3 | 1-1 | 3-2 | 3-1 | 2-1 | 0-0 | | 2-2 | 1-1 | 5-1 | 1-1 | 2-0 | 2-0 |
| 17 | Rushall Olympic | 2-0 | 0-0 | 5-2 | 0-1 | 0-0 | 2-0 | 0-1 | 1-0 | 3-1 | 2-2 | 2-1 | 1-0 | 2-0 | 0-4 | 2-3 | 0-3 | | 1-1 | 1-1 | 1-1 | 0-4 | 1-2 |
| 18 | Stafford Rangers | 4-2 | 1-0 | 0-1 | 1-2 | 1-1 | 3-3 | 0-1 | 1-1 | 5-1 | 0-0 | 1-0 | 2-0 | 2-2 | 1-2 | 1-2 | 1-2 | 1-2 | | 1-1 | 0-1 | 0-0 | 3-1 |
| 19 | Stocksbridge Park Steels | 0-2 | 0-3 | 2-3 | 0-2 | 4-5 | 1-1 | 1-3 | 4-3 | 0-3 | 3-3 | 1-1 | 5-3 | 2-2 | 2-3 | 5-2 | 0-4 | 3-0 | 2-0 | | 1-4 | 3-3 | 1-2 |
| 20 | Whitby Town | 0-4 | 1-3 | 1-3 | 1-1 | 1-1 | 1-1 | 0-1 | 4-1 | 2-0 | 0-2 | 0-4 | 1-0 | 1-1 | 1-0 | 1-2 | 2-4 | 0-1 | 4-0 | 3-2 | | 1-3 | 2-1 |
| 21 | Witton Albion | 0-2 | 0-2 | 2-1 | 2-4 | 1-3 | 3-0 | 1-1 | 5-0 | 0-2 | 1-1 | 2-2 | 3-0 | 2-0 | 3-0 | 2-2 | 2-4 | 2-0 | 3-1 | 1-0 | 4-2 | | 4-3 |
| 22 | Worksop Town | 0-0 | 5-1 | 8-1 | 2-0 | 1-0 | 2-3 | 4-1 | 3-2 | 3-2 | 0-4 | 1-4 | 3-0 | 1-1 | 6-1 | 0-2 | 2-1 | 2-3 | 2-3 | 2-1 | 0-1 | 1-1 | |

 **DIVISION ONE NORTH 2012-13**

| | | P | W | D | L | F | A | GD | Pts |
|---|---|---|---|---|---|---|---|---|---|
| 1 | (P) Skelmersdale United | 42 | 32 | 6 | 4 | 110 | 41 | 69 | 102 |
| 2 | Cammell Laird | 42 | 26 | 8 | 8 | 86 | 58 | 28 | 86 |
| 3 | New Mills | 42 | 26 | 7 | 9 | 107 | 69 | 38 | 85 |
| 4 | (P) Trafford | 42 | 24 | 8 | 10 | 93 | 44 | 49 | 80 |
| 5 | Mossley | 42 | 24 | 8 | 10 | 83 | 48 | 35 | 80 |
| 6 | Ramsbottom United | 42 | 24 | 7 | 11 | 97 | 49 | 48 | 79 |
| 7 | Curzon Ashton | 42 | 22 | 7 | 13 | 98 | 67 | 31 | 73 |
| 8 | Clitheroe | 42 | 21 | 10 | 11 | 66 | 63 | 3 | 73 |
| 9 | Bamber Bridge | 42 | 21 | 7 | 14 | 86 | 58 | 28 | 70 |
| 10 | Warrington Town | 42 | 19 | 12 | 11 | 76 | 54 | 22 | 69 |
| 11 | Burscough | 42 | 14 | 17 | 11 | 81 | 64 | 17 | 59 |
| 12 | Ossett Town | 42 | 14 | 13 | 15 | 67 | 65 | 2 | 55 |
| 13 | Lancaster City (-3pts) | 42 | 15 | 8 | 19 | 70 | 73 | -3 | 50 |
| 14 | Farsley FC | 42 | 13 | 10 | 19 | 72 | 80 | -8 | 49 |
| 15 | Radcliffe Borough | 42 | 11 | 15 | 16 | 68 | 69 | -1 | 48 |
| 16 | Salford City | 42 | 11 | 13 | 18 | 65 | 79 | -14 | 46 |
| 17 | Prescot Cables | 42 | 12 | 10 | 20 | 51 | 67 | -16 | 46 |
| 18 | Harrogate Railway Athletic | 42 | 11 | 8 | 23 | 47 | 89 | -42 | 41 |
| 19 | Wakefield | 42 | 6 | 9 | 27 | 38 | 119 | -81 | 27 |
| 20 | Ossett Albion | 42 | 6 | 7 | 29 | 49 | 96 | -47 | 25 |
| 21 | Goole AFC | 42 | 5 | 8 | 29 | 44 | 89 | -45 | 23 |
| 22 | (R) Garforth Town | 42 | 4 | 4 | 34 | 44 | 157 | -113 | 16 |

**PLAY-OFFS**
Semi-Finals
Cammell Laird 1-0 Mossley
New Mills 0-2 Trafford (AET)

Final (@ Cammell Laird 10/05/13)
Cammell Laird 0-0 Trafford (Trafford won 4-2 on penalties aet)

| | | 1 | 2 | 3 | 4 | 5 | 6 | 7 | 8 | 9 | 10 | 11 | 12 | 13 | 14 | 15 | 16 | 17 | 18 | 19 | 20 | 21 | 22 |
|---|---|---|---|---|---|---|---|---|---|---|---|---|---|---|---|---|---|---|---|---|---|---|---|
| 1 | Bamber Bridge | | 2-1 | 0-0 | 1-3 | 3-0 | 4-0 | 5-0 | 3-0 | 4-1 | 4-3 | 2-2 | 1-4 | 3-2 | 4-0 | 2-1 | 3-1 | 1-1 | 1-2 | 0-2 | 1-0 | 2-0 | 0-0 |
| 2 | Burscough | 1-0 | | 2-2 | 0-0 | 5-1 | 0-0 | 3-1 | 1-4 | 0-0 | 0-3 | 2-1 | 1-1 | 1-2 | 4-2 | 0-2 | 2-2 | 4-1 | 1-3 | 1-1 | 1-1 | | |
| 3 | Cammell Laird | 3-2 | 4-2 | | 3-2 | 1-2 | 2-4 | 2-0 | 1-0 | 0-1 | 1-0 | 1-0 | 2-0 | 3-2 | 4-2 | 5-2 | 3-2 | 3-1 | 3-2 | 3-2 | 1-1 | 2-1 | 2-1 |
| 4 | Clitheroe | 2-1 | 3-2 | 2-1 | | 2-1 | 0-0 | 3-1 | 3-1 | 3-3 | 1-0 | 1-0 | 0-0 | 3-2 | 0-2 | 2-0 | 0-3 | 1-3 | 2-2 | 1-7 | 2-0 | 2-2 | 2-1 |
| 5 | Curzon Ashton | 4-2 | 2-5 | 1-1 | 1-1 | | 3-2 | 6-0 | 3-2 | 3-0 | 4-1 | 3-0 | 4-3 | 3-2 | 0-1 | 2-2 | 0-2 | 1-0 | 3-1 | 1-6 | 0-0 | 10-1 | 4-2 |
| 6 | Farsley AFC | 1-1 | 1-2 | 1-3 | 3-0 | 1-1 | | 5-0 | 1-1 | 2-3 | 2-3 | 0-4 | 1-2 | 2-0 | 4-0 | 1-1 | 2-0 | 1-1 | 5-3 | 1-5 | 3-4 | 3-0 | 0-3 |
| 7 | Garforth Town | 0-3 | 1-5 | 0-4 | 0-2 | 1-6 | 1-3 | | 0-0 | 1-2 | 3-4 | 0-6 | 3-4 | 2-4 | 0-6 | 1-4 | 2-2 | 0-5 | 0-2 | 0-3 | 2-4 | 1-1 | 2-5 |
| 8 | Goole AFC | 0-2 | 2-2 | 0-2 | 1-2 | 0-2 | 0-3 | 6-2 | | 1-0 | 1-3 | 0-4 | 2-3 | 3-1 | 2-0 | 0-1 | 1-2 | 0-0 | 0-0 | 1-2 | 1-2 | 1-2 | 1-2 |
| 9 | Harrogate Railway Athletic | 1-2 | 1-6 | 1-3 | 4-2 | 0-2 | 2-2 | 2-3 | 3-0 | | 0-4 | 0-1 | 1-4 | 1-3 | 1-2 | 1-3 | 2-2 | 0-2 | 2-0 | 3-2 | 1-0 | 1-1 | 1-2 |
| 10 | Lancaster City | 4-2 | 2-2 | 1-2 | 2-2 | 3-2 | 1-1 | 4-1 | 2-2 | 2-1 | | 0-0 | 1-2 | 1-0 | 2-3 | 3-1 | 2-2 | 0-5 | 0-1 | 1-3 | 0-0 | 0-1 | 1-1 |
| 11 | Mossley | 1-0 | 3-1 | 1-3 | 2-3 | 1-2 | 3-0 | 7-0 | 2-1 | 3-0 | 2-0 | | 0-4 | 2-0 | 2-1 | 4-1 | 2-0 | 0-4 | 2-2 | 0-2 | 3-2 | 2-2 | 1-0 |
| 12 | New Mills | 1-5 | 1-2 | 1-1 | 1-2 | 2-1 | 3-0 | 9-2 | 3-1 | 4-1 | 3-1 | 2-2 | | 5-1 | 2-1 | 1-4 | 1-0 | 2-1 | 1-1 | 1-2 | 6-0 | 1-1 | 1-6 |
| 13 | Ossett Albion | 0-1 | 1-1 | 1-2 | 0-1 | 2-0 | 2-0 | 0-1 | 3-2 | 0-2 | 0-3 | 3-3 | 1-4 | | 0-2 | 0-0 | 1-2 | 1-6 | 2-0 | 1-4 | 0-8 | 2-3 | 1-2 |
| 14 | Ossett Town | 2-1 | 2-2 | 3-0 | 1-1 | 1-4 | 3-3 | 5-5 | 0-2 | 0-0 | 1-2 | 0-1 | 3-3 | 1-1 | | 1-1 | 0-0 | 0-1 | 3-2 | 0-1 | 0-4 | 6-0 | 2-2 |
| 15 | Prescot Cables | 2-3 | 0-0 | 0-2 | 0-2 | 1-3 | 0-1 | 1-0 | 2-1 | 2-2 | 3-2 | 1-2 | 1-2 | 2-1 | 1-2 | | 1-1 | 2-0 | 0-3 | 0-1 | 1-1 | 4-0 | 1-1 |
| 16 | Radcliffe Borough | 2-2 | 1-1 | 0-3 | 1-3 | 3-1 | 2-2 | 6-2 | 1-1 | 1-2 | 2-0 | 1-2 | 2-3 | 1-1 | 1-2 | 1-0 | | 2-2 | 1-1 | 0-2 | 2-0 | 4-0 | 2-2 |
| 17 | Ramsbottom United | 2-2 | 3-1 | 3-3 | 3-0 | 3-4 | 1-2 | 6-0 | 2-1 | 4-0 | 2-0 | 1-2 | 2-3 | 4-3 | 1-1 | 3-0 | 3-2 | | 5-1 | 0-2 | 2-1 | 2-1 | 0-0 |
| 18 | Salford City | 2-4 | 2-6 | 2-2 | 1-1 | 1-1 | 2-0 | 3-0 | 3-0 | 1-1 | 1-0 | 1-2 | 1-2 | 0-0 | 1-2 | 1-1 | 2-3 | | 0-3 | 3-3 | 5-2 | 1-1 | 1-1 |
| 19 | Skelmersdale United | 2-1 | 3-3 | 6-1 | 3-0 | 3-2 | 4-0 | 3-1 | 2-2 | 4-0 | 3-1 | 2-1 | 3-3 | 4-1 | 2-1 | 3-1 | 2-1 | 3-2 | | 1-2 | 2-0 | 1-1 | |
| 20 | Trafford | 2-0 | 0-0 | 0-1 | 3-0 | 0-3 | 3-2 | 3-0 | 5-1 | 4-0 | 3-0 | 2-0 | 2-0 | 2-2 | 2-1 | 1-2 | 4-1 | 2-1 | 6-0 | 0-2 | | 7-0 | 3-2 |
| 21 | Wakefield | 0-5 | 1-1 | 2-1 | 0-3 | 2-1 | 0-5 | 0-2 | 3-1 | 0-0 | 1-4 | 1-6 | 3-5 | 1-1 | 0-3 | 1-2 | 2-2 | 1-2 | 0-3 | 0-2 | 0-1 | | 1-2 |
| 22 | Warrington Town | 3-1 | 1-2 | 0-2 | 2-1 | 3-2 | 2-1 | 1-4 | 7-2 | 4-0 | 1-3 | 0-0 | 4-1 | 2-1 | 0-0 | 2-0 | 1-0 | 0-3 | 2-1 | 0-1 | 1-1 | 4-1 | |

# DIVISION ONE SOUTH 2012-13

| | | P | W | D | L | F | A | GD | Pts |
|---|---|---|---|---|---|---|---|---|---|
| 1 | (P) Kings Lynn Town | 42 | 28 | 8 | 6 | 86 | 46 | 40 | 92 |
| 2 | Coalville Town | 42 | 25 | 11 | 6 | 108 | 44 | 64 | 86 |
| 3 | Belper Town | 42 | 23 | 13 | 6 | 95 | 42 | 53 | 82 |
| 4 | (P) Stamford | 42 | 23 | 7 | 12 | 97 | 58 | 39 | 76 |
| 5 | Chasetown | 42 | 21 | 11 | 10 | 83 | 51 | 32 | 74 |
| 6 | Sutton Coldfield Town | 42 | 22 | 8 | 12 | 81 | 61 | 20 | 74 |
| 7 | Halesowen Town | 42 | 23 | 5 | 14 | 79 | 65 | 14 | 74 |
| 8 | Northwich Victoria | 42 | 19 | 10 | 13 | 88 | 58 | 30 | 67 |
| 9 | Sheffield FC | 42 | 18 | 9 | 15 | 85 | 82 | 3 | 63 |
| 10 | Leek Town | 42 | 15 | 14 | 13 | 72 | 60 | 12 | 59 |
| 11 | Gresley FC | 42 | 16 | 10 | 16 | 75 | 77 | -2 | 58 |
| 12 | Carlton Town | 42 | 16 | 8 | 18 | 67 | 68 | -1 | 56 |
| 13 | Brigg Town | 42 | 14 | 11 | 17 | 62 | 76 | -14 | 53 |
| 14 | Rainworth Miners Welfare | 42 | 14 | 9 | 19 | 59 | 75 | -16 | 51 |
| 15 | Market Drayton Town | 42 | 13 | 11 | 18 | 68 | 78 | -10 | 50 |
| 16 | Loughborough Dynamo | 42 | 13 | 10 | 19 | 75 | 75 | 0 | 49 |
| 17 | Newcastle Town | 42 | 11 | 13 | 18 | 45 | 58 | -13 | 46 |
| 18 | Kidsgrove Athletic | 42 | 12 | 7 | 23 | 75 | 89 | -14 | 43 |
| 19 | Romulus | 42 | 11 | 9 | 22 | 52 | 78 | -26 | 42 |
| 20 | Lincoln United | 42 | 9 | 9 | 24 | 64 | 102 | -38 | 36 |
| 21 | Mickleover Sports | 42 | 7 | 13 | 22 | 51 | 92 | -41 | 34 |
| 22 | (R) Hucknall Town | 42 | 4 | 4 | 34 | 39 | 171 | -132 | 16 |

## PLAY-OFFS
Semi-Finals
Belper Town 2-4 Stamford (AET)
Coalville Town 1-2 Chasetown

Final (@ Stamford 10/05/13)
Stamford 2-1 Chasetown

| | | 1 | 2 | 3 | 4 | 5 | 6 | 7 | 8 | 9 | 10 | 11 | 12 | 13 | 14 | 15 | 16 | 17 | 18 | 19 | 20 | 21 | 22 |
|---|---|---|---|---|---|---|---|---|---|---|---|---|---|---|---|---|---|---|---|---|---|---|---|
| 1 | Belper Town | | 1-1 | 1-1 | 3-0 | 1-1 | 1-1 | 4-1 | 2-0 | 1-1 | 1-1 | 1-1 | 3-0 | 3-1 | 5-0 | 0-3 | 1-1 | 3-1 | 1-2 | 9-0 | 2-2 | 4-0 | 1-0 |
| 2 | Brigg Town | 2-2 | | 3-0 | 0-1 | 0-3 | 3-3 | 2-2 | 1-0 | 3-1 | 1-1 | 3-2 | 2-0 | 1-1 | 2-0 | 2-1 | 1-3 | 0-3 | 3-2 | 0-5 | 0-3 | 2-3 | 2-1 |
| 3 | Carlton Town | 0-1 | 5-2 | | 2-2 | 3-2 | 0-1 | 1-2 | 1-0 | 4-2 | 2-2 | 3-2 | 1-1 | 1-2 | 2-3 | 0-1 | 1-0 | 1-2 | 0-0 | 2-0 | 2-2 | 2-3 | 2-3 |
| 4 | Chasetown | 1-1 | 2-0 | 5-0 | | 1-4 | 3-4 | 3-0 | 4-0 | 6-1 | 0-1 | 0-0 | 3-1 | 3-0 | 0-1 | 1-1 | 2-0 | 0-1 | 3-0 | 3-2 | 5-1 | 3-1 | 2-2 |
| 5 | Coalville Town | 1-1 | 2-1 | 5-1 | 1-1 | | 1-1 | 0-1 | 5-0 | 4-3 | 0-0 | 6-2 | 2-1 | 0-0 | 2-2 | 6-1 | 4-1 | 1-0 | 3-0 | 3-1 | 3-1 | 1-0 | 2-0 |
| 6 | Gresley | 1-0 | 2-4 | 0-2 | 1-4 | 1-2 | | 3-2 | 5-2 | 2-1 | 1-2 | 1-1 | 0-0 | 3-2 | 2-0 | 1-1 | 1-3 | 2-1 | 3-0 | 0-1 | 2-3 | 1-3 | 2-1 |
| 7 | Halesowen Town | 1-3 | 2-1 | 1-1 | 1-5 | 4-2 | | | 2-1 | 4-3 | 1-0 | 2-2 | 5-0 | 3-0 | 1-0 | 1-3 | 5-0 | 2-3 | 1-1 | 5-0 | 2-3 | 1-1 | 2-1 |
| 8 | Hucknall Town | 0-5 | 1-6 | 0-3 | 3-2 | 1-9 | 1-3 | 0-4 | | 0-5 | 1-3 | 1-6 | 1-1 | 1-7 | 2-4 | 0-2 | 0-1 | 1-2 | 1-8 | 1-3 | 0-5 | 2-2 | 2-3 |
| 9 | Kidsgrove Athletic | 2-2 | 3-1 | 1-2 | 0-1 | 1-1 | 5-3 | 1-0 | 4-0 | | 1-2 | 3-3 | 2-1 | 3-2 | 2-2 | 1-1 | 4-1 | 0-1 | 3-0 | 0-0 | 1-4 | 1-3 | 0-2 |
| 10 | King's Lynn Town | 1-2 | 3-2 | 0-0 | 1-0 | 3-1 | 2-2 | 3-2 | 2-4 | 3-1 | | 2-0 | 5-2 | 2-0 | 3-0 | 7-0 | 3-2 | 1-0 | 2-0 | 3-0 | 2-1 | 2-1 | 2-0 |
| 11 | Leek Town | 1-2 | 1-1 | 2-1 | 1-1 | 0-4 | 1-2 | 0-2 | 5-1 | 2-1 | 1-1 | | 3-1 | 0-1 | 3-0 | 3-1 | 1-2 | 1-1 | 2-2 | 5-1 | 0-1 | 3-0 | 2-1 |
| 12 | Lincoln United | 2-4 | 1-0 | 2-4 | 2-2 | 2-1 | 5-2 | 1-2 | 0-1 | 1-4 | 2-3 | 1-2 | | 1-3 | 2-1 | 1-1 | 3-2 | 1-1 | 3-1 | 0-3 | 2-6 | 1-1 | 3-2 |
| 13 | Louthborough Dynamo | 0-0 | 1-1 | 2-4 | 3-0 | 0-2 | 1-1 | 0-2 | 13-0 | 5-1 | 3-5 | 0-3 | 1-2 | | 1-5 | 4-2 | 0-3 | 1-3 | 0-0 | 2-0 | 4-1 | 0-2 | 0-2 |
| 14 | Market Drayton Town | 3-2 | 1-1 | 1-4 | 0-1 | 2-5 | 0-1 | 2-3 | 2-4 | 2-0 | 0-1 | 1-1 | 3-3 | 4-1 | | 3-3 | 3-1 | 2-3 | 3-1 | 1-0 | 6-3 | 0-1 | 1-0 |
| 15 | Mickleover Sports | 0-0 | 0-2 | 2-2 | 0-3 | 0-5 | 0-4 | 3-2 | 4-0 | 0-3 | 1-3 | 0-1 | 0-1 | 1-1 | 2-2 | | 0-1 | 0-2 | 1-0 | 0-1 | 3-3 | 1-2 | 2-2 |
| 16 | Newcastle Town | 1-2 | 1-1 | 1-0 | 4-0 | 2-1 | 3-1 | 2-3 | 1-1 | 0-4 | 0-0 | 1-1 | 2-2 | 0-0 | 0-1 | 1-1 | | 1-1 | 0-0 | 0-2 | 0-1 | 0-0 | 0-2 |
| 17 | Northwich Victoria | 1-2 | 2-0 | 2-3 | 0-1 | 3-0 | 2-2 | 3-0 | 10-0 | 1-1 | 0-4 | 3-3 | 4-4 | 1-1 | 4-1 | 1-3 | 2-0 | | 2-0 | 3-1 | 3-2 | 3-4 | 0-1 |
| 18 | Rainworth Miners Welfare | 1-3 | 1-2 | 2-0 | 0-2 | 1-1 | 2-1 | 0-2 | 4-1 | 3-1 | 2-2 | 1-0 | 3-4 | 0-0 | 2-2 | 4-2 | 3-2 | 0-0 | | 2-1 | 1-2 | 0-4 | 1-0 |
| 19 | Romulus | 0-3 | 1-1 | 0-2 | 1-3 | 0-1 | 0-2 | 0-1 | 7-2 | 1-0 | 1-2 | 1-1 | 3-1 | 2-4 | 1-1 | 2-2 | 1-1 | 2-2 | 2-3 | | 2-1 | 0-2 | 1-1 |
| 20 | Sheffield | 1-5 | 1-2 | 2-0 | 2-2 | 3-3 | 1-2 | 0-3 | 3-3 | 3-0 | 2-0 | 0-2 | 2-2 | 1-2 | 3-1 | 2-2 | 1-0 | 2-1 | 4-1 | 2-0 | | 2-1 | 2-3 |
| 21 | Stamford | 4-1 | 3-0 | 1-2 | 1-2 | 1-1 | 2-2 | 4-1 | 8-0 | 4-1 | 4-1 | 0-1 | 5-1 | 1-2 | 3-2 | 5-2 | 3-0 | 5-3 | 1-2 | 4-1 | 0-2 | | 0-0 |
| 22 | Sutton Coldfield Town | 2-1 | 5-0 | 1-0 | 4-4 | 0-4 | 4-2 | 2-0 | 4-0 | 4-3 | 3-1 | 2-2 | 4-3 | 2-1 | 0-0 | 2-1 | 2-0 | 0-5 | 5-1 | 1-1 | 4-0 | 2-4 | |

# LEAGUE CHALLENGE CUP 2012-13

## PRELIMINARY ROUND

| | | |
|---|---|---|
| New Mills | 0–4 | Leek Town |
| Romulus | 2–1 | Gresley |
| Salford City | 0–1 | **CURZON ASHTON** |
| Sheffield | 5–3 | Harrogate Railway |
| Athletic | | |

## ROUND 1

| | | |
|---|---|---|
| Bamber Bridge | 1–2* | Cammell Laird |
| Burscough | 2–1 | Ramsbottom United |
| Coalville Town | 4–6* | Rainworth M. W. |
| Farsley | 2–1 | Ossett Albion |
| Garforth Town | 1–2 | Sheffield |
| Halesowen Town | 1–3* | Carlton Town |
| Hucknall Town | 0–4 | Brigg Town |
| King's Lynn Town | 1–2 | Stamford |
| Lancaster City | 0–1 | **CURZON ASHTON** |
| Lincoln United | 1–4 | Mickleover Sports |
| Mossley | 1–7 | Warrington Town |
| Newcastle Town | 1–2 | Market Drayton Town |
| Northwich Victoria | 2–0 | Kidsgrove Athletic |
| Ossett Town | 3–1* | Belper Town |
| Radcliffe Borough | 4–5 | Clitheroe |
| Romulus | 0–2 | Chasetown |
| Skelmersdale Utd | 7–1 | Prescot Cables |
| Sutton Coldfield T. | 4–2 | Loughborough Dynamo |
| Trafford | 3–1 | Leek Town |
| Wakefield | 2–3 | Goole |

## ROUND 2

| | | |
|---|---|---|
| Brigg Town | 3–5* | Sheffield |
| Carlton Town | 2–1 | Ossett Town |
| Chasetown | 1–5 | Northwich Victoria |
| **CURZON ASHTON** | 2–0 | Burscough |
| Farsley | 4–1 | Clitheroe |
| Goole | 0–4 | Rainworth M. W. |
| Market Drayton T. | 1–0 | Sutton Coldfield Town |
| Mickleover Sports | 4–3* | Stamford |
| Skelmersdale Utd | 2–2* | Cammell Laird (0-3p) |
| Trafford | 3–2 | Warrington Town |

## ROUND 3

| | | |
|---|---|---|
| Witton Albion | 3–1 | AFC Fylde |
| Ashton United | 1–2 | F.C. Utd of Manchester |
| **NORTH FERRIBY UTD** | 6–3 | Sheffield |
| Northwich Victoria | 1–0 | Market Drayton Town |
| Chorley | 2–3 | Cammell Laird |
| **CURZON ASHTON** | 3–0 | Kendal Town |
| Farsley | 3–1 | Whitby Town |
| Ilkeston | 1–2 | Eastwood Town |
| Marine | 3–0 | Trafford |
| Matlock Town | 2–1 | Carlton Town |
| Mickleover Sports | 1–4 | Grantham Town |
| Rainworth Miners Wel. | 2–0* | Buxton |
| Rushall Olympic | 1–0 | Hednesford Town |
| Stafford Rangers | 1–2 | Nantwich Town |
| Stocksbridge P.S. | 3–5 | Blyth Spartans |
| Worksop Town | 4–1 | Frickley Athletic |

## ROUND 4

| | | |
|---|---|---|
| Witton Albion | 4–3 | F.C. Utd of Manchester |
| Blyth Spartans | 1–2 | **NORTH FERRIBY UTD** |
| Eastwood Town | 2–0 | Rainworth M. W. |
| Farsley | 2–1 | Worksop Town |
| Grantham Town | 1–2 | Matlock Town |
| Marine | 1–2 | Cammell Laird |
| Nantwich Town | 1–3 | **CURZON ASHTON** |
| Rushall Olympic | 1–2 | Northwich Victoria |

## QUARTER FINALS

| | | |
|---|---|---|
| Eastwood Town | 0–5 | **NORTH FERRIBY UTD** |
| Cammell Laird | 3–1* | Northwich Victoria |
| Matlock Town | 3–1 | Farsley |
| **CURZON ASHTON** | 0–4 | Witton Albion |

## SEMI-FINALS

| | | |
|---|---|---|
| **NORTH FERRIBY UTD** | 2–1 | Cammell Laird |
| Matlock Town | 1–2 | **CURZON ASHTON** |

## FINAL

| | | |
|---|---|---|
| **CURZON ASHTON** | 1–1* | **NORTH FERRIBY UTD** |
| | (1-2p) | |

\* AET

# Northern Premier League Premier Division Statistics 2012-13

| | MCV | MCD | MCwW | MCwD | MCSG | MCwS | TGS | MCCS | TNCS |
|---|---|---|---|---|---|---|---|---|---|
| AFC Fylde | 6 | 2 | 6 | 10 | 17 | 1 | 7 | 3 | 18 |
| Ashton United | 4 | 3 | 5 | 8 | 9 | 3 | 10 | 5 | 13 |
| Blyth Spartans | 3 | 4 | 6 | 6 | 11 | 2 | 9 | 1 | 5 |
| Buxton | 3 | 2 | 4 | 9 | 12 | 2 | 11 | 3 | 15 |
| Chorley | 5 | 4 | 7 | 8 | 16 | 1 | 8 | 2 | 13 |
| Eastwood Town | 2 | 8 | 31 | 4 | 6 | 3 | 18 | 1 | 1 |
| FC United | 8 | 3 | 5 | 10 | 16 | 2 | 4 | 2 | 12 |
| Frickley Athletic | 2 | 4 | 8 | 3 | 12 | 2 | 12 | 2 | 8 |
| Grantham Town | 2 | 8 | 13 | 6 | 8 | 2 | 12 | 2 | 9 |
| Hednesford Town | 6 | 2 | 4 | 11 | 34 | 1 | 3 | 5 | 17 |
| Ilkeston | 5 | 2 | 8 | 8 | 10 | 2 | 10 | 2 | 10 |
| Kendal Town | 3 | 12 | 12 | 3 | 8 | 2 | 12 | 1 | 3 |
| Marine | 4 | 4 | 6 | 10 | 10 | 3 | 15 | 2 | 12 |
| Matlock Town | 4 | 3 | 7 | 7 | 11 | 3 | 15 | 2 | 8 |
| Nantwich Town | 3 | 5 | 7 | 6 | 8 | 3 | 15 | 1 | 7 |
| North Ferriby United | 6 | 2 | 3 | 12 | 22 | 1 | 4 | 4 | 15 |
| Rushall Olympic | 4 | 3 | 4 | 6 | 10 | 2 | 10 | 2 | 14 |
| Stafford Rangers | 3 | 4 | 6 | 8 | 14 | 3 | 13 | 2 | 12 |
| Stocksbridge PS | 3 | 5 | 11 | 4 | 6 | 2 | 12 | 1 | 3 |
| Whitby Town | 4 | 6 | 7 | 7 | 15 | 2 | 8 | 2 | 10 |
| Witton Albion | 5 | 2 | 5 | 8 | 11 | 1 | 6 | 3 | 12 |
| Worksop Town | 4 | 4 | 4 | 8 | 8 | 2 | 10 | 3 | 11 |

MCV - Most Consecutive Victories
MCD - Most Consecutive Defeatss
MCwW - Most Consecutive without a Win
MCwD - Most Consecutive without a defeat
MCSG - Most Consecutive Scoring Games
MCwS - Most Consecutive without Scoring
TGS - Total Games without Scoring
MCCS - Most Consecutive Clean Sheets
TNCS - Total Number of Clean Sheets

## Goalscorers with at least Ten goals in League, FA Cup and FA Trophy in 2012-2013

| | | | | | | | Total Individual Scorers | Hat tricks | Pens | OG scored by opponents |
|---|---|---|---|---|---|---|---|---|---|---|
| AFC Fylde | Michael Barnes | 21 | Adam Farrell | 18 | James Dean | 15 | 16 + 2 ogs | 3 | 4 | 2 FC United, Whitby Town |
| Ashton United | Aaron Burns | 22 | | | | | 18 + 2 | 5 | 1 | 2 Matlock, Stocksbridge PS |
| Blyth Spartans | | | | | | | 20 + 0 | 8 | | |
| Buxton | Mark Reed | 23 | Lee Morris | 17 | | | 17 + 0 | 7 | 4 | |
| Chorley | Darren Stephenson | 13 | | | | | 11 + 1 | 4 | 1 | 1 Frickley Athletic |
| Eastwood Town | | | | | | | 15 + 2 | 3 | | 2 |
| FC United | Mike Norton | 19 | Matt Wolfenden | 18 | Tom Greaves | 10 | | | | |
| | | | | | Jerome Wright | 10 | 18 + 1 | 3 | 1 | 1 Cammell Laird |
| Frickley Athletic | Gavin Allott | 22 | | | | | 14 + 1 | | 3 | 1 Eastwood Town |
| Grantham Town | | | | | | | 20 + 0 | 4 | | |
| Hednesford Town | Elliott Durrell | 29 | Neil Harvey | 17 | Aaron Rey | 12 | 17 + 0 | 12 | | |
| Ilkeston | Kane Richards | 13 | Aaron Hoddon | 11 | Gary Richards | 10 | 21 + 3 | 2 | | 3 Witton Albion |
| Kendal Town | Danny Mitchley | 10 | Mason McGeechan | 10 | | | 21 + 2 | 4 | 1 | 2 North Ferriby, Stafford R'gers |
| Marine | Nick Rogan | 15 | Marcus Carver | 10 | | | 18 + 0 | | | |
| Matlock Town | Lewis McMahon | 17 | Massiah McDonald | 13 | | | 19 + 2 | 8 | | 2 Ashton United, Blyth Spartans |
| Nantwich Town | Sean Cooke | 14 | | | | | 21 + 2 | 3 | | 2 |
| North Ferriby United | Ryan Kendall | 36 | Anthony Wilson | 15 | Gary Bradshaw | 12 | 15 + 1 | 8 | 2 | 1 Stocksbridge Park Steels |
| Rushall Olympic | Dave Walker | 26 | Ahmed Obeng | 17 | | | 17 + 2 | 4 | 1 | 2 Grantham, North Ferriby |
| Stafford Rangers | Danny Quinn | 20 | | | | | 17 + 0 | 7 | 2 | |
| Stocksbridge PS | Danny South | 15 | Nathan Joynes | 13 | | | 23 + 1 | 2 | 1 | 1 Kendal Town |
| Whitby Town | Nathan Mulligan | 17 | Craig Farrell | 16 | Graeme Armstrong | | 14 + 2 | 6 | 1 | 2 Frickley Athletic, Kendal Town |
| Witton Albion | Shaun Tuck | 21 | Steve Foster | 15 | Joshua Hancock | 14 | | | | |
| | | | | | Danny Andrews | 12 | 17 + 2 | 6 | 2 | 2 Ashton Uited , Whitby Town |
| Worksop Town | Liam Mettam | 23 | Tom Denton | 22 | Ashley Burbeary | 14 | | | | |
| | | | | | Steve Towers | 11 | 13 + 1 | 5 | 3 | 1 Stocksbridge PS |

# A.F.C. FYLDE

**Chairman:** David Haythornthwaite

**Secretary:** Martin Benson    **(T)** 07545 735 154    **(E)** info@afcfylde.co.uk

**Commercial Manager:** Simon Hazelwood    **(T)** 07525 323 775

**Programme Editor:** Chris Park    **(T)** info@afcfylde.co.uk

**Ground Address:** Kellamergh Park, Bryning Lane, Warton, Preston PR4 1TN

**(T)** 01772 682 593    **Manager:** Dave Challinor

2011-12 Squad.
Back Row (L-R): Baldwin (Kit man), Stopforth, Allen, Thorpe, Betts, Whiteside, Steel, MacDonald, Doughty, Stringfellow, Waddington, Wilson, Fraser (Physio).
Front Row: Clarkson (Reserve Team Coach), Penswick, Barnes, Heywood, Kay, Steel, Fuller (Assistant Manager), Mercer (Capt), O'Hanlon, Mercer, Booth, Swarbrick, Jarvis, McNiven (1st Team Coach), Mitchell (Goalkeeping Coach).

## Club Factfile

**Founded:** 1988    **Nickname:**

**Previous Names:** Wesham FC and Kirkham Town amalgamated in 1988 to form Kirkham & Wesham > 2008

**Previous Leagues:** West Lancashire, North West Counties 2007-09

**Club Colours (change):** All white (Blue and red stripes/blue/blue)

**Ground Capacity:** 1,426    **Seats:** 282    **Covered:** 282    **Clubhouse:** Yes    **Shop:** Yes

**Directions:** AFC Fylde is based in an area called 'The Fylde Coast' located between Blackpool and Preston. Kellamergh Park is located in WARTON. EXIT via Junction 3 M55 (signposted A585 Fleetwood/Kirkham). Up approach and turn left towards signs for Kirkham. In around 3/4 mile you will approach a roundabout. Then follow the signs for Wrea Green and Lytham St. Annes (2nd exit) B5259. After another 500 yards you will approach a new roundabout (go straight on) and 1/4 mile you will go over main Preston/Blackpool railway bridge and drop down almost immediately to a small mini roundabout (pub on left called Kingfisher). Carry on straight over this and up to main roundabout (another 200 yards) at junction of main Preston/Blackpool A583. Go straight over roundabout and drive on into Wrea Green Village. At 2nd mini roundabout in the centre of the village (Church on right and Primary School) take left turn into Bryning Lane, signposted on The Green (small white signpost) to Warton (2 miles).The Green will now be on your right as you exit out of the village and in around 1.8 miles you will come to the Birley Arms Pub on your left. Turn left at The Birley Arms Pub Car park and continue to drive through the car park down an access road and park in the Main Club Car Park.

**Previous Grounds:** Coronation Road > 2006

**Record Attendance:** 1,418 v FC United of Manchester, NPL P, 13/10/12.
**Record Victory:** Not known
**Record Defeat:** Not known
**Record Goalscorer:** Not known
**Record Appearances:** Not known
**Additional Records:**

**Senior Honours:**
West Lancashire League 1999-2000, 00-01, 01-02, 03-04, 04-05, 05-06, 06-07.
FA Vase 2007-08.
North West Counties League 2008-09. Northern Premier Division 1 North 2011-12. Lancashire FA Challenge Trophy 2011-12.

### 10 YEAR RECORD

| 03-04 | | 04-05 | | 05-06 | | 06-07 | | 07-08 | | 08-09 | | 09-10 | | 10-11 | | 11-12 | | 12-13 | |
|---|---|---|---|---|---|---|---|---|---|---|---|---|---|---|---|---|---|---|---|
| WYkP | 1 | WYkP | 1 | WYkP | 1 | WYkP | 1 | NWC2 | 2 | NWCP | 1 | NP1N | 13 | NP1N | 5 | NP1N | 1 | NP P | 5 |

# MATCH RESULTS 2012-13

| Date | Comp | H/A | Opponents | Att: | Result | Goalscorers | Pos | No. |
|---|---|---|---|---|---|---|---|---|
| Aug 18 | NPL | A | Ilkeston | 481 | D 1-1 | Sumner 52 | 10 | 1 |
| 21 | NPL | H | Ashton United | 251 | L 1-2 | Dean 6 | 15 | 2 |
| 25 | NPL | H | North Ferriby United | 239 | W 1-0 | Winter 33 | 9 | 3 |
| 27 | NPL | A | Kendal Town | 200 | D 2-2 | Booth 10 (pen) Hughes 51 | 9 | 4 |
| Sept 1 | NPL | H | Whitby Town | 258 | W 4-3 | M.Barnes 3 DORNEY 3 ( 31 65 71) | 9 | 5 |
| 5 | NPL | A | Ashton United | 200 | D 2-2 | Dorney 46 Allen 57 | 11 | 6 |
| 8 | FACQ1 | H | **Ramsbottom United** | 302 | W 3-1 | M.Barnes 32 B Barnes72 Booth 89 |  | 7 |
| 15 | NPL | H | Buxton | 331 | W 5-0 | Booth 36 DEAN 3 (51 55 59) M.Barnes 77 | 9 | 8 |
| 18 | NPL | H | Nantwich Town | 274 | W 3-0 | Allen 53 Dorney 81 M.Barnes 84 | 4 | 9 |
| 22 | FAC Q2 | A | **Bishop Auckland** | 298 | W 2-1 | Dean 26 M.Barnes 57 |  | 10 |
| 29 | FAT Q1 | H | **Marine** | 317 | W 1-0 | M.Barnes 76 |  | 11 |
| Oct 6 | FAC Q3 | H | **Solihull Moors** | 278 | W 4-1 | Booth 12 M.Barnes 29 64 Allen 68 |  | 12 |
| 9 | NPL | H | Witton Albion | 261 | L 1-2 | M.Barnes 37 | 9 | 13 |
| 13 | NPL | H | FC United | 1418 | W 4-2 | Allen 15 32 Farrell 59 M.Barnes 77 |  | 14 |
| 16 | NPL | A | Chorley | 594 | W 4-1 | FARRELL 3 ( 62 83 90) Dorney 69 | 2 | 15 |
| 20 | FAC Q4 | H | **Ilkeston** | 482 | D 1-1 | Farrell 6 |  | 16 |
| 22 | FAC Q4r | A | **Ilkeston** | 696 | W 1-0 | Farrell 2 |  | 17 |
| 27 | FAT Q2 | H | **Nantwich Town** | 261 | D 0-0 |  |  | 18 |
| 30 | FAT Q2r | A | **Nantwich Town** | 181 | D 2-2 | Dean 49 Farrell 69 *aet W 3-1 pens |  | 19 |
| Nov 3 | FAC 1 | H | **Accrington Stanley** | 1213 | L 1-2 | Farrell 90 |  | 20 |
| 10 | FAT Q3 | A | **Solihull Moors** | 155 | L 1-2 | Winter 17 |  | 21 |
| 17 | NPL | H | Worksop Town | 331 | D 2-2 | M.Barnes 57 Farrell 86 | 12 | 22 |
| 20 | NPL | A | Frickley Athletic | 196 | D 1-1 | Buck 73 | 11 | 23 |
| Dec 1 | NPL | H | Grantham Town | 224 | W 5-3 | M.Barnes 3 Winter 12 64 Jarvis 30 Dean 44 | 10 | 24 |
| 15 | NPL | H | Ilkeston | 244 | L 2-3 | M.Barnes 20 Dean 44 | 12 | 25 |
| 18 | NPL | A | Stafford Rangers | 305 | L 2-4 | M.Barnes 9 Dean 51 | 12 | 26 |
| 26 | NPL | H | Kendal Town | 302 | W 4-0 | B.Barnes 29 Dorney 54 68 M.Barnes 72 | 11 | 27 |
| Jan 1 | NPL | A | Marine | 381 | W 4-0 | Farrell 12 Winter 21 78 M. Barnes 69 | 10 | 28 |
| 5 | NPL | A | Buxton | 322 | L 0-2 |  | 13 | 29 |
| 12 | NPL | H | Nantwich Town | 342 | W 3-2 | M.Barnes 4 Booth 23 (pen) McCarthy 36 | 11 | 30 |
| Feb 2 | NPL | H | Chorley | 416 | L 0-1 |  | 12 | 31 |
| 9 | NPL | A | FC United | 2042 | L 1-2 | Stott 4 (og) | 13 | 32 |
| 16 | NPL | H | Stocksbridge PS | 232 | W 4-0 | Booth 16 87 M. Barnes 60 Carden 89 | 12 | 33 |
| 23 | NPL | A | North Ferriby United | 267 | W 1-0 | Dean 79 | 10 | 34 |
| 26 | NPL | A | Eastwood Town | 98 | W 4-1 | Cooke 25 38 Dean 61 81 | 8 | 35 |
| Mar 2 | NPL | A | Blyth Spartans | 357 | W 5-0 | Cooke 2 72 McCarthy 5 20 Dean 25 | 8 | 36 |
| 5 | NPL | A | Hednesford Town | 295 | L 0-2 |  | 9 | 37 |
| 9 | NPL | H | Eastwood Town | 258 | W 5-1 | FARRELL 3( 3 78 80) Booth 24 M.Barnes 87 | 8 | 38 |
| 16 | NPL | A | Grantham Town | 192 | W 2-1 | Farrell 22 Barnes 64 | 7 | 39 |
| 20 | NPL | H | Whitby Town | 203 | W 4-0 | White 45 (og) Farrell 57 (pen) 89 Cooke 65 | 6 | 40 |
| 30 | NPL | H | Matlock Town | 211 | W 3-0 | Booth 4 (pen) Cooke 84 Winter 90 | 6 | 41 |
| Apr 1 | NPL | H | Marine | 304 | W 2-0 | Cooke 22 Farrell 39 | 4 | 42 |
| 6 | NPL | A | Matlock Town | 257 | L 1-2 | Cooke 90 | 6 | 43 |
| 9 | NPL | A | Witton Albion | 421 | W 2-0 | Cooke 28 Farrell 40 | 4 | 44 |
| 13 | NPL | A | Rushall Olympic | 193 | L 0-2 |  | 6 | 45 |
| 16 | NPL | H | Blyth Spartans | 213 | W 1-0 | Barnes 35 | 5 | 46 |
| 20 | NPL | H | Stafford Rangers | 386 | L 0-1 |  | 5 | 47 |
| 23 | NPL | A | Frickley Athletic | 185 | W 3-2 | Barnes 41 McCarthy 45 Farrell 90 | 5 | 48 |
| 25 | NPL | A | Stocksbridge PS | 124 | W 2-0 | Blinkhorn 45 McCarthy 83 | 5 | 49 |
| 27 | NPL | A | Worksop Town | 221 | D 0-0 |  | 5 | 50 |
| 30 | NPL | H | Rushall Olympic | 274 | L 1-3 | McCarthy 69 | 5 | 51 |
| May 4 | NPL | H | Hednesford Town | 563 | L 1-2 | Dean 32 | 5 | 52 |
| 7 | P-Off S-F | A | **Hednesford Town** | 1360 | D 3-3 | Blinkhorn 24 Hinchcliffe 90 Farrell 105 *aet L 1-3 pens |  | 53 |

| GOALSCORERS | Lge | FAC | FAT | Total | Pens | Hat-tricks | Cons Run |  | Lge | FAC | FAT | Total | Pens | Hat-tricks | Cons Run |
|---|---|---|---|---|---|---|---|---|---|---|---|---|---|---|---|
| Barnes | 17 | 4 | 1 | 22 |  |  | 8 | Blinkhorn | 2 |  |  | 2 |  |  |  |
| Farrell | 15 | 3 | 1 | 19 | 1 | 2 | 4 | Buck | 1 |  |  | 1 |  |  |  |
| Dean | 13 | 1 |  | 15 |  | 1 | 3 | Carden | 1 |  |  | 1 |  |  |  |
| Booth | 7 | 2 |  | 9 | 2 |  |  | Hughes | 1 |  |  | 1 |  |  |  |
| Cooke | 9 |  |  | 9 |  |  |  | Jarvis | 1 |  |  | 1 |  |  |  |
| Dorney | 8 |  |  | 8 |  | 1 |  | Sumner | 1 |  |  | 1 |  |  |  |
| Winter | 6 |  | 1 | 7 |  |  |  | Hinchcliffe | 1 |  |  | 1 |  |  |  |
| McCarthy | 6 |  |  | 6 |  |  |  | Own Goals | 2 |  |  | 2 |  |  |  |
| Allen | 4 | 1 |  | 5 |  |  |  | Cons Run - Consecutive scoring games. |  |  |  |  |  |  |  |
| B.Barnes | 1 | 1 |  | 2 |  |  |  |  |  |  |  |  |  |  |  |

# ASHTON UNITED

**Chairman:** David Aspinall
**Secretary:** Andy Finnigan  **(T)** 07866 360200  **(E)** secretary@ashtonutd.com
**Commercial Manager:** Steve Cooper  **(T)** 07796 693 903
**Programme Editor:** Steve Cooper  **(T)** 07796 693 903
**Ground Address:** Hurst Cross, Surrey Street, Ashton-u-Lyne OL6 8DY
**(T)** 0161 339 4158 (Club) 330 1511 (Social)  **Manager:** Craig Robinson

2012-13 Squad - Back row LtoR; Matty Kosylo, Aaron Burns, Matty O' Neill, Chris Lynch, Alex Frost, Terry Smith, Chris Cheetham, Ben Deegan, Matty Burke, Matty Barlow, Kyle Harrop, Sam Hare
Front row LtoR; Dave Haworth (Coach), Danny Lambert, Warren Beattie, Mark Peers, Craig Robinson (Player-assistant manager), Danny Johnson (Manager) Danny Caldecott, Astley Mulholland, Ben Smith, Josh Rose, Callum Hoctor

## Club Factfile

**Founded:** 1878  **Nickname:** Robins
**Previous Names:** Hurst 1878-1947
**Previous Leagues:** Manchester, Lancashire Combination 1912-33, 48-64, 66-68, Midland 1964-66, Cheshire County 1923-48, 68-82, North West Counties 1982-92

**Club Colours (change):** Red and white halves/red/red (Blue & black halves/blue/blue)

**Ground Capacity:** 4,500  **Seats:** 250  **Covered:** 750  **Clubhouse:** Yes  **Shop:** Yes

**Directions**
From the M62 (approx 7.5 miles) Exit at Junction 20, take A627M to Oldham exit (2.5 miles) Take A627 towards Oldham town centre At King Street Roundabout take Park Road Continue straight onto B6194 Abbey Hills Road Follow B6194 onto Lees Road Turn right at the stone cross memorial and 1st right into the ground. From the M60 (approx 2.5 miles); Exit at Junction 23, take A635 for Ashton town centre Follow by-pass to B6194 Mossley Road. At traffic lights turn left into Queens Road Continue onto B6194 Lees Road Turn left at the stone cross memorial and 1st right into the ground.

**Previous Grounds:** Rose HIll 1878-1912

**Record Attendance:** 11,000 v Halifax Town - FA Cup 1st Round 1952
**Record Victory:** 11-3 v Stalybridge Celtic - Manchester Intermediate Cup 1955
**Record Defeat:** 1-11 v Wellington Town - Cheshire League 1946-47
**Record Goalscorer:** Not known
**Record Appearances:** Micky Boyle - 462
**Additional Records:** Paid £9,000 to Netherfield for Andy Whittaker 1994
**Senior Honours:** Received £15,000 from Rotherham United for Karl Marginson 1993
Manchester League 1911-12. Lancs Comb. 1916-17. NWCL Div. Two 1987-88, Div. One 1991-92, League cup 1991-92, Challenge Cup 1991-92.
Manchester Challenge Shield 1992-93. Northern Premier League Division 1 Cup 1994-95, 96-97, 98-99, League Challenge Cup 2010-11.
Manchester Senior Cup 1894-95, 1913-14, 75-76, 77-78. Manchester Premier Cup 1979-80, 82-83, 91092, 2000-01, 01-02, 02-03.

### 10 YEAR RECORD

| 03-04 | | 04-05 | | 05-06 | | 06-07 | | 07-08 | | 08-09 | | 09-10 | | 10-11 | | 11-12 | | 12-13 | |
|---|---|---|---|---|---|---|---|---|---|---|---|---|---|---|---|---|---|---|---|
| NP P | 14 | Conf N | 21 | NP P | 15 | NP P | 18 | NP P | 10 | NP P | 9 | NP P | 12 | NP P | 14 | NP P | 12 | NP P | 10 |

# MATCH RESULTS 2012-13

| Date | Comp | H/A | Opponents | Att: | Result | Goalscorers | Pos | No. |
|------|------|-----|-----------|------|--------|-------------|-----|-----|
| Aug 18 | NPL | H | Worksop Town | 154 | W 5-3 | Deegan 20 62 Robinson 24 Burns 45 Barlow 87 | 2 | 1 |
| 21 | NPL | A | AFC Fylde | 251 | W 2-1 | Peers 34 (pen)  Deegan 87 | 1 | 2 |
| 25 | NPL | A | Eastwood Town | 142 | W 5-0 | Deegan 10 Barlow 19 Robinson 54 Kosylo 70 Mulholland 86 | 1 | 3 |
| 27 | NPL | H | Nantwich Town | 219 | W 2-1 | Baker 26 87 | 1 | 4 |
| Sept 1 | NPL | A | Frickley Athletic | 183 | D 1-1 | Barlow 45 | 1 | 5 |
| 5 | NPL | H | AFC Fylde | 200 | D 2-2 | Peers 26 Burns 87 | 3 | 6 |
| **8** | **FAC Q1** | **A** | **Prescot Cables** | **167** | **W 3-1** | **Burns 7 Lynch 15 Barlow 90** |  | 7 |
| 15 | NPL | H | Grantham Town | 149 | D 1-1 | Kosylo 77 | 4 | 8 |
| 19 | NPL | A | Buxton | 171 | L 1-6 | Johnson 54 | 6 | 9 |
| **22** | **FAC Q2** | **H** | **Marine** | **193** | **L 0-2** |  |  | 10 |
| **29** | **FAT Q1** | **A** | **Ossett Town** | **88** | **L 0-1** |  |  | 11 |
| Oct 6 | NPL | A | Witton Albion | 428 | W 2-0 | Baguley 50 Baker 74 | 3 | 12 |
| 10 | NPL | H | Marine | 186 | L 2-4 | Mulholland 36 Burns 50 | 5 | 13 |
| 13 | NPL | A | Hednesford Town | 489 | W 2-1 | Burns 27 40 | 3 | 14 |
| 23 | NPL | A | Kendal Town | 111 | D 2-2 | Burns 67 90 (pen) | 8 | 15 |
| 27 | NPL | H | Eastwood Town | 103 | W 6-0 | BURNS 4 (17pen 33 44 50) Kosylo 24 Barlow 90 | 4 | 16 |
| 31 | NPL | H | FC United | 503 | L 1-2 | Burns 52 (pen) | 5 | 17 |
| Nov 3 | NPL | A | Stocksbridge PS | 134 | W 3-0 | Bowden-Lovel 36 (og) Hogan 58 Barlow 85 | 3 | 18 |
| 10 | NPL | H | Chorley | 273 | W 3-2 | Burns 16 62 (pen) Lynch 60 | 2 | 19 |
| 17 | NPL | A | Whitby Town | 248 | W 3-1 | Burns 5 (pen) 59  Purewall 56 | 2 | 20 |
| 21 | NPL | H | Ikeston Town | 128 | L 0-3 |  | 3 | 21 |
| 24 | NPL | H | North Ferriby United | 176 | L 0-2 |  | 3 | 22 |
| Dec 15 | NPL | A | Worksop Town | 277 | L 1-5 | Barlow 56 | 5 | 23 |
| Jan 1 | NPL | H | Stafford Rangers | 163 | D 0-0 |  | 5 | 24 |
| 5 | NPL | A | Grantham Town | 222 | W 2-0 | Kosylo  3 Hogan 42 | 6 | 25 |
| 12 | NPL | H | Buxton | 203 | L 0-1 |  | 8 | 26 |
| Feb 2 | NPL | A | Matlock Town | 230 | D 2-2 | Moore 60 (pen) Sheriff 88 | 9 | 27 |
| 9 | NPL | H | Hednesford Town | 153 | D 2-2 | Barlow 64 Hogan 65 | 8 | 28 |
| 16 | NPL | A | Ilkeston | 457 | D 2-2 | Burns 12 Baker 76 | 10 | 29 |
| 19 | NPL | A | Blyth Spartans | 272 | L 1-4 | Burns 1 | 10 | 30 |
| 27 | NPL | H | Kendal Town | 107 | W 4-1 | Burns 26 37 Sheriff 38 46 | 9 | 31 |
| Mar 2 | NPL | A | Nantwich Town | 257 | W 2-0 | Amadi 76 87 | 9 | 32 |
| 6 | NPL | A | Witton Albion | 141 | L 1-3 | Johnson 54 | 10 | 33 |
| 9 | NPL | A | Marine | 302 | D 0-0 |  | 11 | 34 |
| 16 | NPL | H | Rushall Olympic | 140 | L 2-3 | Burns 10  Kosylo 67 | 11 | 35 |
| 27 | NPL | H | Blyth Spartans | 79 | W 2-0 | Amadi 70 Moore 90 | 11 | 36 |
| 30 | NPL | H | Frickley Athletic | 112 | D 0-0 |  | 11 | 37 |
| Apr 1 | NPL | A | Stafford Rangers | 330 | D 0-0 |  | 10 | 38 |
| 6 | NPL | A | Rushall Oympic | 163 | D 0-0 |  | 10 | 39 |
| 10 | NPL | H | Matlock Town | 111 | W 2-0 | Moore 59 Frost 69 (og) | 10 | 40 |
| 13 | NPL | H | Stcksbridge PS | 103 | L 2-3 | Moore 30 81 (pen) | 10 | 41 |
| 20 | NPL | A | Chorley | 563 | D 1-1 | Baguley 64 | 11 | 42 |
| 23 | NPL | A | FC United | 1586 | L 0-3 |  | 11 | 43 |
| 27 | NPL | H | Whitby Town | 114 | D 2-2 | Burke 12 Amadi 61 | 10 | 44 |
| May 4 | NPL | A | North Ferriby United | 626 | L 0-2 |  | 10 | 45 |

| GOALSCORERS | Lge | FAC | FAT | Total | Pens | Hat-tricks | Cons Run | | Lge | FAC | FAT | Total | Pens | Hat-tricks | Cons Run |
|-------------|-----|-----|-----|-------|------|------------|----------|--|-----|-----|-----|-------|------|------------|----------|
| Burns | 21 | 1 |  | 22 | 5 | 1 | 5 | Baguley | 2 |  |  | 2 |  |  |  |
| Barlow | 7 | 1 |  | 8 |  |  |  | Johnson | 2 |  |  | 2 |  |  |  |
| Moore | 5 |  |  | 5 | 2 |  |  | Mulholand | 2 |  |  | 2 |  |  |  |
| Amadi | 4 |  |  | 4 |  |  |  | Robinson | 2 |  |  | 2 |  |  |  |
| Baker | 4 |  |  | 4 |  |  |  | Burke | 1 |  |  | 1 |  |  |  |
| Deegan | 4 |  |  | 4 |  |  |  | Kosylo | 1 |  |  | 1 |  |  |  |
| Kosylo | 4 |  |  | 4 |  |  |  | Peers | 1 |  |  | 1 |  |  |  |
| Hogan | 3 |  |  | 3 |  |  |  | Purewell | 1 |  |  | 1 |  |  |  |
| Lynch | 2 | 1 |  | 3 |  |  |  | Own Goals | 2 |  |  | 2 |  |  |  |
| Sheriff | 3 |  |  | 3 |  |  |  | Cons Run - Consecutive scoring games. | | | | | | | |

# BARWELL

**Chairman:** David Laing
**Secretary:** Mrs Shirley Brown    **(T)** 07961 905 141    **(E)** shirley.brown16@ntlworld.com
**Commercial Manager:** Contact secretary    **(T)**
**Programme Editor:** Dave Richardson    **(T)** 0116 246 0137
**Ground Address:** Kirkby Road Sports Ground, Kirkby Road, Barwell LE9 8FQ
**(T)** 07961 905 141      **Manager:** Jimmy Ginnelly

Back Row (L-R): Viv Coleman (Physio), Martin Hier (Assistant Manager), Jimmy Ginnelly (Manager), Guy Hadland.
Second Row: Liam Castle, Amro Khalid, Tom Weale, Matt West, Luke Barlone, Scott Lower.
Third Row: Richard Lavery, Jamie McAteer, Jamie Towers, Jack Edwards, Jamie Williams, Kevin Charley.
Front Row: Scott Hadland, Mason Rowley, Tom Bates, Casey Gaggini, Paul Spacey, Mark Albrighton.

## Club Factfile

**Founded:** 1992     **Nickname:** Canaries
**Previous Names:** Barwell Athletic FC and Hinckley FC amalgamated in 1992.
**Previous Leagues:** Midland Alliance 1992-2010, Northern Premier League 2010-11. Southern 2011-13.

**Club Colours (change):** Yellow with green trim/green with yellow trim/yellow (Royal blue with white trim/royal blue/royal blue)

**Ground Capacity:** 2,500   **Seats:** 256    **Covered:** 750    **Clubhouse:** Yes   **Shop:** Yes

**Directions**

**FROM M6 NORTH/M42/A5 NORTH:** From M6 North join M42 heading towards Tamworth/Lichfield, leave M42 at Junction 10(Tamworth Services) and turn right onto A5 signposted Nuneaton. Remain on A5 for approx 11 miles, straight on at traffic lights at Longshoot Motel then at next roundabout take first exit signposted A47 Earl Shilton. In about 3 miles at traffic lights go straight on and in 1 mile at roundabout take first exit signposted Barwell. In about 1.5 miles, centre of village, go straight over mini roundabout and then in 20 metres turn right into Kirkby Road. Entrance to complex is 400 metres on right opposite park.
**FROM M1 SOUTH:** From M1 South Take M69 )Signposted Coventry) Take Junction 2 Off M69 (Signposted Hinckley) Follow signs to Hinckley . Go straight on at traffic lights with Holywell Pub on the right. The road bears to the right at next traffic lights turn right signposted Earl Shilton/Leicester. Keep on this road past golf club on right at Hinckley United Ground on left and at large roundabout take second exit signposted Barwell. In about 1.5 miles, centre of village, go straight over mini roundabout and then in 20 metres turn right into Kirkby Road. Entrance to complex is 400 metres on right opposite park.

**Previous Grounds:** None

**Record Attendance:** 1,279 v Whitley Bay, FA Vase Semi-Final 2009-10.
**Record Victory:** Not known
**Record Defeat:** Not known
**Record Goalscorer:** Andy Lucas
**Record Appearances:** Adrian Baker
**Additional Records:**

**Senior Honours:**
Midland Alliance League Cup 2005-06, Champions 2009-10.
Northern Premier Division One South 2010-11.

### 10 YEAR RECORD

| 03-04 | | 04-05 | | 05-06 | | 06-07 | | 07-08 | | 08-09 | | 09-10 | | 10-11 | | 11-12 | | 12-13 | |
|---|---|---|---|---|---|---|---|---|---|---|---|---|---|---|---|---|---|---|---|
| MidAl | 18 | MidAl | 13 | MidAl | 9 | MidAl | 6 | MidAl | 10 | MidAl | 2 | MidAl | 1 | NP1S | 1 | SthP | 9 | SthP | 7 |

# MATCH RESULTS 2012-13

| Date | Comp | H/A | Opponents | Att: | Result | Goalscorers | Pos | No. |
|------|------|-----|-----------|------|--------|-------------|-----|-----|
| Aug 18 | SPL | A | Gosport Borough | 327 | W 2-1 | Adams 45 Barlone 90 | 5 | 1 |
| 21 | SPL | H | Banbury United | 224 | W 4-1 | Spacey 14 Towers 53 90 Hadland 90 | 1 | 2 |
| 25 | SPL | H | Chesham United | 139 | L 1-3 | Towers 90 | 5 | 3 |
| 27 | SPL | A | Stourbridge | 448 | W 2-0 | McAleer 11 Charley 89 | | 4 |
| Sept 1 | SPL | H | Hemel Hempstead | 143 | D 2-2 | Towers 22 Barlone 73 | 4 | 5 |
| 4 | SPL | A | Cambridge City | 225 | L 1-2 | Charley 75 | 8 | 6 |
| 8 | FAC Q1 | H | AFC Wulfrunians | 125 | W 3-0 | Lavery 48 Spacey 85 87 | | 7 |
| 15 | SPL | A | Bashey | 160 | W 5-0 | Barlone 13 16 Lavery 19 West 28 Towers 34 (pen) | 4 | 8 |
| 18 | SPL | A | Bedford Town | 134 | W 2-1 | Lavery 35 West 58 | 4 | 9 |
| 22 | FAC Q2 | H | Bedworth United | 304 | W 3-2 | Spacey 43 Wesley 80 Barlone 85 | | 10 |
| 29 | FAT Q1 | A | Kings Lynn Town | 466 | L 0-1 | | | 11 |
| Oct 6 | FAC Q3 | H | Workington | 217 | D 1-1 | Lavery 90 | | 12 |
| 9 | FAC Q3r | A | Workington | 386 | L 0-2 | | | 13 |
| 13 | SPL | A | St Albans City | 424 | D 4-4 | Gordon 6 (og) Hadland 43 90 Barlone 78 | 7 | 14 |
| 27 | SPL | A | Redditch United | 201 | W 1-0 | Weale 61 | 5 | 15 |
| Nov 10 | SPL | H | Arlesey | 172 | W 2-0 | Towers 1 73 (pen) | 5 | 16 |
| 13 | SPL | H | Chippenham Town | 123 | D 0-0 | | 5 | 17 |
| 17 | SPL | A | AFC Totton | 368 | L 1-2 | Towers 48 | 5 | 18 |
| 24 | SPL | A | St Neots Town | 316 | D 2-2 | Towers 46 Bates 51 | 5 | 19 |
| Dec 1 | SPL | H | Bideford | 134 | D 1-1 | West 60 | 5 | 20 |
| 8 | SPL | A | Frome Town | 155 | W 3-2 | Weale 17 West 31 40 | 5 | 21 |
| 15 | SPL | A | Weymouth | 253 | L 0-1 | | 7 | 22 |
| 18 | SPL | H | Kettering Town | 208 | L 1-2 | Charley 45 | 8 | 23 |
| 26 | SPL | A | Bedworth Town | 280 | D 1-1 | Hadland 47 | 8 | 24 |
| 29 | SPL | A | Chesham United | 220 | D 2-2 | Charley 24 Barlone 45 | 8 | 25 |
| Jan 1 | SPL | H | Stourbridge | 199 | W 2-1 | Barlone 65 Marsden 82 | 7 | 26 |
| 5 | SPL | A | Banbury United | 286 | W 2-1 | Towers 6 11 | 7 | 27 |
| 12 | SPL | A | Cambridge City | 204 | W 1-0 | Edwards 46 | 6 | 28 |
| 29 | SPL | H | Leamington | 357 | L 1-3 | Barlone 68 | 7 | 29 |
| Feb 2 | SPL | H | Hitchin Town | 161 | W 1-0 | Edwards 40 | 6 | 30 |
| 5 | SPL | H | Gsport Borough | 84 | L 1-2 | Rickards 90 | 7 | 31 |
| 9 | SPL | A | Leamington | 552 | W 6-0 | Barlone 3 26 (pen) Lavery 43 90 Weale 67 Hadland 86 | 5 | 32 |
| 16 | SPL | H | AFC Totton | 241 | W 1-0 | Lower 40 | 4 | 33 |
| 19 | SPL | A | Bedford Town | 167 | L 0-3 | | 5 | 34 |
| 23 | SPL | A | Arlesey Town | 108 | W 1-0 | Brown 43 | 5 | 35 |
| Mar 2 | SPL | A | Chippenham Town | 288 | D 1-1 | Hadland 86 | | 36 |
| 4 | SPL | A | Hitchin Town | 200 | W 1-0 | Edwards 72 | 3 | 37 |
| 9 | SPL | H | St Albans City | 241 | L 1-3 | Towers 20 (pen) | 6 | 38 |
| 30 | SPL | A | Hemel Hempstead | 337 | D 1-1 | Charley 52 | 7 | 39 |
| Apr 1 | SPL | H | Bedworth United | 189 | W 2-0 | Gaunt 4 Towers 76 | 6 | 40 |
| 6 | SPL | A | Bideford | 134 | W 2-1 | Barlone 2 Towers 70 | 5 | 41 |
| 9 | SPL | H | Bashley | 104 | D 0-0 | | 5 | 42 |
| 11 | SPL | H | Redditch United | 112 | D 0-0 | | 5 | 43 |
| 13 | SPL | H | St Neots Town | 193 | L 2-3 | Lavery 56 Edwards 76 | 5 | 44 |
| 17 | SPL | A | Kettering Town | 198 | W 2-1 | Newton 32 Barnett 73 | 5 | 45 |
| 20 | SPL | A | Weymouth | 685 | L 1-2 | Newton 75 | 5 | 46 |
| 27 | SPL | H | Frome Town | 304 | D 1-1 | Newton 89 | 7 | 47 |

| GOALSCORERS | Lge | FAC | FAT | Total | Pens | Hat-tricks | Cons Run | | Lge | FAC | FAT | Total | Pens | Hat-tricks | Cons Run |
|-------------|-----|-----|-----|-------|------|------------|----------|--|-----|-----|-----|-------|------|------------|----------|
| Towers | 14 | | | 14 | 3 | | 2 | Brown | 1 | | | 1 | | | |
| Barlone | 11 | 1 | | 12 | 1 | | 2 | Gaunt | 1 | | | 1 | | | |
| Lavery | 5 | 2 | | 7 | | | | Hadland | 1 | | | 1 | | | |
| Hadley | 5 | | | 5 | | | | Lower | 1 | | | 1 | | | |
| West | 5 | | | 5 | 2 | | | Marsden | 1 | | | 1 | | | |
| Charley | 5 | | | 5 | | | | McAleer | 1 | | | 1 | | | |
| Edwards | 4 | | | 4 | | | | Richards | 1 | | | 1 | | | |
| Newton | 3 | | | 3 | | | 3 | Wesley | | 1 | | 1 | | | |
| Spacey | 1 | 2 | | 3 | | | | Own Goals | 1 | | | 1 | | | |
| Weale | 3 | | | 3 | | | | Cons Run - Consecutive scoring games. | | | | | | | |
| Adams | 1 | | | 1 | | | | | | | | | | | |
| Barnett | 1 | | | 1 | | | | | | | | | | | |
| Bates | 1 | | | 1 | | | | | | | | | | | |

# BLYTH SPARTANS

**Chairman:** Tony Platten

**Secretary:** Ian Evans          **(T)** 07905 984 308          **(E)** generalmanager@blythspartans.com

**Commercial Manager:** Contact secretary          **(T)**

**Programme Editor:** Adam Sandcaster          **(T)** 07450 484 071

**Ground Address:** Croft Park, Blyth, Northumberland NE24 3JE

**(T)** 01670 352 373          **Manager:** Tom Wade

October 2012: Blyth substitute Phil Airey lifts the ball over advancing Frickley Athletic goalkeeper Tom Woodhead. His late brace secured a 4-2 win for Blyth; in what was only their second home league success of the season.

## Club Factfile

**Founded:** 1899          **Nickname:** Spartans

**Previous Names:** None

**Previous Leagues:** Northumberland 1901-07, Northern All. 1907-13, 46-47, North Eastern 1913-39, Northern Com. 1945-46, Midland 1958-60, Northern Counties 1960-62, Northern 1962-94, Northern Premier 1994-2006. Conference 2006-13.

**Club Colours (change):** Green & white stripes/black/green (Yellow with green trim/green/green)

**Ground Capacity:** 4,435    **Seats:** 563    **Covered:** 1,000    **Clubhouse:** Yes    **Shop:** Yes

**Directions:** From the Tyne Tunnel, take the A19 signposted MORPETH. At second roundabout take the A189 signposted ASHINGTON. From A189 take A1061 signposted BLYTH. At 1st roundabout follow signs A1061 to BLYTH. Go straight across next two roundabouts following TOWN CENTRE/SOUTH BEECH. At next roundabout turn left onto A193 go straight across next roundabout, and at the next turn right into Plessey Rd and the ground is situated on your left. Team coach should the turn left into William St (3rd left) and reverse up Bishopton St to the designated parking spot.

**Previous Grounds:** None

**Record Attendance:** 10,186 v Hartlepool United - FA Cup 08/12/1956

**Record Victory:** 18-0 v Gateshead Town - Northern Alliance 28/12/1907

**Record Defeat:** 0-10 v Darlington - North Eastern League 12/12/1914

**Record Goalscorer:** Not known.

**Record Appearances:** Eddie Alder - 605 (1965-68)

**Additional Records:** Received £30,000 from Hull City for Les Mutrie

**Senior Honours:**
North Eastern League 1935-36. Northern League 1972-73, 74-75, 75-76, 79-80, 80-81, 81-82, 82-83, 83-84, 86-87, 87-88. Northern League Division 1 1994-95. Northern Premier League Premier Division 2005-06.

### 10 YEAR RECORD

| 03-04 | 04-05 | 05-06 | 06-07 | 07-08 | 08-09 | 09-10 | 10-11 | 11-12 | 12-13 |
|---|---|---|---|---|---|---|---|---|---|
| NP P 21 | NP P 12 | NP P 1 | Conf N 7 | Conf N 18 | Conf N 15 | Conf N 13 | Conf N 9 | Conf N 21 | NP P 16 |

# MATCH RESULTS 2012-13

| Date | Comp | H/A | Opponents | Att: | Result | Goalscorers | Pos | No. |
|------|------|-----|-----------|------|--------|-------------|-----|-----|
| Aug 18 | NPL | A | Witton Albion | 494 | L 1-2 | Dale 14 | 17 | 1 |
| 21 | NPL | H | Stocksbridge PS | 351 | W 5-0 | Melish 47 Dale 50 81 Farrell 88 90 | 7 | 2 |
| 25 | NPL | H | Hednesford Town | 325 | L 1-2 | Airey 3 | 12 | 3 |
| 27 | NPL | A | Whitby Town | 407 | W 3-1 | Airey 6 Kendrick 90 (pen) Dale 90 | | 4 |
| Sept 1 | NPL | H | Marine | 367 | D 3-3 | Kendrick 3 (pen) 62  Farrell 78 | 11 | 5 |
| 4 | NPL | A | Stocksbridge PS | 179 | W 3-2 | Dale 15 Farrell 71 89 | 8 | 6 |
| 8 | FAC Q1 | H | Garforth Town | 401 | W 1-0 | Airey 25 | | 7 |
| 15 | NPL | A | Matlock Town | 286 | W 3-1 | Davis 80 90 Farrell 81 | 7 | 8 |
| 18 | NPL | H | Chorley | 332 | L 1-3 | Airey 30 | 10 | 9 |
| 22 | FAC Q2 | H | Workington | 502 | D 1-1 | Berj 90 | | 10 |
| 29 | FAT Q1 | A | Witton Albion | 313 | L 1-4 | Hassan 90 | | 11 |
| Oct 1 | FAC Q2r | A | Workington | 319 | L 0-1 | | | 12 |
| 13 | NPL | A | Buxton | 342 | L 0-2 | | 13 | 13 |
| 20 | NPL | H | Rushall Olympic | 343 | D 1-1 | Farrell 88 (pen) | 14 | 14 |
| 27 | NPL | H | Frickley Athletic | 288 | W 4-2 | Mason 37 McCorrigan 81 Airey 84 88 | 11 | 15 |
| 31 | NPL | A | Worksop Town | 305 | L 1-8 | Jones 18 | 17 | 16 |
| Nov 3 | NPL | H | Stafford Rangers | 317 | W 1-0 | McGorrigan 10 | 12 | 17 |
| 10 | NPL | A | Grantham Town | 255 | D 2-2 | McGorrigan 49 Mullen 85 | 12 | 18 |
| 17 | NPL | H | Eastwood Town | 267 | W 1-0 | Kendrick 7 | 9 | 19 |
| 24 | NPL | H | Nantwich Town | 299 | D 1-1 | Buchanan 33 | 9 | 20 |
| Dec 1 | NPL | H | FC United | 617 | L 1-2 | Airey 6 | 11 | 21 |
| 8 | NPL | A | Marine | 273 | L 1-5 | Maddison 90 | 12 | 22 |
| 15 | NPL | H | Witton Albion | 222 | L 0-3 | | 15 | 23 |
| 26 | NPL | H | Whitby Town | 320 | D 2-2 | Jennings 72 McGorrigan 73 | 15 | 24 |
| Jan 1 | NPL | A | North Ferriby | 300 | L 2-3 | McGorrigan 29 82 | 16 | 25 |
| 5 | NPL | H | Matlock Town | 311 | W 2-1 | Buchanan 25 Lukic 66 | 15 | 26 |
| 12 | NPL | A | Chorley | 608 | L 0-1 | | 15 | 27 |
| Feb 3 | NPL | A | Frickley Athletic | 224 | L 1-2 | Kendrick 30 | 16 | 28 |
| 9 | NPL | H | Buxton | 301 | D 2-2 | Hubbard 29 (pen)  Utterson 77 | 16 | 29 |
| 16 | NPL | A | Rushall Olympic | 197 | L 2-5 | Maguire 16 Hubbard 54 | 17 | 30 |
| 19 | NPL | H | Ashton United | 272 | W 4-1 | Dale 21 (pen) Mason 45 Maguire 52 87 | 15 | 31 |
| Mar 2 | NPL | H | AFC Hyde | 357 | L 0-5 | | 16 | 32 |
| 5 | NPL | A | Kendall Town | 128 | W 3-1 | Turnbull 8 Mason 74 90 | 15 | 33 |
| 16 | NPL | H | Ilkeston | 326 | W 3-2 | Turnbull 12 Maguire 54  Kendrick 90 (pen) | 15 | 34 |
| 23 | NPL | A | FC United | 1730 | L 1-2 | Kendrick 12 | 15 | 35 |
| 27 | NPL | A | Ashton United | 79 | L 0-2 | | 15 | 36 |
| 30 | NPL | A | Ilkeston Town | 419 | L 1-3 | Kendrick 54 | 15 | 37 |
| Apr 1 | NPL | H | North Ferriby United | 304 | L 0-1 | | 16 | 38 |
| 6 | NPL | H | Worksop Town | 315 | W 3-2 | Dale 70 Hubbard 84 (pen) Mason 88 | 16 | 39 |
| 9 | NPL | A | Hednesford Town | 501 | L 0-3 | | 16 | 40 |
| 13 | NPL | A | Stafford Rangers | 326 | W 4-2 | Maguire 27  Dale 47 Hubbard 56 (pen) 61 (pen) | 16 | 41 |
| 16 | NPL | A | AFC Fylde | 213 | L 0-1 | | 16 | 42 |
| 20 | NPL | H | Grantham Town | 316 | W 1-0 | Maguire 62 | 16 | 43 |
| 27 | NPL | A | Eastwood Town | 122 | W 4-1 | Kendrick 20 Dale 67 Jennings  84 90 | 15 | 44 |
| 30 | NPL | H | Kendal Town | 272 | L 1-3 | Hooks 34 | 16 | 45 |
| May 4 | NPL | A | Nantwich Town | 375 | L 1-2 | Jennings 60 | 16 | 46 |

| GOALSCORERS | Lge | FAC | FAT | Total | Pens | Hat-tricks | Cons Run | | Lge | FAC | FAT | Total | Pens | Hat-tricks | Cons Run |
|-------------|-----|-----|-----|-------|------|------------|----------|---|-----|-----|-----|-------|------|------------|----------|
| Dale | 9 | | 9 | 1 | | | 2 | Turnbull | 2 | | | 2 | | | 2 |
| Kendrick | 9 | | 9 | 2 | | | | Berj | | 1 | | 1 | | | |
| Airey | 6 | 1 | 7 | | | | 2 | Hassan | 1 | | 1 | | | | |
| Farrell | 7 | | 7 | 1 | | | | Hooks | 1 | | 1 | | | | |
| Maguire | 6 | | 6 | | | | 2 | Jones | 1 | | 1 | | | | |
| McCorrigan | 6 | | 6 | | | | | Lukic | 1 | | 1 | | | | |
| Hubbard | 5 | | 5 | 4 | | | 2 | Maddison | 1 | | 1 | | | | |
| Mason | 5 | | 5 | | | | | Melish | 1 | | 1 | | | | |
| Jennings | 4 | | 4 | | | | | Mullen | 1 | | 1 | | | | |
| Buchanan | 2 | | 2 | | | | | Cons Run - Consecutive scoring games. | | | | | | | |
| Davis | 2 | | 2 | | | | | | | | | | | | |

# BUXTON

**Chairman:** David Hopkins

**Secretary:** Don Roberts          **(T)** 07967 822 448          **(E)** admin@buxtonfc.co.uk

**Commercial Manager:** Contact secretary          **(T)**

**Programme Editor:** Mike Barton          **(T)** 07773 947 869

**Ground Address:** The Silverlands, Buxton, Derbyshire SK17 6QH

**(T)** 01298 23197                                        **Manager:** Martin McIntosh

## Club Factfile

**Founded:** 1877          **Nickname:** The Bucks

**Previous Names:** None

**Previous Leagues:** Combination 1891-99, Manchester 1899-1932, Cheshire County 1932-40, 46-73, Northern Premier 1973-98, Northern Counties East 1998-2006

**Club Colours (change):** All blue (All red)

**Ground Capacity:** 4,000    **Seats:** 490    **Covered:** 2,500    **Clubhouse:** Yes    **Shop:** Yes

**Directions**

FROM STOCKPORT (A6): Turn left at first roundabout after dropping down the hill into the town, turn right at next roundabout, right at traffic lights (London Road pub) to Buxton Market Place. After two sets of pedestrian lights turn right at Royles shop then turn immediate left and follow road approx 500 metres to ground (opposite police station.)

FROM BAKEWELL (A6): Turn left at roundabout on to Dale Road and follow road to traffic lights then as above.

FROM MACCLESFIELD/CONGLETON/LEEK: Follow road to Burbage traffic lights and take right fork in the road at the Duke of York pub (Macclesfield Road.) Then at next traffic lights turn left (London Road pub) and follow as above.

FROM ASHBOURNE (A515): Go straight on at first traffic lights (London Road pub) and follow directions as above.

**Previous Grounds:** The Park (Cricket Club) 1877-78. Fields at Cote Heath and Green Lane 1878-84.

**Record Attendance:** 6,000 v Barrow - FA Cup 1st Round 1961-62

**Record Victory:** Not known

**Record Defeat:** Not known

**Record Goalscorer:** Mark Reed - 236 (in 355 + 46 sub appearances 2002-07, 2009-)

**Record Appearances:** David Bainbridge - 642

**Additional Records:** Paid £5,000 to Hyde United for Gary Walker 1989

**Senior Honours:** Received £16,500 from Rotherham for Ally Pickering 1989

Manchester League 1931-32, Lge cup 1925-26, 26-27. Cheshire Co. League 1972-73, Lge Cup 1956-57, 57-58, 68-69. N.C.E. League 2005-06, Presidents Cup 2004-05, 05-06. N.P.L. Division 1 2006-07, President's Cup 1981-82, 2006-07. Derbyshire Senior Cup 1938-39, 45-46, 56-57, 59-60, 71-72, 80-81, 85-86, 86-87, 2008-09.

### 10 YEAR RECORD

| 03-04 | | 04-05 | | 05-06 | | 06-07 | | 07-08 | | 08-09 | | 09-10 | | 10-11 | | 11-12 | | 12-13 | |
|---|---|---|---|---|---|---|---|---|---|---|---|---|---|---|---|---|---|---|---|
| NCEP | 7 | NCEP | 9 | NCEP | 1 | NP 1 | 1 | NP P | 5 | NP P | 14 | NP P | 8 | NP P | 6 | NP P | 13 | NP P | 7 |

# MATCH RESULTS 2012-13

| Date | Comp | H/A | Opponents | Att: | Result | Goalscorers | Pos | No. |
|---|---|---|---|---|---|---|---|---|
| Aug 17 | NPL | A | North Ferriby United | 168 | D 1-1 | Black 90 | 11 | 1 |
| 22 | NPL | H | Marine | 237 | L 1-4 | Nix 5 | 17 | 2 |
| 25 | NPL | H | Whitby Town | 258 | W 2-1 | Roberts 4 Reed 8 (pen) | 11 | 3 |
| 27 | NPL | A | Stocksbridge PS | 226 | W 2-0 | Keane 14 Istead 90 | 10 | 4 |
| Sept 1 | NPL | H | Witton Albion | 339 | D 2-2 | Lugsden 63 Nix 71 (pen) | 10 | 5 |
| 4 | NPL | A | Marine | 218 | L 0-2 | | 13 | 6 |
| 8 | FAC Q1 | A | Quorn | 165 | W 2-1 | Nix 56 (pen) 57 (pen) | | 7 |
| 15 | NPL | A | AFC Fylde | 331 | L 0-5 | | 14 | 8 |
| 19 | NPL | H | Ashton United | 171 | W 6-1 | Lugsden 22 40 Morris 45 (pen) 55 Thewlis 84 Black 88 | 14 | 9 |
| 22 | FAC Q2 | A | Stamford | 201 | W 3-1 | Morris 45 83 Reed 78 | | 10 |
| 29 | FAT Q1 | A | Lincoln United | 107 | W 4-0 | Nix 39 Towey 45 Roberts 47 Morris 61 | | 11 |
| Oct 6 | FAC Q3 | A | Hednesford Town | 498 | D 2-2 | Nix 59 Reed 70 | | 12 |
| 9 | FAC Q3r | H | Hednesford Town | 302 | W 2-1* | Reed 70 Morris 101 | | 13 |
| 13 | NPL | H | Blyth Spartans | 342 | W 2-0 | Deakin 20 Reed 32 | 12 | 14 |
| 16 | NPL | A | Eastwood Town | 195 | W 5-1 | Istead 6 Morris 14 Haggerty 25 Reed 76 Towey 80 | 10 | 15 |
| 20 | FAC Q4 | A | Guiseley | 847 | L 0-2 | | | 16 |
| 24 | NPL | H | Worksop Town | 249 | L 0-3 | | 11 | 17 |
| 27 | FAT Q2 | H | North Ferriby United | 215 | W 2-1 | Towey 59 Lugsden 84 | | 18 |
| 30 | NPL | A | Grantham Town | 177 | D 0-0 | | 10 | 19 |
| Nov 3 | NPL | H | Frickley Athleic | 213 | W 1-0 | Towey 43 | 10 | 20 |
| 10 | FAT Q3 | A | Stamford | 239 | W 2-0 | Reed 38 41 | | 21 |
| 17 | NPL | H | Kendal Town | 271 | L 1-2 | Towey 25 | 13 | 22 |
| 20 | NPL | A | Nantwich Town | 202 | D 2-2 | Istead 23 Reed 70 | 13 | 23 |
| 24 | FAT 1 | A | Grimsby Town | 1369 | D 0-0 | | | 24 |
| Dec 4 | NPL | A | Stafford Rangers | 283 | D 2-2 | Morris 4 Lugsden 45 | | 25 |
| 8 | NPL | A | Witton Albion | 419 | W 4-2 | Duncum 15 MORRIS 3 ( 43 64 73) | 12 | 26 |
| 15 | NPL | H | North Ferriby United | 196 | W 2-0 | Stevens 51 Reed 83 | 9 | 27 |
| 26 | NPL | H | Stocksbridge PS | 240 | W 7-0 | THORNHILL 3 ( 12 55 87) REED 3( 4pen 45 53) Nix 83 | 8 | 28 |
| Jan 1 | NPL | A | Matlock Town | 483 | D 1-1 | Hoggerty 18 | | 29 |
| 5 | NPL | A | AFC Fylde | 322 | W 1-0 | Reed 90 (pen) | 7 | 30 |
| 12 | NPL | A | Ashton United | 203 | W 1-0 | Grant 87 | 6 | 31 |
| Feb 2 | NPL | H | FC United | 1121 | L 0-3 | | 8 | 32 |
| 9 | NPL | A | Blyth Spartans | 301 | D 2-2 | Reed 42 60 | 7 | 33 |
| 16 | NPL | H | Eastwood Town | 291 | W 6-2 | Morris 39 Haggerty 68 Stevens 77 REED 3 ( 80 81 83) | 7 | 34 |
| 27 | NPL | A | Whitby Town | 107 | D 1-1 | Morris 75 (pen) | 7 | 35 |
| Mar 2 | NPL | A | Frickley Athletic | 229 | D 3-3 | Reed 11 74 Stevens 55 | 11 | 36 |
| 5 | NPL | A | Rushall Olympic | 156 | W 1-0 | Morris 70 | 8 | 37 |
| 9 | NPL | H | Stafford Rangers | 329 | W 2-1 | Istead 57 Morris 69 | 7 | 38 |
| 16 | NPL | A | Chorley | 769 | L 1-2 | Thornhill 80 | 10 | 39 |
| 19 | NPL | A | FC United | 1501 | W 2-1 | Haggerty 2 Stevens 58 | 7 | 40 |
| 30 | NPL | A | Hednesford Town | 459 | L 2-3 | Towey 57 Reed 90 | 9 | 41 |
| Apr 1 | NPL | H | Matlock Town | 346 | W 1-0 | Roberts 19 | 9 | 42 |
| 4 | NPL | A | Ilkeston | 387 | D 1-1 | Morris 14 | 9 | 43 |
| 6 | NPL | H | Grantham Town | 274 | D 1-1 | Duncum 45 | 8 | 44 |
| 10 | NPL | H | Ilkeston | 281 | D 0-0 | | 8 | 45 |
| 17 | NPL | A | Hednesford Town | 298 | L 0-2 | | 8 | 46 |
| 20 | NPL | H | Rushall Olympic | 262 | W 2-0 | Thornhill 42 Lugsden 61 | 7 | 47 |
| 21 | NPL | A | Chorley | 234 | D 1-1 | Morris 26 | 7 | 48 |
| 27 | NPL | A | Kendal Town | 165 | L 0-1 | | 7 | 49 |
| May 1 | NPL | H | Nantwich Town | 224 | W 3-1 | Duncum 19 Palmer 87 Reed 90 (pen) | 7 | 50 |
| 4 | NPL | A | Worksop Town | 251 | L 0-2 | | 7 | 51 |

| GOALSCORERS | Lge | FAC | FAT | Total | Pens | Hat-tricks | Cons Run | | Lge | FAC | FAT | Total | Pens | Hat-tricks | Cons Run |
|---|---|---|---|---|---|---|---|---|---|---|---|---|---|---|---|
| Reed | 18 | 3 | 2 | 23 | 2 | 2 | 4 | Stevens | 4 | | | 4 | | | |
| Morris | 13 | 3 | 1 | 17 | 2 | 1 | 3 | Deakin | 1 | | | 1 | | | |
| Nix | 3 | 3 | 1 | 7 | 3 | | | Duncum | 3 | | | 3 | | | |
| Lugsden | 5 | | 1 | 6 | | | | Grant | 1 | | | 1 | | | |
| Towey | 4 | | 2 | 6 | | | | Keane | 1 | | | 1 | | | |
| Haggerty | 4 | | | 4 | | | | Thewlis | 1 | | | 1 | | | |
| Istead | 4 | | | 4 | | | | Palmer | 1 | | | 1 | | | |
| Thornhill | 5 | | | 5 | | 1 | | | | | | | | | |
| Black | 2 | | | 2 | | | | | | | | | | | |
| Roberts | 2 | | 1 | 3 | | | | | | | | | | | |

Cons Run - Consecutive scoring games.

# CHORLEY

**Chairman:** Ken Wright
**Secretary:** Graham Watkinson    **(T)** 07739 952 167    **(E)** info@chorleyfc.com
**Commercial Manager:** John Derbyshire    **(T)**
**Programme Editor:** Josh Vosper    **(T)** 07773 688 936
**Ground Address:** Victory Park Stadium, Duke Street, Chorley, Lancashire PR7 3DU
**(T)** 01257 263 406    **Manager:** Garry Flitcroft

**2012-13 Squad - Back Row (L-R):** Ken Wright (Chairman), Harold Taylor (Secretary), Ashley Parillon, Steve Flitcroft, Ciaran Kilheeney, Adam Roscoe, Andy Robertson, Russell Saunders, Andy Russell, Mark Ross, Chris Denham, Tom Willams, Steve Foster,
Jonathan Gains (Kit Manager), Beverley Webster (Physiotherapist)
**Front Row:** Kieran Walmsley, Jamie Vermiglio, Andy Teague, Jon Smith (Coach), Mike Quigley (Coach), Gary Flitcroft (Manager), Matt Jansen (Player Coach), Porya Ahmadi, Tom Ince, Simon Garner.

## Club Factfile

**Founded:** 1883    **Nickname:** Magpies
**Previous Names:** None
**Previous Leagues:** Lancashire Alliance 1890-94, Lancashire 1894-1903, Lancashire Combination 1903-68, 69-70, Northern Premier 1968-69, 70-72, 82-88, Cheshire County 1970-82, Conference 1988-90

**Club Colours (change):** Black and white stripes/black/black & white hoops (Red/black/red)

**Ground Capacity:** 4,100    **Seats:** 2,800    **Covered:** 900    **Clubhouse:** Yes    **Shop:** Yes

**Directions**

M61 leave at junction 6, follow A6 to Chorley, going past the Yarrow Bridge Hotel on Bolton Road. Turn left at first set of traffic lights into Pilling Lane, first right into Ashley St. Ground 2nd entrance on left.

M6 junction 27, follow Chorley, turn left at lights, A49 continue for 2 ½ miles, turn right onto B5251. Drive through Coppull and into Chorley for about 2 miles. On entering Chorley turn right into Duke Street 200 yards past Plough Hotel. Turn right into Ashby Street after Duke Street school, and first right into Ground.

**Previous Grounds:** Dole Lane 1883-1901, Rangletts Park 1901-05, St George's Park 1905-20

**Record Attendance:** 9,679 v Darwen - FA Cup 1931-32
**Record Victory:** Not known
**Record Defeat:** Not known
**Record Goalscorer:** Peter Watson - 371 (158-66)
**Record Appearances:** Not known
**Additional Records:** Received £30,000 from Newcastle United for David Eatock 1996
**Senior Honours:**
Lancashire Alliance 1892-93. Lancashire League 1896-97, 98-99. Lancashire Combination x11.
Cheshire County League 1975-76, 76-77, 81-82. Northern Premier League 1987-88.
Lancashire FA Trophy x14. Lancashire Combination League cup x3.

## 10 YEAR RECORD

| 03-04 | 04-05 | 05-06 | 06-07 | 07-08 | 08-09 | 09-10 | 10-11 | 11-12 | 12-13 |
|---|---|---|---|---|---|---|---|---|---|
| NP 1   18 | NP 1   16 | NP 1   18 | NP 1   23 | NP1N   14 | NP1N   14 | NP1N   16 | NP1N   3 | NP P   3 | NP P   8 |

# MATCH RESULTS 2012-13

| Date | Comp | H/A | Opponents | Att: | Result | Goalscorers | Pos | No. |
|---|---|---|---|---|---|---|---|---|
| Aug 17 | BSN | A | Stocksbridge Park Steels | 322 | W 5-4 | Kilheeney Roscoe Ince (2) Russell | | 1 |
| 21 | BSN | H | Witton Albion | 625 | L 1-2 | Ince 67 | | 2 |
| 25 | BSN | H | Grantham Town | 529 | W 2-1 | Ince 47 Kilheeney 55 | 8 | 3 |
| 27 | BSN | A | Marine | 446 | L 0-2 | | 8 | 4 |
| Sept 1 | BSN | A | Ilkeston | 658 | W 1-0 | Stephenson | | 5 |
| 4 | BSN | H | Witton Albion | 464 | W 3-1 | Ince 9 (pen) Stephenson 20 70 | 6 | 6 |
| **8** | **FAC Q1** | **H** | **Nantwich Town** | **633** | **W 2-0** | **Kilheeney Stephenson** | | 7 |
| 15 | BSN | A | Hednesford Town | 722 | L 1-2 | Roscoe 28 | 10 | 8 |
| 18 | BSN | H | Blyth Spartans | 332 | W 3-1 | Ince 9 Roscoe 20 Stephenson 70 | | 9 |
| **22** | **FAC Q2** | **H** | **Frickley Athletic** | **642** | **L 1-3** | **1 og.** | | 10 |
| **29** | **FAT Q1** | **H** | **Whitby Town** | **388** | **L 1-3** | **Cunliffe** | | 11 |
| Oct 6 | BSN | A | Eastwood Town | 164 | W 1-0 | Denham 67 | 4 | 12 |
| 9 | BSN | H | Nantwich Town | 546 | D 3-3 | Stephenson 50 Kilheeney 65 76 | | 13 |
| 13 | BSN | A | Rushall Olympic | 355 | D 0-0 | | 4 | 14 |
| 16 | BSN | H | AFC Fylde | 594 | L 1-4 | Kilheeney 23 (pen) | | 15 |
| 20 | BSN | H | Frickley Athletic | 600 | W 5-1 | AHMADI 3( 29 56 pen 76) Whitham 47 Kilheeney 82 | 4 | 16 |
| 23 | BSN | A | Matlock Town | 227 | L 0-1 | | | 17 |
| 27 | BSN | A | Grantham Town | 215 | W 1-0 | Kilheeney 44 | 3 | 18 |
| 30 | BSN | A | Stafford Rangers | 337 | L 0-1 | | | 19 |
| Nov 3 | BSN | H | Worksop Town | 744 | D 1-1 | Teague 17 | 5 | 20 |
| 10 | BSN | A | Ashton United | 273 | L 2-3 | Cunliffe 1 Ince 25 | 6 | 21 |
| 17 | BSN | H | North Ferriby United | 620 | L 0-1 | | 7 | 22 |
| 24 | BSN | H | FC United | 1130 | L 1-2 | Whitham 7 | 7 | 23 |
| Dec 8 | BSN | A | Ilkeston | 405 | L 0-1 | | 9 | 24 |
| 15 | BSN | H | Stocksbridge Park Steels | 459 | D 1-1 | Whitham 51 | 10 | 25 |
| 26 | BSN | H | Marine | 582 | W 1-0 | Stephenson | | 26 |
| 29 | BSN | H | Whitby Town | 553 | L 2-3 | Stephenson 45 Ahmadi 89 | 10 | 27 |
| Jan 1 | BSN | A | Kendal Town | 305 | W 4-1 | Teague 59 74 Roscoe 62 Russell 69 | | 28 |
| 5 | BSN | A | Hednesford Town | 493 | L 1-3 | Russell 88 | 11 | 29 |
| 12 | BSN | H | Blyth Spartans | 608 | W 1-0 | Whitham 69 | 9 | 30 |
| Feb 2 | BSN | A | AFC Fylde | 416 | W 1-0 | Roscoe 90 | 6 | 31 |
| 9 | BSN | H | Rushall Olympic | 506 | L 1-6 | Russell 30 | 9 | 32 |
| 16 | BSN | A | Frickley Athletic | 220 | W 1-0 | Roscoe 1 | 9 | 33 |
| Mar 3 | BSN | H | Matlock Town | 560 | W 1-0 | Ahmadi 88 | 10 | 34 |
| 9 | BSN | A | FC United | 2031 | W 3-1 | Whitham 33 Russell 53 Roscoe 84 | 9 | 35 |
| 16 | BSN | H | Buxton | 769 | W 2-1 | Baker 9 Armodi 74 | 8 | 36 |
| 26 | BSN | A | Nantwich Town | 158 | W 1-0 | Teague 42 | 8 | 37 |
| 30 | BSN | A | Whitby Town | 304 | D 1-1 | O'Brien 39 | 7 | 38 |
| Apr 1 | BSN | H | Kendal Town | 625 | W 5-0 | Roscoe 2 Darkwah 13 Whitham 46 Baker 77 Stephenson 90 | 7 | 39 |
| 6 | BSN | H | Stafford Rangers | 576 | W 2-0 | Roscoe 6 Stephenson 88 | 7 | 40 |
| 13 | BSN | A | Worksop Town | 226 | L 0-1 | | 8 | 41 |
| 20 | BSN | H | Ashton United | 563 | D 1-1 | Stephenson 80 | 8 | 42 |
| 23 | BSN | A | Buxton | 234 | D 1-1 | Stephenson 75 | 8 | 43 |
| 27 | BSN | A | North Ferriby United | 435 | L 0-1 | | 8 | 44 |
| May 4 | BSN | H | Eastwood Town | 831 | W 2-1 | Ince 2 (pen ) Stephenson 83 | 8 | 45 |
| | | | | | | | | 46 |
| | | | | | | | | 47 |
| | | | | | | | | 48 |
| | | | | | | | | 49 |
| | | | | | | | | 50 |
| | | | | | | | | 51 |

| GOALSCORERS | Lge | FAC | FAT | Total | Pens | Hat-tricks | Cons Run |
|---|---|---|---|---|---|---|---|
| Stephenson | 12 | 1 | | 13 | | | 3 |
| Roscoe | 9 | | | 9 | | | 2 |
| Ince | 8 | | | 8 | 2 | | 2 |
| Kilheeney | 7 | 1 | | 8 | 1 | | |
| Ahmadi | 6 | | | 6 | 1 | 1 | |
| Whitham | 6 | | | 6 | | | |
| Russell | 5 | | | 5 | | | 2 |
| Cunliffe | 2 | | 1 | 3 | | | |
| Teague | 3 | | | 3 | | | |
| Baker | 2 | | | 2 | | | |
| Denham | 1 | | | 1 | | | |
| O'Brien | 1 | | | 1 | | | |
| Own Goals | 1 | 1 | | 2 | | | |

Cons Run - Consecutive scoring games.

# DROYLSDEN

**Chairman:** David Pace
**Secretary:** Alan Slater    **(T)** 07989 024 777    **(E)** alans83@btinternet.com
**Commercial Manager:** Stella Quinn    **(T)**
**Programme Editor:** Bryan Pace    **(T)** 0161 335 0129
**Ground Address:** The Butchers Arms Ground, Market Street, Droylsden, M43 7AY
**(T)** 0161 370 1426    **Manager:** David Pace

## Club Factfile

**Founded:** 1892    **Nickname:** The Bloods
**Previous Names:** None
**Previous Leagues:** Manchester, Lancashire Combination 1936-39, 50-68, Cheshire County 1939-50, 68-82, North West Counties 1982-87, Northern Premier 1986-2004
**Club Colours (change):** All red (Yellow/royal blue/royal blue)

**Ground Capacity:** 3,000    **Seats:** 500    **Covered:** 2,000    **Clubhouse:** Yes    **Shop:** Yes

**Directions**

From junction 23 M60 follow signs A635 Manchester, then A662 signed Droylsden, at town centre traffic lights turn right into Market Street, through next set of lights and the main entrance to the ground is 75 yards on your left.

**Previous Grounds:** None

**Record Attendance:** 4,250 v Grimsby, FA Cup 1st Round 1976.
**Record Victory:** 13-2 v Lucas Sports Club
**Record Defeat:** Not known
**Record Goalscorer:** E. Gillibrand - 275 (1931-35)
**Record Appearances:** Paul Phillips - 326
**Additional Records:** Received £11,000 from Crewe Alexandra for Tony Naylor 1990

**Senior Honours:**
Northern Premier League Division 1 1998-99. Conference North 2006-07.
Manchester Premier Cup x3. Manchester Senior Cup x3.

### 10 YEAR RECORD

| 03-04 | 04-05 | 05-06 | 06-07 | 07-08 | 08-09 | 09-10 | 10-11 | 11-12 | 12-13 |
|---|---|---|---|---|---|---|---|---|---|
| NP P   2 | Conf N   3 | Conf N   4 | Conf N   1 | Conf   24 | Conf N   7 | Conf N   5 | Conf N   8 | Conf N   9 | Conf N   21 |

## MATCH RESULTS 2012-13

| Date | Comp | H/A | Opponents | Att: | Result | Goalscorers | Pos | No. |
|------|------|-----|-----------|------|--------|-------------|-----|-----|
| Aug 18 | BSN | H | Boston United | 344 | L 0-1 | | 15 | 1 |
| 21 | BSN | A | Guiseley | 431 | L 1-7 | Rick 76 (pen) | 20 | 2 |
| 25 | BSN | A | Stalybridge Celtic | 546 | D 0-0 | | 20 | 3 |
| 27 | BSN | H | Vauxhall Motors | 550 | W 5-2 | Rick 18 Killeen 39 Logan 41 (pen), Sissons 49 O'Neill 82 | 16 | 4 |
| Sept 1 | BSN | A | Brackley Town | 307 | L 2-3 | Bryan 19 Logan 90 (pen) | 19 | 5 |
| 4 | BSN | H | Harrogate Town | 202 | L 1-3 | O'Neill 78 | 19 | 6 |
| 8 | BSN | H | Solihull Moors | 273 | L 2-4 | Kerr 10 Sissons 87 | 20 | 7 |
| 15 | BSN | A | Worcester City | 325 | L 1-2 | Whitehead 53 (og) | 21 | 8 |
| 22 | FAC Q2 | A | Whitby Town | 202 | L 3-4 | Rick 74 Kerr 85 Hassen 84 (og) | | 9 |
| 29 | BSN | H | Gloucester City | 181 | W 1-0 | Evans 84 | 18 | 10 |
| Oct 3 | BSN | A | Corby Town | 310 | L 0-5 | | 20 | 11 |
| 13 | BSN | A | Gainsborough T | 497 | L 0-3 | | 21 | 12 |
| 20 | BSN | H | Histon | 187 | D 2-2 | Logan 5 Kerr 90 | 21 | 13 |
| 27 | BSN | H | Colwyn Bay | 235 | W 2-0 | Killeen 47 Logan 83 | 19 | 14 |
| 30 | BSN | A | Workington | 363 | L 1-2 | Ellison 37 | 19 | 15 |
| Nov 10 | FAT Q3 | H | Rushall Olympic | 211 | L 1-2 | Logan 89 (pen) | | 16 |
| 17 | BSN | A | FC Halifax Town | 1332 | L 1-4 | Ellison 80 | 21 | 17 |
| Dec 1 | BSN | A | Oxford City | 183 | D 2-2 | Palmer 77 Kerr 81 | 20 | 18 |
| 8 | BSN | H | Bishop's Stortford | 195 | L 1-2 | Logan 45 | 20 | 19 |
| 15 | BSN | A | Boston United | 759 | L 1-5 | Hall 24 | 20 | 20 |
| 26 | BSN | A | Chester | 2934 | L 0-5 | | 21 | 21 |
| Jan 1 | BSN | H | Chester | 1056 | L 3-4 | ELLISON 3 (16 84 90) | 21 | 22 |
| 5 | BSN | H | Brackley Town | 192 | L 0-3 | | 21 | 23 |
| 12 | BSN | A | Solihull Moors | 191 | L 1-2 | Logan 37 | 21 | 24 |
| 29 | BSN | H | Worcester City | 140 | L 0-2 | | 21 | 25 |
| Feb 2 | BSN | A | Histon | 290 | L 1-3 | O'Neill 31 | 21 | 26 |
| 9 | BSN | H | Gainsborough T | 184 | L 1-3 | Hall 55 | 21 | 27 |
| 16 | BSN | H | FC Halifax Town | 643 | L 0-6 | | 21 | 28 |
| 19 | BSN | A | Harrogate Town | 253 | D 1-1 | Ward 41 | 21 | 29 |
| 23 | BSN | A | Bishop's Stortford | 298 | L 1-2 | Lodge 74 | 21 | 30 |
| 26 | BSN | H | Hinckley United | 123 | W 3-2 | Logan 68 (pen) Ahmed 84 Hall 90 | 21 | 31 |
| Mar 2 | BSN | H | Bradford PA | 254 | L 0-7 | | 21 | 32 |
| 5 | BSN | H | Altrincham | 258 | L 0-5 | | 21 | 33 |
| 9 | BSN | H | Guiseley | 211 | L 0-3 | | 21 | 34 |
| 12 | BSN | A | Gloucester City | 349 | L 0-4 | | 21 | 35 |
| 30 | BSN | H | Stalybridge Celtic | 356 | D 1-1 | Langford 53 | 21 | 36 |
| Apr 1 | BSN | A | Vauxhall Motors | 148 | L 0-4 | | 21 | 37 |
| 6 | BSN | H | Corby Town | 139 | D 2-2 | McEvilly 46 (pen) Hall 75 | 21 | 38 |
| 9 | BSN | A | Colwyn Bay | 197 | W 3-1 | O'Neill 19 Gilchrist 37 Logan 43 | 21 | 39 |
| 13 | BSN | A | Bradford Town | 350 | L 0-5 | | 21 | 40 |
| 16 | BSN | H | Workington | 100 | L 0-1 | | 21 | 41 |
| 18 | BSN | A | Hinckley United | 187 | D 2-2 | Ward 71 Sissons 78 | 21 | 42 |
| 20 | BSN | H | Oxford City | 166 | L 1-3 | Gallagher 18 | 21 | 43 |
| 27 | BSN | A | Altrincham | 1274 | L 0-6 | | 21 | 44 |

| GOALSCORERS | Lge | FAC | LC | Total | Pens | Hat-tricks | Cons Run | | Lge | FAC | LC | Total | Pens | Hat-tricks | Cons Run |
|-------------|-----|-----|----|----|------|-----------|----------|------|-----|-----|----|----|------|-----------|----------|
| Logan | 8 | | 1 | 9 | 4 | | 2 | Bryan | 1 | | | 1 | | | |
| Ellison | 5 | | | 5 | | 1 | | Evans | 1 | | | 1 | | | |
| Hall | 4 | | | 4 | | | | Gallagher | 1 | | | 1 | | | |
| Kerr | 3 | 1 | | 4 | | | | Gilchrist | 1 | | | 1 | | | |
| O'Neill | 4 | | | 4 | | | | Langford | 1 | | | 1 | | | |
| Rick | 2 | 1 | | 3 | 1 | | | Lodge | 1 | | | 1 | | | |
| Sissons | 3 | | | 3 | | | | McEvilly | 1 | | | 1 | | | |
| Killeen | 2 | | | 2 | | | | Palmer | 1 | | | 1 | | | |
| Ward | 2 | | | 2 | | | | Own Goals | 1 | 1 | | 2 | | | |
| Ahmed | 1 | | | 1 | | | | Cons Run - Consecutive scoring games. | | | | | | | |

# F.C. UNITED OF MANCHESTER

**Chairman:** Andy Walsh (General Manager)
**Secretary:** Lindsey Howard    **(T)** 0161 273 8950    **(E)** office@fc-utd.co.uk
**Commercial Manager:** Mike Burtonwood    **(T)** 07966 265 353
**Programme Editor:** Tony Howard    **(T)** 0161 273 8950
**Ground Address:** Bury F.C., Gigg Lane, Bury B19 9HR
**(T)** 0161 273 8950    **Manager:** Karl Marginson

2012-13 Squad.

## Club Factfile

**Founded:** 2005    **Nickname:** F.C.
**Previous Names:** None
**Previous Leagues:** North West Counties 2005-07

**Club Colours (change):** Red/white/black (White/black/white)

**Ground Capacity:** 11,840 **Seats:** 11,699 **Covered:** NK    **Clubhouse:** Yes    **Shop:** Yes

**Directions**

**All Main Routes:** Exit M60 at junction 17 (s/p A56 Whitefield, Salford). At roundabout follow signs to `Whitfield A56, Radcliffe (A665), Bury A56' onto the A56. After 0.3 miles go straight over double traffic lights passing McDonalds on LHS (s/p Bury A56, Radcliffe A665). At lights after 0.8 miles (just after the `Bull's Head' pub) bear right (s/p Bury A56). Straight on at lights after 1.0 miles (s/p Town Centre). After 1.0 miles turn right (s/p Football Ground) into Gigg Lane. Ground is on RHS after 0.1 miles.
**From North and East (via M66):** Exit M66 at junction 2 and follow signs to `Bury A58, Football Ground' onto the A58 Rochdale Road. After 0.5 miles turn left at traffic lights by the Crown Hotel (s/p Football Ground) onto Heywood Street. After 0.4 miles turn right at second mini-roundabout (s/p Football Ground, Manchester, Salford B6219) into Wellington Road. At next mini-roundabout turn left into Market Street. Straight on over mini-roundabout after 0.1 miles and right at T-junction after 0.2 miles into Gigg Lane.

**Previous Grounds:** None

**Record Attendance:** 6,731 v Brighton & Hove Albion, FA Cup 2nd Round 08/12/2010
**Record Victory:** 10-2 v Castleton Gabriels 10/12/2005. 8-0 v Squires Gate 14/10/06, Glossop N.E. 28/10/06 & Nelson 05/09/10
**Record Defeat:** 1-5 v Bradford Park Avenue 24/03/2010. 1-5 v Matlock Town 05/09/2010
**Record Goalscorer:** Rory Patterson - 99 (2005-08)
**Record Appearances:** Jerome Wright - 249
**Additional Records:** Simon Carden scored 5 goals against Castleton Gabriels 10/12/2005.
**Senior Honours:** Longest unbeaten run (League): 22 games 03/12/2006 - 18/08/2007.
North West Counties League Division 2 2005-06, Division 1 2006-07.
Northern Premier League Division 1 North Play-off 2007-08.

### 10 YEAR RECORD

| 03-04 | 04-05 | 05-06 | | 06-07 | | 07-08 | | 08-09 | | 09-10 | | 10-11 | | 11-12 | | 12-13 | |
|---|---|---|---|---|---|---|---|---|---|---|---|---|---|---|---|---|---|
| | | NWC2 | 1 | NWC1 | 1 | NP1N | 2 | NP P | 6 | NP P | 13 | NP P | 4 | NP P | 6 | NP P | 3 |

# MATCH RESULTS 2012-13

| Date | Comp | H/A | Opponents | Att: | Result | Goalscorers | Pos | No. |
|---|---|---|---|---|---|---|---|---|
| Aug 18 | NPL | A | Grantham Town | 1220 | W 4-2 | Jones 38 Wright 47 Roca 51 Norton 67 | | 1 |
| 21 | NPL | H | Whitby Town | 1562 | W 3-2 | Norton 6 Wolfenden 54 Cottrell 63 | 3 | 2 |
| 26 | NPL | H | Matlock Town | 1763 | W 4-0 | Norton 41 Roca 51 Jacobs 75 84 | 2 | 3 |
| 27 | NPL | A | Witton Albion | 1352 | D 1-1 | Platt 26 | 3 | 4 |
| Sept 2 | NPL | H | Hednesford Town | 1702 | D 1-1 | Roca 32 | 4 | 5 |
| 5 | NPL | A | Whitby Town | 482 | W 1-0 | Wolfenden 58 | 4 | 6 |
| 8 | FAC Q1 | H | Cammell Laird | 1,024 | W 5-0 | Neville 28 Wright 33 Norton 43 67 Grogan 67 (og) | 4 | 7 |
| 15 | NPL | H | Nantwich Town | 1969 | L 1-2 | Wolfenden 54 | 5 | 8 |
| 18 | NPL | A | Stafford Rangers | 814 | D 1-1 | Wright 16 | 5 | 9 |
| 22 | FAC Q2 | H | Salford City | 1292 | W 3-2 | PLATT    ROCA | | 10 |
| 29 | FAT Q1 | H | Mossley | 861 | D 3-3 | Amadi 73 78 Wright 87 | | 11 |
| Oct 2 | FAT Q1r | A | Mossley | 405 | W 3-1 | Cottrell 19 Platt 58 Birch 81 | | 12 |
| 7 | FAC Q3 | H | Kendal Town | 1186 | W 3-1 | Stott 61 (pen) 81 (pen) Jones 71 | | 13 |
| 13 | NPL | A | AFC Fylde | 1418 | L 2-4 | Norton 37 Daniels 84 | 11 | 14 |
| 20 | FAC Q4 | H | Hereford United | 2212 | L 0-2 | | | 15 |
| 23 | NPL | A | North Ferriby United | 538 | D 1-1 | Wright 38 | 13 | 16 |
| 27 | FAT Q2 | A | Stamford | 749 | L 1-2 | Norton 9 | | 17 |
| 31 | NPL | A | Ashton United | 503 | W 2-1 | Wolfenden 9 19 | 11 | 18 |
| Nov 4 | NPL | H | Eastwood Town | 1692 | W 4-1 | Norton 16 28 Jones 19 Stott 42 (pen) | | 19 |
| 10 | NPL | A | Ilkeston | 1015 | D 1-1 | Platt 10 | 13 | 20 |
| 17 | NPL | H | Rushall Olympic | 1795 | L 0-4 | | 11 | 21 |
| 20 | NPL | H | Marine | 1484 | L 0-1 | | 11 | 22 |
| 24 | NPL | A | Chorley | 1130 | W 2-1 | Norton 36 Tierney 87 | 8 | 23 |
| Dec 1 | NPL | A | Blyth Spartans | 617 | W 2-1 | Stott 14 Norton 50 | 7 | 24 |
| 8 | NPL | A | Hednesford Town | 929 | L 0-1 | | 8 | 25 |
| 15 | NPL | H | Grantham Town | 1539 | W 1-0 | Wolfenden 90 | 8 | 26 |
| Jan 5 | NPL | A | Nantwich Town | 1003 | W 3-2 | Wolfenden 4 Jones 9 Daniels 83 | 8 | 27 |
| 12 | NPL | H | Stafford Rangers | 2131 | W 3-0 | Wright 51 Wolfenden 72 Greaves 76 | 7 | 28 |
| Feb 2 | NPL | H | Buxton | 1121 | W 3-0 | Wolfenden 10 Norton 52 65 | 5 | 29 |
| 9 | NPL | H | AFC Fylde | 2042 | W 2-1 | Wolfenden 47 69 | 4 | 30 |
| 12 | NPL | A | Frickley Athletic | 428 | W 4-2 | Neville 12 Wolfenden 15 Norton 35 Greaves 48 | 4 | 31 |
| 16 | NPL | A | Marine | 1282 | W 3-0 | GREAVES 3 (20 29 55) | 3 | 32 |
| 23 | NPL | H | Ilkeston | 1929 | W 1-0 | Jones 82 | 3 | 33 |
| Mar 4 | NPL | H | North Ferriby United | 2465 | D 1-1 | Greaves 45 | 3 | 34 |
| 7 | NPL | A | Matlock Town | 613 | D 2-2 | Jones 52 59 | 3 | 35 |
| 9 | NPL | H | Chorley Town | 2031 | L 1-3 | Wolfenden 54 | 4 | 36 |
| 16 | NPL | A | Worksop Town | 811 | L 1-4 | Wolfenden 7 | 5 | 37 |
| 19 | NPL | H | Buxton | 1501 | L 1-2 | Wolfenden 39 | 5 | 38 |
| 23 | NPL | H | Blyth Spartans | 1730 | W 2-1 | Norton 81 Greaves 83 | 5 | 39 |
| 30 | NPL | A | Kendal Town | 710 | W 5-1 | Norton 8 Wright 16 19 Stott 54 (Pen) Greaves 65 | | 40 |
| Apr 1 | NPL | H | Stocksbridge PS | 1659 | W 4-0 | Birch 17 Norton 49 Banks 63 Daniels 73 | | 41 |
| 6 | NPL | H | Witton Albion | 1741 | L 0-1 | | 4 | 42 |
| 9 | NPL | H | Kendal Town | 1517 | W 6-0 | Wolfenden 4 DANIELS 3 ( 9 73 85) Giggs 25 Greaves 79 | 3 | 43 |
| 13 | NPL | A | Eastwood Town | 607 | D 2-2 | Banks 45 Norton 89 | 3 | 44 |
| 17 | NPL | A | Stocksbridge PS | 406 | W 3-1 | Wright 39 Jones 47 Daniels 58 | 3 | 45 |
| 21 | NPL | H | Worksop Town | 2761 | W 1-0 | Wolfenden 68 | 3 | 46 |
| 23 | NPL | H | Ashton United | 1586 | W 3-0 | Daniels 13 Stott 33 Wolfenden 44 | 3 | 47 |
| 27 | NPL | A | Rushall Olympic | 1007 | W 1-0 | Stott 58 | 3 | 48 |
| May 4 | NPL | H | Frickley Athletic | 3134 | W 3-0 | Greaves 10 Walwyn 39 Norton 71 | 3 | 49 |
| 7 | P-Off S-F | H | Witton Albion | 2492 | W 3-1 | Wolfenden 9 Mulholland 35 Stott (75 pen) | | 50 |
| 11 | P-Off Final | A | Hednesford Town | 4412 | L 1-2 | Norton 55 | | 51 |

| GOALSCORERS | Lge | FAC | FAT | Total | Pens | Hat-tricks | Cons Run | | Lge | FAC | FAT | Total | Pens | Hat-tricks | Cons Run |
|---|---|---|---|---|---|---|---|---|---|---|---|---|---|---|---|
| Norton | 17 | 2 | 1 | 20 | | | 3 | Cottrell | 1 | | 1 | 2 | | | |
| Wolfenden | 19 | | | 19 | | | 6 | Jacobs | 2 | | | 2 | | | |
| Greaves | 10 | | | 10 | | 1 | | Banks | 1 | | | 1 | | | |
| Wright | 8 | 1 | 1 | 10 | | | | Giggs | 1 | | | 1 | | | |
| Daniels | 8 | | | 8 | | | | Neville | | 1 | | 1 | | | |
| Jones | 7 | 1 | | 8 | | | | Tierney | 1 | | | 1 | | | |
| Stott | 6 | 2 | | 7 | 4 | | 2 | Walwyn | 1 | | | 1 | | | |
| Platt | 2 | 2 | 1 | 5 | | | | Mulholland | 1 | | | 1 | | | |
| Roca | 3 | 1 | | 4 | | | | Own Goals | 1 | 1 | | 2 | | | |
| Amadi | | | 2 | 2 | | | | Cons Run - Consecutive scoring games. | | | | | | | |
| Birch | 1 | | 1 | 2 | | | | | | | | | | | |

# FRICKLEY ATHLETIC

**Chairman:** Gareth Dando
**Secretary:** Steve Pennock    **(T)** 07985 291 074    **(E)** stevepennock99@gmail.com
**Commercial Manager:** Les Bradley    **(T)** 07922 992207
**Programme Editor:** Gareth Dando    **(T)** 07709 098 469
**Ground Address:** Tech5 Stadium, Westfield Lane, South Elmsall, Pontefract WF9 2EQ
**(T)** 01977 642 460    **Manager:** Karl Rose

## Club Factfile

**Founded:** 1910    **Nickname:** The Blues
**Previous Names:** Frickley Colliery
**Previous Leagues:** Sheffield, Yorkshire 1922-24, Midland Counties 1924-33, 34-60, 70-76, Cheshire County 1960-70, Northern Premier 1976-80, Conference 1980-87

**Club Colours (change):** All royal blue (All yellow)

**Ground Capacity:** 2,087    **Seats:** 490    **Covered:** 700    **Clubhouse:** Yes    **Shop:** Yes

**Directions**

From North : Leave A1 to join A639, go over flyover to junction. Turn left and immediately right, signed South Elmsall. Continue to roundabout and take 2nd exit to traffic lights and turn left onto Mill Lane (B6474). Turn right at the T-junction and continue down hill to next T-junction. Turn right and immediately left up Westfield Lane. The ground is signposted to the left after about half a mile.

From South : Exit M18 at J2 onto A1 (North). Leave A1 for A638 towards Wakefield. Continue on A638, going straight on at the first roundabout and turn left at next roundabout to traffic lights. Continue as above from traffic lights.

**Previous Grounds:** None

**Record Attendance:** 6,500 v Rotherham United - FA Cup 1st Round 1971
**Record Victory:** Not known
**Record Defeat:** Not known
**Record Goalscorer:** K Whiteley
**Record Appearances:** Not known
**Additional Records:** Received £12,500 from Boston United for Paul Shirtliff and from Northampton Town for Russ Wilcox

**Senior Honours:**
Sheffield & Hallamshire Senior Cup x11 Most recently 2012-13.

| 10 YEAR RECORD | | | | | | | | | |
|---|---|---|---|---|---|---|---|---|---|
| 03-04 | 04-05 | 05-06 | 06-07 | 07-08 | 08-09 | 09-10 | 10-11 | 11-12 | 12-13 |
| NP P 22 | NP P 18 | NP P 2 | NP P 16 | NP P 14 | NP P 11 | NP P 15 | NP P 18 | NP P 19 | NP P 18 |

# MATCH RESULTS 2012-13

| Date | Comp | H/A | Opponents | Att: | Result | Goalscorers | Pos | No. |
|------|------|-----|-----------|------|--------|-------------|-----|-----|
| Aug 18 | NPL | A | Hednesford Town | 418 | L 2-3 | Ghaichem 29 Johnston 79 | 21 | 1 |
| 21 | NPL | H | Matlock Town | 250 | L 1-2 | Ghaichem 24 | 18 | 2 |
| 25 | NPL | H | Marine | 180 | L 0-2 | | 21 | 3 |
| 27 | NPL | A | North Ferriby United | 207 | L 0-4 | | 21 | 4 |
| Sept 1 | NPL | H | Ashton United | 183 | D 1-1 | Aujla | 19 | 5 |
| 4 | NPL | A | Matlock Town | 255 | L 1-3 | Cotton 67 | 20 | 6 |
| 8 | FAC Q1 | A | **Worksop Town** | 274 | W 2-0 | Auja 57 Allott 62 | | 7 |
| 15 | NPL | A | Rushall Olympic | 164 | L 0-1 | | 21 | 8 |
| 18 | NPL | H | Ilkeston | 212 | W 2-1 | Allott 62 64 | 19 | 9 |
| 22 | FAC Q2 | H | **Chorley** | 642 | W 3-1 | ALLOTT 3 ( 37pen 45 pen 66) | | 10 |
| 29 | FAT Q1 | H | **North Ferriby United** | 146 | L 1-4 | Allott 31 (pen) | | 11 |
| Oct 6 | FAC Q3 | A | **Harrogate United** | 349 | L 2-3 | **Ghaichem 3 Allott 29** | 20 | 12 |
| 13 | NPL | H | Stafford Rangers | 224 | W 2-1 | Hinsley 42 Allott 52 | 20 | 13 |
| 20 | NPL | A | Chorley | 600 | L 1-5 | Allott 8 | 22 | 14 |
| 23 | NPL | H | Eastwood Town | 153 | W 1-0 | Graham 90 (og) | 18 | 15 |
| 27 | NPL | A | Blyth Spartans | 288 | L 2-4 | Hinsley 39 Yates 90 | 19 | 16 |
| 30 | NPL | H | Stocksbridge PS | 200 | W 4-2 | PICTON 3 (25 68 76) Allott 48 | 18 | 17 |
| Nov 3 | NPL | A | Buxton | 243 | L 0-1 | | 18 | 18 |
| 10 | NPL | H | Nantwich Town | 237 | W 3-0 | Hinsley 2 17 Allott 37 | 17 | 19 |
| 17 | NPL | A | Witton Albion | 376 | L 0-5 | | 17 | 20 |
| 20 | NPL | H | AFC Fylde | 196 | D 1-1 | Allott 45 (pen ) | 17 | 21 |
| 24 | NPL | A | Grantham Town | 221 | L 1-2 | Howarth 58 | 18 | 22 |
| Dec 15 | NPL | H | Hednesford Town | 201 | W 2-1 | Hinsley 59 Allott 80 | 18 | 23 |
| 26 | NPL | H | North Ferriby United | 255 | L 2-3 | Howarth 66 Allott 72 (pen) | 18 | 24 |
| 29 | NPL | H | Kendal Town | 208 | W 2-1 | Allott 32 (pen) Picton 66 | 17 | 25 |
| Jan 1 | NPL | A | Whitby Town | 284 | L 1-4 | Picton 31 | 18 | 26 |
| 5 | NPL | H | Rushall Olympic | 220 | D 3-3 | ALLOTT 3 ( 39 56 80) | 14 | 27 |
| 12 | NPL | A | Ilkeston | 433 | L 2-4 | Allott 8 (pen) 74 | 18 | 28 |
| Feb 2 | NPL | H | Blyth Spartans | 224 | W 2-1 | Allott 18 (pen) Hardy 41 | 18 | 29 |
| 6 | NPL | A | Worksop Town | 224 | L 2-3 | Hinsley 1 Picton 21 | 18 | 30 |
| 9 | NPL | A | Stafford Rangers | 398 | D 3-3 | Wood 60 Picton 71 Hardy 90 | 18 | 31 |
| 12 | NPL | H | FC United | 428 | L 2-4 | Picton 54 Wood 66 (pen) | 18 | 32 |
| 16 | NPL | H | Chorley | 220 | L 0-1 | | 18 | 33 |
| 23 | NPL | H | Grantham Town | 217 | D 0-0 | | 18 | 34 |
| Mar 3 | NPL | H | Buxton | 229 | D 3-3 | Yates 13 Wood 17 Hinsley 90 | 18 | 35 |
| 9 | NPL | A | Kendal Town | 120 | W 2-0 | Wood 21 (pen) 41 (pen) | 18 | 36 |
| 16 | NPL | A | Marine | 275 | D 2-2 | Ghaichem 85 Wootton 90 | 18 | 37 |
| 19 | NPL | A | Eastwood Town | 98 | W 1-0 | Burgess 83 | 16 | 38 |
| 30 | NPL | A | Ashton United | 112 | D 0-0 | | 16 | 39 |
| Apr 1 | NPL | H | Whitby Town | 224 | L 0-2 | | 17 | 40 |
| 6 | NPL | A | Stocksbridge PS | 174 | L 3-4 | Howe 25 Allott 57 (pen) Bodwell-Lovell 59 (og) | 18 | 41 |
| 9 | NPL | H | Worksop Town | 202 | D 0-0 | | 17 | 42 |
| 20 | NPL | A | Nantwich Town | 246 | L 2-3 | Wootton 5 Pickton 84 | 18 | 43 |
| 23 | NPL | A | AFC Fylde | 185 | L 2-3 | Wood 38 Yates 74 | 18 | 44 |
| 27 | NPL | H | Witton Albion | 226 | L 0-2 | | 18 | 45 |
| May 4 | NPL | A | FC United | 2124 | L 0-3 | | 18 | 46 |

| GOALSCORERS | Lge | FAC | FAT | Total | Pens | Hat-tricks | Cons Run | | Lge | FAC | FAT | Total | Pens | Hat-tricks | Cons Run |
|-------------|-----|-----|-----|-------|------|-----------|----------|---|-----|-----|-----|-------|------|-----------|----------|
| Allott | 16 | 5 | 1 | 22 | 8 | 2 | 6 | Burgess | 1 | | | 1 | | | |
| Picton | 9 | | | 9 | 1 | | 3 | Cotton | 1 | | | 1 | | | |
| Hinsley | 8 | | | 8 | | | | Howe | 1 | | | 1 | | | |
| Wood | 6 | | | 6 | 3 | | 2 | Johnston | 1 | | | 1 | | | |
| Ghaichem | 3 | 1 | | 4 | | | 2 | Own Goals | 2 | | | 2 | | | |
| Yates | 3 | | | 3 | | | | Cons Run - Consecutive scoring games. | | | | | | | |
| Aija | 1 | 1 | | 2 | | | | | | | | | | | |
| Hardy | 2 | | | 2 | | | | | | | | | | | |
| Howarth | 2 | | | 2 | | | | | | | | | | | |
| Wootton | 2 | | | 2 | | | | | | | | | | | |

# GRANTHAM TOWN

**Chairman:** Peter Railton

**Secretary:** Patrick Nixon          **(T)** 07747 136 033          **(E)** psnixon@hotmail.com

**Commercial Manager:** Steve Cardy          **(T)**

**Programme Editor:** Mike Koranski          **(T)** 01476 562 104

**Ground Address:** South Kesteven Sports Stadium, Trent Road, Gratham NG31 7XQ

**(T)** 01476 591 818 (office)          **Manager:** Gary Sucharewycz

2012-13 Squad.

## Club Factfile

**Founded:** 1874          **Nickname:** Gingerbreads

**Previous Names:** Not known

**Previous Leagues:** Midland Amateur Alliance, Central Alliance 1911-25, 59-61, Midland Counties 1925-59, 61-72, Southern 1972-79, 85-2006, Northern Premier 1979-85

**Club Colours (change):** All red (Navy & sky hoops/neath navy/orange)

**Ground Capacity:** 7,500     **Seats:** 750     **Covered:** 1,950     **Clubhouse:** Yes     **Shop:** Yes

**Directions**

FROM A1 NORTH Leave A1 At A607 Melton Mowbray exit. Turn left at island on slip road into Swingbridge Lane. At T junction turn left into Trent Road ground is 100yds on right.

FROM A52 NOTTINGHAM. Pass over A1 and at first island turn right into housing estate & Barrowby Gate. Through housing estate to T junction. Turn right and then immediately left into Trent road ground is 100 yards on the left.

FROM A607 MELTON MOWBRAY. Pass under A1 and take next left A1 South slip road. At island turn right into Swingbridge Road then as for A1 North above. From all directions follow brown signs for Sports Complex, which is immediately behind the stadium.

**Previous Grounds:** London Road

**Record Attendance:** 3,695 v Southport - FA Trophy 1997-98

**Record Victory:** 13-0 v Rufford Colliery (H) - FA Cup 15/09/1934

**Record Defeat:** 0-16 v Notts County Rovers (A) - Midland Amateur Alliance 22/10/1892

**Record Goalscorer:** Jack McCartney - 416

**Record Appearances:** Chris Gardner - 664

**Additional Records:** Received £20,000 from Nottingham Forest for Gary Crosby

**Senior Honours:**

Southern League Midland Division 1997-98. Lincolnshire Senior Cup x21 Most recently 2011-12. Northern Premier Division 1 South 2011-12.

| 10 YEAR RECORD | | | | | | | | | |
|---|---|---|---|---|---|---|---|---|---|
| 03-04 | 04-05 | 05-06 | 06-07 | 07-08 | 08-09 | 09-10 | 10-11 | 11-12 | 12-13 |
| SthP 22 | SthP 13 | SthP 11 | NP P 22 | NP 1 6 | NP1S 13 | NP1S 11 | NP1S 5 | NP1S 1 | NP P 19 |

# MATCH RESULTS 2012-13

| Date | Comp | H/A | Opponents | Att. | Result | Goalscorers | Pos | No. |
|------|------|-----|-----------|------|--------|-------------|-----|-----|
| Aug 18 | NPL | H | FC United | 1220 | L 2-4 | Grimes 12 Puricloe 53 | 20 | 1 |
| 21 | NPL | A | Stafford Rangers | 474 | W 1-0 | Watt 80 | 10 | 2 |
| 25 | NPL | A | Chorley | 529 | L 0-2 | | 13 | 3 |
| 27 | NPL | H | Worksop Town | 384 | W 3-0 | Puricloe 51 B.Saunders 62 Watt 67 | | 4 |
| Sept 1 | NPL | A | Nantwich Town | 276 | W 2-0 | Potts 10 Ball 45 | 6 | 5 |
| 4 | NPL | H | Stafford Rangers | 270 | D 2-2 | B.Saunders 29 Brindley 58 | 10 | 6 |
| 8 | FAC Q1 | A | Loughborough | 175 | D 2-2 | Brindley 4 McGhee 74 | | 7 |
| 15 | NPL | A | Ashton United | 149 | D 1-1 | Watt 36 | 12 | 8 |
| 18 | NPL | H | Matlock Town | 234 | D 3-3 | Nwadike 38 Watt 72 Higginson 74 | 12 | 9 |
| 22 | FAC Q2 | A | Cambridge City | 379 | L 1-3 | Higginson 58 | | 10 |
| 29 | FAT Q1 | H | Bedford Town | 271 | L 0-2 | | | 11 |
| Oct 6 | NPL | H | Stocksbridge PS | 235 | L 1-2 | Puricloe 67 | 13 | 12 |
| 10 | NPL | A | Whitby Town | 268 | L 0-2 | | 14 | 13 |
| 13 | NPL | A | Kendal Town | 162 | L 0-1 | | 15 | 14 |
| 16 | NPL | H | North Ferriby Utd | 128 | L 2-3 | Lewis 7 Higginson 44 | 15 | 15 |
| 20 | NPL | H | Hednesford Town | 227 | L 2-3 | Grimes 18 Potts 37 | 15 | 16 |
| 27 | NPL | H | Chorley Town | 215 | L 0-1 | | 16 | 17 |
| 30 | NPL | H | Buxton | 177 | D 0-0 | | 17 | 18 |
| Nov 3 | NPL | A | Witton Albion | 429 | W 2-0 | Grimes 32 (pen) Demidh 90 (pen), | 16 | 19 |
| 10 | NPL | H | Blyth Spartans | 255 | D 2-2 | Lewis 20 Potts 79 | 16 | 20 |
| 17 | NPL | A | Marine | 362 | L 0-1 | | 16 | 21 |
| 24 | NPL | H | Frickley Athletic | 221 | W 2-1 | Grimes 3 (pen) 9 | 14 | 22 |
| Dec 1 | NPL | A | AFC Fylde | 224 | L 3-5 | Grimes 67 (pen) McGhee 77 Robinson 80 | 15 | 23 |
| 3 | NPL | A | Ilkeston | 427 | L 0-2 | | 16 | 24 |
| 8 | NPL | H | Nantwich Town | 187 | L 1-4 | S.Saunders 29 | 16 | 25 |
| 15 | NPL | A | FC United | 1539 | L 0-1 | | 16 | 26 |
| 26 | NPL | A | Worksop Town | 347 | L 2-3 | Demidh 31 B.Saunders 58 | 17 | 27 |
| Jan 1 | NPL | H | Eastwood Town | 262 | W 4-0 | McGhee 33 B. Saunders 35 40 S.Saunders 77 | 17 | 28 |
| 5 | NPL | H | Ashton United | 222 | L 0-2 | | 19 | 29 |
| 12 | NPL | A | Matlock Town | 300 | L 2-3 | Brindley 15 Demidh 32 | 19 | 30 |
| Feb 2 | NPL | A | North Ferriby United | 301 | L 1-3 | Smith 41 | 19 | 31 |
| 9 | NPL | H | Kendal Town | 187 | L 3-4 | MacVictor 1 Smith 18 McGhee 61 | 19 | 32 |
| 16 | NPL | A | Hednesford Town | 463 | L 0-3 | | 19 | 33 |
| 23 | NPL | A | Frickley Athletic | 217 | D 0-0 | | 19 | 34 |
| Mar 3 | NPL | H | Ilkeston | 33 | D 1-1 | Meikle 82 | 19 | 35 |
| 9 | NPL | A | Rushall Olympic | 186 | L 1-3 | Nwadike 18 | 19 | 36 |
| 12 | NPL | H | Whitby Town | 100 | L 2-3 | McGhee 53 Smith 56 | 19 | 37 |
| 16 | NPL | H | AFC Fylde | 192 | L 1-2 | Smith 50 | 19 | 38 |
| 30 | NPL | H | Rushall Olympic | 199 | W 2-1 | Hawes 45 Smith 74 | 19 | 39 |
| Apr 1 | NPL | A | Eastwood Town | 187 | D 2-2 | Lewis 30 Watson 85 | 19 | 40 |
| 6 | NPL | A | Buxton | 274 | D 1-1 | Smith 65 | 19 | 41 |
| 13 | NPL | H | Witton Albion | 210 | L 1-3 | Carchedi 25 | 19 | 42 |
| 20 | NPL | A | Blyth Spartans | 316 | L 0-1 | | 20 | 43 |
| 27 | NPL | H | Matrine | 228 | W 1-0 | Lewis 68 | 20 | 44 |
| May 4 | NPL | A | Stocksbridge PS | 168 | W 3-0 | Smith 5 McGhee 62 Carchedi 90 | 19 | 45 |

| GOALSCORERS | Lge | FAC | FAT | Total | Pens | Hat-tricks | Cons Run | | Lge | FAC | FAT | Total | Pens | Hat-tricks | Cons Run |
|-------------|-----|-----|-----|-------|------|-----------|----------|---|-----|-----|-----|-------|------|-----------|----------|
| Smith | 7 | | | 7 | | | 3 | Carchedi | 2 | | | 2 | | | |
| Grimes | 6 | | | 6 | 3 | | 2 | Nwadike | 2 | | | 2 | | | |
| McGhee | 5 | 1 | | 6 | | | | S.Saunders | 2 | | | 2 | | | |
| B.Saunders | 5 | | | 5 | | | 2 | Ball | 1 | | | 1 | | | |
| Lewis | 4 | | | 4 | | | | Hawes | 1 | | | 1 | | | |
| Watt | 4 | | | 4 | | | 2 | MacVictor | 1 | | | 1 | | | |
| Brindley | 2 | 1 | | 3 | | | 2 | Meikle | 1 | | | 1 | | | |
| Demidh | 3 | | | 3 | 1 | | | Robinson | 1 | | | 1 | | | |
| Higginson | 2 | 1 | | 3 | | | 2 | Watson | 1 | | | 1 | | | |
| Puricloe | 3 | | | 3 | | | | Cons Run - Consecutive scoring games. | | | | | | | |
| Potts | 3 | | | 3 | | | | | | | | | | | |

# ILKESTON

**ILKESTON**
FOOTBALL CLUB

**Chairman:** Dave Mantle
**Secretary:** Andrew Raisin    **(T)** 07813 357 393    **(E)** a.raisin@ilkestonfc.co.uk
**Commercial Manager:** Nigel Harrop    **(T)** 07402 758 855
**Programme Editor:** Sam Gascoyne    **(T)** 07735 612 860
**Ground Address:** New Manor Ground, Awsworth Road, Ilkeston, Derbyshire DE7 8JF
**(T)** 0115 944 428    **Manager:** Kevin Wilson

Action from The Robins pre-season friendly against Chelsea which attracted a record crowd of 2,680.
Photo courtesy of Craig Lamont of Craig Lamont Photography.

## Club Factfile

**Founded:** 2010    **Nickname:** The Robins
**Previous Names:** None
**Previous Leagues:** None

**Club Colours (change):** Red/red/red (Orange with black cuffs/orange/orange)

**Ground Capacity:** 3,029    **Seats:** 550    **Covered:** 2,000    **Clubhouse:** Yes    **Shop:** Yes

**Directions**

M1 Junction 26, take the A610 signed Ripley, leave at the first exit on to the A6096 signed Awsworth / Ilkeston, at the next island take the A6096 signed Ilkeston, keep on this road for about half a mile, then turn right into Awsworth Road, Signed Cotmanhay (Coaches can get down this road) the ground is about half a mile on the left hand side down this road. Car Parking available at the ground £1 per car.

**Previous Grounds:** None.

**Record Attendance:** 2,680 v Chelsea - pre-season friendly July 2013. Competitive: 1,670 v Leek Town - NPL Divi.1S P-Off Final 28.4.2012.
**Record Victory:** 7-0 v Sheffield FC - Evo-Stik League D1S P-Off SF 23.4.2012 & v Heanor Town (H) Derbys Sen Cup 2012-13.
**Record Defeat:** 1-5 v Northwich Victoria (H) - FA Trophy Third Qualifying Round 28.11.2011.
**Record Goalscorer:** Gary Ricketts - 32
**Record Appearances:** Ryan Wilson - 88
**Additional Records:**

**Senior Honours:**
Northern Premier League Division One South Play-Off 2011-12.
Derbyshire Senior Challenge Cup 2012-13.

| | | | | 10 YEAR RECORD | | | | | |
|---|---|---|---|---|---|---|---|---|---|
| 03-04 | 04-05 | 05-06 | 06-07 | 07-08 | 08-09 | 09-10 | 10-11 | 11-12 | 12-13 |
| | | | | | | | | NP1S    3 | NP P    12 |

## MATCH RESULTS 2012-13

| Date | Comp | H/A | Opponents | Att: | Result | Goalscorers | Pos | No. |
|------|------|-----|-----------|------|--------|-------------|-----|-----|
| Aug 18 | NPL | H | AFC Fylde | 481 | D 1-1 | Ricketts 55 | 12 | 1 |
| 21 | NPL | A | Rushallm Olympic | 248 | L 1-2 | Reid 90 | 16 | 2 |
| 25 | NPL | A | Nantwich Town | 385 | L 0-1 | | 17 | 3 |
| 27 | NPL | H | Eastwood Town | 795 | W 2-1 | McColl 23 Ricketts 73 | 17 | 4 |
| Sept 1 | NPL | A | Chorley | 652 | L 0-1 | | 17 | 5 |
| 3 | NPL | A | Rushall Olympic | 412 | L 0-1 | | 18 | 6 |
| 8 | FAC Q1 | A | Coalville | 322 | W 1-0 | Wilson 55 (pen) | | 7 |
| 15 | NPL | H | Witton Albion | 499 | L 2-3 | Harrison 7 (og) Booth 51 (og) | 18 | 8 |
| 18 | NPL | A | Frickley Athletic | 212 | L 1-2 | Richards 40 | 18 | 9 |
| 22 | FAC Q2 | H | Belper Town | 519 | D 2-2 | Thomas 39 65 | | 10 |
| 25 | FAC Q2r | A | Belper Town | 320 | W 5-1 | Maguire 18 Hooton 24 Richards 30 Thomas 45 Chambers 64 | | 11 |
| 29 | FAT Q1 | A | Stourbridge | 349 | W 1-0 | Reid 51 | | 12 |
| Oct 6 | FAC Q3 | H | Gresley | 621 | W 4-2 | Hooton 9 Thomas 31 55 Richards 88 | | 13 |
| 13 | NPL | H | Stocksbridge PS | 638 | W 1-0 | Gardner 69 | 19 | 14 |
| 16 | NPL | A | Stafford Rangers | 312 | L 1-2 | Watts 73 | 20 | 15 |
| 20 | FAC Q4 | A | AFC Fylde | 482 | D 1-1 | Gardner 70 | | 16 |
| 22 | FAC Q4r | H | AFC Fylde | 696 | L 0-1 | | | 17 |
| 27 | FAT Q2 | A | Whitby Town | 272 | L 2-4 | Richards 3 Wilson 19 | | 18 |
| 30 | NPL | A | North Ferriby U | 274 | D 1-1 | Ricketts 22 | 23 | 19 |
| Nov 3 | NPL | H | Kendal Town | 401 | D 4-4 | Eades 49 90 Ricketts 84 Watts 87 | 21 | 20 |
| 10 | NPL | H | FC United | 1015 | D 1-1 | Maguire 73 | 22 | 21 |
| 17 | NPL | H | Matlock Town | 612 | L 0-2 | | 21 | 22 |
| 21 | NPL | A | Ashton United | 128 | W 3-0 | Hooton 1, 23 Richards 45 | | 23 |
| 24 | NPL | H | Whitby Town | 563 | W 3-1 | Maguire 10 58 Hooton 15 | 20 | 24 |
| 27 | NPL | A | Hednesford Town | 319 | L 0-2 | | 20 | 25 |
| Dec 1 | NPL | A | Marine | 338 | D 1-1 | Smith 48 | 17 | 26 |
| 3 | NPL | H | Grantham Town | 427 | W 2-0 | Peel 25 Ricketts 90 | 14 | 27 |
| 8 | NPL | H | Chorley | 405 | W 1-0 | Robbins 72 | 14 | 28 |
| 15 | NPL | A | Ashton United | 244 | W 3-2 | Ricketts 19 24 Richards 56 | 13 | 29 |
| 26 | NPL | A | Easrwood Town | 512 | W 4-1 | Richards 12 45 Smith 27 Hooton 55 | 13 | 30 |
| Jan 1 | NPL | H | Worksop Town | 278 | W 2-1 | Hooton 65 Wilson 90 | | 31 |
| 4 | NPL | A | Witton Albion | 454 | D 2-2 | Shehan 24 (og) Partridge 67 | 12 | 32 |
| 12 | NPL | A | Frickley Athletic | 433 | W 4-2 | Maguire 3 58 (pen) Ricketts 6 Hooton 39 | 10 | 33 |
| Feb 2 | NPL | H | Satford Rangers | 515 | L 0-2 | | | 34 |
| 9 | NPL | A | Stocksbridge PS | 185 | D 1-1 | Watts 20 | 11 | 35 |
| 16 | NPL | H | Ashton United | 457 | D 2-2 | Reid 46 82 | 13 | 36 |
| 23 | NPL | A | FC United | 1929 | L 0-1 | | 13 | 37 |
| Mar 2 | NPL | A | Grantham Town | 323 | D 1-1 | Maguire 57 | 13 | 38 |
| 4 | NPL | H | Nantwich Town | 367 | W 3-0 | Richards 1 21 O'Connell 54 | 12 | 39 |
| 16 | NPL | A | Blyth Spartans | 326 | L 2-3 | Ford 24 Hooton 58 | 13 | 40 |
| 30 | NPL | H | Blyth Spartans | 419 | W 3-1 | Hooton 29 (pen) Reid 48 Ricketts 90 | 12 | 41 |
| Apr 1 | NPL | A | Worksop Town | 348 | W 4-1 | Hooton 20 Ricketts 78 Richards 80 90 | 12 | 42 |
| 4 | NPL | H | Buxton | 387 | D 1-1 | Reid 48 | 12 | 43 |
| 6 | NPL | H | North Ferriby United | 417 | D 2-2 | Hooton 35 Russell 63 | 12 | 44 |
| 10 | NPL | A | Buxton | 281 | D 0-0 | | 12 | 45 |
| 13 | NPL | A | Kendal Town | 188 | L 2-3 | Gordon 30 59 | 12 | 46 |
| 20 | NPL | H | Hednesford Town | 529 | L 0-2 | | 13 | 47 |
| 23 | NPL | A | Whitby Town | 247 | W 4-0 | Russell 60 76 Wilson 66 69 | 12 | 48 |
| 27 | NPL | A | Matlock Town | 460 | D 1-1 | Wright 89 | 12 | 49 |
| May 4 | NPL | H | Marine | 427 | W 1-0 | Richards 40 | 12 | 50 |

| GOALSCORERS | Lge | FAC | FAT | Total | Pens | Hat-tricks | Cons Run | | Lge | FAC | FAT | Total | Pens | Hat-tricks | Cons Run |
|-------------|-----|-----|-----|-------|------|------------|----------|---|-----|-----|-----|-------|------|------------|----------|
| Richards | 10 | 2 | 1 | 13 | | | 2 | Watts | 2 | | | 2 | | | |
| Hooton | 10 | 2 | | 12 | | | 2 | Chambers | | 1 | | 1 | | | |
| Ricketts | 10 | | | 10 | | | 2 | Ford | 1 | | | 1 | | | |
| Maguire | 6 | 1 | | 7 | 1 | | | McColl | 1 | | | 1 | | | |
| Eades | 2 | 5 | | 7 | | | | O'Connell | 1 | | | 1 | | | |
| Smith | 5 | | 1 | 6 | | | | Partridge | 1 | | | 1 | | | |
| Thomas | | 5 | | 5 | | | 2 | Peel | 1 | | | 1 | | | |
| Watts | 3 | 1 | 1 | 5 | 1 | | | Robbins | 1 | | | 1 | | | |
| Russell | 3 | | | 3 | | | | Wright | 1 | | | 1 | | | |
| Eades | 2 | | | 2 | | | | Own Goals | 3 | | | 3 | | | |
| Gardner | 1 | 1 | | 2 | | | | Cons Run - Consecutive scoring games. | | | | | | | |
| Gordon | 2 | | | 2 | | | | | | | | | | | |
| Smith | 2 | | | 2 | | | | | | | | | | | |

# Premier Division Action

Here we see Rushall Olympic forward, Lei Brown, win this aerial dual against AFC Fylde at Dales Lane in their 2-0 win.
Photo: Jonathan Holloway.

# KING'S LYNN TOWN

**Chairman:** Keith Chapman

**Secretary:** Norman Cesar  **(T)** 07887 373 956  **(E)** office@kltown.co.uk

**Commercial Manager:** Charlotte Rham  **(T)**

**Programme Editor:** Rob Galliard  **(T)** 01533 773 674

**Ground Address:** The Walks Stadium, Tennyson Road, King's Lynn PE30 5PB

**(T)** 01553 760 060  **Manager:** Gary Setchell

## Club Factfile

**Founded:** 1879  **Nickname:** Linnets

**Previous Names:** King's Lynn > 2010

**Previous Leagues:** N'folk & Suffolk, Eastern Co. 1935-39, 48-54, UCL 1946-48, Midland Co. 1954-58, NPL 1980-81, Southern, Conf

**Club Colours (change):** Yellow with royal blue trim/yellow/yellow (Turquoise/black/turquoise)

**Ground Capacity:** 8,200  **Seats:** 1,200  **Covered:** 5,000  **Clubhouse:** Yes  **Shop:** Yes

**Directions:** At the roundabout, at the junction of A47 and the A17, follow the A47, signposted King's Lynn and Norwich. Travel along the dual carriageway for approx. one and a half miles branching off left, following the signs for Town Centre, onto the Hardwick roundabout. Take the first exit, following the signs for Town Centre, travel through two sets of traffic lights until reaching a further set of traffic lights at the Southgates roundabout. Take the fourth exit onto Vancouver Avenue, and travel for approx. 300 metres, going straight across a mini roundabout, The Walks is a further 200 metres along on the left hand side, with car parking outside the ground. The changing rooms and hospitality suite are located at the rear of the main stand.

**Previous Grounds:** None

**Record Attendance:** Att: 12,937 v Exeter City FAC 1st Rnd 1950-51.

**Record Victory:** Not known

**Record Defeat:** Not known

**Record Goalscorer:** Malcolm Lindsey 321.

**Record Appearances:** Mick Wright 1,152 (British Record)

**Additional Records:**

**Senior Honours:**

Southern League Division 1 East 2003-04, Premier Division 2007-08, League Cup 2004-05.

Northern Premier Division One South 2012-13.

### 10 YEAR RECORD

| 03-04 | 04-05 | 05-06 | 06-07 | 07-08 | 08-09 | 09-10 | 10-11 | 11-12 | 12-13 |
|---|---|---|---|---|---|---|---|---|---|
| SthE 1 | SthP 11 | SthP 3 | SthP 3 | SthP 1 | Conf N 17 | NP P dnf | UCL P 2 | UCL P 2 | NP1S 1 |

# MARINE

**Chairman:** Paul Leary
**Secretary:** Richard Cross      **(T)** 07762 711 714      **(E)** richard@marinefc.com
**Commercial Manager:** contact secretary      **(T)**
**Programme Editor:** Dave McMillan      **(T)** 07949 483 003
**Ground Address:** Arriva Stadium, College Road, Crosby, Liverpool L23 3AS
**(T)** 0151 924 1743      **Manager:** Kevin Lynch

2012-13 Squad - Back Row(L-R): Geoff Maddock, Richard Cross (Secretary), Paul Leary (Chairman), Peter McCormack, Maurice Broderick (Treasurer), Paul Eustace, Barry Godfrey
Middle Row (L-R): Gary Trowler (Kit Manager), Robbie Lawton, Liam Dawson, Alan Burton, Paul Lundon, John Shaw, Liam Duff, Ryan McMahon, Callum Williams, Matty Brown, Danny Grannon, Jonathan Goulding, Nick Rogan, Andy Fowler, Nick McCarthy (Sports Therapist)
Front Row (L-R): Matty Devine, Michael Ordish, Karl Noon, Shaun Dowling, Tony Sayer, Kevin Lynch (Manager), Phil Brazier (Assistant Manager), Liam Rice, Thomas Moore, Marcus Carver
Photo by kind permission of Ray Farley Photography.

## Club Factfile

**Founded:** 1894      **Nickname:** Mariners
**Previous Names:** None
**Previous Leagues:** Liverpool Zingari, Liverpool County Combination, Lancashire Combination 1935-39, 46-69, Cheshire County 1969-79

**Club Colours (change):** White/black/black (Yellow/green/green)

**Ground Capacity:** 3,185  **Seats:** 400  **Covered:** 1,400  **Clubhouse:** Yes  **Shop:** Yes

**Directions**

From the East & South: Leave the M62 at junction 6 and take the M57 to Switch Island at the end.  At the end of the M57 take the A5036 (signposted Bootle & Docks). At the roundabout, at the end of the road (by Docks), turn right onto the A565 following signs for 'Crosby' and 'Marine AFC' and follow this road for 1 mile. After passing the Tesco Express on your right, turn left at the traffic lights (by Merchant Taylors' School) into College Road. The ground is half a mile on your left
From the North: Leave the M6 at junction 26 and join the M58. Travel along the M58 to Switch Island at the end. Take the A5036 (signposted Bootle & Docks) and follow directions above.

**Previous Grounds:** Waterloo Park 1894-1903

**Record Attendance:** 4,000 v Nigeria - Friendly 1949
**Record Victory:** 14-0 v Sandhurst - FA Cup 1st Qualifying Round 01/10/1938
**Record Defeat:** 2-11 v Shrewsbury Town - FA Cup 1st Round 1995
**Record Goalscorer:** Paul Meachin - 200
**Record Appearances:** Peter Smith 952
**Additional Records:** Paid £6,000 to Southport for Jon Penman October 1985
**Senior Honours:** Received £20,000 from Crewe Alexandra for Richard Norris 1996
Northern Premier League Premier Division 1993-94, 84-95.
Lancashire Junior Cup 1978-79, Lancashire Trophy x3. Lancashire Amateur Cup x5. Lancashire Senior Cup x6.
Liverpool Non-League Cup x3. Liverpool Challenge Cup x3.

### 10 YEAR RECORD

| 03-04 | 04-05 | 05-06 | 06-07 | 07-08 | 08-09 | 09-10 | 10-11 | 11-12 | 12-13 |
|---|---|---|---|---|---|---|---|---|---|
| NP P 16 | NP P 15 | NP P 3 | NP P 4 | NP P 7 | NP P 13 | NP P 9 | NP P 9 | NP P 7 | NP P 11 |

# MATCH RESULTS 2012-13

| Date | Comp | H/A | Opponents | Att | Result | Goalscorers | Pos | No. |
|---|---|---|---|---|---|---|---|---|
| Aug 18 | NPL | H | Eastwood Town | 268 | W 2-0 | Carver 27 Fowler 43 | 4 | 1 |
| 21 | NPL | A | Buxton | 237 | W 4-1 | CARVER 3 (42 76 80) Fowler 45 | 1 | 2 |
| 25 | NPL | A | Frickley Athletic | 180 | W 2-0 | Foster 47 (pen) Rogan 71 | 1 | 3 |
| 27 | NPL | H | Chorley | 448 | W 2-0 | Carver 10 Rogan 45 | 1 | 4 |
| Sept 1 | NPL | A | Blyth Spartans | 367 | D 3-3 | Moore 24 (pen) Fowler 57 Noon 88 | 2 | 5 |
| 4 | NPL | H | Buxton | 318 | W 2-0 | Carver 85 90 | 1 | 6 |
| 8 | FAC Q1 | A | Stocksbridge PS | 159 | W 3-0 | Fowler 67 Moore 70 (pen) Dawson 88 | | 7 |
| 15 | NPL | A | Whitby Town | 231 | D 1-1 | Carver 9 | 2 | 8 |
| 18 | NPL | H | Kendal Town | 294 | D 2-2 | Rogan 74 Shaw 90 | 1 | 9 |
| 22 | FAC Q2 | A | Ashton United | 193 | W 2-0 | Dowling 37 Fowler 55 | | 10 |
| 29 | FAT Q1 | A | AFC Hyde | 317 | L 0-1 | | | 11 |
| Oct 6 | FAC Q3 | A | Trafford | 515 | W 3-1 | Rogan 46 Grannon 77 Fowler 88 | | 12 |
| 10 | NPL | A | Ashton United | 186 | W 4-2 | Fowler 10 Rogan 16 Goulding 46 Moore 90 | 1 | 13 |
| 13 | NPL | H | Worksop Town | 607 | L 2-3 | Rogan 26 Dawson 69 | 2 | 14 |
| 16 | NPL | A | Witton Albion | 347 | L 0-2 | | 3 | 15 |
| 20 | FAC Q4 | A | Macclesfield Town | 1189 | L 1-3 | Carver 85 | | 16 |
| 23 | NPL | H | Stafford Rangers | 311 | W 3-1 | Burton 43 Rogan 85 88 | 2 | 17 |
| 27 | NPL | H | Stocksbridge PS | 328 | W 2-1 | Dowling 6 Shaw 69 | 2 | 18 |
| 30 | NPL | A | Hednesford Town | 403 | L 0-2 | | 3 | 19 |
| Nov 3 | NPL | H | Matlock Town | 356 | L 1-3 | Fowler 50 (pen) | 4 | 20 |
| 10 | NPL | A | North Ferriby United | 286 | L 1-3 | Carver 28 | | 21 |
| 17 | NPL | H | Grantham Town | 382 | W 1-0 | Devine 25 | 5 | 22 |
| 20 | NPL | A | FC United | 1484 | W 1-0 | Rogan 83 | 5 | 23 |
| 24 | NPL | A | Stocksbridge PS | 104 | D 2-2 | Grannon 58 64 | 4 | 24 |
| Dec 1 | NPL | H | Ilkeston | 338 | D 1-1 | Rogan 4 | 4 | 25 |
| 8 | NPL | H | Blyth Spartans | 273 | W 5-1 | Dawson 5 56 Noon 14 21 Rogan 80 | 3 | 26 |
| 15 | NPL | A | Eastwood Town | 128 | W 2-1 | Dawson 60 Mitchley 85 | 3 | 27 |
| 26 | NPL | A | Chorley | 582 | L 0-1 | | 3 | 28 |
| Jan 1 | NPL | H | AFC Hyde | 381 | L 0-4 | | | 29 |
| 5 | NPL | H | Whitby Town | 355 | L 2-5 | Mitchley 34 Rogan 56 | 4 | 30 |
| 12 | NPL | A | Kendal Town | 232 | W 3-2 | Rogan 46 71 Jones 56 | 3 | 31 |
| Feb 2 | NPL | H | Witton Albion | 436 | W 3-0 | Goulding 9 Rogan 74 (Pen) Jones 89 | 3 | 32 |
| 9 | NPL | A | Worksop Town | 288 | D 1-1 | Brown 56 | 3 | 33 |
| 16 | NPL | A | FC United | 1282 | L 0-3 | | 4 | 34 |
| 23 | NPL | H | Rushall Olympic | 281 | D 1-1 | Jones 37 | 4 | 35 |
| 26 | NPL | A | Nantwich Town | 162 | W 3-2 | Jones 29 Burton 49 Doherty 70 | 4 | 36 |
| Mar 2 | NPL | A | Stafford Rangers | 455 | D 0-0 | | 4 | 37 |
| 9 | NPL | H | Ashton United | 302 | D 0-0 | | 5 | 38 |
| 16 | NPL | H | Frickley Athletic | 275 | D 2-2 | Jones 25 74 (pen) | 6 | 39 |
| 19 | NPL | A | Rushall Olympic | 163 | L 0-2 | | 5 | 40 |
| 30 | NPL | H | Nantwich Town | 408 | W 2-1 | Jones 50 (pen) Trundle 69 | 7 | 41 |
| Apr 1 | NPL | A | AFC Fylde | 304 | L 0-2 | | 9 | 42 |
| 6 | NPL | A | Hednesford Town | 323 | D 0-0 | | 9 | 43 |
| 13 | NPL | A | Matlock Town | 272 | L 0-1 | | 9 | 44 |
| 20 | NPL | H | North Ferriby United | 472 | L 1-3 | Jones 9 | 10 | 45 |
| 27 | NPL | A | Grantham Town | 228 | L 0-1 | | 11 | 46 |
| May 4 | NPL | A | Ilkeston | 427 | L 0-1 | | 11 | 47 |

| GOALSCORERS | Lge | FAC | FAT | Total | Pens | Hat-tricks | Cons Run | | Lge | FAC | FAT | Total | Pens | Hat-tricks | Cons Run |
|---|---|---|---|---|---|---|---|---|---|---|---|---|---|---|---|
| Rogan | 14 | 1 | | 15 | 1 | | 3 | Mitchley | 2 | | | 2 | | | |
| Carver | 9 | 1 | | 10 | | 1 | 2 | Noon | 2 | | | 2 | | | |
| Fowler | 6 | 3 | | 9 | 1 | | 2 | Shaw | 2 | | | 2 | | | |
| Jones | 8 | | | 8 | 2 | | 2 | Brown | 1 | | | 1 | | | |
| Dawson | 4 | 1 | | 5 | | | 2 | Devine | 1 | | | 1 | | | |
| Grannon | 2 | 1 | | 3 | | | | Doherty | 1 | | | 1 | | | |
| Moore | 2 | 1 | | 3 | 1 | | | Foster | 1 | | | 1 | 1 | | |
| Burton | 2 | | | 2 | | | | Trundle | 1 | | | 1 | | | |
| Dowling | 1 | 1 | | 2 | | | | Cons Run - Consecutive scoring games. | | | | | | | |
| Goulding | 2 | | | 2 | | | | | | | | | | | |

# MATLOCK TOWN

**Chairman:** Tom Wright

**Secretary:** Keith Brown **(T)** 07831 311 427 **(E)** clubshop@matlocktownfc.com

**Commercial Manager:** Tom Wright **(T)** 07850 065 968

**Programme Editor:** Tom Wright **(T)** 07850 065 968

**Ground Address:** Reynolds Stadium, Causeway Lane, Matlock, Derbyshire DE4 3AR

**(T)** 01629 583 866 **Manager:** Mark Atkins

2012-13 Squad
Photo courtesy of Mark Ludbrook from sportsshots.co.uk

## Club Factfile

**Founded:** 1885 **Nickname:** The Gladiators

**Previous Names:** None

**Previous Leagues:** Midland Combination 1894-96, Matlock and District, Derbyshire Senior, Central Alliance 1924-25, 47-61, Central Combination 1934-35, Chesterfield & District 1946-47, Midland Counties 1961-69

**Club Colours (change):** All royal blue (All yellow)

**Ground Capacity:** 5,500 **Seats:** 560 **Covered:** 1,200 **Clubhouse:** Yes **Shop:** Yes

*Directions*

On A615, ground is 500 yards from Town Centre and Matlock BR.

**Previous Grounds:** None

**Record Attendance:** 5,123 v Burton Albion - FA Trophy 1975

**Record Victory:** 10-0 v Lancaster City (A) - 1974

**Record Defeat:** 0-8 v Chorley (A) - 1971

**Record Goalscorer:** Peter Scott

**Record Appearances:** Mick Fenoughty

**Additional Records:** Paid £2,000 for Kenny Clark 1996

**Senior Honours:** Received £10,000 from York City for Ian Helliwell

FA Trophy 1974-75. Anglo Italian Non-League Cup 1979. Derbyshire Senior Cup x7.

| | | | | | 10 YEAR RECORD | | | | | |
|---|---|---|---|---|---|---|---|---|---|---|
| 03-04 | 04-05 | 05-06 | 06-07 | 07-08 | 08-09 | 09-10 | 10-11 | 11-12 | 12-13 |
| NP 1   2 | NP P   11 | NP P   9 | NP P   5 | NP P   16 | NP P   15 | NP P   7 | NP P   11 | NP P   14 | NP P   17 |

# MATCH RESULTS 2012-13

| Date | Comp | H/A | Opponents | Att | Result | Goalscorers | Pos | No. |
|---|---|---|---|---|---|---|---|---|
| Aug 18 | NPL | H | Nantwich Town | 293 | L 0-5 | | 22 | 1 |
| 21 | NPL | A | Frickley Athletic | 250 | W 2-1 | McMahon 79 (pen)  Leesley 83 | 11 | 2 |
| 26 | NPL | A | FC United | 1763 | L 0-4 | | 14 | 3 |
| 29 | NPL | H | Rushall Olympic | 282 | L 0-3 | | | 4 |
| Sept 1 | NPL | A | Stafford Rangers | 435 | L 0-1 | | 18 | 5 |
| 4 | NPL | H | Frickley Athletic | 255 | W 3-1 | McMahon 43 78 Leesley 65 | 17 | 6 |
| 8 | FAC Q1 | H | Belper Town | 460 | D 2-2 | Leesley 6  Tuton 55 | | 7 |
| 11 | FAC Q1r | A | Belper Town | 341 | L 0-3 | | | 8 |
| 15 | NPL | H | Blyth Spartans | 286 | L 1-3 | Hamshaw 11 | 17 | 9 |
| 18 | NPL | A | Grantham Town | 234 | D 3-3 | Nwadike 38 Watt 72 Higginson 74 | 17 | 10 |
| 22 | NPL | H | Stocksbridge PS | 257 | D 1-1 | McMahon 60 (pen) | 16 | 11 |
| 29 | FAT | A | Eastwood Town | 186 | W 2-1 | McMahon 25 McDonald 76 | | 12 |
| Oct 6 | NPL | A | North Ferriby United | 219 | L 1-2 | Leesley 74 | 16 | 13 |
| 13 | NPL | H | Eastwood Town | 371 | L 0-1 | | 18 | 14 |
| 20 | NPL | A | Stocksbridge PS | 191 | W 3-2 | Leesley 37 54 Yates 70 | 16 | 15 |
| 23 | NPL | H | Chorley | 227 | W 1-0 | McDonald 36 | 15 | 16 |
| 27 | FAT Q2 | H | Leek Town | 264 | D 0-0 | | | 17 |
| 31 | FAT Q2r | A | Leek Town | 145 | W 3-1 | McMahon 44 (pen) 83  McDonald 74 | | 18 |
| Nov 3 | NPL | A | Marine | 356 | W 3-1 | McDonald 35 Grayson 39 Lukic 54 | 15 | 19 |
| 10 | FAT Q3 | H | Stalybridge Celtic | 402 | W 2-1 | Lukic 58 McDonald 87 | | 20 |
| 17 | NPL | A | Ilkeston | 612 | W 2-0 | Ashmore 47 McDonald 60 | 14 | 21 |
| 20 | NPL | H | Hednesford Town | 253 | L 2-3 | McDonald 54 Leesley 90 | 14 | 22 |
| 24 | FAT 1 | A | Mansfield Town | 1615 | D 1-1 | McMahon 38 | | 23 |
| 27 | FAT 1r | H | Mansfield Town | 758 | W 2-1 | McMahon 50  McDonald 90 | | 24 |
| Dec 1 | NPL | A | Whtby Town | 237 | L 0-1 | | 16 | 25 |
| 8 | NPL | H | Stafford Rangers | 307 | L 2-3 | Radford 27 Roe 48 | 17 | 26 |
| 15 | FAT 2 | H | Luton Town | 829 | L 1-2 | McMahon 61 (pen) | 17 | 27 |
| 26 | NPL | A | Rushall Olympic | 162 | W 4-0 | McMahon 18 (pen) McDonald 66 75 Hazel 69 | 15 | 28 |
| 29 | NPL | A | Worksop Town | 387 | L 1-6 | McMahon 52 | 16 | 29 |
| Jan 1 | NPL | H | Buxton | 483 | D 1-1 | McMahon 33 | 16 | 30 |
| 5 | NPL | A | Blyth Spartans | 311 | L 1-2 | Sloughter 51 (og) | 17 | 31 |
| 12 | NPL | H | Grantham Town | 300 | W 3-2 | McMahon 5 Grayson 25 McDonald 42 | 17 | 32 |
| Feb 2 | NPL | H | Ashton United | 230 | D 2-2 | Grayson 7 (pen)  Frost 84 (og) | 17 | 33 |
| 9 | NPL | A | Eastwood Town | 178 | D 3-3 | Ashmore 18 66  Foster 70 | 17 | 34 |
| 16 | NPL | A | Nantwich Town | 371 | W 1-0 | Griffiths-Junior  27 | 15 | 35 |
| 23 | NPL | H | Witton Albion | 313 | L 1-2 | Foster 76 | 17 | 36 |
| Mar 2 | NPL | A | Chorley | 560 | L 0-1 | | 17 | 37 |
| 6 | NPL | H | FC United | 613 | D 2-2 | Grayson 37 66 (pen) | 17 | 38 |
| 9 | NPL | A | Hednesford Town | 391 | D 2-2 | McMahon 68 90 (pen) | 17 | 39 |
| 16 | NPL | H | Whtby Town | 271 | D 0-0 | | 17 | 40 |
| 30 | NPL | A | AFC Fylde | 211 | L 0-3 | | 18 | 41 |
| Apr 1 | NPL | A | Buxton | 346 | L 0-1 | | 18 | 42 |
| 6 | NPL | H | AFC Fylde | 257 | W 2-1 | Leesley 6 McDonald 28 | 17 | 43 |
| 10 | NPL | A | Ashton United | 111 | L 0-2 | | 17 | 44 |
| 13 | NPL | H | Marine | 272 | W 1-0 | Leesley 57 | 17 | 45 |
| 17 | NPL | H | North Ferriby United | 261 | L 0-2 | | 17 | 46 |
| 20 | NPL | A | Witton Albion | 574 | L 0-3 | | 17 | 47 |
| 23 | NPL | H | Kendal Town | 223 | W 3-0 | McDonald 24 Foster 29 Algar  32 | 17 | 48 |
| 27 | NPL | H | Ilkeston Town | 460 | D 1-1 | McMahon 12 | 17 | 49 |
| May 2 | NPL | H | Worksop Town | 300 | L 1-5 | Edge 54 | 17 | 50 |
| 4 | NPL | A | Kendal Town | 134 | L 1-4 | Edge 65 | 17 |  |

| GOALSCORERS | Lge | FAC | FAT | Total | Pens | Hat-tricks | Cons Run | | Lge | FAC | FAT | Total | Pens | Hat-tricks | Cons Run |
|---|---|---|---|---|---|---|---|---|---|---|---|---|---|---|---|
| McMahon | 11 | | 6 | 17 | 6 | | 4 | Hamshaw | 1 | | | | | | |
| McDonald | 9 | | 4 | 13 | | | 5 | Hazel | 1 | | | | | | |
| Leesley | 8 | 1 | | 9 | | | 2 | Higginson | 1 | | | | | | |
| Ashmore | 3 | | | 3 | 2 | | | Nwadike | 1 | | | | | | |
| Foster | 3 | | | 3 | | | | Radford | 1 | | | | | | |
| Grayson | 5 | | | 3 | | | 2 | Roe | 1 | | | | | | |
| Edge | 2 | | | 2 | 2 | | 2 | Tuton | | | 1 | | | | |
| Lukic | 1 | | 1 | | | | | Watt | 1 | | | | | | |
| Algar | 1 | | | | | | | Yates | 1 | | | | | | |
| Griffiths-Junior | 1 | | | | | | | Cons Run - Consecutive scoring games. | | | | | | | |

# NANTWICH TOWN

**Chairman:** Jon Gold
**Secretary:** Janet Stubbs     **(T)** 07725 892 922     **(E)** nantwichtownfc@hotmail.co.uk
**Commercial Manager:** n/a     **(T)**
**Programme Editor:** James Brisco     **(T)** 07807 760 600
**Ground Address:** Weaver Stadium, Waterlode, Kingsley Fields, Nantwich, CW5 5BS
**(T)** 01270 621 771     **Manager:** Danny Johnson

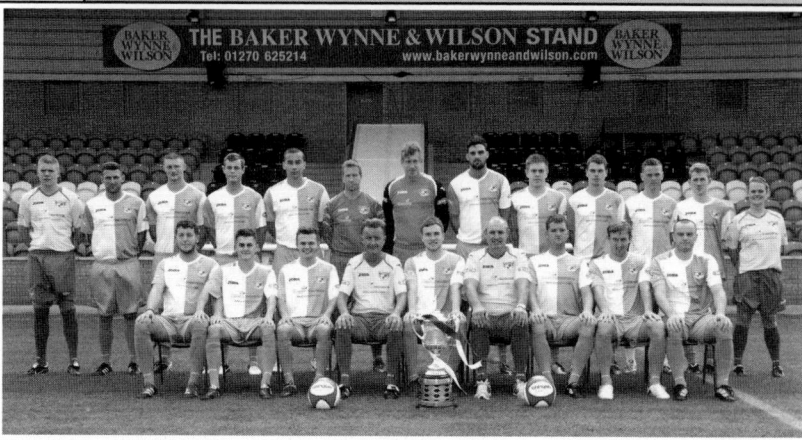

2012-13 Squad - BACK ROW (left to right): Antony Swindells (physio), Kyle Wilson, JJ Bailey, Will Jones, Rod McDonald, Paddy Chesters (goalkeeper coach), Jonny Brain, Mat Bailey, Lewis Short, Niall Maguire, Josh Lane, Zack Foster, Michelle Pennell (head physio).
FRONT ROW (left to right): Matt Lowe, Caspar Hughes, Sean Cooke, Martin Stubbs (assistant manager), Chris Flynn, Jimmy Quinn (manager), Darren Moss, Mark Beesley, Fraser McLachlan. Trophy: Cheshire Senior Cup.
Photo: Simon J Newbury Photography.

## Club Factfile

**Founded:** 1884     **Nickname:** Dabbers
**Previous Names:** Nantwich
**Previous Leagues:** Shropshire & Dist. 1891-92, Combination 1892-94, 1901-10, Cheshire Junior 1894-95, Crewe & Dist. 1895-97, North Staffs & Dist. 1897-1900, Cheshire 1900-01, Manchester 1910-12, 65-68, Lancs. Com. 1912-14, Cheshire Co. 1919-38, 68-82, Crewe & Dist. 1938-39, 47-48, Crewe Am. Comb. 1946-47, Mid-Cheshire 1948-65, North West Co. 1982-2007
**Club Colours (change):** Green/white/green (Yellow/blue/blue)

**Ground Capacity:** 3,500     **Seats:** 350     **Covered:** 495     **Clubhouse:** Yes     **Shop:** Yes

**Directions:** M6 Jun 16 A500 towards Nantwich. Over 4 roundabouts onto A51 towards Nantwich Town Centre, through traffic lights and over railway crossing. Over next r/bout then left at next r/bout past Morrisons supermarket on right. Continue over r/bout through traffic lights. Ground on right at next set of traffic lights.
SATNAV Postcode: CW5 5UP

**Previous Grounds:** London Road/Jackson Avenue (1884-2007)

**Record Attendance:** 5,121 v Winsford United - Cheshire Senior Cup 2nd Round 1920-21
**Record Victory:** 20-0 v Whitchurch Alexandra (home) 1900/01 Cheshire League Division 1, 5 April 1901
**Record Defeat:** 2-16 v Stalybridge Celtic (away) 1932/33 Cheshire County League, 22 Oct 1932
**Record Goalscorer:** John Scarlett 161 goals (1992/3 to 2005/6).     **Goals in a season:** Bobby Jones 60 goals (1946/7)
**Record Appearances:** Not known
**Additional Records:** Gerry Duffy scored 42 during season 1961-62
**Senior Honours:** Record Fee Received undisclosed fee from Crewe Alexandra for Kelvin Mellor - Feb 2008
FA Vase Winners 2005/06. Cheshire Senior Cup Winners 1932/33, 1975/76, 2007/08 & 2011/12. Cheshire County League Champions 1980/81. Mid-Cheshire League Champions 1963/64. North West Counties League Challenge Cup Winners 1994/95. Cheshire Amateur Cup Winners 1895/96 & 1963/64.

### 10 YEAR RECORD

| 03-04 | 04-05 | 05-06 | 06-07 | 07-08 | 08-09 | 09-10 | 10-11 | 11-12 | 12-13 |
|---|---|---|---|---|---|---|---|---|---|
| NWC1   13 | NWC1   16 | NWC1   4 | NWC1   3 | NP1S   3 | NP P   3 | NP P   10 | NP P   17 | NP P   10 | NP P   14 |

# MATCH RESULTS 2012-13

| Date | Comp | H/A | Opponents | Att: | Result | Goalscorers | Pos | No. |
|------|------|-----|-----------|------|--------|-------------|-----|-----|
| Aug 18 | NPL | A | Matlock Town | 293 | W 5-0 | Wilson 16 65 Beesley 35 Cooke 71 Jones 75 | 1 | 1 |
| 21 | NPL | H | Kendal Town | 309 | D 1-1 | Short 59 | 6 | 2 |
| 25 | NPL | H | Ilkeston | 385 | W 1-0 | Cooke 55 | 6 | 3 |
| 27 | NPL | A | Ashton United | 219 | L 1-2 | Cooke 57 | 9 | 4 |
| Sept 1 | NPL | H | Grantham Town | 276 | L 0-3 | | 13 | 5 |
| 4 | NPL | A | Kendal Town | 156 | W 1-0 | Cooke 88 | 9 | 6 |
| 8 | FAC Q1 | A | Chorley | 633 | L 0-2 | | | 7 |
| 15 | NPL | A | FC Unted | 1969 | W 2-1 | Maguire 79 Bailey 87 | 8 | 8 |
| 18 | NPL | H | AFC Fylde | 274 | L 0-3 | | 11 | 9 |
| 22 | NPL | A | Rushall Olympic | 193 | W 3-2 | Smith 41 Jones 45 Cooke 90 | | 10 |
| 29 | FAT Q1 | H | Redditch United | 247 | W 2-1 | Smith 21 Stringfellow 61 (og) | 7 | 11 |
| Oct 6 | NPL | H | Worksop Town | 308 | L 0-5 | | | 12 |
| 9 | NPL | A | Chorley | 546 | D 3-3 | Wilson 9 Cudworth 54 (og) Bailey 81 | 8 | 13 |
| 13 | NPL | A | Whitby Town | 339 | W 2-1 | Bailey 45 Cooke 79 | 6 | 14 |
| 16 | NPL | H | Hednesford Town | 237 | D 1-1 | Smith 79 | 6 | 15 |
| 20 | NPL | A | Eastwood Town | 159 | W 5-1 | Cooke 28 Wilson 60 Short 62 87 Hughes 68 | 6 | 16 |
| 27 | FAT Q2 | A | AFC Fylde | 261 | D 0-0 | | | 17 |
| 30 | FAT Q2r | H | AFC Fylde | 181 | D 2-2 | Flynn 59 Hughes 77 *aet L 1-3 pens | | 18 |
| Nov 3 | NPL | H | North Ferriby United | 260 | L 2-3 | Cooke 23 Everall 30 | 8 | 19 |
| 10 | NPL | A | Frickley Athletic | 237 | L 0-3 | | 8 | 20 |
| 17 | NPL | H | Stafford Rangers | 474 | D 1-1 | Maguire 73 | 8 | 21 |
| 20 | NPL | H | Buxton | 202 | D 2-2 | Everall 33 Lane 86 | 8 | 22 |
| 24 | NPL | A | Blyth Spartans | 299 | D 1-1 | Cooke 76 | 8 | 23 |
| Dec 1 | NPL | H | Stocksbridge PS | 201 | W 4-3 | Lane 10 22 Moss 31 Cooke 80 | 6 | 24 |
| 3 | NPL | A | Grantham Town | 187 | W 4-1 | Everall 35 White 37 Cooke 63 87 (pen) | 6 | 25 |
| Jan 1 | NPL | A | Witton Albion | 526 | D 2-2 | Short 71 Cooke 90 | 8 | 26 |
| 5 | NPL | H | FC United | 1003 | L 2-3 | Cooke 55 Everall 70 | 10 | 27 |
| 12 | NPL | A | AFC Fylde | 342 | L 2-3 | Wilson 69 Hughes 89 | 13 | 28 |
| Feb 2 | NPL | A | Hednesford Town | 403 | L 0-3 | | 14 | 29 |
| 16 | NPL | H | Matlock Town | 371 | L 0-1 | | 14 | 30 |
| 19 | NPL | H | Rushall Olympic | 198 | L 0-2 | | 14 | 31 |
| 23 | NPL | A | Worksop Town | 326 | W 2-0 | Moss 82 Lane 90 | 14 | 32 |
| 26 | NPL | H | Marine | 162 | L 2-3 | Moss 14 Wilson 57 | 14 | 33 |
| Mar 2 | NPL | H | Ashton United | 257 | L 0-2 | | 15 | 34 |
| 4 | NPL | A | Ilkeston | 367 | L 0-3 | | 15 | 35 |
| 26 | NPL | H | Chorley | 158 | L 0-1 | | 16 | 36 |
| 30 | NPL | A | Marine | 408 | L 1-2 | Guest 63 | 17 | 37 |
| Apr 1 | NPL | H | Witton Albion | 388 | W 2-1 | Clayton 23 Bentham 45 | 15 | 38 |
| 6 | NPL | H | Eastwood Town | 186 | W 1-0 | Clayton  56 (pen) | 15 | 39 |
| 9 | NPL | H | Whitby Town | 176 | W 2-1 | Clayton 49 Devenney 54 | 14 | 40 |
| 13 | NPL | A | North Ferriby United | 321 | D 0-0 | | 14 | 41 |
| 20 | NPL | H | Frickley Athletic | 246 | W 3-2 | Clayton 4 Raglan 26 Guest  86 (pen) | 14 | 42 |
| 23 | NPL | A | Stocksbridge PS | 127 | L 2-5 | Clayton 17 Wilson 75 | 14 | 43 |
| 27 | NPL | A | Stafford Rangers | 256 | L 0-2 | | 16 | 44 |
| May 1 | NPL | A | Buxton | 224 | L 1-3 | Bentham 82 | 16 | 45 |
| 4 | NPL | H | Blyth Spartans | 375 | W 2-1 | Clayton 37 Hudson 64 | 14 | 46 |

| GOALSCORERS | Lge | FAC | FAT | Total | Pens | Hat-tricks | Cons Run | | Lge | FAC | FAT | Total | Pens | Hat-tricks | Cons Run |
|-------------|-----|-----|-----|-------|------|------------|----------|---|-----|-----|-----|-------|------|------------|----------|
| Cooke | 14 | | | 14 | 1 | | 4 | Guest | 2 | | | 2 | 1 | | |
| Wilson | 7 | | | 6 | | | | Jones | 2 | | | 2 | | | |
| Clayton | 6 | | | 5 | 1 | | 3 | Maguire | 2 | | | 2 | | | |
| Everall | 4 | | | 4 | | | | Beesley | 1 | | | 1 | | | |
| Lane | 4 | | | 4 | | | | Devenney | 1 | | | 1 | | | |
| Short | 4 | | | 4 | | | | Flynn | | | 1 | 1 | | | |
| Bailey | 3 | | | 3 | | | 2 | Hudson | 1 | | | 1 | | | |
| Moss | 3 | | | 3 | | | 2 | Raglan | 1 | | | 1 | | | |
| Hughes | 2 | | 1 | 3 | | | | White | 1 | | | 1 | | | |
| Smith | 2 | | 1 | 3 | | | 2 | Own Goals | 1 | | 1 | 2 | | | |
| Bentham | 2 | | | 2 | | | | Cons Run - Consecutive scoring games. | | | | | | | |

# RUSHALL OLYMPIC

**Chairman:** John C Allen

**Secretary:** Peter Athersmith     **(T)** 07771 361 002     **(E)** rushallolympic@yahoo.co.uk

**Commercial Manager:** Darren Stockall     **(T)** 07870 236 013

**Programme Editor:** Darren Stockall     **(T)** 07870 236 013

**Ground Address:** Dales Lane off Daw End Lane, Rushall, Nr Walsall WS4 1LJ

**(T)** 01922 641 021     **Manager:** Neil Kitching

2012-13 Squad - Back Row (L-R) – Gary Fitzpatrick, Josh Craddock, Louis Keenan, Decio Gomes, Dave Walker, Kyle Haynes, Mitchell Tolley
Middle Row (L-R) – Lucan Spittle, Leo Brown, Steve Palmer, Tom Burns, Chris Gemmell, Wayne Daniel, Steve Abbott, Michael Clarke, Dave Harrison (Kit Man)
Front Row (L-R) – Andre Landell, Martyn Naylor, Paul Hayward (Goalkeeping Coach), Ian Cooper (First Team Coach), Neil Kitching (Manager), Nick Amos (Assistant Manager), Jonny Haynes, Grant Beckett.
Juniors (L-R) Tom and Danny Kitching. Credit for photo – Steve Walker

## Club Factfile

**Founded:** 1951     **Nickname:** The Pics

**Previous Names:** None

**Previous Leagues:** Walsall Amateur 1952-55, Staffordshire County (South) 1956-78, West Midlands 1978-94, Midland Alliance 1994-2005, Southern 2005-08

**Club Colours (change):** Gold and black/black/black (Red & white/red/red)

**Ground Capacity:** 2,500     **Seats:** 200     **Covered:** 200     **Clubhouse:** Yes     **Shop:** Yes

**Directions:** M6 J10 follow signs for Walsall stay on this dual carriage way for about four miles until you come to the Walsall Arboretum and turn left following signs for Lichfield A461. Go under the bridge and you will come to McDonald's on your right, turn right into Daw End Lane. Go over the canal bridge and turn right opposite the Royal Oak Public House and the ground is on the right.
Alternative: From the A38 to it's junction with the A5 (Muckley Corner Hotel) take the A461 to Walsall after about five miles you will reach some traffic lights in Rushall by Mcdonald's, turn left into Daw End Lane go over the canal bridge and turn right opposite The Royal Oak Public House the ground is on the right.

**Previous Grounds:** Rowley Place 1951-75, Aston University 1976-79

**Record Attendance:** 2,000 v Leeds United Ex players

**Record Victory:** Not known

**Record Defeat:** Not known

**Record Goalscorer:** Graham Wiggin

**Record Appearances:** Alan Dawson - 400+

**Additional Records:**

**Senior Honours:**
West Midlands League 1979-80. Midland Alliance 2004-05.

## 10 YEAR RECORD

| 03-04 | | 04-05 | | 05-06 | | 06-07 | | 07-08 | | 08-09 | | 09-10 | | 10-11 | | 11-12 | | 12-13 | |
|---|---|---|---|---|---|---|---|---|---|---|---|---|---|---|---|---|---|---|---|
| MidAl | 14 | MidAl | 1 | SthW | 10 | SthM | 15 | SthM | 5 | NP1S | 5 | NP1S | 12 | NP1S | 3 | NP P | 8 | NP P | 6 |

# MATCH RESULTS 2012-13

| Date | Comp | H/A | Opponents | Att: | Result | Goalscorers | Pos | No. |
|------|------|-----|-----------|------|--------|-------------|-----|-----|
| ug 18 | NPL | A | Whitby Town | 259 | W 1-0 | Walker 58 | 7 | 1 |
| 1 | NPL | H | Olkeston | 248 | W 2-1 | Walker 21 48 | 5 | 2 |
| 5 | NPL | H | Kendal Town | 202 | W 1-0 | Brown 47 (Pen) | | 3 |
| 7 | NPL | A | Matlock Town | 282 | W 3-0 | Abbott 29 Brown 70 78 | 3 | 4 |
| ept 1 | NPL | H | North Ferriby United | 190 | L 0-3 | | 3 | 5 |
| | NPL | A | Ilkeston Town | 412 | W 1-0 | Brown 53 | | 6 |
| | FAC Q1 | A | Bridgnorth | 141 | L 1-3 | Brown 43 | | 7 |
| 5 | NPL | H | Frickley Athletic | 164 | W 1-0 | Beckett 65 | 1 | 8 |
| 8 | NPL | A | Eastwood Town | 135 | L 1-2 | Walker 86 | 2 | 9 |
| 2 | NPL | H | Nantwich Town | 193 | L 2-3 | Walker 41 Haynes 57 | 2 | 10 |
| 9 | FAT Q1 | H | Woodford United | 101 | W 3-0 | Obeng 56 67 Landell 90 | | 11 |
| )ct 6 | NPL | H | Stafford Rangers | 322 | D 1-1 | Caines 6 | 1 | 12 |
| 3 | NPL | H | Chorley | 355 | D 0-0 | | 5 | 13 |
| 6 | NPL | A | Stocksbridge PS | 102 | L 0-3 | | 6 | 14 |
| '0 | NPL | A | Blyth Spartans | 343 | D 1-1 | Tolley 27 (pen) | 9 | 15 |
| 7 | FAT Q2 | A | Chasetown | 286 | W 3-1 | Walker 14 18 Bragoli 55 | | 16 |
| ,0 | NPL | H | Witton Albion | 210 | L 0-4 | | 10 | 17 |
| Jov 10 | FAT Q3 | A | Droylsden | 211 | W 2-1 | Obeng 82 86 | | 18 |
| 7 | NPL | A | FC United | 1795 | W 4-0 | Islam 24 52 Walker 44 60 | 10 | 19 |
| 4 | FAT 1 | A | Wrexham | 1085 | L 0-5 | | | 20 |
| Dec 8 | NPL | A | North Ferriby United | 243 | D 2-2 | Anderson 79 (og) Craddock 81 | 12 | 21 |
| 5 | NPL | H | Whitby Town | 131 | D 1-1 | Daniel 5 | 14 | 22 |
| '6 | NPL | H | Matlock Town | 162 | L 0-4 | | 14 | 23 |
| Jan 1 | NPL | A | Hednesford Town | 698 | W 4-3 | Daniel 52 Purkiss 70  Walker 71 90 | 14 | 24 |
| | NPL | A | Frickley Athletic | 220 | D 3-3 | Landell 4 Bottomer 20 Walker 45 | 14 | 25 |
| 2 | NPL | H | Eastwood Town | 154 | W 2-0 | Islam 31 Walker 72 (pen) | 14 | 26 |
| eb 2 | NPL | H | Stocksbridge PS | 150 | D 1-1 | Walker  28 (pen) | 13 | 27 |
| | NPL | A | Chorley | 506 | W 6-1 | Obeng 5 Craddock 20  WALKER 4 ( 41 45 60pen 66) | 12 | 28 |
| 2 | NPL | A | Stafford Rangers | 290 | W 2-1 | Obeng 4 6 | 9 | 29 |
| 6 | NPL | H | Blyth Spartans | 197 | W 5-2 | Walker 12 47 Obeng 40 81 Haynes 45 | 8 | 30 |
| 9 | NPL | A | Nantwich Town | 198 | W 2-0 | Smith 6 Walker 12 | 6 | 31 |
| 3 | NPL | A | Marine | 281 | D 1-1 | Obeng 78 (pen) | 6 | 32 |
| Mar 2 | NPL | A | Kendal Town | 180 | W 2-0 | Obeng 25 Landell 87 | 6 | 33 |
| | NPL | H | Buxton | 156 | L 0-1 | | 6 | 34 |
| | NPL | H | Grantham Town | 186 | W 3-1 | Obeng 41 Craddock 60 82 | 6 | 35 |
| 6 | NPL | A | Ashton United | 140 | W 3-2 | Obeng 11 34  Walker 20 | 4 | 36 |
| 9 | NPL | H | Marine | 163 | W 2-0 | Craddock 75 Walker 89 | 4 | 37 |
| 27 | NPL | A | Worksop Town | 247 | W 3-2 | Walker 64 83 Caines 80 | 3 | 38 |
| 0 | NPL | A | Grantham Town | 199 | L 1-2 | Hawes 90 (og) | 4 | 39 |
| Apr 1 | NPL | H | Hednesford Town | 602 | D 2-2 | Walker 42  Daniel 89 | 3 | 40 |
| 5 | NPL | H | Ashton United | 163 | D 0-0 | | 5 | 41 |
| 3 | NPL | H | AFC Fylde | 193 | W 2-0 | Obeng 41 Dovey 87 | 5 | 42 |
| 7 | NPL | H | Worksop Town | 180 | L 1-2 | Craddock 63 | 6 | 43 |
| 20 | NPL | A | Buxton | 262 | L 0-2 | | 6 | 44 |
| 27 | NPL | H | FC United | 1007 | L 0-1 | | 6 | 45 |
| 30 | NPL | A | AFC Fylde | 274 | W 3-1 | Obeng 18 56 McMahon 90 | 6 | 46 |
| May 4 | NPL | A | Witton Albion | 508 | L 0-2 | | 6 | 47 |

| GOALSCORERS | Lge | FAC | FAT | Total | Pens | Hat-tricks | Cons Run | | Lge | FAC | FAT | Total | Pens | Hat-tricks | Cons Run |
|-------------|-----|-----|-----|-------|------|------------|----------|---|-----|-----|-----|-------|------|------------|----------|
| Walker | 24 | | 2 | 26 | 2 | 1 | 5 | Beckett | 1 | | | 1 | | | |
| Obeng | 13 | | 4 | 17 | 1 | | 3 | Bottomley | 1 | | | 1 | | | |
| Brown | 4 | 1 | | 5 | 1 | | 2 | Bragoli | | | 1 | 1 | | | |
| Craddock | 6 | | | 6 | | | | Dovey | 1 | | | 1 | | | |
| Daniel | 3 | | | 3 | | | | McMahon | 1 | | | 1 | | | |
| Islam | 3 | | | 3 | | | | Purkiss | 1 | | | 1 | | | |
| Caines | 2 | | | 2 | | | | Smith | 1 | | | 1 | | | |
| Haynes | 2 | | | 2 | | | | Own Goals | 2 | | | 2 | | | |
| Landell | 2 | | 1 | 3 | | | | Cons Run - Consecutive scoring games. | | | | | | | |
| Abbott | 1 | | | 1 | | | | | | | | | | | |

# Premier Division Action

Gardner (Witton) and Turner (Stocksbridge)
Photo: Keith Clayton.

# SKELMERSDALE UNITED

**Chairman:** Paul Griffiths

**Secretary:** Bryn Jones    **(T)** 07904 911 234    **(E)** skelmersdaleunited@hotmail.com

**Commercial Manager:**              **(T)**

**Programme Editor:** Neil Leatherbarrow    **(T)** 07855 701 512

**Ground Address:** West Lancashire College Stadium, Selby Place, Statham Road WN8 8EF

**(T)** 01695 722 123           **Manager:** Tommy Lawson

## Club Factfile

**Founded:** 1882    **Nickname:** Skem

**Previous Names:** None

**Previous Leagues:** Liverpool County Combination, Lancashire Combination 1891-93, 1903-07, 21-24, 55-56, 76-78, Cheshire County 1968-71, 78-82, Northern Premier 1971-76, North West Counties 1983-2006

**Club Colours (change):** All royal blue (All red)

**Ground Capacity:** 2,300    **Seats:** 240    **Covered:** 500    **Clubhouse:** Yes    **Shop:** Yes

**Directions:** Exit M58 J4 (signposted Skelmersdale), carry straight on at next roundabout (Hope Island) into Glenburn Road, left at next roundabout (Half Mile Island) into Neverstitch Road (signposted Stanley Industrial Estate). Immediately right at next roundabout into Staveley Road and then left into Statham Road. Ground is 500 yards on left in Selby Place.

**Previous Grounds:** None

**Record Attendance:** 7,000 v Slough Town - FA Amateur Cup Semi-final 1967

**Record Victory:** Not known

**Record Defeat:** Not known

**Record Goalscorer:** Stuart Rudd - 230

**Record Appearances:** Robbie Holcroft - 422 including 398 consecutively

**Additional Records:** Paid £2,000 for Stuart Rudd

**Senior Honours:** Received £4,000 for Stuart Rudd

FA Amateur Cup 1970-71. Barassi Anglo-Italian Cup 1970-71.
Northern Premier Division One North 2013-14.
Lancashire Junior Cup x2. Lancashire Non-League Cup x2.

### 10 YEAR RECORD

| 03-04 | | 04-05 | | 05-06 | | 06-07 | | 07-08 | | 08-09 | | 09-10 | | 10-11 | | 11-12 | | 12-13 | |
|-------|---|-------|---|-------|---|-------|----|-------|---|-------|---|-------|---|-------|---|-------|---|-------|---|
| NWC1 | 8 | NWC1 | 6 | NWC1 | 2 | NP 1 | 15 | NP1N | 3 | NP1N | 2 | NP1N | 5 | NP1N | 2 | NP1N | 7 | NP1N | 1 |

# STAFFORD RANGERS

**Chairman:** Ron Woodward
**Secretary:** Mike Hughes      **(T)** 07850 996 386      **(E)** info@staffordrangersfc.co.uk
**Commercial Manager:**      **(T)**
**Programme Editor:** Stuart Maun      **(T)** 07540 124 396
**Ground Address:** Marston Road, Stafford ST16 3BX
**(T)** 01785 602 430      **Manager:** Greg Clowes

2012-13 Squad - Back Row: (Left to Right) Sean Kinsella, Dean Clarke, Danny Quinn, Jermaine Johnson, Christian Dacres, Fabrice Kasiama, Ryan Dicker.
Middle Row: (Left to Right) Mick Hathaway (coach), Luke George, Karl Espley, Oliver Davies, Danny Read, Adam Alcock, Jimmy Turner, Alex Forde, Sid Kelly (kit man).
Front Row: (Left to Right) Kevin Street, Simon Everall, Greg Clowes (manager), Lee Downes, Michael Carr, Liam Walshe, Dorrian Garner (assistant manager), Courtney Pitt, Ryan Brown.

## Club Factfile

**Founded:** 1876      **Nickname:** Rangers
**Previous Names:** None
**Previous Leagues:** Shropshire 1891-93, Birmingham 1893-96, N. Staffs. 1896-1900, Cheshire 1900-01, Birmingham Comb. 1900-12, 46-52, Cheshire County 1952-69, N.P.L. 1969-79, 83-85, Alliance 1979-83, Conf. 1985-95, 2005-11. Southern >2005.

**Club Colours (change):** Black & white stripes/black/black (All red)

**Ground Capacity:** 6,000   **Seats:** 4,264   **Covered:** 3,500   **Clubhouse:** Yes   **Shop:** Yes

**Directions:** M6 Junction 14. Follow signs for Uttoxeter and Stone. Straight over at 1st and 2nd (A34) islands, 3rd right sign posted Common Road and Astonfields Road Ind. Estate. The ground is straight ahead after three quarters of a mile. The route from the Motorway is highlighted by the standard football road signs.

**Previous Grounds:** None

**Record Attendance:** 8,536 v Rotherham United - FA Cup 3rd Round 1975
**Record Victory:** 14-0 v Kidsgrove Athletic - Staffordshire Senior Cup 2003
**Record Defeat:** 0-12 v Burton Town - Birmingham League 1930
**Record Goalscorer:** M. Cullerton - 176
**Record Appearances:** Jim Sargent
**Additional Records:** Paid £13,000 to VS rugby for S. Butterworth
**Senior Honours:** Received £100,000 from Crystal Palace for Stan Collymore
Northern Premier League 1971-72, 84-85. FA trophy 1971-72.
Staffordshire Senior Cup x7

### 10 YEAR RECORD

| 03-04 | | 04-05 | | 05-06 | | 06-07 | | 07-08 | | 08-09 | | 09-10 | | 10-11 | | 11-12 | | 12-13 | |
|---|---|---|---|---|---|---|---|---|---|---|---|---|---|---|---|---|---|---|---|
| SthP | 3 | Conf N | 8 | Conf N | 2 | Conf | 20 | Conf | 23 | Conf N | 18 | Conf N | 16 | Conf N | 20 | NP P | 16 | NP P | 15 |

# MATCH RESULTS 2012-13

| ate | Comp | H/A | Opponents | Att: | Result | Goalscorers | Pos | No. |
|---|---|---|---|---|---|---|---|---|
| ug 18 | NPL | A | Kendal Town | 216 | D 2-2 | Quinn 41 Dacres 63 | 7 | 1 |
|  | NPL | H | Grantham Town | 474 | L 0-1 |  | 17 | 2 |
|  | NPL | H | Stocksbridge PS | 404 | D 1-1 | Jobson 75 | 16 | 3 |
|  | NPL | A | Hednesford Town | 920 | D 2-2 | Quinn 62 87 (Pen) | 16 | 4 |
| ept 1 | NPL | H | Matlock Town | 435 | W 1-0 | Everall 32 | 16 | 5 |
|  | NPL | A | Grantham Town | 270 | D 2-2 | Everall 2 28 | 14 | 6 |
|  | FAC Q1 | A | Stourport Swifts | 171 | D 1-1 | Carr 67 |  | 7 |
|  | FAC Q1r | H | Stourport Swifts | 309 | W 2-1* | Dicker 90 110 |  | 8 |
|  | NPL | A | Worksop Town | 300 | W 3-2 | Carr 7 Espley 61 Quinn 80 (pen) | 13 | 9 |
|  | NPL | H | FC United | 814 | D 1-1 | Dicker 48 | 13 | 10 |
|  | FAC Q2 | A | Gresley | 414 | L 2-3 | Quinn 34 Carr 41 |  | 11 |
|  | FAT Q1 | A | Rugby Town | 206 | D 1-1 | Turner 53 |  | 12 |
| ct 2 | FAT Q1r | H | Rugby Town | 232 | W 1-0* | Quinn 92 (pen) |  | 13 |
|  | NPL | A | Rushall Olympic | 322 | D 1-1 | Turner 22 | 14 | 14 |
|  | NPL | A | Frickley Athletic | 224 | L 1-2 | Quinn 24 | 14 | 15 |
|  | NPL | H | Ilkeston Town | 312 | W 2-1 | Everall 3 47 | 13 | 16 |
|  | NPL | H | North Ferriby United | 450 | L 0-2 |  | 13 | 17 |
|  | NPL | A | Marine | 311 | L1-3 | Quinn 51 | 14 | 18 |
|  | FAT Q2 | H | Ramsbottom United | 341 | W 3-0 | QUINN 3 (11pen 34 65) |  | 19 |
|  | NPL | H | Chorley | 377 | W 1-0 | Quinn 62 | 11 | 20 |
| ov 3 | NPL | A | Blyth Spartans | 317 | L 0-1 |  | 14 | 21 |
|  | FAT Q3 | H | Bradford PA | 419 | W 3-1 | Brown 50 Quinn 71 (pen) Kasiama 87 |  | 22 |
|  | NPL | H | Nantwich Town | 474 | D 1-1 | George 45 | 15 | 23 |
| ec 1 | NPL | A | Eastwood Town | 187 | D 2-2 | Reid 26 Kinsella 90 | 14 | 24 |
|  | NPL | H | Buxton | 282 | D 2-2 | Kasiama 10 43 | 14 | 25 |
|  | NPL | A | Matlock Town | 307 | W 3-2 | Turner 11 Quinn 63 85 | 13 | 26 |
|  | NPL | H | Kendal Town | 364 | W 5-1 | Quinn 4 (pen) Carr 17 Ashton 34 69 Kasiama 90 | 11 | 27 |
|  | NPL | H | AFC Fylde | 305 | W 4-2 | QUINN 3 (3 49 62) Ashton 46 | 9 | 28 |
|  | NPL | H | Hednesford Town | 1124 | L 0-1 |  | 11 | 29 |
| an 1 | NPL | A | Ashton United | 163 | D 0-0 |  | 10 | 30 |
|  | NPL | H | Workso Town | 527 | W 3-1 | Ashton 29 Walshe 33 Kasiama 39 | 9 | 31 |
|  | NPL | A | FC United | 2131 | L 0-3 |  | 12 | 32 |
| eb 2 | NPL | A | Ilkston | 515 | W 2-0 | Ashton 40 Walshe 70 | 10 | 33 |
|  | NPL | H | Frickley Athletic | 398 | D 3-3 | Davcres 14 Kasiama 35 George 87 | 10 | 34 |
| 2 | NPL | H | Rushall Olympic | 290 | L 1-2 | Ashton 45 | 11 | 35 |
| 6 | NPL | A | North Ferriby Town | 232 | D 1-1 | Dacres 76 | 11 | 36 |
| 6 | NPL | H | Witton Albion | 329 | D 0-0 |  | 12 | 37 |
| lar 2 | NPL | H | Marine | 455 | D 0-0 |  | 12 | 38 |
|  | NPL | A | Buxton | 329 | L 1-2 | Carr 22 | 13 | 39 |
| 6 | NPL | H | Eastwood Town | 332 | W 2-0 | Bolton 57 Dacres 85 | 12 | 40 |
| 0 | NPL | A | Witton Albion | 428 | L 1-3 | Carr 9 | 13 | 41 |
| pr 1 | NPL | H | Ashton United | 330 | D 0-0 |  | 14 | 42 |
|  | NPL | A | Chorley | 576 | L 0-2 |  | 14 | 43 |
|  | NPL | A | Stocksbridge PS | 121 | L 0-2 |  | 14 | 44 |
| 3 | NPL | H | Blyth Spartans | 326 | L 2-4 | Quinn 3 (pen) Kinsella 78 (pen) | 15 | 45 |
| 7 | NPL | A | Whitby Town | 174 | L 0-4 |  | 15 | 46 |
| 0 | NPL | A | AFC Fylde | 386 | W 1-0 | Sheldon 26 | 15 | 47 |
| 7 | NPL | H | Nantwich Town | 356 | W 2-0 | Kinsella 15 Turner 69 | 14 | 48 |
| lay 4 | NPL | H | WhitbyTown | 400 | L 0-1 |  | 15 | 49 |

| GOALSCORERS | Lge | FAC | FAT | Total | Pens | Hat-tricks | Cons Run |  | Lge | FAC | FAT | Total | Pens | Hat-tricks | Cons Run |
|---|---|---|---|---|---|---|---|---|---|---|---|---|---|---|---|
| Quinn | 14 | 1 | 5 | 20 | 7 | 2 | 3 | Walsh | 2 |  |  | 2 |  |  |  |
| Ashton | 6 |  |  | 6 |  |  |  | Bolton | 1 |  |  | 1 |  |  |  |
| Carr | 4 | 2 |  | 6 |  |  |  | Brown |  |  | 1 | 1 |  |  |  |
| Kasiama | 5 |  | 1 | 6 |  |  |  | Espley | 1 |  |  | 1 |  |  |  |
| Everall | 5 |  |  | 5 | 2 |  |  | Jobson | 1 |  |  | 1 |  |  |  |
| Dacres | 4 |  |  | 4 |  |  |  | Reid | 1 |  |  | 1 |  |  |  |
| Turner | 3 |  | 1 | 4 |  |  |  | Sheldon | 1 |  |  | 1 |  |  |  |
| Dicker | 1 | 2 |  | 3 |  |  |  | Cons Run - Consecutive scoring games. |  |  |  |  |  |  |  |
| Kinsella | 3 |  |  | 3 | 1 |  |  |  |  |  |  |  |  |  |  |
| George | 2 |  |  | 2 |  |  |  |  |  |  |  |  |  |  |  |

# Premier Division Action

AFC Fylde on the attack against Rushall Olympic in their clash at Dales Lane.
Photo: Jonathan Holloway.

# STAMFORD

**Chairman:** Robert Feetham
**Secretary:** Phil Bee      **(T)** 07772 646 776      **(E)** phil.bee1947@hotmail.co.uk
**Commercial Manager:**                              **(T)**
**Programme Editor:** tbc                            **(T)**
**Ground Address:** Kettering Road, Stamford, Lincs PE9 2JS
**(T)** 01780 763 079                    **Manager:** David Staff

## Club Factfile

**Founded:** 1894      **Nickname:** The Daniels
**Previous Names:** Stamford Town and Rutland Ironworks amalgamated in 1894 to form Rutland Ironworks > 1896
**Previous Leagues:** Peterborough, Northants (UCL) 1908-55, Central Alliance 1955-61, Midland counties 1961-72, United Counties 1972-98, Southern 1998-2007

**Club Colours (change):** All red (White/black/black)

**Ground Capacity:** 2,000   **Seats:** 250   **Covered:** 1,250   **Clubhouse:** Yes   **Shop:** Yes

**Directions**
Travel on A1 Southbound. Leave A1 by A43 slip road.
At junction turn left. Ground is one mile on the left.

**Previous Grounds:** None

**Record Attendance:** 4,200 v Kettering Town - FA Cup 3rd Qualifying Round 1953
**Record Victory:** 13-0 v Peterborough Reserves - Northants League 1929-30
**Record Defeat:** 0-17 v Rothwell - FA Cup 1927-28
**Record Goalscorer:** Bert Knighton - 248
**Record Appearances:** Dick Kwiatkowski - 462
**Additional Records:**

**Senior Honours:**
FA Vase 1979-80. United Counties League x7. Lincolnshire Senior Cup, Senior Shield. Lincolnshire Senior 'A' Cup x3.

### 10 YEAR RECORD

| 03-04 | | 04-05 | | 05-06 | | 06-07 | | 07-08 | | 08-09 | | 09-10 | | 10-11 | | 11-12 | | 12-13 | |
|---|---|---|---|---|---|---|---|---|---|---|---|---|---|---|---|---|---|---|---|
| SthE | 7 | SthE | 21 | SthE | 4 | SthP | 8 | NP P | 20 | NP1S | 7 | NP1S | 10 | NP1S | 19 | NP1S | 7 | NP1S | 4 |

# STOCKSBRIDGE PARK STEELS

**Chairman:** Allen Bethel
**Secretary:** Michael Grimmer    **(T)** 07801 626 725    **(E)** mickgrimmer@gmail.com
**Commercial Manager:** D Cefferty    **(T)** 07788 214 315
**Programme Editor:** Philip Burkenshaw    **(T)** 07713 096 918
**Ground Address:** Look Local Stadium, Bracken Moor Lane, Stocksbridge, Sheffield S36 2AN
**(T)** 0114 288 8305    **Manager:** Darren Schofield

## Club Factfile

**Founded:** 1986    **Nickname:** Steels
**Previous Names:** Stocksbridge Works and Oxley Park merged in 1986
**Previous Leagues:** Northern Counties East 1986-96

**Club Colours (change):** Yellow/blue/blue (Red/white/red)

**Ground Capacity:** 3,500    **Seats:** 400    **Covered:** 1,500    **Clubhouse:** Yes    **Shop:** Yes

**Directions**
From West onto A616. Immediately you reach the Stocksbridge bypass turn Right signed (Stocksbridge West), then continue until you reach the shopping centre approx 1.5 miles. 300 yards past the centre you will see Gordons Autos on your left. Turn right directly opposite signed (Nanny Hill) and continue up the hill for Approx 500 yds, Ground is on the Left.
From M1- From North Junction 36 on to A61 Sheffield to McDonalds Roundabout. From South Junction 35a on to A616 Manchester to McDonalds Roundabout. From McDonalds roundabout on A616 Manchester for approx 6 miles then take Stocksbridge West exit, then continue until you reach the shopping centre approx 1.5 miles. 300yds past the centre you will see Gordons Autos on your Left. Turn right directly opposite signed (Nanny Hill) and continue up the hill for Approx 500yds, ground on Left.

**Previous Grounds:** Stonemoor 1949-51, 52-53

**Record Attendance:** 2,050 v Sheffield Wednesday - opening of floodlights October 1991
**Record Victory:** 17-1 v Oldham Town - FA Cup 2002-03
**Record Defeat:** 0-6 v Shildon
**Record Goalscorer:** Trevor Jones - 145
**Record Appearances:** Not known
**Additional Records:** Paul Jackson scored 10 v Oldham Town in the 2002-03 FA Cup - a FA Cup record
**Senior Honours:** Received £15,000 from Wolverhampton Wanderers for Lee Mills
Northern Counties East Division 1 1991-92, Premier Division 1993-94, League Cup 1994-95.
Sheffield Senior Cup 1951-52, 92-93, 95-96, 98-99

### 10 YEAR RECORD

| 03-04 | | 04-05 | | 05-06 | | 06-07 | | 07-08 | | 08-09 | | 09-10 | | 10-11 | | 11-12 | | 12-13 | |
|---|---|---|---|---|---|---|---|---|---|---|---|---|---|---|---|---|---|---|---|
| NP 1 | 19 | NP 1 | 14 | NP 1 | 6 | NP 1 | 6 | NP1S | 5 | NP1S | 3 | NP P | 11 | NP P | 13 | NP P | 18 | NP P | 20 |

# MATCH RESULTS 2012-13

| Date | Comp | H/A | Opponents | Att: | Result | Goalscorers | Pos | No. |
|---|---|---|---|---|---|---|---|---|
| Aug 18 | NPL | H | Chorley | 322 | L 4-5 | Booker 14 Ellison 24 Darley 48 Fish 69 | 17 | 1 |
| 21 | NPL | A | Blyth Spartans | 351 | L 0-5 | | 22 | 2 |
| 25 | NPL | A | Stafford Rangers | 404 | D 1-1 | Fish 17 | 19 | 3 |
| 27 | NPL | H | Buxton | 226 | L 0-2 | | 20 | 4 |
| Sept 2 | NPL | A | Worksop Town | 243 | L 1-2 | Hunter 78 | 20 | 5 |
| 4 | NPL | H | Blyth Spartans | 179 | L 2-3 | Hogan 51 Boden-Lovell 69 (pen) | 20 | 6 |
| 8 | FAC Q1 | H | Marine | 159 | L 0-3 | | | 7 |
| 15 | NPL | H | Eastwood Town | 127 | D 1-1 | South 89 | 19 | 8 |
| 18 | NPL | A | Witton Albion | 302 | L 0-1 | | 22 | 9 |
| 22 | NPL | A | Matlock Town | 287 | D 1-1 | Bowden-Lovell 90 | 21 | 10 |
| 29 | FAT Q1 | A | New Mills | 155 | L 2-3 | South 35 Bowden-Lovell 80 (pen) | | 11 |
| Oct 6 | NPL | A | Grantham | 235 | W 2-1 | Bowden-Lovell 21 South 45 | 18 | 12 |
| 9 | NPL | H | North Ferriby United | 98 | L 0-4 | | 18 | 13 |
| 13 | NPL | A | Ilkeston Town | 638 | L 0-1 | | 21 | 14 |
| 16 | NPL | H | Rushall Olympic | 102 | W 3-0 | Joynes 25 73  South 54 | 18 | 15 |
| 20 | NPL | H | Matlock Town | 191 | L 2-3 | Joynes 3 Bettney 82 | | 16 |
| 24 | NPL | A | Whitby Town | 242 | L 2-3 | South 45 Joynes 76 | 20 | 17 |
| 27 | NPL | A | Marine | 328 | L 1-2 | South 31 | 21 | 18 |
| 30 | NPL | A | Frickley Athletic | 200 | L 2-4 | Todd 80 South 86 | 21 | 19 |
| Nov 3 | NPL | H | Ashton United | 134 | L 0-3 | | 22 | 20 |
| 10 | NPL | A | Kendal Town | 141 | W 5-0 | South 18 (pen) 32 Qualter 82 (og) Thewlis 66 87 | 20 | 21 |
| 17 | NPL | H | Hednesford Town | 143 | D 3-3 | Callery 8 Hamshaw 68 Thewlis 70 | 20 | 22 |
| 24 | NPL | A | Marine | 104 | D 2-2 | Callery 64 Senior 75 | 20 | 23 |
| Dec 1 | NPL | A | Nantwich Town | 201 | L 3-4 | South 3 Thewlis 84 88 | 21 | 24 |
| 8 | NPL | H | Worksop Town | 187 | L 1-2 | Hamshaw 60 | 21 | 25 |
| 15 | NPL | A | Chorley | 459 | D 1-1 | South 77 | 21 | 26 |
| 26 | NPL | A | Buxton | 240 | L 0-7 | | 21 | 27 |
| Jan 5 | NPL | A | Eastwood Town | 147 | W 2-1 | South 54 Turner 90 | 20 | 28 |
| 12 | NPL | H | Witton Albion | 182 | D 3-3 | Hamshaw 9 South 44 Callery 89 | 20 | 29 |
| Feb 2 | NPL | A | Rushall Olympic | 150 | D 1-1 | Hamshaw 5 | 20 | 30 |
| 9 | NPL | H | Ilkeston | 185 | D 1-1 | Joynes 66 | 21 | 31 |
| 16 | NPL | A | AFC Fylde | 232 | L 0-4 | | 21 | 32 |
| Mar 2 | NPL | H | Whitby Town | 154 | L 1-4 | Thewlis  88 | 21 | 33 |
| 9 | NPL | A | North Ferriby United | 219 | L 1-5 | Denton 39 | 21 | 34 |
| Apr 1 | NPL | A | FC United | 1659 | L 0-4 | | 20 | 35 |
| 6 | NPL | H | Frickley Athletic | 174 | W 4-3 | Bowden-Lovell 14 South 37 | 20 | 36 |
| 9 | NPL | H | Stafford Rangers | 121 | W 2-0 | Callery 2  Swirad 53 | 20 | 37 |
| 13 | NPL | A | Ashton United | 103 | W 3-2 | JOYNES 3 (10 23 79) | 20 | 38 |
| 17 | NPL | H | FC United | 406 | L 1-3 | Joynes 55 | 20 | 39 |
| 20 | NPL | H | Kendal Town | 131 | W 5-3 | Callery 17  South 51 Joynes 54 Swirad 63 Denton 90 | 20 | 40 |
| 21 | NPL | H | Nantwich Town | 127 | W 5-2 | Swirad 25 South 31 Agus 47 Darker 61 Haigh 66 | 20 | 41 |
| 25 | NPL | H | AFC Fylde | 124 | L 0-2 | | 20 | 42 |
| 26 | NPL | A | Hednesford Town | 706 | L 1-4 | Joynes  69 | 20 | 43 |
| May 4 | NPL | H | Grantham Town | 168 | L 0-3 | | 20 | 44 |

| GOALSCORERS | Lge | FAC | FAT | Total | Pens | Hat-tricks | Cons Run | | Lge | FAC | FAT | Total | Pens | Hat-tricks | Cons Run |
|---|---|---|---|---|---|---|---|---|---|---|---|---|---|---|---|
| South | 14 | 1 | | 15 | 1 | | 3 | Darley | 1 | | | 1 | | | |
| Joynes | 13 | | | 13 | | 1 | 3 | Ellison | 1 | | | 1 | | | |
| Bowden-Lovell | 4 | 1 | | 5 | 1 | | 2 | Forbes-Swindler | 1 | | | 1 | | | |
| Callery | 5 | | | 5 | | | 2 | Haigh | 1 | | | 1 | | | |
| Thewlis | 5 | | | 5 | | | 2 | Hogan | 1 | | | 1 | | | |
| Hamshaw | 4 | | | 4 | | | 2 | Hunter | 1 | | | 1 | | | |
| Swirad | 3 | | | 3 | | | 2 | Senior | 1 | | | 1 | | | |
| Denton | 2 | | | 2 | | | | South | 1 | | | 1 | | | |
| Fish | 2 | | | 2 | | | | Todd | 1 | | | 1 | | | |
| Agus | 1 | | | 1 | | | | Turner | 1 | | | 1 | | | |
| Bettney | 1 | | | 1 | | | | Own Goals | 1 | | | 1 | | | |
| Booker | 1 | | | 1 | | | | Cons Run - Consecutive scoring games. | | | | | | | |
| Darker | 1 | | | 1 | | | | | | | | | | | |

# BUY IT IN YOUR NEWSAGENTS EVERY SUNDAY

## BE CLOSE TO THE PASSION

### For online and postal subscriptions
### visit www.thenonleaguefootballpaper.com

### Follow us @TheNonLeaguePaper

# TRAFFORD

**Chairman:** Howard Nelson
**Secretary:** Graham Foxall    **(T)** 07796 864 151    **(E)** davem@traffordfc.co.uk
**Commercial Manager:**    **(T)**
**Programme Editor:** Dave Murray    **(T)** 07551 982 299
**Ground Address:** Shawe View, Pennybridge Lane, Flixton Urmston M41 5DL
**(T)** 0161 747 1727    **Manager:** Garry Vaughan

2012-13 Squad - Back Row (L-R): Manager Garry Vaughan, Sam Lynch, Andy Smart, Warren Collier, Nia Bayunu (Captain), Milton Turner,
Kamahl Whight, Tom Read, Steve Mason, Luke Heron, Billy Burgess, Dion Depeiaza, Martyn Andrews, Haydn Buckley-Smith, Assistant Manager Wayne Goodison.
Front Row: Chris Palmer, Melford Knight, Sam Halligan, Scott Barlow, Paul Nelson, Jack Keightly, Michael Oates, Lewis James, Simon Gallanders, Will Ahern, Paul Ashton, Gareth Thomas, Simon Carden.

## Club Factfile

**Founded:** 1990    **Nickname:** The North
**Previous Names:** North Trafford 1990-94
**Previous Leagues:** Mid Cheshire 1990-92, North West Counties 1992-97, 2003-08, Northern Premier 1997-2003

**Club Colours (change):** All white (All yellow)

**Ground Capacity:** 2,500    **Seats:** 292    **Covered:** 740    **Clubhouse:** Yes    **Shop:** Yes

**Directions**
Anti-Clockwise exit at J10 (Trafford Centre) and turn right towards Urmston B5214. Straight across two roundabouts. First lights turn right into Moorside Road, at next roundabout take second exit in to Bowfell Road. At next lights turn sharp left then immediately right in to Pennybridge Lane next to Bird In Hand Pub, parking on left 100 yards.
Or Leave M60 at J8, taking A6144 towards Lymm, Partington, Carrington. At second set of traffic lights turn right on B5158 towards Flixton. Remain on B5158 crossing railway bridge at Flixton Station and turn right at next set of traffic lights. Passing Bird in Hand Pub take immediate right in to Pennybridge Lane. Parking on left 100 yards.

**Previous Grounds:** Not known

**Record Attendance:** 803 v Flixton - Northern Premier League Division 1 1997-98
**Record Victory:** Not known
**Record Defeat:** Not known
**Record Goalscorer:** Garry Vaughan - 88
**Record Appearances:** Garry Vaughan - 293
**Additional Records:**

**Senior Honours:**
North West Counties Division 1 1996-97, 2007-08.
Manchester Challenge Trophy 2004-05. Northern Premier President's Cup 2008-09.

### 10 YEAR RECORD

| 03-04 | | 04-05 | | 05-06 | | 06-07 | | 07-08 | | 08-09 | | 09-10 | | 10-11 | | 11-12 | | 12-13 | |
|---|---|---|---|---|---|---|---|---|---|---|---|---|---|---|---|---|---|---|---|
| NWC1 | 16 | NWC1 | 12 | NWC1 | 15 | NWC1 | 5 | NWC1 | 1 | NP1N | 15 | NP1N | 12 | NP1N | 14 | NP1N | 12 | NP1N | 4 |

# WHITBY TOWN

**Chairman:** Anthony Graham Manser

**Secretary:** Peter Tyreman    **(T)** 01947 605 153    **(E)**

**Commercial Manager:**    **(T)**

**Programme Editor:** Paul Connolly    **(T)** 07798 746 865

**Ground Address:** Turnbull Ground, Upgang Lane, Whitby, North Yorks YO21 3HZ

**(T)** 01947 604 847    **Manager:** Darren Williams

2012-13 Squad.

## Club Factfile

**Founded:** 1926    **Nickname:** Seasiders

**Previous Names:** Whitby United (pre 1950)

**Previous Leagues:** Northern League 1926-97

**Club Colours (change):** All royal blue (All white)

**Ground Capacity:** 2,680    **Seats:** 622    **Covered:** 1,372    **Clubhouse:** Yes    **Shop:** Yes

**Directions**

On entering Whitby from both the A169 and A171 roads, take the first fork and follow signs for the "West Cliff".
Then turn left at the Spa Shop and Garage, along Love Lane to junction of the A174.
Turn right and the ground is 600 yards on the left.

**Previous Grounds:** None

**Record Attendance:** 4,000 v Scarborough - North Riding Cup 18/04/1965

**Record Victory:** 11-2 v Cargo Fleet Works - 1950

**Record Defeat:** 3-13 v Willington - 24/03/1928

**Record Goalscorer:** Paul Pitman - 382

**Record Appearances:** Paul Pitman - 468

**Additional Records:** Paid £2,500 to Newcastle Blue Star for John Grady 1990
Received £5,000 from Gateshead for Graham Robinson 1997

**Senior Honours:**
Rothmans National Cup 1975-76, 77-78. Northern League 1992-93, 96-97. FA Vase 1996-97.
Northern Premier League Division 1 1997-98.
North Riding Senior Cup x5.

### 10 YEAR RECORD

| 03-04 | 04-05 | 05-06 | 06-07 | 07-08 | 08-09 | 09-10 | 10-11 | 11-12 | 12-13 |
|---|---|---|---|---|---|---|---|---|---|
| NP P  15 | NP P  4 | NP P  6 | NP P  11 | NP P  12 | NP P  19 | NP P  14 | NP P  16 | NP P  17 | NP P  13 |

# MATCH RESULTS 2012-13

| Date | Comp | H/A | Opponents | Att: | Result | Goalscorers | Pos | No. |
|---|---|---|---|---|---|---|---|---|
| Aug 18 | NPL | H | Rushall Olympic | 259 | L 0-1 | | 18 | 1 |
| 21 | NPL | A | FC United | 1562 | L 2-3 | Mulligan 41 84 (pen) | 20 | 2 |
| 25 | NPL | A | Buxton | 258 | L 1-2 | Mulligan 44 | 20 | 3 |
| 27 | NPL | H | Blyth Spartans | 407 | L 1-3 | Mulligan 18 (pen) | 21 | 4 |
| Sept 1 | NPL | A | AFC Hyde | 258 | L 3-4 | Armstrong 45 Burgess 6 White 70 | 21 | 5 |
| 3 | NPL | H | FC United | 482 | L 0-1 | | 21 | 6 |
| 8 | FAC Q1 | A | Ossett Town | 75 | D 1-1 | Mulligan 9 | | 7 |
| 12 | FAC Q1 | H | Ossett Town | 179 | W 1-0 | White 63 | | 8 |
| 15 | NPL | H | Marine | 231 | D 1-1 | Armstrong 34 | 20 | 9 |
| 18 | NPL | A | North Ferriby United | 223 | D 1-1 | Henry 24 (pen) | 21 | 10 |
| 22 | FAC Q2 | H | Droylsden | 202 | W 4-3 | Mulligan 16 89 White 72 Snaith 77 | | 11 |
| 29 | FAT Q1 | A | Chorley | 388 | W 3-1 | Snaith 7 82 Henry 90 | | 12 |
| Oct 6 | FAC Q3 | A | Stalybridge Celtic | 372 | L 1-3 | Portas 5 | | 13 |
| 10 | NPL | H | Grantham | 268 | W 2-0 | Mulligan 22 70 (pen) | 20 | 14 |
| 13 | NPL | H | Nantwich Town | 339 | L 1-2 | Mulligan 31 (pen) | 22 | 15 |
| 17 | NPL | A | Worksop Town | 297 | W 1-0 | Mulligan 65 | 18 | 16 |
| 20 | NPL | A | Witton Albion | 543 | L 2-4 | Henry 26 Janes 56 | 20 | 17 |
| 24 | NPL | H | Stocksbridge PS | 242 | W 3-2 | Henry 32 Mulligan 36 82 (pen) | 16 | 18 |
| 27 | FAT Q2 | H | Ilkeston | 272 | W 4-2 | Snaith 48 Portas 56 Armstrong 62 Corker 84 | | 19 |
| 30 | NPL | A | Kendal Town | 187 | W 4-2 | Armstrong 39 75 Alexander 57(og) Mulligan 60 | 14 | 20 |
| Nov 3 | NPL | H | Hednesford Town | 292 | L 0-2 | | 17 | 21 |
| 10 | FAT Q3 | A | Guiseley | 506 | L 0-7 | | | 22 |
| 17 | NPL | H | Ashton United | 248 | L 1-3 | Mulligan 62 (pen) | 19 | 23 |
| 24 | NPL | A | Ilkeston | 563 | L 1-2 | Purewal 75 | 19 | 24 |
| Dec 1 | NPL | H | Matlock Town | 237 | W 1-0 | Farrell 1 | 18 | 25 |
| 15 | NPL | A | Rushall Olympic | 161 | D 1-1 | Farrell 67 | 19 | 26 |
| 26 | NPL | A | Blyth Spartans | 320 | D 2-2 | Armstrong 5 30 | 19 | 27 |
| 29 | NPL | A | Chorley | 553 | W 3-2 | Farrell 5 Armstrong 39 White 71 | 18 | 28 |
| Jan 1 | NPL | H | Frickley Athletic | 284 | W 4-1 | FARRELL 3 (42 56 72) Corker 64 | | 29 |
| 5 | NPL | A | Marine | 355 | W 5-1 | Armmstrong 26 47 Farrell 30 53 Snaith 86 | 16 | 30 |
| Feb 2 | NPL | H | Worksop Town | 249 | W 2-1 | Farrell 21 34 | 15 | 31 |
| 16 | NPL | H | Witton Albion | 319 | L 1-3 | Farrell 86 | 16 | 32 |
| 23 | NPL | A | Eastwood Town | 147 | W 2-0 | Henry 25 Armstrong 59 | 15 | 33 |
| 27 | NPL | H | Buxton | 202 | D 1-1 | Armstrong 90 | 15 | 34 |
| Mar 2 | NPL | A | Stocksbridge PS | 154 | W 4-1 | Henry 10 48 Portas 27 Farrell 89 | 14 | 35 |
| 6 | NPL | H | North Ferriby United | 242 | L 2-4 | Farrell 20 37 | 14 | 36 |
| 12 | NPL | A | Grantham Town | 100 | W 3-2 | White 6 36 Mulligan 22 | 14 | 37 |
| 16 | NPL | A | Matlock Town | 271 | D 0-0 | | 14 | 38 |
| 20 | NPL | H | AFC Hyde | 203 | L 0-4 | | 14 | 39 |
| 30 | NPL | H | Chorley | 304 | D 1-1 | Farrell 52 (pen) | 14 | 40 |
| Apr 1 | NPL | A | Frickley Athletic | 224 | W 2-0 | McTiernan 40 Yates 70 (og) | 13 | 41 |
| 6 | NPL | H | Kendal Town | 261 | W 1-0 | Snaith 58 | 13 | 42 |
| 9 | NPL | A | Nantwich Town | 176 | L 1-2 | Armstrong 42 (pen) | 13 | 43 |
| 13 | NPL | A | Hednesford Town | 504 | L 0-4 | | 13 | 44 |
| 17 | NPL | H | Stafford Rangers | 174 | W 4-0 | Hassan 64 Farrell 78 Mulligan 82 Portas 90 | 13 | 45 |
| 20 | NPL | H | Eastwood Town | 342 | D 1-1 | Henry 29 | 12 | 46 |
| 23 | NPL | H | Ilkkeston | 247 | L 0-4 | | 13 | 47 |
| 27 | NPL | A | Ashton United | 114 | D 2-2 | Henry 3 McTiernon 88 | 13 | 48 |
| May 4 | NPL | A | Stafford Rangers | 400 | W 1-0 | Robinson 63 | 13 | 49 |

| GOALSCORERS | Lge | FAC | FAT | Total | Pens | Hat-tricks | Cons Run | | Lge | FAC | FAT | Total | Pens | Hat-tricks | Cons Run |
|---|---|---|---|---|---|---|---|---|---|---|---|---|---|---|---|
| Mulligan | 14 | 3 | | 17 | 6 | | 3 | Purewall | 1 | | | 1 | | | |
| Farrell | 16 | | | 16 | 1 | | 5 | McTiernan | 2 | | | 2 | | | |
| Armstrong | 12 | 1 | | 13 | 1 | | 2 | Hassan | 1 | | | 1 | | | |
| Henry | 8 | | 1 | 9 | 1 | | 2 | Robinson | 1 | | | 1 | | | |
| White | 4 | 2 | | 6 | | | | Own Goal | 2 | | | 2 | | | |
| Snaith | 2 | 1 | 3 | 6 | | | 2 | Cons Run - Consecutive scoring games. | | | | | | | |
| Portas | 2 | 1 | 1 | 4 | | | | | | | | | | | |
| Corker | 1 | | 1 | 2 | | | | | | | | | | | |
| Burgess | 1 | | | 1 | | | | | | | | | | | |
| Janes | 1 | | | 1 | | | | | | | | | | | |

# WITTON ALBION

**Chairman:** Mark Harris

**Secretary:** Lisa Duckett    **(T)** 07597 143 886    **(E)** wafc43008@o2.co.uk

**Commercial Manager:** Alison Atkins    **(T)** 07940 574 725

**Programme Editor:** Jamie Thompson    **(T)** 07795 164 710

**Ground Address:** Help for Heros Stadium, Wincham Park, Chapel Street, Wincham, CW9 6DA

**(T)** 01606 430 08    **Manager:** Brian Pritchard

2012-13 Squad. Photo courtesy of the Northwich Guardian.

## Club Factfile

**Founded:** 1887    **Nickname:** The Albion

**Previous Names:** None

**Previous Leagues:** Lancashire Combination, Cheshire County > 1979, Northern Premier 1979-91, Conference 1991-94

**Club Colours (change):** Red & white stripes/blue/red (Navy blue with yellow trim/yellow/yellow)

**Ground Capacity:** 4,500    **Seats:** 650    **Covered:** 2,300    **Clubhouse:** Yes    **Shop:** Yes

**Directions**

**M6 Junction 19:** Follow A556 for Northwich for three miles, through two sets of traffic lights. Turn right at the beginning of the dual carriageway onto A559. After ¾ mile turn right at traffic lights by Slow & Easy Public House, still following A559. After a further ¾ mile turn left a Black Greyhound Public House (signposted). Follow the road through the industrial estate for about ½ mile. Turn left immediately after crossing the canal bridge (signposted) **From M56 Junction 10:** Follow the A558 (Northwich Road) towards Northwich for approximately 6 miles. Turn right at the crossroads by the Black Greyhound Public House (signposted). Follow the road through the industrial estate for about ½ mile. Turn left immediately after crossing the canal bridge (signposted)

**Previous Grounds:** Central Ground (1910-1989)

**Record Attendance:** 3,940 v Kidderminster Harries - FA Trophy Semi-final 13/04/1991

**Record Victory:** 13-0 v Middlewich (H)

**Record Defeat:** 0-9 v Macclesfield Town (A) - 18/09/1965

**Record Goalscorer:** Frank Fidler - 175 (1947-50)

**Record Appearances:** Brian Pritchard - 729

**Additional Records:** Paid £12,500 to Hyde United for Jim McCluskie 1991

**Senior Honours:** Received £11,500 from Chester City for Peter Henderson

Northern Premier League Premier Division 1990-91, Division 1 North Play-offs 2011-12. Cheshire Senior Cup x7.

## 10 YEAR RECORD

| 03-04 | | 04-05 | | 05-06 | | 06-07 | | 07-08 | | 08-09 | | 09-10 | | 10-11 | | 11-12 | | 12-13 | |
|---|---|---|---|---|---|---|---|---|---|---|---|---|---|---|---|---|---|---|---|
| NP P | 5 | NP 1 | 8 | NP 1 | 8 | NP P | 2 | NP P | 2 | NP P | 20 | NP1S | 7 | NP1N | 10 | NP1N | 3 | NP1N | 4 |

# MATCH RESULTS 2012-13

| Date | Comp | H/A | Opponents | Att: | Result | Goalscorers | Pos | No. |
|---|---|---|---|---|---|---|---|---|
| Aug 18 | NPL | H | Blyth Spartans | 494 | W 2-1 | Tuck 10 Gardner 90 (pen) | 6 | 1 |
| 21 | NPL | A | Chorley | 625 | W 2-1 | Wood 15 Gardner 58 | 4 | 2 |
| 25 | NPL | A | Worksop Town | 253 | D 1-1 | Tuck 38 | 5 | 3 |
| 27 | NPL | H | FC United | 1352 | D 1-1 | Harrison 55 | 7 | 4 |
| Sept 1 | NPL | A | Buxton | 339 | D 2-2 | Hancock 28 Fallon 54 | 7 | 5 |
| 4 | NPL | H | Chorley | 484 | L 1-3 | Stott 29 | 9 | 6 |
| 8 | FAC Q1 | A | Burscough | 217 | W 4-2 | Stott 10 36 Andrews 13 Tuck 90 | | 7 |
| 15 | NPL | A | Ilkeston | 499 | W 3-2 | Hancock 27 32 Wood 80 | 11 | 8 |
| 18 | NPL | H | Stocksbridge PS | 302 | W 1-0 | Stott 70 | 8 | 9 |
| 22 | FAC Q2 | A | Kendal Town | 227 | L 2-4 | Stott 1 23 | | 10 |
| 29 | FAT Q1 | H | Blyth Spartans | 313 | W 4-1 | Sheehan 13 Wood 62 Tuck 67 90 | | 11 |
| Oct 6 | NPL | H | Ashton United | 428 | L 0-2 | | 10 | 12 |
| 9 | NPL | A | AFC Fylde | 261 | W 2-1 | Andrews 29 Fallon 40 | 6 | 13 |
| 13 | NPL | A | North Ferriby United | 351 | L 0-2 | | 8 | 14 |
| 16 | NPL | H | Marine | 347 | W 2-0 | Foster 49 Cross 74 | 5 | 15 |
| 20 | NPL | A | Whitby Town | 543 | W 4-2 | Andrews 10 68 Stott 20 McTiernon 86 (og) | 3 | 16 |
| 23 | NPL | A | Hednesford Town | 371 | L 1-2 | Stott 80 | 4 | 17 |
| 27 | FAT Q2 | H | Skelmersdale United | 346 | L 2-3 | Tuck 33 Gardner 40 (pen) | | 18 |
| 30 | NPL | A | Rushall Olympic | 210 | W 4-0 | TUCK 3 ( 35 55 90) Gardner 67 (pen) | 3 | 19 |
| Nov 3 | NPL | H | Grantham Town | 429 | L 0-2 | | 6 | 20 |
| 10 | NPL | A | Eastwood Town | 160 | W 4-3 | TUCK 3 ( 9 66 83) Foster 63 | 4 | 21 |
| 17 | NPL | H | Frickley Athletic | 376 | W 5-0 | ANDREWS 3 ( 9 21 73) Stott 46 James 65 | 3 | 22 |
| 24 | NPL | H | Eastwood Town | 408 | W 3-0 | Tuck 39 66 Foster 41 | 2 | 23 |
| Dec 8 | NPL | H | Buxton | 419 | L 2-4 | Hancock 28 Foster 86 | 4 | 24 |
| 15 | NPL | A | Blyth Spartans | 222 | W 3-0 | Foster 53 Andrews 62 Tuck 68 | 4 | 25 |
| Jan 1 | NPL | H | Nantwich Town | 526 | D 2-2 | Foster 44 Gardner 85 (pen) | 4 | 26 |
| 5 | NPL | H | Ilkesteon | 454 | D 2-2 | Gardner 43 Foster 59 | 3 | 27 |
| 12 | NPL | A | Stocksbridge PS | 182 | D 3-3 | Andrews 30 Tuck 69 Hancock 88 | 4 | 28 |
| Feb 2 | NPL | A | Marine | 438 | L 0-3 | | 4 | 29 |
| 9 | NPL | H | North Ferriby United | 374 | L 2-4 | Meadowcroft 27 Foster 33 | 6 | 30 |
| 16 | NPL | A | Whitby Town | 319 | W 3-1 | Foster 57 Adrews 89 Tuck 90 | 6 | 31 |
| 23 | NPL | A | Matlock Town | 313 | W 2-1 | Gardner 32 (pen) Sheehan 59 | 5 | 32 |
| 26 | NPL | A | Stafford Rangers | 329 | D 0-0 | | 5 | 33 |
| Mar 2 | NPL | H | Hednesford Town | 507 | D 1-1 | Gardner 83 (pen) | 5 | 34 |
| 6 | NPL | A | Ashton United | 141 | W 3-1 | Hancock 21 32 Robinson 45 (og) | 4 | 35 |
| 9 | NPL | H | Worksop Town | 408 | W 4-3 | Foster 9 Glover 66 Hancock 69 Tuck 82 | 3 | 36 |
| 16 | NPL | H | Kendal Town | 370 | W 3-0 | Hancock 26 (pen) 82 Andrews 66 | 3 | 37 |
| 30 | NPL | H | Stafford Rangers | 426 | W 3-1 | Hancock 16 (pen) Tuck 63 Andrews 66 | 3 | 38 |
| Apr 1 | NPL | A | Nantwich Town | 388 | L 1-2 | Foster 77 | 4 | 39 |
| 6 | NPL | A | FC United | 1741 | W 1-0 | Tuck 27 | 3 | 40 |
| 9 | NPL | H | AFC Fylde | 421 | L 0-2 | | 5 | 41 |
| 13 | NPL | A | Grantham Town | 210 | W 3-1 | Hancock 4 32 Tuck 7 | 4 | 42 |
| 17 | NPL | A | Kendal Town | 200 | W 2-1 | Foster 35 Joseph 76 | 4 | 43 |
| 20 | NPL | H | Matlock Town | 574 | W 3-0 | Foster 4 Shaw 90 Andrews 90 | 4 | 44 |
| 27 | NPL | A | Frickley Athletic | 226 | W 2-0 | Foster 30 Harrison 89 | 4 | 45 |
| May 4 | NPL | H | Rushall Olympic | 508 | W 2-0 | Shaw 20 Tuck 69 (pen) | 4 | 46 |
| 7 | P-Off S-F | A | FC United | 2492 | L 1-3 | Hancock 53 (pen) | | 47 |

| GOALSCORERS | Lge | FAC | FAT | Total | Pens | Hat-tricks | Cons Run | | Lge | FAC | FAT | Total | Pens | Hat-tricks | Cons Run |
|---|---|---|---|---|---|---|---|---|---|---|---|---|---|---|---|
| Tuck | 17 | 1 | 3 | 21 | 2 | | 2 | Sheehan | 1 | | 1 | 2 | | | |
| Foster | 15 | | | 15 | | | 5 | Cross | 1 | | | 1 | | | |
| Hancock | 14 | | | 14 | 3 | | 4 | Glover | 1 | | | 1 | | | |
| Andrews | 11 | 1 | | 12 | | | 2 | James | 1 | | | 1 | | | |
| Stott | 5 | 4 | | 9 | | | 2 | Joseph | 1 | | | 1 | | | |
| Gardner | 7 | | 1 | 8 | 6 | | 2 | Meadowcroft | 1 | | | 1 | | | |
| Wood | 2 | | 1 | 3 | | | | Tuck | 1 | | | 1 | | | |
| Fallon | 2 | | | 2 | | | | Own Goals | 2 | | | 2 | | | |
| Harrison | 2 | | | 2 | | | | Cons Run - Consecutive scoring games. | | | | | | | |
| Shaw | 2 | | | 2 | | | | | | | | | | | |

# WORKSOP TOWN

**Chairman:** I Smith

**Secretary:** Keith Ilett     **(T)** 07734 144 961     **(E)** tiger1861@hotmail.co.uk

**Commercial Manager:**     **(T)**

**Programme Editor:** Steve Jarvis     **(T)** 01623 792 047

**Ground Address:** Babbage Way, off Sandy Lane, Worksop S80 1TN

**(T)** 07734 144 961     **Manager:** Mark Shaw

## Club Factfile

**Founded:** 1861     **Nickname:** Tigers

**Previous Names:** Not known

**Previous Leagues:** Midland Co. 1896-98, 1900-30, 49-60, 61-68, 69-74, Sheffield Amateur 1898-99, 1931-33, Central Combination 1933-35, Yorkshire 1935-39, Central Alliance1947-49, 60-61, Northern Premier 1968-69, 74-2004, Conference 2004-07

**Club Colours (change):** Yellow/navy/navy (All red)

**Ground Capacity:**     **Seats:** Yes     **Covered:** Yes     **Clubhouse:** Yes     **Shop:** No

**Directions**

From M1 junc 31 take A57 Worksop after 7 miles carry on to by-pass at 3rd roundabout take 1st exit Sandy Lane industrial estate Ground 1ml on left at side of Tyre Centre.

From A1 junc34 take B6045 Blyth, then take A57 Worksop at 1st set of lights go straight on pass the Hospital on the left,next set of lights straight on, at the next set go under the bridge,the next set of lights turn right,100mts up the road 1st right then turn first left into the ground.

**Previous Grounds:** Central Avenue, Sandy Lane, shared with Ilkeston Town (New Manor Ground)

**Record Attendance:** 8,171 v Chesterfield - FA Cup 1925 (Central Avenue)

**Record Victory:** 20-0 v Staveley - 01/09/1984

**Record Defeat:** 1-11 v Hull City Reserves - 1955-56

**Record Goalscorer:** Kenny Clark - 287

**Record Appearances:** Kenny Clark - 347

**Additional Records:** Paid £5,000 to Grantham Town for Kirk Jackson

**Senior Honours:** Received £47,000 from Sunderland for Jon Kennedy 2000

Sheffield Senior Cup 1923-24, 52-53, 54-55, 65-66, 69-70,72-73, 81-82, 84-85, 94-95, 96-97, 2002-03, 11-12.

Northern Premier League President's Cup 1985-86, 96-97, Chairman's Cup 2001-02.

### 10 YEAR RECORD

| 03-04 | | 04-05 | | 05-06 | | 06-07 | | 07-08 | | 08-09 | | 09-10 | | 10-11 | | 11-12 | | 12-13 | |
|---|---|---|---|---|---|---|---|---|---|---|---|---|---|---|---|---|---|---|---|
| NP P | 7 | Conf N | 17 | Conf N | 9 | Conf N | 21 | NP P | 9 | NP P | 17 | NP P | 18 | NP P | 7 | NP P | 15 | NP P | 9 |

# MATCH RESULTS 2012-13

| Date | Comp | H/A | Opponents | Att: | Result | Goalscorers | Pos | No. |
|---|---|---|---|---|---|---|---|---|
| Aug 18 | NPL | A | Ashton United | 154 | L 3-5 | Mettam 10 41 Towers 45 | 19 | 1 |
| 22 | NPL | H | North Ferriby United | 301 | W 2-1 | Holden 54 Young 86 | 12 | 2 |
| 25 | NPL | H | Witton Albion | 253 | D 1-1 | Towers 44 | 10 | 3 |
| 27 | NPL | A | Grantham Town | 384 | L 0-3 | | 12 | 4 |
| Sept 2 | NPL | H | Stocksbridge PS | 243 | W 2-1 | Mettam 86 Beeson 86 | 14 | 5 |
| 4 | NPL | A | North Ferriby United | 238 | L 0-2 | | 15 | 6 |
| 8 | FAC Q1 | H | **Frickley Athletic** | **274** | **L 0-2** | | | 7 |
| 15 | NPL | H | Stafford Rangers | 300 | L 2-3 | Mettam 41 Denton 45 | 15 | 8 |
| 18 | NPL | A | Hednesford Town | 406 | W 4-0 | Beeson 38 (pen) 59 Denton 68 Young 89 | 14 | 9 |
| 29 | FAT Q1 | A | **Curzon Ashton** | **164** | **W 3-2** | **Miller 17 Mettam 69 Burbeary 88** | | 10 |
| Oct 6 | NPL | A | Nantwich Town | 308 | W 5-0 | Miller 34 Burbeary 35 (pen) King 45 Mettam 73 Denton 79 | 12 | 11 |
| 10 | NPL | H | Eastwood Town | 338 | L 2-3 | Young 10 Mettam 23 | 12 | 12 |
| 13 | NPL | A | Marine | 607 | W 3-2 | DENTON 3 (45 48 67) | 10 | 13 |
| 17 | NPL | H | Whitby Town | 297 | L 0-1 | | 10 | 14 |
| 20 | NPL | H | Kendal Town | 289 | W 3-0 | Denton 42 59 Mettam 63 | 10 | 15 |
| 24 | NPL | A | Buxton | 249 | W 3-0 | Towers 45 Beeson 81 (pen) King 85 | 8 | 16 |
| 27 | FAT Q2 | A | **Halesowen Town** | **265** | **W 1-0** | **Mettam 35** | | 17 |
| 31 | NPL | H | Blyth Spartans | 305 | W 8-1 | Denton 6 Hawes 9 49 Mettam 13 83 Warlow 29 32 Beeson 89 | 6 | 18 |
| Nov 3 | NPL | A | Chorley | 744 | D 1-1 | King 20 | 7 | 19 |
| 10 | FAT Q3 | A | **Chester** | **1410** | **D 2-2** | **Mettam 53 Burbeary 78** | | 20 |
| 14 | FAT Q3r | H | **Chester** | **457** | **W 2-0** | **Young 8 Mettam 17** | | 21 |
| 17 | NPL | A | AFC Fylde | 331 | D 2-2 | Denton 40 90 | 6 | 22 |
| 24 | FAT Q4 | H | **Kings Lynn Town** | **488** | **L 0-1** | | | 23 |
| Dec 6 | NPL | A | Stocksbridge PS | 187 | W 2-1 | Swirad 18 (og) Burbeary 20 | 8 | 24 |
| 15 | NPL | H | Ashton United | 277 | W 5-1 | Burbeary 36 (pen) Mettam 68 Shiels 72 Beeson 76 Towers 90 | 6 | 25 |
| 26 | NPL | H | Grantham Town | 347 | W 3-2 | Denton 36 Mettam 50 Burbeary 71 (pen) | 5 | 26 |
| 29 | NPL | H | Matlock Town | 387 | W 6-1 | Shiels 6 BURBEARY 3 (8 17 19pen) Mettam 26 Denton 67 | 4 | 27 |
| Jan 1 | NPL | H | Ilkeston | 678 | L 1-2 | Denton 84 | 5 | 28 |
| 5 | NPL | A | Stafford Rangers | 527 | L 1-3 | Young 12 | 5 | 29 |
| 12 | NPL | H | Hednesford Town | 390 | L 0-4 | | 5 | 30 |
| Feb 2 | NPL | A | WhitbyTown | 249 | L 1-2 | Burbeary 14 (pen) | 6 | 31 |
| 6 | NPL | H | Frickley Athletic | 224 | W 3-2 | Towers 7 22 Denton 15 | 4 | 32 |
| 9 | NPL | H | Marine | 288 | D 1-1 | Mettam 79 | 5 | 33 |
| 16 | NPL | A | Kendal Town | 215 | W 4-3 | Potts 27 (pen) 49 (pen) Denton 77 84 | 5 | 34 |
| 23 | NPL | H | Nantwich Town | 326 | L 0-2 | | 7 | 35 |
| Mar 2 | NPL | A | Eastwood Town | 209 | W 1-0 | Burbeary 58 | 7 | 36 |
| 9 | NPL | A | Witton Albion | 408 | L 3-4 | Mettam 5 Denton 35 Towers 39 | 9 | 37 |
| 16 | NPL | H | FC United | 811 | W 4-1 | Mettam 51 55 Burbeary 75 (pen) 81 | 8 | 38 |
| 27 | NPL | H | Rushall Olympic | 247 | L 2-3 | Towers 70 Denton 40 | 9 | 39 |
| Apr 1 | NPL | H | Ilkeston | 348 | L 1-4 | Mettam 6 | 11 | 40 |
| 6 | NPL | A | Blyth Spartans | 315 | L 2-3 | Mettam 57 Burbeary 90 | 11 | 41 |
| 9 | NPL | A | Frickley Athletic | 202 | D 0-0 | | 11 | 42 |
| 13 | NPL | H | Chorley | 226 | W 1-0 | Mettam 89 | 11 | 43 |
| 16 | NPL | A | Rushall Olympic | 180 | W 2-1 | Denton 6 Young 45 | 10 | 44 |
| 20 | NPL | A | FC United | 2761 | L 0-1 | | 9 | 45 |
| 27 | NPL | H | AFC Fylde | 221 | D 0-0 | | 9 | 46 |
| May 2 | NPL | A | Matlock Town | 251 | W 5-1 | TOWERS 3( 9 64 71) Denton 42 Potts 80 | 9 | 47 |
| 4 | NPL | H | Buxton | 251 | W 2-0 | Denton 49 Miller 67 | 9 | 48 |

| GOALSCORERS | Lge | FAC | FAT | Total | Pens | Hat-tricks | Cons Run | | Lge | FAC | FAT | Total | Pens | Hat-tricks | Cons Run |
|---|---|---|---|---|---|---|---|---|---|---|---|---|---|---|---|
| Mettam | 19 | | 4 | 23 | | | 3 | Shiels | 2 | | | 2 | | | |
| Denton | 22 | | | 22 | 1 | | 2 | Warlow | 2 | | | 2 | | | |
| Burbeary | 12 | 2 | | 14 | 5 | 1 | 4 | Holden | 1 | | | 1 | | | |
| Towers | 11 | | | 11 | | 1 | | Own Goals | 1 | | | 1 | | | |
| Beeson | 6 | | | 6 | 2 | | | Cons Run - Consecutive scoring games. | | | | | | | |
| Young | 5 | 1 | | 6 | | | | | | | | | | | |
| King | 3 | | | 3 | | | | | | | | | | | |
| Miller | 2 | 1 | | 3 | | | | | | | | | | | |
| Potts | 3 | | | 3 | 2 | | | | | | | | | | |
| Hawes | 2 | | | 2 | | | | | | | | | | | |

# BAMBER BRIDGE

**Chairman:** Terry Gammans
**Secretary:** George Halliwell    **(T)** 07970 042 954    **(E)**
**Commercial Manager:**    **(T)**
**Programme Editor:** Peter Nowell    **(T)** 07766 196 246
**Ground Address:** The Irongate Stadium, Brownedge Road, Bamber Bridge PR5 6UX
**(T)** 01772 909 690    **Manager:** Neil Crowe

## Club Factfile

**Founded:** 1952    **Nickname:** Brig
**Previous Names:** None
**Previous Leagues:** Preston & District 1952-90, North West Counties 1990-93

**Club Colours (change):** White/black/black (All red)

**Ground Capacity:** 3,000    **Seats:** 554    **Covered:** 800    **Clubhouse:** Yes    **Shop:** Yes

**Directions:** Junction 29, A6 (Bamber Bridge by-pass)onto London Way. First roundabout take 3rd exit Brownedge Road (East) then take first right. Ground on left at the bottom of the road.

**Previous Grounds:** King George V, Higher Wallton 1952-86

**Record Attendance:** 2,300 v Czech Republic - Pre Euro '96 friendly
**Record Victory:** 8-0 v Curzon Ashton - North West Counties 1994-95
**Record Defeat:** Not known
**Record Goalscorer:** Not known
**Record Appearances:** Not known
**Additional Records:** Paid £10,000 to Horwich RMI for Mark Edwards
**Senior Honours:** Received £15,000 from Wigan Athletic for Tony Black 1995
ATDC Lancashire Trophy 1994-95.
Northern Premier League Premier Division 1995-96, Challenge Cup 1995-96.

### 10 YEAR RECORD

| 03-04 | 04-05 | 05-06 | 06-07 | 07-08 | 08-09 | 09-10 | 10-11 | 11-12 | 12-13 |
|---|---|---|---|---|---|---|---|---|---|
| NP 1    10 | NP P    21 | NP 1    13 | NP 1    13 | NP1N    5 | NP1N    11 | NP1N    14 | NP1N    7 | NP1N    10 | NP1N    9 |

# BURSCOUGH

**Chairman:** Gary Wright

**Secretary:** Stan Petheridge     **(T)** 07815 954 304     **(E)** stanpeth@fsmail.net

**Commercial Manager:**     **(T)**

**Programme Editor:** Stuart Saint     **(T)** 07791 593 911

**Ground Address:** Victoria Park, Bobby Langton Way, Mart Lane, Burscough L40 0SD

**(T)** 01704 893 237     **Manager:** Derek Goulding

2012-13 Squad

## Club Factfile

**Founded:** 1946     **Nickname:** Linnets

**Previous Names:** None

**Previous Leagues:** Liverpool County Combination 1946-53, Lancashire Combination 1953-70, Cheshire County 1970-82, North West Counties 1982-98, Northern Premier League 1998-2007, Conference 2007-09

**Club Colours (change):** All green (Sky blue/navy/sky)

**Ground Capacity:** 2,500     **Seats:** 270     **Covered:** 1,000     **Clubhouse:** Yes     **Shop:** Yes

**Directions:** M6 to J27. Follow signs for 'Parbold' (A5209), carry on through Newburgh into Burscough passing Briars Hall Hotel on left. Turn right at second mini-roundabout into Junction Lane (signposted 'Burscough & Martin Mere') into village, over canal. Take second left into Mart Lane to ground at end.

**Previous Grounds:** None

**Record Attendance:** 4,798 v Wigan Athletic - FA Cup 3rd Qualifying Round 1950-51

**Record Victory:** 10-0 v Cromptons Rec - 1947 and v Nelson - 1948-49 both Lancashire Combination

**Record Defeat:** 0-9 v Earltown - Liverpool County Combination 1948-49

**Record Goalscorer:** Wes Bridge - 188

**Record Appearances:** Not known

**Additional Records:** Johnny Vincent scored 60 goals during the 1953-64 season

**Senior Honours:** Louis Bimpson scored 7 goals in one game.

North West Counties League Division 1 1982-83. FA Trophy 2002-03. Northern Premier League Premier Division 2006-07. Liverpool Challenge Cup x3. Liverpool Non-League Senior Cup x2.

### 10 YEAR RECORD

| 03-04 | | 04-05 | | 05-06 | | 06-07 | | 07-08 | | 08-09 | | 09-10 | | 10-11 | | 11-12 | | 12-13 | |
|---|---|---|---|---|---|---|---|---|---|---|---|---|---|---|---|---|---|---|---|
| NP P | 19 | NP P | 6 | NP P | 7 | NP P | 1 | Conf N | 8 | Conf N | 21 | NP P | 16 | NP P | 19 | NP P | 22 | NP1N | 11 |

# CAMMELL LAIRD

**Chairman:** Frank Games
**Secretary:** Anthony R Wood     **(T)** 07931 761 429     **(E)** toddywood@hotmail.com
**Commercial Manager:** Philip Wilkinson     **(T)** 07598 090 077
**Programme Editor:** Mark Ridgeway     **(T)** 07807 758 473
**Ground Address:** Kirklands, St Peter's Road, Rock Ferry, Birkenhead CH42 1PY
**(T)** 0151 645 3121     **Manager:** Tony Sullivan

Cammell Laird Football Club 2012/13

## Club Factfile

**Founded:** 1907     **Nickname:** Lairds
**Previous Names:** Kirklands 1922-44.
**Previous Leagues:** West Cheshire, North West Counties

**Club Colours (change):** All royal blue (All yellow)

**Ground Capacity:** 2,000     **Seats:** 150     **Covered:** Yes     **Clubhouse:** Yes     **Shop:** Yes

**Directions**
FROM CHESTER: M53, leave at Junction 5, take third exit on to A41 and travel towards Birkenhead. At New Ferry signpost take B5136 towards New Ferry. After approx 1 mile at sign for Lairds Sports Club, turn right down Proctor Road, ground on the left. FROM LIVERPOOL: Take the Birkenhead Tunnel then A41 signposted North Wales for approx 1 mile. At large roundabout take B5136 signposted New Ferry, Rock Ferry. Follow until 2nd set of traffic lights at Abbotsford pub. Turn left then first right into St Peters Road. Ground at bottom of road on right.

**Previous Grounds:** Prenton Park. Park Road North. Bebington Oval >1922.

**Record Attendance:** 1,700 v Harwich & Parkeston - FA Vase 5th Round 1990-91
**Record Victory:** Not known
**Record Defeat:** Not known
**Record Goalscorer:** Not known
**Record Appearances:** Not known
**Additional Records:**

**Senior Honours:**
North West Counties League Division 2, League Cup and Trophy 2004-05, Division 1 2005-06.
West Cheshire League x19 (Most recently 2000-01). Cheshire Amateur Cup x11.
Wirral Senior Cup.

### 10 YEAR RECORD

| 03-04 | | 04-05 | | 05-06 | | 06-07 | | 07-08 | | 08-09 | | 09-10 | | 10-11 | | 11-12 | | 12-13 | |
|---|---|---|---|---|---|---|---|---|---|---|---|---|---|---|---|---|---|---|---|
| WCh1 | 2 | NWC2 | 1 | NWC1 | 1 | NP 1 | 2 | NP1S | 2 | NP P | 18 | NP1S | 16 | NP1N | 19 | NP1N | 22 | NP1N | 2 |

# CLITHEROE

**Chairman:** Anne Barker
**Secretary:** Colin Wilson          **(T)** 07979 592 238          **(E)** wilsoncfc424370@aol.com
**Commercial Manager:**                              **(T)**
**Programme Editor:** Chris Musson              **(T)** 01254 245 461
**Ground Address:** Shawbridge, off Pendle Road, Clitheroe, Lancashire BB7 1DZ
**(T)** 01200 444 487                              **Manager:** Paul Moore

2012-13 Squad - Back Row (L-R): Kirsty McKillop, Dave Hughes, Jon Stevenson, Chris Smalley, Andy Naylor, Danny Bell, Jack Higgins, Hakan Burton, Will James, Jordan Williams, Rob Flint, Simon Nangle, Paul Moore.
Front Row (L-R): Lee Pugh, Richard Mottram, Louis Edwards, James Gardner, Connor Smith, Marcus Calvert, Ross Dent, Ollie Devenney, Alex Johnson, Alex Johnson.

## Club Factfile

**Founded:** 1877          **Nickname:** The Blues
**Previous Names:** Clitheroe Central 1877-1903.
**Previous Leagues:** Blackburn & District, Lancashire Combination 1903-04, 05-10, 25-82, North West Counties 1982-85

**Club Colours (change):** Royal Blue/royal blue/red (All red)

**Ground Capacity:** 2,400   **Seats:** 250   **Covered:** 1,400   **Clubhouse:** Yes   **Shop:**

**Directions:** M6 junction 31, A59 to Clitheroe (17 miles) at 5th roundabout turn left after half a mile at Pendle Road. Ground is one mile behind Bridge Inn on the right.

**Previous Grounds:** None

**Record Attendance:** 2,050 v Mangotsfield - FA Vase Semi-final 1995-96
**Record Victory:** Not known
**Record Defeat:** Not known
**Record Goalscorer:** Don Francis
**Record Appearances:** Lindsey Wallace - 670
**Additional Records:** Received £45,000 from Crystal Palace for Carlo Nash

**Senior Honours:**
North West Counties League 1984-85, 2003-04.
Lancashire Challenge Trophy 1984-85. East Lancashire Floodlit Trophy 1994-95.

### 10 YEAR RECORD

| 03-04 | | 04-05 | | 05-06 | | 06-07 | | 07-08 | | 08-09 | | 09-10 | | 10-11 | | 11-12 | | 12-13 | |
|---|---|---|---|---|---|---|---|---|---|---|---|---|---|---|---|---|---|---|---|
| NWC1 | 1 | NP 1 | 19 | NP 1 | 16 | NP 1 | 16 | NP1N | 13 | NP1N | 12 | NP1N | 8 | NP1N | 6 | NP1N | 19 | NP1N | 8 |

# CURZON ASHTON

**Chairman:** Harry Galloway
**Secretary:** Robert Hurst    **(T)** 07713 252 310    **(E)** rob@curzon-ashton.co.uk
**Commercial Manager:** Wayne Salkeld    **(T)**
**Programme Editor:** Ian Seymour    **(T)** 07908 721 003
**Ground Address:** Tameside Stadium, Richmond Street, Ashton-u-Lyme OL7 9HG
**(T)** 0161 330 6033      **Manager:** John Flanagan

## Club Factfile

**Founded:** 1963     **Nickname:** Curzon
**Previous Names:** Club formed when Curzon Road and Ashton Amateurs merged.
**Previous Leagues:** Manchester Amateur, Manchester > 1978, Cheshire County 1978-82,
North West Counties 1982-87, 98-2007, Northern Premier 1987-97, Northern Counties East 1997-98,

**Club Colours (change):** All royal blue (All red)

**Ground Capacity:** 4,000    **Seats:** 527    **Covered:** 1,100    **Clubhouse:** Yes    **Shop:** Yes

**Directions**
From Stockport (south) direction Leave the M60 at junc 23 (Ashton-U-Lyne). Turn left at the top of the slip road, go straight through the next set of lights, and bear right (onto Lord Sheldon Way) at the next set. Continue on this road until you come to a set of traffic lights with the Cineworld Cinema on your right. Turn left here onto Richmond St. Over the bridge, across the mini-roundabout and then first left down to the ground. From Oldham (north) direction Leave the M60 at junc 23 (Ashton-U-Lyne) and turn right at the top of the slip road signposted A635 Manchester. Turn right at the second set of traffic lights, sign posted Ashton Moss, and then follow directions as from the south.

**Previous Grounds:** Katherine Street > 204, Stalybridge Celtic FC 2004-06

**Record Attendance:** 1,826 v Stamford - FA Vase Semi-final
**Record Victory:** 7-0 v Ashton United
**Record Defeat:** 0-8 v Bamber Bridge
**Record Goalscorer:** Alan Sykes
**Record Appearances:** Alan Sykes
**Additional Records:**

**Senior Honours:**
Manchester Premier Cup x5

### 10 YEAR RECORD

| 03-04 | | 04-05 | | 05-06 | | 06-07 | | 07-08 | | 08-09 | | 09-10 | | 10-11 | | 11-12 | | 12-13 | |
|-------|--|-------|--|-------|--|-------|--|-------|--|-------|--|-------|--|-------|--|-------|--|-------|--|
| NWC1 | 7 | NWC1 | 4 | NWC1 | 7 | NWC1 | 2 | NP1N | 4 | NP1N | 4 | NP1N | 3 | NP1N | 4 | NP1N | 2 | NP1N | 7 |

# DARLINGTON 1883

**Chairman:** Martin Jesper
**Secretary:** Harry Dunn **(T)** 07807 831 299 **(E)** secretary@dfc1883.co.uk
**Commercial Manager:** **(T)**
**Programme Editor:** Ray Simpson **(T)** 07976 434 111
**Ground Address:** Bishop Auckland FC, Heritage Park, Bishop Auckland, Co. Durham DL14 9AE
**(T)** 01388 604 605 **Manager:** Martin Gray

## Club Factfile

**Founded:** 1883 **Nickname:** The Quakers
**Previous Names:** Darlington FC 1883-2012
**Previous Leagues:** Northern League 1883-1908, 2012-13, North Eastern 1908-21, Football League 1921-89, 91-2010, Conference 1989-90, 10-12.
**Club Colours (change):** White & black hoops/black/black (Pink/dark blue/dark blue)

**Ground Capacity:** **Seats:** **Covered:** **Clubhouse:** Yes **Shop:** Yes

**Directions:** Leave the A1(m) at junction 57 for Darlington. Follow road to roundabout. From here take the first exit off and follow road to second roundabout (Reg Vardy on right). Head straight over and follow signs for Teesside until you reach next roundabout. Turn left here and stadium is on right hand side.

**Previous Grounds:** Feethams > 2003, Reynolds Arena, Hurworth Moor.

**Record Attendance: Record Att:** 21,023 v Bolton Wanderers - League Cup 3rd Round 14/11/1960
**Record Victory:** 9-2 v Lincoln City - Division 3 North 07/01/1928
**Record Defeat:** 0-10 v Doncaster Rovers - Division 4 25/01/1964
**Record Goalscorer:** Alan Walsh - 100, Jerry Best - 80
**Record Appearances:** Ron Greener - 490, John Peverell - 465, Brian Henderson - 463
**Additional Records:** Paid £95,000 to Motherwell for Nick Cusack January 1992.
**Senior Honours:** Received £400,000 from Dundee United for Jason Devos October 1998
Northern League 1895-96, 99-1900, 2012-13. North Eastern League 1912-13, 20-21. Football League Division 3 1924-25, Division 4 1990-91, Division 3 North Cup 1933-34. Durham Senior Cup 1919-20. FA Trophy 2010-11.

### 10 YEAR RECORD

| 03-04 | | 04-05 | | 05-06 | | 06-07 | | 07-08 | | 08-09 | | 09-10 | | 10-11 | | 11-12 | | 12-13 | |
|---|---|---|---|---|---|---|---|---|---|---|---|---|---|---|---|---|---|---|---|
| FL 3 | 18 | FL 2 | 8 | FL 2 | 8 | FL 2 | 11 | FL 2 | 6 | FL 2 | 12 | FL 2 | 24 | Conf | 7 | Conf | 22 | NL 1 | 1 |

**NORTHERN PREMIER DIVISION ACTION:** Spencer (FCUM) pushes Gardner's (Witton) spot kick onto the crossbar.
Photo: Keith Clayton.

# FARSLEY A.F.C.

**Chairman:** John Palmer
**Secretary:** Joshua Greaves   **(T)** 07725 999 758   **(E)** office@farsleyafc.com
**Commercial Manager:** Margaret Palmer   **(T)**
**Programme Editor:** Martin Knox   **(T)** 0113 255 7292
**Ground Address:** Throstle Nest, Newlands, Pudsey, Leeds, LS28 5BE
**(T)** 0113 255 7292   **Manager:** Neil Parsley

2012-13 Squad.

## Club Factfile

**Founded:** 2010   **Nickname:** The Villagers
**Previous Names:** Farsley Celtic > 2010
**Previous Leagues:** Northern Counties East 2010-11.

**Club Colours (change):** Blue & white/blue/white (Yellow, blue & white/blue/blue)

**Ground Capacity:** 4,000   **Seats:** 300   **Covered:** 1,500   **Clubhouse:** Yes   **Shop:** Yes

**Directions**
Farsley is sandwiched between Leeds and Bradford approximately 1 mile from the junction of the Leeds Outer Ring Road (A6110) and the A647 towards Bradford. At the junction, take the B6157 towards Leeds, passing the police station on the left hand side. At New Street (the junction cornered by Go Outdoors) turn left. Newlands is approximately 300 yards on the right. Throstle Nest is situated at the end of Newlands with parking available outside the ground.

**Previous Grounds:** None

**Record Attendance:**
**Record Victory:** 8-0 v Arnold Town (H) Northern Counties East Premier 2010-11.
**Record Defeat:** 5-1 v Tadcaster Albion, President's Cup Final 27/04/11.
**Record Goalscorer:** Not known
**Record Appearances:** Not known
**Additional Records:** None

**Senior Honours:**
Northern Counties East Premier Division 2010-11.

### 10 YEAR RECORD

| 03-04 | 04-05 | 05-06 | 06-07 | 07-08 | 08-09 | 09-10 | 10-11 | | 11-12 | | 12-13 | |
|-------|-------|-------|-------|-------|-------|-------|-------|---|-------|---|-------|----|
| | | | | | | | NCEP | 1 | NP1N | 4 | NP1N | 14 |

# HARROGATE RAILWAY ATHLETIC

**Chairman:** Alan Smith

**Secretary:** Michael Sunley          **(T)** 07970 447 823          **(E)** mike.sunley@btinternet.com

**Commercial Manager:**                                      **(T)**

**Programme Editor:** Michael Sunley                 **(T)** 07970 447 823

**Ground Address:** Station View, Starbeck, Harrogate, North Yorkshire HG2 7JA

**(T)** 01423 883 104                              **Manager:** Billy Miller

## Club Factfile

**Founded:** 1935       **Nickname:** The Rail

**Previous Names:** None

**Previous Leagues:** West Yorkshire, Harrogate & District, Yorkshire 1955-73, 80-82, Northern Counties East 1982-2006

**Club Colours (change):** Red/green/red (All blue)

**Ground Capacity:** 3,500   **Seats:** 800   **Covered:** 600   **Clubhouse:** Yes   **Shop:** No

**Directions:** From All Areas I would suggest using the M1 A1 Link Road heading North. Once on the A1 North stay on it until Junction 47. Exit at Junction 47 and take the 1st Exit at the Roundabout A59 heading towards Knaresborough and Harrogate. At the next Roundabout take the 3rd exit A59 Knaresborough. Stay on the A59 through Knaresborough and on towards Harrogate, after approx 1 mile from Knaresborough you will enter Starbeck. Proceed through Starbeck over the Railway Crossing. Station View is the 1st Right after the Railway Crossing. The Ground is at the far end of Station View. If you are coming from Harrogate towards Knaresborough on the A59 turn left immediately prior to pelican crossing just before the Railway Crossing. The Ground is at the far end of Station View.

**Previous Grounds:** None

**Record Attendance:** 3,500 v Bristol City - FA Cup 2nd Round 2002-03

**Record Victory:** Not known

**Record Defeat:** Not known

**Record Goalscorer:** Not known

**Record Appearances:** Not known

**Additional Records:** Received £1,000 from Guiseley for Colin Hunter

**Senior Honours:**

Northern Counties East Division 2 North & League cup 1983-84, Division 1 1989-99.

| 10 YEAR RECORD | | | | | | | | | |
|---|---|---|---|---|---|---|---|---|---|
| 03-04 | 04-05 | 05-06 | 06-07 | 07-08 | 08-09 | 09-10 | 10-11 | 11-12 | 12-13 |
| NCEP 12 | NCEP 3 | NCEP 3 | NP 1 12 | NP1N 12 | NP1N 18 | NP1N 17 | NP1N 20 | NP1N 21 | NP1N 18 |

# KENDAL TOWN

**Chairman:** Haydon Munslow
**Secretary:** Craig Campbell    **(T)** 07980 660 428    **(E)** info@kendaltownfootballclub.co.uk
**Commercial Manager:** Graham O'Callaghan    **(T)**
**Programme Editor:** Merrill Tummey    **(T)** 07733 135 796
**Ground Address:** The Northgate Stadium, Parkside Road, Kendal, Cumbria LA9 7BL
**(T)** 01539 727 472      **Manager:** Steve Edmondson

KENDAL TOWN F.C.

## Club Factfile

**Founded:** 1919    **Nickname:** Town
**Previous Names:** Netherfield AFC 1919-2000
**Previous Leagues:** Westmorland, North Lancashire Combination 1945-68, Northern Premier 1968-83,
North West Counties 1983-87

**Club Colours (change):** Black and white stripes/black/red (All sky blue)

**Ground Capacity:** 2,490   **Seats:** 450    **Covered:** 1000    **Clubhouse:** Yes   **Shop:** Yes

**Directions:** M6 junction 36, via A590/591/A6 to Kendal (South). At first traffic lights turn right, left at roundabout, right into Parkside Road.
Ground on right over brow of hill.

**Previous Grounds:** None

**Record Attendance:** 5,184 v Grimsby Town - FA Cup 1st Round 1955
**Record Victory:** 11-0 v Great Harwood - 22/03/1947
**Record Defeat:** 0-10 v Stalybridge Celtic - 01/09/1984
**Record Goalscorer:** Tom Brownlee
**Record Appearances:** Not known
**Additional Records:** Received £10,250 from Manchester City for Andy Milner 1995

**Senior Honours:**
Westmorlands Senior Cup x12. Lancashire Senior Cup 2002-03.

### 10 YEAR RECORD

| 03-04 | | 04-05 | | 05-06 | | 06-07 | | 07-08 | | 08-09 | | 09-10 | | 10-11 | | 11-12 | | 12-13 | |
|---|---|---|---|---|---|---|---|---|---|---|---|---|---|---|---|---|---|---|---|
| NP 1 | 21 | NP 1 | 5 | NP 1 | 3 | NP P | 19 | NP P | 11 | NP P | 5 | NP P | 5 | NP P | 8 | NP P | 11 | NP P | 21 |

# LANCASTER CITY

**Chairman:** Stuart Houghton
**Secretary:** Barry Newsham    **(T)** 07759 530 901    **(E)** lancastercityfc@btinternet.com
**Commercial Manager:** Jim Johnstone    **(T)** 07551 642 343
**Programme Editor:** Andrew Satterthwaite    **(T)** 07947 145 915
**Ground Address:** Giant Axe, West Road, Lancaster LA1 5PE
**(T)** 01524 382 238    **Manager:** Darren Peacock

## Club Factfile

**Founded:** 1905    **Nickname:** Dolly Blues
**Previous Names:** None
**Previous Leagues:** Lancashire Combination 1905-70, Northern Premier League 1970-82, 87-2004,
North West Counties 1982-87, Conference 2004-07

**Club Colours (change):** Blue/white/blue (Yellow/blue/yellow)

**Ground Capacity:** 3,064    **Seats:** 513    **Covered:** 900    **Clubhouse:** Yes    **Shop:** Yes

**Directions:** From the South: Exit M6 at Junction 33. At roundabout take the second exit onto the A6, pass through Galgate and then Lancaster University on the right until the next roundabout. Take the second main exit into Lancaster and follow signs for the railway station. At the traffic lights by Waterstones Bookshop turn immediately left. Take the second right onto Station Road and follow downhill on West Road and take the first right into the ground. From the North: Exit M6 at Junction 34 and turn left onto the A683. Follow signs for railway station into City around the one way system. Move over to the right hand side lane at the police station and through traffic lights. Manoeuvre into the left-hand lane until traffic lights at Waterstones Bookshop. Follow directions as from the south.

**Previous Grounds:** None

**Record Attendance:** 7,500 v Carlisle United - FA Cup 1936
**Record Victory:** 8-0 v Leyland Motors (A) - 1983-84
**Record Defeat:** 0-10 v Matlock Town - Northern Premier League Division 1 1973-74
**Record Goalscorer:** David Barnes - 130
**Record Appearances:** Edgar J Parkinson - 591
**Additional Records:** Paid £6,000 to Droylsden for Jamie Tandy
Received £25,000 from Birmingham City for Chris Ward
**Senior Honours:**
Lancashire Junior Cup (ATS Challenge Trophy) 1927-28, 28-29, 30-31, 33-34, 51-52, 74-75.
Northern Premier League Division 1 1995-96.

### 10 YEAR RECORD

| 03-04 | | 04-05 | | 05-06 | | 06-07 | | 07-08 | | 08-09 | | 09-10 | | 10-11 | | 11-12 | | 12-13 | |
|---|---|---|---|---|---|---|---|---|---|---|---|---|---|---|---|---|---|---|---|
| NP P | 8 | Conf N | 13 | Conf N | 15 | Conf N | 24 | NP1N | 11 | NP1N | 7 | NP1N | 2 | NP1N | 8 | NP1N | 6 | NP1N | 13 |

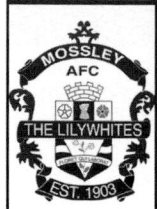

# MOSSLEY

**Chairman:** Vacant
**Secretary:** Harry Hulmes    **(T)** 07944 856 343    **(E)** harry.hulmes@mossleyafc.com
**Commercial Manager:** Steve Burgess    **(T)** steve@mobilevehiclesolutions.co.uk
**Programme Editor:** John Cawthorne    **(T)** 01457 511 053
**Ground Address:** Seel Park, Market Street, Mossley, Lancashire OL5 0ES
**(T)** 01457 832 369                    **Manager:** Peter Band & Lloyd Morrison

## Club Factfile

**Founded:** 1903    **Nickname:** Lilywhites
**Previous Names:** Park Villa 1903-04, Mossley Juniors
**Previous Leagues:** Ashton, South East Lancashire, Lancashire Combination 1918-19, Cheshire County 1919-72,
Northern Premier 1972-95, North West Counties 1995-2004

**Club Colours (change):** White/black/white (All orange)

**Ground Capacity:** 4,500    **Seats:** 200    **Covered:** 1,500    **Clubhouse:** Yes    **Shop:** Yes

**Directions** Exit M60 Junction 23 following A635 Ashton-under-Lyne. Take 3rd exit off roundabout then 3rd exit off next roundabout (Asda) and then 3rd exit off next roundabout signed Mossley A670. At junction turn right on to Mossley Rd through traffic lights. After approx 2.5 miles drop down hill entering Mossley town centre. Passing supermarket on left turn right before next traffic lights. Continue up the hill and left into Market Street. Ground is approx 200 yards on the left.

**Previous Grounds:** None

**Record Attendance:** 7,000 v Stalybridge Celtic 1950
**Record Victory:** Not known
**Record Defeat:** Not known
**Record Goalscorer:** David Moore - 235 (1974-84)
**Record Appearances:** Jimmy O'Connor - 613 (1972-87)
**Additional Records:** Paid £2,300 to Altrincham for Phil Wilson
**Senior Honours:**    Received £25,000 from Everton for Eamonn O'Keefe
Northern Premier League 1978-79, 79-80, Challenge Cup 78-79, Division 1 2005-06.
Manchester Challenge Trophy 2011-12. Manchester Premier Cup 2012-13.

### 10 YEAR RECORD

| 03-04 | | 04-05 | | 05-06 | | 06-07 | | 07-08 | | 08-09 | | 09-10 | | 10-11 | | 11-12 | | 12-13 | |
|---|---|---|---|---|---|---|---|---|---|---|---|---|---|---|---|---|---|---|---|
| NWC1 | 2 | NP 1 | 7 | NP 1 | 1 | NP P | 20 | NP1N | 15 | NP1N | 10 | NP1N | 7 | NP1N | 15 | NP1N | 14 | NP1N | 5 |

# NEW MILLS

**Chairman:** Raymond Coverley
**Secretary:** Duncan Hibbert    **(T)** 07957 482 343    **(E)** newmillsfs@yahoo.co.uk
**Commercial Manager:** n/a    **(T)**
**Programme Editor:** Chris Culkin    **(T)** 07920 054 316
**Ground Address:** Church Lane, New Mills, SK22 4NP
**(T)** 01663 747 435    **Manager:** Roy Soule

## Club Factfile

**Founded:** pre1890    **Nickname:** The Millers
**Previous Names:** New Mills St Georges until 1919
**Previous Leagues:** Manchester, North West Counties, Cheshire

**Club Colours (change):** Amber/amber/black (White/white/black).

**Ground Capacity:** 1,650    **Seats:** 120    **Covered:** 400    **Clubhouse:** Yes    **Shop:**

**Directions**

Via Buxton: Follow the A6 By-Pass, go straight through the roundabout, under railway bridge and about 1 mile further on turn right onto Marsh Lane (Past Furness Vale primary school), this road takes you straight to the ground. Coach drivers should proceed on the A6 a couple of miles turning right opposite the Swan.

From Chesterfield, take the A619 then the A623 and after the hair pin bend at Sparrow pit, proceed down the A623 turning right onto the A6 By-Pass, Follow directions as above.

**Previous Grounds:** Not known

**Record Attendance: Att:** 4,500 v Hyde United, Manchester Junior Cup 09/09/1922
**Record Victory:** 20-3 v Winton United, Manchester Junior Cup 10/11/1962
**Record Defeat:** Not known
**Record Goalscorer:** In a season - Neville Holdgate - 62 1937-38
**Record Appearances:** Not known
**Additional Records:**

**Senior Honours:**
Manchester League Premier Division 1924, 26, 56, 63, 65, 66, 67, 68, 70, 71.
North West Counties Division Two 2007-08, Challenge Cup 2008-09, Premier Division 2010-11.

## 10 YEAR RECORD

| 03-04 | 04-05 | 05-06 | 06-07 | 07-08 | 08-09 | 09-10 | 10-11 | 11-12 | 12-13 |
|---|---|---|---|---|---|---|---|---|---|
| MancP 14 | NWC2 9 | NWC2 12 | NWC2 | NWC2 1 | NWCP 2 | NWCP 2 | NWCP 1 | NP1S 9 | NP1N 3 |

# NORTHWICH VICTORIA

**Chairman:** James Rushe

**Secretary:** Dave Thomas    **(T)** 07798 564 596    **(E)** admin@northwichvics.co.uk

**Commercial Manager:**      **(T)**

**Programme Editor:** David Thomas    **(T)** 07798 564 596

**Ground Address:** Flixton FC, Valley Road, Flixton, Manchester M41 8RQ

**(T)** 0161 458 2903        **Manager:** Lee Ashcroft

## Club Factfile

**Founded:** 1874    **Nickname:** Vics, Greens or Trickies

**Previous Names:** None

**Previous Leagues:** The Combination 1890-92, 1894-98, Football League 1892-94, Cheshire 1898-1900, Manchester 1900-12
Lancashire 1912-19, Cheshire County 1919-68, Northern Premier 1968-79, Conference 1979-2010

**Club Colours (change):** Green and white hoops/white/white (Yellow/blue/blue)

**Ground Capacity:** 6,000   **Seats:** 4,264   **Covered:** 3,500   **Clubhouse:** Yes   **Shop:** Yes

**Directions**

Leave M60 at junction 10, take B5214 signposted Urmston. At second roundabout take 3rd exit, take right only lane on the exit on Daveyhulme Road. Follow this road to Valley Road. Just after left hand bend, 1.5miles. Ground is at far end of the road.

**Previous Grounds:** The Drill Field. Victoria Stadium. Stafford Rangers FC.

**Record Attendance:** 11,290 v Witton Albion - Cheshire League Good Friday 1949

**Record Victory:** 17-0 v Marple Association 1883

**Record Defeat:** 3-10 v Port Vale - 1931

**Record Goalscorer:** Peter Burns - 160 (1955-65)

**Record Appearances:** Ken Jones - 970 (1969-85)

**Additional Records:** Paid £12,000 to Hyde United for Malcolm O'Connor August 1988. Received £50,000 from Leyton Orient for Gary Fletcher June 1921 and from Chester City for Neil Morton October 1990.

**Senior Honours:**
FA Trophy 1983-84.
Conference North 2005-06.
Cheshire Senior Cup x15. Staffordshire Senior Cup x3.

### 10 YEAR RECORD

| 03-04 | | 04-05 | | 05-06 | | 06-07 | | 07-08 | | 08-09 | | 09-10 | | 10-11 | | 11-12 | | 12-13 | |
|---|---|---|---|---|---|---|---|---|---|---|---|---|---|---|---|---|---|---|---|
| Conf | 22 | Conf | 19 | Conf N | 1 | Conf | 13 | Conf | 19 | Conf | 22 | Conf N | 12 | NP P | 12 | NP P | 2 | NP1S | 8 |

# OSSETT ALBION

**Chairman:** Steven Hanks
**Secretary:** Alan Nash     **(T)** 07585 952 295    **(E)** ossettalbion@sky.com
**Commercial Manager:**                  **(T)**
**Programme Editor:** Stephen Hanks     **(T)** 07792 221 088
**Ground Address:** The Warehouse Systems Stadium, Dimple Wells, Ossett, Yorkshire WF5 8JU
**(T)** 01924 273 746           **Manager:** Richard Tracey

2012-13 Squad - Back Row (L-R): S.Holt, R.Tracey, T.Corner, K.Quinn, J.Barford, H.Owen, D.Kelly, J.Mycoe, J.Fox, R.Haslem(Physio)
Front Row: S.Poole, D.Lucas, K.Noble, A.Hayton, S.Nicholson, A.Guiry,
M.Thompson

## Club Factfile

**Founded:** 1944     **Nickname:** Albion
**Previous Names:** Not known
**Previous Leagues:** Heavy Woollen Area 1944-49, West Riding County Amateur 1949-50, West Yorkshire 1950-57,
Yorkshire 1957-82, Northern Counties East 1982-2004

**Club Colours (change):** Gold/black/black (All white)

**Ground Capacity:** 3,000   **Seats:** Yes    **Covered:** 750    **Clubhouse:** Yes    **Shop:** Yes

**Directions:** From M1 Junction 40: Follow Wakefield signs for 200 yards. Turn right at traffic lights (Holiday Inn on the corner). At the end of Queens Drive turn right and then 2nd left onto Southdale Road. At the end of Southdale Road turn right then immediately left onto Dimple Wells Road, the ground is facing. NOTE: There is a weight limit on Southdale Road. Coaches will need to continue on Station Road to the end, turn left, then at the end left again. Take 1st right onto Priory Road following for 200 yards turning left twice.

**Previous Grounds:** Fearn House

**Record Attendance:** 1,200 v Leeds United - Opening of floodlights 1986
**Record Victory:** 12-0 v British Ropes (H) - Yorkshire League Division 2 06/05/1959
**Record Defeat:** 2-11 v Swillington (A) - West Yorkshire League Division 1 25/04/1956
**Record Goalscorer:** John Balmer
**Record Appearances:** Peter Eaton - 800+ (22 years)
**Additional Records:**

**Senior Honours:**
Northern Counties East League Division 1 1986-87, Premier Division 1998-99, 2003-04, League Cup 1983-84, 2002-03.
West Riding County Cup x4.

### 10 YEAR RECORD

| 03-04 | | 04-05 | | 05-06 | | 06-07 | | 07-08 | | 08-09 | | 09-10 | | 10-11 | | 11-12 | | 12-13 | |
|---|---|---|---|---|---|---|---|---|---|---|---|---|---|---|---|---|---|---|---|
| NCEP | 1 | NP 1 | 12 | NP 1 | 14 | NP 1 | 11 | NP1N | 6 | NP1N | 6 | NP1N | 21 | NP1N | 22 | NP1N | 18 | NP1N | 20 |

# OSSETT TOWN

**Chairman:** Graham Firth
**Secretary:** Jacqueline Seed    **(T)** 07936 701 449    **(E)** ossetttownfc@gmail.com
**Commercial Manager:** Graham Willis    **(T)** 01924 266 393
**Programme Editor:** Neil Spofforth    **(T)** 07818 400 808
**Ground Address:** Ingfield, Prospect Road, Ossett, Wakefield WF5 9HA
**(T)** 01924 280 028    **Manager:** Craig Elliott

## Club Factfile

**Founded:** 1936    **Nickname:** Town
**Previous Names:** None
**Previous Leagues:** Leeds 1936-39, Yorkshire 1945-82, Northern Counties East 1983-99

**Club Colours (change):** All red (All blue)

**Ground Capacity:** 4,000    **Seats:** 360    **Covered:** 1,000    **Clubhouse:** Yes    **Shop:** Yes

**Directions**
From M1 Junction 40: Take A638 signposted Ossett Town Centre. Take first left off A638 onto Wakefield Road, sixth left turn into Dale Street (B6120) to traffic lights. Turn left at lights. The Ground is in front of you opposite the bus station. The entrance to the Ground is just before the Esso petrol station.

**Previous Grounds:** Wakefield Road 1936-39. Back Lane.

**Record Attendance:** 2,600 v Manchester United - Friendly 1989
**Record Victory:** 10-1 v Harrogate RA (H) - Northern Counties East 27/04/1993
**Record Defeat:** 0-7 v Easington Colliery - FA Vase 08/10/1983
**Record Goalscorer:** Dave Leadbitter
**Record Appearances:** Steve Worsfold
**Additional Records:** Received £1,350 from Swansea Town for Dereck Blackburn

**Senior Honours:**
West Riding County Cup 1958-59, 81-82

### 10 YEAR RECORD

| 03-04 | 04-05 | 05-06 | 06-07 | 07-08 | 08-09 | 09-10 | 10-11 | 11-12 | 12-13 |
|---|---|---|---|---|---|---|---|---|---|
| NP 1  14 | NP P  16 | NP P  11 | NP P  10 | NP P  18 | NP P  12 | NP P  19 | NP P  21 | NP1N  17 | NP1N  12 |

# PADIHAM

**Chairman:** Frank Heys
**Secretary:** Alan Smith    **(T)** 0777 571 7698    **(E)** alansmithpadihamfc@yahoo.co.uk
**Commercial Manager:**                  **(T)**
**Programme Editor:** Alan Smith        **(T)** 0777 571 7698
**Ground Address:** Arbories Memorial Sports Ground, Well Street, Padiham BB12 8LE
**(T)** 0777 571 7698               **Manager:** Steve Wilkes

## Club Factfile

**Founded:** 1878     **Nickname:** Caldersiders
**Previous Names:** None
**Previous Leagues:** Lancashire Combination. East Lancashire Amateur. North East Lancashire. West Lancashire. North West Counties > 2013.

**Club Colours (change):** All royal blue. (Red/white/black).

**Ground Capacity:** 1,688    **Seats:** 159    **Covered:** Yes    **Clubhouse:** Yes    **Shop:**

**Directions:** M65 to Junction 8, then follow A6068 signposted Clitheroe and Padiham. At traffic lights at bottom of hill turn right into Dean Range/Blackburn Road towards Padiham. At next junction turn into Holland Street opposite church, then into Well St at the side of Hare & Hounds Pub to ground.

**Previous Grounds:** Wyre Street 1878-1916.

**Record Attendance:** Att: 9,000 v Burnley, Dec.1884 (at Calderside Ground).
**Record Victory:**
**Record Defeat:**
**Record Goalscorer:**
**Record Appearances:**
**Additional Records:**

**Senior Honours:**
West Lancashire League 1999-00. North West Counties League 2012-13.

| | | | | | 10 YEAR RECORD | | | | | |
|---|---|---|---|---|---|---|---|---|---|---|
| 03-04 | 04-05 | 05-06 | 06-07 | 07-08 | 08-09 | 09-10 | 10-11 | 11-12 | 12-13 | |
| NWC2 12 | NWC2 4 | NWC2 5 | NWC2 3 | NWC2 12 | NWC1 2 | NWCP 10 | NWCP 4 | NWCP 15 | NWCP 1 | |

# PRESCOT CABLES

**Chairman:** Tony Zeverona

**Secretary:** Doug Lace    **(T)** 07753 143 273    **(E)** prescotcables@hotmail.com

**Commercial Manager:**    **(T)**

**Programme Editor:** Paul Watkinson    **(T)** 0151 426 4593

**Ground Address:** Valerie Park, Eaton Street, Prescot L34 6HD

**(T)** 0151 430 0507    **Manager:** David Powell

2012-13 Squad.

## Club Factfile

**Founded:** 1884    **Nickname:** Tigers

**Previous Names:** Prescot > 1995

**Previous Leagues:** Liverpool County Combination, Lancashire Combination 1897-98, 1918-20, 27-33, 36-76, Mid Cheshire 1976-78, Cheshire County 1978-82, North West Counties 1982-2003

**Club Colours (change):** Amber/black/black (All red)

**Ground Capacity:** 3,000    **Seats:** 500    **Covered:** 600    **Clubhouse:** Yes    **Shop:** Yes

**Directions**

**From North:** M6 to Junction 26, onto M58 to Junction 3. Follow A570 to junction with A580 (East Lancs Road). (Approach junction in right hand lane of the two lanes going straight on). Cross A580 and take first road on right (Bleak Hill Road). Follow this road through to Prescot (2 miles). At traffic lights turn right, straight on at large roundabout (do not follow route onto Prescot by-pass) and right at next lights. 100 yards turn right at Hope and Anchor pub into Hope Street. Club will be in sight at bottom of road. **From South:** M6 to Junction 21a (M62 junction 10). Follow M62 towards Liverpool, to junction 7. Follow A57 to Rainhill and Prescot. Through traffic lights at Fusilier pub, 100 yards turn right at Hope and Anchor pub (as above). **From East:** Follow M62 as described in 'From South' or A580 East Lancs Road to Junction with A570 (Rainford by-pass), turn left and take first right. Follow route as 'From North'.

**Previous Grounds:** None

**Record Attendance:** 8,122 v Ashton National - 1932

**Record Victory:** 18-3 v Great Harwood - 1954-55

**Record Defeat:** 1-12 v Morecambe - 1936-37

**Record Goalscorer:** Freddie Crampton

**Record Appearances:** Harry Grisedale

**Additional Records:**

**Senior Honours:**
Lancashire Combination 1956-57. North West Counties League 2002-03.
Liverpool Non-League Cup x4. Liverpool Challenge Cup x6.

### 10 YEAR RECORD

| 03-04 | | 04-05 | | 05-06 | | 06-07 | | 07-08 | | 08-09 | | 09-10 | | 10-11 | | 11-12 | | 12-13 | |
|---|---|---|---|---|---|---|---|---|---|---|---|---|---|---|---|---|---|---|---|
| NP 1 | 12 | NP P | 5 | NP P | 13 | NP P | 14 | NP P | 13 | NP P | 22 | NP1N | 15 | NP1N | 21 | NP1N | 16 | NP1N | 17 |

# RADCLIFFE BOROUGH

**Chairman:** Vacant

**Secretary:** Graham Fielding    **(T)** 07407 427 028    **(E)** rbfc@hotmail.co.uk

**Commercial Manager:** TNG Events & Promo'    **(T)**

**Programme Editor:** Graham Fielding    **(T)** 07407 427 028

**Ground Address:** Stainton Park, Pilkington Road, Radcliffe, Lancashire M26 3PE

**(T)** 0161 724 8346    **Manager:** Phil Melville

## Club Factfile

**Founded:** 1949    **Nickname:** Boro

**Previous Names:** None

**Previous Leagues:** South East Lancashire, Manchester 1953-63, Lancashire Combination 1963-71,
Cheshire County 1971-82, North West Counties 1982-97

**Club Colours (change):** All blue (all red)

**Ground Capacity:** 3,100    **Seats:** 350    **Covered:** 1,000    **Clubhouse:** Yes    **Shop:** Yes

**Directions:** M62 junction 17 – follow signs for 'Whitefield' and 'Bury'.
Take A665 to Radcliffe via by-pass to Bolton Road. Signposted to turn right into Unsworth Street opposite Turf Hotel.
The Stadium is on the left approximately half a mile turning Colshaw Close East.

**Previous Grounds:** Ashworth Street. Bright Street > 1970.

**Record Attendance:** 2,495 v York City - FA Cup 1st Round 2000-01

**Record Victory:** Not known

**Record Defeat:** Not known

**Record Goalscorer:** Ian Lunt - 147

**Record Appearances:** David Bean - 401

**Additional Records:** Paid £5,000 to Buxton for Gary Walker 1991
Received £20,000 from Shrewsbury Town for Jody Banim 2003

**Senior Honours:**
North West Counties 19984-85. Northern Premier League Division 1 1996-97.

### 10 YEAR RECORD

| 03-04 | 04-05 | 05-06 | 06-07 | 07-08 | 08-09 | 09-10 | 10-11 | 11-12 | 12-13 |
|---|---|---|---|---|---|---|---|---|---|
| NP P  20 | NP P  9 | NP P  18 | NP P  21 | NP1N  16 | NP1N  16 | NP1N  10 | NP1N  18 | NP1N  15 | NP1N  15 |

**NORTHERN PREMIER LEAGUE ACTION:** Ben harrison (Witton) heads past Spencer in the FCUM goal.
Photo: Keith Clayton.

# RAMSBOTTOM UNITED

**Chairman:** Harry Williams

**Secretary:** Graham Shuttleworth    **(T)** 07966 289 434    **(E)** graham@shuttleworth7.orangehome.co.uk

**Commercial Manager:**    **(T)**

**Programme Editor:** Richard Isaacs    **(T)** 07801 529 515

**Ground Address:** The Harry Williams Stadium, Acrebottom (off Bridge Street) BL0 0BS.

**(T)** 07966 289 434      **Manager:** Anthony Johnson

## Club Factfile

**Founded:** 1966     **Nickname:** The Rams

**Previous Names:** None

**Previous Leagues:** Bury Amateur, Bolton Combination & Manchester League

**Club Colours (change):** Blue/blue/white   (Red/black/red).

| **Ground Capacity:** | **Seats:** Yes | **Covered:** Yes | **Clubhouse:** Yes | **Shop:** No |

**Directions**

From South,M66(north) to junction1,take the A56 towards Ramsbottom, after 1 mile turn left at traffic lights down Bury New Road follow the road towards the centre then turn left just before the railway crossing, ground runs parallel with the railway line.

From the North leave the A56 (Edenfield by pass) at the start of the M66, follow the signs for Ramsbottom into the centre turn left down Bridge street then after 100 yards turn immediately right after the railway level crossing ground parallel with railway line.

**Previous Grounds:**

**Record Attendance: Att:** 1,653 v FC United of Manchester 07.04.2007.

**Record Victory:** 9-0 v Stantondale (Home, NWCFL Division Two, 9th November 1996)

**Record Defeat:** 0-7 v Salford City (Away, NWCFL Division One, 16th November 2002)

**Record Goalscorer:** Russell Brierley - 176 (1996-2003). **Record in a season:** Russell Brierley - 38 (1999-2000)

**Record Appearances:** Not known

**Additional Records:**

**Senior Honours:**

North West Counties Division Two 1996-97, Premier Division 2011-12.

### 10 YEAR RECORD

| 03-04 | | 04-05 | | 05-06 | | 06-07 | | 07-08 | | 08-09 | | 09-10 | | 10-11 | | 11-12 | | 12-13 | |
|---|---|---|---|---|---|---|---|---|---|---|---|---|---|---|---|---|---|---|---|
| NWC1 | 17 | NWC1 | 5 | NWC1 | 18 | NWC1 | 8 | NWC1 | 16 | NWCP | 14 | NWCP | 4 | NWCP | 2 | NWCP | 1 | NP1N | 6 |

# SALFORD CITY

**Chairman:** Karen Baird
**Secretary:** Andrew Giblin        **(T)** 07867 823 713        **(E)** andrewgiblin@aol.com
**Commercial Manager:**                **(T)**
**Programme Editor:** Gareth Lyons        **(T)**
**Ground Address:** Moor Lane, Kersal, Salford, Manchester M7 3PZ
**(T)** 0161 792 6287                **Manager:** Barry Massey & Phil Power

2012-13 Squad - Back Row (L-R): Andy Heald (ex-manager), Ritchie Branagan, Nathan Taylor, Aaron Walters, Rob Kinsella, Nathan McDonald, Harry Bockarie.
Front Row: Adie Bellamy, Rees Welsh, Jamie Rother (c), Kris King, Ryan Briody.

## Club Factfile

**Founded:**  1940        **Nickname:** Ammies
**Previous Names:** Salford Central 1940-63, Salford Amateurs 1963 until merger with Anson Villa, Salford F.C. > 1990
**Previous Leagues:** Manchester 1963-80, Cheshire County 1980-82, North West Counties 1982-2008

**Club Colours (change):** Tangerine/black/tangerine (Sky blue/navy blue/sky)

**Ground Capacity:** 8,000  **Seats:** 260    **Covered:** 600    **Clubhouse:** Yes    **Shop:** No

**Directions**
M62 to Junction 17 (Prestwich, Whitefield). Take A56 Bury New Road towards Manchester.
Continue through four sets of traffic lights.
Turn right into Moor Lane. Ground 500 yards on left.
Take first left after ground (Oaklands Road), first left again into Nevile Road and follow along to main entrance.

**Previous Grounds:**

**Record Attendance:** 3,000 v Whickham - FA Vase 1980
**Record Victory:** Not known
**Record Defeat:** Not known
**Record Goalscorer:** Not known
**Record Appearances:** Not known
**Additional Records:**

**Senior Honours:**
Manchester League Premier Division 1975, 76, 77, 79. North West Counties League Cup 2006.

### 10 YEAR RECORD

| 03-04 | 04-05 | 05-06 | 06-07 | 07-08 | 08-09 | 09-10 | 10-11 | 11-12 | 12-13 |
|---|---|---|---|---|---|---|---|---|---|
| NWC1  15 | NWC1  18 | NWC1  5 | NWC1  4 | NWC1  2 | NP1N  20 | NP1N  11 | NP1N  12 | NP1N  13 | NP1N  16 |

# WAKEFIELD

**Chairman:** Simon Turfrey
**Secretary:** Peter Matthews    **(T)** 0794 382 9818    **(E)** simonturfrey@aol.com
**Commercial Manager:** Dan Brownhill    **(T)**
**Programme Editor:** Dan Brownhill    **(T)** 07921 156 561
**Ground Address:** Wakefield Trinity Wildcats, Belle Vue, Wakefield. WF1 5EY
**(T)** 07921 156 561        **Manager:** Paul Lines

## Club Factfile

**Founded:** 1903    **Nickname:** The Bears
**Previous Names:** Emley AFC 1903-2002, Wakefield & Emley AFC 2002-04, 2004-06 Wakefield - Emley AFC
**Previous Leagues:** Huddersfield > 1969, Yorkshire 1969-82, Northern Counties East 1982-89

**Club Colours (change):** All blue ( All yellow)

**Ground Capacity:**    **Seats:** Yes    **Covered:** Yes    **Clubhouse:** Yes   **Shop:** Nk

**Directions** From Wakefield take A368 – Doncaster Road, Belle Vue is on the left hand side behind Superbowl.

**Previous Grounds:** Welfare Ground 1903-2000, Belle Vue 2000-06. Ingfield 2006-12.

**Record Attendance:** 5,134 v Barking - FA Amateur Cup 3rd Round 01/02/1969 at Welfare Ground
**Record Victory:** 12-0 v Ecclesfield Red Rose - Sheffield & Hallamshire Senior Challenge Cup 2nd Round 10/12/1996
**Record Defeat:** 1-7 v Altrincham - Northern Premier League Premier Division 25/04/1998
**Record Goalscorer:** Mick Pamment
**Record Appearances:** Ray Dennis - 762
**Additional Records:** Received £60,000 from Ayr United for Michael Reynolds 1998

**Senior Honours:**
Yorkshire League 1975-76, 77-78, 79-80, 81-82, League Cup 1969-70, 78-79, 81-82.
Northern Counties East 1987-88, 88-89.
Sheffield & Hallamshire Senior Cup 1975-76, 79-80, 80-81, 83-84, 88-89, 90-91, 91-92, 97-98.

### 10 YEAR RECORD

| 03-04 | | 04-05 | | 05-06 | | 06-07 | | 07-08 | | 08-09 | | 09-10 | | 10-11 | | 11-12 | | 12-13 | |
|---|---|---|---|---|---|---|---|---|---|---|---|---|---|---|---|---|---|---|---|
| NP P | 23 | NP P | 13 | NP P | 20 | NP 1 | 21 | NP1N | 7 | NP1N | 9 | NP1N | 18 | NP1N | 16 | NP1N | 20 | NP1N | 19 |

**NORTHERN PREMIER DIVISION ACTION:** Gardner (Witton) tackled by Garner (Chorley). Photo: Keith Clayton.

# WARRINGTON TOWN

**Chairman:** Gary Skeltenbury
**Secretary:** Chris Henshall      **(T)** 07969 123 786      **(E)** info@warringtontown.co.uk
**Commercial Manager:**                         **(T)**
**Programme Editor:** Paul Roach                **(T)** 07982 781 772
**Ground Address:** Cantilever Park, Common Lane, Latchford, Warrington WA4 2RS
**(T)** 01925 653 044                           **Manager:** Shaun Reid

THE WIRE

2012-13 Squad.

## Club Factfile

**Founded:**    1948        **Nickname:** The Town
**Previous Names:** Stockton Heath Albion 1949-61
**Previous Leagues:** Warrington & District 1949-52, Mid Cheshire 1952-78, Cheshire County 1978-82,
North West Counties 1982-90 Northern Premier 1990-97

**Club Colours (change):** Yellow and blue/blue/yellow (Blue & white/white/blue)

**Ground Capacity:** 2,000  **Seats:** 350    **Covered:** 650    **Clubhouse:** Yes    **Shop:** Yes

**Directions**

From M62 Junction 9 Warrington Town Centre: Travel 1 mile south on A49, turn left at traffic lights into Loushers Lane, ground ½ mile on right hand side. From M6 North or South Junction 20: Follow A50 (Warrington signs) for 2 miles, cross Latchford Swingbridge, turn immediate left into Station Road, ground on left.

**Previous Grounds:** London Road 1948-65

**Record Attendance:** 2,600 v Halesowen Town - FA Vase Semi-final 1st leg 1985-86
**Record Victory:** Not known
**Record Defeat:** Not known
**Record Goalscorer:** Steve Hughes - 167
**Record Appearances:** Neil Whalley
**Additional Records:** Paid £50,000 to Preston North End for Liam Watson Received £60,000 from P.N.E. for Liam Watson
**Senior Honours:** Players to progress - Roger Hunt, Liverpool legend and 1966 World Cup winner.
North West Counties 1989-90, Division 2 2000-01, League Cup 1985-86, 87-88, 88-89

| 10 YEAR RECORD | | | | | | | | | |
|---|---|---|---|---|---|---|---|---|---|
| 03-04 | 04-05 | 05-06 | 06-07 | 07-08 | 08-09 | 09-10 | 10-11 | 11-12 | 12-13 |
| NWC1 5 | NP 1 20 | NP 1 19 | NP 1 22 | NP1S 13 | NP1N 19 | NP1N 9 | NP1N 9 | NP1N 11 | NP1N 10 |

# BEDWORTH UNITED

**Chairman:** Peter Randle

**Secretary:** Andy Stickley    **(T)** 07740 869 757    **(E)** andrew.stickley@live.co.uk

**Commercial Manager:** Blake Timms    **(T)**

**Programme Editor:** Alan Robinson    **(T)** 07778 991 586

**Ground Address:** The Oval, Coventry Road, Bedworth CV12 8NN

**(T)** 02476 314 752      **Manager:** Ady Fuller

2013-14 Squad.

## Club Factfile

**Founded:** 1896     **Nickname:** Greenbacks

**Previous Names:** Bedworth Town 1947-68

**Previous Leagues:** Birmingham Combination 1947-54, Birmingham/West Midlands 1954-72. Southern 1972-2013.

**Club Colours (change):** All green (Gold/blue/gold)

**Ground Capacity:** 7,000    **Seats:** 300    **Covered:** 300    **Clubhouse:** Yes    **Shop:** Yes

**Directions:** 1½ miles from M6 J3, take B4113 Coventry–Bedworth Road and after third set of traffic lights (Bedworth Leisure Centre). Ground 200 yards on right opposite cemetery. Coaches to park in Leisure Centre.

**Previous Grounds:** British Queen Ground 1911-39

**Record Attendance:** 5,127 v Nuneaton Borough - Southern League Midland Division 23/02/1982

**Record Victory:** Not known

**Record Defeat:** Not known

**Record Goalscorer:** Peter Spacey - 1949-69

**Record Appearances:** Peter Spacey - 1949-69

**Additional Records:** Paid £1,750 to Hinckley Town for Colin Taylor 1991-92

**Senior Honours:** Received £30,000 from Plymouth Argyle for Richard Landon

Birmingham Combination x2. Birmingham Senior Cup x3. Midland Floodlit Cup 1981-82, 92-93. Southern Division 1 Central Play-offs 2011-12.

### 10 YEAR RECORD

| 03-04 | | 04-05 | | 05-06 | | 06-07 | | 07-08 | | 08-09 | | 09-10 | | 10-11 | | 11-12 | | 12-13 | |
|---|---|---|---|---|---|---|---|---|---|---|---|---|---|---|---|---|---|---|---|
| SthW | 19 | SthW | 15 | SthW | 16 | SthM | 16 | SthM | 15 | SthM | 14 | SthM | 16 | SthC | 15 | SthC | 3 | SthP | 21 |

# BELPER TOWN

**Chairman:** Alan Benfield
**Secretary:** Ian Wright    **(T)** 07768 948 506    **(E)** info@belpertownfc.co.uk
**Commercial Manager:**    **(T)**
**Programme Editor:** David Laughlin    **(T)** 07768 010 604
**Ground Address:** Christchurch Meadow, Bridge Street, Belper DE56 1BA
**(T)** 01773 825 549      **Manager:** Peter Duffield

2012-13 Squad - Back row (L-R): Stacey Plant (Sports Therapist), Richard Adams, Jon Froggatt, Greg Wright, Shaun Roulston, Mark Ward,
Dave Ratcliffe, Aaron Chapman, Colin Marrison, Dan White, Shaun Tuton, Michael Simpkins, David Bennett (Kit Manager),
Front row: Ben Leonard, Aaron Pride, Simon Harrison, Steve Warne, Eric Graves, Mick Godber (Assistant Manager),
Peter Duffield (Manager), Chris Adam, Andy Rushbury, Daryll Thomas, Blake Owen, Glyn Cotton

## Club Factfile

**Founded:** 1883    **Nickname:** Nailers
**Previous Names:** None
**Previous Leagues:** Central Alliance 1957-61, Midland Counties 1961-82, Northern Counties East 1982-97

**Club Colours (change):** Yellow/black/black (All white)

**Ground Capacity:** 2,650   **Seats:** 500    **Covered:** 850    **Clubhouse:** Yes   **Shop:** Yes

**Directions**

From North: Exit M1: Exit junction 28 onto A38 towards Derby. Turn off at A610 (signposted 'Ripley/Nottingham') 4th exit at roundabout towards Ambergate. At junction with A6 (Hurt Arms Hotel) turn left to Belper. Ground on right just past first set of traffic lights. Access to the ground is by the lane next to the church.
From South: Follow A6 north from Derby towards Matlock. Follow A6 through Belper until junction with A517. Ground on left just before traffic lights at this junction. Access to the ground is by the lane next to the church.
NB. Please do not attempt to bring coaches into the ground – these can be parked outside

**Previous Grounds:** Acorn Ground > 1951

**Record Attendance:** 3,200 v Ilkeston Town - 1955
**Record Victory:** 15-2 v Nottingham Forest 'A' - 1956
**Record Defeat:** 0-12 v Goole Town - 1965
**Record Goalscorer:** Mick Lakin - 231
**Record Appearances:** Craig Smithurst - 678
**Additional Records:** Paid £2,000 to Ilkeston Town for Jamie Eaton 2001
Received £2,000 from Hinckley United for Craig Smith
**Senior Honours:**
Central Alliance League 1958-59, Derbyshire Senior Cup 1958-59, 60-61, 62-63, 79-80.
Midland Counties 1979-80. Northern Counties East 1984-85.

### 10 YEAR RECORD

| 03-04 | 04-05 | 05-06 | 06-07 | 07-08 | 08-09 | 09-10 | 10-11 | 11-12 | 12-13 |
|---|---|---|---|---|---|---|---|---|---|
| NP 1   20 | NP 1   17 | NP 1   9 | NP 1   19 | NP 1   8 | NP1S   2 | NP1S   6 | NP1S   14 | NP1S   6 | NP1S   3 |

# BRIGG TOWN

**Chairman:** Kiron Brown
**Secretary:** Martin North          **(T)** 07891 122 242          **(E)** briggtownfc@chessmail.co.uk
**Commercial Manager:**                    **(T)**
**Programme Editor:** Michael Harker          **(T)** 01302 852 404
**Ground Address:** The Hawthorns, Hawthorn Avenue, Brigg DN20 8PG*
**(T)** 01652 651 605                              **Manager:** Michael Gray

2013-2014 Squad

## Club Factfile

**Founded:** 1864          **Nickname:** Zebras
**Previous Names:** Not known
**Previous Leagues:** Lincolnshire 1948-76, Midland Counties 1976-82, Northern Counties East 1982-2004

**Club Colours (change):** Black and white stripes/black/red (All green)

**Ground Capacity:** 2,500   **Seats:** 370   **Covered:** Yes   **Clubhouse:** Yes   **Shop:** Yes

**Directions**
From M180 (Exit 4 - Scunthorpe East) A18 to Brigg. Leave Town via Wrawby Road, following signs for Airport and Grimsby. 100 metres after Sir John Nelthorpe Lower School, and immediately after bus stop/shelter, turn left into Recreation ground (signposted "Football Ground" ) and follow road into club car park.

*SAT NAV postcode DN20 8DT

**Previous Grounds:** Old Manor House Convent, Station Road > 1939, Brocklesby 1939-59

**Record Attendance:** 2,000 v Boston United - 1953
**Record Victory:** Not known
**Record Defeat:** Not known
**Record Goalscorer:** Not known
**Record Appearances:** Not known
**Additional Records:**

**Senior Honours:**
Midland Counties League 1977-78. FA Vase 1995-96, 2002-03. Northern Counties East Premier Division 2000-01.
Lincolnshire League x8, League Cup x5. Lincolnshire 'A' Senior Cup x4. Lincolnshire 'B' Senior Cup x5.

### 10 YEAR RECORD

| 03-04 | | 04-05 | | 05-06 | | 06-07 | | 07-08 | | 08-09 | | 09-10 | | 10-11 | | 11-12 | | 12-13 | |
|---|---|---|---|---|---|---|---|---|---|---|---|---|---|---|---|---|---|---|---|
| NCEP | 3 | NP 1 | 8 | NP 1 | 8 | NP 1 | 17 | NP 1 | 16 | NP1S | 20 | NP1S | 15 | NP1S | 4 | NP1S | 17 | NP1S | 13 |

# CARLTON TOWN

**Chairman:** Michael Garton

**Secretary:** Paul Shelton          **(T)** 07854 586 875          **(E)** info@carltontownfc.co.uk

**Commercial Manager:**          **(T)**

**Programme Editor:** Tim Harris          **(T)** 07873 731 915

**Ground Address:** Bill Stokeld Stadium, Stoek Lane, Gedling, Nottingham NG4 2QP*

**(T)** 0115 940 3192 / 940 2531          **Manager:** Les McJannet

Photo: Keith Clayton.

## Club Factfile

**Founded:** 1904          **Nickname:** Town

**Previous Names:** Sneinton

**Previous Leagues:** Notts Alliance, Central Midlands, Northern Counties East

**Club Colours (change):** Blue & yellow hoops/blue & white/blue & yellow hoops (Navy with yellow & white trim/navy & yellow/navy)

**Ground Capacity:** 1,500   **Seats:** 164   **Covered:** 100   **Clubhouse:** Yes   **Shop:** No

**Directions:** From M1 J26 take A610 to Nottingham Ring Road. Follow signs for Mansfield (A60) for approx 4 miles via 2 roundabouts until reaching junction with A60 at Arnold. Take right turn at Vale Hotel on to Thackerays Lane. Proceed to roundabout and take 3rd exit on to Arno Vale Road. Proceed through traffic lights to top of hill and continue straight on at next lights on to Arnold Lane. Continue past golf course, the old Gedling Colliery and church to mini roundabout. Continue straight on to the old junction with A612. (Southwell) must turn right here and at next set of lights turn left and follow the loop road to the next junction. Take left turn on to the new A612 Gedling By Pass and follow to the next set of traffic lights at Severn Trent Works. Turn left on to Stoke Lane. Entrance to Carlton Town is immediate right. **[Ground must be accessed via the new A612 between Netherfield and Burton Joyce. Football club is signposted in both directions on the approach to the ground).**
*Sat Nav postcode NG4 2QW

**Previous Grounds:**

**Record Attendance:** 1,000 - Radio Trent Charity Match

**Record Victory:** Not known

**Record Defeat:** Not known

**Record Goalscorer:** Not known

**Record Appearances:** Not known

**Additional Records:**

**Senior Honours:**
Notts Alliance League Division 2 1984-85, Division 1 1992-93. Central Midlands Supreme Division 2002-03.
Northern Counties East Division 1 2005-06.
Notts Senior Cup 2012-13.

### 10 YEAR RECORD

| 03-04 | | 04-05 | | 05-06 | | 06-07 | | 07-08 | | 08-09 | | 09-10 | | 10-11 | | 11-12 | | 12-13 | |
|---|---|---|---|---|---|---|---|---|---|---|---|---|---|---|---|---|---|---|---|
| NCE1 | 9 | NCE1 | 3 | NCE1 | 1 | NCEP | 3 | NP 1 | 10 | NP1S | 4 | NP1S | 9 | NP1S | 8 | NP1S | 2 | NP1S | 12 |

NORTHERN PREMIER LEAGUE DIVISION ONE SOUTH - STEP 4

# CHASETOWN

**Chairman:** John Donnelly

**Secretary:** John Richards    **(T)** 07866 902 093    **(E)** chastownfc@gmail.com

**Commercial Manager:** Graham Dicken    **(T)**

**Programme Editor:** Pamela Mullins    **(T)** 07981 192 345

**Ground Address:** The Scholars, Church Street, Chasetown, Walsall WS7 8QL

**(T)** 01543 682 222      **Manager:** Craig Harris

2012-13 Squad - Back row l-r: Jordon Archer, Theo Robinson, Dave Bate, Mark Hands, John Richadrson, Matthew Jukes, Jack Farmer
Lee Evans, Ryan Price, Gavin Saunders, Nick Wellecomme, Greg Downes, Chris Slater, Gary Hay,
Dave Egan, Danny Smith
Front row l-r: John Birt (goalkeeping coach), Dave Reid (first team coach), Johnathan Gould, Danny Ashton, Simon Brown,
Paul Sullivan, Tyronne oconnell-Clarke, Kev Sweeney (assistant manager), Craig Harris (manager) , Andy Westwood, Matty Johnson,
Anthony Maguire, Mark Branch, Chad Degville,
Mick Andrews (sports therapist) Gary Mchale (sports therapist)

## Club Factfile

**Founded:** 1954     **Nickname:** The Scholars

**Previous Names:** Chase Terrace Old Scholars 1954-72

**Previous Leagues:** Cannock Youth 1954-58, Lichfield & District 1958-61, Staffordshire County 1961-72,
West Midlands 1972-94, Midland Alliance 1994-2006, Southern 2006-09

**Club Colours (change):** Royal blue/royal blue/white (All bright red)

**Ground Capacity:** 2,000   **Seats:** 151    **Covered:** 220    **Clubhouse:** Yes   **Shop:** Yes

**Directions** From the M42 junction10 towards Tamworth or from the M6 Junction 11 or 12 towards Cannock or the A38 southbound from Derby - follow signs for A5 towards Brownhills, At the traffic lights at the Terrace Restaurant turn towards Burntwood onto the A5195. Straight over first island towards Chasetown and Hammerwich, over toll road and at second island turn left into Haney Hay Road which leads into Highfields Road signposted Chasetown, up the hill to mini island, then straight on into Church Street past the church on left and school on right. Ground is on the left at end of road. If using M6 Toll exit at junction T6 Burntwood - turn left out of Toll booths and left at second island and follow over toll road as above.

**Previous Grounds:** Burntwood Recreation

**Record Attendance:** 2,420 v Cardiff City - FA Cup 3rd Round January 2008

**Record Victory:** 14-1 v Hanford - Walsall Senior Cup 1991-92

**Record Defeat:** 1-8 v Telford United Reserves - West Midlands League

**Record Goalscorer:** Tony Dixon - 197

**Record Appearances:** Not known

**Additional Records:**

**Senior Honours:**
West Midlands League 1978, League Cup x2.
Midland Alliance 2005-06.
Walsall Senior Cup x2.

### 10 YEAR RECORD

| 03-04 | | 04-05 | | 05-06 | | 06-07 | | 07-08 | | 08-09 | | 09-10 | | 10-11 | | 11-12 | | 12-13 | |
|---|---|---|---|---|---|---|---|---|---|---|---|---|---|---|---|---|---|---|---|
| MidAl | 7 | MidAl | 2 | MidAl | 1 | SthM | | SthM | 7 | SthM | 4 | NP1S | 2 | NP P | 10 | NP P | 20 | NP1S | 5 |

# COALVILLE TOWN

**Chairman:** Glyn Rennocks
**Secretary:** Dan Gallacher    **(T)** 07770 628 561    **(E)** info@coalvilletownfc.co.uk
**Commercial Manager:** Dan Gallacher    **(T)** 07770 628 561
**Programme Editor:** Dan Gallacher    **(T)** 07770 628 561
**Ground Address:** Owen Street Sports Ground, Owen St, Coalville LE67 3DA
**(T)** 01530 833 365        **Manager:** Adam Stevens

_The Ravens_

## Club Factfile

**Founded:** 1994      **Nickname:** The Ravens
**Previous Names:** Ravenstoke Miners Ath. 1926-58. Ravenstoke FC 1958-95. Coalville 1995-98.
**Previous Leagues:** Coalville & Dist. Amateur. North Leicester. Leicestershire Senior. Midland Alliance > 2011.

**Club Colours (change):** Black & white stripes/black with white trim/black with white trim (Red & yellow stripes/red/red)

**Ground Capacity:** 2,000   **Seats:** 240    **Covered:** 240    **Clubhouse:** Yes   **Shop:** Yes

**Directions:** From the M42/A42 take the exit signposted Ashby and follow A511 to Coalville and Leicester. After approx. 3 miles and at the first roundabout take the second exit (A511). At the next roundabout take the 3rd exit into Coalville Town Centre. At the traffic lights go straight over to mini-roundabout then straight on for 50 meters before turning right into Owen Street. Ground is at the top of Owen Street on the left.

**Previous Grounds:** None

**Record Attendance:** 1,500.
**Record Victory:** Not known
**Record Defeat:** Not known
**Record Goalscorer:** Not known
**Record Appearances:** Nigel Simms.
**Additional Records:** 153 goals scored during 2010-11 season.

**Senior Honours:**
Leicestershire Senior Cup 1999-00. Leicestershire Senior 2001-02, 02-03. Midland Football Alliance 2010-11.
Leicestershire Challenge Cup 2012-13.

### 10 YEAR RECORD

| 03-04 | 04-05 | 05-06 | 06-07 | 07-08 | 08-09 | 09-10 | 10-11 | 11-12 | 12-13 |
|---|---|---|---|---|---|---|---|---|---|
| MidAl 8 | MidAl 3 | MidAl 8 | MidAl 18 | MidAl 8 | MidAl 3 | MidAl 2 | MidAl 1 | NP1S 14 | NP1S 2 |

# EASTWOOD TOWN

**Chairman:** Steven Lynch
**Secretary:** Tracie Witton    **(T)** 07973 702 588    **(E)**
**Commercial Manager:**    **(T)**
**Programme Editor:** Paul Braithwaite    **(T)** 07540 701 526
**Ground Address:** Coronation Park, Chewton Street, Eastwood, Notts NG16 3HB
**(T)** 01773 711 819    **Manager:** Chris Shaw & Nick Hawkins

## Club Factfile

**Founded:** 1953    **Nickname:** The Badgers
**Previous Names:** None
**Previous Leagues:** Notts Alliance 1953-61, Central Alliance 1961-67, East Midlands 1967-71, Midland Counties 1971-82, Northern Counties East 1982-87, 2003-04, Northern Premier 1987-2003, 04-09

**Club Colours (change):** Black & white stripes/black/black (Green & white hoops/green/green)

**Ground Capacity:** 5,500   **Seats:** 650   **Covered:** 1,150   **Clubhouse:** Yes   **Shop:** Yes

**Directions**
M1 TRAVELLING SOUTH At junction 27, leave the motorway (A608) Heanor. At roundabout take 3rd exit A608. Past the Sandhills Tavern to a T- junction signposted Brinsley Heanor. Going through Brinsley will take you to Eastwood. At the lights turn left onto Nottingham Road. Look for the Fire Station on your right, then turn 1st right into Chewton Street. Ground is 150 metres on your right.
M1 TRAVELLING NORTH Exit junction 26. At roundabout take exit onto A610 Ripley. Leave the A610 at the first junction signed Ilkeston. Turn right at junction onto B6010, following the signs for Eastwood. Turn 1st left after the Man In Space pub into Chewton Street. Ground is 150 metres on your right.

**Previous Grounds:** Not known

**Record Attendance:** 2,723 v Enfield - FA Amateur Cup February 1965
**Record Victory:** 21-0 v Rufford Colliery - 1954-55
**Record Defeat:** 0-8 v Hucknall Town (A) - 2000-01
**Record Goalscorer:** Martin Wright - 147
**Record Appearances:** Arthur Rowley - 800+ with no bookings (1955-76)
**Additional Records:** Paid £500 to Gainsborough Trinity for Jamie Kay
**Senior Honours:** Recieved £72,500 from Middlesbrough for Richard Liburd
Midland League 1975-76. Northern Premier League Premier Division 2008-09
Notts Senior Cup x11 Most recently 2011-12.

### 10 YEAR RECORD

| 03-04 | 04-05 | 05-06 | 06-07 | 07-08 | 08-09 | 09-10 | 10-11 | 11-12 | 12-13 |
|---|---|---|---|---|---|---|---|---|---|
| NCEP 2 | NP 1 6 | NP 1 7 | NP 1 3 | NP P 4 | NP P 1 | Conf N 10 | Conf N 4 | Conf N 22 | NP P 22 |

**NORTHERN PREMIER DIVISION ACTION:** Sheehan (Witton) and Roscoe (Chorley). Photo: Keith Clayton.

# GOOLE AFC

**Chairman:**
**Secretary:** Andrew Morris    **(T)** 07751 457 254    **(E)**
**Commercial Manager:** Carol Smith    **(T)**
**Programme Editor:** Malcolm Robinson    **(T)**
**Ground Address:** Victoria Pleasure Gardens, Marcus Road, Goole DN14 6WW
**(T)** 01405 762 794 (Match days)      **Manager:** Wayne Benn

2012-13 Squad - Back row L-R: Clive Freeman(asst manager),Graeme Smith(kit man),Daniel Cunningham,Matthew Stirland, Tom Agus,Tim Council,Ryan Pugh,Scott Hartley,Dominic Dickinson,Louis Horne,Brett Lucas,Daniel Cunningham,Andrew Jackson, Ben Neavis(physio)
Front Row L-R:Karl Cunningham,Jack Cross,Des O'Hearne(chairman)Chris Ovington,John Reed(manager),Sam Liversidge, David Taylor,Derry Robson,Nathan Hay.

## Club Factfile

**Founded:** 1997      **Nickname:** The Badgers
**Previous Names:** Goole Town > 1996.
**Previous Leagues:** Central Midlands 1997-98.
                 Northern Counties East 2000-04.

**Club Colours (change):** Red with white trim/white/red (Yellow/black/yellow)

**Ground Capacity:** 3,000    **Seats:** 200    **Covered:** 800    **Clubhouse:** Yes    **Shop:** Yes

**Directions**

Leave the M62 at Junction 36 and follow signs to Goole Town Centre.
Turn right at the 2nd set of traffic lights into Boothferry Road. Turn right again after 300 yards into Carter Street.
The Victoria Pleasure Grounds is at the end of the road. 366 Metres from Goole Railway Station.

**Previous Grounds:** None

**Record Attendance:** 976 v Leeds United - 1999
**Record Victory:** Not known
**Record Defeat:** Not known
**Record Goalscorer:** Kevin Severn (1997-2001)
**Record Appearances:** Phil Dobson - 187 (1999-2001)
**Additional Records:**

**Senior Honours:**
Central Midlands 1997-98.
Northern Counties East Division 1 1999-2000, Premier Division 2003-04.

### 10 YEAR RECORD

| 03-04 | | 04-05 | | 05-06 | | 06-07 | | 07-08 | | 08-09 | | 09-10 | | 10-11 | | 11-12 | | 12-13 | |
|---|---|---|---|---|---|---|---|---|---|---|---|---|---|---|---|---|---|---|---|
| NCEP | 6 | NCEP | 1 | NP 1 | 21 | NP 1 | 7 | NP 1 | 9 | NP1S | 18 | NP1S | 18 | NP1S | 13 | NP1S | 10 | NP1N | 21 |

# GRESLEY

**Chairman:** Barry North
**Secretary:** Reg Shorthouse    **(T)** 07779 049 847    **(E)** reg.shorthouse@gresleyfc.com
**Commercial Manager:**    **(T)**
**Programme Editor:** Robin Mansfield    **(T)** 07855 847 337
**Ground Address:** The Moat Ground, Moat Street, Church Gresley, Derbyshire DE11 9RE
**(T)** 01283 215 316    **Manager:** Gary Norton

2012-13 Squad - Back Row (L-R): Jordi Gough, Dean Oliver, Marc Strzyzewski, Michael Nottingam, Craig Atwood, Kyle Bryant, Marc Goodfellow.
Middle Row: Christina Cooper (physio), Matt Roome, James Jepson, Richard Hanslow, Jamie Barrett, Tom Gutteridge, Dan Douglas, Oliver Hancock, Rob Spencer, Matt Dingley (kit manager).
Front Row: Reg Shorthouse (secretary), Royce Turville, Phil Massingham, Hannah Dingley (coach), Gary Norton (joint manager), Martin Rowe (joint manager), Steve Titterton (asst. Manager), Tom Betteridge, Mickey Lyons, Barry North (chairman).

## Club Factfile

**Founded:** 2009    **Nickname:**
**Previous Names:** Gresley Rovers
**Previous Leagues:** East Midlands 2009-11. Midland Football Alliance 2011-12.

**Club Colours (change):** Red & white/white/red (All white)

**Ground Capacity:**    **Seats:** Yes    **Covered:** Yes    **Clubhouse:** Yes    **Shop:** Yes

**Directions: From the South:** Follow the M42 northbound to Junction 11, turn off onto the A444 toward Burton Upon Trent. Turn right onto the A514 (Castle Road) toward Gresley and follow the road up the hill to the traffic island at the top. Continue on the A514 over the island and take the second road on the left (School Street), the next left into Moat Street where the Moat Ground is located. **From the North-East:** Follow the M1 south to junction 23a, turn off on to the A42 southbound. Continue on the A42 to Ashby-de-la-Zouch then turn off onto the A511 toward Swadlincote. At Woodville turn off the A511 onto the A514 toward Church Gresley, follow the road signs to Gresley, the School Street turn off is second on the right after the Gresley island. Take the first turn on the left in School Street to take you to the ground. **From the North-West:** From Stoke-on-Trent follow the A50 toward Burton-Upon-Trent, turn on to the A511 and continue through Burton. Turn off the A511 onto the A444 toward Nuneaton. Follow the A444 until you reach the turn off for the A514. Turn left onto the A514 (Castle Road) toward Gresley and follow the road up the hill to the traffic island at the top. Continue on the A514 over the island and take the second road on the left (School Street), the next left into Moat Street where the Moat Ground is located.

**Previous Grounds:** None

**Record Attendance:** 861 v Whitehawk (FA Vase Quarter Final 27th Feb 2010)
**Record Victory:** 9-0 v Anstey Nomads 30th August 2010 (EMCL)
**Record Defeat:** 1-5 v Westfields (MFA)
**Record Goalscorer:** Royce Turville - 61
**Record Appearances:** Jamie Barrett - 142
**Additional Records:**

**Senior Honours:**
East Midlands Counties League 2010-11. Midland Alliance 2011-12.

### 10 YEAR RECORD

| 03-04 | 04-05 | 05-06 | 06-07 | 07-08 | 08-09 | 09-10 | 10-11 | 11-12 | 12-13 |
|---|---|---|---|---|---|---|---|---|---|
|  |  |  |  |  |  | EMC  2 | EMC  1 | MidAl  1 | NP1S  11 |

# HALESOWEN TOWN

**Chairman:** Colin Brookes
**Secretary:** Andrew While    **(T)** 07976 769 972    **(E)** info@ht-fc.com
**Commercial Manager:** Mike Burke    **(T)** 07505 102 767
**Programme Editor:** Rob Edmonds    **(T)** 0121 602 0068
**Ground Address:** The Grove, Old Hawne Lane, Halesowen B63 3TB
**(T)** 0121 550 9433                    **Manager:** John Hill

## Club Factfile

**Founded:** 1873    **Nickname:** Yeltz
**Previous Names:** None
**Previous Leagues:** West Midlands 1892-1905, 06-11, 46-86, Birmingham Combination 1911-39

**Club Colours (change):** All blue (Yellow/black/yellow)

**Ground Capacity:** 3,150    **Seats:** 525    **Covered:** 930    **Clubhouse:** Yes    **Shop:** Yes

**Directions:** Leave M5 at Junction 3, follow A456 Kidderminster to first island and turn right (signposted A459 Dudley).
Turn left at next island (signposted A458 Stourbridge).
At next island take third exit into Old Hawne Lane.
Ground about 400 yards on left.

**Previous Grounds:** None

**Record Attendance:** 5,000 v Hendon - FA Cup 1st Round Proper 1954
**Record Victory:** 13-1 v Coventry Amateurs - Birmingham Senior cup 1956
**Record Defeat:** 0-8 v Bilston - West Midlands League 07/04/1962
**Record Goalscorer:** Paul Joinson - 369
**Record Appearances:** Paul Joinson - 608
**Additional Records:** Paid £7,250 to Gresley Rovers for Stuart Evans
                        Received £40,000 from Rushden & Diamonds for Jim Rodwell
**Senior Honours:**
FA Vase 1984-85, 85-86 (R-up 1982-83). Southern League Midland Division 1989-90, Western Division 2001-02.
Birmingham Senior Cup 1983-84, 97-98. Staffordshire Senior Cup 1988-89.
Worcestershire Senior Cup 1951-52, 61-62, 2002-03, 04-05.

### 10 YEAR RECORD

| 03-04 | | 04-05 | | 05-06 | | 06-07 | | 07-08 | | 08-09 | | 09-10 | | 10-11 | | 11-12 | | 12-13 | |
|---|---|---|---|---|---|---|---|---|---|---|---|---|---|---|---|---|---|---|---|
| SthW | 4 | SthP | 9 | SthP | 8 | SthP | 6 | SthP | 3 | SthP | 10 | SthP | 8 | SthP | 21 | Sthsw | 12 | NP1S | 7 |

# KIDSGROVE ATHLETIC

**Chairman:** John Rowley
**Secretary:** Dave Stringer          **(T)** 01782 860 140     **(E)**
**Commercial Manager:**                    **(T)**
**Programme Editor:** Neil Clowes          **(T)** 07950 209 204
**Ground Address:** The Seddon Stadium, Hollinwood Road, Kidsgrove, Staffs ST7 1DQ
**(T)** 01782 782 412                    **Manager:** Ant Buckle

## Club Factfile

**Founded:** 1952     **Nickname:** The Grove
**Previous Names:** None
**Previous Leagues:** Buslem and Tunstall 1953-63, Staffordshire County 1963-66, Mid Cheshire 1966-90,
          North West Counties 1990-2002

**Club Colours (change):** All blue (All red)

**Ground Capacity:** 4,500   **Seats:** 1,000   **Covered:** 800      **Clubhouse:** Yes   **Shop:** Yes

**Directions:** Leave the M6 at Junction 16, join the A500 towards Stoke-on-Trent. Take the 2nd exit signposted Newcastle & Kidsgrove. Top of the slip road, turn left onto A34 Kidsgrove/Congleton. Straight over at roundabout. At 1st set of traffic lights (by Caudwell Arms pub) turn right onto A34. Continue to next set of lights, turn right into Cedar Avenue. Continue then take 2nd right into Lower Ash Road. Take 3rd left into Hollinwood Road, Ground on left at top.

**Previous Grounds:** Vickers and Goodwin 1953-60

**Record Attendance:** 1,903 v Tiverton Town - FA Vase Semi-final 1998
**Record Victory:** 23-0 v Cross Heath W.M.C. - Staffordshire Cup 1965
**Record Defeat:** 0-15 v Stafford Rangers - Staffordshire Senior Cup 20/11/2001
**Record Goalscorer:** Scott Dundas - 53 (1997-98)
**Record Appearances:** Not known
**Additional Records:** Paid £10,000 to Stevenage Borough for Steve Walters
**Senior Honours:** Received £3,000 for Ryan Baker 2003-04
Mid Cheshire League x4, League Cup x3.
North West Counties Division 1 1997-98, 2001-02, Challenge Cup 1997-98.
Staffordshire Senior Cup 2010-11.

### 10 YEAR RECORD

| 03-04 | | 04-05 | | 05-06 | | 06-07 | | 07-08 | | 08-09 | | 09-10 | | 10-11 | | 11-12 | | 12-13 | |
|---|---|---|---|---|---|---|---|---|---|---|---|---|---|---|---|---|---|---|---|
| NP 1 | 22 | NP 1 | 10 | NP 1 | 17 | NP 1 | 8 | NP 1 | 17 | NP1S | 15 | NP1S | 4 | NP1S | 7 | NP1S | 13 | NP1S | 18 |

# LEEK TOWN

**Chairman:** Andrew Wain

**Secretary:** Brain Wain     **(T)** 07967 204 470     **(E)**

**Commercial Manager:**     **(T)**

**Programme Editor:** Tracy Reynolds     **(T)** 07540 161 017

**Ground Address:** Harrison Park, Macclesfield Road, Leek, Cheshire ST13 8LD

**(T)** 01538 399 278     **Manager:** Lee Casswell

## Club Factfile

**Founded:** 1946     **Nickname:** The Blues

**Previous Names:** None

**Previous Leagues:** Staffordshire Co., Manchester 1951-54, 57-73, West Midlands (B'ham) 1954-56, Cheshire Co. 1973-82, North West Counties 1982-87, N.P.L. 1987-94, 95-97, Southern 1994-95, Conference 1997-99

**Club Colours (change):** All blue (Amber & black/amber/black)

**Ground Capacity:** 3,000   **Seats:** 650     **Covered:** 3,000     **Clubhouse:** Yes     **Shop:** Yes

**Directions**

**From the South:** Leave M6 at J15, over roundabout on to the A500, go over the flyover, up the slip road, onto the A50 and follow the signs to Leek. Go straight over the roundabout (Britannia Building on the left) to large set of lights. Go straight across St. Georges Street to top of road to junction, turn left, go down the hill for about a half a mile. The Ground is on the left. **From the North:** Leave M6 at J19. Take Macclesfield signs. Follow into Macclesfield then take A523 Leek/Buxton signs. Follow these to Leek. Ground is situated on the right as you come into Leek. From West Midlands: M6 J15. A500 towards Stoke, over flyover, take A50 past Brittania Stadium. After approx 3 miles join A53 signposted Leek. On entering the town, straight ahead up St Edwards St. (Remainder as above)

**Previous Grounds:** None

**Record Attendance:** 5,312 v Macclesfield Town - FA Cup 1973-74

**Record Victory:** Not known

**Record Defeat:** Not known

**Record Goalscorer:** Dave Sutton - 144

**Record Appearances:** Gary Pearce - 447

**Additional Records:** Paid £2,000 to Sutton Town for Simon Snow

**Senior Honours:** Received £30,000 from Barnsley for Tony Bullock

Northern Premier League 1996-97. Staffordshire Senior Cup 1995-96.

### 10 YEAR RECORD

| 03-04 | | 04-05 | | 05-06 | | 06-07 | | 07-08 | | 08-09 | | 09-10 | | 10-11 | | 11-12 | | 12-13 | |
|---|---|---|---|---|---|---|---|---|---|---|---|---|---|---|---|---|---|---|---|
| NP 1 | 8 | NP P | 7 | NP P | 12 | NP P | 17 | NP P | 19 | NP1S | 9 | NP1S | 8 | NP1S | 16 | NP1S | 5 | NP1S | 10 |

# LINCOLN UNITED

**Chairman:** Malcolm Cowling

**Secretary:** John Wilkinson     **(T)** 07773 284 017     **(E)** johnwilk@live.co.uk

**Commercial Manager:** Allen Crombie     **(T)**

**Programme Editor:** Mark Shillito     **(T)** 07447 501 544

**Ground Address:** NTR Stadium, Ashby Avenue, Hartsholme, Lincoln LN6 0DY

**(T)** 01522 696 400     **Manager:** David Frecklington

Back Row (L-R): Phil McGann, Brendan McDaid, Sam Wilkinson, Josh Raby, David Hone, Sean Wright, Stuart Reddington, Stuart King
David Coyde, Lee Pickering, Darren Dye.
Front: Chris Funnell, Ben Clucas, Joe Butler, Terry Fleming, Ben Garrick, Tom Cowan, Nathan Adams.

## Club Factfile

**Founded:** 1938     **Nickname:** United

**Previous Names:** Lincoln Amateurs > 1954

**Previous Leagues:** Lincolnshire 1945-46, 60-67, Lincoln 1946-60, Yorkshire 1967-82,
Northern Counties East 1982-86, 92-95, Central Midlands 1982-92

**Club Colours (change):** White/white/white & red (All blue)

**Ground Capacity:** 2,714   **Seats:** 400     **Covered:** 1,084     **Clubhouse:** Yes   **Shop:** Yes

**Directions**
Along Lincoln Relief Road (A46) until reaching roundabout with exit for Birchwood. Take this exit which is Skellingthorpe Road for approximately 1 mile, at 30 mph sign turn right into Ashby Avenue. Entrance to ground is 200 yards on right.

**Previous Grounds:** Skew Bridge 1940s, Co-op Sports Ground > 1960s, Hartsholme Cricket Club > 1982

**Record Attendance:** 2,000 v Crook Town - FA Amateur Cup 1st Round 1968

**Record Victory:** 12-0 v Pontefract Colliery - 1995

**Record Defeat:** 0-7 v Huddersfield Town - FA Cup 1st Round 16/11/1991

**Record Goalscorer:** Tony Simmons - 215

**Record Appearances:** Steve Carter - 447

**Additional Records:** Paid £1,000 to Hucknall Town for Paul Tomlinson December 2000

**Senior Honours:** Received £3,000 from Charlton Athletic for Dean Dye July 1991

Northern Counties East Division 1 1985-86, 92-93, Premier Division 1994-95.

### 10 YEAR RECORD

| 03-04 | | 04-05 | | 05-06 | | 06-07 | | 07-08 | | 08-09 | | 09-10 | | 10-11 | | 11-12 | | 12-13 | |
|---|---|---|---|---|---|---|---|---|---|---|---|---|---|---|---|---|---|---|---|
| NP 1 | 4 | NP P | 14 | NP P | 19 | NP P | 15 | NP P | 20 | NP1S | 10 | NP1S | 19 | NP1S | 12 | NP1S | 18 | NP1S | 20 |

# LOUGHBOROUGH DYNAMO

**Chairman:** Frank Fall

**Secretary:** Brian Pugh    **(T)** 07716 846 626    **(E)** contact@loughboroughdynamofc.co.uk

**Commercial Manager:**    **(T)**

**Programme Editor:**    **(T)**

**Ground Address:** Nanpantan Sports Ground, Nanpantan Road, Loughborough LE11 3YE

**(T)** 01509 237 148      **Manager:** Tommy Brookbanks

## Club Factfile

**Founded:** 1955     **Nickname:** Dynamo

**Previous Names:** None

**Previous Leagues:** Loughborough Alliance 1957-66, Leicestershire & District 1966-71, East Midlands 1971-72, Central Alliance 1972-89, Leicestershire Senior 1989-2004, Midland Alliance 2004-08

**Club Colours (change):** Gold/black/gold (Green and white hoops/white/green and white hoops)

**Ground Capacity:** 1,500   **Seats:** 250    **Covered:** Yes    **Clubhouse:** Yes   **Shop:** No

**Directions:** **From M1:** At Junction 23 turn towards Loughborough (A512). At 1st set of traffic lights turn right on to Snells Nook Lane.. At 1st crossroads ("Priory" pub on left) turn left on to Nanpantan Rd. Turn (1st) right after 0.75 miles on to Watermead Lane. The ground is at the end of the lane. **From Leicester (A6):** Turn left at 3rd roundabout on Epinal Way (Ring Road) on to Forest Road. After 2 miles turn (5th) left on to Watermead Lane. **From Nottingham (A60):** Turn right at 1st set of traffic lights in Loughborough. Go through next 4 sets of traffic lights. Turn left at the first roundabout on to Epinal Way straight on at next roundabout and then take the third exit at following roundabout on to Forest Road. After 2 miles turn (5th) left on to Watermead Lane.

**Previous Grounds:** None

**Record Attendance:** Not known

**Record Victory:** Not known

**Record Defeat:** Not known

**Record Goalscorer:** Not known

**Record Appearances:** Not known

**Additional Records:**

**Senior Honours:**

Leicestershire Senior League Division 1 2001-02, Premier Division 2003-04.

Leicestershire Senior Cup 2002-03, 03-04.

### 10 YEAR RECORD

| 03-04 | | 04-05 | | 05-06 | | 06-07 | | 07-08 | | 08-09 | | 09-10 | | 10-11 | | 11-12 | | 12-13 | |
|---|---|---|---|---|---|---|---|---|---|---|---|---|---|---|---|---|---|---|---|
| LeicS | 1 | MidAl | 14 | MidAl | 13 | MidAl | 9 | MidAl | 2 | NP1S | 14 | NP1S | 14 | NP1S | 17 | NP1S | 8 | NP1S | 16 |

# MARKET DRAYTON TOWN

**Chairman:** Bob Mellor
**Secretary:** Brian Garratt    **(T)** 07854 725 957    **(E)** julian@halessawmills.co.uk
**Commercial Manager:**    **(T)**
**Programme Editor:** Clive Jones    **(T)** 07971 403 538
**Ground Address:** Greenfields Sports Ground, Greenfields Lane, Market Drayton TF9 3SL
**(T)** 01630 654 618      **Manager:** Lee Ebdon

## Club Factfile

**Founded:** 1969    **Nickname:**
**Previous Names:** Little Drayton Rangers > 2003
**Previous Leagues:** West Midlands (Regional) 1969-2006, Midland Alliance 2006-09

**Club Colours (change):** All red (All blue)

**Ground Capacity:**    **Seats:**    **Covered:**    **Clubhouse:** Yes    **Shop:** Nk

**Directions**

Take the A41 to Ternhill Island, turn right on A53 for Newcastle-under-Lyne. Straight on at first island (by Muller factory). At next island turn right to town centre (by Gingerbread Inn). Approx 200yds take 2nd right into Greenfields Lane. Ground 150 yards on right, car park opposite.

From Stoke-on-Trent take A53 for Shrewsbury, at Gingerbread Inn turn left for town centre then as above.

**Previous Grounds:** Not known

**Record Attendance:** 440 vs. AFC Telford, Friendly 11/07/09. 229 vs. Witton Albion, Unibond South 25/08/09
**Record Victory:** (League) 9-0 Home vs. Racing Club Warwick 10/03/09
**Record Defeat:** Not known
**Record Goalscorer:** Not known
**Record Appearances:** Not known
**Additional Records:**

**Senior Honours:**
West Midlands (Regional) League 2005-06. Midland Alliance 2008-09.

### 10 YEAR RECORD

| 03-04 | | 04-05 | | 05-06 | | 06-07 | | 07-08 | | 08-09 | | 09-10 | | 10-11 | | 11-12 | | 12-13 | |
|---|---|---|---|---|---|---|---|---|---|---|---|---|---|---|---|---|---|---|---|
| WMP | 7 | WMP | 2 | WMP | 1 | MidAl | 13 | MidAl | 3 | MidAl | 1 | NP1S | 13 | NP1S | 18 | NP1S | 16 | NP1S | 15 |

# MICKLEOVER SPORTS

**Chairman:** Stuart Clarke
**Secretary:** Tony Shaw       **(T)** 07966 197 246     **(E)**
**Commercial Manager:**                                   **(T)**
**Programme Editor:** James Edge          **(T)** 07964 217 945
**Ground Address:** Mickleover Sports Club, Station Road, Mickleover Derby DE3 9FB
**(T)** 01332 512 826                          **Manager:** Glen Kirkwood

## Club Factfile

**Founded:**  1948        **Nickname:** Sports
**Previous Names:** Mickleover Old Boys 1948-93
**Previous Leagues:** Central Midlands 1993-99, Northern Counties East 1999-2009

**Club Colours (change):** Red and black stripes/black/red (All blue)

**Ground Capacity:** 1,500   **Seats:** 280   **Covered:** 500   **Clubhouse:** Yes   **Shop:** Yes

**Directions**

M1 NORTH - J28. A38 to Derby. At Markeaton Island right A52 Ashbourne, 2nd left Radbourne Lane, 3rd Left Station Road 50 yds.

M1 SOUTH – J25. A52 to Derby. Follow signs for Ashbourne, pick up A52 at Markeaton Island (MacDonalds) then as above.

FROM STOKE A50 – Derby. A516 to A38 then as above.

**Previous Grounds:** None

**Record Attendance:** Not known
**Record Victory:** Not known
**Record Defeat:** Not known
**Record Goalscorer:** Not known
**Record Appearances:** Not known
**Additional Records:** Won 16 consecutive League matches in 2009-10 - a Northern Premier League record
**Senior Honours:**
Central Midlands Supreme Division 1998-99. Northern Counties East Division 1 2002-03, Premier Division 2008-09.
Northern Premier League Division 1 South 2009-10.

### 10 YEAR RECORD

| 03-04 | 04-05 | 05-06 | 06-07 | 07-08 | 08-09 | 09-10 | 10-11 | 11-12 | 12-13 |
|---|---|---|---|---|---|---|---|---|---|
| NCEP 13 | NCEP 7 | NCEP 13 | NCEP 7 | NCEP 14 | NCEP 1 | NP1S 1 | NP P 15 | NP P 21 | NP1S 21 |

# NEWCASTLE TOWN

**Chairman:** Alistair Miller

**Secretary:** Ray Tatton     **(T)** 07792 292 849     **(E)** rftatton@tiscali.co.uk

**Commercial Manager:**     **(T)**

**Programme Editor:** Ray Tatton     **(T)** 07792 292 849

**Ground Address:** The Aspire Stadium, Buckmaster Avenue, Clayton, ST5 3BX

**(T)** 01782 662 350     **Manager:** John Diskin

Matt Lowe (Newcastle Town) Lee Molyneux and Matt Tootle (Crewe) during
a pre-season friendly. Photo: Keith Clayton.

## Club Factfile

**Founded:** 1964     **Nickname:** Castle

**Previous Names:** Parkway Hanley, Clayton Park & Parkway Clayton. Merged as NTFC in 1986.

**Previous Leagues:** Newcatle & District, Staffs Co & Mid Cheshire, North West Counties

**Club Colours (change):** Blue/blue/white (All white)

**Ground Capacity:** 4,000    **Seats:** 300    **Covered:** 1,000    **Clubhouse:** Yes    **Shop:** Yes

**Directions**

**FROM M6:** Leave the M6 at Junction 15 and immediately turn left up the bank (signposted A519 Newcastle.) Go to the second roundabout and turn right into Stafford Avenue. Take the first left into Tittensor Road (signposted Newcastle Town FC.) Go to the end and the ground is below in the parkway. (Entrance through the gateway signposted Newcastle Town FC.) **FROM A50 DERBY:** Follow the A50 to the end and join the A500 (signposted M6 South) just past Stoke City Football Ground. Follow the A500 to the Motorway and at the roundabout turn right up the bank (A519 Newcastle.) Go to the second roundabout and turn right into Stafford Avenue. Take the first left into Tittensor Road (signposted Newcastle Town FC.) Go to the end and the ground is below in the parkway. (Entrance through the gateway signposted Newcastle Town FC.)

**Previous Grounds:** None

**Record Attendance:** 3,948 v Notts County - FA Cup 1996

**Record Victory:** Not known

**Record Defeat:** Not known

**Record Goalscorer:** Andy Bott - 149

**Record Appearances:** Dean Gillick - 632

**Additional Records:**

**Senior Honours:**
Mid Cheshire League 1985-86. Walsall Senior Cup 1993-94, 94-95.

### 10 YEAR RECORD

| 03-04 | | 04-05 | | 05-06 | | 06-07 | | 07-08 | | 08-09 | | 09-10 | | 10-11 | | 11-12 | | 12-13 | |
|---|---|---|---|---|---|---|---|---|---|---|---|---|---|---|---|---|---|---|---|
| NWC1 | 6 | NWC1 | 2 | NWC1 | 6 | NWC1 | 12 | NWC1 | 3 | NWCP | 3 | NWCP | 1 | NP1S | 2 | NP1S | 15 | NP1S | 17 |

# RAINWORTH MINERS WELFARE

**Chairman:** Mark Hawkins
**Secretary:** Les Lee    **(T)** 07740 576 958    **(E)**
**Commercial Manager:**    **(T)**
**Programme Editor:** Paul Fryer    **(T)** 07534 530 254
**Ground Address:** Welfare Ground, Kirklington Road, Rainworth, Mansfield NG21 0JY
**(T)** 01623 792 495    **Manager:** Kevin Gee

2012-13 Squad.

## Club Factfile

**Founded:** 1922    **Nickname:** The Wrens
**Previous Names:** Rufford Colliery
**Previous Leagues:** Notts Alliance 1922-03, Central Midlands League 2003-07, Northern Counties East 2007-10

**Club Colours (change):** All White (All royal blue).

**Ground Capacity:** 2,201    **Seats:** 221    **Covered:** 350    **Clubhouse:** Yes    **Shop:** No

**Directions** From M1 (Junction 29) – take A617. At Pleasley turn right onto the new Mansfield Bypass road which is still the A617 and follow to Rainworth. At roundabout with B6020 Rainworth is off to the right, but it is better to go straight over onto the new Rainworth Bypass and then right at the next roundabout (the ground can be seen on the way along the Bypass) At mini roundabout, turn right onto Kirklington Road and go down the hill for ¼ mile – ground and car park on the right
Alternatively you can reach the new A617 Bypass from the A38 via Junction 28 on the M1.    From A614 at roundabout, take the A617 to Rainworth for 1 mile. Left at 1st roundabout into village.  At mini roundabout right into Kirklington road – ¼ mile down hill as above.

**Previous Grounds:** None

**Record Attendance:** 5,071 v Barton Rovers FA Vase SF 2nd Leg, 1982. (A record for a Vase match outside of the final)
**Record Victory:** Not known
**Record Defeat:** Not known
**Record Goalscorer:** Not known
**Record Appearances:** Not known
**Additional Records:**

**Senior Honours:**
Notts Senior Cup Winners 1981-82

### 10 YEAR RECORD

| 03-04 | | 04-05 | | 05-06 | | 06-07 | | 07-08 | | 08-09 | | 09-10 | | 10-11 | | 11-12 | | 12-13 | |
|---|---|---|---|---|---|---|---|---|---|---|---|---|---|---|---|---|---|---|---|
| CM P | 3 | CM Su | 20 | CM Su | 9 | CM Su | 3 | NCE1 | 4 | NCE1 | 2 | NCEP | 2 | NP1S | 20 | NP1S | 19 | NP1N | 14 |

# ROMULUS

**Chairman:** Andrew Wilson
**Secretary:** Peter Lowe     **(T)** 07738 604 391     **(E)** peterwloweuk@yahoo.co.uk
**Commercial Manager:** Andy Mitchell     **(T)**
**Programme Editor:** Paul Dockerill     **(T)** 07711 856 551
**Ground Address:** Sutton Coldfield FC, Central Ground, Coles Lane B72 1NL
**(T)** 0121 354 2997     **Manager:** Richard Evans

## Club Factfile

**Founded:** 1979     **Nickname:** The Roms
**Previous Names:** None
**Previous Leagues:** Midland Combination 1999-2004, Midland Alliance 2004-07, Southern 2007-2010

**Club Colours (change):** Red and white/red/red (Yellow/black/yellow)

**Ground Capacity:** 4,500   **Seats:** 200   **Covered:** 500   **Clubhouse:** Yes   **Shop:** Yes

**Directions**
From M42 Junc 9, take A4097 (Minworth sign). At island, follow signs to Walmley Village. At traffic lights turn right (B4148). After shops turn left at traffic lights into Wylde Green Road. Over railway bridge turn right into East View Road, which becomes Coles Lane.

**Previous Grounds:** Penns Lane.

**Record Attendance:** Not known
**Record Victory:** Not known
**Record Defeat:** Not known
**Record Goalscorer:** Not known
**Record Appearances:** Not known
**Additional Records:** Players who have progress: Dean Sturridge, Stuart Bowen, Luke Rogers, Darius Vassell and Zat Knight.
**Senior Honours:**
Midland Combination Division One 1999-00, Premier Division 2003-04, Challenge Cup 03-04.

### 10 YEAR RECORD

| 03-04 | | 04-05 | | 05-06 | | 06-07 | | 07-08 | | 08-09 | | 09-10 | | 10-11 | | 11-12 | | 12-13 | |
|---|---|---|---|---|---|---|---|---|---|---|---|---|---|---|---|---|---|---|---|
| MCmP | 1 | MidAl | 12 | MidAl | 4 | MidAl | 2 | SthM | 10 | SthM | 11 | SthM | 8 | NP1S | 10 | NP1S | 20 | NP1S | 19 |

# SCARBOROUGH ATHLETIC

**Chairman:** David Holland

**Secretary:** John Clarke  **(T)** 07545 878 467  **(E)**

**Commercial Manager:** Andy Troughton  **(T)** andy@scarboroughathletic.com

**Programme Editor:** Stuart Fairbridge  **(T)** 07850 480 352

**Ground Address:** Bridlington FC, Queensgate, Bridlington, East Yorks YO16 7LN

**(T)** 01262 606 879  **Manager:** Rudy Funk

Scarborough Athletic's 2012-13 U19 Squad.

## Club Factfile

**Founded:** 2007  **Nickname:** The Seadogs

**Previous Names:** Formed after Scarborough F.C. folded in 2007.

**Previous Leagues:** Northern Counties East 2007-13.

**Club Colours (change):** All Red (All orange).

**Ground Capacity:** 3000  **Seats:** 500  **Covered:** 1,200  **Clubhouse:** Yes  **Shop:** No

**Directions**

From South (Hull, Beeford, Barmston): Approach Bridlington on the A165, passing golf course on right and Broadacres Pub, Kingsmead Estate on left. Straight through traffic lights to roundabout by B&Q. Turn right. At traffic lights turn left and over the railway bridge. At roundabout bear left and carry on heading north up Quay Road. After traffic lights turn right into Queensgate. Ground is 800 yards up the road on the right.

From South and West (Driffield, Hull, York): Approach Bridlington on A614. (This was formally the A166). Straight on at traffic lights (Hospital on right) and follow the road round the bend. At roundabout straight across to mini roundabout and bear right (second exit). Follow road around to right and to traffic lights. Straight on. At next traffic lights (just after Kwikfit) turn left into Queensgate. Ground is 800 yards up the road on the right.

From North (Scarborough): Approach Bridlington (Esso garage on right) at roundabout turn left then at mini roundabout second exit. Follow road around to right and to traffic lights. Straight on. At next traffic lights (just after Kwikfit) turn left into Queensgate. Ground is 800 yards up the road on the right.

**Previous Grounds:** None

**Record Attendance:** Att: 791 v Leeds Carnegie N.C.E. Div.1 - 25.04.09.

**Record Victory:** 13-0 v Brodsworth, Northern Counties East, 2009-10.

**Record Defeat:**

**Record Goalscorer:**

**Record Appearances:**

**Additional Records:**

**Senior Honours:**

Northern Counties East Division One 2008-09, Premier 2012-13.

| 10 YEAR RECORD | | | | | | | | | |
|---|---|---|---|---|---|---|---|---|---|
| 03-04 | 04-05 | 05-06 | 06-07 | 07-08 | 08-09 | 09-10 | 10-11 | 11-12 | 12-13 |
| | | | | NCE1 5 | NCE1 1 | NCEP 5 | NCEP 10 | NCEP 3 | NCEP 1 |

# SHEFFIELD

**Chairman:** Richard Tims

**Secretary:** Stephen Hall      **(T)** 07761 207 447    **(E)**

**Commercial Manager:**      **(T)**

**Programme Editor:** Stuart James      **(T)** 07709 225 110

**Ground Address:** The BT Local Business Stadium, Sheffield Road, Dronfield S18 2GD

**(T)** 01246 292 622      **Manager:** Ian Whitehouse

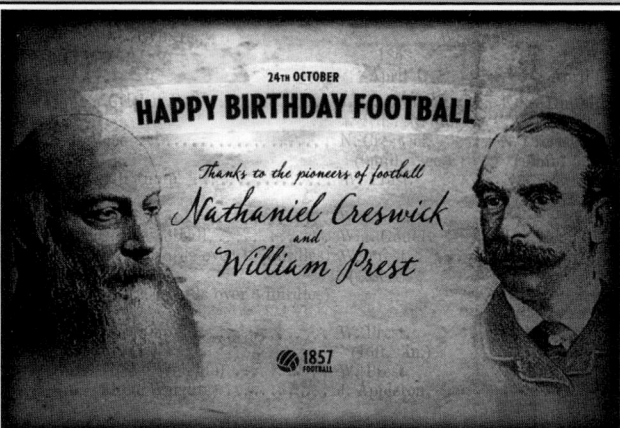

24th of October: Happy Birthday Football! In recognition of the 155th anniversary of the club and in memory of the founders, Nathaniel Creswick and William Prest, the Sheffield FC Foundation celebrated the pioneering spirit of football with fans, clubs and football associations from all over the world. This event has now become "World Football Day" - one day for the global football community to remember and celebrate the pioneers and inventors of the game.

## Club Factfile

**Founded:** 1857    **Nickname:** Not known

**Previous Names:** None

**Previous Leagues:** Yorkshire 1949-82

**Club Colours (change):** Red/black/red (All blue)

**Ground Capacity:** 1,456    **Seats:** 250    **Covered:** 500    **Clubhouse:** Yes    **Shop:** Yes

**Directions**

**From the South** – M1 to Junc 29, A617 into Chesterfield. At Roundabout follow A61 Sheffield. This is a dual carriageway passing over 2 roundabouts. At the 3rd roundabout take the 3rd exit signposted Dronfield. The Coach and Horses Public House is at the bottom of the hill on the right and the BT Local Business Stadium directly behind it. Entrance to the ground is by turning right at the traffic lights and immediate right into the Club Car Park. **From the East** – M18 to M1 north to Junc 33 (Sheffield). Turn towards Sheffield and take the 3rd exit from dual carriageway signposted 'Ring Road / Chesterfield'. Go straight on at traffic island so that you are travelling alongside dual carriageway for a short period. At the junction turn left onto A61 Chesterfield. This is a dual carriageway passing through numerous traffic lights and two traffic islands. Follow Chesterfield sign at all times. After passing Graves Tennis centre on your left, turn left at next traffic island (still signposted Chesterfield). At next traffic island take 2nd exit signposted Dronfield The Coach and Horses Public House is at the bottom of the hill on the right and the BT Local Business Stadium directly behind it. Entrance to the ground is by turning right at the traffic lights and immediate right into the Club Car Park.

**Previous Grounds:** Abbeydale Park, Dore 1956-89, Sheffield Amateur Sports Stadium, Hillsborough Park 1989-91, Don Valley Stadium 1991-97

**Record Attendance:** 2,000 v Barton Rovers - FA Vase Semi-final 1976-77

**Record Victory:** Not known

**Record Defeat:** Not known

**Record Goalscorer:** Not known

**Record Appearances:** Not known

**Additional Records:** Paid £1,000 to Arnold Town for David Wilkins. Received £1,000 from Alfreton for Mick Godber 2002.

**Senior Honours:** World's first ever Football Club.

FA Amateur Cup 1902-03. Northern Counties East Division 1 1988-89, 90-91, League Cup 2000-01, 04-05.
Sheffield and Hallamshire Senior Cup 1993-94, 2004-05, 05-06.

## 10 YEAR RECORD

| 03-04 | | 04-05 | | 05-06 | | 06-07 | | 07-08 | | 08-09 | | 09-10 | | 10-11 | | 11-12 | | 12-13 | |
|---|---|---|---|---|---|---|---|---|---|---|---|---|---|---|---|---|---|---|---|
| NCEP | 4 | NCEP | 4 | NCEP | 4 | NCEP | 2 | NP 1 | 4 | NP1S | 11 | NP1S | 5 | NP1S | 11 | NP1S | 4 | NP1S | 9 |

# SUTTON COLDFIELD TOWN

**Chairman:** Nick Thurston

**Secretary:** Bill Worship          **(T)** 07837 375 369          **(E)** billandpatworship@tiscali.co.uk

**Commercial Manager:**                                   **(T)**

**Programme Editor:** Lyn Coley                     **(T)** 0121 240 5421

**Ground Address:** Central Ground, Coles Lane, Sutton Coldfield B72 1NL

**(T)** 0121 354 2997                                **Manager:** Neil Tooth

## Club Factfile

**Founded:**  1897       **Nickname:** Royals

**Previous Names:** Sutton Coldfield F.C. 1879-1921

**Previous Leagues:** Central Birmingham, Walsall Senior, Staffordshire County, Birmingham Combination 1950-54, West Midlands (Regional) 1954-65, 79-82, Midlands Combination 1965-79

**Club Colours (change):** All blue (All yellow)

**Ground Capacity:** 4,500  **Seats:** 200     **Covered:** 500     **Clubhouse:** Yes     **Shop:** Yes

**Directions** From M42 Junc 9, take A4097 [Minworth sign]. At island, follow signs to Walmley Village. At traffic lights turn right [B4148]. After shops turn left at traffic lights into Wylde Green Road. Over railway bridge turn right into East View Road, which becomes Coles Lane.

**Previous Grounds:** Meadow Plat 1879-89, Coles Lane 1890-1919

**Record Attendance:** 2,029 v Doncaster Rovers - FA Cup 1980-81

**Record Victory:** Not known

**Record Defeat:** Not known

**Record Goalscorer:** Eddie Hewitt - 288

**Record Appearances:** Andy Ling - 550

**Additional Records:** Paid £1,500 to Gloucester for Lance Morrison, to Burton Albion for Micky Clarke and to Atherstone United for

**Senior Honours:**       Steve Farmer 1991. Received £25,000 from West Bromwich Albion for Barry Cowdrill 1979

West Midlands League 1979-80. Midland Combination x2.

### 10 YEAR RECORD

| 03-04 | | 04-05 | | 05-06 | | 06-07 | | 07-08 | | 08-09 | | 09-10 | | 10-11 | | 11-12 | | 12-13 | |
|---|---|---|---|---|---|---|---|---|---|---|---|---|---|---|---|---|---|---|---|
| SthW | 8 | SthW | 18 | SthW | 7 | SthM | 12 | SthM | 4 | SthM | 6 | SthM | 6 | NP1S | 6 | NP1S | 12 | NP1S | 6 |

# Premier Division Action

AFC Fylde keeper, Ben Hinchcliffe, punches clear from this Rushall attack.
Photo: Jonathan Holloway.

Rushall's No.6, Dave Walker, is under pressure in this Fylde attack.
Photo: Jonathan Holloway.

# PREMIER DIVISION 2012-13

| | | P | W | D | L | F | A | GD | Pts |
|---|---|---|---|---|---|---|---|---|---|
| 1 | (P) Leamington | 42 | 30 | 5 | 7 | 85 | 46 | 39 | 95 |
| 2 | Stourbridge | 42 | 25 | 8 | 9 | 94 | 42 | 52 | 83 |
| 3 | Chesham United | 42 | 21 | 12 | 9 | 69 | 48 | 21 | 75 |
| 4 | Hemel Hempstead Town | 42 | 22 | 6 | 14 | 95 | 71 | 24 | 72 |
| 5 | (P) Gosport Borough | 42 | 19 | 13 | 10 | 78 | 43 | 35 | 70 |
| 6 | Arlesey Town | 42 | 21 | 6 | 15 | 70 | 51 | 19 | 69 |
| 7 | Barwell | 42 | 19 | 12 | 11 | 67 | 50 | 17 | 69 |
| 8 | Cambridge City | 42 | 20 | 6 | 16 | 63 | 57 | 6 | 66 |
| 9 | Weymouth | 42 | 18 | 8 | 16 | 59 | 71 | −12 | 62 |
| 10 | Bedford Town | 42 | 18 | 7 | 17 | 61 | 56 | 5 | 61 |
| 11 | St Albans City | 42 | 18 | 6 | 18 | 81 | 71 | 10 | 60 |
| 12 | St Neots Town | 42 | 15 | 7 | 20 | 77 | 77 | 0 | 52 |
| 13 | Hitchin Town | 42 | 15 | 7 | 20 | 62 | 68 | −6 | 52 |
| 14 | A.F.C. Totton | 42 | 15 | 7 | 20 | 62 | 84 | −22 | 52 |
| 15 | Chippenham Town | 42 | 13 | 12 | 17 | 63 | 67 | −4 | 51 |
| 16 | Banbury United | 42 | 14 | 9 | 19 | 60 | 75 | −15 | 51 |
| 17 | Bashley | 42 | 13 | 10 | 19 | 47 | 63 | −16 | 49 |
| 18 | Frome Town | 42 | 11 | 12 | 19 | 40 | 55 | −15 | 45 |
| 19 | Redditch United | 42 | 12 | 7 | 23 | 32 | 65 | −33 | 43 |
| 20 | Bideford | 42 | 11 | 9 | 22 | 58 | 73 | −15 | 42 |
| 21 | (R) Bedworth United | 42 | 11 | 9 | 22 | 39 | 73 | −34 | 42 |
| 22 | (R) Kettering Town (-10pts) | 42 | 8 | 8 | 26 | 47 | 102 | −55 | 22 |

## PLAY-OFFS
### Semi-Finals
Stourbridge 1-2 Gosport Borough
Chesham United 0-2 Hemel Hempstead Town

### Final (@ Hemel Hempstead 06/05/13)
Hemel Hempstead Town 2-2 Gosport Borough (Gosport won 5-4 on penalties)

| | | 1 | 2 | 3 | 4 | 5 | 6 | 7 | 8 | 9 | 10 | 11 | 12 | 13 | 14 | 15 | 16 | 17 | 18 | 19 | 20 | 21 | 22 |
|---|---|---|---|---|---|---|---|---|---|---|---|---|---|---|---|---|---|---|---|---|---|---|---|
| 1 | AFC Totton | | 3-3 | 2-3 | 2-1 | 2-0 | 2-0 | 3-2 | 2-0 | 1-5 | 1-1 | 0-5 | 2-0 | 3-2 | 2-0 | 4-0 | 2-2 | 0-2 | 2-0 | 3-0 | 2-1 | 2-4 | 5-2 |
| 2 | Arlesey Town | 5-0 | | 2-1 | 0-1 | 1-2 | 2-1 | 1-0 | 2-2 | 1-2 | 2-0 | 4-0 | 0-1 | 1-1 | 3-1 | 3-0 | 3-1 | 0-2 | 3-0 | 1-3 | 4-3 | 2-4 | 3-0 |
| 3 | Banbury United | 2-1 | 1-3 | | 1-2 | 3-1 | 1-1 | 1-1 | 1-1 | 2-2 | 1-2 | 1-0 | 1-1 | 2-4 | 4-0 | 2-0 | 0-4 | 3-0 | 0-0 | 2-2 | 3-1 | 0-2 | 1-3 |
| 4 | Barwell | 1-0 | 2-0 | 4-1 | | 0-0 | 2-1 | 2-0 | 1-1 | 1-0 | 1-3 | 0-0 | 1-1 | 1-2 | 2-2 | 1-2 | 1-0 | 1-3 | 0-0 | 1-3 | 2-3 | 2-1 | 0-1 |
| 5 | Bashley | 0-3 | 1-0 | 2-0 | 0-5 | | 0-1 | 1-0 | 4-1 | 0-0 | 1-3 | 2-1 | 2-1 | 1-1 | 0-6 | 3-1 | 0-1 | 0-2 | 0-1 | 2-0 | 2-2 | 0-1 | 1-0 |
| 6 | Bedford Town | 4-1 | 0-0 | 3-1 | 3-0 | 0-1 | | 0-1 | 3-1 | 2-1 | 0-1 | 1-1 | 1-0 | 0-3 | 1-1 | 1-4 | 2-2 | 2-1 | 2-0 | 3-0 | 2-0 | 0-2 | 0-2 |
| 7 | Bedworth United | 2-0 | 2-1 | 0-4 | 1-1 | 0-3 | 2-0 | | 2-1 | 0-2 | 1-1 | 2-2 | 1-0 | 1-1 | 1-2 | 0-1 | 1-0 | 0-3 | 0-0 | 1-1 | 1-3 | 0-3 | 2-0 |
| 8 | Bideford | 1-1 | 1-1 | 1-2 | 1-2 | 0-0 | 0-3 | 3-0 | | 2-1 | 2-1 | 1-2 | 0-0 | 0-2 | 3-2 | 4-0 | 3-2 | 0-1 | 3-2 | 1-0 | 0-0 | 2-2 | 2-1 |
| 9 | Cambridge City | 0-0 | 1-2 | 1-0 | 2-1 | 3-1 | 2-1 | 3-0 | 1-0 | | 1-0 | 2-3 | 1-2 | 0-4 | 0-1 | 1-1 | 0-0 | 1-4 | 1-0 | 2-1 | 0-5 | 2-2 | 2-0 |
| 10 | Chesham United | 6-0 | 1-0 | 3-1 | 2-2 | 3-0 | 2-2 | 3-0 | 1-0 | 1-0 | | 1-1 | 1-1 | 0-3 | 0-0 | 0-0 | 1-1 | 1-1 | 2-1 | 2-1 | 2-1 | 1-1 | 1-2 |
| 11 | Chippenham Town | 3-0 | 1-0 | 0-2 | 1-1 | 1-0 | 0-2 | 1-1 | 1-7 | 4-3 | 2-3 | | 2-2 | 0-0 | 1-2 | 3-0 | 2-4 | 2-3 | 4-3 | 2-2 | 4-0 | 2-2 | 2-0 |
| 12 | Frome Town | 3-1 | 0-1 | 0-0 | 2-3 | 1-1 | 2-3 | 1-3 | 0-1 | 0-3 | 0-0 | 2-0 | | 1-1 | 1-3 | 3-1 | 2-1 | 0-2 | 1-0 | 0-3 | 1-2 | 0-1 | 2-0 |
| 13 | Gosport Borough | 1-0 | 0-1 | 3-2 | 1-2 | 0-0 | 4-0 | 1-0 | 2-0 | 1-2 | 3-1 | 2-3 | 0-0 | | 3-3 | 7-0 | 0-0 | 3-0 | 2-3 | 0-1 | 1-0 | 1-3 | 0-0 |
| 14 | Hemel Hempstead Town | 4-1 | 1-2 | 1-2 | 1-1 | 4-2 | 4-3 | 6-1 | 4-1 | 1-0 | 1-2 | 2-1 | 0-3 | 1-1 | | 5-2 | 8-2 | 1-3 | 4-0 | 1-1 | 2-4 | 2-1 | 1-3 |
| 15 | Hitchin Town | 1-1 | 1-3 | 1-1 | 1-2 | 0-7 | 3-0 | 1-4 | 3-1 | 1-2 | 3-1 | 2-4 | 1-1 | 1-3 | 1-2 | | 3-1 | 1-3 | 0-1 | 2-6 | 1-0 | 0-1 | 1-6 |
| 16 | Kettering Town | 4-0 | 0-1 | 1-2 | 0-1 | 3-2 | 2-0 | 1-1 | 1-0 | 0-3 | 1-3 | 2-1 | 1-0 | 3-2 | 3-4 | | 0-1 | 3-0 | 0-2 | 2-2 | 0-1 | 1-2 | |
| 17 | Leamington | 2-1 | 4-3 | 4-1 | 0-6 | 4-1 | 3-0 | 6-1 | 2-1 | 1-0 | 0-1 | 1-0 | 2-0 | 1-3 | 3-2 | 2-1 | 3-0 | | 2-0 | 2-1 | 3-0 | 1-1 | 1-1 |
| 18 | Redditch United | 2-1 | 0-2 | 0-2 | 0-1 | 0-0 | 0-3 | 0-0 | 2-1 | 2-4 | 0-2 | 1-0 | 2-1 | 0-2 | 1-4 | 4-1 | 0-2 | 1-1 | | 0-2 | 1-0 | 0-4 | 0-0 |
| 19 | St Albans City | 3-0 | 1-0 | 4-0 | 4-4 | 2-2 | 2-2 | 3-0 | 4-3 | 3-2 | 2-6 | 0-2 | 4-0 | 1-6 | 0-1 | 2-1 | 1-1 | 3-0 | 3-0 | | 0-1 | 2-4 | 2-3 |
| 20 | St Neots Town | 1-3 | 1-2 | 3-2 | 2-2 | 2-2 | 1-3 | 3-2 | 5-3 | 2-3 | 3-1 | 0-1 | 0-1 | 2-3 | 6-1 | 4-3 | 2-3 | 0-1 | 1-2 | 3-2 | | 0-0 | 4-2 |
| 21 | Stourbridge | 3-0 | 4-1 | 8-1 | 0-2 | 3-0 | 0-1 | 0-1 | 3-1 | 4-1 | 5-0 | 2-1 | 1-1 | 1-1 | 2-3 | 0-0 | 4-1 | 5-1 | 1-0 | 2-1 | 0-1 | | 5-0 |
| 22 | Weymouth | 3-3 | 2-1 | 1-0 | 2-1 | 1-0 | 0-4 | 2-1 | 4-2 | 0-1 | 0-3 | 0-0 | 2-1 | 3-3 | 0-1 | 0-0 | 3-2 | 0-4 | 0-2 | 2-0 | 3-1 | 1-5 | |

# DIVISION ONE CENTRAL 2012-13

| | | P | W | D | L | F | A | GD | Pts |
|---|---|---|---|---|---|---|---|---|---|
| 1 | (P) Burnham | 42 | 31 | 6 | 5 | 108 | 39 | 69 | 99 |
| 2 | Rugby Town | 42 | 31 | 3 | 8 | 103 | 45 | 58 | 96 |
| 3 | Godalming Town | 42 | 28 | 8 | 6 | 94 | 39 | 55 | 92 |
| 4 | (P) Biggleswade Town | 42 | 26 | 7 | 9 | 97 | 50 | 47 | 85 |
| 5 | Beaconsfield SYCOB | 42 | 26 | 6 | 10 | 81 | 47 | 34 | 84 |
| 6 | Slough Town | 42 | 26 | 5 | 11 | 103 | 50 | 53 | 83 |
| 7 | Royston Town | 42 | 24 | 10 | 8 | 86 | 49 | 37 | 82 |
| 8 | Daventry Town | 42 | 22 | 10 | 10 | 81 | 47 | 34 | 76 |
| 9 | Guildford City | 42 | 20 | 6 | 16 | 86 | 75 | 11 | 66 |
| 10 | Ashford Town | 42 | 17 | 10 | 15 | 85 | 79 | 6 | 61 |
| 11 | Uxbridge | 42 | 19 | 4 | 19 | 78 | 85 | −7 | 61 |
| 12 | Aylesbury | 42 | 16 | 10 | 16 | 76 | 73 | 3 | 58 |
| 13 | Northwood | 42 | 17 | 6 | 19 | 80 | 73 | 7 | 57 |
| 14 | Barton Rovers | 42 | 16 | 5 | 21 | 62 | 78 | −16 | 53 |
| 15 | A.F.C. Hayes | 42 | 13 | 8 | 21 | 73 | 81 | −8 | 47 |
| 16 | Chalfont St Peter (-15pts) | 42 | 18 | 7 | 17 | 76 | 74 | 2 | 46 |
| 17 | Thatcham Town | 42 | 10 | 5 | 27 | 59 | 86 | −27 | 35 |
| 18 | Fleet Town | 42 | 10 | 5 | 27 | 47 | 76 | −29 | 35 |
| 19 | North Greenford United | 42 | 9 | 6 | 27 | 56 | 95 | −39 | 33 |
| 20 | Chertsey Town | 42 | 9 | 4 | 29 | 50 | 98 | −48 | 31 |
| 21 | Leighton Town | 42 | 6 | 5 | 31 | 43 | 121 | −78 | 23 |
| 22 | (R) Woodford United | 42 | 0 | 0 | 42 | 21 | 185 | −164 | 0 |

## PLAY-OFFS
Semi-Finals
Rugby Town 1-0 Beaconsfield SYCOB (AET)
Godalming Town 1-2 Biggleswade Town

Final (@ Rugby Town 06/05/13)
Rugby Town 1-3 Biggleswade Town

| | | 1 | 2 | 3 | 4 | 5 | 6 | 7 | 8 | 9 | 10 | 11 | 12 | 13 | 14 | 15 | 16 | 17 | 18 | 19 | 20 | 21 | 22 |
|---|---|---|---|---|---|---|---|---|---|---|---|---|---|---|---|---|---|---|---|---|---|---|---|
| 1 | AFC Hayes | | 3-1 | 3-4 | 3-1 | 6-0 | 1-1 | 0-3 | 1-3 | 3-0 | 1-1 | 3-1 | 1-2 | 0-6 | 2-2 | 1-3 | 0-3 | 1-1 | 1-2 | 3-0 | 1-3 | 3-2 | 2-1 |
| 2 | Ashford Town (Middlesex) | 2-1 | | 1-1 | 2-2 | 2-1 | 4-0 | 2-3 | 1-1 | 2-1 | 3-2 | 5-0 | 1-5 | 1-3 | 3-1 | 3-2 | 4-0 | 1-1 | 1-4 | 0-1 | 1-1 | 3-5 | 10-0 |
| 3 | Aylesbury | 6-2 | 2-2 | | 2-1 | 2-1 | 3-2 | 2-2 | 2-2 | 3-1 | 0-2 | 1-4 | 0-5 | 1-2 | 1-1 | 1-1 | 3-0 | 1-1 | 0-2 | 1-4 | 3-0 | 5-2 | 7-0 |
| 4 | Barton Rovers | 0-0 | 1-2 | 3-2 | | 1-4 | 1-2 | 1-6 | 1-1 | 3-0 | 1-2 | 2-0 | 0-2 | 3-1 | 3-0 | 2-1 | 2-1 | 1-3 | 0-1 | 2-2 | 2-0 | 1-3 | 2-1 |
| 5 | Beaconsfield SYCOB | 2-2 | 0-2 | 1-1 | 3-1 | | 4-0 | 2-1 | 2-0 | 4-0 | 3-1 | 4-2 | 0-2 | 3-2 | 1-0 | 3-0 | 0-2 | 1-0 | 1-2 | 1-1 | 2-1 | 1-1 | 3-0 |
| 6 | Biggleswade Town | 3-1 | 4-2 | 1-1 | 5-2 | 1-0 | | 0-3 | 5-2 | 5-1 | 0-1 | 1-0 | 3-2 | 2-1 | 5-0 | 2-0 | 2-1 | 1-0 | 2-1 | 3-1 | 2-1 | 3-1 | 2-1 |
| 7 | Burnham | 2-1 | 3-0 | 2-0 | 3-2 | 0-0 | 0-3 | | 1-0 | 2-0 | 2-2 | 1-0 | 1-0 | 3-2 | 6-0 | 1-0 | 1-1 | 2-3 | 1-0 | 5-1 | 2-1 | 7-0 | |
| 8 | Chalfont St Peter | 5-1 | 2-2 | 3-1 | 2-3 | 1-3 | 0-5 | 1-1 | | 2-1 | 1-4 | 2-1 | 2-2 | 2-1 | 1-0 | 1-1 | 0-4 | 1-2 | 0-3 | 1-2 | 2-0 | 3-0 | 7-1 |
| 9 | Chertsey Town | 0-1 | 1-1 | 1-2 | 0-3 | 1-4 | 0-4 | 0-4 | 1-2 | | 1-5 | 1-0 | 1-0 | 1-3 | 2-2 | 2-1 | 3-2 | 1-2 | 1-1 | 1-3 | 2-4 | 3-2 | 4-1 |
| 10 | Daventry Town | 0-2 | 2-1 | 0-0 | 3-0 | 0-1 | 1-1 | 3-4 | 2-1 | 2-0 | | 2-1 | 1-2 | 1-1 | 4-0 | 1-1 | 1-0 | 4-2 | 4-1 | 3-1 | 1-1 | 4-1 | 3-0 |
| 11 | Fleet Town | 0-3 | 2-0 | 1-0 | 0-2 | 0-1 | 0-2 | 1-3 | 3-1 | 0-1 | | 0-3 | 2-1 | 0-1 | 4-0 | 1-2 | 0-0 | 2-1 | 2-5 | 0-2 | 2-4 | 5-0 | |
| 12 | Godalming Town | 1-3 | 3-3 | 1-0 | 1-0 | 0-2 | 1-0 | 1-0 | 4-0 | 1-1 | 1-0 | 2-0 | | 2-0 | 5-0 | 1-1 | 3-0 | 2-2 | 1-2 | 2-1 | 4-1 | 4-0 | |
| 13 | Guildford City | 0-2 | 2-3 | 0-1 | 4-2 | 0-1 | 1-3 | 0-3 | 3-2 | 2-1 | 2-0 | 4-1 | 1-1 | | 1-0 | 3-2 | 3-1 | 2-2 | 2-1 | 1-1 | 2-2 | 2-1 | 4-1 |
| 14 | Leighton Town | 0-5 | 0-1 | 3-5 | 0-2 | 2-4 | 0-4 | 2-3 | 0-3 | 1-4 | 2-3 | 0-0 | 1-4 | 0-6 | | 0-2 | 2-3 | 1-1 | 1-2 | 0-3 | 3-1 | 0-1 | 4-0 |
| 15 | North Greenford United | 3-2 | 1-3 | 0-1 | 1-2 | 0-2 | 0-0 | 0-3 | 3-2 | 4-1 | 1-2 | 1-3 | 2-4 | 5-4 | 3-4 | | 1-3 | 1-2 | 1-2 | 1-3 | 0-3 | 3-4 | 1-0 |
| 16 | Northwood | 5-3 | 1-3 | 3-2 | 2-2 | 2-3 | 1-1 | 1-2 | 1-3 | 1-1 | 3-1 | 1-2 | 1-2 | 3-0 | 1-1 | | 2-3 | 0-3 | 2-1 | 2-1 | 3-0 | 5-1 | |
| 17 | Royston Town | 2-0 | 2-0 | 3-2 | 3-0 | 3-2 | 3-1 | 1-1 | 4-2 | 1-0 | 2-1 | 0-0 | 1-0 | 3-2 | 8-0 | 2-0 | 2-2 | | 2-1 | 2-0 | 2-0 | 4-2 | |
| 18 | Rugby Town | 2-1 | 4-0 | 3-0 | 5-0 | 3-0 | 2-2 | 2-3 | 2-1 | 2-1 | 2-0 | 2-0 | 0-3 | 6-1 | 5-0 | 3-0 | 1-2 | 2-1 | | 0-4 | 4-2 | 6-2 | 2-1 |
| 19 | Slough Town | 2-1 | 6-1 | 4-3 | 3-1 | 1-1 | 3-1 | 2-0 | 0-1 | 3-0 | 1-1 | 3-1 | 2-3 | 1-2 | 5-1 | 3-0 | 5-0 | 3-1 | 2-3 | | 4-1 | 1-3 | 4-0 |
| 20 | Thatcham Town | 1-1 | 3-2 | 1-2 | 2-1 | 1-2 | 1-4 | 0-2 | 0-1 | 2-0 | 0-4 | 2-4 | 1-2 | 1-3 | 1-0 | 0-2 | 1-4 | 0-2 | 0-1 | 0-2 | | 2-1 | 5-0 |
| 21 | Uxbridge | 1-0 | 2-2 | 2-1 | 0-1 | 0-2 | 1-0 | 2-3 | 1-2 | 2-0 | 2-2 | 1-1 | 1-4 | 3-2 | 5-1 | 2-1 | 1-0 | 0-2 | 1-2 | 3-2 | 5-4 | | 4-0 |
| 22 | Woodford United | 1-3 | 0-2 | 0-1 | 0-2 | 0-6 | 0-10 | 0-7 | 1-5 | 3-7 | 0-4 | 0-2 | 1-2 | 0-3 | 4-5 | 2-5 | 0-5 | 1-4 | 0-7 | 1-4 | 1-8 | 0-2 | |

# DIVISION ONE SOUTH & WEST 2012-13

| | | P | W | D | L | F | A | GD | Pts |
|---|---|---|---|---|---|---|---|---|---|
| 1 | (P) Poole Town | 42 | 30 | 8 | 4 | 82 | 36 | 46 | 98 |
| 2 | (P) Hungerford Town | 42 | 26 | 6 | 10 | 71 | 44 | 27 | 84 |
| 3 | Merthyr Town | 42 | 24 | 11 | 7 | 84 | 38 | 46 | 83 |
| 4 | Swindon Supermarine | 42 | 25 | 6 | 11 | 79 | 51 | 28 | 81 |
| 5 | Paulton Rovers | 42 | 23 | 6 | 13 | 64 | 54 | 10 | 75 |
| 6 | Yate Town | 42 | 21 | 6 | 15 | 69 | 63 | 6 | 69 |
| 7 | Sholing* | 42 | 20 | 8 | 14 | 87 | 56 | 31 | 68 |
| 8 | Shortwood United | 42 | 20 | 7 | 15 | 62 | 45 | 17 | 67 |
| 9 | North Leigh | 42 | 19 | 4 | 19 | 70 | 69 | 1 | 61 |
| 10 | Cinderford Town | 42 | 17 | 8 | 17 | 61 | 66 | −5 | 59 |
| 11 | Cirencester Town (-1pt) | 42 | 15 | 13 | 14 | 54 | 57 | −3 | 57 |
| 12 | Wimborne Town | 42 | 15 | 10 | 17 | 59 | 60 | −1 | 55 |
| 13 | Mangotsfield United | 42 | 15 | 10 | 17 | 53 | 61 | −8 | 55 |
| 14 | Evesham United | 42 | 14 | 9 | 19 | 49 | 58 | −9 | 51 |
| 15 | Clevedon Town | 42 | 12 | 13 | 17 | 61 | 67 | −6 | 49 |
| 16 | Tiverton Town | 42 | 11 | 14 | 17 | 51 | 58 | −7 | 47 |
| 17 | Didcot Town | 42 | 12 | 10 | 20 | 59 | 76 | −17 | 46 |
| 18 | Taunton Town | 42 | 12 | 8 | 22 | 59 | 85 | −26 | 44 |
| 19 | Bridgwater Town | 42 | 10 | 10 | 22 | 52 | 78 | −26 | 40 |
| 20 | Abingdon United | 42 | 10 | 8 | 24 | 42 | 66 | −24 | 38 |
| 21 | Bishop's Cleeve | 42 | 10 | 7 | 25 | 49 | 66 | −17 | 37 |
| 22 | (R) Winchester City (-3pts) | 42 | 9 | 2 | 31 | 42 | 105 | −63 | 26 |

* Sholing resigned at the end of the season.

## PLAY-OFFS
### Semi-Finals
Hungerford Town 4-2 Paulton Rovers (AET)
Merthyr Town 2-2 Swindon Supermarine (Merthyr won 3-2 on penalties AET)

### Final @ Hungerford Town 06/05/13)
Hungerford Town 3-1 Merthyr Town (AET)

| | 1 | 2 | 3 | 4 | 5 | 6 | 7 | 8 | 9 | 10 | 11 | 12 | 13 | 14 | 15 | 16 | 17 | 18 | 19 | 20 | 21 | 22 |
|---|---|---|---|---|---|---|---|---|---|---|---|---|---|---|---|---|---|---|---|---|---|---|
| 1 Abingdon United | | 2-0 | 3-1 | 3-0 | 0-2 | 3-1 | 0-1 | 1-0 | 0-0 | 1-2 | 0-0 | 0-2 | 0-0 | 0-4 | 1-3 | 0-2 | 1-3 | 3-0 | 2-0 | 1-3 | 1-2 | 1-2 |
| 2 Bishops Cleeve | 2-0 | | 1-1 | 1-4 | 0-3 | 1-0 | 4-1 | 3-0 | 1-2 | 2-2 | 2-3 | 1-2 | 0-1 | 1-1 | 0-1 | 0-2 | 1-2 | 3-0 | 2-3 | 1-3 | 5-1 | 0-2 |
| 3 Bridgwater Town | 3-0 | 3-0 | | 1-0 | 1-1 | 0-2 | 1-1 | 1-1 | 1-2 | 1-1 | 0-1 | 1-4 | 1-3 | 1-4 | 2-2 | 0-5 | 0-4 | 0-3 | 0-0 | 0-0 | 3-0 | 1-2 |
| 4 Cinderford Town | 1-0 | 2-1 | 2-1 | | 1-2 | 2-1 | 3-3 | 3-2 | 1-0 | 1-1 | 0-0 | 4-3 | 3-1 | 1-2 | 3-2 | 1-2 | 0-1 | 2-1 | 1-3 | 0-1 | 2-0 | 2-2 |
| 5 Cirencester Town | 2-1 | 2-4 | 1-6 | 2-2 | | 3-1 | 2-0 | 1-3 | 0-3 | 1-0 | 0-3 | 1-3 | 0-1 | 3-2 | 0-1 | 0-0 | 2-1 | 1-1 | 1-1 | 3-1 | 1-4 | 1-1 |
| 6 Clevedon Town | 2-3 | 1-1 | 1-1 | 1-1 | 3-2 | | 1-1 | 1-1 | 2-5 | 2-2 | 1-2 | 2-1 | 0-1 | 0-0 | 3-1 | 0-0 | 1-2 | 1-1 | 3-1 | 3-1 | 1-4 | 1-1 |
| 7 Didcot Town | 1-0 | 0-1 | 0-2 | 1-1 | 2-2 | 2-1 | | 0-1 | 1-2 | 2-3 | 0-1 | 1-0 | 3-4 | 0-4 | 1-0 | 1-0 | 1-2 | 3-0 | 4-1 | 2-2 | 5-2 | 2-0 |
| 8 Evesham United | 1-1 | 1-0 | 0-1 | 1-2 | 0-0 | 3-2 | 2-4 | | 0-1 | 0-2 | 1-1 | 1-0 | 0-2 | 2-3 | 1-0 | 1-2 | 0-2 | 2-4 | 2-0 | 3-0 | 0-2 | 3-0 |
| 9 Hungerford Town | 2-0 | 1-0 | 2-0 | 3-2 | 0-1 | 1-3 | 6-1 | 2-1 | | 2-1 | 0-4 | 4-2 | 2-1 | 0-0 | 3-0 | 3-1 | 1-0 | 3-2 | 1-0 | 0-0 | 1-1 | 1-1 |
| 10 Mangotsfield United | 2-1 | 3-0 | 1-0 | 1-3 | 0-1 | 4-3 | 1-0 | 0-0 | 1-0 | | 0-2 | 2-0 | 3-3 | 0-3 | 0-0 | 2-3 | 1-2 | 2-2 | 3-1 | 1-2 | 10-0 | 1-2 |
| 11 Merthyr Town | 3-2 | 2-1 | 1-0 | 1-2 | 3-0 | 1-0 | 3-0 | 3-0 | 0-0 | 1-1 | | 2-2 | 2-2 | 1-0 | 3-2 | 2-0 | 0-3 | 3-1 | 2-0 | 2-0 | 10-0 | 1-2 |
| 12 North Leigh | 5-3 | 1-3 | 3-1 | 2-1 | 1-0 | 1-3 | 4-2 | 1-3 | 1-4 | 1-1 | 1-3 | | 0-0 | 4-0 | 3-1 | 1-1 | 2-1 | 0-2 | 1-3 | 2-0 | 2-0 | 1-2 |
| 13 Paulton Rovers | 1-0 | 1-0 | 1-4 | 2-0 | 1-0 | 0-1 | 0-0 | 1-1 | 0-2 | 2-0 | 2-1 | 3-1 | | 1-2 | 2-0 | 4-1 | 3-1 | 3-3 | 2-1 | 0-3 | 2-1 | 3-2 |
| 14 Poole Town | 1-1 | 1-0 | 2-1 | 4-0 | 3-0 | 2-0 | 4-1 | 1-0 | 1-1 | 1-0 | 3-2 | 1-0 | 1-0 | | 2-1 | 3-0 | 2-0 | 4-1 | 2-0 | 1-0 | 2-0 | 2-3 |
| 15 Sholing | 3-0 | 3-0 | 8-1 | 2-0 | 2-3 | 4-2 | 2-2 | 7-1 | 1-2 | 2-1 | 2-2 | 5-0 | 1-0 | 1-1 | | 2-0 | 5-1 | 4-0 | 2-2 | 1-0 | 4-1 | 3-1 |
| 16 Shortwood United | 3-0 | 1-0 | 0-2 | 1-2 | 0-0 | 1-1 | 1-0 | 2-1 | 1-0 | 0-1 | 1-0 | 3-1 | 5-0 | 2-3 | 2-3 | | 3-0 | 2-1 | 2-2 | 2-2 | 4-0 | 1-0 |
| 17 Swindon Supermarine | 2-1 | 2-0 | 2-1 | 2-1 | 1-1 | 1-2 | 2-0 | 0-0 | 1-0 | 3-1 | 2-2 | 4-3 | 2-1 | 5-1 | 3-1 | 2-2 | | 3-0 | 2-1 | 1-2 | 4-0 | 3-0 |
| 18 Taunton Town | 1-1 | 3-2 | 3-0 | 4-1 | 0-0 | 3-2 | 1-5 | 0-2 | 2-0 | 2-2 | 1-2 | 0-2 | 0-2 | 1-1 | 2-2 | 0-1 | 3-2 | | 0-0 | 1-0 | 4-3 | 2-5 |
| 19 Tiverton Town | 0-0 | 1-1 | 1-1 | 0-0 | 1-2 | 1-0 | 2-2 | 2-2 | 1-3 | 0-1 | 1-1 | 1-2 | 3-4 | 1-2 | 1-0 | 2-1 | 0-2 | 2-1 | | 2-0 | 3-0 | 2-0 |
| 20 Wimborne Town | 2-2 | 1-1 | 4-3 | 1-3 | 2-2 | 0-0 | 2-2 | 0-1 | 1-3 | 3-1 | 0-3 | 2-1 | 0-1 | 0-2 | 0-1 | 1-0 | 2-1 | 5-1 | 2-0 | | 1-0 | 5-1 |
| 21 Winchester City | 0-1 | 0-2 | 1-3 | 1-0 | 0-4 | 0-2 | 4-0 | 1-3 | 0-1 | 3-4 | 0-3 | 0-2 | 2-1 | 1-3 | 0-2 | 1-2 | 1-3 | 3-2 | 0-0 | 1-4 | | 2-1 |
| 22 Yate Town | 1-2 | 1-1 | 2-1 | 3-1 | 3-1 | 1-1 | 2-1 | 1-2 | 4-2 | 1-0 | 0-3 | 0-2 | 3-0 | 1-3 | 0-1 | 3-1 | 1-0 | 0-0 | 2-1 | 2-1 | 6-1 | |

# LEAGUE CUP

## PRELIMINARY ROUND

| | | |
|---|---|---|
| Aylesbury | 2-1 | Barton Rovers |
| Bishops Cleeve | 3-3* | Evesham United (5-4p) |

## ROUND 1  *MISSING BIGGLESWADE T.*
*KETTERING T.*

| | | |
|---|---|---|
| Bedford Town | 5-0 | Leighton Town |
| Fleet Town | 0-4 | Northwood |
| Tiverton Town | 3-2 | Taunton Town |
| Beaconsfield SYCOB | 2-0 | Chesham United |
| Hitchin Town | 2-0 | St Neots Town |
| Abingdon United | 3-5 | Daventry Town |
| Hayes | 3-1 | Uxbridge |
| Aylesbury | 3-2 | Cambridge City |
| Banbury United | 1-2 | North Leigh |
| Bedworth United | 1-2* | Barwell |
| Bedworth United | 1-0 | Royston Town |
| Bridgwater Town | 1-1* | Bideford (5-4p) |
| Burnham | 1-2 | Ashford Town |
| Chalfont St Peter | 0-1 | Slough Town |
| Chippenham Town | 0-3 | Paulton Rovers |
| Cinderford Town | 5-1 | Bishops Cleeve |
| Merthyr Town | 0-2 | Yate Town |
| North Greenford U. | 4-2 | Godalming Town |
| Poole Town | 3-0 | Weymouth |
| St Albans City | 2-3 | Hemel Hempstead T. |
| Stourbridge | 4-1 | Redditch United |
| Thatcham Town | 0-6 | Hungerford Town |
| Woodford United | 1-5 | Didcot Town |
| Frome Town | 1-0 | Cirencester Town |
| Guildford City | 3-5* | Chertsey Town |
| Swindon Supermarine | 0-1 | Shortwood United |
| Wimborne Town | 3-0 | Bashley |
| Sholing | 2-1 | AFC Totton |
| Mangotsfield United | 2-1 | Clevedon Town |
| Rugby Town | 1-2 | Leamington |
| Winchester City | 3-3* | Gosport Borough (1-4p) |

## ROUND 2

| | | |
|---|---|---|
| Hungerford Town | 0-1 | North Leigh |
| Mangotsfield United | 1-3 | Shortwood United |
| Arlesey Town | 2-2* | Biggleswade T. (4-3p) |
| Bedford Town | 3-2* | Hitchin Town |
| Chertsey Town | 1-5 | Hemel Hempstead T. |
| Daventry Town | 2-3 | Barwell |
| Didcot Town | 1-0 | Beaconsfield SYCOB |
| North Greenford U. | 2-6 | AFC Hayes |
| Northwood | 1-0 | Ashford Town |
| Stourbridge | 1-2 | Leamington |
| Wimborne Town | 3-0 | Poole Town |
| Yate Town | 1-2 | Cinderford Town |
| Frome Town | 5-2 | Bridgwater Town |
| Sholing | 1-0 | Gosport Borough |
| Aylesbury | 0-1* | Slough Town |
| Tiverton Town | 1-4 | Paulton Rovers |

## ROUND 3

| | | |
|---|---|---|
| Barwell | 0-1 | Leamington |
| Bedford Town | 1-2 | Arlesey Town |
| North Leigh | 2-4 | Cinderford Town |
| Northwood | 2-1 | Hemel Hempstead T. |
| Shortwood United | 2-3 | Didcot Town |
| Slough Town | 3-1* | AFC Hayes |
| Frome Town | 3-2* | Paulton Rovers |
| Sholing | 4-3* | Wimborne Town |

## QUARTER FINALS

| | | |
|---|---|---|
| Arlesey Town | 6-0 | Didcot Town |
| Frome Town | 3-2 | Sholing |
| Leamington | 3-1 | Cinderford Town |
| Slough Town | 2-1 | Northwood |

## SEMI-FINALS

| | | |
|---|---|---|
| Leamington | 1-2 | Arlesey Town |
| Frome Town | 2-1 | Slough Town |

## FINAL (2 Legs)

| | | |
|---|---|---|
| Arlesey Town | 1-0 | Frome Town |
| Frome Town | 1-1* | Arlesey Town |

Arlesey Town win 2-1 on aggregate.

*AET

## Southern League Premier Division Statistics 2012-13

| | MCV | MCD | MCwW | MCwD | MCSG | MCwS | TGS | MCCS | TNCS |
|---|---|---|---|---|---|---|---|---|---|
| AFC Totton | 6 | 3 | 6 | 8 | 21 | 3 | 9 | 3 | 13 |
| Arlesey Town | 4 | 4 | 5 | 6 | 12 | 2 | 11 | 3 | 17 |
| Banbury United | 2 | 3 | 8 | 3 | 11 | 2 | 9 | 3 | 9 |
| Barwell | 4 | 2 | 4 | 5 | 11 | 2 | 7 | 3 | 15 |
| Bashley | 3 | 4 | 8 | 5 | 4 | 3 | 19 | 2 | 12 |
| Bedford Town | 4 | 3 | 5 | 7 | 6 | 3 | 14 | 3 | 13 |
| Bedworth United | 3 | 6 | 12 | 4 | 9 | 4 | 16 | 3 | 10 |
| Bideford | 2 | 6 | 11 | 5 | 13 | 3 | 12 | 2 | 7 |
| Cambridge City | 3 | 4 | 4 | 7 | 10 | 2 | 10 | 2 | 14 |
| Chesham United | 7 | 3 | 5 | 17 | 29 | 3 | 8 | 2 | 12 |
| Chippenham Town | 3 | 3 | 17 | 5 | 7 | 3 | 13 | 3 | 10 |
| Frome Town | 3 | 3 | 7 | 4 | 3 | 3 | 18 | 3 | 13 |
| Gosport Borough | 4 | 3 | 6 | 23 | 8 | 2 | 10 | 3 | 19 |
| Hemel Hempstead | 4 | 4 | 4 | 5 | 15 | 1 | 3 | 2 | 9 |
| Hitchin Town | 2 | 4 | 6 | 4 | 13 | 2 | 9 | 3 | 14 |
| Kettering | 3 | 11 | 14 | 6 | 17 | 4 | 15 | 3 | 8 |
| Leamington | 6 | 2 | 4 | 12 | 19 | 2 | 5 | 4 | 17 |
| Redditch United | 2 | 5 | 8 | 4 | 6 | 5 | 25 | 2 | 11 |
| St Albans City | 5 | 3 | 5 | 5 | 11 | 3 | 9 | 1 | 11 |
| St Neots Town | 5 | 4 | 8 | 5 | 17 | 3 | 10 | 2 | 6 |
| Stourbridge | 8 | 2 | 4 | 8 | 12 | 2 | 9 | 3 | 14 |
| Weymouth | 6 | 4 | 5 | 6 | 7 | 4 | 15 | 2 | 11 |

MCV - Most Consecutive Victories
MCD - Most Consecutive Defeatss
MCwW - Most Consecutive without a Win
MCwD - Most Consecutive without a defeat
MCSG - Most Consecutive Scoring Games
MCwS - Most Consecutive without Scoring
TGS - Total Games without Scoring
MCCS - Most Consecutive Clean Sheets
TNCS - Total Number of Clean Sheets

### Goalscorers with at least Ten goals in League, FA Cup and FA Trophy in 2012-2013

| | Individual Scorers | | | Total Individual Scorers | Hat tricks | Pens | OG scored by opponents |
|---|---|---|---|---|---|---|---|
| AFC Totton | Richard Gillespie 24 | Dave Allen 11 | Michael Gosney 10 | 16 + 1 ogs | 3 | | 1 Bedworth United |
| Arlesey Town | Drew Roberts 30 | Chris Dillon 16 | | 13 + 2 | 10 | | 2 Cambridge City , Gosport Boro |
| Banbury United | Albi Skendi 10 | | | 19 + 0 | 2 | 1 | |
| Barwell | Jamie Towers 14 | Luke Barlone 12 | | 21 + 1 | 4 | | 1 St Albans City |
| Bashley | | | | 19 + 1 | | | 1 Poole Town |
| Bedford Town | | | | 14 + 2 | 4 | 1 | 2 Leamington, St NeotsTown |
| Bedworth United | Mitchell Piggon 11 | | | 16 + 0 | 1 | | |
| Bideford | Sean Downing 16 | Kevin Squire 12 | | 14 + 1 | 5 | | 1 Weymouth |
| Cambridge City | Craig Hammond 20 | Adam Marriott 16 | | 19 + 1 | 8 | 1 | 1 Billericay Town |
| Chesham United | Simon Thomas 23 | James Potton 11 | | 15 + 3 | 6 | 3 | 3 Chippenham, Hitchin, Weymouth |
| Chippenham Town | Alan Griffin 18 | Lee Phillips 15 | | 15 + 1 | 9 | | 1 Frome Town |
| Frome Town | | | | 14 + 2 | 1 | | 2 Hitchin Town, Kettering Town |
| Gosport Borough | Justin Bennett 20 | Rory Williams 16 | Danny Wooden 15 / Adam Wilde 10 | 18 + 1 | 2 | 3 | 1 Bashley |
| Hemel Hempstead | Dave Pearce 22 | Matt Nolan 21 | Charlie Mpi 14 | 18 + 1 | 1 | 1 | 1 Leamington |
| Hitchin Town | John Frendo 42 | | | 18 + 1 | 13 | 5 | 1 Chesham United |
| Kettering | | | | 17 + 3 | 8 | | 3 Bidford, Chippenham Town |
| Leamington | Matty Dodd 13 | Liam Daly 12 | Ricky Johnson 12 | 7 | | 2 | 1 Hemel Hempstead |
| | Stefan Moore 12 | Lee Chilton 11 | Richard Batchelor 10 | 17 + 1 | 8 | 2 | |
| Redditch United | | | | 16 + 1 | | | 1 Chippenham Town |
| St Albans City | Greg Ngoyi 14 | Chris Henry 11 | Sean Shields 11 | | | | 1 Kettering Town |
| | | | Lewis Toomey 11 | 25 + 1 | 9 | 3 | |
| St Neots Town | Ben Mackey 23 | Louis Hilliard 11 | Dan Jacob 11 | 22 + 1 | 8 | 2 | 1 Barwell |
| Stourbridge | Luke Benbow 18 | Ben Billingham 17 | Sean Geddes 12 | 17 + 1 | 2 | 3 | 1 Banbury United |
| Weymouth | Mark Ford 18 | Ben Joyce 18 | | 12 + 1 | 3 | 2 | 1 Totton & Ealing |

# AFC TOTTON

**Chairman:** Andy Straker (Interim)
**Secretary:** Alec Hayter            **(T)**                    **(E)** alechayter@onetel.com
**Commercial Manager:**                                **(T)**
**Programme Editor:** Stephen Cain          **(T)** stephen.cain@trescal.com
**Ground Address:** Testwood Stadium, Salisbury Road, Calmore, Totton SO40 2RW
**(T)** 02380 868 981                              **Manager:** Stephen Riley

1886  2011
125 Years

## Club Factfile

**Founded:**  1886        **Nickname:** Stags
**Previous Names:** Totton FC until merger with Totton Athletic in 1975
**Previous Leagues:** Hampshire 1982-86, Wessex 1986-2008

**Club Colours (change):** All blue (All yellow)

**Ground Capacity:** 3,000   **Seats:** 500   **Covered:** 500   **Clubhouse:** Yes   **Shop:** Yes

**Directions**
From the M27 Junction 2. From the east take the first exit at the roundabout or from the west take the third exit at the roundabout.
Take the first left within 100 yards, signposted Totton Central.
At the T junction turn left and you will find the entrance to the ground approximately 1 mile on the left hand side, just before the Calmore Roundabout.

**Previous Grounds:** South testwood Park 1886-1933.

**Record Attendance:** 600 v Windsor & Eton - FA Cup 4th Qualifying Round 1982-83
**Record Victory:** Not known
**Record Defeat:** Not known
**Record Goalscorer:**  Not known
**Record Appearances:** James Sherlington
**Additional Records:**

**Senior Honours:**
Hampshire League 1981-82, 84-85. Wessex League Premier Division 2007-08.
Southern League Division South & West 2010-11.
Hampshire Senior Cup 2010-11.

### 10 YEAR RECORD

| 03-04 | | 04-05 | | 05-06 | | 06-07 | | 07-08 | | 08-09 | | 09-10 | | 10-11 | | 11-12 | | 12-13 | |
|---|---|---|---|---|---|---|---|---|---|---|---|---|---|---|---|---|---|---|---|
| Wex | 8 | Wex1 | 8 | Wex1 | 4 | WexP | 2 | WexP | 1 | Sthsw | 3 | Sthsw | 2 | Sthsw | 1 | SthP | 3 | SthP | 14 |

# MATCH RESULTS 2012-13

| Date | Comp | H/A | Opponents | Att: | Result | Goalscorers | Pos | No. |
|---|---|---|---|---|---|---|---|---|
| Aug 18 | SPL | A | Frome Town | 249 | L 1-3 | Gillespie 20 | 19 | 1 |
| 21 | SPL | H | Chesham United | 335 | D 1-1 | Hill 90 | 17 | 2 |
| 25 | SPL | H | Stourbridge | 267 | L 2-4 | Gillespie 15 Coutts 28 | 20 | 3 |
| 27 | SPL | A | Hemel Hempstead | 333 | L 1-4 | Allen 20 | 20 | 4 |
| Sept 1 | SPL | H | Bedford Town | 306 | W 2-0 | Gillespie 5 27 | 18 | 5 |
| 4 | SPL | A | Weymouth | 635 | D 3-3 | Coutts 20 Bottomly 27 Gillespie 41 | 18 | 6 |
| 8 | FAC Q1 | A | Swindon Supermarine | 131 | W 6-0 | Gillespie 12 64 Allen 19 56 Gosney 27 81 | | 7 |
| 15 | SPL | A | St Neots Town | 336 | W 3-1 | Allen 47 69 Davis 87 | 13 | 8 |
| 18 | SPL | H | Bideford | 267 | W 2-0 | Gillespie 24 73 | 9 | 9 |
| 22 | FAC Q2 | A | Truro City | 424 | W 3-2 | Gillespie 27 Allen 46 Gosney 79 | | 10 |
| 29 | FAT Q1 | H | Bideford | 288 | W 2-0 | Coutts 7 Hill 47 | | 11 |
| Oct 6 | FAC Q3 | H | Merthyr Town | 539 | W 3-2 | Davies 18 Gillespie 23 Allen 33 | | 12 |
| 13 | SPL | A | Redditch United | 190 | L 1-2 | Mason 89 | 15 | 13 |
| 20 | FAC Q4 | H | Cambridge City | 674 | L 2-3 | Jones 8 Valentine 90 | | 14 |
| 27 | FAT Q2 | H | Gosport Borough | 349 | W 3-2 | Gillespie 9 Hill 23 Whisken 59 | | 15 |
| Nov 3 | SPL | A | St Albans City | 397 | W 3-0 | Whisken 9 Gosney 20 Davies 70 | 12 | 16 |
| 6 | SPL | A | Bashley | 282 | W 3-0 | Coutts 39 Allen 79 Gillespie 82 | 8 | 17 |
| 10 | FAT Q3 | H | Basingstoke Town | 368 | W 3-0 | Davies 45 Coutts 50 Allen 60 | | 18 |
| 13 | SPL | H | Hitchin Town | 268 | D 2-2 | Gillespie 34 Whisken 42 | 8 | 19 |
| 17 | SPL | H | Barwell | 368 | W 2-1 | Gillespie 75 Hill 80 | 8 | 20 |
| 24 | FAT 1 | A | Forest Green Rovers | 523 | L 1-2 | Racine 71 og | | 21 |
| 27 | SPL | A | Chippenham Town | 295 | L 0-3 | | 11 | 22 |
| Dec 1 | SPL | A | Leamington | 554 | L 1-2 | Gosney 54 | 13 | 23 |
| 8 | SPL | H | Bedworth United | 263 | W 3-2 | Allen 26 Gosney 32 Kemp 75 (og) | 9 | 24 |
| 15 | SPL | A | Cambridge City | 319 | D 0-0 | | 10 | 25 |
| 18 | SPL | A | Banbury United | 116 | L 1-2 | Gosney 22 | 12 | 26 |
| 26 | SPL | A | Gosport Borough | 372 | L 0-1 | | 15 | 27 |
| Jan 1 | SPL | H | Hemel Hempstead | 297 | W 2-0 | Allen 47 Gillespie 82 | 13 | 28 |
| 5 | SPL | A | Chesham United | 326 | L 0-6 | | 14 | 29 |
| 15 | SPL | H | Kettering Town | 229 | W 4-0 | Gillespie 25 42 Whitely 69 Chiedozie 72 | 12 | 30 |
| 19 | SPL | A | Bideford Town | 168 | D1-1 | Gillespie 47 | 12 | 31 |
| 26 | SPL | H | St Neots Town | 352 | W 2-1 | Gosney 39 (pen) Cargill 47 | 11 | 32 |
| Feb 2 | SPL | H | Bashley | 438 | W 2-0 | Gillespie 3 Davies 79 | 9 | 33 |
| 5 | SPL | H | Weymouth | 329 | W 5-2 | Gillespie 40 Hill 62 Whitley 66 Coutts 82 Cargill 86 | 7 | 34 |
| 9 | SPL | A | Hitchin Town | 269 | L 0-4 | | 8 | 35 |
| 12 | SPL | A | Stourbridge | 260 | L 0-3 | | 9 | 36 |
| 16 | SPL | A | Barwell | 241 | L 0-1 | | 10 | 37 |
| 19 | SPL | H | Arlesey Town | 235 | D 3-3 | Coutts 58 Gillespie 65 (pen) Whisken 74 | 10 | 38 |
| 23 | SPL | H | Banbury United | 308 | L 2-3 | Brown 2 Whisken 20 | 10 | 39 |
| Mar 2 | SPL | A | Kettering Town | 322 | D 1-1 | Hill 76 | 12 | 40 |
| 9 | SPL | H | Redditch United | 605 | W 2-0 | Roberts 43 Davies 60 | 11 | 41 |
| 12 | SPL | H | Frome Town | 243 | W 2-0 | Brown 44 Cargill 81 | 10 | 42 |
| 16 | SPL | A | St Albans City | 328 | L 0-3 | | 10 | 43 |
| 30 | SPL | A | Bedford Town | 224 | L 1-4 | Gosney 19 (pen) | 12 | 44 |
| Apr 1 | SPL | H | Gosport Borough | 426 | W 3-2 | Gillespie 45 Gosney 73 Roberts 90 | 12 | 45 |
| 6 | SPL | H | Leamington | 368 | L 0-2 | | 12 | 46 |
| 13 | SPL | A | Arlesey Town | 105 | L 0-5 | | 12 | 47 |
| 20 | SPL | H | Cambridge City | 306 | L 1-5 | Gillespie 89 | 13 | 48 |
| 23 | SPL | H | Chippenham Town | 284 | L 0-5 | | 13 | 49 |
| 27 | SPL | A | Bedworth United | 137 | L 0-2 | | 14 | 50 |

| GOALSCORERS | Lge | FAC | FAT | Total | Pens | Hat-tricks | Cons Run | | Lge | FAC | FAT | Total | Pens | Hat-tricks | Cons Run |
|---|---|---|---|---|---|---|---|---|---|---|---|---|---|---|---|
| Gillespie | 19 | 4 | 1 | 24 | 1 | | 2 | Whitley | 2 | | | 2 | | | |
| Allen | 6 | 4 | 1 | 11 | | | 2 | Bottomly | 1 | | | 1 | | | |
| Gosney | 7 | 3 | | 10 | 2 | | 2 | Jones | | 1 | | 1 | | | |
| Coutts | 5 | | 2 | 7 | | | | Mason | 1 | | | 1 | | | |
| Davies | 4 | 1 | | 6 | | | | Valentine | | 1 | | 1 | | | |
| Hill | 4 | | 2 | 6 | | | | Xhiedozie | 1 | | | 1 | | | |
| Whisken | 4 | | 1 | 5 | | | 2 | Own Goals | 1 | | 1 | 2 | | | |
| Cargill | 3 | | | 3 | | | | Cons Run - Consecutive scoring games. | | | | | | | |
| Brown | 2 | | | 2 | | | | | | | | | | | |
| Roberts | 2 | | | 2 | | | | | | | | | | | |

# ARLESEY TOWN

**Chairman:** Manny Cohen
**Secretary:** Chris Sterry      **(T)** 07540 201 473      **(E)** chris.sterry@ntlworld.com
**Commercial Manager:**                              **(T)**
**Programme Editor:** Jason Marshall          **(T)** jasonmarshall1@live.co.uk
**Ground Address:** Armadillo Stadium, Hitchin Road, Arlesey SG15 6RS
**(T)** 01462 734 504                              **Manager:** Zema Abbey

## Club Factfile

**Founded:** 1891      **Nickname:** The Blues
**Previous Names:** None
**Previous Leagues:** Biggleswade & Dist., Bedfordshire Co. (South Midlands) 1922-26, 27-28, Parthenon, London 1958-60, United Co. 1933-36, 82-92, Spartan South Mid. 1992-2000, Isthmian 2000-04, 06-08, Southern 2004-07
**Club Colours (change):** Light blue/dark blue/dark blue (Yellow/black/black)

**Ground Capacity:** 2,920      **Seats:** 150      **Covered:** 600      **Clubhouse:** Yes      **Shop:** Yes

**Directions**

From the A1 exit at Baldock(J10) and follow the signs for Stotfold then Arlesey. You will enter Arlesey from the area known as Church End, this is the opposite end of Arlesey, but as there is only one main street just follow keep driving until you pass the Biggs Wall building and the ground is on your left.

Coming of the M1 at Luton and follow the signs for Hitchin, pass Hitchin Town FC on the Shefford Road and turn right into Turnpike Lane, this is Ickleford. Follow the road out of Ickleford and bear left away from the Letchworth turning, the ground is a little further on, on the right.

**Previous Grounds:** The Bury. Lamb Meadow.

**Record Attendance:** 2,000 v Luton Town Reserves - Bedfordshire Senior Cup 1906
**Record Victory:** Not known
**Record Defeat:** Not known
**Record Goalscorer:** Not known
**Record Appearances:** Gary Marshall
**Additional Records:**

**Senior Honours:**
South Midlands Premier Division x5. United Counties Premier Division 1984-85. FA Vase 1994-95.
Isthmian League Division 3 2000-01. Southern League Division 1 Central 2010-11.
Bedfordshire Senior Cup 1965-66, 78-79, 96-97, 2010-11.

### 10 YEAR RECORD

| 03-04 | | 04-05 | | 05-06 | | 06-07 | | 07-08 | | 08-09 | | 09-10 | | 10-11 | | 11-12 | | 12-13 | |
|-------|---|-------|----|-------|----|-------|----|-------|----|-------|----|-------|---|-------|---|-------|----|-------|---|
| Isth1N | 8 | SthE | 14 | SthE | 10 | Isth1N | 18 | Isth1N | 15 | SthC | 18 | SthC | 9 | SthC | 1 | SthP | 18 | SthP | 6 |

# MATCH RESULTS 2012-13

| Date | Comp | H/A | Opponents | Att: | Result | Goalscorers | Pos | No. |
|---|---|---|---|---|---|---|---|---|
| Aug 18 | SPL | A | Stourbridge | 175 | L 1-4 | Hatch 54 | 21 | 1 |
| 21 | SPL | H | Bedford Town | 240 | W 2-1 | Hibbert 15 Roberts 48 | 12 | 2 |
| 25 | SPL | H | Bedworth United | 130 | W 1-0 | Goss 13 | 7 | 3 |
| 27 | SPL | A | Hitchin Town | 573 | W 1-0 | Roberts 31 | 5 | 4 |
| Sept 1 | SPL | H | Gosport Borough | 121 | D 1-1 | Molineux 88 (og) | 6 | 5 |
| 4 | SPL | A | Hemel Hempstead | 308 | W 2-1 | Marsh 10 Roberts 53 | 4 | 6 |
| 8 | FAC Q1 | A | Barton Rovers | 152 | W 1-0 | Roberts 2 (pen) | | 7 |
| 15 | SPL | A | Leamington | 536 | L 3-4 | Dillon 17 Roberts 27 (pen) 54 (pen) | 7 | 8 |
| 18 | SPL | H | Chesham United | 135 | W 2-0 | Prosper 16 Dillon 21 | 6 | 9 |
| 22 | FAC Q2 | H | Dulwich Hamlet | 156 | W 1-0 | Roberts 90 | | 10 |
| 29 | FAT Q1 | A | St Albans City | 335 | W 2-1 | Roberts 23 (pen) Dillon 58 | | 11 |
| Oct 6 | FAC Q3 | H | Brackley Town | 227 | W 4-3 | Prosper 2 7 Goss 3 Blackett 63 | | 12 |
| 9 | SPL | A | St Albans City | 277 | L 0-1 | | 8 | 13 |
| 13 | SPL | A | Chippenham Town | 331 | D 0-0 | | 8 | 14 |
| 20 | FAC Q4 | A | Didcot Town | 414 | W 1-0 | Frater 28 | | 15 |
| 27 | FAT Q2 | A | Cray Wanderers | 96 | D 0-0 | | | 16 |
| 30 | FAT Q2r | H | Cray Wanderers | 100 | L 2-3 | Hatch 6 Roberts 46 | | 17 |
| Nov 3 | FAC 1 | A | Coventry City | 6594 | L 0-3 | | | 18 |
| 10 | SPL | A | Barwell | 172 | L 0-2 | | 11 | 19 |
| 13 | SPL | H | Bashley | 107 | L 1-2 | Roberts 56 | 12 | 20 |
| 17 | SPL | H | Kettering Town | 242 | W 3-0 | Frater 43 Roberts 57 65 | 10 | 21 |
| Dec 1 | SPL | H | St Neots Town | 267 | W 4-3 | Farrell 41 Roberts 43 88 Dillon 85 | 10 | 22 |
| 8 | SPL | A | Weymouth | 676 | L 1-2 | Hibbert 65 | 12 | 23 |
| 15 | SPL | H | Frome Town | 10 | L 0-1 | | 12 | 24 |
| 26 | SPL | A | Canbridge City | 385 | W 2-1 | Marsh 52 Dillon 64 | 11 | 25 |
| Jan 1 | SPL | H | Hitchin Town | 536 | W 3-1 | Dillon 3 16 Roberts 23 (pen) | 11 | 26 |
| 5 | SPL | A | Bedford Town | 306 | D 0-0 | | 10 | 27 |
| 12 | SPL | H | Hemel Hempstead T | 216 | W 3-1 | Roberts 7 (pen) 58 (pen) Dillon 78 | 10 | 28 |
| 15 | SPL | A | Banbury United | 125 | W 3-1 | Hatch 11 Dillon 44 Roberts 49 | 6 | 29 |
| 26 | SPL | H | Leamington | 290 | L 0-2 | | 7 | 30 |
| Feb 2 | SPL | H | St Albans City | 261 | L 1-3 | Goss 32 | 11 | 31 |
| 9 | SPL | A | Bideford | 181 | D 1-1 | Gordon 55 | 11 | 32 |
| 17 | SPL | A | Kettering Town | 317 | W 3-1 | Marsh 4 Roberts 36 (pen) 45 | 11 | 33 |
| 19 | SPL | A | AFC Totton | 235 | D 3-3 | Dillon 20 Roberts 73 (pen) 89 | 11 | 34 |
| 23 | SPL | H | Barwell | 108 | L 0-1 | | 12 | 35 |
| Mar 2 | SPL | A | Bashley | 105 | L 0-1 | | 14 | 36 |
| 5 | SPL | H | Bideford | 85 | D 2-2 | Thorne 32 45 | 14 | 37 |
| 9 | SPL | H | Chippenham Town | 104 | W 4-0 | Roberts 46 50 Dillon 60 Forsythe 89 | 12 | 38 |
| 12 | SPL | A | Chesham United | 207 | L 0-1 | | 12 | 39 |
| 26 | SPL | H | Redditch United | 80 | W 3-0 | Hibbert 17 Dillon 40 Goss 54 | 13 | 40 |
| 30 | SPL | A | Gosport Borough | 459 | W 1-0 | Dillon 81 | 10 | 41 |
| Apr 1 | SPL | H | Cambridge City | 210 | L 1-2 | Pepper 89 (og) | 10 | 42 |
| 4 | SPL | A | Redditch United | 94 | W 2-0 | Forsythe 53 Hatch 57 | 10 | 43 |
| 6 | SPL | A | St Neots Town | 273 | W 2-1 | Dillon 58 Roberts 75 | 10 | 44 |
| 11 | SPL | H | Banbury United | 87 | W 2-1 | Marsh 80 Hibbert 90 | 9 | 45 |
| 13 | SPL | H | AFC Totton | 105 | W 5-0 | Thorne 2 Roberts 6 45 Prosper 10 Dillon 70 | 7 | 46 |
| 16 | SPL | H | Stourbridge | 115 | L 2-4 | Dillon 50 Roberts 67 | 7 | 47 |
| 20 | SPL | A | Frome Town | 185 | W 1-0 | Farrell 83 | 7 | 48 |
| 23 | SPL | A | Bedworth United | 115 | L 1-2 | Roberts 47 (pen) | 7 | 49 |
| 27 | SPL | H | Weymouth | 186 | W 3-0 | Roberts 52 Marsh 65 Prosper 69 | 6 | 50 |

| GOALSCORERS | Lge | FAC | FAT | Total | Pens | Hat-tricks | Cons Run | | Lge | FAC | FAT | Total | Pens | Hat-tricks | Cons Run |
|---|---|---|---|---|---|---|---|---|---|---|---|---|---|---|---|
| Roberts | 26 | 2 | 2 | 30 | 10 | | 3 | Frater | 1 | 1 | | 2 | | | |
| Dillon | 15 | 1 | | 16 | 2 | | | Blackett | | 1 | | 1 | | | |
| Marsh | 5 | | | 5 | | | | Gordon | 1 | | | 1 | | | |
| Prosper | 3 | 2 | | 5 | | | | Own Goals | 2 | | | 2 | | | |
| Goss | 3 | 1 | | 4 | | | | Cons Run - Consecutive scoring games. | | | | | | | |
| Hatch | 3 | | 1 | 4 | | | | | | | | | | | |
| Hibbert | 4 | | | 4 | | | | | | | | | | | |
| Thorne | 3 | | | 3 | | | | | | | | | | | |
| Farrell | 2 | | | 2 | | | | | | | | | | | |
| Forsythe | 2 | | | 2 | | | | | | | | | | | |

# BANBURY UNITED

**Chairman:** Paul Jones
**Secretary:** Barry Worlsey　　**(T)** 07941 267 567　　**(E)** bworsley@btinternet.com
**Commercial Manager:** Nigel Porter, Richard　　**(T)**
**Programme Editor:** David Shadbolt　　**(T)** djshadbolt@tiscali.o.uk
**Ground Address:** Spencer Stadium, off Station Road, Banbury OX16 5TA
**(T)** 01295 263 354　　　　　　　**Manager:** Ady Fuller

## Club Factfile

**Founded:** 1931　　**Nickname:** Puritans
**Previous Names:** Spencer Villa 1931-34. Banbury Spencer. Club reformed in 1965 as Banbury United
**Previous Leagues:** Banbury Junior 1933-34, Oxon Senior 1934-35, Birmingham Combination 1935-54,
　　　　　　　　　West Midlands 1954-66, Southern 1966-90, Hellenic 1991-2000

**Club Colours (change):** Red with gold trim/red/red/ (White/blue/blue)

**Ground Capacity:** 6,500　　**Seats:** 250　　**Covered:** 50　　**Clubhouse:** Yes　　**Shop:** Yes

**Directions**
From M40, Junction 11, head towards Banbury, over first roundabout, left at next roundabout into Concorde Avenue. Straight on at next roundabout, taking left hand lane, and turn left at traffic lights, turn first right into Station Approach. At station forecourt and car park, take narrow single track road on extreme right and follow to Stadium.(Direct SatNav to OX16 5AB).

**Previous Grounds:** Middleton Road 1931-34.

**Record Attendance:** 7,160 v Oxford City - FA Cup 3rd Qualifying Round 30/10/1948
**Record Victory:** 12-0 v RNAS Culham - Oxon Senior Cup 1945-46
**Record Defeat:** 2-11 v West Bromwich Albion 'A' - Birmingham Combination 1938-39
**Record Goalscorer:** Dick Pike and Tony Jacques - 222 (1935-48 and 1965-76 respectively)
**Record Appearances:** Jody McKay - 576
**Additional Records:** Paid £2,000 to Oxford United for Phil Emsden
**Senior Honours:**　Received £20,000 from Derby County for Kevin Wilson 1979
Hellenic Premier 1999-2000. Oxford Senior Cup 1978-79, 87-88, 2003-04.

### 10 YEAR RECORD

| 03-04 | 04-05 | 05-06 | 06-07 | 07-08 | 08-09 | 09-10 | 10-11 | 11-12 | 12-13 |
|---|---|---|---|---|---|---|---|---|---|
| SthE　8 | SthP　17 | SthP　7 | SthP　13 | SthP　9 | SthP　19 | SthP　12 | SthP　16 | SthP　16 | SthP　16 |

# MATCH RESULTS 2012-13

| Date | Comp | H/A | Opponents | Att: | Result | Goalscorers | Pos | No. |
|------|------|-----|-----------|------|--------|-------------|-----|-----|
| Aug 18 | SPL | H | St Albans City | 253 | D 2-2 | Johnson 80 88 | 9 | 1 |
| 21 | SPL | A | Barwell | 224 | L 1-4 | Talabi 47 | 18 | 2 |
| 25 | SPL | A | Kettering Town | 526 | D 1-1 | Talabi 31 | 19 | 3 |
| 27 | SPL | H | Redditch United | 254 | D 0-0 | | | 4 |
| Sept 1 | SPL | A | St Neots Town | 332 | L 2-3 | Johnson 23 O'Grady 53 | 19 | 5 |
| 4 | SPL | H | Bideford | 163 | D 1-1 | Confue 60 | 19 | 6 |
| 8 | FAC Q1 | A | Hungerford Town | 104 | D 1-1 | Johnson 53 | | 7 |
| 12 | FAC Q1r | H | Hungerford Town | 145 | L 0-2 | | | 8 |
| 15 | SPL | H | Chippenham Town | 234 | W 1-0 | Ashton 73 | 15 | 9 |
| 22 | SPL | A | Stourbridge | 351 | L 1-8 | Coronado 74 | 20 | 10 |
| 29 | FAT Q1 | H | Wimborne Town | 146 | D 1-1 | Coronado 37 | | 11 |
| Oct 2 | FAT Q1r | A | Wimborne Town | 99 | D 3-3 | Coranado 38 Gray 90 103 *aet L 5-6 pens | | 12 |
| 9 | SPL | H | Frome Town | 167 | D 1-1 | Blossom 7 | 20 | 13 |
| 13 | SPL | H | Weymouth | 352 | L 1-3 | Lorraine 43 | 20 | 14 |
| 20 | SPL | A | Bedworth United | 201 | W 4-0 | Isaac 2, 7 Polk 20 Agyernon-Prempeh | 18 | 15 |
| Nov 13 | SPL | A | Gosport Borough | 303 | L 2-3 | Lorraine 50 Talabi 56 | | 16 |
| 17 | SPL | A | Hitchin Town | 364 | W 2-1 | Blossom 38 Talabi 81 | 17 | 17 |
| 24 | SPL | H | Hemel Hempstead U | 123 | W 4-0 | Lorraine 14 Skendi 64 Talabi 69 (pen) 79 | 17 | 18 |
| Dec 1 | SPL | A | Chesham United | 298 | L 1-2 | Lorraine 3 | 19 | 19 |
| 4 | SPL | A | Cambridge City | 225 | L 0-1 | | 17 | 20 |
| 8 | SPL | H | Bashley | 208 | W 3-1 | Isaac 27 Talabi 60 Skendi 75 | 16 | 21 |
| 15 | SPL | A | Bedford Town | 226 | L 1-3 | Agyeman-Prempeh 2 | 19 | 22 |
| 18 | SPL | H | AFC Totton | 116 | W 2-1 | Lait 73 Shariff 78 | 15 | 23 |
| 22 | SPL | A | St Albans City | 334 | L 0-4 | | 15 | 24 |
| 26 | SPL | H | Leamington | 465 | W 3-0 | Bridges 34 70 (pen) Skendi 49 | 14 | 25 |
| Jan 5 | SPL | H | Barwell | 286 | L 1-2 | Martin 43 | 16 | 26 |
| 12 | SPL | A | Bideford | 191 | W 2-1 | Martin 30 Blossom 60 | 14 | 27 |
| 15 | SPL | H | Arlesey Town | 125 | L 1-3 | Shariff 82 | 15 | 28 |
| 26 | SPL | A | Chippenham Town | 311 | W 2-0 | N'Guesson 30 Isaac 40 | 13 | 29 |
| 29 | SPL | H | Kettering Town | 147 | W 2-0 | Isaac 14 Sheriff 29 | 12 | 30 |
| Feb 2 | SPL | A | Frome Town | 205 | D 0-0 | | 12 | 31 |
| 9 | SPL | H | Gosport Borough | 223 | L 2-4 | Shariff 42 Bridges 81 (pen) | 13 | 32 |
| 16 | SPL | H | Hitchin Town | 216 | L 0-4 | | 14 | 33 |
| 19 | SPL | A | Redditch United | 121 | W 2-0 | Skendi 48 Blossom 54 | 12 | 34 |
| 23 | SPL | A | AFC Totton | 308 | W 3-2 | Isaac 37 Skendi 60 Hopkins 90 | 11 | 35 |
| Mar 2 | SPL | H | Bedworth United | 269 | D 1-1 | Hopkins 13 | 13 | 36 |
| 5 | SPL | H | Stourbridge | 126 | L 0-2 | | 13 | 37 |
| 9 | SPL | A | Weymouth | 764 | L 0-1 | | 14 | 38 |
| 30 | SPL | H | St Neots Town | 292 | W 3-1 | SKENDI (4 20 72) | 14 | 39 |
| Apr 1 | SPL | A | Leamington | 734 | L 1-4 | Hpkins 50 | 14 | 40 |
| 6 | SPL | H | Chesham United | 234 | L 1-2 | Talabi 6 | 14 | 41 |
| 11 | SPL | A | Arlesey Town | 87 | L 1-2 | Isaac 79 | 14 | 42 |
| 13 | SPL | A | Hemel Hemptead T | 306 | W 2-1 | Talabi 15 Isaac 69 | 14 | 43 |
| 16 | SPL | H | Cambridge City | 114 | D 2-2 | Polk 27 Skendl 78 | 14 | 44 |
| 20 | SPL | H | Bedford Town | 258 | D 1-1 | Skendl 51 | 14 | 45 |
| 27 | SPL | A | Bashley United | 196 | L 0-2 | | 16 | 46 |

| GOALSCORERS | Lge | FAC | FAT | Total | Pens | Hat-tricks | Cons Run | | Lge | FAC | FAT | Total | Pens | Hat-tricks | Cons Run |
|-------------|-----|-----|-----|-------|------|-----------|----------|---|-----|-----|-----|-------|------|-----------|----------|
| Skendi | 10 | | | 10 | | 1 | 2 | Agyeman-Prempeh | 2 | | | 2 | | | |
| Talabi | 9 | | 1 | 9 | | | 3 | Gray | | | 2 | 2 | | | |
| Isaac | 8 | | | 8 | | | 2 | Martin | 2 | | | 2 | | | 2 |
| Blossom | 4 | | | 4 | | | | Polk | 2 | | | 2 | | | |
| Lorraine | 4 | | | 4 | | | 2 | Ashton | 1 | | | 1 | | | |
| Johnson | 3 | 1 | | 4 | | | | Confue | 1 | | | 1 | | | |
| Shariff | 4 | | | 4 | | | | Lait | 1 | | | 1 | | | |
| Bridges | 3 | | | 3 | 1 | | | N'Guesson | 1 | | | 1 | | | |
| Cornado | 1 | | 2 | 3 | | | 3 | O'Grady | 1 | | | 1 | | | |
| Hopkins | 3 | | | 3 | | | | Cons Run - Consecutive scoring games. | | | | | | | |

# BASHLEY

**Chairman:** Mike Cranidge
**Secretary:** Colin Bell          **(T)**          **(E)** thebellfamily24@btinternet.com
**Commercial Manager:** Ian Roberts          **(T)**
**Programme Editor:** Richard Millbery          **(T)** rw_millbery@lineone.net
**Ground Address:** Bashley Road Ground, Bashley Road, New Milton, Hampshire BH25 5RY
**(T)** 01425 620 280          **Manager:**

## Club Factfile

**Founded:** 1947     **Nickname:** The Bash
**Previous Names:** None
**Previous Leagues:** Bournemouth 1953-83, Hampshire 1983-86, Wessex 1986-89, Southern 1989-2004, Isthmian 2004-06

**Club Colours (change):** Gold/black/black (White/blue/blue)

**Ground Capacity:** 4,250   **Seats:** 250   **Covered:** 1,200   **Clubhouse:** Yes   **Shop:** Yes

**Directions**

Take the A35 from Lyndhurst towards Christchurch, turn left onto B3058 towards New Milton.
The ground is on the left hand side in Bashley village.

**Previous Grounds:** None

**Record Attendance:** 3,500 v Emley - FA Vase Semi-final 1st Leg 1987-88
**Record Victory:** 21-1 v Co-Operative (A) - Bournemouth League 1964
**Record Defeat:** 2-20 v Air Speed (A) - Bournemouth League 1957
**Record Goalscorer:** Richard Gillespie - 134
**Record Appearances:** John Bone - 829
**Additional Records:** Paid £7,500 to Newport (IOW) for Danny Gibbons and from Dorchester Tn for David Elm. Received £15,000 from
**Senior Honours:** Salisbury for Craig Davis, from Eastleigh for Paul Sales and from AFC Bournemouth for Wade Elliott.
Wessex League 1986-87, 87-88, 88-89. Southern League Southern Division 1989-90, Division 1 South & West 2006-07.

### 10 YEAR RECORD

| 03-04 | | 04-05 | | 05-06 | | 06-07 | | 07-08 | | 08-09 | | 09-10 | | 10-11 | | 11-12 | | 12-13 | |
|---|---|---|---|---|---|---|---|---|---|---|---|---|---|---|---|---|---|---|---|
| SthE | 11 | Isth1 | 14 | Isth1 | 9 | Sthsw | 1 | SthP | 5 | SthP | 14 | SthP | 7 | SthP | 11 | SthP | 13 | SthP | 17 |

## MATCH RESULTS 2012-13

| Date | Comp | H/A | Opponents | Att: | Result | Goalscorers | Pos | No. |
|------|------|-----|-----------|------|--------|-------------|-----|-----|
| Aug 18 | SPL | A | Cambridge City | 243 | L 1-3 | Green 63 | 20 | 1 |
| 21 | SPL | H | Frome Town | 227 | W 2-1 | Stokoe 26 66 | 11 | 2 |
| 25 | SPL | H | Hemel Hempstead | 159 | L 0-6 | | 17 | 3 |
| 27 | SPL | A | Gosport Borough | 307 | D 0-0 | | 16 | 4 |
| Sept 1 | SPL | H | Bedworth United | 152 | W 1-0 | Middleton 90 | 11 | 5 |
| 4 | SPL | A | Chesham United | 291 | L 0-3 | | 14 | 6 |
| 8 | FAC Q1 | H | Gosport Borough | 205 | D 1-1 | Gradwell 1 | | 7 |
| 11 | FAC Q1r | A | Gosport Borough | 182 | L 2-3 | Hill 53 Stokoe 75 | | 8 |
| 15 | SPL | H | Barwell | 160 | L 0-5 | | 19 | 9 |
| 18 | SPL | A | Chippenham Town | 241 | L 0-1 | | 21 | 10 |
| 29 | FAT Q1 | A | Poole Town | 351 | D 1-1 | Brooks 49 (og) | | 11 |
| Oct 2 | FAT Q1r | H | Poole Town | 171 | L 0-4 | | | 12 |
| 6 | SPL | A | Kettering Town | 304 | W 7-0 | Stokoe 29 47 Foster 51 53 Farren 71 Vokes 82 89 | 14 | 13 |
| 13 | SPL | H | Leamington | 229 | L 0-2 | Dodds 27 Taylor 87 | 18 | 14 |
| 27 | SPL | H | Bideford | 155 | W 4-1 | Gradwell 45 Gamble 49 Stephenson 66 73 | 13 | 15 |
| Nov 3 | SPL | A | St Neots Town | 389 | D 2-2 | Richardson 55 Jenkinson 66 | 14 | 16 |
| 6 | SPL | H | AFC Totton | 282 | L 0-3 | | 16 | 17 |
| 13 | SPL | A | Arlesey Town | 107 | W 2-1 | Gamble 36 Jenkinson 89 (pen) | 14 | 18 |
| 17 | SPL | A | Bedford Town | 234 | W 1-0 | Strickland 87 | 8 | 19 |
| Dec 1 | SPL | H | St Albans City | 158 | W 2-0 | Gamble 40 89 | 11 | 20 |
| 6 | SPL | A | Banbury United | 208 | L 1-3 | Richardson 77 | 13 | 21 |
| 15 | SPL | H | Stourbridge | 182 | L 0-1 | | 13 | 22 |
| 18 | SPL | H | Hitchin Town | 92 | L 0-1 | | 14 | 23 |
| 26 | SPL | A | Weymouth | 820 | L 0-1 | | 17 | 24 |
| Jan 1 | SPL | H | Gosport Borough | 190 | D 1-1 | Gamble 38 | 18 | 25 |
| 5 | SPL | A | Frome Town | 171 | D 1-1 | Gamble 70 (pen) | 18 | 26 |
| Feb 2 | SPL | A | AFC Totton | 438 | L 0-2 | | 19 | 27 |
| 5 | SPL | H | Cambridge City | 109 | D 0-0 | | 18 | 28 |
| 9 | SPL | H | Kettering | 178 | W 3-1 | Gradwell 74 Knight 77 Stokoe 88 | 18 | 29 |
| 16 | SPL | H | Bedford Town | 185 | L 0-1 | | 18 | 30 |
| 23 | SPL | A | Hitchin Town | 243 | L 2-3 | Casey 12 Stephenson 53 | 19 | 31 |
| 26 | SPL | H | Chippenham Town | 87 | W 2-1 | Gamble 9 Stokoe 15 | 17 | 32 |
| Mar 2 | SPL | H | Arlesey Town | 105 | W 1-0 | Middleton 45 | 16 | 33 |
| 5 | SPL | A | Redditch United | 95 | D 0-0 | | 16 | 34 |
| 9 | SPL | A | Leamington | 462 | L 1-4 | Knight 27 | 16 | 35 |
| 19 | SPL | H | Chesham United | 103 | L 1-3 | Oliver 7 | 16 | 36 |
| 23 | SPL | A | Bideford | 161 | D 0-0 | | 16 | 37 |
| 26 | SPL | A | Weymouth | 128 | L 2-4 | Knight 48 Gamble 90 | 16 | 38 |
| 30 | SPL | A | Bedworth United | 149 | W 3-0 | Gamble 44 (pen) Gradwell 62 Stokoe 80 | 16 | 39 |
| Apr 1 | SPL | H | Weymouth | 304 | W 1-0 | Richardson 80 | 15 | 40 |
| 6 | SPL | A | St Albans City | 305 | D 2-2 | Richardson 25 Oliver 47 | 14 | 41 |
| 9 | SPL | A | Barwell | 104 | D 0-0 | | 15 | 42 |
| 16 | SPL | H | St Neots Town | 114 | D 2-2 | Moth 26 Richardson 89 | 15 | 43 |
| 18 | SPL | H | Redditch United | 88 | L 0-1 | | 15 | 44 |
| 20 | SPL | A | Stourbridge | 647 | L 0-3 | | 16 | 45 |
| 27 | SPL | H | Banbury United | 196 | W 2-0 | Gamble 48, 90 | | 46 |

| GOALSCORERS | Lge | FAC | FAT | Total | Pens | Hat-tricks | Cons Run | | Lge | FAC | FAT | Total | Pens | Hat-tricks | Cons Run |
|-------------|-----|-----|-----|-------|------|------------|----------|---|-----|-----|-----|-------|------|------------|----------|
| Gamble | 11 | | | 11 | 2 | | 2 | Casey | 1 | | | 1 | | | |
| Stokoe | 7 | 1 | | 8 | | | | Dodds | 1 | | | 1 | | | |
| Richardson | 5 | | | 5 | 2 | | | Farren | 1 | | | 1 | | | |
| Gradwell | 3 | 1 | | 4 | | | | Green | 1 | | | 1 | | | |
| Knight | 3 | | | 3 | | | | Hill | | 1 | | 1 | | | |
| Stephenson | 3 | | | 3 | | | | Moth | 1 | | | 1 | | | |
| Foster | 2 | | | 2 | | | | Strickland | 1 | | | 1 | | | |
| Jenkinson | 2 | | | 2 | 1 | | | Taylor | 1 | | | 1 | | | |
| Middleton | 2 | | | 2 | | | | Own Goals | | | 1 | | | | |
| Oliver | 2 | | | 2 | | | | Cons Run - Consecutive scoring games. | | | | | | | |
| Vokes | 2 | | | 2 | | | | | | | | | | | |

# BEDFORD TOWN

**Chairman:** David Howell
**Secretary:** Dave Swallow    **(T)** 07939 812 965    **(E)** david.swallow@bedfordeagles.net
**Commercial Manager:**    **(T)**
**Programme Editor:** Dave Swallow    **(T)** david.swallow@bedfordeagles.net
**Ground Address:** The Eyrie, Meadow Lane, Cardington, Bedford MK44 3SB
**(T)** 01234 831 558    **Manager:** Lee Bearman

2012-13 Squad - Back Row (L-R): Josh Beech, Gareth Price, Michael Built, Jamaine Ivy, Mark Bell, Nick Beasant, Ian Brown (Captain), Dan Crowie, Greg Ling, Seb Simpson, Steve Kinniburgh, Chris Gibbons (Physio), Adam Sandy (Assistant Manager)

Front Row: Ollie Wilkinson, Leigh Stevens, Callum Lewis, David Howell (Chairman), Nick Platnauer (Manager), Paul Cooper, Eugene Libertucci, Ashley Fuller

## Club Factfile

**Founded:** 1989    **Nickname:** The Eagles
**Previous Names:** Original Bedford Town founded in 1908 folded in 1982
**Previous Leagues:** South Midlands 1989-94, Isthmian 1994-2004, Southern 2004-06, Conference 2006-07

**Club Colours (change):** All blue (Gold with black trim/black/black)

**Ground Capacity:** 3,000    **Seats:** 300    **Covered:** 1,000    **Clubhouse:** Yes    **Shop:** Yes

**Directions**

From A1: Take A603 from Sandy to Bedford, go through Willington and ground is a mile and a half on right, signposted Meadow Lane. From M1: Off at Junction 13, take A421, carry on A421 onto Bedford Bypass and take A603 Sandy turn off. Ground is on left.

**Previous Grounds:** Allen Park, Queens Park, Bedford Park Pitch 1991-93

**Record Attendance:** 3,000 v Peterborough United - Ground opening 06/08/1993
**Record Victory:** 9-0 v Ickleford and v Cardington
**Record Defeat:** 0-5 v Hendon
**Record Goalscorer:** Jason Reed
**Record Appearances:** Eddie Lawley
**Additional Records:**

**Senior Honours:**
Isthmian League Division 2 1998-99. Bedfordshire Senior Cup 1994-95. Southern League Play-offs 2005-06.

### 10 YEAR RECORD

| 03-04 | | 04-05 | | 05-06 | | 06-07 | | 07-08 | | 08-09 | | 09-10 | | 10-11 | | 11-12 | | 12-13 | |
|---|---|---|---|---|---|---|---|---|---|---|---|---|---|---|---|---|---|---|---|
| Isth P | 15 | SthP | 5 | SthP | 5 | Conf S | 22 | SthP | 19 | SthP | 15 | SthP | 18 | SthP | 17 | SthP | 10 | SthP | 10 |

# MATCH RESULTS 2012-13

| Date | Comp | H/A | Opponents | Att: | Result | Goalscorers | Pos | No. |
|------|------|-----|-----------|------|--------|-------------|-----|-----|
| Aug 18 | SPL | H | Leamington | 335 | D 2-2 | Mace 43 (og) Beasant 72 | 15 | 1 |
| 21 | SPL | A | Arlesey Town | 240 | L 1-2 | Beasant 56 | 15 | 2 |
| 25 | SPL | A | Bideford | 174 | W 3-0 | Beasant 10 60 (pen) Fuller 75 | 9 | 3 |
| 27 | SPL | H | Kettering Town | 538 | D 1-1 | Beasant 59 | 10 | 4 |
| Sept 1 | SPL | A | AFC Totton | 306 | L 0-2 | | 14 | 5 |
| 4. | SPL | H | Redditch United | 213 | W 2-1 | Beasant 66 Grimes 79 | 12 | 6 |
| 8. | FAC Q1 | A | **Waltham Abbey** | **149** | **L 0-1** | | | 7 |
| 15 | SPL | H | Bedworth United | 260 | L 0-1 | | 12 | 8 |
| 18 | SPL | A | Barwell | 134 | L 1-2 | Peacock 20 | 16 | 9 |
| 29 | FAT Q1 | A | **Grantham Town** | **271** | **W 2-0** | **Bell 14 Peacock 48** | | 10 |
| Oct 2 | SPL | A | Chippenham Town | 207 | W 2-0 | Grimes 61 Peacock 79 | 10 | 11 |
| 6 | SPL | H | Bideford | 244 | W 3-1 | Ivy 16 Bell 34 Fuller 51 (pen) | 8 | 12 |
| 9 | SPL | H | Stourbridge | 224 | W 2-0 | Ivy 37 Peacock 58 | 5 | 13 |
| 13 | SPL | A | Chesham United | 401 | D 2-2 | Beech 41 Bell 84 | 6 | 14 |
| 20 | SPL | H | Hemel Hmpstead T | 389 | L 0-3 | | 6 | 15 |
| 27 | FAT Q2 | H | **Maidstone United** | **402** | **L 2-3** | **Ivy 81 Built 90** | | 16 |
| Nov 3 | SPL | H | Gosport Borough | 210 | W 1-0 | Ivy 27 | 5 | 17 |
| 10 | SPL | A | Cambridge City | 357 | L 1-2 | Built 9 | 7 | 18 |
| 13 | SPL | A | St Albans City | 293 | D 2-2 | Lewis 14 75 | 7 | 19 |
| 17 | SPL | H | Bashley | 234 | L 0-1 | | 7 | 20 |
| Dec 1 | SPL | H | Weymouth | 231 | L 0-2 | | 12 | 21 |
| 8 | SPL | A | Hitchin Town | 358 | L 0-2 | | 14 | 22 |
| 15 | SPL | H | Banbury United | 226 | W 3-1 | Green 5 32 Bell 85 | 12 | 23 |
| 19 | SPL | A | Frome Town | 119 | W 3-2 | Lewis 18 Bell 40 Green 68 | 9 | 24 |
| 26 | SPL | H | St Neots Town | 567 | W 3-0 | Green 60 Bell 68 Built 85 | 7 | 25 |
| Jan 2 | SPL | A | Kettering Town | 456 | L 0-3 | | 7 | 26 |
| 5 | SPL | H | Arlesey Town | 306 | D 0-0 | | 9 | 27 |
| 12 | SPL | A | Redditch United | 148 | W 3-0 | Green 40 Ivy 76 Beasant 87 | 8 | 28 |
| Feb 2 | SPL | A | Stourbridge | 448 | W 1-0 | Beasant 62 | 8 | 29 |
| 9 | SPL | H | Chippenham Town | 220 | D 1-1 | Kinniburgh 90 | 10 | 30 |
| 16 | SPL | A | Bashley | 185 | W 1-0 | Green 58 | 9 | 31 |
| 19 | SPL | H | Barwell | 167 | W 3-0 | Green 27 Gysai 59 Built 75 | 7 | 32 |
| 23 | SPL | H | Cambridge City | 351 | W 2-1 | Beech 45 W.Green 90 | 7 | 33 |
| Mar 5 | SPL | A | Bedworth United | 122 | L 0-2 | | 8 | 34 |
| 9 | SPL | H | Chesham United | 261 | L 0-1 | | 10 | 35 |
| 19 | SPL | A | Leamington | 381 | L 0-3 | | 11 | 36 |
| 30 | SPL | H | AFC Totton | 224 | W 4-1 | Beasant 12 Libertucci 34 Ivy 48 Peacock 90 | 11 | 37 |
| Apr 1 | SPL | A | St Neots Town | 532 | W 3-1 | Nkinga 68 (og) Ivy 83 Davis 87 | 11 | 38 |
| 6 | SPL | A | Weymouth | 548 | W 4-0 | PEACOCK 3 ( 55 64 74) W,Green 90 | 11 | 39 |
| 9 | SPL | A | Gosport Brorough | 306 | L 0-4 | | 11 | 40 |
| 13 | SPL | H | Frome Town | 227 | L 0-1 | | 11 | 41 |
| 14 | SPL | A | Kettering Town | 189 | L 1-3 | Hockley 39 (pen) | 11 | 42 |
| 16 | SPL | H | St Albans City | 205 | W 2-0 | Lewis 44 Built 90 | 8 | 43 |
| 20 | SPL | A | Banbury United | 258 | D 1-1 | Lewis 72 (pen) | 10 | 44 |
| 27 | SPL | H | Hitchin Town | 432 | L 1-4 | Kinniburgh 88 | 10 | 45 |

| GOALSCORERS | Lge | FAC | FAT | Total | Pens | Hat-tricks | Cons Run | | Lge | FAC | FAT | Total | Pens | Hat-tricks | Cons Run |
|-------------|-----|-----|-----|-------|------|------------|----------|---|-----|-----|-----|-------|------|------------|----------|
| Beasant | 9 | | | 9 | 1 | | 4 | Kinniburgh | 2 | | | 2 | | | |
| Green | 9 | | | 9 | | | 3 | Davis | 1 | | | 1 | | | |
| Peacock | 7 | 1 | | 8 | | 1 | 3 | Gysai | 1 | | | 1 | 1 | | |
| Ivy | 6 | | 1 | 7 | | | 2 | Hockley | 1 | | | 1 | | | |
| Bell | 5 | | 1 | 6 | | | 3 | Libertucci | 1 | | | 1 | | | |
| Built | 4 | | 1 | 5 | | | | Own Goals | 2 | | | | | | |
| Lewis | 5 | | | 5 | 1 | | 2 | Cons Run - Consecutive scoring games. | | | | | | | |
| Beech | 4 | | | 4 | | | | | | | | | | | |
| Fuller | 2 | | | 2 | 1 | | | | | | | | | | |
| Grimes | 2 | | | 2 | | | | | | | | | | | |

# BIDEFORD

**Chairman:** Roy Portch
**Secretary:** Kevin Tyrrell  **(T)** 07929 078 613  **(E)** k.tyrrell@talktalk.net
**Commercial Manager:** Darren Hollyoak  **(T)**
**Programme Editor:** Ian Knight  **(T)** ianknight@bidefordafc.co.uk
**Ground Address:** The Sports Ground, Kingsley Road, Bideford EX39 2LH
**(T)** 01237 474 974  **Manager:** Sean Joyce

## Club Factfile

**Founded:** 1949  **Nickname:** The Robins
**Previous Names:** Bideford Town
**Previous Leagues:** Devon & Exeter 1947-49, Western 1949-72, 75-2010, Southern 1972-75

**Club Colours (change):** All red (All blue)

**Ground Capacity:** 6,000  **Seats:** 375  **Covered:** 1,000  **Clubhouse:** Yes  **Shop:**

**Directions**
Exit M5 at J.27. A361 to Barnstaple. Turn left onto A39 to Bideford.
9 miles turn left into town.
Ground on right hand side as entering town centre.

**Previous Grounds:** None

**Record Attendance:** 6,000 v Gloucester City - FA Cup 4th Qualifying Round
**Record Victory:** Not known
**Record Defeat:** Not known
**Record Goalscorer:** Tommy Robinson - 259
**Record Appearances:** Derek May - 527
**Additional Records:**

**Senior Honours:**
Western League 1963-64, 70-71, 71-72, 81-82, 82-83, 2001-02, 03-04, 04-05, 05-06, 09-10, Division 1 1951-52, Division 3 1949-50.
Southern Division 1 South & West 2011-12.
Devon Senior Cup 1979-80

### 10 YEAR RECORD

| 03-04 | | 04-05 | | 05-06 | | 06-07 | | 07-08 | | 08-09 | | 09-10 | | 10-11 | | 11-12 | | 12-13 | |
|---|---|---|---|---|---|---|---|---|---|---|---|---|---|---|---|---|---|---|---|
| WestP | 1 | WestP | 1 | WestP | 1 | WestP | 4 | WestP | 6 | WestP | 6 | WestP | 1 | Sthsw | 10 | Sthsw | 1 | SthP | 20 |

# MATCH RESULTS 2012-13

| Date | Comp | H/A | Opponents | Att: | Result | Goalscorers | Pos | No. |
|---|---|---|---|---|---|---|---|---|
| Aug 18 | SPL | A | Bedworth United | 212 | L 1-2 | Downing 12 | 15 | 1 |
| 21 | SPL | H | Gosport Borough | 197 | L 0-2 | | 15 | 2 |
| 25 | SPL | H | Bedford Town | 174 | L 0-3 | | 21 | 3 |
| 272 | SPL | A | Weymouth | 673 | L 2-4 | Laight 16 Dixon 65 (og) | 21 | 4 |
| Sept 1 | SPL | H | Chesham United | 117 | W 2-1 | Vassell 65 Groves 76 (pen) | 21 | 5 |
| 4 | SPL | A | Banbury United | 183 | D 1-1 | Vassell 90 | 21 | 6 |
| 8 | FAC Q1 | H | Bodmin Town | 208 | D 2-2 | Squire 44 Downing 89 | | 7 |
| 12 | FAC Q1r | A | Bodmin Town | 220 | W 3-2* | Laight 20 Groves 110 Downing 114 | | 8 |
| 15 | SPL | H | Redditch United | 177 | W 3-2 | Downing 50 Andrew 60 Sampson 85 | 18 | 9 |
| 18 | SPL | A | AFC Totton | 267 | L 0-2 | | 19 | 10 |
| 22 | FAC Q2 | A | Gosport Borough | 232 | L 0-2 | | | 11 |
| 29 | FAT Q1 | A | AFC Totton | 288 | L 0-2 | | | 12 |
| Oct 6 | SPL | A | Bedford Town | 244 | L 1-3 | Andrew 15 | 20 | 13 |
| 20 | SPL | H | Stourbridge | 207 | D 2-2 | Downing 10 Squire 60 | 21 | 14 |
| 27 | SPL | A | Bashley | 155 | L 1-4 | Squire 88 | 21 | 15 |
| Nov 3 | SPL | H | Hitchin Town | 198 | W 3-2 | Barker 3 Downing 5 Hockley 80 (pen) | 20 | 16 |
| 6 | SPL | H | Chippenham Town | 108 | L 1-2 | Squire 65 | 20 | 17 |
| 10 | SPL | A | St Neots Town | 324 | L 3-5 | Groves 73 Bye 77 Downing 78 | 20 | 18 |
| 17 | SPL | H | St Albans City | 186 | W 1-0 | Farkins 75 | 19 | 19 |
| 27 | SPL | H | Kettering Town | 106 | W 4-0 | Andrew 24 Downing 35 80 Squire 87 | 19 | 20 |
| Dec 1 | SPL | A | Barwell | 134 | D 1-1 | Squire 58 | 18 | 21 |
| 8 | SPL | H | Hemel Hempstead T | 197 | W 3-2 | Squire 30 70 Groves 55 | 20 | 22 |
| 15 | SPL | A | Leamington | 429 | L 1-2 | Squire 25 | 17 | 23 |
| 26 | SPL | A | Frome Town | 228 | W 1-0 | Furzer 62 | 15 | 24 |
| Jan 1 | SPL | H | Weymouth | 373 | W 2-1 | Andrew 55 70 | 14 | 25 |
| 5 | SPL | A | Gosport Borough | 379 | L 0-2 | | 15 | 26 |
| 12 | SPL | H | Banbury United | 181 | L 1-2 | Andrew 90 | 16 | 27 |
| 19 | SPL | H | AFC Totton | 168 | D 1-1 | Andrew 34 | 16 | 28 |
| Feb 2 | SPL | A | Chippenham Town | 291 | W 7-1 | Squire 18 81 Harper-Penman 41 Bye 45, Downing 53 56 Andrew 73 | 15 | 29 |
| 9 | SPL | H | Arlesey Town | 181 | D 1-1 | Clifford 63 | 15 | 30 |
| 16 | SPL | A | S Albans City | 370 | L 3-4 | Downing 44 89 Groves 85 (pen) | 15 | 31 |
| 19 | SPL | H | Bedworth United | 132 | W 3-0 | Hockley 26 81 (pen) Andrew 65 | 15 | 32 |
| 23 | SPL | H | St Neots Town | 183 | D 0-0 | | 15 | 33 |
| 26 | SPL | H | Cambridge City | 87 | W 2-1 | Downing 18 Squire 90 | 14 | 34 |
| Mar 2 | SPL | A | Stourbridge | 509 | L 1-3 | Downing 78 | 15 | 35 |
| 5 | SPL | A | Arlesey Town | 75 | D 2-2 | Groves 4 42 | 15 | 36 |
| 16 | SPL | A | Hitchin Town | 321 | L 0-1 | | 15 | 37 |
| 23 | SPL | H | Bashley | 161 | D 0-0 | | 15 | 38 |
| 30 | SPL | A | Chesham United | 450 | L 0-1 | | 15 | 39 |
| Apr 1 | SPL | H | Frome Town | 187 | D 0-0 | | 15 | 40 |
| 6 | SPL | H | Barwell | 134 | L 1-2 | Hockley 50 (pen) | 16 | 41 |
| 9 | SPL | A | Redditch United | 109 | L 1-2 | Downing 35 | 16 | 42 |
| 13 | SPL | A | Cambridge City | 296 | L 0-1 | | 17 | 43 |
| 14 | SPL | A | Kettering | 189 | L 1-3 | Hockley 35 (pen) | 17 | 44 |
| 20 | SPL | H | Leamington | 360 | L 0-1 | | 20 | 45 |
| 27 | SPL | A | Hemel Hempstead T | 583 | L 1-4 | Groves 43 | 20 | 46 |

| GOALSCORERS | Lge | FAC | FAT | Total | Pens | Hat-tricks | Cons Run | | Lge | FAC | FAT | Total | Pens | Hat-tricks | Cons Run |
|---|---|---|---|---|---|---|---|---|---|---|---|---|---|---|---|
| Downing | 14 | 2 | | 16 | | | 3 | Farkins | 1 | | | 1 | | | |
| Squire | 11 | 1 | | 12 | | | 4 | Furzer | 1 | | | 1 | | | |
| Andrew | 9 | | | 9 | | | 3 | Harper-Penman | 1 | | | 1 | | | |
| Groves | 7 | 1 | | 8 | 2 | | | Sampson | 1 | | | 1 | | | |
| Laight | 1 | 1 | | 2 | | | | Own Goal | | | | 1 | | | |
| Bye | 2 | | | 2 | | | | Cons Run - Consecutive scoring games. | | | | | | | |
| Vassell | 2 | | | 2 | | | 2 | | | | | | | | |
| Hockley | 5 | | | 5 | 3 | | | | | | | | | | |
| Barker | 1 | | | 1 | | | | | | | | | | | |
| Clifford | 1 | | | 1 | | | | | | | | | | | |

# BIGGLESWADE TOWN

**Chairman:** Maurice Dorrington
**Secretary:** Andy McDonnell    **(T)** 07879 802 105    **(E)** andy.mcdonnell@ntlworld.com
**Commercial Manager:**    **(T)**
**Programme Editor:** David Simpson    **(T)** simpson_david@hotmail.co.uk
**Ground Address:** The Carlsberg Stadium, Langford Road, Biggleswade SG18 9JJ
**(T)** 01767 315 547    **Manager:** Chris Nunn

## Club Factfile

**Founded:** 1874    **Nickname:** The Waders
**Previous Names:** Biggleswade FC
**Previous Leagues:** Biggleswade & District, Bedford & District, Spartan South Midlands 1951-55, 80-2009, Eastern Counties 1955-63, United Counties 1963-80

**Club Colours (change):** White with green trim/green/green (Blue & black stripes/blue/blue & black)

**Ground Capacity:** 3,000    **Seats:** 300    **Covered:** 400    **Clubhouse:** Yes    **Shop:**

**Directions:** From the south – up the A1, past the first roundabout (Homebase) signposted Biggleswade. At next roundabout (Sainsburys) turn right onto A6001. As you approach the Town Centre, go straight over the mini roundabout following signs for Langford (Teal Road). At traffic lights, turn right (still heading towards Langford). Continue along Hitchin Street over two mini roundabouts and as you pass under the A1, the ground entrance is 200 yards on the right. From the north – exit A1 at the Sainsburys roundabout and follow instructions as above.

**Previous Grounds:** Fairfield

**Record Attendance:** 2,000
**Record Victory:** Not known
**Record Defeat:** Not known
**Record Goalscorer:** Not known
**Record Appearances:** Not known
**Additional Records:**

**Senior Honours:**
Spartan South Midlands Premier Division 2008-09. Bedfordshire Premier Cup 2009. Bedfordshire Senior Challenge Cup 2012-13.

### 10 YEAR RECORD

| 03-04 | 04-05 | 05-06 | 06-07 | 07-08 | 08-09 | 09-10 | 10-11 | 11-12 | 12-13 |
|---|---|---|---|---|---|---|---|---|---|
| SSM P 15 | SSM P 10 | SSM P 15 | SSM P 18 | SSM P 3 | SSM P 1 | SthM 12 | SthC 4 | SthC 8 | SthC 4 |

# BURNHAM

**Chairman:** Gary Reeves
**Secretary:** Alan King  **(T)** 07899 941 414  **(E)** burnhamfcsec@aol.com
**Commercial Manager:**  **(T)**
**Programme Editor:** Gareth Stoneman  **(T)** gms.burnhamfc@gmail.com
**Ground Address:** The Gore, Wymers Wood Road, Burnham, Slough SL1 8JG
**(T)** 01628 668 654  **Manager:** Martin Stone

Ryan Blake (Burnham) takes on Aaron Blaxall (Fleet) in a pre-season friendly.
Photo: Keith Clayton.

### Club Factfile

**Founded:** 1878  **Nickname:** The Blues
**Previous Names:** Burnham & Hillingdon 1985-87
**Previous Leagues:** Hellenic 1971-77, 95-99, Athenian 1977-84, London Spartan 1984-85, Southern 1985-95

**Club Colours (change):** Blue and white halves/blue/blue (Red and black hoops/red/red)

**Ground Capacity:** 2,500  **Seats:** Yes  **Covered:** Yes  **Clubhouse:** Yes  **Shop:** Yes

**Directions:** Approx. 2 miles from M4 junction 7 and 5 miles from M40 junction 2. From M40 take A355 to A4 signposted Maidenhead. From M4 take A4 towards Maidenhead until you reach roundabout with Sainsbury Superstore on left. Turn right into Lent Rise Road and travel approx 11/2 miles over 2 double roundabouts. 100 yards after second double roundabout fork right into Wymers Wood Road. Ground entrance on right.

**Previous Grounds:** Baldwin Meadow until 1920s

**Record Attendance:** 2,380 v Halesowen Town - FA Vase 02/04/1983
**Record Victory:** 18-0 v High Duty Alloys - 1970-71
**Record Defeat:** 1-10 v Ernest Turner Sports - 1963-64
**Record Goalscorer:** Fraser Hughes - 65 (1969-70)
**Record Appearances:** Not known
**Additional Records:**

**Senior Honours:**
Hellenic League 1975-76, 98-99, League Cup 1975-76, 98-99, Division 1 Cup 1971-72.
Southern League Division One Central 2012-13.

### 10 YEAR RECORD

| 03-04 | | 04-05 | | 05-06 | | 06-07 | | 07-08 | | 08-09 | | 09-10 | | 10-11 | | 11-12 | | 12-13 | |
|---|---|---|---|---|---|---|---|---|---|---|---|---|---|---|---|---|---|---|---|
| SthE | 17 | SthW | 9 | SthW | 4 | Sthsw | 3 | Sthsw | 10 | Sthsw | 17 | SthM | 3 | SthC | 14 | SthC | 15 | SthC | 1 |

# CAMBRIDGE CITY

**Chairman:** Kevin Satchell
**Secretary:** Andy Dewey          **(T)** 07720 678 585     **(E)** andy@cambridgecityfc.com
**Commercial Manager:** Paul Hammond          **(T)** 07505 904 119
**Programme Editor:** Chris Farrington          **(T)** ccfc.editor@googlemail.com
**Ground Address:** City Ground, Milton Road, Cambridge CB4 1UY
**(T)** 01223 233 226                    **Manager:** Gary Roberts

2012-13 Squad - Back Row (L-R): Charlie Death, Christian Lester, Dave Theobald, Craig Hammond, Zac Barrett, Enol Ordonez, Lee Chaffey, Jack Dekanski, Victor Torres, Joey Abbs.
Front Row: Joe Miller (Therapist),Tom Pepper, Pat Bexfield, Neil Midgley, Gary Roberts (Manager), Adrian Cambridge, Robbie Nightingale, Lee Clift, David Prada, Brian Chapman (Kit Man).

## Club Factfile

**Founded:** 1908      **Nickname:** Lilywhites
**Previous Names:** Cambridge Town 1908-51
**Previous Leagues:** Bury & District 1908-13, 19-20, Anglian 1908-10, Southern Olympian 1911-14, Southern Amateur 1913-35, Spartan 1935-50, Athenian 1950-58, Southern 1958-2004

**Club Colours (change):** White/black/white (All light blue)

**Ground Capacity:** 2,722   **Seats:** 526    **Covered:** 220    **Clubhouse:** Yes   **Shop:** Yes

**Directions:** Take Junction 13 on M11 and head for City Centre. At mini roundabout turn left then straight on at traffic lights. The road then runs parallel with the river. On reaching traffic lights controlling entry to one way system, get into middle lane up beside Staples Office Furniture and follow lane behind Staples where it becomes nearside lane. Stay in this lane until road straightens then take first left. Ground is behind Westbrook Centre.

**Previous Grounds:** None

**Record Attendance:** 12,058 v Leytonstone - FA Amateur Cup 1st Round 1949-50
**Record Victory:** Not known
**Record Defeat:** Not known
**Record Goalscorer:** Gary Grogan
**Record Appearances:** Mal Keenan
**Additional Records:** Paid £8,000 to Rushden & Diamonds for Paul Coe
**Senior Honours:** Received £100,000 from Millwall for Neil Harris 1998
Southern League 1962-63, Southern Division 1985-86.
Suffolk Senior Cup 1909-10. East Anglian x9. Cambridgeshire Professional Cup 2012-13.

### 10 YEAR RECORD

| 03-04 | | 04-05 | | 05-06 | | 06-07 | | 07-08 | | 08-09 | | 09-10 | | 10-11 | | 11-12 | | 12-13 | |
|---|---|---|---|---|---|---|---|---|---|---|---|---|---|---|---|---|---|---|---|
| SthP | 8 | Conf S | 2 | Conf S | 7 | Conf S | 13 | Conf S | 14 | SthP | 4 | SthP | 6 | SthP | 4 | SthP | 5 | SthP | 8 |

# MATCH RESULTS 2012-13

| Date | Comp | H/A | Opponents | Att: | Result | Goalscorers | Pos | No. |
|---|---|---|---|---|---|---|---|---|
| Aug 18 | SPL | H | Bashley | 243 | W 3-1 | Delanski 10 Hammond 34 86 | 3 | 1 |
| 21 | SPL | A | St Albans City | 363 | L 2-3 | Chaffey 54 Bryant 73 | 8 | 2 |
| 25 | SPL | A | Chippenham Town | 258 | L 3-4 | Bryant 28 Hammond 44 (pen) Theobald 50 | 13 | 3 |
| 27 | SPL | H | St Neots Town | 514 | L 0-5 | | 17 | 4 |
| Sept 1 | SPL | A | Leamington | 502 | L 0-1 | | 20 | 5 |
| 4 | SPL | H | Barwell | 225 | W 2-1 | Hammond 58 Bryant 90 | 16 | 6 |
| 8 | FAC Q1 | H | Huntingdon Town | 240 | W 7-0 | HAMMOND 4 (3 15 36 52) Cambridge 19 Abbs 60 Pepper 65 | 14 | 7 |
| 15 | SPL | H | Frome Town | 315 | L 1-2 | Hammond 28 | 21 | 8 |
| 18 | SPL | A | Kettering Town | 399 | W 2-1 | Hammond 84 87 | 14 | 9 |
| 22 | FAC Q2 | H | Grantham | 379 | W 3-1 | Theobald 36 Hammond 53 60 | 9 | 10 |
| 29 | FAT Q1 | A | Enfield Town | 281 | L 1-4 | Bryant 13 | | 11 |
| Oct 6 | FAC Q3 | H | Billericay Town | 394 | D 1-1 | Oares 49 (og) | | 12 |
| 9 | FAC Q3r | A | Billericay Town | 364 | W 4-2 | Bryant 39 48 Hammond 65 (pen) 68 | | 13 |
| 13 | SPL | A | Gosport Borough | 340 | W 2-1 | Bryant 35 Hammond 90 | 14 | 14 |
| 20 | FAC Q4 | A | AFC Totton | 674 | W 3-2 | Theobald 2 Cambridge 36 Prada 62 | | 15 |
| 23 | SPL | A | Hemel Hempstead | 313 | L 0-1 | | 14 | 16 |
| Nov 3 | FAC 1 | H | MK Dons | 1564 | D 0-0 | | | 17 |
| 6 | SPL | H | Bedworth United | 247 | W 3-0 | Lewis 57 Prada 64 Marriott 82 | 13 | 18 |
| 10 | SPL | H | Bedford Town | 357 | W 2-1 | Marriott 18 Nightingale 83 (pen) | 9 | 19 |
| 13 | FAC 1r | A | MK Dons | 4126 | L 1-6 | Theobald 60 | | 20 |
| 17 | SPL | A | Weymouth | 513 | W 1-0 | Lewis 67 | 8 | 21 |
| 20 | SPL | H | Chesham United | 228 | W 1-0 | Theobald 30 | 7 | 22 |
| Dec 1 | SPL | H | Stourbridge | 285 | D 2-2 | Brighton 68 Marriott 90 | 7 | 23 |
| 4 | SPL | H | Banbury United | 225 | W 1-0 | Marriott 54 | 6 | 24 |
| 8 | SPL | A | Redditch United | 173 | W 4-2 | Marriott 20 63 Nightingale 26 Fuller 58 | 6 | 25 |
| 10 | SPL | A | Hitchin Town | 285 | W 3-0 | Hammond 39 (pen) 41 Bryant 90 | 3 | 26 |
| 15 | SPL | H | AFC Totton | 319 | D 0-0 | | 4 | 27 |
| 26 | SPL | H | Arlesey Town | 385 | L 1-2 | Marriott 57 | 5 | 28 |
| Jan 1 | SPL | A | St Neots Town | 627 | W 3-2 | Brighton 1 Marriott 59 Allen 62 | 3 | 29 |
| 5 | SPL | H | St Albans City | 326 | W 2-1 | Hammond 73 (pen) 88 | 3 | 30 |
| 12 | SPL | A | Barwell | 204 | L 0-1 | | 4 | 31 |
| Feb 2 | SPL | A | Bedworth United | 187 | W 2-0 | Nighingale 61 (pen) Marriott 75 | 4 | 32 |
| 5 | SPL | A | Bashley | 109 | D 0-0 | | 4 | 33 |
| 9 | SPL | H | Hemel Hempstead | 397 | L 0-1 | | 5 | 34 |
| 16 | SPL | H | Weymouth | 380 | W 2-0 | Prada 5 Nightingale 80 (pen) | 5 | 35 |
| 23 | SPL | A | Bedford Town | 351 | L 1-2 | Marriott 26 | 8 | 36 |
| 26 | SPL | A | Bideford | 87 | L 1-2 | Darling 75 | 8 | 37 |
| Mar 5 | SPL | H | Kettering Town | 212 | D 1-1 | Cambridge 83 | 8 | 38 |
| 9 | SPL | H | Gosport Borough | 228 | L 0-4 | | 9 | 39 |
| 27 | SPL | A | Frome Town | 125 | W 3-0 | Marriott 13 70 Culver 33 | 9 | 40 |
| Apr 1 | SPL | A | Arlesey Town | 210 | W 2-1 | Fuller 20 Prada 81 | 9 | 41 |
| 3 | SPL | H | Hitchin Town | 235 | D 0-0 | | 9 | 42 |
| 6 | SPL | A | Stourbridge | 363 | L 1-4 | Marriott 24 | 11 | 43 |
| 9 | SPL | H | Chippenham Town | 224 | L 2-3 | Hicks 54 (pen) Griffin 65 (og) | 11 | 44 |
| 13 | SPL | H | Bideford | 296 | W 1-0 | Marriott 73 | 8 | 45 |
| 16 | SPL | A | Banbury United | 144 | D 2-2 | Blanchett 70 Marriott 86 | 9 | 46 |
| 20 | SPL | A | AFC Totton | 306 | W 5-1 | Pepper 7 80 Nightingale 19 Cambridge 41 Darling 75 | 8 | 47 |

| GOALSCORERS | Lge | FAC | FAT | Total | Pens | Hat-tricks | Cons Run | | Lge | FAC | FAT | Total | Pens | Hat-tricks | Cons Run |
|---|---|---|---|---|---|---|---|---|---|---|---|---|---|---|---|
| Hammond | 12 | 8 | | 20 | 4 | 1 | 5 | Lewis | 2 | | | 2 | | | |
| Marriott | 16 | | | 16 | | | 3 | Abbs | | 1 | | 1 | | | |
| Bryant | 5 | 2 | 1 | 8 | | | 2 | Allen | 1 | | | 1 | | | |
| Nightingale | 5 | | | 5 | 3 | | | Blanchett | 1 | | | 1 | | | |
| Theobald | 3 | 3 | | 5 | | | | Chaffey | 1 | | | 1 | | | |
| Cambridge | 2 | 2 | | 4 | | | | Culver | 1 | | | 1 | | | |
| Prada | 3 | 1 | | 4 | | | | Delanski | 1 | | | 1 | | | |
| Pepper | 2 | 1 | | 3 | | | | Hicks | 1 | | | 1 | 1 | | |
| Brighton | 2 | | | 2 | | | | Own Goals | 1 | 1 | | 2 | | | |
| Darling | 2 | | | 2 | | | | Cons Run - Consecutive scoring games. | | | | | | | |
| Fuller | 2 | | | 2 | | | | | | | | | | | |

# CHESHAM UNITED

**Chairman:** Brian McCarthy

**Secretary:** Alan Lagden          **(T)**          **(E)** secretary@cheshamunited.co.uk

**Commercial Manager:** Julie Cawood          **(T)** julie.cawood@cheshamunited.co.uk

**Programme Editor:** Steve Doman          **(T)** programme@cheshamunited.co.uk

**Ground Address:** The Meadow, Amy Lane, Amersham Road, Chesham HP5 1NE

**(T)** 01494 783 964                    **Manager:** Andy Leese

## Club Factfile

**Founded:** 1917          **Nickname:** The Generals

**Previous Names:** Chesham Town and Chesham Generals merged in 1917 to form Chesham United.

**Previous Leagues:** Spartan 1917-47, Corinthian 1947-63, Athenian 1963-73, Isthmian 1973-2004

**Club Colours (change):** All claret (Yellow/black/yellow)

**Ground Capacity:** 5,000     **Seats:** 284     **Covered:** 2,500     **Clubhouse:** Yes     **Shop:** Yes

**Directions**

From M25 Junction 20 take A41 (Aylesbury), leave A41 at turn-off for Chesham (A416), pass through Ashley Green into Chesham. Follow signs to Amersham, still on A416 pass two petrol stations opposite each other and at next roundabout take third exit into ground.
From M1 Junction 8 follow signs for Hemel Hempstead then joining the A41 for Aylesbury, then as above.

**Previous Grounds:** None

**Record Attendance:** 5,000 v Cambridge United - FA Cup 3rd Round 05/12/1979

**Record Victory:** Not known

**Record Defeat:** Not known

**Record Goalscorer:** John Willis

**Record Appearances:** Martin Baguley - 600+

**Additional Records:** Received £22,000 from Oldham Athletic for Fitz Hall

**Senior Honours:**
Isthmian League 1992-93, Division 1 1986-87, 97-97. Berks & Bucks Senior Cup x12.

### 10 YEAR RECORD

| 03-04 | | 04-05 | | 05-06 | | 06-07 | | 07-08 | | 08-09 | | 09-10 | | 10-11 | | 11-12 | | 12-13 | |
|---|---|---|---|---|---|---|---|---|---|---|---|---|---|---|---|---|---|---|---|
| Isth1N | 4 | SthP | 12 | SthP | 22 | Sthsw | 15 | SthM | 6 | SthM | 5 | SthM | 4 | SthP | 6 | SthP | 4 | SthP | 3 |

# MATCH RESULTS 2012-13

| Date | Comp | H/A | Opponents | Att: | Result | Goalscorers | Pos | No. |
|---|---|---|---|---|---|---|---|---|
| Aug 18 | SPL | H | St Neots Town | 354 | W 2-1 | Wilson 24 Waters 57 | 7 | 1 |
| 21 | SPL | A | AFC Totton | 335 | D 1-1 | Si Thomas 7 | 6 | 2 |
| 25 | SPL | A | Barwell | 139 | W 3-1 | Fotheringham 33 Wilson 39 Si Thomas 81 | 4 | 3 |
| 27 | SPL | H | St Albans City | 518 | W 2-1 | Fotheringham 9 20 | | 4 |
| Sept 1 | SPL | A | Bideford | 117 | L 1-2 | Si Thomas 55 (Pen) | 5 | 5 |
| 4 | SPL | H | Bashley | 291 | W 3-0 | Talbot 19 Chennels 43 Rolfe 54 | 3 | 6 |
| 8 | FAC Q1 | H | Northwood | 252 | L 0-1 | | | 7 |
| 15 | SPL | H | Gosport Borough | 270 | L 0-3 | | 6 | 8 |
| 18 | SPL | A | Arlesey Town | 135 | L 0-2 | | 8 | 9 |
| 29 | FAT Q1 | A | Bishop's Cleeve | 96 | W 2-1 | Chennells 48 Si Thomas 87 | | 10 |
| Oct 6 | SPL | A | Stourbridge | 436 | L 0-5 | | 11 | 11 |
| 9 | SPL | H | Hemel Hempstead T | 376 | D 0-0 | | 10 | 12 |
| 13 | SPL | H | Bedford Town | 401 | D 2-2 | Potton 17 Chennells 90 | 9 | 13 |
| 27 | FAT Q2 | H | Taunton Town | 214 | W 5-1 | Si.THOMAS 3 (10 pen 67 88) Potton 30 Little 35 | | 14 |
| Nov 3 | SPL | A | Bedworth United | 168 | D 1-1 | McGleish 21 | 11 | 15 |
| 10 | FAT Q3 | A | Canvey Island | 275 | D 1-1 | Fotheringham 31 | | 16 |
| 13 | FAT Q3r | H | Canvey Island | 241 | W 2-1 | Chennells 44 Little 88 | | 17 |
| 17 | SPL | A | Frome Town | 188 | D 0-0 | | 18 | 18 |
| 18 | SPL | A | Cambridge City | 228 | L 0-1 | | 18 | 19 |
| 24 | FAT 1 | H | Bath City | 301 | W 2--1 | Watters 19 Si Thomas 26 | | 20 |
| Dec 1 | SPL | H | Banbury United | 298 | W 3-1 | Watters 5 Little 39 44 | 14 | 21 |
| 4 | SPL | H | Weymouth | 217 | L 1-2 | Wells 21 (og) | 16 | 22 |
| 9 | SPL | A | Kettering Town | 253 | L 1-3 | Fagan 31 | 18 | 23 |
| 12 | FAT 2 | H | Barrow | 470 | L 1-5 | Wilson 86 | | 24 |
| 26 | SPL | H | Chippenham Town | 302 | D 1-1 | Si Thomas 67 | 19 | 25 |
| 29 | SPL | H | Barwell | 220 | D 2-2 | Potton 78 Little 87 | 18 | 26 |
| Jan 1 | SPL | A | St Albans City | 615 | W 6-2 | Si THOMAS 3 (10 pen 40 63 pen) Effiong 47 52 Chennells 90 | 17 | 27 |
| 5 | SPL | H | AFC Totton | 326 | W 6-0 | Si THOMAS 4 ( 12 32 50 58) Effiong 39 Fotheringham 74 13 | | 28 |
| 8 | SPL | H | Redditch United | 258 | W 2-1 | Wilson18 Wales 86 | 10 | 29 |
| 26 | SPL | A | Gosport Borough | 320 | L 1-3 | Potton 40 | 14 | 30 |
| Feb 2 | SPL | A | Hemel Hempstead T | 489 | W 2-1 | Wales 87 Chennells 90 | 13 | 31 |
| 5 | SPL | A | St Neots Town | 176 | L 1-3 | Si Thomas 50 | 14 | 32 |
| 9 | SPL | H | Stourbridge | 311 | D 1-1 | Potton 51 | 14 | 33 |
| 16 | SPL | H | Frome Town | 250 | D 1-1 | Potton 47 | 13 | 34 |
| 23 | SPL | A | Leamington | 501 | W 1-0 | Wales 65 | 13 | 35 |
| 25 | SPL | A | Hitchin Town | 239 | W 3-1 | Potton 23 Stewart 80 (og) Effiong 90 | 11 | 36 |
| Mar 2 | SPL | H | Canbridge City | 419 | W 1-0 | Effiong 2 | 10 | 37 |
| 5 | SPL | H | Leamington | 231 | D 1-1 | Potton 44 | 10 | 38 |
| 9 | SPL | A | Bedford Town | 261 | W1-0 | Watters 26 | 8 | 39 |
| 12 | SPL | H | Arlesey Town | 207 | W1-0 | Little 1 | 8 | 40 |
| 19 | SPL | A | Bashley | 103 | W 3-1 | Si Thomas 30 Effiong 39 Watters 73 | 8 | 41 |
| 23 | SPL | A | Weymouth | 673 | W 3-0 | Potton 18 39 Si Thomas 55 | 6 | 42 |
| 30 | SPL | H | Bideford | 450 | W 1-0 | Potton 30 | 4 | 43 |
| Apr 1 | SPL | A | Chippenham Town | 292 | W 3-2 | Kyriacou 7 Williams 17 (og) Effiong 61 | 4 | 44 |
| 6 | SPL | A | Banbury Town | 234 | W 2-1 | Wales 8 Effiong 43 | 4 | 45 |
| 13 | SPL | H | Hitchin Town | 409 | D 1-1 | Si Thomas 20 (pen) | 4 | 46 |
| 16 | SPL | H | Bedworth Town | 260 | W 3-0 | Effiong 27 Si Thomas 45 59 (pen) | 3 | 47 |
| 20 | SPL | A | Redditch United | 278 | W 2-0 | Lambert 37 (pen) Si Thomas 53 | 3 | 48 |
| 27 | SPL | H | Kettering Town | 355 | D 0-0 | | 3 | 49 |
| 30 | P-Off S-F | H | Hemel Hempstead T | 1136 | L 0-2 | | | 50 |

| GOALSCORERS | Lge | FAC | FAT | Total | Pens | Hat-tricks | Cons Run | | Lge | FAC | FAT | Total | Pens | Hat-tricks | Cons Run |
|---|---|---|---|---|---|---|---|---|---|---|---|---|---|---|---|
| Thomas | 18 | | 5 | 23 | 6 | 3 | 3 | Kyriacou | 1 | | | 1 | | | |
| Potton | 10 | | 1 | 11 | | | 2 | Lambert | 1 | | | 1 | | | |
| Effiong | 9 | | | 9 | | | 2 | McGleish | 1 | | | 1 | | | |
| Chennels | 4 | | 2 | 6 | | | | Rolfe | 1 | | | 1 | | | |
| Little | 4 | | 2 | 6 | | | | Talbot | 1 | | | 1 | | | |
| Fotheringham | 4 | | 1 | 5 | | | 2 | Own Goals | 3 | | | | | | |
| Watters | 4 | | 1 | 5 | | | 2 | Cons Run - Consecutive scoring games. | | | | | | | |
| Wales | 4 | | | 4 | | | | | | | | | | | |
| Wilson | 3 | | 1 | 4 | | | | | | | | | | | |
| Fagan | 1 | | | 1 | | | | | | | | | | | |

# CHIPPENHAM TOWN

**Chairman:** John Applegate
**Secretary:** Angela Townsley    **(T)** 07909 634 875    **(E)** angelatownsley_chiptownfc@talktalk.net
**Commercial Manager:** Paul Applegate    **(T)**
**Programme Editor:** Will Hulbert    **(T)** angelatownsley_chiptownfc@talktalk.net
**Ground Address:** Hardenhuish Park, Bristol Road, Chippenham SN14 6LR
**(T)** 01249 650 400    **Manager:** Nathan Rudge

BACK ROW: Matty Bown, Pete Hussey, Mani Randhawa, Ashley Williams, Scott Lye, Dave Gilroy, Alex Kite, Alan Griffin, Josh Dempsey, Toby Osman, Lee Phillips, James Guthrie, Luke Ballinger, Scott Garraway.
Coach / Goal/K Coach / Physio
FRONT ROW: Dean Griffiths, Iain Harvey, Shaun Lamb, Scott Rogers, Nathan Rudge, Richard Fey, Steve Casey, Brandon Barnes, Josh Egan, Tom Seery.
Player Manager / Assist Manager
2012- 2013 SEASON

## Club Factfile

**Founded:** 1873    **Nickname:** The Bluebirds
**Previous Names:** None
**Previous Leagues:** Hellenic, Wiltshire Senior, Wiltshire Premier, Western

**Club Colours (change):** All royal blue (Green/black/black)

**Ground Capacity:** 3,000    **Seats:** 300    **Covered:** 1,000    **Clubhouse:** Yes    **Shop:** Yes

**Directions:** Exit 17 from M4. Follow A350 towards Chippenham for three miles to first roundabout, take second exit (A350); follow road to third roundabout (junction with A420). Turn left and follow signs to town centre. Ground is 1km on left hand side adjacent to pedestrian controlled traffic lights. Car/Coach park next to traffic lights.

**Previous Grounds:** Played at four different locations before moving in to Hardenhuish on 24/09/1919.

**Record Attendance:** 4,800 v Chippenham United - Western League 1951
**Record Victory:** 9-0 v Dawlish Town (H) - Western League
**Record Defeat:** 0-10 v Tiverton Town (A) - Western League
**Record Goalscorer:** Dave Ferris
**Record Appearances:** Ian Monnery
**Additional Records:**

**Senior Honours:**
Western League 1951-52. Les Phillips Cup 1999-2000. Wiltshire Senior Cup. Wiltshire Senior Shield x4.

### 10 YEAR RECORD

| 03-04 | | 04-05 | | 05-06 | | 06-07 | | 07-08 | | 08-09 | | 09-10 | | 10-11 | | 11-12 | | 12-13 | |
|---|---|---|---|---|---|---|---|---|---|---|---|---|---|---|---|---|---|---|---|
| SthP | 21 | SthP | 2 | SthP | 4 | SthP | 7 | SthP | 4 | SthP | 8 | SthP | 3 | SthP | 7 | SthP | 11 | SthP | 15 |

# MATCH RESULTS 2012-13

| Date | Comp | H/A | Opponents | Att: | Result | Goalscorers | Pos | No. |
|---|---|---|---|---|---|---|---|---|
| Aug 18 | SPL | A | Hemel Hempstead Town | 202 | L 1-2 | Griffin 41 | 16 | 1 |
| 21 | SPL | H | Weymouth | 364 | D 2-2 | Ballinger 4 Phillips 14 | 16 | 2 |
| 25 | SPL | H | Cambridge City | 258 | W 4-3 | Phillips 16 Ballinger 20 Griffin 33 (Pen) 52 | 10 | 3 |
| 27 | SPL | A | Frome Town | 429 | L 0-2 | | 14 | 4 |
| Sept 1 | SPL | H | Hitchin Town | 315 | L 2-4 | Griffin 2 (Pen) Phillips 46 | 16 | 5 |
| 4 | SPL | A | Gosport Borough | 260 | W 3-2 | Ballinger 4 (pen) 34 (pen) Phillips 83 | 12 | 6 |
| 8 | FAC Q1 | H | Mangotsfield Town | 303 | W 3-1 | Roberts 39 Phillips 51 Ballinger 67 | | 7 |
| 15 | SPL | A | Banbury United | 234 | L 0-1 | | 16 | 8 |
| 18 | SPL | H | Bashley | 241 | W 1-0 | Griffiths 81 | 11 | 9 |
| 22 | FAC Q2 | A | Bishop's Cleeve | 187 | W 2-1 | Barnes 62 Lye 70 | | 10 |
| 29 | FAT Q1 | H | Swindon Supermarine | 280 | W 4-0 | Griffin 4 67 Griffiths 23 47 | | 11 |
| Oct 2 | SPL | H | Bedford Town | 207 | L 0-2 | | 12 | 12 |
| 6 | FAC Q3 | H | Badshot Lea | 367 | W 3-1 | Barnes 7 Phillips 30 Egan 70 | | 13 |
| 13 | SPL | H | Arlesey Town | 331 | D 0-0 | | 17 | 14 |
| 20 | FAC Q4 | A | Gloucester City | 675 | L 0-1 | | | 15 |
| 27 | FAT Q2 | H | Sholing | 237 | L 1-2 | Ballinger 77 | 18 | 16 |
| Nov 3 | SPL | A | Leamington | 621 | L 0-1 | | | 17 |
| 6 | SPL | A | Bideford | 108 | W 2-1 | Griffin 83 89 | 13 | 18 |
| 10 | SPL | H | Bedworth United | 286 | D 1-1 | Griffin 88 | 18 | 19 |
| 13 | SPL | A | Barwell | 123 | D 0-0 | | 16 | 20 |
| 17 | SPL | A | Redditch United | 187 | L 0-1 | | 17 | 21 |
| 24 | SPL | A | St Albans City | 312 | W 2-0 | Knighton 24 Griffin 85 | 15 | 22 |
| 27 | SPL | H | AFC Totton | 295 | W 3-0 | Knighton 29 55 Phillips 65 | 9 | 23 |
| Dec 1 | SPL | H | Kettering Town | 335 | W 3-0 | Knighton 18 Ballinger 50 Phillips 68 | 6 | 24 |
| 8 | SPL | A | Stourbridge | 317 | L 1-2 | Griffiths 30 | 7 | 25 |
| 15 | SPL | H | St Neots Town | 217 | D 2-2 | Knighton 7 Ballinger 82 | 9 | 26 |
| 26 | SPL | A | Chesham United | 302 | D 1-1 | Kite 78 | 11 | 27 |
| Jan 1 | SPL | H | Frome Town | 478 | D 2-2 | Bennett 7 (og) Griffin 26 | 12 | 28 |
| 5 | SPL | A | Weymouth | 679 | D 0-0 | | 12 | 29 |
| 12 | SPL | H | Gosport Borough | 371 | D 0-0 | | 13 | 30 |
| 26 | SPL | H | Banbury United | 311 | L 0-2 | | 15 | 31 |
| Feb 2 | SPL | H | Bideford | 291 | L 1-7 | Knighton 51 | 16 | 32 |
| 5 | SPL | H | Hemel Hempstead Town | 195 | L 1-2 | Guthrie 57 | 16 | 33 |
| 9 | SPL | A | Bedford Town | 220 | D 1-1 | Griffiths 2 | 16 | 34 |
| 16 | SPL | H | Redditch Town | 318 | L 2-3 | Prada 5 Nightingale 80 (pen) | 16 | 35 |
| 23 | SPL | A | Bedworth United | 146 | D 2-2 | Phillips 56 83 | 16 | 36 |
| 26 | SPL | A | Bashley | 87 | L 1-2 | Phillips 28 | 16 | 37 |
| Mar 2 | SPL | H | Barwell | 288 | D 1-1 | Phillips 85 (pen) | 17 | 38 |
| 9 | SPL | A | Arlesey Town | 104 | L 0-4 | | 18 | 39 |
| 30 | SPL | A | Hitchin Town | 304 | L 1-2 | Griffin 8 | 20 | 40 |
| Apr 1 | SPL | H | Chesham United | 292 | L 2-3 | Griffin 4 (pen) Guthrie 22 | 20 | 41 |
| 6 | SPL | A | Kettering | 292 | W 4-2 | Griffin 14 Phillips 27 58 McClennon 77 | 19 | 42 |
| 9 | SPL | A | Cambridge City | 224 | W 3-2 | Phillips 31 Griffin 41 45 | 18 | 43 |
| 13 | SPL | H | St Albans City | 342 | W 4-3 | Phillips 5 Osman 34 Guthrie 55 Knighton 75 | 18 | 44 |
| 16 | SPL | H | Leamington | 588 | L 0-2 | | 19 | 45 |
| 20 | SPL | A | St Neots Town | 389 | W 1-0 | Griffiths 7 | 17 | 46 |
| 23 | SPL | A | AFC Totton | 284 | W 5-0 | Kite 47 Griffiths 49 Griffin 54 (Pen) 83 McClennan 62 | 16 | 47 |
| 27 | SPL | H | Stourbridge | 473 | W 4-0 | Griffiths 9 18 Kite 28 Guthrie 49 | 15 | 48 |

| GOALSCORERS | Lge | FAC | FAT | Total | Pens | Hat-tricks | Cons Run |
|---|---|---|---|---|---|---|---|
| Griffin | 16 | | 2 | 18 | 4 | | 4 |
| Phillips | 14 | 2 | | 15 | 2 | | 3 |
| Griffiths | 7 | | 2 | 9 | | | |
| Ballinger | 6 | 1 | 1 | 8 | 2 | | 2 |
| Knighton | 7 | | | 7 | | | 3 |
| Guthrie | 4 | | | 4 | | | |
| Kite | 3 | | | 3 | | | |
| Barnes | | 2 | | 2 | | | |
| McClennan | 2 | | | 2 | | | |
| Egan | | 1 | | 1 | | | |

| | Lge | FAC | FAT | Total | Pens | Hat-tricks | Cons Run |
|---|---|---|---|---|---|---|---|
| Lye | | 1 | | 1 | | | |
| Nightingale | 1 | | | 1 | | 1 | |
| Osman | 1 | | | 1 | | | |
| Prada | 1 | | | 1 | | | |
| Roberts | | 1 | | 1 | | | |
| Own Goals | 1 | | | 1 | | | |
| Cons Run - Consecutive scoring games. | | | | | | | |

# CORBY TOWN

**Chairman:** Kevin Ingram
**Secretary:** Gerry Lucas　　(T) 07932 6333 43　　(E) gerry21@gmail.com
**Commercial Manager:** John Laws　　(T)
**Programme Editor:** Hannah Ingram　　(T) info@corbytown.co.uk
**Ground Address:** Steel Park, Jimmy Kane Way, Rockingham Road, Corby NN17 2FB
(T) 01536 406 640　　　　　　　　**Manager:** Chris Plummer

2012-13 Squad - Back row (L-R): Nathan Fox, Nethaniel Wedderburn, Greg Kaziboni, Sam Ives, Ryan Semple, Tom McGowan
Middle: Kenny Williams, Lewis Webb, Avelino Vieira, Josh Moreman, Paul Walker, Liam Richardson,
George, James McCafferty, Scott Tomkins.
Front row: Leon McKenzie, Ricky Miller, Ian Sampson, Chris Plummer, Tom Ingram, Jason Crowe.
Missing: Nathan Horne, Jon Stead, Pierrick Briand.

## Club Factfile

**Founded:** 1947　　**Nickname:** The Steelmen
**Previous Names:** Stewart & Lloyds (Corby) > 1947
**Previous Leagues:** United Counties 1935-52. Midland 1952-58. Southern 1958-2009

**Club Colours (change):** White/black/black (Pink/black & white/pink)

**Ground Capacity:** 3,893　　**Seats:** 577　　**Covered:** 1,575　　**Clubhouse:** Yes　　**Shop:** Yes

**Directions:** From A14, Exit at Jnc 7, Keep left, at first roundabout take A6003 Oakham/Uppingham stay on this road for approx. 7 miles (ignore signs for Corby to your right en route) straight over two roundabouts at second B.P. petrol station on right. At next roundabout approx 1 mile ahead turn right onto A6116 for 300 yards entrance to Ground between Rugby Club and Rockingham Forest Hotel (Great Western).

**Previous Grounds:** Occupation Road 1948-85.

**Record Attendance:** 2,240 v Watford - Friendly 1986-87
**Record Victory:** Not known
**Record Defeat:** Not known
**Record Goalscorer:** David Holbauer - 159 (1984-95)
**Record Appearances:** Derek Walker - 601
**Additional Records:** Paid £2,700 to Barnet for Elwun Edwards 1981
**Senior Honours:** Received £20,000 from Oxford United for Matt Murphy 1993
United Counties League 1950-51, 51-52. Southern League Premier Division 2008-09.
Northants Senior Cup x7 Most recently 2012-13.

## 10 YEAR RECORD

| 03-04 | | 04-05 | | 05-06 | | 06-07 | | 07-08 | | 08-09 | | 09-10 | | 10-11 | | 11-12 | | 12-13 | |
|---|---|---|---|---|---|---|---|---|---|---|---|---|---|---|---|---|---|---|---|
| SthE | 15 | SthW | 12 | SthE | 2 | SthP | 20 | SthP | 16 | SthP | 1 | Conf N | 6 | Conf N | 13 | Conf N | 17 | Conf N | 20 |

# MATCH RESULTS 2012-13

| Date | Comp | H/A | Opponents | Att: | Result | Goalscorers | Pos | No. |
|------|------|-----|-----------|------|--------|-------------|-----|-----|
| Aug 18 | BSN | H | Vauxhall Motors | 548 | L 0-1 | | 14 | 1 |
| 21 | BSN | A | Solihull Moors | 195 | L 0-3 | | 19 | 2 |
| 25 | BSN | A | Worcester City | 738 | L 1-5 | Webb 54 | 22 | 3 |
| 27 | BSN | H | Brackley Town | 644 | L 0-4 | | 22 | 4 |
| Sept 1 | BSN | H | Bradford PA | 381 | L 4-5 | McKenzie 41 49 Moreman 89 90 | 22 | 5 |
| 8 | BSN | A | Workington | 394 | W 3-2 | Moreman 27 Galinski 51 Vierra 55 | 21 | 6 |
| 15 | BSN | H | Colwyn Bay | 411 | W 3-1 | Moreman 27 Semple 70 McKenzie 90 | 20 | 7 |
| 18 | BSN | A | Oxford City | 261 | L 0-2 | | 20 | 8 |
| 22 | FAC Q2 | H | Leamington | 516 | W 3-2 | McGowan 37 Moreman 48 79 | | 9 |
| 29 | BSN | A | Gainsborough Trinity | 516 | D 2-2 | Ives 21 Semple 22 | 20 | 10 |
| Oct 3 | BSN | H | Droylsden | 310 | W 5-0 | MOREMAN 3 ( 2 75 90)  Moyo 46 (og) Wedderburn 90 | 16 | 11 |
| 6 | FAC Q3 | A | Histon | 330 | D 1-1 | Malone 47 | | 12 |
| 10 | FAC Q3r | H | Histon | 510 | W 2-1 | Moreman 44 Semple 64 | | 13 |
| 13 | BSN | H | Altrincham | 572 | L 2-5 | Piergianni 56 Kaziboni 90 | 19 | 14 |
| 20 | FAC Q4 | H | Hendon | 692 | L 1-2 | Moreman 8 | | 15 |
| 31 | BSN | H | Gloucester City | 237 | W 3-2 | Semple 45 Piergianni 50 Ives 64 | 16 | 16 |
| Nov 3 | BSN | A | Histon | 305 | W 4-3 | Kaziboni 35 40 Malone 39  Moreman 69 | 14 | 17 |
| 10 | FAT Q3 | A | Wealdsone | 406 | D 1-1 | Ives 51 | | 18 |
| 14 | FAT Q3r | H | Wealdstone | 280 | W 3-2 | Ives 45 Piergianni 82 Moreman 90 | | 19 |
| 17 | BSN | H | Oxford City | 299 | D 1-1 | Piergianni 89 | 15 | 20 |
| 24 | FAT 1 | H | Hayes & Yeading | 322 | W 3-2 | Piergianni 56 Crowe 82 McKenzie 90 | | 21 |
| 27 | BSN | A | Chester | 1853 | L 1-2 | Hughes 71 | 16 | 22 |
| Dec 1 | BSN | A | Bishops Stortford | 317 | L 1-2 | Semple 36 | 16 | 23 |
| 8 | BSN | H | Hinckley United | 300 | W 5-3 | McGowan 7 Moreman 33 Hughes 45 88  Semple 59 | 16 | 24 |
| 15 | FAT 2 | A | Tamworh | 683 | D 1-1 | Hughes 90 | | 25 |
| 19 | FAT 2r | H | Tamworth | 300 | L 2-4 | Malone 52 Hughes 64 (pen) | | 26 |
| 26 | BSN | A | Boston United | 1176 | D 1-1 | Ives 51 | 17 | 27 |
| Jan 2 | BSN | H | Boston United | 572 | W 2-1 | Webb 24 Malone 90 | 17 | 28 |
| 5 | BSN | H | Histon | 410 | D 0-0 | | 17 | 29 |
| 8 | BSN | A | Guiseley | 328 | L 1-2 | Moreman 32 | 17 | 30 |
| 12 | BSN | A | Stalybridge Celtic | 422 | W 2-1 | Piergianni 5  Crowe 68 | 14 | 31 |
| 29 | BSN | A | Harrogate Town | 99 | L 1-6 | Greer 78 | 14 | 32 |
| Feb 2 | BSN | H | FC Halifax Town | 439 | L 1-5 | McGowan  43 | 15 | 33 |
| 9 | BSN | A | Altrincham | 774 | L 1-2 | Semple 25 | 17 | 34 |
| 16 | BSN | H | Chester | 768 | L 1-2 | Malone 90 | 18 | 35 |
| 23 | BSN | A | Bradford PA | 285 | L 1-2 | Semple 83 | 19 | 36 |
| 27 | BSN | H | Bishops Stortford | 263 | D 2-2 | Vierra 5 (pen) Semple 28 | 19 | 37 |
| Mar 2 | BSN | A | Colwyn Bay | 278 | L 0-1 | | 19 | 38 |
| 6 | BSN | H | Guiseley | 229 | L 2-3 | Semple 45 Ivey-Ward 78 | 19 | 39 |
| 9 | BSN | H | Stalybridge Celtic | 266 | W 1-0 | Moreman 26 | 19 | 40 |
| 16 | BSN | H | Harrogate Town | 273 | L 0-2 | | 19 | 41 |
| 20 | BSN | H | Solihull Moors | 272 | L 2-3 | Moreman 8 Piergianni 90 | 19 | 42 |
| 26 | BSN | A | Vauxhall Motors | 106 | D 1-1 | King 69 | 19 | 43 |
| 30 | BSN | H | Worcester City | 275 | W 1-0 | King 3 (Pen) | 19 | 44 |
| Apr 1 | BSN | A | Brackley Town | 391 | W 4-2 | Semple 27 41 King 53 Piergianni 70 | 19 | 45 |
| 6 | BSN | A | Droylsden | 139 | D 2-2 | King 47 76 | 19 | 46 |
| 8 | BSN | A | Hinckley United | 255 | L 3-6 | McGowan 37  60 King 53 (pen) | 19 | 47 |
| 11 | BSN | A | FC Halifax Town | 838 | L 0-2 | | 19 | 48 |
| 13 | BSN | H | Workington | 314 | L 1-3 | Malone 38 | 19 | 49 |
| 20 | BSN | A | Gloucester City | 355 | W 1-0 | Wedderburn 86 | 19 | 50 |
| 27 | BSN | H | Gainsborough Trinity | 1856 | D 0-0 | | 20 | 51 |

| GOALSCORERS | Lge | FAC | LC | Total | Pens | Hat-tricks | Cons Run | | Lge | FAC | LC | Total | Pens | Hat-tricks | Cons Run |
|-------------|-----|-----|-----|-------|------|------------|----------|--|-----|-----|-----|-------|------|------------|----------|
| Moreman | 12 | 4 | 1 | 17 | 1 | | 3 | Crowe | 1 | | 1 | 2 | | | |
| Semple | 11 | 1 | | 12 | | | 2 | Vierra | 2 | | | 2 | 1 | | |
| Piergianni | 6 | | 2 | 8 | | | | Webb | 2 | | | 2 | | | |
| King | 6 | | | 6 | 2 | | | Wedderburn | 2 | | | 2 | | | |
| Malone | 4 | 1 | 1 | 6 | | | | Galinski | 1 | | | 1 | | | |
| Hughes | 3 | | 2 | 5 | 1 | | | Greer | 1 | | | 1 | | | |
| Ives | 3 | | 2 | 5 | | | | Ivey-Ward | 1 | | | 1 | | | |
| McGowan | 4 | 1 | | 5 | | | | Own Goal | 1 | | | 1 | | | |
| McKenzie | 3 | | 1 | 4 | | | | Cons Run - Consecutive scoring games. | | | | | | | |
| Kaziboni | 3 | | | 3 | | | | | | | | | | | |

# FROME TOWN

**Chairman:** Jeremy Alderman

**Secretary:** Ian Pearce        **(T)** 07811 511 222        **(E)** ian@frometownfc.co.uk

**Commercial Manager:** Ivan Carver        **(T)** 07981 583 786

**Programme Editor:** Andrew Meaden        **(T)** 01225 776 678

**Ground Address:** Aldersmith Stadium, Badgers Hill, Berkley Road, Frome BA11 2EH

**(T)** 01373 464 087        **Manager:** Derek Graham

## Club Factfile

**Founded:** 1904        **Nickname:** The Robins

**Previous Names:** None

**Previous Leagues:** Wiltshire Premier 1904, Somerset Senior 1906-19, Western 1919, 63-2009

**Club Colours (change):** All red (Yellow/blue/yellow)

**Ground Capacity:** 2,000    **Seats:** 150    **Covered:** 200    **Clubhouse:** Yes    **Shop:** Yes

**Directions:** From Bath, take A36 and then A361. At third roundabout, follow A361 and at fourth roundabout take A3098. Take first right and ground is one mile on left hand side. From south follow A36 (Warminster) and take A3098 to Frome. At T Junction turn right and take second exit at roundabout. Ground is first right and follow road for one mile on left hand side.

**Previous Grounds:** None

**Record Attendance:** 8,000 v Leyton Orient - FA Cup 1st Round 1958

**Record Victory:** Not Known

**Record Defeat:** Not Known

**Record Goalscorer:** Not Known

**Record Appearances:** Not Known

**Additional Records:**

**Senior Honours:**
Somerset County League 1906-07, 08-09, 10-11.
Western League Division 1 1919-20, 2001-02, Premier Division 1962-63, 78-79.
Somerset Senior Cup 1932-33, 33-34, 50-51 Somerset Premier Cup 1966-67, 68-69 (shared), 82-83, 2008-09.

### 10 YEAR RECORD

| 03-04 | 04-05 | 05-06 | 06-07 | 07-08 | 08-09 | 09-10 | 10-11 | 11-12 | 12-13 |
|---|---|---|---|---|---|---|---|---|---|
| WestP  3 | WestP  3 | WestP  7 | WestP  3 | WestP  4 | WestP  2 | Sthsw  6 | Sthsw  4 | SthP  12 | SthP  18 |

# MATCH RESULTS 2012-13

| Date | Comp | H/A | Opponents | Att: | Result | Goalscorers | Pos | No. |
|------|------|-----|-----------|------|--------|-------------|-----|-----|
| Aug 18 | SPL | H | AFC Totton | 240 | W 3-1 | Evans 33 Powell 39 Woods 73 | 4 | 1 |
| 21 | SPL | A | Bashley | 227 | L 1-2 | Powell 83 (pen) | 12 | 2 |
| 25 | SPL | A | St Albans City | 336 | L 0-4 | | 16 | 3 |
| 27 | SPL | H | Chippenham Town | 429 | W 2-0 | Smith 12 Lapham 70 | 12 | 4 |
| Sept 1 | SPL | A | Kettering Town | 500 | D 1-1 | Powell 34 | 10 | 5 |
| 4 | SPL | H | Leamington | 229 | L 0-2 | | 13 | 6 |
| 8 | FAC Q1 | A | Larkhall Athletic | 185 | D 0-0 | | | 7 |
| 12 | FAC Q1r | H | Larkhall Athletic | 204 | W 4-0 | Powell 5 46 Woods 38 Perrott 73 | | 8 |
| 15 | SPL | A | Cambridge City | 315 | W 2-1 | Smith 28 Jeffries 36 | 9 | 9 |
| 19 | SPL | H | Weymouth | 323 | W 2-0 | Perrott 39 Evans 47 | 9 | 10 |
| 22 | FAC Q2 | H | Weston-s-Mare | 256 | L 0-2 | | | 11 |
| 29 | FAT Q1 | H | Taunton Town | 131 | L 0-1 | | | 12 |
| Oct 6 | SPL | H | St Neots Town | 210 | L 1-2 | Powell 60 | 9 | 13 |
| 9 | SPL | A | Banbury United | 167 | D 1-1 | Thompson 41 | 9 | 14 |
| 13 | SPL | A | Hitchin Town | 311 | L 0-2 | | 10 | 15 |
| 20 | SPL | H | Redditch United | 173 | W 1-0 | Powell 56 | 9 | 16 |
| Nov 3 | SPL | H | Hemel Hempstead U | 155 | L 1-3 | Gilroy 29 | 9 | 17 |
| 10 | SPL | A | Stourbridge | 384 | D 1-1 | Powell 9 | 8 | 18 |
| 17 | SPL | H | Chesham United | 188 | D 0-0 | | 11 | 19 |
| Dec 1 | SPL | A | Bedworth Town | 130 | L 0-1 | | 16 | 20 |
| 8 | SPL | H | Barwell | 155 | L 2-3 | Evans 62 Lapham 63 | 18 | 21 |
| 15 | SPL | A | Arlesey Town | 111 | W 1-0 | Gilroy 52 | 16 | 22 |
| 19 | SPL | H | Bedford Town | 119 | L 2-3 | Perrott 61 Jeffries 88 | 16 | 23 |
| 26 | SPL | H | Bideford | 228 | L 0-1 | | 18 | 24 |
| Jan 1 | SPL | A | Chippenham Town | 478 | D 2-2 | Perott 75 D.Evans 90 | 19 | 25 |
| 5 | SPL | H | Bashley | 171 | D 1-1 | Gilroy 53 | 19 | 26 |
| 12 | SPL | A | Leamington | 524 | L 0-2 | | 19 | 27 |
| 15 | SPL | A | Gosport Borough | 179 | D 0-0 | | 18 | 28 |
| Feb 2 | SPL | H | Banbury United | 205 | D 0-0 | | 17 | 29 |
| 9 | SPL | A | St Neots Town | 268 | W 1-0 | Perrott 3 | 17 | 30 |
| 12 | SPL | A | Weymouth | 457 | L 1-2 | Jeffries 74 | 17 | 31 |
| 16 | SPL | A | Chesham United | 250 | D 1-1 | Smith 17 | 17 | 32 |
| 20 | SPL | H | St Albans City | 108 | L 0-3 | | 17 | 33 |
| 23 | SPL | H | Stourbridge | 177 | L 0-1 | | 18 | 34 |
| Mar 2 | SPL | A | Redditch United | 190 | L 1-2 | Hulbert 58 | 20 | 35 |
| 9 | SPL | H | Hitchin Town | 263 | W 2-1 | Gilbert 39 (og) Copp 51 | 17 | 36 |
| 12 | SPL | A | AFC Totton | 243 | L 0-2 | | 17 | 37 |
| 27 | SPL | H | Cambridge City | 125 | L 0-3 | | 18 | 38 |
| 30 | SPL | H | Kettering Town | 222 | W 3-1 | Baggeridge 51 Eze 65 (og) Bryant 90 | 18 | 39 |
| Apr 1 | SPL | A | Bideford | 187 | D 0-0 | | 18 | 40 |
| 6 | SPL | H | Bedorth United | 209 | L 1-2 | Ballinger 78 | 18 | 41 |
| 13 | SPL | A | Bedford Town | 227 | W 1-0 | Smith 50 | 19 | 42 |
| 16 | SPL | A | Hemel Hempstead T | 217 | W 3-0 | Ballinger 59 &0 (pen)  Hulbert 88 | 17 | 43 |
| 20 | SPL | H | Arlesey Town | 185 | L 0-1 | | 18 | 44 |
| 23 | SPL | H | Gosport Borough | 165 | D 1-1 | Ballinger 28 | 18 | 45 |
| 27 | SPL | A | Barwell | 304 | D 1-1 | Smith 80 | 18 | 46 |

| GOALSCORERS | Lge | FAC | FAT | Total | Pens | Hat-tricks | Cons Run | | Lge | FAC | FAT | Total | Pens | Hat-tricks | Cons Run |
|-------------|-----|-----|-----|-------|------|-----------|----------|--|-----|-----|-----|-------|------|-----------|----------|
| Powell | 6 | 2 | | 8 | | | 2 | Copp | 1 | | | 1 | | | |
| Evans | 4 | 1 | | 5 | | | | Baggeridge | 1 | | | 1 | | | |
| Smith | 5 | | | 5 | | | | Bryant | 1 | | | 1 | | | |
| Ballinger | 4 | | | 4 | 1 | | | Thompson | 1 | | | 1 | | | |
| Perrott | 4 | | | 4 | | | | Own Goals | 2 | | | 2 | | | |
| Gilroy | 3 | | | 3 | | | | Cons Run - Consecutive scoring games. | | | | | | | |
| Jeffries | 3 | | | 3 | | | | | | | | | | | |
| Hulbert | 2 | | | 2 | | | | | | | | | | | |
| Lapham | 2 | | | 2 | | | | | | | | | | | |
| Woods | 1 | 1 | | 2 | | | | | | | | | | | |

# HEMEL HEMPSTEAD TOWN

**Chairman:** David Boggins
**Secretary:** Dean Chance      **(T)** 07858 990 550      **(E)** dean.chance@ntlworld.com
**Commercial Manager:** Tony Conway      **(T)**
**Programme Editor:** Tony Conway      **(T)** tonyconway@yahoo.com
**Ground Address:** Vauxhall Road, Adeyfield Road, Hemel Hempstead HP2 4HW
**(T)** 01442 259 777                    **Manager:** Stuart Maynard & Dean Brennan

## Club Factfile

**Founded:** 1885      **Nickname:** The Tudors
**Previous Names:** Hemel Hempstead FC
**Previous Leagues:** Spartan 1922-52, Delphian 1952-63, Athenian 1963-77, Isthmian 1977-2004

**Club Colours (change):** Red with white trim/red/red (Lime green & black/black/black)

**Ground Capacity:** 3,152    **Seats:** 300    **Covered:** 900    **Clubhouse:** Yes    **Shop:** Yes

**Directions**
Leave M1 at Junction 8 - follow dual carriageway over two roundabouts.
Get into outside lane and after 100 yards turn right.
Follow road to mini-roundabout turn left, next large roundabout take third exit into ground car park.

**Previous Grounds:** Crabtree Lane

**Record Attendance:** 3,500 v Tooting & Mitcham - Amateur Cup 1962 (Crabtree Lane)
**Record Victory:** Not known
**Record Defeat:** Not known
**Record Goalscorer:** Dai Price
**Record Appearances:** John Wallace - 1012
**Additional Records:**

**Senior Honours:**
Isthmian League Division 3 1998-99. Herts Senior Cup x8 Most recently 2012-13. Herts Charity Cup x6.

| | | | | | 10 YEAR RECORD | | | | | |
|---|---|---|---|---|---|---|---|---|---|---|
| 03-04 | 04-05 | 05-06 | 06-07 | 07-08 | 08-09 | 09-10 | 10-11 | 11-12 | 12-13 | |
| Isth1N 6 | SthP 19 | SthW 4 | SthP 5 | SthP 7 | SthP 5 | SthP 20 | SthP 15 | SthP 19 | SthP 4 | |

# MATCH RESULTS 2012-13

| Date | Comp | H/A | Opponents | Att: | Result | Goalscorers | Pos | No. |
|------|------|-----|-----------|------|--------|-------------|-----|-----|
| Aug 18 | SPL | H | Chippenham Town | 202 | W 2-1 | Pearce 5 Campana 49 | 8 | 1 |
| 21 | SPL | A | Kettering Town | 569 | W 2-1 | King 65 Nolan 84 | 3 | 2 |
| 25 | SPL | A | Bashley | 159 | W 6-0 | Mpi 5 Osobu 20 70 Pearce 67 Nolan 85 88 | 1 | 3 |
| 27 | SPL | H | AFC Totton | 333 | W 4-1 | MPI 3 (50 56 78) Campana 60 | 1 | 4 |
| Sept 1 | SPL | A | Barwell | 143 | D 2-2 | Nolan 9 Mpi 28 | 1 | 5 |
| 4 | SPL | H | Arlesey Town | 308 | L 1-2 | Pearce 47 | 2 | 6 |
| 8 | FAC Q1 | H | Waltham Abbey | 258 | L 2-5 | Mpi 30 Bakare 49 | | 7 |
| 15 | SPL | A | Weymouth | 607 | W 1-0 | Mpi 34 | 2 | 8 |
| 18 | SPL | H | St Neots Town | 246 | L 2-4 | Nolan 26 Bakare 61 | 3 | 9 |
| 29 | FAT Q1 | A | Bridgwater Town | 113 | D 2-2 | O'Leary 64 (pen) Pearce 69 | | 10 |
| Oct 2 | FAT Q1r | H | Bridgwater Town | 93 | L 1-3 | O'Leary 82 | | 11 |
| 6 | SPL | A | Redditch United | 167 | W 4-1 | Nolan 6 54 Pearce 29 57 | | 12 |
| 9 | SPL | A | Chesham United | 376 | D 0-0 | | 2 | 13 |
| 13 | SPL | H | Bedworth United | 444 | W 6-1 | Nolan 3 41 Parkes 63 85 O'Leary 70 Osobu 80 | 1 | 14 |
| 20 | SPL | A | Bedford Town | 389 | W 3-0 | Nolan 9 Parkes 56 (pen) Osobu 90 | 1 | 15 |
| 24 | SPL | H | Cambridge City | 313 | W 1-0 | Nolan 64 | | 16 |
| 27 | SPL | H | Leamington | 477 | L 1-3 | Owen 48 (og) | 1 | 17 |
| Nov 3 | SPL | A | Frome Town | 155 | W 3-1 | O'Leary 35 (pen) Pearce 45 Nolan 90 | 1 | 18 |
| 10 | SPL | A | Gosport Borough | 298 | D 3-3 | Pearce 22 Mpi 55 80 | 1 | 19 |
| 17 | SPL | H | Stourbridge | 352 | W 2-1 | Nolan 48 Parkes 67 | 1 | 20 |
| 24 | SPL | A | Bsnbury United | 123 | L 0-4 | | 1 | 21 |
| Dec 1 | SPL | H | Redditch United | 246 | W 4-0 | PEARCE 3 (7 25 78) O'Leary 80 | 1 | 22 |
| 8 | SPL | A | Bideford | 197 | L 2-3 | Pearce 18 Bruce 80 | 1 | 23 |
| 15 | SPL | H | Hitchin Town | 416 | W 8-2 | Nolan 20 Howes 34 O'Toole 48 Campano 53 Osubo 59 Pearce 66 Mpi 71 88 | 1 | 24 |
| 26 | SPL | H | St Albans City | 787 | D 1-1 | Parkes 58 | 1 | 25 |
| Jan 1 | SPL | A | AFC Totton | 297 | L 0-2 | | 1 | 26 |
| 5 | SPL | H | Kettering Town | 443 | W 5-2 | Pearce 2 75 King 6 Nolan 23 Mpi 34 | 1 | 27 |
| 12 | SPL | A | Arlesey Town | 216 | L 1-3 | Nolan 4 | 1 | 28 |
| Feb 2 | SPL | H | Chesham United | 489 | L 1-2 | Nolan 1 | 2 | 29 |
| 5 | SPL | A | Chippenham Town | 195 | W 2-1 | May 1 Osobu 7 | 2 | 30 |
| 9 | SPL | A | Cambrdge City | 397 | W 1-0 | May | 2 | 31 |
| 16 | SPL | A | Stourport | 664 | W 3-2 | Pearce 26 Diarra 36 Charles 58 | 2 | 32 |
| 23 | SPL | H | Gosport Borough | 280 | D 1-1 | Hutton 26 | 2 | 33 |
| 26 | SPL | A | St Neots Town | 218 | L 1-6 | Parkes 70 | 2 | 34 |
| Mar 2 | SPL | H | Bedford Town | 464 | W 4-3 | Campana 44 Nolan 45 Osobu79 Maissiat 90 | 2 | 35 |
| 5 | SPL | H | Weymouth | 223 | L 1-3 | Nolan 63 | 2 | 36 |
| 19 | SPL | A | Bedworth United | 120 | W 2-1 | Pearce 8 King 65 | 3 | 37 |
| 26 | SPL | H | Bashley | 128 | W 4-2 | Pearce 24 May 27 Mpi 38 47 | 2 | 38 |
| 30 | SPL | H | Barwell | 337 | D 1-1 | Talbot 28 | 2 | 39 |
| Apr 1 | SPL | A | St Albans City | 560 | W 1-0 | Hutton 57 | 2 | 40 |
| 13 | SPL | H | Banbury United | 306 | L 1-2 | Pearce 79 | 3 | 41 |
| 16 | SPL | H | Frome Town | 217 | L 0-3 | | 4 | 42 |
| 20 | SPL | A | Hitchin Town | 353 | L 2-3 | O'Leary 30 Pearce 48 | 4 | 43 |
| 23 | SPL | A | Leamington | 539 | L 2-3 | Pearce 55 Maisiatt 90 | 4 | 44 |
| 27 | SPL | H | Bedford Town | 583 | W 4-1 | Nolan 12 66 Charles 50 Pearce 52 | 4 | 45 |
| 30 | P-Off S-F | A | Chesham United | 1136 | W 2-0 | Charles 24 53 | | 46 |
| May 6 | P-Off Final | H | Gosport Borough | 2254 | D 2-2 | Hutton 85 Osubu 90 *aet L 4-5 pens | | 47 |

| GOALSCORERS | Lge | FAC | FAT | Total | Pens | Hat-tricks | Cons Run | | Lge | FAC | FAT | Total | Pens | Hat-tricks | Cons Run |
|-------------|-----|-----|-----|-------|------|------------|----------|---|-----|-----|-----|-------|------|------------|----------|
| Pearce | 21 | 1 | | 22 | 1 | | 3 | May | 3 | | | 3 | | | 2 |
| Nolan | 21 | | | 21 | | | 3 | Bakare | 1 | 1 | | 2 | | | |
| Mpi | 13 | 1 | | 14 | | | | Maisiatt | 2 | | | 2 | | | |
| Osobu | 8 | | | 8 | | | 2 | Bruce | 1 | | | 1 | | | |
| O'Leary | 4 | | 2 | 6 | 1 | | 2 | Diarra | 1 | | | 1 | | | |
| Parkes | 6 | | | 6 | | | | House | 1 | | | 1 | | | |
| Campana | 4 | | | 4 | | | | O'Toole | 1 | | | 1 | | | |
| Charles | 4 | | | 4 | | | 2 | Talbot | 1 | | | 1 | | | |
| Hutton | 3 | | | 3 | | | | Own Goal | 1 | | | 1 | | | |
| King | 3 | | | 3 | | | | Cons Run - Consecutive scoring games. | | | | | | | |

# HINCKLEY UNITED

**Chairman:** Mike Sutton
**Secretary:** Ray Baggott      **(T)** 07802 355 249      **(E)** raybaggott@yahoo.co.uk
**Commercial Manager:** Paul Moss      **(T)**
**Programme Editor:** Ray Baggott      **(T)** raybaggott@yahoo.co.uk
**Ground Address:** The Greene King Stadium, Leicester Road, Hinckley LE10 3DR
**(T)** 01455 840 088      **Manager:** Carl Heggs

## Club Factfile

**Founded:** 1997      **Nickname:** United
**Previous Names:** Today's club was formed when Hinckley Athletic and Hinckley Town merged in 1997
**Previous Leagues:** As United: Southern 1997-2004

**Club Colours (change):** Red with blue trim/blue with red trim/red (Orange with black trim/black/black)

**Ground Capacity:** 4,329      **Seats:** 630      **Covered:** 2,695      **Clubhouse:** Yes      **Shop:** Yes

**Directions:** M1 J21 take M69 (Coventry) or M6 J2 take M69 (Leicester). M69 J2 take A5 North. At 3rd roundabout (Dodwells). Take 2nd exit A47 Earl Shilton & Industrial Estates, follow A47 over three roundabouts & a set of traffic lights at next roundabout take 3rd exit B4668. Stadium is 100 yards on right.

**Previous Grounds:** Middlefield Lane. deMontfort Park Stadium.

**Record Attendance:** 2,889 v Nuneaton Borough - Conference North 26/12/2006
**Record Victory:** 9-1 v Rocester (A) - 28/08/2000
**Record Defeat:** 1-7 v Stalybridge Celtic (A) - Conference North 03/03/2009
**Record Goalscorer:** Dave Sadler - 83 in 180 games
**Record Appearances:** Neil Cartwright - 398 (1999-2010)
**Additional Records:** Received £30,000 from Luton Town for Andre Gray, March 2012.
**Senior Honours:** Paid £5,000 to Kiddrminster Harriers for Matt Lewis, December 2003.
Southern League Division 1 Western 2000-01

### 10 YEAR RECORD

| 03-04 | | 04-05 | | 05-06 | | 06-07 | | 07-08 | | 08-09 | | 09-10 | | 10-11 | | 11-12 | | 12-13 | |
|---|---|---|---|---|---|---|---|---|---|---|---|---|---|---|---|---|---|---|---|
| SthP | 6 | Conf N | 12 | Conf N | 10 | Conf N | 4 | Conf N | 19 | Conf N | 10 | Conf N | 7 | Conf N | 15 | Conf N | 20 | Conf N | 22 |

# MATCH RESULTS 2012-13

| Date | Comp | H/A | Opponents | Att: | Result | Goalscorers | Pos | No. |
|------|------|-----|-----------|------|--------|-------------|-----|-----|
| Aug 18 | BSN | H | Harrogate Town | 301 | L 0-2 | | 19 | 1 |
| 21 | BSN | A | Brackley Town | 303 | L 0-5 | | 21 | 2 |
| 25 | BSN | A | Boston United | 1105 | W 2-1 | Wint 32  Bragoli 68 | 16 | 3 |
| 27 | BSN | H | Histon | 363 | L 0-1 | | 20 | 4 |
| Sept 1 | BSN | A | Stalybridge Celtic | 467 | L 0-4 | | 21 | 5 |
| 8 | BSN | H | FC Halifax Town | 522 | L 0-2 | | 22 | 6 |
| 15 | BSN | A | Vauxhall Motors | 173 | L 1-2 | Newton 76 | 22 | 7 |
| 22 | FAC Q2 | H | Tividale | 145 | W 5-3 | Cole 8  Wint 25 Newton 30 (pen) 70  Lane 81 | | 8 |
| 29 | BSN | A | Workington | 291 | L 1-2 | Newton 32 | 22 | 9 |
| Oct 2 | BSN | H | Oxford City | 234 | L 0-2 | | 22 | 10 |
| 6 | FAC Q3 | H | Ossett Albion | 270 | D 2-2 | Headley 76 Harrop 79 | | 11 |
| 9 | FAC Q3r | A | Ossett Albion | 280 | L 0-1 | | | 12 |
| 13 | BSN | A | Colwyn Bay | 318 | L 2-3 | Wint 7 48 | 22 | 13 |
| 20 | BSN | H | Colwyn Bay | 315 | L 1-3 | Wint 45 | 22 | 14 |
| 27 | BSN | H | Gloucester City | 316 | L 0-3 | | 22 | 15 |
| 30 | BSN | A | Gainsborough Trinity | 451 | L 0-5 | | 22 | 16 |
| Nov 4 | BSN | H | Worcester City | 359 | L 0-5 | | 22 | 17 |
| 10 | FAT Q3 | A | Gainsborough Trinity | 357 | D 1-1 | Cole 48 | | 18 |
| 13 | FAT Q3r | H | Gainsborough Trinity | 181 | L 1-4 | Wint 41 | | 19 |
| 17 | BSN | A | Altrincham | 768 | L 0-8 | | 22 | 20 |
| 19 | BSN | A | Bradford PA | 301 | L 0-4 | | 22 | 21 |
| Dec 1 | BSN | H | Guiseley | 192 | L 0-3 | | 22 | 22 |
| 8 | BSN | A | Corby Town | 300 | L 3-5 | Headley 44 90 Brown 52 | 22 | 23 |
| 15 | BSN | A | Harrogate Town | 1440 | L 0-5 | | 22 | 24 |
| 26 | BSN | A | Solihull Moors | 208 | L 0-1 | | 22 | 25 |
| 29 | BSN | A | Chester | 2701 | L 0-3 | | 22 | 26 |
| Jan 1 | BSN | H | Solihull Moors | 338 | D 1-1 | Cole 36 | 22 | 27 |
| 5 | BSN | H | Stalybridge Celtic | 306 | L 0-3 | | 22 | 28 |
| 12 | BSN | H | Chester | 648 | L 0-6 | | 22 | 29 |
| 29 | BSN | H | Brackley Town | 152 | L 1-3 | Headley 76 | 22 | 30 |
| Feb 2 | BSN | A | Oxford City | 319 | L 2-6 | Brown 52 Towers 73 | 22 | 31 |
| 5 | BSN | H | Vauxhall Motors | 151 | L 0-6 | | 22 | 32 |
| 16 | BSN | A | Bishop's Stortford | 388 | D 1-1 | Brown 35 | 22 | 33 |
| 23 | BSN | H | Workington | 238 | D 1-1 | Richards 70 | 22 | 34 |
| 26 | BSN | A | Droylsden | 123 | L 2-3 | Richards 18 Canavan 86 | 22 | 35 |
| Mar 2 | BSN | H | Gainsborough Trinity | 333 | L 0-2 | | 22 | 36 |
| 5 | BSN | A | FC Halifax Town | 900 | L 0-7 | | 22 | 37 |
| 9 | BSN | A | Gloucester City | 293 | L 1-4 | Lane 37 | 22 | 38 |
| 30 | BSN | H | Boston United | 353 | L 2-4 | Brown 57 Conway 88 | 22 | 39 |
| Apr 1 | BSN | A | Histon | 318 | L 1-2 | Richards 39 | 22 | 40 |
| 6 | BSN | H | Bradford PA | 250 | L 1-4 | Pickering 46 | 22 | 41 |
| 8 | BSN | H | Corby Town | 255 | W 6-3 | Lane 4 (pen) Canavan 5 RICHARDS 3( 25 61 85) Headley 35 | 22 | 42 |
| 11 | BSN | A | Worcester City | 828 | L 1-3 | Brown 90 | 22 | 43 |
| 18 | BSN | H | Droylsden | 187 | D 2-2 | Canavan 20 30 | 22 | 44 |
| 20 | BSN | A | Altrincham | 534 | L 0-6 | | 22 | 45 |
| 23 | BSN | H | Bishop's Stortford | 204 | L 1-5 | Richards 76 | 22 | 46 |
| 27 | BSN | A | Guiseley | 750 | W 4-2 | Richards 15 45 Canavan 75 Hurren 80 | 22 | 47 |

| GOALSCORERS | Lge | FAC | LC | Total | Pens | Hat-tricks | Cons Run | | Lge | FAC | LC | Total | Pens | Hat-tricks | Cons Run |
|-------------|-----|-----|-----|-------|------|------------|----------|--|-----|-----|-----|-------|------|------------|----------|
| Richards | 9 | | | 9 | 1 | | 2 | Harrop | | 1 | | 1 | | | |
| Wint | 4 | 1 | 1 | 6 | | | | Hurren | 1 | | | 1 | | | |
| Brown | 5 | | | 5 | | | | Pickering | 1 | | | 1 | | | |
| Canavan | 5 | | | 5 | | | | Towers | 1 | | | 1 | | | |
| Headley | 4 | 1 | | 5 | | | | Cons Run - Consecutive scoring games. | | | | | | | |
| Newton | 2 | 2 | | 4 | 1 | | | | | | | | | | |
| Cole | 1 | 1 | 1 | 3 | | | | | | | | | | | |
| Lane | 2 | 1 | | 3 | 1 | | | | | | | | | | |
| Bragoli | 1 | | | 1 | | | | | | | | | | | |
| Conway | 1 | | | 1 | | | | | | | | | | | |

# HITCHIN TOWN

**Chairman:** Terry Barratt
**Secretary:** Roy Izzard  **(T)** 07803 202 498  **(E)** roy.izzard@hitchintownfc.co.uk
**Commercial Manager:**  **(T)**
**Programme Editor:** Neil Jensen  **(T)** neil.jensen@db.com
**Ground Address:** Top Field, Fishponds Road, Hitchin SG5 1NU
**(T)** 01462 459 028 (match days only)  **Manager:** Mark Burke

2012-13 Squad.

## Club Factfile

**Founded:** 1865  **Nickname:** Canaries
**Previous Names:** Hitchin FC 1865-1911. Re-formed in 1928
**Previous Leagues:** Spartan 1928-39, Herts & Middlesex 1939-45, Athenian 1945-63, Isthmian 1964-2004

**Club Colours (change):** Yellow/green/green (All green)

**Ground Capacity:** 5,000  **Seats:** 500  **Covered:** 1,250  **Clubhouse:** Yes  **Shop:** Yes

**Directions**
From East A1 to J8 onto A602 to Hitchin.
At Three Moorhens Pub roundabout, take third exit (A600) towards Bedford, over next roundabout and lights, turn right at next roundabout, turnstiles on left, parking 50 yards on.

**Previous Grounds:** None

**Record Attendance:** 7,878 v Wycombe Wanderers - FA Amateur Cup 3rd Round 08/02/1956
**Record Victory:** 13-0 v Cowley and v RAF Uxbridge - both Spartan League 1929-30
**Record Defeat:** 0-10 v Kingstonian (A) and v Slough Town (A) - 1965-66 and 1979-80 respectively
**Record Goalscorer:** Paul Giggle - 214 (1968-86)
**Record Appearances:** Paul Giggle - 769 (1968-86)
**Additional Records:** Paid £2,000 to Potton United for Ray Seeking
**Senior Honours:**  Received £30,000 from Cambridge United for Zema Abbey, January 2000
AFA Senior Cup 1931-32. London Senior Cup 1969-70. Isthmian League Division 1 1992-93.
Herts Senior Cup x19 (a record)

### 10 YEAR RECORD

| 03-04 | | 04-05 | | 05-06 | | 06-07 | | 07-08 | | 08-09 | | 09-10 | | 10-11 | | 11-12 | | 12-13 | |
|---|---|---|---|---|---|---|---|---|---|---|---|---|---|---|---|---|---|---|---|
| Isth P | 20 | SthP | 18 | SthP | 14 | SthP | 11 | SthP | 18 | SthP | 20 | SthC | 2 | SthC | 2 | SthP | 14 | SthP | 13 |

# MATCH RESULTS 2012-13

| Date | Comp | H/A | Opponents | Att: | Result | Goalscorers | Pos | No. |
|---|---|---|---|---|---|---|---|---|
| Aug 18 | SPL | H | Redditch United | 252 | W 3-0 | Gilbert 35 Lincoln 48  Gregson 90 | | 1 |
| 21 | SPL | A | St Neots Town | 390 | W 3-2 | Delderfield 6 9  Fontanelle 49 | 2 | 2 |
| 25 | SPL | A | Leamington | 381 | L 0-3 | | 6 | 3 |
| 27 | SPL | H | Arlesey Town | 573 | L 0-1 | | 6 | 4 |
| Sept 1 | SPL | A | Chippenham Town | 315 | W 4-2 | Delderfield 9 Frendo 18 Gregson 22 Donnelly 28 | 8 | 5 |
| 3 | SPL | H | St Albans City | 491 | L 0-2 | | 9 | 6 |
| 8 | FAC Q1 | A | Ware | 181 | W 5-0 | Lincoln 14 89 FRENDO 3 (48 pen 58 68 pen) | 8 | 7 |
| 15 | SPL | H | Stourbridge | 408 | L 0-1 | | 10 | 8 |
| 18 | SPL | A | Bedworth Town | 153 | L 0-1 | | 13 | 9 |
| 22 | FAC Q2 | A | Whitehawk | 144 | D 1-1 | Donnelly 56 | | 10 |
| 24 | FAC Q2r | H | Whitehawk | 185 | W 5-0 | Gregson 5 Frendo 24 (pen) 46 Gilbert 65 Lewis 69 | | 11 |
| 29 | FAT Q1 | H | Sittingbourne | 198 | W 3-1 | Donnelly 40 Bickerstaff 77 Frendo 90 | | 12 |
| Oct 6 | FAC Q3 | A | Hastings United | 459 | D 2-2 | Frendo 14 Burke 26 | | 13 |
| 8 | FAC Q3r | H | Hastings United | 298 | L 1-2 | Frendo 58 (pen) | | 14 |
| 13 | SPL | H | Frome Town | 311 | W 2-0 | Frendo 28 C.Stewart 69 | 13 | 15 |
| 20 | SPL | A | Weymouth | 650 | L 2-3 | Frendo 1 Burke 16 | 14 | 16 |
| 27 | FAT Q2 | A | Wingate & Finchley | 101 | D 2-2 | Frendo 37 78 (Pen) | | 17 |
| 29 | FAT Q2r | H | Wingate & Finchley | 171 | W 3-0 | BURKE 3 ( 17 52 76) | | 18 |
| Nov 3 | SPL | A | Bideford | 198 | L 2-3 | Frendo 15 (pen) 16 | 16 | 19 |
| 10 | FAT Q3 | A | Tonbridge Angels | 513 | L 1-2 | Frendo 29 (pen) | | 20 |
| 13 | SPL | A | AFC Totton | 268 | D 2-2 | King 13 Frendo 37 (pen) | 13 | 21 |
| 17 | SPL | H | Banbury United | 364 | L 1-2 | Frendo 74 | 21 | 22 |
| Dec 1 | SPL | A | Gosport Borough | 299 | D 0-0 | | 21 | 23 |
| 8 | SPL | H | Bedford Town | 358 | W 2-0 | Frendo 18 52 | 21 | 24 |
| 10 | SPL | H | Cambridge City | 285 | L 0-3 | | 21 | 25 |
| 15 | SPL | A | Hemel Hempstead | 416 | L 2-8 | Frendo 65 (pen) Delderfield 84 | 21 | 26 |
| 18 | SPL | A | Bashley | 92 | W 1-0 | Frendo 2 | 20 | 27 |
| 26 | SPL | H | Kettering Town | 428 | L 3-4 | FRENDO 3 (42 pen 54 pen 77)) | 20 | 28 |
| Jan 1 | SPL | A | Arlesey Town | 536 | L 1-3 | Frendo 41 | 20 | 29 |
| 12 | SPL | A | St Albans City | 381 | D 1-1 | Woolley 56 | 20 | 30 |
| 26 | SPL | H | Stourbridge | 444 | L 1-4 | Frendo  3 | 20 | 31 |
| 28 | SPL | H | St Neots Town | 265 | D 2-2 | Gregson 72 Noone 85 | 20 | 32 |
| Feb 2 | SPL | A | Barwell | 161 | L 0-1 | | 20 | 33 |
| 9 | SPL | H | AFC Totton | 269 | W 4-0 | FRENDO 3 (44 pen 51 69) Woolley 62 | 20 | 34 |
| 16 | SPL | A | Banbury United | 216 | W 4-0 | FRENDO 3 ( 34 39 63)  Gregson 61 | 19 | 35 |
| 19 | SPL | H | Leamington | 350 | L 1-0 | | 19 | 36 |
| 23 | SPL | H | Bashley | 243 | W 3-2 | Frendo 6 10 Gregson 64 | 18 | 37 |
| 26 | SPL | H | Chesham United | 239 | L 1-3 | Frendo 53 (pen) | 18 | 38 |
| May 2 | SPL | H | Weymouth | 264 | L 1-2 | Dillon 71 | 19 | 39 |
| 4 | SPL | H | Barwell | 200 | L 0-1 | | 19 | 40 |
| 9 | SPL | A | Frome Town | 263 | L 1-2 | Toomey 11 | 21 | 41 |
| 16 | SPL | H | Bideford | 321 | W 1-0 | Toomey 52 | 17 | 42 |
| 30 | SPL | H | Chippenham Town | 304 | W 2-1 | Gilbert 22 Toomey 40 | 17 | 43 |
| Apr 1 | SPL | A | Kettering | 220 | L 1-3 | Reny 58 | 17 | 44 |
| 3 | SPL | H | Cambridge City | 235 | D 0-0 | | 17 | 45 |
| 6 | SPL | H | Gosport Borough | 256 | W 1-0 | Frendo 70 | 17 | 46 |
| 8 | SPL | H | Bedworth United | 243 | D 1-1 | Frendo 82 | 17 | 47 |
| 13 | SPL | A | Chesham United | 409 | D 1-1 | Gudgeon 24 (og) | 16 | 48 |
| 16 | SPL | A | Redditch United | 164 | W 2-0 | Webb 12 Frendo 37 | 16 | 49 |
| 20 | SPL | H | Hemel Hempstead T | 353 | W 3-2 | TOOMEY 3 ( 10 44 45) | 15 | 50 |
| 27 | SPL | A | Bedford Town | 432 | W 4-1 | FRENDO 3 ( 60 82 84 ) King 63 | 13 | 51 |

| GOALSCORERS | Lge | FAC | FAT | Total | Pens | Hat-tricks | Cons Run | | Lge | FAC | FAT | Total | Pens | Hat-tricks | Cons Run |
|---|---|---|---|---|---|---|---|---|---|---|---|---|---|---|---|
| Frendo | 31 | 7 | 4 | 42 | 13 | 5 | 7 | Bickerstaff | | | 1 | 1 | | | |
| Gregson | 5 | 1 | | 6 | | | | Dillon | 1 | | | 1 | | | |
| Toomey | 6 | | | 6 | 1 | | 3 | Fontanelle | 1 | | | 1 | | | |
| Burke | 1 | 1 | 3 | 5 | | 1 | | Lewis | | 1 | | 1 | | | |
| Delderfield | 4 | | | 4 | | | | Noone | 1 | | | 1 | | | |
| Gilbert | 2 | 1 | 1 | 3 | | | | Remy | 1 | | | 1 | | | |
| Lincoln | 1 | 2 | | 3 | | | | Stewart | 1 | | | 1 | | | |
| Woolley | 2 | 1 | | 3 | | | | Webb | 1 | | | 1 | | | |
| Donnelly | 1 | 1 | | 2 | | | | Own Goals | 1 | | | 1 | | | |
| King | 2 | | | 2 | | | | Cons Run - Consecutive scoring games. | | | | | | | |

# HUNGERFORD TOWN

**Chairman:** Steve Skipworth
**Secretary:** John Smyth          **(T)**                    **(E)** john.smyth@saxon-brands.com
**Commercial Manager:** Ron Tarry, Ray Brown,   **(T)**
**Programme Editor:** John Smyth          **(T)** john.smyth@saxon-brands.com
**Ground Address:** Bulpitt Lane, Hungerford RG17 0AY
**(T)** 01488 682 939                              **Manager:** Bobby Wilkinson

Celebrations after lifting the Basingstoke Senior Cup.
Back row. Ryan Crockford, Ian Herring, Ian Hobbs (Goalkeeping coach), Jack Wild, John Boardman, Paul Strudley,Carl Davis, Mark Hughes, Luke brewer,Scott Davis, Matt Day, Harry Goodyear, Lea Barkus (coach) Ben Ashby (coach)
Front row. Alan O'Brien, Sean Wood, Dean Stow, Scott Rees, Diak John, Bobby Wilkinson (Manager)

## Club Factfile

**Founded:** 1886     **Nickname:** The Crusaders
**Previous Names:** None
**Previous Leagues:** Newbury & District, Swindon & District, Hellenic 1958-78, 2003-09, Isthmian 1978-2003

**Club Colours (change):** White/royal blue/royal blue (All red)

**Ground Capacity:** 2,500   **Seats:** 170    **Covered:** 400    **Clubhouse:** Yes   **Shop:** Yes

**Directions:** From M4 Junction, take A338 to Hungerford. First Roundabout turn right on to A4, next roundabout first left, 100 yards roundabout 1st left up High Street, go over three roundabouts, at fourth roundabout turn first left signposted 'Football Club'. Take second left into Bulpitt Lane, go over crossroads, ground on left.

**Previous Grounds:** None

**Record Attendance:** 1,684 v Sudbury Town - FA Vase Semi-final 1988-89
**Record Victory:** Not known
**Record Defeat:** Not known
**Record Goalscorer:** Ian Farr - 268
**Record Appearances:** Dean Bailey and Tim North - 400+
**Additional Records:** Paid £4,000 to Yeovil Town for Joe Scott
**Senior Honours:**     Received £3,800 from Barnstaple Town for Joe Scott
Hellenic Division 1 1970-71, Premier Division 2008-09, League Cup 2006-07, 07-08.
Berks & Bucks Senior Cup 1981-82. Basingstoke Senior Cup 2012-13.
Isthmian representatives in Anglo Italian Cup 1981.

### 10 YEAR RECORD

| 03-04 | | 04-05 | | 05-06 | | 06-07 | | 07-08 | | 08-09 | | 09-10 | | 10-11 | | 11-12 | | 12-13 | |
|---|---|---|---|---|---|---|---|---|---|---|---|---|---|---|---|---|---|---|---|
| Hel P | 6 | Hel P | 17 | Hel P | 16 | Hel P | 3 | Hel P | 3 | Hel P | 1 | Sthsw | 17 | Sthsw | 7 | Sthsw | 5 | Sthsw | 2 |

# POOLE TOWN

**Chairman:** Clive Robbins
**Secretary:** Bill Reid          **(T)** 01794  517 991     **(E)** secretary@pooletownfc.co.uk
**Commercial Manager:** Mark Bumford          **(T)**
**Programme Editor:** Ian Claxton          **(T)** ian.claxton@btinternet.com
**Ground Address:** Tatnam Ground, Oakdale School, School Lane, Poole BH15 3JR
**(T)** 07771 604 289 (Match days)          **Manager:** Tommy Killick

Team line up before their league match against Shortwood United.
Photo: Peter Barnes.

## Club Factfile

**Founded:** 1880          **Nickname:** The Dolphins
**Previous Names:** Poole Rovers 1884, Poole Hornets 1886 - amalgamated on 20.09.1890 to form Town. Know as Poole & St. Mary's 1919-20.
**Previous Leagues:** Dorset 1896-1903, 04-05, 10-11. Hampshire 1903-04, 05-10, 11-23, 34-35, 96-2004. Western 1923-26, 30-34, 35-57.
          Southern 1926-30, 57-96. Wessex 2004-11.

**Club Colours (change):** Red & white halves/red/white

**Ground Capacity:** 2,000     **Seats:** 154     **Covered:** 200     **Clubhouse:** Yes     **Shop:** Yes

**Directions:** Follow the A35 into Poole and at the roundabout by the fire station take the second exit into Holes Bay Road (A350). At next roundabout take 1st exit onto Broadstone Way (A349) and turn right at Wessex Gate East traffic lights into Willis Way. Turn right into Fleets Way and continue until you see Poole Motor Cycles. Turn left into Palmer Road opposite Poole Motor Cycles and take first right into School Lane which will take you into the Club/School car park. The ground is on the right hand side. Nearest Railway Station: Poole (3/4 mile)

**Previous Grounds:** Ye Old Farm Ground. Wimborne Road Rec > 1933. Poole Stadium 1933-94. Hamworthy Utd FC 1994-96. Holt Utd 1996.

**Record Attendance:** Att: 10,224 v Queens Park Rangers, FA Cup 1st Rnd Replay, 1946 (at Poole Stadium).
**Record Victory:** 11-0 v Horndean (A) Hampshire League 11/02/1998
**Record Defeat:** 1-8 v East Cowes VA (A) Hampshire League 01/05/2001.
**Record Goalscorer:** Not known
**Record Appearances:** Not known
**Additional Records:** Got to 3rd Round of FA Cup in 1926 v Everton. Transfer fee paid £5,000 for Nicky Dent 1990.
**Senior Honours:** Transfer fee received £70,000 for Charlie Austin from Swindon Town 2009.
Western League 1956-57. Dorset Senior Cup x13 Most recently 2012-13.
Wessex League Champions 2008-09, 09-10, 10-11. Southern Division One South & West 2012-13.

### 10 YEAR RECORD

| 03-04 | 04-05 | 05-06 | 06-07 | 07-08 | 08-09 | 09-10 | 10-11 | 11-12 | 12-13 |
|---|---|---|---|---|---|---|---|---|---|
| HantP   3 | Wex2   2 | Wex1   8 | WexP   4 | WexP   4 | WexP   1 | WexP   1 | WexP   1 | Sthsw   2 | Sthsw   1 |

# REDDITCH UNITED

**Chairman:** Chris Swan
**Secretary:** Dave Jones          **(T)**                    **(E)** secretaryrufc@ymail.com
**Commercial Manager:**                    **(T)**
**Programme Editor:** Sallie Swan & Craig Swan  **(T)** programmeeditor.reds@yahoo.com
**Ground Address:** Valley Stadium, Bromsgrove Road, Redditch B97 4RN
**(T)** 01527 67450                    **Manager:** Liam McDonald

## Club Factfile

**Founded:** 1891          **Nickname:** The Reds
**Previous Names:** Redditch Town
**Previous Leagues:** Birmingham combination 1905-21, 29-39, 46-53, West Midlands 1921-29, 53-72,
Southern 1972-79, 81-2004, Alliance 1979-80. Conference 2004-11.

**Club Colours (change):** Red/black/black (All blue)

**Ground Capacity:** 5,000   **Seats:** 400   **Covered:** 2,000   **Clubhouse:** Yes   **Shop:** Yes

**Directions:** M42 J2, at island first exit onto the A441 for 2 miles, next island first exit onto Birmingham Road A441 for 1.2 miles then at island third exit onto Middlehouse Lane B4184 for 0.3 miles. At traffic lights (next to the fire station) turn left onto Birmingham Road for 0.2 miles then turn right into Clive Road for 0.3 miles. At island take first exit onto Hewell Road for 0.2 miles then at 'T' junction right onto Windsor Street for 0.1 miles. At traffic lights (next to bus station) continue straight ahead onto Bromsgrove Road for 0.3 miles and at the brow of the hill, turn right into the ground's entrance.

**Previous Grounds:** HDA Sports Ground, Millsborough Road

**Record Attendance:** 5,500 v Bromsgrove Rovers - Wets Midlands League 1954-55
**Record Victory:** Not known
**Record Defeat:** Not known
**Record Goalscorer:** Not known
**Record Appearances:** Not known
**Additional Records:** Paid £3,000 to Halesowen Town for Paul Joinson
**Senior Honours:**     Received £40,000 from Aston Villa for David Farrell
Worcestershire Senior Cup 1893-94, 29-30, 74-75, 76-76, 2007-08.
Birmingham Senior Cup 1924-25, 31-32, 38-39, 76-77, 2004-05.
Southern League Division 1 North 1975-76, Western Division 2003-04. Staffordshire Senior Cup 1990-91.

### 10 YEAR RECORD

| 03-04 | | 04-05 | | 05-06 | | 06-07 | | 07-08 | | 08-09 | | 09-10 | | 10-11 | | 11-12 | | 12-13 | |
|---|---|---|---|---|---|---|---|---|---|---|---|---|---|---|---|---|---|---|---|
| SthW | 1 | Conf N | 9 | Conf N | 20 | Conf N | 19 | Conf N | 13 | Conf N | 14 | Conf N | 19 | Conf N | 21 | SthP | 15 | SthP | 19 |

# MATCH RESULTS 2012-13

| Date | Comp | H/A | Opponents | Att: | Result | Goalscorers | Pos | No. |
|---|---|---|---|---|---|---|---|---|
| Aug 18 | SPL | A | Hitchin Town | 252 | L 0-3 | | 22 | 1 |
| 1 | SPL | H | Bedford Town | 200 | D 0-0 | | 19 | 2 |
| 5 | SPL | A | Gosport Borough | 336 | W 3-2 | Banks 17 65 Fuller 75 | 12 | 3 |
| 7 | SPL | A | Banbury United | 254 | D 0-0 | | 12 | 4 |
| ept 1 | SPL | H | Weymouth | 240 | D 0-0 | | 13 | 5 |
| | SPL | A | Bedford Town | 213 | L 1-2 | Richards 32 | 15 | 6 |
| | FAC Q1 | H | Hednesford Town | 276 | L 0-3 | | | 7 |
| 5 | SPL | A | Bideford | 177 | L 2-3 | Deards 78 Danks 88 | 20 | 8 |
| 8 | SPL | H | Leamington | 269 | D 1-1 | Richards 27 | 18 | 9 |
| 9 | FAT Q1 | A | Nantwich Town | 274 | L 1-2 | Richards 71 | | 10 |
| Oct 6 | SPL | H | Hemel Hempstead T | 167 | L 1-4 | Deards 37 | 19 | 11 |
| | SPL | A | St Neots Town | 290 | W 2-1 | Grandison 46 Deards 55 | 14 | 12 |
| 3 | SPL | H | AFC Totton | 190 | W 2-1 | Creswell 36 McDonald 58 | 11 | 13 |
| 0 | SPL | A | Frome Town | 173 | L 0-1 | | 12 | 14 |
| 7 | SPL | H | Barwell | 201 | L 0-1 | | 14 | 15 |
| Nov 6 | SPL | H | St Albans City | 119 | L 0-2 | | 17 | 16 |
| 0 | SPL | A | Kettering Town | 487 | W 1-0 | Reid 90 | 15 | 17 |
| 7 | SPL | H | Chippenham Town | 187 | W 1-0 | Moran 13 | 11 | 18 |
| Dec 1 | SPL | A | Hemel Hempstead T | 246 | L 0-4 | | 17 | 19 |
| | SPL | H | Cambridge City | 173 | L 2-4 | Hylton 81 Cresswell 88 | 20 | 20 |
| 6 | SPL | A | Stourbridge | 512 | L 0-1 | | 21 | 21 |
| an 8 | SPL | A | Chesham United | 258 | L 1-2 | Oshungbure 45 | 21 | 22 |
| 2 | SPL | H | Bedford Town | 146 | L 0-3 | | 21 | 23 |
| Feb 2 | SPL | H | St Neots Town | 160 | W 1-0 | Richards 45 | 21 | 24 |
| | SPL | A | St Albans City | 322 | L 0-3 | | 21 | 25 |
| 6 | SPL | A | Chippenham Town | 318 | W 3-2 | Tindle 35 (og) Hylton 81 Richards 90 | 21 | 26 |
| 9 | SPL | H | Banbury United | 121 | L 0-2 | | 21 | 27 |
| 3 | SPL | H | Kettering Town | 610 | W 4-1 | Charlton 22 Richards 38 42 Washbourne 90 | 20 | 28 |
| 6 | SPL | A | Bedworth United | 120 | D 0-0 | | 18 | 29 |
| Mar 2 | SPL | H | Frome Town | 190 | W 2-1 | Richards 34 McDonald 90 | 18 | 30 |
| | SPL | H | Bashley | 95 | D 0-0 | | 18 | 31 |
| | SPL | A | AFC Totton | 605 | L 0-2 | | 19 | 32 |
| 2 | SPL | A | Leamington | 301 | L 0-2 | | 19 | 33 |
| 9 | SPL | H | Gosport Borough | 101 | L 0-2 | | 20 | 34 |
| 6 | SPL | A | Arlesey Town | 80 | L 0-3 | | 20 | 35 |
| 0 | SPL | A | Weymouth | 651 | W 2-0 | Richards 56 Thompson-Brown 76 | 19 | 36 |
| Apr 1 | SPL | H | Stourbridge | 321 | L 0-4 | | 19 | 37 |
| | SPL | H | Arlesey Town | 94 | L 0-2 | | 20 | 38 |
| | SPL | H | Bideford | 109 | W 2-1 | Sammons 74 Deards 80 | 20 | 39 |
| 1 | SPL | A | Barwell | 112 | D 0-0 | | 20 | 40 |
| 6 | SPL | H | Hitchin Town | 164 | L 0-2 | | 20 | 41 |
| 8 | SPL | A | Bashley | 88 | W 1-0 | Sammons 71 | 18 | 42 |
| 0 | SPL | H | Chesham United | 278 | L 0-2 | | 19 | 43 |
| 7 | SPL | A | Cambridge City | 814 | L 0-1 | | 19 | 44 |

| GOALSCORERS | Lge | FAC | FAT | Total | Pens | Hat-tricks | Cons Run | | Lge | FAC | FAT | Total | Pens | Hat-tricks | Cons Run |
|---|---|---|---|---|---|---|---|---|---|---|---|---|---|---|---|
| Richards | 8 | 1 | | 8 | | | 2 | Fuller | 1 | | | 1 | | | |
| Deards | 4 | | | 4 | | | 2 | Moran | 1 | | | 1 | | | |
| Banks | 2 | | | 2 | | | | Oshungbure | 1 | | | 1 | | | |
| Cresswell | 2 | | | 2 | | | | Reid | 1 | | | 1 | | | |
| Hylton | 2 | | | 2 | | | | Washbourne | 1 | | | 1 | | | |
| McDonald | 2 | | | 2 | | | | Thompson-Brown | 1 | | | 1 | | | |
| Sammons | 2 | | | 2 | | | | Own Goal | 1 | | | 1 | | | |
| Charlton | 1 | | | 1 | | | | Cons Run - Consecutive scoring games. | | | | | | | |
| Danks | 1 | | | 1 | | | | | | | | | | | |
| Grandison | 1 | | | 1 | | | | | | | | | | | |

# ST ALBANS CITY

**Chairman:** Nick Archer

**Secretary:** Steve Eames   **(T)** 01727 848914   **(E)** steveeames@sacfc.co.uk

**Commercial Manager:** Sabra Swinton   **(T)** 01727 847 407

**Programme Editor:** Lee Wood   **(T)** leewood@queenswaypublishing.co.uk

**Ground Address:** Clarence Park, York Road, St. Albans, Herts AL1 4PL

**(T)** 01727 848 914       **Manager:** James Gray

2012-13 Squad.

## Club Factfile

**Founded:** 1908   **Nickname:** The Saints

**Previous Names:** None

**Previous Leagues:** Herts County 1908-10, Spartan 1908-20, Athenian 1920-23, Isthmian 1923-2004, Conference 2004-11.

**Club Colours (change):** Yellow/blue/yellow (Sky blue/navy/sky blue)

**Ground Capacity:** 5,007   **Seats:** 667   **Covered:** 1,900   **Clubhouse:** Yes   **Shop:** Yes

**Directions:** From the M25 (Clockwise) Exit M25 at junction 21A(A405). Follow signs to St. Albans from slip road. At Noke Hotel roundabout (Shell garage will be straight ahead), bear right on A405 and stay on A405 until London Colney roundabout (traffic light controlled). Turn left onto A1081. Follow road for approx 1 mile until mini roundabout (Great Northern pub on left). Turn right into Alma Road. At traffic lights turn right into Victoria Street and continue to junction with Crown pub. Go straight across into Clarence Road, ground is first on left about 50 yards past junction or take the next turning on the left into York Road, ground entrance is at the end of the road on the left. From the M25 (Counter-clockwise) Exit M25 at junction 22 (A1081). Follow signs to St. Albans from slip road. At London Colney roundabout (traffic light controlled) exit onto A1081. Follow road for approx 1 mile until mini roundabout (Great Northern pub on left). Turn right into Alma Road. At traffic lights turn right into Victoria Street and continue to junction with Crown pub. Go straight across into Clarence Road, ground is first on left about 50 yards past junction or take the next turning on the left into York Road, ground entrance is at the end of the road on the left.

**Previous Grounds:** None

**Record Attendance:** 9,757 v Ferryhill Athletic - FA Amateur Cup 1926

**Record Victory:** 14-0 v Aylesbury United (H) - Spartan League 19/10/1912

**Record Defeat:** 0-11 v Wimbledon (H) - Isthmian League 1946

**Record Goalscorer:** Billy Minter - 356 (Top scorer for 12 consecutive season from 1920-32)

**Record Appearances:** Phil Wood - 900 (1962-85)

**Additional Records:** Paid £6,000 to Yeovil Town for Paul Turner August 1957

**Senior Honours:** Received £92,759 from Southend United for Dean Austin 1990

Athenian League 1920-21, 21-22. Isthmian League 1923-24, 26-27, 27-28.

London Senior Cup 1970-71.

### 10 YEAR RECORD

| 03-04 | | 04-05 | | 05-06 | | 06-07 | | 07-08 | | 08-09 | | 09-10 | | 10-11 | | 11-12 | | 12-13 | |
|---|---|---|---|---|---|---|---|---|---|---|---|---|---|---|---|---|---|---|---|
| Isth P | 19 | Conf S | 14 | Conf S | 2 | Conf | 24 | Conf S | 19 | Conf S | 12 | Conf S | 13 | Conf S | 22 | SthP | 8 | SthP | 11 |

# MATCH RESULTS 2012-13

| Date | Comp | H/A | Opponents | Att: | Result | Goalscorers | Pos | No. |
|---|---|---|---|---|---|---|---|---|
| Aug 18 | SPL | A | Banbury United | 253 | D 2-2 | Toomey 45  Ujah 90 | 12 | 1 |
| 21 | SPL | H | Cambridge City | 363 | W 3-2 | Hayles 13 Toomey 44 67 (pen) | 5 | 2 |
| 25 | SPL | H | Frome Town | 336 | W 4-0 | Graham 1 Hayles 7 Toomey 25 Shields 64 | 2 | 3 |
| 27 | SPL | A | Chesham United | 518 | L 1-2 | Toomey 51 (Pen) | 5 | 4 |
| Sept 1 | SPL | H | Stourbridge | 395 | L 2-4 | Gray 21 Shields (Shaun) 38 | 9 | 5 |
| 3 | SPL | A | Hitchin Town | 491 | W 2-0 | Hayles 7 Henry 29 | 7 | 6 |
| 8 | FAC Q1 | A | Harrow Borough | 219 | W 3-1 | Hayles 14 50 Shields 76 | | 7 |
| 15 | SPL | H | Kettering Town | 498 | W 2-1 | Toomey 23 56 | 5 | 8 |
| 18 | SPL | A | Gosport Borough | 242 | W 1-0 | Toomey 26 | 5 | 9 |
| 22 | FAC Q2 | A | Ashford T (Mdx) | 179 | W 6-2 | SHIELDS 3 (7 23 30) Hyde 35 Martin 48 Henry 75 | | 10 |
| 29 | FAT Q1 | H | Arlesey Town | 335 | L 1-2 | Ujah 18 | | 11 |
| Oct 6 | FAC Q3 | H | Lowestoft Town | 506 | L 0-1 | | | 12 |
| 9 | SPL | H | Arlesey Town | 277 | W 1-0 | Shields 18 | 3 | 13 |
| 13 | SPL | H | Barwell | 424 | D 4-4 | DIARRA (28 40 70) Hyde 59 (pen) | 5 | 14 |
| 20 | SPL | A | St Neots Town | 518 | L 2-3 | Toomey 22 Shields 88 | 5 | 15 |
| Nov 3 | SPL | A | AFC Totton | 397 | L 0-3 | | 7 | 16 |
| 6 | SPL | A | Redditch United | 119 | W 2-0 | Hayles 66 87 | 5 | 17 |
| 10 | SPL | H | Weymouth | 457 | L 2-3 | Ujah 37 Onieva 51 | 6 | 18 |
| 13 | SPL | H | Bedford Town | 293 | D 2-2 | Henry 62 Hayles 88 | 6 | 19 |
| 17 | SPL | A | Bideford Town | 186 | L 0-1 | | 6 | 20 |
| 24 | SPL | H | Chippenham Town | 312 | L 0-2 | | 6 | 21 |
| Dec 1 | SPL | A | Bashley | 158 | L 0-2 | | 9 | 22 |
| 8 | SPL | H | Leamington | 356 | W 3-0 | Martin 16 Ijaha 44 Taylor 64 | 7 | 23 |
| 15 | SPL | A | Bedworth United | 183 | W 3-1 | SHIELDS 3 (10 19 43) | 6 | 24 |
| 22 | SPL | H | Banbury United | 334 | W 4-0 | Graham 23 Ngoyi 39 Henry 77 Toomey 89 | 5 | 25 |
| 26 | SPL | A | Hemel Henpstead | 787 | D 1-1 | Charles 90 | 5 | 26 |
| Jan 1 | SPL | H | Chesham United | 615 | L 2-6 | Eadie 31 Toomey 72 | 6 | 27 |
| 5 | SPL | A | Cambridge City | 502 | L 1-2 | Ngoyi 23 | 7 | 28 |
| Feb 2 | SPL | A | Arlesey Town | 261 | W 3-1 | Ngoyi 9 (pen) 81 Urquart 46 | 7 | 29 |
| 9 | SPL | H | Redditch United | 322 | W 3-0 | Wadkins 66 Henry 82 Ngoyi  90 | 7 | 30 |
| 12 | SPL | H | Hitchin Town | 381 | D 1-1 | Henry 83 | 7 | 31 |
| 16 | SPL | H | Bideford Town | 370 | W 4-3 | Seeby  5 Comley 45 (pen) Henry  78 87 | 7 | 32 |
| 20 | SPL | A | Frome Town | 108 | W 3-0 | Seeby 32 Henry 50 Comley 90 | 7 | 33 |
| 23 | SPL | A | Weymouth | 586 | L 0-2 | | 9 | 34 |
| 26 | SPL | H | Gosport Borough | 205 | L 1-6 | Ngoyi 71 (pen) | 9 | 35 |
| Mar 2 | SPL | H | St Neots Town | 446 | L 0-1 | | 9 | 36 |
| 9 | SPL | A | Barwell | 241 | W 3-1 | Keenleyside 33 Ngoyi 72 Shaw 90 | 7 | 37 |
| 13 | SPL | A | Kettering Town | 154 | W 6-2 | Urquart 6 Comley 27 Eze 50 (og) Ngoyi 57 77  Bailey 87 | 7 | 38 |
| 16 | SPL | H | AFC Totton | 328 | W 3-0 | Ngoyi 4 Henry 16 Wadkins 57 | 7 | 39 |
| 30 | SPL | A | Stourbridge | 469 | L 1-2 | Ngoyi 86 (pen) | 8 | 40 |
| Apr 1 | SPL | H | Hemel Hempstead U | 560 | L 0-1 | | 8 | 41 |
| 6 | SPL | H | Bashley | 305 | D 2-2 | Godfrey 18 Keeleyside 62 | 9 | 42 |
| 13 | SPL | A | Chippenham Town | 342 | L 3-4 | Godfrey 30 Bruce 42  Ngoyi 45 (pen) | 10 | 43 |
| 16 | SPL | A | Bedford Town | 205 | L 0-2 | | 11 | 44 |
| 20 | SPL | H | Bedworth United | 327 | W 3-0 | Bailey 9 Henry 71 Ngoyi 90 | 11 | 45 |
| 27 | SPL | A | Leamington | 1027 | L 1-2 | Ngoyi 89 | 11 | 46 |

| GOALSCORERS | Lge | FAC | FAT | Total | Pens | Hat-tricks | Cons Run | | Lge | FAC | FAT | Total | Pens | Hat-tricks | Cons Run |
|---|---|---|---|---|---|---|---|---|---|---|---|---|---|---|---|
| Henry | 10 | 1 | | 11 | | | 2 | Martin | 1 | 1 | | 2 | | | |
| Ngoyi | 14 | | | 14 | 2 | | 4 | Seeby | 2 | | | 2 | | | 2 |
| Shields | 7 | 4 | | 11 | | 2 | | Urquart | 2 | | | 2 | | | |
| Toomey | 11 | | | 11 | 2 | | 4 | Wadkins | 2 | | | 2 | | | |
| Hayles | 6 | 2 | | 8 | 3 | | 2 | Bruce | 1 | | | 1 | | | |
| Comley | 3 | | | 3 | 1 | | | Charles | 1 | | | 1 | | | |
| Diarra | 3 | | | 3 | | 1 | | Eadie | 1 | | | 1 | | | |
| Ujah | 2 | 1 | | 3 | | | | Gray | 1 | | | 1 | | | |
| Bailey | 2 | | | 2 | | | | Ijaha | 1 | | | 1 | | | |
| Godfrey | 2 | | | 2 | | | 2 | Onieva | 1 | | | 1 | | | |
| Graham | 2 | | | 2 | | | | Shaw | 1 | | | 1 | | | |
| Hyde | 1 | 1 | | 2 | 1 | | | Taylor | 1 | | | 1 | | | |
| Keenleyside | 2 | | | 2 | | | | Own Goals | 1 | | | 1 | | | |
| | | | | | | | | Cons Run - Consecutive scoring games. | | | | | | | |

# ST. NEOTS TOWN

**Chairman:** Mike Kearns

**Secretary:** Peter Naylor    **(T)** 07702 400 205    **(E)** secretary@stneotsfc.com

**Commercial Manager:**    **(T)**

**Programme Editor:** Mark Davies    **(T)** mark@blueprwandesign.co.uk

**Ground Address:** Hunts Post Community Stadium, Cambridge Road, St Neots, PE19 6SN

**(T)** 01480 470 012      **Manager:** Iain Parr

ST NEOTS TOWN FC

## Club Factfile

**Founded:** 1879    **Nickname:** Saints

**Previous Names:** St Neots 1879-1924. St. Neots & District 1924-1951.

**Previous Leagues:** S Midlands, Cent. Alliance, UCL, Eastern Co., Hunts, United Counties > 2011.

**Club Colours (change):** All dark blue (All red)

**Ground Capacity:** 3,000    **Seats:** 250    **Covered:** 850    **Clubhouse:** Yes    **Shop:** No

**Directions**

From St Neots town centre, take the B1428 Cambridge Road, after going under the railway bridge, turn left at the first roundabout into Dramsell Rise. Follow the road up the hill to Kester Way and the ground. If approaching from Cambridge on the A428, turn right at the first roundabout as you approach St Neots onto the Cambridge Road. At the second roundabout, turn right into Dramsell Rise and follow as above. If travelling via the A1, follow signs for the A428 Cambridge. Go straight over roundabout with Tescos on left hand side, then turn left at next roundabout. Follow final instructions above as if approaching from Cambridge.

**Previous Grounds:** Rowley Park >2008.

**Record Attendance:** Att: 2,000 v Wisbech 1966

**Record Victory:** Not known

**Record Defeat:** Not known

**Record Goalscorer:** Not known

**Record Appearances:** Not known

**Additional Records:**

**Senior Honours:**
United Counties League 1967-68, 2010-11. Division One 1994-95.Southern League Division 1 Central 2011-12.
Huntingdonshire Senior Cup x36 Most recently 2012-13. Huntingdonshire Premier Cup 2001-02.

### 10 YEAR RECORD

| 03-04 | 04-05 | 05-06 | 06-07 | 07-08 | 08-09 | 09-10 | 10-11 | 11-12 | 12-13 |
|-------|-------|-------|-------|-------|-------|-------|-------|-------|-------|
| UCL P 4 | UCL P 14 | UCL P 4 | UCL P 17 | UCL P 8 | UCL P 17 | UCL P 2 | UCL P 1 | SthC 1 | SthP 12 |

# MATCH RESULTS 2012-13

| Date | Comp | H/A | Opponents | Att: | Result | Goalscorers | Pos | No. |
|------|------|-----|-----------|------|--------|-------------|-----|-----|
| Aug 18 | SPL | A | Chesham United | 354 | L 1-2 | Mackey 21 | 18 | 1 |
| 21 | SPL | H | Hitchin Town | 390 | L 2-3 | Stewart 25 61 | 20 | 2 |
| 25 | SPL | H | Weymouth | 251 | W 4-2 | Mackey 11 Moore 24 Lee 51 Hilliard 65 | 14 | 3 |
| 27 | SPL | A | Cambridge City | 514 | W 5-0 | Moore 1 MACKEY 3 ( 9 41pen 72) Jacob 53 | 10 | 4 |
| Sept 1 | SPL | H | Banbury United | 332 | W 3-2 | Moore 17 Jacob 77 79 | 7 | 5 |
| 4 | SPL | A | Bedworth United | 202 | W 3-1 | Moore 6 Gent 31 Thorne 69 | 5 | 6 |
| 8 | FAC Q1 | H | **Peterborough NS** | **342** | **W 5-0** | **Jacob 11 Adjei 45 Mackey 49 60 (pen) Moore 72** | | 7 |
| 15 | SPL | H | AFC Totton | 336 | L 1-3 | Moore 7 | 8 | 8 |
| 18 | SPL | A | Hemel Hempstead T | 246 | W 4-2 | Moore 32 Mackey 56 Hilliard 67 Jacob 75 | 7 | 9 |
| 22 | FAC Q2 | A | **Boreham Wood** | **432** | **L 1-2** | **Hilliard 75** | | 10 |
| 29 | FAT Q1 | A | **Chasetown** | **224** | **L 2-3** | **Jacob 76 Thorne 90** | | 11 |
| Oct 6 | SPL | A | Frome Town | 210 | W 2-1 | Adjei 57 Hilliard 72 | 4 | 12 |
| 9 | SPL | H | Redditch United | 290 | L 1-2 | Mackey 56 (pen) | 5 | 13 |
| 13 | SPL | A | Stourbridge | 743 | W 1-0 | Hilliard 7 | 3 | 14 |
| 20 | SPL | H | St Albans City | 518 | W 3-2 | Thorne 45 Moone 56 Jusuff 78 | 2 | 15 |
| Nov 3 | SPL | H | Bashley | 389 | D 2-2 | Jacob 21 Moore 74 | 3 | 16 |
| 10 | SPL | H | Bideford | 324 | W 5-3 | Gent 19 Duncliffe 22 Mackey 31(pen) 52 Hilliard 32 | 2 | 17 |
| 17 | SPL | A | Leamington | 707 | L 0-3 | | 3 | 18 |
| 24 | SPL | H | Barwell | 316 | D 2-2 | Moore 18 Mackey (82 pen) | 3 | 19 |
| Dec 1 | SPL | A | Arlesey Town | 267 | L 3-4 | Davis 3 Mackey 53 Hilliard 57 | 3 | 20 |
| 8 | SPL | H | Gosport Borough | 280 | L 2-3 | Mackey 3 70 (pen) | 5 | 21 |
| 15 | SPL | A | Chippenham Town | 317 | D 2-2 | Gent 68 Mackey 88 (pen) | 5 | 22 |
| 26 | SPL | A | Bedford Town | 567 | L 0-3 | | 7 | 23 |
| 29 | SPL | A | Weymouth | 701 | L 1-3 | Calver 24 | 9 | 24 |
| Jan 1 | SPL | H | Cambridge City | 627 | L 2-3 | Yusuff 12 Jacob 19 | 9 | 25 |
| 12 | SPL | H | Bedworth United | 265 | W 3-2 | Mackey 25 Hilliard 28 63 | 11 | 26 |
| 26 | SPL | A | AFC Totton | 352 | L 1-2 | Mackey 72 (pen) | 11 | 27 |
| 28 | SPL | A | Hitchin Town | 265 | D 2-2 | Mackey 45 62 | 14 | 28 |
| Feb 2 | SPL | A | Redditch United | 160 | L 0-1 | | 10 | 29 |
| 5 | SPL | H | Chesham United | 176 | W 3-1 | Jacob 18 Hoyte 52 Davis 56 | 12 | 30 |
| 9 | SPL | H | Frome Town | 268 | L 0-1 | | 12 | 31 |
| 16 | SPL | H | Leamingtrn | 434 | L 0-1 | | 14 | 32 |
| 23 | SPL | A | Bideford Town | 183 | D 0-0 | | 12 | 33 |
| 26 | SPL | H | Hemel Hempstead Town | 218 | W 6-1 | Jacob 39 54 Ogbona 50 MACKEY 3 ( 77 82 89) | 11 | 34 |
| Mar 2 | SPL | A | St Albans City | 446 | W 1-0 | Asante 90 | 11 | 35 |
| 9 | SPL | H | Stourbridge | 336 | D 0-0 | | 13 | 36 |
| 23 | SPL | H | Kettering Town | 379 | W 4-3 | Sear 59 Auger 78 Asante 88 Hilliard 90 | 11 | 37 |
| 30 | SPL | A | Banbury United | 292 | L 1-3 | Adjei 78 | 13 | 38 |
| Apr 1 | SPL | H | Bedford Town | 532 | L 1-3 | Davis 23 | 13 | 39 |
| 6 | SPL | H | Arlesey Town | 273 | L1-2 | Hilliard 18 | 13 | 40 |
| 10 | SPL | A | Kettering Town | 187 | L 0-1 | | 13 | 41 |
| 13 | SPL | A | Barwell | 193 | W 3-2 | Auger 25 Lavery 34 (og) Werndley 48 | 13 | 42 |
| 16 | SPL | A | Bashley | 114 | D 2-2 | Loudon 16 Wood 68 | 12 | 43 |
| 20 | SPL | H | Chippenham Town | 389 | L 0-1 | | 12 | 44 |
| 27 | SPL | A | Gosport Borough | 511 | L 0-1 | | 13 | 45 |

| GOALSCORERS | Lge | FAC | FAT | Total | Pens | Hat-tricks | Cons Run | | Lge | FAC | FAT | Total | Pens | Hat-tricks | Cons Run |
|-------------|-----|-----|-----|-------|------|------------|----------|--|-----|-----|-----|-------|------|------------|----------|
| Mackey | 21 | 2 | | 23 | 8 | 2 | 4 | Calver | 1 | | | 1 | | | |
| Hilliard | 10 | 1 | | 11 | | | 2 | Duncliffe | 1 | | | 1 | | | |
| Jacob | 9 | 1 | 1 | 11 | | | | Hoyte | 1 | | | 1 | | | |
| Moore | 8 | 1 | | 9 | | | 7 | Lee | 1 | | | 1 | | | |
| Davis | 3 | | | 3 | | | | Loudon | 1 | | | 1 | | | |
| Gent | 3 | | | 3 | | | | Moone | 1 | | | 1 | | | |
| Thorne | 2 | 1 | | 3 | | | | Ogbona | 1 | | | 1 | | | |
| Adjei | 2 | | | 2 | | | | Sear | 1 | | | 1 | | | |
| Asante | 2 | | | 2 | | | | Werndley | 1 | | | 1 | | | |
| Auger | 2 | | | 2 | | | | Wood | 1 | | | 1 | | | |
| Jusuff | 2 | | | 2 | | | | Own Goals | 1 | | | 1 | | | |
| Stewart | 2 | | | 2 | | | | Cons Run - Consecutive scoring games. | | | | | | | |

# STOURBRIDGE

**Chairman:** Andy Pountney
**Secretary:** Clive Eades    **(T)** 07958 275 986    **(E)** clive1974eades@gmail.com
**Commercial Manager:**    **(T)**
**Programme Editor:** Nigel Gregg    **(T)** ng004f7624@blueyonder.co.uk
**Ground Address:** War Memorial Athletic Ground, High Street, Amblecote DY8 4HN
**(T)** 01384 394 040 / 444 075      **Manager:** Gary Hackett

Stourbridge debutant Ben Mackey shoots past Weymouth keeper, Simon Evans, to score the opening goal in the first minute in their 5-0 home win. Photo: Jonathan Holloway

### Club Factfile

**Founded:** 1876    **Nickname:** The Glassboys
**Previous Names:** Stourbridge Standard 1876-87
**Previous Leagues:** West Midlands (Birmingham League) 1892-1939, 54-71, Birmingham Combination 1945-53, Southern 1971-2000

**Club Colours (change):** Red and white stripes/red/red (Yellow with green trim/green/yellow)

**Ground Capacity:** 2,000    **Seats:** 250    **Covered:** 750    **Clubhouse:** Yes    **Shop:** Yes

**Directions**
From Stourbridge Ring-Road follow signs A491 to Wolverhampton.
The ground is on the left within 300 yards immediately beyond the third traffic lights and opposite the Royal Oak public house.

**Previous Grounds:** None

**Record Attendance:** 5,726 v Cardiff City - Welsh Cup Final 1st Leg 1974
**Record Victory:** Not known
**Record Defeat:** Not known
**Record Goalscorer:** Ron Page - 269
**Record Appearances:** Ron Page - 427
**Additional Records:** Received £20,000 from Lincoln City for Tony Cunningham 1979

**Senior Honours:**
Southern League Division 1 North 1973-74, Midland Division 90-91, League Cup 92-93. Midland Alliance 2001-02, 02-03.
Worcestershire Junior Cup 1927-28. Hereford Senior Cup 1954-55. Birmingham Senior Cup x3.
Worcestershire Senior Cup x11 Most recently 2012-13.

### 10 YEAR RECORD

| 03-04 | 04-05 | 05-06 | 06-07 | 07-08 | 08-09 | 09-10 | 10-11 | 11-12 | 12-13 |
|---|---|---|---|---|---|---|---|---|---|
| MidAl 9 | MidAl 8 | MidAl 2 | SthM 7 | SthM 3 | SthP 16 | SthP 9 | SthP 8 | SthP 6 | SthP 2 |

# MATCH RESULTS 2012-13

| Date | Comp | H/A | Opponents | Att: | Result | Goalscorers | Pos | No. |
|---|---|---|---|---|---|---|---|---|
| Aug 18 | SPL | H | Arlesey Town | 175 | W 4-1 | Rock 21 Billingham 34 Geddes 74 Knight 90 | 1 | 1 |
| 21 | SPL | A | Leamington | 417 | D 1-1 | Bennett 71 | 4 | 2 |
| 25 | SPL | A | AFC Totton | 267 | W 4-2 | Dovey 23 45 Bennett 44 Rock 67 | 3 | 3 |
| 27 | SPL | H | Barwell | 448 | L 0-2 | | 5 | 4 |
| Sept 1 | SPL | A | St Albans City | 395 | W 4-2 | McCone 14 49 Broadhurst 31 Knight 80 | 3 | 5 |
| | SPL | H | Kettering | 486 | D 0-0 | | 6 | 6 |
| 8 | FAC Q2 | A | Leamington | 602 | D 2-2 | Knight 3 Geddes 72 | 6 | 7 |
| 11 | FAC Q2r | H | Leamington | 440 | L 1-0 | Billingham 3 | | 8 |
| 15 | SPL | A | Hitchin Town | 408 | W 1-0 | Benbow 80 | 3 | 9 |
| 18 | SPL | H | Banbury United | 351 | W 8-1 | Canavan 2 Geddes 20 Ashton 32 (og) | 2 | |
| | | | | | | ROCK 3 (46 76 82) McCone 58 Hendry 78 | | 10 |
| 29 | FAT Q1 | H | Ilkeston | 349 | L 0-1 | | | 11 |
| Oct 6 | SPL | H | Chesham United | 436 | W 5-0 | Benbow 14 45 Bennett 46 Billingham 73 Broadhurst 84 | 1 | 12 |
| 9 | SPL | A | Bedford Town | 224 | L 0-2 | | 1 | 13 |
| 13 | SPL | H | St Neots Town | 743 | L 0-1 | | 4 | 14 |
| 20 | SPL | A | Bideford | 207 | D 2-2 | Billingham 1 Canavan 5 | 3 | 15 |
| 27 | SPL | H | Bedworth United | 405 | L 0-1 | | 4 | 16 |
| Nov 3 | SPL | A | Weymouth | 607 | W 5-1 | Benbow 41 Geddes 46 Rock 70 Billingham 75 Evans 84 | 4 | 17 |
| 10 | SPL | H | Frome Town | 384 | D 1-1 | Billingham 51 | 4 | 18 |
| 17 | SPL | A | Hemel Hempstead | 352 | L 1-2 | Geddes 51 (pen) | 4 | 19 |
| 24 | SPL | H | Gosport Borough | 251 | D 1-1 | Benbow 56 | 4 | 20 |
| Dec 1 | SPL | A | Cambridge City | 285 | D 2-2 | Billingham 45 Benbow 58 | 4 | 21 |
| 8 | SPL | H | Chippenham Town | 317 | W 2-1 | Geddes 71 (Pen) Benbow 90 | 3 | 22 |
| 15 | SPL | A | Bashley | 182 | W 1-0 | Evans 72 | 4 | 23 |
| 26 | SPL | H | Redditch United | 512 | W 1-0 | McPike 87 | 3 | 24 |
| Jan 1 | SPL | A | Barwell | 199 | L 1-2 | Canavan 33 | 4 | 25 |
| 5 | SPL | H | Leamington | 667 | W 5-1 | Fitzpatrick 12 Billingham 20 73 Evans 35 Benbow 73 | 4 | 26 |
| 12 | SPL | A | Kettering Town | 517 | W 1-0 | Geddes 65 (pen) | 3 | 27 |
| 26 | SPL | H | Hitchin Town | 444 | W 4-1 | BENBOW 3 ( 2 54 60) Geddes 80 (pen) | 3 | 28 |
| Feb 2 | SPL | H | Bedford Town | 448 | L 0-1 | | 3 | 29 |
| 9 | SPL | A | Chesham United | 311 | D 1-1 | Spray 35 | 3 | 30 |
| 12 | SPL | H | AFC Totton | 260 | W 3-0 | BILLINGHAM 3 ( 45 70 78) | 3 | 31 |
| 16 | SPL | H | Hemel Hempstead | 664 | L 2-3 | Canavan 80 Billingham 89 | 3 | 32 |
| 23 | SPL | A | Frome Town | 183 | W 1-0 | Oliver 72 | 3 | 33 |
| Mar 2 | SPL | A | Bideford | 509 | W 3-1 | Geddes 68 (pen) Benbow 84 88 | | 34 |
| 5 | SPL | A | Banbury United | 126 | W 2-0 | Benbow 43 Bennett 79 | 3 | 35 |
| 9 | SPL | A | St Neots Town | 336 | D 0-0 | | 2 | 36 |
| 16 | SPL | H | Weymouth | 519 | W 5-0 | MACKEY 3 ( 1 8 78) Canavan 36 Billingham 90 | 2 | 37 |
| 30 | SPL | H | St Albans City | 469 | W 2-1 | Billingham 3 Benbow 47 | 3 | 38 |
| Apr 1 | SPL | A | Stourbridge | 321 | W 4-0 | Geddes 27 (pen) Benbow 33 Mackey 38 69 | 3 | 39 |
| 6 | SPL | H | Cambridge City | 363 | W 4-1 | Bennett 30 Benbow 51 Fitzpatrick 77 Geddes 84 | 2 | 40 |
| 10 | SPL | A | Bedworth United | 200 | W 3-0 | Mackey 37 89 Benbow 59 | 2 | 41 |
| 13 | SPL | A | Gosport Borough | 403 | W 3-1 | Geddes 22 Billingham 50 90 | 2 | 42 |
| 16 | SPL | A | Arlesey Town | 115 | W 4-2 | Geddes 24 Fitzpatrick 53 73 Mackey 90 | 2 | 43 |
| 20 | SPL | H | Bashley | 647 | W 3-0 | Broadhurst 40 Knight 68 Fitzpatrick 88 | 2 | 44 |
| 27 | SPL | A | Chipenham Town | 473 | L 0-4 | | 2 | 45 |
| 30 | P-Off S-F | H | Gosport Borough | 993 | L 1-2 | Bennett 27 | | 46 |

| GOALSCORERS | Lge | FAC | FAT | Total | Pens | Hat-tricks | Cons Run | | Lge | FAC | FAT | Total | Pens | Hat-tricks | Cons Run |
|---|---|---|---|---|---|---|---|---|---|---|---|---|---|---|---|
| Benbow | 18 | | | 18 | | 1 | 4 | Evans | 3 | | | 3 | | | |
| Billingham | 16 | 1 | | 17 | | 1 | 2 | McCone | 3 | | | 3 | | | |
| Geddes | 12 | 1 | | 12 | 2 | | 2 | Dovey | 2 | | | 2 | | | |
| Mackey | 8 | | | 8 | | 1 | | Hendry | 1 | | | 1 | | | |
| Bennett | 6 | | | 6 | | | 2 | McPike | 1 | | | 1 | | | |
| Rock | 6 | | | 6 | | | | Oliver | 1 | | | 1 | | | |
| Canavan | 5 | | | 5 | | | | Spray | 1 | | | 1 | | | |
| Fitzpatrick | 5 | | | 5 | | | | Own Goals | 1 | | | 1 | | | |
| Knight | 3 | 1 | | 4 | | | | Cons Run - Consecutive scoring games. | | | | | | | |
| Broadhurst | 3 | | | 3 | | | | | | | | | | | |

# TRURO CITY

**Chairman:** Peter Masters
**Secretary:** tbc      **(T)**      **(E)** info@truocityfc.net
**Commercial Manager:**      **(T)**
**Programme Editor:** Dave Deacon      **(T)** davedeacs@hotmail.com
**Ground Address:** Treyew Road, Truro, Cornwall TR1 2TH
**(T)** 01872 225 400 / 278 853 (Social Club)      **Manager:** Steve Massey

Photo: Keith Clayton.

## Club Factfile

**Founded:** 1889      **Nickname:** City, White Tigers, The Tinmen
**Previous Names:** None
**Previous Leagues:** Cornwall County, Plymouth & District, South Western, Western 2006-08, Southern 2008-11.

**Club Colours (change):** All white (Red & black stripes/red/red)

**Ground Capacity:** 3,500    **Seats:** 1,675    **Covered:** Yes    **Clubhouse:** Yes    **Shop:**

**Directions:** On arriving at Exeter, leave the M5 at junction 31 and join the A30. Travel via Okehampton, Launceston, and Bodmin.. At the end of the dual carriageway (windmills on right hand side) take left hand turning signposted Truro. After approximately 7 miles turn right at traffic lights, travel downhill crossing over three roundabouts, following signs for Redruth. Approximately 500 metres after third roundabout signed 'Arch Hill', ground is situated on left hand side.

**Previous Grounds:** None

**Record Attendance:** 1,400 v Aldershot - FA Vase
**Record Victory:** Not known
**Record Defeat:** Not known
**Record Goalscorer:** Not known
**Record Appearances:** Not known
**Additional Records:** Most League points and goals in a season:
**Senior Honours:** 115 points & 185 goals, Western League Division One (42 games) 2006-07.
South Western League 1960-61, 69-70, 92-93, 95-96, 97-98. Western League Division 1 2006-07, Premier Division 07-08.
FA Vase 2006-07. Southern League Division 1 South & West 2008-09, Premier Division 2010-11.
Cornwall Senior Cup x15

### 10 YEAR RECORD

| 03-04 | | 04-05 | | 05-06 | | 06-07 | | 07-08 | | 08-09 | | 09-10 | | 10-11 | | 11-12 | | 12-13 | |
|---|---|---|---|---|---|---|---|---|---|---|---|---|---|---|---|---|---|---|---|
| SWest | 15 | SWest | 6 | SWest | 2 | West1 | 1 | WestP | 1 | Sthsw | 1 | SthP | 11 | SthP | 1 | Conf S | 14 | Conf S | 22 |

# MATCH RESULTS 2012-13

| Date | Comp | H/A | Opponents | Att: | Result | Goalscorers | Pos | No. |
|------|------|-----|-----------|------|--------|-------------|-----|-----|
| Aug 17 | BSS | A | Billericay Town | 402 | L 1-2 | Wild 48 (og) | 20 | 1 |
| 21 | BSS | H | Havant & Waterlooville | 390 | D 3-3 | Watkins 18 50 Ash 69 (pen) | 15 | 2 |
| 25 | BSS | H | Salisbury City | 336 | D 1-1 | Moore 8 | 16 | 3 |
| 27 | BSS | A | Weston -s-Mare | 870 | W 2-0 | Moore 30 Yetton 67 | 10 | 4 |
| Sept 1 | BSS | H | Boreham Wood | 329 | W 2-0 | Yetton 27 Wlliams 54 | 5 | 5 |
| 4 | BSS | A | Basingstoke Town | 301 | L 2-3 | Yetton 38 Moore 70 | 8 | 6 |
| 8 | BSS | A | Maidenhead United | 274 | L 0-8 | | 22 | 7 |
| 15 | BSS | H | Bromley | 538 | L 0-1 | | 22 | 8 |
| 22 | FAC Q2 | H | AFC Totton | 424 | L 2-3 | Yetton 2 Williams 90 | | 9 |
| 29 | BSS | A | Chelmsford City | 820 | L 2-3 | Yetton 14 Afful 42 | 22 | 10 |
| Oct 2 | BSS | H | Bath City | 344 | W 2-1 | Yetton 30 87 | 22 | 11 |
| 23 | BSS | A | Staines Town | 271 | L 0-1 | | 22 | 12 |
| 27 | BSS | H | Sutton United | 613 | L 1-2 | Watkins 3 | 22 | 13 |
| 30 | BSS | A | Farnborough | 343 | L 1-4 | Martin 72 | 22 | 14 |
| Nov 4 | BSS | H | AFC Hornchurch | 414 | W 3-2 | Moore 45 50 Watkins 66 | 22 | 15 |
| 10 | FAT Q3 | A | Farnborough | 320 | L 2-3 | Watkins 44 Ash 90 | | 16 |
| 17 | BSS | A | Eastbourne Borough | 514 | L 0-1 | | 22 | 17 |
| Dec 1 | BSS | H | Tonbridge Angels | 346 | W 2-0 | Martin 47 (pen) Moore 89 | 22 | 18 |
| 4 | BSS | H | Dover Athletic | 279 | L 0-3 | | 22 | 19 |
| 8 | BSS | A | Boreham Wood | 200 | D 0-0 | | 22 | 20 |
| 15 | BSS | H | Maidenhead United | 384 | L 0-1 | | 22 | 21 |
| Jan 1 | BSS | A | Dorchester Town | 520 | D 2-2 | Moore 41 Ash 90 | 22 | 22 |
| 5 | BSS | A | Welling United | 508 | L 3-4 | Moore 26 32 Watkins 27 | 22 | 23 |
| 12 | BSS | H | Billericay Town | 421 | L 2-4 | Watts 56 Moore 80 | 22 | 24 |
| 15 | BSS | A | Salisbury City | 533 | L 3-4 | Hayles 45 Moore 47 Watts 69 | 22 | 25 |
| 26 | BSS | H | Chelmsford City | 421 | L 1-2 | Broad 90 | 22 | 26 |
| Feb 2 | BSS | A | Dover Athletic | 824 | L 2-3 | Cooke 55 Moore 57 | 22 | 27 |
| 9 | BSS | A | Hayes & Yeading | 495 | W 2-1 | Watkins 39 Moore 81 | 22 | 28 |
| 16 | BSS | H | Staines Town | 478 | L 0-3 | | 22 | 29 |
| 19 | BSS | A | Dorchester Town | 314 | L 1-2 | Watts 24 | 22 | 30 |
| 23 | BSS | A | Bath City | 574 | D 1-1 | Watkins 90 | 22 | 31 |
| 26 | BSS | H | Weston-s-Mare | 226 | L 1-2 | Hayles 83 | 22 | 32 |
| Mar 2 | BSS | H | Hayes & Yeading | 378 | W 3-1 | Afful 39 Watkins 58 90 | 22 | 33 |
| 9 | BSS | A | Bromley | 343 | L 0-4 | | 22 | 34 |
| 12 | BSS | A | Sutton United | 360 | W 1-0 | Watts 82 | 22 | 35 |
| 23 | BSS | H | Welling United | 448 | L 0-3 | | 22 | 36 |
| 30 | BSS | A | Havant & Waterlooville | 715 | L 0-1 | | 22 | 37 |
| Apr 1 | BSS | H | Basingstoke Town | 385 | D 2-2 | Watkins 20 Ash 63 | 22 | 38 |
| 6 | BSS | H | Eastbourne Borough | 316 | D 2-2 | Yetton 19 Hayles 82 | 22 | 39 |
| 9 | BSS | H | Eastleigh | 201 | L 1-3 | Yetton 85 | 22 | 40 |
| 13 | BSS | A | AFC Hornchurch | 282 | W 2-1 | Yetton 47 Watkins 63 | 22 | 41 |
| 20 | BSS | H | Farnborough | 384 | D 3-3 | Wright 2 4 Kendall 88 | 22 | 42 |
| 23 | BSS | A | Eastleigh | 1320 | L 1-3 | Hayles 40 | 22 | 43 |
| 27 | BSS | A | Tonbridge Angels | 582 | W 3-2 | Hayles 14 52 | 22 | 44 |

| GOALSCORERS | Lge | FAC | FAT | Total | Pens | Hat-tricks | Cons Run | | Lge | FAC | FAT | Total | Pens | Hat-tricks | Cons Run |
|-------------|-----|-----|-----|-------|------|------------|----------|---|-----|-----|-----|-------|------|------------|----------|
| Moore | 13 | | | 13 | | | 4 | Broad | 1 | | | 1 | | | |
| Watkins | 11 | | 1 | 12 | | | 2 | Cooke | 1 | | | 1 | | | |
| Yetton | 9 | 1 | | 10 | | | 3 | Kendall | 1 | | | 1 | | | |
| Hayles | 6 | | | 6 | | | | Own Goals | 1 | | | 1 | | | |
| Ash | 3 | | 1 | 4 | 1 | | | Cons Run - Consecutive scoring games. | | | | | | | |
| Watts | 4 | | | 4 | | | | | | | | | | | |
| Afful | 2 | | | 2 | | | | | | | | | | | |
| Martin | 2 | | | 2 | 1 | | | | | | | | | | |
| Williams | 1 | 1 | | 2 | | | | | | | | | | | |
| Wright | 2 | | | 2 | | | | | | | | | | | |

SOUTHERN LEAGUE PREMIER DIVISION - STEP 3

# WEYMOUTH

**Chairman:** Nigel Biddlecombe
**Secretary:** Nigel Biddlecombe    **(T)** 07880 508 240    **(E)** biddie@weymoff.com
**Commercial Manager:**    **(T)**
**Programme Editor:** Ian White    **(T)** whiteij7544@btinterneti.com
**Ground Address:** Bob Lucas Stadium, Radipole Lane, Weymouth DT4 9XJ
**(T)** 01305 785 558      **Manager:** Brendan King

2012-13 Squad.

## Club Factfile

**Founded:** 1890    **Nickname:** The Terras
**Previous Names:** None
**Previous Leagues:** Dorset, Western 1907-23, 28-49, Southern 1923-28, 49-79, 89-2005, Alliance/Conference 1979-89, 2005-10

**Club Colours (change):** All claret with sky blue trim

**Ground Capacity:** 6,600   **Seats:** 800   **Covered:** Yes   **Clubhouse:** Yes   **Shop:** Yes

**Directions**
Approach Weymouth from Dorchester on the A354.
Turn right at first roundabout onto Weymouth Way, continue to the next roundabout then turn right (signposted Football Ground).
At the next roundabout take third exit into the ground.

**Previous Grounds:** Recreation Ground > 1987.

**Record Attendance:** 4,995 v Manchester United - Ground opening 21/10/97
**Record Victory:** Not known
**Record Defeat:** Not known
**Record Goalscorer:** W 'Farmer' Haynes - 275
**Record Appearances:** Tony Hobsons - 1,076
**Additional Records:** Paid £15,000 to Northwich Victoria for Shaun Teale
Received £100,000 from Tottenham Hotspur for Peter Guthrie 1988
**Senior Honours:**
Southern League 1964-65, 65-66. Conference South 2005-06.
Dorset Senior Cup x27

### 10 YEAR RECORD

| 03-04 | | 04-05 | | 05-06 | | 06-07 | | 07-08 | | 08-09 | | 09-10 | | 10-11 | | 11-12 | | 12-13 | |
|---|---|---|---|---|---|---|---|---|---|---|---|---|---|---|---|---|---|---|---|
| SthP | 2 | Conf S | 7 | Conf S | 1 | Conf | 11 | Conf | 18 | Conf | 23 | Conf S | 22 | SthP | 18 | SthP | 17 | SthP | 9 |

## MATCH RESULTS 2012-13

| Date | Comp | H/A | Opponents | Att: | Result | Goalscorers | Pos | No. |
|------|------|-----|-----------|------|--------|-------------|-----|-----|
| Aug 18 | SPL | H | Kettering | 901 | D 0-0 | | 14 | 1 |
| 21 | SPL | A | Chippenham Town | 364 | D 2-2 | Smith 34 Walker 48 (pen) | 14 | 2 |
| 25 | SPL | A | St Neots Town | 251 | L 2-4 | Ford 62 Walker 90 (pen) | 18 | 3 |
| 27 | SPL | H | Bideford | 673 | W 4-2 | JOYCE 3 ( 26 55 60) Duff 50 | 14 | 4 |
| Sept 1 | SPL | A | Redditch United | 240 | D 0-0 | | 12 | 5 |
| 4 | SPL | H | AFC Totton | 635 | D 3-3 | Walker 25 Smith 26 73 | 11 | 6 |
| 8 | FACQ1 | A | **Totton & Eling** | 230 | D 2-2 | Joyce 11 Walker 59 | | 7 |
| 11 | FAC Q1r | H | **Totton & Eling** | 356 | W 3-0 | Feeney 23 (og) Duff 29 Joyce 30 | | 8 |
| 15 | SPL | H | Hemel Hempstead T | 607 | L 0-1 | | 14 | 9 |
| 19 | SPL | A | Frome Town | 323 | L 0-2 | | 17 | 10 |
| 22 | FAC Q2 | A | **Basingstoke Town** | 324 | L 1-3 | Joyce 17 | | 11 |
| 29 | FAT Q1 | H | **Tiverton Town** | 402 | W 3-0 | Groves 4 Smith 73 Dean 90 | | 12 |
| Oct 2 | SPL | H | Gosport Borough | 413 | D 3-3 | Palmer 58 Joyce 63 Ford 69 | 17 | 13 |
| 6 | SPL | A | Bedworth United | 204 | L 0-2 | | 18 | 14 |
| 13 | SPL | A | Banbury United | 340 | W 3-1 | Critchell 7 Joyce 34 65 | 16 | 15 |
| 20 | SPL | H | Hitchin Town | 650 | W 3-2 | FORD 3 ( 15 47 60) | 11 | 16 |
| 27 | FAT Q2 | A | **Shortwood Town** | 366 | L 1-2 | Ford 37 | | 17 |
| Nov 3 | SPL | H | Stourbridge | 607 | L 1-5 | Ford 44 | 13 | 18 |
| 10 | SPL | A | St Albans City | 457 | W 3-2 | Ford 35 84 Joyce 39 | | 19 |
| 17 | SPL | H | Cambridge City | 4513 | L 0-1 | | 15 | 20 |
| Dec 1 | SPL | A | Bedford Town | 231 | W 2-0 | Joyce 48 Duff 69 | 15 | 21 |
| 4 | SPL | A | Chesham United | 217 | W 2-1 | Duff 24 Walker 57 | 13 | 22 |
| 8 | SPL | H | Arlesey Town | 676 | W 2-1 | Joyce 4 50 | 13 | 23 |
| 15 | SPL | H | Barwell | 253 | W 1-0 | Ford 15 | 8 | 24 |
| 26 | SPL | H | Bashley | 820 | W 1-0 | Duff 34 | 6 | 25 |
| 29 | SPL | H | St Neots Town | 701 | W 3-1 | Walker 29 Ford 55 Poole 82 | 5 | 26 |
| Jan 1 | SPL | A | Bideford | 373 | L 1-2 | Smith 65 | 5 | 27 |
| 5 | SPL | H | Chipp[enham Town | 679 | D 0-0 | | 6 | 28 |
| 16 | SPL | H | Leamington | 422 | L 0-4 | | 7 | 29 |
| Feb 2 | SPL | A | Gosport Borough | 401 | D 0-0 | | 10 | 30 |
| 5 | SPL | A | AFC Totton | 329 | L 2-5 | Joyce  37 45 | 11 | 31 |
| 9 | SPL | H | Bedworth United | 512 | W 2-1 | Ford 6 20 | 9 | 32 |
| 12 | SPL | H | Frome Town | 457 | W 2-1 | Reed 29 Smith 55 (pen) | 8 | 33 |
| 16 | SPL | A | Cambridge City | 380 | L 0-2 | | 8 | 34 |
| 20 | SPL | A | Kettering Town | 187 | W 6-1 | Ford 6 22 Palmer 32 Reed 62 | 7 | 35 |
| 23 | SPL | H | St Albans City | 586 | W 2-0 | Critchell 6  Ford 15 | 5 | 36 |
| Mar 2 | SPL | A | Hitchin Town | 354 | W 2-1 | Joyce 29 Walker 53 | 6 | 37 |
| 5 | SPL | A | Hemel Hempstead T | 223 | W 3-1 | Joyce 45 Ford 48 Palmer 61 | 4 | 38 |
| 9 | SPL | H | Banbury United | 764 | W 1-0 | Palmer 87 | 4 | 39 |
| 23 | SPL | H | Chesham United | 673 | L 0-3 | | 6 | 40 |
| 30 | SPL | H | Redditch United | 651 | L 0-2 | | 6 | 41 |
| Apr 1 | SPL | A | Bashley | 304 | L 0-1 | | 7 | 42 |
| 6 | SPL | H | Bedford Town | 548 | L 0-4 | | 7 | 43 |
| 13 | SPL | A | Leamington | 891 | D 1-1 | Joyce 78 | 9 | 44 |
| 20 | SPL | H | Barwell | 685 | W 2-1 | McConnell 19 Ford 42 | 9 | 45 |
| 27 | SPL | A | Arlesey Town | 186 | L 0-3 | | 9 | 46 |

| GOALSCORERS | Lge | FAC | FAT | Total | Pens | Hat-tricks | Cons Run | | Lge | FAC | FAT | Total | Pens | Hat-tricks | Cons Run |
|-------------|-----|-----|-----|-------|------|-----------|----------|---|-----|-----|-----|-------|------|-----------|----------|
| Ford | 17 | | 1 | 18 | | 1 | 4 | Groves | 1 | | | 1 | | | |
| Joyce | 15 | 3 | | 18 | | 1 | 2 | McConnell | 1 | | | 1 | | | |
| Walker | 6 | 1 | | 7 | 2 | | 2 | Poole | 1 | | | 1 | | | |
| Duff | 4 | 1 | | 5 | | | 2 | Cons Run - Consecutive scoring games. | | | | | | | |
| Smith | 5 | | 1 | 6 | 1 | | | | | | | | | | |
| Palmer | 4 | | | 4 | | | | | | | | | | | |
| McCone | 3 | | | 3 | | | | | | | | | | | |
| Critchell | 2 | | | 2 | | | | | | | | | | | |
| Reed | 2 | | | 2 | | | | | | | | | | | |
| Dean | 1 | | | 1 | | | | | | | | | | | |

# AFC HAYES

**Chairman:** Barry Stone
**Secretary:** Barry Crump          **(T)**                    **(E)** afchayesfootballsec@hotmail.co.uk
**Commercial Manager:**                    **(T)**
**Programme Editor:** Graham White          **(T)** grassrootspublications@btconnect.com
**Ground Address:** Farm Park, Kingshill Avenue, Hayes UB4 8DD
**(T)** 020 8845 0110                    **Manager:** Ian Crane

## Club Factfile

**Founded:** 1974      **Nickname:** The Brook
**Previous Names:** Brook House > 2007.
**Previous Leagues:** Spartan South Midlands, Isthmian

**Club Colours (change):** Blue and white stripes/blue/blue (Yellow & black stripes/black/yellow)

**Ground Capacity:** 2,000   **Seats:** 150   **Covered:** 200   **Clubhouse:** Yes   **Shop:** No

**Directions**
From the A40 McDonalds Target roundabout take A312 south towards Hayes.
At White Hart roundabout take third exit into Yeading Lane.
Turn right at first traffic lights into Kingshill Avenue.
Ground approx one miles on the right-hand side.

**Previous Grounds:** None

**Record Attendance:** Not known
**Record Victory:** Not known
**Record Defeat:** Not known
**Record Goalscorer:** Not known
**Record Appearances:** Not known
**Additional Records:**

**Senior Honours:**
Spartan South Midlands Premier South 1997-98, Premier Cup 1999-2000, Challenge Trophy 2003-04.
Isthmian Associate Members Trophy 2005-06.
Middlesex Senior Cup 2008-09.

### 10 YEAR RECORD

| 03-04 | 04-05 | 05-06 | 06-07 | 07-08 | 08-09 | 09-10 | 10-11 | 11-12 | 12-13 |
|---|---|---|---|---|---|---|---|---|---|
| IsltP ~8 | ConfS 12 | GonfS 20 | ConfS 20 | Sthsw 14 | Sthsw 9 | Sthsw 21 | SthC 19 | SthC 10 | SthC 15 |

SSMP 2 ISN 2 3 isN 2 3 STN SW 18

---

# DOWNLOAD THE DIRECTORY FOR FREE!

The Non-League Club Directory is also avaialble as a download on the platforms listed to the right. As a reader of the Directory we'd like to offer you the chance to sample it for FREE until the season ends.

Including all that's in the this paperback edition, the download will have the added benefit of being updated as the season progresses. Including photos, previews and reports the Directory will grow as the season goes on.

If you would like to take us up on this offer please send your request for a FREE subsription to tw.publications@btinternet.com
Please quote: NLD14APP

# ASHFORD TOWN (MIDDLESEX)

**Chairman:** Dave Baker

**Secretary:** Geoff Knock  **(T)** 07928 101 876  **(E)** football.secretary@atmfc.co.uk

**Commercial Manager:**  **(T)**

**Programme Editor:** Phil Marshall  **(T)** club.manager@atmfc.co.uk

**Ground Address:** Robert Parker Stadium, Stanwell, Staines TW19 7BH

**(T)** 01784 245 908  **Manager:** Paul Burgess

## Club Factfile

**Founded:** 1958  **Nickname:** Ash Trees

**Previous Names:** Ashford Albion 1958-64.

**Previous Leagues:** Hounslow & District 1964-68, Surrey Intermediate 1968-82, Surrey Premier 1982-90, Combined Counties 1990-2000, Isthmian 2000-04, 06-10, Southern 2004-06

**Club Colours (change):** Tangerine and white stripes/black/tangerine (Blue/white/blue)

**Ground Capacity:** 2,550  **Seats:** 250  **Covered:** 250  **Clubhouse:** Yes  **Shop:** No

**Directions:** M25 junction 13, A30 towards London, third left at footbridge after Ashford Hospital crossroads, ground sign posted after 1/4 mile on the right down Short Lane, two miles from Ashford (BR) and Hatton Cross tube station.

**Previous Grounds:** Clockhouse Lane Recreation 1958-85.

**Record Attendance:** 992 v AFC Wimbledon - Isthmian League Premier Division 26/09/2006

**Record Victory:** Not known

**Record Defeat:** Not known

**Record Goalscorer:** Andy Smith

**Record Appearances:** Alan Constable - 650

**Additional Records:** Received £10,000 from Wycombe Wanderers for Dannie Bulman 1997

**Senior Honours:**
Surrey Premier League 1982-90. Combined Counties League 1994-95, 95-96, 96-97, 97-98.
Middlesex Charity Cup 2000-01. Middlesex Premier Cup 2006-07. Isthmian League Cup 2006-07.

### 10 YEAR RECORD

| 03-04 | | 04-05 | | 05-06 | | 06-07 | | 07-08 | | 08-09 | | 09-10 | | 10-11 | | 11-12 | | 12-13 | |
|---|---|---|---|---|---|---|---|---|---|---|---|---|---|---|---|---|---|---|---|
| Isth1S | 12 | SthW | 6 | SthW | 2 | Isth P | 17 | Isth P | 6 | Isth P | 10 | Isth P | 20 | SthC | 16 | SthC | 9 | SthC | 10 |

# AYLESBURY

**Chairman:** Danny Martone
**Secretary:** Ian Brown          **(T)** 07947 338 462     **(E)** brownzola@aol.com
**Commercial Manager:** Grahame Faulconbridge  **(T)**
**Programme Editor:** Christine Martone       **(T)** martone040@hotmail.com
**Ground Address:** Haywood Way, Aylesbury, Bucks. HP19 9WZ
**(T)** 01296 421 101                              **Manager:** Craig Faulconbridge

Photo: Keith Clayton.

## Club Factfile

**Founded:**  1930     **Nickname:** The Moles
**Previous Names:** Negretti & Zambra FC 1930-54, Stocklake 1954-2000, Haywood United > 2000, Haywood FC 2000-06, Aylesbury Vale 2006-09.
**Previous Leagues:** Aylesbury District. Wycombe & District. Chiltern, Spartan South Midlands

**Club Colours (change):** Red with black trim/black/red (Silver & white/red/red)

**Ground Capacity:**       **Seats:** Yes     **Covered:** Yes     **Clubhouse:** Yes   **Shop:** No

**Directions:** When entering Aylesbury from all major routes, join the ring road and follow signposts for A41 Bicester and Waddesdon. leave the ring road at the roundabout by the Texaco Garage and Perry dealership. From the Texaco Garage cross straight over four roundabouts. At the fifth roundabout with the Cotton Wheel Pub on the right hand side, turn right into Jackson Road. Take the second left into Haywood Way, club is at the bottom of the road. If entering Aylesbury from Bicester (A41), turn left into Jackson Road by the Cotton Wheel Pub, and then second left into Haywood Way.

**Previous Grounds:** Negretti & Zambra King's Cross 1930-49. Stocklake Industrial Estate 1949-87.

**Record Attendance:** Not known
**Record Victory:** Not known
**Record Defeat:** Not known
**Record Goalscorer:** Not known
**Record Appearances:** Not known
**Additional Records:** Not known

**Senior Honours:**
Spartan South Midlands League Division 1 2003-04, Premier Division 2009-10.
Wycombe Senior Cup 1994-95.

## 10 YEAR RECORD

| 03-04 | | 04-05 | | 05-06 | | 06-07 | | 07-08 | | 08-09 | | 09-10 | | 10-11 | | 11-12 | | 12-13 | |
|---|---|---|---|---|---|---|---|---|---|---|---|---|---|---|---|---|---|---|---|
| SSM1 | 1 | SSM P | 3 | SSM P | 5 | SSM P | 5 | SSM P | 9 | SSM P | 15 | SSM P | 1 | SthC | 8 | SthC | 20 | SthC | 12 |

# AYLESBURY UNITED

**Chairman:** Graham Read
**Secretary:** Steve Baker    **(T)** 07768 353 265    **(E)** stevepb42@hotmail.com
**Commercial Manager:**    **(T)**
**Programme Editor:** Steve Baker    **(T)** stevepb42@hotmail.com
**Ground Address:** Leighton Town FC, Lake Street, Leighton Buzzard, Beds LU7 1RX
**(T)** 01296 487 367 (Office)      **Manager:** Tony Joyce

2012-13 Squad - Back row (L-R): Steve Baker (Secretary), Vicky Baker (Physiotherapist), Gary Hawksworth (Assistant Manager), Craig Preston, Sam Slatter, Joey Acheampong, Joe Donaldson, Steve Hatch, Jack Sillitoe, John Mulholland, Ben Baines, Michael Korpala, Stacey Field, Ron Schmidt (Kit Man), Graham Read (Chairman). Front row: Russell Clark, Ian Cooper, Paul Edgeworth, Craig Townsend, Tony Joyce (Manager), Jack Wood, Warren Garcia, Lee Bircham, Tom Barnett.

## Club Factfile

**Founded:** 1897    **Nickname:** The Ducks
**Previous Names:** None
**Previous Leagues:** Post War: Spartan >1951, Delphian 51-63, Athenian 63-76, Southern 76-88, 2004-10, Conf. 88-89, Isthmian 89-2004. Spartan South Midlands 2010-13.

**Club Colours (change):** Green & white/white/white (Orange/black/black)

**Ground Capacity:** 2,800   **Seats:** 155    **Covered:** 300    **Clubhouse:** Yes   **Shop:** No

**Directions:** From Aylesbury: Take the A418 towards Leighton Buzzard and at the bypass turn right onto the A505. Go straight over the first two roundabouts; then turn left at the third onto the A4146. Stay on the A4146 at the next two roundabouts (second exit, first exit), then carry straight on at the next mini-roundabout. The entrance to the ground is about 50 yards after this mini-roundabout on the left. Car parking is on your left as you turn. Travel from the Midlands using the M1: Leave the M1 at junction 15 and take the A508 towards Milton Keynes. After 9 miles you will reach the A5 roundabout. Take the first exit and travel about 8 miles to the roundabout at the end of the dual carriageway. Take the second exit and follow the A5 towards Dunstable. After about 3 miles you will arrive at another roundabout (Flying Fox pub is on your left) take the third exit towards Heath & Reach and Leighton Buzzard. Follow this road for about 4 miles until you arrive at a large roundabout in Leighton Buzzard then take the first exit. At the next roundabout take the second exit, you will then go through 2 sets of lights. The ground and car park is on the right, immediately after the lights and opposite a petrol station.

**Previous Grounds:** Turnfurlong Lane. Buckingham Road >2006

**Record Attendance:** Turnfurlong Lane - 7,440 v Watford FAC 1st Rnd 1951-52. Buckingham Road - 6,031 v England 04/06/1988.
**Record Victory:** 10-0 v Hornchurch & Upminster (H), Delphain League 17/04/1954
**Record Defeat:** 0-9 v Bishop's Stortford (A), Delphian League 08/10/1955
**Record Goalscorer:** Cliff Hercules - 301 (1984-2002)
**Record Appearances:** Cliff Hercules - 651+18 (1984-2002)
**Additional Records:**

**Senior Honours:**
Southern League 1987-88. Berks & Bucks Senior Cup x5 2012-13. Isthmian Cup 1994-95.

### 10 YEAR RECORD

| 03-04 | | 04-05 | | 05-06 | | 06-07 | | 07-08 | | 08-09 | | 09-10 | | 10-11 | | 11-12 | | 12-13 | |
|---|---|---|---|---|---|---|---|---|---|---|---|---|---|---|---|---|---|---|---|
| Isth P | 24 | SthP | 10 | SthP | 21 | SthM | 6 | SthM | 8 | SthM | 10 | SthM | 22 | SSM P | 6 | SSM P | 4 | SSM P | 2 |

# BARTON ROVERS

**Chairman:** Darren Whiley
**Secretary:** Iain Rennie      **(T)**          **(E)**
**Commercial Manager:**            **(T)**
**Programme Editor:** Kev King      **(T)** programme@bartonrovers.com
**Ground Address:** Sharpenhoe Road, Barton-le-Clay, Bedford MK45 4SD
**(T)** 01582 707 772          **Manager:** Dan Kennoy

Back Row (L-R): Keith West, Dan Kennoy, Dave Parkinson, Luke Rowland, Andrew Iwediuno, Geoff Baffo, Nick Gardner, Richard Wilmot, Kyle Forster, James Ferguson, Nat Peacock, Colm Kierans, Adam Fisher, Annmarie Novis, Chris Wing.

Front Row: Ricky Case, Rhys Hoenes, Danny Payne, James Bent, Tommy Hull, Phil Smeaton, Niran Vaughan, Ashley Grinham, Jermaine Hall.

## Club Factfile

**Founded:** 1898     **Nickname:** Rovers
**Previous Names:** None
**Previous Leagues:** Luton & district 1947-54, South Midlands 1954-79, Isthmian 1979-2004

**Club Colours (change):** Royal blue with white trim/royal blue/royal blue with white bands (Yellow with black trim/black/yellow)

**Ground Capacity:** 4,000   **Seats:** 160    **Covered:** 1,120    **Clubhouse:** Yes   **Shop:** Yes

**Directions**

Leave M1 at J12 head towards Harlington.
Follow signs through Sharpenhoe Village to Barton.
At T-junction in village turn right, continue 500 yards and turn right into ground on concrete roadway adjacent to playing fields.

**Previous Grounds:** None

**Record Attendance:** 1,900 v Nuneaton Borough - FA Cup 4th Qualifying Round 1976
**Record Victory:** Not known
**Record Defeat:** Not known
**Record Goalscorer:** Richard Camp - 152 (1989-98)
**Record Appearances:** Tony McNally - 598 (1988-2005)
**Additional Records:** Paid £1,000 to Hitchin Town for B. Baldry 1980
**Senior Honours:** Received £1,000 from Bishop's Stortford for B. Baldry 1981
South Midlands League 1970-71, 71-72, 72-73, 74-75, 75-76, 76-77.
Bedfordshire Senior Cup 1971-72, 72-73, 80-81, 81-82, 89-90, 97-98, 98-99. Bedfordshire Premier Cup 1995-96.

### 10 YEAR RECORD

| 03-04 | 04-05 | 05-06 | 06-07 | 07-08 | 08-09 | 09-10 | 10-11 | 11-12 | 12-13 |
|---|---|---|---|---|---|---|---|---|---|
| Isth1N 18 | SthE 8 | SthE 19 | SthM 20 | SthM 11 | SthM 17 | SthM 21 | SthC 12 | SthC 11 | SthC 14 |

# BEACONSFIELD SYCOB

**Chairman:** Fred Deanus (Chief Exec.)
**Secretary:** Robin Woolman      **(T)**      **(E)** robin.woolman@btinternet.com
**Commercial Manager:** Paul Hughes, Paul      **(T)**
**Programme Editor:** Karl McKenzie      **(T)** karlmckenzie1@hotmail.co.uk
**Ground Address:** Holloways Park, Windsor Road, Beaconsfield, Bucks HP9 2SE
**(T)** 01494 676 868      **Manager:** James Pritchard

## Club Factfile

**Founded:** 1994      **Nickname:** The Rams
**Previous Names:** Slough YCOB and Beaconsfield United merged in 1994
**Previous Leagues:** Spartan South Midlands 1004-2004, 07-08, Southern 2004-07

**Club Colours (change):** Red and white quarters/white with red trim/red and white (Yellow with blue trim/blue/yellow & blue)

| Ground Capacity: | Seats: | Covered: | Clubhouse: Yes | Shop: |
|---|---|---|---|---|

**Directions**

Leave Junction 2 of M40, take A355 towards Slough, 50 yards off roundabout turn left and at next roundabout turn complete right, coming back towards A355 to continue across A355, then turn right and 150 yards on left is sign to club. Go through gate and clubhouse is 200 yards on right.

**Previous Grounds:** None

**Record Attendance:** Not known
**Record Victory:** Not known
**Record Defeat:** Not known
**Record Goalscorer:** Allan Arthur
**Record Appearances:** Allan Arthur
**Additional Records:**

**Senior Honours:**
Spartan South Midlands 2000-01, 03-04, 07-08. Berks and Bucks Senior Trophy 2003-04

### 10 YEAR RECORD

| 03-04 | | 04-05 | | 05-06 | | 06-07 | | 07-08 | | 08-09 | | 09-10 | | 10-11 | | 11-12 | | 12-13 | |
|---|---|---|---|---|---|---|---|---|---|---|---|---|---|---|---|---|---|---|---|
| SSM P | 1 | SthE | 14 | SthW | 13 | Sthsw | 22 | SSM P | 1 | Sthsw | 4 | SthM | 19 | SthC | 22 | SthC | 5 | SthC | 5 |

# CHALFONT ST PETER

**Chairman:** Dennis Mair

**Secretary:** John Carroll       **(T)** 07950 981 008       **(E)** jc.chalfontfc@fsmail.net

**Commercial Manager:** Charlotte Mair       **(T)** 01753 885 797

**Programme Editor:** Ian Doorbar       **(T)** 07985 943 395

**Ground Address:** Mill Meadow, Gravel Hill, Amersham Road, Chalfont St Peter  SL9 9QX

**(T)** 01753  886 477       **Manager:** Danny Edwards

## Club Factfile

**Founded:** 1926       **Nickname:** Saints

**Previous Names:** None

**Previous Leagues:** G W Comb. Parthernon. London. Spartan. L Spartan. Athenian. Isthmian, Spartan South Midlands 2006-11.

**Club Colours (change):** Red/green/red. (All yellow).

**Ground Capacity:** 4,500   **Seats:** 220   **Covered:** 120   **Clubhouse:** Yes   **Shop:** Yes

**Directions**
Follow A413 (Amersham Road).
The ground is adjacent to the Chalfont Community Centre off Gravel Hill which is part of the A413.
Players and officials can park inside the ground.
The A413 is the Denham to Aylesbury road.

**Previous Grounds:** None

**Record Attendance: Att:** 2,550 v Watford benefit match 1985   **App:** Colin Davies

**Record Victory:** Not known

**Record Defeat:** Not known

**Record Goalscorer:** Not known

**Record Appearances:** Not known

**Additional Records:**

**Senior Honours:**
Isthmian Lge Div 2 87-88, Berks & Bucks Intermediate Cup 52-53.
Spartan South Midlands Premier Division 2010-11.

### 10 YEAR RECORD

| 03-04 | | 04-05 | | 05-06 | | 06-07 | | 07-08 | | 08-09 | | 09-10 | | 10-11 | | 11-12 | | 12-13 | |
|---|---|---|---|---|---|---|---|---|---|---|---|---|---|---|---|---|---|---|---|
| Isth2 | 14 | Isth2 | 11 | Isth2 | 8 | SSM P | 6 | SSM P | 2 | SSM P | 3 | SSM P | 2 | SSM P | 1 | SthC | 12 | SthC | 16 |

# CHERTSEY TOWN

**Chairman:** Steve Powers
**Secretary:** Chris Gay          **(T)** 07713 473 313     **(E)** chrisegay@googlemail.com
**Commercial Manager:** Sue Powers, Wendy     **(T)**
**Programme Editor:** Chris Gay                    **(T)** chrisegay@googlemail.com
**Ground Address:** Alwyns Lane, Chertsey, Surrey KT16 9DW
**(T)** 01932 561 774                    **Manager:** David Johnston

2012-2013 Squad - Back Row L-R: Matt Holley, Rob Carrick, Alex Fostick, Lewis Fostick, Gavin Quintyre, Kai Francis, Jordan Kennedy, Michael Blount, Dave Melling, Matt Morris, Matt Powell, John Pomroy, Dayo Oshitola. Front Row: Matt Brunt, Jermiele Johnson, Justin Gray, Neil Woodyer, David Johnston, Chris Payne, Tom McGarry, Rob Carr.

## Club Factfile

**Founded:** 1890      **Nickname:** Curfews
**Previous Names:** None
**Previous Leagues:** Metropolitan. Spartan. Athenian. Isthmian, Combined Counties 2006-11.

**Club Colours (change):** Royal blue & white stripes/royal blue/royal blue (All red)

**Ground Capacity:** 3,000   **Seats:** 240    **Covered:** 760    **Clubhouse:** Yes   **Shop:** Yes

**Directions:** Leave M25 at junction 11, East on St. Peters Way (A317). Left at roundabout in Chertsey Road (A317). Left into Eastworth Road (A317). Straight on into Chilsey Green Road (A320), 3rd exit on roundabout (towards Staines) (A320). 1st right after car showrooms into St. Ann's Road (B375). Right at Coach & Horses in Grove Road (residential). Alwyns Lane is very narrow and not suitable for large motor coaches.

**Previous Grounds:**

**Record Attendance: Att:** 2150 v Aldershot Town, Isthmian Div.2 04/12/93. **Goals:** Alan Brown (54) 1962-63.
**Record Victory:** Not known
**Record Defeat:** Not known
**Record Goalscorer:** Not known
**Record Appearances:** Not known
**Additional Records:**

**Senior Honours:**
Surrey Senior Champions 1959, 61, 62. Isthmian League Cup 1994.

## 10 YEAR RECORD

| 03-04 | | 04-05 | | 05-06 | | 06-07 | | 07-08 | | 08-09 | | 09-10 | | 10-11 | | 11-12 | | 12-13 | |
|---|---|---|---|---|---|---|---|---|---|---|---|---|---|---|---|---|---|---|---|
| Isth2 | 4 | Isth2 | 6 | Isth2 | 6 | CCP | 8 | CCP | 8 | CCP | 3 | CCP | 2 | CCP | 2 | SthC | 17 | SthC | 20 |

# DAVENTRY TOWN

**Chairman:** Iain Humphrey
**Secretary:** Nigel Foster     **(T)** 07454 521 773     **(E)** dtfcsecretary@sky.com
**Commercial Manager:** Jim Davis     **(T)**
**Programme Editor:** Nigel Foster     **(T)** 07454 521 773
**Ground Address:** Communications Park, Browns Road, Daventry, Northants NN11 4NS
**(T)** 01327 311 239        **Manager:** Darran Foster

2012-13 Squad.

## Club Factfile

**Founded:** 1886     **Nickname:** The Town
**Previous Names:** Not known
**Previous Leagues:** Northampton Town (pre-1987), Central Northways Comb 1987-89, United Counties 1989-2010.

**Club Colours (change):** Purple/white/purple (White/purple/white)

**Ground Capacity:** 2,000   **Seats:** 250    **Covered:** 250    **Clubhouse:** Yes   **Shop:**

**Directions**
From Northampton or J.16 of the M1, follow A45 westbound into Daventry, crossing the A5 on the way.
At first roundabout bear left along A45 Daventry Bypass.
At next roundabout go straight over onto Browns Road.
The Club is at the top of this road on the left.

**Previous Grounds:** Not known

**Record Attendance:** 850 v Utrecht (Holland) - 1989
**Record Victory:** Not known
**Record Defeat:** Not known
**Record Goalscorer:** Not known
**Record Appearances:** Not known
**Additional Records:**

**Senior Honours:**
United Counties League Division 1 1989-90, 90-91, 2000-01, 2007-08, Premier Division 2009-10.

### 10 YEAR RECORD

| 03-04 | 04-05 | 05-06 | 06-07 | 07-08 | 08-09 | 09-10 | 10-11 | 11-12 | 12-13 |
|-------|-------|-------|-------|-------|-------|-------|-------|-------|-------|
| UCL P | UCL P | UCL P | UCL P | UCL 1   1 | UCL P   7 | UCL P   1 | SthC   2 | SthC   16 | SthC   8 |

# DUNSTABLE TOWN

**Chairman:** Roger Dance

**Secretary:** Malcolm Aubrey  **(T)**     **(E)** malcolm.aubrey@openreach.co.uk

**Commercial Manager:** Robin Head  **(T)**

**Programme Editor:** Paul Harris  **(T)** hpauljharris@aol.com

**Ground Address:** Creasey Park Stadium, Brewers Hill Rd, Dunstable LU6 1BB

**(T)** 07798 716 263     **Manager:** Darren Croft & Paul Reeves

Celebrations after clinching the Spartan South Midlands title.
Photo: Gordon Whittington.

## Club Factfile

**Founded:** 1883   **Nickname:** The Blues

**Previous Names:** Dunstable Town 1883-1976. Dunstable FC 1976-98.

**Previous Leagues:** Metropolitan & District 1950-61, 64-65. United Counties 1961-63. Southern 1965-76, 2004-09.
Spartan South Midlands 1998-2003, 09-13. Isthmian 2003-04.

**Club Colours (change):** Blue & white (Red & white)

**Ground Capacity:** 3,500   **Seats:** 350   **Covered:** 1000   **Clubhouse:** Yes   **Shop:** Yes

**Directions**

From the south: When travelling on the A5, go straight across the lights in the centre of Dunstable. Turn left at the next main set of lights into Brewers Hill Road. You will immediately pass the Fire Station on your left. Carry on until you hit the first roundabout, Go over the roundabout and take the immediate right into Creasey Park Drive. From the north: When travelling south on the A5, go through the chalk cutting and over the first set of traffic lights. At the next set of lights, turn right into Brewers Hill Road. Then proceed as above. From the East: Turn right at the traffic lights in the centre of Dunstable. Turn left at the next main set of traffic lights into Brewers Hill Road. Then proceed as above. From the east: When coming into Dunstable, go straight across the first roundabout you come to. Then turn left at the double mini-roundabout into Drovers Way. Follow this road for about 1/2 mile as it bears to the right and becomes Brewers Hill Road. Go over two mini-roundabouts and just before you hit the larger roundabout, turn left into Creasey Park Drive.

**Previous Grounds:** Kingsway 1950-58.

**Record Attendance:** 10,000 (approx) v Manchester United, friendly, July 1974

**Record Victory:** 12-0 v Welwyn Garden City, Spartan South Midlands League 2009-10.

**Record Defeat:** 0-13 v Arsenal, Metropolitan League

**Record Goalscorer:** Not known

**Record Appearances:** Not known

**Additional Records:** Received £25,000 from Reading for Kerry Dixon 1980.

**Senior Honours:**
Spartan South Midlands Division One 1999-00, Premier 2002-03, 12-13.
Bedfordshire Senior Cup 1895–96, 1956–57, 59–60, 79–80, 82–83, 85–86, 86–87, 87–88, 88–89, 2002–03, 06–07, 08–09.
Bedfordshire Premier Cup 1980–81, 82–83, 90–91, 2006–07, 11-12.

### 10 YEAR RECORD

| 03-04 | | 04-05 | | 05-06 | | 06-07 | | 07-08 | | 08-09 | | 09-10 | | 10-11 | | 11-12 | | 12-13 | |
|---|---|---|---|---|---|---|---|---|---|---|---|---|---|---|---|---|---|---|---|
| Isth1N | 5 | SthP | 20 | SthW | 21 | SthM | 11 | SthM | 13 | SthM | 21 | SSM P | 7 | SSM P | 7 | SSM P | 2 | SSM P | 1 |

# EGHAM TOWN

**Chairman:** Patrick Bennett

**Secretary:** Daniel Bennett   **(T)** 07932 612 424   **(E)** sales@beautiful-bathrooms.co.uk

**Commercial Manager:**   **(T)**

**Programme Editor:** Stephen Bennett   **(T)** patonofwalton@btconnect.com

**Ground Address:** Runnymead Stadium, Tempest Road, Egham TW20 8XD

**(T)** 01784 435 226 or 01784 437055   **Manager:** Lee Passmore

## Club Factfile

**Founded:** 1877   **Nickname:** Sarnies
**Previous Names:** Runnymead Rovers 1877-1905. Egham F.C. 05-63.
**Previous Leagues:** Spartan. Athenian. Isthmian. Southern. Combined Counties 2006-13.

**Club Colours (change):** Red & white (Green & black)

**Ground Capacity:** 5500   **Seats:** 262   **Covered:** 3300   **Clubhouse:** Yes   **Shop:** No

**Directions**
From M25 - J13 - Take the A30, heading south. The road runs parallel with the M25 briefly, and sweeps round a sharp left hand bend, under the M25. Stay right, down to the r'about in front of you just the other side of the M25. Go round the r'about and back under the M25.This road is called The Causeway. Carry on down this road, over the small r'about at Sainsbury's and at the bigger r'about turn right (signposted B3376 - Thorpe, Chertsey, Woking). Proceed down Thorpe Rd, over a level crossing, to a mini r'about, go over, and on the left, after the green turn into Pond Road. Left into Wards Place then first right and you will see the entrance to the football ground.

**Previous Grounds:** Moved to Recreation Ground - now Runnymead Stadium - in 1963.

**Record Attendance:** 1400 v Wycombe Wanderers, FAC 2nd Qual. 1972-73.
**Record Victory:** Not known
**Record Defeat:** Not known
**Record Goalscorer:** Mark Butler (153).
**Record Appearances:** Dave Jones (850+).
**Additional Records:**

**Senior Honours:**
Spartan League Champions 1971-72. Athenian League Division 2 Champions.
Combined Counties League 2012-13.

### 10 YEAR RECORD

| 03-04 | | 04-05 | | 05-06 | | 06-07 | | 07-08 | | 08-09 | | 09-10 | | 10-11 | | 11-12 | | 12-13 | |
|---|---|---|---|---|---|---|---|---|---|---|---|---|---|---|---|---|---|---|---|
| Isth1S | 22 | SthW | 22 | Isth2 | 5 | CCP | 10 | CCP | 12 | CCP | 13 | CCP | 4 | CCP | 13 | CCP | 4 | CCP | 1 |

# KETTERING TOWN

**Chairman:** Imraan Ladak

**Secretary:** Bob Brown     **(T)**     **(E)** info@ketteringtownfc.co.uk

**Commercial Manager:**     **(T)**

**Programme Editor:** Paul Cooke     **(T)** companioncooke@btinternet.com

**Ground Address:** Latimer Park, Burton Latimer, Kettering NN15 5PS

**(T)** 01536 217 006     **Manager:** Dean Thomas

## Club Factfile

**Founded:** 1872     **Nickname:** The Poppies

**Previous Names:** Kettering > 1924

**Previous Leagues:** Midland 1892-1900, also had a team in United Counties 1896-99, Southern 1900-30, 1950-79, 2001-02, Birmingham 1930-50, Alliance/Conference 1979-2001, 02-03, Isthmian 2003-04

**Club Colours (change):** Red & black (Blue & white)

**Ground Capacity:**     **Seats:** Yes     **Covered:** Yes     **Clubhouse:** Yes     **Shop:**

**Directions:** From Junction 10 of the A14 turn due South at the roundabout onto Kettering Road (signposted Burton Latimer). After 200 yards turn right at the roundabout onto Attendiez Way. Go over the next roundabout and follow the road around Morrison's warehouse. The road becomes Polwell Lane and the entrance to Latimer Park is on the left just after Morrison's warehouse.
If approaching from the South, take the A6 to its junction with the A14 and follow the directions above or, if travelling up the A509 turn right at the roundabout just after Isham (signposted Burton Latimer) onto Station Road and continue for half a mile past the Weetabix and Alumasc factories before turning left onto Polwell Lane. The entrance to Latimer Park is on the right after 50 yards.

**Previous Grounds:** North Park, Green Lane, Rockingham Road > 2011. Nene Park 2011-13.

**Record Attendance:** 11,536 v Peterborough - FA Cup 1st Round replay 1958-59

**Record Victory:** 16-0 v Higham YMCI - FA Cup 1909

**Record Defeat:** 0-13 v Mardy - Southern League Division Two 1911-12

**Record Goalscorer:** Roy Clayton - 171 (1972-81)

**Record Appearances:** Roger Ashby

**Additional Records:** Paid £25,000 to Macclesfield for Carl Alford 1994. Recieved £150,000 from Newcastle United for Andy Hunt

**Senior Honours:**

Southern League 1927-28, 56-57, 72-73, 2001-02. Conference North 2007-08.

### 10 YEAR RECORD

| 03-04 | | 04-05 | | 05-06 | | 06-07 | | 07-08 | | 08-09 | | 09-10 | | 10-11 | | 11-12 | | 12-13 | |
|---|---|---|---|---|---|---|---|---|---|---|---|---|---|---|---|---|---|---|---|
| Isth P | 9 | Conf N | 4 | Conf N | 6 | Conf N | 2 | Conf N | 1 | Conf | 8 | Conf | 6 | Conf | 14 | Conf | 24 | SthP | 22 |

# LEIGHTON TOWN

**Chairman:** Terry McCafferty
**Secretary:** (T) (E)
**Commercial Manager:** (T)
**Programme Editor:** Andrew Parker (T) andrewparker-leightontownnfc@virginmedia.com
**Ground Address:** Lake Street, Leighton Buzzard, Beds LU7 1RX
**(T)** 01525 373 311 **Manager:** Danny Greany

James Gray (Leighton) opens the scoring against MK Dons while Antony Kay looks on during this pre-season friendly. Photo: Keith Clayton.

## Club Factfile

**Founded:** 1885 **Nickname:** Reds
**Previous Names:** Leighton United 1922-63
**Previous Leagues:** Leighton & District, South Midlands 1922-24, 26-29, 46-54, 55-56, 76-92, Spartan 1922-53, 67-74, United Counties 1974-76, Isthmian

**Club Colours (change):** Red & white (Yellow & blue)

**Ground Capacity:** 2,800 **Seats:** 155 **Covered:** 300 **Clubhouse:** Yes **Shop:** No

**Directions:** Ground is situated just south of Town Centre on the A4146 Leighton Buzzard to Hemel Hemstead Road. Entrance to car park and ground is opposite Morrisons Supermarket Petrol Station. 1/2 mile south of town centre.

**Previous Grounds:** Wayside

**Record Attendance:** 1,522 v Aldershot Town - Isthmian League Division 3 30/01/1993
**Record Victory:** v Met Railway (H) - Spartan League 1925-26
**Record Defeat:** 0-12 v Headington United (A) - Spartan League 18/10/1947
**Record Goalscorer:** Not known
**Record Appearances:** Not known
**Additional Records:**

**Senior Honours:**
South Midlands League 1966-67, 91-92. Isthmian League Division 2 2003-04.
Bedfordshire Senior Cup 1926-27, 67-68, 69-70, 92-93.

### 10 YEAR RECORD

| 03-04 | | 04-05 | | 05-06 | | 06-07 | | 07-08 | | 08-09 | | 09-10 | | 10-11 | | 11-12 | | 12-13 | |
|-------|---|-------|----|-------|---|-------|----|-------|---|-------|---|-------|----|-------|---|-------|----|-------|----|
| Isth2 | 1 | SthE | 10 | SthW | 8 | SthM | 18 | SthM | 9 | SthM | 8 | SthM | 10 | SthC | 7 | SthC | 13 | SthC | 21 |

# MARLOW

**Chairman:** Terry Staines
**Secretary:** Paul Burdell  **(T)** 07961 145 949  **(E)** marlow.fc@virgin.net
**Commercial Manager:**  **(T)**
**Programme Editor:** Terry Staines  **(T)** terry.staines@ntlworld.com
**Ground Address:** Alfred Davies Memorial Ground, Oak tree Road, Marlow SL7 3ED
**(T)** 01628 483 970  **Manager:** Mark Bartley

Celebrations after lifting the Hellenic League title.

## Club Factfile

**Founded:** 1870  **Nickname:** The Blues
**Previous Names:** Great Marlow
**Previous Leagues:** Reading & District, Spartan 1908-10, 28-65, Gt Western Suburban, Athenian 1965-84, Isthmian 1984-2004. Southern 2004-12. Hellenic 2012-13.

**Club Colours (change):** All royal blue (All red)

**Ground Capacity:** 3,000  **Seats:** 250  **Covered:** 600  **Clubhouse:** Yes  **Shop:**

**Directions** From M40 (Junction 4 High Wycombe) or M4 (Junction 8/9 Maidenhead) take A404, leave at the A4155 junction signposted Marlow. Follow A4155 towards Marlow then turn right at Esso service station into Maple Rise.
At crossroads follow straight ahead into Oak Tree Road.
Ground 100 yards on left.

**Previous Grounds:** Crown ground 1870-1919, Star Meadow 1919-24

**Record Attendance:** 3,000 v Oxford United - FA Cup 1st Round 1994
**Record Victory:** Not known
**Record Defeat:** Not known
**Record Goalscorer:** Kevin Stone
**Record Appearances:** Mick McKeown - 500+
**Additional Records:** Paid £5,000 to Sutton United for Richard Evans
**Senior Honours:** Received £8,000 from Slough Town for David Lay
Isthmian League Division 1 1987-88, League Cup 92-93. Hellenic League Premier Division 2012-13.
Berks & Bucks Senior Cup x11

### 10 YEAR RECORD

| 03-04 | | 04-05 | | 05-06 | | 06-07 | | 07-08 | | 08-09 | | 09-10 | | 10-11 | | 11-12 | | 12-13 | |
|---|---|---|---|---|---|---|---|---|---|---|---|---|---|---|---|---|---|---|---|
| Isth1S | 16 | SthW | 13 | SthW | 6 | Sthsw | 7 | Sthsw | 9 | SthM | 9 | SthM | 15 | SthC | 11 | SthC | 22 | Hel P | 1 |

# NORTH GREENFORD UNITED

**Chairman:** John Bivens
**Secretary:** Mrs Barbara Bivens　**(T)** 07915 661 580　**(E)** barbarabivens@talktalk.net
**Commercial Manager:**　　　　　　　　　　　**(T)**
**Programme Editor:** Graham Wither　　　　**(T)** grassrootspublications@btconnect.com
**Ground Address:** Berkeley Fields, Berkley Avenue, Greenford UB6 0NX
**(T)** 0208 422 8923　　　　　　　　　**Manager:** Jon-Barrie Bates

## Club Factfile

**Founded:** 1944　　**Nickname:** Blues
**Previous Names:** None
**Previous Leagues:** London Spartan, Combined Counties 2002-10

**Club Colours (change):** Royal blue & white (Yellow & red)

**Ground Capacity:** 2,000　**Seats:** 150　**Covered:** 100　**Clubhouse:** Yes　**Shop:** No

**Directions:** A40 going towards London. At the Greenford Flyover come down the slip road, keep in the left hand lane, turn left onto the Greenford Road (A4127). At the third set of traffic lights, turn right into Berkeley Av. Go to the bottom of the road. There is a large car park. We are on the right hand side.

**Previous Grounds:**

**Record Attendance:** 985 v AFC Wimbledon
**Record Victory:** Not known
**Record Defeat:** Not known
**Record Goalscorer:** John Hill - 98
**Record Appearances:** Not known
**Additional Records:**

**Senior Honours:**
Combined Counties League Premier Division 2009-10

### 10 YEAR RECORD

| 03-04 | | 04-05 | | 05-06 | | 06-07 | | 07-08 | | 08-09 | | 09-10 | | 10-11 | | 11-12 | | 12-13 | |
|---|---|---|---|---|---|---|---|---|---|---|---|---|---|---|---|---|---|---|---|
| CCP | 14 | CCP | 2 | CCP | 13 | CCP | 5 | CCP | 6 | CCP | 2 | CCP | 1 | SthC | 20 | SthC | 18 | SthC | 19 |

# NORTHWOOD

**Chairman:** Ian Barry
**Secretary:** Alan Evans      **(T)** 07960 744 349      **(E)** alan.evansnfc@btopenworld.com
**Commercial Manager:**      **(T)**
**Programme Editor:** Ken Green      **(T)** ken.green01@ntlworld.com
**Ground Address:** Northwood Park, Chestnut Avenue, Northwood, Middlesex HA6 1HR
**(T)** 01923 827 148      **Manager:** Mark Burgess

April 2013

## Club Factfile

**Founded:** 1926      **Nickname:** Woods
**Previous Names:** Northwood United 1926-1945.
**Previous Leagues:** Harrow & Wembley 1932-69, Middlesex 1969-78, Hellenic 1979-84, London Spartan 1984-93,
Isthmian 1993-2005, 2007-10, Southern 2005-07

**Club Colours (change):** All red (Yellow & blue)

**Ground Capacity:** 3,075      **Seats:** 308      **Covered:** 932      **Clubhouse:** Yes      **Shop:** No

**Directions:** M25 Junction 18, take A404 through Rickmansworth to Northwood. After passing under grey railway bridge, take first right into Chestnut Avenue. Ground is in grounds of Northwood Park, entrance is 400 metres on left. (Ground is 20 minutes from J.18).

**Previous Grounds:** Northwood Recreation Ground 1926-1928. Northwood Playing Fields 1928-1971.

**Record Attendance:** 1,642 v Chlesea - Friendly July 1997
**Record Victory:** 15-0 v Dateline (H) - Middlesex Intermediate Cup 1973
**Record Defeat:** 0-8 v Bedfont - Middlesex League 1975
**Record Goalscorer:** Not known
**Record Appearances:** Chris Gell - 493+
**Additional Records:** Lawrence Yaku scored 61 goals during season 1999-2000

**Senior Honours:**
Isthmian League Division 1 North 2002-03, Charity Shield 2002.
Middlesex Premier Cup 1994-95.

### 10 YEAR RECORD

| 03-04 | 04-05 | 05-06 | 06-07 | 07-08 | 08-09 | 09-10 | 10-11 | 11-12 | 12-13 |
|---|---|---|---|---|---|---|---|---|---|
| Isth P    21 | Isth P    17 | SthP    19 | SthP    22 | Isth1N    10 | Isth1N    6 | Isth1N    10 | SthC    20 | SthC    7 | SthC    13 |

# POTTERS BAR TOWN

**Chairman:** Peter Waller

**Secretary:** Alan Evans    **(T)** 0783 363 2965    **(E)** potters_bar_sec@hotmail.co.uk

**Commercial Manager:** Jeff Barnes    **(T)** 07785 765 793

**Programme Editor:** Jeff Barnes    **(T)** jeff@jeffbarnes.co.uk

**Ground Address:** Pakex Stadium, Parkfield, Watkins Rise, Potters Bar EN6 1QN

**(T)** 01707 654 833    **Manager:** Adam Lee

Photo: Alan Coomes.

## Club Factfile

**Founded:** 1960    **Nickname:** Grace or Scholars

**Previous Names:** None

**Previous Leagues:** Barnet & District 1960-65, North London Combination 1965-68, Herts Senior County 1968-91, Spartan South Midlands 1991-2005, Southern 2005-06. Isthmian 2006-13.

**Club Colours (change):** Maroon/white/white (All yellow)

---

**Ground Capacity:** 2,000    **Seats:** 150    **Covered:** 250    **Clubhouse:** Yes    **Shop:** Yes

**Directions:** M25 junction 24 enter Potters Bar along Southgate Road (A111) turn right into High Street at first lights (A1000) then left into The Walk after half a mile. Ground is 200 yards on the right - opposite Potters Bar Cricket Club.

**Previous Grounds:** None

---

**Record Attendance:** 268 v Wealdstone - FA Cup 1998 (4,000 watched a charity match in 1997)

**Record Victory:** Not known

**Record Defeat:** Not known

**Record Goalscorer:** Not known

**Record Appearances:** Not known

**Additional Records:**

**Senior Honours:**
Spartan South Midlands League Premier 1996-97, 2004-05.

### 10 YEAR RECORD

| 03-04 | 04-05 | 05-06 | 06-07 | 07-08 | 08-09 | 09-10 | 10-11 | 11-12 | 12-13 |
|---|---|---|---|---|---|---|---|---|---|
| SSM P 4 | SSM P 1 | SthE 15 | Isth1N 14 | Isth1N 17 | Isth1N 19 | Isth1N 14 | Isth1N 13 | Isth1N 12 | Isth1N 10 |

# ROYSTON TOWN

**Chairman:** Steve Jackson
**Secretary:** Terry McKinnell    **(T)** 07772 086 709    **(E)** terry.mckinnell@talktalk.net
**Commercial Manager:**    **(T)**
**Programme Editor:** Kelly Taylor    **(T)** info@abaconsultants.com
**Ground Address:** Garden Walk, Royston, Herts, SG8 7HP
**(T)** 01763 241 204    **Manager:** Paul Attfield

2012-13 Squad.

## Club Factfile

**Founded:** 1872    **Nickname:** Crows
**Previous Names:** None
**Previous Leagues:** Cambridgeshire & Herts Co. Isthmian

**Club Colours (change):** White & black (Red & white)

**Ground Capacity:**    **Seats:** Yes    **Covered:** Yes    **Clubhouse:** Yes    **Shop:**

**Directions**
From A505 (Town Bypass) take A10 towards town centre (signposted London).
Go straight on at next roundabout.
Garden Walk is on the left after the 3rd set of pedestrian lights (opposite Catholic Church).
Entrance to ground is approx 75 metres on left.

**Previous Grounds:** Royston Heath, Mackerell Hall and Newmarket Road before acquiring Garden Walk in 1931.

**Record Attendance:** Att: 876 v Aldershot Town, 1993-94.
**Record Victory:**
**Record Defeat:**
**Record Goalscorer:**
**Record Appearances:**
**Additional Records:**
**Senior Honours:**
Herts County Champions 1976-77. South Midlands Div.1 1978-79, 2008-09, Premier Division 2011-12.

### 10 YEAR RECORD

| 03-04 | | 04-05 | | 05-06 | | 06-07 | | 07-08 | | 08-09 | | 09-10 | | 10-11 | | 11-12 | | 12-13 | |
|-------|---|-------|---|-------|---|-------|---|------|---|------|---|-------|---|-------|---|-------|---|------|---|
| SSM P | 13 | SSM P | 16 | SSM P | 18 | SSM P | 20 | SSM1 | 5 | SSM1 | 1 | SSM P | 4 | SSM P | 3 | SSM P | 1 | SthC | 7 |

# RUGBY TOWN

**Chairman:** Brian Melvin
**Secretary:** Doug Wilkins **(T)** 07976 284 614 **(E)** dougwilkins44@hotmail.com
**Commercial Manager:** **(T)**
**Programme Editor:** Neil Melvin **(T)** neil@melbros.com
**Ground Address:** Butlin Road, Rugby, Warwicks CV21 3SD
**(T)** 01788 844 806 **Manager:** Dave Stringer

## Club Factfile

**Founded:** 1956 **Nickname:** The Valley

**Previous Names:** Valley Sports 1956-71, Valley Sport Rugby 1971-73, VS Rugby 1973-2000, Rugby United 2000-05

**Previous Leagues:** Rugby & District 1956-62, Coventry & Partnership, North Warwickshire 1963-69, United Counties 1969-75
West Midlands 1975-83

**Club Colours (change):** Sky blue & white (All maroon)

**Ground Capacity:** 6,000 **Seats:** 750 **Covered:** 1,000 **Clubhouse:** Yes **Shop:** Yes

**Directions**
From M6 J.1 North and South, take A426 signed Rugby at third island turn left into Boughton Road.
Continue along Boughton Road after passing under viaduct turn right at traffic lights, B5414 up the hill take second left at mini island into Butlin Road.

**Previous Grounds:** None

**Record Attendance:** 3,961 v Northampton Town - FA Cup 1984
**Record Victory:** 10-0 v Ilkeston Town - FA Trophy 04/09/1985
**Record Defeat:** 1-11 v Ilkeston Town (A) - 18/04/1998
**Record Goalscorer:** Danny Conway - 124
**Record Appearances:** Danny Conway - 374
**Additional Records:** Paid £3,500 for R Smith, I Crawley and G Bradder
**Senior Honours:** Received £15,000 from Northampton Town for Terry Angus
FA Vase 1982-83. Southern League Midland Division 1986-87. Midland Combination Division 1 2001-02.
Birmingham Senior Cup 1988-89, 91-92

## 10 YEAR RECORD

| 03-04 | 04-05 | 05-06 | 06-07 | 07-08 | 08-09 | 09-10 | 10-11 | 11-12 | 12-13 |
|---|---|---|---|---|---|---|---|---|---|
| MCmP 3 | | SthP 15 | SthP 17 | SthP 15 | SthP 17 | SthP 22 | SthC 6 | SthC 6 | SthC 2 |

# ST. IVES TOWN

**Chairman:** Paul Reason & Sheldon Francis
**Secretary:** Simon Clark     **(T)** 07884 398 770     **(E)** simon.clark@stivestownfc.co.uk
**Commercial Manager:** Mark Taylor     **(T)**
**Programme Editor:** Simon Clark     **(T)** 07884 398 770
**Ground Address:** Westwood Road, St. Ives PE27 6WU
**(T)** 01480 463 207     **Manager:** Warren Everdell & Jez Hall

2012-13 Squad - Back Row (l-r): Richard Philps, Junior McDougald, Dan Newman, Jon Gull, Arron Last, Niall Conroy-Owen, Lee Ellison, Ozie Foster, Scott Fielding, Jamie Alsop, Guy Last, Dun Ruscillo, Errol McCammon.
Front Row (l-r): David Cobb, Matt Bannister, Morgan Phillips, Warren Everdell, Jez Hall, Stuart Cobb, James Hall, Scott Everdell, Grant Robbins.

## Club Factfile

**Founded:** 1887     **Nickname:** Saints
**Previous Names:** None
**Previous Leagues:** Cambridgeshire, Central Amateur, Hunts, Peterborough & District. United Counties > 2013.

**Club Colours (change):** White & black (All yellow)

**Ground Capacity:**     **Seats:** Yes     **Covered:** Yes     **Clubhouse:** Yes    **Shop:** No

**Directions:** From A1123 Houghton Road rurn right at traffic lights into Ramsey Road. After Fire Station turn right into Westwood Road. Ground at end of road on right hand side immediately before St Ivo Recreation Centre Car Park.

**Previous Grounds:** Meadow Lane.

**Record Attendance:** 767 v Needham Market, FA Vase 5th Rnd 2007-08. 801 v Cambridge United, pre-season friendly, 2009-10.
**Record Victory:**
**Record Defeat:**
**Record Goalscorer:**
**Record Appearances:**
**Additional Records:**

**Senior Honours:**
Hunts Senior Cup 1900/01, 1911/12, 1922/23, 1925/26, 1929/30, 1981/82, 1986/87, 1987/88, 2006/07, 2008/09, 2011-12. Hunts Premier Cup 2006-07, 2008/09. United Counties League Cup 2009-10.

### 10 YEAR RECORD

| 03-04 | | 04-05 | | 05-06 | | 06-07 | | 07-08 | | 08-09 | | 09-10 | | 10-11 | | 11-12 | | 12-13 | |
|---|---|---|---|---|---|---|---|---|---|---|---|---|---|---|---|---|---|---|---|
| UCL 1 | 10 | UCL 1 | 3 | UCL P | 9 | UCL P | 10 | UCL P | 5 | UCL P | 6 | UCL P | 10 | UCL P | 11 | UCL P | 3 | UCL P | 2 |

# SLOUGH TOWN

**Chairman:** Steve Easterbrook
**Secretary:** Kath Lathey     **(T)** 07792 126 124     **(E)** gensec@sloughtownfc.net
**Commercial Manager:**     **(T)**
**Programme Editor:** Glen Riley     **(T)** programme@sloughtownfc.net
**Ground Address:** Sharing with Beaconsfield SYCOB, Holloways Park, Slough Rd HP9 2SG
**(T)** 01494 676 868     **Manager:** Neil Baker & Jon Underwood

## Club Factfile

**Founded:** 1890     **Nickname:** The Rebels
**Previous Names:** None
**Previous Leagues:** Southern Alliance 1892-93, Berks & Bucks 1901-05, Gt Western Suburban 1909-19, Spartan 1920-39, Herts & Middx 1940-45, Corinthian 1946-63, Athenian 1963-73, Isthmian 1973-90, 94-95, Conf. 1990-94

**Club Colours (change):** Amber/navy blue/amber (All green)

**Ground Capacity:** 3,500    **Seats:** 200    **Covered:** Yes    **Clubhouse:** Yes    **Shop:** Yes

**Directions:** Leave M40 at Junction 2, take A355 towards Slough, only 50 yards off the roundabout on the A355 is slip road on right with sign giving Club name. Turn right through gate and clubhouse is 200 metres on the right. The ground is 'signposted' from both sides of the carriageway (A355).

**Previous Grounds:**

**Record Attendance:** 8,000 v Liverpool - Schoolboys 1976
**Record Victory:** 17-0 v Railway Clearing House - 1921-22
**Record Defeat:** 1-11 v Chesham Town - 1909-10
**Record Goalscorer:** Tony Norris - 84 (1925-26)
**Record Appearances:** Terry Reardon - 458 (1964-81)
**Additional Records:** Paid £18,000 to Farnborough Town for Colin Fielder
**Senior Honours:** Received £22,000 from Wycombe Wanderers for Steve Thompson
Isthmian League 1980-81, 89-90. Athenian League x3. Berks & Bucks Senior Cup x10.

### 10 YEAR RECORD

| 03-04 | 04-05 | 05-06 | 06-07 | 07-08 | 08-09 | 09-10 | 10-11 | 11-12 | 12-13 |
|---|---|---|---|---|---|---|---|---|---|
| Isth1S 4 | Isth P 13 | Isth P 17 | Isth P 22 | Sthsw 21 | Sthsw 16 | SthM 5 | SthC 5 | SthC 2 | SthC 6 |

# UXBRIDGE

**Chairman:** Alan Holloway
**Secretary:** Roger Stevens    **(T)** 01895 236 879    **(E)** sec@uxbridgefc.co.uk
**Commercial Manager:** Colin Evans    **(T)** 07505 140 788
**Programme Editor:** Sharon Madigan    **(T)** program.editor@uxbridgefc.co.uk
**Ground Address:** Honeycroft Road, West Drayton, Middlesex UB7 8HX
**(T)** 01895 443 557    **Manager:** Tony Choules

Back Row: Karis Baker (Ass't Physio), Gary Mills (Chief Scout), Patrick Lynott, Gavin Brown, Max Howell, Damian Panter, Mark Dennison, John Peacock
Matthew Elston-Bull, Nicke Kabamba, Tyrone Rowe-McKenzie, Jake Jenkins, Stuart Farrell, Daniel Julienne, Scott Everley (Ass't Physio), Stuart Everley (Club Physio)
Front Row: Danny Tilbury, Shaun Lucien, Andrew Capewell, Mark Smith, Paul Mill (1st Team Ass't Manager) Tony Choules (Club Manager)
Wayne Carter (Captain) Kevin Warner, Matt Woods, Chris Moore

2012-13 Squad.

## Club Factfile

**Founded:** 1871      **Nickname:** The Reds
**Previous Names:** Uxbridge Town 1923-45
**Previous Leagues:** Southern 1894-99, Gt Western Suburban 1906-19, 20-23, Athenian 1919-20, 24-37, 63-82, Spartan 1937-38, London 1938-46, Gt Western Comb. 1939-45, Corinthian 1946-63, Isthmian

**Club Colours (change):** Red/white/red (Sky blue/navy/navy)

**Ground Capacity:** 3,770   **Seats:** 339    **Covered:** 760    **Clubhouse:** Yes    **Shop:**

**Directions:** M4 to Junction 4 (Heathrow), take A408 towards Uxbridge for 1 mile, turn left into Horton Road. Ground 1/2 mile on right.

**Previous Grounds:** RAF Stadium 1923-48, Cleveland Road 1948-78

**Record Attendance:** 1,000 v Arsenal - Opening of the floodlights 1981
**Record Victory:** Not known
**Record Defeat:** Not known
**Record Goalscorer:** Phil Duff - 153
**Record Appearances:** Roger Nicholls - 1,054
**Additional Records:**

**Senior Honours:**
Middlesex Senior Cup 1893-94, 95-96, 1950-51, 2000-01. London Challenge Cup 1993-94, 96-97, 98-99.

### 10 YEAR RECORD

| 03-04 | | 04-05 | | 05-06 | | 06-07 | | 07-08 | | 08-09 | | 09-10 | | 10-11 | | 11-12 | | 12-13 | |
|---|---|---|---|---|---|---|---|---|---|---|---|---|---|---|---|---|---|---|---|
| Isth1N | 13 | SthE | 4 | SthE | 14 | Sthsw | 8 | Sthsw | 5 | Sthsw | 13 | Sthsw | 15 | SthC | 13 | SthC | 4 | SthC | 11 |

# BISHOP'S CLEEVE

**Chairman:** David Walker
**Secretary:** Nigel Green  (T) 07919 518 880  (E) negreen@tiscali.co.uk
**Commercial Manager:**  (T)
**Programme Editor:** Nigel Green  (T) nigelgreen@bishopscleeve.com
**Ground Address:** Kayte Lane, Bishop's Cleeve, Cheltenham GL52 3PD
(T) 01242 676 166  **Manager:** Alex Sykes

2012-13 Squad - Back Row L-R; Sam Avery, Ryan Clarke, Louie Barnfather, Iain Sercombe, James Nortei, Alex Hoyle, Sam O'Neil
Middle Row L-R; Alice Wood (Physio), Jon Crowford, Mike Davis, Stuart Midwinter, Jake Lee, Mike Tambling, Lamin Sankoh, Dean Ackland (Coach)
Front Row L-R; Will Gayton, Lee Davis, Matt Rose (Asst. Manager), Michael Jackson (Capt), Alex Sykes (Manager), Adam Mace, Carl Brown

## Club Factfile

**Founded:** 1892  **Nickname:** Villagers
**Previous Names:**
**Previous Leagues:** Cheltenham, North Gloucestershire, Hellenic 1983-2006

**Club Colours (change):** Green, black & white (Blue & white)

**Ground Capacity:** 1,500  **Seats:** 50  **Covered:** 50  **Clubhouse:** Yes  **Shop:** Yes

**Directions:** From Cheltenham take A435 towards Evesham.
Pass racecourse, take right at traffic lights then first left into Kayte Lane.
Ground 1/2 mile on left.

**Previous Grounds:** Stoke Road and ground shared with Moreton Town, Wollen Sports, Highworth Town and Forest Green Rovers

**Record Attendance:** 1,300 v Cheltenham Town - July 2006
**Record Victory:** Not known
**Record Defeat:** Not known
**Record Goalscorer:** Kevin Slack
**Record Appearances:** John Skeen
**Additional Records:**

**Senior Honours:**
Hellenic League Division 1 1986-87, Premier League Cup 1988.
Gloucestershire Junior Cup North. Gloucestershire Senior Amateur Cup North x3.

### 10 YEAR RECORD

| 03-04 | 04-05 | 05-06 | 06-07 | 07-08 | 08-09 | 09-10 | 10-11 | 11-12 | 12-13 |
|---|---|---|---|---|---|---|---|---|---|
| Hel P 3 | Hel P 3 | Hel P 2 | SthM 13 | SthM 12 | Sthsw 18 | Sthsw 11 | Sthsw 15 | Sthsw 11 | Sthsw 21 |

# BRIDGWATER TOWN 1984

**Chairman:** Alan Hurford
**Secretary:** Roger Palmer     **(T)** 07587 775 227     **(E)** palmer449@btinternet.com
**Commercial Manager:**               **(T)**
**Programme Editor:** Roger Palmer       **(T)** palmer449@btinternet.com
**Ground Address:** Fairfax Park, College Way, Bath Road, Bridgwater, Somerset TA6 4TZ
**(T)** 01278 446 899               **Manager:** Richard Fey

## Club Factfile

**Founded:** 1984     **Nickname:** The Robins
**Previous Names:** Bridgwater Town
**Previous Leagues:** Somerset Senior, Western

**Club Colours (change):** Red, white & black (Yellow & blue)

**Ground Capacity:** 2,500   **Seats:** 128    **Covered:** 500     **Clubhouse:** Yes    **Shop:** Yes

**Directions:** Southbound from Bristol M5 J.23- enter town on A39 from Glastonbury. Ground is between Bridgwater College and Rugby Ground by railway bridge.
Northbound from Taunton – M5 J.24- enter town on A38, follow signs for Glastonbury (A39). Ground is between Bridgwater College and Rugby Ground as you pass over railway bridge.

**Previous Grounds:** None

**Record Attendance:** 1,112 v Taunton Town - 26/02/1997
**Record Victory:** Not Known
**Record Defeat:** Not Known
**Record Goalscorer:** Not Known
**Record Appearances:** Not Known
**Additional Records:**

**Senior Honours:**
Somerset Senior League x3. Somerset Senior Cup 1993-94, 95-96. Western League Division 1 1995-96.

### 10 YEAR RECORD

| 03-04 | | 04-05 | | 05-06 | | 06-07 | | 07-08 | | 08-09 | | 09-10 | | 10-11 | | 11-12 | | 12-13 | |
|---|---|---|---|---|---|---|---|---|---|---|---|---|---|---|---|---|---|---|---|
| WestP | 6 | WestP | 6 | WestP | 11 | WestP | 2 | Sthsw | 6 | Sthsw | 7 | Sthsw | 3 | Sthsw | 18 | Sthsw | 15 | Sthsw | 19 |

# CINDERFORD TOWN

**Chairman:** Ashley Saunders

**Secretary:** Robert Maskell    **(T)** 07835 511 774    **(E)** maskellbilly@yahoo.co.uk

**Commercial Manager:**    **(T)**

**Programme Editor:** Liam Maskell    **(T)** liam.maskell@gmail.com

**Ground Address:** The Causeway, Hildene, Cinderford, Gloucestershire GL14 2QH

**(T)** 01594 827 147 / 822 039    **Manager:** Steve Peters

Cinderford Town's Greg Lewis is denied a goal by Shortwood United's James Coates.
Photo: Peter Barnes

## Club Factfile

**Founded:** 1922    **Nickname:** The Foresters

**Previous Names:** None

**Previous Leagues:** Gloucestershire Northern Senior 1922-39, 60-62, Western 1946-59, Warwickshire Combination 1963-64, West Midlands 1965-69, Gloucestershire Co. 1970-73, 85-89, Midland Comb. 1974-84, Hellenic 1990-95

**Club Colours (change):** White & black (All yellow)

**Ground Capacity:** 3,500    **Seats:** 250    **Covered:** 1,000    **Clubhouse:** Yes    **Shop:** Yes

**Directions** Take A40 west out of Gloucester, then A48 for 8 miles. Turn right at Elton Garage onto A4151 (Forest of Dean). Continue through Littledean, climb steep hill, turn right at crossroads (football ground), then second left into Latimer Road. Or if coming from Severn Bridge take A48 Chepstow through Lydney, Newnham then left at Elton Garage – then as above.

**Previous Grounds:** Mousel Lane, Royal Oak

**Record Attendance:** 4,850 v Minehead - Western League 1955-56

**Record Victory:** 13-0 v Cam Mills - 1938-39

**Record Defeat:** 0-10 v Sutton Coldfield - 1978-79

**Record Goalscorer:** Not known

**Record Appearances:** Russel Bowles - 528

**Additional Records:**

**Senior Honours:**
Western League Division 2 1956-57. Midland Combination 1981-82. Hellenic Premier Division 1994-95, League Cup 94-95.
Gloucestershire Senior Amateur Cup North x6. Gloucestershire Junior Cup North 1980-81.
Gloucestershire Senior Cup 2000-01.

### 10 YEAR RECORD

| 03-04 | 04-05 | 05-06 | 06-07 | 07-08 | 08-09 | 09-10 | 10-11 | 11-12 | 12-13 |
|---|---|---|---|---|---|---|---|---|---|
| SthW 20 | SthW 16 | SthW 15 | SthM 9 | SthM 16 | SthM 11 | Sthsw 16 | Sthsw 12 | Sthsw 10 | Sthsw 10 |

# CIRENCESTER TOWN

**CIRENCESTER TOWN**
FOOTBALL CLUB

**Chairman:** Stephen Abbley
**Secretary:** Scott Griffin      **(T)** 01285 654543      **(E)** scott.griffin@cirentownfc.plus.com
**Commercial Manager:**                        **(T)**
**Programme Editor:** Scott Griffin            **(T)** scott.griffin@cirentownfc.plus.com
**Ground Address:** The Corinium Stadium, Kingshill Lane, Cirencester GL7 1HS
**(T)** 01285 654 543                          **Manager:** Brian Hughes

Cirencester 'keeper, Glyn Garner, gathers the ball safely against Poole Town.
Photo: Peter Barnes.

## Club Factfile

**Founded:** 1889      **Nickname:** Centurions
**Previous Names:** None
**Previous Leagues:** Hellenic

**Club Colours (change):** Red & black (Orange & white)

**Ground Capacity:** 4,500   **Seats:** 550   **Covered:** 1,250   **Clubhouse:** Yes   **Shop:** Yes

**Directions**
Leave bypass at Burford Road roundabout.
Aim for Stow, turn right at traffic lights, then right again at next junction, first left into Kingshill Lane.
Ground 500 yards on right.

**Previous Grounds:** Smithfield Stadium

**Record Attendance:** 2,600 v Fareham Town - 1969
**Record Victory:** Not known
**Record Defeat:** Not known
**Record Goalscorer:** Not known
**Record Appearances:** Not known
**Additional Records:** Paid £4,000 to Gloucester City for Lee Smith

**Senior Honours:**
Hellenic League Premier Division 1995-96.
Gloucestershire Senior Amateur Cup 1989-90. Gloucestershire County Cup 1995-96.

### 10 YEAR RECORD

| 03-04 | | 04-05 | | 05-06 | | 06-07 | | 07-08 | | 08-09 | | 09-10 | | 10-11 | | 11-12 | | 12-13 | |
|---|---|---|---|---|---|---|---|---|---|---|---|---|---|---|---|---|---|---|---|
| SthW | 3 | SthP | 7 | SthP | 18 | SthP | 21 | Sthsw | 14 | Sthsw | 5 | SthP | 13 | SthP | 22 | Sthsw | 11 | | |

# CLEVEDON TOWN

**Chairman:** Steve Spicer

**Secretary:** Brian Rose     **(T)** 07768 100 632     **(E)** brian.rose@blueyonder.co.uk

**Commercial Manager:**     **(T)**

**Programme Editor:** Dave Wright     **(T)** smallwavedave@hotmail.com

**Ground Address:** Hand Stadium, Davis Lane, Clevedon BS21 6TG

**(T)** 01275 871 600        **Manager:** Micky Bell

2012-13 Squad - Back row (left to right) John Roberts (Kit Manager), Jack McKenna, Curtis Jack, Cameron Ricketts, Steve Kingdon, Lee Matthews,
Ben Murray, Aaron Robbins, Jordan Walker, Jonny Moss, Adie Adams, Jenny Moore (Physio).
Front row (left to right) Bawan Hussain, Jack Flurry, Alex Russell, Paul McLoughlin (Coach), Steve Spicer (Chairman),
Micky Bell (Manager), Matt Fisher, Adam Mahdi, Reeko Best.

## Club Factfile

**Founded:** 1880     **Nickname:** Seasiders

**Previous Names:** Clevedon FC and Ashtonians merged in 1974

**Previous Leagues:** Weston & District, Somerset Senior, Bristol Charity, Bristol & District, Bristol Suburban, Western 1974-93

**Club Colours (change):** Burgandy & blue (Blue & white)

**Ground Capacity:** 3,500   **Seats:** 300    **Covered:** 1,600    **Clubhouse:** Yes    **Shop:** Yes

**Directions**
Exit J20 from M5, at bottom of slip road, turn left at roundabout into Central Way.
At next roundabout turn left to Kenn Road.
Stay on Kenn Road out of town, cross river, take 1st left into Davis Lane, over motorway.
Ground 200m on right.

**Previous Grounds:** Dial Hill until early 1890s, Teignmouth Road > 1991

**Record Attendance:** 2,300 v Billingham Synthonia - FA Amateur Cup 1952-53

**Record Victory:** 18-0 v Dawlish Town (H) - Western League Premier Division 24/04/1993

**Record Defeat:** 3-13 v Yate YMCA (A) - Bristol Combination 1967-68

**Record Goalscorer:** Not known

**Record Appearances:** Not known

**Additional Records:**

**Senior Honours:**
Somerset Senior Cup 1901-02, 04-05, 28-29, 2000-01, 01-02. Somerset Premier Cup x4.
Southern League Western Division 1992-93, 2005-06, Midland Division 1998-99.

### 10 YEAR RECORD

| 03-04 | | 04-05 | | 05-06 | | 06-07 | | 07-08 | | 08-09 | | 09-10 | | 10-11 | | 11-12 | | 12-13 | |
|---|---|---|---|---|---|---|---|---|---|---|---|---|---|---|---|---|---|---|---|
| SthW | 11 | SthW | 4 | SthW | 1 | SthP | 18 | SthP | 11 | SthP | 18 | SthP | 21 | Sthsw | 20 | Sthsw | 20 | Sthsw | 15 |

# DIDCOT TOWN

**Chairman:** John Bailey
**Secretary:** Pat Horsman    **(T)** 07882 154 612    **(E)** didcot@fernring.co.uk
**Commercial Manager:**    **(T)**
**Programme Editor:** Steve Clare    **(T)** steveclare@didcottownfc.co.uk
**Ground Address:** Draycott Engineering Loop Meadow Stadium, Bowmont Water, Didcot OX11 7GA
**(T)** 01235 813 138      **Manager:** Andy Wallbridge

## Club Factfile

**Founded:** 1907      **Nickname:** Railwaymen
**Previous Names:** Didcot Village and Northbourne Wanderers amalgamated to form Didcot Town in 1907.
**Previous Leagues:** Metropolitan 1957-63, Hellenic 1963-2006

**Club Colours (change):** Red & white (Blue & gold)

**Ground Capacity:** 5,000   **Seats:** 250     **Covered:** 200     **Clubhouse:** Yes    **Shop:** Yes

**Directions:** From A34 take A4130 towards Didcot.
At first roundabout take first exit, at next roundabout take third exit, then straight across next two roundabouts.
At fifth roundabout turn right into Avon Way.
Follow Avon Way for 1/2 mile till you get to a mini roundabout.
Straight across it, ground is on the left after 100 yards, in Bowmont Water.

**Previous Grounds:** Fleet Meadow. Edmonds Park. Cow Lane. Haydon Road. Station Road 1923-99.

**Record Attendance:** 1,512 v Jarrow roofing - FA Vase Semi-final 2005
**Record Victory:** Not known
**Record Defeat:** Not known
**Record Goalscorer:** Ian Concanon
**Record Appearances:** Not known
**Additional Records:**

**Senior Honours:**
Hellenic League Premier Division 1953-54, 2005-06, Division 1 1976-77, 87-88, League Cup x6.
FA Vase 2004-05. Berks & Bucks Senior Trophy 2001-02, 02-03, 05-06.

### 10 YEAR RECORD

| 03-04 | 04-05 | 05-06 | 06-07 | 07-08 | 08-09 | 09-10 | 10-11 | 11-12 | 12-13 |
|---|---|---|---|---|---|---|---|---|---|
| Hel P 5 | Hel P 2 | Hel P 1 | Sthsw 10 | Sthsw 3 | Sthsw 5 | SthP 15 | SthP 19 | Sthsw 16 | Sthsw 17 |

# EVESHAM UNITED

**Chairman:** Jim Cockerton
**Secretary:** Mike Peplow        **(T)** 07889 011 539        **(E)** footballsecretary@eveshamunitedfcl.com
**Commercial Manager:** Bern Jordan        **(T)**
**Programme Editor:** Mike Peplow        **(T)** 07889 011 539
**Ground Address:** Jubilee Stadium, Cheltenham Rd, Evesham WR11 2LZ
**(T)** 01386 442 303        **Manager:** Shaun Cunnington

## Club Factfile

**Founded:** 1945    **Nickname:** The Robins
**Previous Names:** Not known
**Previous Leagues:** Worcester, Birmingham Combination, Midland Combination 1951-55, 65-92, West Midlands (Regional) 1955-62

**Club Colours (change):** Red and white stripes/white/red (Blue and white stripes/blue/blue)

**Ground Capacity:**        **Seats:** Yes        **Covered:** Yes        **Clubhouse:** Yes        **Shop:** Yes

**Directions**

**FROM M5 NORTH:** Leave M5 motorway at Junction 7 and follow B4084 through Pershore onto Evesham. At traffic lights in Evesham with River Avon and Bridge on left, take right hand lane and turn right into Cheltenham Road signposted A46, M5 Southbound, Oxford and Cheltenham. Continue through two sets of traffic lights passing Tesco Garage and Ambulance Station on left before reaching roundabout. Ground situated on right at roundabout. **FROM M5 SOUTH:** Leave M5 motorway at Junction 9 signposted Tewkesbury and Evesham. Take 3rd exit signposted Ashchurch and Evesham. Follow A46 (Evesham) through Beckford before reaching roundabout on outskirts of Evesham. Ground situated on left at roundabout. **FROM M42:** Leave M42 motorway at Junction 3 (A435) signposted Redditch and Evesham. Continue on A435 (Evesham) through Studley then A46 until reaching roundabout on outskirts of Evesham. Take left hand exit onto Evesham by-pass (A46), signposted M5 South, Cheltenham and Oxford. Proceed on by-pass going over three r'abouts before reaching ground, which is situated on 4th r'about at end of by-pass.

**Previous Grounds:** The Crown Meadow > 1968, Common Reed 1968-2006. Ground shared with Worcester City 2006-12.

**Record Attendance:** 2,338 v West Bromwich Albion - Friendly 18/07/1992
**Record Victory:** 11-3 v West Heath United
**Record Defeat:** 1-8 v Ilkeston Town
**Record Goalscorer:** Sid Brain
**Record Appearances:** Rob Candy
**Additional Records:** Paid £1,500 to Hayes for Colin Day 1992
**Senior Honours:** Received £5,000 from Cheltenham Town for Simon Brain
Midland Combination Premier Division 1991-92, Division 1 1965-66, 67-68, 68-69.
Southern League Division 1 Midlands 2007-08.
Worcestershire Senior Urn x2

### 10 YEAR RECORD

| 03-04 | | 04-05 | | 05-06 | | 06-07 | | 07-08 | | 08-09 | | 09-10 | | 10-11 | | 11-12 | | 12-13 | |
|---|---|---|---|---|---|---|---|---|---|---|---|---|---|---|---|---|---|---|---|
| SthW | 14 | SthW | 3 | SthP | 20 | SthM | 5 | SthM | 1 | SthP | 9 | SthP | 16 | SthP | 12 | SthP | 20 | Sthsw | 14 |

# FLEET TOWN

**Chairman:** Steve Cantle

**Secretary:** John Goodyear     **(T)**        **(E)**

**Commercial Manager:** Vacant      **(T)**

**Programme Editor:** Martin Griffiths     **(T)** mgriffiths@ntlworld.com

**Ground Address:** Calthorpe Park, Crookham Road, Fleet, Hants GU51 5FA

**(T)** 01252 623 804          **Manager:** Craig Davis

Photo: Keith Clayton.

## Club Factfile

**Founded:** 1890     **Nickname:** The Blues

**Previous Names:** Fleet FC 1890-1963

**Previous Leagues:** Hampshire 1961-77, Athenian, Combined Counties, Chiltonian, Wessex 1989-95, 2000-02, Southern 1995-2000, 02-04, 07-08, Isthmian 2004-07, 2008-11.

**Club Colours (change):** All blue (Yellow & black/black/yellow & black)

**Ground Capacity:** 2,000   **Seats:** 250    **Covered:** 250    **Clubhouse:** Yes    **Shop:** Yes

**Directions:** Leave the M3 at Junction 4a, and follow the signs for Fleet. Head along the A3013, Fleet Road. Carry on along the street passing the main shopping street, through several pedestrian crossings for about 1 mile. When you get to the Oatsheaf Pub crossroads head straight across. Ground is 300yds down the hill on the right.

**Previous Grounds:** Watsons Meadow > 1923.

**Record Attendance:** 1,336 v AFC Wimbledon, Isthmian League 08/01/2005

**Record Victory:** 15-0 v Petersfield , Wessex League 26/12/1994

**Record Defeat:** 0-7 v Bashley, Southern League 12/04/2004

**Record Goalscorer:** Mark Frampton - 428

**Record Appearances:** Mark Frampton - 250

**Additional Records:** Paid £3,000 to Aldershot for Mark Russell

**Senior Honours:**
Wessex League 1994-95.
Aldershot Senior Cup 1993, 95, 96, 2000, 08, 09, 10. Basingstoke Senior Cup 2006, 08, 10. Hampshire Senior Cup 2009.

### 10 YEAR RECORD

| 03-04 | | 04-05 | | 05-06 | | 06-07 | | 07-08 | | 08-09 | | 09-10 | | 10-11 | | 11-12 | | 12-13 | |
|---|---|---|---|---|---|---|---|---|---|---|---|---|---|---|---|---|---|---|---|
| SthE | 22 | Isth1 | 19 | Isth1 | 14 | Isth1S | 5 | Sthsw | 2 | Isth1S | 3 | Isth1S | 6 | Isth1S | 13 | SthC | 21 | SthC | 18 |

# GODALMING TOWN

**Chairman:** Kevin Young

**Secretary:** Glenn Moulton     **(T)**       **(E)** secretary@godalmingtownfc.co.uk

**Commercial Manager:** Kevin Marshall    **(T)** commercial@godalmingtownfc.co.uk

**Programme Editor:** Nick Mitchell      **(T)** info@godalmingtownfc.co.uk

**Ground Address:** Weycourt, Meadrow, Guildford, Surrey GU7 3JE

**(T)** 01483 417 520              **Manager:** Andy Hunt

## Club Factfile

**Founded:** 1950      **Nickname:** The G's

**Previous Names:** Godalming United 1950-71. Godalming & Farncombe 1971-79. Godalming Town 1979-92. Godalming & Guildford 1992-2005.

**Previous Leagues:** Combined Counties, Southern 2006-08

**Club Colours (change):** Yellow & green (White & black)

**Ground Capacity:** 3,000   **Seats:** 200    **Covered:** 400    **Clubhouse:** Yes   **Shop:** Yes

**Directions**

A3100 from Guildford, pass the Manor Inn on the left and then the petrol station on the right. Wey Court is 50 yards further along the road on the right hand side.

A3100 from Godalming, pass the Three Lions pub on the left and then turn left into Wey Court immediately after the Leathern Bottle pub.

Parking: Please note that the club car park is for players and officials only. Spectators are asked to use the public car park next door to the ground.

**Previous Grounds:** Recreation Ground 1950-71. Brief spell at Broadwater Park whilst work was done on Weycourt.

**Record Attendance:** 1,305 v AFC Wimbledon - 2002

**Record Victory:** Not Known

**Record Defeat:** Not Known

**Record Goalscorer:** Not Known

**Record Appearances:** Not Known

**Additional Records:**

**Senior Honours:**
Combined Counties League Premier Division 1983-84, 2005-06.
Surrey Senior Cup 2012-13.

### 10 YEAR RECORD

| 03-04 | | 04-05 | | 05-06 | | 06-07 | | 07-08 | | 08-09 | | 09-10 | | 10-11 | | 11-12 | | 12-13 | |
|---|---|---|---|---|---|---|---|---|---|---|---|---|---|---|---|---|---|---|---|
| CCP | 11 | CCP | 4 | CCP | 1 | Isth1S | 22 | Sthsw | 12 | Isth1S | 9 | Isth1S | 4 | Isth1S | 17 | Isth1S | 5 | SthC | 3 |

# GUILDFORD CITY

**Chairman:** Vacant

**Secretary:** Barry Underwood      **(T)** 07912 689 953      **(E)** barry.underwood@guildfordcityfc.co.uk

**Commercial Manager:** Kevin Parker      **(T)**

**Programme Editor:** Jack Underwood      **(T)** jack.underwood@guildfordcityfc.co.uk

**Ground Address:** Spectrum Leisure Centre, Parkway, Guildford GU1 1UP

**(T)** 01483 443 322      **Manager:** Dean Thomas

2012-13 Squad.

## Club Factfile

**Founded:** 1996      **Nickname:** The City

**Previous Names:** AFC Guildford 1996-2005. Guildford United 2005-06.

**Previous Leagues:** Surrey Senior.

**Club Colours (change):** Red, white & black (Yellow & blue)

**Ground Capacity:** 1100      **Seats:** 269      **Covered:** Yes      **Clubhouse:** Yes      **Shop:** Yes

**Directions:** From Guildford main line station, take no.100 shuttle bus to Spectrum. From London Road Station walk via Stoke Park. From A3, exit at Guildford – follow signs to leisure centre.

**Previous Grounds:** None

**Record Attendance:** Att: 211 v Godalming & Guildford, 2004

**Record Victory:**

**Record Defeat:**

**Record Goalscorer:**

**Record Appearances:**

**Additional Records:** Combined Counties Division 1 Champions 2003-04, Premier Division 2010-11.

**Senior Honours:**

Southern League 1937-38, 55-56, League cup 1962-63, 66-67.

Combined Counties Division One 2003-04, Premier Division 2010-11, 11-12

## 10 YEAR RECORD

| 03-04 | | 04-05 | | 05-06 | | 06-07 | | 07-08 | | 08-09 | | 09-10 | | 10-11 | | 11-12 | | 12-13 | |
|---|---|---|---|---|---|---|---|---|---|---|---|---|---|---|---|---|---|---|---|
| CC1 | 1 | CCP | 12 | CCP | 17 | CCP | 21 | CCP | 2 | CCP | 20 | CCP | 7 | CCP | 1 | CCP | 1 | SthC | 9 |

# MANGOTSFIELD UNITED

**Chairman:** Mike Richardson

**Secretary:** David Jones  **(T)** 07903 655 723  **(E)** davidj693@hotmail.co.uk

**Commercial Manager:** Shaun Honour  **(T)** 07795 533 120

**Programme Editor:** Bob Smale  **(T)** bob_smale@yahoo.co.uk

**Ground Address:** Cossham Street, Mangotsfield, Bristol BS16 9EN

**(T)** 0117 956 0119      **Manager:** Richard Thompson

Lee Marshall heads the ball towards goal with Marcus Duharty in the background, during this pre-season friendly against Cribbs Friends Life. Photo: Peter Coddington.

## Club Factfile

**Founded:** 1950  **Nickname:** The Field

**Previous Names:** None

**Previous Leagues:** Bristol & District 1950-67. Avon Premier Combination 1967-72. Western 1972-2000.

**Club Colours (change):** Maroon, sky blue & white (yellow & black)

**Ground Capacity:** 2,500 **Seats:** 300 **Covered:** 800 **Clubhouse:** Yes **Shop:** Yes

**Directions:** Exit the M32 at Junction 1 and follow the A4174 towards Downend following signs to Mangotsfield. Turn left into Cossham Street, the ground is approx 300 yards on the right.

**Previous Grounds:** None

**Record Attendance:** 1,253 v Bath City - F.A. Cup 1974

**Record Victory:** 17-0 v Hanham Sports (H) - 1953 Bristol & District League

**Record Defeat:** 3-13 v Bristol City United - Bristol & District League Division 1

**Record Goalscorer:** John Hill

**Record Appearances:** John Hill - 600+

**Additional Records:** In the last 10 matches of the 2003/04 season, the club went 738 minutes (just over 8 games) without scoring and then finished the campaign with 13 goals in the last two, which included a 9-0 away win.

**Senior Honours:**

Gloucestershire Senior Cup 1968-69, 75-76, 2002-03, 12-13. Somerset Premier Cup 1987-88. Western League 1990-91. Southern League Division One West 2004-05. Gloucestershire F.A. Trophy x6.

### 10 YEAR RECORD

| 03-04 | | 04-05 | | 05-06 | | 06-07 | | 07-08 | | 08-09 | | 09-10 | | 10-11 | | 11-12 | | 12-13 | |
|---|---|---|---|---|---|---|---|---|---|---|---|---|---|---|---|---|---|---|---|
| SthW | 13 | SthW | 1 | SthP | 10 | SthP | 9 | SthP | 14 | SthP | 22 | Sthsw | 9 | Sthsw | 3 | Sthsw | 14 | Sthsw | 13 |

# MERTHYR TOWN

**THE MARTYRS**

**M.T.F.C.**

**Chairman:** Meurig Price
**Secretary:** Jamie Mack      **(T)** 07823 776 422      **(E)** merthysec@gmail.com
**Commercial Manager:**                                              **(T)**
**Programme Editor:** Malcolm Johnson      **(T)** malc.johnson@talk21.com
**Ground Address:** Penydarren Park, Park Terrance, Merthyr Tydfil CF47 8RF
**(T)** 07980 363 675                              **Manager:** Garry Shephard

## Club Factfile

**Founded:**  2010      **Nickname:** Martyrs
**Previous Names:**  None
**Previous Leagues:**  Western League 2010-12.

**Club Colours (change):**  White & black (All yellow)

**Ground Capacity:**      **Seats:** Yes      **Covered:** Yes      **Clubhouse:** Yes      **Shop:**

**Directions:** Leave the M4 at Junction 32 and join the A470 to Merthyr Tydfil. After approx 22 miles at the fourth roundabout take 3rd exit. At next roundabout go straight on and go straight on through two sets of traffic lights. At third set turn left (ground signposted Merthyr Tydfil FC from here). After 50 yards take first right, then first right just after Catholic Church into Park Terrace. The ground is at the end of the road approx. 200 yards on.

**Previous Grounds:** None

**Record Attendance:**
**Record Victory:**
**Record Defeat:**
**Record Goalscorer:**
**Record Appearances:**
**Additional Records:**

**Senior Honours:**
Western League Division One 2010-11, Premier Division 2011-12.

| | | | | | 10 YEAR RECORD | | | | | |
|---|---|---|---|---|---|---|---|---|---|---|
| 03-04 | 04-05 | 05-06 | 06-07 | 07-08 | 08-09 | 09-10 | 10-11 | 11-12 | 12-13 | |
| | | | | | | | West1    1 | WestP    1 | Sthsw    3 | |

# NORTH LEIGH

**Chairman:** Peter King

**Secretary:** Keith Huxley    **(T)** 01993 851 497    **(E)** huxley893@btinterneti.com

**Commercial Manager:**    **(T)**

**Programme Editor:** Mike Burnell    **(T)** 01993 845 507

**Ground Address:** Eynsham Hall Park, North Leigh, Witney, Oxon OX29 6SL

**(T)** 07583 399 577      **Manager:** Mark Gee

After winning the Oxford Senior Cup in May 2012.

## Club Factfile

**Founded:** 1908    **Nickname:** The Millers

**Previous Names:** None

**Previous Leagues:** Witney & District, Hellenic 1990-2008

**Club Colours (change):** Yellow/black/yellow (Dark blue with red trim)

**Ground Capacity:** 2,000    **Seats:** 100    **Covered:** 200    **Clubhouse:** Yes    **Shop:** No

**Directions**

Ground is situated off A4095 Witney to Woodstock road, three miles east of Witney.
Entrance 300 yards east of main park entrance.

**Previous Grounds:** None

**Record Attendance:** 426 v Newport County - FA Cup 3rd Qualifying Round 16/10/2004

**Record Victory:** Not known

**Record Defeat:** Not known

**Record Goalscorer:** P Coles

**Record Appearances:** P King

**Additional Records:**

**Senior Honours:**

Hellenic Premier Division 2001-02, 02-03, 07-08. Oxon Charity Cup x2.
Oxfordshire Senior Cup 2011-12.

### 10 YEAR RECORD

| 03-04 | | 04-05 | | 05-06 | | 06-07 | | 07-08 | | 08-09 | | 09-10 | | 10-11 | | 11-12 | | 12-13 | |
|---|---|---|---|---|---|---|---|---|---|---|---|---|---|---|---|---|---|---|---|
| Hel P | 8 | Hel P | 7 | Hel P | 4 | Hel P | 2 | Hel P | 1 | Sthsw | 8 | Sthsw | 10 | Sthsw | 6 | Sthsw | 6 | Sthsw | 9 |

# PAULTON ROVERS

**Chairman:** David Bissex

**Secretary:** Chris Fenwick    **(T)** 07760 377 302    **(E)** footballsecretary.prfc@gmail.com

**Commercial Manager:**    **(T)**

**Programme Editor:** Peter Lord    **(T)** 07886 015 330

**Ground Address:** Athletic Ground, Winterfield Road, Paulton, Bristol BS39 7RF

**(T)** 01761 412 907    **Manager:** Nick Bunyard

2012-13 Squad - Back Row L-R: Paul Milsom (Asst Manager), Andy Crabtree (Coach), Josh Jeffries, James Vincent, Craig Loxton, Stuart Pearson, Joe Bushin, Kyle Phillips, Marcus Mapstone, Scott Brice, Nick McCootie,
Nick Bunyard (Manager), Maizie Phillips (Physio)/
Front Row L-R: James Billing, Steve Bridges, Joe Viner, Ben Lacey, Stuart Tovey, Dan Cleverley (Captain),
Brandon Barnes, Mike Reaney.

## Club Factfile

**Founded:** 1881    **Nickname:** The Robins or Rovers

**Previous Names:** Not known

**Previous Leagues:** Wiltshire Premier, Somerset Senior, Western

**Club Colours (change):** All maroon (All blue with yellow trim)

**Ground Capacity:** 5,000    **Seats:** 253    **Covered:** 2,500    **Clubhouse:** Yes    **Shop:** Yes

**Directions**

From A39 at Farrington Gurney, follow A362 marked Radstock for two miles.
Turn left at roundabout, take B3355 to Paulton and ground is on the right.

**Previous Grounds:** Chapel Field, Cricket Ground, Recreation Ground

**Record Attendance:** 2,000 v Crewe Alexandra - FA Cup 1906-07

**Record Victory:** Not known

**Record Defeat:** Not known

**Record Goalscorer:** Graham Colbourne

**Record Appearances:** Steve Tovey

**Additional Records:**

**Senior Honours:**

Somerset Senior Cup x12.

Somerset Premier Cup 2012-13.

### 10 YEAR RECORD

| 03-04 | | 04-05 | | 05-06 | | 06-07 | | 07-08 | | 08-09 | | 09-10 | | 10-11 | | 11-12 | | 12-13 | |
|---|---|---|---|---|---|---|---|---|---|---|---|---|---|---|---|---|---|---|---|
| WestP | 2 | SthW | 8 | SthW | 17 | Sthsw | 2 | Sthsw | 7 | Sthsw | 10 | Sthsw | 7 | Sthsw | 11 | Sthsw | 7 | Sthsw | 5 |

# SHORTWOOD UNITED

**Chairman:** Peter Webb

**Secretary:** Mark Webb    **(T)** 07792 323784    **(E)** squish.shortwoodfc@live.co.uk

**Commercial Manager:** Jim Cunneen    **(T)** 07714 661 797

**Programme Editor:** Paul Benneyworth    **(T)** swoodprog@btinternet.com

**Ground Address:** Meadowbank, Shortwood, Nailsworth GL6 0SJ

**(T)** 01453 833 936      **Manager:** John Evans

Shortwood United's Alton Axton and James Coates try to penetrate
the Cinderford Town defence. Photo: Peter Barnes.

## Club Factfile

**Founded:** 1900    **Nickname:** The Wood

**Previous Names:** None.

**Previous Leagues:** Gloucestershire County. Hellenic >2012.

**Club Colours (change):** Red & white/black/black.

**Ground Capacity:** 2,000   **Seats:** 50    **Covered:** 150    **Clubhouse:** Yes    **Shop:** No

**Directions**

When entering Nailsworth from Stroud turn right at mini roundabout, when coming from Cirencester go straight over roundabout, and when from Bath turn left at mini roundabout.

Proceed up Spring Hill 30 yards turn left at Raffles Wine Warehouse, straight through town turn left at Brittannia Pub carry on for 1 mile until you come to Shortwood village you will see sign post on fork in the road keep to the left follow on for quarter of a mile ground opposite church.

**Previous Grounds:** Played at Nailsworth Playing Field, Table Land and Wallow Green before moving to Meadowbank in 1972.

**Record Attendance:** Att: 1,000 v Forest Green Rovers, FA Vase 5th Rnd 1982.

**Record Victory:**

**Record Defeat:**

**Record Goalscorer:** Peter Grant.

**Record Appearances:** Peter Grant.

**Additional Records:** Gloucestershire Lge Champions 1981-82.

**Senior Honours:**

Hellenic League Champions 1984-85, 91-92.

Gloucestershire Senior Cup (x 2).

| | | | | **10 YEAR RECORD** | | | | | |
|---|---|---|---|---|---|---|---|---|---|
| 03-04 | 04-05 | 05-06 | 06-07 | 07-08 | 08-09 | 09-10 | 10-11 | 11-12 | 12-13 |
| Hel P 19 | Hel P 15 | Hel P 15 | Hel P 8 | Hel P 5 | Hel P 2 | Hel P 2 | Hel P 6 | Hel P 2 | Sthsw 8 |

# STRATFORD TOWN

**Chairman:** Craig Hughes
**Secretary:** Brian Rose     **(T)** 07833 776 834     **(E)** brian_rose@nfumutual.co.uk
**Commercial Manager:** Melanie Tweedle     **(T)**
**Programme Editor:** Mark Bickley     **(T)** markbickley@hotmail.com
**Ground Address:** The DCS Stadium, Knights Lane, Tiddington, Stratford Upon Avon CV37 7BZ
**(T)** 01789 269 336     **Manager:**

## Club Factfile

**Founded:** 1943     **Nickname:** The Town
**Previous Names:** Straford Rangers 1943-49. Stratford Town Amateurs 1964-70.
**Previous Leagues:** Worcestershire/Midland Comb. Birmingham & Dist. W.Mid (Reg). Hellenic. Midland Alliance > 2013.

**Club Colours (change):** All royal blue. (Tangerine/black/tangerine)

**Ground Capacity:**     **Seats:** Yes     **Covered:** Yes     **Clubhouse:** Yes     **Shop:** Yes

**Directions:** From Town Centre follow signs for Banbury (A422) and Oxford (A3400). Cross Clopton Bridge and turn immediately left onto B4086 towards Wellesbourne. After approx 1 mile you enter the village of Tiddington. Turn 1st right into Knights Lane. Ground is approx 800 yards on right (100 yards after school).

**Previous Grounds:** A number of pitches before Alcester Road by the late 1940s.

**Record Attendance: Att:** 1,078 v Aston Villa, Birmingham Senior Cup, Oct. 1996.
**Record Victory:** Not known
**Record Defeat:** Not known
**Record Goalscorer:** Not known
**Record Appearances:** Not known
**Additional Records:**

**Senior Honours:**
Worcestershire/Midland Combination 1956-57, 86-87.
Birmingham Senior Cup 1962-63. Midland Alliance 2012-13, League Cup 2002-03, 03-04, 10-11.

### 10 YEAR RECORD

| 03-04 | 04-05 | 05-06 | 06-07 | 07-08 | 08-09 | 09-10 | 10-11 | 11-12 | 12-13 |
|---|---|---|---|---|---|---|---|---|---|
| MidAl 3 | MidAl 11 | MidAl 15 | MidAl 4 | MidAl 7 | MidAl 6 | MidAl 3 | MidAl 5 | MidAl 8 | MidAl 1 |

# SWINDON SUPERMARINE

**Chairman:** Jez Webb
**Secretary:** Judi Moore    **(T)** 07785 970 954    **(E)** judimoore6@aol.com
**Commercial Manager:** Vacant    **(T)**
**Programme Editor:** Keith Yeomans    **(T)** supermarinefc@aol.com
**Ground Address:** The Webbs Stadium, South Marston, Swindon SN3 4BZ
**(T)** 01793 828 778      **Manager:** Dave Webb

## Club Factfile

**Founded:** 1992     **Nickname:** Marine
**Previous Names:** Club formed after the amalgamation of Swindon Athletic and Supermarine
**Previous Leagues:** Wiltshire, Hellenic 1992-2001.

**Club Colours (change):** All blue (All red)

**Ground Capacity:** 3,000   **Seats:** 300    **Covered:** 300    **Clubhouse:** Yes    **Shop:** Yes

**Directions**

From M5 Junction 11a, take the A417 to Cirencester, then A419 Swindon. At the A361 junction by Honda Factory take road to Highworth. After one mile Club is on 4th roundabout.

From M4 Junction 15, take A419 towards Swindon Cirencester, take A361, then as above .

From A420 Swindon take A419 to Cirencester, near Honda factory take A361, then as above.

**Previous Grounds:** Supermarine: Vickers Airfield > Mid 1960s

**Record Attendance:** 1,550 v Aston Villa
**Record Victory:** Not known
**Record Defeat:** Not known
**Record Goalscorer:** Damon York - 136 (1990-98)
**Record Appearances:** Damon York - 314 (1990-98)
**Additional Records:** Paid £1,000 to Hungerford Town for Lee Hartson

**Senior Honours:**
Hellenic League Premier Division 1997-98, 2000-01, Challenge Cup 97-97, 99-2000.

### 10 YEAR RECORD

| 03-04 | | 04-05 | | 05-06 | | 06-07 | | 07-08 | | 08-09 | | 09-10 | | 10-11 | | 11-12 | | 12-13 | |
|---|---|---|---|---|---|---|---|---|---|---|---|---|---|---|---|---|---|---|---|
| SthW | 17 | SthW | 19 | SthW | 5 | Sthsw | 4 | SthP | 12 | SthP | 13 | SthP | 14 | SthP | 10 | SthP | 21 | Sthsw | 4 |

# TAUNTON TOWN

**Chairman:** Kevin Sturmey

**Secretary:** Martin Dongworth    **(T)** 07791 948 686    **(E)** secretary@tauntontown.com

**Commercial Manager:** Martyn Rogers    **(T)** 07850 420 488

**Programme Editor:** Martin Dongworth    **(T)** 07791 948 686

**Ground Address:** Wordsworth Drive, Taunton, Somerset TA1 2HG

**(T)** 01823 278 191                    **Manager:** Leigh Robinson

## Club Factfile

**Founded:** 1947    **Nickname:** The Peacocks

**Previous Names:** None

**Previous Leagues:** Western 1954-77, 83-2002, Southern 1977-83

**Club Colours (change):** Claret & sky blue (yellow & blue)

**Ground Capacity:** 2,500    **Seats:** 300    **Covered:** 1,000    **Clubhouse:** Yes    **Shop:** Yes

**Directions**

From M5 Junction 25 follow signs to Town Centre.
Proceed along Toneway then bear left at roundabout into Chritchard Way.
At traffic lights proceed into Wordsworth Drive and the ground is on the left.

**Previous Grounds:** None

**Record Attendance:** 3,284 v Tiverton Town - FA Vase Semi-final 1999

**Record Victory:** 12-0 v Dawlish Town (A) - FA Cup Preliminary Round 28/08/1993

**Record Defeat:** 0-8 v Cheltenham Town (A) - FA Cup 2nd Qualifying Round 28/09/1991

**Record Goalscorer:** Tony Payne

**Record Appearances:** Tony Payne

**Additional Records:** Reg Oram scored 67 in one season

**Senior Honours:**

Western League 1968-69, 89-90, 95-96, 98-99, 99-2000, 2000-01. FA Vase 2000-01.
Somerset Premier Cup 2002-03, 05-06.

### 10 YEAR RECORD

| 03-04 | | 04-05 | | 05-06 | | 06-07 | | 07-08 | | 08-09 | | 09-10 | | 10-11 | | 11-12 | | 12-13 | |
|---|---|---|---|---|---|---|---|---|---|---|---|---|---|---|---|---|---|---|---|
| SthW | 15 | SthW | 17 | SthW | 18 | Sthsw | 5 | Sthsw | 18 | Sthsw | 20 | Sthsw | 19 | Sthsw | 9 | Sthsw | 17 | Sthsw | 18 |

# THATCHAM TOWN

**Chairman:** Eric Bailey
**Secretary:** Alan Lovegrove     **(T)** 07817 723 846     **(E)** mail@alanlovegrove.wanadoo.co.uk
**Commercial Manager:** Duncan Groves     **(T)**
**Programme Editor:** Andy Morris     **(T)** acmorris@madasafish.com
**Ground Address:** Waterside Park, Crookham Hill, Thatcham, Berks RG19 4PA
**(T)** 01635 862 016     **Manager:** Scott Tarr

2012-13 Squad.

## Club Factfile

**Founded:** 1895     **Nickname:** The Kingfishers
**Previous Names:** Not known
**Previous Leagues:** Hellenic 1974-82, Athenian 1982-84, London Spartan 1984-86, Wessex 1986-2006

**Club Colours (change):** Blue and white stripes/blue/blue (Red/black/black)

**Ground Capacity:** 3,000    **Seats:** 300    **Covered:** 300     **Clubhouse:** Yes    **Shop:** Yes

**Directions:**
A4 Thatcham at Sony roundabout turn into Pipers Way.
At next roundabout turn left, crossing over the railway line.
Entrance to Waterside Park 300 metres on left-hand side.

**Previous Grounds:** Station Road 1946-52, Lancaster Close 1952-92

**Record Attendance:** 1,400 v Aldershot - FA Vase
**Record Victory:** Not known
**Record Defeat:** Not known
**Record Goalscorer:** Not known
**Record Appearances:** Not known
**Additional Records:**

**Senior Honours:**
Hellenic League 1974-75. Wessex League 1995-96.

### 10 YEAR RECORD

| 03-04 | | 04-05 | | 05-06 | | 06-07 | | 07-08 | | 08-09 | | 09-10 | | 10-11 | | 11-12 | | 12-13 | |
|---|---|---|---|---|---|---|---|---|---|---|---|---|---|---|---|---|---|---|---|
| Wex | 10 | Wex1 | 3 | Wex1 | 2 | Sthsw | 6 | Sthsw | 15 | Sthsw | 6 | Sthsw | 12 | Sthsw | 5 | Sthsw | 8 | SthC | 17 |

# TIVERTON TOWN

**Chairman:** Dave Wright
**Secretary:** Ramsey Findlay    **(T)** 07761 261 990    **(E)** ramsayfindlay@hotmail.co.uk
**Commercial Manager:** John Fournier    **(T)** 07980 543 634
**Programme Editor:** Alan Reidy    **(T)** alanreidy@tiscali.co.uk
**Ground Address:** Ladysmead, Bolham Road, Tiverton, Devon EX16 6SG
**(T)** 01884 252 397      **Manager:** John Clarkson

## Club Factfile

**Founded:** 1913     **Nickname:** Tivvy
**Previous Names:** None
**Previous Leagues:** Devon and Exeter, Western

**Club Colours (change):** All yellow (All white)

**Ground Capacity:** 3,500   **Seats:** 520   **Covered:** 2,300   **Clubhouse:** Yes   **Shop:** Yes

**Directions**
M5 Junction 27, follow A361 to Tiverton's second exit at roundabout, turning left.
Continue for about 400 yards, crossing roundabout until reaching mini-roundabout.
Carry on straight across. Ground is 200 yards on right.

**Previous Grounds:** None

**Record Attendance:** 3,000 v Leyton Orient - FA Cup 1st Round Proper 1994-95
**Record Victory:** 10-0 v Exmouth Town, Devon St Lukes Cup 16/02/1994
**Record Defeat:** 2-6 v Stafford Rangers (A) - Southern League 2001-02 & Heavitree United, Les Philips Cup 29/11/1997
**Record Goalscorer:** Phil Everett
**Record Appearances:** Not known
**Additional Records:**

**Senior Honours:**
FA Vase 1997-98, 98-99. Western League x5. Southern League Cup 2006-07.
Devon Senior Cup 1955-56, 65-66. East Devon Senior Cup x7.

### 10 YEAR RECORD

| 03-04 | | 04-05 | | 05-06 | | 06-07 | | 07-08 | | 08-09 | | 09-10 | | 10-11 | | 11-12 | | 12-13 | |
|---|---|---|---|---|---|---|---|---|---|---|---|---|---|---|---|---|---|---|---|
| SthP | 15 | SthP | 8 | SthP | 12 | SthP | 15 | SthP | 17 | SthP | 12 | SthP | 19 | SthP | 20 | Sthsw | 9 | Sthsw | 16 |

# WIMBORNE TOWN

**Chairman:** Paul Miller
**Secretary:** Peter Barham    **(T)** 07956 833 316    **(E)** barhamp@tiscali.co.uk
**Commercial Manager:** Paul Miller    **(T)**
**Programme Editor:** Graham Dunn    **(T)** magpies.graham@gmail.com
**Ground Address:** The Cuthbury, Cowgrove Road, Wimborne, Dorset, BH21 4EL
**(T)** 01202 884 821    **Manager:** Steve Cuss

The Wimborne defence clear this Shortwood corner during this league encounter.
Photo: Peter Barnes.

## Club Factfile

**Founded:** 1878    **Nickname:** Magpies
**Previous Names:** None
**Previous Leagues:** Dorset, Dorset Combination, Western 1981-86, Wessex 1986-2010

**Club Colours (change):** Black and white stripes/black/black (Sky blue & navy blue)

**Ground Capacity:** 3,250    **Seats:** 275    **Covered:** 425    **Clubhouse:** Yes    **Shop:** Yes

**Directions**
On the Wimborne To Blandford Road (B3082), turn left into Cowgrove Road just past Victoria Hospital. Postcode for Sat nav is BH21 4EL.

**Previous Grounds:** None

**Record Attendance:** 3,250 v Bamber Bridge
**Record Victory:** Not known
**Record Defeat:** Not known
**Record Goalscorer:** Jason Lovell
**Record Appearances:** James Sturgess
**Additional Records:**

**Senior Honours:**
FA Vase 1991-92. Wessex League 1991-92, 93-94, 99-2000.
Dorset Senior Amateur Cup 1936-37, 63-64.

### 10 YEAR RECORD

| 03-04 | | 04-05 | | 05-06 | | 06-07 | | 07-08 | | 08-09 | | 09-10 | | 10-11 | | 11-12 | | 12-13 | |
|---|---|---|---|---|---|---|---|---|---|---|---|---|---|---|---|---|---|---|---|
| Wex | 2 | Wex1 | 7 | Wex1 | 12 | WexP | 6 | WexP | 3 | WexP | 4 | WexP | 2 | Sthsw | 19 | Sthsw | 19 | Sthsw | 12 |

# YATE TOWN

**Chairman:** Colin Pick
**Secretary:** Terry Tansley   **(T)** 07875 272 126   **(E)** admin@yatetownfc.com
**Commercial Manager:**   **(T)**
**Programme Editor:** Terry Tansley   **(T)** admin@yatetownfc.com
**Ground Address:** Lodge Road, Yate, Bristol BS37 7LE
**(T)** 01454 228 103   **Manager:** Robert Cousins

2013-14 Squad.

## Club Factfile

**Founded:** 1906   **Nickname:** The Bluebells
**Previous Names:** Yate Rovers 1906-1930s. Yate YMCA 1933-58.
**Previous Leagues:** Bristol Premier Combination > 1968, Gloucestershire County 1968-83, Hellenic 1983-89, 2000-03, Southern 1989-2000

**Club Colours (change):** White/blue navy/white (All yellow)

**Ground Capacity:** 2,000   **Seats:** 236   **Covered:** 400   **Clubhouse:** Yes   **Shop:** Yes

**Directions**
From East: leave M4 J18, enter Yate on A432 via Chipping Sodbury bypass. Turn right at first small roundabout (Link Road), straight over next roundabout into Goose Green Way, over more roundabouts and 2 major sets of traffic lights. Turn right at third set of lights (by The Fox), then immediately left into Lodge Road. Ground 200m on right. From North: M5 (South) exit J14, B4509/B4060 into Chipping Sodbury. Turn right into Chipping Sodbury High Street, down Bowling Hill and right at first roundabout into Goose Green Way – then as above. From South: Leave M5 at J15, then join M5. Leave M4 at J19, take second exit onto M32. Leave M32 at J1, at roundabout take first exit onto A4174. Continue on A4174 over traffic lights, then at roundabout take first exit onto A432. Enter Yate on A432, at traffic lights turn left into Stover Road (B4059), then at roundabout take second exit – still on B4059. Left at traffic lights (Fox PH) and immediately left into Lodge Road.

**Previous Grounds:** Yate Aerodrome 1954-60. Sunnyside Lane 1960-84.

**Record Attendance:** 2,000 v Bristol Rovers v Bristol Rovers Past XI - Vaughan Jones testimonial 1990
**Record Victory:** 13-3 v Clevedon - Bristol Premier Combination 1967-68
**Record Defeat:** Not known
**Record Goalscorer:** Kevin Thaws
**Record Appearances:** Gary Hewlett
**Additional Records:** Paid £2,000 to Chippenham Town for Matt Rawlings 2003
**Senior Honours:** Received £15,000 from Bristol Rovers for Mike Davis
Hellenic League 1987-88, 88-89. Gloucestershire Senior Cup 2004-05, 05-06.

## 10 YEAR RECORD

| 03-04 | 04-05 | 05-06 | 06-07 | 07-08 | 08-09 | 09-10 | 10-11 | 11-12 | 12-13 |
|---|---|---|---|---|---|---|---|---|---|
| SthW 16 | SthW 2 | SthP 6 | SthP 14 | SthP 10 | SthP 21 | Sthsw 13 | Sthsw 14 | Sthsw 13 | Sthsw 6 |

# Division One South & West Action

Poole Town defender, Will Spetch, clears the ball from
Evesham striker Roland Agbor during their 3-2 away win. Photo: Jonathan Holloway.

Poole Town player, Steve Devlin (left, light shirt)
looks to tackle this Evesham midfielder at The Jubilee Stadium. Photo: Jonathan Holloway.

# PREMIER DIVISION 2012-13

| | | P | W | D | L | F | A | GD | Pts |
|---|---|---|---|---|---|---|---|---|---|
| 1 | (P) Whitehawk | 42 | 25 | 13 | 4 | 88 | 42 | 46 | 88 |
| 2 | Lowestoft Town | 42 | 23 | 11 | 8 | 71 | 38 | 33 | 80 |
| 3 | Wealdstone | 42 | 22 | 13 | 7 | 70 | 38 | 32 | 79 |
| 4 | (P) Concord Rangers | 42 | 22 | 10 | 10 | 80 | 54 | 26 | 76 |
| 5 | East Thurrock United | 42 | 18 | 16 | 8 | 65 | 45 | 20 | 70 |
| 6 | Metropolitan Police | 42 | 20 | 10 | 12 | 65 | 56 | 9 | 70 |
| 7 | Bury Town | 42 | 19 | 9 | 14 | 66 | 64 | 2 | 66 |
| 8 | Canvey Island | 42 | 18 | 10 | 14 | 60 | 55 | 5 | 64 |
| 9 | Margate | 42 | 17 | 11 | 14 | 61 | 49 | 12 | 62 |
| 10 | Hendon | 42 | 16 | 12 | 14 | 48 | 50 | -2 | 60 |
| 11 | Kingstonian | 42 | 18 | 5 | 19 | 63 | 62 | 1 | 59 |
| 12 | Leiston | 42 | 13 | 17 | 12 | 55 | 57 | -2 | 56 |
| 13 | Hampton & Richmond | 42 | 13 | 14 | 15 | 58 | 56 | 2 | 53 |
| 14 | Bognor Regis Town | 42 | 15 | 8 | 19 | 48 | 58 | -10 | 53 |
| 15 | Harrow Borough | 42 | 12 | 9 | 21 | 53 | 71 | -18 | 45 |
| 16 | Enfield Town | 42 | 13 | 5 | 24 | 60 | 83 | -23 | 44 |
| 17 | Cray Wanderers | 42 | 10 | 13 | 19 | 60 | 85 | -25 | 43 |
| 18 | Wingate & Finchley | 42 | 12 | 6 | 24 | 56 | 82 | -26 | 42 |
| 19 | Lewes | 42 | 9 | 13 | 20 | 59 | 75 | -16 | 40 |
| 20 | Carshalton Athletic | 42 | 12 | 4 | 26 | 55 | 76 | -21 | 40 |
| 21 | (R) Thurrock (-3pts) | 42 | 11 | 8 | 23 | 40 | 62 | -22 | 38 |
| 22 | (R) Hastings United | 42 | 8 | 15 | 19 | 39 | 62 | -23 | 39 |

## PLAY-OFFS
Semi-Finals
Lowestoft Town 1-0 East Thurrock United
Wealdstone 1-2 Concord Rangers

Final (@: Lowestoft Town 06/05/13)
Lowestoft Town 1-2 Concord Rangers

| | | 1 | 2 | 3 | 4 | 5 | 6 | 7 | 8 | 9 | 10 | 11 | 12 | 13 | 14 | 15 | 16 | 17 | 18 | 19 | 20 | 21 | 22 |
|---|---|---|---|---|---|---|---|---|---|---|---|---|---|---|---|---|---|---|---|---|---|---|---|
| 1 | Bognor Regis Town | | 5-1 | 2-2 | 2-1 | 0-1 | 0-2 | 1-0 | 0-0 | 0-5 | 0-3 | 1-0 | 3-1 | 0-1 | 1-1 | 3-1 | 0-2 | 0-2 | 0-0 | 1-0 | 0-1 | 1-3 | 1-0 |
| 2 | Bury Town | 2-0 | | 1-0 | 1-1 | 0-4 | 0-2 | 1-2 | 2-1 | 0-1 | 0-1 | 1-0 | 1-2 | 1-0 | 3-3 | 2-1 | 1-1 | 2-2 | 0-2 | 3-1 | 0-0 | 1-3 | 4-2 |
| 3 | Canvey Island | 1-1 | 0-1 | | 4-2 | 0-2 | 1-0 | 2-1 | 3-4 | 0-0 | 3-0 | 1-1 | 0-3 | 4-3 | 2-0 | 0-0 | 0-2 | 3-1 | 0-1 | 2-0 | 2-0 | 1-2 | 3-2 |
| 4 | Carshalton Athletic | 0-2 | 1-3 | 0-2 | | 1-2 | 2-1 | 1-1 | 3-2 | 3-0 | 3-1 | 1-0 | 1-2 | 1-3 | 1-3 | 3-3 | 2-0 | 4-0 | 1-1 | 0-1 | 0-2 | 0-1 | 1-2 |
| 5 | Concord Rangers | 1-3 | 3-2 | 3-0 | 6-3 | | 0-4 | 2-2 | 3-0 | 2-1 | 1-2 | 4-0 | 1-2 | 0-3 | 0-0 | 3-6 | 1-1 | 2-1 | 5-1 | 1-1 | 2-2 | 2-2 | 4-1 |
| 6 | Cray Wanderers | 1-3 | 2-2 | 1-1 | 3-2 | 0-2 | | 2-2 | 1-5 | 2-0 | 2-1 | 0-3 | 0-1 | 1-3 | 0-0 | 2-2 | 1-1 | 0-4 | 1-2 | 0-1 | 0-3 | 1-2 | 3-4 |
| 7 | East Thurrock United | 4-4 | 1-3 | 2-0 | 4-0 | 3-1 | 1-1 | | 2-0 | 1-2 | 2-0 | 1-1 | 2-2 | 1-0 | 0-2 | 0-0 | 2-2 | 1-0 | 0-2 | 1-1 | 0-2 | 1-1 | 2-0 |
| 8 | Enfield Town | 0-1 | 2-3 | 0-2 | 1-2 | 0-1 | 1-3 | 2-3 | | 0-2 | 2-0 | 1-0 | 6-3 | 1-1 | 1-0 | 2-1 | 2-3 | 0-3 | 4-0 | 1-1 | 1-2 | 1-3 | 2-1 |
| 9 | Hampton & Richmond | 1-0 | 2-3 | 2-2 | 0-1 | 1-1 | 1-3 | 0-3 | 4-2 | | 0-0 | 1-0 | 1-2 | 0-1 | 3-3 | 2-1 | 1-1 | 1-2 | 0-0 | 1-0 | 3-1 | 1-0 | 3-3 |
| 10 | Harrow Borough | 3-2 | 3-1 | 1-3 | 1-0 | 1-2 | 3-3 | 2-3 | 4-2 | 4-3 | | 0-1 | 1-1 | 1-0 | 1-3 | 0-2 | 3-3 | 0-2 | 2-3 | 4-1 | 0-0 | 3-1 | 1-2 |
| 11 | Hastings United | 1-1 | 0-1 | 0-0 | 1-4 | 2-2 | 1-1 | 1-1 | 3-2 | 0-0 | 2-0 | | 1-2 | 1-0 | 0-1 | 3-3 | 1-4 | 2-2 | 1-2 | 1-1 | 1-1 | 0-2 | 2-1 |
| 12 | Hendon | 1-0 | 2-2 | 1-2 | 3-1 | 2-2 | 0-0 | 0-0 | 2-3 | 0-3 | 1-2 | 2-0 | | 1-0 | 2-1 | 2-2 | 0-1 | 0-1 | 1-1 | 1-0 | 0-0 | 1-1 | 0-2 |
| 13 | Kingstonian | 1-0 | 0-2 | 1-2 | 2-1 | 0-1 | 9-3 | 0-2 | 1-2 | 0-0 | 4-2 | 0-1 | 2-1 | | 3-1 | 3-1 | 0-1 | 3-3 | 1-0 | 1-0 | 2-0 | 2-3 | 0-1 |
| 14 | Leiston | 1-1 | 0-0 | 1-1 | 1-0 | 0-3 | 1-1 | 5-4 | 3-1 | 2-2 | 1-0 | 3-1 | 0-1 | 2-2 | | 1-1 | 0-0 | 1-2 | 0-2 | 2-1 | 1-1 | 0-2 | 3-0 |
| 15 | Lewes | 1-0 | 2-3 | 1-2 | 2-1 | 0-3 | 2-2 | 1-1 | 1-2 | 2-2 | 1-1 | 1-2 | 0-0 | 1-2 | 0-1 | | 2-1 | 2-0 | 1-2 | 1-2 | 1-0 | 2-3 | 3-1 |
| 16 | Lowestoft Town | 1-2 | 1-0 | 2-0 | 2-3 | 4-1 | 4-1 | 0-0 | 0-0 | 5-3 | 3-0 | 1-0 | 1-0 | 1-3 | 1-1 | 2-0 | | 1-0 | 2-1 | 0-1 | 3-0 | 0-0 | 3-0 |
| 17 | Margate | 3-0 | 3-1 | 2-2 | 3-1 | 0-2 | 0-1 | 0-1 | 2-0 | 2-1 | 0-0 | 1-1 | 2-0 | 1-2 | 2-0 | 1-1 | 2-1 | | 1-2 | 3-1 | 2-4 | 2-1 | 2-0 |
| 18 | Metropolitan Police | 3-2 | 3-1 | 2-1 | 1-0 | 0-2 | 2-4 | 2-2 | 2-1 | 1-0 | 1-1 | 4-0 | 2-1 | 4-1 | 0-1 | 1-3 | 1-0 | | 1-2 | 0-1 | 2-5 | 2-1 | |
| 19 | Thurrock | 1-2 | 0-3 | 0-1 | 1-3 | 0-1 | 5-1 | 0-2 | 1-0 | 0-0 | 3-0 | 1-1 | 1-2 | 4-0 | 0-3 | 2-0 | 1-2 | 1-1 | 0-4 | | 0-0 | 0-3 | 1-2 |
| 20 | Wealdstone | 1-0 | 2-3 | 2-0 | 3-0 | 2-1 | 2-0 | 1-1 | 4-0 | 3-2 | 2-0 | 3-0 | 2-1 | 5-2 | 2-0 | 6-1 | 0-0 | 2-1 | 1-0 | 2-2 | | 1-1 | 2-3 |
| 21 | Whitehawk | 3-0 | 2-2 | 5-4 | 2-0 | 1-0 | 2-0 | 1-0 | 6-0 | 0-0 | 0-0 | 2-2 | 0-0 | 2-0 | 5-1 | 3-1 | 1-3 | 1-1 | 1-1 | 5-1 | 1-1 | | 3-1 |
| 22 | Wingate & Finchley | 1-3 | 1-3 | 0-1 | 1-0 | 0-0 | 4-4 | 0-1 | 1-2 | 0-3 | 2-1 | 2-2 | 0-1 | 3-0 | 2-2 | 2-4 | 3-2 | 1-0 | 1-3 | 0-1 | 1-1 | 2-3 | |

# DIVISION ONE NORTH 2012-13

|  |  | P | W | D | L | F | A | GD | Pts |
|---|---|---|---|---|---|---|---|---|---|
| 1 | (P) Grays Athletic | 42 | 32 | 6 | 4 | 96 | 38 | 58 | 102 |
| 2 | Maldon & Tiptree | 42 | 27 | 8 | 7 | 101 | 47 | 54 | 89 |
| 3 | (P) Thamesmead Town | 42 | 28 | 4 | 10 | 85 | 49 | 36 | 88 |
| 4 | Witham Town | 42 | 24 | 7 | 11 | 71 | 47 | 24 | 79 |
| 5 | Aveley | 42 | 24 | 6 | 12 | 92 | 58 | 34 | 78 |
| 6 | Heybridge Swifts | 42 | 21 | 10 | 11 | 102 | 55 | 47 | 73 |
| 7 | Soham Town Rangers | 42 | 22 | 7 | 13 | 95 | 75 | 20 | 73 |
| 8 | Romford | 42 | 19 | 7 | 16 | 72 | 72 | 0 | 64 |
| 9 | Brentwood Town | 42 | 17 | 8 | 17 | 63 | 62 | 1 | 59 |
| 10 | Potters Bar Town | 42 | 15 | 13 | 14 | 64 | 68 | −4 | 58 |
| 11 | Cheshunt (-3pts) | 42 | 16 | 10 | 16 | 75 | 73 | 2 | 55 |
| 12 | Waltham Abbey | 42 | 15 | 8 | 19 | 60 | 70 | −10 | 53 |
| 13 | Chatham Town | 42 | 13 | 13 | 16 | 59 | 65 | −6 | 52 |
| 14 | Wroxham | 42 | 12 | 14 | 16 | 68 | 64 | 4 | 50 |
| 15 | Needham Market | 42 | 12 | 13 | 17 | 61 | 62 | −1 | 49 |
| 16 | Tilbury (-18pts) | 42 | 18 | 9 | 15 | 69 | 62 | 7 | 45 |
| 17 | A.F.C. Sudbury | 42 | 12 | 9 | 21 | 57 | 84 | −27 | 45 |
| 18 | Waltham Forest | 42 | 10 | 10 | 22 | 54 | 72 | −18 | 40 |
| 19 | Ware | 42 | 10 | 6 | 26 | 59 | 105 | −46 | 36 |
| 20 | Redbridge (-1pt) | 42 | 7 | 6 | 29 | 42 | 105 | −63 | 26 |
| 21 | Harlow Town (-10pts) | 42 | 9 | 8 | 25 | 45 | 82 | −37 | 25 |
| 22 | (R) Ilford | 42 | 4 | 8 | 30 | 32 | 105 | −73 | 20 |

## PLAY-OFFS
### Semi-Finals
Maldon & Tiptree 3-1 Aveley
Thamesmead Town 3-2 Witham Town

### Final (@ Maldon 05/05/13)
Maldon & Tiptree 2-2 Thamesmead Town (Thamesmead won 4-1 on penalties)

|  |  | 1 | 2 | 3 | 4 | 5 | 6 | 7 | 8 | 9 | 10 | 11 | 12 | 13 | 14 | 15 | 16 | 17 | 18 | 19 | 20 | 21 | 22 |
|---|---|---|---|---|---|---|---|---|---|---|---|---|---|---|---|---|---|---|---|---|---|---|---|
| 1 | AFC Sudbury |  | 2-3 | 0-4 | 1-1 | 1-3 | 3-1 | 3-2 | 0-2 | 0-1 | 2-1 | 0-0 | 1-1 | 6-1 | 3-6 | 0-2 | 1-1 | 1-1 | 2-0 | 1-0 | 2-0 | 0-1 | 2-4 |
| 2 | Aveley | 4-1 |  | 3-0 | 5-1 | 0-1 | 1-0 | 1-2 | 3-0 | 2-2 | 2-1 | 2-3 | 1-0 | 2-1 | 4-1 | 1-1 | 1-2 | 0-1 | 2-1 | 3-1 | 3-1 | 1-4 |  |
| 3 | Brentwood Town | 1-0 | 0-2 |  | 0-0 | 2-0 | 0-1 | 0-0 | 3-2 | 3-1 | 0-2 | 1-0 | 3-1 | 1-1 | 1-3 | 6-3 | 0-1 | 1-1 | 0-2 | 2-0 | 4-0 | 3-2 | 1-1 |
| 4 | Chatham Town | 2-0 | 1-2 | 2-1 |  | 2-2 | 1-4 | 2-1 | 1-0 | 1-0 | 0-2 | 0-2 | 1-2 | 2-1 | 5-0 | 0-0 | 2-3 | 1-2 | 4-0 | 2-4 | 2-3 | 0-2 | 1-1 |
| 5 | Cheshunt | 1-0 | 4-2 | 1-0 | 2-2 |  | 1-2 | 1-2 | 0-0 | 3-0 | 2-0 | 1-3 | 1-0 | 1-1 | 2-3 | 2-3 | 0-3 | 3-1 | 5-1 | 4-2 | 2-3 | 3-2 | 0-0 |
| 6 | Grays Athletic | 6-0 | 3-1 | 4-1 | 1-1 | 1-4 |  | 4-1 | 3-0 | 2-1 | 2-0 | 1-1 | 4-1 | 3-0 | 3-2 | 2-2 | 3-0 | 4-2 | 3-5 | 3-1 | 2-0 | 1-1 | 4-0 |
| 7 | Harlow Town | 1-2 | 3-4 | 0-5 | 1-2 | 2-2 | 1-2 |  | 0-2 | 3-0 | 0-1 | 0-3 | 0-1 | 1-0 | 2-3 | 3-6 | 0-4 | 1-0 | 0-0 | 1-1 | 0-2 | 2-2 | 2-0 |
| 8 | Heybridge Swifts | 4-2 | 1-1 | 1-3 | 2-2 | 3-2 | 1-2 | 0-1 |  | 3-0 | 1-0 | 2-2 | 2-1 | 11-0 | 3-0 | 2-8 | 2-2 | 4-2 | 3-1 | 4-0 | 2-2 | 3-1 | 1-1 |
| 9 | Ilford | 1-1 | 0-5 | 0-1 | 1-3 | 3-3 | 0-2 | 2-1 | 0-6 |  | 0-3 | 1-6 | 1-1 | 2-1 | 0-2 | 1-3 | 0-0 | 0-1 | 1-4 | 2-2 | 3-3 | 2-7 | 1-3 |
| 10 | Maldon & Tiptree | 3-1 | 0-0 | 5-1 | 4-3 | 6-1 | 2-1 | 9-1 | 1-0 | 1-0 |  | 1-0 | 3-2 | 2-2 | 1-1 | 4-1 | 1-0 | 3-3 | 0-0 | 5-2 | 4-3 | 2-1 | 4-0 |
| 11 | Needham Market | 1-3 | 4-1 | 1-1 | 0-1 | 2-2 | 0-1 | 2-2 | 2-2 | 3-0 | 1-3 |  | 0-2 | 2-1 | 2-2 | 2-3 | 0-5 | 1-1 | 0-0 | 1-6 | 2-0 | 1-3 | 0-0 |
| 12 | Potters Bar Town | 4-1 | 0-5 | 3-0 | 0-0 | 3-2 | 0-2 | 0-0 | 1-1 | 1-0 | 2-2 | 2-2 |  | 3-2 | 2-2 | 1-3 | 2-4 | 0-2 | 1-0 | 1-1 | 2-2 | 2-2 | 2-1 |
| 13 | Redbridge | 1-0 | 1-4 | 0-3 | 1-3 | 2-1 | 0-1 | 0-4 | 0-8 | 1-1 | 0-4 | 1-4 | 0-2 |  | 0-5 | 2-4 | 3-4 | 1-3 | 0-1 | 2-2 | 0-1 | 1-4 |  |
| 14 | Romford | 5-2 | 2-1 | 3-4 | 0-0 | 0-0 | 1-2 | 2-0 | 0-5 | 1-0 | 0-3 | 1-0 | 2-1 | 1-2 |  | 2-3 | 1-4 | 2-1 | 3-1 | 2-2 | 4-1 | 0-1 | 1-0 |
| 15 | Soham Town Rangers | 7-2 | 3-3 | 2-2 | 1-0 | 2-4 | 1-2 | 2-1 | 0-4 | 1-2 | 0-2 | 3-2 | 3-0 | 3-0 | 1-1 |  | 4-2 | 1-1 | 1-3 | 2-1 | 1-3 | 0-1 | 3-3 |
| 16 | Thamesmead Town | 1-0 | 3-2 | 1-2 | 4-0 | 2-3 | 1-2 | 2-1 | 4-1 | 4-0 | 2-1 | 0-3 | 3-2 | 1-0 | 3-1 | 1-0 |  | 1-0 | 3-0 | 2-1 | 1-0 | 0-1 | 2-1 |
| 17 | Tilbury | 1-1 | 1-3 | 1-1 | 5-1 | 2-1 | 0-1 | 1-0 | 2-1 | 3-2 | 2-4 | 2-1 | 2-2 | 4-1 | 1-2 | 0-1 | 0-1 |  | 0-2 | 1-0 | 6-1 | 2-1 | 3-2 |
| 18 | Waltham Abbey | 0-2 | 1-2 | 2-4 | 1-1 | 4-0 | 1-1 | 1-5 | 5-1 | 0-3 | 2-0 | 2-0 | 0-0 | 4-0 | 0-2 | 1-2 | 1-2 | 2-2 |  | 1-2 | 3-0 | 2-1 |  |
| 19 | Waltham Forest | 2-2 | 2-1 | 1-0 | 0-0 | 2-2 | 0-3 | 3-0 | 0-1 | 3-1 | 2-0 | 0-1 | 1-4 | 0-0 | 0-0 | 1-2 | 1-2 | 1-2 | 0-3 |  | 2-3 | 1-2 | 0-0 |
| 20 | Ware | 1-2 | 1-4 | 2-1 | 0-3 | 1-2 | 1-5 | 2-3 | 0-5 | 1-1 | 2-3 | 1-2 | 1-3 | 1-1 | 1-3 | 0-3 | 0-1 | 1-0 | 3-2 | 2-0 |  | 2-4 | 4-3 |
| 21 | Witham Town | 1-1 | 0-2 | 2-0 | 2-2 | 1-0 | 0-0 | 0-1 | 0-0 | 4-0 | 3-2 | 1-0 | 2-3 | 1-2 | 1-0 | 2-1 | 2-1 | 2-0 | 3-0 | 2-1 | 4-1 |  | 1-0 |
| 22 | Wroxham | 2-3 | 1-1 | 2-0 | 1-1 | 0-1 | 0-1 | 3-0 | 3-0 | 2-0 | 2-2 | 1-1 | 0-0 | 1-3 | 5-0 | 0-3 | 4-3 | 2-3 | 2-2 | 3-3 | 4-1 | 0-1 |  |

# DIVISION ONE SOUTH 2012-13

| | | P | W | D | L | F | A | GD | Pts |
|---|---|---|---|---|---|---|---|---|---|
| 1 | (P) Dulwich Hamlet | 42 | 28 | 5 | 9 | 91 | 42 | +49 | 89 |
| 2 | (P) Maidstone United | 42 | 26 | 10 | 6 | 96 | 39 | +57 | 88 |
| 3 | Faversham Town | 42 | 22 | 11 | 9 | 74 | 57 | +17 | 77 |
| 4 | Hythe Town | 42 | 22 | 10 | 10 | 78 | 55 | +23 | 76 |
| 5 | Folkestone Invicta | 42 | 19 | 14 | 9 | 73 | 49 | +24 | 71 |
| 6 | Leatherhead | 42 | 22 | 4 | 16 | 66 | 44 | +22 | 70 |
| 7 | Ramsgate | 42 | 20 | 10 | 12 | 60 | 44 | +16 | 70 |
| 8 | Burgess Hill Town | 42 | 16 | 15 | 11 | 54 | 46 | +8 | 63 |
| 9 | Sittingbourne | 42 | 16 | 13 | 13 | 67 | 56 | +11 | 61 |
| 10 | Worthing | 42 | 16 | 9 | 17 | 77 | 74 | +3 | 57 |
| 11 | Eastbourne Town | 42 | 16 | 9 | 17 | 62 | 61 | +1 | 57 |
| 12 | Merstham | 42 | 16 | 8 | 18 | 67 | 76 | −9 | 56 |
| 13 | Crawley Down Gatwick | 42 | 15 | 10 | 17 | 72 | 70 | +2 | 55 |
| 14 | Corinthian-Casuals | 42 | 10 | 16 | 16 | 39 | 54 | −15 | 46 |
| 15 | Horsham | 42 | 12 | 9 | 21 | 54 | 77 | −23 | 45 |
| 16 | Tooting & Mitcham United | 42 | 12 | 9 | 21 | 52 | 75 | −23 | 45 |
| 17 | Whitstable Town | 42 | 12 | 8 | 22 | 53 | 71 | −18 | 44 |
| 18 | Walton & Hersham | 42 | 11 | 11 | 20 | 48 | 77 | −29 | 44 |
| 19 | Herne Bay | 42 | 10 | 13 | 19 | 44 | 69 | −25 | 43 |
| 20 | Chipstead | 42 | 11 | 9 | 22 | 54 | 80 | −26 | 42 |
| 21 | Three Bridges | 42 | 11 | 7 | 24 | 58 | 83 | −25 | 40 |
| 22 | Walton Casuals | 42 | 9 | 10 | 23 | 50 | 90 | −40 | 37 |

## PLAY-OFFS
### Semi-Finals
Maidstone United 1-0 Folkestone Invicta
Faversham Town 3-0 Hythe Town

### Final (@ Maidstone 04/05/13)
Maidstone United 3-0 Faversham Town

| | 1 | 2 | 3 | 4 | 5 | 6 | 7 | 8 | 9 | 10 | 11 | 12 | 13 | 14 | 15 | 16 | 17 | 18 | 19 | 20 | 21 | 22 |
|---|---|---|---|---|---|---|---|---|---|---|---|---|---|---|---|---|---|---|---|---|---|---|
| 1 Burgess Hill Town | | 3-1 | 2-1 | 0-3 | 3-3 | 0-0 | 0-1 | 1-3 | 2-0 | 4-1 | 0-1 | 1-1 | 0-2 | 2-1 | 2-0 | 2-0 | 2-1 | 1-3 | 2-0 | 3-1 | 2-0 | 3-1 |
| 2 Chipstead | 0-0 | | 2-2 | 1-5 | 0-1 | 2-5 | 1-2 | 1-3 | 2-2 | 3-1 | 1-4 | 0-2 | 1-4 | 0-1 | 3-0 | 1-0 | 3-0 | 3-3 | 2-2 | 1-0 | 2-2 | 0-4 |
| 3 Corinthian-Casuals | 0-1 | 1-1 | | 0-1 | 1-0 | 2-1 | 1-2 | 1-1 | 1-1 | 0-0 | 1-3 | 0-2 | 1-3 | 2-2 | 0-2 | 1-1 | 4-4 | 0-0 | 0-1 | 0-0 | 5-1 | 1-4 |
| 4 Crawley Down Gatwick | 5-0 | 3-2 | 0-1 | | 3-1 | 2-1 | 2-4 | 4-3 | 3-1 | 1-1 | 1-2 | 0-3 | 0-0 | 0-1 | 1-1 | 0-3 | 3-1 | 0-4 | 4-0 | 3-1 | 1-1 | 1-0 |
| 5 Dulwich Hamlet | 1-1 | 2-1 | 3-0 | 3-1 | | 4-2 | 1-1 | 2-0 | 2-1 | 4-0 | 0-2 | 3-1 | 1-1 | 4-1 | 3-0 | 3-1 | 2-0 | 2-2 | 3-0 | 5-0 | 3-0 | 3-0 |
| 6 Eastbourne Town | 2-1 | 3-0 | 0-0 | 2-1 | 2-0 | | 1-1 | 1-1 | 2-3 | 3-1 | 0-2 | 0-0 | 0-3 | 3-2 | 0-1 | 2-2 | 0-3 | 1-0 | 4-3 | 0-2 | 2-0 | 0-1 |
| 7 Faversham Town | 2-1 | 0-2 | 0-0 | 1-1 | 0-2 | 3-3 | | 0-1 | 1-1 | 3-1 | 3-2 | 1-0 | 0-4 | 4-1 | 1-1 | 3-0 | 2-2 | 1-0 | 1-4 | 7-0 | 1-4 | 1-2 |
| 8 Folkestone Invicta | 1-1 | 3-2 | 0-0 | 2-1 | 0-2 | 2-2 | 2-2 | | 1-0 | 2-1 | 1-1 | 2-0 | 2-2 | 1-3 | 3-1 | 0-0 | 3-1 | 1-0 | 5-0 | 3-0 | 2-1 | 2-1 |
| 9 Herne Bay | 1-1 | 0-1 | 1-3 | 4-3 | 1-3 | 1-0 | 0-3 | 3-2 | | 2-1 | 0-0 | 0-1 | 1-3 | 0-3 | 0-2 | 0-0 | 0-0 | 0-1 | 2-1 | 0-4 | 1-1 | 1-4 |
| 10 Horsham | 0-1 | 4-1 | 1-1 | 1-4 | 1-4 | 1-3 | 1-2 | 2-1 | 0-1 | | 3-4 | 1-0 | 1-1 | 1-0 | 0-2 | 4-3 | 4-1 | 3-1 | 0-0 | 2-0 | 2-0 | 0-0 |
| 11 Hythe Town | 2-2 | 0-1 | 3-1 | 2-1 | 1-0 | 2-4 | 2-2 | 2-1 | 0-1 | 1-0 | | 2-3 | 3-4 | 0-0 | 0-2 | 1-1 | 1-0 | 5-2 | 1-1 | 1-0 | 2-0 | 2-2 |
| 12 Leatherhead | 0-1 | 0-1 | 0-1 | 4-0 | 1-0 | 3-2 | 3-1 | 1-1 | 1-0 | 1-2 | 0-1 | | 0-1 | 3-1 | 1-2 | 0-1 | 1-1 | 2-2 | 3-1 | 4-0 | 1-0 | 1-3 |
| 13 Maidstone United | 0-0 | 3-0 | 2-0 | 2-2 | 5-0 | 2-0 | 1-2 | 2-2 | 2-0 | 3-0 | 1-1 | 2-3 | | 2-0 | 2-1 | 2-1 | 3-1 | 3-0 | 4-5 | 1-1 | 2-0 | 2-2 |
| 14 Merstham | 1-1 | 1-4 | 0-0 | 2-4 | 3-1 | 3-1 | 1-2 | 2-1 | 2-4 | 2-2 | 1-4 | 3-1 | 1-3 | | 0-2 | 2-1 | 0-1 | 2-1 | 2-1 | 1-0 | 2-1 | 0-3 |
| 15 Ramsgate | 1-1 | 1-0 | 0-0 | 4-1 | 0-3 | 0-0 | 2-0 | 1-1 | 3-1 | 4-0 | 2-4 | 4-1 | 1-0 | 1-1 | | 1-3 | 1-1 | 1-2 | 1-2 | 0-1 | 1-2 | 2-0 |
| 16 Sittingbourne | 2-1 | 2-2 | 3-0 | 2-2 | 3-1 | 1-0 | 1-1 | 0-1 | 2-2 | 2-1 | 1-0 | 0-1 | 2-1 | 2-2 | 0-1 | | 5-2 | 2-0 | 3-2 | 1-1 | 1-1 | 1-2 |
| 17 Three Bridges | 0-0 | 4-1 | 1-2 | 3-1 | 1-2 | 0-2 | 0-0 | 0-3 | 4-1 | 2-1 | 1-3 | 0-3 | 1-3 | 2-3 | 1-2 | 2-3 | | 1-0 | 2-3 | 3-2 | 3-2 | 2-2 |
| 18 Tooting & Mitcham United | 1-1 | 1-1 | 3-0 | 1-0 | 0-2 | 0-1 | 1-2 | 0-5 | 0-1 | 0-3 | 3-2 | 0-3 | 0-5 | 2-4 | 1-3 | 2-2 | 0-2 | | 1-1 | 0-2 | 3-2 | 5-2 |
| 19 Walton & Hersham | 0-1 | 1-0 | 1-0 | 2-1 | 0-4 | 2-2 | 1-0 | 1-1 | 4-2 | 1-1 | 2-2 | 1-3 | 0-4 | 1-0 | 0-2 | 0-5 | 2-0 | 0-1 | | 1-1 | 1-2 | 0-2 |
| 20 Walton Casuals | 0-5 | 1-4 | 0-1 | 1-1 | 0-2 | 1-2 | 1-2 | 1-3 | 1-1 | 3-1 | 1-3 | 0-2 | 0-3 | 6-6 | 1-1 | 4-1 | 2-3 | 0-1 | 2-2 | | 0-3 | 1-6 |
| 21 Whitstable Town | 2-4 | 1-0 | 0-2 | 0-0 | 1-2 | 2-0 | 2-3 | 2-1 | 1-1 | 2-2 | 1-2 | 0-5 | 2-3 | 1-0 | 0-1 | 1-2 | 2-1 | 0-4 | 3-0 | 1-1 | | 4-0 |
| 22 Worthing | 0-0 | 3-0 | 1-2 | 2-2 | 1-4 | 0-3 | 3-5 | 1-1 | 2-2 | 1-2 | 3-4 | 1-3 | 2-0 | 4-2 | 2-1 | 3-1 | 3-4 | 2-0 | 0-0 | 3-4 | 0-2 | |

# LEAGUE CUP 2012-13

## ROUND 1

| | | |
|---|---|---|
| Cheshunt | 1-2 | Soham Town Rangers |
| Chipstead | 0-3 | Three Bridges |

## ROUND 2

| | | |
|---|---|---|
| Aveley | 5-0 | East Thurrock United |
| Chatham Town | 0-2 | Harrow Borough |
| Wealdstone | 3-2 | Ramsgate AFC |
| Sudbury | 0-3 | Leiston King's |
| Burgess Hill Town | 0-0 | Bognor Regis Town (3-4p |
| Canvey Island | 6-0 | Ilford16 October 2012 |
| Corinthian-Casuals | 1-1 | Walton Casuals (3-4p) |
| Faversham Town | 4-3 | Cray Wanderers |
| Grays Athletic | 0-3 | Waltham Forest |
| Harlow Town | 0-2 | Witham Town |
| Hastings United | 1-0 | Lewes |
| Horsham | 2-1 | Walton & Hersham |
| Leatherhead | 0-0 | Carshalton Athletic (1-4p) |
| Maidstone United | 4-0 | Sittingbourne |
| Maldon & Tiptree | 0-3 | Bury Town |
| Margate | 0-4 | Met Police |
| Needham Market | 6-1 | Ware |
| Redbridge | 1-0 | Potters Bar Town |
| Soham Town Rangers | 1-1 | Lowestoft Town (4-2p) |
| Thamesmead Town | 4-3 | Waltham Abbey |
| Three Bridges | 5-4 | Hampton & Richmond |
| Thurrock | 2-0 | Wingate & Finchley |
| Whitehawk | 5-0 | Merstham |
| Whitstable Town | 4-3 | Hythe Town |
| Worthing | 3-2 | Crawley Down Gatwick |
| Wroxham | 4-2 | Heybridge Swifts |
| Eastbourne Town | 1-2 | **DULWICH HAMLET** |
| Enfield Town | 0-1 | Brentwood Town |
| Folkestone Invicta | 2-2 | Kingstonian (2-4p) |
| Hendon | 2-2 | Tilbury (0-3p) |
| Herne Bay | 2-2 | Tooting & Mitcham (7-6p) |
| Romford | 1-4 | **CONCORD RANGERS** |

## ROUND 3

| | | |
|---|---|---|
| Aveley | 2-1 | Tilbury |
| Bognor Regis Town | 0-1 | Whitehawk |
| Carshalton Athletic | 1-2 | Wealdstone |
| **DULWICH HAMLET** | 5-1 | Herne Bay |
| Faversham Town | 0-1 | Thamesmead Town |
| Harrow Borough | 0-1 | Kingstonian |
| Hastings United | 6-4 | Three Bridges |
| Leiston | 1-1 | Soham Town Rangers (3-5 p) |
| Redbridge | 0-9 | **CONCORD RANGERS** |
| Thurrock | 0-0 | Brentwood Town (4-3p) |
| Whitstable Town | 0-2 | Maidstone United |
| Witham Town | 2-4 | Bury Town |
| Wroxham | 1-1 | Needham Market (4-3p) |
| Metropolitan Police | 5-3 | Walton Casuals |
| Waltham Forest | 3-1 | Canvey Island |
| Horsham | 1-2 | Worthing |

## ROUND 4

| | | |
|---|---|---|
| **CONCORD RANGERS** | 2-1 | Bury Town |
| Thamesmead Town | 2-2 | Aveley (4-3p) |
| Thurrock | 1-1 | Waltham Forest (6-5p) |
| Whitehawk | 2-0 | Maidstone United |
| Worthing | 2-3 | Hastings United |
| Wroxham | 0-0 | Soham Town Rangers (7-6 p) |
| **DULWICH HAMLET** | 1-0 | Wealdstone |

## QUARTER FINAL

| | | |
|---|---|---|
| Hastings United | 4-3 | Whitehawk |
| Thamesmead Town | 0-0 | Thurrock (4-2p) |
| **CONCORD RANGERS** | 2-0 | Wroxham |
| **DULWICH HAMLET** | 4-1 | Kingstonian |

## SEMI FINALS

| | | |
|---|---|---|
| **CONCORD RANGERS** | 3-0 | Hastings Town |
| **DULWICH HAMLET** | 1-1 | Thamesmead Town (5-3p) |

## FINAL

| | | |
|---|---|---|
| **CONCORD RANGERS** | 3-2* | **DULWICH HAMLET** |
| | | *AET |

# Isthmian League Premier Division Statistics 2012-13

| | MCV | MCD | MCwW | MCwD | MCSG | MCwS | TGS | MCCS | TNCS |
|---|---|---|---|---|---|---|---|---|---|
| Bognor Regis Town | 2 | 4 | 7 | 4 | 6 | 4 | 17 | 2 | 10 |
| Bury Town | 5 | 4 | 4 | 9 | 10 | 3 | 10 | 4 | 11 |
| Canvey Island | 3 | 3 | 7 | 5 | 10 | 4 | 15 | 3 | 13 |
| Carshalton Athletic | 4 | 8 | 8 | 4 | 12 | 2 | 14 | 2 | 8 |
| Concord Rangers | 6 | 3 | 3 | 8 | 17 | 3 | 5 | 3 | 17 |
| Cray Wanderers | 2 | 5 | 8 | 5 | 13 | 3 | 13 | 1 | 9 |
| East Thurrock United | 6 | 2 | 6 | 15 | 17 | 1 | 7 | 3 | 20 |
| Enfield Town | 2 | 6 | 8 | 5 | 8 | 3 | 12 | 2 | 8 |
| Hampton & Richmond B | 3 | 3 | 8 | 10 | 16 | 3 | 14 | 6 | 20 |
| Harrow Borough | 2 | 5 | 7 | 3 | 5 | 3 | 16 | 1 | 8 |
| Hastings United | 2 | 3 | 18 | 10 | 8 | 2 | 17 | 2 | 8 |
| Hendon | 3 | 2 | 7 | 9 | 14 | 2 | 11 | 2 | 16 |
| Kingstonian | 3 | 5 | 6 | 4 | 7 | 3 | 13 | 2 | 8 |
| Leiston | 4 | 8 | 6 | 10 | 23 | 3 | 13 | 3 | 11 |
| Lewes | 2 | 6 | 6 | 5 | 10 | 1 | 9 | 2 | 9 |
| Lowestoft Town | 3 | 2 | 3 | 20 | 9 | 1 | 8 | 3 | 21 |
| Margate | 4 | 5 | 7 | 10 | 10 | 3 | 12 | 4 | 13 |
| Metropolitan Police | 5 | 2 | 4 | 12 | 22 | 2 | 7 | 2 | 13 |
| Thurrock | 3 | 5 | 7 | 3 | 10 | 2 | 15 | 2 | 11 |
| Wealdstone | 3 | 2 | 4 | 13 | 14 | 1 | 8 | 3 | 18 |
| Whitehawk | 6 | 1 | 3 | 13 | 15 | 2 | 7 | 4 | 17 |
| Wingate & Finchley | 2 | 4 | 8 | 4 | 14 | 3 | 12 | 1 | 6 |

MCV - Most Consecutive Victories
MCD - Most Consecutive Defeatss
MCwW - Most Consecutive without a Win
MCwD - Most Consecutive without a defeat
MCSG - Most Consecutive Scoring Games
MCwS - Most Consecutive without Scoring
TGS - Total Games without Scoring
MCCS - Most Consecutive Clean Sheets
TNCS - Total Number of Clean Sheets

## Goalscorers with at least Ten goals in League, FA Cup and FA Trophy in 2012-2013

| | Individual Scorers | | | | | | Total Individual Scorers | Hat tricks | Pens | OG scored by opponents |
|---|---|---|---|---|---|---|---|---|---|---|
| Bognor Regis Town | James Crane | 11 | | | | | 17 + 0 ogs | 4 | | |
| Bury Town | John Sands | 26 | Sam Reed | 11 | Craig Parker | 10 | 19 + 1 | 6 | 1 | Concord Rangers |
| Canvey Island | Bradley Woods-Garness | 21 | Rob King | 13 | Jay Curran | 10 | 13 + 2 | 4 | 1 | 2 East Thurrock U , Uxbridge |
| Carshalton Athletic | Nat Pinney | 22 | | | | | 17 + 1 | 5 | 3 | Harrow Borough |
| Concord Rangers | Tony Stokes | 24 | Harry Elmes | 14 | Jason Hallett | 13 | 16 + 0 | 5 | 2 | |
| Cray Wanderers | Leigh Bremner | 24 | Paul Vines | 10 | | | 17 + 0 | 2 | | |
| East Thurrock United | Sam Higgins | 20 | Sam Collins | 15 | David Bryant | 10 | 13 + 1 | 3 | | 1 Hampton & Richmond |
| Enfield Town | Liam Hope | 22 | Scott McGleish | 12 | | | 14 + 1 | 5 | 3 | 1 Hendon |
| Hampton & Richmond B | Charlie Moone | 24 | | | | | 19 + 1 | 2 | | 1 Bognor Regis Town |
| Harrow Borough | Simon Akinola | 11 | | | | | 17 + 1 | 4 | | 1 Lowestoft Town |
| Hastings United | Bradley Goldberg | 11 | | | | | 15 + 0 | 3 | | |
| Hendon | | | | | | | 22 + 2 | 3 | | 2 Enfield Town |
| Kingstonian | Andre McCollin | 17 | Matt Pattison | 16 | | | 18 + 0 | 3 | 2 | |
| Leiston | Gareth Heath | 21 | Emanuel Osie | 11 | | | 14 + 1 | 2 | | 1 Harrow Borough |
| Lewes | Nathan Crabb | 12 | | | | | 16 + 1 | 1 | 1 | 1 Cray Wanderers |
| Lowestoft Town | Jack Defty | 21 | Chris Henderson | 14 | | | 16 + 1 | 5 | 1 | 1 Harrow Borough |
| Margate | Tommy Whitnell | 10 | | | | | 15 + 1 | 3 | | 1 Cray Wanderers |
| Metropolitan Police | Jonte Smith | 19 | David Knight | 13 | | | 19 + 2 | 3 | 1 | 2 Bury Town, Hastings United |
| Thurrock | | | | | | | 17 + 4 | 3 | | 4 Leiston, Lewes, Welling U, Wingate & Finchley |
| Wealdstone | Richard Jolly | 19 | Peter Dean | 12 | | | 15 + 4 | 2 | 1 | 4 Harrow Borough, Margate, Merstham, Thurrock |
| Whitehawk | Danny Mills | 12 | James Fraser | 10 | Sam Gargan | 10 | | 6 | 2 | |
| | | | | | Michael Malcolm | 10 | 24 + 0 | | 2 | |
| Wingate & Finchley | Leon Smith | 10 | | | | | 23 + 0 | 1 | | |

# AFC HORNCHURCH

**Chairman:** Colin McBride
**Secretary:** Peter Butcher          **(T)** 07918 645 109          **(E)** peter.butcher5@btinternet.com
**Commercial Manager:** Peter Butcher          **(T)** 07918 645 109
**Programme Editor:** Peter Butcher          **(T)** 07918 645 109
**Ground Address:** The Stadium, Bridge Avenue, Upminster, Essex RM14 2LX
**(T)** 01708 220 080                    **Manager:** Jim McFarlane

## Club Factfile

**Founded:** 2005          **Nickname:** The Urchins
**Previous Names:** Formed in 2005 after Hornchurch F.C. folded
**Previous Leagues:** Essex Senior 2005-06. Isthmian 2006-12. Conference 2012-13.

**Club Colours (change):** Red and white stripes/black/black

**Ground Capacity:** 3,500    **Seats:** 800    **Covered:** 1,400    **Clubhouse:** Yes    **Shop:** Yes

**Directions**

Bridge Avenue is off A124 between Hornchurch and Upminster.

**Previous Grounds:** None

**Record Attendance:** 3,500 v Tranmere Rovers - FA Cup 2nd Round 2003-04
**Record Victory:** Not known
**Record Defeat:** Not known
**Record Goalscorer:** Not known
**Record Appearances:** Not known
**Additional Records:** Won the Essex League with a record 64 points in 2005-06

**Senior Honours:**
Since reformation in 2005: Essex Senior League, League Cup and Memorial Trophy 2005-06.
Isthmian League Division 1 North 2006-07, Premier Division Play-offs 2011-12.
Essex Senior Cup 2012-13.

### 10 YEAR RECORD

| 03-04 | | 04-05 | | 05-06 | | 06-07 | | 07-08 | | 08-09 | | 09-10 | | 10-11 | | 11-12 | | 12-13 | |
|---|---|---|---|---|---|---|---|---|---|---|---|---|---|---|---|---|---|---|---|
| Isth P | 5 | Conf S | 17 | ESen | 1 | Isth1N | 1 | Isth P | 4 | Isth P | 6 | Isth P | 9 | Isth P | 10 | Isth P | 2 | Conf S | 20 |

# MATCH RESULTS 2012-13

| Date | Comp | H/A | Opponents | Att: | Result | Goalscorers | Pos | No. |
|------|------|-----|-----------|------|--------|-------------|-----|-----|
| Aug 17 | BSS | A | Salisbury City | 663 | L 1-2 | Tuohy 44 | 17 | 1 |
| 21 | BSS | H | Boreham Wood | 270 | D 1-1 | L.Smith 36 | 18 | 2 |
| 25 | BSS | H | Dover Athletic | 1105 | L 0-1 | | 19 | 3 |
| 27 | BSS | A | Billericay Town | 647 | D 1-1 | McKenzie 67 | 18 | 4 |
| Sept 1 | BSS | H | Weston-s-Mare | 245 | D 0-0 | | 18 | 5 |
| 4 | BSS | A | Bromley | 408 | L 0-4 | | 19 | 6 |
| 8 | BSS | A | Basingstoke Town | 359 | W 2-0 | Tuohy 30 (pen) Smith 64 | 18 | 7 |
| 15 | BSS | H | Dorchester Town | 273 | W1-0 | Smith 33 | 15 | 8 |
| 22 | FAC Q2 | A | Billericay Town | 509 | L 1-3 | Smith 90 | | 9 |
| 29 | BSS | H | Farnborough | 263 | D 1-1 | Smith 6 (pen) | 17 | 10 |
| Oct 2 | BSS | A | Maidenhead United | 245 | W 4-2 | Tuohy 23 58 Bowditch 39 Brown 44 (og) | 14 | 11 |
| 6 | BSS | H | Havant & Waterlooville | 215 | D 2-2 | Tuohy 22 McKenzie 83 | 9 | 12 |
| 13 | BSS | A | Staines Town | 347 | L 1-3 | Gray 81 | 14 | 13 |
| 20 | BSS | H | Eastbourne Borough | 278 | L 0-1 | | 15 | 14 |
| 27 | BSS | A | Bath City | 509 | L 1-3 | Gray 21 | 18 | 15 |
| 30 | BSS | H | Chelmsford City | 515 | L 0-2 | | 20 | 16 |
| Nov 3 | BSS | A | Truro City | 414 | L 2-3 | McKenzie 57 90 | 20 | 17 |
| 10 | FAT Q3 | H | Bishop's Stortford | 301 | L 2-3 | Curley 23 Mackenzie 47 | | 18 |
| 17 | BSS | H | Eastleigh | 298 | W 1-0 | Daniel 6 | 18 | 19 |
| Dec 1 | BSS | A | Hayes & Yeading | 141 | W 3-1 | Love 5 Curley 16 McKenzie 90 | 16 | 20 |
| 8 | BSS | A | Weston-s-Mare | 256 | L 0-1 | | 18 | 21 |
| 15 | BSS | H | Basingstoke Town | 260 | W 3-0 | McKenzie 48 56 Gray 73 | 12 | 22 |
| 26 | BSS | H | Welling United | 483 | L 0-3 | | 15 | 23 |
| 29 | BSS | H | Billericay Town | 503 | W 1-0 | Eyong 29 | 8 | 24 |
| Jan 1 | BSS | A | Welling United | 670 | L 0-4 | | 11 | 25 |
| 5 | BSS | A | Havant & Waterlooville | 641 | L 2-5 | Smith 81 Gray 84 | 14 | 26 |
| 12 | BSS | H | Salisbury City | 270 | D 2-2 | Tuohy 81 (pen) 90 (pen) | 16 | 27 |
| 26 | BSS | H | Tonbridge Angels | 362 | D 1-1 | Smith 75 | 16 | 28 |
| Feb 2 | BSS | A | Eastbourne Borough | 544 | D 1-1 | Spencer 69 | 16 | 29 |
| 9 | BSS | H | Sutton United | 352 | D 1-1 | Gray 90 | 18 | 30 |
| 16 | BSS | H | Maidenhead United | 338 | L 0-2 | | 20 | 31 |
| 19 | BSS | A | Tonbridge Angels | 304 | L 0-1 | | 20 | 32 |
| 23 | BSS | H | Staines Town | 234 | D 1-1 | Tuohy 90 (pen) | 20 | 33 |
| Mar 2 | BSS | A | Farnborough | 386 | D 1-1 | Tuohy 70 | 20 | 34 |
| 9 | BSS | H | Bath City | 340 | W 2-1 | Tuohy 60 Smith 80 | 19 | 35 |
| 13 | BSS | A | Chelmsford City | 428 | W 4-1 | Tuohy 3 (pen) St Aimie 9 L.Smith 84 Rainford 72 (og) | 17 | 36 |
| 26 | BSS | A | Dover Athletic | 483 | L 0-1 | | 19 | 37 |
| 29 | BSS | A | Boreham Wood | 287 | L 1-2 | St Aimie 66 | 20 | 38 |
| Apr 1 | BSS | H | Bromley | 316 | W 1-0 | St Aimie 90 | 17 | 39 |
| 6 | BSS | A | Eastleigh | 504 | L 0-1 | | 18 | 40 |
| 9 | BSS | A | Dorchester Town | 327 | L 1-3 | Noel 58 | 18 | 41 |
| 13 | BSS | H | Truro City | 282 | L 1-2 | May-52 | 20 | 42 |
| 20 | BSS | A | Sutton United | 516 | L1-4 | Gray 74 | 20 | 43 |
| 27 | BSS | H | Hayes & Yeading | 281 | W 2-0 | Tuohy 54 57 | 20 | 44 |

| GOALSCORERS | Lge | FAC | LC | Total | Pens | Hat-tricks | Cons Run | | Lge | FAC | LC | Total | Pens | Hat-tricks | Cons Run |
|-------------|-----|-----|----|-------|------|------------|----------|---|-----|-----|----|-------|------|------------|----------|
| Tuohy | 12 | | | 12 | 5 | | 4 | May | 1 | | | 1 | | | |
| Mackenzie | 8 | | 1 | 9 | | | | Noel | 1 | | | 1 | | | |
| Smith | 8 | 1 | | 9 | 1 | | | Spencer | 1 | | | 1 | | | |
| Gray | 6 | | | 6 | | | | Own Goals | 2 | | | 2 | | | |
| St Aimie | 3 | | | 3 | | | | Cons Run - Consecutive scoring games. | | | | | | | |
| Curley | 1 | | 1 | 2 | | | | | | | | | | | |
| Bowditch | 1 | | | 1 | | | | | | | | | | | |
| Daniel | 1 | | | 1 | | | | | | | | | | | |
| Eyong | 1 | | | 1 | | | | | | | | | | | |
| Love | 1 | | | 1 | | | | | | | | | | | |

# BILLERICAY TOWN

**Chairman:** Steve Kent

**Secretary:** Ian Ansell    **(T)** 0795 897 8154    **(E)** secretary@billericaytownfc.co.uk

**Commercial Manager:**    **(T)**

**Programme Editor:** Gary Clark    **(T)** 07702 018 590

**Ground Address:** New Lodge, Blunts Wall Road, Billericay CM12 9SA

**(T)** 01277 652 188    **Manager:** Craig Edwards

## Club Factfile

**Founded:** 1880    **Nickname:** Town or Blues

**Previous Names:** None

**Previous Leagues:** Romford & District 1890-1914, Mid Essex 1918-47, South Essex Combination 1947-66, Essex Olympian 1966-71, Essex Senior 1971-77, Athenian 1977-79. Isthmian 1979-2012. Conference 2012-13.

**Club Colours (change):** Blue & white

**Ground Capacity:** 3,500    **Seats:** 424    **Covered:** 2,000    **Clubhouse:** Yes    **Shop:** Yes

**Directions** From the M25 (J29) take the A127 to the Basildon/Billericay (A176) turn-off, (junction after the Old Fortune of War r'about). Take second exit at r'about (Billericay is signposted). Then straight over (2nd exit) at the next roundabout. Continue along that road until you enter Billericay. At the first r'about take the first available exit. At the next r'about (with Billericay School on your left) go straight over (1st exit). At yet another r'about!, turn left into the one-way system. Keep in the left-hand lane and go straight over r'about. At first set of lights, turn left. Blunts Wall Road is the second turning on your right.

**Previous Grounds:** None

**Record Attendance:** 3,841 v West Ham United - Opening of Floodlights 1977

**Record Victory:** 11-0 v Stansted (A) - Essex Senior League 05/05/1976

**Record Defeat:** 3-10 v Chelmsford City (A) - Essex Senior Cup 04/01/1993

**Record Goalscorer:** Freddie Claydon - 273

**Record Appearances:** J Pullen - 418

**Additional Records:** Leon Gutzmore scored 51 goals during the 1997-98 season.

**Senior Honours:**    Received £22,500+ from West Ham United for Steve Jones November 1992

FA Vase 1975-76, 76-77, 78-79. Essex Senior Cup 1975-76. Athenian League 1978-79. Isthmian Premier Division 2011-12. Essex Senior Trophy x2.

### 10 YEAR RECORD

| 03-04 | | 04-05 | | 05-06 | | 06-07 | | 07-08 | | 08-09 | | 09-10 | | 10-11 | | 11-12 | | 12-13 | |
|---|---|---|---|---|---|---|---|---|---|---|---|---|---|---|---|---|---|---|---|
| Isth P | 22 | Isth P | 2 | Isth P | 7 | Isth P | 4 | Isth P | 10 | Isth P | 11 | Isth P | 13 | Isth P | 11 | Isth P | 1 | Conf S | 21 |

# MATCH RESULTS 2012-13

| Date | Comp | H/A | Opponents | Att: | Result | Goalscorers | Pos | No. |
|------|------|-----|-----------|------|--------|-------------|-----|-----|
| Aug 18 | BSS | H | Truro City | 402 | W 2-1 | Wild 21 Lechmere 87 | 4 | 1 |
| 21 | BSS | A | Hayes & Yeading | 267 | L 2-4 | Poole 50 (pen 73 (pen) | 12 | 2 |
| 25 | BSS | A | Eastbourne Borough | 705 | L 1-2 | Poole 47 (pen) | 15 | 3 |
| 27 | BSS | H | AFC Hornchurch | 647 | D 1-1 | Lechmere 12 | 16 | 4 |
| Sept 1 | BSS | A | Bath City | 611 | L 1-2 | Poole 59 (pen) | 16 | 5 |
| 4 | BSS | H | Tonbridge Angels | 369 | D 3-3 | Green 8 Swaine 37 Poole 57 | 15 | 6 |
| 8 | BSS | H | Eastleigh | 503 | W 4-0 | Poole 21 (Pen) Charles-Smith 28  Wild 53  Green 65 | 11 | 7 |
| 15 | BSS | A | Staines Town | 363 | W 2-1 | Osborn 39 Swaine 88 | 8 | 8 |
| 22 | FAC Q2 | H | AFC Hornchurch | 509 | W 3-1 | LECHMERE 3 (13 67 89) |  | 9 |
| 29 | BSS | H | Basingstoke Town | 479 | L 1-3 | Swaine 55 | 14 | 10 |
| Oct 1 | BSS | A | Boreham Wood | 242 | L 0-3 |  | 18 | 11 |
| 6 | FAC Q3 | A | Cambridge City | 394 | D 1-1 | Theobald 52 (og) |  | 12 |
| 9 | FAC Q3r | H | Cambridge City | 364 | L 2-4 | Poole 37 84 (pen) |  | 13 |
| 13 | BSS | H | Dorchester Town | 477 | W 3-1 | Taylor 19 Lechmere 61 Poole 66 | 13 | 14 |
| 20 | BSS | H | Havant & Waterlooville | 401 | W 3-1 | Collis 18 Osborn 29 56 | 13 | 15 |
| Nov 3 | BSS | H | Weston s Mare | 395 | D 0-0 |  | 15 | 16 |
| 10 | FAT Q3 | H | Enfield Town | 417 | W 3-2 | Swaine 2 Poole 4 May 60 |  | 17 |
| 17 | BSS | A | Bromley | 450 | W 1-0 | May | 11 | 18 |
| 20 | BSS | A | Dover Athletic | 607 | L 1-4 | Edwards 37 | 11 | 19 |
| 24 | FAT 1 | H | Cambridge United | 537 | L 0-3 |  |  | 20 |
| 27 | BSS | A | Welling United | 408 | L 2-5 | Edwards 72 Benjamin 90 |  | 21 |
| Dec 1 | BSS | H | Dover Athletic | 501 | L 1-2 | Swaine 88 | 13 | 22 |
| 10 | BSS | H | Bath City | 388 | W 2-0 | May 42 Swaine 88 | 10 | 23 |
| 29 | BSS | A | AFC Hornchurch | 503 | L 0-1 |  | 12 | 24 |
| Jan 1 | BSS | H | Chelmsford City | 1211 | L 0-1 |  | 15 | 25 |
| 8 | BSS | A | Eastleigh | 344 | L 0-5 |  | 19 | 26 |
| 12 | BSS | A | Truro City | 421 | W 4-2 | MAY 4 (5 49 69 76) | 15 | 27 |
| Feb 4 | BSS | A | Chelmsford Town | 918 | D 1-1 | Poole 19 | 13 | 28 |
| 9 | BSS | A | Maidenhead United | 301 | L 2-3 | Swaine 33 May 86 | 21 | 29 |
| 16 | BSS | A | Salisbury City | 764 | L 0-2 |  | 21 | 30 |
| 23 | BSS | H | Bromley | 427 | L 2-3 | Osborn 16 Poole 90 | 21 | 31 |
| 26 | BSS | A | Dorchester Town | 308 | L 1-6 | Taylor 71 | 21 | 32 |
| Mar 2 | BSS | A | Basingstoke Town | 419 | D 3-3 | Swaine 22 Osborn 35 Smith 82 | 21 | 33 |
| 5 | BSS | H | Farnborough | 229 | W 2-1 | May 13 Poole 51 | 20 | 34 |
| 12 | BSS | A | Havant & Waterlooville | 355 | L 0-5 |  | 21 | 35 |
| 16 | BSS | H | Welling United | 519 | L 1-2 | Ashton 88 | 21 | 36 |
| 19 | BSS | H | Sutton United | 293 | L 2-4 | Taylor 40 44 | 21 | 37 |
| 27 | BSS | H | Boreham Wood | 212 | D 1-1 | Osborn 14 | 21 | 38 |
| 30 | BSS | H | Hayes & Yeadng | 424 | W 4-1 | Osborn 53 May 59 83 Wild 80 | 21 | 39 |
| Apr 1 | BSS | A | Tonbridge Angels | 595 | D 1-1 | Poole 44 | 21 | 40 |
| 6 | BSS | A | Sutton United | 566 | L 0-3 |  | 21 | 41 |
| 9 | BSS | H | Eastbourne Borough | 317 | L 1-2 | Hudson 47 | 21 | 42 |
| 13 | BSS | H | Salisbury City | 374 | L 1-2 | Swaine 2 | 21 | 43 |
| 16 | BSS | H | Staines Town | 263 | L 2-3 | Hudson 34 71 | 21 | 44 |
| 20 | BSS | A | Weston-s-Mare | 320 | L 0-1 |  | 21 | 45 |
| 23 | BSS | A | Farnborough | 297 | L 3-4 | Swaine 38 Poole 44 79 | 21 | 46 |
| 27 | BSS | H | Maidenhead United | 340 | W 1-0 | May | 21 | 47 |

| GOALSCORERS | Lge | FAC | LC | Total | Pens | Hat-tricks | Cons Run | | Lge | FAC | LC | Total | Pens | Hat-tricks | Cons Run |
|-------------|-----|-----|----|----|------|-----------|----------|---|-----|-----|----|----|------|-----------|----------|
| Poole | 13 | 2 | 1 | 16 | 6 |  | 2 | Ashton | 1 |  |  | 1 |  |  |  |
| May | 11 |  | 1 | 12 | 1 |  | 2 | Benjamin | 1 |  |  | 1 |  |  |  |
| Swaine | 9 |  | 1 | 10 |  |  | 2 | Charles-Smith | 1 |  |  | 1 |  |  |  |
| Osborn | 7 |  |  | 7 |  |  |  | Collis | 1 |  |  | 1 |  |  |  |
| Lechmere | 3 | 3 |  | 6 | 1 |  |  | Smith | 1 |  |  | 1 |  |  |  |
| Taylor | 4 |  |  | 4 |  |  |  | Own Goal |  | 1 |  | 1 |  |  |  |
| Hudson | 3 |  |  | 3 |  |  |  | Cons Run - Consecutive scoring games. | | | | | | | |
| Wild | 3 |  |  | 3 |  |  |  | | | | | | | | |
| Edwards | 2 |  |  | 2 |  |  |  | | | | | | | | |
| Green | 2 |  |  | 2 |  |  |  | | | | | | | | |

# BOGNOR REGIS TOWN

**Chairman:** Dominic Reynolds
**Secretary:** Simon Cook          **(T)** 07527 455 167          **(E)** sajcook2@aol.com
**Commercial Manager:** n/a          **(T)**
**Programme Editor:** Rob Garforth          **(T)** 07791 591 375
**Ground Address:** Nyewood Lane, Bognor Regis PO21 2TY
**(T)** 01243 822 325                              **Manager:** Jamie Howell

## Club Factfile

**Founded:** 1883          **Nickname:** The Rocks
**Previous Names:** None
**Previous Leagues:** West Sussex 1896-1926, Brighton & Hove District 1926-27, Sussex County 1927-72, Southern League 1972-81, Isthmian 1982-2004, Conference 2004-09

**Club Colours (change):** White with green trim/green/white (Gold/black/gold)

**Ground Capacity:** 4,100   **Seats:** 350   **Covered:** 2,600   **Clubhouse:** Yes   **Shop:** Yes

**Directions:** West along sea front from pier past Aldwick shopping centre then turn right into Nyewood Lane.

**Previous Grounds:** None

**Record Attendance:** 3,642 v Swnsea City - FA Cup 1st Round replay 1984
**Record Victory:** 24-0 v Littlehampton - West Sussex League 1913-14
**Record Defeat:** 0-19 v Shoreham - West Sussex League 1906-07
**Record Goalscorer:** Kevin Clements - 206
**Record Appearances:** Mick Pullen - 967 (20 seasons)
**Additional Records:** Paid £2,000 for Guy Rutherford 1995-96. Received £10,500 from Brighton & Hove for John Crumplin and
**Senior Honours:** Geoff Cooper, and from Crystal Palace for Simon Rodger.
Sussex Professional Cup 1973-74. Sussex Senior Cup x9.
Isthmian League Division 1 South Play-offs 2011-12.

### 10 YEAR RECORD

| 03-04 | | 04-05 | | 05-06 | | 06-07 | | 07-08 | | 08-09 | | 09-10 | | 10-11 | | 11-12 | | 12-13 | |
|---|---|---|---|---|---|---|---|---|---|---|---|---|---|---|---|---|---|---|---|
| Isth P | 10 | Conf S | 9 | Conf S | 12 | Conf S | 12 | Conf S | 18 | Conf S | 21 | Isth P | 22 | Isth1S | 2 | Isth1S | 2 | Isth P | 14 |

# MATCH RESULTS 2012-13

| Date | Comp | H/A | Opponents | Att: | Result | Goalscorers | Pos | No. |
|------|------|-----|-----------|------|--------|-------------|-----|-----|
| Aug 18 | RPL | A | Concord Rangers | 212 | W 3-1 | Robinson 31 Moon 39 Crane 60 | 2 | 1 |
| 21 | RPL | H | Metropolitan Police | 512 | D 0-0 | | 8 | 2 |
| 25 | RPL | H | East Thurrock U | 441 | W 1-0 | Johnson 51 | 3 | 3 |
| 27 | RPL | A | Leiston | 225 | D 1-1 | Harper 80 | 5 | 4 |
| Sept 1 | RPL | H | Margate | 521 | L 0-2 | | 9 | 5 |
| 8 | FAC Q1 | H | **Epsom & Ewell** | **368** | **W 4-0** | **Johnson 12 32 Dodd 65 Crane 78** | | 6 |
| 15 | RPL | A | Wingate & Finchley | 124 | W 3-1 | Dodd 55 Moon 72 Tuck 90 | 7 | 7 |
| 22 | FAC Q2 | A | **Maidenhead United** | **316** | **L 2-4** | **Dodd 55 Moon 65** | | 8 |
| 29 | FAT Q1 | H | **Ilford** | **321** | **W 4-0** | **Dodd 30 Harper 35 73 Crane 44** | | 9 |
| Oct 6 | RPL | H | Wealdstone | 448 | L 0-1 | | 8 | 10 |
| 9 | RPL | A | Carshalton Athletic | 204 | W 2-0 | Kempson 34 Walshe 44 | 6 | 11 |
| 13 | RPL | A | Canvey Island | 476 | D 1-1 | Crane 16 | 6 | 12 |
| 20 | RPL | H | Enfield Town | 472 | D 0-0 | | 6 | 13 |
| 23 | RPL | H | Harrow Borough | 357 | L 0-3 | | 7 | 14 |
| 27 | FAT Q2 | H | **Bridgwater Town** | **313** | **W 3-0** | **Robinson 38 (pen) 75 (pen) Whyte 43.** | | 15 |
| Nov 3 | RPL | H | Thurrock | 444 | W 1-0 | Crane 45 | 5 | 16 |
| 10 | FAT Q3 | H | **Havant & Waterlooville** | **702** | **L 1-4** | **Crane 19** | | 17 |
| 13 | RPL | A | Hastings United | 359 | D 1-1 | Robinson 34 | | 18 |
| 17 | RPL | A | Lowestoft Town | 634 | W 2-1 | Crane 39 Harper 47 | 5 | 19 |
| Dec 1 | RPL | H | Bury Town | 425 | W 5-1 | Dodd 41 Robinson 67 Stockford 83 Crane 88 90 | 4 | 20 |
| 8 | RPL | A | Kingstonian | 358 | L 0-1 | | 6 | 21 |
| 15 | RPL | H | Hendon | 340 | W 3-1 | Whyte 74 Dodd 83 Wollers 90 | 5 | 22 |
| 26 | RPL | A | Lewes | 883 | L 0-1 | | 5 | 23 |
| Jan 1 | RPL | H | Whitehawk | 626 | L 1-3 | Robinson 28 (pen) | 6 | 24 |
| 5 | RPL | H | Carshalton Athletic | 389 | W 2-1 | Beck 7 Robinson 36 (pen) | 6 | 25 |
| 12 | RPL | A | Wealdstone | 396 | L 0-1 | | 8 | 26 |
| 16 | RPL | H | Cray Wanderers | 126 | W 3-1 | Robinson 13 Crane 43 Whyte 73 | 6 | 27 |
| 23 | RPL | A | Enfield Town | 434 | W 1-0 | Crane 35 | 5 | 28 |
| Feb 3 | RPL | H | Kingstonian | 552 | L 0-1 | | 6 | 29 |
| 9 | RPL | A | Hendon | 213 | L 0-1 | | 7 | 30 |
| 16 | RPL | H | Cray Wanderers | 441 | L 0-2 | | 9 | 31 |
| 19 | RPL | A | East Thurrock U | 127 | D 4-4 | Thompson 27 85 Pearce 34 Whyte 82 | 8 | 32 |
| 23 | RPL | A | Bury Town | 320 | L 0-2 | | 10 | 33 |
| Mar 2 | RPL | H | Concord Rangers | 390 | L 0-1 | | 11 | 34 |
| 9 | RPL | A | Margate | 415 | L 0-3 | | 13 | 35 |
| 16 | RPL | H | Wingate & Finchley | 357 | W1-0 | Dodd 27 | 12 | 36 |
| 19 | RPL | H | Hampton & Richmond B | 330 | L 0-5 | | 12 | 37 |
| 26 | RPL | H | Leiston | 264 | D 1-1 | Pearce 40 | 12 | 38 |
| 29 | RPL | A | Whitehawk | 271 | L 0-3 | | 13 | 39 |
| Apr 1 | RPL | H | Lewes | 409 | W 3-1 | Pearce 38 73 Wills 71 | 12 | 40 |
| 6 | RPL | H | Hastings United | 303 | W 1-0 | Thompson 68 | 12 | 41 |
| 9 | RPL | H | Canvey Island | 264 | D 2-2 | Kempson 19 31 | 12 | 42 |
| 13 | RPL | A | Thurrock | 184 | W 2-1 | S.Pearce 69 Thompson 87 | 12 | 43 |
| 17 | RPL | A | Metropolitan Police | 139 | L 2-3 | Thompson 2 Dodd 58 | 12 | 44 |
| 20 | RPL | H | Lowestoft Town | 448 | L 0-2 | | 13 | 45 |
| 25 | RPL | A | Harrow Borough | 132 | L 2-3 | Pearce 4 Woods 35 | 14 | 46 |
| 27 | RPL | A | Hampton & Richmond B | 525 | L 0-1 | | 14 | 47 |

| GOALSCORERS | Lge | FAC | FAT | Total | Pens | Hat-tricks | Cons Run | | Lge | FAC | FAT | Total | Pens | Hat-tricks | Cons Run |
|-------------|-----|-----|-----|-------|------|-----------|----------|--|-----|-----|-----|-------|------|-----------|----------|
| Crane | 8 | 1 | 2 | 11 | | | 2 | Beck | 1 | | | 1 | | | |
| Robinson | 6 | | 2 | 8 | 4 | | 2 | Stockford | 1 | | | 1 | | | |
| Dodd | 5 | 2 | 1 | 8 | | | 4 | Tuck | 1 | | | 1 | | | |
| Pearce | 6 | | | 6 | | | | Walshe | 1 | | | 1 | | | |
| Thompson | 5 | | | 5 | | | 2 | Wills | 1 | | | 1 | | | |
| Harper | 2 | | 2 | 4 | | | | Wollers | 1 | | | 1 | | | |
| Whyte | 3 | | 1 | 4 | | | | Woods | 1 | | | 1 | | | |
| Johnson | 1 | 2 | | 3 | | | | Cons Run - Consecutive scoring games. | | | | | | | |
| Kempson | 3 | | | 3 | | | | | | | | | | | |
| Moon | 2 | 1 | | 3 | | | | | | | | | | | |

# BURY TOWN

**Chairman:** Russell Ward
**Secretary:** Mrs Wendy Turner    **(T)** 07795 661 959    **(E)** wturner@burytownfc.freeserve.co.uk
**Commercial Manager:** n/a    **(T)**
**Programme Editor:** Christopher Ward    **(T)** 07778 571 812
**Ground Address:** Ram Meadow, Cotton Lane, Bury St Edmunds IP33 1XP
**(T)** 01284 754 721    **Manager:** Richard Wilkins

## Club Factfile

**Founded:** 1872    **Nickname:** The Blues

**Previous Names:** Bury St Edmunds 1872-1885, 1895-1908. Bury Town 1885-95. Bury United 1908-23.

**Previous Leagues:** Norfolk & Suffolk Border, Essex & Suffolk Border, Eastern Counties 1935-64, 76-87, 97-2006, Metropolitan 1964-71, Southern 1971-76, 87-97

**Club Colours (change):** All blue (orange/black/orange)

**Ground Capacity:** 3,500    **Seats:** 300    **Covered:** 1,500    **Clubhouse:** Yes    **Shop:** Yes

**Directions**
Follow signs to Town Centre from A14. At second roundabout take first left into Northgate Street then left into Mustow Street at T junction at lights and left again into Cotton Lane. Ground is 350 yards on the right.

**Previous Grounds:** Kings Road 1888-1978

**Record Attendance:** 2,500 v Enfield - FA Cup 1986
**Record Victory:** Not known
**Record Defeat:** Not known
**Record Goalscorer:** Doug Tooley
**Record Appearances:** Doug Tooley
**Additional Records:** Paid £1,500 to Chelmsford City for Mel Springett
**Senior Honours:** Received £5,500 from Ipswich Town for Simon Milton
Eastern Counties League 1963-64.
Suffolk Premier Cup x10 Most recently 2012-13.
Southern League Division One Central 2010/11

### 10 YEAR RECORD

| 03-04 | | 04-05 | | 05-06 | | 06-07 | | 07-08 | | 08-09 | | 09-10 | | 10-11 | | 11-12 | | 12-13 | |
|---|---|---|---|---|---|---|---|---|---|---|---|---|---|---|---|---|---|---|---|
| ECP | 9 | ECP | 2 | ECP | 2 | Isth1N | 17 | Isth1N | 7 | SthC | 7 | SthC | 1 | Isth P | 3 | Isth P | 5 | Isth P | 7 |

# MATCH RESULTS 2012-13

| Date | Comp | H/A | Opponents | Att: | Result | Goalscorers | Pos | No. |
|------|------|-----|-----------|------|--------|-------------|-----|-----|
| Aug 18 | RPL | H | Carshalton Athletic | 312 | D 1-1 | Sands 47 | 9 | 1 |
| 21 | RPL | A | Thurrock | 412 | W 3-0 | Bullard 18 Clark 37 Blake 90 | 5 | 2 |
| 25 | RPL | A | Hendon | 139 | D 2-2 | Blake 26 Cook 43 | 8 | 3 |
| 27 | RPL | H | Canvey Island | 420 | W 1-0 | Bullard 34 | 6 | 4 |
| Sept 1 | RPL | A | Hastings United | 340 | W 1-0 | Blake 81 | 4 | 5 |
| 8 | FAC Q1 | H | **Canvey Island** | **375** | **W 3-0** | **Clark 44 (pen) 63 Reed 83** |  | 6 |
| 15 | RPL | H | Kingstonian | 451 | W1-0 | Clark 56 | 3 | 7 |
| 22 | FAC Q2 | H | **Wingate & Finchley** | **366** | **W 2-1** | **Reed 33 Clark 68** |  | 8 |
| 29 | FAT Q1 | H | **Whitehawk** | **301** | **D 0-0** |  |  | 9 |
| Oct 2 | FATQ1r | A | **Whitehawk** | **50** | **L 0-1** |  |  | 10 |
| 6 | FAC Q3 | H | **Hampton & Richmond B** | **405** | **W 4-0** | **Reed 9 66 Ingram 34 Hall 84** |  | 11 |
| 13 | RPL | H | Harrow Borough | 532 | L 0-1 |  | 7 | 12 |
| 20 | FAC Q4 | A | **Dorchester Town** | **555** | **L 1-3** | **Hall 89** |  | 13 |
| 23 | RPL | A | Cray Wanderers | 134 | D 2-2 | Parker 76 Sands 90 | 10 | 14 |
| Nov 3 | RPL | H | Whitehawk | 372 | L 1-3 | Sands 7 | 9 | 15 |
| 10 | RPL | H | Lewes | 320 | W 2-1 | Reed 2 Hitching 83 | 8 | 16 |
| 13 | RPL | A | East Thurrock United | 151 | W 3-1 | Sands 48 Blake 61 Kennedy 67 | 6 | 17 |
| 17 | RPL | A | Margate | 348 | L 1-3 | Nunn 3 | 6 | 18 |
| 24 | RPL | H | Wngate & Finchley | 282 | W 4-2 | Sands 24 46 Coulson 48 Reed 82 | 4 | 19 |
| Dec 1 | RPL | A | Bognor Regis Town | 425 | L 1-5 | Sands 55 | 7 | 20 |
| 8 | RPL | A | Hampton & Richmond B | 252 | W 3-2 | Sands 48 Parker 57 64 (pen) | 4 | 21 |
| 15 | RPL | H | Metropolitan Police | 288 | L 0-2 |  | 7 | 22 |
| 18 | RPL | H | Leiston | 325 | D 3-3 | Sands 64 68 Tann 71 | 7 | 23 |
| Jan 1 | RPL | A | Enfield Town | 368 | W 3-2 | Patrick 20 Sands 82 89 | 7 | 24 |
| 5 | RPL | A | Leiston | 356 | D 0-0 |  | 7 | 25 |
| 12 | RPL | H | East Thurrock United | 320 | L 1-2 | Sands 51 | 9 | 26 |
| 16 | RPL | A | Canvey Island | 201 | W 1-0 | Sands 24 | 7 | 27 |
| 26 | RPL | H | Concord Rangrs | 375 | L 0-4 |  | 8 | 28 |
| Feb 2 | RPL | H | Hampton & Richmond B | 301 | L 0-1 |  | 8 | 29 |
| 5 | RPL | A | Harrow Borough | 94 | L 1-3 | Sands 47 | 8 | 30 |
| 9 | RPL | A | Metropolitan Police | 102 | L 1-3 | Sands 84 | 9 | 31 |
| 16 | RPL | A | Wingate & Finchley | 113 | W 3-1 | Sands 11 30  Parker 65 | 10 | 32 |
| 19 | RPL | H | Hendon | 252 | L 1-2 | Parker 90 | 10 | 33 |
| 23 | RPL | H | Bognor Regis Town | 320 | W 2-0 | Sands 5 29 | 9 | 34 |
| 26 | RPL | H | Thurrock | 260 | W 3-1 | Parker 10 Reed 23 78 | 7 | 35 |
| Mar 2 | RPL | A | Carshalton Athletic | 271 | W 3-1 | Parker 41 (Pen) Sands 49 55 | 5 | 36 |
| 16 | RPL | A | Kingstonian | 274 | W 2-0 | Whiteley 11 Parker 65 (pen) | 7 | 37 |
| 19 | RPL | H | Concord Rangers | 218 | L 2-3 | Fry 45 (og) Logan 63 | 8 | 38 |
| 30 | RPL | H | Enfield Town | 320 | W 2-1 | Sands 55 Nunn 90 | 8 | 39 |
| Apr 1 | RPL | A | Lowestoft | 873 | L 0-1 |  | 8 | 40 |
| 3 | RPL | H | Cray Wanderers | 235 | L 0-2 |  | 8 | 41 |
| 6 | RPL | H | Wealdstone | 479 | D 0-0 |  | 8 | 42 |
| 9 | RPL | A | Wealdstone | 507 | W 3-2 | Reed 32 62 Sands 76 | 6 | 43 |
| 13 | RPL | A | Whitehawk | 181 | D 2-2 | Reed 3 Short 82 | 9 | 44 |
| 16 | RPL | H | Lowestoft Town | 594 | D 1-1 | Parker 20 (pen) | 9 | 45 |
| 20 | RPL | H | Margate | 425 | D 2-2 | Sands  49 Tann 85 | 9 | 46 |
| 23 | RPL | H | Hastings United | 304 | W 1-0 | Key 60 | 7 | 47 |
| 27 | RPL | H | Lewes | 816 | W 3-2 | Key 28 Parker 33 (pen) Sands 90 | 7 |  |

| GOALSCORERS | Lge | FAC | FAT | Total | Pens | Hat-tricks | Cons Run |  | Lge | FAC | FAT | Total | Pens | Hat-tricks | Cons Run |
|-------------|-----|-----|-----|-------|------|------------|----------|--|-----|-----|-----|-------|------|------------|----------|
| Sands | 26 |  |  | 26 |  |  | 3 | Cook | 1 |  |  | 1 |  |  |  |
| Parker | 10 |  |  | 10 | 5 |  | 3 | Coulson | 1 |  |  | 1 |  |  |  |
| Reed | 7 | 4 |  | 11 |  |  |  | Hitching | 1 |  |  | 1 |  |  |  |
| Clark | 2 | 3 |  | 5 | 1 |  | 3 | Ingram |  | 1 |  | 1 |  |  |  |
| Blake | 4 |  |  | 4 |  |  |  | Kennedy | 1 |  |  | 1 |  |  |  |
| Bullard | 2 |  |  | 2 |  |  |  | Patrick | 1 |  |  | 1 |  |  |  |
| Hall |  | 2 |  | 2 |  |  |  | Short | 1 |  |  | 1 |  |  |  |
| Key | 2 |  |  | 2 |  |  | 2 | Whiteley | 1 |  |  | 1 |  |  |  |
| Nunn | 2 |  |  | 2 |  |  |  | Own Goals | 1 |  |  | 1 |  |  |  |
| Tann | 2 |  |  | 2 |  |  |  | Cons Run - Consecutive scoring games. |  |  |  |  |  |  |  |
| Logan | 1 |  |  | 1 |  |  |  |  |  |  |  |  |  |  |  |

# CANVEY ISLAND

**Chairman:** George Frost
**Secretary:** Gary Sutton    **(T)** 0779 002 5828    **(E)** gary.sutton@sky.com
**Commercial Manager:** n/a    **(T)**
**Programme Editor:** Glen Eckett    **(T)** 07740 921 532
**Ground Address:** The Prospects Stadium, Park Lane, Canvey Island, Essex SS8 7PX
**(T)** 01268 682 991      **Manager:** Danny Heale

## Club Factfile

**Founded:** 1926    **Nickname:** The Gulls
**Previous Names:** None
**Previous Leagues:** Southend & District, Thurrock & Thames Combination, Parthenon, Metropolitan, Greater London 1964-71, Essex Senior 1971-95, Isthmian 1995-2004, Conference 2004-06

**Club Colours (change):** Yellow and sky blue/sky blue/yellow (White with sky blue trim/white with sky blue trim/sky blue)

**Ground Capacity:** 4,100    **Seats:** 500    **Covered:** 827    **Clubhouse:** Yes    **Shop:** Yes

**Directions**
A130 from A13 or A127 at Sadlers Farm roundabout.
One mile through Town Centre, first right past old bus garage.

**Previous Grounds:** None

**Record Attendance:** 3,553 v Aldershot Town - Isthmian League 2002-03
**Record Victory:** Not Known
**Record Defeat:** Not Known
**Record Goalscorer:** Andy Jones
**Record Appearances:** Steve Ward
**Additional Records:** Paid £5,000 to Northwich Victoria for Chris Duffy
**Senior Honours:**    Received £4,500 from Farnborough Town for Brian Horne
Isthmian Division 1 1993-94, Premier Division 2003-04.
FA Trophy 2000-01. Essex Senior Cup 1998-99, 2000-01, 2001-02.

### 10 YEAR RECORD

| 03-04 | | 04-05 | | 05-06 | | 06-07 | | 07-08 | | 08-09 | | 09-10 | | 10-11 | | 11-12 | | 12-13 | |
|---|---|---|---|---|---|---|---|---|---|---|---|---|---|---|---|---|---|---|---|
| Isth P | 1 | Conf N | 18 | Conf N | 4 | Isth1N | 6 | Isth1N | 5 | Isth P | 12 | Isth P | 16 | Isth P | 6 | Isth P | 8 | Isth P | 8 |

# MATCH RESULTS 2012-13

| Date | Comp | H/A | Opponents | Att: | Result | Goalscorers | Pos | No. |
|------|------|-----|-----------|------|--------|-------------|-----|-----|
| Aug 18 | RPL | A | Wingate & Finchley | 130 | W 1-0 | Woods-Garness 48 | 5 | 1 |
| 21 | RPL | H | Leiston | 305 | W 2-0 | Heale 14 King 39 (pen) | 3 | 2 |
| 25 | RPL | H | Hampton & Waterloovile | 332 | D 0-0 | | 5 | 3 |
| 27 | RPL | A | Bury Town | 420 | L 0-2 | | 7 | 4 |
| Sept 1 | RPL | H | Lewes | 320 | D 0-0 | | 7 | 5 |
| 8 | FAC Q1 | A | Bury Town | 375 | L 0-3 | | | 6 |
| 15 | RPL | H | Metropolitan Police | 135 | L 1-2 | Curran 3 | 9 | 7 |
| 29 | FAT Q1 | H | Wroxham | 261 | D 0-0 | | | 8 |
| Oct 2 | FAT Q1r | A | Wroxham | 154 | W 2-1 | Curran 35 Miller 117 *aet | | 9 |
| 6 | RPL | A | Leiston | 201 | D 1-1 | Dobinson 62 | 9 | 10 |
| 9 | RPL | H | Whitehawk | 212 | L 1-2 | Woods-Garness 1 | 7 | 11 |
| 13 | RPL | H | Bognor Regis Town | 476 | D 1-1 | Woods-Garness 22 | 10 | 12 |
| 20 | RPL | A | Harrow Borough | 141 | W 3-1 | Dobinson 42 Woods-Garness 59 Dumas 64 | 9 | 13 |
| 23 | RPL | H | Margate | 252 | W 3-1 | WOODS-GARNESS 3 ( 24 61 70) | 7 | 14 |
| 27 | FAT Q2 | A | Uxbridge | 152 | D 3-3 | King 8 79 Curran 20 | | 15 |
| 30 | FAT Q2r | H | Uxbridge | 176 | W 4-2 | Carter 5 (og) Dennis 59  King 65 (pen) 71 (pen) | | 16 |
| Nov 2 | RPL | H | Enfield Town | 382 | L 3-4 | King 34 65 Dobinson 38 | 8 | 17 |
| 10 | FAT Q3 | H | Chesham United | 275 | D 1-1 | Dennis 6 | | 18 |
| 17 | RPL | A | Hastings Unitd | 410 | D 0-0 | | 11 | 19 |
| Dec 1 | RPL | H | Kingstonian | 302 | W 4-3 | Hawes 29 L.Dennis 30 King 44 Woods-Garness 89 | 10 | 20 |
| 8 | RPL | H | Cray Wanderers | 271 | W 1-0 | Woods-Garness 84 | 9 | 21 |
| 15 | RPL | A | Carshalton Athletic | 208 | W 2-0 | Curran 3 54 | 8 | 22 |
| 26 | RPL | A | Concord Rangers | 338 | L 0-3 | | 10 | 23 |
| Jan 1 | RPL | H | East Thurrock | 349 | W 2-1 | Peddie 66 (og) Woods-Garness 71 | 10 | 24 |
| 5 | RPL | A | Whitehawk | 159 | L 4-5 | Hawes 30 Curran 40 Dennis 56 Chatting 65 | 10 | 25 |
| 8 | RPL | A | Hendon | 158 | W 2-1 | Curran14 Woods-Garness 53 | 7 | 26 |
| 12 | RPL | H | East Thurrock | 328 | W 2-0 | Woods-Garness 20-74 | 4 | 27 |
| 16 | RPL | H | Bury Town | 201 | L 0-1 | | 5 | 28 |
| 26 | RPL | H | Harrow Borough | 304 | W 3-0 | Woods-Garness 65 King 68  Curran 90 | 3 | 29 |
| Feb 5 | RPL | H | Wealdstone | 222 | W 2-0 | Orlu  34 67 | 3 | 30 |
| 9 | RPL | H | Carshalton Athletic | 311 | W 4-2 | Curran 19 Woods-Garness 27 85 Hawes 36 | 3 | 31 |
| 16 | RPL | H | Hendon | 321 | L 0-3 | | 4 | 32 |
| 19 | RPL | A | Lowestoft | 436 | L 0-2 | | 4 | 33 |
| 23 | RPL | A | Kingstonian | 277 | W 2-1 | Rowe 70 Woods-Garness 82 | 3 | 34 |
| Mar 2 | RPL | H | Wingate & Finchley | 310 | W 3-2 | Woods-Garness 38 Hawes 76 Curran 84 | 3 | 35 |
| 9 | RPL | A | Lewes | 526 | W 2-1 | King 19 (pen) Dobinson 80 | 3 | 36 |
| 16 | RPL | H | Metropolitan Police | 234 | L 0-1 | | 5 | 37 |
| 19 | RPI | A | Cray Wanderers | 124 | D 1-1 | Woods-Garness 53 | 5 | 38 |
| 23 | RPL | A | Margate | 405 | D 2-2 | King 1 Woods-Garness 7 | 6 | 39 |
| 29 | RPL | A | East Thurrock | 315 | L 0-2 | | 6 | 40 |
| Apr 1 | RPL | H | Concord Rangers | 616 | L 0-2 | | 7 | 41 |
| 6 | RPL | H | Lowestoft Town | 331 | L 0-2 | | 7 | 42 |
| 9 | RPL | A | Bognor Regis Town | 264 | D 2-2 | King 17 Kavanagh 74 | 7 | 43 |
| 13 | RPL | A | Enfield Town | 330 | W 2-0 | Woods-Garness 20 Miller 73 | 8 | 44 |
| 17 | RPL | A | Thurrock | 218 | W 1-0 | King 48 | 6 | 45 |
| 20 | RPL | H | Hastings United | 402 | D 1-1 | Chatting 45 | 7 | 46 |
| 25 | RPL | A | Hampton & Richmond B | 131 | D 2-2 | | 6 | 47 |
| 27 | RPL | A | Wealdstone | 803 | L 0-2 | | 8 | 48 |

| GOALSCORERS | Lge | FAC | FAT | Total | Pens | Hat-tricks | Cons Run | | Lge | FAC | FAT | Total | Pens | Hat-tricks | Cons Run |
|-------------|-----|-----|-----|-------|------|------------|----------|---|-----|-----|-----|-------|------|------------|----------|
| Woods-Garness | 21 | | | 21 | | 1 | 4 | Heale | 1 | | | 1 | | | |
| Rob King | 9 | | 4 | 13 | 3 | | | Rowe | 1 | | | 1 | | | |
| Jay Curran | 8 | | 2 | 10 | | | | Kavanagh | 1 | | | 1 | | | |
| Dennis | 2 | | 2 | 4 | | | | Own Goals | 2 | | 1 | 2 | | | |
| Dobinson | 4 | | | 4 | 1 | | | Cons Run - Consecutive scoring games. | | | | | | | |
| Hawes | 4 | | | 4 | | | | | | | | | | | |
| Orlu | 2 | | | 2 | | | | | | | | | | | |
| Chattiing | 2 | | | 2 | | | | | | | | | | | |
| Miller | 1 | | 1 | 2 | | | | | | | | | | | |
| Dumas | 1 | | | 1 | | | | | | | | | | | |

# CARSHALTON ATHLETIC

**Chairman:** Paul Dipre

**Secretary:** Chris Blanchard    **(T)** 07583 817 519    **(E)** chrisblanchard@carshaltonathletic.co.uk

**Commercial Manager:** n/a    **(T)**

**Programme Editor:** Chris Blanchard    **(T)** 07583 817 519

**Ground Address:** War Memorial Sports Ground, Colston Avenue, Carshalton SM5 2PW

**(T)** 07583 817 519    **Manager:** Tommy Williams

## Club Factfile

**Founded:** 1905    **Nickname:** Robins

**Previous Names:** None

**Previous Leagues:** Southern Suburban > 1911, Surrey Senior 1922-23, London 1923-46, Corinthian 1946-56, Athenian 1956-73, Isthmian 1973-2004, Conference 2004-06

**Club Colours (change):** All red

**Ground Capacity:** 8,000    **Seats:** 240    **Covered:** 4,500    **Clubhouse:** Yes    **Shop:** Yes

**Directions**

Turn right out of Carshalton Station exit,
turn right again,
and then left into Colston Avenue.

**Previous Grounds:** None

**Record Attendance:** 7,800 v Wimbledon - London Senior Cup

**Record Victory:** 13-0 v Worthing - Isthmian League Cup 28/01/1991

**Record Defeat:** 0-11 v Southall - Athenian League March 1963

**Record Goalscorer:** Jimmy Bolton - 242

**Record Appearances:** Jon Warden - 504

**Additional Records:** Paid £15,000 to Enfield for Curtis Warmington

**Senior Honours:**    Received £30,000 from Crystal Palace for Ian Cox

Isthmian League Division 1 South 2002-03.

Surrey Senior Shield 1975-76. London Challenge Cup 1991-92. Surrey Senior Cup x3.

### 10 YEAR RECORD

| 03-04 | | 04-05 | | 05-06 | | 06-07 | | 07-08 | | 08-09 | | 09-10 | | 10-11 | | 11-12 | | 12-13 | |
|---|---|---|---|---|---|---|---|---|---|---|---|---|---|---|---|---|---|---|---|
| Isth P | 7 | Conf S | 19 | Conf S | 21 | Isth P | 13 | Isth P | 18 | Isth P | 4 | Isth P | 17 | Isth P | 13 | Isth P | 16 | Isth P | 20 |

# MATCH RESULTS 2012-13

| Date | Comp | H/A | Opponents | Att: | Result | Goalscorers | Pos | No. |
|---|---|---|---|---|---|---|---|---|
| Aug 18 | RPL | A | Bury Town | 312 | D 1-1 | Vines 51 | 10 | 1 |
| 21 | RPL | H | Lewes | 305 | D 3-3 | Roberts 44 Sogbanmu 44 Taylor 57 | 12 | 2 |
| 25 | RPL | H | Concord Rangers | 340 | L 1-2 | Taylor 75 | 16 | 3 |
| 27 | RPL | A | Wingate & Finchley | 173 | L 0-1 | | 18 | 4 |
| Sept 1 | RPL | H | East Thurrock United | 675 | D 1-1 | Sogbanmu 81 | 18 | 5 |
| 8 | FAC Q1 | A | Pagham | 140 | D 0-0 | | | 6 |
| 11 | FAC Q1r | H | Pagham | 151 | W 3-0 | Harding 38 Sogbanmu 43 Taylor 68 | | 7 |
| 15 | RPL | A | Harrow Borough | 140 | L 0-1 | | 20 | 8 |
| 22 | FAC Q2 | H | Chalfont St Peter | 185 | L 0-1 | | | 9 |
| 29 | FAT Q1 | H | Heybridge Swifts | 172 | W 3-0 | Mills 12 68 Harding 40 | | 10 |
| Oct 9 | RPL | H | Bognor Regis Town | 204 | L 0-2 | | 20 | 11 |
| 13 | RPL | H | Hastings United | 204 | W 1-0 | Clarke 70 | 19 | 12 |
| 20 | RPL | A | Kingstonian | 357 | L 1-2 | Mills 4 | 20 | 13 |
| 23 | RPL | A | Whitehawk | 121 | L 0-1 | | 21 | 14 |
| 27 | FAT Q2 | A | Kings Lynn Town | 497 | L 1-6 | Sogbanmu 9 | | 15 |
| Nov 3 | RPL | H | Lowestoft | 181 | W 2-0 | Adelokun 88 Pinney 90 | 18 | 16 |
| 10 | RPL | A | Concord Rangers | 122 | L 3-6 | Pinney 6 Sogbanmu 19 Pinnock 90 | 19 | 17 |
| 13 | RPL | A | Cray Wanderers | 175 | L 2-3 | Pinney 33 Roberts 41 | 19 | 18 |
| 17 | RPL | A | Wealdstone | 422 | L 0-3 | | 19 | 19 |
| 24 | RPL | H | Thurrock | 157 | L 0-1 | | 22 | 20 |
| Dec 1 | RPL | A | Leiston | 178 | L 0-1 | | 22 | 21 |
| 8 | RPL | A | Hendon | 147 | L 1-3 | Clarke 56 | 22 | 22 |
| 11 | RPL | A | Margate | 228 | L 1-3 | Pigden 56 | 22 | 23 |
| 15 | RPL | H | Canvey Island | 208 | L 0-2 | | 22 | 24 |
| 26 | RPL | A | Hampton & Richmond | 269 | W 1-0 | Pinney 36 | 22 | 25 |
| Jan 1 | RPL | H | Met Police | 193 | D 1-1 | Pinney 37 | 22 | 26 |
| 5 | RPL | A | Bognor Regis Town | 389 | L 1-2 | Pinney 24 | 22 | 27 |
| 8 | RPL | H | Enfield Town | 180 | W 3-2 | PINNEY 3 ( 40 (pen) 50 (pen) 60) | 22 | 28 |
| 12 | RPL | H | Cray Wanderers | 201 | W 2-1 | Adelakun 31 Nolan 83 | 22 | 29 |
| 26 | RPL | H | Kingstonian | 391 | L 1-3 | Sogbanmu 74 | 22 | 30 |
| Feb 2 | RPL | H | Hendon | 188 | L 1-2 | Pinney 45 (pen) | 22 | 31 |
| 9 | RPL | A | Canvey Island | 311 | L 2-4 | Pinney 6 Adelakun 49 | 22 | 32 |
| 16 | RPL | A | Thurrock | 228 | W 3-1 | Pinney 17 85  Gomez-Pico 52 | 21 | 33 |
| 19 | RPL | H | Wingate & Finchley | 89 | L 1-2 | Pinney 51 | 22 | 34 |
| 23 | RPL | H | Leiston | 128 | L 1-3 | Walker 52 | 22 | 35 |
| Mar 2 | RPL | H | Bury Town | 271 | L 1-3 | Sogbanmu 22 | 22 | 36 |
| 9 | RPL | A | East Thurrock United | 201 | L 0-4 | | 22 | 37 |
| 19 | RPL | A | Lewes | 405 | L 1-2 | Ashton 1 | 22 | 38 |
| 23 | RPL | A | Whitehawk | 158 | L 0-2 | | 22 | 39 |
| 26 | RPL | H | Harrow Borough | 75 | W 3-1 | Peacock 36 (og) Gomez-Pico 51 Pinney 80 | 22 | 40 |
| 30 | RPL | A | Metropolitan Police | 115 | L 0-1 | | 22 | 41 |
| Apr 1 | RPL | H | Hampton & Richmond | 207 | W 3-0 | BRADFORD 3 (2 4 61 pen) | 22 | 42 |
| 6 | RPL | H | Margate | 272 | W 4-0 | O'Toole 10 PINNEY 3 ( 32 62 (pen) 90) | 22 | 43 |
| 13 | RPL | A | Lowestoft Town | 770 | W 3-1 | Ashton 2 Pigden  35 Pinney 52 | 22 | 44 |
| 18 | RPL | A | Hastings United | 480 | W 4-1 | Pigden 4 Ashton 53 Sogbanmu 57 Pinney 82 (pen) | 20 | 45 |
| 20 | RPL | H | Wealdstone | 388 | L 0-2 | | 21 | 46 |
| 27 | RPL | A | Enfield Town | 382 | W 2-1 | Pinney 61 84 | 21 | 47 |

| GOALSCORERS | Lge | FAC | FAT | Total | Pens | Hat-tricks | Cons Run | | Lge | FAC | FAT | Total | Pens | Hat-tricks | Cons Run |
|---|---|---|---|---|---|---|---|---|---|---|---|---|---|---|---|
| Pinney | 22 | | | 22 | 4 | 2 | | Harding | | 1 | 1 | 2 | | | |
| Sogbanmu | 6 | 1 | 1 | 8 | | | | Roberts | 2 | | | 2 | | | |
| Adelakun | 3 | | | 3 | | | | Nolan | 1 | | | 1 | | | |
| Ashton | 3 | | | 3 | | | | O'Toole | 1 | | | 1 | | | |
| Bradford | 3 | | | 3 | 1 | 1 | | Pinnock | 1 | | | 1 | | | |
| Mills | 1 | | 2 | 3 | | | | Vines | 1 | | | 1 | | | |
| Pigden | 3 | | | 3 | | | | Walker | 1 | | | 1 | | | |
| Taylor | 2 | 1 | | 3 | | | | Own Goal | 1 | | | 1 | | | |
| Clarke | 2 | | | 2 | | | | Cons Run - Consecutive scoring games. | | | | | | | |
| Gomez-Pico | 2 | | | 2 | | | | | | | | | | | |

# CRAY WANDERERS

**Chairman:** Gary Hillman
**Secretary:** Kerry Phillips    **(T)** 07718 353 583    **(E)** kerryphillips@hotmail.com
**Commercial Manager:** n/a    **(T)**
**Programme Editor:** Phil Babbs    **(T)** 07977 828 252
**Ground Address:** Bromley FC, Hayes Lane, Bromley, Kent BR2 9EF
**(T)** 020 8460 5291    **Manager:** Ian Jenkins

The team line up before their FA Cup 2nd Qualifying Round tie against Thamesmead Town. Photo: Alan Coomes.

## Club Factfile

**Founded:** 1860    **Nickname:** Wanderers or Wands
**Previous Names:** Cray Old Boys (immediately after WW1); Sidcup & Footscray (start of WW2).
**Previous Leagues:** Kent 1894-1903, 1906-07, 1909-1914, 1934-38, 1978-2004; West Kent & South Suburban Leagues (before WW1); London 1920-1934, 1951-1959; Kent Amateur 1938-1939, 1946-1951; South London Alliance 1943-1946; Aetolian 1959-1964; Greater London 1964-1966; Metropolitan 1966-1971; Met. London 1971-1975: London Spartan 1975-1978.
**Club Colours (change):** Amber/black/black (Pale blue/white/pale blue)

**Ground Capacity:** 5,000    **Seats:** 1,300    **Covered:** 2,500    **Clubhouse:** Yes    **Shop:** Yes

**Directions**
**From M25:** Leaving the motorway at junction 4, follow the A21 to Bromley and London, for approximately 4 miles and then fork left onto the A232 signposted Croydon/Sutton. At the second set of traffic lights, turn right into Baston Road (B265), following it for about two miles as it becomes Hayes Street and then Hayes Lane. Cray Wanderers FC is on the right hand side of the road just after the mini roundabout. There is ample room for coaches to drive down the driveway, turn round and park.

**Previous Grounds:** Star Lane (1860s), Derry Downs (until 1898), Fordcroft (1898-1936), Twysdens (1936-1939), St Mary Cray Rec (1940s),
**Previous Grounds: Cont.** Northfield Farm (1950-51), Tothills (aka Fordcroft, 1951-1955), Grassmeade (1955-1973), Oxford Road (1973-1998).

**Record Attendance:** (Grassmeade) 2,160vLeytonstone – FA Am.C 3rd Rd, 1968-69; (Oxford R) 1,523vStamford – FAV QF 79-80; (Hayes L) 1,082vAFC Wim. – 04-05
**Record Victory:** 15-0 v Sevenoaks - 1894-95.
**Record Defeat:** 2-15 (H) and 0-14 (A) v Callenders Athletic - Kent Amateur League, 1947-48.
**Record Goalscorer:** Ken Collishaw 274 (1954-1965)
**Record Appearances:** John Dorey - 500 (1961-72).
**Additional Records:** Unbeaten for 28 Ryman League games in 2007-2008.

**Senior Honours:**
Kent League 1901-02, 80-81, 2002-03, 03-04 (League Cup 83-84, 2002-03); London League 1956-57, 57-58 (League Cup 54-55); Aetolian League 1962-63 (League Cup 63 -64); Greater London League 1965-66 (League Cup 64-65, 65-66); Met. Lge Cup 1970-71; Met. London League & League Cup 1974-75; London Spartan League 1976-77, 77 -78. Kent Amateur Cup 1930-31, 62-63, 63-64, 64-65. Kent Senior Trophy 1992-93, 2003-04.

### 10 YEAR RECORD

| 03-04 | 04-05 | 05-06 | 06-07 | 07-08 | 08-09 | 09-10 | 10-11 | 11-12 | 12-13 |
|---|---|---|---|---|---|---|---|---|---|
| Kent P    1 | Isth1    6 | Isth1    11 | Isth1S    12 | Isth1S    3 | Isth1S    2 | Isth P    15 | Isth P    9 | Isth P    9 | Isth P    17 |

# MATCH RESULTS 2012-13

| Date | Comp | H/A | Opponents | Att: | Result | Goalscorers | Pos | No. |
|------|------|-----|-----------|------|--------|-------------|-----|-----|
| Aug 18 | RPL | A | Leiston | 199 | D 1-1 | Willy 199 | 11 | 1 |
| 21 | RPL | H | Whitehawk | 155 | L 1-2 | Bremner 79 | 15 | 2 |
| 25 | RPL | H | Harrow Borough | 111 | W 2-1 | Williams 34 Bremner 68 | 11 | 3 |
| 27 | RPL | A | East Thurrrock United | 161 | L 1-2 | Willy 3 | 13 | 4 |
| Sept 1 | RPL | H | Metropolitan Police | 182 | D 1-1 | Willy 89 | 13 | 5 |
| 9 | FAC Q1 | A | **Greenwich Borough** | 84 | **W 1-0** | **Willy 20** | | 6 |
| 15 | RPL | A | Lewes | 665 | D 2-2 | Power 16 Bremner 34 (pen) | 14 | 7 |
| 22 | FAC Q2 | H | **Thamesmead T** | 92 | **W 3-1** | **Williams 54 Bremner 84 90** | | 8 |
| 29 | FAT Q1 | A | **Thamesmead T** | 40 | **W 1-0** | **Bremner (pen) 42** | | 9 |
| Oct 6 | FAC Q3 | H | **Chelmsford City** | 350 | **L 1-2** | **Saunders 45** | | 10 |
| 13 | RPL | A | Enfield Town | 433 | W 3-1 | Clark 4 Stavinou 45 Bremner 88 | 12 | 11 |
| 20 | RPL | A | Concord Rangers | 161 | W 4-0 | Bremner 5 Vines 77 89 Hamici 90 | 10 | 12 |
| 23 | RPL | H | Bury Town | 134 | D 2-2 | Vines 24 Willy 90 | 10 | 13 |
| 27 | FAT Q2 | H | **Arlesey Town** | 96 | **D 0-0** | | | 14 |
| 30 | FAT Q2r | A | **Arlesey Town** | 100 | **W 3-2** | **Vines 20 53 Hamid 119** | | 15 |
| Nov 3 | RPL | H | Wealdstone | 222 | L 0-3 | | 10 | 16 |
| 11 | FAT Q3 | H | **Welling United** | 262 | **L 0-1** | | | 17 |
| 13 | RPL | H | Carshalton Athletic | 175 | W 3-2 | Bremner 23 (pen) 66 Vines71 | 9 | 18 |
| 17 | RPL | A | Hampton & Richmond B | 369 | W 3-1 | Bremner 14 Vines 37 Day 65 | 10 | 19 |
| 28 | RPL | A | Hendon | 102 | D 0-0 | | 8 | 20 |
| Dec 5 | RPL | H | Lowestoft Town | 109 | D 1-1 | Vines 81 | 8 | 21 |
| 8 | RPL | A | Canvey Island | 271 | L 0-1 | | 11 | 22 |
| 16 | RPL | H | Kingstonian | 201 | L 1-3 | Clark 90 | 12 | 23 |
| 26 | RPL | A | Margate | 408 | W 1-0 | Bremner 19 | 12 | 24 |
| 29 | RPL | A | Harrow Borough | 137 | D 3-3 | Vines 54 Jones 62 Phillips 75 | 11 | 25 |
| Jan 2 | RPL | H | Concord Rangers | 155 | L 0-2 | | 11 | 26 |
| 6 | RPL | H | Hendon | 213 | L 0-1 | | 12 | 27 |
| 8 | RPL | A | Thurrock | 158 | L 1-5 | Vines 58 | 13 | 28 |
| 12 | RPL | A | Carshalton Athletic | 201 | L 1-2 | Bremner 26 (pen) | 14 | 29 |
| 16 | RPL | H | Bognor Regis Town | 126 | L 1-3 | Bremner 18 | 14 | 30 |
| 24 | RPL | A | Hastings United | 247 | D 1-1 | Bremner 44 (pen) | 14 | 31 |
| Feb 5 | RPL | H | Enfield Town | 142 | L 1-5 | Power 72 | 15 | 32 |
| 9 | RPL | A | Kingstonian | 278 | L 3-9 | Phillips 53 Bremner 68 (pen) Saunders 71 | 16 | 33 |
| 16 | RPL | A | Bognor Regis T | 441 | W 2-0 | Power 54 Stavrinou 59 | 16 | 34 |
| 23 | RPL | H | Hastings United | 150 | L 0-3 | | 17 | 35 |
| 26 | RPL | A | Whitehawk | 90 | L 0-2 | | 17 | 36 |
| Mar 3 | RPL | H | Lieston | 145 | D 0-0 | | 17 | 37 |
| 5 | RPL | H | Wingate & Finchley | 85 | L 3-4 | Bremner 66 Booth 85 Fray 88 | 18 | 38 |
| 9 | RPL | A | Metropolitan Police | 105 | W 4-2 | Bremner 13 (pen) 48 Booth 52 Saunders 64 | 17 | 39 |
| 19 | RPL | H | Canvey Island | 124 | D 1-1 | Booth 25 | 17 | 40 |
| Apr 1 | RPL | H | Margate | 246 | L 0-4 | | 17 | 41 |
| 3 | RPL | A | Bury Town | 235 | W 2-0 | Bremner 31 Clark 36 | 16 | 42 |
| 6 | RPL | H | Thurrock | 117 | L 0-1 | | 17 | 43 |
| 9 | RPL | A | Lowestoft Town | 462 | L 1-4 | Power 69 (pen) 17 | 17 | 44 |
| 13 | RPL | A | Wealdstone | 549 | L 0-2 | | 19 | 45 |
| 17 | RPL | H | East Thurrock United | 130 | D 2-2 | Phillips 18 Bremner 75 | 18 | 46 |
| 20 | RPL | H | Hampton & Richmond B | 172 | W 2-0 | Phillips 62 Power 90 | 17 | 47 |
| 23 | RPL | H | Lewes | 248 | D 2-2 | Bremner 35 Young 45 | 17 | 48 |
| 27 | RPL | A | Wingate & Finchley | 129 | D 4-4 | Long 11 Power 58 Bremner 77 90 | 17 | 49 |

| GOALSCORERS | Lge | FAC | FAT | Total | Pens | Hat-tricks | Cons Run | | Lge | FAC | FAT | Total | Pens | Hat-tricks | Cons Run |
|-------------|-----|-----|-----|-------|------|-----------|----------|---|-----|-----|-----|-------|------|-----------|----------|
| Bremner | 21 | 2 | 1 | 24 | 1 | | 3 | Fray | 1 | | | 1 | | | |
| Vines | 8 | | 2 | 10 | | | 2 | Hamici | 1 | | | 1 | | | |
| Power | 7 | | | 7 | 1 | | | Hamid | | | 1 | 1 | | | |
| Willy | 4 | 1 | | 5 | | | 3 | Jones | 1 | | | 1 | | | |
| Phillips | 4 | | | 4 | | | | Long | 1 | | | 1 | | | |
| Booth | 3 | | | 3 | | | 3 | Stavrinou | 1 | | | 1 | | | |
| Clark | 3 | | | 3 | | | | Young | 1 | | | 1 | | | |
| Saunders | 2 | 1 | | 3 | | | | Cons Run - Consecutive scoring games. | | | | | | | |
| Williams | 1 | | 1 | 2 | | | | | | | | | | | |
| Day | 1 | | | 1 | | | | | | | | | | | |

www.non-leagueclubdirectory.co.uk    369

# SOCCER BOOKS LIMITED

## 72 ST. PETERS AVENUE (Dept. NLD)
## CLEETHORPES
## N.E. LINCOLNSHIRE
## DN35 8HU
## ENGLAND
### Tel. 01472 696226    Fax 01472 698546

Web site   www.soccer-books.co.uk
e-mail   info@soccer-books.co.uk

Established in 1982, Soccer Books Limited has one of the largest ranges of English-Language soccer books available. We continue to expand our stocks even further to include many more titles including German, French, Spanish and Italian-language books.

With well over 200,000 satisfied customers over the past 30 years, we supply books to virtually every country in the world but have maintained the friendliness and accessibility associated with a small family-run business. The range of titles we sell includes:

**YEARBOOKS** – All major yearbooks including editions of the Sky Sports Football Yearbook (previously Rothmans), Supporters' Guides, South American Yearbooks, North & Central American Yearbooks, Asian Football Yearbooks, Yearbooks of African Football, Non-League Club Directories, Almanack of World Football.

**CLUB HISTORIES** – Complete Statistical Records, Official Histories, Definitive Histories plus many more including photographic books.

**WORLD FOOTBALL** – World Cup books, European Championships History, Statistical histories for the World Cup, European Championships, South American and European Club Cup competitions and foreign-language Season Preview Magazines for dozens of countries.

**BIOGRAPHIES & WHO'S WHOS** – of Managers and Players plus Who's Whos etc.

**ENCYCLOPEDIAS & GENERAL TITLES** – Books on Stadia, Hooligan and Sociological studies, Histories and hundreds of others, including the weird and wonderful!

**DVDs** – Season reviews for British clubs, histories, European Cup competition finals, World Cup matches and series reviews, player profiles and a selection of almost 60 F.A. Cup Finals with many more titles becoming available all the time.

For a printed listing showing a selection of our titles, contact us using the information at the top of this page. Alternatively, our web site offers a secure ordering system for credit and debit card holders and Paypal users and lists our full range of 2,000 new books and 400 DVDs.

# DULWICH HAMLET

**Chairman:** Jack Payne
**Secretary:** Martin Eede          **(T)** 0795 739 5948          **(E)** eede.martin@gmail.com
**Commercial Manager:** n/a          **(T)**
**Programme Editor:** John Lawrence          **(T)** john_lawrence@hotmail.co.uk
**Ground Address:** Champion Hill Stadium, Dog Kennell Hill, Edgar Kail Way SE22 8BD
**(T)** 0207 274 8707          **Manager:** Gavin Rose

The Isthmian Division One South Championship winning squad.
Back Row: Erhun Aksel Öztümer, Ellis Green, Dominic Weston, Suliaman Bangura, Ethan Pinnock, Vernon Francis, James Tedder,
Phil Wilson, Carl Wilson-Denis, Josh Turner, Luke Hickie, Lewis Gonsalves, Kalvin Morath-Gibbs.
Front Row: Laura McPherson (Physiotherapist), Frankie Sawyer, Dean Carpenter, Kevin James (Coach), Gavin Rose (Manager),
Junior Kadi (Assistant Manager), Ahmed Deen, Peter Adeniyi, Nyren Clunis, Corinna Kehaya (Physiotherapist)

## Club Factfile

**Founded:** 1889     **Nickname:** Hamlet
**Previous Names:** None
**Previous Leagues:** Camberwell 1894-97, Southern Suburban 1897-1900, 01-07, Dulwich 1900-01, Spartan 1907-08

**Club Colours (change):** Navy blue and pink/navy blue/navy blue (White/black/black)

**Ground Capacity:** 3,000     **Seats:** 500     **Covered:** 1,000     **Clubhouse:** Yes     **Shop:** Yes

**Directions**
East Dulwich station, 200 yards.
Denmark Hill station, 10 minutes walk.
Herne Hill station then bus 37 stops near ground.
Buses 40 & 176 from Elephant & Castle, 185 from Victoria.

**Previous Grounds:** Woodwarde Rd 1893-95,College Farm 95-96,Sunray Ave 1896-02,Freeman's Gd,Champ Hill 02-12,Champ Hill (old grd)12-92

**Record Attendance:** 1,835 v Southport - FA Cup 1998-99
**Record Victory:** Not known
**Record Defeat:** Not known
**Record Goalscorer:** Edgar Kail - 427 (1919-33)
**Record Appearances:** Reg Merritt - 576 (1950-66)
**Additional Records:** Received £35,000 from Charlton Athletic for Chris Dickson 2007

**Senior Honours:**
FA Amateur Cup 1919-20, 31-32, 33-34, 36-37.
Isthmian League Premier Division x4, Division One 1977-78, Division One South 2012-13. London Senior Cup x5. Surrey Senior Cup x16.
London Challenge Cup 1998-99.

## 10 YEAR RECORD

| 03-04 | 04-05 | 05-06 | 06-07 | 07-08 | 08-09 | 09-10 | 10-11 | 11-12 | 12-13 |
|---|---|---|---|---|---|---|---|---|---|
| Isth1S 7 | Isth1 15 | Isth1 13 | Isth1S 8 | Isth1S 6 | Isth1S 12 | Isth1S 12 | Isth1S 5 | Isth1S 3 | Isth1S 1 |

# EAST THURROCK UNITED

**Chairman:** Brian Mansbridge

**Secretary:** Neil Speight    **(T)** 0788 531 3435    **(E)** speight.n@sky.com

**Commercial Manager:** n/a      **(T)**

**Programme Editor:** Neil Speight      **(T)** 0788 531 3435

**Ground Address:** Rookery Hill, Corringham, Essex SS17 9LB

**(T)** 01375 644 166             **Manager:** John Coventry

2012-13 Squad - Back (from left): Payan Patel (Physio), Kris Newby, Sam Higgins, Steve Sheehan, Spencer Harrison, Richard Wray, Jamie Riley,
Simon Peddie, Lewis Bentley, Ross Parmenter, Kye Ruel, Neil Gray (GK coach). Front: Sam Collins, Ryan Sammons, John Coventry (Manager) Reiss Gilbey (Capt), Jay Devereux (Assistant manager), Matt Hall, Tom Stephen.

## Club Factfile

**Founded:** 1969     **Nickname:** Rocks

**Previous Names:** Corringham Social > 1969 (Sunday side)

**Previous Leagues:** South Essex Combination, Greater London, Metropolitan 1972-75, London Spartan 1975-79, Essex Senior 1979-92, Isthmian 1992-2004, Southern 2004-05

**Club Colours (change):** Amber with black trim/black/black (Black & white stripes/black/black)

**Ground Capacity:** 3,500   **Seats:** 160    **Covered:** 1,000    **Clubhouse:** Yes    **Shop:** Yes

**Directions**

From A13 London-Southend road,
take A1014 at Stanford-le-Hope for two and half miles,
Ground is on the left.

**Previous Grounds:** Billet, Stanford-le-Hope 1970-73, 74-76, Grays Athletic 1973-74, Tilbury FC 1977-82, New Thames Club 1982-84

**Record Attendance:** 1,215 v Woking FA Cup 2003

**Record Victory:** 7-0 v Coggeshall (H) - Essex Senior League 1984

**Record Defeat:** 0-9 v Eton Manor (A) - Essex Senior League 1982

**Record Goalscorer:** Graham Stewart - 102

**Record Appearances:** Glen Case - 600+

**Additional Records:** £22,000 from Leyton Orient for Greg Berry 1990

**Senior Honours:**
Isthmian League Division Three 1999-2000, Division One North 2010-11. East Anglian Cup 2002-03.

## 10 YEAR RECORD

| 03-04 | 04-05 | 05-06 | 06-07 | 07-08 | 08-09 | 09-10 | 10-11 | 11-12 | 12-13 |
|---|---|---|---|---|---|---|---|---|---|
| Isth1N 12 | SthE 2 | Isth P 12 | Isth P 16 | Isth P 20 | Isth1N 2 | Isth1N 5 | Isth1N 1 | Isth P 10 | Isth P 5 |

## MATCH RESULTS 2012-13

| Date | Comp | H/A | Opponents | Att: | Result | Goalscorers | Pos | No. |
|------|------|-----|-----------|------|--------|-------------|-----|-----|
| Aug 18 | RPL | H | Kingstonian | 224 | D 1-1 | Ruel 61 | 12 | 1 |
| 21 | RPL | A | Wealdstone | 412 | D 1-1 | Newby 67 | 13 | 2 |
| 25 | RPL | A | Bognor Regis Town | 441 | L 0-1 | | 17 | 3 |
| 27 | RPL | H | Cray Wanderers | 161 | D 1-1 | Gilbey 55 | 16 | 4 |
| Sept 1 | RPL | A | Carshalton Athletic | 675 | D 1-1 | Collins 58 | 16 | 5 |
| 8 | FAC Q1 | H | Witham Town | 155 | W 2-0 | Newby 27 Gilbey 28 | | 6 |
| 15 | RPL | H | Hendon | 141 | W 2-0 | Araba 32 Higgins 66 | 11 | 7 |
| 22 | FAC Q2 | A | Kingstonian | 306 | W 3-2 | Newby 9  Higgins 42 75 (pen) | | 8 |
| 29 | FAT Q1 | H | Hastings United | 143 | W 4-0 | Ruel 12 Araba 6 51 Higgins 67 | | 9 |
| Oct 6 | FAC Q3 | H | Maidstone United | 364 | W 3-0 | Higgins 23 (pen) Gilbey 35 Newby 88 | | 10 |
| 9 | RPL | A | Enfield Town | 314 | W 3-2 | Collins 70 Araba 82 Newby 89 | 9 | 11 |
| 13 | RPL | A | Met Police | 122 | D 2-2 | Higgins 12 Araba 21 | 9 | 12 |
| 20 | FAC Q4 | A | Chelmsford City | 902 | D 2-2 | Harrison 14 Newby 90 | | 13 |
| 23 | FAC Q4r | H | Chelmsford City | 595 | D 4-4 | Higgins 1 95 Collins 90 Newby 120 *aet Lost 3-5 pens | | 14 |
| 27 | FAT Q2 | H | Thurrock | 138 | D1-1 | Higgins 30 | | 15 |
| Nov 3 | RPL | H | Hampton & Richmond B | 158 | L 1-2 | Gilbey 86 | 14 | 16 |
| 13 | RPL | H | Bury Town | 151 | L 1-3 | Collins 30 | 15 | 17 |
| 17 | RPL | A | Wingate & Finchley | 109 | W 1-0 | Ruel 3 | 14 | 18 |
| 24 | RPL | H | Leiston | 135 | D 2-2 | Gilbey 20 Araba 45 | 15 | 19 |
| Dec 1 | RPL | A | Lewes | 433 | D 1-1 | Newby 67 | 15 | 20 |
| 4 | RPL | H | Margate | 146 | D 0-0 | | 12 | 21 |
| 8 | RPL | A | Harrowe Borough | 113 | W 3-2 | Collins 5 Newby 37 Araba 63 | 12 | 22 |
| 15 | RPL | A | Lowestoft Town | 201 | L 0-2 | | 14 | 23 |
| 18 | RPL | H | Whitehawk | 141 | D 1-1 | Obaze 55 | 14 | 24 |
| Jan 1 | RPL | A | Canvey Island | 349 | L 1-2 | Collins 34 | 15 | 25 |
| 5 | RPL | H | Enfield Town | 215 | W 2-0 | Collins 17 Bryant 41 | 15 | 26 |
| 12 | RPL | A | Bury Town | 320 | W 2-1 | Collins 58 Ruel 71 | 11 | 27 |
| Feb 5 | RPL | A | Hastings United | 346 | D 1-1 | Ruel 68 | 13 | 28 |
| 9 | RPL | A | Lowestoft Town | 553 | D 0-0 | | 13 | 29 |
| 16 | RPL | A | Leiston | 189 | L 4-5 | COLLINS 3 ( 10 39 57) Bryant 26 | 14 | 30 |
| 19 | RPL | H | Bognor Regis Town | 127 | D 4-4 | Gilbey 39 Ruel 43 Bryant 71 90 | 14 | 31 |
| 23 | RPL | H | Lewes | 125 | W 1-0 | Higgins 10 (pen) | 14 | 32 |
| 26 | RPL | H | Wealdstone | 117 | L 0-2 | | 14 | 33 |
| Mar 2 | RPL | A | Kingstonian | 269 | W 2-0 | Higgins 10 Lawson 66 | 13 | 34 |
| 5 | RPL | H | Thurrock | 119 | W 1-0 | Bryant 17 | 11 | 35 |
| 9 | RPL | H | Carshalton Athletic | 201 | W 4-0 | Parmenter 33 Sammonds 45 Bryant 51 Higgins 62 | 10 | 36 |
| 19 | RPL | H | Metropolitan Police | 121 | D 2-2 | Bryant 43 Lawson 81 | 11 | 37 |
| 26 | RPL | A | Concord Rangers | 163 | D 2-2 | Bryant 45 Ruel 60 | 11 | 38 |
| 29 | RPL | A | Canvey Island | 315 | W 2-0 | Lawson 12 Higgins 73 | 10 | 39 |
| Apr 1 | RPL | A | Thurrock | 236 | W 2-0 | Bryant 7 Stephen 43 | 9 | 40 |
| 6 | RPL | A | Concord Rangers | 210 | W 3-1 | Higgins 21 (Pen) 53 Collins 38 | 9 | 41 |
| 9 | RPL | A | Margate | 241 | W 1-0 | Bryant 29 | 8 | 42 |
| 10 | RPL | A | Hendon | 145 | D 0-0 | | 6 | 43 |
| 13 | RPL | A | Hampton & Richmond B | 293 | W 3-0 | Collins 23  31 Chiweshe 52 (og) | 6 | 44 |
| 16 | RPL | A | Cray Wanderers | 130 | D 2-2 | Higgins 12 (pen) 85 | 5 | 45 |
| 20 | RPL | H | Wingate & Finchley | 201 | W 2-0 | Higgins  51 Collins  68 | 5 | 46 |
| 23 | RPL | H | Harrow Borough | 145 | W 2-0 | Higgins 4 47 | 5 | 47 |
| 25 | RPL | H | Hastings United | 242 | W 1-0 | Ruel 29 | 5 | 48 |
| 27 | RPL | A | Whitehawk | 438 | L 0-1 | | 5 | 49 |

| GOALSCORERS | Lge | FAC | FAT | Total | Pens | Hat-tricks | Cons Run | | Lge | FAC | FAT | Total | Pens | Hat-tricks | Cons Run |
|-------------|-----|-----|-----|-------|------|-----------|----------|--|-----|-----|-----|-------|------|-----------|----------|
| Higgins | 13 | 5 | 2 | 20 | 3 | | 4 | Parmenter | 1 | | | 1 | | | |
| Collins | 14 | 1 | | 15 | | 1 | 3 | Sammonds | 1 | | | 1 | | | |
| Bryant | 10 | | | 10 | | | 4 | Stephen | 1 | | | 1 | | | |
| Newby | 4 | 5 | | 9 | | | 2 | Own Goals | 1 | | | 1 | | | |
| Ruel | 7 | | 1 | 8 | | | | Cons Run - Consecutive scoring games. | | | | | | | |
| Araba | 5 | | 2 | 7 | | | | | | | | | | | |
| Gilbey | 4 | 2 | | 6 | | | | | | | | | | | |
| Lawson | 3 | | | 3 | | | | | | | | | | | |
| Harrison | | 1 | | 1 | | | | | | | | | | | |
| Obaze | 1 | | | 1 | | | | | | | | | | | |

# ENFIELD TOWN

**Chairman:** Paul Millington
**Secretary:** Scott Miller    **(T)** 07903 495 199    **(E)** hibs1173@hotmail.com
**Commercial Manager:** n/a    **(T)**
**Programme Editor:** Ciaron Glennon    **(T)** 07730 953 813
**Ground Address:** Queen Elizabeth Stadium, Donkey Lane, Enfield EN1 3PL
**(T)** 0208 350 4064        **Manager:** Steve Newing

2012-13 Squad - Back row: Michael Ewang, Joe O'Brien, Dave Kendall, Jordan Lockie, Liam Hope, Phil Kane, Mark Kirby, Dean Pennant, Gary Burrell, Mitch Hahn, Leon Osei, Danny Barber, Joe Stevens, Adam Wallace.
Front row: Jeyasiva Sivapathasundaram, Tyler Campbell, Neil Johnston, Bryan Hammatt, Noel Imber, Jason Dale (assistant manager), Steve Newing (manager), Peter Hammatt (coach), James Chalk, Craig McKay, Walid Matata, Lee Allen, Michael Bardle.
The trophy is the Supporters Direct Cup. Enfield Town beat Wrexham 3-1 to win it.

## Club Factfile

**Founded:** 2001     **Nickname:** ET's or Towners
**Previous Names:** Broke away from Enfield F.C. in 2001
**Previous Leagues:** Essex Senior League

**Club Colours (change):** White/blue/blue (Red & yellow hoops/red/red & yellow hoops)

**Ground Capacity:**    **Seats:** Yes    **Covered:** Yes    **Clubhouse:**    **Shop:**

**Directions**

From the M25: Head towards London on the A10 from junction 25. Turn right into Carterhatch Lane at the Halfway House pub. Donkey Lane is first left after the pub.

From London/North Circular Road: Head north up the A10 and turn left to Carterhatch Lane at the Halfway House pub. Donkey Lane is first left after the pub.

**Previous Grounds:** Brimsdown Rovers FC 2001-2010

**Record Attendance:** 562 v Enfield - Middlesex Charity Cup 2002-03
**Record Victory:** 7-0 v Ilford (A) - 29/04/2003
**Record Defeat:** Not known
**Record Goalscorer:** Dan Clarke - 68
**Record Appearances:** Stuart Snowden - 147
**Additional Records:**

**Senior Honours:**
Essex Senior League 2002-03, 04-05. Isthmian League Division 1 North Play-offs 2011-12.

### 10 YEAR RECORD

| 03-04 | | 04-05 | | 05-06 | | 06-07 | | 07-08 | | 08-09 | | 09-10 | | 10-11 | | 11-12 | | 12-13 | |
|---|---|---|---|---|---|---|---|---|---|---|---|---|---|---|---|---|---|---|---|
| ESen | 4 | ESen | 1 | SthE | 3 | Isth1N | 3 | Isth1N | 12 | Isth1N | 12 | Isth1N | 4 | Isth1N | 6 | Isth1N | 2 | Isth P | 16 |

# MATCH RESULTS 2012-13

| Date | Comp | H/A | Opponents | Att: | Result | Goalscorers | Pos | No. |
|------|------|-----|-----------|------|--------|-------------|-----|-----|
| Aug 18 | RPL | A | Lewes | 511 | W 2-1 | Kirby 40 Hope 55 | 15 | 1 |
| 21 | RPL | H | Wingate & Finchley | 373 | W 2-1 | Kirby 3 90 | 4 | 2 |
| 25 | RPL | H | Whitehawk | 375 | L 1-3 | Hope 14 | 7 | 3 |
| 27 | RPL | A | Metropolitan Police | 155 | D 2-2 | Kirby 14 Johnson 41 | 7 | 4 |
| Sept 1 | RPL | H | Hampton & Richmond B. | 320 | L 0-2 | | 11 | 5 |
| 8 | FAC Q1 | H | St Margaretsbury | 346 | W 2-0 | Campbell  Hope | | 6 |
| 15 | RPL | A | Margate | 483 | L 0-2 | | 13 | 7 |
| 22 | FAC Q2 | H | Bishop's Stortford | 460 | L 1-4 | Campbell | | 8 |
| 29 | FAT Q1 | H | Cambridge City | 281 | W 4-1 | Lockie 8 Kirby 23 Hope 57  Wallace 80 | | 9 |
| Oct 9 | RPL | H | East Thurrock United | 314 | L 2-3 | Campbell 8 Hope 48 | 14 | 10 |
| 13 | RPL | H | Cray Wanderers | 433 | L 1-3 | Wallace 56 | 18 | 11 |
| 20 | RPL | A | Bognor Regis Town | 472 | D 0-0 | | 17 | 12 |
| 27 | FAT Q2 | A | Concord Rangers | 148 | W 2-0 | Hope 13 (pen) O'Brien 79 | | 13 |
| Nov 3 | RPL | A | Canvey Island | 382 | W 4-3 | HOPE 3 ( 19 37 56) O'Brien  41 | 16 | 14 |
| 6 | RPL | A | Hastings United | 297 | L 2-3 | Campbell 48 White 52 | 17 | 15 |
| 10 | FAT Q3 | A | Billericay Town | 417 | L 2-3 | Campbell 68 Wallace 69 | | 16 |
| 13 | RPL | H | Harrow Borough | 303 | W 2-0 | Hunt 67 Wallace 74 | 15 | 17 |
| 17 | RPL | H | Hendon | 411 | W 6-3 | HOPE 3 ( 45 64 pen 68) Campbell 55 Bardle 50 Cousins 77 (og) | 12 | 18 |
| Dec 1 | RPL | H | Lowestoft Town | 381 | L 2-3 | Hunt 11 Wallace 25 | 14 | 19 |
| 8 | RPL | H | Thurrock | 327 | D 1-1 | Wallace 19 | 14 | 20 |
| 15 | RPL | A | Wealdstone | 562 | L 0-4 | | 16 | 21 |
| 26 | RPL | A | Leiston | 230 | L 1-3 | Hahn 57 | 16 | 22 |
| 29 | RPL | A | Whitehawk | 163 | L 0-6 | | 18 | 23 |
| Jan 1 | RPL | H | Bury Town | 368 | L 2-3 | McGleish 68 Kendall 90 | 19 | 24 |
| 5 | RPL | A | East Thurrock United | 215 | L 0-2 | | 20 | 25 |
| 8 | RPL | A | Carshalton Athletic | 180 | L 2-3 | McGleish  33 75 | 18 | 26 |
| 12 | RPL | H | Hastings United | 354 | W 1-0 | McGleish 77 | 17 | 27 |
| 26 | RPL | H | Bognor Regis Town | 434 | L 0-1 | | 18 | 28 |
| Feb 5 | RPL | A | Cray Wanderers | 142 | W 5-2 | McGLEISH 3 ( 23 45 53) Wallace 82 90 | 18 | 29 |
| 9 | RPL | H | Wealdstone | 506 | L 1-2 | Campbell 59 | 18 | 30 |
| 12 | RPL | H | Metropolitan Police | 255 | W 4-0 | Wallace 5 McGleish 12 89 Bardle 85 | 16 | 31 |
| 16 | RPL | H | Kingstonian | 432 | D 1-1 | McGleish 27 (pen) | 17 | 32 |
| 23 | RPL | A | Lowestoft Town | 623 | D 0-0 | | 15 | 33 |
| 26 | RPL | A | Wingate & Finchley | 149 | W 2-1 | McGleish 37 Kirby 61 | 15 | 34 |
| Mar 2 | RPL | H | Lewes | 414 | W 2-1 | McGleish 30 Hammatt 34 | 15 | 35 |
| 5 | RPL | H | Concord Rangers | 252 | L 0-1 | | 15 | 36 |
| 16 | RPL | H | Margate | 397 | L 0-3 | | 15 | 37 |
| 23 | RPL | A | Concord Rangers | 282 | L 0-3 | | 15 | 38 |
| 27 | RPL | A | Kingstonian | 214 | W 2-1 | Hope 52 85 | 15 | 39 |
| 30 | RPL | A | Bury Town | 320 | L 1-2 | Hope 29 | 15 | 40 |
| Apr 1 | RPL | H | Leiston | 298 | W 1-0 | Hope 33 | 15 | 41 |
| 4 | RPL | A | Hampton & Richmond B. | 202 | L 2-4 | Hope 11 66 (pen) | 15 | 42 |
| 6 | RPL | A | Harrow Borough | 248 | L 2-4 | Hope 24 82 | 15 | 43 |
| 10 | RPL | H | Canvey Island | 330 | L 0-2 | | 15 | 44 |
| 20 | RPL | A | Hendon | 220 | W 3-2 | O'Brien 3  Campbell 15 Hope 35 | 15 | 45 |
| 23 | RPL | A | Thurrock | 212 | L 0-1 | | 26 | 46 |
| 27 | RPL | H | Carshalton Athletic | 382 | L 1-2 | Hope 9 (pen) | 16 | 47 |

| GOALSCORERS | Lge | FAC | FAT | Total | Pens | Hat-tricks | Cons Run | | Lge | FAC | FAT | Total | Pens | Hat-tricks | Cons Run |
|-------------|-----|-----|-----|-------|------|------------|----------|---|-----|-----|-----|-------|------|------------|----------|
| Hope | 19 | 1 | 2 | 22 | 3 | 2 | 5 | Johnson | 1 | | | 1 | | | |
| McGleish | 12 | | | 12 | 1 | 1 | 2 | Kendall | 1 | | | 1 | | | |
| Wallace | 7 | | 2 | 9 | | | | Lockie | | | 1 | | | | |
| Campbell | 5 | 2 | 1 | 8 | | | | White | 1 | | | 1 | | | |
| Kirby | 5 | | 1 | 6 | | | | Own Goals | 1 | | | 1 | | | |
| Bardle | 2 | | | 2 | | | | Cons Run - Consecutive scoring games. | | | | | | | |
| Hunt | 2 | | | 2 | | | | | | | | | | | |
| O'Brien | 2 | | 1 | 3 | | | | | | | | | | | |
| Hahn | 1 | | | 1 | | | | | | | | | | | |
| Hammett | 1 | | | 1 | | | | | | | | | | | |

# Click Back in Time!

Over 36 years of publishing the Non-League Club Directory has filled a room full of information and photographs covering the game we know and love.

What we intend, over time, is to create a website that shares with you everything we have accumulated, which we hope will bring back some fond memories of season's gone by.

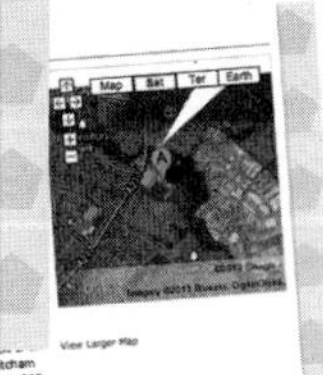

A unique look back at how the game has evolved since the 1940s will also make for interesting reading, including league tables from season's gone by.

Log on to **www.non-leagueclubdirectory.co.uk** today and see how many faces from teams gone by you recognise

# GRAYS ATHLETIC

**Chairman:** Keith Burns
**Secretary:** Val Pepperell   **(T)** 07931 731 358   **(E)** graysathleticfc@hotmail.co.uk
**Commercial Manager:** Chris Jones, Steve   **(T)**
**Programme Editor:** Chris Jones   **(T)** cmjones007@hotmail.com
**Ground Address:** Rush Green Sports & Leisure Centre, Rush Green Road, Romford RM7 0LU
**(T)** 07752 161 633     **Manager:** Hakan Hayrettin

Champions!! The squad celebrate winning the Isthmian Division One North title.
Photo: Peter Jackson.

## Club Factfile

**Founded:** 1890   **Nickname:** The Blues
**Previous Names:** None
**Previous Leagues:** Athenian 1912-14, 58-83, London 1914-24, 26-39, Kent 1924-26, Corinthian 1945-58, Isthmian 1958-2004, Conference 2004-10

**Club Colours (change):** All royal blue (All white)

**Ground Capacity:**   **Seats:**   **Covered:**   **Clubhouse:** Yes   **Shop:** No

**Directions**
At junction 8, exit onto M25 toward Dartford, Continue onto A282, Partial toll road.
At junction 31, take the A1090/A1306 exit to Thurrock (Lakeside)/Purfleet/W Thurrock/A126 Toll road.
At the roundabout, take the 3rd exit onto Arterial Road Purfleet/A1306
Continue to follow A1306. Go through 3 roundabouts
At the roundabout, take the 3rd exit onto Rainham Rd/A125.
At the roundabout, take the 1st exit onto Dagenham Rd/A1112
Continue to follow A1112 at the roundabout, take the 2nd exit onto Rainham Rd S/A1112
At the roundabout, take the 2nd exit onto Wood Ln/A124 continue to follow A124. Destination will be on the left

**Previous Grounds:** Recreation Ground Bridge Road. Rookery Hill (East Thurrock Utd).

**Record Attendance:** 9,500 v Chelmsford City - FA Cup 4th Qualifying Round 1959
**Record Victory:** 12-0 v Tooting & Mitcham United - London League 24/02/1923
**Record Defeat:** 0-12 v Enfield (A) - Athenian League 20/04/1963
**Record Goalscorer:** Harry Brand - 269 (1944-52)
**Record Appearances:** Phil Sammons - 673 (1982-97)
**Additional Records:**

**Senior Honours:**
Conference South 2004-05. FA Trophy 2004-05, 05-06. Isthmian Division One North 2012-13.
Essex Senior Cup x8

### 10 YEAR RECORD

| 03-04 | | 04-05 | | 05-06 | | 06-07 | | 07-08 | | 08-09 | | 09-10 | | 10-11 | | 11-12 | | 12-13 | |
|---|---|---|---|---|---|---|---|---|---|---|---|---|---|---|---|---|---|---|---|
| Isth P | 6 | Conf S | 1 | Conf | 3 | Conf | 19 | Conf | 10 | Conf | 19 | Conf | 23 | Isth1N | 10 | Isth1N | 5 | Isth1N | 1 |

# HAMPTON & RICHMOND BOROUGH

**Chairman:** Steve McPherson
**Secretary:** Nick Hornsey      **(T)** 07768 861 446      **(E)** secretary@hamptonfc.net
**Commercial Manager:** n/a      **(T)**
**Programme Editor:** James Waddan      **(T)** 07572 867 744
**Ground Address:** Accord Beveree Stadium, Beaver Close, Station Road, Hampton TW12 2BX
**HRBFC**      **(T)** 0208 8979 2456      **Manager:** Paul Barry

2012-13 Squad - Back Row (L-R): Mo Harkin, Malvin Kamara, Joe Benjamin, Max Hustwick, Paul Johnson, Rodney Chiweshe, Billy Jeffreys, Lloyd Anderson, Dean Inman, Joe Turner, Elliot Bent, Charlie Moone, James Simmonds, Richard Johnson (Physio)
Front Row: Neil Jenkins, Karle Carder, Gary Holloway, Nigel Edgecombe (Coach), Paul Barry (Coach), Mark Harper (Manager), Andy Smith (Assistant Manager), Anson Cousins, Tom Hickey, Alan Bray.

## Club Factfile

**Founded:** 1921      **Nickname:** Beavers or Borough
**Previous Names:** Hampton > 1999
**Previous Leagues:** Kingston & District, South West Middlesex, Surrey Senior 1959-64, Spartan 1964-71, Athenian 1971-73, Isthmian 1973-2007

**Club Colours (change):** Red with blue flash/blue/red (Sky blue/white/sky blue)

**Ground Capacity:** 3,000   **Seats:** 300   **Covered:** 800   **Clubhouse:** Yes   **Shop:** Yes

**Directions:** From M25; Exit M25 at Junction 10 (M3 Richmond). Exit M3 at Junction 1 and take 4th exit (Kempton Park, Kingston). After approximately 3 miles turn left in to High Street, Hampton. Immediately turn left on to Station Road. The entrance to the ground is 200 yards on the right hand side.

**Previous Grounds:** None

**Record Attendance:** 2,520 v AFC Wimbledon - 11/10/2005
**Record Victory:** 11-1 v Eastbourne United - Isthmian League Division 2 South 1991-92
**Record Defeat:** 0-13 v Hounslow Town - Middlesex Senior Cup 1962-63
**Record Goalscorer:** Peter Allen - 176 (1964-73)
**Record Appearances:** Tim Hollands - 750 (1977-95)
**Additional Records:** Paid £3,000 to Chesham United for Matt Flitter June 2000
**Senior Honours:** Received £40,000 from Queens Park Rangers for Leroy Phillips
Isthmian League Premier Division 2006-07.
Spartan League x4. London Senior Cup x2. Middlesex Senior Challenge Cup 2011-12.

### 10 YEAR RECORD

| 03-04 | 04-05 | 05-06 | 06-07 | 07-08 | 08-09 | 09-10 | 10-11 | 11-12 | 12-13 |
|---|---|---|---|---|---|---|---|---|---|
| Isth1S 5 | Isth P 6 | Isth P 5 | Isth P 1 | Conf S 3 | Conf S 2 | Conf S 14 | Conf S 18 | Conf S 21 | Isth P 13 |

# MATCH RESULTS 2012-13

| Date | Comp | H/A | Opponents | Att: | Result | Goalscorers | Pos | No. |
|------|------|-----|-----------|------|--------|-------------|-----|-----|
| Aug 18 | RPL | H | Hastings United | 296 | W 1-0 | Hustwick 43 | 6 | 1 |
| 21 | RPL | A | Hendon | 180 | W 3-0 | Kamara 16 Benjamin 34 Moone 54 | 2 | 2 |
| 25 | RPL | A | Canvey Island | 332 | D 0-0 | | 2 | 3 |
| 27 | RPL | H | Thurrock | 427 | W 1-0 | Moone 38 | 1 | 4 |
| Sept 1 | RPL | A | Enfield Town | 320 | W 2-0 | Bates 67 Moone 82 | 1 | 5 |
| 3 | FAC 1 | A | **AFC Kempston** | **101** | **W 3-0** | **Bates 13 Moone 25  Benjamin** | | 6 |
| 15 | RPL | H | Lowestoft | 509 | D 1-1 | Moone 19 | 2 | 7 |
| 22 | FAC Q2 | A | **Waltham Forest** | **89** | **W 1-0** | **Moone 85** | | 8 |
| 29 | FAT Q1 | A | **Hythe Town** | **202** | **D 1-1** | **Harkin 46** | | 9 |
| Oct 2 | FAT Q1r | A | **Hythe Town** | **151** | **W 4-0** | **MOONE 3  Kamara** | | 10 |
| 6 | FAC Q3 | A | **Bury Town** | **405** | **L 0-4** | | | 11 |
| 9 | RPL | H | Lewes | 296 | W 2-1 | Turner 27 Ledgister 74 | 2 | 12 |
| 13 | RPL | H | Whitehawk | 616 | W 1-0 | Moone 84 | 1 | 13 |
| 20 | RPL | A | Leiston | 209 | D 2-2 | Hickey 90 Holloway 90 | 1 | 14 |
| 27 | FAT Q2 | H | **Three Bridges** | **229** | **W 1-0** | **Kamara 87** | | 15 |
| 29 | RPL | A | Wealdstone | 588 | L 2-3 | Ledgister  Hickey | 1 | 16 |
| Nov 3 | RPL | A | East Thurrock U | 158 | W 2-1 | Simmonds 2 Ledgister 8 | 1 | 17 |
| 6 | RPL | A | Concord Rangers | 214 | L 1-2 | Bettamere 83 | 1 | 18 |
| 10 | FAT Q3 | A | **Leiston** | **201** | **D 1-1** | **Moone 16** | | 19 |
| 14 | FAT 3Qr | H | **Leiston** | **163** | **W 3-2** | **Moone (2) Hickey** | | 20 |
| 17 | RPL | H | Cray Wanderers | 369 | L 1-3 | Moone 29 | 4 | 21 |
| 24 | FAT 1 | H | **Chelmsford City** | **241** | **D 1-1** | **Moone 63** | | 22 |
| Dec 1 | RPL | H | Margate | 339 | L 1-2 | Holloway 24 | 6 | 23 |
| 8 | RPL | H | Bury Town | 252 | L 2-3 | Jenkins 28 Moone 72 | 8 | 24 |
| 10 | FAT 1r | A | **Chelmsford City** | **301** | **L 2-3** | **Jenkins 43 Bettamer 80** | | 25 |
| 15 | RPL | A | Wingate & Finchley | 131 | W 3-0 | Bates 43 Hickey 79 Turner 87 | 6 | 26 |
| 18 | RPL | A | Harrow Borough | 148 | L 3-4 | Moone 41 Bettamer 82 Holloway 88 | 8 | 27 |
| 26 | RPL | H | Carshalton Athletic | 269 | L 0-1 | | 9 | 28 |
| Jan 1 | RPL | A | Kingstonian | 476 | D 0-0 | | 11 | 29 |
| 6 | RPL | A | Lewes | 558 | D 2-2 | Moone 31 (pen) Turner 43 | 11 | 30 |
| Feb 2 | RPL | A | Bury Town | 301 | W 1-0 | Moone 69 | 10 | 31 |
| 9 | RPL | H | Wingate & Finchley | 269 | D 3-3 | Moss 25 Moone 51 76 | 11 | 32 |
| 19 | RPL | A | Thurrock | 134 | D 0-0 | | 11 | 33 |
| 23 | RPL | A | Margate | 354 | L 1-2 | Moone 80 | 13 | 34 |
| 26 | RPL | H | Hendon | 201 | L 1-2 | Moone 60 | 14 | 35 |
| Mar 2 | RPL | A | Hastings United | 422 | D 0-0 | | 14 | 36 |
| 5 | RPL | H | Metropolitan Police | 132 | D 0-0 | | 14 | 37 |
| 12 | RPL | H | Concord Rangers | 139 | D 1-1 | Moone 71 (pen) | 14 | 38 |
| 16 | RPL | A | Lowestoft Town | 527 | L 3-5 | Taggart 39 51 Moss 45 | 14 | 39 |
| 19 | RPL | A | Bognor Regis Town | 330 | W 5-0 | MOSS 3 (25 38 39) Stoner 57 (og) Murray 90 | 13 | 40 |
| 26 | RPL | A | Whitehawk | 104 | D 0-0 | | 14 | 41 |
| 30 | RPL | H | Kingstonian | 589 | L 0-1 | | 14 | 42 |
| Apr 1 | RPL | A | Carshalton Athletic | 207 | L 0-3 | | 14 | 43 |
| 4 | RPL | H | Enfield Town | 202 | W 4-2 | Turner 14 89 Bettamee 39 Simmonds 63 | 13 | 44 |
| 6 | RPL | A | Metropolitan Police | 222 | L 0-1 | | 14 | 45 |
| 9 | RPL | H | Leiston | 169 | D 3-3 | Simmonds 52 Holloway 68 Moss 78 | 14 | 46 |
| 13 | RPL | H | East Thurrock U | 293 | L 0-3 | | 14 | 47 |
| 16 | RPL | H | Harrow Borough | 154 | D 0-0 | | 14 | 48 |
| 18 | RPL | H | Wealdstone | 326 | W 3-1 | Powell  16 Jefferies 69 Turner 90 | 14 | 49 |
| 20 | RPL | A | Cray Wanderers | 172 | L 0-2 | | 14 | 50 |
| 25 | RPL | A | Canvey Island | 131 | D 2-2 | Bray 55 Holloway 85 | 14 | 51 |
| 27 | RPL | H | Bognor Regis Town | 525 | W 1-0 | Turner 64 | 13 | 52 |

| GOALSCORERS | Lge | FAC | FAT | Total | Pens | Hat-tricks | Cons Run | | Lge | FAC | FAT | Total | Pens | Hat-tricks | Cons Run |
|-------------|-----|-----|-----|-------|------|-----------|----------|--|-----|-----|-----|-------|------|-----------|----------|
| Moone | 15 | 2 | 7 | 24 | 2 | | 5 | Jenkins | 1 | | 1 | 2 | | | 2 |
| Turner | 7 | | | 7 | | | | Taggart | 2 | | | 2 | | | |
| Moss | 6 | | | 6 | | 1 | | Bray | 1 | | | 1 | | | |
| Holloway | 5 | | | 5 | | | | Harkin | | | 1 | 1 | | | |
| Bettamere | 3 | | 1 | 4 | | | | Hustwick | 1 | | | 1 | | | |
| Hickey | 3 | | 1 | 4 | | | | Jefferies | 1 | | | 1 | | | |
| Bates | 2 | 1 | | 3 | | | 2 | Murray | 1 | | | 1 | | | |
| Kamara | 1 | | 2 | 3 | | | | Powell | 1 | | | 1 | | | |
| Ledgister | 3 | | | 3 | | | | Own Goals | 1 | | | 1 | | | |
| Simmonds | 3 | | | 3 | | | | Cons Run - Consecutive scoring games. | | | | | | | |
| Benjamin | 1 | 1 | | 2 | | | | | | | | | | | |

# HARROW BOROUGH

**Chairman:** Peter Rogers

**Secretary:** Peter Rogers    **(T)** 0795 618 5685    **(E)** peter@harrowboro.co.uk

**Commercial Manager:** n/a     **(T)**

**Programme Editor:** Peter Rogers    **(T)** 0795 618 5685

**Ground Address:** Earlsmead, Carlyon Avenue, South Harrow HA2 8SS

**(T)** 0844 561 1347     **Manager:** Dave Anderson

2012-13 Squad - Back Row: Ola Williams, Gary Burrell, Michael Barima, Jon Munday, Michael Peacock, Steve Ferguson.
Middle Row: Peter Webber, Bill Tumbridge, Alwayne Jones, Jamie Jackson, Danny Leech, Elvijs Putnins,
Evandro Delgado, Peter Rogers.
Front Row: Simeon Akinola, Gary Jones, Rob Wolleaston, Darron Wilkinson, Dave Anderson , Jason Goodliffe, Joakim Ehui,
James Burgess, Jordan Lawal.

## Club Factfile

**Founded:** 1933     **Nickname:** Boro

**Previous Names:** Roxonian 1933-38, Harrow Town 1938-66

**Previous Leagues:** Harrow & District 1933-34, Spartan 1934-40, 45-58, West Middlesex Combination 1940-41, Middlesex Senior 1941-45,
Delphian 1956-63, Athenian 1963-75

**Club Colours (change):** Red with white trim/red/red (Blue with white trim/blue/blue)

**Ground Capacity:** 3,070   **Seats:** 350    **Covered:** 1,000    **Clubhouse:** Yes    **Shop:** Yes

**Directions**
From the M25 junction 16, take the M40 East towards Uxbridge and London. Continue onto A40, passing Northolt Aerodrome on the left hand side. At the Target Roundabout junction (A312) turn left towards Northolt.
Just after passing Northolt Underground Station on the left hand side, turn left at the next set of traffic lights, onto Eastcote Lane, becoming Field End Road.
At next roundabout, turn right onto Eastcote Lane. At a small parade of shops, take the turning on the right into Carlyon Avenue. Earlsmead is the second turning on the right.

**Previous Grounds:** Northcult Road 1933-34.

**Record Attendance:** 3,000 v Wealdstone - FA Cup 1st Qualifying Road 1946

**Record Victory:** 13-0 v Handley Page (A) - 18/10/1941

**Record Defeat:** 0-8 on five occasions

**Record Goalscorer:** Dave Pearce - 153

**Record Appearances:** Les Currell - 582, Colin Payne - 557, Steve Emmanuel - 522

**Additional Records:**

**Senior Honours:**
Isthmian League 1983-84.
Middlesex Senior Cup 1982-83, 92-93. Middlesex Premier Cup 1981-82.
Middlesex Senior Charity Cup 1979-80, 92-93, 2005-06, 06-07

### 10 YEAR RECORD

| 03-04 | 04-05 | 05-06 | 06-07 | 07-08 | 08-09 | 09-10 | 10-11 | 11-12 | 12-13 |
|---|---|---|---|---|---|---|---|---|---|
| Isth P   17 | Isth P   16 | Isth P   16 | Isth P   19 | Isth P   16 | Isth P   14 | Isth P   14 | Isth P   5 | Isth P   17 | Isth P   15 |

# MATCH RESULTS 2012-13

| Date | Comp | H/A | Opponents | Att: | Result | Goalscorers | Pos | No. |
|------|------|-----|-----------|------|--------|-------------|-----|-----|
| Aug 18 | RPL | H | Thurrock | 114 | W 4-1 | Wooleaston 9 Jones 13 51 (pen) Akinola 16 | 1 | 1 |
| 20 | RPL | A | Kingstonian | 296 | L 2-4 | Akinola 15 Jones 90 | 10 | 2 |
| 25 | RPL | A | Cray Wanderers | 111 | L 1-2 | Ehul 90 | 13 | 3 |
| 27 | RPL | H | Hastings United | 131 | L 0-1 | | 16 | 4 |
| Sept 1 | RPL | A | Lowestoft Town | 591 | L 0-3 | | 19 | 5 |
| 8 | FAC Q1 | H | St Albans City | 219 | L 1-3 | Ehul 39 | | 6 |
| 15 | RPL | H | Carshalton Athletic | 140 | W1-0 | Burrell 87 | 16 | 7 |
| 29 | FAT Q1 | A | Whitstable Town | 161 | L 0-2 | | | 8 |
| Oct 9 | RPL | A | Wingate & Finchley | 101 | L 1-2 | Akinola 20 | 16 | 9 |
| 13 | RPL | A | Bury Town | 532 | W 1-0 | Tararov 11 | 14 | 10 |
| 20 | RPL | H | Canvey Island | 141 | L 1-3 | Ehul 49 | 15 | 11 |
| 23 | RPL | A | Bognor Regis Town | 357 | W 3-0 | Akinola 46 80 Peacock 64 | 11 | 12 |
| Nov 3 | RPL | H | Concord Rangers | 104 | L 1-2 | Akinola 73 | 12 | 13 |
| 10 | RPL | H | Margate | 132 | L 0-2 | | 14 | 14 |
| 13 | RPL | A | Enfield Town | 303 | L 0-2 | | 14 | 15 |
| 17 | RPL | A | Lewes | 479 | D 1-1 | Akinola 50 | 17 | 16 |
| Dec 1 | RPL | A | Whitehawk | 201 | D 0-0 | | 16 | 17 |
| 8 | RPL | H | East Thurrock United | 113 | L 2-3 | Merrifield 32 Akinola 77 | 18 | 18 |
| 15 | RPL | A | Leiston | 199 | L 0-1 | | 18 | 19 |
| 18 | RPL | H | Hampton & Richmond B | 148 | W 4-3 | Lucien 25 Leech 35 Peacock 51 Jones 76 (pen) | 17 | 20 |
| 26 | RPL | H | Wealdstone | 661 | D 0-0 | | 17 | 21 |
| 29 | RPL | H | Cray Wanderers | 137 | D 3-3 | Putnins (GK) 1 Sankoh 42 Akinola 80 | 16 | 22 |
| Jan 5 | RPL | H | Wingate & Finchley | 156 | L 1-2 | Sankoh 24 | 17 | 23 |
| 12 | RPL | A | Metropolitan Police | 125 | D 1-1 | Ofuse-Hene 34 | 19 | 24 |
| 26 | RPL | A | Canvey Island | 304 | L 0-3 | | 20 | 25 |
| 29 | RPL | H | Metropolitan Police | 103 | L 2-3 | Merrifield 27 Leech 71 | 20 | 26 |
| Feb 5 | RPL | H | Bury Town | 94 | W 3-1 | Peacock 33 Akinola 54 Sankoh 81 | 19 | 27 |
| 9 | RPL | H | Leiston | 123 | L 1-3 | Lucien 66 | 19 | 28 |
| 23 | RPL | H | Whitehawk | 91 | W 3-1 | Jones 45 (pen) Lucien 45 Williams 68 | 19 | 29 |
| 26 | RPL | H | Kingstonian | 147 | W 1-0 | Jones 36 (pen) | 16 | 30 |
| Mar 2 | RPL | A | Thurrock | 168 | L 0-3 | | 16 | 31 |
| 5 | RPL | A | Hendon | 153 | W 2-1 | Sankoh 9 Leech 46 | 16 | 32 |
| 9 | RPL | H | Lowestoft Town | 204 | D 3-3 | Reynolds 7 (og) Lucien 23 27 | 16 | 33 |
| 26 | RPL | A | Carshalton Athletic | 75 | L 1-3 | Lucien 70 | 16 | 34 |
| 30 | RPL | H | Hendon | 90 | D 1-1 | Wolleaston 4 | 16 | 35 |
| Apr 1 | RPL | A | Wealdstone | 841 | L 0-2 | | 18 | 36 |
| 6 | RPL | H | Enfield Town | 248 | W 4-2 | Sankoh 6 50 Akinola71 Wolleaston 72 | 16 | 37 |
| 9 | RPL | H | Hastings United | 337 | L 0-2 | | 16 | 38 |
| 13 | RPL | A | Concord Rangers | 183 | W 2-1 | Olima 5 Lucien 59 | 16 | 39 |
| 16 | RPL | A | Hampton & Richmond B | 154 | D 0-0 | | 15 | 40 |
| 20 | RPL | H | Lewes | 154 | L 0-2 | | 16 | 41 |
| 23 | RPL | A | East Thurrock United | 145 | L 0-2 | | 16 | 42 |
| 25 | RPL | A | Bognor Regis Town | 132 | W 3-2 | Berry 16 Williams 45 Bola 77 | 15 | 43 |
| 27 | RPL | A | Margate | 305 | D 0-0 | | 15 | 44 |

| GOALSCORERS | Lge | FAC | FAT | Total | Pens | Hat-tricks | Cons Run | | Lge | FAC | FAT | Total | Pens | Hat-tricks | Cons Run |
|-------------|-----|-----|-----|-------|------|------------|----------|--|-----|-----|-----|-------|------|------------|----------|
| Akinola | 11 | | | 11 | | | 2 | Berry | 1 | | | 1 | | | |
| Lucien | 7 | | | 7 | | | 2 | Bola | 1 | | | 1 | | | |
| Jones | 6 | | | 6 | 4 | | 2 | Burrell | 1 | | | 1 | | | |
| Sankoh | 6 | | | 6 | | | | Olima | 1 | | | 1 | | | |
| Ehul | 2 | 1 | | 3 | | | | Ofuse-Hene | 1 | | | 1 | | | |
| Leech | 3 | | | 3 | | | | Putnins (GK) | 1 | | | 1 | | | |
| Peacock | 3 | | | 3 | | | | Tararov | 1 | | | 1 | | | |
| Wolleaston | 3 | | | 3 | | | | Own Goals | 1 | | | 1 | | | |
| Merrifield | 2 | | | 2 | | | | Cons Run - Consecutive scoring games. | | | | | | | |
| Williams | 2 | | | 2 | | | | | | | | | | | |

# HENDON

**Chairman:** Simon Lawrence
**Secretary:** Graham Etchell    **(T)** 07973 698 552    **(E)** hendonfc@freenetname.co.uk
**Commercial Manager:** n/a     **(T)**
**Programme Editor:** Graham Etchell     **(T)** hendonfc@freenetname.co.uk
**Ground Address:** Harrow Borough FC, Earlsmead, Carlyon Avenue, South Harrow HA2 8SS
**(T)**            **Manager:** Gary McCann

The team line up before their FA Cup 3rd Qualifying match versus Eastbourne Borough.
Photo: Roger Turner.

## Club Factfile

**Founded:** 1908     **Nickname:** Dons or Greens
**Previous Names:** Christ Church Hampstead > 1908, Hampstead Town > 1933, Golders Green > 1946
**Previous Leagues:** Finchley & District 1908-11, Middlesex 1910-11, London 1911-14, Athenian 1914-63

**Club Colours (change):** All green & white (All tangerine)

**Ground Capacity:** 2,450   **Seats:** 350    **Covered:** 950    **Clubhouse:** Yes    **Shop:**

**Directions**

From the M25 junction 16, take the M40 East towards Uxbridge and London. Continue onto A40, passing Northolt Aerodrome on the left hand side. At the Target Roundabout junction (A312) turn left towards Northolt.
Just after passing Northolt Underground Station on the left hand side, turn left at the next set of traffic lights, onto Eastcote Lane, becoming Field End Road.
At next roundabout, turn right onto Eastcote Lane. At a small parade of shops, take the turning on the right into Carlyon Avenue. Earlsmead is the second turning on the right.

**Previous Grounds:** Claremont Road. Vale Farm (Wembley FC).

**Record Attendance:** 9,000 v Northampton Town - FA Cup 1st Round 1952
**Record Victory:** 13-1 v Wingate - Middlesex County Cup 02/02/1957
**Record Defeat:** 2-11 v Walthamstowe Avenue, Athenian League 09/11/1935
**Record Goalscorer:** Freddie Evans - 176 (1929-35)
**Record Appearances:** Bill Fisher - 787 - (1940-64)
**Additional Records:** Received £30,000 from Luton Town for Iain Dowie

**Senior Honours:**
FA Amateur Cup 1959-60, 64-65, 71-72. Isthmian League 1964-65, 72-73. European Amateur Champions 1972-73.
Athenian League x3. London Senior Cup 1963-64, 68-69. Middlesex Senior Cup x14

### 10 YEAR RECORD

| 03-04 | 04-05 | 05-06 | 06-07 | 07-08 | 08-09 | 09-10 | 10-11 | 11-12 | 12-13 |
|---|---|---|---|---|---|---|---|---|---|
| Isth P   4 | Isth P   11 | Isth P   19 | Isth P   14 | Isth P   7 | Isth P   16 | Isth P   10 | Isth P   15 | Isth P   7 | Isth P   10 |

# MATCH RESULTS 2012-13

| Date | Comp | H/A | Opponents | Att: | Result | Goalscorers | Pos | No. |
|------|------|-----|-----------|------|--------|-------------|-----|-----|
| Aug 18 | RPL | A | Margate | 313 | L 0-2 | | 21 | 1 |
| 21 | RPL | H | Hampton & Richmond | 180 | L 0-3 | | 21 | 2 |
| 25 | RPL | H | Hendon | 139 | D 2-2 | Hall 21 77 | 21 | 3 |
| 27 | RPL | A | Whitehawk | 145 | D 0-0 | | 20 | 4 |
| Sept 1 | RPL | H | Concord Rangers | 157 | D 2-2 | Mazzone 15 Ngoyi 79 | 20 | 5 |
| 8 | FAC Q1 | H | Potters Bar Town | 119 | D 1-1 | McLaren | | 6 |
| 11 | FAC Q1r | A | Potters Bar Town | 139 | W 3-0 | Shulton, Cracknell, Mazzone | | 7 |
| 15 | RPL | A | East Thurrock U | 141 | L 0-2 | | 21 | 8 |
| 22 | FAC Q2 | H | Lewes | 166 | W 3-0 | Cracknell 44 Charles 51 Murray 90 | | 9 |
| 29 | FAT Q1 | A | Leiston | 186 | L 1-2 | Charles | | 10 |
| 6 | FAC Q3 | A | Eastbourne Borough | 439 | D 2-2 | Ngoyi 47 72 | | 11 |
| 9 | FAC Q3r | H | Eastbourne Borough | 150 | W 2-1* | Murray 120 (pen) Rankin 128 | | 12 |
| 13 | RPL | H | Leiston | 179 | W 2-1 | Ngoyi 9 15 | 21 | 13 |
| 20 | FAC Q4 | A | Corby Town | 692 | W 2-1 | Ngoyi 37 Murray 63 | | 14 |
| 23 | RPL | H | Metropolitan Police | 161 | D 1-1 | Mazzone 23 | 20 | 15 |
| Nov 3 | FAC 1 | A | Aldershot | 1822 | L 1-2 | Cracknell 28 | | 16 |
| 10 | RPL | H | Lowestoft Town | 168 | L 0-1 | | 21 | 17 |
| 13 | RPL | A | Lewes | 323 | D 0-0 | | 21 | 18 |
| 17 | RPL | A | Enfield Town | 411 | L 3-6 | Mazzone 48 Kilby 70 (og) Aite-Quakrim 90 | 22 | 19 |
| 20 | RPL | H | Cray Wanderers | 102 | D 0-0 | | 20 | 20 |
| Dec 2 | RPL | A | Wealdstone | 437 | L 1-2 | Aite-Quakrim 89 | 21 | 21 |
| 8 | RPL | H | Carshalton | 147 | W 3-1 | Owusu-Bekde 38 Aite-Quakrim 43 Diedhiou 84 | 21 | 22 |
| 10 | RPL | A | Kingstonian | 254 | L 1-2 | Osusu-Bekde 90 | 21 | 23 |
| 15 | RPL | A | Bognor Regis Town | 340 | L 1-3 | Cracknell 90 | 21 | 24 |
| 18 | RPL | A | Thurrock | 164 | W 2-1 | Hall 77 Curtis 90 (pen) | 19 | 25 |
| 26 | RPL | A | Wingate & Finchley | 182 | W 1-0 | Owusu-Bekde 90 (pen) | 18 | 26 |
| Jan 1 | RPL | A | Cray Wanderers | 213 | W 1-0 | Aite-Quakrim 89 | 18 | 27 |
| 8 | RPL | H | Canvey Island | 158 | L 1-2 | Cracknell 30 | 18 | 28 |
| 12 | RPL | H | Kingstonian | 212 | W 1-0 | Connors 41 | 16 | 29 |
| Feb 2 | RPL | A | Carshalton Athletic | 188 | W 2-0 | Angol 7 Sonner 19 | 13 | 30 |
| 5 | RPL | H | Whitehawk | 136 | D 1-1 | Cracknell 18 | 13 | 31 |
| 9 | RPL | H | Bognor Regis Town | 213 | W 1-0 | Angol 79 | 12 | 32 |
| 16 | RPL | A | Canvey Island | 321 | W 3-0 | Cracknell 11 Morias 58 Rankin 90 | 11 | 33 |
| 19 | RPL | A | Bury Town | 252 | W 2-1 | Morias 9 McLaren 82 | 11 | 34 |
| 23 | RPL | H | Wealdstone | 402 | D 0-0 | | 12 | 35 |
| 26 | RPL | A | Hampton & Richmond B | 201 | W 2-1 | Morias 31(pen) 38 | 10 | 36 |
| Mar 2 | RPL | H | Margate | 194 | D 0-0 | | 10 | 37 |
| 5 | RPL | H | Harrow Borough | 153 | L 1-2 | Currie 54 (pen) | 11 | 38 |
| 26 | RPL | H | Thurrock | 91 | W 1-0 | Rankin 59 | 10 | 39 |
| 30 | RPL | A | Harrow Borough | 90 | D 1-1 | Flegg 90 | 11 | 40 |
| Apr 1 | RPL | A | Wingate & Finchley | 148 | L 0-2 | | 11 | 41 |
| 4 | RPL | A | Concord Rangers | 122 | W 2-1 | Cracknell 40 Maclaren 89 | 11 | 42 |
| 6 | RPL | H | Lewes | 131 | D 2-2 | Cracknell 15 K Maclaren 32 | 11 | 43 |
| 10 | RPL | H | East Thurrock U | 145 | D 0-0 | | 11 | 44 |
| 13 | RPL | A | Hastings United | 401 | W 2-1 | McCluskie 57 McLaren 87 | 11 | 45 |
| 16 | RPL | A | Hastings United | 154 | W 2-0 | O'Leary 21 Rankin 90 | 10 | 46 |
| 18 | RPL | A | Leiston | 152 | W 1-0 | Connors 70 | 9 | 47 |
| 20 | RPL | H | Enfield Town | 220 | L 2-3 | Diedhiou 51 O'Brien 77 (og) | 10 | 48 |
| 23 | RPL | A | Metropolitan Police | 113 | L 1-2 | K.Smith 90 | 10 | 49 |
| 27 | RPL | A | Lowestoft Town | 890 | L 0-1 | | 10 | 50 |

| GOALSCORERS | Lge | FAC | FAT | Total | Pens | Hat-tricks | Cons Run | | Lge | FAC | FAT | Total | Pens | Hat-tricks | Cons Run |
|-------------|-----|-----|-----|-------|------|------------|----------|--|-----|-----|-----|-------|------|------------|----------|
| Cracknell | 6 | 3 | | 9 | | | 2 | Connors | 2 | | | 2 | | | |
| Ngoyi | 3 | 3 | | 6 | | | | Diedhiou | 2 | | | 2 | | | |
| McLaren | 4 | 1 | | 5 | | | 2 | Currie | 1 | | | 1 | 1 | | |
| Aite-Quakrim | 4 | | | 4 | | | 2 | Curtis | 1 | | | 1 | 1 | | |
| Mazzone | 3 | 1 | | 4 | | | | Flegg (19) | 1 | | | 1 | | | |
| Morias | 4 | | | 4 | | | 2 | McCluskie | 1 | | | 1 | | | |
| Rankin | 3 | 1 | | 4 | | | | O'Leary | 1 | | | 1 | | | |
| Hall | 3 | | | 3 | | | | Shulton | | 1 | | 1 | | | |
| Murray | | 3 | | 3 | | | | Smith | 1 | | | 1 | | | |
| Owusu-Bekde | 3 | | | 3 | 1 | | 2 | Sonner | 1 | | | 1 | | | |
| Angol | 2 | | | 2 | | | | Own Goals | 2 | | | 2 | | | |
| Charles | | 1 | 1 | 2 | | | | Cons Run - Consecutive scoring games. | | | | | | | |

# KINGSTONIAN

**Chairman:** John Fenwick

**Secretary:** Gerry Petit          **(T)** 0785 937 7778          **(E)** gandjpetit149@tiscali.co.uk

**Commercial Manager:** n/a          **(T)**

**Programme Editor:** Robert Wooldridge          **(T)** 07884 074 668

**Ground Address:** Kingsmeadow Stadium, Kingston Road, Kingston KT1 3PB

**(T)** 0208 330 6869          **Manager:** Alan Dowson

2012-13 Squad - Back row (L-R): James Street, Allan Tait, Kieran Murphy, Byron Napper, Aaron Goode, Dominic Sterling, Gary MacDonald, Tom Hutchinson, Simon Huckle, Mark Francis.
Middle row: Mark Hams, Mat Somner, Bashiru Alimi, Karl Murray, Rob Tolfrey, Alan Dowson, Jake Whincup, Craig Mullen, Saheed Sankoh, Matt Pattison, Martin Tyler, Gerry Petit.
Front row: Paul Ferrie, Goma Lambu, Charles Ofosu-Hene, Dean Lodge, Stuart Duff, Andre McCollin, Wade Small, Mark Nwokeji, Sam Clayton, Alan Smith.

## Club Factfile

**Founded:** 1885          **Nickname:** The K's

**Previous Names:** Kingston & Suburban YMCA 1885-87, Saxons 1887-90, Kingston Wanderers 1893-1904, Old Kingstonians 1908-19

**Previous Leagues:** Kingston & District, West Surrey, Southern Suburban, Athenian 1919-29, Isthmian 1929-98, Conference 1998-2001

**Club Colours (change):** Red and white hoops/black/red & white (Yellow with blue piping/blue/blue)

**Ground Capacity:** 4,262     **Seats:** 1,080     **Covered:** 2,538     **Clubhouse:** Yes     **Shop:** Yes

**Directions**
Take Cambridge Road from Town Centre (A2043) to Malden Road.
From A3 turn off at New Malden and turn left onto A2043.
Ground is 1 mile on the left which is half a mile from Norbiton BR.

**Previous Grounds:** Several > 1921, Richmond Road 1921-89

**Record Attendance:** 4,582 v Chelsea - Freindly

**Record Victory:** 15-1 v Delft - 1951

**Record Defeat:** 0-11 v Ilford - Isthmian League 13/02/1937

**Record Goalscorer:** Johnnie Wing - 295 (1948-62)

**Record Appearances:** Micky Preston - 555 (1967-85)

**Additional Records:** Paid £18,000 to Rushden & Diamonds for David Leworthy 1997

**Senior Honours:** Received £150,000 from West Ham United for Gavin Holligan 1999

FA Amateur Cup 1932-33. Isthmian League 1933-34, 36-37, 97-98, Division 1 South 2008-09.
FAT Trophy 1998-99, 99-2000. Athenian League x2. London Senior Cup x3. Surrey Senior Cup x3.

### 10 YEAR RECORD

| 03-04 | | 04-05 | | 05-06 | | 06-07 | | 07-08 | | 08-09 | | 09-10 | | 10-11 | | 11-12 | | 12-13 | |
|---|---|---|---|---|---|---|---|---|---|---|---|---|---|---|---|---|---|---|---|
| Isth P | 18 | Isth P | 22 | Isth1 | 7 | Isth1S | 13 | Isth1S | 7 | Isth1S | 1 | Isth P | 5 | Isth P | 7 | Isth P | 11 | Isth P | 11 |

# MATCH RESULTS 2012-13

| Date | Comp | H/A | Opponents | Att: | Result | Goalscorers | Pos | No. |
|---|---|---|---|---|---|---|---|---|
| Aug 17 | RPL | A | East Thurrock United | 313 | D 1-1 | Lodge 33 | 13 | 1 |
| 21 | RPL | H | Harrow Borough | 296 | L 4-2 | Lodge 19 (pen) 75 McCollin 53 Goode 55 | 6 | 2 |
| 25 | RPL | H | Margate | 335 | D 3-3 | McDonald 29 McCollin 48 Murphy 84 | 9 | 3 |
| 27 | RPL | A | Concord Rangers | 152 | W 3-0 | McCollin 29 64 Pattison 34 | 5 | 4 |
| 2 | RPL | H | Leiston | 338 | W 3-1 | Goode 14 Small 34 Pattison 54 | 5 | 5 |
| 3 | FAC Q1 | A | Guildford City | 295 | W 3-0 | Mullen (2) Pattison | | 6 |
| 15 | RPL | A | Bury Town | 451 | L 0-1 | | 5 | 7 |
| 22 | FAC Q2 | H | East Thurrock United | 306 | L 2-3 | Lodge 59 Pattison 85 | | 8 |
| Oct 1 | FAT Q1 | H | **Eastbourne Town** | **290** | **W 2-1** | **Small 76 82** | | 9 |
| 6 | RPL | H | Lewes | 326 | W 3-1 | Small 9 38 Lodge 76 | 1 | 10 |
| 8 | RPL | A | Wealdstone | 494 | L 2-5 | McCollin 3 McDonald 8 | | 11 |
| 13 | RPL | A | Lowestoft | 815 | W 3-1 | McCollin 11 78 Pattison 45 | 2 | 12 |
| 20 | RPL | H | Carshalton Athletic | 357 | W 2-1 | Pattison 2 Huckle 9 | 2 | 13 |
| 28 | FAT Q2 | H | **Burnham** | **261** | **W 2-1** | **McCollin 6 41** | | 14 |
| Nov 3 | RPL | H | Wingate & Finchley | 332 | L 0-1 | | 4 | 15 |
| 10 | FAT Q3 | H | **Brentwood Town** | **291** | **D 2-2** | **Mullen 52 Hutchinson 61** | | 16 |
| 13 | FAT Q3r | A | **Brentwood Town** | **320** | **W 4-1** | **Pattison 6 23 Murphy 9 Munn 21** | | 17 |
| 17 | RPL | A | Thurrock | 220 | L 0-4 | | 8 | 18 |
| 24 | FAT 1 | H | **Dartford** | **508** | **L 0-4** | | | 19 |
| Dec 1 | RPL | A | Canvey Island | 302 | L 3-4 | McCOLLIN 3 ( 7 49 59) | 11 | 20 |
| 3 | RPL | H | Bognor Regis Town | 358 | W 1-0 | McCollin 43 (pen) | 10 | 21 |
| 10 | RPL | H | Hendon | 254 | W 2-1 | Murphy 19 Pattison 39 | 7 | 22 |
| 16 | RPL | A | Cray Wanderers | 201 | W 3-1 | Small 77 McCollin 86 Pattison 90 | 6 | 23 |
| 26 | RPL | A | Metropolitan Police | 241 | L 1-4 | Small 11 | 6 | 24 |
| Jan 1 | RPL | H | Hampton & Richmond | 476 | D 0-0 | | 6 | 25 |
| 5 | RPL | H | Wealdstone | 451 | W 2-0 | Pattison 65 McCollin 79 | 4 | 26 |
| 12 | RPL | A | Hendon | 212 | L 0-1 | | 7 | 27 |
| 26 | RPL | A | Carshalton Athletic | 391 | W 3-1 | Pattison 38 Goode  51 Korangten 53 | 7 | 28 |
| Feb 2 | RPL | A | Bognor Regis Town | 552 | W 1-0 | Small 87 | 4 | 29 |
| 9 | RPL | H | Cray Wanderers | 278 | W 9-3 | Korangten 31 90 TAYLOR 3 (43 50 70) | | |
| | | | | | | Pattison 45 83 McCollin 67 Vines 80 | | 30 |
| 16 | RPL | A | Enfield Town | 432 | D 1-1 | Vines 88 | 5 | 31 |
| 18 | RPL | A | Whitehawk | 187 | L 0-2 | | | 32 |
| 23 | RPL | H | Canvey Island | 277 | L 1-2 | McCollin 24 | 7 | 33 |
| 26 | RPL | A | Harrow Borough | 147 | L 0-1 | | 8 | 34 |
| Mar 2 | RPL | H | East Thurrock United | 269 | L 0-2 | | 9 | 35 |
| 17 | RPL | H | Bury Town | 274 | L 0-2 | | 9 | 36 |
| 23 | RPL | A | Lewes | 686 | W 2-1 | Pattison  34 Vines 90 | 9 | 37 |
| 26 | RPL | A | Lowestoft Town | 256 | L 0-1 | | 9 | 38 |
| 28 | RPL | H | Enfield Town | 214 | L 1-2 | Somner 36 | 9 | 39 |
| 30 | RPL | A | Hampton & Richmond B | 589 | W 1-0 | Somner 11 | 9 | 40 |
| Apr 2 | RPL | H | Metropolitan Police | 259 | W 1-0 | Pattison 69 | 9 | 41 |
| 6 | RPL | H | Whitehawk | 305 | L 2-3 | Wanadio 42 Sweeney 58 | 10 | 42 |
| 8 | RPL | H | Hastings United | 245 | L 0-1 | | 10 | 43 |
| 13 | RPL | A | Wingate & Finchley | 212 | L 0-3 | | 13 | 44 |
| 16 | RPL | A | Margate | 185 | W 2-1 | Sweeney 37  Vines 56 | 11 | 45 |
| 20 | RPL | H | Thurrock | 241 | W 1-0 | Taylor 83 | 11 | 46 |
| 22 | RPL | H | Concord Rangers | 205 | L 0-1 | | 11 | 47 |
| 24 | RPL | A | Leiston | 182 | D 2-2 | Okai 85 Vines 90 (pen) | 11 | 48 |
| 27 | RPL | A | Hastings United | 511 | L 0-1 | | 11 | 49 |

| GOALSCORERS | Lge | FAC | FAT | Total | Pens | Hat-tricks | Cons Run | | Lge | FAC | FAT | Total | Pens | Hat-tricks | Cons Run |
|---|---|---|---|---|---|---|---|---|---|---|---|---|---|---|---|
| McCollin | 15 | | 2 | 17 | 1 | 1 | 3 | McDonald | 2 | | | 2 | | | |
| Pattison | 12 | 2 | 2 | 16 | | | 3 | Somner | 2 | | | 2 | | 2 | |
| Small | 6 | | 2 | 8 | | | 2 | Sweeney | 2 | | | 2 | | | |
| Lodge | 4 | 1 | | 5 | 1 | | 2 | Huckle | 1 | | 1 | 1 | | | |
| Vines | 5 | | | 5 | | | 2 | Hutchinson | | | 1 | 1 | | | |
| Taylor | 4 | | | 4 | 1 | | | Munn | | | 1 | 1 | | | |
| Goode | 3 | | | 3 | | | | Okai | 1 | | | 1 | | | |
| Korangton | 3 | | | 3 | | | | Wanadio | 1 | | | 1 | | | |
| Mullen | | 2 | 1 | 3 | | | | Cons Run - Consecutive scoring games. | | | | | | | |
| Murphy | 2 | | 1 | 3 | | | | | | | | | | | |

# LEISTON

**Chairman:** Andrew Crisp
**Secretary:** David Rees     **(T)** 07977 782 559    **(E)** gagrees@aol.com
**Commercial Manager:** n/a    **(T)**
**Programme Editor:** Mark Barber    **(T)** 07792 292 134
**Ground Address:** LTAA, Victory Road, Leiston IP16 4DQ
**(T)** 01728 830 308      **Manager:** Danny Laws

## Club Factfile

**Founded:** 1880    **Nickname:** The Blues
**Previous Names:** None
**Previous Leagues:** Suffolk & Ipswich, Eastern Counties > 2011.

**Club Colours (change):** Blue/white/red (All red)

**Ground Capacity:** 2,500   **Seats:** 124   **Covered:** 500   **Clubhouse:**   **Shop:**

**Directions:** Take junction 28 off the M25, take the A12/A1023 exit to Chelmsford/Romford/Brentwood, keep left at the fork, follow signs for Chelmsford/A12 (E) and merge onto A12, at the roundabout, take the 3rd exit onto the A14 ramp, merge onto A14, at junction 58, exit toward A12, keep left at the fork, follow signs for Lowestoft/Woodbridge/A12 (N) and merge onto A12, go through 7 roundabouts, turn right onto A1094, turn left onto Snape Rd/B1069, continue to follow B1069, turn left onto Victory Rd, ground will be on the left.

**Previous Grounds:** Leiston Recreation Ground 1880-1918.

**Record Attendance: Att:** 271 v AFC Sudbury, 13.11.04.
**Record Victory:** Not known
**Record Defeat:** Not known
**Record Goalscorer:** Lee McGlone - 60 (League).
**Record Appearances:** Tim Sparkes - 154 (League).
**Additional Records:**

**Senior Honours:**
Eastern Counties League Premier Division 2010-11. Isthmian League Division 1 North 2011-12.

### 10 YEAR RECORD

| 03-04 | | 04-05 | | 05-06 | | 06-07 | | 07-08 | | 08-09 | | 09-10 | | 10-11 | | 11-12 | | 12-13 | |
|---|---|---|---|---|---|---|---|---|---|---|---|---|---|---|---|---|---|---|---|
| EC1 | 3 | ECP | 10 | ECP | 9 | ECP | 5 | ECP | 9 | ECP | 7 | ECP | 3 | ECP | 1 | Isth1N | 1 | Isth P | 12 |

# MATCH RESULTS 2012-13

| Date | Comp | H/A | Opponents | Att: | Result | Goalscorers | Pos | No. |
|------|------|-----|-----------|------|--------|-------------|-----|-----|
| Aug 17 | RPL | H | Cray Wanderers | 199 | D 1-1 | Hammond 32 | 14 | 1 |
| 21 | RPL | A | Canvey Island | 305 | L 0-2 | | 18 | 2 |
| 25 | RPL | A | Wealdstone | 415 | L 0-2 | | 20 | 3 |
| 27 | RPL | H | Bognor RegisTown | 225 | D 1-1 | Thrower 69 | 20 | 4 |
| Sept 2 | RPL | A | Kingstonian | 338 | L 1-3 | G.Heath 48 | 22 | 5 |
| | FAC Q1 | H | **Southend Manor** | **153** | **W 5-1** | **G.Heath (2), Ottley-Gooch, Henry, J Heath** | | 6 |
| 15 | RPL | H | Hastings United | 206 | W 3-1 | Thrower 8 Henry 19 G.Heath 75 | 18 | 7 |
| 22 | FAC Q2 | A | **Badshot Lea** | **100** | **L 2-4** | G Heath 40 (pen) Wray 57 | | 8 |
| 29 | FAT Q1 | H | **Hendon** | **186** | **W 2-1** | Thrower, Henry | | 9 |
| Oct 6 | RPL | H | Canvey Island | 201 | D 1-1 | G.Heath 40 | 17 | 10 |
| 13 | RPL | A | Hendon | 179 | L 1-2 | Osei 35 | 20 | 11 |
| 20 | RPL | H | Hampton & Ricmond B | 209 | D 2-2 | Osei 59 G.Heath 88 | 19 | 12 |
| 27 | FAT Q2 | A | **Metropolitan Police** | **153** | **D 1-1** | **Thrower 12** | | 13 |
| 30 | FAT Q2r | A | **Metropolitan Police** | **150** | **W 4-3** | **Henry 52 G.Heath 72  Hammond 75 Osei 87** | | 14 |
| Nov 3 | RPL | H | Lewes | 186 | D 1-1 | Stone 78 | 20 | 15 |
| 6 | RPL | H | Margate | 153 | L 1-2 | G.Heath 19 | 20 | 16 |
| 10 | FAT Q3 | H | **Hampton & Richmond B** | **201** | **D 1-1** | **G.Heath 55** | | 17 |
| 17 | RPL | A | Whitehawk | 142 | L 1-4 | Jefford 36 | 21 | 18 |
| 24 | RPL | A | East Thurrock United | 135 | D 2-2 | Brothers 49 Osei 80 | 20 | 19 |
| 27 | RPL | A | Wingate & Finchley | 106 | D 2-2 | Stone 56 Osei 82 | 19 | 20 |
| Dec 1 | RPL | H | Carshalton Athletic | 178 | W 1-0 | Ottley-Gooch 73 | 19 | 21 |
| 8 | RPL | A | Metropolitan Police | 105 | W 1-0 | Osei 71 | 16 | 22 |
| 15 | RPL | H | Harrow Borough | 199 | W 1-0 | Peacock 89 (og) | 15 | 23 |
| 18 | RPL | A | Bury Town | 325 | D 3-3 | Osei 14 Hunt 24 Jefford 66 | 15 | 24 |
| 26 | RPL | H | Enfield Town | 230 | W 3-1 | G.Heath 24 78 Osei 54 | 14 | 25 |
| Jan 1 | RPL | A | Lowestoft | 751 | D 1-1 | D.Heath 29 | 14 | 26 |
| 5 | RPL | H | Bury Town | 356 | D 0-0 | | 14 | 27 |
| 29 | RPL | H | Wealdstone | 202 | D 1-1 | Osei 78 | 14 | 28 |
| Feb 5 | RPL | H | Metropolitan Police | 111 | L 0-2 | | 15 | 29 |
| 9 | RPL | A | Harrow Borough | 123 | W 3-1 | G.Heath 9 (pen) 83 Brothers 56 | 14 | 30 |
| 16 | RPL | H | East Thurrock United | 189 | W 5-4 | Brothers 4 Ottley-Gooch 8 Head 29 G.Heath 35 Osei 62 | 13 | 31 |
| 21 | RPL | A | Thurrock | 156 | W 3-0 | G.Heath 14 (pen) Head 47 Osei 56 | 11 | 32 |
| 23 | RPL | A | Carshalton Athletic | 128 | W 3-1 | G.Heath 48 Ottley-Gooch 63 Stone 82 | 11 | 33 |
| 26 | RPL | A | Leiston | 200 | L 0-2 | | 12 | 34 |
| Mar 3 | RPL | A | Cray Wanderers | 145 | D 0-0 | | 12 | 35 |
| 16 | RPL | A | Hastings United | 327 | W 1-0 | Henry 58 | 11 | 36 |
| 26 | RPL | A | Bognor Regis T | 264 | D 1-1 | Brothers  M 23 | 12 | 37 |
| 30 | RPL | H | Lowestoft | 656 | D 0-0 | | 12 | 38 |
| Apr 1 | RPL | A | Enfield Town | 298 | L 0-1 | | 14 | 39 |
| 6 | RPL | H | Wingate & Finchley | 194 | W 3-0 | Hammond 18 Brothers 58 Winter 77 | 12 | 40 |
| 9 | RPL | A | Hamptn & Richmond B | 169 | D 3-3 | Winter 38 49 G Heath 56 | 11 | 41 |
| 11 | RPL | H | Thurrock | 144 | W 2-1 | G.Heath 13 Winter 59 | 10 | 42 |
| 13 | RPL | A | Lewes | 479 | W 1-0 | G Heath 77 | 10 | 43 |
| 16 | RPL | H | Concord Rangers | 150 | L 0-3 | | 12 | 44 |
| 18 | RPL | H | Hendon | 152 | L 0-1 | | 12 | 45 |
| 21 | RPL | H | Whitehawk | 365 | L 0-2 | | 12 | 46 |
| 24 | RPL | H | Kingstonian | 182 | D 2-2 | G.Heath 46 Henry 80 | 12 | 47 |
| 27 | RPL | A | Concord Rangers | 243 | D 0-0 | | 12 | 48 |

| GOALSCORERS | Lge | FAC | FAT | Total | Pens | Hat-tricks | Cons Run | | Lge | FAC | FAT | Total | Pens | Hat-tricks | Cons Run |
|-------------|-----|-----|-----|-------|------|-----------|----------|---|-----|-----|-----|-------|------|-----------|----------|
| G Heath | 16 | 3 | 2 | 21 | 2 | | 4 | Jefford | 2 | | | 2 | | | |
| Osie | 10 | | 1 | 11 | | | 2 | D.Heath | 1 | | | 1 | | | |
| Henry | 3 | 1 | 2 | 6 | | | | J.Heath | | | 1 | 1 | | | |
| Brothers | 5 | | | 5 | | | | Hunt | 1 | | | 1 | | | |
| Ottley-Gooch | 3 | 1 | | 4 | | | | Wray | | 1 | | 1 | | | |
| Thrower | 2 | | 2 | 4 | | | | Own Goals | 1 | | | 1 | | | |
| Winter | 4 | | | 4 | | | | Cons Run - Consecutive scoring games. | | | | | | | |
| Hammond | 2 | | 1 | 3 | | | | | | | | | | | |
| Stone | 3 | | | 3 | | | | | | | | | | | |
| Head | 2 | | | 2 | | | 2 | | | | | | | | |

# LEWES

**Chairman:** Terry Parris
**Secretary:** Kevin Brook    **(T)** 07785 074 081    **(E)** clubsecretary@lewesfc.com
**Commercial Manager:** Clive Burgess    **(T)** 07852 233 943
**Programme Editor:** Stuart Fuller    **(T)** 07947 078 530
**Ground Address:** The Dripping Pan, Mountfield Road, Lewes, East Sussex BN7 2XD
**(T)** 01273 470 820      **Manager:** Garry Wilson

2012-13 Squad - Back row (L-R): Ray Bugg (kit manager), Steve Brinkhurst, Jay Conroy, Steve Robinson, Pawel Szelemej, Kieron Thorp, Chris Breach, Lewis Hamilton, Callum Dunne, Lee Cooper, Sam Piper (assistant kit man).
Front row: Karl Beckford, Charlie Leach, Arron Hopkinson, Nathan Crabb, Simon Wormull (manager),
Nick Brown (1st team coach & U18 manager), Layton Schaaf, Max Howell, Jack Walder, Dan Bolwell.

## Club Factfile

**Founded:** 1885    **Nickname:** Rooks
**Previous Names:** None
**Previous Leagues:** Mid Sussex 1886-1920, Sussex County 1920-65, Athenian 1965-77, Isthmian 1977-2004, Conference 2004-11.

**Club Colours (change):** Red and black stripes/black/black

**Ground Capacity:** 3,000   **Seats:** 400    **Covered:** 1,400    **Clubhouse:** Yes    **Shop:** Yes

**Directions**

After leaving the M23, follow the A23 to Brighton. On the outskirts of Brighton join the A27 eastbound. Stay on the A27 for about 5 miles. At the roundabout take first exit into Lewes. Follow this road until you reach traffic lights outside Lewes Prison. Turn right at the lights and follow the road down the hill until you reach a mini roundabout outside the Swan public house. Turn left at roundabout into Southover High Street and continue over next mini roundabout outside the Kings Head public house. At the next roundabout go straight over into Mountfield Road. The Dripping Pan is on your right.

**Previous Grounds:** Played at Convent Field for two seasons before WWI

**Record Attendance:** 2,500 v Newhaven - Sussex County League 26/12/1947
**Record Victory:** Not known
**Record Defeat:** Not known
**Record Goalscorer:** 'Pip' Parris - 350
**Record Appearances:** Terry Parris - 662
**Additional Records:** Paid £2,000 for Matt Allen
**Senior Honours:** Received £2,500 from Brighton & Hove Albion for Grant Horscroft
Mid Sussex League 1910-11, 13-14. Sussex County League 1964-65.
Sussex Senior Cup 1964-65, 70-71, 84-85, 2000-01, 05-06. Athenian League Division 2 1967-68, Division 1 1969-70.
Isthmian League Division 2 2001-02, Division 1 South 2003-04. Conference South 2007-08

### 10 YEAR RECORD

| 03-04 | | 04-05 | | 05-06 | | 06-07 | | 07-08 | | 08-09 | | 09-10 | | 10-11 | | 11-12 | | 12-13 | |
|---|---|---|---|---|---|---|---|---|---|---|---|---|---|---|---|---|---|---|---|
| Isth1S | 1 | Conf S | 4 | Conf S | 4 | Conf | 9 | Conf S | 1 | Conf | 24 | Conf S | 19 | Conf S | 21 | Isth P | 6 | Isth P | 19 |

# MATCH RESULTS 2012-13

| ate | Comp | H/A | Opponents | Att: | Result | Goalscorers | Pos | No. |
|---|---|---|---|---|---|---|---|---|
| ug 18 | RPL | H | Enfield | 511 | W 1-0 | Beckford 13 | 7 | 1 |
|  | RPL | A | Carshalton Athletic | 170 | D 3-3 | Brinkhurst 16 Thomas 39 67 | 14 | 2 |
| 5 | RPL | A | Thurrock | 196 | L 0-2 |  | 19 | 3 |
| 7 | RPL | H | Wealdstone | 589 | W 1-0 | Beckford 81 (pen) | 15 | 4 |
| ept 1 | RPL | A | Canvey Island | 320 | D 0-0 |  | 15 | 5 |
|  | FAC Q1 | A | Redhill | 200 | W 3-1 | Crabb 23 Wickham 36 88 |  | 6 |
| 5 | RPL | H | Cray Wanderers | 665 | D 2-2 | Vines 41 (og) Howell 90 | 15 | 7 |
| 2 | FAC Q2 | A | Hendon | 166 | L 0-3 |  |  | 8 |
| ct 1 | FAT Q1 | H | Lowestoft | 407 | W 1-0 | Godfrey 45 |  | 9 |
|  | RPL | H | Kingstonian | 326 | L 1-3 | Thomas 20 | 16 | 10 |
|  | RPL | A | Hampton & Ricmond B | 296 | L 1-2 | Thomas 29 | 17 | 11 |
| 3 | RPL | A | Margate | 542 | D 1-1 | Beckford 90 | 17 | 12 |
| 0 | RPL | H | Wingate & Finchley | 502 | W 3-1 | Thomas 35 50 Breach 75 | 12 | 13 |
| 7 | FAT Q2 | A | Brentwood Town | 118 | D 3-3 | Beckford 37 (pen) Crabb 65 Breach 73 |  | 14 |
| 0 | FAT Q2r | H | Brentwood Town |  | L 0-3 |  |  | 15 |
| ov 3 | RPL | A | Leiston | 186 | D 1-1 | Breach 25 | 15 | 16 |
| 0 | RPL | A | Bury Town | 320 | L 1-2 | Beckford 60 | 16 | 17 |
| 3 | RPL | H | Hendon | 323 | D 0-0 |  | 14 | 18 |
| 7 | RPL | H | Harrow Borough | 479 | D 1-1 | Thomas 52 | 15 | 19 |
| 0 | RPL | H | Lowestoft Town | 247 | W 2-0 | Godfrey 23 Walder 79 | 13 | 20 |
| 4 | RPL | A | Metropolitan Police | 110 | D 1-1 | Breach 55 | 13 | 21 |
| ec 2 | RPL | H | East Thurrock Town | 433 | D 1-1 | Godfrey 26 | 13 | 22 |
|  | RPL | H | Whitehwak | 674 | L 2-3 | Walder 34 Godfrey 47 | 15 | 23 |
| 5 | RPL | A | Concord Rangers | 108 | W 6-3 | CRABB 3(1 84 90 pen) Godfrey 14 Breach 37 Dollery 66 | 13 | 24 |
| 5 | RPL | H | Bognor Regis Town | 883 | W 1-0 | Crabb 80 | 13 | 25 |
| 9 | RPL | H | Thurrock | 493 | L 1-2 | Donaghey 42 | 13 | 26 |
| an 1 | RPL | A | Hastings United | 717 | D 3-3 | Walder 16 Wormull 40 Beckford 78 (pen) | 11 | 27 |
|  | RPL | H | Hampton & Richond B | 558 | D 2-2 | Brinkhurst 19 Schaaf 62 | 11 | 28 |
| 2 | RPL | A | Lowestoft | 580 | L 0-2 |  | 13 | 29 |
| eb 2 | RPL | A | Whitehawk | 485 | L 1-3 | Donaghey 66 | 14 | 30 |
|  | RPL | A | Wingate | 104 | W 4-2 | Godfrey 22 Breach 43 Brinkhurst 47 Fergany 87 | 13 | 31 |
|  | RPL | H | Concord Rangers | 442 | L 0-3 |  | 15 | 32 |
| 6 | RPL | H | Metropolitan Police | 546 | L 1-2 | Brewer 28 | 15 | 33 |
| 9 | RPL | A | Wealdstone | 520 | L 1-6 | Brinkhurst 45 | 15 | 34 |
| 3 | RPL | A | East Thurrock U | 125 | L 0-1 |  | 16 | 35 |
| lar 2 | RPL | A | Enfield Town | 414 | L 1-2 | Godfrey 73 | 17 | 36 |
|  | RPL | H | Canvey Island | 526 | L 1-2 | Malins 10 | 19 | 37 |
| 9 | RPL | H | Carshalton Athletic | 405 | W 2-1 | Godfrey 36 Beckford 69 (pen) |  | 38 |
| 3 | RPL | H | Kingstonian | 686 | L 1-2 | Crabb 60 | 18 | 39 |
| 0 | RPL | H | Hastings United | 788 | L 1-2 | Beckford 77 (pen) | 18 | 40 |
| pr 1 | RPL | A | Bognor Regis Town | 409 | L 1-3 | Brinkhurst 57 | 19 | 41 |
|  | RPL | A | Hendon | 131 | D 2-2 | Wormull 45 (pen) Godfrey 86 | 20 | 42 |
| 0 | RPL | H | Margate | 411 | W 2-0 | Crabb 45 Brinkhurst 90 | 20 | 43 |
| 3 | RPL | H | Leiston | 479 | L 0-1 |  | 20 | 44 |
| 0 | RPL | H | Harrow Borough | 154 | W 2-0 | Crabb 42 53 | 18 | 45 |
| 3 | RPL | A | Cray Wanderers | 248 | D 2-2 | Crabb 80 93 | 19 | 46 |
| 7 | RPL | H | Bury Town | 816 | L 2-3 | Brinkhurst 52 Dunne 77 | 20 | 47 |

| GOALSCORERS | Lge | FAC | FAT | Total | Pens | Hat-tricks | Cons Run |  | Lge | FAC | FAT | Total | Pens | Hat-tricks | Cons Run |
|---|---|---|---|---|---|---|---|---|---|---|---|---|---|---|---|
| Crabb | 10 | 1 | 1 | 12 | 1 | 1 | 2 | Dollery | 1 |  |  | 1 |  |  |  |
| Godfrey | 8 | 1 |  | 9 |  |  | 3 | Dunn | 1 |  |  | 1 |  |  |  |
| Beckford | 7 | 1 |  | 8 |  |  |  | Ferguson | 1 |  |  | 1 |  |  |  |
| Brinkhurst | 7 |  |  | 7 |  |  |  | Howell | 1 |  |  | 1 |  |  |  |
| Thomas | 7 |  |  | 7 |  |  | 2 | Malins | 1 |  |  | 1 |  |  |  |
| Breach | 5 |  |  | 5 |  |  |  | Schaaf | 1 |  |  | 1 |  |  |  |
| Walder | 3 |  |  | 3 |  |  |  | Own Goal | 1 |  |  | 1 |  |  |  |
| Donaghey | 2 |  |  | 2 |  |  |  | Cons Run - Consecutive scoring games. |  |  |  |  |  |  |  |
| Wormull | 2 |  |  | 2 |  |  |  |  |  |  |  |  |  |  |  |
| Brewer | 1 |  |  | 1 |  |  |  |  |  |  |  |  |  |  |  |

# LOWESTOFT TOWN

**Chairman:** Gary Keyzor
**Secretary:** Terry Lynes    **(T)** 0793 087 2947    **(E)** terrylynes@fsmail.net
**Commercial Manager:** n/a      **(T)**
**Programme Editor:** Terry Lynes      **(T)** 0793 087 2947
**Ground Address:** Crown Meadow, Love Road, Lowestoft NR32 2PA
**(T)** 01502 573 818      **Manager:** Micky Chapman and Ady Gallagher

2012-13 Squad - Back Row (L-R): Erkan Okay, Osiris, Amando, Danny Cunningham, Sam Gaughran, Chris Henderson, Stuart Ainsley, Joe Clark.
Middle Row: Greg Crane, Dan Gleeson, Nathen Stone, Scott Mitchell, Jake Jessup, Andy Reynolds, Jack Defty, Joe Francis, Lee Smith, Michael Frew.
Front Row: Emma Scoggins, Andrew Fisk, Adam Smith, George Neeve, Ady Gallagher, Mick Chapman, Craig Fleming, Robert Eagle, Aaron Jones, Avril Soards.

## Club Factfile

**Founded:** 1880      **Nickname:** The Trawler Boys or Blues
**Previous Names:** Original club merged with Kirkley in 1887 to form Lowestoft and became Lowestoft Town in 1890
**Previous Leagues:** North Suffolk 1897-35, Eastern Counties 1935-2009

**Club Colours (change):** All royal blue (All white)

**Ground Capacity:** 3,000   **Seats:** 466    **Covered:** 500    **Clubhouse:** Yes   **Shop:** Yes

**Directions**

Just off A12.
Ten minutes from Lowestoft BR.

**Previous Grounds:** None

**Record Attendance:** 5,000 v Watford - FA Cup 1st Round 1967
**Record Victory:** Not Known
**Record Defeat:** Not Known
**Record Goalscorer:** Not Known
**Record Appearances:** Not Known
**Additional Records:**

**Senior Honours:**
Eastern Counties League 1935-36 (shared), 37-38, 62-63, 64-65, 65-66, 66-67, 67-68, 69-70, 70-71, 77-78, 2005-06, 08-09.
Isthmian League Division 1 North 2009-10.
Suffolk Senior Cup 1902-03, 22-23, 25-26, 31-32, 35-36, 46-47, 47-48, 48-49, 55-56.

### 10 YEAR RECORD

| 03-04 | | 04-05 | | 05-06 | | 06-07 | | 07-08 | | 08-09 | | 09-10 | | 10-11 | | 11-12 | | 12-13 | |
|---|---|---|---|---|---|---|---|---|---|---|---|---|---|---|---|---|---|---|---|
| ECP | 8 | ECP | 4 | ECP | 1 | ECP | 3 | ECP | 11 | ECP | 1 | Isth1N | 1 | Isth P | 4 | Isth P | 3 | Isth P | 2 |

# MATCH RESULTS 2012-13

| ate | Comp | H/A | Opponents | Att: | Result | Goalscorers | Pos | No. |
|---|---|---|---|---|---|---|---|---|
| ug 18 | RPL | A | Whitehawk | 135 | W 3-1 | Henderson 62 70 Cockrill 63 | 3 | 1 |
|  | RPL | H | Concord Rangers | 668 | W 4-1 | Cockrill 7 Mitchell 42 Henderson 53 Frew 85 | 1 | 2 |
| 5 | RPL | H | Metropolitan Police | 640 | W 2-1 | Defty 54 Smith 58 | 1 | 3 |
| 7 | RPL | A | Margate | 440 | L 1-2 | Defty 41 | 2 | 4 |
| ept 1 | RPL | H | Harrow Borough | 591 | W 3-0 | Crane 5 Gleeson 18 Henderson 53 | 2 | 5 |
|  | FAC Q1 | A | Tilbury | 134 | W 2-0 | Frew 5 Mitchell 75 |  | 6 |
| 5 | RPL | A | Hampton & Richmond B | 509 | D 1-1 | Defty 10 | 4 | 7 |
| 2 | FAC Q2 | A | Wealdstone | 413 | W 2-1 | Henderson 35 Frew 56 |  | 8 |
| ct 1 | FAT Q1 | A | Lewes | 407 | L 0-1 |  |  | 9 |
|  | FAC Q3 | A | St Albans City | 506 | W 1-0 | Francis 59 |  | 10 |
| 3 | RPL | A | Kingstonian | 845 | L 1-3 | Francis 45 | 7 | 11 |
| 0 | FAC Q4 | A | Braintree Town | 634 | L 2-3 | Henderson 37 Frew 79 |  | 12 |
| 3 | RPL | H | Wingate & Finchley | 447 | W 3-0 | Henderson 6 Smith 33 Francis 40 |  | 13 |
| ov 3 | RPL | A | Carshalton Athletic | 181 | L 0-2 |  | 7 | 14 |
| 0 | RPL | A | Hendon | 168 | W 1-0 | Henderson 10 | 6 | 15 |
| 7 | RPL | H | Bognor Regis Town | 634 | L 1-2 | Cockrill 71 (pen) | 9 | 16 |
| 0 | RPL | A | Lewes | 247 | L 1-2 | Francis 15 | 10 | 17 |
| ec 1 | RPL | A | Enfield Town | 381 | W 3-2 | Defty 29 Henderson 47 Frew 82 | 8 | 18 |
|  | RPL | A | Cray Wanderers | 140 | D 1-1 | Cockrill 79 (pen) | 8 | 19 |
|  | RPL | H | Wealdstone | 576 | W 3-0 | DEFTY 3 ( 21 49 86) | 5 | 20 |
| 5 | RPL | A | East Thurrock | 201 | W 2-0 | Cockrill 36 (pen) Defty 81 | 4 | 21 |
| an 1 | RPL | H | Leiston | 751 | D 1-1 | Defty 88 | 8 | 22 |
| 2 | RPL | H | Lewes | 580 | W 2-0 | Saker 54 Defty 73 | 6 | 23 |
| eb 9 | RPL | H | East Thurrock | 553 | D 0-0 |  | 10 | 24 |
| 2 | RPL | H | Margate | 394 | W 1-0 | Defty 5 | 6 | 25 |
| 5 | RPL | A | Hastings United | 435 | W 4-1 | Defty 18 45  Henderson 73  Dawkins 90 | 6 | 26 |
| 9 | RPL | H | Canvey Island | 436 | W 2-0 | Smith 73 (pen)  Defty 67 | 4 | 27 |
| 3 | RPL | H | Enfield Town | 523 | D 0-0 |  | 4 | 28 |
| 6 | RPL | A | Concord Rangers | 65 | D 1-1 | Smith 65 | 5 | 29 |
| lar 2 | RPL | H | Whitehawk | 871 | D 0-0 |  | 6 | 30 |
|  | RPL | H | Hastings Town | 480 | W 1-0 | Henderson 51 | 4 | 31 |
|  | RPL | A | Harrow Borough | 204 | D 3-3 | Defty 17 A.Smith 35 Olima 78 (og) | 5 | 32 |
| 3 | RPL | A | Metropolitan Police | 101 | W 3-1 | Defty 10 60  Okay 24 | 4 | 33 |
| 6 | RPL | H | Hampton & Richmond B | 527 | W 5-3 | Mitchell 4 Henderson  33 Defty 53 82 Frew 88 | 3 | 34 |
| 5 | RPL | A | Kingstonian | 256 | W 1-0 | Okay 37 | 3 | 35 |
| 0 | RPL | A | Leiston | 656 | D 0-0 |  | 4 | 36 |
| pr 1 | RPL | H | Bury Town | 873 | W 1-0 | Henderson 69 | 4 | 37 |
|  | RPL | A | Thurrock | 393 | L 0-1 |  | 4 | 38 |
|  | RPL | A | Canvey Island | 331 | W 2-0 | Eagle 40 Defty 42 | 3 | 39 |
|  | RPL | H | Cray Wanderers | 462 | W 4-1 | Defty 22 Okay 27 Henderson 31 Williams 45 | 3 | 40 |
| 3 | RPL | H | Carshalton Athletic | 770 | L 2-3 | L.Smith 1 73 (pen) | 3 | 41 |
| 6 | RPL | A | Bury Town | 594 | D 1-1 | L.Smith 83 | 3 | 42 |
| 8 | RPL | A | Thurrock | 184 | W 2-1 | Araba 53 Dawkin 89 | 3 | 43 |
| 9 | RPL | A | Bognor Regis Town | 448 | W 2-0 | Frew 23 Okay 80 | 2 | 44 |
| 3 | RPL | A | Wealdsone | 772 | D 0-0 |  | 2 | 45 |
| 5 | RPL | A | Wingate & Finchley | 175 | L 2-3 | Benjamin 5 Araba 65 | 2 | 46 |
| 7 | RPL | A | Hendon | 890 | W 1-0 | Frew 65 | 2 | 47 |
| lay 1 | P-Off S-F | H | East Thurrock United | 1182 | W 1-0 | Henderson 80 |  | 48 |
|  | P-Off F | H | Concord Rangers | 2490 | L 1-2 | Mitchell 21 |  | 49 |

| GOALSCORERS | Lge | FAC | FAT | Total | Pens | Hat-tricks | Cons Run |  | Lge | FAC | FAT | Total | Pens | Hat-tricks | Cons Run |
|---|---|---|---|---|---|---|---|---|---|---|---|---|---|---|---|
| Defty | 21 |  | 21 |  |  | 1 | 3 | Benjamn | 1 |  |  | 1 |  |  |  |
| Henderson | 13 | 2 |  | 15 |  |  | 2 | Crane | 1 |  |  | 1 |  |  |  |
| Frew | 5 | 3 |  | 8 |  |  |  | Eagle | 1 |  |  | 1 |  |  |  |
| Smith | 8 |  |  | 8 | 2 |  |  | Gleeson | 1 |  |  | 1 |  |  |  |
| Cockrill | 5 |  |  | 5 | 3 |  |  | Saker ) | 1 |  |  | 1 |  |  |  |
| Francis | 3 | 1 |  | 4 |  |  |  | Williams | 1 |  |  | 1 |  |  |  |
| Okay | 4 |  |  | 4 |  |  |  | Own Goal | 1 |  |  | 1 |  |  |  |
| Mitchell | 3 | 1 |  | 3 |  |  |  | Cons Run - Consecutive scoring games. |  |  |  |  |  |  |  |
| Araba | 2 |  |  | 2 |  |  |  |  |  |  |  |  |  |  |  |
| Dawkins | 2 |  |  | 2 |  |  |  |  |  |  |  |  |  |  |  |

# NON LEAGUE DAY

## Saturday
## 7th September

 **Support your local club**

# nonleagueday.co.uk

# MAIDSTONE UNITED

**Chairman:** (Chief Exec.) Bill Williams

**Secretary:** Ian Tucker          **(T)** 07968 505 888          **(E)** itucker@maidstoneunited.co.uk

**Commercial Manager:** n/a                    **(T)**

**Programme Editor:** Ian Tucker                    **(T)** mufcprogramme@btopenworld.com

**Ground Address:** The Gallagher Stadium, James Whatman Way, Maidstone, Kent ME14 1LQ

**(T)** 01622 753 817                    **Manager:** Jay Saunders

The team line up before a match during their promotion winning season.
Phtoo: Roger Turner

## Club Factfile

**Founded:** 1992          **Nickname:** The Stones

**Previous Names:** None

**Previous Leagues:** Kent County, Kent

**Club Colours (change):** Amber/black/black

**Ground Capacity:**          **Seats:** Yes          **Covered:** Yes          **Clubhouse:** Yes          **Shop:** Yes

**Directions**

M20 (junction 6) and M2 (junction 3).
Follow signs to Maidstone on the A229.
At the White Rabbit roundabout, take the third exit on to James Whatman Way.

**Previous Grounds:** London Road 1992-2001, Central Park (Sittingbourne) 2001-02 11-12, The Homelands 2002-11.

**Record Attendance:** 1,589 v Gillingham - Friendly

**Record Victory:** 12-1 v Aylesford - Kent League 1993-94

**Record Defeat:** 2-8 v Scott Sports - 1995-96

**Record Goalscorer:** Richard Sinden - 98

**Record Appearances:** Aaron Lacy - 187

**Additional Records:** Paid £2,000 for Steve Jones - 2000

**Senior Honours:**
Kent League 2001-02, 05-06, League cup 2005-06. Isthmian Division 1 South 2006-07.
Kent Senior Trophy 2002-03.

### 10 YEAR RECORD

| 03-04 | | 04-05 | | 05-06 | | 06-07 | | 07-08 | | 08-09 | | 09-10 | | 10-11 | | 11-12 | | 12-13 | |
|---|---|---|---|---|---|---|---|---|---|---|---|---|---|---|---|---|---|---|---|
| Kent P | 4 | Kent P | 4 | Kent P | 1 | Isth1S | 1 | Isth P | 17 | Isth P | 15 | Isth P | 18 | Isth P | 20 | Isth1S | 6 | Isth1S | 2 |

# MARGATE

**Chairman:** Keith Piper
**Secretary:** Ken Tomlinson    **(T)** 0771 003 3566    **(E)** ken.tomlinson@margate-fc.com
**Commercial Manager:** n/a    **(T)**
**Programme Editor:** Neil Wyatt    **(T)** 07806 865 2092
**Ground Address:** Hartsdown Park, Hartsdown Road, Margate, Kent CT9 5QZ
**(T)** 01843 221 769    **Manager:** Simon Osborn & Craig Holloway

2012-13 Squad.

## Club Factfile

**Founded:** 1896    **Nickname:** The Gate
**Previous Names:** None
**Previous Leagues:** Kent 1911-23, 24-28, 29-33, 37-38, 46-59. Southern 1933-37, 59-2001, Conference 2001-04

**Club Colours (change):** Royal blue & white hoops/royal blue/white

**Ground Capacity:** 3,000    **Seats:** 350    **Covered:** 1,750    **Clubhouse:** Yes    **Shop:** Yes

**Directions:** From M25 continue onto M26 merge onto M20, at junction 7, exit onto Sittingbourne Rd/A249 toward Sheerness/Canterbury/Ramsgate, continue to follow A249, take the ramp onto M2, continue onto A299 (signs for Margate/Ramsgate) keep right at the fork, at the roundabout, take the 2nd exit onto Canterbury Rd (Birchington)/A28 continue to follow A28, turn right onto The Square/A28 continue to follow A28, turn right onto George V Ave/B2052, turn right onto Hartsdown Rd/B2052, ground will be on the left.

**Previous Grounds:** At least six before moving to Hartsdown in 1939.

**Record Attendance:** 14,500 v Tottenham Hotspur - FA Cup 3rd Round 1973
**Record Victory:** 8-0 v Tunbridge Wells (H) - 1966-67, v Chatham Town (H) - 1987-88 and v Stalybridge Celtic (H) - 2001-02
**Record Defeat:** 0-11 v AFC Bournemouth (A) - FA Cup 20/11/1971
**Record Goalscorer:** Jack Palethorpe scored 66 during 1929-30
**Record Appearances:** Bob Harrop
**Additional Records:** Paid £5,000 to Dover Athletic for Steve Cuggy
**Senior Honours:**
Southern League Premier Division 1935-36, 2000-01, Division 1 1962-63, Division 1 South 1977-78.

## 10 YEAR RECORD

| 03-04 | | 04-05 | | 05-06 | | 06-07 | | 07-08 | | 08-09 | | 09-10 | | 10-11 | | 11-12 | | 12-13 | |
|---|---|---|---|---|---|---|---|---|---|---|---|---|---|---|---|---|---|---|---|
| Conf | 16 | Conf S | 21 | Isth P | 14 | Isth P | 6 | Isth P | 9 | Isth P | 19 | Isth P | 19 | Isth P | 16 | Isth P | 15 | Isth P | 9 |

# MATCH RESULTS 2012-13

| Date | Comp | H/A | Opponents | Att: | Result | Goalscorers | Pos | No. |
|---|---|---|---|---|---|---|---|---|
| Aug 18 | RPL | H | Hendon | 313 | W 2-0 | Avery 65 Rook 78 | 4 | 1 |
| 21 | RPL | A | Hastings United | 349 | D 2-2 | Stubbs 80 (pen) Beales 84 | 7 | 2 |
| 25 | RPL | A | Kingstonian | 335 | D 3-3 | Long 3 Whitnell 13 27 | 10 | 3 |
| 2 | RPL | H | Lowestoft Town | 440 | W 2-1 | Whitnell 40 Long 65 | 9 | 4 |
| Sept 1 | RPL | A | Bognor Regis Town | 521 | W 2-0 | Murphy 67 Dolby 86 | 9 | 5 |
| 8 | FAC Q1 | A | Faversham Town | 409 | D 2-2 | Long 13 Rook 75 | | 6 |
| 11 | FAC Q1r | H | Faversham Town | 387 | W 3-0 | Rook 13 Long 60 Murphy 79 | | 7 |
| 15 | RPL | H | Enfield Town | 483 | W 2-0 | Rook 7 Murphy 33 | 1 | 8 |
| 22 | FAC Q2 | A | Aveley | 131 | W 4-1 | Dolby Long Corneillle Rhodes | | 9 |
| 29 | FAT Q1 | H | Maidstone United | 475 | W 1-2 | Dolby 85 | | 10 |
| Oct 6 | FAC Q3 | H | Slough Town | 410 | L 0-1 | | | 11 |
| 9 | RPL | H | Concord Rangers | 217 | L 0-2 | | 4 | 12 |
| 13 | RPL | H | Lewes | 542 | D 1-1 | Long 35 | 5 | 13 |
| 20 | RPL | A | Thurrock | 320 | D 1-1 | Murphy 49 | 5 | 14 |
| 23 | RPL | A | Canvey Island | 252 | L 1-3 | Stubbs 86 | 6 | 15 |
| 27 | RPL | H | Hastings United | 257 | D 1-1 | Stubbs 49 | 4 | 16 |
| Nov 6 | RPL | A | Leiston | 153 | W 2-1 | Stubbs 30 (pen) Avery 45 | 5 | 17 |
| 10 | RPL | A | Harrow Borough | 132 | W 2-0 | Whitnell 38 Avery 65 | 3 | 18 |
| 17 | RPL | H | Bury Town | 348 | W 3-1 | Whitnell 50 Stubbs 74 Avery 86 | 2 | 19 |
| Dec 1 | RPL | A | Hampton & Richmond | 339 | W 2-1 | Stubbs 13 Bodkin 37 | 2 | 20 |
| 4 | RPL | A | East Thurrock United | 146 | D 0-0 | | 1 | 21 |
| 8 | RPL | H | Wingate & Finchley | 346 | W 2-0 | Beales 61 Rhodes 85 | 1 | 22 |
| 11 | RPL | H | Carshalton Athletic | 228 | W 3-1 | Corneille 38 62 Bodkin 63 | 1 | 23 |
| 26 | RPL | H | Cray Wanderers | 408 | L 0-1 | | 1 | 24 |
| Jan 5 | RPL | A | Concord Rangers | 228 | L 1-2 | Rook 45 | 2 | 25 |
| Feb 2 | RPL | A | Wingate & Finchley | 172 | L 0-1 | | 7 | 26 |
| 9 | RPL | H | Whitehawk | 418 | W 2-1 | Rhodes 59 63 | 6 | 27 |
| 12 | RPL | A | Lowestoft Town | 394 | L 0-1 | | 7 | 28 |
| 16 | RPL | A | Wealdstone | 647 | L 1-2 | Stubbs 1 | 7 | 29 |
| 20 | RPL | A | Metropolitan Police | 129 | L 0-1 | | 8 | 30 |
| 23 | RPL | H | Hampton & Richmond B | 354 | W 2-1 | Purcell 54 Rhodes 84 | 8 | 31 |
| 26 | RPL | H | Leiston | 200 | W 2-0 | Purcell 34 80 | 7 | 32 |
| Mar 2 | RPL | A | Hendon | 194 | D 0-0 | | 7 | 33 |
| 9 | RPL | H | Bognor Regis Town | 415 | W 3-0 | Ibe 13 Whitnell 29 66 | 6 | 34 |
| 16 | RPL | A | Enfield Town | 397 | W 3-0 | Rook 23 63 Ibe 47 | 6 | 35 |
| 19 | RPL | A | Whitehawk | 149 | D 1-1 | Beales 20 | 6 | 36 |
| 23 | RPL | H | Canvey Island | 405 | D 2-2 | Bodkin 23 Hand 90 (pen) | 6 | 37 |
| 26 | RPL | H | Wealdstone | 236 | L 2-4 | Ibe 3 Whitnell 55 | 6 | 38 |
| 30 | RPL | H | Thurrock | 326 | W 3-1 | Ibe 19 79 Whitnell 44 | 5 | 39 |
| Apr 1 | RPL | A | Cray Wanderers | 216 | W 4-0 | Burgess (og) 34 Dolby 41 Ibe 50 66 | 5 | 40 |
| 6 | RPL | A | Carshalton Athletic | 272 | L 0-4 | | 5 | 41 |
| 9 | RPL | H | East Thurrock United | 241 | L 0-1 | | 6 | 42 |
| 10 | RPL | A | Lewes | 411 | L 0-2 | | 7 | 43 |
| 13 | RPL | H | Metropolitan Police | 382 | L 1-2 | Ibe 25 | 7 | 44 |
| 16 | RPL | H | Kingstonian | 185 | L 1-2 | Whitnell 77 | 8 | 45 |
| 20 | RPL | A | Bury Town | 425 | D 2-2 | Pooley 64 79 | 8 | 46 |
| 27 | RPL | H | Harrow Borough | 305 | D 0-0 | | 9 | 47 |

| GOALSCORERS | Lge | FAC | FAT | Total | Pens | Hat-tricks | Cons Run | | Lge | FAC | FAT | Total | Pens | Hat-tricks | Cons Run |
|---|---|---|---|---|---|---|---|---|---|---|---|---|---|---|---|
| Whitnell | 10 | | | 10 | | | 2 | Bodkin | 3 | | | 3 | | | |
| Ibe | 8 | | | 8 | | | 3 | Corneille | 2 | 1 | | 3 | | | |
| Stubbs | 7 | | | 7 | 2 | | 3 | Purcell | 3 | | | 3 | | | 2 |
| Long | 3 | 3 | | 6 | | | 2 | Pooley | 2 | | | 2 | | | |
| Dolby | 2 | 1 | 1 | 5 | | | 2 | Hand | 1 | | | 1 | 1 | | |
| Rhodes | 4 | 1 | | 5 | | | | Own Goals | 1 | | | 1 | | | |
| Rook | 5 | 2 | | 5 | | | 3 | Cons Run - Consecutive scoring games. | | | | | | | |
| Avery | 4 | | | 4 | | | | | | | | | | | |
| Murphy | 3 | 1 | | 4 | | | 2 | | | | | | | | |
| Beales | 3 | | | 3 | | | | | | | | | | | |

# METROPOLITAN POLICE

**Chairman:** Des Flanders
**Secretary:** Tony Brooking　　**(T)** 0796 133 4523　　**(E)** tony.brooking@met.police.uk
**Commercial Manager:** n/a　　**(T)**
**Programme Editor:** Richard Peirce　　**(T)** 07802 864 203
**Ground Address:** Imber Court, Ember Lane, East Molesey, Surrey KT8 0BT
**(T)** 0208 398 7358　　　　　　　　　　　　　　　**Manager:** Jim Cooper

The team line up before their FA Cup Qualifying round tie against
Beckenham Town. Photo: Alan Coomes.

## Club Factfile

**Founded:** 1919　　**Nickname:** The Blues
**Previous Names:** None
**Previous Leagues:** Spartan 1928-60, Metropolitan 1960-71, Southern 1971-78

**Club Colours (change):** All blue (All red)

**Ground Capacity:** 3,000　**Seats:** 297　　**Covered:** 1,800　　**Clubhouse:** Yes　　**Shop:** No

**Directions**
From London A3 take A309 towards Scilly Isles roundabout then right into Hampton Court Way.
Left at first roundabout into Imber Court Road. Ground is in 300 yards.

**Previous Grounds:** None

**Record Attendance:** 4,500 v Kingstonian - FA Cup 1934
**Record Victory:** 10-1 v Tilbury - 1995
**Record Defeat:** 1-11 v Wimbledon - 1956
**Record Goalscorer:** Mario Russo
**Record Appearances:** Pat Robert
**Additional Records:**

**Senior Honours:**
Spartan League x7.
Middlesex Senior Cup 1927-28, Surrey Senior Cup 1932-33. London Senior Cup 2009-10.
Isthmian League Division One South 2010-11.

## 10 YEAR RECORD

| 03-04 | | 04-05 | | 05-06 | | 06-07 | | 07-08 | | 08-09 | | 09-10 | | 10-11 | | 11-12 | | 12-13 | |
|---|---|---|---|---|---|---|---|---|---|---|---|---|---|---|---|---|---|---|---|
| Isth1S | 20 | Isth1 | 5 | Isth1 | 4 | Isth1S | 6 | Isth1S | 4 | Isth1S | 4 | Isth1S | 10 | Isth1S | 1 | Isth P | 12 | Isth P | 6 |

# MATCH RESULTS 2012-13

| Date | Comp | H/A | Opponents | Att: | Result | Goalscorers | Pos | No. |
|------|------|-----|-----------|------|--------|-------------|-----|-----|
| Aug 18 | RPL | A | Wealdstone | 415 | L 0-1 | | 17 | 1 |
| 21 | RPL | H | Bognor Regis Town | 512 | D 0-0 | | | 2 |
| 25 | RPL | A | Lowestoft Town | 640 | L 1-2 | Palmer 90 | 18 | 3 |
| 27 | RPL | H | Enfield Town | 155 | D 2-2 | Ty Smith 23 Newton 40 | 16 | 4 |
| Sept 1 | RPL | A | Cray Wanderers | 182 | W 2-1 | J Smith 20 55 | 14 | 5 |
| 8 | FAC Q1 | A | Beckenham Town | 70 | W 7-1 | J.SMITH (5) Crook 1 (og) | | 6 |
| 15 | RPL | H | Canvey Island | 135 | W 2-1 | Sutherland 47 68 | 10 | 7 |
| 22 | FAC Q2 | A | Berkhamstead | 204 | W 3-0 | J.Smith 56 58 (pen) Tyrell 78 | | 8 |
| 29 | FAT Q1 | A | Redbridge | 37 | W 5-0 | J.Smith , Bourne Newton (2) Tait | | 9 |
| Oct 6 | FAC Q3 | A | Dereham Town | 328 | D 1-1 | Brown | | 10 |
| 10 | FAC Q3r | H | Dereham Town | 191 | W 2-0 | J.Smith 23 T Smith 40 | | 11 |
| 13 | RPL | H | East Thurrock | 122 | D 2-2 | J.Smith 23 Palmer 40 | 13 | 12 |
| 20 | FAC Q4 | A | South Park | 643 | W 3-0 | Newton 18 J.Smith 48 85 | | 13 |
| 23 | RPL | A | Hendon | 161 | D 1-1 | T.Smith 45 | 12 | 14 |
| 27 | FAT Q2 | A | Leiston | 153 | D 1-1 | J.Smith 42 | | 15 |
| 30 | FAT Q2r | H | Leiston | 150 | L 3-4 | Bird 50 Tait 70 78 | | 16 |
| Nov 3 | FAC 1 | H | Crawley Town | 1485 | L 1-2 | Tait 83 | | 17 |
| 10 | RPL | H | Hastings United | 157 | W 4-0 | J.Smith 9 49 (pen) Dickson 17 (og) Tait 19 | 11 | 18 |
| 13 | RPL | A | Whitehawk | 115 | D 1-1 | Tait 19 | 11 | 19 |
| 17 | RPL | A | Concord Rangers | 210 | L 1-5 | J. Smith 7 | 13 | 20 |
| 24 | RPL | H | Lewes | 110 | D 1-1 | J.Smith 85 (pen) | 14 | 21 |
| Dec 2 | RPL | A | Wingate & Finchley | 89 | W 3-1 | Brown 32 Whickham 55 Sutherland 71 | 12 | 22 |
| 8 | RPL | H | Leiston | 105 | L 0-1 | Clayton 52 Knight 58 83 Newton 82 | 13 | 23 |
| 15 | RPL | A | Bury Town | 288 | W 2-0 | Tait 20 Kennedy 42 (og) | 12 | 24 |
| 26 | RPL | H | Kingstonian | 241 | W 4-1 | | 12 | 25 |
| Jan 1 | RPL | A | Carshalton Athletic | 193 | D 1-1 | Newton 41 | 12 | 26 |
| 12 | RPL | H | Harrow Borough | 125 | D 1-1 | Sutherland 13 | 12 | 27 |
| 26 | RPL | H | Whitehawk | 165 | L 2-5 | T.Smith 56 Watkins 70 | 12 | 28 |
| 29 | RPL | A | Harrow Borough | 103 | W 3-2 | T.Smith 58 Knight 79 Watkins 88 | 10 | 29 |
| Feb 5 | RPL | A | Leiston | 111 | W 2-0 | T.Smith 51 Watkins 59 | 9 | 30 |
| 9 | RPL | H | Bury Town | 102 | W 3-1 | Newton 17  Watkins 21 Collins 77 | 8 | 31 |
| 12 | RPL | A | Enfield Town | 255 | L 0-4 | | 8 | 32 |
| 16 | RPL | A | Lewes | 546 | W 2-1 | Collins 31 Nookes 65 | 8 | 33 |
| 20 | RPL | H | Margate | 129 | W 1-0 | Kavanagh 64 | 6 | 34 |
| 23 | RPL | H | Wingate & Finchley | 101 | W 2-1 | Reynolds 82 T.Smith 89 | 6 | 35 |
| Mar 2 | RPL | H | Wealdstone | 275 | L 0-1 | | 8 | 36 |
| 5 | RPL | A | Hampton & Richond B | 132 | D 0-0 | | 8 | 37 |
| 9 | RPL | H | Cray Wanderers | 105 | L 2-4 | Reynolds 36 Knight 85 | 8 | 38 |
| 13 | RPL | A | Lowestoft Town | 101 | L 1-3 | Knight 86 | 8 | 39 |
| 16 | RPL | A | Canvey Island | 234 | W 1-0 | Knight 34 | 8 | 40 |
| 19 | RPL | A | East Thurrock | 121 | D 2-2 | Nookes 47 Knight 90 | 8 | 41 |
| 26 | RPL | A | Hastings United | 219 | W 2-1 | Newton 63  C.Collins 84 | 7 | 42 |
| 30 | RPL | H | Carshalton Athletic | 115 | W 1-0 | Collins 62 | 7 | 43 |
| Apr 2 | RPL | A | Kingstonian | 259 | L 0-1 | | 8 | 44 |
| 6 | RPL | H | Hampton & Richmond B | 222 | W 1-0 | Knight 55 | 6 | 45 |
| 9 | RPL | H | Thurrock | 106 | L 1-2 | Knight 61 | 7 | 46 |
| 13 | RPL | A | Margate | 382 | W 2-1 | Crook 35  Knight 49 | 5 | 47 |
| 17 | RPL | H | Bognor Regis Town | 139 | W 3-2 | Collins 9 59 Knight 74 | 5 | 48 |
| 20 | RPL | H | Concord Rangers | 120 | L 0-2 | | 6 | 49 |
| 23 | RPL | H | Hendon | 113 | W 2-1 | Newton 33 Collins 39 | 6 | 50 |
| 27 | RPL | A | Thurrock | 208 | W 4-0 | Collins 17 Knight 51 56 Tait 83 | 6 | 51 |

| GOALSCORERS | Lge | FAC | FAT | Total | Pens | Hat-tricks | Cons Run | | Lge | FAC | FAT | Total | Pens | Hat-tricks | Cons Run |
|-------------|-----|-----|-----|-------|------|-----------|----------|---|-----|-----|-----|-------|------|-----------|----------|
| Smith | 7 | 10 | 2 | 19 | 3 | 1 | 3 | Reynolds | 2 | | | 2 | | | |
| Knight | 13 | | | 13 | | | 4 | Bird | | | 1 | 1 | | | |
| Newton | 6 | 1 | 2 | 9 | | | | Bourne | | | 1 | 1 | | | |
| Collins | 8 | | | 8 | | | | Clayton | 1 | | | 1 | | | |
| Tait | 4 | 1 | 3 | 8 | | | | Crook | 1 | | | 1 | | | |
| T.Smith | 6 | 1 | | 7 | | | | Kavanagh | 1 | | | 1 | | | |
| Sutherland | 4 | | | 4 | | | | Tyrell | | 1 | | 1 | | | |
| Watkins | 4 | | | 4 | | | | Whickham | 1 | | | 1 | | | |
| Brown | 1 | 1 | | 2 | | | | Own Goals | 2 | | | 2 | | | |
| Nookes | 2 | | | 2 | | | | Cons Run - Consecutive scoring games. | | | | | | | |
| Palmer | 2 | | | 2 | | | | | | | | | | | |

# THAMESMEAD TOWN

**Chairman:** Terry Hill

**Secretary:** David Joy     **(T)** 0799 061 2495     **(E)** davejoyo@yahoo.co.uk

**Commercial Manager:** n/a     **(T)**

**Programme Editor:** Albert Panting     **(T)** 07957 194 640

**Ground Address:** Bayliss Avenue, Thamesmead, London SE28 8NJ

**(T)** 020 8311 4211     **Manager:** Keith McMahon

The team line up before their match against Cray Wanderers in the 2nd Qualifying Round of the FA Cup. Photo: Alan Coomes.

## Club Factfile

**Founded:** 1970     **Nickname:** The Mead

**Previous Names:** None

**Previous Leagues:** Spartan 1987-91, Kent 1991-2008

**Club Colours (change):** All green (All light blue)

**Ground Capacity:** 400     **Seats:** 161     **Covered:** 125     **Clubhouse:** Yes     **Shop:**

**Directions**

From the A2 take the A2018 exit toward Dartford/Wilmington, at the roundabout, take the 1st exit onto Shepherd's Ln/A2018.
At the roundabout, take the 1st exit onto Rochester Way. Slight right at Swan Ln, continue onto Station Rd.
At the roundabout, take the 1st exit onto Crayford Rd/A207, continue to follow A207, slight right to stay on A207, turn left at London Rd/A2000 continue to follow A2000, turn right at Perry St/A2000.
At the roundabout, take the 2nd exit onto Northend Rd/A206, continue to follow A206. Go through 1 roundabout.
At the roundabout, take the 2nd exit onto Bronze Age Way/A2016, continue to follow A2016. Go through 1 roundabout.
At the roundabout, take the 2nd exit onto Eastern Way/A2016. Take the ramp. At the roundabout, take the 3rd exit onto Carlyle Rd/A2041.
At the roundabout, take the 3rd exit onto Crossway. Turn right at Bayliss Ave, take the 1st left onto Chadwick Way. Ground will be on the left.

**Previous Grounds:** Crossways. Meridian Sports Ground > 1985.

**Record Attendance:** 400 v Wimbledon - Ground opening 1988

**Record Victory:** 9-0 v Kent Police - Kent League 19/04/1994

**Record Defeat:** Not known

**Record Goalscorer:** Delroy D'Oyley

**Record Appearances:** Not known

**Additional Records:**

**Senior Honours:**
Kent Senior Trophy 2004-05. Kent Premier 2007-08

### 10 YEAR RECORD

| 03-04 | | 04-05 | | 05-06 | | 06-07 | | 07-08 | | 08-09 | | 09-10 | | 10-11 | | 11-12 | | 12-13 | |
|---|---|---|---|---|---|---|---|---|---|---|---|---|---|---|---|---|---|---|---|
| Kent P | 2 | Kent P | 8 | Kent P | 3 | Kent P | 4 | Kent P | 1 | Isth1N | 18 | Isth1N | 7 | Isth1N | 17 | Isth1N | 10 | Isth1N | 3 |

# WEALDSTONE

**Chairman:** Howard Krais

**Secretary:** Paul Fruin          **(T)** 0779 003 8095          **(E)** paul@pfruin.orangehome.co.uk

**Commercial Manager:** n/a          **(T)**

**Programme Editor:** Mark Hyde          **(T)** 07721 893 861

**Ground Address:** St. Georges Stadium, Grosvenor Vale, Ruislip, Middlesex HA4 6JQ

**(T)** 01895 637 487          **Manager:** Gordon Bartlett

## Club Factfile

**Founded:** 1899     **Nickname:** The Stones

**Previous Names:** None

**Previous Leagues:** Willesden & District 1899-1906, 08-13, London 1911-22, Middlesex 1913-22, Spartan 1922-28, Athenian 1928-64, Isthmian 1964-71, 95-2006, Southern 1971-79, 81-82, 88-95, Conference 1979-81, 82-88

**Club Colours (change):** All blue with white trim (Yellow with blue trim/blue/yellow)

**Ground Capacity:** 2,300     **Seats:** 300     **Covered:** 450     **Clubhouse:** Yes     **Shop:**

**Directions**

**From the M1:** Follow Signs for Heathrow Airport on the M25. Come off at Junction 16 onto the A40, come off at The Polish War Memorial junction A4180 sign posted to Ruislip, continue on West End Road, right into Grosvenor Vale after approx 1.5 miles, the ground is at the end of the road.

**From the M25:** Follow Take Junction 16 Off M25 onto A40. Then come off at The Polish War Memorial junction A4180 sign posted to Ruislip, continue on West End Road, right into Grosvenor Vale after approx 1.5 miles, the ground is at the end of the road.

**From the M4:** Junction 4B, take the M25 towards Watford, come off Junction 16 and join A40, come off at The Polish War Memorial junction A4180 sign posted to Ruislip, continue on West End Road, right into Grosvenor Vale after approx 1.5 miles, the ground is at the end of the road.

**Previous Grounds:** Lower Mead Stadium, Watford FC, Yeading FC, Northwood FC  *EDGWARE TOWN FC*

**Record Attendance:** 13,504 v Leytonstone - FA Amateur Cup 4th Round replay 05/03/1949 (at Lower Mead Stadium)

**Record Victory:** 22-0 v The 12th London Regiment (The Rangers) - FA Amateur Cup 13/10/1923

**Record Defeat:** 0-14 v Edgware Town (A) - London Senior Cup 09/12/1944

**Record Goalscorer:** George Duck - 251

**Record Appearances:** Charlie Townsend - 514

**Additional Records:** Paid £15,000 to Barnet for David Gipp

**Senior Honours:** Received £70,000 from Leeds United for Jermaine Beckford

Athenian League 1951-52. Southern League Division 1 South 1973-74, Southern Division 1981-82. Conference 1984-85. Isthmian League Division 3 1996-97. FA Amateur Cup 1965-66. London Senior Cup 1961-62. FA Trophy 1984-85. Middlesex Senior Cup x11

### 10 YEAR RECORD

| 03-04 | | 04-05 | | 05-06 | | 06-07 | | 07-08 | | 08-09 | | 09-10 | | 10-11 | | 11-12 | | 12-13 | |
|---|---|---|---|---|---|---|---|---|---|---|---|---|---|---|---|---|---|---|---|
| Isth1N | 7 | Isth P | 18 | Isth P | 18 | Sth P | 19 | Isth P | 13 | Isth P | 7 | Isth P | 6 | Isth P | 12 | Isth P | 4 | Isth P | 3 |

# MATCH RESULTS 2012-13

| Date | Comp | H/A | Opponents | Att | Result | Goalscorers | Pos | No. |
|---|---|---|---|---|---|---|---|---|
| Aug 18 | RPL | H | Metropolitan Police | 415 | W 1-0 | Jolly 26 | 8 | 1 |
| 21 | RPL | A | East Thurrock United | 412 | D 1-1 | Jolly 42 | 9 | 2 |
| 25 | RPL | H | Leiston | 415 | W 2-0 | Fitzgerald 42 Pett 69 | 4 | 3 |
| 27 | RPL | A | Lewes | 589 | L 0-1 | | 6 | 4 |
| Sept 1 | RPL | H | Whitehawk | 402 | D 1-1 | Chappell 45 | 6 | 5 |
| 8 | FAC Q1 | H | Biggleswade Town | 302 | W 2-0 | Jolly, Dean | | 6 |
| 15 | RPL | A | Concord Rangers | 225 | D 2-2 | Jolly 48 Chappell 42 | 8 | 7 |
| 22 | FAC Q2 | H | Lowestoft Town | 413 | L 1-2 | Cronin 52 (pen) | | 8 |
| 29 | FAT Q1 | H | Chertsey Town | 254 | W 3-1 | Jolly 41 57 Dean 90 | | 9 |
| Oct 6 | RPL | A | Bognor Regis Town | 448 | W 1-0 | Jolly 51 | 7 | 10 |
| 8 | RPL | H | Kingstonian | 494 | W 5-2 | Jolly, Dyer, Dean, Pett. Webb | 1 | 11 |
| 13 | RPL | H | Thurrock | 703 | D 2-2 | Brooks 45 Yiga 75 (og) | 4 | 12 |
| 27 | FAT Q2 | A | Merstham | 245 | W 6-2 | Graves 5 (og) Dean 6 20 Jolly 9 Dyer 80 Kirks 85 | | 13 |
| 29 | RPL | H | Hampton & Richmond B | 588 | W 3-2 | Dyer 48 Cronin 59 Jolly 89 | 3 | 14 |
| Nov 3 | RPL | A | Cray Wanderers | 222 | W 3-0 | Jolly 2 65 Dyer 19 | 3 | 15 |
| 10 | FAT Q3 | H | Corby Town | 405 | D 1-1 | Dyer 73 | | 16 |
| 17 | RPL | H | Carshalton Athletic | 422 | W 3-0 | Pett 27Jolly 42 Baidoo 80 | 3 | 17 |
| Dec 1 | RPL | H | Hendon | 437 | W 2-1 | Chappell 47 Webb 88 | 3 | 18 |
| 8 | RPL | A | Lowestoft Town | 576 | L 0-3 | | 3 | 19 |
| 15 | RPL | H | Enfield Town | 562 | W 4-0 | Jolly 27 Parker 49 Moore 47 89 | 3 | 20 |
| 26 | RPL | A | Harrow Borough | 661 | D 0-0 | | 3 | 21 |
| Jan 1 | RPL | H | Wingate & Finchley | 512 | L 2-3 | Jolly 83 Webb 84 | 4 | 22 |
| 5 | RPL | A | Kingstonian | 451 | L 0-2 | | 5 | 23 |
| 8 | RPL | A | Hastings United | 547 | D 1-1 | Dyer 56 | 3 | 24 |
| 12 | RPL | H | Bognor Regis Town | 396 | W 1-0 | Dyer 73 | 2 | 25 |
| 26 | RPL | H | Hastings United | 523 | W 3-0 | Cronin 34 (Pen) Dean 58 68 | 2 | 26 |
| 29 | RPL | A | Leiston | 202 | D 1-1 | Pett 27 | 3 | 27 |
| Feb 5 | RPL | A | Canvey Island | 222 | L 0-2 | | 5 | 28 |
| 9 | RPL | A | Enfield Town | 506 | W 2-1 | Parker 50 Dyer 73 | 4 | 29 |
| 16 | RPL | H | Margate | 647 | W 2-1 | Parker 84 89 | 2 | 30 |
| 18 | RPL | H | Lewes | 520 | W 6-1 | DEAN 4 (10 32 43 48) Jolly 29 Chappell 41 | 2 | 31 |
| 23 | RPL | A | Hendon | 402 | D 0-0 | | 2 | 32 |
| 26 | RPL | A | East Thurrock United | 117 | W 2-0 | Dean 35 Parker 50 | 2 | 33 |
| Mar 2 | RPL | A | Metropolitan Police | 275 | W 1-0 | Pett 51 | 2 | 34 |
| 9 | RPL | A | Whitehawk | 587 | D 1-1 | Dyer 76 | 2 | 35 |
| 13 | RPL | A | Thurrock | 189 | D 0-0 | | 2 | 36 |
| 26 | RPL | A | Margate | 236 | W 4-2 | Pett 22 25 Bodkin 65 (og) McGleish 66 | 2 | 37 |
| 28 | RPL | H | Concord Rangers | 610 | W 2-2 | James 87 Pett 90 | 2 | 38 |
| 30 | RPL | A | Wingate & Finchley | 326 | D 1-1 | Jolly 9 | 2 | 39 |
| Apr 1 | RPL | H | Harrow Borough | 841 | W 2-0 | Cronin 37 Leach 45 (og) | 2 | 40 |
| 6 | RPL | A | Bury Town | 479 | D 0-0 | | 2 | 41 |
| 9 | RPL | A | Bury Town | 507 | L 2-3 | Moore 47 McGleish 55 | 3 | 42 |
| 13 | RPL | H | Cray Wanderers | 549 | W 2-0 | McGleish 6 More 69 | 2 | 43 |
| 18 | RPL | A | Hampton & Richmond B | 326 | L 1-3 | McGleish 5 | 2 | 44 |
| 20 | RPL | A | Carshalton Athletic | 388 | W 2-0 | McGleish 18 Pett 68 | 3 | 45 |
| 23 | RPL | H | Lowestoft Town | 772 | D 0-0 | | 3 | 46 |
| 27 | RPL | A | Canvey Island | 803 | W 2-0 | Jolly 50 69 | 3 | 47 |
| May 1 | P-Offs S-F | H | Concord Rangers | 1055 | L 1-2 | King 90 (og) *aet | | 48 |

| GOALSCORERS | Lge | FAC | FAT | Total | Pens | Hat-tricks | Cons Run | | Lge | FAC | FAT | Total | Pens | Hat-tricks | Cons Run |
|---|---|---|---|---|---|---|---|---|---|---|---|---|---|---|---|
| Jolly | 15 | 1 | 3 | 19 | | | 3 | Baidoo | 1 | | | 1 | | | |
| Dean | 8 | 1 | 3 | 12 | 1 | | | Brooks | 1 | | | 1 | | | |
| Dyer | 7 | | 2 | 9 | | | | Fitzgerald | 1 | | | 1 | | | |
| Pett | 9 | | | 9 | | | | James | 1 | | | 1 | | | |
| McGleish | 5 | | | 5 | | | | Kirks | | | 1 | 1 | | | |
| Parker | 5 | | | 5 | | | | Own Goals | 4 | | 1 | 5 | | | |
| Chappell | 4 | | | 4 | | | | Cons Run - Consecutive scoring games. | | | | | | | |
| Cronin | 3 | 1 | | 4 | 2 | | | | | | | | | | |
| Moore | 4 | | | 4 | | | | | | | | | | | |
| Webb | 3 | | | 3 | | | | | | | | | | | |

# WINGATE & FINCHLEY

**Chairman:** Aron Sharpe

**Secretary:** David Thrilling  **(T)** 0797 700 7746  **(E)** secretary@wingatefinchley.com

**Commercial Manager:** n/a  **(T)**

**Programme Editor:** Paul Lerman  **(T)** 07736 282 218

**Ground Address:** Harry Abraham Stadium, Summers Lane, Finchley N12 0PD

**(T)** 020 8446 2217  **Manager:** Daniel Nielson

## Club Factfile

**Founded:** 1991  **Nickname:** Blues

**Previous Names:** Wingate (founded 1946) and Finchley (founded late 1800s) merged in 1991

**Previous Leagues:** South Midlands 1991-95, Isthmian 1995-2004, Southern 2004-2006

**Club Colours (change):** Royal blue with navy piping/royal blue with navy piping/navy (White with gold piping/black/black)

**Ground Capacity:** 8,500  **Seats:** 500  **Covered:** 500  **Clubhouse:** Yes  **Shop:** No

**Directions**

The simplest way to get to The Harry Abrahams Stadium is to get on to the A406 North Circular Road.
If coming from the West (eg via M1), go past Henlys Corner (taking the left fork after the traffic lights) and then drive for about 1 mile. The exit to take is the one immediately after a BP garage. Take the slip road and then turn right at the lights onto the A1000.
If coming from the East (eg via A10, M11) take the A1000 turn off. At the end of the slip road turn left at the lights. Go straight over the next set of lights. Then after 100m pass through another set of lights, then at the next set of lights turn right into Summers Lane. The Abrahams Stadium is a few hundred metres down on the right hand side.

**Previous Grounds:** None

**Record Attendance:** 528 v Brentwood Town (Division One North Play-Off) 2010/11

**Record Victory:** 9-1 v Winslow (South Midlands League) 23/11/1991

**Record Defeat:** 0-9 v Edgware - Isthmian Division 2 15/01/2000

**Record Goalscorer:** Marc Morris 650 (including with Wingate FC) FA Record for one Club

**Record Appearances:** Marc Morris 720 (including with Wingate FC)FA Record for one Club

**Additional Records:**

**Senior Honours:**
Isthmian League Cup 2010-11.
London Senior Cup 2010-11.

### 10 YEAR RECORD

| 03-04 | 04-05 | 05-06 | 06-07 | 07-08 | 08-09 | 09-10 | 10-11 | 11-12 | 12-13 |
|---|---|---|---|---|---|---|---|---|---|
| Isth1N 11 | SthE 12 | SthE 12 | Isth1N 9 | Isth1N 18 | Isth1N 7 | Isth1N 3 | Isth1N 3 | Isth P 13 | Isth P 18 |

# DOWNLOAD THE DIRECTORY FOR FREE!

The Non-League Club Directory is also avaialble as a download on the platforms listed to the right. As a reader of the Directory we'd like to offer you the chance to sample it for FREE until the season ends.

Including all that's in the this paperback edition, the download will have the added benefit of being updated as the season progresses. Including photos, previews and reports the Directory will grow as the season goes on.

If you would like to take us up on this offer please send your request for a FREE subsription to tw.publications@btinternet.com
Please quote: NLD14APP

# MATCH RESULTS 2012-13

| Date | Comp | H/A | Opponents | Att: | Result | Goalscorers | Pos | No. |
|------|------|-----|-----------|------|--------|-------------|-----|-----|
| Aug 18 | RPL | H | Canvey Island | 130 | L 0-1 | | 18 | 1 |
| 21 | RPL | A | Enfield Town | 34 | L 1-2 | Docker 65 (pen) | 19 | 2 |
| 25 | RPL | A | Hastings United | 298 | L 1-2 | Smith 40 | 22 | 3 |
| 27 | RPL | H | Carshalton Athletic | 173 | W 1-0 | Smith 60 | 22 | 4 |
| Sept 1 | RPL | A | Thurrock | 128 | W 2-1 | Smith 58 Pinto 67 | 12 | 5 |
| 8 | FAC Q1 | H | **Royston Town** | **124** | **D 1-1** | Laird 18 | | 6 |
| 11 | FAC Q1r | A | **Royston Town** | **101** | **W 3-2\*** | Smith 53 Pinto 70 101 | | 7 |
| 15 | RPL | H | Bognor Regis T | 124 | L 1-3 | Smith 73 | 17 | 8 |
| 22 | FAC Q2 | A | **Bury Town** | **366** | **L 1-2** | **Smith 39** | | 9 |
| 29 | FAT Q1 | H | **Potters Bar** | **91** | **W 2-1** | **Kyriacou 29 Jones 39** | | 10 |
| Oct 6 | RPL | A | Whitehawk | 73 | L 1-2 | Morris 14 | 18 | 11 |
| 9 | RPL | H | Harrow Borough | 101 | W 2-1 | Fowler 68 Karagul 73 | 10 | 12 |
| 13 | RPL | H | Concord Rangers | 262 | D 0-0 | | 11 | 13 |
| 20 | RPL | A | Lewes | 502 | L 1-3 | Baptiste 71 | 13 | 14 |
| 23 | RPL | A | Lowestoft Town | 447 | L 0-3 | | 15 | 15 |
| 27 | FAT Q2 | H | **Hitchin Town** | **101** | **D 2-2** | **Gardiner 30 Pinto 32** | | 16 |
| 29 | FAT Q2r | A | **Hitchin Town** | **171** | **L 0-3** | | | 17 |
| Nov 3 | RPL | A | Kingstonian | 332 | W 1-0 | Henry 56. | 11 | 18 |
| 17 | RPL | H | East Thurock Utd. | 109 | L 0-1 | | 18 | 19 |
| 24 | RPL | A | Bury Town | 282 | L 2-4 | Karagul 25 Smith 55 | 18 | 20 |
| 27 | RPL | A | Leiston | 106 | D 2-2 | Gardiner 60 Smith 79 | 16 | 21 |
| Dec 1 | RPL | H | Metropolitan Police | 89 | L 1-3 | Fowler 15 | 17 | 22 |
| 8 | RPL | A | Margate | 346 | L 0-2 | | 19 | 23 |
| 15 | RPL | H | Hampton & Richmond B | 131 | L 0-3 | | 19 | 24 |
| 26 | RPL | H | Hendon | 182 | L 0-1 | | 20 | 25 |
| 29 | RPL | H | Hastings United | 140 | D 2-2 | Brown 49 Shulton 90 | 21 | 26 |
| Jan 1 | RPL | A | Wealdstone | 512 | W 3-2\* | Brown 28 41 O'Sullivan 60 | 18 | 27 |
| 5 | RPL | A | Harrow Borough | 156 | W 2-1 | Thomas 8 O'Sullivan 66 | 16 | 28 |
| 12 | RPL | H | Whitehawk | 133 | L 2-3 | Thomas 47 Brown 71 | 18 | 29 |
| Feb 2 | RPL | A | Margate | 172 | W 1-0 | Thomas 19 | 17 | 30 |
| 5 | RPL | H | Lewes | 104 | L 2-4 | O'Sullivan 10 Thomas 84 | 17 | 31 |
| 9 | RPL | A | Hampton & Richmond B | 269 | D 3-3 | Bellotti 16 82 Brown 53 | 17 | 32 |
| 16 | RPL | H | Bury Town | 113 | L 1-3 | Bellotti 62 | 18 | 33 |
| 19 | RPL | A | Carshalton Athletic | 89 | W 2-1 | Rifat 38 Scarlett 44 | 18 | 34 |
| 23 | RPL | A | Metropolitan Police | 101 | L 1-2 | Scarlett 13 | 18 | 35 |
| 26 | RPL | H | Enfield Town | 149 | L 1-2 | Bellotti 3 | 19 | 36 |
| Mar 2 | RPL | A | Canvey Island | 310 | L 2-3 | Bellotti 18 66 | 19 | 37 |
| 5 | RPL | A | Cray Wanderers | 85 | W 4-3 | Rifat 52 Thomas 60 67 Mackie 89 | 18 | 38 |
| 7 | RPL | A | Concord Rangers | 164 | L 1-4 | Bellotti 3 | 18 | 39 |
| 10 | RPL | H | Thurrock | 166 | L 0-1 | | 18 | 40 |
| 16 | RPL | A | Bognor Regis Town | 357 | L 0-1 | | 18 | 41 |
| 30 | RPL | H | Wealdstone | 342 | D 1-1 | Mackie 36 | 19 | 42 |
| Apr 1 | RPL | A | Hendon | 148 | W 2-0 | Mackie 58 Smith 86 | 17 | 43 |
| 8 | RPL | A | Leiston | 194 | L 0-3 | | 19 | 44 |
| 13 | RPL | H | Kingstonian | 212 | W 3-0 | McCall 15 Smith 50 (pen) Christian 88 | 18 | 45 |
| 20 | RPL | A | East Thurrock U | 201 | L 0-2 | | 20 | 46 |
| 25 | RPL | H | Lowestoft Town | 175 | W 3-2 | Scott 28 Mackie 48 Rifat 77 | 18 | 47 |
| 27 | RPL | H | Cray Wanderers | 129 | D 4-4 | Bellotti 2 71 Thomas 18 27 | 18 | 48 |

| GOALSCORERS | Lge | FAC | FAT | Total | Pens | Hat-tricks | Cons Run | | Lge | FAC | FAT | Total | Pens | Hat-tricks | Cons Run |
|-------------|-----|-----|-----|-------|------|------------|----------|---|-----|-----|-----|-------|------|------------|----------|
| Smith | 8 | 2 | | 10 | | | 3 | Christian | 1 | | | 1 | | | |
| Bellotti | 9 | | | 9 | | | 2 | Docker | 1 | | | 1 | 1 | | |
| Thomas | 8 | | | 8 | | | 4 | Henry | 1 | | | 1 | | | |
| Brown | 5 | | | 5 | | | 2 | Jones | | | 1 | 1 | | | |
| Mackie | 4 | | | 4 | | | 2 | Kyriaco | | | 1 | 1 | | | |
| Pinto | 1 | 2 | 1 | 4 | | | | Laird | | 1 | | 1 | | | |
| O'Sullivan | 3 | | | 3 | | | 2 | McCall | 1 | | | 1 | | | |
| Rifat | 3 | | | 3 | | | | Morris | 1 | | | 1 | | | |
| Fowler | 2 | | | 2 | | | | Scott | 1 | | | 1 | | | |
| Gardiner | 1 | | 1 | 2 | | | | Shulton | 1 | | | 1 | | | |
| Karagul | 2 | | | 2 | | | | | | | | | | | |
| Scarlett | 2 | | | 2 | | | | Cons Run - Consecutive scoring games. | | | | | | | |
| Baptiste | 1 | | | 1 | | | | | | | | | | | |

# AFC SUDBURY

**Chairman:** Philip Turner
**Secretary:** Davis Webb  **(T)** 07885 327 510  **(E)** dave-afc@supanet.com
**Commercial Manager:** n/a  **(T)**
**Programme Editor:** Darren Theobald  **(T)** theobaldd@hotmail.co.uk
**Ground Address:** The Mel Group Stadium, King's Marsh Brundon Lane, Sudbury CO10 7HN
**(T)** 01787 376 213  **Manager:** David Batch

2012-13 Squad - Back row L/R Barry Lakin (asst manager) Duane Clarke (kit boy) Lee Boylan Tom Webb Stuart Fergus Danny Charge James smith Danny Gay Ben Tracey Bradley Thomas Ian Cousins Leon Antoine Eljay Worrell Tony Brightwell (phsio) James Baker Chris Tracey (manager)
Front row L/R David Bryant David Cowley Robbie Martin Ben Smith Michael Shinn Sam Clarke Adam Dalby Russell Pond

## Club Factfile

**Founded:** 1999  **Nickname:** Yellows
**Previous Names:** Sudbury Town (1874) and Sudbury Wanderers (1958) merged in 1999
**Previous Leagues:** Eastern Counties 1999-2006, Isthmian 2006-08, Southern 2008-10

**Club Colours (change):** Yellow/blue/yellow (All red)

**Ground Capacity:** 2,500  **Seats:** 200  **Covered:** 1,500  **Clubhouse:** Yes  **Shop:** Yes

**Directions**

From Braintree: Take A131 through Halstead to Sudbury. On descending hill into Sudbury turn left at first set of traffic lights (Kings Head), and then take the first right into Brundon Lane. The road narrows before reaching ground on the right hand side.

From Colchester, Bury St Edmunds and Ipswich: Enter Sudbury and follow signs for Halstead/Chelmsford. Go aross the river bridge and go under the old rail bridge, then turn right at the traffic lights (Kings Head) into Bulmer Road and the first right again into Brundon Lane. The road narrows before reaching ground on the right hand side.

**Previous Grounds:** The Priory Stadium

**Record Attendance:** 1,800
**Record Victory:** Not known
**Record Defeat:** Not known
**Record Goalscorer:** Gary Bennett - 172
**Record Appearances:** Paul Betson - 376
**Additional Records:**

**Senior Honours:**
Eastern Counties League 2000-01, 01-02, 02-03, 03-04, 04-05.
Suffolk Premier Cup 2002, 2003, 2004.

## 10 YEAR RECORD

| 03-04 | | 04-05 | | 05-06 | | 06-07 | | 07-08 | | 08-09 | | 09-10 | | 10-11 | | 11-12 | | 12-13 | |
|---|---|---|---|---|---|---|---|---|---|---|---|---|---|---|---|---|---|---|---|
| ECP | 1 | ECP | 1 | ECP | 3 | Isth1N | 5 | Isth1N | 2 | SthM | | SthM | 14 | Isth1N | 7 | Isth1N | 8 | Isth1N | 17 |

# AVELEY

**Chairman:** Graham Gennings
**Secretary:** Craig Johnston    **(T)** 0794 643 8540    **(E)** craigjohnston@aveleyfc.freeserve.co.uk
**Commercial Manager:** n/a    **(T)**
**Programme Editor:** Craig Johnston    **(T)** craigjohnston@aveleyfc.freeserve.co.uk
**Ground Address:** Mill Field, Mill Road, Aveley, Essex RM15 4SJ
**(T)** 01708 865 940    **Manager:** Justin Gardner

2012-13 Squad - Back row (L-R): Jessica Fox, Carey Eastwood, Marc Sontag, Jordan Cox, Ronnie Worster, Jay Leader (c), David McCartney, Alfred Kamara, Paul Burnett, Ricky Edwards, Sheldon Sellears, Tom Querry, Kevin Head.
Front row: Ellis Sands, Jack Stevenson, Charlie Stevenson, Gary Nesbit, Justin Gardner, Victor Renner, Billy Holland, Junior Appiah, Shane Oakley.

## Club Factfile

**Founded:** 1927    **Nickname:** The Millers
**Previous Names:** None
**Previous Leagues:** Thurrock Combination 1946-49, London 1949-57, Delphian 1957-63, Athenian 1963-73, Isthmian 1973-2004, Southern 2004-06

**Club Colours (change):** All blue (All red)

**Ground Capacity:** 4,000    **Seats:** 400    **Covered:** 400    **Clubhouse:** Yes    **Shop:** No

**Directions** London - Southend A1306, turn into Sandy Lane at Aveley.

**Previous Grounds:** None

**Record Attendance:** 3,741 v Slough Town - FA Amateur Cup 27/02/1971
**Record Victory:** 11-1 v Histon - 24/08/1963
**Record Defeat:** 0-8 v Orient, Essex Thameside Trophy
**Record Goalscorer:** Jotty Wilks - 214
**Record Appearances:** Ken Riley - 422
**Additional Records:**

**Senior Honours:**
Athenian League 1970-71. Isthmian League Division 1 North 2008-09.
Thameside Trophy 1980, 2005, 2007.

### 10 YEAR RECORD

| 03-04 | | 04-05 | | 05-06 | | 06-07 | | 07-08 | | 08-09 | | 09-10 | | 10-11 | | 11-12 | | 12-13 | |
|---|---|---|---|---|---|---|---|---|---|---|---|---|---|---|---|---|---|---|---|
| Isth1N | 14 | SthE | 17 | SthE | 20 | Isth1N | 15 | Isth1N | 11 | Isth1N | 1 | Isth P | 3 | Isth P | 19 | Isth P | 20 | Isth P | 5 |

# BARKINGSIDE

**Chairman:** Jimmy Flanagan
**Secretary:** Jimmy Flanagan    **(T)** 07956 894 194    **(E)** confclothing@aol.com
**Commercial Manager:** n/a        **(T)**
**Programme Editor:** Jimmy Flanagan      **(T)**
**Ground Address:** Oakside Stadium, Station Road, Barkingside IG6 1NB
**(T)** 020 8552 3995        **Manager:** Matt Frew

## Club Factfile

**Founded:** 1898      **Nickname:** The Side / Sky Blues
**Previous Names:** None
**Previous Leagues:** London. Greater London. Met London. Spartan, South Midlands. Essex Senior > 2013.

**Club Colours (change):** Sky blue & navy/navy blue/navy blue. (All orange)

**Ground Capacity:** 3,000    **Seats:** 350      **Covered:** 850      **Clubhouse:** Yes    **Shop:** No

**Directions:** A12 from London, turn left off Eastern Avenue into Horns Road, Barkingside (Greengate). Right into Craven Gardens, right again into Carlton Drive and left into Station Road. Go over bridge and ground is on the right. Adjacent to Barkingside Underground Station (Central Line).

**Previous Grounds:** Barkingside High Road. Barkingside Recreation Ground.

**Record Attendance: Att:** 957 v Arsenal Reserves, London League, 1957.
**Record Victory:**
**Record Defeat:**
**Record Goalscorer:**
**Record Appearances:**
**Additional Records:** Greater London League 1964-65. Spartan League 1996-97.

**Senior Honours:**
London Senior Cup 1996-97. Spartan South Midlands League Premier Division 1998-99. Essex Senior Cup 2008-09.

### 10 YEAR RECORD

| 03-04 | | 04-05 | | 05-06 | | 06-07 | | 07-08 | | 08-09 | | 09-10 | | 10-11 | | 11-12 | | 12-13 | |
|---|---|---|---|---|---|---|---|---|---|---|---|---|---|---|---|---|---|---|---|
| ESen | 11 | ESen | 4 | ESen | 4 | ESen | 3 | ESen | 3 | ESen | 5 | ESen | 9 | ESen | 15 | ESen | 8 | ESen | 2 |

# BRENTWOOD TOWN

**Chairman:** Brian Hallett
**Secretary:** John Layden  (T) 07835 850 167  (E) john.leyden5@yahoo.co.uk
**Commercial Manager:** n/a  (T)
**Programme Editor:** Ken Hobbs  (T) 07958 232 829
**Ground Address:** The Arena, Brentwood Centre, Doddinghurst Road, Brentwood CM15 9NN
**(T)** 07768 006 370  **Manager:** Les Whitton

## Club Factfile

**Founded:** 1954  **Nickname:** Blues
**Previous Names:** Manor Athletic, Brentwood Athletic, Brentwood F.C.
**Previous Leagues:** Romford & District, South Essex Combination, London & Essex Border, Olympian, Essex Senior

**Club Colours (change):** Sky blue/white/white (All claret)

**Ground Capacity:** 1,000  **Seats:** 150  **Covered:** 250  **Clubhouse:** Yes  **Shop:** No

**Directions:** From High Street (Wilson's Corner) turn north into Ongar Road. Then at third mini roundabout turn right into Doddinghurst Road.

**Previous Grounds:** King George's Playing Fields (Hartswood), Larkins Playing Fields 1957-93

**Record Attendance:** 472 v West Ham United - 27/07/2004
**Record Victory:** Not known
**Record Defeat:** Not known
**Record Goalscorer:** Not known
**Record Appearances:** Not known
**Additional Records:**

**Senior Honours:**
Essex Senior League 2000-01, 2006-07, League Cup 1975-76, 78-79, 90-91, 2006-07.
Essex Olympian League Cup 1967-68.

### 10 YEAR RECORD

| 03-04 | 04-05 | 05-06 | 06-07 | 07-08 | 08-09 | 09-10 | 10-11 | 11-12 | 12-13 |
|---|---|---|---|---|---|---|---|---|---|
| ESen 14 | ESen 14 | ESen 8 | ESen 1 | Isth1N 6 | Isth1N 3 | Isth1N 12 | Isth1N 5 | Isth1N 9 | Isth1N 9 |

# BURNHAM RAMBLERS

**Chairman:** William Hannan
**Secretary:** Shaun Pugh    **(T)** 0752 509 9914    **(E)** secretarybrfc@sapugh.gotadsl.co.
**Commercial Manager:** n/a    **(T)**
**Programme Editor:** Martin Leno    **(T)** 07702 592 418
**Ground Address:** Leslie Fields Stadium, Springfield Road CM0 8TE
**(T)** 01621 784 383    **Manager:** Keith Wilson

## Club Factfile

**Founded:** 1900    **Nickname:** Ramblers
**Previous Names:** None
**Previous Leagues:** North Essex. Mid-Essex. Olympian. South East Essex. Essex Senior > 2013.

**Club Colours (change):** Navy & sky blue stripes/navy/sky blue (All red).

**Ground Capacity:** 2,000    **Seats:** 156    **Covered:** 300    **Clubhouse:** Yes    **Shop:** No

**Directions:** **A12** Proceed along the A12 until you reach the turn off for Maldon. Carry on through Danbury and then follow the signs for Burnham on Crouch (B1010). *Just before you get to Burnham on Crouch there is a garage on the left-hand side. Springfield Road is about quarter of a mile past the garage on the right. Turn right into Springfield Road, then take the second turning on the right and then first right and drive through the gates of the ground. **A127** Proceed along the A127, and take the A130 turn off sign-posted to Chelmsford. At Rettendon Turnpike (a large roundabout), take the A132 to South Woodham Ferrers. Burnham on Crouch is sign-posted from there (B1012 and then B1010). Continue from * above. **A13** Proceed along A13 and take the A130 turn off sign-posted to Chelmsford. At Rettendon Turnpike (a large roundabout) take the A132 to South Woodham Ferrers. Burnham on Crouch is sign-posted from there (B1012 and then B1010). Continue from * above.

**Previous Grounds:** None

**Record Attendance:** Att: 1,500 v Arsenal, opening of stand.
**Record Victory:**
**Record Defeat:**
**Record Goalscorer:**
**Record Appearances:**
**Additional Records:**

**Senior Honours:**
Essex Senior League 2012-13.

| | 10 YEAR RECORD | | | | | | | | |
|---|---|---|---|---|---|---|---|---|---|
| 03-04 | 04-05 | 05-06 | 06-07 | 07-08 | 08-09 | 09-10 | 10-11 | 11-12 | 12-13 |
| ESen 12 | ESen 2 | ESen 5 | ESen 5 | ESen 8 | ESen 7 | ESen 3 | ESen 7 | ESen 4 | ESen 1 |

# CHATHAM TOWN

**Chairman:** Jeff Talbot
**Secretary:** Henry Longhurst    **(T)** 0796 746 5554    **(E)** h.longhurst@sky.com
**Commercial Manager:** n/a        **(T)**
**Programme Editor:** Rachel Willett       **(T)** rachel.willett1987@yahoo.co.uk
**Ground Address:** Maidstone Road Sports Ground, Maidstone Road, Chatham ME4 6LR
**(T)** 01634 812 194         **Manager:** Kevin Watson

## CHATHAM TOWN FOOTBALL CLUB

2012-13 Squad - Back Row- Jamie Lawrence, Rodrigue Ndiane, Lee Hales, Jack Jeffery, Ryan Laker, Jack Pallen, Garry Tilley
Middle Row-Terry Groom (physio), Jean-Michel Sigre, Harry Smith, Tony Kessell, Tim Roberts, Kes Metitiri, Steve Binks (Director)
Front Row- Ryan Palmer, Matt Newman, Kevin Watson (Manager) Keith Levitt (Ass/ Manager) Brad Potter (Capt) Matt Solly

## Club Factfile

**Founded:** 1882     **Nickname:** Chats
**Previous Names:** Chatham FC 1882-1974, Medway FC 1974-79
**Previous Leagues:** Southern 1894-1900, 1920-21, 27-29, 83-88, 2001-, Kent 1894-96, 1901-1905, 29-59, 68-83, 88-2001,
                       Aetolian 1959-64, Metropolitan 1964-68

**Club Colours (change):** Red & black stripes/black/black (Blue & black stripes/blue/blue)

**Ground Capacity:** 2,000   **Seats:** 600    **Covered:** 600    **Clubhouse:** Yes   **Shop:** Yes

**Directions**
Exit the M2 at junction 3, and follow directions for Chatham & Town Centre. You will then pass a Homebase & Toys 'R' Us on the left hand side. Continue straight over the roundabout and then there is a split in the road, where you bear right for chatham this is Maidstone Road. Follow this, continuing straight over the cross roads and you will see a petrol station on the left. Bournville Road is opposite the petrol station on the left. Ground entrance is first left.

**Previous Grounds:** Great Lines, Chatham 1882-90

**Record Attendance:** 5,000 v Gillingham - 1980
**Record Victory:** Not known
**Record Defeat:** Not known
**Record Goalscorer:** Not known
**Record Appearances:** Not known
**Additional Records:** Received Transfer fee of £500. FA Cup Quarter finalists 1888/89.

**Senior Honours:**
Kent League 1894-95, 1903-04, 04-05, 71-72, 73-74, 75-76, 76-77, 79-80, 2000-01. Aetolian League 1963-64.
Kent Senior Cup 1885-86, 86-87, 87-88, 88-89, 94-95,1904-05, 10-11, 18-19. Kent Senior Shield 1919-20.

### 10 YEAR RECORD

| 03-04 | 04-05 | 05-06 | 06-07 | 07-08 | 08-09 | 09-10 | 10-11 | 11-12 | 12-13 |
|---|---|---|---|---|---|---|---|---|---|
| SthE   13 | SthE   11 | SthE   17 | Isth1S   16 | Isth1S   18 | Isth1N   10 | Isth1S   17 | Isth1S   21 | Isth1N   15 | Isth1N   13 |

# CHESHUNT

**Chairman:** Dean Williamson
**Secretary:** Alex Kalinic  **(T)** 0775 483 1800  **(E)** clubsecretary@cheshuntfc.com
**Commercial Manager:** n/a  **(T)**
**Programme Editor:** Alex Kalinic  **(T)** 0775 483 1800
**Ground Address:** Cheshunt Stadium, Theobalds Lane, Cheshunt, Herts EN8 8RU
**(T)** 01992 625 793  **Manager:** Tony Faulkner

2012-13 Squad

## Club Factfile

**Founded:** 1946  **Nickname:** Ambers
**Previous Names:**
**Previous Leagues:** London 1947-51, 56-59, Delphian 1952-55, Aetolian 1960-62, Spartan 1963-64, 88-93, Athenian 1965-76, Isthmian 1977-87, 94-2005, Southern 2006-08

**Club Colours (change):** Amber/black/black (Sky blue/white/sky blue)

**Ground Capacity:** 3,500  **Seats:** 424  **Covered:** 600  **Clubhouse:** Yes  **Shop:** No

**Directions**
M25, junction 25 take A10 north towards Hertford.
Third exit at roundabout towards Waltham Cross A121.
First exit at roundabout towards Cheshunt B176.
Under railway bridge then left onto Theobalds Lane.
Ground is 800 yard on the right.

**Previous Grounds:** Gothic Sports Ground 1946-47. College Road 1947-50. Brookfield Lane 1950-52, 53-58.

**Record Attendance:** 5,000
**Record Victory:**  v Bromley - FA Amateur Cup 2nd Round 28/01/1950
**Record Defeat:** 0-10 v Etonn Manor - London League 17/04/1956
**Record Goalscorer:**  Eddie Sedgwick - 148 (1967-72, 1980)
**Record Appearances:** John Poole - 526 (1970-76, 79-83)
**Additional Records:** Received £10,000 from Peterborough United for Lloyd Opara
**Senior Honours:**
London League Premier Division 1950, Division 1 1948, 49. Athenian League Premier Division 1976, Division 1 1968.
Spartan League 1963. Isthmian League Division 2 2003.
London Charity Cup 1974. East Anglian Cup 1975. Herts Charity Cup 2006, 2008.

## 10 YEAR RECORD

| 03-04 | | 04-05 | | 05-06 | | 06-07 | | 07-08 | | 08-09 | | 09-10 | | 10-11 | | 11-12 | | 12-13 | |
|---|---|---|---|---|---|---|---|---|---|---|---|---|---|---|---|---|---|---|---|
| Isth1N | 3 | Isth P | 19 | SthP | 16 | SthP | 16 | SthP | 22 | Isth1N | 14 | Isth1N | 15 | Isth1N | 18 | Isth1N | 18 | Isth1N | 11 |

# DEREHAM TOWN

**Chairman:** Simon Barnes
**Secretary:** Nigel Link          **(T)** 07885 144 039     **(E)** patnige1954@fsmail.net
**Commercial Manager:**                              **(T)**
**Programme Editor:** Simon Barnes          **(T)** 07766 318 550
**Ground Address:** Aldiss Park, Norwich Road, Dereham, Norfolk NR20 3PX
**(T)** 01362 690 460                              **Manager:** Matt Henman

Celebrations after winning the Eastern Counties title!

## Club Factfile

**Founded:** 1884      **Nickname:** Magpies
**Previous Names:** Dereham and Dereham Hobbies.
**Previous Leagues:** Norwich District. Dereham & District. Norfolk & Suffolk. Anglian Comb. Eastern Counties > 2013.

**Club Colours (change):** White & black/black/black. (Green & white/green/green)

**Ground Capacity:** 3,000  **Seats:** 50      **Covered:** 500      **Clubhouse:** Yes   **Shop:** Yes

**Directions:** Take the A47 towards Swaffham & Dereham. Do not take first slip road into Dereham. Carry on along the by-pass and take the second slip road, onto the B1110, sign posted B1147 to Bawdeswell, Swanton Morley and the Dereham Windmill. Follow the slip road round and Aldiss Park is 500 yards on your right.

**Previous Grounds:** None

**Record Attendance:** Att: 3000 v Norwich City, Friendly, 07/2001.
**Record Victory:**
**Record Defeat:**
**Record Goalscorer:**
**Record Appearances:**
**Additional Records:**

**Senior Honours:**
Anglian Combination Division 1 Champions 1989-90, Premier Division 97-98. Norfolk Senior Cup 2005-06, 06-07.
Eastern Counties Premier Division 2012-13.

### 10 YEAR RECORD

| 03-04 | | 04-05 | | 05-06 | | 06-07 | | 07-08 | | 08-09 | | 09-10 | | 10-11 | | 11-12 | | 12-13 | |
|---|---|---|---|---|---|---|---|---|---|---|---|---|---|---|---|---|---|---|---|
| ECP | 18 | ECP | 15 | ECP | 12 | ECP | 6 | ECP | 4 | ECP | 4 | ECP | 10 | ECP | 2 | ECP | 10 | ECP | 1 |

# ERITH & BELVEDERE

**THE DERES**

**FOUNDED 1922**

**Chairman:** John McFadden

**Secretary:** Adam Peters **(T)** 07984 090 805 **(E)** clubsec_erithandbelvederefc@live.com

**Commercial Manager:** n/a **(T)**

**Programme Editor:** Brian Spurrell / Martin Tarrant **(T)** 07713 189 912

**Ground Address:** Welling FC, Park View Road, Welling, DA16 1SY

**(T)** 07984 090 805 **Manager:** Chris Cosgrove & Martin Ford

The team and fans enjoy the club's success in winning the Kent League title.
Photo: Alan Coomes.

## Club Factfile

**Founded:** 1922 **Nickname:** Deres

**Previous Names:** Belvedere & District FC (Formed 1918 restructured 1922)

**Previous Leagues:** Kent. London. Corinthian. Athenian. Southern. Kent League 2005-13.

**Club Colours (change):** Blue & white quarters/blue/blue. (Red & white quarters/red/red)

**Ground Capacity:** 4,000 **Seats:** 1,070 **Covered:** 1,000 **Clubhouse:** Yes **Shop:** Yes

**Directions**

M25 to Dartford then A2 towards London.
Take Bexleyheath/Blackfen/Sidcup,turn off (six miles along A2) then follow A207 signed welling.
Ground is 1 mile From A2 on main road towards Welling High Street.

**Previous Grounds:** Park View, Belvedere 1922-99.

**Record Attendance:** 5,573 v Crook C.W., FA Amateur Cup 19/02/1949

**Record Victory:** 14-1 v Orpington, Kent Senior Cup, 14/03/1942

**Record Defeat:** 0-15 v Ashford, Kent League, 28/04/1937

**Record Goalscorer:** Colin Johnson - 284 (61-71).

**Record Appearances:** Dennis Crawford - 504 (56-71).

**Additional Records:**

**Senior Honours:**
Kent League 1981-82, 2012-13. London Senior Cup 1944-45.

### 10 YEAR RECORD

| 03-04 | | 04-05 | | 05-06 | | 06-07 | | 07-08 | | 08-09 | | 09-10 | | 10-11 | | 11-12 | | 12-13 | |
|---|---|---|---|---|---|---|---|---|---|---|---|---|---|---|---|---|---|---|---|
| SthE | 21 | SthE | 21 | Kent P | 4 | Kent P | 7 | Kent P | 7 | Kent P | 8 | Kent P | 12 | Kent P | 5 | Kent P | 2 | Kent P | 1 |

# HARLOW TOWN

**Chairman:** John Barnett
**Secretary:** Ray Dyer  **(T)** 07545 100 823  **(E)** harlowtownfc@aol.com
**Commercial Manager:** n/a  **(T)**
**Programme Editor:** Mark Kettley  **(T)** sundayonly1@aol.com
**Ground Address:** Barrows Farm Std, off Elizabeth Way, The Pinnacles, Harlow CM19 5BE
**(T)** 01279 443 196  **Manager:** Danny Chapman

## Club Factfile

**Founded:** 1879  **Nickname:** Hawks
**Previous Names:** None
**Previous Leagues:** East Hertfordshire > 1932, Spartan 1932-39, 46-54, London 1954-61, Delphian 1961-63, Athenian 1963-73, Isthmian 1973-92, Inactive 1992-93, Southern 2004-06

**Club Colours (change):** All red (White/black/black)

**Ground Capacity:** 3,500  **Seats:** 500  **Covered:** 500  **Clubhouse:** Yes  **Shop:** Yes

**Directions**
Barrows Farm is situated on the western side of town just off of the Roydon Road (A1169) on the Pinnacles Industrial Estate.
If coming into Harlow from the M11 (North or South) exit at Junction 7 and follow the A414 until the first roundabout where you turn left onto the A1169. Follow the A1169 signed for Roydon until you see the ground ahead of you at the Roydon Road roundabout. Go straight over the roundabout and the entrance to the ground is on the left.
If coming into town from the west on the A414 turn right at the first roundabout (the old ground was straight ahead) signed Roydon A1169. Follow the A1169 for approx 1 mile and the entrance to the ground is on the right.

**Previous Grounds:** Marigolds 1919-22, Green Man Field 1922-60

**Record Attendance:** 9,723 v Leicester City - FA Cup 3rd Round replay 08/01/1980
**Record Victory:** 14-0 v Bishop's Stortford - 11/04/1925
**Record Defeat:** 0-11 v Ware (A) - Spartan Division 1 East 06/03/1948
**Record Goalscorer:** Dick Marshall scored 64 during 1928-29
**Record Appearances:** Norman Gladwin - 639 (1949-70)
**Additional Records:**

**Senior Honours:**
Athenian League Division 1 1971-72. Isthmian League Division 1 1978-79, Division 2 North 1988-89.
Essex Senior cup 1978-79

### 10 YEAR RECORD

| 03-04 | 04-05 | 05-06 | 06-07 | 07-08 | 08-09 | 09-10 | 10-11 | 11-12 | 12-13 |
|---|---|---|---|---|---|---|---|---|---|
| Isth1N 10 | SthE 15 | SthE 9 | Isth1N 2 | Isth P 15 | Isth P 20 | Isth1N 22 | Isth1N 4 | Isth1N 7 | Isth1N 21 |

# HEYBRIDGE SWIFTS

**Chairman:** Nick Bowyer

**Secretary:** Jill Hedgecock   **(T)** 07522 158 487   **(E)** blackwater1@sky.com

**Commercial Manager:** n/a   **(T)**

**Programme Editor:** Jill Hedgecock   **(T)** 07522 158 487

**Ground Address:** Scraley Road, Heybridge, Maldon, Essex CM9 8JA

**(T)** 01621 852 978   **Manager:** Mark Hawkes

## Club Factfile

**Founded:** 1880   **Nickname:** Swifts

**Previous Names:** Heybridge FC.

**Previous Leagues:** Essex & Suffolk Border, North Essex, South Essex, Essex Senior 1971-84

**Club Colours (change):** Black and white stripes/black/black (Yellow/white/white)

**Ground Capacity:** 3,000  **Seats:** 550  **Covered:** 1,200  **Clubhouse:** Yes  **Shop:** Yes

**Directions:** Leave Maldon on the main road to Colchester, pass through Heybridge then turn right at sign to Tolleshunt Major (Scraley Road). The ground is on the right.

**Previous Grounds:** One before Scraley Road.

**Record Attendance:** 2,477 v Woking - FA Trophy 1997

**Record Victory:** Not known

**Record Defeat:** Not known

**Record Goalscorer:** Julian Lamb - 115 (post War)

**Record Appearances:** Hec Askew - 500+. John Pollard - 496

**Additional Records:** Paid £1,000 for Dave Rainford and for Lee Kersey. Received £35,000 from Southend United for Simon Royce

**Senior Honours:** Isthmian League Division 2 North 1989-90, Essex Senior League x3. Essex Junior Cup 1931-32. East Anglian Cup 1993-94, 94-95.

### 10 YEAR RECORD

| 03-04 | 04-05 | 05-06 | 06-07 | 07-08 | 08-09 | 09-10 | 10-11 | 11-12 | 12-13 |
|---|---|---|---|---|---|---|---|---|---|
| Isth P  16 | Isth P  7 | Isth P  2 | Isth P  12 | Isth P  12 | Isth P  21 | Isth1N  6 | Isth1N  9 | Isth1N  16 | Isth1N  6 |

# MALDON & TIPTREE

**Chairman:** Ed Garty
**Secretary:** Phil Robinson    **(T)** 0775 906 6636    **(E)** robbophil@hotmail.com
**Commercial Manager:** n/a    **(T)**
**Programme Editor:** Richard Buckby    **(T)** 07711 089 128
**Ground Address:** Wallace Binder Ground, Park Drive, Maldon CM9 6XX
**(T)** 01621 853 762    **Manager:** Terry Spillane

## Club Factfile

**Founded:** 2010    **Nickname:** The Hoops
**Previous Names:** Maldon Town (1975) and Tiptree United (1933) merged in 2010 to form today's club
**Previous Leagues:** None

**Club Colours (change):** Blue and red stripes/blue/blue (All orange)

**Ground Capacity:** 2,800    **Seats:** 155    **Covered:** 300    **Clubhouse:** Yes    **Shop:**

**Directions**
From M25 junction 28 travel north on A12 until A414 to Maldon.
Turn right at Safeways roundabout, then over next two roundabouts.
Ground is on the right.

**Previous Grounds:** None

**Record Attendance:** Not known
**Record Victory:** Not known
**Record Defeat:** Not known
**Record Goalscorer:** Not known
**Record Appearances:** Not known
**Additional Records:**

**Senior Honours:**
None

### 10 YEAR RECORD

| 03-04 | 04-05 | 05-06 | 06-07 | 07-08 | 08-09 | 09-10 | 10-11 | | 11-12 | | 12-13 | |
|-------|-------|-------|-------|-------|-------|-------|-------|---|-------|---|-------|---|
| | | | | | | | Isth1N | 8 | Isth1N | 11 | Isth1N | 2 |

# NEEDHAM MARKET

**Chairman:** Keith Nunn
**Secretary:** Mark Easlea          **(T)** 0779 545 6502          **(E)** m.easlea@sky.com
**Commercial Manager:** n/a                                        **(T)**
**Programme Editor:** Alan Jopling                                  **(T)** 07824 878 707
**Ground Address:** Bloomfields, Quinton Road, Needham Market IP6 8DA
**(T)** 01449 721 000                                        **Manager:** Mark Morsley

## Club Factfile

**Founded:** 1919          **Nickname:** The Marketmen
**Previous Names:** None
**Previous Leagues:** Suffolk & Ipswich Senior, Eastern Counties

**Club Colours (change):** All red (Yellow/black/black)

**Ground Capacity:** 1,000     **Seats:** 250     **Covered:** 250     **Clubhouse:** Yes     **Shop:** Yes

**Directions**
Quinton Road is off Barretts Lane which in turn is off Needham Market High Street.

**Previous Grounds:** Young's Meadow 1919. Crowley Park >1996.

**Record Attendance:** 750 v Ipswich Town - Suffolk Premier Cup 2007
**Record Victory:** 10-1 v I[swich Wanderers (A) , FA Cup Preliminary Round, 01/09/2007
**Record Defeat:** 2-6 v Lowestoft Town (A), FA Trophy First round Qualifier, 19/10/2010
**Record Goalscorer:** Craig Parker - 111 (2007-2011) Most goals in a season - Craig Parker 40 (2011-11).
**Record Appearances:** Rhys Barber - 334 (2006-2012)
**Additional Records:** Most goals scored in a season - 196 in 70 games (2007-08)

**Senior Honours:**
Suffolk Senior Cup 1989-90, 2004-05. Suffolk & Ipswich Senior League 1995-96. East Anglian Cup 2006-07.
Eastern Counties Premier Division 2009-10.

### 10 YEAR RECORD

| 03-04 | | 04-05 | | 05-06 | | 06-07 | | 07-08 | | 08-09 | | 09-10 | | 10-11 | | 11-12 | | 12-13 | |
|---|---|---|---|---|---|---|---|---|---|---|---|---|---|---|---|---|---|---|---|
| EC1 | 14 | EC1 | 2 | ECP | 6 | ECP | 4 | ECP | 2 | ECP | 3 | ECP | 1 | Isth1N | 2 | Isth1N | 4 | Isth1N | 16 |

# REDBRIDGE

**Chairman:** Imran Merchant
**Secretary:** Bob Holloway    **(T)** 0789 069 9907    **(E)** r.holloway338@btinternet.com
**Commercial Manager:** n/a    **(T)**
**Programme Editor:** Adam Silver    **(T)** 07796 880 824
**Ground Address:** Oakside Stadium, Station Road, Barkingside, Ilford IG6 1NB
**(T)** 020 8550 3611    **Manager:** Dave Ross & Ricky Eaton

## Club Factfile

**Founded:** 1958    **Nickname:** Motormen
**Previous Names:** Ford United 1958-2004
**Previous Leagues:** Aetolian 1959-64, Greater London 1964-71, Metropolitan 1971-74, Essex Senior 1974-97, Isthmian 1997-2004, Conference 2004-05

**Club Colours (change):** Red with black trim/black/black (White and red/red/red)

**Ground Capacity:** 3,000    **Seats:** 350    **Covered:** 1,000    **Clubhouse:** Yes    **Shop:** Yes

**Directions**
A12 from London, turn left off Eastern Avenue into Horns Road, Barkingside (Greengate). Right into Craven Gardens, right again into Carlton Drive and left into Station Road. Go over bridge and ground is on the right. Adjacent to Barkingside Underground Station (Central Line).

**Previous Grounds:** Ford Sports & Social Club > 2000

**Record Attendance:** 58,000 v Bishop Auckland
**Record Victory:** Not known
**Record Defeat:** Not known
**Record Goalscorer:** Jeff Wood - 196
**Record Appearances:** Roger Bird
**Additional Records:**

**Senior Honours:**
Aetolian League 1959-60, 61-62. Greater London League 1970-71. Essex Senior League 1991-92, 96-97.
Isthmian League Division 3 1998-99, Division 1 2001-02,

| | | | | | 10 YEAR RECORD | | | | | |
|---|---|---|---|---|---|---|---|---|---|---|
| 03-04 | 04-05 | 05-06 | 06-07 | 07-08 | 08-09 | 09-10 | 10-11 | 11-12 | 12-13 | |
| Isth P  13 | Conf S  22 | Isth P  22 | Isth1N  16 | Isth1N  3 | Isth1N  8 | Isth1N  18 | Isth1N  16 | Isth1N  6 | Isth1N  20 | |

# ROMFORD

**Chairman:** Steve Gardener
**Secretary:** Colin Ewenson    **(T)** 0797 371 7074    **(E)** ewenson@aol.com
**Commercial Manager:** n/a    **(T)**
**Programme Editor:** Keith Preston    **(T)** 07876 237 918
**Ground Address:** Thurrock FC, South Way, Ship Lane, Aveley RM19 1YN
**(T)** 01708 865 492    **Manager:** Paul Martin

## Club Factfile

**Founded:** 1876    **Nickname:** Boro
**Previous Names:** Original club founded in 1876 folded during WW1, Reformed in 1929 folded again in 1978 and reformed in 1992
**Previous Leagues:** Athenian 1931-39, Isthmian 1945-59, 97-2002, Southern 1959-78, Essex Senior 1992-96, 2002-09

**Club Colours (change):** Blue and yellow stripes/blue/blue (Red and black/black/black)

**Ground Capacity:** 4,500    **Seats:** 300    **Covered:** 1,000    **Clubhouse:** Yes    **Shop:**

**Directions:** Approaching the ground from the North - along the M25 in a clockwise direction. Leave the motorway at junction 30. At the roundabout take the second exit and stay in the left hand lane. This leads to a large roundabout controlled by traffic lights. The fifth exit is Ship Lane and the ground is approximately 50 yards on the right hand side. Approaching the ground from the South - anti-clockwise on the M25. When going through the Dartford Tunnel take the left hand bore. On coming out of the tunnel take the first exit - junction 31. This leads to a large roundabout controlled by traffic lights. Take the third exit which is Ship Lane. The ground is situated approximately 50 yards on the right hand side.

**Previous Grounds:** The Mill Field (Aveley FC).

**Record Attendance:** 820 v Leatherhead - Isthmian Division 2
**Record Victory:** Not known
**Record Defeat:** Not known
**Record Goalscorer:** Danny Benstock
**Record Appearances:** S Horne - 234
**Additional Records:**

**Senior Honours:**
Essex Senior League 1995-96, 2008-09. Isthmian League Division 2 1996-97.

### 10 YEAR RECORD

| 03-04 | 04-05 | 05-06 | 06-07 | 07-08 | 08-09 | 09-10 | 10-11 | 11-12 | 12-13 |
|---|---|---|---|---|---|---|---|---|---|
| ESen 5 | ESen 5 | ESen 12 | ESen 2 | ESen 5 | ESen 1 | Isth1N 13 | Isth1N 12 | Isth1N 13 | Isth1N 8 |

# SOHAM TOWN RANGERS

**Chairman:** Colin Murfit
**Secretary:** Mark Bailey **(T)** 07903 289 938 **(E)** mvbailey@fsmail.net
**Commercial Manager:** n/a **(T)**
**Programme Editor:** n/a **(T)**
**Ground Address:** Julius Martin Lane, Soham, Ely, Cambridgeshire CB7 5EQ
**(T)** 01353 720 732 **Manager:** Steve Fallon

## Club Factfile

**Founded:** 1947 **Nickname:** Town or Rangers
**Previous Names:** Soham Town and Soham Rangers merged in 1947
**Previous Leagues:** Peterborough & District, Eastern Counties 1963-2008, Southern 2008-11.

**Club Colours (change):** All green with white trim

**Ground Capacity:** 2,000 **Seats:** 250 **Covered:** 1,000 **Clubhouse:** Yes **Shop:** Yes

**Directions** Take the turning off the A14 for Soham/Ely. Join the A142 following signs for Ely/Soham. On approaching Soham at the Q8 Petrol Station, continue down the Soham by-pass for approx. 1.5 miles. Turn left after the Bypass Motel, continue bearing left across the Common into Bushel Lane, at end of road, turn right into Hall Street. Julius Martin Lane is 2nd left.

**Previous Grounds:**

**Record Attendance:** 3,000 v Pegasus - FA Amateur Cup 1963
**Record Victory:** Not known
**Record Defeat:** Not known
**Record Goalscorer:** Not known
**Record Appearances:** Not known
**Additional Records:**

**Senior Honours:**
Eastern Counties League Premier Division 2007-08

### 10 YEAR RECORD

| 03-04 | | 04-05 | | 05-06 | | 06-07 | | 07-08 | | 08-09 | | 09-10 | | 10-11 | | 11-12 | | 12-13 | |
|---|---|---|---|---|---|---|---|---|---|---|---|---|---|---|---|---|---|---|---|
| ECP | 5 | ECP | 7 | ECP | 10 | ECP | | ECP | 1 | SthC | 15 | SthC | 11 | SthC | 17 | Isth1N | 19 | Isth1N | 7 |

# THURROCK

**Chairman:** Tommy South
**Secretary:** Mark Southgate    **(T)** 07979 525 117    **(E)** mark.southgate@purcom.com
**Commercial Manager:** n/a    **(T)**
**Programme Editor:** Mark Kettlety    **(T)** 07940 322 612
**Ground Address:** South Way, Ship Lane, Grays, Essex RM19 1YN
**(T)** 01708 865 492    **Manager:** Mark Stimson

2012-13 Squad.

## Club Factfile

**Founded:** 1985    **Nickname:** Fleet
**Previous Names:** Purfleet > 2003
**Previous Leagues:** Essex Senior 1985-89, Isthmian 1989-2004

**Club Colours (change):** Yellow/green/green (All purple)

**Ground Capacity:** 4,500   **Seats:** 300   **Covered:** 1,000   **Clubhouse:** Yes   **Shop:** Yes

**Directions:** Approaching the ground from the North - along the M25 in a clockwise direction. Leave the motorway at junction 30. At the roundabout take the second exit and stay in the left hand lane. This leads to a large roundabout controlled by traffic lights. The fifth exit is Ship Lane and the ground is approximately 50 yards on the right hand side. Approaching the ground from the South - anticlockwise on the M25. When going through the Dartford Tunnel take the left hand bore. On coming out of the tunnel take the first exit - junction 31. This leads to a large roundabout controlled by traffic lights. Take the third exit which is Ship Lane. The ground is situated approximately 50 yards on the right hand side.

**Previous Grounds:** None

**Record Attendance:** 2,572 v West Ham United - Friendly 1998
**Record Victory:** 10-0 v Stansted (H) - Essex Senior Lge 1986-87 and v East Ham United (A) - Essex Senior Lge 1987-88
**Record Defeat:** 0-6 v St Leonards Stamco (A) - FA Trophy 1996-97 and v Sutton United (H) - Isthmian League 1997-98
**Record Goalscorer:** George Georgiou - 106
**Record Appearances:** Jimmy McFarlane - 632
**Additional Records:**

**Senior Honours:**
Isthmian League Division 2 1991-92.
Essex Senior Cup 2003-04, 05-06.

### 10 YEAR RECORD

| 03-04 | | 04-05 | | 05-06 | | 06-07 | | 07-08 | | 08-09 | | 09-10 | | 10-11 | | 11-12 | | 12-13 | |
|---|---|---|---|---|---|---|---|---|---|---|---|---|---|---|---|---|---|---|---|
| Isth P | 3 | Conf S | 3 | Conf S | 10 | Conf S | 18 | Conf S | 12 | Conf S | 20 | Conf S | 10 | Conf S | 20 | Conf S | 22 | Isth P | 21 |

# TILBURY

**Chairman:** Daniel Nash
**Secretary:** Anthony Mercer   **(T)** 07718 881 593   **(E)** amercer67@googlemail.com
**Commercial Manager:** n/a   **(T)**
**Programme Editor:** Mark Kettlety   **(T)** 07940 322 612
**Ground Address:** Chadfields, St Chads Road, Tilbury, Essex RM18 8NL
**(T)** 01375 843 093   **Manager:** Paul Vaughan

## Club Factfile

**Founded:** 1895   **Nickname:** The Dockers
**Previous Names:**
**Previous Leagues:** Grays & District/South Essex, Kent 1927-31, London, South Essex Combination (Wartime), Corinthian 1950-57, Delphian 1962-63, Athenian 1963-73, Isthmian 1973-2004, Essex Senior 2004-05

**Club Colours (change):** Black & white stripes/black/red (Red/red/white)

**Ground Capacity:** 4,000   **Seats:** 350   **Covered:** 1,000   **Clubhouse:** Yes   **Shop:** No

**Directions:** A13 Southend bound go left at Chadwell St Mary's turning, then right after 400 metres and right again at roundabout (signed Tilbury). Right into St Chads Road after five miles, first right into Chadfields for ground.

**Previous Grounds:** A couple before moving in to Chafields in 1946-47.

**Record Attendance:** 5,500 v Gorleston - FA Cup 1949
**Record Victory:** Not known
**Record Defeat:** Not known
**Record Goalscorer:** Ross Livermore - 282 in 305 games
**Record Appearances:** Nicky Smith - 424 (1975-85)
**Additional Records:** Received £2,000 from Grays Athletic for Tony Macklin 1990 and from Dartford for Steve Connor 1985

**Senior Honours:**
Athenian League 1968-69. Isthmian League Division 1 1975-76.
Essex Senior Cup x4.

### 10 YEAR RECORD

| 03-04 | | 04-05 | | 05-06 | | 06-07 | | 07-08 | | 08-09 | | 09-10 | | 10-11 | | 11-12 | | 12-13 | |
|---|---|---|---|---|---|---|---|---|---|---|---|---|---|---|---|---|---|---|---|
| Isth1N | 22 | SthE | 22 | ESen | 3 | Isth1N | 19 | Isth1N | 20 | Isth1N | 11 | Isth1N | 11 | Isth1N | 19 | Isth1N | 3 | Isth1N | 16 |

# VICKERS CRAYFORD DARTFORD ATHLETIC

**Chairman:** Gary Rump
**Secretary:** Chris Dudley    **(T)** 07803 700 261    **(E)** chris.dudley@ntlworld.com
**Commercial Manager:** n/a        **(T)**
**Programme Editor:** Brian Norris       **(T)** 07746 028 506
**Ground Address:** VCD Athletic Club, Oakwood, Old Road, Crayford DA1 4DN
**(T)** 01322 524 262               **Manager:** Tony Russell

## Club Factfile

**Founded:** 1916     **Nickname:** The Vickers
**Previous Names:** Vickers (Erith). Vickers (Crayford)
**Previous Leagues:** Dartford & District. Kent County. Isthmian

**Club Colours (change):** Green & white/white (Blue/black/black)

**Ground Capacity:**     **Seats:** Yes    **Covered:** Yes    **Clubhouse:** Yes   **Shop:** No

**Directions:** Follow A2 until you reach the exit for A220/A223 towards Bexleyheath and Crayford. At the roundabout, take the second exit on to Bourne Road/A223. After just over half a mile, turn right onto the A207 London Road. Keep left at the fork, then turn left onto Crayford High Street/A2000. Where the A2000 bends right, go straight on to pick up Old Road, and the ground is on your right.

**Previous Grounds:** Groundshared with Thamesmead (5 seasons), Lordswood (2) and Greenwich Boro' (1) whilst waiting for planning at Oakwood.

**Record Attendance:** 13,500 Away v Maidstone, 1919.
**Record Victory:**
**Record Defeat:**
**Record Goalscorer:**
**Record Appearances:**
**Additional Records:**

**Senior Honours:**
Kent County League 1996-97. Kent League 2008-09.
Kent Senior Trophy 2005-06, 08-09.

### 10 YEAR RECORD

| 03-04 | 04-05 | 05-06 | 06-07 | 07-08 | 08-09 | 09-10 | 10-11 | 11-12 | 12-13 |
|---|---|---|---|---|---|---|---|---|---|
| Kent P 3 | Kent P 5 | Kent P 6 | Kent P 2 | Kent P 2 | Kent P 1 | Isth1N 8 | Kent P 3 | Kent P 3 | Kent P 2 |

# WALTHAM ABBEY

**Chairman:** John Martin
**Secretary:** David Hodges　　**(T)** 07742 364 447　　**(E)** walthamabbeyfc@btconnect.com
**Commercial Manager:** n/a　　**(T)**
**Programme Editor:** n/a　　**(T)**
**Ground Address:** Capershotts, Sewardstone Road, Waltham Abbey, Essex EN9 1LU
**(T)** 01992 711 287　　　　　　　　　　**Manager:** Paul Wickenden

2012-13 Squad - Back Row (L-R): B.Jones,D.Elmes,L.Maxwell,C.Mann, J.Bransgrove, M.Attard, C.Wheeler, D.Aboiye.
Front Row: A.Coley, E.Osei, J.Peagram, C.Akers, T.Bruno, P.Wickenden (Manager) R.Wickenden (Assistant Manager), J.Daveney,
M.Bedford, T.Laxton, L.Bristow

## Club Factfile

**Founded:** 1944　　**Nickname:** Abbotts
**Previous Names:** Abbey Sports amalgamated with Beechfield Sports in 1974 to form Beechfields. Club then renamed to Waltham Abbey in 1976
**Previous Leagues:** Spartan, Essex & Herts Border, Essex Senior

**Club Colours (change):** Green and white hoops/white/green (All blue)

**Ground Capacity:** 2,000　**Seats:** 300　　**Covered:** 500　　**Clubhouse:** Yes　　**Shop:** No

**Directions**

Exit M25 at junction 26 and take 2nd left at roundabout into Honey Lane (A121).
At the Sewardstone roundabout, take third right into Sewarstone Road which takes you over the M25.
Ground is first right before cemetery.

**Previous Grounds:** None

**Record Attendance:** Not known
**Record Victory:** Not known
**Record Defeat:** Not known
**Record Goalscorer:** Not known
**Record Appearances:** Not known
**Additional Records:**

**Senior Honours:**
London Spartan League Division 1 1977-78, Senior Division 1978-79.
London Senior Cup 1999. Essex Senior Cup 2004-05.

### 10 YEAR RECORD

| 03-04 | | 04-05 | | 05-06 | | 06-07 | | 07-08 | | 08-09 | | 09-10 | | 10-11 | | 11-12 | | 12-13 | |
|---|---|---|---|---|---|---|---|---|---|---|---|---|---|---|---|---|---|---|---|
| ESen | 6 | ESen | 3 | ESen | 2 | Isth1N | 10 | Isth1N | 14 | Isth1N | 4 | Isth1N | 21 | Isth1N | 11 | Isth1N | 14 | Isth1N | 12 |

# WALTHAM FOREST

**Chairman:** Turgut Esendagli
**Secretary:** Tony Brazier    **(T)** 0771 564 0171    **(E)** bjmapbr@ntlworld.com
**Commercial Manager:** n/a    **(T)**
**Programme Editor:** Andrzej Perkins    **(T)** 07789 816 303
**Ground Address:** Wadham Lodge, Kitchener Road, Walthamstow E17 4JP
**(T)** 02085 272 444    **Manager:** Olawale Ojelabi

## Club Factfile

**Founded:** 1995    **Nickname:** The Stags
**Previous Names:** Leyton Pennant formed when Leyton and Walthamstow Pennant merged in 1995. Changed to Waltham Forest in 2003.
**Previous Leagues:** Isthmian 2003-04, Southern 2004-06

**Club Colours (change):** White/blue/blue (Orange/black/orange)

**Ground Capacity:** 3,500    **Seats:** 216    **Covered:** Yes    **Clubhouse:** Yes    **Shop:**

**Previous Grounds:** Wadham Lodge 1995-2008. Groundshared with Ilford FC 2008-13.

**Record Attendance:** Not known
**Record Victory:** Not known
**Record Defeat:** Not known
**Record Goalscorer:** Not known
**Record Appearances:** Not known
**Additional Records:**

**Senior Honours:**
None

### 10 YEAR RECORD

| 03-04 | | 04-05 | | 05-06 | | 06-07 | | 07-08 | | 08-09 | | 09-10 | | 10-11 | | 11-12 | | 12-13 | |
|---|---|---|---|---|---|---|---|---|---|---|---|---|---|---|---|---|---|---|---|
| Isth1N | 16 | SthE | 9 | SthE | 8 | Isth1N | 8 | Isth1N | 19 | Isth1N | 20 | Isth1N | 16 | Isth1N | 21 | Isth1N | 17 | Isth1N | 18 |

# WARE

**Chairman:** Mike Varney
**Secretary:** Sean Mynott    **(T)** 07812 097 924    **(E)** seanmynott@aol.com
**Commercial Manager:** n/a    **(T)**
**Programme Editor:** Mark Kettlety    **(T)** 07940 322 612
**Ground Address:** Wodson Park, Wadesmill Road, Ware, Herts SG12 0UQ
**(T)** 01920 462 064    **Manager:** Nicholas Ironton

## Club Factfile

**Founded:** 1892    **Nickname:** Blues
**Previous Names:** None
**Previous Leagues:** East Herts, North Middlesex 1907-08, Herts County 1908-25, Spartan 1925-55, Delphian 1955-63, Athenian 1963-75

**Club Colours (change):** Blue with white piping/blue/blue (Amber/black/amber)

**Ground Capacity:** 3,300    **Seats:** 500    **Covered:** 312    **Clubhouse:** Yes    **Shop:** Yes

**Directions:** A10 off junction A602 and B1001 turn right at roundabout after 300 yards and follow Ware sign, past Rank factory. Turn left at main road onto A1170 (Wadesmill Road) Stadium is on the right after 3/4 mile.

**Previous Grounds:** Highfields, Canons Park, London Road, Presdales Lower Park 1921-26

**Record Attendance:** 3,800 v Hendon - FA Amateur Cup 1956-57
**Record Victory:** 10-1 v Wood Green Town
**Record Defeat:** 0-11 v Barnet
**Record Goalscorer:** George Dearman scored 98 goals during 1926-27
**Record Appearances:** Gary Riddle - 654
**Additional Records:**

**Senior Honours:**
Isthmian League Division 2 2005-06.
East Anglian Cup 1973-74. Herts Senior Cup x5.

| 10 YEAR RECORD | | | | | | | | | |
|---|---|---|---|---|---|---|---|---|---|
| 03-04 | 04-05 | 05-06 | 06-07 | 07-08 | 08-09 | 09-10 | 10-11 | 11-12 | 12-13 |
| Isth2  8 | Isth2  10 | Isth2  1 | Isth1N  7 | Isth1N  4 | Isth1N  9 | Isth1N  19 | Isth1N  14 | Isth1N  21 | Isth1N  19 |

# WITHAM TOWN

**Chairman:** Tony Last
**Secretary:** Kevin Carroll   **(T)** 07743 827 505   **(E)** kpcarroll1@gmail.com
**Commercial Manager:** n/a   **(T)**
**Programme Editor:** Steve Parker   **(T)** 07984 177 888
**Ground Address:** Spicer McColl Stadium, Spa Road, Witham CM8 1UN
**(T)** 01376 511 198   **Manager:** Garry Kimble

2012-13 Squad.

## Club Factfile

**Founded:** 1947   **Nickname:** Town
**Previous Names:** None.
**Previous Leagues:** Mid. Essex. Essex & Suff. B. Essex Senior 1971-87. Isthmian 1987-2009

**Club Colours (change):** White/blue/green (All yellow).

**Ground Capacity:** 2,500   **Seats:** 157   **Covered:** 780   **Clubhouse:** Yes   **Shop:** No

**Directions:** From M25: At junction 28, take the A12/A1023 exit to Chelmsford/Romford/Brentwood.
At the roundabout, take the 1st exit onto the A12 ramp to Chelmsford/Harwich/A120.
Merge onto A12. At junction 21, exit onto Hatfield Rd/B1389 toward Witham.
Go through 2 roundabouts. Turn left onto Spinks Lane. Turn right onto Highfields Road.
Turn left ground will be on the right.

**Previous Grounds:** None

**Record Attendance:** Att: 800 v Billericay Town, Essex Senior Lge, May 1976.
**Record Victory:** Not known
**Record Defeat:** Not known
**Record Goalscorer:** Colin Mitchell.
**Record Appearances:** Keith Dent.
**Additional Records:**
**Senior Honours:**
Essex Senior League 1970-71, 85-86, 2011-12.

| | 10 YEAR RECORD | | | | | | | | |
|---|---|---|---|---|---|---|---|---|---|
| 03-04 | 04-05 | 05-06 | 06-07 | 07-08 | 08-09 | 09-10 | 10-11 | 11-12 | 12-13 |
| Isth2  6 | Isth2  5 | Isth2  2 | Isth1N  20 | Isth1N  20 | Isth1N  21 | ESen  2 | ESen  3 | ESen  1 | Isth1N  4 |

# WROXHAM

**Chairman:** Tom Jarrett
**Secretary:** Chris Green     **(T)** 07508 219 072     **(E)** secretary@wroxhamfc.com
**Commercial Manager:** n/a     **(T)**
**Programme Editor:** Mark Kettlety     **(T)** 07940 322 612
**Ground Address:** Trafford Park, Skinners Lane, Wroxham NR12 8SJ
**(T)** 01603 783 536     **Manager:** Pawel Guziejko

2012-13 Squad.

## Club Factfile

**Founded:** 1892     **Nickname:** Yachtsmen
**Previous Names:** None
**Previous Leagues:** East Norfolk. Norwich City. East Anglian. Norwich & Dist. Anglian Comb.

**Club Colours (change):** Blue/white/blue (White/blue/white)

**Ground Capacity:** 2,500     **Seats:** 50     **Covered:** 250     **Clubhouse:** Yes     **Shop:** No

**Directions**
From Norwich, turn left at former Castle Pub and keep left to ground.
Under two miles from Wroxham & Hoveton BR. Buses 722,724 and 717.

**Previous Grounds:** Norwich Road, The Avenue and Keys Hill. Moved in to Trafford Park around the time of WWII.

**Record Attendance: Att:** 1,011 v Wisbech Town, Eastern Co. Lge, 16.03.93.
**Record Victory:** Not known
**Record Defeat:** Not known
**Record Goalscorer:** Matthew Metcalf
**Record Appearances:** Stu Larter.
**Additional Records:**

**Senior Honours:**
Anglian County League 1981-82, 82-83, 83-84, 84-85, 86-87.
Eastern Counties League Division One 1988-89, Prem 91-92, 92-93, 93-94, 96-97, 97-98, 98-99, 2006-07, 11-12.
Norfolk Senior Cup 1992-93, 95-96, 97-98, 99-00, 03-04.

### 10 YEAR RECORD

| 03-04 | 04-05 | 05-06 | 06-07 | 07-08 | 08-09 | 09-10 | 10-11 | 11-12 | 12-13 |
|---|---|---|---|---|---|---|---|---|---|
| ECP 3 | ECP 5 | ECP 8 | ECP 1 | ECP 3 | ECP 5 | ECP 8 | ECP 3 | ECP 1 | Isth1N 14 |

# BURGESS HILL TOWN

**Chairman:** Kevin Newell

**Secretary:** Tim Spencer    **(T)** 0781 264 2498    **(E)** timspencer57@hotmail.com

**Commercial Manager:** n/a    **(T)**

**Programme Editor:** Colin Bowman    **(T)** 078164 96487

**Ground Address:** Leylands Park, Maple Drive, Burgess Hill, West Sussex RH15 8DL

**(T)** 01444 254 832      **Manager:** Richard Wilkins

## Club Factfile

**Founded:** 1882    **Nickname:** Hillians

**Previous Names:** None

**Previous Leagues:** Mid Sussex, Sussex County > 2003, Southern 2003-04

**Club Colours (change):** Green & black stripes/black/black (Yellow & black/black/black)

**Ground Capacity:** 2,250   **Seats:** 307   **Covered:** Yes    **Clubhouse:** Yes   **Shop:** Yes

**Directions**
Turn east from A273 London Road into Leylands Road,
take 4th left sign posted Leyland Park.
Nearest station is Wivelsfield.

**Previous Grounds:** None

**Record Attendance:** 2,005 v AFC Wimbledon - Isthmian League Division 1 2004-05

**Record Victory:** Not known

**Record Defeat:** Not known

**Record Goalscorer:** Ashley Carr - 208

**Record Appearances:** Paul Williams - 499

**Additional Records:**

**Senior Honours:**
Sussex County League x6 (Most recently 2001-02, 02-03).
Sussex Senior Cup 1883-84, 84-85, 85-86.

### 10 YEAR RECORD

| 03-04 | | 04-05 | | 05-06 | | 06-07 | | 07-08 | | 08-09 | | 09-10 | | 10-11 | | 11-12 | | 12-13 | |
|---|---|---|---|---|---|---|---|---|---|---|---|---|---|---|---|---|---|---|---|
| SthE | 9 | Isth1 | 10 | Isth1 | 19 | Isth1S | 14 | Isth1S | 12 | Isth1S | 19 | Isth1S | 7 | Isth1S | 7 | Isth1S | 20 | Isth1S | 8 |

# CHIPSTEAD

**Chairman:** Geoff Corner
**Secretary:** Heather Armstrong  **(T)** 07525 443 802  **(E)** heather.chipsteadfc@virginmedia.com
**Commercial Manager:** n/a  **(T)**
**Programme Editor:** Mark Budd  **(T)** mgbudd70@yahoo.co.uk
**Ground Address:** High Road, Chipstead, Surrey CR5 3SF
**(T)** 01737 553 250  **Manager:** John Hampshire

2012-13 Squad - Back Row (L-R): Tony Parsons, Malcolm Cooper, Ray Freeman, George Murphy, Luke coleman, Matt York, Rob Watkins, Martin Grant, Michael Eacott, Mike Haverin, Steve Newman, Owen Davies, Ocean Toya, Roy Jacobson.
Front Row: Paul gorman, Colin Hartburn, Karl Gibbs, Adam Fletcher, Colin Turner, Mark Tompkins, Jason Goodchild, Bruce Hogg, Russell Bedford, Fabian Batchelor, Danny Carroll.

## Club Factfile

**Founded:** 1906  **Nickname:** Chips
**Previous Names:** None
**Previous Leagues:** Surrey Intermediate 1962-82, Surrey Premier 1982-86, Combined Counties 1986-2007

**Club Colours (change):** Green and white hoops/green/black (All red)

**Ground Capacity:** 2,000  **Seats:** 150  **Covered:** 200  **Clubhouse:** Yes  **Shop:** Yes

**Directions**
From the Brighton Road north bound,
go left into Church Lane and left into Hogcross Lane.
High Road is on the right.

**Previous Grounds:** None

**Record Attendance:** 1,170
**Record Victory:** Not known
**Record Defeat:** Not known
**Record Goalscorer:** Mick Nolan - 124
**Record Appearances:** Not known
**Additional Records:**

**Senior Honours:**
Combined Counties Premier 1989-90, 2006-07.

| 10 YEAR RECORD | | | | | | | | | |
|---|---|---|---|---|---|---|---|---|---|
| 03-04 | 04-05 | 05-06 | 06-07 | 07-08 | 08-09 | 09-10 | 10-11 | 11-12 | 12-13 |
| CCP  8 | CCP  8 | CCP  14 | CCP  1 | Isth1S  15 | Isth1S  21 | Isth1S  19 | Isth1S  10 | Isth1S  12 | Isth1S  20 |

# CORINTHIAN CASUALS

**Chairman:** Brian Vandervilt

**Secretary:** Gary Weir **(T)** 07508 707 740 **(E)** secretary@corinthian-casuals.com

**Commercial Manager:** n/a **(T)**

**Programme Editor:** Rob Cavallini **(T)** 07712 861 099

**Ground Address:** King George's Field, Queen Mary Close, Hook Rise South, KT6 7NA

**(T)** 0208 397 3368 **Manager:** Kim Harris

2012-13 Squad - Back Row L-R: Sam Labinjo, David Ocquaye, Adam Cheadle, Dave Hodges, Jordan Cheadle, Aaron Gough, Danny Bracken, Adam Peck, Danny Dudley, Francois Gabbidon, Joe Hicks, Steve Goddard, Joel Thompson. Front Row L- R: Olakunle Akinwande, Matt Ellis, Midi Nsugba, Tom Jelley, Jason Turley, Ben Ewing, Jamie Byatt, Joe Davies, Rob Stevenson, Daniel Green.

## Club Factfile

**Founded:** 1939 **Nickname:** Casuals

**Previous Names:** Casuals and Corinthians merged in 1939

**Previous Leagues:** Isthmian 1939-84, Spartan 1984-96, Combined Counties 1996-97

**Club Colours (change):** Chocolate and pink halves/chocolate/chocolate (All blue)

**Ground Capacity:** 2,000 **Seats:** 161 **Covered:** 700 **Clubhouse:** Yes **Shop:** Yes

**Directions:** The ground is situated just off the A3 not far from the Tolworth roundabout. If you are travelling from the M25 you can join the A3 at junction 10 towards London. Stay on the A3 until you reach the 50mph speed limit, continue under the Hook roundabout and move into the lefthand lane for ca. 174 yds. Bear LEFT onto Hook Rise North for 0.2 mile (Tolworth Junction). At roundabout, take the FOURTH exit (as if you were going to rejoin the A3 going towards Portsmouth) then almost immediately take slip road on left onto Hook Rise South for 0.5 mile. If you are travelling from London on the A3 take the Tolworth Junction exit. At roundabout, take the SECOND exit (as if you were going to rejoin the A3 going towards Portsmouth) then almost immediately take slip road on left onto Hook Rise South for 0.5 mile. Turn LEFT into Queen Mary Close. Ground and car park under railway bridge on right hand side. Youth Section pitches and changing rooms are in the park on the left.

**Previous Grounds:** Kennington Oval, shared with Kingstonian and Dulwich Hamlet

**Record Attendance:** Not known

**Record Victory:** Not known

**Record Defeat:** Not known

**Record Goalscorer:** Cliff West - 219

**Record Appearances:** Simon Shergold - 526

**Additional Records:**

**Senior Honours:**
London Spartan League Senior Division 1985-86.
Surrey Senior Cup 2010-11.

### 10 YEAR RECORD

| 03-04 | 04-05 | 05-06 | 06-07 | 07-08 | 08-09 | 09-10 | 10-11 | 11-12 | 12-13 |
|---|---|---|---|---|---|---|---|---|---|
| Isth1S 23 | Isth1 13 | Isth1 23 | Isth1S 22 | Isth1S 20 | Isth1S 20 | Isth1S 13 | Isth1S 20 | Isth1S 13 | Isth1S 14 |

# CRAWLEY DOWN GATWICK

**Chairman:** Brian Suckling
**Secretary:** Richard Munn    **(T)** 07909 578 134    **(E)** richardmunn@hotmail.co.uk
**Commercial Manager:** Matthew York    **(T)** 07582 531 794
**Programme Editor:** Michael Martin    **(T)** 07973 620 759
**Ground Address:** The Haven Sportsfield, Hophurst Lane, Crawley Down RH10 4LJ
**(T)** 01342 717 140    **Manager:** Simon Wormull

## Club Factfile

**Founded:** 1993    **Nickname:** The Anvils
**Previous Names:** Crawley Down United > 1993. Crawley Down Village > 1999. Crawley Down > 2012.
**Previous Leagues:** Mid Sussex, Sussex County > 2011.

**Club Colours (change):** All Red (All white)

**Ground Capacity:** 1,000    **Seats:**    **Covered:** 50    **Clubhouse:** Yes    **Shop:**

**Directions**

**From the North:** Turn off the M23 at Junction 10 signposted East Grinstead At the roundabout at the Copthorne Hotel, take the 2nd exit, signed A264 East Grinstead. At the next roundabout (Duke's Head) take the 3rd exit, B2028 south, toward Turners Hill After approx. 1 mile turn left into Sandy Lane. (just after entering the 30mph zone and a telephone box in the layby on the right). At the end of Sandy Lane (war memorial on the right), turn left signed Felbridge. After a couple of bends the Haven Centre is on your left. **From the East:** Travel through East Grinstead on the A22 until the Junction with the A264 at the Felbridge Traffic lights. Turn left (Sign posted Crawley) and after 100 Meters take the Left Fork towards Crawley Down. Approx 1.5 Miles Haven Centre on Right. **From the South:** Travel North through Turners Hill on the B2028 after approx 2 Miles take the 2nd turning on your right (Vicarage Road). This is a Right fork and is sited just after passing over a small bridge. Follow Vicarage Road for approx 1/2 Mile past Junction with Sandy Lane and The Haven Centre is 200 Meters on your left.

**Previous Grounds:** None

**Record Attendance:** 404 v East Grinstead Town 96
**Record Victory:** Not known
**Record Defeat:** Not known
**Record Goalscorer:** Not known
**Record Appearances:** Not known
**Additional Records:**

**Senior Honours:**
Sussex County Division One 2010-11.

### 10 YEAR RECORD

| 03-04 | | 04-05 | | 05-06 | | 06-07 | | 07-08 | | 08-09 | | 09-10 | | 10-11 | | 11-12 | | 12-13 | |
|---|---|---|---|---|---|---|---|---|---|---|---|---|---|---|---|---|---|---|---|
| SxC2 | 11 | SxC2 | 10 | SxC2 | 5 | SxC2 | 16 | SxC2 | 6 | SxC2 | 3 | SxC1 | 8 | SxC1 | 1 | Isth1S | 16 | Isth1S | 13 |

# EASTBOURNE TOWN

**Chairman:** David Jenkins
**Secretary:** Mark Potter      **(T)** 0772 084 6857      **(E)** markpotter@eastbournera.fsnet.co.uk
**Commercial Manager:** n/a      **(T)**
**Programme Editor:** Mark Potter      **(T)** 0772 084 6857
**Ground Address:** The Saffrons, Compton Place Road, Eastbourne BN21 1EA
**(T)** 01323 724 328                                    **Manager:** Kevin Laundon

## Club Factfile

**Founded:** 1881      **Nickname:** Town
**Previous Names:** Devonshire Park 1881-89
**Previous Leagues:** Southern Amateur 1907-46, Corinthian 1960-63, Athenian 1963-76, Sussex County 1976-2007

**Club Colours (change):** Navy & yellow/navy/navy (Red/gold/red)

**Ground Capacity:** 3,000      **Seats:** 200      **Covered:** Yes      **Clubhouse:** Yes      **Shop:** No

**Directions**

Come into Eastbourne following the signs for Eastbourne Railway Station. When arriving at the railway station mini-roundabout turn right into Grove Road, (opposite from the station) and carry on past the Police Station and Town Hall (the large clock building.) Go straight over at the junction past the Caffyns car showroom (you can see the ground on your right), then take the first right turn into Compton Place Road and the entrance to The Saffrons car park is 100 yards on the right.

**Previous Grounds:** Devonshire Park 1881-1886

**Record Attendance:** 7,378 v Hastings United - 1953
**Record Victory:** Not known
**Record Defeat:** Not known
**Record Goalscorer:** Not known
**Record Appearances:** Not known
**Additional Records:**

**Senior Honours:**
Sussex County League 1976-77, Sussex Senior Cup x12.
Sussex RUR Charity Cup x3. AFA Senior Cup x2.

| 10 YEAR RECORD | | | | | | | | | |
|---|---|---|---|---|---|---|---|---|---|
| 03-04 | 04-05 | 05-06 | 06-07 | 07-08 | 08-09 | 09-10 | 10-11 | 11-12 | 12-13 |
| SxC1    5 | SxC1    10 | SxC1    5 | SxC1    1 | Isth1S    19 | Isth1S    13 | Isth1S    22 | Isth1S    18 | Isth1S    14 | Isth1S    11 |

# FAVERSHAM TOWN

**Chairman:** Ray Leader
**Secretary:** Mrs Wendy Walker    **(T)** 0778 963 8367    **(E)** wendy-walker@hotmail.co.uk
**Commercial Manager:** n/a                    **(T)**
**Programme Editor:** Mark Downs              **(T)** 07840 079 992
**Ground Address:** Salters Lane, Faversham Kent ME13 8ND
**(T)** 01795 591 900                          **Manager:** Ray Turner

## Club Factfile

**Founded:**   1884          **Nickname:** Lillywhites
**Previous Names:** Faversham Invicta, Faversham Services, Faversham Railway and Faversham Rangers pre War.
**Previous Leagues:** Metropolitan, Athenian, Kent

**Club Colours (change):** White/black/black (All yellow)

**Ground Capacity:** 2,000   **Seats:** 200   **Covered:** 1,800   **Clubhouse:** Yes   **Shop:**

**Directions:** From the M25 continue onto M26 9.9 miles. Continue onto M20 8.1 miles. Exit onto Slip Road (M20 J7) 0.2 miles. Bear left 0.1 miles. Continue onto Sittingbourne Road A249 0.9 miles. Bear right onto Detling Hill A249 4.6 miles. Bear left 0.1 miles. Continue onto Slip Road (M2 J5) 0.4 miles. Continue onto M2 10.5 miles. Exit onto Slip Road (M2 J6) 0.1 miles. Turn left onto Ashford Road A251 0.5 miles. Turn right onto Canterbury Road A2 0.2 miles. Turn right onto Westwood Place 0.1 miles.

**Previous Grounds:** Moved in to Salters Lane in 1948.

**Record Attendance:** Not Known
**Record Victory:** Not Known
**Record Defeat:** Not Known
**Record Goalscorer:** Not Known
**Record Appearances:** Not Known
**Additional Records:**

**Senior Honours:**
Kent League 1969-70, 70-71, 89-90, 2009-10.

### 10 YEAR RECORD

| 03-04 | 04-05 | 05-06 | 06-07 | 07-08 | 08-09 | 09-10 | 10-11 | 11-12 | 12-13 |
|-------|-------|-------|-------|-------|-------|-------|-------|-------|-------|
|       |       |       | Kent P 12 | Kent P 13 | Kent P 4 | Kent P 1 | Isth1S 8 | Isth1S 17 | Isth1S 3 |

# FOLKESTONE INVICTA

**Chairman:** Mark Jenner
**Secretary:** Richard Murrill    **(T)** 07810 864 228    **(E)** richardmurrill@gmail.com
**Commercial Manager:** n/a    **(T)**
**Programme Editor:** Richard Murrill    **(T)** 07810 864 228
**Ground Address:** The Fullicks Stadium, Cheriton Road CT19 5JU
**(T)** 01303 257 461    **Manager:** Neil Cugley

2012-13 Squad - Back Row (L-R): Mick Dix (Asst Manager), Neil Cugley (Manager), Willy Webb (Kit Manager), Brian Merryman (Director), Alex Bartlett (Physio), Dave Williams (Physio).
Middle Row: Josh Burchell, Frankie Chappell, Liam Dickson, Jack Delo, Roddy Hayward, Ryan Philpott, Darren Marsden, Stuart King.
Front Row: Lee Gledhill, James Everitt, Liam Friend (C), Roland Edge, Paul Jones, Josh Vincent.

## Club Factfile

**Founded:** 1936    **Nickname:** The Seasiders
**Previous Names:** None
**Previous Leagues:** Kent 1990-98, Southern 1998-2004

**Club Colours (change):** Black & amber stripes/black with amber trim/black (White & sky stripes/sky/sky)

**Ground Capacity:** 4,000    **Seats:** 900    **Covered:** Yes    **Clubhouse:** Yes    **Shop:** Yes

**Directions**
Leave the M20 motorway at junction 13, and head south onto the A20 (Cherry Garden Avenue). At the traffic lights, turn left onto the A2034 (Cheriton Road), pass the Harvey Grammar School and Stripes club - the ground is next left before Morrisons' supermarket; opposite the cemetery. Some car parking is available at Stripes.

**Previous Grounds:** South Road Hythe > 1991, County League matches on council pitches

**Record Attendance:** 7,881 v Margate - Kent Senior Cup 1958
**Record Victory:** 13-0 v Faversham Town - Kent League Division 1
**Record Defeat:** 1-7 v Crockenhill - Kent League Division 1
**Record Goalscorer:** Not Known
**Record Appearances:** Not Known
**Additional Records:**

**Senior Honours:**
None

### 10 YEAR RECORD

| 03-04 | 04-05 | 05-06 | 06-07 | 07-08 | 08-09 | 09-10 | 10-11 | 11-12 | 12-13 |
|---|---|---|---|---|---|---|---|---|---|
| SthE  5 | Isth P  13 | Isth P  13 | Isth P  18 | Isth1S  21 | Isth1S  11 | Isth1S  2 | Isth P  22 | Isth1S  4 | Isth1S  5 |

# GUERNSEY

**GUERNSEY FOOTBALL CLUB**

**Chairman:** Steve Dewsnip

**Secretary:** Mark Le Tissier    **(T)** 07781 119 169    **(E)** mark.letissier@guernseyfc.com

**Commercial Manager:** n/a    **(T)**

**Programme Editor:** Andy Richards    **(T)** 07447 907 595

**Ground Address:** Footes Lane Stadium, St Peter Port, Guernsey GY1 2UL

**(T)** 01481 747 279      **Manager:** Tony Vance

Taken before the FA Vase Second Round match against Erith Town.
Back row (L-R): Angus Mackay, Dom Heaume, Alex Le Prevost, Chris Tardif, Jamie Dodd, Simon Geall.
Front: Dave Rihoy, Sam Cochrane, Glyn Dyer, Ross Allen, Ryan-Zico Black.
Photo: Alan Coomes

## Club Factfile

**Founded:** 2011    **Nickname:** Green Lions

**Previous Names:** None

**Previous Leagues:** Combined Counties 2011-13.

**Club Colours (change):** Green & white/white/green (Sky blue/sky blue/white)

**Ground Capacity:** 5,000   **Seats:** Yes   **Covered:** Yes   **Clubhouse:** Yes   **Shop:**

**Directions:** The ground is located centrally in the island, is easily accessible with parking for several hundred cars in the immediate vicinity and on a regular bus route stopping immediately outside the stadium. It is approximately three miles north easterly from Guernsey Airport and one mile west from St Peter Port, the island's capital.

**Previous Grounds:** None

**Record Attendance:** 4,290 v. Spennymoor Town, FA Vase semi-final first leg, 23/03/2013

**Record Victory:** 9-0 v Sheerwater (H), Combined Counties Premier, 24/09/2011

**Record Defeat:** 2-4 v Colliers Wood United (A), Combined counties Premier, 24/04/2013

**Record Goalscorer:** Ross Allen - 110

**Record Appearances:** Dom Heaume - 93 (5 as substitute)

**Additional Records:**

**Senior Honours:**
Combined Counties League Division One 2011-12, Premier Challenge Cup 2011-12.

### 10 YEAR RECORD

| 03-04 | 04-05 | 05-06 | 06-07 | 07-08 | 08-09 | 09-10 | 10-11 | 11-12 | 12-13 |
|-------|-------|-------|-------|-------|-------|-------|-------|-------|-------|
|       |       |       |       |       |       |       |       | CC1   1 | CCP   2 |

# HASTINGS UNITED

**Chairman:** David Walters
**Secretary:** Tony Cosens   **(T)** 0771 265 4288   **(E)** richardcosens@btinternet.com
**Commercial Manager:** n/a   **(T)**
**Programme Editor:** Dan Willett   **(T)** 07590 568 432
**Ground Address:** The Pilot Field, Elphinstone Road, Hastings TN34 2AX
**(T)** 01424 444 635   **Manager:** Sean Ray

The team line up before their FA Cup Fourth Qualifying Round tie v Blackfield & Langley.
Photo: Roger Turner.

## Club Factfile

**Founded:** 1894   **Nickname:** The Us
**Previous Names:** Hastings and St Leonards Amateurs, Hastings Town > 2002
**Previous Leagues:** South Eastern 1904-05, Southern 1905-10, Sussex County 1921-27, 52-85, Southern Amateur 1927-46, Corinthian 1946-48

**Club Colours (change):** Claret/white/white (Light blue/claret/claret)

**Ground Capacity:** 4,050   **Seats:** 800   **Covered:** 1,750   **Clubhouse:** Yes   **Shop:** Yes

**Directions**
From A1 turn left at third roundabout into St Helens Road.
Then left after one mile into St Helens Park Road leading into Downs Road.
Turn left at T-junction at the end of the road. Ground is 200 yards on the right.

**Previous Grounds:** Bulverhythe Recreation > 1976

**Record Attendance:** 4,888 v Nottingham Forest - Friendly 23/06/1996
**Record Victory:** Not Known
**Record Defeat:** Not Known
**Record Goalscorer:** Terry White scored 33 during 1999-2000
**Record Appearances:** Not Known
**Additional Records:** Paid £8,000 to Ashford Town for Nicky Dent
**Senior Honours:** Received £30,000 from Nottingham Forest for Paul Smith
Southern League Division 1 1991-92, 2001-01, League Cup 1994-95.

### 10 YEAR RECORD

| 03-04 | | 04-05 | | 05-06 | | 06-07 | | 07-08 | | 08-09 | | 09-10 | | 10-11 | | 11-12 | | 12-13 | |
|---|---|---|---|---|---|---|---|---|---|---|---|---|---|---|---|---|---|---|---|
| SthE | 18 | Isth1 | 11 | Isth1 | 12 | Isth1S | 4 | Isth P | 14 | Isth P | 17 | Isth P | 7 | Isth P | 18 | Isth P | 18 | Isth P | 22 |

# HERNE BAY

**Chairman:** Trevor Kennett
**Secretary:** John Bathurst  **(T)** 07788 718 745  **(E)** johnbhbfc@aol.com
**Commercial Manager:** n/a  **(T)**
**Programme Editor:** Steve Barton  **(T)** 07507 614 868
**Ground Address:** Safety Net Stadium, Winch's Field, Stanley Gardens, Herne Bay CT6 5SG
**(T)** 01227 374 156  **Manager:** Sam Denly

## Club Factfile

**Founded:** 1886  **Nickname:** The Bay
**Previous Names:** None.
**Previous Leagues:** East Kent. Faversham & Dist. Cantebury & Dist. Kent Am. Athenian.

**Club Colours (change):** Blue & white strips/blue/blue (Yellow/black/black)

**Ground Capacity:** 3,000  **Seats:** 200  **Covered:** 1,500  **Clubhouse:** Yes  **Shop:** Yes

**Directions**
From M25 exit onto Sittingbourne Rd/A249 toward Sheerness.
Continue to follow A249. At the roundabout, take the 1st exit onto the M2 ramp to Canterbury/Dover/Ramsgate.
Merge onto M2. Continue onto Thanet Way/A299.
Continue to follow A299. Take the A291 exit toward Canterbury/Herne Bay.
At the roundabout, take the 2nd exit onto A291. At the roundabout, take the 1st exit onto Canterbury Rd/B2205.
Turn left onto Spenser Rd. Take the 1st left onto Stanley Gardens.
Take the 1st left to stay on Stanley Gardens.

**Previous Grounds:** Mitchell's Athletic Ground. Herne Bay Memorial Park.

**Record Attendance:** 2,303 v Margate, FA Cup 4th Qual. 1970-71.
**Record Victory:** 19-3 v Hythe Wanderers - Feb 1900.
**Record Defeat:** 0-11 v 7th Dragon Guards - Oct 1907.
**Record Goalscorer:**
**Record Appearances:**
**Additional Records:** Most League Victories in a Season: 34 - 1996-97.

**Senior Honours:**
Kent League 1991-92, 93-94, 96-97, 97-98, 2011-12, Premier Cup 1996-97, 2009-10, 2010-11.
Kent Senior Trophy 1978-79, 1996-97.

### 10 YEAR RECORD

| 03-04 | | 04-05 | | 05-06 | | 06-07 | | 07-08 | | 08-09 | | 09-10 | | 10-11 | | 11-12 | | 12-13 | |
|---|---|---|---|---|---|---|---|---|---|---|---|---|---|---|---|---|---|---|---|
| Kent P | 10 | Kent P | 2 | Kent P | 7 | Kent P | 9 | Kent P | 6 | Kent P | 6 | Kent P | 2 | Kent P | 2 | Kent P | 1 | Isth1S | 19 |

# HORSHAM

**Chairman:** Kevin Borrett
**Secretary:** Annie Raby          **(T)** 07800 922 442          **(E)** ivan.raby@btinternet.com
**Commercial Manager:** n/a          **(T)**
**Programme Editor:** Jeff Barrett          **(T)** 07712 888 980
**Ground Address:** Horsham YMCA, Gorings Mead, Horsham RH13 5BP
**(T)** 01403 266 888                    **Manager:** Simon Colbran

## Club Factfile

**Founded:**   1881          **Nickname:** Hornets
**Previous Names:**
**Previous Leagues:** West Susses Senior, Sussex County 1926-51, Metropolitan 1951-57, Corinthian 1957-63, Athenian 1963-73

**Club Colours (change):** Amber and green/green/amber (White/black/white)

**Ground Capacity:** 1,575   **Seats:** 150     **Covered:** 200     **Clubhouse:** Yes    **Shop:**

**Directions**
Travel north on the A23, turning off onto the A272 at Bolney. Continue on the A272 to Cowfold then follow the A281 to Horsham. On entering the outskirts of the town, follow the A281 (Brighton Road) a short distance and Gorings Mead is a turning on the left. The entrance to the ground is at the bottom of Gorings Mead.

**Previous Grounds:** Horsham Park, Hurst Park, Springfield Park

**Record Attendance:** 8,000 v Swindon - FA Cup 1st Round Novmber 1966
**Record Victory:** 16-1 v Southwick - Sussex County League 1945-46
**Record Defeat:** 1-11 v Worthing - Sussex Senior Cup 1913-14
**Record Goalscorer:**  Mick Browning
**Record Appearances:**  Mark Stepney
**Additional Records:**

**Senior Honours:**
Athenian League Division 1 1972-73. Sussex Senior Cup x7

| | | | | | 10 YEAR RECORD | | | | |
|---|---|---|---|---|---|---|---|---|---|
| 03-04 | 04-05 | 05-06 | 06-07 | 07-08 | 08-09 | 09-10 | 10-11 | 11-12 | 12-13 |
| Isth1S   15 | Isth1   3 | Isth1   2 | Isth1S   9 | Isth P   11 | Isth P   13 | Isth P   11 | Isth P   17 | Isth P   22 | Isth1S   15 |

# HYTHE TOWN

**Chairman:** John Dowsett

**Secretary:** Martin Giles    **(T)** 07908 763 101    **(E)** martinrgiles@sky.com

**Commercial Manager:** n/a    **(T)**

**Programme Editor:** Martin Whybrow    **(T)** 07787 124 794

**Ground Address:** Reachfields Stadium, Fort Road, Hythe CT21 6JS

**(T)** 01303 264 932 / 238 256      **Manager:** Scott Porter

The team before their FA Trophy First Qualifying Round tie v Hampton & Richmond.
Photo: Alan Coomes.

## Club Factfile

**Founded:** 1910    **Nickname:** Town

**Previous Names:** Hythe Town 1910-1992, Hythe United 1992-2001

**Previous Leagues:** Kent Amateur League, Kent League, Southern League, Kent County League, Kent League.

**Club Colours (change):** All red (All blue)

**Ground Capacity:** 3,000   **Seats:** 350    **Covered:** 2,400    **Clubhouse:** Yes    **Shop:** No

**Directions:** The Reachfields Stadium is easily accessible from the M20 motorway. Leave the M20 at junction 11, then at the roundabout take the 3rd exit onto the B2068, signposted Hastings, Hythe. At the next roundabout take the 2nd exit onto Ashford Road, A20. Continue forward onto Ashford Road, A20. Entering Newingreen, at the T-junction turn left onto Hythe Road, A261, signposted Hythe. Continue forward down London Road, A261. Entering Hythe, continue forward at the traffic lights onto Scanlons Bridge Road, A2008.
Turn right at the next set of lights onto Dymchurch Road, A259. Either take the 1st left down Fort Road and turn right at the end of Fort Road for the car-park, or after a few hundred yards turn left onto the Reachfields estate. Follow the road round and the stadium will be on your right.

**Previous Grounds:** South Road.

**Record Attendance:** 2,147 v Yeading, FA Vase Semi-Final, 1990.

**Record Victory:** 10-1 v Sporting Bengal, 2008-09

**Record Defeat:** 1-10 v Swanley Furness, 1997-98

**Record Goalscorer:** Dave Cook - 113

**Record Appearances:** Jason Brazier - 350

**Additional Records:**

**Senior Honours:**
Kent League 1988-89, 2010-11.
Kent Senior Cup 2011-12.
Kent Senior Trophy 1990-91.

### 10 YEAR RECORD

| 03-04 | 04-05 | 05-06 | 06-07 | 07-08 | 08-09 | 09-10 | 10-11 | 11-12 | 12-13 |
|---|---|---|---|---|---|---|---|---|---|
| Kent P   6 | Kent P   6 | Kent P   12 | Kent P   6 | Kent P   4 | Kent P   2 | Kent P   3 | Kent P   1 | Isth1S   8 | Isth1S   4 |

# LEATHERHEAD

**Chairman:** Peter Ashdown
**Secretary:** Jean Grant    **(T)** 07966 710 089    **(E)** jeanlisagrant@blackberry.orange.co.uk
**Commercial Manager:** n/a    **(T)**
**Programme Editor:** Neil Grant    **(T)** 07816 772 857
**Ground Address:** Fetcham Grove, Guildford Road, Leatherhead, Surrey KT22 9AS
**(T)** 01372 360 151      **Manager:** Richard Brady

Back Row (L-R): Elliott Thompson, Bentley Graham, Dan Palfrey, Tom Bradbrook, Chris Boulter, Matt Reed, Joe Goldsmith, Jerry Nnamani, Billy Manners, Charlie Holness, Greg Andrews, Tim Ward(kitman).
Front Row: Kev Terry, Louis Chin, Sam Blackman, Kevin Taylor(Physio), Richard Brady(Manager), Pat Gradley(Assistant), Tommy Hutchings, Jamie Coyle, Adam Gross.

## Club Factfile

**Founded:** 1946    **Nickname:** The Tanners
**Previous Names:** None
**Previous Leagues:** Surrey Senior 1946-50, Metropolitan 1950-51, Delphian 1951-58, Corinthian 1958-63, Athenian 1963-72

**Club Colours (change):** Green/white/green (All red)

**Ground Capacity:** 3,400   **Seats:** 200    **Covered:** 45    **Clubhouse:** Yes    **Shop:** Yes

**Directions:** M25 junction 9 to Leatherhead, follow signs to Leisure Centre, ground adjacent.
Half a mile from Leatherhead BR.

**Previous Grounds:** None

**Record Attendance:** 5,500 v Wimbledon - 1976
**Record Victory:** 13-1 v Leyland Motors - Surrey Senior League 1946-47
**Record Defeat:** 1-11 v Sutton United
**Record Goalscorer:** Steve Lunn scored 46 goals during 1996-97
**Record Appearances:** P Caswell - 200
**Additional Records:** Paid £1,500 to Croydon for B Salkeld
Received £1,500 from Croydon for B Salkeld
**Senior Honours:** Athenian League 1963-64.
Surrey Senior Cup 1968-69. Isthmian League cup 1977-78.

### 10 YEAR RECORD

| 03-04 | | 04-05 | | 05-06 | | 06-07 | | 07-08 | | 08-09 | | 09-10 | | 10-11 | | 11-12 | | 12-13 | |
|---|---|---|---|---|---|---|---|---|---|---|---|---|---|---|---|---|---|---|---|
| Isth1S | 13 | Isth1 | 7 | Isth1 | 10 | Isth1S | 11 | Isth1S | 17 | Isth1S | 15 | Isth1S | 5 | Isth1S | 4 | Isth P | 19 | Isth1S | 6 |

# MERSTHAM

**Chairman:** Chris Chapman
**Secretary:** Richard Baxter    **(T)** 0772 029 0027    **(E)** richardbaxter01@hotmail.com
**Commercial Manager:**    **(T)**
**Programme Editor:** Kevin Austen    **(T)** 07911 853 353
**Ground Address:** Moatside Stadium, Weldon Way, Merstham, Surrey RH1 3QB
**(T)** 01737 644 046      **Manager:** Hayden Bird

## Club Factfile

**Founded:** 1905     **Nickname:** Moatsiders
**Previous Names:** None
**Previous Leagues:** Redhill & District, Surrey Senior 1964-78, London Spartan 1978-84, Combined Counties 1984-2008

**Club Colours (change):** Amber & black/black/amber (All blue)

**Ground Capacity:** 2,500   **Seats:** 174   **Covered:** 100   **Clubhouse:** Yes   **Shop:** No

**Directions:**
Leave Merstham village (A23) by School Hill,
take 5th right (Weldon Way).
Clubhouse and car park on the right.
Ten minutes walk from Merstham BR.

**Previous Grounds:** None

**Record Attendance:** 1,587 v AFC Wimbledon - Combined Counties League 09/11/2002
**Record Victory:** Not Known
**Record Defeat:** Not Known
**Record Goalscorer:** Not Known
**Record Appearances:** Not Known
**Additional Records:**

**Senior Honours:**
Combined Counties League Premier Division 2007-08.

### 10 YEAR RECORD

| 03-04 | | 04-05 | | 05-06 | | 06-07 | | 07-08 | | 08-09 | | 09-10 | | 10-11 | | 11-12 | | 12-13 | |
|---|---|---|---|---|---|---|---|---|---|---|---|---|---|---|---|---|---|---|---|
| CCP | 12 | CCP | 16 | CCP | 2 | CCP | 2 | CCP | 1 | Isth1S | 8 | Isth1S | 16 | Isth1S | 19 | Isth1S | 9 | Isth1S | 12 |

# PEACEHAVEN & TELSCOMBE

**Chairman:** Lenard Edwards
**Secretary:** Derek Earley    **(T)** 07717 178 483    **(E)** derek@peacehavenfc.com
**Commercial Manager:** n/a    **(T)**
**Programme Editor:** Andrew Melbourne    **(T)** 07818 062 071
**Ground Address:** The Sports Park, Piddinghoe Ave, Peacehaven, BN10 8RH
**(T)** 01273 582 471    **Manager:** Shaun Saunders

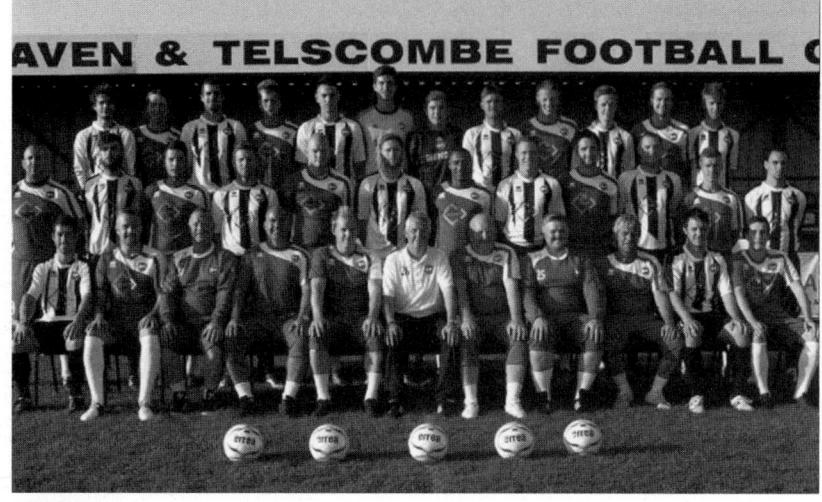

## Club Factfile

**Founded:** 1923    **Nickname:**
**Previous Names:** Formed when Peacehaven Rangers and Telscombe Tye merged.
**Previous Leagues:** Sussex County > 2013.

**Club Colours (change):** All black & white (All white)

**Ground Capacity:**    **Seats:** Yes    **Covered:** Yes    **Clubhouse:** Yes    **Shop:**

**Directions:** From Brighton on A259, over roundabout & Piddinghoe Ave. is next left after 2nd set of lights-ground at end. From Newhaven, Piddinghoe Ave. is 1st right after 1st set of lights. 3 miles from Newhaven(BR). Peacehaven is served by Brighton to Newhaven & Eastbourne buses.

**Previous Grounds:** The Tye.

**Record Attendance:**
**Record Victory:**
**Record Defeat:**
**Record Goalscorer:**
**Record Appearances:**
**Additional Records:**

**Senior Honours:**
Sussex County Division One 1978-79, 81-82, 82-83, 91-92, 92-93, 94-95, 95-96, 2012-13. Division Three 2005-06, Division Two 2008-09.

### 10 YEAR RECORD

| 03-04 | | 04-05 | | 05-06 | | 06-07 | | 07-08 | | 08-09 | | 09-10 | | 10-11 | | 11-12 | | 12-13 | |
|---|---|---|---|---|---|---|---|---|---|---|---|---|---|---|---|---|---|---|---|
| SxC2 | 12 | SxC2 | 17 | SxC3 | 1 | SxC2 | 5 | SxC2 | 4 | SxC2 | 1 | SxC1 | 2 | SxC1 | 3 | SxC1 | 5 | SxC1 | 1 |

# RAMSGATE

**Chairman:** Paul Jefcoate

**Secretary:** Martin Able    **(T)** 0795 899 3959    **(E)** secretary@ramsgate-fc.co.uk

**Commercial Manager:** n/a      **(T)**

**Programme Editor:** Steve Redford    **(T)** 07977 453 775

**Ground Address:** Southwood Stadium, Prices Avenue, Ramsgate, Kent CT11 0AN

**(T)** 01843 591 662      **Manager:** Tim Dixon

2012-13 Squad - Back Row (left to right): Darren Beale (Asst Manager), Foy Turner (Director), Warren Schulz, Joe Kennett, Ben Laslett, Danny Twyman, Ashley Bourne, Shannon Harris, Ollie Gray, Luke Wheatley, Dean Hill, Steve Nolan (Coach), Richard Lawson (Chairman).
Front Row (left to right): Liam Beale (Asst Physio), Steve O'Brien, Ashley Groombridge, Tom Chapman, Macauley Murray, Sam Gore, Michael Yianni, Charlie Walsh, Iona McCarvill (Physio), Ken Harding (Kit), Tim Dixon (Manager).

## Club Factfile

**Founded:** 1945      **Nickname:** Rams

**Previous Names:** Ramsgate Athletic > 1972

**Previous Leagues:** Kent 1949-59, 1976-2005, Southern 1959-76

**Club Colours (change):** All red (Yellow/black/black)

**Ground Capacity:** 5,000   **Seats:** 400    **Covered:** 600    **Clubhouse:** Yes    **Shop:** Yes

**Directions**

Approach Ramsgate via A299 (Canterbury/London) or A256 (Dover/Folkestone) to Lord of Manor roundabout.
Follow the signpost to Ramsgate along Canterbury Road East, counting via 2nd exit of the 1st roundabout.
At the 2nd roundabout, continue towards Ramsgate on London Road (2nd exit).
Take the 3rd turning on the left, into St Mildred's Avenue, then 1st left into Queen Bertha Road.
After the right hand bend, take left into Southwood Road, and 1st left into Prices Ave. The stadium is at the end of Prices Avenue.

**Previous Grounds:** None

**Record Attendance:** 5,200 v Margate - 1956-57
**Record Victory:** 11-0 & 12-1 v Canterbury City - Kent League 2000-01
**Record Defeat:** Not Known
**Record Goalscorer:** Mick Willimson
**Record Appearances:** Not Known
**Additional Records:**

**Senior Honours:**
Kent League Division 1 1949-50, 55-56, 56-57, Premier League 1998-99, 2004-05, Kent League Cup x6.
Isthmian League Division 1 2005-06, League Cup 2007-08.
Kent Senior Cup 1963-64, Kent Senior Trophy x3.

### 10 YEAR RECORD

| 03-04 | | 04-05 | | 05-06 | | 06-07 | | 07-08 | | 08-09 | | 09-10 | | 10-11 | | 11-12 | | 12-13 | |
|-------|---|-------|---|-------|---|-------|---|-------|---|-------|----|--------|----|--------|---|--------|----|--------|---|
| Kent P | 9 | Kent P | 1 | Isth1 | 1 | Isth P | 8 | Isth P | 5 | Isth P | 22 | Isth1S | 14 | Isth1S | 9 | Isth1S | 10 | Isth1S | 7 |

# REDHILL

**Chairman:** John Park
**Secretary:** Phil Whatling    **(T)** 07929 742 081    **(E)** phil.whatling@btinternet.com
**Commercial Manager:** n/a    **(T)**
**Programme Editor:** David Challinor    **(T)** 07512 685 026
**Ground Address:** Kiln Brow, Three Arch Road, Redhill, Surrey  RH1 5AE
**(T)** 01737 762 129    **Manager:** Mike Maher

## Club Factfile

**Founded:** 1894    **Nickname:** Reds/Lobsters
**Previous Names:** None
**Previous Leagues:** E & W Surrey. Spartan. Southern Sub. London. Athenian. Sussex County > 2013.

**Club Colours (change):** Red & white/red/red. (Yellow/blue/blue).

**Ground Capacity:** 2,000    **Seats:** 150    **Covered:** 150    **Clubhouse:** Yes    **Shop:** Yes

**Directions**

On left hand side of A23 two and a half miles south of Redhill.

**Previous Grounds:** Wiggie 1894-1896. Memorial Park 1896-1984.

**Record Attendance:** 8,000 v Hastings U FA Cup 1956
**Record Victory:**
**Record Defeat:**
**Record Goalscorer:** Steve Turner 119
**Record Appearances:** Brian Medlicott 766
**Additional Records:**

**Senior Honours:**
London League 1922-23. Athenian League 1924-25, 83-84.
Surrey Senior Cup 1928-29, 65-66.

| | 10 YEAR RECORD | | | | | | | | |
|---|---|---|---|---|---|---|---|---|---|
| 03-04 | 04-05 | 05-06 | 06-07 | 07-08 | 08-09 | 09-10 | 10-11 | 11-12 | 12-13 |
| SxC1  11 | SxC1  13 | SxC1  18 | SxC1  15 | SxC1  8 | SxC1  7 | SxC1  5 | SxC1  8 | SxC1  10 | SxC1  2 |

# SITTINGBOURNE

**Chairman:** Maurice Dunk
**Secretary:** John Pltts    **(T)** 07909 995 210    **(E)** johncp49@hotmail.com
**Commercial Manager:** n/a    **(T)**
**Programme Editor:** John Pitts    **(T)** 07909 995 210
**Ground Address:** WEM Stadium, Woodstock Park, Broadoak Road, Sittingbourne ME9 8AG
**(T)** 01795 410 777    **Manager:** Jim Ward and Danny Ward

## Club Factfile

**Founded:** 1886    **Nickname:** Brickies
**Previous Names:** Sittingbourne United 1881-86
**Previous Leagues:** Kent 1894-1905, 1909-27, 30-39, 45-59, 68-91, South Eastern 1905-09, Southern 1927-30, 59-67

**Club Colours (change):** Red with black stripes/black/black (All blue)

**Ground Capacity:** 3,000    **Seats:** 300    **Covered:** 600    **Clubhouse:** Yes    **Shop:** Yes

**Directions**
From the M2 exit at Junction 5, take A249 towards Sheerness, leave A249 at 1st junction, raised section to Key Street roundabout, take A2 to Sittingbourne.
One way system to town centre, first right into Park Road, Follow signs to Kent Science Park, Park Road becomes Gore Court Road, Gore Court Road becomes Woodstock Road, Woodstock Road becomes Ruins Barn Road.
When houses disappear approximately half a mile, take left as signposted Kent Science Park/Sittingbourne Research Centre into Broadoak Road, down hill passed Research Centre on right, carry on up hill, take left into car park Woodstock Park.
SatNav postcode: ME9 8AG

**Previous Grounds:** Sittingbourne Rec. 1881-90, Gore Court 1890-92, The Bull Ground 1892-1990. Central Park 1990-2001

**Record Attendance:** 5,951 v Tottenham Hotspur - Friendly 26/01/1993
**Record Victory:** 15-0 v Orpington, Kent League 1922-23)
**Record Defeat:** 0-10 v Wimbledon, SL Cup 1965-66)
**Record Goalscorer:** Not Known
**Record Appearances:** Not Known
**Additional Records:** Paid £20,000 to Ashford Town for Lee McRobert 1993
**Senior Honours:** Received £210,000 from Millwall for Neil Emblem and Michael Harle 1993
Southern League Southern Division 1992-93, 95-96. Kent League x7, League cup x4.
Kent Senior Cup 1901-02, 28-29, 29-30, 57-58.

## 10 YEAR RECORD

| 03-04 | | 04-05 | | 05-06 | | 06-07 | | 07-08 | | 08-09 | | 09-10 | | 10-11 | | 11-12 | | 12-13 | |
|---|---|---|---|---|---|---|---|---|---|---|---|---|---|---|---|---|---|---|---|
| SthE | 10 | SthE | 19 | SthE | 18 | Isth1S | 10 | Isth1S | 9 | Isth1S | 6 | Isth1S | 9 | Isth1S | 11 | Isth1S | 19 | Isth1S | 9 |

# THREE BRIDGES

**Chairman:** Paul Terry

**Secretary:** Lorraine Bonner      **(T)** 07701 011 513      **(E)** lorraine.bonner@lw.com

**Commercial Manager:** Russell Rego      **(T)**

**Programme Editor:** Alf Blackler      **(T)** 07758 745 372

**Ground Address:** Jubilee Field, Three Bridges Rd, Crawley, RH10 1LQ

**(T)** 01293 442 000      **Manager:** Paul Falli

## Club Factfile

**Founded:** 1901      **Nickname:** Bridges

**Previous Names:** Three Bridges Worth 1936-52, Three Bridges Utd 53-64

**Previous Leagues:** Mid Sussex, E Grinstead, Redhill & Dist 36-52

**Club Colours (change):** Amber & black stripes/black/black. (Blue & white stripes /blue/blue)

**Ground Capacity:** 3,500      **Seats:** 120      **Covered:** 600      **Clubhouse:** Yes      **Shop:**

**Directions**
Leave the M23 at Junction 10 heading towards Crawley on the A2011 (Crawley Avenue). At the roundabout take the first left heading towards Three Bridges Train Station (Hazelwick Avenue). Pass Tesco on your left and head straight over the roundabout (second exit). As you approach the traffic lights remain in the right hand side lane. After turning right in to Haslett Avenue at these lights move immediately in to the right turn lane at the next set of lights. Turn right at these lights in to Three Bridges Road. Follow the road round to the left then turn left after one hundred yards in to Jubilee Walk (directly opposite the Plough Pub). Follow the road to the end and turn right (still Jubilee Walk) and head straight on where Three Bridges Jubilee Field Stadium is at the far end.

**Previous Grounds:** None

**Record Attendance:** 2,000 v Horsham 1948

**Record Victory:** Not known

**Record Defeat:** Not known

**Record Goalscorer:** Not known

**Record Appearances:** John Malthouse

**Additional Records:**

**Senior Honours:**
Sussex RUR Cup 1982-83. Sussex County League Division One 2011-12.

| 10 YEAR RECORD | | | | | | | | | |
|---|---|---|---|---|---|---|---|---|---|
| 03-04 | 04-05 | 05-06 | 06-07 | 07-08 | 08-09 | 09-10 | 10-11 | 11-12 | 12-13 |
| SxC1 4 | SxC1 7 | SxC1 15 | SxC1 12 | SxC1 6 | SxC1 5 | SxC1 7 | SxC1 5 | SxC1 1 | Isth1S 21 |

# TOOTING & MITCHAM UNITED

**Chairman:** Steve Adkins

**Secretary:** Jackie Watkins **(T)** 07890 102 737 **(E)** jackie@tmunited.org

**Commercial Manager:** n/a **(T)**

**Programme Editor:** Michael Woods **(T)** tmufcprog@gmail.com

**Ground Address:** Imperial Fields, Bishopsford Road, Morden, Surrey SM4 6BF

**(T)** 020 8685 6193 **Manager:** Roberto Forzoni

## Club Factfile

**Founded:** 1932 **Nickname:** The Terrors

**Previous Names:** Tooting Town (Founded in 1887) and Mitcham Wanderers (1912) merged in 1932 to form Tooting & Mitcham FC.

**Previous Leagues:** London 1932-37, Athenian 1937-56

**Club Colours (change):** Black and white stripes/black/black (blue/white/blue)

**Ground Capacity:** 3,500 **Seats:** 600 **Covered:** 1,200 **Clubhouse:** Yes **Shop:** Yes

**Directions**

M25 junction 8, take the A217 northbound, this goes through Tadworth and Cheam. It's dual carriageway most of the way, although long stretches have a 40mph speed limit. This leads to a major roundabout with lights (Rose Hill). Take the third exit (Mitcham A217), this is Bishopsford Road and the ground is a mile further on. Go through two sets of lights, the road dips, and the entrance is on the right opposite a petrol station.

From the South: M25 junction 7, M23 then A23 northbound. Turn left onto the A237 after passing under a railway bridge at Coulsdon South station. Through Hackbridge and Beddington, then turn left onto the A239. Turn left again at lights by Mitcham Cricket Green into the A217, the ground is 800 yards on the left.

**Previous Grounds:** Sandy Lane, Mitcham

**Record Attendance:** 17,500 v Queens Park Rangers - FA Cup 2nd Round 1956-57 (At Sandy Lane)

**Record Victory:** 11-0 v Welton Rovers - FA Amateur Cup 1962-63

**Record Defeat:** 1-8 v Kingstonian - Surrey Senior Cup 1966-67

**Record Goalscorer:** Alan Ives - 92

**Record Appearances:** Danny Godwin - 470

**Additional Records:** Paid £9,000 to Enfield for David Flint
Received £10,000 from Luton Town for Herbie Smith

**Senior Honours:**
Athenian League 1949-50, 54-55. Isthmian League 1975-76, 59-60, Division 2 2000-01. Full Members Cup 1992-93. London Senior Cup 1942-43, 48-49, 58-59, 59-60, 2006-07, 07-08. Surrey Senior cup 1937-38, 43-44, 44-45, 52-53, 59-60, 75-76, 76-77, 77-78, 2007-07. Surrey Senior Shield 1951-52, 60-61, 61-62, 65-66. South Thames Cup 1969-70.

## 10 YEAR RECORD

| 03-04 | 04-05 | 05-06 | 06-07 | 07-08 | 08-09 | 09-10 | 10-11 | 11-12 | 12-13 |
|---|---|---|---|---|---|---|---|---|---|
| Isth1S 11 | Isth1 8 | Isth1 6 | Isth1S 2 | Isth1S 2 | Isth P 9 | Isth P 12 | Isth P 14 | Isth P 21 | Isth1S 16 |

# WALTON & HERSHAM

**Chairman:** Alan Smith
**Secretary:** Michael Groom    **(T)** 0771 023 0694    **(E)** mhgroom@aol.com
**Commercial Manager:** n/a      **(T)**
**Programme Editor:** Mark Massingham    **(T)** 07985 507 299
**Ground Address:** Sports Ground, Stompond Lane, Walton-on-Thames KT12 1HF
**(T)** 01932 245 263      **Manager:** Steve Baker

## Club Factfile

**Founded:** 1945      **Nickname:** Swans
**Previous Names:** Walton FC (Founded in 1895) amalgamated with Hersham FC in 1945.
**Previous Leagues:** Surrey Senior, Corinthian 1945-50, Athenian 1950-71

**Club Colours (change):** All red (Yellow/blue/yellow)

**Ground Capacity:** 5,000   **Seats:** 400    **Covered:** 2,500    **Clubhouse:** Yes    **Shop:** Yes

**Directions**
From Walton Bridge go over and along New Zealand Avenue,
down one way street and up A244 Hersham Road.
Ground is second on the right.

**Previous Grounds:** None

**Record Attendance:** 10,000 v Crook Town - FA Amateur Cup 6th Round 1951-52
**Record Victory:** 10-0 v Clevedon - FA Amateur Cup 1960
**Record Defeat:** 3-11 v Kingstonian - Surrey Shield 1958
**Record Goalscorer:** Reg Sentance - 220 (During 11 seasons)
**Record Appearances:** Terry Keen - 449 (During 11 seasons)
**Additional Records:** Paid £6,000. Received £150,000 from Bristol Rovers for Nathan Ellington 1999.

**Senior Honours:**
Athenian League 1968-69.
FA Amateur Cup 1972-73. Barassi Cup 1973-74.
Surrey Senior Cup x6. London Senior Cup.

### 10 YEAR RECORD

| 03-04 | | 04-05 | | 05-06 | | 06-07 | | 07-08 | | 08-09 | | 09-10 | | 10-11 | | 11-12 | | 12-13 | |
|---|---|---|---|---|---|---|---|---|---|---|---|---|---|---|---|---|---|---|---|
| Isth1S | 9 | Isth1 | 2 | Isth P | 9 | Isth P | 19 | Isth1S | 10 | Isth1S | 14 | Isth1S | 8 | Isth1S | 6 | Isth1S | 11 | Isth1S | 18 |

# WALTON CASUALS

**Chairman:** Tony Gale
**Secretary:** Gus Schofield    **(T)** 07949 981 598    **(E)** g.schofield1@ntlworld.com
**Commercial Manager:** n/a    **(T)**
**Programme Editor:** David Symonds    **(T)** 07720 557 530
**Ground Address:** The Waterside Stadium, Waterside Drive, Walton KT12 2JP
**(T)** 01932 787 749      **Manager:** Mike Sullivan

2012-13 Squad - Back L to R – Dick Errington (Physio), Mark Norman( Fitness Coach), AJ Morrison, Jon Boswell, Jahmahl King, Sean Bradley, Gareth Williams, Kieran Campbell, Brendan Sebuliba, Ashley Thompson, Robb Sheridan, Matt Druce, Steve Honey(Goalkeeping Coach), Kwaku Agyeman ( Fitness Coach).
Front L-R – Michael Corbett, James Hamsher, Marlon Wallen, Sol Patterson-Bohner, Craig Lewington, Martin Beard ( Head Coach), Mick Sullivan (Manager ), Peter Thomas (Assistant Manager), Hassan Nyang, Byron Brown, Sam Robinson, Matt Robinson.

## Club Factfile

**Founded:** 1948    **Nickname:** The Stags
**Previous Names:**
**Previous Leagues:** Surrey Intermediate, Surrey Senior, Suburban, Surrey Premier, Combined Counties

**Club Colours (change):** Tangerine/black/black

**Ground Capacity:** 2,000   **Seats:** 153    **Covered:** 403    **Clubhouse:** Yes    **Shop:** Yes

**Directions**
Left off Terrace Road at first major roundabout out of Walton centre.
Ground is next to The Xcel Leisure Centre.

**Previous Grounds:** Elm Grove Rec. 1948-69. Franklyn Road 1969-71. Stompond Lane 1971-72. Liberty Lane 1972-80.

**Record Attendance:** 1,748 v AFC Wimbledon - Combined Counties League 12/04/2004
**Record Victory:** Not Known
**Record Defeat:** Not Known
**Record Goalscorer:** Greg Ball - 77
**Record Appearances:** Craig Carley - 234
**Additional Records:**

**Senior Honours:**
Combined Counties League Premier Division 2004-05, League Cup 1999-2000.

| 10 YEAR RECORD | | | | | | | | | |
|---|---|---|---|---|---|---|---|---|---|
| 03-04 | 04-05 | 05-06 | 06-07 | 07-08 | 08-09 | 09-10 | 10-11 | 11-12 | 12-13 |
| CCP 7 | CCP 1 | Isth1 15 | Isth1S 17 | Isth1S 16 | Isth1S 17 | Isth1S 21 | Isth1S 12 | Isth1S 15 | Isth1S 22 |

# WHITSTABLE TOWN

**Chairman:** Gary Johnson

**Secretary:** Phil Gurr    **(T)** 07840 827 796    **(E)** secretary@whitstabletownfc.co.uk

**Commercial Manager:** n/a    **(T)**

**Programme Editor:** Andy Short    **(T)** 07920 068 449

**Ground Address:** The Belmont Ground, Belmont Road, Belmont, Whitstable CT5 1QP

**(T)** 01227 266 012      **Manager:** Nicky Southall

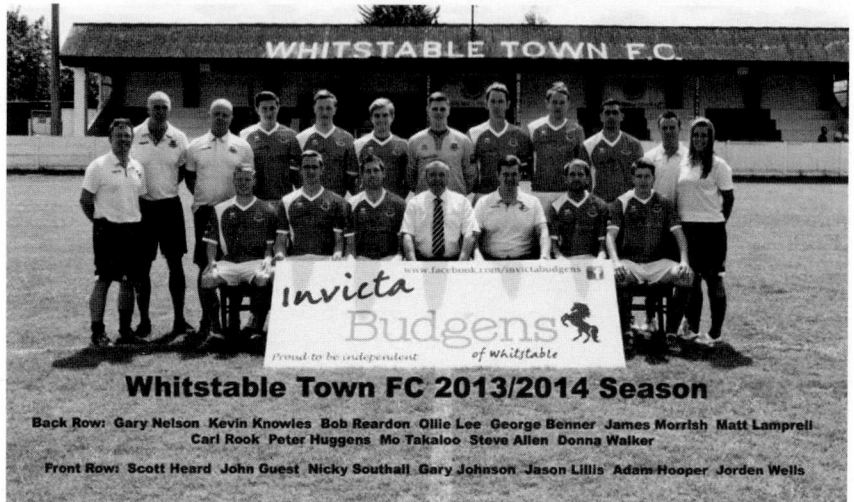

Whitstable Town FC 2013/2014 Season

Back Row: Gary Nelson · Kevin Knowles · Bob Reardon · Ollie Lee · George Benner · James Morrish · Matt Lamprell · Carl Rook · Peter Huggens · Mo Takaloo · Steve Allen · Donna Walker

Front Row: Scott Heard · John Guest · Nicky Southall · Gary Johnson · Jason Lillis · Adam Hooper · Jorden Wells

Picture courtesy of Les Biggs.

## Club Factfile

**Founded:** 1886    **Nickname:** Oystermen or Natives

**Previous Names:**

**Previous Leagues:** East Kent 1897-1909, Kent 1909-59, Aetolian 1959-60, Kent Amateur 1960-62, 63-64, South East Anglian 1962-63, Greater London 1964-67, Kent 1967-2007

**Club Colours (change):** Red & white/white/red (Yellow/blue/yellow)

**Ground Capacity:** 2,000   **Seats:** 500   **Covered:** 1,000   **Clubhouse:** Yes   **Shop:** Yes

**Directions**

From Thanet Way (A299) turn left at Tesco roundabout and Millstrood Road.
Ground at bottom of road,
400 yards from Whitstable BR station.

**Previous Grounds:**

**Record Attendance:** 2,500 v Gravesend & Northfleet - FA Cup 19/10/1987

**Record Victory:** Not known

**Record Defeat:** Not known

**Record Goalscorer:** Barry Godfrey

**Record Appearances:** Frank Cox - 429 (1950-60)

**Additional Records:**

**Senior Honours:**
Kent Amateur Cup 1928-29.
Kent League 2006-07, League Trophy 2006-07.

### 10 YEAR RECORD

| 03-04 | | 04-05 | | 05-06 | | 06-07 | | 07-08 | | 08-09 | | 09-10 | | 10-11 | | 11-12 | | 12-13 | |
|---|---|---|---|---|---|---|---|---|---|---|---|---|---|---|---|---|---|---|---|
| Kent P | 5 | Kent P | 3 | Kent P | 5 | Kent P | 10 | Isth1S | 14 | Isth1S | 16 | Isth1S | 18 | Isth1S | 15 | Isth1S | 18 | Isth1S | 17 |

# WORTHING

**Chairman:** Mrs Deborah McKail
**Secretary:** Gareth Nicholas  **(T)** 01903 236 449  **(E)** garethbnicholas@hotmail.co.uk
**Commercial Manager:** n/a  **(T)**
**Programme Editor:** Alistar McKail  **(T)** 07760 110 308
**Ground Address:** Woodside Road, Worthing, West Sussex BN14 7HQ
**(T)** 01903 239 575  **Manager:** Lee Brace

## Club Factfile

**Founded:** 1886  **Nickname:** Rebels
**Previous Names:** None
**Previous Leagues:** West Sussex 1896-1904, 1905-14, 19-20, Brighton Hove & District 1919-20, Sussex County 1920-40, Corinthian 1948-63, Athenian 1963-77

**Club Colours (change):** All red (All yellow)

**Ground Capacity:** 3,650  **Seats:** 500  **Covered:** 1,500  **Clubhouse:** Yes  **Shop:**

**Directions**
A24 or A27 to Grove Lodge roundabout.
A24 (Town Centre exit) and right into South Farm Road.
Over five roundabouts take last on right (Pavilion Road) before level crossing.
Woodside Road on right, ground on left. 1/2 mile from BR.

**Previous Grounds:** None

**Record Attendance:** 3,600 v Wimbledon - FA Cup 14/11/1936
**Record Victory:** 25-0 v Littlehampton (H) - Sussex League 1911-12
**Record Defeat:** 0-14 v Southwick (A) - Sussex County League 1946-47
**Record Goalscorer:** Mick Edmonds - 276
**Record Appearances:** Mark Knee - 414
**Additional Records:** Received £7,500 from Woking for Tim Read 1990

**Senior Honours:**
Sussex League 1920-21, 21-22, 26-27, 28-29, 30-31, 33-34, 38-39. Sussex League West 1945-46.
Isthmian League Division 2 1981-82, 92-93, Division 1 1982-83.
Sussex Senior Cup x21.

### 10 YEAR RECORD

| 03-04 | | 04-05 | | 05-06 | | 06-07 | | 07-08 | | 08-09 | | 09-10 | | 10-11 | | 11-12 | | 12-13 | |
|---|---|---|---|---|---|---|---|---|---|---|---|---|---|---|---|---|---|---|---|
| Isth1S | 2 | Isth P | 10 | Isth P | 8 | Isth P | 20 | Isth1S | 5 | Isth1S | 5 | Isth1S | 3 | Isth1S | 14 | Isth1S | 7 | Isth1S | 10 |

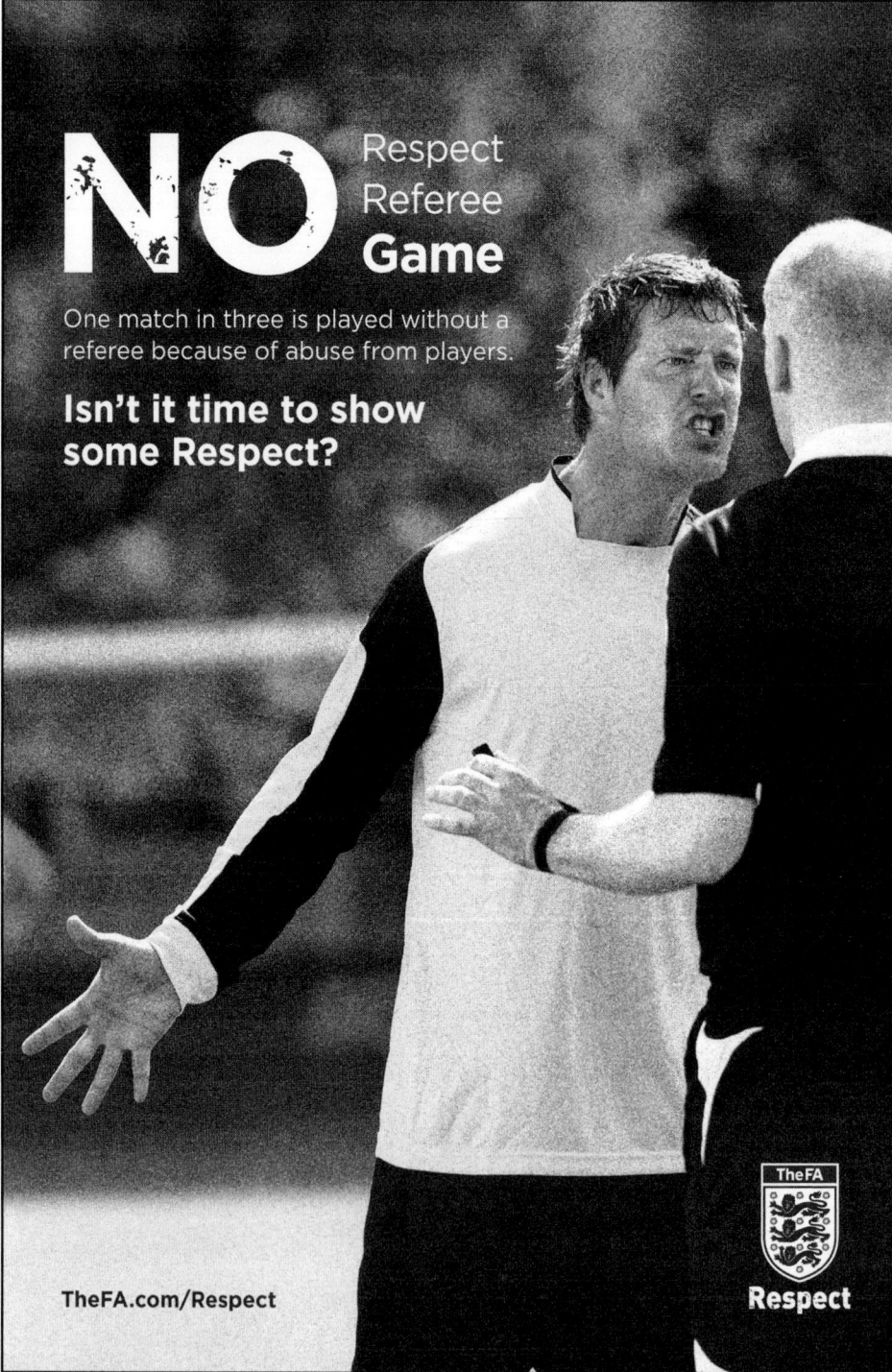

# COMBINED COUNTIES LEAGUE

**Sponsored by:** Cherry Red Records
**Founded:** 1978
**Recent Champions:**
2008: Merstham
2009: Bedfont Green
2010: North Greenford United
2011: Guildford City
2012: Guildford City
**combinedcountiesleague.co.uk**

| PREMIER DIVISION | P | W | D | L | F | A | Pts |
|---|---|---|---|---|---|---|---|
| 1 (P) Egham Town | 42 | 31 | 5 | 6 | 113 | 48 | 98 |
| 2 (P) Guernsey | 42 | 30 | 6 | 6 | 131 | 56 | 96 |
| 3 Cove | 42 | 23 | 9 | 10 | 90 | 62 | 78 |
| 4 South Park | 42 | 23 | 8 | 11 | 96 | 60 | 77 |
| 5 Epsom & Ewell | 42 | 23 | 6 | 13 | 85 | 72 | 75 |
| 6 Windsor | 42 | 22 | 5 | 15 | 103 | 88 | 71 |
| 7 Badshot Lea | 42 | 20 | 5 | 17 | 74 | 63 | 65 |
| 8 Farnham Town | 42 | 19 | 4 | 19 | 64 | 71 | 61 |
| 9 Hanworth Villa | 42 | 17 | 9 | 16 | 86 | 75 | 60 |
| 10 Molesey | 42 | 17 | 9 | 16 | 70 | 63 | 60 |
| 11 Raynes Park Vale | 42 | 18 | 4 | 20 | 75 | 83 | 58 |
| 12 Horley Town | 42 | 16 | 9 | 17 | 59 | 67 | 57 |
| 13 Bedfont Sports | 42 | 16 | 8 | 18 | 60 | 63 | 56 |
| 14 Croydon | 42 | 15 | 5 | 22 | 70 | 103 | 50 |
| 15 Wembley | 42 | 14 | 7 | 21 | 47 | 61 | 49 |
| 16 Camberley Town | 42 | 13 | 10 | 19 | 56 | 72 | 49 |
| 17 Chessington & Hook United | 42 | 13 | 10 | 19 | 63 | 92 | 49 |
| 18 Colliers Wood United | 42 | 15 | 1 | 26 | 84 | 95 | 46 |
| 19 Hartley Wintney | 42 | 13 | 4 | 25 | 71 | 107 | 43 |
| 20 Ash United | 42 | 11 | 9 | 22 | 70 | 90 | 42 |
| 21 (R) Sandhurst Town | 42 | 13 | 2 | 27 | 68 | 103 | 41 |
| 22 (R) Dorking | 42 | 10 | 5 | 27 | 59 | 100 | 35 |

## EL RECORDS PREMIER CHALLENGE CUP

**ROUND 1**

| | | | |
|---|---|---|---|
| Dorking | v | Banstead Athletic | 4-1 |
| Hanworth Villa | v | Hartley Wintney | 5-0 |
| Windsor | v | Colliers Wood United | 1-2 |
| Warlingham | v | Egham Town | 2-4 |
| Croydon | v | Epsom Athletic | 6-5 |
| Wembley | v | Frimley Green | 3-1 |
| South Kilburn | v | Ash United | 3-1 |
| Farnham Town | v | Epsom & Ewell | 2-3 |

**ROUND 2**

| | | | |
|---|---|---|---|
| CB Hounslow United | v | Sandhurst Town | 1-5 |
| Staines Lammas | v | Molesey | 0-3 |
| Camberley Town | v | Cobham | 3-5 |
| Dorking | v | Hanworth Villa | 1-3 |
| Horley Town | v | Farleigh Rovers | 3-0 |
| Colliers Wood United | v | South Park | 1-3 |
| Chessington & Hook Utd | v | Cove | 4-1 |
| Knaphill | v | Mole Valley SCR | 1-3 |
| Sheerwater | v | Egham Town | 0-4 |
| Croydon | v | Worcester Park | 2-1 |
| Wembley | v | South Kilburn | 2-1 |
| Raynes Park Vale | v | Westfield | 4-3 |
| Eversley & California | v | AFC Croydon Athletic | 2-3 |
| Spelthorne Sports | v | Badshot Lea | 1-2 |
| Bedfont Sports | v | Epsom & Ewell | 1-3 |
| Guernsey | v | Feltham | 3-1 |

**ROUND 3**

| | | | |
|---|---|---|---|
| Sandhurst Town | v | Molesey | 3-2 |
| Cobham | v | Hanworth Villa | 4-3 |
| Horley Town | v | South Park | 1-2 |
| Chessington & Hook Utd | v | Mole Valley SCR | 1-2 aet |
| Egham Town | v | Croydon | 7-1 |
| Wembley | v | Raynes Park Vale | 2-1 aet |
| AFC Croydon Athletic | v | Badshot Lea | 3-2 |
| Epsom & Ewell | v | Guernsey | 2-0 |

**QUARTER FINALS**

| | | | |
|---|---|---|---|
| Sandhurst Town | v | Cobham | 0-2 |
| South Park | v | Mole Valley SCR | 2-1 |
| Egham Town | v | Wembley | 4-0 |
| AFC Croydon Athletic | v | Epsom & Ewell | 2-6 |

**SEMI FINALS**

| | | | |
|---|---|---|---|
| Cobham | v | South Park | 2-3 |
| Egham Town | v | Epsom & Ewell | 0-1 |

**FINAL**

| | | | |
|---|---|---|---|
| South Park | v | Epsom & Ewell | 0-3 |

| PREMIER DIVISION | 1 | 2 | 3 | 4 | 5 | 6 | 7 | 8 | 9 | 10 | 11 | 12 | 13 | 14 | 15 | 16 | 17 | 18 | 19 | 20 | 21 | 22 |
|---|---|---|---|---|---|---|---|---|---|---|---|---|---|---|---|---|---|---|---|---|---|---|
| 1 Ash United | | 4-1 | 1-0 | 6-0 | 0-1 | 0-3 | 3-1 | 4-0 | 0-3 | 3-2 | 2-3 | 1-5 | 5-1 | 1-3 | 0-0 | 1-2 | 0-2 | 5-2 | 0-3 | 1-2 | 1-7 |
| 2 Badshot Lea | 3-1 | | 3-2 | 0-1 | 2-0 | 1-0 | 1-2 | 1-2 | 2-1 | 0-3 | 2-3 | 0-1 | 2-2 | 2-1 | 3-0 | 1-2 | 0-1 | 1-5 | 2-0 | 0-3 | 1-0 | 1-4 |
| 3 Bedfont Sports | 1-1 | 0-3 | | 3-2 | 3-1 | 4-1 | 2-1 | 3-2 | 0-0 | 0-2 | 1-2 | 2-1 | 1-2 | 2-2 | 2-1 | 0-3 | 1-2 | 1-0 | 3-2 | 2-1 | 1-0 | 0-3 |
| 4 Camberley Town | 2-0 | 2-3 | 0-0 | | 2-0 | 2-1 | 0-3 | 0-0 | 0-1 | 2-3 | 1-2 | 1-1 | 1-0 | 2-2 | 2-1 | 2-2 | 2-1 | 1-3 | 1-4 | 1-0 | 0-2 | 0-0 |
| 5 Chessington & Hook United | 0-2 | 1-1 | 1-1 | 1-1 | | 2-4 | 2-6 | 0-0 | 4-2 | 1-8 | 2-3 | 3-3 | 1-4 | 3-0 | 1-0 | 2-0 | 1-1 | 0-4 | 3-0 | 0-3 | 2-1 | 2-2 |
| 6 Colliers Wood United | 1-3 | 0-2 | 1-2 | 0-1 | 4-0 | | 1-2 | 5-2 | 2-4 | 0-0 | 3-4 | 1-5 | 4-2 | 4-2 | 3-4 | 2-0 | 2-1 | 3-4 | 3-1 | 1-2 | 1-2 | 2-3 |
| 7 Cove | 3-2 | 2-4 | 0-1 | 2-1 | 2-2 | 3-2 | | 5-2 | 3-0 | 1-1 | 1-1 | 3-2 | 0-3 | 2-1 | 4-1 | 2-0 | 1-1 | 1-0 | 1-1 | 0-2 | 3-2 |
| 8 Croydon | 3-2 | 1-1 | 2-0 | 3-2 | 1-0 | 5-1 | 0-1 | | 3-1 | 4-2 | 1-2 | 0-1 | 4-7 | 1-1 | 2-1 | 3-1 | 3-3 | 4-2 | 3-2 | 0-6 | 0-2 | 0-1 |
| 9 Dorking | 2-2 | 0-2 | 0-4 | 5-1 | 6-3 | 2-0 | 3-4 | 5-3 | | 0-0 | 0-1 | 3-2 | 0-6 | 0-6 | 0-2 | 2-3 | 3-2 | 0-0 | 0-1 | 2-4 | 0-0 | 1-2 |
| 10 Egham Town | 4-0 | 3-2 | 1-0 | 4-3 | 4-1 | 4-1 | 3-1 | 3-0 | 3-1 | | 3-0 | 4-0 | 3-1 | 2-1 | 1-6 | 3-0 | 7-1 | 2-0 | 2-1 | 0-2 | 1-0 | 3-1 |
| 11 Epsom & Ewell | 5-2 | 1-0 | 0-4 | 2-1 | 0-1 | 3-2 | 1-6 | 2-6 | 3-2 | 2-0 | | 3-1 | 2-5 | 2-1 | 2-4 | 4-1 | 1-0 | 6-1 | 4-0 | 1-1 | 2-0 | 1-3 |
| 12 Farnham Town | 2-1 | 0-1 | 1-0 | 1-3 | 2-1 | 1-4 | 3-2 | 3-0 | 0-2 | 2-1 | 1-1 | | 1-2 | 2-1 | 4-1 | 2-0 | 1-3 | 0-1 | 1-0 | 1-1 | 1-1 | 3-1 |
| 13 Guernsey | 1-1 | 1-1 | 5-2 | 2-2 | 0-2 | 5-3 | 1-2 | 8-0 | 1-0 | 5-2 | 2-0 | 1-0 | | 5-1 | 8-1 | 4-1 | 3-2 | 4-3 | 3-2 | 1-0 | 3-0 | 5-2 |
| 14 Hanworth Villa | 2-2 | 3-3 | 3-0 | 2-3 | 2-1 | 1-4 | 2-0 | 1-3 | 4-0 | 0-2 | 3-2 | 1-3 | 2-1 | | 2-2 | 3-1 | 1-2 | 0-0 | 1-0 | 2-2 | 2-0 | 6-1 |
| 15 Hartley Wintney | 3-2 | 0-6 | 4-2 | 2-1 | 0-1 | 2-0 | 0-0 | 2-1 | 2-3 | 1-3 | 0-4 | 2-3 | 3-4 | 2-7 | | 0-1 | 2-6 | 2-2 | 0-4 | 2-1 | 1-2 | 1-4 |
| 16 Horley Town | 2-1 | 3-2 | 2-0 | 1-2 | 4-2 | 3-0 | 1-0 | 3-0 | 4-3 | 1-1 | 1-1 | 1-0 | 1-2 | 3-1 | | 1-0 | 3-2 | 1-2 | 1-2 | 1-1 | 1-1 |
| 17 Molesey | 2-2 | 1-0 | 2-1 | 2-2 | 0-2 | 0-2 | 0-3 | 5-1 | 2-0 | 0-3 | 0-0 | 2-0 | 1-1 | 1-2 | 0-1 | 1-1 | | 3-2 | 3-0 | 2-1 | 0-2 | 0-1 |
| 18 Raynes Park Vale | 0-0 | 3-2 | 1-0 | 1-2 | 2-5 | 2-4 | 3-1 | 2-1 | 3-1 | 1-2 | 2-3 | 3-0 | 1-5 | 2-1 | 2-1 | 1-0 | 1-6 | | 0-1 | 0-4 | 0-1 | 2-3 |
| 19 Sandhurst Town | 2-5 | 3-2 | 0-6 | 3-0 | 1-3 | 1-4 | 2-2 | 2-3 | 3-1 | 0-3 | 2-1 | 5-1 | 0-2 | 1-2 | 1-0 | 1-1 | 1-6 | 3-4 | | 3-5 | 2-4 | 0-1 |
| 20 South Park | 2-1 | 0-1 | 1-1 | 4-0 | 4-4 | 3-2 | 2-2 | 1-0 | 1-0 | 4-4 | 1-3 | 4-1 | 0-2 | 1-1 | 2-6 | 4-1 | 3-1 | 4-2 | 2-5 | | 2-1 | 3-0 |
| 21 Wembley | 2-2 | 0-2 | 1-1 | 0-3 | 0-0 | 1-3 | 2-1 | 2-0 | 3-1 | 0-2 | 1-4 | 2-3 | 0-2 | 1-2 | 2-2 | 2-1 | 1-3 | 1-2 | 1-2 | | 1-0 |
| 22 Windsor | 7-0 | 2-6 | 2-1 | 4-2 | 1-2 | 4-2 | 3-3 | 6-0 | 5-2 | 2-8 | 0-0 | 2-1 | 1-6 | 3-6 | 5-2 | 1-2 | 2-1 | 6-2 | 1-5 | 2-0 | |

## COMBINED COUNTIES - STEP 5/6

### DIVISION ONE

| | | P | W | D | L | F | A | Pts |
|---|---|---|---|---|---|---|---|---|
| 1 | (P) Frimley Green | 34 | 26 | 2 | 6 | 98 | 39 | 80 |
| 2 | (P) Mole Valley SCR | 34 | 23 | 6 | 5 | 78 | 31 | 75 |
| 3 | (P) Westfield | 34 | 24 | 3 | 7 | 67 | 42 | 75 |
| 4 | Eversley & California | 34 | 21 | 5 | 8 | 103 | 49 | 68 |
| 5 | Spelthorne Sports | 34 | 20 | 6 | 8 | 83 | 54 | 66 |
| 6 | South Kilburn | 33 | 19 | 7 | 7 | 66 | 42 | 64 |
| 7 | Staines Lammas | 33 | 17 | 7 | 9 | 77 | 62 | 58 |
| 8 | AFC Croydon Athletic | 34 | 17 | 3 | 14 | 71 | 63 | 54 |
| 9 | Epsom Athletic | 34 | 15 | 4 | 15 | 69 | 69 | 49 |
| 10 | Worcester Park | 34 | 14 | 6 | 14 | 75 | 60 | 48 |
| 11 | Cobham | 34 | 13 | 3 | 18 | 59 | 69 | 42 |
| 12 | Warlingham | 32 | 10 | 4 | 18 | 67 | 94 | 34 |
| 13 | Knaphill | 34 | 11 | 1 | 22 | 48 | 79 | 34 |
| 14 | Feltham | 34 | 9 | 6 | 19 | 59 | 76 | 33 |
| 15 | Sheerwater | 34 | 9 | 5 | 20 | 43 | 76 | 32 |
| 16 | Farleigh Rovers | 34 | 8 | 4 | 22 | 47 | 93 | 28 |
| 17 | Banstead Athletic | 34 | 5 | 10 | 19 | 40 | 68 | 25 |
| 18 | CB Hounslow United | 34 | 2 | 0 | 32 | 34 | 118 | 6 |

### LEMON RECORDS DIV. ONE CHALLENGE CUP

**ROUND 1**

| | | | |
|---|---|---|---|
| Banstead Athletic | v | CB Hounslow United | 3-1 |
| AFC Croydon Athletic | v | Epsom Athletic | 3-0 |

**ROUND 2**

| | | | |
|---|---|---|---|
| Spelthorne Sports | v | Staines Lammas | 1-6 |
| Worcester Park | v | Frimley Green | 4-1 |
| Feltham | v | South Kilburn | 2-0 |
| Knaphill | v | Westfield | 2-1 |
| Mole Valley SCR | v | Cobham | 2-4 |
| Eversley & California | v | Sheerwater | 5-0 |
| Farleigh Rovers | v | Warlingham | 4-1 |
| Banstead Athletic | v | AFC Croydon Athletic | 1-3 |

**QUARTER FINALS**

| | | | |
|---|---|---|---|
| Staines Lammas | v | Worcester Park | 5-1 |
| Feltham | v | Knaphill | 4-3 |
| Cobham | v | Eversley & California | 1-2 |
| Farleigh Rovers | v | AFC Croydon Athletic | 0-7 |

**SEMI FINALS**

| | | | |
|---|---|---|---|
| Staines Lammas | v | Feltham | 2-0 |
| Eversley & California | v | AFC Croydon Athletic | 1-2 |

**FINAL**

| | | | |
|---|---|---|---|
| Staines Lammas | v | AFC Croydon Athletic | 0-5 |

### RESERVE DIVISION

| | | P | W | D | L | F | A | Pts |
|---|---|---|---|---|---|---|---|---|
| 1 | Raynes Park Vale | 22 | 19 | 1 | 2 | 79 | 24 | 58 |
| 2 | Farnham Town (-3pts) | 22 | 17 | 2 | 3 | 89 | 25 | 50 |
| 3 | Worcester Park | 22 | 13 | 1 | 8 | 52 | 43 | 40 |
| 4 | CB Hounslow United | 22 | 11 | 5 | 6 | 54 | 40 | 38 |
| 5 | Farleigh Rovers | 22 | 10 | 5 | 7 | 41 | 25 | 35 |
| 6 | Warlingham | 22 | 10 | 3 | 9 | 47 | 55 | 33 |
| 7 | Westfield (-3pts) | 22 | 10 | 2 | 10 | 51 | 44 | 29 |
| 8 | Ash United (-3pts) | 21 | 10 | 1 | 10 | 53 | 51 | 28 |
| 9 | Sandhurst Town | 22 | 7 | 1 | 14 | 33 | 66 | 22 |
| 10 | Frimley Green | 22 | 5 | 2 | 15 | 35 | 65 | 17 |
| 11 | Knaphill | 21 | 5 | 2 | 14 | 34 | 66 | 17 |
| 12 | Sheerwater | 22 | 0 | 3 | 19 | 16 | 80 | 3 |

### RESERVE CHALLENGE CUP

**ROUND 1**

| | | | |
|---|---|---|---|
| CB Hounslow United | v | Farnham Town | 0-4 |
| Warlingham | v | Knaphill | 0-2 |
| Westfield | v | Sandhurst Town | 2-2, 4-3p |
| Farleigh Rovers | v | Worcester Park | 1-5 |

**QUARTER FINALS**

| | | | |
|---|---|---|---|
| Ash United | v | Farnham Town | 1-5 |
| Raynes Park Vale | v | Knaphill | 1-0 |
| Sheerwater | v | Westfield | 0-2 |
| Frimley Green | v | Worcester Park | 1-2 aet |

**SEMI FINALS**

| | | | |
|---|---|---|---|
| Farnham Town | v | Raynes Park | 1-2 |
| Westfield | v | Worcester Park | 1-2 |

**FINAL**

| | | | |
|---|---|---|---|
| Raynes Park | v | Worcester Park | 2-0 |

### DIVISION ONE

| DIVISION ONE | 1 | 2 | 3 | 4 | 5 | 6 | 7 | 8 | 9 | 10 | 11 | 12 | 13 | 14 | 15 | 16 | 17 | 18 |
|---|---|---|---|---|---|---|---|---|---|---|---|---|---|---|---|---|---|---|
| 1 AFC Croydon Athletic | | 4-0 | 4-1 | 3-2 | 3-0 | 0-1 | 5-2 | 0-1 | 1-3 | 7-2 | 0-1 | 3-1 | 1-2 | 0-1 | 1-2 | 0-3 | 0-2 | 1-0 |
| 2 Banstead Athletic | 2-3 | | 6-1 | 1-2 | 0-3 | 1-1 | 1-1 | 0-4 | 1-1 | 0-1 | 1-1 | 2-2 | 0-2 | 3-3 | 2-2 | 5-3 | 0-1 | 2-1 |
| 3 CB Hounslow United | 3-6 | 0-2 | | 3-4 | 0-4 | 0-1 | 1-3 | 1-2 | 3-5 | 1-0 | 1-0 | 0-2 | 1-4 | 0-2 | 1-3 | 1-3 | 0-2 | 0-2 |
| 4 Cobham | 2-1 | 3-0 | 1-0 | | 3-4 | 0-4 | 4-0 | 2-1 | 1-2 | 0-1 | 1-1 | 2-1 | 2-4 | 3-3 | 1-2 | 6-1 | 1-3 | 0-7 |
| 5 Epsom Athletic | 2-1 | 2-0 | 5-0 | 3-1 | | 0-3 | 2-2 | 3-2 | 2-3 | 5-3 | 0-2 | 0-1 | 2-5 | 0-1 | 0-2 | 4-4 | 1-2 | 3-0 |
| 6 Eversley & California | 6-1 | 2-1 | 6-0 | 3-2 | 7-3 | | 6-1 | 2-2 | 0-3 | 3-0 | 0-6 | 1-2 | 3-0 | 6-3 | 4-3 | 7-1 | 2-0 | 0-1 |
| 7 Farleigh Rovers | 3-4 | 1-1 | 2-0 | 1-2 | 2-3 | 0-6 | | 3-1 | 2-1 | 2-1 | 4-5 | 4-2 | 0-1 | 0-1 | 0-2 | 1-4 | 0-3 | 1-1 |
| 8 Feltham | 1-3 | 3-0 | 5-0 | 2-1 | 1-2 | 0-3 | 5-1 | | 1-3 | 1-2 | 3-3 | 6-2 | 0-0 | 1-2 | 3-2 | 2-2 | 2-3 | 0-2 |
| 9 Frimley Green | 6-2 | 1-0 | 7-0 | 0-1 | 3-0 | 1-0 | 5-0 | 4-0 | | 3-0 | 3-2 | 2-1 | 2-1 | 1-3 | 1-2 | 4-0 | 2-1 | 1-3 |
| 10 Knaphill | 2-3 | 2-1 | 4-1 | 0-2 | 0-4 | 2-3 | 3-0 | 2-1 | 0-5 | | 1-2 | 4-0 | 2-4 | 1-3 | 0-1 | 3-1 | 0-2 | 4-2 |
| 11 Mole Valley SCR | 4-0 | 3-0 | 3-0 | 3-0 | 2-2 | 1-0 | 3-0 | 5-0 | 1-1 | 1-0 | | 3-0 | 0-1 | 3-1 | 4-3 | 1-2 | 0-1 | 1-2 |
| 12 Sheerwater | 1-2 | 0-0 | 3-1 | 1-1 | 1-0 | 2-1 | 3-2 | 1-2 | 2-3 | 2-1 | 1-3 | | 2-0 | 2-3 | 1-3 | 0-0 | 1-4 | 0-3 |
| 13 South Kilburn | 1-1 | 1-1 | 2-1 | 2-0 | 0-1 | 0-2 | 1-3 | 3-2 | 1-3 | 5-0 | 1-1 | 5-1 | | 3-2 | 0-2 | C-C | 1-0 | 2-2 |
| 14 Spelthorne Sports | 1-1 | 4-3 | 4-1 | 2-1 | 2-1 | 3-4 | 3-1 | 3-1 | 2-2 | 5-0 | 1-3 | 3-1 | 2-3 | | 2-2 | 6-1 | 1-1 | 4-0 |
| 15 Staines Lammas | 2-3 | 4-0 | 5-4 | 3-2 | 3-3 | 2-2 | 6-0 | 2-2 | 3-2 | 4-2 | 0-4 | 0-0 | 0-4 | 2-1 | | 2-3 | 3-5 | 2-1 |
| 16 Warlingham | 0-1 | 1-1 | 2-4 | 1-3 | 3-1 | 1-7 | 3-2 | 7-3 | 2-4 | 1-2 | 0-1 | 3-2 | 1-2 | 1-4 | A-A | | 1-2 | 3-7 |
| 17 Westfield | 0-3 | 2-1 | 4-1 | 2-1 | 4-3 | 1-0 | 3-0 | 3-2 | 0-4 | 2-0 | 2-2 | 2-0 | 1-1 | 2-1 | 0-2 | 4-3 | | 1-0 |
| 18 Worcester Park | 3-3 | 1-2 | 5-0 | 4-2 | 0-1 | 4-4 | 1-1 | 3-0 | 2-4 | 1-3 | 0-1 | 7-2 | 1-2 | 0-1 | 3-1 | 2-6 | 3-2 | |

## CLUB MOVEMENTS

**Premier Division - In:** Alton Town (S - Wessex Premier). Frimley Green (P). Mole Valley SCR (P). Westfield (P).
**Out:** Dorking (R). Egham Town (P - Southern Div.1 Central). Guernsey (P - Isthmian Div.1 South). Sandhurst Town (R).
**Division One - In:** Bedfont & Feltham (Name Change from Feltham FC). Dorking (R). Sandhurst Town (R).
**Out:** Frimley Green (P). Mole Valley SCR (P). Warlingham (W - Surrey Elite Intermediate League). Westfield (P).

## ALTON TOWN

Founded: 1947          Nickname: The Brewers

**Secretary:** Jim McKell          **(T)** 07740 099 374          **(E)** jim@altontownfc.com

**Chairman:** Jim McKell          **Manager:** Colin Fielder          **Prog Ed:** Jim McKell

**Ground:** Alton (Bass) Sports Ground, Anstey Road, Alton, Hants GU34 2RL          **(T)**

**Capacity:** 2,000  **Seats:** 200   **Covered:** 250   **Midweek Matchday:** Tuesday          **Clubhouse:** Yes   **Shop:** No

**Colours(change):** White/black/black
**Previous Names:** Present club formed in 1990 when Alton Town and Bass Alton merged.
**Previous Leagues:** Hampshire League > 2002. Wessex 2002-13.
**Records:**
**Senior Honours:** Hants Senior Cup 1958, 1969, 1972 & 1978. Hampshire Champions 2001-02.

**10 YEAR RECORD**

| 03-04 | | 04-05 | | 05-06 | | 06-07 | | 07-08 | | 08-09 | | 09-10 | | 10-11 | | 11-12 | | 12-13 | |
|---|---|---|---|---|---|---|---|---|---|---|---|---|---|---|---|---|---|---|---|
| Wex1 | 18 | Wex1 | 19 | Wex1 | 20 | WexP | 17 | WexP | 14 | WexP | 19 | WexP | 18 | WexP | 13 | WexP | 10 | WexP | 18 |

## ASH UNITED

Founded: 1911          Nickname: Green Army

**Secretary:** Paul Blair          **(T)** 07837 832 323          **(E)** sec@ashunited.co.uk

**Chairman:** Kevin Josey          **Manager:** Alan Reed          **Prog Ed:** Paul Burch

**Ground:** Shawfields Stadium, Youngs Drive off Shawfield Road, Ash, GU12 6RE.          **(T)** 01252 320 385 / 345 757

**Capacity:** 2500  **Seats:** 152   **Covered:** 160   **Midweek Matchday:** Tuesday          **Clubhouse:** Yes   **Shop:** No

**Colours(change):** All green.
**Previous Names:** None
**Previous Leagues:** Surrey Intermediate
**Records:** Att: 914 v AFC Wimbledon Combined Co 2002-03. **Goals:** Shaun Mitchell (216). **Apps:** Paul Bonner (582).
**Senior Honours:** Aldershot Senior Cup 1998-99, 01-02.

**10 YEAR RECORD**

| 03-04 | | 04-05 | | 05-06 | | 06-07 | | 07-08 | | 08-09 | | 09-10 | | 10-11 | | 11-12 | | 12-13 | |
|---|---|---|---|---|---|---|---|---|---|---|---|---|---|---|---|---|---|---|---|
| CCP | 9 | CCP | 13 | CCP | 3 | CCP | 4 | CCP | 15 | CCP | 9 | CCP | 11 | CCP | 18 | CCP | 13 | CCP | 20 |

## BADSHOT LEA

Founded: 1907          Nickname: Baggies

**Secretary:** Mrs Nicky Staszkiewicz          **(T)** 07921 466 858          **(E)** nstaszkiewicz@ashgatepublishing.com

**Chairman:** Mark Broad          **Manager:** Nick Snowden & Ryan Scott          **Prog Ed:** Peter Collison

**Ground:** Ash United, Shawfields Stadium, Youngs Drive off Shawfield Rd, Ash, GU12 6RE.          **(T)** 01252 320 385

**Capacity:** 2,500  **Seats:** 152   **Covered:** 160   **Midweek Matchday:** Tuesday          **Clubhouse:** Yes   **Shop:** No

**Colours(change):** Claret & blue/blue/claret
**Previous Names:**
**Previous Leagues:** Surrey Intermediate. Hellenic > 2008.
**Records:** Att: 276 v Bisley, 16.04.07.
**Senior Honours:**

**10 YEAR RECORD**

| 03-04 | | 04-05 | | 05-06 | | 06-07 | | 07-08 | | 08-09 | | 09-10 | | 10-11 | | 11-12 | | 12-13 | |
|---|---|---|---|---|---|---|---|---|---|---|---|---|---|---|---|---|---|---|---|
| Hel1E | 14 | Hel1E | 7 | Hel1E | 12 | Hel1E | 3 | Hel P | 11 | CCP | 7 | CCP | 10 | CCP | 6 | CCP | 17 | CCP | 7 |

## BEDFONT SPORTS

Founded: 2000          Nickname: The Eagles

**Secretary:** David Sturt          **(T)** 07712 824 112          **(E)** dave.sturt2@blueyonder.co.uk

**Chairman:** David Reader          **Manager:** Gavin Bamford          **Prog Ed:** Terry Reader

**Ground:** Bedfont Sports Club, Hatton Road, Bedfont TW14 8JA          **(T)** 0208 831 9067

**Capacity:** 3,000  **Seats:** Yes   **Covered:** 200   **Midweek Matchday:** Tuesday          **Clubhouse:**      **Shop:**

**Colours(change):** Red & black hoops/black/red & black hoops
**Previous Names:** Bedfont Sunday became Bedfont Sports in 2000 - Bedfont Eagles (1978) merged with the club shortly afterwards.
**Previous Leagues:** Middlesex County > 2009
**Records:**
**Senior Honours:** Middlesex County Premier Cup 2009-10.

**10 YEAR RECORD**

| 03-04 | 04-05 | 05-06 | 06-07 | 07-08 | 08-09 | 09-10 | | 10-11 | | 11-12 | | 12-13 | |
|---|---|---|---|---|---|---|---|---|---|---|---|---|---|
| | | | | | | CC1 | 9 | CC1 | 4 | CC1 | 2 | CCP | 13 |

## CAMBERLEY TOWN

Founded: 1895 — Nickname: Reds or Town

**Secretary:** Ben Clifford — **(T)** 07876 552 210 — **(E)** benjaminclifford@sky.com
**Chairman:** Christopher Goff — **Manager:** Daniel Turkington — **Prog Ed:** Andy Vaughan
**Ground:** Krooner Park, Wilton Road, Camberley, Surrey GU15 2QW — **(T)** 01276 65392
**Capacity:** 1,976 **Seats:** 196 **Covered:** 300 **Midweek Matchday:** Tuesday — **Clubhouse:** Yes **Shop:** Yes

**Colours(change):** Red and white stripes/red & blue/red
**Previous Names:** None
**Previous Leagues:** Surrey Senior Lge. Spartan Lge. Athenian Lge. Isthmian Lge.
**Records:** Att: 2066 v Aldershot Town, Isthmian Div.2 25/08/90. **Apps:** Brian Ives.
**Senior Honours:**

**10 YEAR RECORD**

| 03-04 | | 04-05 | | 05-06 | | 06-07 | | 07-08 | | 08-09 | | 09-10 | | 10-11 | | 11-12 | | 12-13 | |
|---|---|---|---|---|---|---|---|---|---|---|---|---|---|---|---|---|---|---|---|
| Isth2 | 10 | Isth2 | 12 | Isth2 | 14 | CCP | 7 | CCP | 3 | CCP | 5 | CCP | 3 | CCP | 4 | CCP | 6 | CCP | 16 |

## CHESSINGTON & HOOK UNITED

Founded: 1921 — Nickname: Chessey

**Secretary:** Chris Blackie — **(T)** 07748 877 704 — **(E)** kandcblackie@googlemail.com
**Chairman:** Graham Ellis — **Manager:** Paul Norris — **Prog Ed:** Eric Wicks
**Ground:** Chalky Lane, Chessington, Surrey KT9 2NF — **(T)** 01372 602 263
**Capacity:** 3000 **Seats:** 167 **Covered:** 600 **Midweek Matchday:** Tuesday — **Clubhouse:** Yes **Shop:** No

**Colours(change):** All blue
**Previous Names:** Chessington United.
**Previous Leagues:** Surrey Senior. Surrey County Premier.
**Records:**
**Senior Honours:**

**10 YEAR RECORD**

| 03-04 | | 04-05 | | 05-06 | | 06-07 | | 07-08 | | 08-09 | | 09-10 | | 10-11 | | 11-12 | | 12-13 | |
|---|---|---|---|---|---|---|---|---|---|---|---|---|---|---|---|---|---|---|---|
| CCP | 10 | CCP | 3 | CCP | 8 | CCP | 11 | CCP | 11 | CCP | 19 | CCP | 6 | CCP | 12 | CCP | 20 | CCP | 17 |

## COLLIERS WOOD UNITED

Founded: 1874 — Nickname: The Woods

**Secretary:** Tony Hurrell — **(T)** 07956 983 947 — **(E)** collierswoodutd@btconnect.com
**Chairman:** Tony Eldridge — **Manager:** Mark Douglas — **Prog Ed:** Chris Clapham
**Ground:** Wibandune Sports Gd, Lincoln Green, Wimbledon SW20 0AA — **(T)** 0208 942 8062
**Capacity:** 2000 **Seats:** 102 **Covered:** 100 **Midweek Matchday:** Wednesday — **Clubhouse:** Yes **Shop:** Yes

**Colours(change):** Blue & black stripes/black/black
**Previous Names:** Vandyke Colliers United
**Previous Leagues:** Surrey County Senior Lge.
**Records:** Att: 151 v Guildford City 06/08/2010. **Win:** 9-1 v Bedfont 05/03/2008.
**Senior Honours:**

**10 YEAR RECORD**

| 03-04 | | 04-05 | | 05-06 | | 06-07 | | 07-08 | | 08-09 | | 09-10 | | 10-11 | | 11-12 | | 12-13 | |
|---|---|---|---|---|---|---|---|---|---|---|---|---|---|---|---|---|---|---|---|
| CC1 | 2 | CCP | 14 | CCP | 4 | CCP | 13 | CCP | 7 | CCP | 14 | CCP | 19 | CCP | 11 | CCP | 19 | CCP | 18 |

## COVE

Founded: 1897 — Nickname:

**Secretary:** Graham Brown — **(T)** 07713 250 093 — **(E)** covefc1897@aol.com
**Chairman:** Matthew Hutton — **Manager:** Anthony Millerick — **Prog Ed:** Graham Brown
**Ground:** Oak Farm Fields, 7 Squirrels Lane, Farnborough GU14 8PB — **(T)** 01252 543 615
**Capacity:** 2500 **Seats:** 110 **Covered:** 100 **Midweek Matchday:** Tuesday — **Clubhouse:** Yes **Shop:** No

**Colours(change):** Yellow/black/yellow
**Previous Names:** None
**Previous Leagues:** Isthmian League. Hampshire.
**Records:** Att: 1798 v Aldershot Town, Isthmian Div.3 01/05/93.
**Senior Honours:** Aldershot Senior Cup x6 Most recently 2012-13.

**10 YEAR RECORD**

| 03-04 | | 04-05 | | 05-06 | | 06-07 | | 07-08 | | 08-09 | | 09-10 | | 10-11 | | 11-12 | | 12-13 | |
|---|---|---|---|---|---|---|---|---|---|---|---|---|---|---|---|---|---|---|---|
| CCP | 24 | CCP | 20 | CCP | 16 | CCP | 18 | CCP | 4 | CCP | 6 | CCP | 12 | CCP | 9 | CCP | 11 | CCP | 3 |

# CROYDON
Founded: 1953 Nickname: The Trams

**Secretary:** Antonio Di Natale **(T)** 07758 815 040 **(E)** croydonfc1953@gmail.com

**Chairman:** Dickson Gill **Manager:** Aaron Smith **Prog Ed:** Simon Hawkins

**Ground:** Croydon Sports Arena, Albert Road, South Norwood SE25 4QL **(T)** 0208 654 8555

**Capacity:** 8,000 **Seats:** 500 **Covered:** 1,000 **Midweek Matchday:** Wednesday **Clubhouse:** Yes **Shop:** Yes

**Colours(change):** All sky blue
**Previous Names:** Croydon Amateurs > 1974.
**Previous Leagues:** Surrey Senior. Spartan. Athenian. Isthmian > 2006. Kent 2006-09.
**Records:** **Att:** 1,450 v Wycombe Wders, FA Cup 4th Qual. 1975. **Goalscorer:** Alec Jackson - 111. **Apps:** Alec Jackson - 452 (1977-88).
**Senior Honours:**

**10 YEAR RECORD**

| 03-04 | 04-05 | 05-06 | 06-07 | 07-08 | 08-09 | 09-10 | 10-11 | 11-12 | 12-13 |
|---|---|---|---|---|---|---|---|---|---|
| Isth1S 21 | Isth1 22 | Isth2 10 | Kent P 3 | Kent P 12 | Kent P 9 | CCP 16 | CCP 20 | CCP 16 | CCP 14 |

# EPSOM & EWELL
Founded: 1918 Nickname: E's

**Secretary:** Peter Beddoe **(T)** 07767 078 132 **(E)** p.beddoe1@ntlworld.com

**Chairman:** Tony Jeffcoate **Manager:** Lyndon Buckwell **Prog Ed:** Steven Dyke

**Ground:** Chipstead FC, High Road, Chipstead, Surrey CR5 3SF **(T)** 01737 553 250

**Capacity:** 2,000 **Seats:** 150 **Covered:** 200 **Midweek Matchday:** Tuesday **Clubhouse:** Yes **Shop:** No

**Colours(change):** Royal blue & white hoops/royal blue/royal blue
**Previous Names:** Epsom T (previously Epsom FC) merged with Ewell & Stoneleigh in 1960
**Previous Leagues:** Corinthian Lge. Athenian Lge. Surrey Senior Lge. Isthmian Lge.
**Records:** **Att:** 5000 v Kingstonian, FAC 2Q 15/10/49. **Goals:** Tommy Tuite - 391. **Apps:** Graham Morris - 658.
**Senior Honours:**

**10 YEAR RECORD**

| 03-04 | 04-05 | 05-06 | 06-07 | 07-08 | 08-09 | 09-10 | 10-11 | 11-12 | 12-13 |
|---|---|---|---|---|---|---|---|---|---|
| Isth1S 24 | Isth2 14 | Isth2 15 | CCP 17 | CCP 10 | CCP 4 | CCP 5 | CCP 10 | CCP 14 | CCP 5 |

# FARNHAM TOWN
Founded: 1906 Nickname: The Town

**Secretary:** Ross Moore **(T)** 07810 698 272 **(E)** rossjm22@gmail.com

**Chairman:** Ray Bridger **Manager:** Paul Tanner **Prog Ed:** Ross Moore

**Ground:** Memorial Ground, West Street, Farnham GU9 7DY **(T)** 01252 715 305

**Capacity:** 1,500 **Seats:** 50 **Covered:** **Midweek Matchday:** Tuesday **Clubhouse:** **Shop:**

**Colours(change):** Claret & sky blue/white, claret & sky blue/sky blue
**Previous Names:**
**Previous Leagues:** Spartan 1973-75, London Spartan 1975-80, Combined Co. 1980-92, 93-2006, Isthmian 1992-93 (resigned pre-season).
**Records:**
**Senior Honours:** Combined Counties League 1990-91, 91-92, Division 1 2006-07.

**10 YEAR RECORD**

| 03-04 | 04-05 | 05-06 | 06-07 | 07-08 | 08-09 | 09-10 | 10-11 | 11-12 | 12-13 |
|---|---|---|---|---|---|---|---|---|---|
| CCP 22 | CCP 21 | CCP 21 | CC1 1 | CC1 5 | CC1 8 | CC1 11 | CC1 2 | CCP 12 | CCP 8 |

# FRIMLEY GREEN
Founded: 1919 Nickname: The Green

**Secretary:** Mark O'Grady **(T)** 07812 026 390 **(E)** mogradyuk@yahoo.co.uk

**Chairman:** Mark O'Grady **Manager:** Paul Miles **Prog Ed:** Mark O'Grady

**Ground:** Frimley Green Rec. Ground, Frimley Green, Camberley GU16 6JY **(T)** 01252 835 089

**Capacity:** 2000 **Seats:** No **Covered:** Yes **Midweek Matchday:** Tuesday **Clubhouse:** **Shop:**

**Colours(change):** All blue
**Previous Names:**
**Previous Leagues:** Surrey Senior. London Spartan. Combined Counties 1981-94. Surrey County Premier 1999-2002.
**Records:** **Record Att:** 1,152 v AFC Wimbledon 2002-03. **Win:** 6-1 v Farnham Town 21/12/02. **Defeat:** 1-7 v Walton Casuals 2002/03.
**Senior Honours:** Combined Counties League Division One 2012-13.

**10 YEAR RECORD**

| 03-04 | 04-05 | 05-06 | 06-07 | 07-08 | 08-09 | 09-10 | 10-11 | 11-12 | 12-13 |
|---|---|---|---|---|---|---|---|---|---|
| CCP 20 | CCP 15 | CCP 18 | CC1 13 | CC1 6 | CC1 16 | CC1 13 | CC1 15 | CC1 10 | CC1 1 |

COMBINED COUNTIES - STEP 5/6

## HANWORTH VILLA
Founded: 1976     Nickname: The Vilans

**Secretary:** Dave Brown    **(T)** 07971 650 297    **(E)** david.h.brown@btconnect.com
**Chairman:** Gary Brunning    **Manager:** Lee Stevenson    **Prog Ed:** Gary Brunning
**Ground:** Rectory Meadows, Park Road, Hanworth TW13 6PN    **(T)** 020 8831 9391
**Capacity:** 600   **Seats:** 100   **Covered:** Yes   **Midweek Matchday:** Tuesday    **Clubhouse:** Yes   **Shop:**

**Colours(change):** Red & white/black/black
**Previous Names:**
**Previous Leagues:** Hounslow & District Lge. West Middlesex Lge. Middlesex County League.
**Records:**
**Senior Honours:** West Middlesex Div. 1 & Div. 2 Champions. Middlesex County Champions 2002-03, 04-05.

**10 YEAR RECORD**

| 03-04 | 04-05 | 05-06 | 06-07 | 07-08 | 08-09 | 09-10 | 10-11 | 11-12 | 12-13 |
|---|---|---|---|---|---|---|---|---|---|
| MidCo 4 | MidCo 1 | CC1 7 | CC1 6 | CC1 2 | CC1 2 | CCP 17 | CCP 5 | CCP 3 | CCP 9 |

## HARTLEY WINTNEY
Founded: 1897     Nickname: The Row

**Secretary:** Gerry Wykes    **(T)** 07720 474 214    **(E)** gerald.wykes@sky.com
**Chairman:** Luke Mullen    **Manager:** Ben Dillon    **Prog Ed:** Luke Mullen
**Ground:** Memorial Playing Fields,Green Lane, Hartley Wintney RG27 8DL    **(T)** 01252 843 586
**Capacity:** 2,000   **Seats:** 113   **Covered:** Yes   **Midweek Matchday:** Tuesday    **Clubhouse:** Yes   **Shop:** Yes

**Colours(change):** Orange & black/orange/orange
**Previous Names:** None
**Previous Leagues:** Founder members of the Home Counties League (renamed Combined Counties League)
**Records:** 1,392 v AFC Wimbledon , 25/01/02.
**Senior Honours:** Combined Counties League 1982-83.

**10 YEAR RECORD**

| 03-04 | 04-05 | 05-06 | 06-07 | 07-08 | 08-09 | 09-10 | 10-11 | 11-12 | 12-13 |
|---|---|---|---|---|---|---|---|---|---|
| CCP 15 | CCP 23 | CC1 5 | CC1 16 | CC1 3 | CCP 21 | CC1 5 | CC1 7 | CC1 3 | CCP 19 |

## HORLEY TOWN
Founded: 1896     Nickname: The Clarets

**Secretary:** Mrs Nicky Maybury    **(T)** 07753 216 403    **(E)** maybury@hotmail.com
**Chairman:** Mark Sale    **Manager:** Trevor Smith    **Prog Ed:** Mark Sale
**Ground:** The New Defence, Court Lodge Road, Horley RH6 8SP    **(T)** 01293 822 000
**Capacity:** 1800   **Seats:** 101   **Covered:** Yes   **Midweek Matchday:** Tuesday    **Clubhouse:** Yes   **Shop:** Yes

**Colours(change):** Sky blue/claret/claret
**Previous Names:** Horley >1975
**Previous Leagues:** Surrey Senior, London Spartan, Athenian, Surrey County Senior, Crawley & District
**Records:** Att: 1,500 v AFC Wimbledon, 2003-04. **Goalscorer:** Alan Gates. **Win:** 12-1 v Egham. **Defeat:** 2-8 v Redhill 1956/57.
**Senior Honours:**

**10 YEAR RECORD**

| 03-04 | 04-05 | 05-06 | 06-07 | 07-08 | 08-09 | 09-10 | 10-11 | 11-12 | 12-13 |
|---|---|---|---|---|---|---|---|---|---|
| CCP 17 | CCP 7 | CCP 5 | CC1 2 | CCP 5 | CCP 12 | CCP 14 | CCP 16 | CCP 7 | CCP 12 |

## MOLE VALLEY SCR
Founded: 1978     Nickname: Commoners

**Secretary:** Darren Salmon    **(T)** 07596 537 933    **(E)** scrfc@outlook.com
**Chairman:** Alan Salmon    **Manager:** Darren Salmon    **Prog Ed:** Gary Brigden
**Ground:** Cobham FC, Leg of Mutton Field, Anvil Lane, Downside Bridge Road KT11 1AA    **(T)** 01932 866 386
**Capacity:** 500   **Seats:** No   **Covered:** Yes   **Midweek Matchday:** Wednesday    **Clubhouse:** Yes   **Shop:** Yes

**Colours(change):** All blue
**Previous Names:** Inrad FC. Centre 21 FC . SCR Plough, SCR Grapes, SRC Litten Tree, SCR Kingfisher
**Previous Leagues:** South Eastern Combination.
**Records:**
**Senior Honours:** **Previous Names:** Inrad FC. Centre 21 FC . SCR Plough, SCR Grapes, SRC Litten Tree, SCR Kingfisher.
    **Previous Leagues:** South Eastern Combination.

**10 YEAR RECORD**

| 03-04 | 04-05 | 05-06 | 06-07 | 07-08 | 08-09 | 09-10 | 10-11 | 11-12 | 12-13 |
|---|---|---|---|---|---|---|---|---|---|
| | | | | | CC1 4 | CC1 1 | CCP 8 | CCP 21 | CC1 2 |

# MOLESEY
Founded: 1953     Nickname: The Moles

**Secretary:** Tracy Teague    **(T)** 07939 387 277    **(E)** teaguetracy90@yahoo.co.uk
**Chairman:** Tracy Teague    **Manager:** Steve Webb    **Prog Ed:** Peter Lelliott
**Ground:** 412 Walton Road, West Molesey KT8 2JG.    **(T)** 020 8979 4283 (Clubhouse)
**Capacity:** 4,000 **Seats:** 160 **Covered:** Yes **Midweek Matchday:** Tuesday    **Clubhouse:** Yes **Shop:** Yes

**Colours(change):** White/black/black.
**Previous Names:** None.
**Previous Leagues:** Surrey Senior. Spartan. Athethian. Isthmian.
**Records:**
**Senior Honours:** **Record Att:** 1,255 v Sutton United, Surrey Senior Cup sem-final 1966. **Goalscorer:** Michael Rose (139). **Apps:** Frank Hanley (453).

**10 YEAR RECORD**

| 03-04 | | 04-05 | | 05-06 | | 06-07 | | 07-08 | | 08-09 | | 09-10 | | 10-11 | | 11-12 | | 12-13 | |
|---|---|---|---|---|---|---|---|---|---|---|---|---|---|---|---|---|---|---|---|
| Isth1S | 19 | Isth1 | 16 | Isth1 | 17 | Isth1S | 15 | Isth1S | 22 | CCP | 11 | CCP | 8 | CCP | 3 | CCP | 5 | CCP | 10 |

# RAYNES PARK VALE
Founded: 1995     Nickname: The Vale

**Secretary:** Paul Armour    **(T)** 07980 914 211    **(E)** paul.armour2@btinternet.com
**Chairman:** Lee Dobinson    **Manager:** Gavin Bolger    **Prog Ed:**
**Ground:** Prince George's Playing Field, Raynes Park SW20 9NB    **(T)** Jon Morris
**Capacity:** 1500 **Seats:** 120 **Covered:** 100 **Midweek Matchday:** Tuesday    **Clubhouse:** Yes **Shop:** No

**Colours(change):** Blue/blue/red
**Previous Names:** Raynes Park > 1995 until merger with Malden Vale.
**Previous Leagues:** Surrey County Premier Lge. Isthmian.
**Records:** **Att:** 1871 v AFC Wimbledon (At Carshalton Athletic).
**Senior Honours:**

**10 YEAR RECORD**

| 03-04 | | 04-05 | | 05-06 | | 06-07 | | 07-08 | | 08-09 | | 09-10 | | 10-11 | | 11-12 | | 12-13 | |
|---|---|---|---|---|---|---|---|---|---|---|---|---|---|---|---|---|---|---|---|
| CCP | 16 | CCP | 9 | CCP | 9 | CCP | 15 | CCP | 19 | CCP | 8 | CCP | 18 | CCP | 15 | CCP | 9 | CCP | 11 |

# SOUTH PARK
Founded: 1897     Nickname:

**Secretary:** Nick Thatcher    **(T)** 07817 613 674    **(E)** spfcsecretary@hotmail.co.uk
**Chairman:** Colin Puplett    **Manager:** Joe McElligott    **Prog Ed:** Nick Thatcher
**Ground:** King George's Field, Whitehall Lane, South Park RH2 8LG    **(T)** 01737 245 963
**Capacity:** 700 **Seats:** 100 **Covered:** Yes **Midweek Matchday:** Tuesday    **Clubhouse:** Yes **Shop:** Yes

**Colours(change):** All red
**Previous Names:** South Park & Reigate Town 2001-03.
**Previous Leagues:** Crawley & District > 2006.
**Records:** **Att:** 230 v Warlingham 10/08/2007.
**Senior Honours:**

**10 YEAR RECORD**

| 03-04 | 04-05 | 05-06 | 06-07 | | 07-08 | | 08-09 | | 09-10 | | 10-11 | | 11-12 | | 12-13 | |
|---|---|---|---|---|---|---|---|---|---|---|---|---|---|---|---|---|
| | | | CC1 | 7 | CC1 | 12 | CC1 | 14 | CC1 | 6 | CC1 | 3 | CCP | 8 | CCP | 4 |

# WEMBLEY
Founded: 1946     Nickname: The Lions

**Secretary:** Mrs Jean Gumm    **(T)** 07876 125 784    **(E)** wembleyfc@aol.com
**Chairman:** Brian Gumm    **Manager:** Ian Bates    **Prog Ed:** Richard Markiewicz
**Ground:** Vale Farm, Watford Road, Sudbury, Wembley HA0 3HG.    **(T)** 0208 904 8169
**Capacity:** 2450 **Seats:** 350 **Covered:** 950 **Midweek Matchday:** Tuesday    **Clubhouse:** Yes **Shop:** No

**Colours(change):** Red & white/red/red
**Previous Names:** None
**Previous Leagues:** Middlesex Lge. Spartan. Delphian. Corinthian. Athenian. Isthmian.
**Records:** **Att:** 2654 v Wealdstone, FA Amateur Cup 1952-53. **Goals:** Bill Handraham (105). **Apps:** Spud Murphy (505).
**Senior Honours:**

**10 YEAR RECORD**

| 03-04 | | 04-05 | | 05-06 | | 06-07 | | 07-08 | | 08-09 | | 09-10 | | 10-11 | | 11-12 | | 12-13 | |
|---|---|---|---|---|---|---|---|---|---|---|---|---|---|---|---|---|---|---|---|
| Isth2 | 11 | Isth2 | 13 | Isth2 | 11 | CCP | 3 | CCP | 14 | CCP | 17 | CCP | 15 | CCP | 14 | CCP | 10 | CCP | 15 |

# WESTFIELD
Founded: 1953     Nickname: The Field

**Secretary:** Michael Lawrence    **(T)** 07780 684 416    **(E)** michaelgeorgelawrence@hotmail.com

**Chairman:** Stephen Perkins    **Manager:** John Comer    **Prog Ed:** Pat Kelly

**Ground:** Woking Park, off Elmbridge Lane, Kingfield, Woking GU22 9BA    **(T)** 01483 771 106

**Capacity:** 1000   **Seats:** Yes   **Covered:** Yes   **Midweek Matchday:** Tuesday    **Clubhouse:** Yes   **Shop:**

**Colours(change):** Yellow/black/black
**Previous Names:** None
**Previous Leagues:** Surrey Senior
**Records:**
**Senior Honours:** Surrey Senior League 1972-73, 73-74.

**10 YEAR RECORD**

| 03-04 | | 04-05 | | 05-06 | | 06-07 | | 07-08 | | 08-09 | | 09-10 | | 10-11 | | 11-12 | | 12-13 | |
|---|---|---|---|---|---|---|---|---|---|---|---|---|---|---|---|---|---|---|---|
| CCP | 19 | CCP | 10 | CCP | 11 | CC1 | 10 | CC1 | 4 | CC1 | 13 | CC1 | 16 | CC1 | 13 | CC1 | 8 | CC1 | 3 |

# WINDSOR
Founded: 1892     Nickname: The Royalists

**Secretary:** Steve Rowland    **(T)** 07887 770 630    **(E)** secretary@windsorfc.net

**Chairman:** Kevin Stott    **Manager:** Mick Woodham    **Prog Ed:** Matthew Stevens

**Ground:** Stag Meadow, St Leonards Road, Windsor, Berks SL4 3DR    **(T)** 01753 860 656

**Capacity:** 3,085   **Seats:** 302   **Covered:** 650   **Midweek Matchday:** Tuesday    **Clubhouse:** Yes   **Shop:** Yes

**Colours(change):** All red
**Previous Names:** Windsor & Eton 1892-2011.
**Previous Leagues:** W.Berks, Gt Western, Suburban, Athenian 22-29,63-81, Spartan 29-32, Gt W.Comb. Corinthian 45-50, Met 50-60, Delphian 60-63, Isth 63-06, Sth06-11
**Records:** 8,500 - Charity Match
**Senior Honours:** Athenian League 1979-80, 80-81. Isthmian League Division 1 1983-84. Southern League Division 1 South & West 2009-10.
Berks & Bucks Senior Cup x11.

**10 YEAR RECORD**

| 03-04 | | 04-05 | | 05-06 | | 06-07 | | 07-08 | | 08-09 | | 09-10 | | 10-11 | | 11-12 | | 12-13 | |
|---|---|---|---|---|---|---|---|---|---|---|---|---|---|---|---|---|---|---|---|
| Isth1S | 3 | Isth P | 15 | Isth P | 21 | Sthsw | 14 | Sthsw | 8 | Sthsw | 2 | Sthsw | 1 | SthP | Exp | CCP | 2 | CCP | 6 |

# PREMIER DIVISION GROUND DIRECTIONS

**ALTON TOWN - Alton (Bass) Sports Ground, Anstey Road, Alton, Hants GU34 2RL**
Leave the A31 at the B3004 signposted to Alton. Follow the road round to the left passing Anstey Park on the right, the ground is then immediately on the left – opposite the turning into Anstey Lane. Postcode for Satellite Navigation systems GU34 2RL

**ASH UNITED - Youngs Drive GU12 6RE - 01252 320 385**
FROM M3: Get off the M3 at J4, onto the A331: Take 3rd Exit off to Woking. Up to the roundabout turn left into Shawfields Road, follow road for about 500 yards, Football Ground is on the left, take next turning on your left into Youngs Drive where club is 50yards on. FROM M25: Get onto the A3 heading to Guildford/Portsmouth. Keep on this until you reach the A31(Hog's Back). Then go onto the A31 until you reach the exit for the A331 to Aldershot. Follow the signs for Aldershot, which will be the 1st exit off the A331.When you reach the roundabout take the exit for Woking, which will be the 3rd exit off. Up to the roundabout turn left into Shawfields Road, then as above.

**BADSHOT LEA - See Ash United FC.**

**BEDFONT SPORTS - Bedfont Sports Club TW14 9QT**
From Junction 13, M25 – Staines. At Crooked Billet roundabout turn right onto the A30 Signposted C. London, Hounslow. At Clockhouse Roundabout take the 2nd exit onto the A315 Signposted Bedfont. Turn left onto Hatton Road. Arrive on Hatton Road, Bedfont Sports Club.

**CAMBERLEY TOWN - Krooner Park GU15 2QW - 01276 65392**
Exit M3 Motorway at Junction 4. At the end of the slip road take the right hand land signposted A331, immediately take the left hand lane signposted Frimley and Hospital (Red H Symbol) and this will lead you up onto the A325. Continue to the roundabout and turn left onto the B3411 (Frimley Road) Continue past Focus DIY store on Left and stay on B3411 for approx 1.5 miles. At the next Mini roundabout turn left into Wilton Road, proceed through industrial estate (past the Peugeot garage) and the entrance to the ground is right at the end.

**CHESSINGTON & HOOK UNITED - Chalky Lane KT9 2NF - 01372 745 777**
Chalky Lane is off A243 (Opposite Chessington World of Adventures) which leads to Junction 9 on M25 or Hook Junction on the A3.

**COLLIERS WOOD UTD - Wibbandune Sports Ground SW20 0AA - 0208 942 8062**
On A3 Southbound 1 mile from Robin Hood Gate.

**COVE - Squirrel Lane GU14 8PB - 01252 543 615**
From M3 junction 4, follow signs for A325, then follow signs for Cove FC.

**CROYDON - Croydon Sports Arena, Albert Road, South Norwood SE25 4QL - 0208 654 8555**
From M25: Exit at either Junction 6 and then take the A22 to Purley Cross and then join the A23 London Road and then directions below from Purley, or exit at Junction 7 and take the A23 London Road all the way. From Streatham and Norbury: Take the A23 London Road to the roundabout at Thornton Heath, continue down the A23 Thornton Road. Then take the 1st on the Right past the No Entry road (Fairlands Avenue), Silverleigh Road, 50 yards, at the fork, keep left (signposted Croydon Athletic FC) into Trafford Road, then Mayfield Road (which is a continuation of Trafford Road) Go to the end of Mayfield Road, then left at the last house. Follow the lane, passed allotments, past an open car park space and continue along the lane to our club car park.

**EPSOM & EWELL - Chipstead FC, High Road, Chipstead, Surrey CR5 3SF - 01737 553250**
From the Brighton Road north bound, go left into Church Lane and left into Hogcross Lane. High Road is on the right.

**FARNHAM TOWN - Memorial Ground, West St. GU9 7DY - 01252 715 305**
Follow A31 to Coxbridge roundabout (passing traffic lights at Hickleys corner. Farnham station to left.) At next roundabout take 3rd exit into Farnham town centre. At the mini roundabout take 2nd exit. The ground is to the left.

**FRIMLEY GREEN - Frimley Green Recreation Groand GU16 6SY - 01252 835 089**
Exit M3 at junction 4 and follow the signs to Frimley High Street. At the mini roundabout in front of the White Hart public house turn into Church Road. At the top of the hill by the Church the road bends right and becomes Frimley Green Road. Follow the road for approx of a mile, go over the mini roundabout which is the entrance to Johnson's Wax factory, and the Recreation Ground is the second turning on the left, just past Henley Drive, which is on your right.

**HANWORTH VILLA - Rectory Meadows, Park Road TW13 6PN - 0208 831 9391**
From M25 and M3 once on the M3 towards London. This becomes the A316, take the A314 (Hounslow Rd) exit signposted Feltham & Hounslow. Turn left onto Hounslow Rd, at the second mini round about (Esso garage on the corner) turn left into Park Rd. Continue down Park Road past the Hanworth Naval Club on the right and Procter's Builders Merchants on the left. Follow the road around the 90 degree bend and continue to the end of the road past the Hanworth Village Hall. Once past the two houses next to the village hall turn left into Rectory Meadows.

**HARTLEY WINTNEY - Memorial Playing Fields RG27 8DL - 01252 843 586**
On entering Hartley Wintney via the A30 take the turn at the mini roundabout signposted A323 Fleet. Take the 1st right turn, Green Lane, which has St John's Church on the corner. Continue down Green Lane for about 800 metres and turn right into car park, which has a shared access with Greenfields School. Turn left at St John's Church if coming down the A323 from Fleet.

**HORLEY TOWN - The New Defence RH6 8RS - 07545 697 234**
From centre of town go North up Victoria where it meets the A23, straight across to Vicarage Lane, 2nd left into Court Lodge Road follow it through estate and we are behind adult education centre.

**MOLE VALLEY SCR - Cobham FC, Leg of Mutton Field - 07787 383 407**
From Cobham High Street, turn right into Downside Bridge Road and turn right into Leg of Mutton Field.

**MOLESEY - 412 Walton Road West KT8 0JG - 0208 979 4283**
Take A3 towards Cobham/London & exit at Esher-Sandown turn. 1st exit at roundabout to A244 through Esher to Marquis of Granby Pub. 1st exit A309 at next roundabout. 1st exit at end of road turn right, follow until mini roundabout left into Walton Road after 1 mile ground on left.

**RAYNES PARK VALE - Prince Georges Fields SW20 9NB - 0208 540 8843**
Exit Raynes Park station into Grand Drive cross Bushey Road at the traffic lights continue up Grand Drive for 400 yards entrance on the left follow drive to clubhouse. From the A3. Onto Bushey Road towards South Wimbledon. Grand Drive on the right, ground in Grand Drive on the left hand side.

**SOUTH PARK - King George's Field RH2 8LG - 01737 245 963**
From junction 8 of the M25, take A217 and follow signs to Gatwick. Follow through the one way system via Reigate town centre and continue on until traffic lights and crossroads by The Angel public house, turn right at these lights, into Prices Lane, and continue on road. After a sharp right bend into Sandcross Lane past Reigate Garden Centre. Take next left after school into Whitehall Lane.

**WEMBLEY - Vale Farm, Watford Road HA0 3AG - 0208 904 8169**
From Sudbury Town Station 400 yards along Watford Road.

**WESTFIELD - Woking Park, off Elmbridge Lane GU22 7AA - 01483 771 106**
Follow signs to Woking Leisure Centre on the A247.

**WINDSOR - Stag Meadow, St Leonards Road, Windsor, Berks SL4 3DR - 01753 860 656**
Exit M4 at Junction 6, follow dual carriageway (signposted Windsor) to large roundabout at end, take third exit into Imperial Road, turn left at T-junction into St Leonards Road. Ground approx ½ mile on right opposite Stag & Hounds public house.

# DIVISION ONE

## AFC CROYDON ATHLETIC
Founded: 2012    Nickname: The Rams

**Secretary:** Peter Smith  **(T)** 07907 588 496  **(E)** secretary@afccroydonathletic.co.uk
**Chairman:** Paul Smith  **Manager:** Anthony Williams  **Prog Ed:** Peter Smith
**Ground:** Croydon Sports Arena, Albert Road, South Norwood, London SE25 4QL  **(T)** 020 8654 8555  **Capacity:** 8,000
**Colours(change):** All maroon

**ADDITIONAL INFORMATION: Record Att:** 1,372 v AFC Wimbledon 2004-05
**Previous Names:** Norwood FC and Wandsworth FC amalgamated in 1986 to form Wandsworth & Norwood > 1990.
Croydon Athletic 1990-2012.
**Honours:** London Spartan League 1994-95. Isthmian League Division 3 2001-02, Division 1 South 2009-10.

## BANSTEAD ATHLETIC
Founded: 1944    Nickname: A's

**Secretary:** Terry Molloy  **(T)** 07958 436 483  **(E)** terrymolloy@leyfield.eclipse.co.uk
**Chairman:** Terry Molloy  **Manager:** Jack Johnson  **Prog Ed:** Bob Lockyar
**Ground:** Merland Rise, Tadworth, Surrey KT20 5JG  **(T)** 01737 350 982  **Capacity:** 3500
**Colours(change):** Amber & black/black/black

**ADDITIONAL INFORMATION:**
**Previous Leagues:** London Spartan League. Athenian League. Isthmian > 2006.
**Honours:** London Spartan LC 1965-67. Athenian LC 190-82.
**Record Att:** 1400 v Leytonstone, FA Amateur Cup 1953. **Goals:** Harry Clark. **Apps:** Dennis Wall.

## BEDFONT & FELTHAM
Founded: 2012    Nickname:

**Secretary:** Scott Savoy  **(T)** 07539 219 924  **(E)** ssavoyffc@msn.com
**Chairman:** Brian Barry  **Manager:** Wayne Tisson  **Prog Ed:** Rob Healey
**Ground:** The Orchard, Hatton Road, Bedfont TW14 9QT  **(T)** 020 8890 7264  **Capacity:** 1200
**Colours(change):** Yellow & blue/blue/blue

**ADDITIONAL INFORMATION:**
**Previous Names:** Bedfont FC and Feltham (1946) amalgamated in May 2012 but had to wait until 2013-14 before changing the name.

## CB HOUNSLOW UNITED
Founded: 1989    Nickname:

**Secretary:** Stephen Hosmer  **(T)** 07900 604 936  **(E)** stephen.hosmer@btinternet.com
**Chairman:** Frank James  **Prog Ed:** Stephen Hosmer
**Ground:** Bedfont & Feltham FC, The Orchard, Hatton Road, Bedfont TW14 9QT  **(T)** 0208 890 7264  **Capacity:** 1200
**Colours(change):** All dark blue

**ADDITIONAL INFORMATION:**
**Previous League:** Middlesex County.

## COBHAM
Founded: 1892    Nickname: Hammers

**Secretary:** Ken Reed  **(T)** 07850 211 165  **(E)** cobhamfootballclub@hotmail.com
**Chairman:** Chris Palmer  **Manager:** Kevin Petters  **Prog Ed:** Sam Merison
**Ground:** The Reg Madgwick Stadium, Leg O'Mutton Field, Anvil Lane, Cobham KT11 1AA  **(T)** 01932 866 386  **Capacity:** 2000
**Colours(change):** All red

**ADDITIONAL INFORMATION: Att:** 2000 - Charity game 1975.
**Honours:** Combined Counties League Cup 2001-02.

## DORKING
Founded: 1880    Nickname: The Chicks

**Secretary:** Ray Collins  **(T)** 07795 231816  **(E)** ray.collins@hotmail.co.uk
**Chairman:** Jack Collins  **Manager:** Glynn Stephens  **Prog Ed:** Bryan Bletso
**Ground:** Meadowbank, Mill Lane, Dorking Surrey RH4 1DX  **(T)** 01306 884 112  **Capacity:** 3500
**Colours(change):** Green & white hoops/green & white/green

**ADDITIONAL INFORMATION:**
**Previous Names:** Guildford & Dorking (when club merged 1974). Dorking Town 1977-82.
**Previous Leagues:** Corinthian, Athenian, Isthmian > 2006.
**Record Att:** 4500 v Folkstone Town FAC 1955 & v Plymouth Argyle FAC 1993. **Goals:** Andy Bushell. **Apps:** Steve Lunn.

## EPSOM ATHLETIC
Founded: 1997    Nickname: The Blue Stallions

**Secretary:** Paul Burstow  **(T)** 07821 537 177  **(E)** mintybunt@hotmail.com
**Chairman:** Paul Burstow  **Manager:** Luke Reynolds  **Prog Ed:** Simon Stevens
**Ground:** Chessington & Hook Utd Fc, Chalky Lane, Chessington, Surrey KT9 2NF  **(T)** 01372 745 777  **Capacity:** 3,000
**Colours(change):** All navy blue with white trim

**ADDITIONAL INFORMATION:**
**Previous League:** Surrey Elite > 2012.
**Honours:** Surrey Elite 2011-12.

# EVERSLEY & CALIFORNIA

Founded: 2012    Nickname: Wild Boars

**Secretary:** Martin McMahon    **(T)** 07834 363 053    **(E)** mljmcmahon@hotmail.com
**Chairman:** David Bland    **Manager:** Ian Savage    **Prog Ed:** Paul Latham
**Ground:** ESA Sports Complex, Fox Lane, Eversley RG27 0NS    **(T)** 0118 973 2400    **Capacity:** 300+
**Colours(change):** Yellow & royal blue stripes/royal blue/royal blue

**ADDITIONAL INFORMATION:**
**Previous League:** Surrey Elite Intermediate.
**Honours:** Surrey Elite Intermediate 2008-09.

# FARLEIGH ROVERS

Founded: 1922    Nickname: The Foxes

**Secretary:** Peter Collard    **(T)** 07545 444 820    **(E)** peter.collard@aquatots.com
**Chairman:** Mark Whittaker    **Manager:** Tim Moffatt    **Prog Ed:** Peter Collard
**Ground:** Parsonage Field, Harrow Road, Warlingham CR6 9EX    **(T)** 01883 626 483    **Capacity:** 500
**Colours(change):** Black & red stripes/black/black

**ADDITIONAL INFORMATION:**
**Previous League:** Surrey County Premier.
**Honours:** Surrey County Premier 1982-83.

# KNAPHILL

Founded: 1924    Nickname: The Knappers

**Secretary:** Bryan Freeman    **(T)** 07876 162 904    **(E)** knaphillfc.honsecretary@gmail.com
**Chairman:** David Freeman    **Manager:** Phil Ruggles    **Prog Ed:** Lisa Harding
**Ground:** Brookwood Country Park, Redding Way, Knaphill GU21 2AY    **(T)** 01483 475 150    **Capacity:** 750
**Colours(change):** Red/black/red

**ADDITIONAL INFORMATION: Att:** 323 v Guernsey. **Goalscorer:** Matt Baker - 24.
**Honours:** Woking & District League 1978-79. Surrey Intermediate League Division One 2005-06, Premier 06-07.

# SANDHURST TOWN

Founded: 1910    Nickname: Fizzers

**Secretary:** Anne Brummer    **(T)** 07725 878 460    **(E)** secretarystfc@hotmail.co.uk
**Chairman:** Tony Dean    **Manager:** Salvatore Diprima    **Prog Ed:** Sarah Heard
**Ground:** Bottom Meadow, Memorial Ground, Yorktown Rd, GU47 9BJ    **(T)** 01252 878 768    **Capacity:** 1000
**Colours(change):** Red/black/black.

**ADDITIONAL INFORMATION:**
**Previous Leagues:** Reading & District. East Berkshire. Aldershot Senior. Chiltonian.
**Record Att:** 2,449 v AFC Wimbledon, Combined Counties 17.08.2002.
**Honours:** Aldershot FA Senior Invitation Challenge Cup 2000-01, 05-06. Combined Counties Premier Challenge Cup 2010-11.

# SHEERWATER

Founded: 1958    Nickname: Sheers

**Secretary:** Trevor Wenden    **(T)** 07791 612 008    **(E)** trevor.wenden2@ntlworld.com
**Chairman:** Chris Wye    **Manager:** John Cook    **Prog Ed:** Trevor Wenden
**Ground:** Sheerwater Recreation Ground, Blackmore Crescent, Woking GU21 5QJ    **(T)** 07791 612 008    **Capacity:** 1,000
**Colours(change):** All royal blue

**ADDITIONAL INFORMATION:**
**Previous League:** Surrey County Premier.

# SOUTH KILBURN

Founded: 2005    Nickname: SK

**Secretary:** Mrs Amanda Jennings    **(T)** 07595 256 309    **(E)** jenningsmandy@ymail.com
**Chairman:** Dennis Woolcock    **Manager:** Mick Jennings
**Ground:** Vale Farm, Watford Road, North Wembley HA0 3HE    **(T)** 0208 908 6545
**Colours(change):** White & black/black/black

**ADDITIONAL INFORMATION: Att:** 65 v Rayners Lane 25/08/2008.

# SPELTHORNE SPORTS

Founded: 1922    Nickname: Spelly

**Secretary:** Chris Devlin    **(T)** 07956 321 558    **(E)** secretary@spelthornesportsfc.co.uk
**Chairman:** Ian Croxford    **Manager:** Paul Johnson    **Prog Ed:** Chris Devlin
**Ground:** Spelthorne Sports Club, 296 Staines Rd West, Ashford Common, TW15 1RY    **(T)** 01932 961 055
**Colours(change):** Blue & white stripes/blue/white

**ADDITIONAL INFORMATION:**
**Previous League:** Surrey Elite Intermediate.
**Honours:** Surrey Elite Intermediate League 2010-11.

## STAINES LAMMAS
Founded: 1926     Nickname:

**Secretary:** Bob Parry     **(T)** 07771 947 757     **(E)** bobandtracey1@btopenworld.com
**Chairman:** Greg Clarke     **Manager:** Steve Willmore     **Prog Ed:** Clive Robertson
**Ground:** Ashford Tn (Mx) FC, The Robert Parker Stadium, Short Lane, Stanwell TW19 7BH     **(T)** 01784 245 908     **Capacity:** 2550
**Colours(change):** All blue

**ADDITIONAL INFORMATION:**
**Record Att:** 107 v Hanworth Villa, January 2006. **Goalscorer:** Jay Coombs - 270+ **Win:** 19-1 v Cranleigh (Surrey Senior Lge) 19/03/03.
**Honours:** Combined Counties Division 1 2007-08, 08-09.

## WORCESTER PARK
Founded: 1921     Nickname: The Skinners

**Secretary:** Kristina Maitre     **(T)** 07768 179 938     **(E)** kristinajayne@hotmail.co.uk
**Chairman:** Sam Glass     **Manager:** John Di Palma     **Prog Ed:** Darren Talbot
**Ground:** Skinners Field, Green Lane, Worcester Park, Surrey KT4 8AJ     **(T)** 0208 337 4995
**Colours(change):** All blue

**ADDITIONAL INFORMATION:**
**Previous League:** Surrey County Premier.
**Honours:** Surrey County Premier/Senior League 1999-2000, 2000-01. Combined Counties Division One 2010-11.

# DIVISION ONE GROUND DIRECTIONS

**AFC CROYDON ATHLETIC - Croydon Sports Arena, Albert Road, South Norwood, London SE25 4QL**
From M25: Exit at either Junction 6 and then take the A22 to Purley Cross and then join the A23 London Road and then directions below from Purley, or exit at Junction 7 and take the A23 London Road all the way. From Streatham and Norbury: Take the A23 London Road to the roundabout at Thornton Heath, continue down the A23 Thornton Road. Then take the 1st on the Right past the No Entry road (Fairlands Avenue), Silverleigh Road, 50 yards, at the fork, keep left (signposted Croydon Athletic FC) into Trafford Road, then Mayfield Road (which is a continuation of Trafford Road) Go to the end of Mayfield Road, then left at the last house. Follow the lane, passed allotments, past an open car park space and continue along the lane to our club car park.

**BANSTEAD ATHLETIC - Merland Rise KT20 5JG - 01737 350 982**
From M25 junction 8 follow signs to Banstead Sports Centre.

**BEDFONT & FELTHAM - The Orchard, Hatten Road TW14 9QT - 0208 890 7264**
Hatton Road runs alongside the A30 at Heathrow. Ground is opposite the Duke of Wellington Public House.

**CB HOUNSLOW UNITED - See Bedfont & Feltham**

**COBHAM - Leg of Mutton Field - 07787 383 407**
From Cobham High Street, turn right into Downside Bridge Road and turn right into Leg of Mutton Field.

**DORKING - Meadowbank Stadium RH4 1DX - 01306 884 112**
Dorking Football Club's Meadowbank ground is very close to the town centre and only a ten minute walk from any of the three railway stations that serve the town.
Deepdene and Dorking West are on the (First Great Western Link) Reading to Gatwick Airport line. Dorking is on the (South West Trains) Horsham to London Waterloo line.
Follow the signs for the town centre from all stations. Meadowbank is on Mill Lane which is well signposted from the High Street.

**EPSOM ATHLETIC - Chessington & Hook United FC, Chalky Lane KT9 2NF - 01372 745 777**
Chalky Lane is off A243 (Opposite Chessington World of Adventures) which leads to Junction 9 on M25 or Hook Junction on the A3.

**EVERSLEY & CALIFORNIA - ESA Sports Complex, Fox Lane, Eversley RG27 0NS - 0118 973 2400**
Leave the M3 at junction 4a signposted Fleet/Farnborough. At the roundabout take the 2nd exit towards Yateley.
At the roundabout take the 2nd exit towards Yateley. At the roundabout take the 2nd exit towards Yateley.
At the roundabout take the 1st exit and proceed through Yateley on the Reading Road. At the roundabout take the 2nd exit and follow the road for about 1 mile. Turn right down the first turning for Fox Lane and then follow the road round to the right where the ground will be signposted.

**FARLEIGH ROVERS - Parsonage Field, Harrow Road CR6 9EX - 01883 626 483**
From M25 junction 6 left at lights up Godstone Hill (Caterham bypass) to roundabout. Take fourth turning off of roundabout. Up Succombs Hill then right into Westhall Rd. Right at the green then second left into Farleigh Rd. Left at mini round about continue still on Farleigh Road. Right at the Harrow Pub. This is Harrow Road. Right at the end of the houses and the ground is behind the houses.

**KNAPHILL - Brookwood Country Park GU21 2AY - 01483 475 150**
From A3: A322 from Guildford through towards Worplesdon. At Fox Corner rounabaout, take 2bd exit onto Bagshot Road, A322 signposted Bagshot. Pat West Hill Golf Club, at traffice lights turn right onto Brookwood Lye Road, A324 signposted Woking. Turn left into Hermitage Road on A324, up to roundabout, take 1st exit onto Redding Way, then 1st left entering driveway towards car park and ground.

**SANDHURST TOWN - Bottom Meadow GU47 9BJ - 01252 878 768**
Situated on A321 approx 5 miles from Junction 4 on M3, or approx 8 miles from junction 10 on the M4 Park in Council Offices car park and walk down tarmac footpath beside the stream to ground.

**SHEERWATER - Sheerwater Recreation Ground GU21 5QJ - 01932 348 192**
From M25(J11) take the A320 towards Woking, At Six Cross roundabout take the exit to Monument Road. At the lights turn left into Eve Road for Sheerwater Estate. First left is Blackmore Crescent, Entrance is Quarter of a mile on left.

**SOUTH KILBURN - Vale Farm, Watford Road HA0 3HE - 0208 908 6545**
Leave A40 onto A404, Watford Road, continue along Watford Road, you will see the sign for Vale Farm Sports Ground on right.

**SPELTHORNE SPORTS - 296 Staines Rd West, Ashford Common, TW15 1RY - 01932 783 625**
From M25 (J13) take the A30 exit to London (W)/Hounslow/Staines. At the roundabout, take the 1st exit onto Staines Bypass/A30 heading to London(W)/Hounslow/Staines/Kingston/A308. Turn left onto Staines Bypass/A308
Continue to follow A308. Go through 1 roundabout. Make a U-turn at Chertsey Rd. Ground will be on the left.

**STAINES LAMMAS - Ashford T (Mx), The Robert Parker Std, Short Lane, Stanwell TW19 7BH - 01784 245908**
M25 junction 13, A30 towards London, third left at footbridge after Ashford Hospital crossroads, ground sign posted after 1/4 mile on the right down Short Lane, two miles from Ashford (BR) and Hatton Cross tube station.

**WORCESTER PARK- Skinners Field, Green Lane KT4 8AJ - 0208 337 4995**
From M25, come off at A3 turn off and head towards London, then come off at Worcester Park turn off, stay on this road until you pass station on your left and go under bridge, then take first left which is Green Lane, ground is 500 yards on the left.

# NON LEAGUE DAY

# Saturday
# 7th September

 **Support your local club**

# nonleagueday.co.uk

# EAST MIDLAND COUNTIES LEAGUE

**Sponsored by:** No sponsor
**Founded:** 2008
**Recent Champions:**
2009: Kirby Muxloe SC
2010: Dunkirk
2011: Gresley
2012: Heanor Town
emc-fl.com

| | | P | W | D | L | F | A | Pts |
|---|---|---|---|---|---|---|---|---|
| 1 | (P) Basford United | 36 | 31 | 2 | 3 | 97 | 29 | 95 |
| 2 | Barrow Town | 36 | 27 | 3 | 6 | 95 | 31 | 84 |
| 3 | Thurnby Nirvana | 36 | 25 | 3 | 8 | 94 | 35 | 78 |
| 4 | Borrowash Victoria | 36 | 21 | 5 | 10 | 92 | 50 | 68 |
| 5 | Holwell Sports | 36 | 20 | 4 | 12 | 81 | 55 | 64 |
| 6 | Blaby & Whetstone Athletic | 36 | 19 | 5 | 12 | 73 | 47 | 62 |
| 7 | Aylestone Park (-3pts) | 36 | 19 | 4 | 13 | 71 | 52 | 58 |
| 8 | Graham St Prims (-3pts) | 36 | 18 | 6 | 12 | 68 | 62 | 57 |
| 9 | Holbrook Sports | 36 | 16 | 5 | 15 | 68 | 66 | 53 |
| 10 | Radcliffe Olympic | 36 | 14 | 3 | 19 | 68 | 78 | 45 |
| 11 | Bardon Hill | 36 | 12 | 8 | 16 | 65 | 67 | 44 |
| 12 | Lutterworth Athletic | 36 | 10 | 7 | 19 | 60 | 71 | 37 |
| 13 | Gedling Miners Welfare | 36 | 9 | 8 | 19 | 58 | 96 | 35 |
| 14 | Anstey Nomads | 36 | 9 | 7 | 20 | 41 | 92 | 34 |
| 15 | Ellistown | 36 | 8 | 9 | 19 | 56 | 101 | 33 |
| 16 | St Andrews | 36 | 9 | 5 | 22 | 56 | 95 | 32 |
| 17 | Ibstock United | 36 | 9 | 5 | 22 | 53 | 96 | 32 |
| 18 | Greenwood Meadows | 36 | 7 | 9 | 20 | 56 | 85 | 30 |
| 19 | Radford | 36 | 8 | 4 | 24 | 48 | 92 | 28 |

## LEAGUE CUP

**ROUND 1**

| | | | |
|---|---|---|---|
| Radcliffe Olympic | v | Holwell Sports | 2-1 |
| Greenwood Meadows | v | Borrowash Victoria | 0-3 |
| Thurnby Nirvana | v | Gedling Miners Welfare | 5-0 |

**ROUND 2**

| | | | |
|---|---|---|---|
| Anstey Nomads | v | Borrowash Victoria | 2-2 |
| R - Borrowash Victoria | v | Anstey Nomads | 4-1 |
| Barrow Town | v | Blaby & Whetstone Athletic | 2-3 |
| Ellistown | v | Aylestone Park | 2-3 |
| Graham St Prims | v | Radford | 3-2 |
| Ibstock United | v | Basford United | 0-4 |
| Radcliffe Olympic | v | Lutterworth Athletic | 1-3 |
| St Andrews | v | Thurnby Nirvana | 2-4 |
| Holbrook Sports | v | Bardon Hill | 0-2 |

**QUARTER FINALS**

| | | | |
|---|---|---|---|
| Aylestone Park | v | Bardon Hill | 1-2 |
| Thurnby Nirvana | v | Graham St Pims | 3-4 |
| Borrowash Victoria | v | Blaby & Whetstone Athletic | 2-3 |
| Lutterworth Athletic | v | Basford United | 1-1 |
| R - Basford United | v | Lutterworth Athletic | 6-3 |

**SEMI FINALS**

| | | | |
|---|---|---|---|
| Bardon Hill | v | Basford United | 1-5 |
| Graham St Pims | v | Blaby & Whetstone Athletic | 1-0 |

**FINAL**

| | | | |
|---|---|---|---|
| Graham St Prims | v | Basford United | 0-2 |

| | | 1 | 2 | 3 | 4 | 5 | 6 | 7 | 8 | 9 | 10 | 11 | 12 | 13 | 14 | 15 | 16 | 17 | 18 | 19 |
|---|---|---|---|---|---|---|---|---|---|---|---|---|---|---|---|---|---|---|---|---|
| 1 | Anstey Nomads | | 1-0 | 2-2 | 0-6 | 2-4 | 1-4 | 0-3 | 1-1 | 1-4 | 2-3 | 2-2 | 2-1 | 2-1 | 0-4 | 1-1 | 1-2 | 1-7 | 0-2 | 3-1 |
| 2 | Aylestone Park | 3-2 | | 1-2 | 1-2 | 1-3 | 2-0 | 1-6 | 5-1 | 3-0 | 2-2 | 1-0 | 0-1 | 2-3 | 1-0 | 3-0 | 0-1 | 3-0 | 7-1 | 1-1 |
| 3 | Bardon Hill | 1-1 | 2-3 | | 2-1 | 0-1 | 4-0 | 4-2 | 2-3 | 3-1 | 0-0 | 2-2 | 1-3 | 2-3 | 5-2 | 6-0 | 2-1 | 4-1 | 4-0 | 0-2 |
| 4 | Barrow Town | 4-0 | 3-0 | 2-0 | | 0-1 | 2-1 | 0-1 | 2-0 | 0-0 | 1-1 | 3-3 | 3-0 | 2-3 | 3-0 | 5-2 | 4-0 | 3-0 | 2-1 | 4-0 |
| 5 | Basford United | 3-0 | 0-1 | 2-1 | 1-0 | | 2-0 | 2-0 | 7-1 | 5-2 | 3-3 | 5-2 | 4-0 | 3-0 | 8-0 | 3-2 | 2-1 | 4-0 | 2-0 | 2-1 |
| 6 | Blaby & Whetstone Athletic | 2-1 | 2-2 | 5-0 | 0-1 | 0-1 | | 2-3 | 2-0 | 3-1 | 2-3 | 3-1 | 2-0 | 1-2 | 2-0 | 2-0 | 2-1 | 3-1 | 3-0 | 0-2 |
| 7 | Borrowash Victoria | 5-0 | 3-1 | 1-0 | 3-4 | 6-1 | 2-2 | | 1-4 | 2-2 | 3-0 | 1-0 | 2-0 | 0-0 | 2-1 | 2-1 | 2-1 | 5-0 | 5-1 | 1-3 |
| 8 | Ellistown | 2-2 | 1-5 | 2-2 | 0-3 | 0-5 | 2-2 | 1-2 | | 1-1 | 1-1 | 3-1 | 0-0 | 2-5 | 1-5 | 3-1 | 2-3 | 3-1 | 0-3 | 0-6 |
| 9 | Gedling Miners Welfare | 1-2 | 2-2 | 0-4 | 0-4 | 0-3 | 2-0 | 1-8 | 3-1 | | 0-1 | 2-4 | 3-2 | 1-1 | 5-0 | 4-4 | 4-3 | 2-1 | 0-3 | 1-1 |
| 10 | Graham St Prims | 0-1 | 1-2 | 6-2 | 1-7 | 0-3 | 0-4 | 2-3 | 1-2 | 2-0 | | 2-1 | 1-0 | 3-1 | 2-1 | 4-0 | 3-1 | 2-1 | 2-2 | 0-2 |
| 11 | Greenwood Meadows | 0-1 | 1-0 | 3-3 | 1-2 | 2-2 | 1-5 | 0-0 | 2-3 | 4-1 | 0-5 | | 2-3 | 1-1 | 1-3 | 4-1 | 1-6 | 3-1 | 2-2 | 1-0 |
| 12 | Holbrook Sports | 4-0 | 0-1 | 3-1 | 2-3 | 0-3 | 1-1 | 1-1 | 1-1 | 5-3 | 2-1 | 3-1 | | 0-3 | 2-1 | 2-1 | 3-0 | 2-5 | 3-0 | 0-4 |
| 13 | Holwell Sports | 7-2 | 1-2 | 2-1 | 1-2 | 0-2 | 1-4 | 3-2 | 5-1 | 5-0 | 3-2 | 1-2 | 1-3 | | 1-2 | 0-2 | 2-1 | 3-0 | 2-0 | 2-2 |
| 14 | Ibstock United | 1-1 | 0-4 | 0-1 | 1-3 | 1-2 | 0-2 | 2-8 | 4-2 | 3-2 | 1-2 | 3-3 | 3-1 | 1-2 | | 0-6 | 3-1 | 2-2 | 1-1 | 0-4 |
| 15 | Lutterworth Athletic | 5-0 | 2-0 | 2-4 | 1-2 | 3-1 | 1-2 | 2-1 | 6-1 | 2-2 | 1-2 | 2-1 | 1-1 | 0-3 | 2-2 | | 0-1 | 1-2 | 4-1 | 2-1 |
| 16 | Radcliffe Olympic | 3-1 | 2-0 | 4-0 | 1-3 | 0-1 | 1-1 | 2-3 | 1-1 | 2-3 | 2-3 | 2-0 | 3-7 | 0-5 | 3-2 | 4-2 | | 2-2 | 3-2 | 3-1 |
| 17 | Radford | 0-1 | 2-5 | 3-6 | 0-4 | 0-1 | 1-3 | 1-0 | 2-8 | 1-1 | 0-2 | 2-0 | 1-5 | 1-5 | 3-1 | 1-0 | 2-3 | | 0-2 | 0-2 |
| 18 | St Andrews | 1-3 | 2-3 | 2-1 | 1-1 | 0-3 | 1-5 | 3-2 | 3-0 | 2-4 | 2-3 | 5-3 | 1-6 | 1-2 | 2-3 | 1-1 | 6-3 | 0-4 | | 0-2 |
| 19 | Thurnby Nirvana | 2-1 | 2-3 | 2-1 | 0-1 | 0-2 | 4-1 | 2-1 | 5-2 | 5-0 | 4-2 | 4-1 | 6-1 | 3-1 | 4-0 | 3-0 | 4-1 | 3-0 | 5-1 | |

## CLUB MOVEMENTS

**In:** Arnold Town (R - Northern Counties East Premier for breach of rules). Ellistown & Ibstock United (Merger of Ellistown and Ibstock United). Stapenhill (P - Leicestershire Senior). Sutton Town AFC (P - Central Midlands South).
**Out:** Basford United (P - Northern Counties East). Ellistown (NC). Ibstock United (NC). Lutterworth Athletic (S - United Counties Division One).

## ANSTEY NOMADS

Founded: 1947    Nickname: Nomads

**Secretary:** Chris Hillebrandt       **(T)** 0794 685 6430       **(E)** chille1055@hotmail.com
**Chairman:** Tony Ford       **Manager:** Mark Poulton       **Prog Ed:** Helen Preston-Hayes
**Ground:** Cropston Road, Anstey, Leicester LE7 7BP       **(T)** 0116 236 4868
**Colours(change):** Red & white stripes/black/red (All blue)

**ADDITIONAL INFORMATION: Att:** 4,500 v Hayes, 2nd Round FA Amateru Cup.
Leicestershire Senior League 1951-52, 53-54, 81-82, 82-83, 2008-09. Leicestershire Senior Cup 1994-95.

## ARNOLD TOWN

Founded: 1989    Nickname: Eagles

**Secretary:** Graham Peck       **(T)** 07815 458 196       **(E)** graham@peckgraham.orangehome.co.uk
**Chairman:** Graham Peck       **Manager:** Graham Walker       **Prog Ed:** Mick Gretton
**Ground:** Eagle Valley, Oxton Road, Arnold, Nottingham NG5 8PS       **(T)** 0115 965 6000
**Colours(change):** All maroon. (Yellow/blue/yellow)

**ADDITIONAL INFORMATION:**
**Previous Leagues:** Central Midland 1989-93. Northern Counites East 1993-2013.
**Record Att:** 3,390 v Bristol Rovers FAC 1-Dec 1967   **Goalscorer:** Peter Fletcher - 100. **App:** Pete Davey - 346. **Win:** 10-1 **Defeat:** 0-7
**Honours:** Northern Counties East 1985-86. Central Midlands 92-93. Northern Counties Div.1 93-94.

## AYLESTONE PARK

Founded: 1968    Nickname:

**Secretary:** Mrs Frances Hargrave       **(T)** 07563 713 700       **(E)** beaumonttownfc@hotmail.co.uk
**Chairman:** Bob Stretton       **Manager:** Stuart Spencer & Frank Benjamin
**Ground:** Mary Linwood Recreation Ground, Saffron Lane, Leicester LE6 6TG       **(T)** 0116 278 5485
**Colours(change):** Red/black/black (All blue)

**ADDITIONAL INFORMATION:**
**Previous Name:** Aylestone Park Old Boys > 2007.
**Previous Leagues:** Leicestershire Senior 1992-2012.
**Honours:** Leicestershire Senior Cup 2012-13.

## BARDON HILL

Founded:    Nickname:

**Secretary:** Adrian Bishop       **(T)** 07999 879 841       **(E)** ade_bish@hotmail.co.uk
**Chairman:**       **Manager:** Don Gethfield       **Prog Ed:** Adrian Bishop
**Ground:** Bardon Close, Coalville, Leicester LE67 4BS       **(T)** 01530 815 569
**Colours(change):** All royal blue

**ADDITIONAL INFORMATION:**
**Previous Name:** Bardon Hill Sports
**Previous League:** Leics Senior.

## BARROW TOWN

Founded: Late 1800s    Nickname:

**Secretary:** Andy Dermott       **(T)** 07875 291 365       **(E)** a.dermott514@btinternet.com
**Chairman:** Michael Bland       **Manager:** Steve Alexander       **Prog Ed:** Andy Dermott
**Ground:** Riverside Park, Bridge Street, Quorn, Leicestershire LE12 8EN       **(T)** 07999 879 841
**Colours(change):** Royal blue/royal blue/white (All red)

**ADDITIONAL INFORMATION:**
**Previous League:** Leicestershire Senior.
**Honours:** Leicester Senior League Division One 1992-93.

## BLABY & WHETSTONE ATHLETIC

Founded:    Nickname:

**Secretary:** Sue Warner       **(T)** 07757 513 333       **(E)** suewarner2@aol.com
**Chairman:** Mark Jenkins       **Manager:** Steve Orme       Roger Morris
**Ground:** Warwick Road, Whetstome, Leicester LE8 6LW       **(T)** 0116 275 1182
**Colours(change):** All navy blue (Yellow & blue/yellow/yellow)

**ADDITIONAL INFORMATION:**
**Previous Lge:** Leicestershire Senior > 2011.

## BORROWASH VICTORIA

Founded:    Nickname:

**Secretary:** John Robinson       **(T)**       **(E)** jarobinson@rocketmail.com
**Chairman:** Frazer Watson       **Manager:** Kevin Bunting       **Prog Ed:** Adrian Randle
**Ground:** Watkinsons Construction Bowl, Borrowash Rd, Spondon, Derby DE21 7PH       **(T)** 01332 669 688
**Colours(change):** Red & white stripes/black/black (All blue)

**ADDITIONAL INFORMATION:**
**Previous League:** Central Midlands

## ELLISTOWN & IBSTOCK UNITED    Founded: 2013    Nickname:

**Secretary:** Sue Matthews   **(T)** 07791 963 618    **(E)** suematthews7@hotmail.com
**Chairman:** Andy Roach   **Manager:** Richard Hill & Paul Brown   **Prog Ed:** David Craggs
**Ground:** Terrace Road, Terrace Road, Ellistown, Leicestershire LE67 1GD   **(T)** 01530 230 159
**Colours(change):**
**ADDITIONAL INFORMATION:**
Formed when Ellistown and Ibstock United merged in the summer of 2013.

## GEDLING MINERS WELFARE    Founded:    Nickname:

**Secretary:** Norman Hay   **(T)** 07748 138 732    **(E)** norman.hay@virginmedia.com
**Chairman:** Vic Hulme   **Manager:** Jonathan Simpson   **Prog Ed:** Ian Williams
**Ground:** Plains Social Club, Plains Road, Mapperley, Nottingham NG3 5RH   **(T)** 0115 926 6300
**Colours(change):** Yellow/blue/yellow (All red)
**ADDITIONAL INFORMATION:**
**Previous League:** Central Midlands

## GRAHAM ST. PRIMS    Founded: 1904    Nickname: Prims

**Secretary:** Peter Davis   **(T)** 01332 332 092    **(E)** j.davis16@sky.com
**Chairman:** John Lindsay (Vice)   **Manager:** Mark Webster   **Prog Ed:** Edward Davis
**Ground:** Asterdale Sports Centre, Borrowash Road, Spondon, Derbyshire DE21 7PH   **(T)** 07969 160 574
**Colours(change):** Red/black/black (All royal blue)
**ADDITIONAL INFORMATION:**
**Previous League:** Central Midlands

## GREENWOOD MEADOWS    Founded: 1987    Nickname:

**Secretary:** Christine Burton   **(T)** 0771 253 0706    **(E)** christineburton@live.co.uk
**Chairman:** Mark Burton   **Manager:** Nev Silcock   **Prog Ed:** Martin Asher
**Ground:** Lenton Lane Ground, Lenton Lane, Nr Clifton Bridge, Nottingham NG7 2SA   **(T)** 07712 530 706
**Colours(change):** Green/black/green (Yellow/green/yellow)
**ADDITIONAL INFORMATION:**
**Previous League:** Central Midlands

## HOLBROOK SPORTS    Founded: 1931    Nickname:

**Secretary:** Amanda Bradley   **(T)**    **(E)**
**Chairman:** Howard Williams   **Manager:** Paul Romney
**Ground:** JJN Ground, Shaw Lane, Holbrook, Derbyshire DE56 0TG   **(T)** 01332 880 259
**Colours(change):** All blue (Black & yellow/black/black)
**ADDITIONAL INFORMATION:**
**Previous Names:** Holbrook, Holbrook Miners Welfare
**Previous League:** Central Midlands

## HOLWELL SPORTS    Founded:    Nickname:

**Secretary:** Martin Rooney   **(T)** 07957 618046    **(E)** holwellsportsguy@btinternet.com
**Chairman:** Len Hallows   **Manager:** Simon Daws
**Ground:** Welby Road, Asfordby Hill, Melton Mowbray, Leicestershire LE14 3RD   **(T)** 07873 134 181
**Colours(change):** Green & gold/green/green & gold (All sky blue)
**ADDITIONAL INFORMATION:**
**Previous League:** Leicestershire Senior

## RADCLIFFE OLYMPIC    Founded: 1876    Nickname: Olympic

**Secretary:** Andrew Royce   **(T)**    **(E)** mail@radcliffeolympic.co.uk
**Chairman:** Rick Bright   **Manager:** Kevin Waddley   **Prog Ed:** Brendan Richardson
**Ground:** The Rec. Grd, Wharfe Lane, Radcliffe on Trent, Nottingham NG12 2AN   **(T)** 07825 285 024
**Colours(change):** All navy blue (All red)
**ADDITIONAL INFORMATION:**
**Previous Leagues:** Notts Alliance, Central Midlands

## RADFORD
Founded: 1964    Nickname:

**Secretary:** John Holt    **(T)** 07508 384 276    **(E)** vote4holt@hotmail.co.uk
**Chairman:** Bob Thomas    **Manager:** Iain McCulloch and Alf Stacey    **Prog Ed:** John Holt
**Ground:** Selhurst Street, Off Radford Road, Nottingham NG7 5EH    **(T)** 0115 942 3250
**Colours(change):** All claret (All sky blue)

**ADDITIONAL INFORMATION:**
**Previous Names:** Manlove & Allots 1964-71. Radford Olympic 1971-87.
**Previous Leagues:** Nottinghamshire Sunday 1964-78. East Midlands Regional 1978-83. Central Midlands 1983-2008.
Honours: East Midlands Regional League 1982-83. Central Midlands League Senior Cup 1983-84.

## ST. ANDREWS
Founded:    Nickname:

**Secretary:** Les Botting    **(T)** 07793 500 937    **(E)** standrewsfc@btconnect.com
**Chairman:** Andy Ward    **Prog Ed:** Darren Creed
**Ground:** Canal Street, Aylestone, Leicester LE2 8LX    **(T)** 0116 283 9298
**Colours(change):** Black & white/black/black (All blue)

**ADDITIONAL INFORMATION:**
**Previous League:** Leicestershire Senior

## STAPENHILL
Founded: 1947    Nickname:

**Secretary:** John Holmes    **(T)** 07805 411 307    **(E)**
**Chairman:** Martin Furness    **Manager:** Micky Wood
**Ground:** Edge Hill, Maple Grove, Stapenhill DE15 9NN.    **(T)** 01283 562 471
**Colours(change):** All red. (Black & white/black/black).

**ADDITIONAL INFORMATION:**
**Previous Leagues:** Leicestershire Senior > 2007, 2008-13. Midland Combination. Midland Alliance 2007-08.

## SUTTON TOWN AFC
Founded: 2007    Nickname: The Snipes

**Secretary:** Tim Naylor    **(T)**    **(E)**
**Chairman:**    **Manager:** Dean Short    **Prog Ed:** Dean Parrish
**Ground:** The Fieldings, Huthwaite Road, Sutton in Ashfield, Nottinghamshire NG17 2HB    **(T)**    **Capacity:** 2,500
**Colours(change):** All maroon

**ADDITIONAL INFORMATION:**
**Previous Leagues:** Central Midlands
**Honours:** Central Midlands League South Division 2012-13.

## THURNBY NIRVANA
Founded: 2008    Nickname:

**Secretary:** Zak Hajat    **(T)** 07811 843 136    **(E)** nirvanafc@hotmail.com
**Chairman:** Pat Darby    **Manager:** Damion Qualiey    **Prog Ed:** Chris Tonge
**Ground:** Dakyn Road, Thurnby Lodge, Leicester LE5 2ED    **(T)** 0116 243 3308
**Colours(change):** All green (Red & black/black/black)

**ADDITIONAL INFORMATION:**
**Previous Name:** Thurnby Rangers and Leicester Nirvana merged to form today's club in 2008.
**Previous League:** Leicestershire Senior

# EASTERN COUNTIES

2012-13 - Mildenhall Town.    2012-13 - Newmarket Town. Photos: Alan Coomes.

# EASTERN COUNTIES LEAGUE

**Sponsored by:** Thurlow Nunn
**Founded:** 1935
**Recent Champions:**
2008: Soham Town Rangers
2009: Lowestoft Town
2010: Needham Market
2011: Leiston
2012: Wroxham
**ridgeonsleague.co.uk**

| PREMIER DIVISION | | P | W | D | L | F | A | Pts |
|---|---|---|---|---|---|---|---|---|
| 1 | (P) Dereham Town | 38 | 28 | 3 | 7 | 85 | 35 | 87 |
| 2 | Wisbech Town | 38 | 25 | 8 | 5 | 85 | 40 | 83 |
| 3 | Gorleston | 38 | 23 | 8 | 7 | 91 | 37 | 77 |
| 4 | Brantham Athletic | 38 | 22 | 7 | 9 | 85 | 50 | 73 |
| 5 | Godmanchester Rovers | 38 | 19 | 10 | 9 | 76 | 49 | 67 |
| 6 | Walsham-le-Willows | 38 | 19 | 8 | 11 | 71 | 59 | 65 |
| 7 | Mildenhall Town | 38 | 19 | 7 | 12 | 66 | 54 | 64 |
| 8 | Hadleigh United | 38 | 18 | 7 | 13 | 67 | 52 | 61 |
| 9 | Stanway Rovers | 38 | 17 | 10 | 11 | 49 | 39 | 61 |
| 10 | Haverhill Rovers | 38 | 16 | 7 | 15 | 73 | 59 | 55 |
| 11 | Ely City | 38 | 15 | 7 | 16 | 71 | 63 | 52 |
| 12 | Kirkley & Pakefield | 38 | 13 | 13 | 12 | 57 | 68 | 52 |
| 13 | Norwich United | 38 | 14 | 6 | 18 | 55 | 52 | 48 |
| 14 | Felixstowe & Walton United | 38 | 13 | 6 | 19 | 54 | 69 | 45 |
| 15 | Woodbridge Town | 38 | 11 | 8 | 19 | 52 | 72 | 41 |
| 16 | CRC | 38 | 9 | 8 | 21 | 56 | 83 | 35 |
| 17 | Diss Town | 38 | 7 | 10 | 21 | 43 | 82 | 31 |
| 18 | Wivenhoe Town | 38 | 6 | 8 | 24 | 30 | 85 | 26 |
| 19 | Thetford Town | 38 | 6 | 6 | 26 | 41 | 85 | 24 |
| 20 | FC Clacton | 38 | 4 | 5 | 29 | 44 | 118 | 17 |

## LEAGUE CUP

**PRELIMINARY ROUND**

| | | | |
|---|---|---|---|
| Brantham Athletic | v | Cornard United | 7-0 |
| Brightlingsea Regent | v | Braintree Town Res | 2-4 |
| Ely City | v | Downham Town | 6-0 |
| Swaffham Town | v | Fakenham Town | 2-1 |
| Whitton United | v | Woodbridge Town | 2-1 |
| Wisbech Town | v | March Town United | 4-0 |

**ROUND 1**

| | | | |
|---|---|---|---|
| Brantham Athletic | v | Wivenhoe Town | 7-0 |
| Debenham LC | v | Team Bury | 2-1 |
| Dereham Town | v | Great Yarmouth Town | 3-0 |
| FC Clacton | v | Stanway Rovers | 0-3 |
| Godmanchester Rovers | v | Cambridge University Press | 0-1 |
| Gorleston | v | Diss Town | 1-0 |
| Haverhill Rovers | v | Halstead Town | 5-1 |
| Ipswich Wanderers | v | Felixstowe & Walton United | 1-6 |
| Long Melford | v | Braintree Town Res | 1-4 |
| Mildenhall Town | v | Ely City | 1-0 |
| Saffron Walden Town | v | CRC | 0-3 |
| Stowmarket Town | v | Whitton United | 1-2 |
| Swaffham Town | v | Kirkley & Pakefield | 0-4 |
| Thetford Town | v | Norwich United | 2-1 |
| Walsham-le-Willows | v | Hadleigh United | 2-3 |
| Wisbech Town | v | Newmarket Town | 3-1 |

**ROUND 2**

| | | | |
|---|---|---|---|
| Braintree Town Res | v | CRC | 1-2 |
| Cambridge University Press | v | Dereham Town | 2-1 |
| Gorleston | v | Mildenhall Town | 2-1 |
| Hadleigh United | v | Haverhill Rovers | 0-1 |
| Kirkley & Pakefield | v | Debenham LC | 5-1 |
| Stanway Rovers | v | Brantham Athletic | 2-1 |
| Whitton United | v | Felixstowe & Walton United | 3-6 |
| Wisbech Town | v | Thetford Town | 2-1 |

**QUARTER FINALS**

| | | | |
|---|---|---|---|
| Cambridge University Press | v | CRC | 3-2 |
| Felixstowe & Walton Utd | v | Gorleston | 2-1 |
| Kirkley & Pakefield | v | Wisbech Town | 1-3 |
| Stanway Rovers | v | Haverhill Rovers | 3-1 |

**SEMI FINALS**

| | | | |
|---|---|---|---|
| Wisbech Town | v | Cambridge University Press | 2-0 |
| Felixstowe & Walton Utd | v | Stanway Rovers | 1-2 |

**FINAL**

| | | | |
|---|---|---|---|
| Stanway Rovers | v | Wisbech Town | 1-2 |

| PREMIER DIVISION | 1 | 2 | 3 | 4 | 5 | 6 | 7 | 8 | 9 | 10 | 11 | 12 | 13 | 14 | 15 | 16 | 17 | 18 | 19 | 20 |
|---|---|---|---|---|---|---|---|---|---|---|---|---|---|---|---|---|---|---|---|---|
| 1 Brantham Athletic | | 4-0 | 1-0 | 1-1 | 1-1 | 7-0 | 0-3 | 5-0 | 1-1 | 1-3 | 3-2 | 1-1 | 5-1 | 2-1 | 0-1 | 6-3 | 4-3 | 2-1 | 1-1 | 4-1 |
| 2 CRC | 2-4 | | 0-2 | 1-4 | 2-2 | 0-3 | 3-2 | 1-1 | 0-2 | 2-0 | 3-4 | 1-2 | 1-1 | 0-5 | 1-3 | 4-0 | 1-3 | 1-2 | 2-0 | 4-1 |
| 3 Dereham Town | 3-0 | 4-0 | | 4-1 | 3-2 | 5-0 | 2-1 | 1-0 | 2-1 | 2-1 | 1-0 | 4-1 | 1-4 | 0-1 | 2-0 | 4-2 | 5-0 | 2-3 | 3-0 | 1-0 |
| 4 Diss Town | 1-4 | 2-5 | 1-1 | | 2-2 | 3-2 | 0-1 | 1-1 | 1-1 | 1-1 | 0-2 | 1-2 | 2-4 | 1-4 | 2-0 | 2-1 | 0-2 | 2-6 | 0-0 | 0-1 |
| 5 Ely City | 1-2 | 2-1 | 1-2 | 2-1 | | 4-2 | 4-0 | 2-3 | 2-0 | 1-3 | 2-1 | 2-2 | 1-2 | 2-0 | 1-0 | 4-1 | 1-1 | 1-2 | 4-1 | 0-2 |
| 6 FC Clacton | 0-4 | 2-2 | 0-4 | 0-2 | 2-5 | | 2-2 | 1-6 | 0-3 | 1-4 | 3-2 | 0-1 | 0-3 | 0-2 | 2-2 | 1-1 | 3-2 | 1-2 | 2-1 | 1-2 |
| 7 Felixstowe & Walton United | 3-3 | 3-3 | 0-2 | 2-0 | 2-0 | 4-1 | | 0-2 | 0-2 | 0-4 | 3-2 | 3-3 | 1-1 | 0-2 | 0-1 | 0-2 | 1-2 | 1-0 | 2-0 | 2-1 |
| 8 Godmanchester Rovers | 1-0 | 2-3 | 2-1 | 3-0 | 3-2 | 6-0 | 3-2 | | 0-0 | 2-2 | 3-2 | 3-1 | 4-0 | 0-2 | 1-2 | 2-3 | 2-0 | 0-2 | 9-0 | 1-1 |
| 9 Gorleston | 0-2 | 6-1 | 2-0 | 5-1 | 8-1 | 10-2 | 4-1 | 1-2 | | 1-0 | 3-2 | 1-1 | 1-1 | 5-1 | 3-0 | 2-0 | 0-0 | 2-3 | 1-1 | 5-2 |
| 10 Hadleigh United | 0-1 | 2-1 | 4-1 | 2-1 | 2-0 | 2-1 | 0-1 | 1-3 | 2-0 | | 1-0 | 2-3 | 0-1 | 2-1 | 1-1 | 4-2 | 0-2 | 4-1 | 0-0 | 1-1 |
| 11 Haverhill Rovers | 1-2 | 2-1 | 1-2 | 2-2 | 2-0 | 2-1 | 3-1 | 5-1 | 0-3 | 2-2 | | 5-0 | 1-3 | 2-2 | 0-2 | 4-4 | 1-2 | 0-3 | 3-1 | 3-0 |
| 12 Kirkley & Pakefield | 0-2 | 3-0 | 0-3 | 1-1 | 0-4 | 2-2 | 1-1 | 2-2 | 0-3 | 4-3 | 0-2 | | 0-3 | 2-0 | 2-0 | 3-0 | 2-3 | 1-3 | 3-1 | 2-1 |
| 13 Mildenhall Town | 0-1 | 2-0 | 1-3 | 5-2 | 1-1 | 4-1 | 3-2 | 1-2 | 1-2 | 1-2 | 0-0 | 4-3 | | 2-1 | 1-2 | 4-2 | 0-3 | 0-3 | 4-0 | 2-1 |
| 14 Norwich United | 3-1 | 0-2 | 0-1 | 0-3 | 1-3 | 2-1 | 3-0 | 1-1 | 1-2 | 2-0 | 0-1 | 0-1 | 1-2 | | 0-2 | 1-2 | 2-1 | 0-0 | 4-0 | 1-1 |
| 15 Stanway Rovers | 1-0 | 1-1 | 2-2 | 1-1 | 2-1 | 2-1 | 3-0 | 0-1 | 2-2 | 0-1 | 0-0 | 1-2 | 2-0 | 3-2 | | 4-0 | 0-1 | 0-0 | 0-0 | 3-1 |
| 16 Thetford Town | 1-1 | 0-2 | 1-1 | 0-1 | 1-2 | 1-0 | 0-1 | 0-2 | 1-2 | 1-3 | 1-2 | 1-1 | 0-1 | 0-1 | 0-1 | | 1-2 | 1-5 | 1-1 | 2-0 |
| 17 Walsham-le-Willows | 1-4 | 3-2 | 0-3 | 2-0 | 2-0 | 4-3 | 1-0 | 1-1 | 2-4 | 4-2 | 1-5 | 0-0 | 1-1 | 2-1 | 3-0 | | | 1-3 | 7-0 | 3-0 |
| 18 Wisbech Town | 4-2 | 2-2 | 0-1 | 6-0 | 1-0 | 3-1 | 2-0 | 0-0 | 0-2 | 3-1 | 2-2 | 3-3 | 1-0 | 2-2 | 3-1 | 4-1 | 1-1 | | 3-1 | 3-1 |
| 19 Wivenhoe Town | 0-3 | 0-0 | 1-1 | 3-0 | 0-6 | 2-0 | 3-6 | 0-2 | 1-0 | 2-4 | 1-3 | 0-0 | 0-1 | 2-1 | 0-1 | 1-3 | 0-1 | | | 3-0 |
| 20 Woodbridge Town | 4-0 | 2-1 | 1-3 | 2-0 | 2-2 | 5-2 | 1-3 | 1-2 | 0-1 | 1-0 | 0-2 | 2-2 | 1-1 | 1-2 | 3-2 | 4-3 | 3-1 | 0-2 | 2-1 | |

## EASTERN COUNTIES - STEP 5/6

| DIVISION ONE | P | W | D | L | F | A | Pts |
|---|---|---|---|---|---|---|---|
| 1 Cambridge University Press | 34 | 25 | 7 | 2 | 94 | 32 | 82 |
| 2 (P) Newmarket Town | 34 | 24 | 4 | 6 | 84 | 34 | 76 |
| 3 (P) Brightlingsea Regent | 34 | 22 | 6 | 6 | 90 | 29 | 72 |
| 4 Ipswich Wanderers | 34 | 18 | 9 | 7 | 67 | 38 | 63 |
| 5 Fakenham Town | 34 | 19 | 6 | 9 | 62 | 37 | 63 |
| 6 Saffron Walden Town | 34 | 17 | 11 | 6 | 73 | 32 | 62 |
| 7 Whitton United | 34 | 17 | 6 | 11 | 87 | 46 | 57 |
| 8 Braintree Town Reserves | 34 | 18 | 3 | 13 | 86 | 65 | 57 |
| 9 Swaffham Town | 34 | 17 | 3 | 14 | 76 | 55 | 54 |
| 10 Great Yarmouth Town | 34 | 15 | 7 | 12 | 70 | 64 | 52 |
| 11 Halstead Town | 34 | 15 | 4 | 15 | 70 | 63 | 49 |
| 12 Team Bury | 34 | 13 | 6 | 15 | 62 | 72 | 45 |
| 13 Long Melford (-1pt) | 34 | 8 | 8 | 18 | 46 | 81 | 31 |
| 14 March Town United (-1pt) | 34 | 8 | 5 | 21 | 38 | 84 | 28 |
| 15 Debenham LC | 34 | 8 | 3 | 23 | 57 | 91 | 27 |
| 16 Downham Town | 34 | 8 | 3 | 23 | 41 | 84 | 27 |
| 17 Stowmarket Town | 34 | 5 | 4 | 25 | 41 | 100 | 19 |
| 18 Cornard United | 34 | 1 | 1 | 32 | 17 | 154 | 4 |

## DIVISION ONE LEAGUE CUP

**PRELIMINARY ROUND**

| | | | |
|---|---|---|---|
| Cornard United | v | Stowmarket Town | 1-0 |
| Saffron Walden Town | v | Braintree Town Reserves | 1-5 |

**ROUND 1**

| | | | |
|---|---|---|---|
| Brightlingsea Regent | v | Whitton United | 1-0 |
| Cornard United | v | Braintree Town Reserves | 0-10 |
| Debenham LC | v | Ipswich Wanderers | 2-5 |
| Downham Town | v | Newmarket Town | 1-3 |
| Fakenham Town | v | Great Yarmouth Town | 2-3 |
| Long Melford | v | Halstead Town | 0-1 |
| March Town United | v | Cambridge University Press | 1-0 |
| Swaffham Town | v | Team Bury | 5-3 |

**QUARTER FINALS**

| | | | |
|---|---|---|---|
| Great Yarmouth Town | v | March Town United | 3-1 |
| Ipswich Wanderers | v | Braintree Town Reserves | 2-0 |
| Newmarket Town | v | Halstead Town | 2-1 |
| Swaffham Town | v | Brightlingsea Regent | 0-2 |

**SEMI FINALS**

| | | | |
|---|---|---|---|
| Great Yarmouth Town | v | Ipswich Wanderers | 0-0 |

*Great Yarmouth won on penalties.*

| | | | |
|---|---|---|---|
| Newmarket Town | v | Brightlingsea Regent | 0-3 |

**FINAL**

| | | | |
|---|---|---|---|
| Brightlingsea Regent | v | Great Yarmouth Town | 1-0 |

| DIVISION ONE | 1 | 2 | 3 | 4 | 5 | 6 | 7 | 8 | 9 | 10 | 11 | 12 | 13 | 14 | 15 | 16 | 17 | 18 |
|---|---|---|---|---|---|---|---|---|---|---|---|---|---|---|---|---|---|---|
| 1 Braintree Town Res | | 0-2 | 2-3 | 5-0 | 2-1 | 6-2 | 1-0 | 5-2 | 3-4 | 1-2 | 3-0 | 1-3 | 3-2 | 2-2 | 1-0 | 1-3 | 8-2 | 2-1 |
| 2 Brightlingsea Regent | 2-3 | | 1-0 | 3-0 | 6-2 | 2-2 | 1-1 | 1-2 | 5-1 | 4-2 | 3-1 | 1-2 | 2-0 | 1-1 | 4-0 | 2-1 | 2-1 | 2-2 |
| 3 Cambridge University Press | 3-0 | 1-1 | | 9-0 | 3-1 | 3-0 | 1-1 | 2-0 | 2-1 | 0-2 | 2-0 | 3-1 | 2-2 | 2-2 | 3-0 | 2-1 | 8-2 | 2-2 |
| 4 Cornard United | 0-4 | 0-5 | 2-5 | | 1-2 | 0-4 | 0-4 | 0-5 | 0-2 | 0-4 | 2-3 | 1-2 | 0-4 | 0-9 | 1-2 | 0-4 | 2-2 | 0-7 |
| 5 Debenham LC | 2-6 | 0-4 | 0-4 | 14-0 | | 1-4 | 1-2 | 6-4 | 2-1 | 1-1 | 4-0 | 2-2 | 1-2 | 0-2 | 1-1 | 1-0 | 1-2 | 1-3 |
| 6 Downham Town | 4-2 | 1-1 | 0-1 | 3-1 | 4-1 | | 0-4 | 2-1 | 0-2 | 1-2 | 1-3 | 2-3 | 1-3 | 1-1 | 3-2 | 0-2 | 0-4 | 0-3 |
| 7 Fakenham Town | 3-2 | 2-1 | 0-0 | 4-0 | 1-2 | 2-0 | | 1-1 | 0-3 | 1-1 | 5-0 | 3-0 | 0-2 | 1-3 | 2-0 | 2-1 | 3-0 | 1-0 |
| 8 Great Yarmouth Town | 1-3 | 1-1 | 3-4 | 3-1 | 7-4 | 2-0 | 3-0 | | 3-3 | 0-0 | 0-0 | 1-3 | 2-3 | 1-1 | 2-1 | 2-1 | 0-1 | 4-2 |
| 9 Halstead Town | 2-3 | 0-2 | 0-1 | 7-0 | 3-0 | 4-1 | 2-1 | 2-3 | | 0-2 | 6-0 | 3-0 | 3-4 | 1-0 | 2-1 | 1-1 | 1-3 | 0-5 |
| 10 Ipswich Wanderers | 2-3 | 0-4 | 1-2 | 0-1 | 3-0 | 6-1 | 1-2 | 2-1 | 3-1 | | 2-1 | 2-0 | 0-1 | 3-0 | 4-2 | 2-2 | 2-2 | 1-0 |
| 11 Long Melford | 1-8 | 0-6 | 2-5 | 5-1 | 5-0 | 2-1 | 1-3 | 1-2 | 2-2 | 1-2 | | 0-0 | 0-4 | 1-1 | 2-2 | 2-1 | 1-1 | 2-1 |
| 12 March Town United | 1-1 | 1-6 | 1-2 | 2-1 | 2-0 | 1-2 | 1-2 | 1-2 | 0-3 | 0-4 | 0-3 | | 0-1 | 2-3 | 1-0 | 1-6 | 0-6 | 0-3 |
| 13 Newmarket Town | 1-1 | 0-1 | 0-2 | 4-0 | 4-2 | 1-0 | 4-4 | 5-1 | 3-0 | 1-1 | 1-0 | 3-0 | | 0-1 | 7-0 | 4-0 | 4-1 | 2-0 |
| 14 Saffron Walden Town | 3-0 | 1-0 | 1-1 | 6-1 | 1-0 | 3-0 | 0-1 | 0-1 | 4-0 | 1-1 | 2-1 | 4-1 | 1-2 | | 6-0 | 3-1 | 4-0 | 0-0 |
| 15 Stowmarket Town | 4-0 | 0-6 | 0-6 | 11-1 | 2-1 | 4-0 | 0-2 | 1-2 | 1-4 | 0-3 | 2-5 | 2-2 | 0-4 | 2-2 | | 0-5 | 0-2 | 1-7 |
| 16 Swaffham Town | 3-1 | 0-5 | 0-3 | 3-1 | 6-1 | 5-0 | 3-2 | 2-5 | 4-1 | 2-2 | 4-0 | 2-0 | 1-2 | 1-0 | 2-0 | | 4-1 | 4-2 |
| 17 Team Bury | 3-1 | 0-2 | 2-3 | 1-0 | 1-2 | 3-1 | 0-2 | 3-1 | 2-2 | 1-3 | 2-2 | 2-1 | 1-2 | 2-2 | 4-0 | 2-1 | | 2-3 |
| 18 Whitton United | 1-2 | 3-1 | 1-4 | 6-0 | 2-0 | 3-0 | 2-0 | 2-2 | 2-3 | 1-1 | 2-0 | 7-1 | 3-2 | 2-3 | 3-0 | 4-0 | 4-1 | |

## CLUB MOVEMENTS

**Premier Division - In:** Brightlingsea Regent (P). Newmarket Town (P).
**Out:** Dereham Town (P - Isthmian Division One North). Wisbech Town (S - United Counties Premier).
**Division One - In:** AFC Sudbury Reserves (S - Eastern Counties Reserves Div.1).
Dereham Town Reserves (S - Eastern Counties Reserves Prem).
Haverhill Borough, formerly Haverhill Sports Association (P - Essex & Suffolk Border).
Needham Market Reserves (S - Eastern Counties Reserves Prem).
**Out:** Brightlingsea Regent (P). Cambridge University Press (W - Cambridgeshire Senior). Newmarket Town (P).

## BRANTHAM ATHLETIC
Founded: 1887     Nickname:

**Secretary:** Barry Felgate    **(T)** 07890 130583    **(E)** branthamathfc@hotmail.co.uk

**Chairman:** Peter Crowhurst    **Manager:** Tony Hall    **Prog Ed:** Barry Felgate

**Ground:** Brantham Leisure Centre, New Village, Brantham CO11 1RZ.    **(T)** 01206 392 506

**Capacity:** 1,200   **Seats:** 200   **Covered:** 200   **Midweek Matchday:** Tuesday    **Clubhouse:** Yes

**Colours(change):** All blue. (Red and black/black/black)
**Previous Names:** Brantham & Stutton United 1996-98.
**Previous Leagues:** Eastern Counties. Suffolk & Ipswich.
**Records:** Att: 1,700 v VS Rugby, FA Vase 5R 1982-83.
**Senior Honours:** Suffolk & Ipswich Senior League Champions 2007-08.

**10 YEAR RECORD**

| 03-04 | 04-05 | 05-06 | 06-07 | 07-08 | 08-09 | 09-10 | 10-11 | 11-12 | 12-13 |
|---|---|---|---|---|---|---|---|---|---|
| | S&I 1   2 | S&I S   14 | S&I S   4 | S&I S   1 | EC1   8 | EC1   3 | ECP   13 | ECP   3 | ECP   4 |

## BRIGHTLINGSEA REGENT
Founded: Pre     Nickname: The Tics

**Secretary:** Tom Rothery    **(T)** 07528 840 890    **(E)** t.rothery@sky.com

**Chairman:** Terry Doherty    **Manager:** James Webster

**Ground:** North Road, Brightlingsea, Essex CO7 0PL    **(T)** 01206 304 199

**Capacity:**   **Seats:**   **Covered:**   **Midweek Matchday:** Tuesday    **Clubhouse:** Yes

**Colours(change):** Red & black stripes/red/red (Purple/black/black)
**Previous Names:**
**Previous Leagues:** Essex & Suffolk Border > 2011.
**Records:**
**Senior Honours:** Essex & Suffolk Border League 2010-11.

**10 YEAR RECORD**

| 03-04 | 04-05 | 05-06 | 06-07 | 07-08 | 08-09 | 09-10 | 10-11 | 11-12 | 12-13 |
|---|---|---|---|---|---|---|---|---|---|
| | | | | | | | EsSuP   1 | EC1   5 | EC1   3 |

## CRC
Founded:     Nickname:

**Secretary:** Julie Ankers    **(T)** 07782 120 354    **(E)** julieankers@cambridge-united.co.uk

**Chairman:** Robert Smith    **Manager:** Mark Bonner

**Ground:** Cambridge Utd FC, R Costings Abbey Stad, Newmarket Road CB5 8LN    **(T)** 07782 120 354

**Capacity:** 9,217   **Seats:** 200   **Covered:**   **Midweek Matchday:** Wednesday    **Clubhouse:** Yes   **Shop:** Yes

**Colours(change):** Amber/black/black (All white)
**Previous Names:** None.
**Previous Leagues:** None
**Records:**
**Senior Honours:**

**10 YEAR RECORD**

| 03-04 | 04-05 | 05-06 | 06-07 | 07-08 | 08-09 | 09-10 | 10-11 | 11-12 | 12-13 |
|---|---|---|---|---|---|---|---|---|---|
| | | | ECP   17 | ECP   13 | ECP   2 | ECP   2 | ECP   11 | ECP   8 | ECP   16 |

## DISS TOWN
Founded: 1888     Nickname: Tangerines

**Secretary:** Steve Flatman    **(T)** 07855 531 341    **(E)** pam@dissfc.wanadoo.co.uk

**Chairman:** Richard Upson    **Manager:** Richard Daniels    **Prog Ed:** Gary Enderby

**Ground:** Brewers Green Lane, Diss, Norfolk IP22 4QP    **(T)** 01379 651 223

**Capacity:**   **Seats:**   **Covered:**   **Midweek Matchday:** Tuesday    **Clubhouse:** Yes

**Colours(change):** Tangerine/navy/tangerine (Sky blue/navy/sky blue)
**Previous Names:**
**Previous Leagues:** Anglian Combination
**Records:** 1,731 v Atherton LR, FA Vase Semi Final, 19.03.94.
**Senior Honours:** Eastern Counties Division One 1991-92. FA Vase winners 1993-94.

**10 YEAR RECORD**

| 03-04 | 04-05 | 05-06 | 06-07 | 07-08 | 08-09 | 09-10 | 10-11 | 11-12 | 12-13 |
|---|---|---|---|---|---|---|---|---|---|
| ECP   4 | ECP   12 | ECP   11 | ECP   20 | EC1   4 | EC1   9 | EC1   5 | EC1   3 | ECP   16 | ECP   17 |

## ELY CITY

Founded: 1885     Nickname: Robins

**Secretary:** Derek Oakey    **(T)** 07720 542 882    **(E)** derek.oakey@tesco.net
**Chairman:** Robert Button    **Manager:** Alan Alsop    **Prog Ed:** Barnes Print
**Ground:** Unwin Sports Ground, Downham Road, Ely CB6 2SH    **(T)** 01353 662 035
**Capacity:** 1,500 **Seats:** 150 **Covered:** 350 **Midweek Matchday:** Tuesday    **Clubhouse:** Yes **Shop:** Yes

**Colours(change):** All red. (All blue).
**Previous Names:** None.
**Previous Leagues:** Peterborough. Central Alliance.
**Records:** Att: 260 v Soham, Eastern Counties Div.1, 12.04.93.
**Senior Honours:** Cambridgeshire Senior Cup 1947-48. Eastern Counties Division 1 1996-97.
Cambridgeshire Invitation Cup 2011-12, 12-13.

**10 YEAR RECORD**

| 03-04 | | 04-05 | | 05-06 | | 06-07 | | 07-08 | | 08-09 | | 09-10 | | 10-11 | | 11-12 | | 12-13 | |
|---|---|---|---|---|---|---|---|---|---|---|---|---|---|---|---|---|---|---|---|
| EC1 | 10 | EC1 | 9 | EC1 | 7 | EC1 | 4 | EC1 | 2 | ECP | 14 | ECP | 9 | ECP | 15 | ECP | 2 | ECP | 11 |

## FC CLACTON

Founded: 1892     Nickname: The Seasiders

**Secretary:** Barry Leatherdale    **(T)** 07545 998 242    **(E)** secretary@fcclacton.com
**Chairman:** David Ballard    **Manager:** Ray Turner    **Prog Ed:** Martin Oswick
**Ground:** Rush Green Bowl, Rush Green Rd, Clacton-on-Sea CO16 7BQ    **(T)** 07792 352 187
**Capacity:** 3,000 **Seats:** 200 **Covered:** Yes **Midweek Matchday:** Tuesday    **Clubhouse:** Yes **Shop:** Yes

**Colours(change):** White & royal blue/royal blue/royal blue. (Yellow/black/black).
**Previous Names:** Clacton Town > 2007
**Previous Leagues:** Eastern Counties. Essex County. Southern League.
**Records:** Att: 3,505 v Romford, FA Cup 1952 at Old Road.
**Senior Honours:** Eastern Counties Division 1 1994-95, 98-99.

**10 YEAR RECORD**

| 03-04 | | 04-05 | | 05-06 | | 06-07 | | 07-08 | | 08-09 | | 09-10 | | 10-11 | | 11-12 | | 12-13 | |
|---|---|---|---|---|---|---|---|---|---|---|---|---|---|---|---|---|---|---|---|
| ECP | 6 | ECP | 8 | ECP | 22 | ECP | 21 | EC1 | 10 | EC1 | 7 | EC1 | 2 | ECP | 16 | ECP | 15 | ECP | 20 |

## FELIXSTOWE & WALTON UNITED

Founded: 2000     Nickname: Seasiders

**Secretary:** Kevin Witchalls    **(T)** 07912 304 453    **(E)** kevin.witchalls@btinternet.com
**Chairman:** Andy Wilding    **Manager:** Steve Buckle    **Prog Ed:** Adam Whalley
**Ground:** Goldstar Ground, Dellwood Avenue, Felixstowe IP11 9HT    **(T)** 01394 282 917
**Capacity:** 2,000 **Seats:** 200 **Covered:** 200 **Midweek Matchday:** Tuesday    **Clubhouse:** Yes **Shop:** Yes

**Colours(change):** Red & white stripes/white/red. (Yellow & blue/yellow/yellow).
**Previous Names:** Felixstowe Port & Town and Walton United merged in July 2000.
**Previous Leagues:** None
**Records:**
**Senior Honours:**

**10 YEAR RECORD**

| 03-04 | | 04-05 | | 05-06 | | 06-07 | | 07-08 | | 08-09 | | 09-10 | | 10-11 | | 11-12 | | 12-13 | |
|---|---|---|---|---|---|---|---|---|---|---|---|---|---|---|---|---|---|---|---|
| EC1 | 15 | EC1 | 17 | EC1 | 2 | ECP | 13 | ECP | 8 | ECP | 12 | ECP | 7 | ECP | 18 | ECP | 18 | ECP | 14 |

## GODMANCHESTER ROVERS

Founded: 1911     Nickname: Goody/Rovers

**Secretary:** Roger Carpenter    **(T)** 07552 771 338    **(E)** rogergrfc@gmail.com
**Chairman:** Keith Gabb    **Manager:** David Hurst & Neville Nania    **Prog Ed:** Sue Hurst
**Ground:** Bearscroft Lane, Godmanchester, Huntingdon, Cambs PE29 2LQ    **(T)** 07774 830507
**Capacity:** **Seats:** **Covered:** Yes **Midweek Matchday:** Wednesday    **Clubhouse:** Yes

**Colours(change):** Blue & white stripes/blue/blue (Red & white stripes/red/red)
**Previous Names:** None
**Previous Leagues:**
**Records:** Att: 138 v Cambridge City Reserves, Dec. 2003.
**Senior Honours:** Eastern Counties League Division One 2011-12.

**10 YEAR RECORD**

| 03-04 | | 04-05 | | 05-06 | | 06-07 | | 07-08 | | 08-09 | | 09-10 | | 10-11 | | 11-12 | | 12-13 | |
|---|---|---|---|---|---|---|---|---|---|---|---|---|---|---|---|---|---|---|---|
| EC1 | 7 | EC1 | 20 | EC1 | 14 | EC1 | 17 | EC1 | 16 | EC1 | 10 | EC1 | 12 | EC1 | 9 | EC1 | 1 | ECP | 5 |

# GORLESTON
Founded: 1887          Nickname: The Cards

**Secretary:** Ann Santon          **(T)** 07597 926 329          **(E)** santonmicks@aol.com

**Chairman:** Alan Gordon          **Manager:** Stuart Larter          **Prog Ed:** Colin Bray

**Ground:** Emerald Park, Woodfarm Lane, Gorleston, Norfolk NR31 9AQ          **(T)** 01493 602 802

**Capacity:**          **Seats:** Yes          **Covered:** Yes          **Midweek Matchday:** Tuesday          **Clubhouse:** Yes

**Colours(change):** All green (Red/black/black)
**Previous Names:** None
**Previous Leagues:** Anglian Combination
**Records:** Record Att: 4,473 v Orient, FA Cup 1st Round, 29.11.51.
**Senior Honours:** Norfolk & Suff. Lge (x 7). Norfolk Senior Cup x16 Most recently 2011-12.
Anglian Comb 1968-69. Eastern Counties 1952-53, 72-73, 79-80, 80-81. Division One 1995-96, 2010-11.

### 10 YEAR RECORD
| 03-04 | | 04-05 | | 05-06 | | 06-07 | | 07-08 | | 08-09 | | 09-10 | | 10-11 | | 11-12 | | 12-13 | |
|---|---|---|---|---|---|---|---|---|---|---|---|---|---|---|---|---|---|---|---|
| ECP | 20 | ECP | 21 | EC1 | 18 | EC1 | 14 | EC1 | 8 | EC1 | 6 | EC1 | 4 | EC1 | 1 | ECP | 12 | ECP | 3 |

# HADLEIGH UNITED
Founded: 1892          Nickname: Brettsiders

**Secretary:** Louise Hay          **(T)** 07962 274 986          **(E)** louise.hay1@yahoo.co.uk

**Chairman:** Rolf Beggerow          **Manager:** Stuart Crawford          **Prog Ed:** Nick Barwick

**Ground:** Millfield, Tinkers Lane, Duke St, Hadleigh IP7 5NF          **(T)** 01473 822 165

**Capacity:** 3,000 **Seats:** 250          **Covered:** 500          **Midweek Matchday:** Tuesday          **Clubhouse:** Yes

**Colours(change):** White/blue/blue (All blue)
**Previous Names:** None
**Previous Leagues:** Suffolk & Ipswich.
**Records:** Att: 518 v Halstead Town, FA Vase replay, 17.01.95.
**Senior Honours:** Suffolk & Ipswich League Champions 1953-54, 56-57, 73-74, 76-77, 78-79.
Suffolk Senior Cup 1968-69, 71-72, 82-83, 2003-04. Eastern Counties League Champions 1993-94.

### 10 YEAR RECORD
| 03-04 | | 04-05 | | 05-06 | | 06-07 | | 07-08 | | 08-09 | | 09-10 | | 10-11 | | 11-12 | | 12-13 | |
|---|---|---|---|---|---|---|---|---|---|---|---|---|---|---|---|---|---|---|---|
| EC1 | 18 | EC1 | 16 | EC1 | 21 | EC1 | 9 | EC1 | 5 | EC1 | 2 | ECP | 18 | ECP | 9 | ECP | 11 | ECP | 8 |

# HAVERHILL ROVERS
Founded: 1886          Nickname: Rovers

**Secretary:** Julie Ankers          **(T)** 07782 120 354          **(E)** julesankers@gmail.com

**Chairman:** Alastair Shulver          **Manager:** Dean Greygoose

**Ground:** The New Croft, Chalkstone Way, Haverhill, Suffolk CB9 0BW          **(T)** 01440 702 137

**Capacity:** 3,000 **Seats:** 200          **Covered:** 200          **Midweek Matchday:** Tuesday          **Clubhouse:** Yes

**Colours(change):** All red. (All green).
**Previous Names:** None.
**Previous Leagues:** East Anglian. Essex & Suffolk Border.
**Records:**
**Senior Honours:** Essex & Suffolk Border League Champions 1947-48, 62-63, 63-64.
Eastern Counties League Cup 1964-65, League Champions 78-79. Suffolk Senior Cup 1995-96.

### 10 YEAR RECORD
| 03-04 | | 04-05 | | 05-06 | | 06-07 | | 07-08 | | 08-09 | | 09-10 | | 10-11 | | 11-12 | | 12-13 | |
|---|---|---|---|---|---|---|---|---|---|---|---|---|---|---|---|---|---|---|---|
| EC1 | 11 | EC1 | 5 | EC1 | 8 | EC1 | 2 | ECP | 10 | ECP | 21 | ECP | 12 | ECP | 8 | ECP | 14 | ECP | 10 |

# KIRKLEY & PAKEFIELD
Founded: 1886          Nickname: The Kirks

**Secretary:** Ian Wardrope          **(T)**          **(E)**

**Chairman:** Robert Jenkerson          **Manager:** Jamie Godbold

**Ground:** K. & P. Community Sports & S. Club, Walmer Rd, Lowestoft NR33 7LE          **(T)** 01502 513 549

**Capacity:** 2,000 **Seats:** 150          **Covered:** 150          **Midweek Matchday:** Wednesday          **Clubhouse:** Yes          **Shop:** Yes

**Colours(change):** All blue with white trim (All maroon).
**Previous Names:** Kirkley. Kirkley & Waveney 1929-33. Merged with Pakefield in 2007.
**Previous Leagues:** Norfolk & Suffolk. Anglian Combination.
**Records:** Att: 1,125 v Lowestoft Town. **Goalscorer:** Barry Dale - 241. **Apps:** Barry Dale - 495.
**Senior Honours:** Suffolk Senior Cup 1900-01, 01-02, 24-25, 00-01, 01-02. Anglian Combination League 2001-02, 02-03.

### 10 YEAR RECORD
| 03-04 | | 04-05 | | 05-06 | | 06-07 | | 07-08 | | 08-09 | | 09-10 | | 10-11 | | 11-12 | | 12-13 | |
|---|---|---|---|---|---|---|---|---|---|---|---|---|---|---|---|---|---|---|---|
| EC1 | 5 | EC1 | 3 | ECP | 14 | ECP | 7 | ECP | 6 | ECP | 6 | ECP | 4 | ECP | 12 | ECP | 13 | ECP | 12 |

# MILDENHALL TOWN
Founded: 1898 — Nickname: The Hall

**Secretary:** Brian Hensby **(T)** 07932 043 261 **(E)** bhensby@talktalk.net
**Chairman:** Martin Tuck **Manager:** Christian Appleford **Prog Ed:** Frank Marshall
**Ground:** Recreation Way, Mildenhall, Suffolk IP28 7HG **(T)** 01638 713 449
**Capacity:** 2,00 **Seats:** 50 **Covered:** 200 **Midweek Matchday:** Tuesday **Clubhouse:** Yes **Shop:** Yes

**Colours(change):** Amber/black/black. (Red & white/white/red).
**Previous Names:** None
**Previous Leagues:** Bury & District. Cambridgeshire. Cambridgeshire Premier.
**Records:** Att: 450 v Derby County, Friendly, July 2001.
**Senior Honours:**

### 10 YEAR RECORD
| 03-04 | | 04-05 | | 05-06 | | 06-07 | | 07-08 | | 08-09 | | 09-10 | | 10-11 | | 11-12 | | 12-13 | |
|---|---|---|---|---|---|---|---|---|---|---|---|---|---|---|---|---|---|---|---|
| ECP | 12 | ECP | 6 | ECP | 5 | ECP | 2 | ECP | 5 | ECP | 11 | ECP | 6 | ECP | 5 | ECP | 7 | ECP | 7 |

# NEWMARKET TOWN
Founded: 1877 — Nickname: The Jockeys

**Secretary:** Elaine Jeakins **(T)** 01638 663 637 **(E)** elaine.jeakins@ntlworld.com
**Chairman:** John Olive **Manager:** Kevin Grainger & Carl Johnson **Prog Ed:** Elaine Jeakins
**Ground:** Town Ground, Cricket Field Road, Off Cheveley Rd, Newmarket CB8 8BT **(T)** 01638 663 637
**Capacity:** 2,750 **Seats:** 144 **Covered:** 250 **Midweek Matchday:** Wednesday **Clubhouse:** Yes **Shop:** Yes

**Colours(change):** Yellow/blue/yellow (Blue/blue/yellow)
**Previous Names:** None
**Previous Leagues:** Bury Senior. Ipswich Senior. Essex & Suffolk B. United Counties.
**Records:** Att: 2,701 v Abbey United (now Cambridge Utd) FA Cup, 01.10.49.
**Senior Honours:** Suffolk Senior Cup 1934-35, 93-94. Suffolk Premier Cup 1993-94, 94-95, 96-97. Eastern Counties League Division 1 2008-09.

### 10 YEAR RECORD
| 03-04 | | 04-05 | | 05-06 | | 06-07 | | 07-08 | | 08-09 | | 09-10 | | 10-11 | | 11-12 | | 12-13 | |
|---|---|---|---|---|---|---|---|---|---|---|---|---|---|---|---|---|---|---|---|
| ECP | 10 | ECP | 13 | ECP | 17 | ECP | 12 | ECP | 21 | EC1 | 1 | ECP | 16 | ECP | 19 | ECP | 20 | EC1 | 2 |

# NORWICH UNITED
Founded: 1903 — Nickname: Planters

**Secretary:** Keith Cutmore **(T)** 07788 437 515 **(E)** secretary.nufc@hotmail.co.uk
**Chairman:** John Hilditch **Manager:** Damian Hilton **Prog Ed:** Barnes Print
**Ground:** Plantation Park, Blofield, Norwich NR13 4PL **(T)** 01603 716 963
**Capacity:** 3,000 **Seats:** 100 **Covered:** 1,000 **Midweek Matchday:** Tuesday **Clubhouse:** Yes **Shop:** Yes

**Colours(change):** Yellow & blue/blue/blue. (All red)
**Previous Names:** Poringland & District > 1987
**Previous Leagues:** Norwich & District. Anglian Combination
**Records:** Att: 401 v Wroxham, Eastern Co. Lge, 1991-92. **Goalscorer:** M. Money. **Apps:** Tim Sayer.
**Senior Honours:** Anglian Combination Senior Cup 1983-84. Eastern Counties League Division One 1990-91, 01-02.

### 10 YEAR RECORD
| 03-04 | | 04-05 | | 05-06 | | 06-07 | | 07-08 | | 08-09 | | 09-10 | | 10-11 | | 11-12 | | 12-13 | |
|---|---|---|---|---|---|---|---|---|---|---|---|---|---|---|---|---|---|---|---|
| ECP | 11 | ECP | 14 | ECP | 20 | ECP | 16 | ECP | 15 | ECP | 19 | ECP | 15 | ECP | 6 | ECP | 9 | ECP | 13 |

# STANWAY ROVERS
Founded: 1956 — Nickname: Rovers

**Secretary:** Danny Coyle **(T)** 07581 056 174 **(E)** stanwayrovers@fsmail.net
**Chairman:** Roy Brett **Manager:** Barry Larkin
**Ground:** Hawthorns, New Farm Road, Stanway, Colchester CO3 0PG **(T)** 01206 578 187
**Capacity:** 1,500 **Seats:** 100 **Covered:** 250 **Midweek Matchday:** Wednesday **Clubhouse:** Yes **Shop:** Yes

**Colours(change):** Yellow/black/black. (Claret & sky/sky/claret).
**Previous Names:** None.
**Previous Leagues:** Colchester & East Essex. Essex & Suffolk Border.
**Records:** Att: 210 v Harwich & P, Eastern Co. Lge Div.1, 2004.
**Senior Honours:** Eastern Counties League Division 1 Champions 2005-06, League Cup 2008-09.

### 10 YEAR RECORD
| 03-04 | | 04-05 | | 05-06 | | 06-07 | | 07-08 | | 08-09 | | 09-10 | | 10-11 | | 11-12 | | 12-13 | |
|---|---|---|---|---|---|---|---|---|---|---|---|---|---|---|---|---|---|---|---|
| EC1 | 4 | EC1 | 6 | EC1 | 1 | ECP | 14 | ECP | 7 | ECP | 9 | ECP | 5 | ECP | 7 | ECP | 5 | ECP | 9 |

# THETFORD TOWN
Founded: 1883   Nickname:

**Secretary:** Bob Richards  **(T)** 07795 255 160  **(E)** bobrich60@talktalk.net
**Chairman:** Mick Bailey  **Manager:** Mark Scott
**Ground:** Recreation Ground, Mundford Road, Thetford, Norfolk IP24 1NB  **(T)** 01842 766 120
**Capacity:**  **Seats:** Yes  **Covered:** Yes  **Midweek Matchday:** Tuesday  **Clubhouse:** Yes

**Colours(change):** Claret/blue/blue (Blue & claret/claret/claret)
**Previous Names:** None
**Previous Leagues:** Founder member of Eastern Counties League
**Records:** **Att:** 394 v Diss Town, Norfolk Senior Cup, 1991.
**Senior Honours:** Norfolk Senior Cup 1947-48, 90-91. Norfolk & Suffolk League 1954-55.

**10 YEAR RECORD**

| 03-04 | | 04-05 | | 05-06 | | 06-07 | | 07-08 | | 08-09 | | 09-10 | | 10-11 | | 11-12 | | 12-13 | |
|---|---|---|---|---|---|---|---|---|---|---|---|---|---|---|---|---|---|---|---|
| EC1 | 19 | EC1 | 19 | EC1 | 22 | EC1 | 11 | EC1 | 13 | EC1 | 16 | EC1 | 11 | EC1 | 5 | EC1 | 2 | ECP | 19 |

# WALSHAM-LE-WILLOWS
Founded: 1888   Nickname: The Willows

**Secretary:** Gordon Ross  **(T)** 07742 111 892  **(E)** gordonaross@aol.com
**Chairman:** Mike Powles  **Manager:** Paul Smith
**Ground:** The Meadow, Summer Road, Walsham-le-Willows IP31 3AH  **(T)** 01359 259 298
**Capacity:**  **Seats:** 100  **Covered:** 100  **Midweek Matchday:** Wednesday  **Clubhouse:** Yes

**Colours(change):** White with red stripe/red/red (Light blue & white/black/blue)
**Previous Names:** None
**Previous Leagues:** Bury & District. Suffolk & Ipswich.
**Records:**
**Senior Honours:** Suffolk & Ipswich Senior League Champions 2001-02, 02-03. Suffolk Senior Cup 2005-06.
Eastern Counties League Division 1 Champions 2006-07.

**10 YEAR RECORD**

| 03-04 | | 04-05 | | 05-06 | | 06-07 | | 07-08 | | 08-09 | | 09-10 | | 10-11 | | 11-12 | | 12-13 | |
|---|---|---|---|---|---|---|---|---|---|---|---|---|---|---|---|---|---|---|---|
| S&I S | 2 | EC1 | 4 | EC1 | 5 | EC1 | 1 | ECP | 16 | ECP | 10 | ECP | 13 | ECP | 17 | ECP | 17 | ECP | 6 |

# WIVENHOE TOWN
Founded: 1925   Nickname: The Dragons

**Secretary:** Lorraine Rogers  **(T)** 07531 134 001  **(E)** lorraine.rogers@btopenworld.com
**Chairman:** Mo Osman  **Manager:** Mo Osman
**Ground:** Broad Lane, Elmstead Road, Wivenhoe CO7 7HA  **(T)** 01206 827 144
**Capacity:** 2876  **Seats:** 161  **Covered:** 1300  **Midweek Matchday:** Tuesday  **Clubhouse:** Yes  **Shop:** Yes

**Colours(change):** All blue (Yellow with blue sleevs/yellow/yellow)
**Previous Names:** Wivenhoe Rangers.
**Previous Leagues:** Brightlingsea & District. Colchester & East Essex. Essex & Suffolk Border, Essex Senior, Isthmian
**Records:** **Att:** 1,912 v Runcorn, FA Trophy, 1st Round, Feb. 1990. **Goalscorer:** (258 in 350 games). **Apps:** Keith Bain (538).
**Senior Honours:** Isthmian Division 2 North 1987-88. Division 1 1989-90. Essex Senior Trophy 1987-88.

**10 YEAR RECORD**

| 03-04 | | 04-05 | | 05-06 | | 06-07 | | 07-08 | | 08-09 | | 09-10 | | 10-11 | | 11-12 | | 12-13 | |
|---|---|---|---|---|---|---|---|---|---|---|---|---|---|---|---|---|---|---|---|
| Isth1N | 17 | SthE | 5 | SthE | 6 | Isth1N | 11 | Isth1N | 22 | ECP | 17 | ECP | 20 | ECP | 20 | ECP | 19 | ECP | 18 |

# WOODBRIDGE TOWN
Founded: 1885   Nickname: The Woodpeckers

**Secretary:** Daniel Frost  **(T)**  **(E)** frostdan@ntlworld.com
**Chairman:** John Beecroft  **Manager:** Mark Scopes
**Ground:** Notcutts Park, Fynn Road, Woodbridge IP12 4LS  **(T)** 01394 385 308
**Capacity:** 3,000  **Seats:** 50  **Covered:** 200  **Midweek Matchday:** Wednesday  **Clubhouse:** Yes  **Shop:** No

**Colours(change):** Black & white stripes/black/black. (All red).
**Previous Names:** None.
**Previous Leagues:** Ipswich & District. Suffolk & Ipswich.
**Records:** **Att:** 3,000 v Arsenal, for the opening of the floodlights, 02.10.90.
**Senior Honours:** Suffolk Senior Cup 1885, 77-78, 92-93, 93-94.
Ipswich & District Senior Champions 1912-13. Suffolk & Ipswich Senior 1988-89.

**10 YEAR RECORD**

| 03-04 | | 04-05 | | 05-06 | | 06-07 | | 07-08 | | 08-09 | | 09-10 | | 10-11 | | 11-12 | | 12-13 | |
|---|---|---|---|---|---|---|---|---|---|---|---|---|---|---|---|---|---|---|---|
| ECP | 17 | ECP | 17 | ECP | 16 | ECP | 9 | ECP | 17 | ECP | 18 | ECP | 19 | ECP | 10 | ECP | 6 | ECP | 15 |

# DIVISION ONE

## AFC SUDBURY RESERVES
Founded: 1999    Nickname: AFC

**Secretary:** Delia Pearce    **(T)** 07710 663 084    **(E)** delia.pearce@yahoo.co.uk
**Chairman:** Philip Turner    **Manager:** Ian Manby
**Ground:** The Mel Group Stadium, King's Marsh Brundon Lane, Sudbury CO10 7HN    **(T)** 01787 376 213
**Colours(change):** Yellow & blue

**ADDITIONAL INFORMATION:**

## BRAINTREE TOWN RESERVES
Founded:    Nickname:

**Secretary:** Paul Tyler    **(T)** 07769 978 142    **(E)** paulstyler@hotmail.co.uk
**Chairman:** Jon Emin    **Manager:** Mark Sansom    **Prog Ed:** Mark Sansom
**Ground:** The Amlin Stadium, Clockhouse Way, Cressing Road, Braintree, Essex CM7 3RD    **(T)** 01376 345 617    **Capacity:** 4,000
**Colours(change):** Royal blue/royal blue & orange/orange (Orange/white/orange)

**ADDITIONAL INFORMATION:**

## CORNARD UNITED
Founded: 1964    Nickname: Ards

**Secretary:** Chris Symes    **(T)** 07811 096 832    **(E)** chrissymes@hotmail.com
**Chairman:** Chris Symes    **Manager:** Mark Hoskin    **Prog Ed:** Chris Symes
**Ground:** Blackhouse Lane, Great Cornard, Sudbury, Suffolk CO10 0NL    **(T)** 07811 096 832
**Colours(change):** Blue & white/blue/blue (Gold & black/black/black)

**ADDITIONAL INFORMATION:**
**Record Att:** 400 v Colchester United 1997. **Goalscorer:** Andy Smiles. **Apps:** Keith Featherstone.
**Honours:** Essex & Suffolk Border League Champions 1988-89. Eastern Counties Div. 1 1989-90. Suffolk Senior Cup 89-90.

## DEBENHAM LC
Founded: 1991    Nickname: The Hornets

**Secretary:** Dan Snell    **(T)** 07840 246 837    **(E)** snelly1992@hotmail.co.uk
**Chairman:** Philip Alden & Kevin Snell    **Manager:** Paul Grainger    **Prog Ed:** Martyn Clarke
**Ground:** Debenham Leisure Centre, Gracechurch Street, Debenham IP14 6BL    **(T)** 01728 861 101    **Capacity:** 1,000
**Colours(change):** Yellow/black/yellow. (All navy blue).

**ADDITIONAL INFORMATION: Record Att:** 400. **Goalscorer:** Lee Briggs. **Apps:** Steve Nelson.
**Previous Name:** Debenham Angels > 2005.
**Previous League:** Suffolk & Ipswich > 2005.

## DEREHAM TOWN RESERVES
Founded:    Nickname:

**Secretary:** Nigel Link    **(T)** 07885 144 039    **(E)** 07885 144 039
**Chairman:** Mike Baldry    **Manager:** Matt Henman    **Prog Ed:** Barnes Print
**Ground:** Aldiss Park, Norwich Road, Dereham, Norfolk NR20 3PX    **(T)** 01362 690 460
**Colours(change):** Black & white stripes/black/black (Green & white stripes/green/green)

**ADDITIONAL INFORMATION:**

## DOWNHAM TOWN
Founded: 1881    Nickname: Town

**Secretary:** George Dickson    **(T)** 07834 329 781    **(E)** george.dickson@britishsugar.com
**Chairman:** Sandra Calvert    **Prog Ed:** Barnes Print
**Ground:** Memorial Field, Lynn Road, Downham Market PE38 9QE    **(T)** 01366 388 424
**Colours(change):** All red (All blue)

**ADDITIONAL INFORMATION:**
**Record Att:** 325 v Wells Town, Norfolk Senior Cup, 1998-99. **Honours:** Peterborough Senior Cup 1962, 63, 67, 72, 87.
Peterborough League 1963, 74, 79, 87, 88. Norfolk Senior Cup 1964, 66.

## FAKENHAM TOWN
Founded: 1884    Nickname: Ghosts

**Secretary:** Glen Mallett    **(T)**    **(E)** glenmallett@fakenhamtownfc.co.uk
**Chairman:** Geoffrey Saunders    **Manager:** Wayne Anderson    **Prog Ed:** Barnes Print
**Ground:** Clipbush Park, Clipbush Lane, Fakenham, Norfolk NR21 8SW    **(T)** 07540 778 379
**Colours(change):** Amber & black stripes/black/amber (Blue & white stripes/blue/blue)

**ADDITIONAL INFORMATION:**
**Record Att:** 1,100 v Watford, official opening of new ground.
**Honours:** Norfolk Senior Cup 1970-71, 72-73, 73-74, 91-92, 93-94, 94-95.

# GREAT YARMOUTH TOWN

Founded: 1897     Nickname:

**Secretary:** Len Beresford    **(T)** 01493 859 587    **(E)** sandysauce@hotmail.com

**Chairman:** Colin Jones    **Manager:** Mike Derbyshire    **Prog Ed:** Superjakko

**Ground:** The Wellesley, Sandown Road, Great Yarmouth NR30 1EY    **(T)** 01493 656 099    **Capacity:** 3,600

**Colours(change):** Yellow & black stripes/black/yellow (All claret)

**ADDITIONAL INFORMATION:**
**Record Att:** 8,944 v Crystal Palace FA Cup R1 52-53. **Goalscorer:** Gordon South - 298 (1927-47). **Apps:** Mark Vincent - 700 (84-05).
**Honours:** Eastern Counties League Champions 1968-69, Division 1 2009-10. Norfolk Senior Cup (x 12)

# HALSTEAD TOWN

Founded: 1879     Nickname: The Town

**Secretary:** Steve Webber    **(T)** 07848 822 802    **(E)** halsteadtownfc@aol.com

**Chairman:** Jimmy Holder    **Manager:** Mark Benterman    **Prog Ed:** Barnes Print

**Ground:** Rosemary Lane, Broton Industrial Estate, Halstead, Essex CO9 1HR    **(T)** 01787 472 082

**Colours(change):** Black & white/black/black (All blue)

**ADDITIONAL INFORMATION:**
**Record Att:** 4,000 v Walthamstowe Avenue, Essex Senior Cup 1949.
**Honours:** Eastern Counties Champions 1994-95, 95-96. Div.1 2002-03. Essex Senior Trophy 1994-95, 96-97.

# HAVERHILL BOROUGH

Founded: 2011     Nickname:

**Secretary:**    **(T)**    **(E)**

**Chairman:** Barry Geoghegan    **Manager:** Ben Cowling

**Ground:** The New Croft, Chalkestone Way, Haverhill, Suffolk CB9 0LD    **(T)** 01440 702 137    **Capacity:** 3,000

**Colours(change):** All red

**ADDITIONAL INFORMATION:**
**Previous Names:** Haverhill Sports Association > 2013.
**Previous Leagues:** Essex & Suffolk Border > 2013.

# IPSWICH WANDERERS

Founded: 1983     Nickname: Wanderers

**Secretary:** Paul Crickmore    **(T)** 07577 745 778    **(E)** iwfc@hotmail.co.uk

**Chairman:** Terry Fenwick    **Manager:** Glenn Read

**Ground:** SEH Sports Centre, Humber Doucy Lane, Ipswich IP4 3NR    **(T)** 01473 728 581

**Colours(change):** Blue/blue/white

**ADDITIONAL INFORMATION:**
**Record Att:** 335 v Woodbridge, Eastern Counties League 1993-94.
**Honours:** Eastern Counties Div.1 Champions 1997-98, 04-05. Suffolk Senior Cup 2012-13.

# LONG MELFORD

Founded: 1868     Nickname: The Villagers

**Secretary:** Richard Powell    **(T)** 07897 751 298    **(E)** richard.j.powell@hotmail.co.uk

**Chairman:** Colin Woodhouse    **Manager:** Jules Mumford    **Prog Ed:** Andy Cussans

**Ground:** Stoneylands Stadium, New Road, Long Melford, Suffolk CO10 9JY    **(T)** 01787 312 187

**Colours(change):** Black & white stripes/black/black (All red)

**ADDITIONAL INFORMATION:**
**Honours:** Essex & Suffolk Border Champions x5. Suffolk Senior Cup x8.

# MARCH TOWN UNITED

Founded: 1885     Nickname: Hares

**Secretary:** Raymond Bennett    **(T)** 07944 721 312    **(E)** r.bennett639@btinternet.com

**Chairman:** Phil White    **Manager:** Paul Crosbie    Gary Wesley

**Ground:** GER Sports Ground, Robin Goodfellow Lane, March, Cambs PE15 8HS    **(T)** 01354 653 073

**Colours(change):** Amber & black/black/black (All blue)

**ADDITIONAL INFORMATION:**
**Record Att:** 7,500 v King's Lynn, FA Cup 1956.
**Honours:** United Counties League 1953-54. Eastern Counties 1987-88.

# NEEDHAM MARKET RESERVES

Founded: 1919     Nickname: The Marketmen

**Secretary:** Mark Easlea    **(T)** 0779 545 6502    **(E)** m.easlea@sky.com

**Chairman:** Keith Nunn (Interim)    **Manager:** Kevin Horlock

**Ground:** Bloomfields, Quinton Road, Needham Market IP6 8DA. Tel: 01449 721 000    **(T)**    **Capacity:** 1,000

**Colours(change):**

**ADDITIONAL INFORMATION:**

## SAFFRON WALDEN TOWN

Founded: 1872     Nickname: The Bloods

**Secretary:** Brian Wilson     **(T)** 07747 500 659     **(E)** secretary@swtfc.com
**Chairman:** Melvyn Seymour     **Manager:** Colin Wallington & Stuart Wardley
**Ground:** 1 Catons Lane, Saffron Walden, Essex CB10 2DU     **(T)** 01799 520 980
**Colours(change):** Red & black

**ADDITIONAL INFORMATION:**
**Record Goalscorer:** Alec Ramsey - 192. **Apps:** Les Page - 538. **Honours:** Essex Senior League 1973-74, 99-00.
Eastern Counties 1982-83. Essex Senior Challenge Trophy 1982-83, 83-84, 84-85.
**Previous Lge:** Eastern Counties > 2011. Folded in 2011 reformed for 2012-13 season.

## STOWMARKET TOWN

Founded: 1883     Nickname: Gold and Blacks

**Secretary:** Amber Wilkie     **(T)** 07747 774 030     **(E)** footballsecretary@stowmarkettownfc.co.uk
**Chairman:** Neil Sharp     **Manager:** Rick Andrews     **Prog Ed:** Lal Moss
**Ground:** Greens Meadow, Bury Road, Stowmarket, Suffolk IP14 1JQ     **(T)** 01449 612 533
**Colours(change):** Gold & black/black/black (All red)

**ADDITIONAL INFORMATION:**
**Previous League:** Essex & Suffolk Border. **Record Att:** 1,200 v Ipswich Town, friendly, July 1994.
**Honours:** Suffolk Senior Cup x10

## SWAFFHAM TOWN

Founded: 1892     Nickname: Pedlars

**Secretary:** Ray Ewart     **(T)** 01760 724 581     **(E)** rayewart@aol.com
**Chairman:** Wayne Hardy     **Manager:** Paul Hunt     **Prog Ed:** Barnes Print
**Ground:** Shoemakers Lane, Swaffham, Norfolk PE37 7NT     **(T)** 01760 722 700
**Colours(change):** Black & white stripes/black/black

**ADDITIONAL INFORMATION:**
**Record Att:** 250 v Downham Town, Eastern Counties League Cup, 03.09.91.
**Honours:** Eastern Counties Division 1 2000-01.

## TEAM BURY

Founded: 2005     Nickname:

**Secretary:** Ross Wilding     **(T)** 07971 199 810     **(E)** ross.wilding@wsc.ac.uk
**Chairman:** Alan Collen     **Manager:** Ross Wilding     **Prog Ed:** Ross Wilding
**Ground:** Bury Town FC, Ram Meadow, Cotton Lane, Bury St Edmunds IP33 1XP     **(T)** 01284 754 721
**Colours(change):** All blue (All red)

**ADDITIONAL INFORMATION:**

## WHITTON UNITED

Founded: 1926     Nickname:

**Secretary:** Phil Pemberton     **(T)** 07429 116 538     **(E)** pemby64@hotmail.com
**Chairman:** Mark Richards     **Manager:** Paul Bugg     **Prog Ed:** Phil Pemberton
**Ground:** King George V Playing Fields, Old Norwich Road, Ipswich IP1 6LE     **(T)** 01473 464 030
**Colours(change):** Green and white

**ADDITIONAL INFORMATION:**
**Record Att:** 528 v Ipswich Town, 29.11.95.
**Honours:** Suffolk & Ipswich League 1946-47, 47-48, 65-66, 67-68, 91-92, 92-93. Suffolk Senior Cup 1958-59, 62-63, 92-93.
Suffolk Premier Cup 2011-12.

# GROUND DIRECTIONS

**BRANTHAM ATHLETIC - Brantham Leisure Centre CO11 1RZ - 01206 392 506**
Turn off the A12 heading towards East Bergholt, stay on the B1070 through East Bergholt and go straight across
the roundabout with the A137. Turn left immediately at the T-junction and follow this road around the sharp curve
to the right and turn right immediately before the Village Hall. Follow this road around the sharp left hand turn
and the Social Club and the car park are on the right.

**BRIGHTLINGSEA REGENT - North Road, Brightlingsea, Essex CO7 0PL - 01206 304 199**
Take exit 28 off M25, take slip road left for A12 toward Brentwood / Chelmsford / Romford, turn left onto slip road, merge
onto A12, take slip road left for A120, take slip road left for A133, at roundabout, take 2nd exit, turn left onto B1029 /
Great Bentley Road, turn right onto B1027 / Tenpenny Hill, and then immediately turn left onto B1029 / Brightlingsea
Road, turn left to stay on B1029 / Ladysmith Avenue, bear left onto Spring Road, turn left onto North Road.

**CRC - The Trade Recruitment Stadium CB5 8LN - 01223 566 500**
Exit the A14 at the fourth junction (situated east of Cambridge), up the slip road to the roundabout (sign posted
Stow-Cum-Quy). Turn right onto the A1303, and return westwards towards Cambridge. Go straight over the first
roundabout, passing Marshall Airport to the left. Go straight over two sets of traffic lights to a roundabout. The
Ground's floodlights can be seen from here and McDonald's is on the right.

**DISS TOWN - Brewers Green Lane IP22 4QP - 01379 651 223**
Off B1066 Diss -Thetford road near Roydon school. One and a half miles from Diss (BR).

**ELY CITY - Unwin Sports Ground CB6 2SH - 01353 662 035**
Follow signs for Kings Lynn/Downham Market as you approach Ely. Don't go into the city centre. After the Little Chef roundabout (junction of A10/A142) continue for approx half a mile until the next roundabout. Turn left for Little Downham (the B1411). There is also a sign for a Golf Course. The Golf Course is part of a Sports Complex which includes the football club. After turning left at the roundabout take another left after only about 50 metres into the Sports Complex entrance. The football club is at the end of the drive past the rugby club and tennis courts.

**FC CLACTON - Rush Green Bowl CO16 7BQ - 01255 432 590**
Leave the A12 at junction 29, then at roundabout take the 1st exit, then merge onto the A120 (sign posted Clacton, Harwich). Branch left, then merge onto the A133 (sign posted Clacton). Continue along the A133 following signs to Clacton until St Johns Roundabout (tiled Welcome to Clacton sign) take the 4th exit onto St Johns Rd - B1027 (sign posted St Osyth) Entering Clacton On Sea B1027 (fire station on left). B1027 At second mini-roundabout turn left onto Cloes Lane (Budgens on right). Continue down Cloes Lane for about 1/2 mile, passing St.Clares School on your right, at traffic lights, turn right onto Rush Green Rd. Rush Green Bowl will then appear on the right after 1/4 mile.

**FELIXSTOWE & WALTON - Town Ground, Dellwood Ave IP11 9HT - 01394 282 917**
The A12 meets the A14 (Felixstowe to M1/M6 trunk road) at Copdock interchange, just to the South of Ipswich. For Felixstowe take the A14 heading east over the Orwell Bridge. Follow the A14, for approx. 14 miles until you come to a large roundabout with a large water tower on your right, take the 1st exit off the roundabout, which is straight on. Take the first exit at the next roundabout, straight ahead again. At the next roundabout take the fourth exit onto Beatrice Avenue, take the first left into Dellwood Avenue. The ground is 100 yards down on the left behind tall wooden fencing.

**GODMANCHESTER ROVERS - Bearscroft Lane PE29 2LQ - 07774 830 507**
From A14 turn off for Godmanchester. Take A1198 towards Wood Green Animal Shelter, Bearscroft Lane is half mile from A14 on the left.

**GORLESTON - Emerald Park, Woodfarm Lane NR31 9AQ - 01493 602 802**
On Magdalen Estate follow signs to Crematorium, turn left and follow road to ground.

**HADLEIGH UNITED - Millfield, Tinkers Lane IP7 5NG - 01473 822 165**
On reaching Hadleigh High Street turn into Duke Street (right next to Library), continue on for approximately 150 metres and take left turn into narrow lane immediately after going over small bridge, continue to end of the lane where you will find the entrance to club car park.

**HAVERHILL ROVERS - The New Croft, Chalkstone Way CB9 0LD - 01440 702 137**
Take the A143 in to Haverhill and, at the roundabout by Tesco, turn left and then right in the one in front of the store. Carry on over the next roundabout past Aldi on the left and past the Sports Centre, Cricket Club and garage on the left. Just after the Workspace Office Solutions building take a right towards the town centre towards Parking (South). The drive way into Hamlet Croft is a small turning on the left just after Croft Lane (look for the sign for Tudor Close).

**KIRKLEY & PAKEFIELD - K & P Community & Sports Club, Walmer Road, NR33 7LE - 01502 513 549.**
From A12 to Lowestoft town centre and go over roundabout at Teamways Garage and past Teamways Pub. Take next left into Walmer Road.

**MILDENHALL TOWN - Recreation Way, Mildenhall, Suffolk IP28 7HG - 01638 713449 (club)**
Next to swimming pool and car park a quarter of a mile from town centre.

**NEWMARKET TOWN - Town Ground, Cricket Field Road CB8 8BG - 01638 663 637 (club).**
Four hundred yards from Newmarket BR.Turn right into Green Road and right at cross roads into new Cheveley Rd. Ground is at top on left.

**NORWICH UNITED - Plantation Park, Blofield, Norwich, Norfolk NR13 4PL - 01603 716963**
Off the A47.

## EASTERN COUNTIES - STEP 5/6

**STANWAY ROVERS - `Hawthorns', New Farm Road CO3 0PG - 01206 578 187**
Leave A12 at Jct 26 to A1124. Turn right(from London)or left from Ipswich onto Essex Yeomanry Way. A1124 towards Colchester 1st right into Villa Rd,then left into Chaple Rd, and left into New Farm Rd. Ground 400 yds on left.Nearest BR station is Colchester North.

**THETFORD TOWN - Recreation Ground, Munford Road IP24 1NB - 01842 766 120**
Off bypass (A11) at A143 junction - ground 800 yards next to sports ground.

**WALSHAM LE WILLOWS - Walsham Sports Club, Summer Road IP31 3AH 01359 259 298**
From Bury - Diss road (A143) turn off down Summer Lane in Walsham-le-Willows and ground is on the right.

**WIVENHOE TOWN - Broad Lane, Elmstead Road CO7 7HA - 01206 825 380**
The ground is situated off the B1027 to the north of Wivenhoe.

**WOODBRIDGE TOWN - Notcutts Park, Seckford Hall Road IP12 4DA - 01394 385 308**
From Lowestoft turn left into Woodbridge at last roundabout (or first roundabout from Ipswich). Take first turning left and first left again. Drive to ground at end of road on left.

## DIVISION ONE

**AFC SUDBURY RESERVES - The Mel Group Stadium, King's Marsh Brundon Lane, Sudbury CO10 7HN**
From Colchester, Bury St Edmunds and Ipswich: Enter Sudbury and follow signs for Halstead/Chelmsford. Go aross the river bridge and go under the old rail bridge, then turn right at the traffic lights (Kings Head) into Bulmer Road and the first right again into Brundon Lane. The road narrows before reaching ground on the right hand side.
**BRAINTREE TOWN RESERVES - The Amlin Stadium, Clockhouse Way, Cressing Rd, Braintree CM7 3RD**
Leave M11 at junction 8A (for Stansted Airport) and follow A120 towards Braintree and Colchester for 17 miles. At Gallows Corner roundabout (with WestDrive Kia on your right) take first exit into Cressing Road. Clockhouse Way and the entrance to the ground are three quarters of a mile on the left and are clearly sign-posted.
**CORNARD UNITED - Blackhouse Lane CO10 0NL - 07811 096 382**
Left off roundabout on A134 coming from Ipswich/Colchester into Sudbury, follow signs for Country Park - ground is immediately opposite along Blackhouse Lane.
**DEBENHAM LC - Debenham Leisure Centre IP14 6BL - 01728 861 101**
Approach Ipswich along the A14. Turn left at junction 51 onto the A140 signposted towards Norwich. After approx 4 miles turn right towards Mickfield and follow the road into Debenham turning left into Gracechurch Street. Debenham Leisure Centre is approx 1 mile on the right hand side.
**DOWNHAM TOWN - Memorial Field, Lynn Road          PE38 9QE - 01366 388 424**
One and a quarter miles from Downham Market (BR) - continue to town clock, turn left and ground is three quarters of a mile down Lynn Road.
**FAKENHAM TOWN - Clipbush Pk, Clipbush Lane NR21 8SW - 01328 855 859**
Corner of A148 & Clipbush Lane.
**GREAT YARMOUTH TOWN - The Wellesley, Sandown Road NR30 1EY - 01493 656 099**
Just off Marine Parade 200 yards north of the Britannia Pier. Half a mile from the BR station.
**HALSTEAD TOWN - Rosemary Lane CO9 1HR - 01787 472 082**
From A1311 Chelmsford to Braintree road follow signs to Halstead.
**HAVERHILL BOROUGH - Haverhill Rovers FC, The New Croft, Chalkestone Way, Haverhill CB9 0LD**
See Haverhill Rovers for directions.
**IPSWICH WANDERERS - SEH Sports Centre IP4 3NR 01473 728 581**
**LONG MELFORD - Stoneylands Stadium CO10 9JY - 01787 312 187**
Turn down St Catherine Road off Hall St (Bury-Sudbury road) and then turn left into New Road.
**MARCH TOWN UNITED - GER Sports Ground PE15 8HS - 01354 653 073**
5 mins from town centre, 10 mins from BR station.
**NEEDHAM MARKET RESERVES - Bloomfields, Quinton Road, Needham Market IP6 8DA.**
**SAFFRON WALDEN TOWN - Catons Lane CB10 2DU - 01799 522 789**
Into Castle Street off Saffron-W High St. Then left at T jct and 1st left by Victory Pub.
**STOWMARKET TOWN - Greens Meadow, Bury Road IP14 1JQ - 01449 612 533**
About 800 yards from Stowmarket station (BR).Turn right at lights and head out of town over roundabout into Bury Road, Ground is on the right.
**SWAFFHAM TOWN - Shoemakers Lane PE37 7NT - 01760 722 700**
**TEAM BURY - Ram Meadow, Cotton Lane IP33 1XP - 01284 754 721**
**WHITTON UNITED - King George V Playing Fields IP1 6LE - 01473 464 030**
Turn off A14, junction A1156 approx 3 miles west of A12/A14 junction.

# ESSEX SENIOR LEAGUE

**Sponsored by:** No sponsor
**Founded:** 1971
**Recent Champions:**
2008: Concord Rangers
2009: Romford
2010: Witham Town
2011: Enfield 1893
2012: Witham Town
**essexseniorfootballleague.moonfruit.com**

| | P | W | D | L | F | A | Pts |
|---|---|---|---|---|---|---|---|
| (P) Burnham Ramblers | 36 | 25 | 7 | 4 | 92 | 46 | 82 |
| (P) Barkingside | 36 | 22 | 7 | 7 | 72 | 40 | 73 |
| Takeley (-3pts) | 36 | 22 | 7 | 7 | 85 | 49 | 70 |
| Great Wakering Rovers | 36 | 19 | 8 | 9 | 97 | 54 | 65 |
| Eton Manor | 36 | 20 | 5 | 11 | 86 | 61 | 65 |
| Barking | 36 | 17 | 9 | 10 | 68 | 49 | 60 |
| Southend Manor | 36 | 15 | 11 | 10 | 78 | 50 | 56 |
| Haringey & Waltham Dev. | 36 | 15 | 8 | 13 | 70 | 65 | 53 |
| Enfield 1893 | 36 | 14 | 9 | 13 | 66 | 59 | 51 |
| London Bari | 36 | 13 | 12 | 11 | 63 | 60 | 51 |
| Sporting Bengal United | 36 | 11 | 11 | 14 | 79 | 95 | 44 |
| Bethnal Green United | 36 | 11 | 10 | 15 | 61 | 73 | 43 |
| Basildon United | 36 | 12 | 5 | 19 | 52 | 79 | 41 |
| Sawbridgeworth Town | 36 | 10 | 9 | 17 | 67 | 87 | 39 |
| Hullbridge Sports | 36 | 9 | 8 | 19 | 53 | 70 | 35 |
| London APSA | 36 | 8 | 11 | 17 | 46 | 70 | 35 |
| Stansted | 36 | 7 | 13 | 16 | 48 | 69 | 34 |
| Clapton | 36 | 3 | 12 | 21 | 37 | 76 | 21 |
| Bowers & Pitsea | 36 | 4 | 8 | 24 | 42 | 110 | 20 |

## LEAGUE CUP

**ROUND 1 (2 LEGS - HOME & AWAY)**

| | | | |
|---|---|---|---|
| London Bari | v | Sawbridgeworth Town | 2-2 - 5-0 |
| Southend Manor | v | Burnham Ramblers | 2-3 - 3-3 |
| Bethnal Green United | v | Takeley | 1-2 - 2-1 |

**ROUND 2**

| | | | |
|---|---|---|---|
| London Bari | v | Clapton | 1-1 - 4-1 |
| Great Wakering Rovers | v | Hullbridge Sports | 6-2 - 2-1 |
| Eton Manor | v | Haringey & Waltham D. | 2-1 - 4-3 |
| Bowers & Pitsea | v | Basildon United | 2-1 - 2-1 |
| Barking | v | Sporting Bengal Utd | 4-0 - 1-2 |
| London APSA | v | Barkingside | 2-2 - 0-0, 4-2p |
| Enfield 1893 | v | Stansted | 3-3 - 3-2 |
| Burnham Ramblers | v | Bethnal Green United | 0-1 - 5-0 |

**QUARTER FINALS**

| | | | |
|---|---|---|---|
| London Bari | v | Great Wakering Rovers | 2-0 - 3-2 |
| Eton Manor | v | Bowers & Pitsea | 3-2 - 2-5 |
| Barking | v | Barkingside | 1-3 - 1-1 |
| Enfield 1893 | v | Burnham Ramblers | 0-2 - 2-1 |

**SEMI FINALS**

| | | | |
|---|---|---|---|
| London Bari | v | Bowers & Pitsea | 2-1 - 1-4 |
| Barkingside | v | Burnham Ramblers | 1-1 - 2-1 |

**FINAL**

| | | | |
|---|---|---|---|
| Bowers & Pitsea | v | Barkingside | 1-9 |

| | 1 | 2 | 3 | 4 | 5 | 6 | 7 | 8 | 9 | 10 | 11 | 12 | 13 | 14 | 15 | 16 | 17 | 18 | 19 |
|---|---|---|---|---|---|---|---|---|---|---|---|---|---|---|---|---|---|---|---|
| 1 Barking | | 1-1 | 2-1 | 1-2 | 3-3 | 0-2 | 3-1 | 2-2 | 1-2 | 2-1 | 3-1 | 2-2 | 1-2 | 1-0 | 2-0 | 3-3 | 5-2 | 3-0 | 0-0 |
| 2 Barkingside | 2-0 | | 0-1 | 2-0 | 3-1 | 2-3 | 1-1 | 2-1 | 4-1 | 0-5 | 2-1 | 2-0 | 1-1 | 2-3 | 5-1 | 0-1 | 4-1 | 3-2 | 1-0 |
| 3 Basildon United | 0-3 | 1-3 | | 2-1 | 3-1 | 2-3 | 3-1 | 1-3 | 0-4 | 2-1 | 0-1 | 3-2 | 3-0 | 2-3 | 1-1 | 2-7 | 1-4 | 1-1 | 2-2 |
| 4 Bethnal Green United | 2-1 | 0-2 | 3-2 | | 3-0 | 1-2 | 2-3 | 2-2 | 3-2 | 2-0 | 2-2 | 1-1 | 2-2 | 3-1 | 2-1 | 2-2 | 2-3 | 0-2 | 2-2 |
| 5 Bowers & Pitsea | 1-4 | 0-3 | 1-2 | 1-1 | | 1-5 | 0-0 | 1-4 | 2-0 | 1-6 | 3-4 | 1-5 | 2-4 | 0-2 | 6-2 | 0-5 | 5-4 | 2-2 | 1-5 |
| 6 Burnham Ramblers | 1-1 | 1-1 | 2-0 | 2-3 | 7-0 | | 3-3 | 3-2 | 1-4 | 1-1 | 4-1 | 1-1 | 5-0 | 2-2 | 6-3 | 2-0 | 5-3 | 5-2 | 0-0 |
| 7 Clapton | 0-2 | 0-2 | 0-2 | 3-3 | 3-1 | 2-3 | | 1-3 | 0-6 | 2-2 | 2-3 | 0-1 | 0-1 | 0-3 | 0-0 | 1-1 | 1-2 | 1-1 | 0-1 |
| 8 Enfield 1893 | 3-0 | 1-3 | 0-1 | 2-0 | 0-0 | 3-2 | 2-0 | | 3-2 | 1-0 | 1-2 | 3-3 | 1-0 | 2-0 | 6-1 | 2-1 | 1-1 | 3-2 | 0-3 |
| 9 Eton Manor | 2-1 | 2-0 | 3-3 | 2-2 | 4-0 | 0-2 | 3-2 | 2-1 | | 0-2 | 2-1 | 5-2 | 0-0 | 1-2 | 5-1 | 2-1 | 4-1 | 1-3 | 3-1 |
| 10 Great Wakering Rovers | 1-1 | 1-2 | 3-0 | 3-1 | 5-0 | 0-2 | 2-2 | 4-2 | 7-2 | | 3-2 | 3-1 | 4-1 | 1-3 | 2-0 | 3-1 | 5-2 | 4-1 | 2-5 |
| 11 Haringey & Waltham Development | 1-2 | 1-2 | 2-0 | 6-1 | 4-0 | 1-2 | 2-1 | 2-2 | 0-4 | 0-3 | | 3-1 | 1-0 | 2-1 | 5-2 | 2-2 | 2-2 | 2-2 | 0-4 |
| 12 Hullbridge Sports | 1-3 | 2-4 | 3-0 | 3-0 | 0-1 | 0-1 | 2-0 | 2-2 | 1-2 | 1-5 | 1-0 | | 4-0 | 2-2 | 1-1 | 1-3 | 1-4 | 2-2 | 2-3 |
| 13 London APSA | 1-0 | 0-4 | 0-1 | 1-3 | 2-2 | 3-0 | 2-4 | 1-1 | 3-2 | 1-3 | 1-2 | 0-1 | | 3-1 | 1-2 | 3-3 | 2-2 | 2-2 | 1-3 |
| 14 London Bari | 1-1 | 1-0 | 4-2 | 2-1 | 2-0 | 0-1 | 1-1 | 3-1 | 2-2 | 2-2 | 2-2 | 2-0 | 1-1 | | 1-1 | 2-2 | 3-3 | 1-2 | 1-3 |
| 15 Sawbridgeworth Town | 2-4 | 2-2 | 4-1 | 5-1 | 3-3 | 1-3 | 2-2 | 2-1 | 2-3 | 3-2 | 3-2 | 4-2 | 3-4 | 3-2 | | 0-3 | 1-1 | 1-2 | 1-1 |
| 16 Southend Manor | 2-3 | 0-0 | 2-2 | 3-3 | 1-1 | 0-1 | 5-0 | 4-1 | 4-0 | 2-2 | 0-2 | 2-0 | 1-0 | 4-1 | 2-0 | | 4-1 | 4-1 | 1-3 |
| 17 Sporting Bengal United | 1-5 | 4-4 | 4-2 | 0-3 | 4-1 | 1-4 | 1-0 | 3-2 | 3-3 | 4-4 | 2-2 | 3-0 | 1-1 | 2-0 | 1-6 | 1-6 | | 2-0 | 2-5 |
| 18 Stansted | 0-1 | 0-2 | 0-3 | 2-1 | 3-0 | 0-1 | 0-0 | 1-1 | 0-1 | 2-2 | 3-3 | 0-2 | 1-1 | 2-3 | 0-2 | 2-2 | 2-2 | | 1-4 |
| 19 Takeley | 3-1 | 0-1 | 5-0 | 3-1 | 2-0 | 2-4 | 5-0 | 2-1 | 0-5 | 0-3 | 0-3 | 2-0 | 3-1 | 3-3 | 2-1 | 2-0 | 4-3 | 2-2 | |

## ESSEX SENIOR - STEP 5

### Reserve Division East

| | | P | W | D | L | F | A | Pts |
|---|---|---|---|---|---|---|---|---|
| 1 | Canvey Island Reserves | 18 | 15 | 2 | 1 | 54 | 13 | 47 |
| 2 | Tilbury Reserves | 18 | 14 | 4 | 0 | 51 | 12 | 46 |
| 3 | Thurrock Reserves | 18 | 12 | 2 | 4 | 68 | 16 | 38 |
| 4 | East Thurrock Reserves | 18 | 8 | 3 | 7 | 36 | 31 | 27 |
| 5 | Burnham Ramblers Reserves | 18 | 6 | 5 | 7 | 23 | 46 | 23 |
| 6 | Great Wakering Rovers Reserves | 18 | 6 | 2 | 10 | 33 | 33 | 20 |
| 7 | Bowers & Pitsea Reserves | 18 | 6 | 2 | 10 | 34 | 49 | 20 |
| 8 | Hullbridge Sports Reserves | 18 | 4 | 2 | 12 | 24 | 63 | 14 |
| 9 | Takeley Reserves | 18 | 3 | 3 | 12 | 30 | 51 | 12 |
| 10 | Stansted Reserves | 18 | 3 | 1 | 14 | 20 | 59 | 10 |

### Reserve Division West

| | | P | W | D | L | F | A | Pts |
|---|---|---|---|---|---|---|---|---|
| 1 | Enfield Town Reserves | 16 | 11 | 2 | 3 | 71 | 19 | 35 |
| 2 | Romford Reserves | 16 | 8 | 5 | 3 | 38 | 23 | 29 |
| 3 | Grays Athletic Reserves | 14 | 8 | 2 | 4 | 42 | 23 | 26 |
| 4 | Enfield 1893 Reserves | 16 | 7 | 5 | 4 | 39 | 47 | 26 |
| 5 | Barking Reserves | 15 | 7 | 2 | 6 | 33 | 19 | 23 |
| 6 | Waltham Abbey Reserves | 16 | 6 | 3 | 7 | 26 | 38 | 21 |
| 7 | Bethnal Green Utd Reserves | 16 | 6 | 1 | 9 | 37 | 41 | 19 |
| 8 | Sawbridgeworth Town Reserves | 15 | 4 | 1 | 10 | 26 | 63 | 13 |
| 9 | London APSA Reserves | 16 | 2 | 1 | 13 | 21 | 60 | 7 |

## GORDON BRASTED MEMORIAL CUP

### ROUND 1

| | | | |
|---|---|---|---|
| Barking | v | Sporting Bengal United | 2-4 |
| London APSA | v | Southend Manor | 1-5 |
| Great Wakering Rovers | v | Enfield 1893 | 0-3 |

### ROUND 2

| | | | |
|---|---|---|---|
| Bowers & Pitsea | v | Barkingside | 0-2 |
| Hullbridge Sports | v | Sporting Bengal United | 1-2 |
| Basildon United | v | Eton Manor | 2-2, 5-4p |
| Clapton | v | Burnham Ramblers | 0-3 |
| London Bari | v | Southend Manor | 2-1 |
| Takeley | v | Stansted | 0-1 |
| Haringey & Waltham Dev. | v | Bethnal Green United | 1-3 |
| Sawbridgeworth Town | v | Enfield 1893 | 1-3 |

### QUARTER FINALS

| | | | |
|---|---|---|---|
| Barkingside | v | Sporting Bengal United | 3-2 |
| Basildon United | v | Burnham Ramblers | 1-3 |
| London Bari | v | Stansted | 2-0 |
| Bethnal Green United | v | Enfield 1893 | 0-2 |

### SEMI FINALS

| | | | |
|---|---|---|---|
| Barkingside | v | Burnham Ramblers | 0-2 |
| London Bari | v | Enfield 1893 | 1-3 |

### FINAL

| | | | |
|---|---|---|---|
| Burnham Ramblers | v | Enfield 1893 | 8-2 |

## CLUB MOVEMENTS

**Premier Division - In:** FC Romania (P - Middlesex County Premier Division). Ilford (R - Isthmian Div.1 North).

Greenhouse London (NC from Haringey & Waltham Development). Tower Hamlets (NC from Bethnal Green).

**Out:** Barkingside (P - Isthmian Div.1 North). Bethnal Green (NC to Tower Hamlets. Burnham Ramblers (P - Isthmian Div.1

North). Haringey & Waltham Development (NC to Greenhouse London).

# Click Back in Time!

Over 36 years of publishing the Non-League Club Directory has filled a room full of information and photographs covering the game we know and love.

What we intend, over time, is to create a website that shares with you everything we have accumulated, which we hope will bring back some fond memories of season's gone by.

A unique look back at how the game has evolved since the 1940s will also make for interesting reading, including league tables from season's gone by.

Log on to **www.non-leagueclubdirectory.co.uk** today
and see how many faces from teams gone by you recognise

# BARKING
Founded: 1880     Nickname: The Blues

**Secretary:** Peter Ball    **(T)** 07790 594 530    **(E)** secretary@barking-fc.co.uk
**Chairman:** Rob O'Brien    **Manager:** Mick O'Shea    **Prog Ed:** Ashley Hanson
**Ground:** Mayesbrook Park, Lodge Avenue, Dagenham RM8 2JR    **(T)** 0776 458 7112
**Capacity:** 2,500 **Seats:** 200 **Covered:** 600 **Midweek Matchday:** Tuesday    **Clubhouse:** Yes **Shop:** Yes

**Colours(change):** All blue.
**Previous Names:** Barking Rov. Barking Woodville. Barking Working Lads Institute, Barking Institute. Barking T. Barking & East Ham U.
**Previous Leagues:** South Essex, London, Athenian. Isthmian. Southern.
**Records:** **Att:** 1,972 v Aldershot, FA Cup 2nd Rnd, 1978. **Goalscorer:** Neville Fox - 241 (65-73). **Apps:** Bob Makin - 566.
**Senior Honours:** Essex Senior Cup 1893-94, 95-96, 1919-20, 45-46, 62-63, 69-70, 89-90. London Senior Cup 1911-12, 20-21, 26-27, 78-79.

**10 YEAR RECORD**

| 03-04 | 04-05 | 05-06 | 06-07 | 07-08 | 08-09 | 09-10 | 10-11 | 11-12 | 12-13 |
|---|---|---|---|---|---|---|---|---|---|
| Isth1N 23 | SthE 6 | SthE 5 | ESen 6 | ESen 9 | ESen 12 | ESen 8 | ESen 6 | ESen 7 | ESen 6 |

# BASILDON UNITED
Founded: 1963     Nickname:

**Secretary:** Richard Mann    **(T)** 0796 435 6642    **(E)** rm006e7184@blueyonder.co.uk
**Chairman:** Paul Smith    **Manager:** Laurie Carter    **Prog Ed:** Richard Mann
**Ground:** The Stadium, Gardiners Close, Basildon SS14 3AW    **(T)** 01268 520 268
**Capacity:** 2,000 **Seats:** 400 **Covered:** 1,000 **Midweek Matchday:** Wednesday    **Clubhouse:** Yes **Shop:** No

**Colours(change):** Gold/black/black. (All red).
**Previous Names:** Armada Sports.
**Previous Leagues:** Grays & Thurrock. Greater London. Essex Senior. Athenian. Isthmian.
**Records:** **Att:** 4,000 v West Ham, ground opening 11.08.70.
**Senior Honours:** Isthmian League Division 2 Champions 1983-84.

**10 YEAR RECORD**

| 03-04 | 04-05 | 05-06 | 06-07 | 07-08 | 08-09 | 09-10 | 10-11 | 11-12 | 12-13 |
|---|---|---|---|---|---|---|---|---|---|
| ESen 7 | ESen 7 | ESen 11 | ESen 10 | ESen 16 | ESen 8 | ESen 12 | ESen 12 | ESen 18 | ESen 13 |

# BOWERS & PITSEA
Founded: 1946     Nickname:

**Secretary:** Lee Stevens    **(T)** 07910 626 727    **(E)** lee-stevens@sky.com
**Chairman:** Barry Hubbard    **Manager:** John Doyle    **Prog Ed:** Lee Stevens
**Ground:** Len Salmon Stadium, Crown Avenue, Pitsea, Basildon SS13 2BE    **(T)** 01268 581 977
**Capacity:** 2,000 **Seats:** 200 **Covered:** 1,000 **Midweek Matchday:** Wednesday    **Clubhouse:** Yes **Shop:** Yes

**Colours(change):** All claret. (All sky blue).
**Previous Names:** Bowers United > 2004.
**Previous Leagues:** Thurrock & Thameside Combination. Olympian.
**Records:** **Att:** 1,800 v Billericay Town, FA Vase.
**Senior Honours:**

**10 YEAR RECORD**

| 03-04 | 04-05 | 05-06 | 06-07 | 07-08 | 08-09 | 09-10 | 10-11 | 11-12 | 12-13 |
|---|---|---|---|---|---|---|---|---|---|
| ESen 8 | ESen 10 | ESen 15 | ESen 4 | ESen 7 | ESen 11 | ESen 17 | ESen 14 | ESen 15 | ESen 19 |

# CLAPTON
Founded: 1878     Nickname: Tons

**Secretary:** Shirley Doyle    **(T)** 0798 358 8883    **(E)** ShirleyDoyle@claptonfc.com
**Chairman:** John Murray Smith    **Manager:** Chris Wood
**Ground:** The Old Spotted Dog, Upton Lane, Forest Gate E7 9NU    **(T)** 0794 400 9386
**Capacity:** 2,000 **Seats:** 100 **Covered:** 180 **Midweek Matchday:** Tuesday    **Clubhouse:** Yes **Shop:** No

**Colours(change):** Red & white stripes/black/red (Black & red stripes/red/red)
**Previous Names:** None
**Previous Leagues:** Southern (founder member). London. Isthmian (founder member).
**Records:** **Att:** 12,000 v Tottenham Hotspur, FA Cup, 1898-99. First English club to play on the continent, beating a Belgian XI in 1890.
**Senior Honours:** Isthmian League Champions 1910-11, 22-23, Division 2 1982-83. Essex Senior Cup (x 4).

**10 YEAR RECORD**

| 03-04 | 04-05 | 05-06 | 06-07 | 07-08 | 08-09 | 09-10 | 10-11 | 11-12 | 12-13 |
|---|---|---|---|---|---|---|---|---|---|
| Isth2 15 | Isth2 16 | Isth2 16 | ESen 14 | ESen 11 | ESen 16 | ESen 16 | ESen 17 | ESen 17 | ESen 18 |

## ENFIELD 1893 FC

Founded: 1893  Nickname:

**Secretary:** Mark Wiggs  (T) 0795 764 7820  (E) enfieldfc@ntlworld.com
**Chairman:** Steve Whittington  **Manager:** Luke Giddings  **Prog Ed:** Mark Kettlety
**Ground:** Goldsdown Road, Enfield, Middlesex EN3 7RP  (T) 01438 210 073
**Capacity:** 500  **Seats:** 300  **Covered:** Yes  **Midweek Matchday:** Wednesday  **Clubhouse:** Yes

**Colours(change):** White/blue/white. (Yellow/blue/yellow).
**Previous Names:** Enfield Spartans > 1900. Enfield > 2007.
**Previous Leagues:** Tottenham & District, North Middlesex, London, Athenian, Isthmian, Alliance, Southern
**Records:** Att: 10,000 v Spurs, floodlight opening at Southbury Rd., 10.10.62. **Goals:** Tommy Lawrence - 191 (1959-64). **Apps:** Andy Pape - 643 (85-92 93-99)
**Senior Honours:** FA Trophy 1981-82, 87-88. Alliance League 1982-83, 85-86. FA Amateur Cup 1966-67, 69-70. Essex Senior League 2010-11.

**10 YEAR RECORD**

| 03-04 | | 04-05 | | 05-06 | | 06-07 | | 07-08 | | 08-09 | | 09-10 | | 10-11 | | 11-12 | | 12-13 | |
|---|---|---|---|---|---|---|---|---|---|---|---|---|---|---|---|---|---|---|---|
| Isth1N | 24 | Isth2 | 2 | SthE | 16 | Isth1N | 13 | ESen | 2 | ESen | 2 | ESen | 4 | ESen | 1 | ESen | 7 | ESen | 9 |

## ETON MANOR

Founded: 1901  Nickname: The Manor

**Secretary:** Enrique Nespereira  (T) 07740 457 686  (E)
**Chairman:** Reg Curtis  **Manager:** Kieren King  **Prog Ed:** Reg Curtis
**Ground:** Waltham Abbey FC, Capershotts, Sewardstone Road, Waltham Abbey EN9 1LU  (T) 01992 711 287
**Capacity:** 2,500  **Seats:** 200  **Covered:** 600  **Midweek Matchday:** Monday  **Clubhouse:** Yes

**Colours(change):** Sky blue & navy. (Black & white/black/black).
**Previous Names:** Wildernes Leyton.
**Previous Leagues:** London. Greater London. Metropolitan.
**Records:** Att: 600 v Leyton Orient, opening of floodlights. **Goalscorer:** Dave Sams.
**Senior Honours:**

**10 YEAR RECORD**

| 03-04 | | 04-05 | | 05-06 | | 06-07 | | 07-08 | | 08-09 | | 09-10 | | 10-11 | | 11-12 | | 12-13 | |
|---|---|---|---|---|---|---|---|---|---|---|---|---|---|---|---|---|---|---|---|
| ESen | 9 | ESen | 12 | ESen | 13 | ESen | 11 | ESen | 4 | ESen | 6 | ESen | 15 | ESen | 8 | ESen | 14 | ESen | 5 |

## F.C. ROMANIA

Founded: 2006  Nickname:

**Secretary:** Emil Vintila  (T) 07907 944 409  (E) emilvintila17@yahoo.co.uk
**Chairman:** Ion Vintila  **Manager:** Ion Vintila
**Ground:** Cheshunt FC, Theobalds Lane, Cheshunt, Herts EN8 8RU  (T) 01992 625 793
**Capacity:** 3,500  **Seats:** 424  **Covered:** 600  **Midweek Matchday:**  **Clubhouse:** Yes

**Colours(change):** Yellow/blue/yellow (All orange)
**Previous Names:** None
**Previous Leagues:** Middlesex County 2006-13.
**Records:**
**Senior Honours:**

**10 YEAR RECORD**

| 03-04 | 04-05 | 05-06 | 06-07 | 07-08 | 08-09 | 09-10 | 10-11 | 11-12 | | 12-13 | |
|---|---|---|---|---|---|---|---|---|---|---|---|
| | | | | | | | | MidxP | 2 | MidxP | 2 |

## GREAT WAKERING ROVERS

Founded: 1919  Nickname: Rovers

**Secretary:** Daniel Ellis  (T) 07828 048 671  (E) danielellis@hotmail.co.uk
**Chairman:** Roy Ketteridge  **Manager:** Dan Trenkel  **Prog Ed:** Dan Ellis
**Ground:** Burroughs Park, Little Wakering Hall Lane, Gt Wakering SS3 0HH  (T) 01702 217 812
**Capacity:** 2,500  **Seats:** 150  **Covered:** 300  **Midweek Matchday:**  **Clubhouse:** Yes  **Shop:** No

**Colours(change):** Green and white stripes/white/green
**Previous Names:** Not known
**Previous Leagues:** Southend & Dist. 1919-81, Southend All. 1981-89, Essex Inter 1989-92, Essex Sen 1992-99, Isth. 1999-2004, Sthn 2004-05
**Records:** 1,150 v Southend United - Friendly 19/07/2006
**Senior Honours:** Essex Senior League 1994-95. Isthmian League Division 3.

**10 YEAR RECORD**

| 03-04 | | 04-05 | | 05-06 | | 06-07 | | 07-08 | | 08-09 | | 09-10 | | 10-11 | | 11-12 | | 12-13 | |
|---|---|---|---|---|---|---|---|---|---|---|---|---|---|---|---|---|---|---|---|
| Isth1N | 21 | SthE | 20 | SthE | 13 | Isth1N | 12 | Isth1N | 13 | Isth1N | 13 | Isth1N | 9 | Isth1N | 15 | Isth1N | 22 | ESen | 4 |

# GREENHOUSE LONDON
Founded: 2000    Nickname:

**Secretary:** Lindsay Boyaram    **(T)** 0743 212 1547    **(E)**

**Chairman:** Burk Gravis

**Ground:** Haringey Boro' FC, Coles Park, White Hart Lane N17 7JP    **(T)**

**Capacity:**    **Seats:**    **Covered:**    **Midweek Matchday:** Wednesday    **Clubhouse:** Yes    **Shop:** No

**Colours(change):** All red
**Previous Names:** Mauritius Sports merged with Walthamstow Avenue & Pennant 2007. Mauritius Sports Association 2009-11. Haringey & Waltham Development 2011-13
**Previous Leagues:** London Intermediate 2001-03. Middlesex County 2003-2007.
**Records:**
**Senior Honours:**

**10 YEAR RECORD**

| 03-04 | 04-05 | 05-06 | 06-07 | 07-08 | 08-09 | 09-10 | 10-11 | 11-12 | 12-13 |
|---|---|---|---|---|---|---|---|---|---|
| | | | | ESen 13 | ESen 15 | ESen 18 | ESen 11 | ESen 12 | ESen 8 |

# HARINGEY BOROUGH
Founded: 1907    Nickname: Borough

**Secretary:** John Bacon    **(T)** 07979 050 190    **(E)** baconjw@hotmail.com

**Chairman:** Aki Achillea    **Manager:** Tom Loizu    **Prog Ed:** John Bacon

**Ground:** Coles Park, White Hart Lane, Tottenham, London N17 7JP    **(T)** 0208 889 1415 (Matchday)

**Capacity:** 2,500    **Seats:** 280    **Covered:** yes    **Midweek Matchday:**    **Clubhouse:** Yes    **Shop:** No

**Colours(change):** Yellow/green/yellow
**Previous Names:** Tufnell Park 1907
**Previous Leagues:** London, Isthmian, Spartan, Delphian, Athenian, Spartan South Midlands > 2013.
**Records:** **Att:** 400
**Senior Honours:** London Senior Cup 1912-13, 90-91, Athenian League 1913-14

**10 YEAR RECORD**

| 03-04 | 04-05 | 05-06 | 06-07 | 07-08 | 08-09 | 09-10 | 10-11 | 11-12 | 12-13 |
|---|---|---|---|---|---|---|---|---|---|
| SSM P 18 | SSM P 18 | SSM P 19 | SSM P 21 | SSM1 2 | SSM P 18 | SSM P 15 | SSM P 8 | SSM P 5 | SSM P 9 |

# HULLBRIDGE SPORTS
Founded: 1945    Nickname:

**Secretary:** Mrs Beryl Petre    **(T)** 01702 230 630    **(E)** beryl@petre1942.fsnet.co.uk

**Chairman:** Andrew Burgess    **Prog Ed:** Beryl Petre

**Ground:** Lower Road, Hullbridge, Hockley Essex SS5 6BJ    **(T)** 01702 230 420

**Capacity:** 1,500    **Seats:** 60    **Covered:** 60    **Midweek Matchday:** Tuesday    **Clubhouse:** Yes    **Shop:** No

**Colours(change):** Royal blue & white stripes/royal/royal.
**Previous Names:** None
**Previous Leagues:** Southend & District. Southend Alliance.
**Records:** **Att:** 800 v Blackburn Rovers, FA Youth Cup 1999-00.
**Senior Honours:**

**10 YEAR RECORD**

| 03-04 | 04-05 | 05-06 | 06-07 | 07-08 | 08-09 | 09-10 | 10-11 | 11-12 | 12-13 |
|---|---|---|---|---|---|---|---|---|---|
| ESen 16 | ESen 15 | ESen 14 | ESen 12 | ESen 14 | ESen 9 | ESen 11 | ESen 9 | ESen 11 | ESen 15 |

# ILFORD
Founded: 1987    Nickname: The Foxes

**Secretary:** Marion Chilvers    **(T)** 07710 285571    **(E)** rogerchilvers@aol.com

**Chairman:** Roger Chilvers    **Manager:** Martin Haywood    **Prog Ed:** Len Llewellyn

**Ground:** Cricklefield Stadium, 486 High Road, Ilford, Essex IG1 1UE    **(T)** 020 8514 8352

**Capacity:** 3,500    **Seats:** 216    **Covered:** Yes    **Midweek Matchday:**    **Clubhouse:** Yes    **Shop:** No

**Colours(change):** Blue and white hoops/blue/blue (All red)
**Previous Names:** Reformed as Ilford in 1987 after the original club merged with Leytonstone in 1980.
**Previous Leagues:** Spartan 1987-94, Essex Senior 1996-2004, Isthmian 2004-05, 2006-13, Southern 2005-06.
**Records:** Not known
**Senior Honours:** Isthmian League Division Two 2004-05.

**10 YEAR RECORD**

| 03-04 | 04-05 | 05-06 | 06-07 | 07-08 | 08-09 | 09-10 | 10-11 | 11-12 | 12-13 |
|---|---|---|---|---|---|---|---|---|---|
| ESen 2 | Isth2 1 | SthE 21 | Isth1N 21 | Isth1N 21 | Isth1N 17 | Isth1N 20 | Isth1N 20 | Isth1N 20 | Isth1N 22 |

## LONDON APSA

Founded: 1993    Nickname:

**Secretary:** Zabir Bashir    **(T)** 07956 660 699    **(E)** zabirbashir23@hotmail.com

**Chairman:** Zulfi Ali

**Ground:** Terrence McMillan Stadium, Maybury Road, London E13 8RZ    **(T)**
**Capacity:**    **Seats:**    **Covered:**    **Midweek Matchday:**    **Clubhouse:**

**Colours(change):** All blue (Green & white/green & white/green)
**Previous Names:** Ahle Sunnah
**Previous Leagues:** Asian League.
**Records:**
**Senior Honours:**

**10 YEAR RECORD**

| 03-04 | | 04-05 | | 05-06 | | 06-07 | | 07-08 | | 08-09 | | 09-10 | | 10-11 | | 11-12 | | 12-13 | |
|---|---|---|---|---|---|---|---|---|---|---|---|---|---|---|---|---|---|---|---|
| ESen | 15 | ESen | 13 | ESen | 9 | ESen | 13 | ESen | 17 | ESen | 14 | ESen | 13 | ESen | 10 | ESen | 13 | ESen | 16 |

## LONDON BARI

Founded: 1995    Nickname:

**Secretary:** Ricky Eaton    **(T)** 07534 913 087    **(E)**

**Chairman:** Imran Merchant

**Ground:** The Old Spotted Dog, Upton Lane, Forest Gate E7 9NU    **(T)**
**Capacity:** 2,000 **Seats:** 100 **Covered:** 180 **Midweek Matchday:**    **Clubhouse:** Yes

**Colours(change):** Yellow/black/black
**Previous Names:** Bari FC.
**Previous Leagues:** South Essex 1995-98. Asian League. Essex Sunday Corinthian League > 2012.
**Records:**
**Senior Honours:**

**10 YEAR RECORD**

| 03-04 | 04-05 | 05-06 | 06-07 | 07-08 | 08-09 | 09-10 | 10-11 | 11-12 | | 12-13 | |
|---|---|---|---|---|---|---|---|---|---|---|---|
| | | | | | | | | EsxSC | 1 | ESen | 10 |

## SAWBRIDGEWORTH TOWN

Founded: 1890    Nickname: Robins

**Secretary:** Paula Worsdell    **(T)**    **(E)** sawbosec@hotmail.com

**Chairman:** Steve Day    **Manager:** Marc Das

**Ground:** Crofters End, West Road, Sawbridgeworth CM21 0DE    **(T)** 01279 722 039
**Capacity:** 2,500 **Seats:** 175 **Covered:** 300 **Midweek Matchday:** Tuesday    **Clubhouse:** Yes    **Shop:** No

**Colours(change):** Red & black/black/black. (Green/green/white).
**Previous Names:** Sawbridgeworth > 1976.
**Previous Leagues:** Stortford. Spartan. Herts County. Essex Olympian.
**Records:**    **Att:** 610 v Bishops Stortford.
**Senior Honours:**

**10 YEAR RECORD**

| 03-04 | | 04-05 | | 05-06 | | 06-07 | | 07-08 | | 08-09 | | 09-10 | | 10-11 | | 11-12 | | 12-13 | |
|---|---|---|---|---|---|---|---|---|---|---|---|---|---|---|---|---|---|---|---|
| ESen | 3 | ESen | 8 | ESen | 6 | ESen | 8 | ESen | 12 | ESen | 13 | ESen | 10 | ESen | 16 | ESen | 6 | ESen | 14 |

## SOUTHEND MANOR

Founded: 1955    Nickname: The Manor

**Secretary:** Stephen Durant    **(T)** 01702 301 573    **(E)** sdurant@hotmail.co.uk

**Chairman:** Steven Robinson    **Manager:** Leon Woodford

**Ground:** The Arena, Southchurch Pk, Lifstan Way, Southend SS1 2TH    **(T)** 01702 615 577
**Capacity:** 2,000 **Seats:** 500 **Covered:** 700 **Midweek Matchday:** Tuesday    **Clubhouse:** Yes    **Shop:** No

**Colours(change):** Yellow/black/yellow. (White/red/red).
**Previous Names:** None
**Previous Leagues:** Southend Borough Combination. Southend & District Alliance.
**Records:**    **Att:** 1,521 v Southend United, opening floodlights, 22.07.91.
**Senior Honours:** Essex Senior League Champions 1990-91. Essex Senior Trophy 92-93.

**10 YEAR RECORD**

| 03-04 | | 04-05 | | 05-06 | | 06-07 | | 07-08 | | 08-09 | | 09-10 | | 10-11 | | 11-12 | | 12-13 | |
|---|---|---|---|---|---|---|---|---|---|---|---|---|---|---|---|---|---|---|---|
| ESen | 10 | ESen | 6 | ESen | 10 | ESen | 9 | ESen | 6 | ESen | 4 | ESen | 7 | ESen | 5 | ESen | 2 | ESen | 7 |

# SPORTING BENGAL UNITED

Founded: 1996    Nickname: Bengal Tigers.

**Secretary:** Khayrul Alam    **(T)** 0207 392 2126    **(E)** bfauk@btconnect.com

**Chairman:** Aroz Miah    **Manager:** Mamun Chowdhury

**Ground:** Mile End Stadium, Rhodeswell Rd, Off Burdett Rd E14 4TW    **(T)** 020 8980 1885

**Capacity:**    **Seats:** Yes    **Covered:**    **Midweek Matchday:** Wednesday    **Clubhouse:**

**Colours(change):** All royal blue (All yellow).
**Previous Names:** None.
**Previous Leagues:** Asian League. London Intermediate, Kent 2003-11.
**Records:** **Att:** 4,235 v Touring Phalco Mohammedan S.C.
**Senior Honours:**

**10 YEAR RECORD**

| 03-04 | 04-05 | 05-06 | 06-07 | 07-08 | 08-09 | 09-10 | 10-11 | 11-12 | 12-13 |
|---|---|---|---|---|---|---|---|---|---|
| Kent P 17 | Kent P 14 | Kent P 15 | Kent P 17 | Kent P 17 | Kent P 17 | Kent P 15 | Kent P 15 | ESen 10 | ESen 11 |

# STANSTED

Founded: 1902    Nickname: Blues

**Secretary:** Tom Williams    **(T)** 07921 403 842    **(E)** stanstedfc@yahoo.co.uk

**Chairman:** Glyn Warwick    **Manager:** Dave Roach

**Ground:** Hargrave Park, Cambridge Road, Stansted CM24 8DL    **(T)** 01279 812 897

**Capacity:** 2,000 **Seats:** 200 **Covered:** 400 **Midweek Matchday:** Tuesday    **Clubhouse:** Yes    **Shop:** No

**Colours(change):** All royal blue (All red).
**Previous Names:** None.
**Previous Leagues:** Spartan. London. Herts County.
**Records:** **Att:** 828 v Whickham, FA Vase, 1983-84.
**Senior Honours:**

**10 YEAR RECORD**

| 03-04 | 04-05 | 05-06 | 06-07 | 07-08 | 08-09 | 09-10 | 10-11 | 11-12 | 12-13 |
|---|---|---|---|---|---|---|---|---|---|
| ESen 13 | ESen 11 | ESen 16 | ESen 16 | ESen 10 | ESen 10 | ESen 1 | ESen 2 | ESen 16 | ESen 17 |

# TAKELEY

Founded: 1903    Nickname:

**Secretary:** Michael Rabey    **(T)** 0783 184 5466    **(E)** mcrab@btinternet.com

**Chairman:** Pat Curran    **Manager:** Steve Castle

**Ground:** Station Road, Takeley, Bishop's Stortford CM22 6SQ    **(T)** 01279 870 404

**Capacity:**    **Seats:**    **Covered:**    **Midweek Matchday:** Tuesday    **Clubhouse:**

**Colours(change):** All royal blue with white trim. (All red with white trim).
**Previous Names:** None.
**Previous Leagues:** Essex Intermediate/Olympian.
**Records:**
**Senior Honours:** Essex Olympian League 2001-02.

**10 YEAR RECORD**

| 03-04 | 04-05 | 05-06 | 06-07 | 07-08 | 08-09 | 09-10 | 10-11 | 11-12 | 12-13 |
|---|---|---|---|---|---|---|---|---|---|
| EssxO 6 | EssxO 8 | EssxO 9 | EssxO 3 | EssxO 2 | ESen 3 | ESen 6 | ESen 13 | ESen 3 | ESen 3 |

# TOWER HAMLETS

Founded: 2000    Nickname: Green Army

**Secretary:** Akhtar Imran Ahmed    **(T)** 07590 568 422    **(E)** akhtarx@hotmail.com

**Chairman:** Mohammed Nural Hoque    **Manager:** Anton Stephenson    **Prog Ed:** Akhtar Imran Ahmed

**Ground:** Mile End Stadium, Rhodeswell Rd, Poplar E14 7TW    **(T)** 020 8980 1885

**Capacity:** 2,000 **Seats:** Yes **Covered:** Yes **Midweek Matchday:** Wednesday    **Clubhouse:**

**Colours(change):** Green & white/green/white
**Previous Names:** Bethnal Green United 2000-2013.
**Previous Leagues:** Middlesex 2000-09.
**Records:**
**Senior Honours:**

**10 YEAR RECORD**

| 03-04 | 04-05 | 05-06 | 06-07 | 07-08 | 08-09 | 09-10 | 10-11 | 11-12 | 12-13 |
|---|---|---|---|---|---|---|---|---|---|
| Midx1 2 | MidxP 7 | | | MidxP 8 | MidxP 1 | ESen 5 | ESen 4 | ESen 9 | ESen 12 |

# THE NON-LEAGUE PAPER

**ESSENTIAL READING FOR FOLLOWERS OF THE NATIONAL GAME**

## BUY IT IN YOUR NEWSAGENTS EVERY SUNDAY

## BE CLOSE TO THE PASSION

# HELLENIC LEAGUE

| **Sponsored by:** Uhlsport |
|---|
| **Founded:** 1953 |
| **Recent Champions:** |
| 2008: North Leigh |
| 2009: Hungerford Town |
| 2010: Almondsbury Town |
| 2011: Wantage Town |
| 2012: Oxford City Nomads |
| **hellenicleague.co.uk** |

## LEAGUE CHALLENGE CUP

**ROUND 1**

| | | | |
|---|---|---|---|
| AFC Hinksey | v | Wokingham & Emmb' | 2-3 |
| Chalfont Wasps | v | Carterton | 4-2 |
| Cheltenham Sar's | v | Finchampstead | 5-2 |
| Chinnor | v | Flackwell Heath | 1-3 |
| Clanfield | v | Purton | 2-1 aet |
| Cricklade Town | v | Ascot United | 4-2 |
| Didcot Town | v | Shrivenham | 0-3 |
| Easington Sports | v | Fairford Town | 3-2 |
| Henley Town | v | Lydney Town | 3-4 aet |
| Hook Norton | v | Headington Amateurs | 4-5 aet |
| Kidlington | v | Maidenhead United | 3-1 |
| Lambourn Sports | v | Holyport | 3-2 |
| Letcombe | v | Thame United | 1-3 |
| Malmesbury Vic's | v | Penn & Tylers Grn | 1-2 aet |
| North Leigh | v | Milton United | 1-2 |
| Thatcham Town | v | New College Swindon | 3-0 |
| Wantage Town | v | Wootton Bassett Town | 2-0 |
| Witney Town | v | Bracknell Town | 3-2 |
| Woodley Town | v | Abingdon Town | 0-1 |

**ROUND 2**

| | | | |
|---|---|---|---|
| Ardley United | v | Lydney Town | 4-2 |
| Binfield | v | Tytherington Rocks | 3-1 |
| Brimscombe & Thrupp | v | Milton United | 7-1 |
| Highworth Town | v | Shrivenham | 2-1 |
| Old Woodstock Town | v | Cheltenham Saracens | 2-4 |
| Rayners Lane | v | Clanfield | 3-1 |
| Reading Town | v | Wantage Town | 1-3 |
| Headington Amateurs | v | Witney Town | 5-6 aet |
| Kidlington | v | Highmoor-Ibis | 3-2 aet |
| Lambourn Sports | v | Slimbridge | 1-0 |
| Thame United | v | Newbury | 1-3 |
| Penn & Tylers Green | v | Cricklade Town | 4-0 |
| Abingdon Town | v | Wokingham & Emmb | 2-1 |
| Chalfont Wasps | v | Thatcham Town Res | 3-0 |
| Flackwell Heath | v | Marlow | 1-1 5-6p |
| Easington Sports | v | Oxford City Nomads | 1-3 |

**ROUND 3**

| | | | |
|---|---|---|---|
| Ardley United | v | Abingdon Town | 5-0 |
| Brimscombe & Thrupp | v | Binfield | 2-1 |
| Cheltenham Saracens | v | Penn & Tylers Green | 8-2 |
| Highworth Town | v | Marlow | 1-4 |
| Kidlington | v | Newbury | HW |
| Lambourn Sports | v | Wantage Town | 2-3 |
| Rayners Lane | v | Oxford City Nomads | 2-3 |
| Witney Town | v | Chalfont Wasps | 7-0 |

| PREMIER DIVISION | | P | W | D | L | F | A | Pts |
|---|---|---|---|---|---|---|---|---|
| 1 | (P) Marlow | 36 | 29 | 6 | 1 | 123 | 40 | 93 |
| 2 | Wantage Town | 36 | 24 | 5 | 7 | 77 | 41 | 77 |
| 3 | Binfield | 36 | 21 | 5 | 10 | 80 | 39 | 68 |
| 4 | Oxford City Nomads | 36 | 20 | 6 | 10 | 65 | 51 | 66 |
| 5 | Ardley United | 36 | 19 | 5 | 12 | 85 | 64 | 62 |
| 6 | Slimbridge | 36 | 18 | 7 | 11 | 65 | 49 | 61 |
| 7 | Ascot United | 36 | 17 | 9 | 10 | 75 | 54 | 60 |
| 8 | Wokingham & Emmbrook | 36 | 16 | 10 | 10 | 65 | 43 | 58 |
| 9 | Thame United | 36 | 16 | 9 | 11 | 72 | 52 | 57 |
| 10 | Flackwell Heath | 36 | 17 | 5 | 14 | 85 | 64 | 56 |
| 11 | Cheltenham Saracens | 36 | 17 | 5 | 14 | 69 | 77 | 56 |
| 12 | Highmoor Ibis | 36 | 14 | 3 | 19 | 75 | 81 | 45 |
| 13 | Kidlington | 36 | 13 | 3 | 20 | 72 | 93 | 42 |
| 14 | Holyport | 36 | 12 | 4 | 20 | 64 | 78 | 40 |
| 15 | Newbury | 36 | 10 | 8 | 18 | 64 | 76 | 38 |
| 16 | Highworth Town | 36 | 9 | 8 | 19 | 53 | 75 | 35 |
| 17 | Reading Town | 36 | 5 | 8 | 23 | 41 | 85 | 23 |
| 18 | Abingdon Town | 36 | 6 | 3 | 27 | 29 | 107 | 21 |
| 19 | Shrivenham | 36 | 3 | 3 | 30 | 31 | 121 | 12 |

Witney Town - record expunged.

| PREMIER DIVISION | 1 | 2 | 3 | 4 | 5 | 6 | 7 | 8 | 9 | 10 | 11 | 12 | 13 | 14 | 15 | 16 | 17 | 18 | 19 |
|---|---|---|---|---|---|---|---|---|---|---|---|---|---|---|---|---|---|---|---|
| 1 Abingdon Town | | 1-8 | 3-1 | 0-1 | 2-2 | 2-4 | 0-9 | 1-2 | 0-4 | 0-4 | 1-3 | 4-0 | 0-2 | 0-1 | 1-2 | 0-1 | 0-5 | 0-5 | 1-3 |
| 2 Ardley United | 5-0 | | 2-1 | 0-4 | 5-0 | 2-1 | 2-4 | 2-1 | 5-3 | 4-3 | 1-1 | 1-2 | 1-3 | 3-2 | 3-2 | 2-2 | 2-1 | 6-1 | 1-2 |
| 3 Ascot United | 4-1 | 1-2 | | 0-2 | 3-0 | 4-1 | 1-0 | 2-2 | 5-2 | 0-3 | 1-1 | 6-3 | 0-0 | 2-0 | 3-2 | 1-0 | 3-1 | 1-3 | 1-1 |
| 4 Binfield | 6-1 | 1-3 | 0-0 | | 2-1 | 3-2 | 1-2 | 5-0 | 2-0 | 1-2 | 1-2 | 2-1 | 2-3 | 2-1 | 5-0 | 1-1 | 3-1 | 1-1 | 2-1 |
| 5 Cheltenham Saracens | 1-1 | 0-2 | 3-1 | 0-4 | | 3-1 | 7-3 | 2-1 | 2-1 | 4-1 | 1-1 | 1-1 | 5-1 | 3-2 | 2-0 | 2-3 | 4-2 | 0-2 | 2-1 |
| 6 Flackwell Heath | 2-0 | 2-1 | 2-3 | 3-5 | 3-4 | | 4-2 | 5-1 | 3-2 | 0-1 | 3-1 | 2-2 | 3-2 | 6-0 | 3-0 | 0-3 | 2-3 | 2-3 | 1-1 |
| 7 Highmoor Ibis | 2-0 | 3-0 | 1-3 | 0-3 | 0-5 | 0-2 | | 2-0 | 4-1 | 1-1 | 1-4 | 4-2 | 1-3 | 4-0 | 4-0 | 2-3 | 1-3 | 3-4 | 1-1 |
| 8 Highworth Town | 2-0 | 1-4 | 0-4 | 0-0 | 4-1 | 0-0 | 2-4 | | 0-1 | 4-3 | 1-6 | 3-1 | 1-0 | 0-3 | 10-1 | 4-0 | 1-1 | 0-1 | 0-3 |
| 9 Holyport | 3-0 | 1-1 | 1-5 | 0-2 | 3-0 | 1-5 | 1-3 | 1-0 | | 8-3 | 1-4 | 0-1 | 1-1 | 1-1 | 3-0 | 2-3 | 1-2 | 0-3 | 0-5 |
| 10 Kidlington | 3-1 | 2-2 | 3-2 | 1-8 | 5-1 | 2-1 | 4-3 | 5-1 | 0-1 | | 0-4 | 4-2 | 2-3 | 4-1 | 5-2 | 1-2 | 0-2 | 1-4 | 1-3 |
| 11 Marlow | 8-1 | 4-0 | 4-1 | 4-1 | 6-0 | 3-2 | 4-1 | 5-4 | 4-0 | 2-1 | | 4-2 | 5-1 | 5-1 | 4-0 | 2-0 | 2-2 | 4-1 | 2-1 |
| 12 Newbury | 9-1 | 2-1 | 2-2 | 1-0 | 1-2 | 0-1 | 0-2 | 2-1 | 0-3 | 7-2 | 2-6 | | 1-1 | 4-2 | 1-0 | 2-4 | 0-0 | 2-3 | 1-1 |
| 13 Oxford City Nomads | 2-0 | 5-2 | 2-1 | 1-0 | 0-0 | 3-3 | 4-2 | 2-0 | 5-3 | 3-1 | 0-0 | 3-2 | | 0-2 | 4-1 | 2-0 | 2-0 | 0-1 | 1-0 |
| 14 Reading Town | 0-1 | 0-1 | 1-4 | 1-1 | 2-4 | 0-2 | 4-1 | 2-2 | 0-3 | 2-2 | 0-1 | 1-1 | 3-1 | | 1-1 | 0-2 | 2-2 | 0-1 | 1-4 |
| 15 Shrivenham | 0-2 | 0-6 | 1-3 | 2-4 | 1-2 | 2-8 | 0-3 | 0-0 | 1-5 | 1-0 | 1-4 | 1-4 | 0-3 | 6-2 | | 0-2 | 0-5 | 1-4 | 0-3 |
| 16 Slimbridge | 0-1 | 3-0 | 1-2 | 2-1 | 4-1 | 2-1 | 4-0 | 1-2 | 3-3 | 1-0 | 3-5 | 1-1 | 0-1 | 2-2 | 3-3 | | 0-1 | 4-0 | 1-1 |
| 17 Thame United | 2-1 | 1-2 | 2-2 | 0-1 | 1-3 | 2-2 | 3-1 | 2-2 | 5-0 | 1-2 | 3-1 | 2-1 | 2-1 | 2-0 | 4-0 | 1-2 | | 3-3 | 3-2 |
| 18 Wantage Town | 0-0 | 1-1 | 1-1 | 1-0 | 5-0 | 1-2 | 4-0 | 3-1 | 1-2 | 3-0 | 0-3 | 2-0 | 1-0 | 3-0 | 4-0 | 1-0 | 2-1 | | 0-1 |
| 19 Wokingham & Emmbrook | 1-2 | 3-2 | 1-1 | 1-3 | 2-1 | 0-1 | 1-1 | 0-0 | 1-0 | 4-2 | 3-3 | 2-1 | 5-0 | 4-1 | 1-1 | 1-2 | 0-0 | 1-4 | |

# HELLENIC LEAGUE - STEP 5/6

| DIVISION ONE EAST | P | W | D | L | F | A | Pts |
|---|---|---|---|---|---|---|---|
| 1 Rayners Lane | 28 | 17 | 6 | 5 | 81 | 36 | 57 |
| 2 Headington Amateurs | 28 | 15 | 8 | 5 | 69 | 41 | 53 |
| 3 Woodley Town | 28 | 13 | 11 | 4 | 52 | 34 | 50 |
| 4 Penn & Tylers Green | 28 | 14 | 5 | 9 | 56 | 44 | 47 |
| 5 (P) Bracknell Town | 28 | 13 | 7 | 8 | 60 | 38 | 46 |
| 6 Chinnor | 28 | 13 | 7 | 8 | 59 | 51 | 46 |
| 7 Maidenhead United Reserves | 28 | 13 | 6 | 9 | 72 | 56 | 45 |
| 8 Easington Sports | 28 | 12 | 6 | 10 | 52 | 41 | 42 |
| 9 Chalfont Wasps | 28 | 12 | 5 | 11 | 55 | 57 | 41 |
| 10 Finchampstead | 28 | 11 | 7 | 10 | 56 | 49 | 40 |
| 11 AFC Hinksey | 28 | 11 | 3 | 14 | 81 | 60 | 36 |
| 12 Thatcham Town Reserves | 28 | 9 | 1 | 18 | 48 | 81 | 28 |
| 13 Didcot Town Reserves | 28 | 8 | 2 | 18 | 41 | 67 | 26 |
| 14 Milton United | 28 | 7 | 4 | 17 | 43 | 87 | 25 |
| 15 Henley Town | 28 | 1 | 4 | 23 | 31 | 114 | 7 |

| DIVISION ONE WEST | P | W | D | L | F | A | Pts |
|---|---|---|---|---|---|---|---|
| 1 (P) Brimscombe & Thrupp | 30 | 25 | 3 | 2 | 95 | 20 | 78 |
| 2 (P) Wootton Bassett Town | 30 | 22 | 3 | 5 | 75 | 40 | 69 |
| 3 Tytherington Rocks | 30 | 19 | 5 | 6 | 87 | 42 | 62 |
| 4 Fairford Town | 30 | 19 | 4 | 7 | 65 | 38 | 58 |
| 5 Carterton | 30 | 17 | 6 | 7 | 73 | 45 | 57 |
| 6 Old Woodstock Town | 30 | 15 | 3 | 12 | 59 | 52 | 48 |
| 7 Cricklade Town | 30 | 13 | 6 | 11 | 73 | 58 | 45 |
| 8 Hook Norton | 30 | 12 | 7 | 11 | 47 | 60 | 43 |
| 9 Lambourn Sports | 30 | 10 | 7 | 13 | 50 | 57 | 37 |
| 10 Lydney Town | 30 | 12 | 1 | 17 | 55 | 66 | 37 |
| 11 Clanfield | 30 | 9 | 9 | 12 | 48 | 61 | 36 |
| 12 North Leigh Reserves | 30 | 10 | 3 | 17 | 55 | 79 | 33 |
| 13 Purton | 30 | 8 | 3 | 19 | 56 | 80 | 27 |
| 14 New College Swindon | 30 | 6 | 1 | 23 | 36 | 88 | 19 |
| 15 Malmesbury Victoria | 30 | 5 | 3 | 22 | 36 | 75 | 18 |
| 16 Letcombe | 30 | 1 | 10 | 19 | 47 | 96 | 13 |

## LEAGUE CHALLENGE CUP continued...

**QUARTER FINALS**
| | | | |
|---|---|---|---|
| Ardley United | v | Wantage Town | 1-2 |
| Cheltenham Saracens | v | Brimscombe & Thrupp | 1-0 |
| Kidlington | v | Marlow | 2-6 |
| Oxford City Nomads | v | Bye (Witney Withdrew) | |

**SEMI FINALS**
| | | | |
|---|---|---|---|
| Cheltenham Saracens | v | Wantage Town | 2-0 |
| Marlow | v | Oxford City Nomads | 1-3 |

**FINAL**
| | | | |
|---|---|---|---|
| Cheltenham Saracens | v | Oxford City Nomads | 1-2 |

## FLOODLITE CUP

**ROUND 1**
| | | | |
|---|---|---|---|
| Abingdon Town | v | Lydney Town | 1-3 |
| Ascot United | v | Hook Norton | 3-3 |
| *Hook Norton win on penalties.* | | | |
| Brimscombe & Thrupp | v | Kidlington | 2-1 |
| Burnham | v | Milton United | 4-0 |
| Cirencester Town | v | Thame United | 1-2 |
| Maidenhead United | v | Binfield | 5-3 |
| Malmesbury Victoria | v | Carterton | 2-1 |
| North Leigh | v | Thatcham Town | 1-2 |
| Shrivenham | v | Wootton Bassett Town | 4-1 |

**ROUND 2**
| | | | |
|---|---|---|---|
| Ardley United | v | Didcot Town | 7-1 |
| Chinnor | v | Wantage Town | 1-2 |
| Fairford Town | v | Bracknell Town | 2-2 |
| *Fairford Town win on penalties.* | | | |
| Highmoor-Ibis | v | Shrivenham | 1-2 |
| Highworth Town | v | Thame United | 3-1 |
| Holyport | v | Lydney Town | 4-1 |
| New College Swindon | v | Cheltenham Saracens | 0-2 |
| Rayners Lane | v | Oxford City Nomads | 3-2 |
| Shortwood United | v | Marlow | 2-4 |
| Hook Norton | v | Slimbridge | 3-3 |
| *Slimbridge win on penalties.* | | | |
| Burnham | v | Reading Town | 1-3 |
| Maidenhead United | v | Clanfield | 3-0 |
| Malmesbury Victoria | v | Newbury | 2-4 |
| Thatcham Town | v | Henley Town | 3-1 |
| Witney Town | v | Brimscombe & Thrupp | 1-3 |
| Wokingham & Emm' | v | Flackwell Heath | 2-1 |

**ROUND 3**
| | | | |
|---|---|---|---|
| Ardley United | v | Wokingham & Emm' | 3-1 |
| Brimscombe & Thrupp | v | Reading Town | 4-0 |
| Highworth Town | v | Cheltenham Saracens | 3-1 |
| Fairford Town | v | Shrivenham | 6-2 |
| Holyport | v | Wantage Town | 0-3 |
| Maidenhead United | v | Thatcham Town | 2-0 |
| Rayners Lane | v | Marlow | 1-3 |
| Slimbridge | v | Newbury | 5-3 |

**QUARTER FINALS**
| | | | |
|---|---|---|---|
| Ardley United | v | Slimbridge | 3 0 |
| Brimscombe & Thrupp | v | Maidenhead United | HW |
| Fairford Town | v | Marlow | 2 1 |
| Wantage Town | v | Cheltenham | 1 0 |

**SEMI FINALS**
| | | | |
|---|---|---|---|
| Brimscombe & Thrupp | v | Wantage Town | 1-2 |
| Fairford Town | v | Ardley United | 1-2 |

**FINAL**
| | | | |
|---|---|---|---|
| Ardley Town | v | Wantage Town | 2-0 |

## SUPPLEMENTARY CUP

**ROUND 1**
| | | | |
|---|---|---|---|
| Finchampstead | v | Cricklade Town | 5-2 |
| AFC Hinksey | v | Ascot United | 0-4 |
| Letcombe | v | Didcot Town Reserves | 1-3 |

**ROUND 2**
| | | | |
|---|---|---|---|
| Bracknell Town | v | Headington Amateurs | 4-6 |
| Clanfield | v | Ascot United | 3-1 |
| Flackwell Heath | v | Didcot Town Reserves | 2-0 |
| Henley Town | v | Carterton | 2-5 |
| Highmoor Ibis | v | New College Swindon | 7-1 |
| Holyport | v | Chinnor | 2-1 |
| Hook Norton | v | Slimbridge | 1-5 |
| Lydney Town | v | Old Woodstock Town | 8-4 |
| Malmesbury Victoria | v | Maidenhead Utd Res | AW |
| Milton United | v | Fairford Town | AW |
| Purton | v | Easington Sports | 3-2 |
| Shrivenham | v | North Leigh Res | 1-4 |
| Thame United | v | Reading Town | 4-0 |
| Thatcham Town Res | v | Woodley Town | 2-2 |
| *Thatcham Town win on penalties.* | | | |
| Tytherington Rocks | v | Finchampstead | 3-1 |
| Wootton Bassett Town | v | Wokingham & Emm' | 0-5 |

**ROUND 3**
| | | | |
|---|---|---|---|
| Carterton | v | Fairford Town | 3-1 |
| Headington Amateurs | v | Lydney Town | 1-1 |
| *Headington Amateurs win on penalties.* | | | |
| Highmoor Ibis | v | Tytherington Rocks | 0-2 |
| North Leigh Res | v | Wokingham | 3-3 |
| *Wokingham win on penalties.* | | | |
| Purton | v | Clanfield | 2-1 |
| Slimbridge | v | Maidenhead Utd Res | HW |
| Thatcham Town Res | v | Thame United | 0-3 |
| Flackwell Heath | v | Holyport | 3-2 |

**QUARTER FINALS**
| | | | |
|---|---|---|---|
| Carterton | v | Purton | 5-1 |
| Flackwell Heath | v | Headington Amateurs | 2-3 |
| Wokingham & Emm' | v | Tytherington Rocks | 1-3 |
| Slimbridge | v | Thame United | 2-1 |

**SEMI FINALS**
| | | | |
|---|---|---|---|
| Slimbridge | v | Tytherington Rocks | 0-0 |
| *Slimbridge win on penalties.* | | | |
| Carterton | v | Headington Amateurs | 1-2 |

**FINAL**
| | | | |
|---|---|---|---|
| Slimbridge | v | Headington Amateurs | 0-1 |

## CHAIRMAN'S RESERVE DIVISION ONE CUP

**FINAL**
| | | | |
|---|---|---|---|
| Binfield | v | Corencester Town | 0-1 |

## PRESIDENT'S RESERVE DIVISION TWO CUP

**2012-13 COMPETITION WAS CANCELLED.**

| DIVISION ONE EAST | 1 | 2 | 3 | 4 | 5 | 6 | 7 | 8 | 9 | 10 | 11 | 12 | 13 | 14 | 15 |
|---|---|---|---|---|---|---|---|---|---|---|---|---|---|---|---|
| 1 AFC Hinksey | | 1-5 | 6-3 | 7-0 | 5-0 | 3-4 | 0-4 | 1-4 | 8-0 | 2-4 | 1-2 | 3-2 | 1-3 | 7-1 | 5-3 |
| 2 Bracknell Town | 3-0 | | 7-0 | 2-2 | 4-1 | 3-2 | 1-3 | 0-0 | 1-1 | 1-3 | 3-1 | 1-3 | 1-2 | 2-0 | 1-1 |
| 3 Chalfont Wasps | 1-1 | 4-1 | | 2-3 | 2-5 | 3-2 | 4-1 | 6-1 | 5-0 | 1-2 | 3-2 | 2-1 | 1-4 | 1-4 | 1-1 |
| 4 Chinnor | 2-1 | 1-1 | 1-2 | | 8-3 | 2-1 | 1-1 | 0-5 | 2-1 | 3-1 | 9-2 | 0-0 | 1-3 | 3-0 | 0-0 |
| 5 Didcot Town Reserves | 0-3 | 0-2 | 0-1 | 2-3 | | 0-3 | 1-2 | 0-1 | 4-0 | 0-0 | 2-2 | 4-2 | 0-3 | 2-1 | 2-1 |
| 6 Easington Sports | 0-3 | 1-1 | 3-0 | 4-0 | 2-1 | | 1-1 | 1-1 | 3-0 | 2-0 | 3-0 | 4-1 | 2-4 | 1-3 | 0-2 |
| 7 Finchampstead | HW | 1-3 | 0-1 | 2-1 | 1-4 | 0-1 | | 3-3 | 2-0 | 2-6 | 8-0 | 3-1 | 1-2 | 3-3 | 1-1 |
| 8 Headington Amateurs | 2-2 | 0-3 | 2-0 | 1-1 | 1-0 | 2-0 | 2-0 | | 8-0 | 3-2 | 1-0 | 1-2 | 4-0 | 9-2 | 0-3 |
| 9 Henley Town | 1-7 | 2-3 | 1-5 | 3-4 | 0-4 | 2-2 | 0-7 | 3-4 | | 1 2-8 | 0-1 | 1-8 | 0-5 | 3-4 | 0-3 |
| 10 Maidenhead United Reserves | 4-3 | 3-1 | 2-4 | 2-1 | 3-2 | 0-0 | 5-1 | 1-1 | 4-1 | | 1-4 | 2-2 | 5-2 | 2-3 | 4-4 |
| 11 Milton United | 2-8 | 1-5 | 1-1 | 0-4 | 1-2 | 1-5 | 2-1 | 3-5 | 2-2 | 3-6 | | 3-1 | 0-1 | 2-1 | 1-1 |
| 12 Penn & Tylers Green | HW | 1-0 | 0-0 | 2-1 | 2-1 | 2-0 | 2-2 | 5-1 | 4-2 | 1-1 | 2-0 | | 1-3 | 0-2 | 1-4 |
| 13 Rayners Lane | 5-1 | 1-1 | 2-2 | 0-2 | 7-0 | 2-0 | 3-3 | 1-1 | 3-3 | 4-0 | 7-2 | 0-3 | | 10-0 | 0-1 |
| 14 Thatcham Town Reserves | 4-1 | 1-4 | 3-0 | 0-1 | 2-0 | 3-4 | 1-2 | 1-3 | 0-1 | 2-1 | 2-4 | 2-5 | 0-4 | | 1-3 |
| 15 Woodley Town | 1-1 | 2-0 | 1-0 | 3-3 | 5-1 | 1-1 | 0-1 | 3-2 | 3-2 | 1-0 | 2-1 | 1-2 | 0-0 | 3-2 | |

| DIVISION ONE WEST | 1 | 2 | 3 | 4 | 5 | 6 | 7 | 8 | 9 | 10 | 11 | 12 | 13 | 14 | 15 | 16 |
|---|---|---|---|---|---|---|---|---|---|---|---|---|---|---|---|---|
| 1 Brimscombe & Thrupp | | 1-0 | 5-0 | 3-0 | 9-1 | 6-1 | 2-2 | 4-2 | 2-0 | 6-0 | 1-0 | 7-1 | 3-0 | 3-2 | 0-1 | 2-0 |
| 2 Carterton | 0-1 | | 3-1 | 0-4 | 1-1 | 5-1 | 3-2 | 3-1 | 2-2 | 3-1 | 5-2 | 5-1 | 4-2 | 6-1 | 2-2 | 1-3 |
| 3 Clanfield | 1-1 | 0-0 | | 1-1 | 2-1 | 3-1 | 4-3 | 4-1 | 0-4 | 4-1 | 2-1 | 0-3 | 1-3 | 2-2 | 3-1 | 4-1 |
| 4 Cricklade Town | 3-4 | 2-2 | 6-3 | | 0-1 | 2-3 | 1-0 | 6-0 | 2-1 | 3-0 | 4-1 | 3-3 | 1-3 | 2-1 | 1-2 | 0-0 |
| 5 Fairford Town | 2-1 | 0-2 | 0-0 | 4-1 | | 1-1 | 7-2 | 2-1 | 1-0 | 3-0 | 3-1 | 2-1 | 1-0 | 6-1 | 1-0 | 3-4 |
| 6 Hook Norton | 1-3 | 2-2 | 3-2 | 3-2 | 1-1 | | 2-1 | 0-0 | 4-2 | 2-0 | 3-1 | 1-4 | 2-1 | 3-1 | 0-4 | 1-2 |
| 7 Lambourn Sports | 0-4 | 0-2 | 0-5 | 2-2 | 2-1 | 1-1 | | 4-1 | 2-1 | 3-0 | 2-0 | 4-2 | 1-2 | 1-1 | 2-3 | 1-2 |
| 8 Letcombe | 1-3 | 1-5 | 2-2 | 1-7 | 0-4 | 2-2 | 0-0 | | 3-4 | 2-2 | 4-0 | 1-6 | 4-4 | 1-7 | 2-2 | 1-2 |
| 9 Lydney Town | 0-4 | 2-6 | 3-0 | 3-1 | 1-2 | 2-1 | 4-2 | 3-1 | | 4-1 | 3-1 | 1-0 | 2-3 | 2-5 | 1-2 | 0-3 |
| 10 Malmesbury Victoria | 0-1 | 0-1 | 1-1 | 1-4 | 0-2 | 1-2 | 0-2 | 0-0 | 2-0 | | 5-1 | 1-5 | 8-2 | 2-1 | 0-7 | 0-2 |
| 11 New College Swindon | 0-3 | 0-3 | 3-0 | 0-6 | 2-4 | 0-2 | 2-2 | 4-1 | 2-3 | 3-2 | | 0-2 | 3-1 | 1-3 | 0-4 | 1-5 |
| 12 North Leigh Reserves | 1-1 | 2-1 | 3-3 | 5-3 | 0-6 | 1-3 | 0-3 | 4-2 | 3-1 | 2-0 | 1-2 | | 0-3 | 3-1 | 1-5 | 0-5 |
| 13 Old Woodstock Town | 0-1 | 2-0 | 0-0 | 1-2 | 2-0 | 1-0 | 3-0 | 3-2 | 2-0 | 3-1 | 4-1 | 3-0 | | 2-2 | 0-2 | 2-5 |
| 14 Purton | 1-6 | 1-3 | 1-0 | 2-3 | 0-1 | 6-0 | 1-4 | 3-3 | 2-4 | 3-2 | 1-2 | 2-0 | 0-3 | | 1-4 | 1-2 |
| 15 Tytherington Rocks | 0-6 | 1-2 | 4-1 | 7-0 | 1-3 | 2-2 | 0-2 | 3-3 | 3-2 | 4-2 | 3-0 | 4-0 | 4-3 | 7-1 | | 3-0 |
| 16 Wootton Bassett Town | 0-2 | 6-1 | 4-1 | 1-1 | 2-1 | 2-0 | 2-2 | 3-2 | 0-3 | 3-0 | 4-2 | 4-3 | 3-1 | 3-1 | 2-1 | |

| DIVISION TWO EAST | P | W | D | L | F | A | Pts |
|---|---|---|---|---|---|---|---|
| 1 (P) Burnham Reserves | 24 | 16 | 4 | 4 | 49 | 20 | 52 |
| 2 Thame United Reserves | 24 | 15 | 3 | 6 | 51 | 24 | 48 |
| 3 Binfield Reserves | 24 | 14 | 4 | 6 | 64 | 39 | 46 |
| 4 Finchampstead Reserves | 24 | 14 | 4 | 6 | 42 | 28 | 46 |
| 5 Easington Sports Reserves | 24 | 13 | 3 | 8 | 31 | 35 | 39 |
| 6 Ascot United Reserves | 24 | 10 | 5 | 9 | 46 | 42 | 35 |
| 7 Penn & Tylers Green Reserves | 24 | 10 | 4 | 10 | 44 | 47 | 34 |
| 8 Slough Town Reserves | 24 | 10 | 3 | 11 | 53 | 41 | 33 |
| 9 Holyport Reserves | 24 | 9 | 3 | 12 | 50 | 54 | 30 |
| 10 Rayners Lane Reserves | 24 | 8 | 4 | 12 | 54 | 47 | 28 |
| 11 Bracknell Town Reserves | 24 | 7 | 1 | 16 | 37 | 68 | 22 |
| 12 Chinnor Reserves | 24 | 5 | 4 | 15 | 25 | 53 | 19 |
| 13 Kidlington Reserves | 24 | 2 | 4 | 18 | 26 | 74 | 10 |

| DIVISION TWO WEST | P | W | D | L | F | A | Pts |
|---|---|---|---|---|---|---|---|
| 1 (P) Shortwood United Reserves | 22 | 18 | 1 | 3 | 70 | 18 | 55 |
| 2 Brimscombe & Thrupp Reserves | 22 | 16 | 2 | 4 | 72 | 30 | 50 |
| 3 Cirencester Town 'Dev' | 22 | 15 | 3 | 4 | 83 | 35 | 48 |
| 4 Highworth Town Reserves | 22 | 13 | 2 | 7 | 62 | 45 | 41 |
| 5 Wootton Bassett Town Reserves | 22 | 12 | 1 | 9 | 46 | 35 | 37 |
| 6 Cheltenham Saracens Reserves | 22 | 10 | 0 | 12 | 66 | 47 | 30 |
| 7 Wantage Town Reserves | 22 | 9 | 2 | 11 | 43 | 53 | 29 |
| 8 Fairford Town Reserves | 22 | 8 | 2 | 12 | 45 | 60 | 26 |
| 9 Old Woodstock Town Reserves | 22 | 7 | 1 | 14 | 34 | 66 | 22 |
| 10 Shrivenham Reserves | 22 | 4 | 5 | 13 | 36 | 65 | 17 |
| 11 Hook Norton Reserves | 22 | 5 | 2 | 15 | 31 | 62 | 17 |
| 12 Letcombe Reserves | 22 | 4 | 1 | 17 | 23 | 95 | 13 |

## CLUB MOVEMENTS

**Premier Division - In:** Brimscombe & Thrupp (P). Bracknell Town (P). Wootton Bassett Town (P).
**Out:** Marlow (P - Southern Div.1 Central). Slimbridge (S - Western League Premier). Witney Town (WS). Wokingham & Emmbrook (R).

**Division One East - In:** Burnham Reserves (P). Wokingham & Emmbrook (R).
**Out:** Bracknell Town (P). Easington Sports (S - Div.1 West). Thatcham Town Reserves (W).

**Division One West - In:** Easington Sports (S - Div.1 East). Shortwood United Reserves (P). Tuffley Rovers (P- Gloucestershire County)
**Out:** Brimscombe & Thrupp (P). Lambourne Sports (W - joined North Berkshire).

## ABINGDON TOWN

Founded: 1870　　　Nickname: The Abbots

**Secretary:** Wendy Larman　　**(T)** 01235 763 985　　**(E)** thomas.larman@btinternet.com

**Chairman:** Tom Larman　　**Manager:** Shaun Smith　　**Prog Ed:** Kenny More

**Ground:** Culham Road, Abingdon OX14 3HP　　**(T)** 01235 521 684

**Capacity:** 3,000　**Seats:** 271　**Covered:** 1,771　**Midweek Matchday:** Tuesday　**Clubhouse:** Yes　**Shop:** Yes

| | |
|---|---|
| **Colours(change):** | All yellow and green |
| **Previous Names:** | Abingdon FC (merged with St Michaels in 1899) > 1928. |
| **Previous Leagues:** | Reading Senior, Reading & District, Oxfordshire Senior, North Berkshire, Spartan, Isthmian |
| **Records:** | Att: 4,000 v Swindon Town, Maurice Owen Benefit, 1950. |
| **Senior Honours:** | Berks & Bucks Senior Cup 58-59. Spartan Lge 88-89. Isthmian Lge Div.2 South 90-91. |

**10 YEAR RECORD**

| 03-04 | | 04-05 | | 05-06 | | 06-07 | | 07-08 | | 08-09 | | 09-10 | | 10-11 | | 11-12 | | 12-13 | |
|---|---|---|---|---|---|---|---|---|---|---|---|---|---|---|---|---|---|---|---|
| Isth2 | 9 | Isth2 | 7 | Hel P | 18 | Hel P | 18 | Hel P | 19 | Hel P | 19 | Hel P | 12 | Hel P | 14 | Hel P | 11 | Hel P | 18 |

## ABINGDON UNITED

Founded: 1946　　　Nickname: The U's

**Secretary:** John Blackmore　　**(T)** 07747 615 691　　**(E)** john.blackmore2@ntlworld.com

**Chairman:** Mrs Deborah Blackmore　　**Manager:** Richie Bourne　　**Prog Ed:** Bill Fletcher

**Ground:** The North Court, Northcourt Road, Abingdon OX14 1PL　　**(T)** 01235 203 203

**Capacity:** 2,000　**Seats:** 158　**Covered:** 258　**Midweek Matchday:**　　**Clubhouse:** Yes

| | |
|---|---|
| **Colours(change):** | All yellow |
| **Previous Names:** | Not known |
| **Previous Leagues:** | North Berkshire 1949-58, Hellenic 1958-2006 |
| **Records:** | 1,500 v Oxford United - Friendly 1994 |
| **Senior Honours:** | Hellenic League Division 1 1981-82, League Cup 1965-66. Berks & Bucks Senior Trophy x2. |

**10 YEAR RECORD**

| 03-04 | | 04-05 | | 05-06 | | 06-07 | | 07-08 | | 08-09 | | 09-10 | | 10-11 | | 11-12 | | 12-13 | |
|---|---|---|---|---|---|---|---|---|---|---|---|---|---|---|---|---|---|---|---|
| Hel P | 11 | Hel P | 5 | Hel P | 3 | Hel P | 18 | Sthsw | 16 | Sthsw | 15 | Sthsw | 14 | Sthsw | 16 | Sthsw | 18 | Sthsw | 20 |

## ARDLEY UNITED

Founded: 1945　　　Nickname:

**Secretary:** Norman Stacey　　**(T)** 07711 009198　　**(E)** ardley.house@virgin.net

**Chairman:** Norman Stacey　　**Manager:** Kevin Brock　　**Prog Ed:** Tom Sawyer

**Ground:** The Playing Fields, Oxford Road, Ardley OX27 7NZ　　**(T)** 07711 009 198

**Capacity:** 1,000　**Seats:** 100　**Covered:** 200　**Midweek Matchday:** Tuesday　**Clubhouse:** Yes　**Shop:** No

| | |
|---|---|
| **Colours(change):** | All sky blue. |
| **Previous Names:** | None |
| **Previous Leagues:** | Oxford Senior. |
| **Records:** | Att: 278 v Kidlington, 29.08.05. |
| **Senior Honours:** | Hellenic League Division One 1996-97, 97-98. |

**10 YEAR RECORD**

| 03-04 | | 04-05 | | 05-06 | | 06-07 | | 07-08 | | 08-09 | | 09-10 | | 10-11 | | 11-12 | | 12-13 | |
|---|---|---|---|---|---|---|---|---|---|---|---|---|---|---|---|---|---|---|---|
| Hel1W | 5 | Hel P | 18 | Hel P | 10 | Hel P | 4 | Hel P | 13 | Hel P | 5 | Hel P | 7 | Hel P | 3 | Hel P | 3 | Hel P | 5 |

## ASCOT UNITED

Founded: 1965　　　Nickname: Yellaman

**Secretary:** Mark Gittoes　　**(T)** 07798 701995　　**(E)** mark.gittoes@ascotunited.net

**Chairman:** Mike Harrison　　**Manager:** Jeff Lamb

**Ground:** Ascot Racecourse, Car Park 10, Winkfield Rd, Ascot SL5 7RA　　**(T)** 01344 291 107

**Capacity:**　**Seats:**　**Covered:**　**Midweek Matchday:** Tuesday　**Clubhouse:** Yes

| | |
|---|---|
| **Colours(change):** | Yellow/blue/yellow |
| **Previous Names:** | None. |
| **Previous Leagues:** | Reading Senior. |
| **Records:** | Att: 1,149 - 19/08/2011. |
| **Senior Honours:** | |

**10 YEAR RECORD**

| 03-04 | | 04-05 | | 05-06 | | 06-07 | | 07-08 | | 08-09 | | 09-10 | | 10-11 | | 11-12 | | 12-13 | |
|---|---|---|---|---|---|---|---|---|---|---|---|---|---|---|---|---|---|---|---|
| ReadS | 6 | ReadS | 3 | ReadS | 4 | ReadS | 1 | Hel1E | 4 | Hel1E | 2 | Hel P | 15 | Hel P | 12 | Hel P | 14 | Hel P | 7 |

# BINFIELD
Founded: 1892     Nickname: Moles

**Secretary:** Rob Challis     **(T)** 07515 336989     **(E)** robchallis@binfieldfc.com

**Chairman:** Bob Bacon     **Manager:** Mark Tallentire     **Prog Ed:** Colin Byers

**Ground:** Stubbs Lane off Hill Farm Lane, Binfield RG42 5NR     **(T)** 01344 860 822

**Capacity:**    **Seats:** yes    **Covered:** yes    **Midweek Matchday:** Monday     **Clubhouse:** Yes

**Colours(change):** All red.
**Previous Names:** None.
**Previous Leagues:** Ascot & District. Great Western Combination. Reading & Dist. Chiltonian.
**Records:** **Att:** 1000+ Great Western Combination.
**Senior Honours:** Hellenic League Division 1 East 2008-09.

### 10 YEAR RECORD

| 03-04 | 04-05 | 05-06 | 06-07 | 07-08 | 08-09 | 09-10 | 10-11 | 11-12 | 12-13 |
|---|---|---|---|---|---|---|---|---|---|
| Hel1E 5 | Hel1E 5 | Hel1E 8 | Hel1E 11 | Hel1E 9 | Hel1E 1 | Hel P 8 | Hel P 2 | Hel P 8 | Hel P 3 |

# BRACKNELL TOWN
Founded: 1896     Nickname: The Robins

**Secretary:** Darrell Freeland     **(T)** 07712 473 142     **(E)** club@bracknelltownfc.com

**Chairman:** Ian Nugent     **Manager:** Danny Oliphant & Stephen Nebbett

**Ground:** Larges Lane Bracknell RG12 9AN     **(T)** 01344 412 305

**Capacity:** 2,500 **Seats:** 190    **Covered:** 400    **Midweek Matchday:** Tuesday     **Clubhouse:** Yes    **Shop:** Yes

**Colours(change):** Red and white hoops/red/red
**Previous Names:** None
**Previous Leagues:** Great Western Comb., Surrey Senior 1963-70, London Spartan 1970-75, Isthmian 1984-2004, Southern 2004-10
**Records:** **Att:** 2,500 v Newquay - FA Amateur Cup 1971. **Goalscorer:** Justin Day. **Apps:** James Woodcock.
**Senior Honours:**

### 10 YEAR RECORD

| 03-04 | 04-05 | 05-06 | 06-07 | 07-08 | 08-09 | 09-10 | 10-11 | 11-12 | 12-13 |
|---|---|---|---|---|---|---|---|---|---|
| Isth1S 14 | SthW 20 | SthW 19 | Sthsw 19 | Sthsw 20 | Sthsw | Sthsw 22 | Hel P 16 | Hel P 21 | Hel1E 5 |

# BRIMSCOMBE & THRUPP
Founded: 1886     Nickname: Lilywhites

**Secretary:** John Mutton     **(T)** 01453 757 880     **(E)** johncolin123@gmail.com

**Chairman:** Clive Baker     **Manager:** Phil Baker     **Prog Ed:** Clive Baker

**Ground:** 'The Meadow', London Road, Brimscombe Stroud, Gloucestershire GL5 2SH     **(T)** 07833 231 464

**Capacity:**    **Seats:**    **Covered:**    **Midweek Matchday:** Tuesday     **Clubhouse:** Yes

**Colours(change):** White/blue/blue.
**Previous Names:** Brimscombe AFC 1886- late 1970s. Brimscombe and Thrupp merged.
**Previous Leagues:** Gloucestershire County
**Records:**
**Senior Honours:** Gloucestershire County League 2010-11. Hellenic League Div.1 West 2012-13.

### 10 YEAR RECORD

| 03-04 | 04-05 | 05-06 | 06-07 | 07-08 | 08-09 | 09-10 | 10-11 | 11-12 | 12-13 |
|---|---|---|---|---|---|---|---|---|---|
| | | | | | | GlCo 5 | GlCo 1 | Hel1W 4 | Hel1W 1 |

# CHELTENHAM SARACENS
Founded: 1964     Nickname: Sara's

**Secretary:** Debbie Organ     **(T)** 07578 035 311     **(E)**

**Chairman:** Mark Griffiths     **Manager:** Gerry Oldham

**Ground:** Petersfield Park, Tewkesbury Road GL51 9DY     **(T)** 01242 584 134

**Capacity:**    **Seats:** Yes    **Covered:** Yes    **Midweek Matchday:** Wednesday     **Clubhouse:** Yes

**Colours(change):** All navy blue
**Previous Names:**
**Previous Leagues:**
**Records:** **Att:** 327 v Harrow Hill 31/08/2003.
**Senior Honours:** Glouscestershire Senior Cup 1991-92. Hellenic League Division 1 1999-2000.

### 10 YEAR RECORD

| 03-04 | 04-05 | 05-06 | 06-07 | 07-08 | 08-09 | 09-10 | 10-11 | 11-12 | 12-13 |
|---|---|---|---|---|---|---|---|---|---|
| Hel1W 13 | Hel1W 6 | Hel1E 8 | Hel1W 6 | Hel1W 5 | Hel1W 12 | Hel1W 4 | Hel1W 3 | Hel P 15 | Hel P 11 |

# FLACKWELL HEATH
Founded: 1907     Nickname: Heath

**Secretary:** Geoff Turner     **(T)** 07988 779 390     **(E)** flackwellheathfc@hotmail.co.uk

**Chairman:** Geoff Turner     **Manager:** Graham Malcolm     Geoff Turner

**Ground:** Wilks Park, Magpie Lane, Heath End Rd, Flackwell Hth HP10 9EA.     **(T)** 01628 523 892

**Capacity:** 2,000 **Seats:** 150   **Covered:** Yes   **Midweek Matchday:** Tuesday     **Clubhouse:** Yes   **Shop:** No

**Colours(change):** All red.
**Previous Names:** None.
**Previous Leagues:** Great Western Combination. Hellenic. Isthmian.
**Records:** **Att:** 1,500 v Oxford United, charity match, 1966. **Goalscorer:** Tony Wood. **Apps:** Lee Elliott.
**Senior Honours:**

| 10 YEAR RECORD | | | | | | | | | |
|---|---|---|---|---|---|---|---|---|---|
| 03-04 | 04-05 | 05-06 | 06-07 | 07-08 | 08-09 | 09-10 | 10-11 | 11-12 | 12-13 |
| Isth2 5 | Isth2 9 | Isth2 4 | Isth1N 22 | Hel P 9 | Hel P 16 | Hel P 4 | Hel P 8 | Hel P 4 | Hel P 10 |

# HIGHMOOR-IBIS
Founded: 2001     Nickname: Mighty Moor

**Secretary:** Chris Gallimore     **(T)** 01189 588 518     **(E)** chris.gallimore@sjpp.co.uk

**Chairman:** Martin Law     **Manager:** Shane Small-King

**Ground:** Palmer Park Stadium, Wokingham Road, Reading RG6 1LF     **(T)** 01189 375 080

**Capacity:**   **Seats:**   **Covered:**   **Midweek Matchday:** Monday     **Clubhouse:**

**Colours(change):** All blue
**Previous Names:** Highmoor and Ibis merged to form today's club in 2001.
**Previous Leagues:** Reading > 2011.
**Records:**
**Senior Honours:** Reading League Senior Division 2003-04, 10-11.

| 10 YEAR RECORD | | | | | | | | | |
|---|---|---|---|---|---|---|---|---|---|
| 03-04 | 04-05 | 05-06 | 06-07 | 07-08 | 08-09 | 09-10 | 10-11 | 11-12 | 12-13 |
| ReadS 1 | ReadS 4 | ReadS 3 | ReadS 2 | ReadS 6 | ReadS 2 | ReadS 4 | ReadS 1 | Hel1E 2 | Hel P 12 |

# HIGHWORTH TOWN
Founded: 1893     Nickname: Worthians

**Secretary:** Fraser Haines     **(T)** 01793 861 109     **(E)** fraserhaines@btinternet.com

**Chairman:** Rohan Haines     **Manager:** John Fisher     **Prog Ed:** Mike Markham

**Ground:** Elm Recreation Ground, Highworth SN6 7DD     **(T)** 01793 766 263

**Capacity:** 2,000 **Seats:** 150   **Covered:** 250   **Midweek Matchday:** Tuesday     **Clubhouse:** Yes   **Shop:** No

**Colours(change):** Red/black/red.
**Previous Names:** None.
**Previous Leagues:** Swindon & District. Wiltshire.
**Records:** **Att:** 2,000 v QPR, opening of floodlights. **Goalscorer:** Kevin Higgs. **Apps:** Rod Haines.
**Senior Honours:** Hellenic League Champions 2004-05.

| 10 YEAR RECORD | | | | | | | | | |
|---|---|---|---|---|---|---|---|---|---|
| 03-04 | 04-05 | 05-06 | 06-07 | 07-08 | 08-09 | 09-10 | 10-11 | 11-12 | 12-13 |
| Hel P 9 | Hel P 1 | Hel P 12 | Hel P 15 | Hel P 6 | Hel P 6 | Hel P 9 | Hel P 4 | Hel P 6 | Hel P 16 |

# HOLYPORT
Founded: 1934     Nickname: The Villagers

**Secretary:** Lyn Davies     **(T)** 07824 605 731     **(E)** Lyn.davies@rbwm.gov.uk

**Chairman:** Tony Andrews     **Manager:** Derek Sweetman     **Prog Ed:** Richard Tyrell

**Ground:** Summerleaze Village SL6 8SP     **(T)** 07702 369 708 / 07879 041 359

**Capacity:**   **Seats:**   **Covered:**   **Midweek Matchday:** Tuesday     **Clubhouse:** Yes

**Colours(change):** Claret/green/claret
**Previous Names:** None
**Previous Leagues:** None
**Records:** **Att:** 218 v Eton Wick, 2006. **Goalscorer:** Jamie Handscomb - 78. **Apps:** Sam Jones - 216.
**Senior Honours:** Norfolkian Senior Cup 1999-2000. Hellenic League Division One East 2010-11.

| 10 YEAR RECORD | | | | | | | | | |
|---|---|---|---|---|---|---|---|---|---|
| 03-04 | 04-05 | 05-06 | 06-07 | 07-08 | 08-09 | 09-10 | 10-11 | 11-12 | 12-13 |
| Hel1E 17 | Hel1E 15 | Hel1E 14 | Hel1E 9 | Hel1E 7 | Hel1E 5 | Hel1E 3 | Hel1E 1 | Hel P 13 | Hel P 14 |

# KIDLINGTON
**Founded:** 1909    **Nickname:**

**Secretary:** David Platt   **(T)** 07956 531 185   **(E)** david.platt45@googlemail.com
**Chairman:** Gary Johnson   **Manager:** Martin Wilkinson   **Prog Ed:** Les Deabill
**Ground:** Yarnton Road, Kidlington, Oxford OX5 1AT   **(T)** 01865 841 526
**Capacity:**   **Seats:** Yes   **Covered:** Yes   **Midweek Matchday:** Tuesday   **Clubhouse:** Yes   **Shop:** No

**Colours(change):** All green
**Previous Names:** None.
**Previous Leagues:** Oxford Senior.
**Records:** **Att:** 2,500 v Showbiz XI, 1973.
**Senior Honours:**

**10 YEAR RECORD**

| 03-04 | 04-05 | 05-06 | 06-07 | 07-08 | 08-09 | 09-10 | 10-11 | 11-12 | 12-13 |
|---|---|---|---|---|---|---|---|---|---|
| Hel1W 12 | Hel1W 3 | Hel P 20 | Hel P 9 | Hel P 15 | Hel P 9 | Hel P 11 | Hel P 7 | Hel P 18 | Hel P 13 |

# NEWBURY
**Founded:** 1887    **Nickname:** The Town

**Secretary:** Knut Riemann   **(T)** 07855 031 000   **(E)** kriemann@yahoo.com
**Chairman:** Keg Moss   **Manager:** Keg Moss & Martyn Benson (Temp)
**Ground:** Faraday Road, Newbury RG14 2AD   **(T)** 01635 41031
**Capacity:**   **Seats:**   **Covered:**   **Midweek Matchday:** Tuesday   **Clubhouse:** Yes

**Colours(change):** Amber & black/black/amber & black
**Previous Names:** Old London Apprentice > 2005. O L A Newbury 2005-2007.
**Previous Leagues:** Reading Senior > 2008.
**Records:** **Att:** 246 v Kintbury Rangers 27/12/2008.
**Senior Honours:** Hellenic League 1978-79, 80-81, Division One East 2011-12. Athenian League 1982-83.

**10 YEAR RECORD**

| 03-04 | 04-05 | 05-06 | 06-07 | 07-08 | 08-09 | 09-10 | 10-11 | 11-12 | 12-13 |
|---|---|---|---|---|---|---|---|---|---|
| Read3 2 | Read2 1 | Read1 4 | Read1 1 | ReadS 2 | Hel1E 3 | Hel1E 16 | Hel1E 3 | Hel1E 1 | Hel P 15 |

# OXFORD CITY NOMADS
**Founded:** 1936    **Nickname:** The Nomads

**Secretary:** Colin Taylor   **(T)** 07817 885 396   **(E)** ctoxford@btinternet.com
**Chairman:** Brian Cox   **Manager:** Chris Fontaine   **Prog Ed:** Colin Taylor
**Ground:** Court Place Farm Stadium, Marsh Lane, Marston OX3 0NQ   **(T)** 01865 744 493
**Capacity:** 3,000 **Seats:** 300   **Covered:** 400   **Midweek Matchday:** Wednesday   **Clubhouse:** Yes   **Shop:** Yes

**Colours(change):** Blue & white hoops/blue/blue.
**Previous Names:** Quarry Nomads > 2005.
**Previous Leagues:** Chiltonian.
**Records:** **Att:** 334 v Headington Amateurs, 25.08.03.
**Senior Honours:** Hellenic League Premier Division 2011-12.

**10 YEAR RECORD**

| 03-04 | 04-05 | 05-06 | 06-07 | 07-08 | 08-09 | 09-10 | 10-11 | 11-12 | 12-13 |
|---|---|---|---|---|---|---|---|---|---|
| Hel1W 7 | Hel1W 15 | Hel1E 11 | Hel1E 12 | Hel1W 9 | Hel1W 3 | Hel P 10 | Hel P 17 | Hel P 1 | Hel P 4 |

# READING TOWN
**Founded:** 1966    **Nickname:** Town

**Secretary:** Richard Grey   **(T)**   **(E)** richardigrey@aol.com
**Chairman:** Roland Ford   **Manager:** Colin Millard   **Prog Ed:** Richard Wickson
**Ground:** Reading Town Sports Ground, Scours Lane, Reading RG30 6AY   **(T)** 0118 945 3555
**Capacity:** 2000 **Seats:** 120   **Covered:** 200   **Midweek Matchday:** Tuesday   **Clubhouse:** Yes   **Shop:** No

**Colours(change):** Red/black/black
**Previous Names:** Lower Burghfield, XI Utd, Vincents Utd, Reading Garage, ITS Reading T.
**Previous Leagues:** Chiltonian Lge. Combined Counties.
**Records:** **Att:** 1067 v AFC Wimbledon, Combined Counties 03.05.03.
**Senior Honours:**

**10 YEAR RECORD**

| 03-04 | 04-05 | 05-06 | 06-07 | 07-08 | 08-09 | 09-10 | 10-11 | 11-12 | 12-13 |
|---|---|---|---|---|---|---|---|---|---|
| CCP 3 | CCP 19 | CCP 10 | CCP 9 | CCP 13 | Hel P 8 | Hel P 3 | Hel P 13 | Hel P 7 | Hel P 17 |

# SHRIVENHAM

Founded: 1900   Nickname: Shrivy

**Secretary:** Andy Timbrell **(T)** 07999 133 439 **(E)** timbrell.andrew63@btinternet.com

**Chairman:** Neil Sutton **Manager:** Dave Turner & Mark Stevens **Prog Ed:** Matty Hirst

**Ground:** The Recreation Ground, Shrivenham SN6 8BJ **(T)** 07767 371 414

**Capacity:** **Seats:** **Covered:** **Midweek Matchday:** Tuesday **Clubhouse:** Yes

**Colours(change):** Blue & white hoops/blue/blue.
**Previous Names:** None.
**Previous Leagues:** North Berkshire.
**Records:** Att: 800 v Aston Villa, 21.05.2000.
**Senior Honours:** Hellenic Division One West 2004-05.

### 10 YEAR RECORD

| 03-04 | 04-05 | 05-06 | 06-07 | 07-08 | 08-09 | 09-10 | 10-11 | 11-12 | 12-13 |
|---|---|---|---|---|---|---|---|---|---|
| Hel1W 3 | Hel1W 1 | Hel P 8 | Hel P 10 | Hel P 8 | Hel P 18 | Hel P 16 | Hel P 20 | Hel P 16 | Hel P 19 |

# THAME UNITED

Founded: 1883   Nickname: United

**Secretary:** Vince Saunders **(T)** **(E)**

**Chairman:** Jake Collinge **Manager:** Mark West **Prog Ed:** Jake Collinge

**Ground:** The ASM Stadium, Meadow View Pk, Tythrop Wa, Thame, Oxon, OX9 3RN **(T)** 01844 214 401

**Capacity:** 2,500 **Seats:** Yes **Covered:** Yes **Midweek Matchday:** Tuesday **Clubhouse:** Yes

**Colours(change):** Red & black/black/black.
**Previous Names:** Thame F.C.
**Previous Leagues:** Oxon Senior. Hellenic. South Midlands. Isthmian. Southern.
**Records:** Att: 1,035 v Aldershot, Isthmian Div.2, 04.04.94. **Goalscorer:** Not known. **Apps:** Steve Mayhew.
**Senior Honours:** Isthmian Division 2 1994-95.

### 10 YEAR RECORD

| 03-04 | 04-05 | 05-06 | 06-07 | 07-08 | 08-09 | 09-10 | 10-11 | 11-12 | 12-13 |
|---|---|---|---|---|---|---|---|---|---|
| Isth1N 15 | SthW 11 | SthW 22 | Hel P 20 | Hel1E 10 | Hel1E 9 | Hel1E 1 | Hel P 10 | Hel P 9 | Hel P 9 |

# WANTAGE TOWN

Founded: 1892   Nickname: Alfredians

**Secretary:** John Culley **(T)** 07921 243 263 **(E)** john_clly@yahoo.co.uk

**Chairman:** Tony Woodward **Manager:** Gary Ackling **Prog Ed:** Ros Shepperd

**Ground:** Alfredian Park, Manor Road, Wantage OX12 8DW **(T)** 01235 764 781

**Capacity:** 1,500 **Seats:** 50 **Covered:** 300 **Midweek Matchday:** Tuesday **Clubhouse:** Yes **Shop:** No

**Colours(change):** Green & white hoops/white/green.
**Previous Names:** None.
**Previous Leagues:** Swindon & District. North Berkshire. Reading & District.
**Records:** Att: 550 v Oxford United, July 2003.
**Senior Honours:**

### 10 YEAR RECORD

| 03-04 | 04-05 | 05-06 | 06-07 | 07-08 | 08-09 | 09-10 | 10-11 | 11-12 | 12-13 |
|---|---|---|---|---|---|---|---|---|---|
| Hel1E 1 | Hel P 10 | Hel P 9 | Hel P 11 | Hel P 12 | Hel P 11 | Hel P 5 | Hel P 1 | Hel P 12 | Hel P 2 |

# WOOTTON BASSETT TOWN

Founded: 1882   Nickname:

**Secretary:** Ian Thomas **(T)** 07714 718 122 **(E)** ian.thomas@wbtfc.co.uk

**Chairman:** Andy Walduck **Manager:** Jeff Roberts **Prog Ed:** Mark Smedley

**Ground:** Gerard Buxton Sport Ground, Rylands Way SN4 8AW **(T)** 01793 853 880

**Capacity:** 2,000 **Seats:** None **Covered:** 350 **Midweek Matchday:** Tuesday **Clubhouse:** Yes **Shop:** No

**Colours(change):** Blue & yellow/blue/yellow.
**Previous Names:** None.
**Previous Leagues:** Wiltshire.
**Records:** Record Att: 2,103 v Swindon Town, July 1991. **Goalscorer:** Brian 'Tony' Ewing. **Apps:** Steve Thomas.
**Senior Honours:** Previous Leagues: Wiltshire.

### 10 YEAR RECORD

| 03-04 | 04-05 | 05-06 | 06-07 | 07-08 | 08-09 | 09-10 | 10-11 | 11-12 | 12-13 |
|---|---|---|---|---|---|---|---|---|---|
| Hel P 16 | Hel P 21 | Hel1W 5 | Hel1W 11 | Hel1W 15 | Hel1W 4 | Hel1W 2 | Hel P 15 | Hel1W 5 | Hel1W 2 |

## AFC HINKSEY
Founded: 2005    Nickname:

**Secretary:** Stuart Parsons   **(T)** 07975 723 123    **(E)** afchinksey@rocketmail.com
**Chairman:** Gavin Preston   **Manager:** Kevin McMahon    **Prog Ed:** Chris Warmington
**Ground:** Abingdon Town FC Culham Road Abingdon OX14 3HP    **(T)** 07975 723 123
**Colours(change):** Purple/black/black

**ADDITIONAL INFORMATION:**
**Previous League:** Oxfordshire Senior > 2012.
**Honours:** Oxfordshire Senior League 2011-12.

## BURNHAM RESERVES
Founded:    Nickname: The Blues

**Secretary:** Alan King   **(T)** 07899 941 414    **(E)** burnhamfcsec@aol.com
**Chairman:** Alan King   **Manager:** Merv Lloyd    **Prog Ed:** Gareth Stoneman
**Ground:** The Gore, Wymers Wood Road, Burnham, Slough SL1 8JG    **(T)** 01628 668 654
**Colours(change):** Blue & white

**ADDITIONAL INFORMATION:**

## CHALFONT WASPS
Founded: 1922    Nickname: The Stingers

**Secretary:** Bob Cakeboard   **(T)** 07895 094 579    **(E)** robert.cakeboard@btinternet.com
**Chairman:** Steve Waddington   **Manager:** Martin Kenealy    **Prog Ed:** Alan Yeomans
**Ground:** Crossleys, Bowstridge Lane Chalfont, St Giles HP8 4QN    **(T)** 01494 875 050
**Colours(change):** Yellow and black stripes/black/black

**ADDITIONAL INFORMATION:**
**Record Att:** 82 v Didcot Town 17/12/2005.
**Honours:** Hellenic League Division 1 East 2007-08.

## CHINNOR
Founded: 1971    Nickname:

**Secretary:** Elaine Barker   **(T)** 07843 056 215    **(E)** elaine-barker6@btinternet.com
**Chairman:** Terry Devine
**Ground:** Station Road, Chinnor, Oxon OX39 4PV    **(T)** 01844 352 579
**Colours(change):** Yellow & black

**ADDITIONAL INFORMATION:**
**Previous League:** Oxfordshire Senior.
**Record Att:** 306 v Oxford Quarry Nomads, 29.08.2005.

## DIDCOT TOWN RESERVES
Founded: 1907    Nickname: Railwaymen

**Secretary:** Pat Horsman   **(T)** 07882 154 612    **(E)** didcot@fernring.co.uk
**Chairman:** John Bailey   **Manager:** Mark Janes & Neal McDermaid   **Prog Ed:** Steve Clare
**Ground:** Loop Meadow Stadium, Bowmont Water, Didcot OX11 7GA    **(T)** 01235 813 138    **Capacity:** 5,000
**Colours(change):** Red & white/white/red & white

**ADDITIONAL INFORMATION:**
**Previous League:** Hellenic Reserves.

## FINCHAMPSTEAD
Founded: 1952    Nickname: Finches

**Secretary:** Nick Markman   **(T)** 07793 866 324    **(E)** njm826@btinternet.com
**Chairman:** Richard Laugharne   **Manager:** Jon Laugharne    **Prog Ed:** Nick Markman
**Ground:** *Memorial Park The Village, Finchampstead RG40 4JR    **(T)** 0118 9732 890
**Colours(change):** Sky blue & white/sky/sky

**ADDITIONAL INFORMATION:**
**Record Att:** 425 v Sandhurst, 1958-59.
**Honours:** Chiltonian League 1987-88. Reading Senior Challenge Cup 1986-87. Hellenic League Division 1 East 2001-02.
*Matches will also be played at Eversley & California's (UCL Div.1) Fox Lane early in the season and for floodlit games.

## HEADINGTON AMATEURS
Founded: 1949    Nickname: A's

**Secretary:** Donald Light   **(T)** 07764 943 778    **(E)** donald.light@ntlworld.com
**Chairman:** Donald Light   **Manager:** Luke Cuff    **Prog Ed:** Donald Light
**Ground:** The Pavillion, Barton Recreation Ground, Oxford OX3 9LA    **(T)** 01865 762 974
**Colours(change):** All red

**ADDITIONAL INFORMATION:**
**Record Att:** 250 v Newport AFC, 1991. **Goalscorer:** Tony Penge. **Apps:** Kent Drackett.
**Honours:** Oxfordshire Senior League 1972-73, 73-74, 75-76, 76-77, Division 1 1968-69. Hellenic League Division One West 2010-11.

## HENLEY TOWN
Founded: 1871     Nickname: Lillywhites

**Secretary:** Tony Kingston     **(T)** 07712 139 592     **(E)** kingstontony6@gmail.com
**Chairman:** Jack Hollidge     **Manager:** Cyril Fairchild     **Prog Ed:** Tony Kingston
**Ground:** The Triangle Ground, Mill Lane, Henley RG9 4HB     **(T)** 07758 376 369
**Colours(change):** Red & white

**ADDITIONAL INFORMATION: Att:** 2000+ v Reading, 1922. **Goalscorer:** M. Turner.
Hellenic League Div.1 1963-64, 67-68, Div.1 East 2000-01. Chiltonian League Division 1 1987-88. Premier 1999-00.

## MAIDENHEAD UNITED RESERVES
Founded: 1870     Nickname: Magpies

**Secretary:** Ken Chandler     **(T)** 07863 183 872     **(E)** kenneth.chandler@btinternet.com
**Chairman:** Peter Griffin     **Manager:** Sam Lock
**Ground:** York Road, Maidenhead, Berkshire SL6 1SF     **(T)** 01628 636 314     **Capacity:** 4,500
**Colours(change):** Black & white stripe/black/red

**ADDITIONAL INFORMATION: Previous League:** Hellenic Reserves.

## MILTON UNITED
Founded: 1909     Nickname: Miltonians

**Secretary:** Vacant     **(T)**     **(E)** milton.united.fc@hotmail.co.uk
**Chairman:** Andy Burchette     **Manager:** Paul Bedwell     **Prog Ed:** A M Print & copy
**Ground:** Potash Lane, Milton Heights, OX13 6AG     **(T)** 01235 832 999
**Colours(change):** Claret & sky/claret & sky/claret

**ADDITIONAL INFORMATION:**
**Record Att:** 608 Carterton v Didcot Town, League Cup Final, 07.05.05. **Goalscorer:** Nigel Mott.
**Honours:** Hellenic League 1990-91.

## PENN & TYLERS GREEN
Founded: 1905     Nickname:

**Secretary:** Andrea Latta     **(T)** 07904 538 868     **(E)** hsvlatta1955@yahoo.co.uk
**Chairman:** Tony Hurst     **Manager:** Giovanni Sepede
**Ground:** French School Meadows, Elm Road, Penn, Bucks HP10 8LF     **(T)** 01494 815 346
**Colours(change):** Blue & white stripes/blue/blue

**ADDITIONAL INFORMATION:**
**Previous League:** Chiltonian (Founder member).
**Record Att:** 125 v Chalfont Wasps, August 2000.

## RAYNERS LANE
Founded: 1933     Nickname: The Lane

**Secretary:** Tony Pratt     **(T)** 01895 233 853     **(E)** richard.mitchell@tesco.net
**Chairman:** Martin Noblett     **Manager:** Mick Bradshaw
**Ground:** Tithe Farm Social Club, Rayners Lane, South Harrow HA2 0XH     **(T)** 0208 868 8724
**Colours(change):** Yellow/green/yellow

**ADDITIONAL INFORMATION:**
**Record Att:** 550 v Wealdstone 1983.
**Honours:** Hellenic League Division 1 1982-83, Division One West 2012-13.

## WOKINGHAM & EMMBROOK
Founded: 2004     Nickname: Satsumas

**Secretary:** Natalie Bateman     **(T)** 075570 79865     **(E)** j.rance@crown-golf.co.uk
**Chairman:** Paul Rance     **Manager:** Dan Bateman & Matt Eggleston
**Ground:** Emmbrook Sports & Social Club Lowther Road, Wokingham. RG41 1JB     **(T)** 0118 9780209
**Colours(change):** Orange/black/black.

**ADDITIONAL INFORMATION: Record Att:** 305 v Binfield, 25.03.2005.
**Honours:** Reading Senior 2008-09, 11-12, 12-13.

## WOODLEY TOWN
Founded: 1904     Nickname: Town

**Secretary:** John Mailer     **(T)** 07883 341 628     **(E)** john_mailer@hotmail.co.uk
**Chairman:** Mark Rozzier     **Manager:** Louie Tallett     **Prog Ed:** Mark Beaven
**Ground:** East Park Farm, Park Lane, Charvil, Berks RG10 9TR     **(T)** 07703 474 555
**Colours(change):** All navy blue

**ADDITIONAL INFORMATION:**
**Previous League:** Reading.
**Honours:** Reading Football League Senior Division 2008-09. Berkshire Trophy Centre Senior Cup 2008-09.

## CARTERTON

Founded: 1922     Nickname:

**Secretary:** Elaine Bunyan     **(T)** 07912 308 092     **(E)** info@cartertonfc.com
**Chairman:** Tom Amer     **Manager:** Mark Moss
**Ground:** Kilkenny Lane, Carterton, Oxfordshire OX18 1DY.     **(T)** 01993 842 410     **Capacity:** 1,500
**Colours(change):** Red/green/red.

**ADDITIONAL INFORMATION:** Record Att: 650 v Swindon Town, July 2001. **Goalscorer:** Phil Rodney.

## CLANFIELD

Founded: 1890     Nickname: Robins

**Secretary:** Terry Maycock     **(T)** 07747 742 239     **(E)** maycocktel@aol.com
**Chairman:** John Osborne     **Manager:** Jason Court
**Ground:** Radcot Road, Clanfield OX18 2ST     **(T)** 01367 810 314
**Colours(change):** All red

**ADDITIONAL INFORMATION:**
**Record Att:** 197 v Kidlington August 2002.
**Honours:** Hellenic League Division 1 1969-70.

## CRICKLADE TOWN

Founded: 1897     Nickname: Crick

**Secretary:** Rebecca Ross     **(T)** 07970 066 581     **(E)** alisdair.ross@venuesevent.com
**Chairman:** Alisdair Ross     **Manager:** Graham Jackson     **Prog Ed:** Kevin Midgley
**Ground:** Cricklade Leisure Centre, Stones Lane, Cricklade SN6 6JW     **(T)** 01793 750 011
**Colours(change):** Green/black/black

**ADDITIONAL INFORMATION:**
**Record Att:** 170 v Trowbridge Town 2003-04.
**Honours:** Wiltshire League 2000-01.

## EASINGTON SPORTS

Founded: 1946     Nickname: The Clan

**Secretary:** Angela Clives     **(T)** 07815 325 905     **(E)** aclives@btinternet.com
**Chairman:** Neil Clarke     **Manager:** Craig Pearman
**Ground:** Addison Road, Banbury OX16 9DH     **(T)** 01295 257 006
**Colours(change):** Red & white/black/black, red & white

**ADDITIONAL INFORMATION:**
**Record Att:** 258 v Hook Norton.
**Hnours:** Oxfordshire Senior League 1957-58, 58-59. Division 1 1965-66. Oxfordshire Senior Ben Turner Trophy 1970-71.

## FAIRFORD TOWN

Founded: 1891     Nickname: Town

**Secretary:** William Beach     **(T)** 07919 940 909     **(E)** wbeach007@btinternet.com
**Chairman:** Mike Tanner     **Manager:** Paul Braithwaite
**Ground:** Cinder Lane, London Road, Fairford GL7 4AX     **(T)** 01285 712 071     **Capacity:** 2,000
**Colours(change):** All red.

**ADDITIONAL INFORMATION:** Att: 1,525 v Coventry City, friendly, July 2000. **Goalscorer:** Pat Toomey.

## HOOK NORTON

Founded: 1898     Nickname: Hooky

**Secretary:** Garnet Thomas     **(T)** 07866 035 642     **(E)** thomasz@tiscali.co.uk
**Chairman:** Garnet Thomas     **Manager:** Mark Boyland     **Prog Ed:** Alan White
**Ground:** The Bourne, Hook Norton OX15 5PB     **(T)** 01608 737 132
**Colours(change):** Royal blue/royal blue/white

**ADDITIONAL INFORMATION:**
**Record Att:** 244 v Banbury United, 12/12/98.
**Honours:** Oxfordshire Senior League 1999-00, 00-01. Hellenic League Division 1 West 2001-02.

## LETCOMBE

Founded: 1910     Nickname: Brooksiders

**Secretary:** Des Williams     **(T)** 07765 144 985     **(E)** deswilliams45@btinternet.com
**Chairman:** Dennis Stock     **Manager:** Alan Gifford     **Prog Ed:** Russell Stock
**Ground:** Bassett Road, Letcombe Regis OX12 9JU     **(T)** 07765 144 985
**Colours(change):** All purple

**ADDITIONAL INFORMATION:**
**Record Att:** 203 v Old Woodstock Town, 29/08/04.
**Honours:** North Berkshire League Division One 1989-90. Chiltonian League Division One 1990-91.

## LYDNEY TOWN
**Founded:** 1911    **Nickname:** The Town

**Secretary:** Roger Sansom    **(T)** 07887 842 125    **(E)** rsansom@glatfelter.com
**Chairman:** Peter Elliott    **Manager:** Mark Lee    **Prog Ed:** Roger Sansom
**Ground:** Lydney Recreation Ground, Swan Road, Lydney GL15 5RU    **(T)** 01594 844 523
**Colours(change):** Black & white stripes/black/black & white

**ADDITIONAL INFORMATION:**
**Record Att:** 375 v Ellwood, 05.11.05.
**Honours:** Gloucestershire County League 2005-06. Hellenic League Division 1 West 2006-07.

## MALMESBURY VICTORIA
**Founded:**    **Nickname:** The Vics

**Secretary:** Julie Exton    **(T)** 07595 725 263    **(E)** jmexton@aol.com
**Chairman:** Phil Exton    **Manager:** Gareth Davies    **Prog Ed:** Phil Exton
**Ground:** Flying Monk Ground, Gloucester Road, SN16 0AJ    **(T)** 01666 822 141
**Colours(change):** Black & white/black/red

**ADDITIONAL INFORMATION:**
**Record Att:** 261 v Cirencester United, 25.08.02.
**Honours:** Wiltshire League 1999-00. Wiltshire Senior Cup 01-02.

## NEW COLLEGE ACADEMY
**Founded:** 1984    **Nickname:** College

**Secretary:** Rob Hopkins    **(T)** 07739 914 888    **(E)** rob.hopkins@newcollege.ac.uk
**Chairman:** Paul Bodin    **Manager:** Rob Hopkins    **Prog Ed:** Rob Hopkins
**Ground:** Sumpermarine RFC Sports & Social, Supermarine Rd, South Marston SN3 4BZ    **(T)** 01793 824 828
**Colours(change):** All royal blue

**ADDITIONAL INFORMATION: Previous League:** Wiltshire > 2011.

## NORTH LEIGH RESERVES
**Founded:** 1908    **Nickname:** The Millers

**Secretary:** Keith Huxley    **(T)** 01993 851497    **(E)** keith.huxley08@tiscali.co.uk
**Chairman:** Peter King    **Manager:** Mark Gee    **Prog Ed:** Mike Burnell
**Ground:** Eynsham Hall Park Sports Ground OX29 6PN.    **(T)** 07775 818 066    **Capacity:** 2,000
**Colours(change):** Yellow/black/yellow

**ADDITIONAL INFORMATION:**
**Previous Leagues:** Hellenic Reserves.

## OLD WOODSTOCK TOWN
**Founded:** 1998    **Nickname:**

**Secretary:** Ian Whelan    **(T)** 07714 267224    **(E)** i.whelan@ntlworld.com
**Chairman:** Ted Saxton    **Manager:** Clint Ross
**Ground:** New Road, Woodstock OX20 1PD    **(T)** 07748 152 243    **Capacity:** 1,000
**Colours(change):** Royal blue & red/royal/royal.

**ADDITIONAL INFORMATION:**
**Previous Names:** Woodstock Town (1911) and Old Woodstock (1920) merged in 1998 to form today's club.
**Record Att:** 258 v Kidlington, 27.08.01.
**Honours:** Oxfordshire Senior League 1998-99.

## PURTON
**Founded:** 1923    **Nickname:** The Reds

**Secretary:** Alan Eastwood    **(T)** 07950 889 177    **(E)** alan.eastwood830@ntlworld.com
**Chairman:** Alan Eastwood    **Manager:** Chris Pethick    **Prog Ed:** Alan Eastwood
**Ground:** The Red House, Purton SN5 4DY    **(T)** 01793 770 262 (MD)
**Colours(change):** All red

**ADDITIONAL INFORMATION:**
**Honours:** Wiltshire League 1945-46, 46-47, 47-48. Wiltshire County League 1985-86. Hellenic League Division 1 1995-96, Division 1 West 2003-04. Wiltshire Senior Cup 1938-39, 48-49, 50-51, 54-55, 87-88, 88-89, 94-95.

## SHORTWOOD UNITED RESERVES
**Founded:**    **Nickname:**

**Secretary:** Mark Webb    **(T)** 07792 323 784    **(E)** squish.shortwoodfc@live.co.uk
**Chairman:** Peter Webb    **Manager:** Des Meredith
**Ground:** Meadowbank, Shortwood, Nailsworth GL6 0SJ    **(T)** 01453 833 936
**Colours(change):** Red & white stripes/black/black

**ADDITIONAL INFORMATION:**
**Previous League:** Gloucestershire Northern Senior.
**Honours:** Gloucestershire Northern Senior League 2011-12. Hellenic Division 2 West 2012-13.

## TUFFLEY ROVERS

Founded:      Nickname:

**Secretary:** Neil Spiller     **(T)** 07545 492 261     **(E)** neil.spiller@tuffleyroversfc.co.uk
**Chairman:** Roy Craddock     **Manager:** Doug Foxwell
**Ground:** Glevum Park Lower Tuffley Lane, Tuffley, Gloucester. GL2 5DT     **(T)** 07708 361 808     **Capacity:** 1,000
**Colours(change):** Sky blue and claret

**ADDITIONAL INFORMATION:**
**Previous League:** Gloucestershire County.

## TYTHERINGTON ROCKS

Founded: 1896      Nickname: The Rocks

**Secretary:** Graham Shipp     **(T)** 07811 318 424     **(E)** tramar1618@btinternet.com
**Chairman:** Ted Travell     **Manager:** Gary Powell     **Prog Ed:** Mark Brown
**Ground:** Hardwicke Playing Field, Tytherington Glos GL12 8UJ     **(T)** 07837 555 776
**Colours(change):** Amber & black/black/black

**ADDITIONAL INFORMATION:**
**Previous League:** Gloucestershire County.
**Record Att:** 424 v Winterbourne United, 26/08/2007.

# GROUND DIRECTIONS

## PREMIER DIVISION

**ABINGDON TOWN - Culham Road OX14 3HP - 01235 521 684**
From Town Centre follow signs for Culham, go over bridge, ground is 300 yards on right.

**ABINGDON UNITED - The North Court, Northcourt Road, Abingdon OX14 1PL - 01235 203 203**
From the north – Leave A34 at Abingdon north turning. Ground on right at first set of traffic lights.
From the south – Enter Town Centre, leave north on A4183 (Oxford Road).
Ground on left after one mile.

**ARDLEY UNITED - The Playing Fields OX27 7NZ - 07711 009 198**
From M40 Junction 10 take B430 towards Middleton Stoney the ground is on the right hand side after mile. From Oxford take B430 through Weston-on-the-Green & Middleton Stoney then on the left hand side after passing Church in village.

**ASCOT UNITED - Ascot Racecourse SL5 7RA - 07798 701 995**
From Ascot High Street, with Ascot Racecourse on the left, follow the A329 to the mini-roundabout, at the end of the High Street, turn left on Winkfield Rd, go through road underpass and take the first right (signposted Car Park 7&8). Follow the track past the Ascot United welcome sign, through gates into the large car park and the ground is approx. 600m further on.

**BINFIELD - Hill Farm Lane RG42 5NR - 01344 860 822**
From M4 Junction 10 take A329 signposted Wokingham & Binfield, at roundabout take 1st exit. Go through 1st set of traffic lights, turn left at 2nd set opposite Travel Lodge. Follow road through village over two mini-roundabouts, at 'T' junction with church in front of you turn right. Take left filter road after 150 yards into Stubbs Lane. Ground is on left at end of short lane.

**BRACKNELL TOWN - Larges Lane Bracknell RG12 9AN - 01344 412 305**
Leave M4 at J10, take A329M signposted Wokingham & Bracknell. Follow road for 5 miles, over roundabout, pass Southern industrial estate (Waitrose etc.) on right to a 2nd roundabout with traffic lights; take 2nd exit and follow signposts for M3. At next roundabout take 1st exit. At next roundabout take 3rd exit, Church Road dual carriageway. This brings you to another roundabout with Bracknell & Wokingham college on right and Old Manor PH on left, take 5th exit for Ascot - A329. Go down hill on dual carriageway, London Road to next roundabout take 4th exit back up the dual carriageway, London Road, Larges Lane last left turn before reaching roundabout again. Ground 200 yards on right.

**BRIMSCOMBE & THRUPP** - 'The Meadow', London Road, Brimscombe Stroud, Gloucestershire GL5 2SH - 07833 231 464
9 miles north of Cirencester on A419. 2 miles south of Stroud on A419.

**CHELTENHAM SARACENS - PETERSFIELD PARK GL51 9DY - 01242 584 134**
Follow directions into Cheltenham following signs for railway station. At Station roundabout take Gloucester Road, in a Northerly direction for approx 2 miles. Turn left at lights past Tesco entrance onto Tewkesbury Rd, follow road past 'The Range' store over railway bridge. Take 1st left and then 1st left again, then left into service road into car park.

**FLACKWELL HEATH - Wilks Park, Magpie Lane HP10 9EA - 01628 523 892**
Junction 4 of M40 Follow signs A404 (High Wycombe) Turn right at traffic lights halfway down Marlow Hill, signposted Flackwell Heath. Ground three (3) miles on left.

**HIGHMOOR - IBIS - Palmer Park Stadium, Wokingham Road, Reading RG6 1LF - 01189 375 080**
From A4 ( Also indicated as London Road Reading) At the KIngs Road/A 329 Junction turn into the A329 the Palmer Park ground is approx. 300 metres on the left.

**HIGHWORTH TOWN - Elm Recreation Ground SN6 7DD - 01793 766 263**
Enter Town on A361, turn into The Green by Veterinary Surgery, Ground and Car Park 100 yards on left.

**HOLYPORT - Summerleaze Village SL6 8SP - 07702 369 708**
From the A4 Maidenhead take the B4447 towards Cookham after   mile turn right into Ray Mill Road West, at the T-junction turn left into Blackamoor Lane. As road bends sharply you will see the entrance to the ground on left, signposted Holyport FC. Please observe speed limit down track to the ground.

**KIDLINGTON - Yarnton Road OX5 1AT - 01865 841 526**
From Kidlington Roundabout take A4260 into Kidlington. After 3rd set of traffic lights take 2nd left into Yarnton Road. Ground 300 yards on left, just past Morton Avenue.

**NEWBURY - Faraday Road RG14 2AD - 01635 41031**
Leave M4 at junction 13 taking Newbury road. Take A4 towards Thatcham, then take 1st right by 'Topp Tiles' into Faraday Road, ground is at end of road.

**OXFORD CITY NOMADS - Court Place Farm Stadium OX3 0NQ - 01865 744 493**
From South:  From Newbury travel along the A34 towards Oxford turn onto Ring Road heading towards London (East). Follow Ring Road over 5 roundabouts to the Green Road roundabout signposted London, M40 East. Go straight over towards Banbury. A fly-over is visible, turn left onto the slip road and follow road to Court Place Farm Stadium on left. From North:  At the North Oxford roundabout, travel towards London M40 on the Eastern by-pass, turn off at the flyover, the ground is visible to the left as you go over bridge.

**READING TOWN - Scours Lane RG30 6AY - 0118 945 3555**
Leave M4 at junction 12 and take A4 towards Reading. Turn left at 1st lights go through Tilehurst Centre turn right into Norcot Road then left into Oxford Road and 1st right into Scours Lane.

**SHRIVENHAM - The Recreation Ground SN6 8BJ - 07767 371 414**
Shrivenham village is signposted off A420 Oxford to Swindon road, six miles east of Swindon, four miles west of Faringdon. Drive through village turn into Highworth Road, ground is on right, car park on left.

**THAME UNITED - The ASM Stadium, Meadow View Park, Tythrop Wa, Thame, Oxon, OX9 3RN 01844 214 401.** From the west: At the Oxford Road roundabout on the edge of Thame take the first left (sign posted Aylesbury) and follow the by-pass. At the next roundabout take the third exit on to Tythrop Way. The ground is 200 yards on the left.
From the east: Leave the M40 at Junction 6 and follow the signposts to Thame. On arriving in Thame, take the first right on to Wenman Road (B4012). Stay on the B4012 as it by-passes Thame, going straight over two roundabouts. The ground is on the right, directly off the by-pass, approximately half a mile after you pass Chinnor Rugby Club.

**WANTAGE TOWN - Alfredian Park, Manor Road OX12 8DW - 01235 764 781**
Proceed to Market Square. Take road at southeast corner (Newbury Street signposted to Hungerford). Continue for approximately a quarter of a mile take right turning into the ground. Clearly marked 'Wantage Town FC'.

**WOOTTON BASSETT - Gerard Buxton Sports Ground    SN4 8AW - 01793 853 880**
Leave M4 at junction 16 and proceed towards Wootton Bassett Town Centre. Take 1st left after BP Petrol Station in Longleaze. Take 3rd turning on right into Rylands Way. Ground 150 metres on right hand side. Approaching from Calne or Devizes Area - proceed through Wootton Bassett Town Centre, take first right after Shell Garage into Longleaze then follow previous instructions.

# DIVISION 1 EAST
**AFC HINKSEY - Abingdon Town FC Culham Road Abingdon OX14 3HP**
From Abingdon town centre follow signs for Culham, go over bridge, ground is 300 yards on right

**BURNHAM RESERVES - The Gore, Wymers Wood Road, Burnham, Slough SL1 8JG**
**01628 668 654**
Approximately 2 miles from the M4 junction 7 and 5 miles from the M40 junction 2. From M40 take A355 to A4 signposted Maidenhead. From M4 take A4 towards Maidenhead until you reach roundabout with Sainsbury Superstore on left. Turn right into Lent Rise Road. Travel approximately 1½ miles over two double roundabouts, 100 yards after second double roundabout fork right into Wymers Wood Road. Ground entrance on right.

**CHALFONT WASPS - Crossleys Bowstridge Lane HP8 4QN - 01494 875 050**
A413 to Chalfont St Giles, follow signposts for village centre. Bowstridge Lane is 400 yards on left immediately after the shops. Crossleys is 400 yards along Bowstridge Lane on the right. Ground is directly ahead.

**CHINNOR - Station Road OX39 4PV - 01844 352 579**
Leave M40 at junction 6 and follow B4009 sign posted Princes Risborough. After 3 miles enter Chinnor and turn left at Crown PH roundabout. Ground is 400 yards on right.

**DIDCOT TOWN RESERVES - Loop Meadow Stadium OX11 7GA - 01235 813 138**
From A34 take A4130 towards Didcot, at first roundabout take first exit, at next roundabout take third exit, then straight across next two roundabouts, at 5th roundabout turn right into Avon Way, ground is on the left. Also footpath direct from Didcot Railway Station.

**FINCHAMPSTEAD - Memorial Park, The Village RG40 4JR - 0118 973 2890**
A321 from Wokingham, then fork right onto B3016. At the Greyhound Public House turn right onto the B3348. The ground is 200 yards on the right.

**HEADINGTON AM' - Barton Recreation Ground OX3 9LA - 01865 760 489**
A40 from London take last exit at Headington Roundabout. A40 from Witney take first exit. Take first left after leaving roundabout into North Way. Follow North Way to end where road merges to become Barton Village Road. Ground at bottom of hill on left.

**HENLEY TOWN - The Triangle Ground RG9 4HB - 01491 411 083**
From Henley Town Centre take the A4155 towards Reading. Mill Lane is approximately one mile from the Town Centre on the left immediately before the Jet Garage. From M4 Junction 11 head towards Reading on the A33 inner distribution road then follow A4155 signed to Henley, turn right into Mill Lane after the Jet Garage. Ground & Car Park on the left over the Railway Bridge.

**MAIDENHEAD UNITED RESERVES - York Road, Maidenhead, Berkshire SL6 1SF**
**01628 636 314**
The Ground is in the town centre. 200 yards from the station and two minutes walk from the High Street. Access from M4 Junctions 7 or 8/9.

**MILTON UNITED - Potash Lane OX13 6AG - 01235 832 999**
Exit A34 at Milton, 10 miles south of Oxford & 12 miles north of junction 13 of M4. Take A4130 towards Wantage approximately 200 metres turn 1st left then right into Milton Hill. Ground 400 metres on the left.

**PENN & TYLERS GREEN - French School Meadows HP10 8LF - 01494 815 346**
From West - 'M40 to High Wycombe leave at J4. Follow A404 to Amersham, via Wycombe. Stay on A404 up the hill past railway station approx. 3 miles at Hazlemere Crossroads turn right onto the B474 signposted to Penn and Beaconsfield. Continue for approx. one mile go past three new houses on left, turn into Elm Road, the ground is on the left. From East -Leave M40 at Junction 2 and take the road signed Beaconsfield. From Beaconsfield follow the road through Penn towards Hazlemere, pass the pond on green and entrance to ground is on the right had side of road before the hill.

**RAYNERS LANE - The Farm Social Club HA2 0XH - 0208 868 8724**
From A40 Polish War Memorial turn left into A4180 (West End Road), approx. 500 metres turn right into Station Approach, at traffic lights turn right into Victoria Road. At next roundabout continue straight on to traffic lights at junction with Alexandra Avenue (Matrix Bar & Restaurant on left). Continue straight on over traffic lights and take second turning on left into Rayners Lane. Ground is approximately half a mile on the left.

**WOKINGHAM & EMMB' - Emmbrook Sports & Social Club Lowther Rd, Wokingham. RG41 1JB 0118 9780 209**

**WOODLEY TOWN - East Park Farm, Park Lane RG10 9TR - 07703 474 555**
Take A4, Bath Road & exit onto A3032 at @Wee Waif' roundabout to Twyford & Charvil. Take right exit at mini-roundabout into Park Lane then 2nd exit at mini-roundabout on Park Lane then left turn into East Park Farm. After-match Hospitality is at the Earley Home Guard Club.

# DIVISION 1 WEST

**CARTERTON - Kilkenny Lane OX18 1DY - 01993 842 410**
Leave A40 follow B4477 for Carterton continue along Monahan Way turning right at roundabout, at traffic lights turn right onto Upavon Way. At next set of lights turn right onto B4020 to Burford. Take 2nd right into Swinbrook Road carry onto Kilkenny Lane, a single-track road). Ground & car park 200 metres on left hand side.

**CLANFIELD - Radcot Road OX18 2ST - 01367 810 314**
Situated on A4095 at southern end of village, 8 miles west of Witney and 4 miles east of Faringdon.

**CRICKLADE TOWN - Cricklade Leisure Centre SN6 6JW - 01793 750 011**
Cricklade is eight miles North of Swindon signposted off the A419. Leisure Centre is signposted off the B4040 Malmesbury Road.

**EASINGTON SPORTS - Addison Road OX16 9DH - 01295 257 006**
From North/South M40- Leave M40 at J11, follow A422 to Banbury, 2nd r'about take A4260 to Adderbury. Go through three sets of traffic lights, at top of hill at T-junc' turn left. Take 3rd right into Addison Rd. From South West A361 – Entering Banbury take 1st right turning into Springfield Av after 'The Easington' PH. Follow road, take T-junc' right into Grange Rd, 1st right into Addison Rd. Ground on left at end of road.

**FAIRFORD TOWN - Cinder Lane London Road GL7 4AX - 01285 712 071**
Take A417 from Lechlade, turn left down Cinder Lane 150 yards after 40 mph sign. From Cirencester take Lechlade Road, turn right down Cinder Lane 400 yards after passing the Railway Inn.

**HOOK NORTON - The Bourne OX15 5PB - 01608 737 132**
From Oxford – A44 to junction with A361 turn right, take 1st left to a 'T' junction, turn right & enter village, after 30 MPH turn left then 1st right into 'The Bourne', take 1st left into ground.

**LETCOMBE - Bassett Road OX12 9JU - 07765 144 985**
Take the B4507 from Wantage (Sign posted White Horse). Turn left after half a mile to Letcombe Regis. Ground on Far side of Village, on the right hand side of road.

**LYDNEY TOWN - Lydney Recreation Ground GL15 5RU - 01594 844 523**
From Gloucester – take Lydney road off A48 down Highfield Hill and into the town centre. Take 1st left into Swan Road after 2nd set of pelican lights. From Chepstow – at by-pass roundabout take Lydney road. Go over railway crossing then take 2nd right into Swan Road.

**MALMESBURY VICTORIA - Flying Monk Ground SN16 0AJ**
Off A429 signpost Cirencester take B4014 to Tetbury. First left signpost Town Centre Ground on right directly after Somerfield supermarket, narrow right turning into ground behind supermarket.

**NEW COLLEGE SWINDON - Supermarine RFC Sports & Social Supermarine Road South Marston Swindon SN3 4BZ - 01793 824 828**
From M5 Junction 11a, take the A417 to Cirencester, then A419 Swindon. At the A361 junction by Honda Factory take road to Highworth. After one mile Club is on 4th roundabout.
From M4 Junction 15, take A419 towards Swindon Cirencester, take A361, then as above .
From A420 Swindon take A419 to Cirencester, near Honda factory take A361, then as above.

**NORTH LEIGH RESERVES - Eynsham Hall Park Sports Ground OX29 6PN - 07775 818 066**
Ground situated on A4095 Witney to Woodstock road, three miles east of Witney. Entrance 300 yards east of main park entrance.

**OLD WOODSTOCK TOWN - New Road, Woodstock OX20 1PD - 07748 152 243**
A44 from Oxford, turn right opposite The Crown into Hensington Road. After half a mile road bends to right, take 1st turning right into New Road. Ground on left.

**PURTON - The Red House SN5 4DY - 01793 770 262 MD**
Red House is near Village Hall Square; Purton is well signposted from all directions, situated on the B4041 Wootton Bassett to Cricklade Road, NW of Swindon.

**SHORTWOOD UNITED RESERVES - Meadowbank, Shortwood, Nailsworth GL6 0SJ 01453 833 936**
When entering Nailsworth from Stroud turn right at mini roundabout, when coming from Cirencester go straight over roundabout, and when from Bath turn left at mini roundabout.
Proceed up Spring Hill 30 yards turn left at Raffles Wine Warehouse, straight through town turn left at Brittannia Pub carry on for 1 mile until you come to Shortwood village you will see sign post on fork in the road keep to the left follow on for quarter of a mile ground opposite church.

**TYTHERINGTON ROCKS - Hardwicke Playing Field GL12 8UJ - 07837 555 776**
From M5 Junction 14 take A38 for Bristol. Tytherington turn-off is approximately three (3) miles. Enter village, ground is signposted.

**WINTERBOURNE UNITED - Oakland Park, Alomondsbury, Bristol BS32 4AG - 07976 255 666**
From M4 (West) leave at junction 20 to M5 (Sth West). Leave immediately at junction 16 (A38 Thornbury), turn right onto A38, then first left 100 yards from junction, in front of Motorway Police HQ, Ground next door. Signposted from A38 'Gloucestershire FA HQ'.

2012-13 - Wantage Town (Hellenic Premier).

Photo: Roger Turner

2012-13 Kent Invicta Champions - Phoenix Sports.

Photo: Alan Coomes.

# KENT INVICTA LEAGUE

**Sponsored by:** No sponsor
**Founded:** 2011

### Recent Champions
### 2012: Bly Spartans

|  |  | P | W | D | L | F | A | Pts |
|---|---|---|---|---|---|---|---|---|
| 1 | (P) Phoenix Sports | 30 | 25 | 3 | 2 | 108 | 26 | 78 |
| 2 | Hollands & Blair | 30 | 24 | 2 | 4 | 96 | 25 | 74 |
| 3 | (P) Ashford United | 30 | 20 | 6 | 4 | 79 | 32 | 66 |
| 4 | Bearsted | 30 | 18 | 3 | 9 | 82 | 43 | 57 |
| 5 | Seven Acre & Sidcup | 30 | 15 | 5 | 10 | 59 | 46 | 50 |
| 6 | Lydd Town | 30 | 15 | 5 | 10 | 63 | 59 | 50 |
| 7 | Bridon Ropes | 30 | 14 | 6 | 10 | 51 | 35 | 48 |
| 8 | Sutton Athletic | 30 | 12 | 5 | 13 | 41 | 41 | 41 |
| 9 | Orpington | 30 | 12 | 4 | 14 | 35 | 64 | 40 |
| 10 | Eltham Palace | 29 | 10 | 6 | 13 | 49 | 74 | 36 |
| 11 | Kent Football United | 29 | 8 | 5 | 16 | 43 | 67 | 29 |
| 12 | Rusthall | 30 | 8 | 5 | 17 | 38 | 81 | 29 |
| 13 | Crockenhill | 30 | 7 | 4 | 19 | 44 | 84 | 25 |
| 14 | Woodstock Park | 30 | 6 | 4 | 20 | 33 | 58 | 22 |
| 15 | Meridian | 30 | 6 | 3 | 21 | 40 | 80 | 21 |
| 16 | Lewisham Borough | 30 | 5 | 2 | 23 | 38 | 84 | 17 |

## CHALLENGE TROPHY

**PRELIMINARY ROUND**

| Ashford United | v | Crown Alexandra | 4-0 |
|---|---|---|---|

**ROUND 1**

| Bearsted | v | Seven Acre & Sidcup | 3-1 |
|---|---|---|---|
| Lewisham Borough | v | Ashford United | 3-2 |
| Sutton Athletic | v | Orpington | 3-2 |
| Bridon Ropes | v | Rustall | 2-0 |
| Woodstock Park | v | Kent Football United | 5-1 |
| Phoenix Sports | v | Eltham Palace | 5-0 |
| Lydd Town | v | Crockenhill | 3-0 |
| Hollands & Blair | v | Meridian | 2-0 |

**QUARTER FINALS**

| Hollands & Blair | v | Bridon Ropes | 7-2 |
|---|---|---|---|
| Phoenix Sports | v | Sutton Athletic | 4-1 |
| Woodstock Park | v | Bearsted | 0-6 |
| Lewisham Borough | v | Lydd Town | 0-4 |

**SEMI FINALS**

| Bearstead | v | Lydd Town | 0-3 |
|---|---|---|---|
| Phoenix Sports | v | Hollands & Blair | 1-2 |

**FINAL**

| Hollands & Blair | v | Phoenix Sports | 4-3 |
|---|---|---|---|

| | | 1 | 2 | 3 | 4 | 5 | 6 | 7 | 8 | 9 | 10 | 11 | 12 | 13 | 14 | 15 | 16 |
|---|---|---|---|---|---|---|---|---|---|---|---|---|---|---|---|---|---|
| 1 | Ashford Utd | | 2-0 | 0-0 | 4-0 | 2-0 | 1-3 | 3-2 | 5-0 | 7-2 | 3-0 | 5-0 | 1-2 | 4-4 | 5-2 | 2-1 | 5-1 |
| 2 | Bearsted | 3-1 | | 4-1 | 2-0 | 5-0 | 1-2 | 1-2 | 3-1 | 1-2 | 7-0 | 7-0 | 4-4 | 4-1 | 2-0 | 2-1 | 2-1 |
| 3 | Bridon Ropes | 1-1 | 3-5 | | 4-0 | 7-0 | 2-0 | 3-0 | 1-1 | 2-2 | 0-2 | 1-0 | 3-2 | 2-1 | 0-2 | 1-0 | 4-1 |
| 4 | Crockenhill | 0-2 | 2-5 | 1-4 | | 3-3 | 1-3 | A | 4-3 | 0-4 | 1-1 | 0-2 | 1-2 | 1-3 | 3-6 | 1-1 | 2-1 |
| 5 | Eltham Palace | 2-2 | 2-2 | 0-1 | 3-2 | | 0-4 | 4-3 | 1-0 | 0-1 | 4-3 | 2-2 | 1-3 | 3-2 | 0-3 | 3-2 | 0-2 |
| 6 | Hollands & Blair | 0-2 | 2-1 | 3-0 | 8-0 | 8-1 | | 3-0 | 5-0 | 2-2 | 2-1 | 6-2 | 2-3 | 0-0 | 2-0 | 3-2 | H |
| 7 | Kent Football Utd | 1-1 | 1-1 | 0-2 | 4-1 | | 0-3 | | 2-0 | 1-2 | 5-0 | 0-2 | 0-6 | 1-2 | 0-4 | 0-3 | 3-2 |
| 8 | Lewisham Boro' | 2-6 | 0-3 | 0-1 | 2-5 | 0-4 | 1-5 | 4-2 | | 0-4 | 2-1 | 0-1 | 2-4 | 2-3 | 1-2 | 0-1 | 5-1 |
| 9 | Lydd Town | 1-3 | 0-5 | 0-0 | 1-4 | 2-3 | 2-4 | 3-3 | 3-2 | | 8-1 | 2-1 | 1-0 | 6-1 | 1-2 | 2-5 | 1-1 |
| 10 | Meridian | 1-3 | 1-4 | 0-3 | 7-1 | 1-1 | 0-5 | 2-2 | 2-3 | 0-2 | | 1-2 | 0-4 | 1-4 | 1-3 | 2-3 | 2-0 |
| 11 | Orpington | 0-5 | 4-2 | 2-1 | 1-1 | 1-5 | 0-4 | 0-1 | 2-0 | 0-2 | 2-1 | | 0-6 | 2-1 | 3-3 | 0-1 | HW |
| 12 | Phoenix Sports | 3-0 | 4-1 | 3-2 | 4-0 | 3-1 | 1-0 | 3-1 | 7-1 | 5-0 | 2-0 | 2-0 | | 12-0 | 6-1 | 2-2 | 2-1 |
| 13 | Rusthall | 1-2 | 0-2 | 0-0 | 1-4 | 0-2 | 0-7 | 2-3 | 2-1 | 4-2 | 1-4 | 3-4 | 0-6 | | 1-1 | H | |
| 14 | Seven Acre & Sid' | 0-1 | 3-1 | 2-0 | 0-2 | 3-0 | 0-2 | 6-3 | 1-3 | 1-2 | 1-2 | 1-0 | 0-0 | 1-1 | | 5-1 | 1-1 |
| 15 | Sutton Athletic | 0-0 | 0-2 | 2-1 | 2-0 | 5-2 | 0-3 | 1-1 | 2-1 | 0-1 | 1-0 | 0-0 | 1-3 | 2-0 | 1-3 | | 1-0 |
| 16 | Woodstock Park | 0-1 | 3-0 | 2-1 | 1-4 | 2-2 | 2-5 | 3-2 | 1-1 | 1-2 | 1-3 | 1-2 | 0-4 | 2-0 | 1-3 | 1-0 | |

## CLUB MOVEMENTS

**Premier Division - In:** Fleet Leisure (P - Kent County Premier Division). Glebe (N). Meridian VP (NC from Meridian).

**Out:** Ashford United (P - Southern Counties East). Meridian (NC to Meridian VP). Phoenix Sports (P - Southern Counites East). Woodstock Park (W - now in Kent County Div.2 East).

2012-13 - Bearsted.

Photo: Alan Coomes

2012-13 - Eltham Athletic.

Photo: Alan Coomes.

## BEARSTED

Founded: 1895    Nickname:

**Secretary:** Roy Benton    **(T)** 07849 809 875    **(E)** benton951@aol.com
**Chairman:**    **Manager:** Tony Cornwell    **Prog Ed:** Janine Harris
**Ground:** Otham Sports Club, Honey Lane, Otham, Maidstone ME15 8RG    **(T)** 07860 360 280
**Colours(change):** White/blue/blue (All yellow)

**ADDITIONAL INFORMATION:**
**Previous League:** Kent County > 2011.

## BRIDON ROPES

Founded: 1935    Nickname:

**Secretary:** Richard Clements    **(T)** 07884 457 852    **(E)** rich.clements@live.co.uk
**Chairman:** Clive Smith    **Manager:** Ben Kotey    **Prog Ed:** Reggie Boatswain
**Ground:** Meridian Sports & Social Club, Charlton Park Lane, Charlton, London SE7 8QS    **(T)** 0208 8561923
**Colours(change):** Blue & white/blue/blue (All red)

**ADDITIONAL INFORMATION:**
**Previous Lge:** Kent County > 2011.

## CROCKENHILL

Founded: 1946    Nickname:

**Secretary:** Steve Cullen    **(T)** 07702 886 966    **(E)** steve@crockenhillfc.co.uk
**Chairman:**    **Prog Ed:** Alan Curnich
**Ground:** Wested Meadow Ground, Eynesford Road, Crockenhill, Kent BR8 8EJ    **(T)** 01322 666 767
**Colours(change):** Red & white stripes/black/black (Yellow & black stripes/yellow/yellow)

**ADDITIONAL INFORMATION:**
**Previous Lge:** Kent County > 2011.

## ELTHAM PALACE

Founded: 1961    Nickname:

**Secretary:** Liam Kelly    **(T)** 07825 997 598    **(E)** elthampalace@gmail.com
**Chairman:**    **Manager:** Neil Proctor    **Prog Ed:** Liam Kelly
**Ground:** Green Court Sports Club, Green Court Rd, Crockenhill, Kent BR8 8HF    **(T)**
**Colours(change):** All royal blue (All yellow)

**ADDITIONAL INFORMATION:**

## FLEET LEISURE

Founded: 1927    Nickname:

**Secretary:** Dave Hughes    **(T)** 07725 961 273    **(E)** fleetleisurefc@aol.com
**Chairman:**    **Prog Ed:** Dave Hughes
**Ground:** Rochester United FC, Rede Court Road, Strood, Kent ME2 3TU    **(T)** 01634 710 577
**Colours(change):** All red (Yellow/black/yellow)

**ADDITIONAL INFORMATION:**
**Previous Name:** Beauwater FC
**Previous League:** Kent County > 2013.

## GLEBE

Founded: 2013    Nickname:

**Secretary:** Nikola Curtis    **(T)** 07875 036 907    **(E)** nikola.curtis@ntlworld.com
**Chairman:** Rocky McMillan    **Prog Ed:** Rocky McMillan
**Ground:** Holmesdale FC, Oakley Road, Bromley, Kent BR2 8HG    **(T)** 07903 274 178
**Colours(change):** Red & black/black/black (White/red/red)

**ADDITIONAL INFORMATION:**

## HOLLANDS & BLAIR

Founded: 1970    Nickname: Blair

**Secretary:** Laurence Plummer    **(T)** 07540 841 799    **(E)** laurence.plummer@btinternet.com
**Chairman:** Barry Peirce    **Manager:** Paul Piggott    **Prog Ed:** Laurence Plummer
**Ground:** Star Meadow Sports Club, Darland Avenue, Gillingham, Kent ME7 3AN    **(T)** 01634 573839
**Colours(change):** All red (Yellow & blue)

**ADDITIONAL INFORMATION:**
**Previous Lge:** Kent County > 2011.
**Honours:** Kent County 2010-11.

2012-13 - Lewisham Borough.

Photo: Alan Coomes

2012-13 - Meridian.

Photo: Alan Coomes.

## KENT FOOTBALL UNITED

Founded:    Nickname:

**Secretary:** Roy MacNeil     **(T)** 07968 661 929     **(E)** roymacneil@tiscali.co.uk
**Chairman:**     **Prog Ed:** Bradley Ambridge
**Ground:** Oakwood (VCD Ath. FC) Old Road, Crayford, Kent DA1 4DN     **(T)** 07501 684 838
**Colours(change):** Blue & white/blue/blue (Yellow & black/black/black)
**ADDITIONAL INFORMATION:**

## LEWISHAM BOROUGH

Founded: 2003     Nickname: The Boro

**Secretary:** Ray Simpson & Juliet Walker     **(T)** 07958 946 236     **(E)** grancan_jamaica@yahoo.co.uk
**Chairman:** Ray Simpson     **Manager:** Willie O'Sullivan     **Prog Ed:** Ray Simpson & Juliet Walker
**Ground:** Ladywell Arena, Silvermere Road, Catford, London SE6 4QX     **(T)**
**Colours(change):** All royal blue (All yellow)
**ADDITIONAL INFORMATION:**
**Previous Lge:** Kent county > 2011.

## LYDD TOWN

Founded: 1885     Nickname:

**Secretary:** Bruce Marchant     **(T)** 01303 275 403     **(E)** brucemarchant@hotmail.com
**Chairman:**     **Prog Ed:** Dave Johncock
**Ground:** The Lindsey Field, Dengemarsh Road, Lydd, Kent TN29 9JH     **(T)** 01797 321 904
**Colours(change):** Green & red/green/red (Blue & white stripes/blue/blue)
**ADDITIONAL INFORMATION:**
**Previous Lge:** Kent County > 2011.

## MERIDIAN VP

Founded: 1995     Nickname:

**Secretary:** Dwinder Tamma     **(T)** 07977 274 179     **(E)** dtamna@meridianfc.co.uk
**Chairman:** Dwinder Tamma     **Manager:** Darrell Queeley     **Prog Ed:** Dwinder Tamma
**Ground:** Meridian Sports & Social Club, 110 Charlton Park Lane, London SE7 8QS     **(T)** 0208 856 1923
**Colours(change):** All sky blue (All red)
**ADDITIONAL INFORMATION:**
**Previous Lge:** Kent County > 2011.
**Previous Name:** Meridan 1995-2013.

## ORPINGTON

Founded: 1939     Nickname:

**Secretary:** Paul Wade     **(T)** 01689 889 619     **(E)** paul.wade@virgin.net
**Chairman:**     **Prog Ed:** Phil Alder
**Ground:** Green Court Road, Crockenhill, Kent BR8 8HJ     **(T)** 07940 355 595
**Colours(change):** Amber/black/amber (All blue)
**ADDITIONAL INFORMATION:**
**Previous Lge:** Kent County > 2011.

## RUSTHALL

Founded: 1890     Nickname:

**Secretary:** Alan Hawkins     **(T)** 01892 532 212     **(E)** hawkins48@btinternet.com
**Chairman:** John Ronaldson     **Manager:** Gary Sharman     **Prog Ed:** Alan Hawkins
**Ground:** Jockey Farm, Nellington Road, Rusthall, Tunbridge Wells, Kent TN4 8SH     **(T)** 07865 396 299
**Colours(change):** Green & white stripes/green/green (Blue & black/black/black)
**ADDITIONAL INFORMATION:**
**Previous Lge:** Kent County > 2011.

## SEVEN ACRE & SIDCUP

Founded: 1900     Nickname:

**Secretary:** Lee Hill     **(T)** 07834 583 395     **(E)** lhsasfc@gmail.com
**Chairman:** Steve Reader     **Manager:** Danny Wakeling     **Prog Ed:** John Brand
**Ground:** Sidcup & District Conservative Club, Oxford Road, Sidcup, Kent, DA14 6LW.     **(T)** 020 8300 2987
**Colours(change):** Red & black/black/black (Green/black/black)
**ADDITIONAL INFORMATION:**
**Previous Lge:** Kent County > 2011.

# SUTTON ATHLETIC

Founded: 1898    Nickname:

**Secretary:** Guy Eldridge  **(T)**  **(E)**
**Chairman:** Micky Kelleher    **Manager:** James Collins    **Prog Ed:** John Ball
**Ground:** The Pavillion Lower Road, Sports Ground, Lower Road, Hextable, Kent BR8 7RZ  **(T)** 07788 446 495
**Colours(change):**  Green & white/green/green (Black & white/black/white)

**ADDITIONAL INFORMATION:**
**Previous League:** Kent County > 2011.
**Previous Names:** Sutton United > 2012.

2012-13 - Seven Acre & Sidcup.    Photo: Alan Coomes.

2012-12 - Sutton Athletic.    Photo: Alan Coomes.

# MIDLAND COMBINATION

**Sponsored by:** Athium Limited

**Founded:** 1927

**Recent Champions:**
2008: Coleshill Town. 2009: Loughborough University
2010: Heath Hayes. 2011: Heather St. Johns. 2012: Continental Star

**midcomb.com**

| PREMIER DIVISION | P | W | D | L | F | A | Pts |
|---|---|---|---|---|---|---|---|
| 1 (P) Walsall Wood | 34 | 25 | 5 | 4 | 75 | 31 | 80 |
| 2 Littleton | 34 | 19 | 8 | 7 | 75 | 39 | 65 |
| 3 Earlswood Town | 34 | 18 | 9 | 7 | 86 | 47 | 63 |
| 4 Nuneaton Griff | 34 | 19 | 4 | 11 | 71 | 53 | 61 |
| 5 Brocton | 34 | 17 | 7 | 10 | 76 | 51 | 58 |
| 6 Bromsgrove Sporting (-3pts) | 34 | 18 | 6 | 10 | 73 | 54 | 57 |
| 7 Southam United | 34 | 16 | 6 | 12 | 69 | 59 | 54 |
| 8 Bolehall Swifts | 34 | 16 | 6 | 12 | 56 | 49 | 54 |
| 9 Atherstone Town (-3pts) | 34 | 17 | 5 | 12 | 63 | 52 | 53 |
| 10 Lichfield City | 34 | 16 | 5 | 13 | 68 | 62 | 53 |
| 11 Stafford Town | 34 | 15 | 7 | 12 | 73 | 52 | 52 |
| 12 Coventry Copsewood | 34 | 13 | 10 | 11 | 58 | 55 | 49 |
| 13 Pershore Town | 34 | 9 | 12 | 13 | 56 | 69 | 39 |
| 14 Pelsall Villa | 34 | 8 | 4 | 22 | 39 | 75 | 28 |
| 15 Blackwood | 34 | 6 | 9 | 19 | 47 | 83 | 27 |
| 16 Pilkington XXX | 34 | 6 | 5 | 23 | 46 | 102 | 23 |
| 17 Racing Club Warwick | 34 | 5 | 4 | 25 | 42 | 92 | 19 |
| 18 Castle Vale JKS | 34 | 4 | 6 | 24 | 46 | 94 | 18 |

Bloxwich United AFC - record expunged.

| DIVISION ONE | P | W | D | L | F | A | Pts |
|---|---|---|---|---|---|---|---|
| 1 (P) Alvis | 34 | 29 | 2 | 3 | 122 | 32 | 89 |
| 2 Hampton | 34 | 25 | 4 | 5 | 99 | 38 | 79 |
| 3 Cadbury Athletic | 34 | 23 | 5 | 6 | 105 | 33 | 74 |
| 4 Archdale '73 | 34 | 23 | 2 | 9 | 94 | 58 | 71 |
| 5 Stretton Eagles | 34 | 21 | 3 | 10 | 86 | 52 | 66 |
| 6 Phoenix United (-3pts) | 34 | 22 | 2 | 10 | 100 | 51 | 65 |
| 7 Fairfield Villa | 34 | 19 | 2 | 13 | 84 | 56 | 59 |
| 8 Knowle | 34 | 18 | 2 | 14 | 73 | 48 | 56 |
| 9 West Midlands Police | 34 | 17 | 3 | 14 | 71 | 69 | 54 |
| 10 Aston | 34 | 17 | 2 | 15 | 72 | 81 | 53 |
| 11 FC Glades Sporting | 34 | 16 | 4 | 14 | 60 | 54 | 52 |
| 12 Feckenham | 34 | 12 | 6 | 16 | 59 | 77 | 42 |
| 13 Chelmsley Town | 34 | 9 | 5 | 20 | 48 | 78 | 32 |
| 14 Greenhill | 34 | 7 | 6 | 21 | 39 | 86 | 27 |
| 15 Shirley Town | 34 | 5 | 6 | 23 | 34 | 83 | 21 |
| 16 Droitwich Spa | 34 | 6 | 3 | 25 | 36 | 91 | 21 |
| 17 Coton Green | 34 | 3 | 3 | 28 | 28 | 116 | 12 |
| 18 (R) Northfield Town | 34 | 3 | 2 | 29 | 28 | 135 | 11 |

| PREMIER DIVISION | 1 | 2 | 3 | 4 | 5 | 6 | 7 | 8 | 9 | 10 | 11 | 12 | 13 | 14 | 15 | 16 | 17 | 18 |
|---|---|---|---|---|---|---|---|---|---|---|---|---|---|---|---|---|---|---|
| 1 Atherstone Town | | 4-0 | 0-1 | 3-2 | 1-0 | 3-0 | 6-2 | 1-2 | 4-2 | 0-1 | 1-0 | 3-1 | 3-0 | 3-1 | 3-1 | 2-1 | 0-1 | 0-3 |
| 2 Blackwood | 3-0 | | 2-2 | 1-1 | 1-4 | 3-2 | 2-1 | 2-5 | 2-2 | 3-5 | 1-4 | 1-1 | 3-3 | 1-1 | 2-1 | 0-1 | 2-1 | 1-0 |
| 3 Bolehall Swifts | 1-2 | 2-1 | | 1-0 | 0-0 | 3-0 | 0-3 | 1-3 | 1-0 | 3-0 | 1-2 | 0-2 | 1-2 | 3-2 | 3-0 | 1-1 | 2-1 | 1-1 |
| 4 Brocton | 1-4 | 5-0 | 4-3 | | 2-3 | 5-3 | 4-3 | 1-0 | 2-1 | 0-2 | 0-1 | 1-0 | 1-1 | 4-1 | 5-0 | 2-1 | 1-1 | 2-2 |
| 5 Bromsgrove Sporting | 2-2 | 4-3 | 1-1 | 3-2 | | 5-1 | 2-0 | 3-3 | 4-1 | 1-3 | 0-4 | 3-0 | 0-2 | 5-0 | 5-2 | 2-1 | 1-0 | 0-4 |
| 6 Castle Vale JKS | 1-1 | 3-2 | 0-1 | 2-5 | 0-2 | | 2-2 | 0-2 | 0-2 | 1-3 | 3-5 | 2-1 | 2-2 | 2-2 | 3-0 | 1-2 | 1-2 | 1-5 |
| 7 Coventry Copsewood | 1-1 | 4-2 | 3-1 | 1-3 | 3-3 | 2-2 | | 1-1 | 2-1 | 1-1 | 0-3 | 3-1 | 2-1 | 5-0 | 4-2 | 1-1 | 0-4 | 0-2 |
| 8 Earlswood Town | 6-1 | 4-0 | 1-3 | 1-1 | 1-0 | 1-0 | 2-2 | | 1-3 | 1-1 | 2-2 | 5-1 | 4-1 | 4-0 | 2-1 | 3-0 | 3-1 | 4-0 |
| 9 Lichfield City | 1-4 | 0-0 | 4-3 | 0-1 | 2-0 | 2-1 | 1-0 | 3-2 | | 1-2 | 2-1 | 2-1 | 2-1 | 3-1 | 5-2 | 1-2 | 3-3 | 0-3 |
| 10 Littleton | 1-1 | 1-1 | 2-0 | 1-1 | 0-3 | 5-1 | 3-1 | 2-2 | 4-2 | | 3-0 | 5-0 | 1-1 | 2-2 | 5-1 | 3-0 | 1-0 | 2-3 |
| 11 Nuneaton Griff | 1-2 | 3-1 | 3-1 | 1-4 | 3-1 | 6-1 | 1-1 | 4-3 | 4-1 | 1-0 | | 3-1 | 2-0 | 1-2 | 1-0 | 1-4 | 1-5 | 0-1 |
| 12 Pelsall Villa | 2-1 | 2-1 | 0-2 | 0-5 | 2-3 | 4-0 | 1-1 | 2-4 | 0-3 | 1-0 | 1-2 | | 3-3 | 4-2 | 0-2 | 2-4 | 0-3 | 1-2 |
| 13 Pershore Town | 3-1 | 4-2 | 0-5 | 3-1 | 2-2 | 1-0 | 1-2 | 1-3 | 1-1 | 0-1 | 2-2 | 2-0 | | 4-0 | 2-2 | 3-3 | 0-0 | 1-2 |
| 14 Pilkington XXX | 2-1 | 1-0 | 1-3 | 0-4 | 0-5 | 1-5 | 0-1 | 1-1 | 1-5 | 5-3 | 2-5 | 0-1 | 3-3 | | 3-2 | 2-3 | 1-5 | 1-3 |
| 15 Racing Club Warwick | 2-3 | 2-2 | 1-2 | 2-0 | 2-1 | 4-0 | 0-2 | 1-5 | 2-2 | 0-7 | 1-2 | 1-2 | 0-4 | 3-1 | | 0-2 | 1-1 | 1-3 |
| 16 Southam United | 4-0 | 3-2 | 1-2 | 2-2 | 4-1 | 5-2 | 0-2 | 1-1 | 4-3 | 0-3 | 2-1 | 3-1 | 5-1 | 1-3 | 3-2 | | 2-3 | 1-1 |
| 17 Stafford Town | 2-2 | 6-0 | 2-2 | 1-3 | 1-2 | 3-2 | 0-2 | 3-2 | 2-5 | 0-1 | 4-1 | 1-1 | 5-1 | 5-3 | 5-0 | 1-0 | | 0-4 |
| 18 Walsall Wood | 1-0 | 1-0 | 4-0 | 3-1 | 1-2 | 2-2 | 1-0 | 3-2 | 1-2 | 2-1 | 0-0 | 2-0 | 5-0 | 2-1 | 2-1 | 4-2 | 2-1 | |

## CUP FINALS

**THE LES JAMES CHALLENGE CUP**
Brocton v Walsall Wood 2-0

**CHALLENGE TROPHY**
Redditch United Reserves v Tamworth Reserves 4-3

**PRESIDENTS CUP**
Cadbury Athletic v Phoenix United 0-2

**CHALLENGE URN**
Cadbury Athletic Reserves v Coton Green Reserves 1-0

**CHALLENGE VASE**
FC Stratford v Sutton United 2-4

**CHALLENGE BOWL UNDER 21'S**
Rugby Town Juniors U21s v Worcestershire College of Tech. 3-0

### DIVISION TWO

| | | P | W | D | L | F | A | Pts |
|---|---|---|---|---|---|---|---|---|
| 1 | (P) Barnt Green Spartak | 32 | 23 | 6 | 3 | 93 | 49 | 75 |
| 2 | (P) Sutton United (-1pt) | 32 | 22 | 6 | 4 | 103 | 32 | 71 |
| 3 | Perrywood | 32 | 22 | 5 | 5 | 78 | 42 | 71 |
| 4 | Polesworth | 32 | 20 | 5 | 7 | 105 | 69 | 65 |
| 5 | Alcester Town | 32 | 18 | 6 | 8 | 90 | 49 | 60 |
| 6 | Barton United | 32 | 18 | 4 | 10 | 69 | 49 | 58 |
| 7 | Henley Forest | 32 | 13 | 8 | 11 | 69 | 58 | 47 |
| 8 | Coventry Spires | 32 | 12 | 6 | 14 | 62 | 69 | 42 |
| 9 | Enville Athletic | 32 | 13 | 3 | 16 | 56 | 82 | 42 |
| 10 | FC Stratford | 32 | 12 | 5 | 15 | 58 | 61 | 41 |
| 11 | Leamington Hibernian | 32 | 10 | 8 | 14 | 46 | 47 | 38 |
| 12 | Clements '83 | 32 | 10 | 3 | 19 | 54 | 82 | 33 |
| 13 | Kenilworth Town KH | 32 | 8 | 8 | 16 | 47 | 69 | 32 |
| 14 | Burntwood Town | 32 | 9 | 5 | 18 | 53 | 85 | 32 |
| 15 | Coventry Spartans | 32 | 8 | 3 | 21 | 52 | 78 | 27 |
| 16 | Inkberrow | 32 | 6 | 1 | 25 | 37 | 79 | 19 |
| 17 | Rugeley Rangers | 32 | 3 | 8 | 21 | 38 | 110 | 17 |

### RESERVE DIVISION ONE

| | | P | W | D | L | F | A | Pts |
|---|---|---|---|---|---|---|---|---|
| 1 | Redditch United Reserves | 24 | 14 | 6 | 4 | 67 | 35 | 48 |
| 2 | Gresley Reserves | 24 | 14 | 5 | 5 | 68 | 36 | 47 |
| 3 | Chasetown Reserves | 24 | 13 | 4 | 7 | 58 | 30 | 43 |
| 4 | Quorn Reserves | 24 | 12 | 5 | 7 | 39 | 36 | 41 |
| 5 | Banbury United Reserves | 24 | 12 | 4 | 8 | 38 | 32 | 40 |
| 6 | Loughborough Uni Reserves | 24 | 11 | 6 | 7 | 64 | 54 | 39 |
| 7 | Tamworth Reserves | 24 | 11 | 4 | 9 | 46 | 44 | 37 |
| 8 | Lichfield City Reserves | 24 | 10 | 2 | 12 | 40 | 52 | 32 |
| 9 | Coalville Town Reserves | 24 | 9 | 5 | 10 | 37 | 54 | 32 |
| 10 | Loughborough Dynamo Res (-5pts) | 24 | 7 | 5 | 12 | 40 | 49 | 23 |
| 11 | Boldmere St. Michael's R | 24 | 7 | 1 | 16 | 37 | 57 | 22 |
| 12 | Barwell Reserves | 24 | 6 | 3 | 15 | 39 | 64 | 21 |
| 13 | Stratford Town Reserves | 24 | 3 | 4 | 17 | 35 | 65 | 13 |

### RESERVE DIVISION TWO

| | | P | W | D | L | F | A | Pts |
|---|---|---|---|---|---|---|---|---|
| 1 | Bromsgrove Sporting | 22 | 18 | 3 | 1 | 89 | 25 | 57 |
| 2 | Atherstone Town Reserves | 22 | 14 | 0 | 8 | 79 | 43 | 42 |
| 3 | Walsall Wood Reserves | 22 | 10 | 8 | 4 | 46 | 28 | 38 |
| 4 | Knowle Reserves | 22 | 11 | 5 | 6 | 46 | 38 | 38 |
| 5 | Cadbury Athletic Reserves | 22 | 9 | 4 | 9 | 50 | 59 | 31 |
| 6 | Continental Star Res. (-3pts) | 22 | 9 | 4 | 9 | 39 | 41 | 28 |
| 7 | Brocton Reserves | 22 | 7 | 6 | 9 | 51 | 51 | 27 |
| 8 | Coton Green Reserves (-3pts) | 22 | 7 | 6 | 9 | 31 | 61 | 24 |
| 9 | Racing Club Warwick Reserves | 21 | 6 | 5 | 10 | 46 | 48 | 23 |
| 10 | Tipton Town Reserves | 22 | 4 | 8 | 10 | 40 | 49 | 20 |
| 11 | Castle Vale JKS Reserves | 21 | 5 | 2 | 14 | 23 | 69 | 17 |
| 12 | Droitwich Spa Reserves | 21 | 3 | 5 | 13 | 17 | 38 | 14 |

### CLUB MOVEMENTS

**Premier Division - In:** Alvis (P). Studley (R - Midland Football Alliance).
**Out:** Bloxwich United AFC (F). Walsall Wood (P - Midland Football Alliance).

**Division One - In:** Barnt Green Spartak (P). Sutton United (P).
**Out:** Alvis (P). Greenhill (W). Northfield Town (R). Stretton Eagles (W).

**Division Two - In:** Coventry United (N). Austrey Rangers (N). Badsey Rangers (P - Stratford Football Alliance Div.2). Northfield Town (R). Paget Rangers (P - Birmingham AFC Div.2). Rostance Edwards (P - Wolverhampton Combination).
**Out:** Barnt Green Spartak (P). Clements '83 (W). Coventry Spartans (W - Coventry Alliance). Coventry Spires (W). Henley Forest (W). Sutton United (P). Young Warriors (W).

## ALVIS SPORTING CLUB

Founded:     Nickname:

**Secretary:** Nicola Rynolds     **(T)** 07962 322 838     **(E)** nicola541@btinternet.com
**Chairman:** Don Corrigan
**Ground:** The Pavilion, Copsewood Sports & Soc Club, Allard Way, Binley, Coventry, CV3 1JP   **(T)**
**Colours(change):** Sky blue/navy/sky blue

**ADDITIONAL INFORMATION:**
**Honours:** Midland Combination Division One 2012-13.

## ATHERSTONE TOWN

Founded: 2004     Nickname: The Adders

**Secretary:** Graham Read     **(T)** 01908 211 166     **(E)** grahamgdr777@aol.com
**Chairman:** Robert Weale
**Ground:** Sheepy Road, Atherston, Warwickshire CV9 3AD     **(T)** 01827 717 829
**Colours(change):** Red and white stripes/black/black

**ADDITIONAL INFORMATION:**
**Previous Leagues:** Midland Combination 2004-06. Midland Alliance 2006-08, 11-12. Southern 2008-11.
**Honours:** Midland Combination Division 1 2004-05, Premier Division 2005-06. Midland Alliance 2007-08.

## BLACKWOOD

Founded: 1964     Nickname:

**Secretary:** Terry Moyens     **(T)** 07811378 652     **(E)** terrymoyens@blueyonder.co.uk
**Chairman:** Malcom Hudson     Jim Brogan
**Ground:** The Coppice, Tythe Barn Lane, Shirley, Solihull, West Midlands, B90 1PH     **(T)**
**Colours(change):** Blue & black stripes/black/black

**ADDITIONAL INFORMATION:**
**Honours:** Midland Combination Division Three 2009-10, Division Two 2010-11, Division One 2011-12.

## BOLEHILL SWIFTS

Founded: 1953     Nickname:

**Secretary:** Philip Crowley     **(T)** 07702 786 722     **(E)** bolehallswifts.philcrowley@hotmail.co.uk
**Chairman:** Les Fitzpatrick
**Ground:** Rene Road, Bolehall, Tamworth, Staffordshire B77 3NN     **(T)**
**Colours(change):** All yellow.

**ADDITIONAL INFORMATION:**
**Honours:** Midland Combination Division 2 1984-85.

## BROCTON

Founded: 1937     Nickname:

**Secretary:** Terry Homer     **(T)** 07791 841 774     **(E)** terryhomer@yahoo.co.uk
**Chairman:** Brian Townsend
**Ground:** Silkmore Lane Sports Grd, Silkmore Lane, Stafford, Staffordshire ST17 4JH     **(T)**
**Colours(change):** Green & white/white/green

**ADDITIONAL INFORMATION:**

## BROMSGROVE SPORTING

Founded: 2009     Nickname: The Rouslers

**Secretary:** David Stephens     **(T)** 07955 121 966     **(E)** dave@bromsgrovesporting.co.uk
**Chairman:** John Teece
**Ground:** The Victoria Ground, Birmingham Road, Bromsgrove, Worcs, B61 0DR     **(T)** 01527 876949     **Capacity:** 4,893
**Colours(change):** Red & white stripes/blue/blue

**ADDITIONAL INFORMATION:**

## CASTLE VALE JKS

Founded: 1998     Nickname:

**Secretary:** John Deeble     **(T)** 07916 641 106     **(E)** dibbs107@hotmail.co.uk
**Chairman:** Duval Palgrave
**Ground:** Vale Stadium, Farnborough Road, Castle Vale, Birmingham B35 7DA     **(T)**
**Colours(change):** Yellow & royal blue/royal blue/yellow & royal blue

**ADDITIONAL INFORMATION:**
**Honours:** Midland Combination Division 1 2008-09.

## COVENTRY COPSEWOOD
Founded: 1923     Nickname:

**Secretary:** David Wilson    **(T)** 07807 969 327     **(E)** copsewoodfc@hotmail.co.uk
**Chairman:** Robert Abercrombie
**Ground:** Copsewood Sports & Social Club, Allard Way, Binley, Coventry CV3 1JP    **(T)**
**Colours(change):** All blue

**ADDITIONAL INFORMATION:**
**Previous Names:** G.P.T. Coventry > 2000, Coventry Marconi > 2005.
**Honours:** Midland Combination Challenge Cup 2006-07.

## EARLSWOOD TOWN
Founded: 1968     Nickname:

**Secretary:** Clive Faulkner    **(T)** 07866 122 254     **(E)** faulkner-c1@sky.com
**Chairman:** Graham Ashford
**Ground:** Bromsgrove Sp FC, The Victoria Ground, Birmingham Road, Bromsgrove, B61 0DR    **(T)**
**Colours(change):** Red & white stripes/black/red

**ADDITIONAL INFORMATION:**
**Honours:** Midland Combination League Division One 2010-11.

## LICHFIELD CITY
Founded: 1970     Nickname:

**Secretary:** Michael Tyler    **(T)** 07756 521 301     **(E)** tylermick1954@hotmail.co.uk
**Chairman:** Darren Leaver
**Ground:** Brownsfield Park, Brownsfield Road, Lichfield, Staffs, WS13 6AY    **(T)**
**Colours(change):** Blue with white V/blue/blue

**ADDITIONAL INFORMATION:**

## LITTLETON
Founded: 1890     Nickname:

**Secretary:** Mrs M Brighton    **(T)** 01386 832 906     **(E)** mbrighton1@hotmail.co.uk
**Chairman:** Colin Emms
**Ground:** 5 Acres, Pebworth Road, North Littleton, Evesham, Worcs, WR11 8QL    **(T)**
**Colours(change):** Red/white/red

**ADDITIONAL INFORMATION:**

## NUNEATON GRIFF
Founded: 1972     Nickname:

**Secretary:** Peter Kemp    **(T)** 07944 457 250     **(E)** nuneatongriff@virginmedia.com
**Chairman:** John Gore
**Ground:** The Pingles Stadium, Avenue Road, Nuneaton, Warwickshire CV11 4LX    **(T)**
**Colours(change):** Blue & white/blue/blue

**ADDITIONAL INFORMATION:**
**Honours:** Midland Combination Premier Division 1999-2000, 00-01.

## PELSALL VILLA
Founded: 1898     Nickname:

**Secretary:** Glen Hooker    **(T)** 07854 003 879     **(E)** pelsallvillafc@hotmail.co.uk
**Chairman:** Shaun Mason
**Ground:** The Bush Ground, Walsall Road, Walsall, West Midlands WS3 4BP    **(T)**
**Colours(change):** Red & black stripes/black/black

**ADDITIONAL INFORMATION:**

## PERSHORE TOWN
Founded: 1988     Nickname:

**Secretary:** Jane Conway    **(T)** 07841 377 788     **(E)** jane.chamberlain@homecall.co.uk
**Chairman:** Ken Tallis
**Ground:** King George V Playing Field, King George's Way, Pershore WR10 1QU    **(T)**
**Colours(change):** Blue & white/blue/blue

**ADDITIONAL INFORMATION:**
**Previous League:** Midland Alliance (Founder members).
**Honours:** Midland Combination Division 2 1989-90, Premier 1993-94.

## PILKINGTON XXX

Founded: 2002     Nickname:

Secretary: Ms Kim Holland     **(T)** 07432 784 340     **(E)** pilkingtonxxx@gmail.com
Chairman: Darren McGinley
Ground: TSA Sports Ground, Eckersall Road, Kings Norton, Birmingham B38 8SR     **(T)**
Colours(change): Red & navy/red/red

ADDITIONAL INFORMATION:
Previous Name: Burman Hi-Ton > 2002.
Honours: Midland Combination Division 2 2001-02.

## RACING CLUB WARWICK

Founded: 1919     Nickname: Racers

Secretary: Pat Murphy     **(T)** 07926 188 553     **(E)** pja.murphy@hotmail.co.uk
Chairman: Andrew Cowlard
Ground: Townsend Meadow, Hampton Road, Warwick, Warwickshire CV34 6JP     **(T)** 01926 495 786
Colours(change): Amber & gold/black/black

ADDITIONAL INFORMATION:
Record Att: 1,280 v Leamington FC, Midland All.26/12/2005. **Goalscorer:** Steve Edgington - 200. **Apps:** Steve Cooper - 600+
Honours: Midland Combination Premier Division 1987-88.

## SOUTHAM UNITED

Founded: 1905     Nickname:

Secretary: Charles Hill     **(T)** 07802 949 781     **(E)** charles@southamunitedfc.com
Chairman: Charles Hill     Barry Shearsby (Caretaker)
Ground: Banbury Road, Southam, Warwickshire CV47 2BJ     **(T)**
Colours(change): Yellow/blue/blue

ADDITIONAL INFORMATION:
Honours: Midland Combination Division 3 1980-81.

## STAFFORD TOWN

Founded: 1976     Nickname:

Secretary: David Howard     **(T)** 07789 110 923     **(E)** staffordtown@hotmail.co.uk
Chairman: Gordon Evans     Adam Cunningham
Ground: Evans Park, Riverway, Stafford ST16 3TH     **(T)**
Colours(change): All red

ADDITIONAL INFORMATION:
Previous Leagues: Midland Combination 1977-84. Staffordshire 1984-93. West Midlands (Regional) 1993-2012.
Previous Names: Stafford > 1981.

## STUDLEY

Founded: 1971     Nickname: Bees

Secretary: Bob Fletcher     **(T)** 07745 310 077     **(E)** bobtheat@hotmail.co.uk
Chairman: Bob Fletcher     **Manager:** Paul Smith
Ground: The Beehive, Abbeyfields Drive, Studley B80 7BE     **(T)** 01527 853 817     **Capacity:** 1,500
Colours(change): Sky blue/navy/sky blue

ADDITIONAL INFORMATION: Previous Names: Studley BKL > 2002.
Previous Leagues: Redditch & Sth Warwicks Sunday Combination. Midland Combination. Midland Alliance > 2013.
Record Att: 810 v Leamington 2003-04. Goalscorer: Brian Powell. Apps: Lee Adams - 523.
Honours: Midland Combination Div.1 1991-92. Worcestershire FA Senior Urn 00-01,01-02, 02-03.

### MIDLAND COMBINATION DIVISION ONE CONSTITUTION 2013-14

| | | |
|---|---|---|
| ARCHDALE '73 | County Sports Ground, Claines Lane, Worcester WR3 7SS | 07736 309670 |
| ASTON | Coleshill Town FC Pack Meadow, Packington Lane, Coleshill, B46 3JQ | 07412 008047 |
| BARNT GREEN SPARTAK | TSA Sports Ground, Eckersall Road, Kings Norton, Birmingham, B38 8SR | 07806 298217 |
| CADBURY ATHLETIC | Cadbury Recreation Ground, Bournville Lane, Birmingham, B30 1LA | 07725 868328 |
| CHELMSLEY TOWN | The Pavilion, Coleshill Road, Marston Green, Birmingham B37 7HW | 07736 296246 |
| COTON GREEN | New Mill Lane, Fazeley, Tamworth, B78 3RX | 01889 585526 |
| DROITWICH SPA | Droitwich Spa Leisure Centre, Briar Mill, Droitwich WR9 0RZ | 01905 771212 |
| FAIRFIELD VILLA | Recreation Ground, Stourbridge Road, Fairfield, Bromsgrove B61 9LZ | 01527 877049 |
| FC GLADES SPORTING | Earlswood Town FC, The Pavilions, Malthouse Lane, Earlswood, B94 5DX | 07790 583693 |
| FECKENHAM | Studley Sports & Social Club, Eldorado Close, Studley B80 7HP | 01527 852671 |
| HAMPTON | Field Lane Sports Ground, Lugtrout Lane, Solihull B91 2RT | 07786 915274 |
| KNOWLE | Hampton Road, Knowle, Solihull B93 0NX | 01564 779807 |
| PHOENIX UNITED | Vale Stadium, Farnborough Road, Castle Vale, Birmingham, B35 7BE | 07565 523361 |
| SHIRLEY TOWN | Tilehouse Lane, Whitlocks End, Solihull B90 1PN | 07800 769595 |
| SUTTON UNITED | Hollyfield Road, Sutton Coldfield, B75 7SE | 07779 029621 |
| WEST MIDLANDS POLICE | Tally Ho! Traing Centre, Pershore Road, Edgbaston, Birmingham B5 7RD | 07771 920801 |

## MIDLAND COMBINATION DIVISION TWO CONSTITUTION 2013-14

| | | |
|---|---|---|
| ALCESTER TOWN | Stratford Road, Oversley Green, Alcester, Warwickshire, B49 6LN | 07970 148893 |
| AUSTREY RANGERS | Austrey Fields, Garborough Lane, off Newton Lane, Austrey, Warwickshire, CV9 3EG | 07966 654718 |
| BADSEY RANGERS | Badsey Recreation Ground, Sands Lane, Badsey, Evesham, Worcs, WR11 7EZ | 07799 441466 |
| BARTON UNITED | Holland SC, Efflinch Lane, Barton-under-Needwood, Burton-upon-Trent DE13 8ET | 01283 713972 |
| BURNTWOOD TOWN | Burntwood Leisure Centre, High Street, Chasetown, WS7 3XH | 07806 600833 |
| COVENTRY UNITED | Westwood Heath Sports Grd, Westwood Heath Rd, Westwood Heath, Coventry, CV4 8GP | 07863 563943 |
| ENVILLE ATHLETIC | Enville Athletic Club, Hall Drive, Enville, Stourbridge DY7 5HB | 01384 872368 |
| FC STRATFORD | Knights Lane, Tiddington, Stratford-upon-Avon CV37 7BZ | 07957 694473 |
| INKBERROW | Sands Road, Inkberrow, Worcester WR7 4HJ | 07834 826102 |
| KENILWORTH TOWN KH | Gypsy Lane, Kenilworth, Warwickshire, CV8 1FA | 07946 144831 |
| LEAMINGTON HIBERNIAN | Ajax Park, Hampton Road, Warwick CV35 8HA | 01926 495786 |
| NORTHFIELD TOWN | Shenley Lane Community Centre, Shenley Lane, Selly Oak, Birmingham B29 4HZ | 07967 204921 |
| PAGET RANGERS | Trevor Brown Memorial Ground, Church Road, Great Barr, Birmingham, B73 5RY | 07795 007749 |
| PERRYWOOD | Neel Park, Droitwich Road, Perdiswell, Worcester WR3 7SN | 07808 768222 |
| POLESWORTH | North Warks Sports & Social, Hermitage Hill, Polesworth, Tamworth B78 1HS | 01827 892482 |
| ROSTANCE EDWARDS | The Red Lion Ground, Somerfield Road, Walsall, WS3 2EH | 07879 405452 |
| RUGELEY RANGERS | Brereton Social FC, Armitage Lane, , Staffordshire, WS15 1ED | 07805 988182 |

# GROUND DIRECTIONS

**ALVIS SPORTING CLUB - The Pavilion, Copsewood Sports & Social Club, Allard Way, Binley, Coventry, CV3 1JP**
M6 South: Leave at junction 2 and follow A4600 signs for City Centre. Go over 3 roundabouts and past 1 set of traffic lights, on reaching the 2nd set of traffic lights with Coventry Oak pub on left, turn left down Hipswell Highway. Follow road for 1 mile and reach another set of lights (Fire Station is on left and Mill Pool pub is on right). Go over lights and the ground is 300 yards on the left.
From M40: Follow A46 signs to Coventry and Leicester, stay on this road until very end, you then reach a roundabout with a flyover, go round the roundabout following M69 signs. This road takes you past Asda and you reach a set of traffic lights with a roundabout. Take 2nd left turn off the roundabout, again following M69 signs, This is Allard Way and takes you past Matalan on left, Go under railway bridge and ground is 400 yards on the right. A45 from Birmingham Direction: Follow A45 until reaching a slip road signposted A46, this slip road has the Festival Pub on left side of it. It is after a roundabout with big Peugeot car showroom on left. Go down slip road and take 2nd exit. , this is another slip road leading to A46, signposted B4114 Coventry. Follow road until reaching roundabout with a flyover, and then follow as M40 directions above

**ATHERSTONE TOWN - Sheepy Road, Atherston, Warwickshire CV9 3AD - 01827 717 829**
Take M42 towards Atherstone. Exit at Junction 10. Travel southbound on A5 towards Nuneaton for approximately 4 miles. At third roundabout take first exit to Holly Lane Industrial Estate. Over railway bridge (Aldi HQ on left). At the next roundabout turn right onto Rowlands Way. Ground is 300 yards on the right. Car park and street parking in Rowlands Way.

**BLACKWOOD - Ground: Hampton Sports Club, Field Lane , Solihull , West Midlands , B91 2RT**
From M42 North or South: Exit motorway at junction 5 (signposted Solihull). Take 1st Exit left (A41). Continue on A41 until you reach 1st set of traffic lights and turn right into Hampton Lane, after approx 1/2 mile turn left into Field Lane, ground is approx 3/4 mile on the right hand side.

**BOLEHILL SWIFTS - Rene Road, Bolehall, Tamworth, Staffordshire B77 3NN**
Exit M42 at Junction 10, take A5 towards Tamworth, exit A5 at 2nd exit (Glascote & Amington Industrial Estate). Turn right onto Marlborough Way, at next island turn left (B5000), turn right into Argyle Street (opposite chip shop). At T-junction, turn left into Amington Road, drive over the canal bridge, and turn 2nd right into Leedham Avenue. Take right fork into Rene Road. Club is situated 150 yards on right immediately after school.

**BROCTON - Ground: Silkmore Lane Sports Ground, Silkmore Lane , Stafford , Staffordshire , ST17 4JH**
From M6 J13 take A449 towards Stafford for 1.5 miles until reaching traffic lights by Esso petrol station. Turn right at lights into Rickescote Road, follow road round over railway bridge to mini island, at island bear left into Silkmore Lane. At next mini island take 4th exit for entrance to ground. From Lichfield/Rugeley. After passing Staffs Police HQ at Baswick go downhill past BMW garage and pub to large island, take 1st exit into Silkmore Lane, at next mini island take 2nd exit into ground entrance. Do not turn into Lancaster Road or Silkmore Crescent as directed by Sat Navs.

**BROMSGROVE SPORTING - Ground: The Victoria Ground, Birmingham Road, Bromsgrove, Worcs, B61 0DR**
From M5 J4 take A38 to Bromsgrove, after island at M42 J1, take 1st right at Traffic Lights (signposted Bromsgrove North). Ground is 1000 metres on right (opposite Tesco Garage). From M42 J1, follow above directions from islands.

**CASTLE VALE JKS - Ground: Vale Stadium, Farnborough Road, Castle Vale , Birmingham , West Midlands , B35 7DA**
From M6 Junction 5 turn right at the island onto the A452 to island with Spitfire sculpture, turn right into Tangmere Drive, then right into Farnborough Road. Ground is on the right hand side after approximately 1/2 mile.

**COVENTRY COPSEWOOD - Ground: Copsewood Sports & Social Club, Allard Way, Binley , Coventry , West Midlands , CV3 1HQ**
M6 South: Leave at junction 2 and follow A4600 signs for City Centre. Go over 3 roundabouts and past 1 set of traffic lights, on reaching the 2nd set of traffic lights with Coventry Oak pub on left, turn left down Hipswell Highway. Follow road for 1 mile and reach another set of lights (Fire Station is on left and Mill Pool pub is on right). Go over lights and the ground is 300 yards on the left. From M40: Follow A46 signs to Coventry and Leicester, stay on this road until very end, you then reach a roundabout with a flyover, go round the roundabout following M69 signs. This road takes you past Asda and you reach a set of traffic lights with a roundabout. Take 2nd left turn off the roundabout, again following M69 signs, This is Allard Way and takes you past Matalan on left, Go under railway bridge and ground is 400 yards on the right. A45 from Birmingham Direction: Follow A45 until reaching a slip road signposted A46, this slip road has the Festival Pub on left side of it. It is after a roundabout with big Peugeot car showroom on left. Go down slip road and take 2nd exit. , this is another slip road leading to A46, signposted B4114 Coventry. Follow road until reaching roundabout with a flyover, and then follow as M40 directions above.

**EARLSWOOD TOWN - Ground: The Victoria Ground, Birmingham Road, Bromsgrove, Worcs, B61 0DR**
From M5 J4 take A38 to Bromsgrove, after island at M42 J1, take 1st right at Traffic Lights (signposted Bromsgrove North). Ground is 1000 metres on right (opposite Tesco Garage). From M42 J1, follow above directions from islands.

**LICHFIELD CITY - Ground: Brownsfield Park, Brownsfield Road , Lichfield , Staffordshire , WS13 6AY**
From M42 J10, follow A5 towards Brownhills, or J9 and follow A446 to Lichfield, then follow signs for A38 Lichfield/Derby. From Swinfen Roundabout take 3rd exit for A38 north and then take next off A38 onto A5192 (Cappers Lane). Follow A5192 through 2 islands onto Eastern Avenue. The Ground is on the right at the top of the hill next to Norgreen factory. From M6 J12, follow A5 towards Lichfield then A38 to Lichfield Derby, then follow instructions as above.

**LITTLETON - Ground: Five Acres, Pebworth Road, North Littleton , Evesham , Worcestershire , WR11 8QL**
Get on A46 and aim for Bidford-on-Avon, leave A46 at Bidford roundabout and follow signs for B439 (Bidford 0.5 miles). Come to roundabout in Bidford and take exit B4085 (Cleeve Prior), over a very narrow bridge controlled by traffic lights, straight over crossroads following sign to Honeybourne Broadway. Straight on for approx. 3 miles signpost right turn for the Littletons at crossroads, the ground is 1.25 miles on the right.

**NUNEATON GRIFF - Ground: The Pingles Stadium, Avenue Road , Nuneaton , Warwickshire , CV11 4LX**
From M5, M42 & M6: Take M6 south to junction 3 and leave by turning left onto A444 (Nuneaton). Stay on A444 through Bermuda Park, McDonalds and George Eliot Hospital roundabouts until reaching large roundabout with footbridge over road. Carry straight on (2nd exit) and downhill, taking right hand lane. At bottom of hill you reach Coton Arches Island, take 2nd exit (A4252 Avenue Road) and travel 1/2 mile to Cedar Tree Pub traffic lights, turn left into Stadium car park service road. It is unsuitable for coaches to turn around in. From A5: Travel south following signs for Nuneaton. After passing through Atherstone travel for 2 1/2 miles until junction with A444. At this junction (Royal Red Gate Pub) turn right at staggered junction and continue on A444 through Caldecote and Weddington into Nuneaton. Join one-way system at Graziers Arms by turning left and immediately take right hand lane for 300 yards and follow A444 for Coventry. At Third Island turn left on to dual carriageway (Coton Road) for 1/2 mile and turn left at Coton Arches island on to A4252 (Avenue Road) then as above.

**PELSALL VILLA - Ground: The Bush Ground, Walsall Road , Walsall , West Midlands , WS3 4BP**
Leave M6 at junction 7 sign-posted A34 Birmingham. Take A34 towards Walsall to 1st lights, turn right (marked Ring Road) across 3 islands. At large island at the bottom of the hill, take last exit marked Lichfield. Up hill and across next island to traffic lights, continue to next set of lights and turn left (B4154 Pelsall). Go over Railway Bridge to Old Bush Public House, the ground is next to the public house signposted Pelsall Cricket Club. From Birmingham East: Follow A452 from Spitfire Island then follow signs towards Brownhills. At the traffic lights at the Shire Oak P.H, turn left onto A461 (Walsall) and pass the entrance to Walsall Wood FC. At the traffic lights in Shelfield (The Spring Cottage PH) turn right (signposted Pelsall). At the next set of traffic lights turn left, the Bush is approx 400 yards on left. From: Coventry: Take A45 to Stonebridge Island, turn right onto A452 but then keep to the right following A446 (signposted Lichfield). Follow the A446 to Bassett's Pole Island. Take the 3rd exit onto A38 (Lichfield). Leave the A38 at sliproad for the A5 and take the 2nd exit at the island. Follow the A5 over next 2 islands and at Muckley Corner turn left (inside lane) to join A461. Go straight on at the traffic lights and follow directions as above.

**PERSHORE TOWN - Ground: King George V Playing Field, King George's Way , Pershore , Worcestershire , WR10 1QU**
M5 Junction 7, take B4080 (formerly A44) to Pershore. On entering the town turn left at 2nd set of traffic lights (signposted Leisure Centre). The ground is 300 yards on the left hand side.

## MIDLAND COMBINATION - STEP 6/7

**PILKINGTON XXX - Ground: Triplex Sports, Eckersall Road, Kings Norton , Birmingham , West Midlands , B38 8SR**
From Cotteridge A441 through and past Kings Norton Station, 150 yards turn right across dual carriageway at petrol station, approximately 300 yards there is a sharp bend, turn right. Ground is on right.

**RACING CLUB WARWICK - Ground: Hampton Road , Warwick , Warwickshire , CV34 6JP**
M40 Junction 15, signposted Warwick. At roundabout with traffic lights take A429 to Warwick. Follow this road for 1/2 mile and you will come to houses on your left. Take the 2nd turn on the left into Shakespeare Avenue. Follow to T-junction. Turn right into Hampton Road. Entrance to ground is 50 yards on left.

**SOUTHAM UNITED - Ground: Banbury Road , Southam , Warwickshire , CV47 2BJ**
From Birmingham: M40 Junction 12, exit to A4451 to Southam. Approximately 6 1/2 miles to an island in Southam, turn right, at 2nd island turn right again, ground is 100 yards on right. From Coventry: take A423 Banbury Road; the ground is approximately 12 1/2 miles from Coventry

**STAFFORD TOWN - Evans Park, Riverway, Stafford ST16 3TH**
From M6 junction 13, take A449 towards Stafford for 1½ miles until reaching traffic lights by an Esso petrol station. Turn right at the lights into Rickerscote Road, follow the road round over railway bridge to a mini island. At the island bear left into Silkmore Lane, after approximately 600 yards take the 2nd exit at the mini island and carry on until a large island, take the 2nd exit towards Stafford town centre (A34 Lichfield Road). Go over the railway bridge with Alstrom factory on the left hand side. Straight on at 1st set of traffic lights, then bear left at next set of lights (A518 Uttoxeter) and follow road round with B&Q and Argos on your left hand side. At the roundabout (with KFC and Pizza Hut in front of you) take the 2nd exit (A518 Uttoxeter) and follow to traffic lights. Go straight over lights into Riverway, the ground entrance is approximately 80 yards on the right hand side. Follow the driveway behind the cricket pavilion to the stadium entrance.

**STUDLEY - Ground: The Beehive, Abbeyfields Drive, Studley, B80 7BF**
From M42 Junction 3, take exit towards Redditch (A435). Head South for 5 miles, Abbeyfield Drive is on the left hand side ½ mile past "The Boot" Public House, adjacent to a sharp left hand bend.

## DIVISION ONE

**ARCHDALE '73 - Ground: County Sports Ground, Claines Lane , Worcester , Worcestershire , WR3 7SS**
M5 to Junction 6, take A449 (link road) signposted Kidderminster, down to the bottom, at island turn sharp left into Claines Lane, continue past church on right, ground is on the left (about 1/2 mile).

**ASTON - Ground: Pack Meadow, Packington Lane, Coleshill, Warwickshire, B46 3JQ**
Exit M6 at Junction 4, take A446 signposted Lichfield, turn right across dual carriageway onto B4117 to Coleshill. After scholl on right, turn right into Packington Lane, ground is 0.5 miles of the left.

**BARNET GREEN SPARTAK - Ground: TSA Sports Ground, Eckersall Road, Kings Norton, Birmingham, B38 8SR**
From Cotteridge A441 through and past Kings Norton Station, 150 yards turn right across dual carriageway at petrol station, approximately 300 yards there is a sharp bend, turn right. Ground is on right.

**CADBURY ATHLETIC - Ground: Cadbury Recreation Ground, Bournville Lane, Birmingham, B30 1LA**
From M5 Junction 4: Take A38 to Birmingham, turn right at Selly Oak lights (A4040), travel 1 mile down Oak Tree Lane/ Linden Road to Bournville Lane, turn left, the ground is on the left. From M42 Junction 2: Take A441 to Birmingham through Kings Norton to Cotteridge, take Watford Road (A4040) for 1 mile to Bourneville Lane, and turn right, ground on left. From Birmingham City Centre: Take A38 Bristol Road to Selly Oak Lights, turn left, travel 1 mile down Oak Tree Lane/Linden Road to Bournville Lane, turn left, ground on right. Note: All routes in the South of Birmingham are well signposted for "Cadbury World". Following these will lead to our ground. (A-Z Page 105 2E)

**CHELMSLEY TOWN - Ground: The Pavilion, Coleshill Road, Marston Green, Birmingham, B37 7HW**
M6 junction 4, if travelling south, turn left at the motorway island, if travelling north turn right. Turn 1st left into Coleshill Heath Road, straight on at island, 2nd right into Coleshill Road and then 2nd right into ground.

**COTON GREEN - Ground: New Mill Lane, Fazeley , Tamworth , Staffordshire , B78 3RX**
From M42 junction 9, take A446 exit towards The Belfry, at the next island turn right towards Tamworth and Drayton Manor Park (A4091), continue for approximately 4 miles, past entrance to Drayton Mark Park on your left, continue over the canal with 'Debbies Boat Hire' on your right and 'Fazeley Marina' on your left. As you enter Fazeley you need to turn right immediately after the start of the 30mph speed limit, into New Mill Lane (there is a right filter lane). Once in New Mill Lane, follow lane past houses, turn right at the bottom and follow into car park.

**DROITWICH SPA - Ground: Droitwich Spa Leisure Centre, Briar Mill , Droitwich , Worcestershire , WR9 0RZ**
M5 junction 5, take A38 to Droitwich, At traffic lights by Chateau Impney, go onto dual carriageway, at roundabout take 1st exit (Kidderminster Road), pass Homebase and take next right into Salwarpe Road. Go straight over at next roundabout, next right into Briarmill Road and ground is behind the all weather complex.

**FAIRFIELD VILLA - Ground: Recreation Ground, Stourbridge Road, Fairfield , Bromsgrove , Worcestershire , B61 9LZ**
From M42 Junction 1: Take A38 North to junction 4 M5 and then take A491 towards Stourbridge, travel 2 miles to next roundabout, then left onto B4091 up into Fairfield Village. Go past Swan Public House and approximately 200 yards on your left you will see a school warning sign and telephone booth. Turn left here, up drive to ground. From M5 Junction 4: See above From A38 South to M5 junction 4: see above.

**FC GLADES SPORTING - Ground: Earlswood Town FC, The Pavilions, Malthouse Lane, Earlswood, B94 5DX**

**FECKENHAM - Ground: Studley Sports & Social Club, Eldorado Close , Studley , Warwickshire , B80 7HP**
Leave M42 at junction 3 then, at roundabout, take the 3rd exit onto the A435, signposted Redditch / Evesham. At the next roundabout take the 2nd exit staying on the A435, at the next roundabout, take the 2nd exit onto the B4092, signposted Astwood Bank, then take the 3rd turning on the right into Eldorado Close. Leave the M5 south at junction 4. At the roundabout take the 2nd exit onto the A38, signposted Bromsgrove. Travel for approximately 3 miles then turn onto the A448, signposted Redditch, the A448 will then merge with the A4189. At the next roundabout take the 3rd turning staying on the A4189. At the next roundabout take the 2nd turning still on the A4189, at the next roundabout take the 3rd turning onto the A435 signposted Evesham. At the next roundabout take the 2nd exit, staying on the A435. At the next roundabout take the 2nd exit onto the B4092, signposted Astwood Bank, then take the 3rd turning on the right into Eldorado Close.

**HAMPTON - Ground: Hampton Sports Club, Field Lane , Solihull , West Midlands , B91 2RT**
From M42 North or South: Exit motorway at junction 5 (signposted Solihull). Take 1st Exit left (A41). Continue on A41 until you reach 1st set of traffic lights and turn right into Hampton Lane, after approx 1/2 mile turn left into Field Lane, ground is approx 3/4 mile on the right hand side.

**KNOWLE - Ground: Hampton Road, Knowle , Solihull , West Midlands , B93 0NX**
Directions: M42 Junction 5, A4140 to Knowle, turn left at Toby Carvery into Hampton Road. Ground is 200 yards on right.

**PHOENIX UNITED - Ground: Vale Stadium, Farnborough Road, Castle Vale, Birmingham, B35 7BE**
From M6 Junction 5 turn right at the island onto the A452 to island with Spitfire sculpture, turn right into Tangmere Drive, then right into Farnborough Road, Ground is on the right hand side after approximately ½ mile.

**SHIRLEY TOWN - Ground: Tilehouse Lane, Shirley , Solihull , West Midlands , B90 1PH**
Directions: Tanworth Lane after 150yds, turn right into Dickens Heath Road (Chiswick Green Inn on Left). Follow road to island, take 3rd exit and then after 100 yards go right into Tythe Barn Lane. Follow road then approx 3/4 miles at T junction turn right into Tilehouse Lane. Ground 200 yds on Right (opposite Whitlock's End Station car park). From West & M42: Leave @ J3 onto A435 to Birmingham. After 1 1/2 miles (Beckets Island) take 4th Exit (signposted Earlswood) entering Station Road. After 3/4 miles bear right over railway bridge entering Norton Lane. After 1/4 miles turn left into Lowbrook Road. After 1/4 mile at crossroads turn left into Tilehouse lane. After 1 mile approx ground is on right hand side (opposite Whitlock's End Station Car Park).

**SUTTON UNITED - Ground: Hollyfield Road, Sutton Coldfield, B75 7SE**
If approaching from Sutton Coldfield, follow signs to Good Hope Hospital, the Hospital will be on your left as you go the hill. At the traffic lights, turn right and 300 metres on your right will be an entrance at the side of St Chad's Church, the gates are clearly signposted SUFC.
If approaching from Birmingham on the Tyburn Road, follow signs for Sutton Coldfield, go through Walmley Village, keeping on the Walmley Road until the Reddicap Pub which will be on your left. Go straight over the lights onto Hollyfield Road, 300 metres on your left will be an entrance at the side of St Chad's Church. The gates are clearly signposted SUFC.

**WEST MIDLANDS POLICE - Ground: Tally Ho Training Centre, Pershore Road, Edgbaston , Birmingham , West Midlands , B5 7RD**
Directions: From M5: Exit at junction 3, take A456 Hagley Road to 'Five Ways', turn right on to Islington Row, turn right at traffic lights at Bristol Road. Turn left at next set of traffic lights into Priory Road, then right into Pershore Road. Tally Ho! is on your left. From M6: Exit at junction 6; take Aston Expressway (A38) through Queensway underpasses emerging in Bristol Street/Bristol Road. Turn left at traffic lights at junction with Priory Road. Turn right at next set of traffic lights. Pershore Road and Tally Ho! is on your left (A-Z Reference 3G Page 89).

# MIDLAND FOOTBALL ALLIANCE

**Sponsored by:** Baker Joiner
**Founded:** 1994

**Recent Champions:**
2008: Atherstone Town
\009: Market Drayton Town
2010: Barwell
2011: Coalville Town
2012: Gresey
**midlandfootballalliance.co.uk**

| | | P | W | D | L | F | A | Pts |
|---|---|---|---|---|---|---|---|---|
| 1 | (P) Stratford Town | 42 | 28 | 7 | 7 | 106 | 46 | 91 |
| 2 | Westfields | 42 | 28 | 6 | 8 | 103 | 52 | 90 |
| 3 | Gornal Athletic | 42 | 25 | 11 | 6 | 86 | 58 | 86 |
| 4 | Loughborough University | 42 | 23 | 6 | 13 | 89 | 39 | 75 |
| 5 | Stourport Swifts | 42 | 21 | 10 | 11 | 89 | 47 | 73 |
| 6 | Tipton Town | 42 | 21 | 9 | 12 | 91 | 65 | 72 |
| 7 | Bridgnorth Town | 42 | 19 | 10 | 13 | 62 | 54 | 67 |
| 8 | Tividale | 42 | 20 | 6 | 16 | 81 | 69 | 66 |
| 9 | Boldmere St. Michaels | 42 | 19 | 6 | 17 | 77 | 74 | 63 |
| 10 | Dunkirk | 42 | 18 | 8 | 16 | 69 | 69 | 62 |
| 11 | Alvechurch | 42 | 18 | 8 | 16 | 70 | 75 | 62 |
| 12 | Kirby Muxloe | 42 | 15 | 8 | 19 | 60 | 74 | 53 |
| 13 | Rocester | 42 | 13 | 13 | 16 | 66 | 66 | 52 |
| 14 | Coventry Sphinx | 42 | 15 | 5 | 22 | 47 | 68 | 50 |
| 15 | Coleshill Town | 42 | 13 | 8 | 21 | 52 | 69 | 47 |
| 16 | Continental Star | 42 | 13 | 7 | 22 | 57 | 78 | 46 |
| 17 | Causeway United | 42 | 11 | 11 | 20 | 52 | 67 | 44 |
| 18 | Heath Hayes | 42 | 12 | 7 | 23 | 64 | 111 | 43 |
| 19 | Highgate United | 42 | 11 | 9 | 22 | 65 | 100 | 42 |
| 20 | Heather St. John's | 42 | 11 | 7 | 24 | 49 | 83 | 40 |
| 21 | (R) Studley | 42 | 9 | 11 | 22 | 51 | 84 | 38 |
| 22 | (R) Ellesmere Rangers | 42 | 9 | 8 | 25 | 52 | 90 | 33 |

## LEAGUE CUP

**ROUND 1**

| | | | |
|---|---|---|---|
| Coventry Sphinx | v | Coleshill Town | 3-2 |
| Alvechurch | v | Westfields | 2-3 |
| Gornal Athletic | v | Ellesmere Rangers | 3-1 |
| Heather St John's | v | Rocester | 3-6 |
| Highgate United | v | Stourport Swifts | 2-0 |
| Tividale | v | Causeway United | 1-3 |

**ROUND 2**

| | | | |
|---|---|---|---|
| Gornal Athletic | v | Bridgnorth Town | 0-1 |
| Kirby Muxloe | v | Rocester | 1-2 |
| Loughborough University | v | Dunkirk | 3-1 |
| Causeway United | v | Tipton Town | 1-2 |
| Coventry Sphinx | v | Boldmere St Michaels | 2-3 |
| Straford Town | v | Highgate United | 1-3 |
| Studley | v | Westfields | 0-1 |
| Continental Star | v | Heath Hayes | 2-1 |

**QUARTER FINALS**

| | | | |
|---|---|---|---|
| Tipton Town | v | Bridgnorth Town | 4-2 |
| Boldmere St Michaels | v | Continental Star | 1-0 |
| Highgate United | v | Westfields | 1-3 |
| Rocester | v | Loughborough University | 1-2 |

**SEMI FINALS (OVER 2 LEGS)**

| | | | |
|---|---|---|---|
| Loughborough University | v | Tipton Town | 3-2 |
| Tipton Town | v | Loughborough University | 1-2 |
| Boldmere St Michaels | v | Westfields | 1-1 |
| Westfields | v | Boldmere St Michaels | 6-2 |

**FINAL**

| | | | |
|---|---|---|---|
| Loughborough University | v | Westfields | 2-0 |

| | | 1 | 2 | 3 | 4 | 5 | 6 | 7 | 8 | 9 | 10 | 11 | 12 | 13 | 14 | 15 | 16 | 17 | 18 | 19 | 20 | 21 | 22 |
|---|---|---|---|---|---|---|---|---|---|---|---|---|---|---|---|---|---|---|---|---|---|---|---|
| 1 | Alvechurch | | 3-2 | 1-0 | 0-3 | 4-1 | 2-2 | 1-0 | 1-2 | 4-2 | 0-1 | 1-0 | 0-0 | 1-2 | 1-4 | 1-4 | 0-1 | 1-1 | 1-3 | 3-2 | 2-4 | 2-2 | 2-1 |
| 2 | Boldmere St. Michaels | 2-1 | | 3-0 | 1-1 | 0-2 | 1-2 | 0-0 | 3-2 | 2-1 | 1-4 | 1-2 | 0-1 | 3-2 | 1-0 | 0-1 | 1-0 | 1-3 | 3-5 | 4-0 | 1-2 | 3-4 | 0-4 |
| 3 | Bridgnorth Town | 2-2 | 2-2 | | 1-0 | 0-0 | 2-1 | 2-1 | 2-1 | 1-1 | 1-1 | 3-1 | 4-1 | 5-1 | 1-2 | 1-0 | 2-2 | 2-0 | 1-2 | 2-0 | 1-3 | 1-3 | 0-1 |
| 4 | Causeway United | 1-1 | 5-2 | 0-1 | | 2-1 | 3-2 | 2-0 | 0-1 | 1-2 | 0-0 | 3-0 | 1-1 | 1-0 | 2-2 | 0-3 | 3-3 | 1-1 | 1-2 | 1-1 | 1-3 | 1-2 | 0-0 |
| 5 | Coleshill Town | 0-3 | 0-2 | 1-3 | 0-0 | | 1-2 | 0-2 | 2-3 | 2-0 | 0-1 | 2-1 | 1-0 | 1-2 | 3-0 | 1-1 | 1-4 | 0-1 | 2-2 | 2-2 | 1-5 | 0-1 | |
| 6 | Continental Star | 0-1 | 1-2 | 0-2 | 1-3 | 1-0 | | 1-1 | 1-1 | 2-0 | 1-2 | 1-2 | 2-2 | 3-1 | 4-1 | 1-0 | 2-2 | 3-0 | 3-1 | 4-1 | 0-2 | 0-1 | 1-1 |
| 7 | Coventry Sphinx | 0-1 | 0-4 | 1-0 | 1-0 | 1-4 | 3-2 | | 0-2 | 2-1 | 3-1 | 1-2 | 1-1 | 1-2 | 1-0 | 0-3 | 1-3 | 0-5 | 2-1 | 1-0 | 4-2 | 1-2 | 1-2 |
| 8 | Dunkirk | 3-2 | 1-1 | 1-2 | 3-1 | 2-1 | 2-1 | 2-0 | | 0-0 | 1-4 | 2-2 | 6-1 | 4-1 | 4-1 | 0-2 | 2-1 | 1-6 | 1-2 | 1-3 | 1-2 | 3-1 | 1-2 |
| 9 | Ellesmere Rangers | 3-4 | 0-0 | 0-0 | 1-2 | 1-1 | 1-2 | 0-0 | 0-1 | | 2-4 | 2-0 | 2-3 | 1-2 | 2-1 | 1-3 | 1-3 | 1-3 | 0-7 | 1-0 | 4-2 | 2-2 | 1-4 |
| 10 | Gornal Athletic | 4-1 | 3-1 | 1-1 | 2-0 | 0-1 | 3-0 | 3-1 | 4-2 | 3-2 | | 2-2 | 1-1 | 2-2 | 0-0 | 1-2 | 3-2 | 2-0 | 3-1 | 2-2 | 0-1 | 1-1 | 1-2 |
| 11 | Heath Hayes | 2-6 | 1-2 | 3-2 | 3-2 | 4-0 | 0-4 | 0-2 | 3-0 | 3-2 | 0-2 | | 1-0 | 1-8 | 1-1 | 1-4 | 2-1 | 1-3 | 2-2 | 2-1 | 2-4 | 4-3 | 1-1 |
| 12 | Heather St. John's | 2-3 | 1-5 | 1-3 | 2-1 | 0-4 | 0-1 | 1-0 | 0-3 | 0-2 | 2-4 | 5-1 | | 2-0 | 0-0 | 3-1 | 0-1 | 2-4 | 0-1 | 1-2 | 0-2 | 3-1 | 3-3 |
| 13 | Highgate United | 3-3 | 3-4 | 3-0 | 2-1 | 2-1 | 1-0 | 0-4 | 3-2 | 2-2 | 1-1 | 4-4 | 1-3 | | 1-4 | 0-0 | 0-2 | 0-2 | 1-2 | 2-0 | 1-1 | 2-3 | 0-3 |
| 14 | Kirby Muxloe | 1-2 | 2-0 | 0-2 | 3-1 | 1-2 | 1-0 | 0-2 | 1-1 | 1-1 | 1-3 | 4-1 | 2-1 | 2-2 | | 2-1 | 1-2 | 2-1 | 0-3 | 2-1 | 0-0 | 0-3 | 0-5 |
| 15 | Loughborough University | 0-1 | 7-0 | 0-1 | 1-0 | 1-0 | 0-0 | 3-1 | 1-1 | 3-0 | 7-0 | 6-0 | 1-2 | 4-0 | 1-2 | | 5-1 | 4-0 | 0-2 | 3-1 | 3-1 | 0-1 | 4-2 |
| 16 | Rocester | 0-1 | 1-2 | 2-2 | 4-2 | 0-2 | 4-0 | 2-0 | 0-1 | 2-3 | 5-1 | 3-2 | 2-0 | 2-0 | 2-3 | 0-3 | | 1-1 | 1-1 | 2-3 | 0-2 | 1-1 | 1-2 |
| 17 | Stourport Swifts | 1-2 | 1-4 | 1-1 | 1-1 | 5-1 | 3-1 | 1-1 | 2-2 | 3-0 | 0-1 | 4-0 | 1-0 | 7-0 | 3-0 | 1-1 | 4-0 | | 2-1 | 2-2 | 1-0 | 4-0 | 3-1 |
| 18 | Stratford Town | 2-1 | 1-0 | 3-1 | 7-0 | 2-1 | 9-0 | 4-0 | 2-2 | 4-1 | 0-2 | 1-1 | 2-1 | 4-2 | 2-1 | 2-3 | 1-1 | 1-1 | | 4-0 | 3-0 | 3-1 | 0-2 |
| 19 | Studley | 1-1 | 0-2 | 0-2 | 3-1 | 1-5 | 2-2 | 1-0 | 0-1 | 2-1 | 0-2 | 4-0 | 0-1 | 2-2 | 3-3 | 1-1 | 1-1 | 2-1 | 0-3 | | 5-2 | 0-0 | 1-2 |
| 20 | Tipton Town | 4-2 | 2-3 | 1-2 | 1-2 | 3-0 | 4-0 | 1-3 | 2-0 | 4-0 | 3-3 | 4-3 | 0-0 | 5-3 | 2-1 | 0-0 | 2-2 | 1-0 | 3-3 | 4-1 | | 1-0 | 2-2 |
| 21 | Tividale | 1-0 | 0-4 | 2-1 | 2-0 | 1-1 | 5-1 | 1-3 | 2-0 | 2-3 | 1-2 | 5-3 | 4-2 | 5-0 | 2-0 | 0-0 | 0-3 | 1-4 | 7-0 | 1-0 | | | 3-4 |
| 22 | Westfields | 6-1 | 3-2 | 5-0 | 0-2 | 1-2 | 2-1 | 5-1 | 4-0 | 3-2 | 0-2 | 3-0 | 5-0 | 2-1 | 7-2 | 2-1 | 2-2 | 1-0 | 1-2 | 2-1 | 2-1 | 2-0 | |

**CLUB MOVEMENTS**
**Premier Division - In:** AFC Wulfrunians (P - West Midlands). Quorn - (S - United Counties Premier).
Shepshed Dynamo (S - United Counties Premier). Walsall Wood (P - Midland Combination Premier).
**Out:** Bridgnorth Town (F - May 2013). Ellesmere Rangers (R - West Midlands). Stratford Town (P - Southern Div.1 S&W).
Studley (R - Midland Combination).

# A.F.C. WULFRUNIANS

Founded: 2005          Nickname:

**Secretary:** Ian Davies          **(T)** 07989 953 738          **(E)** jaki.davies1512@btinternet.com

**Chairman:** Ian Round

**Ground:** Castlecroft Stadium, Castlecroft Road, Wolverhampton WV3 8NA          **(T)** 01902 761410

**Capacity:**          **Seats:** Yes     **Covered:** Yes     **Midweek Matchday:**          **Clubhouse:** Yes

**Colours(change):** Red & white/black/red (All blue)
**Previous Names:** None
**Previous Leagues:** West Midlands (Regional).
**Records:**
**Senior Honours:** West Midlands (Regional) League Division Two 2005-06, Premier Division 2008-09, 12-13.

### 10 YEAR RECORD

| 03-04 | 04-05 | 05-06 | | 06-07 | | 07-08 | | 08-09 | | 09-10 | | 10-11 | | 11-12 | | 12-13 | |
|---|---|---|---|---|---|---|---|---|---|---|---|---|---|---|---|---|---|
| | | WM2 | 1 | WM1 | 2 | WMP | 6 | WMP | 1 | WMP | 3 | WMP | 3 | WMP | 5 | WMP | 1 |

# ALVECHURCH

Founded: 1929          Nickname: The Church

**Secretary:** Stephen Denny          **(T)** 07710 012 733          **(E)** alvechurchfc@btinternet.com

**Chairman:** Richard Thorndike

**Ground:** Lye Meadow, Redditch Road, Alvechurch B48 7RS          **(T)** 0121 445 2929

**Capacity:** 3,000 **Seats:** 100     **Covered:** 300     **Midweek Matchday:** Tuesday          **Clubhouse:** Yes          No

**Colours(change):** Yellow/black/black. (All blue).
**Previous Names:** Alvechurch FC >1992. Re-formed in 1994.
**Previous Leagues:** Midland Combination
**Records:**
**Senior Honours:** Since 1994: Midland Combination Premier 2002-03. Worcestershire Senior Urn 03-04, 04-05, 12-13.

### 10 YEAR RECORD

| 03-04 | | 04-05 | | 05-06 | | 06-07 | | 07-08 | | 08-09 | | 09-10 | | 10-11 | | 11-12 | | 12-13 | |
|---|---|---|---|---|---|---|---|---|---|---|---|---|---|---|---|---|---|---|---|
| MidAl | 19 | MidAl | 15 | MidAl | 14 | MidAl | 10 | MidAl | 14 | MidAl | 10 | MidAl | 7 | MidAl | 20 | MidAl | 13 | MidAl | 11 |

# BOLDMERE ST. MICHAELS

Founded: 1883          Nickname: The Mikes

**Secretary:** Rob Paterson          **(T)** 07528 177 046          **(E)** paterson_r3@sky.com

**Chairman:** Keith Fielding

**Ground:** Trevor Brown Memorial Ground, Church Road, Boldmere B73 5RY          **(T)** 0121 373 4435

**Capacity:** 2,500 **Seats:** 230     **Covered:** 400     **Midweek Matchday:** Tuesday          **Clubhouse:** Yes

**Colours(change):** White with red & black/black/black with white trim (All yellow & blue)
**Previous Names:** None.
**Previous Leagues:** West Midlands (Regional). Midland Combination.
**Records:**
**Senior Honours:** AFA Senior Cup 1947-48. Midland Combination Premier 1985-86, 88-89, 89-90.

### 10 YEAR RECORD

| 03-04 | | 04-05 | | 05-06 | | 06-07 | | 07-08 | | 08-09 | | 09-10 | | 10-11 | | 11-12 | | 12-13 | |
|---|---|---|---|---|---|---|---|---|---|---|---|---|---|---|---|---|---|---|---|
| MidAl | 15 | MidAl | 10 | MidAl | 10 | MidAl | 7 | MidAl | 4 | MidAl | 4 | MidAl | 6 | MidAl | 3 | MidAl | 12 | MidAl | 9 |

# CAUSEWAY UNITED

Founded: 1957          Nickname:

**Secretary:** Frank Webb          **(T)** 07977 599 847          **(E)**

**Chairman:** Carl Burley

**Ground:** Halesowen Town FC, The Grove, Old Hawne Lane, Halesowen B63 3TB          **(T)** 0121 550 9433

**Capacity:**          **Seats:**     **Covered:**     **Midweek Matchday:** Tuesday          **Clubhouse:** Yes

**Colours(change):** All blue. (All white).
**Previous Names:** None.
**Previous Leagues:** West Midlands (Regional).
**Records:** **Att:** 150. **Apps:** Malcolm Power - 300+
**Senior Honours:**

### 10 YEAR RECORD

| 03-04 | | 04-05 | | 05-06 | | 06-07 | | 07-08 | | 08-09 | | 09-10 | | 10-11 | | 11-12 | | 12-13 | |
|---|---|---|---|---|---|---|---|---|---|---|---|---|---|---|---|---|---|---|---|
| Isth P | 17 | MidAl | 16 | MidAl | 19 | MidAl | 17 | MidAl | 6 | MidAl | 9 | MidAl | 12 | MidAl | 10 | MidAl | 7 | MidAl | 17 |

## COLESHILL TOWN

Founded: 1894 — Nickname:

**Secretary:** David Brown — **(T)** 07799 075 828 — **(E)** dave.brown@skanska.co.uk
**Chairman:** Paul Billing — As secretary
**Ground:** Pack Meadow, Packington Lane, Coleshill B46 3JQ — **(T)** 01675 463 259
**Capacity:** **Seats:** **Covered:** **Midweek Matchday:** Tuesday **Clubhouse:** Yes

**Colours(change):** White/blue/red (Yellow/black/yellow)
**Previous Names:** None.
**Previous Leagues:** Midland Combination.
**Records:**
**Senior Honours:** Midland Combination Division Two 1969-70. Premier 07-08.

**10 YEAR RECORD**

| 03-04 | 04-05 | 05-06 | 06-07 | 07-08 | 08-09 | 09-10 | 10-11 | 11-12 | 12-13 |
|---|---|---|---|---|---|---|---|---|---|
| MCmP 18 | MCmP 9 | MCmP 11 | MCmP 4 | MCmP 1 | MidAl 11 | MidAl 8 | MidAl 12 | MidAl 16 | MidAl 15 |

## CONTINENTAL STAR

Founded: 1973 — Nickname:

**Secretary:** Keith John — **(T)** 07956 429 046 — **(E)** keith.john6@hotmail.co.uk
**Chairman:** Keith John
**Ground:** Rushall Olympic FC, Dales Lane, Rushall, Walsall, West Midlands WS4 1LJ — **(T)** 01922 641 021
**Capacity:** **Seats:** **Covered:** **Midweek Matchday:** **Clubhouse:**

**Colours(change):** Yellow/blue/blue (Red/black/white)
**Previous Names:** Handsworth Continental Star 2001-02.
**Previous Leagues:** Midland Combination 1993-2012.
**Records:**
**Senior Honours:** Midland Combination Division 2 1995-96, Premier Division 2011-12.

**10 YEAR RECORD**

| 03-04 | 04-05 | 05-06 | 06-07 | 07-08 | 08-09 | 09-10 | 10-11 | 11-12 | 12-13 |
|---|---|---|---|---|---|---|---|---|---|
| MCmP 19 | MCmP 20 | MCmP 22 | MCmP 19 | MCmP 18 | MCmP 17 | MCmP 14 | MCmP 11 | MCmP 1 | MidAl 16 |

## COVENTRY SPHINX

Founded: 1946 — Nickname: Sphinx

**Secretary:** Jackie McGowan — **(T)** 07843 477 799 — **(E)** jackie.mcgowan@coventrysphinx.co.uk
**Chairman:** Dannie Cahill
**Ground:** Sphinx Spts & Social Club, Sphinx Drive, Coventry CV3 1WA — **(T)** 02476 451 361
**Capacity:** **Seats:** Yes **Covered:** Yes **Midweek Matchday:** Tuesday **Clubhouse:** Yes

**Colours(change):** Sky blue & white stripes/navy/navy or sky blue (Yellow & black stripes/black/yellow).
**Previous Names:** Sphinx > 1995.
**Previous Leagues:** Midland Combination.
**Records:**
**Senior Honours:** Midland Combination Premier 2006-07.

**10 YEAR RECORD**

| 03-04 | 04-05 | 05-06 | 06-07 | 07-08 | 08-09 | 09-10 | 10-11 | 11-12 | 12-13 |
|---|---|---|---|---|---|---|---|---|---|
| MCmP 4 | MCmP 2 | MCmP 2 | MCmP 1 | MidAl 19 | MidAl 7 | MidAl 9 | MidAl 16 | MidAl 3 | MidAl 14 |

## DUNKIRK

Founded: 1946 — Nickname: The Boatmen

**Secretary:** Steve Throssell — **(T)** 07903 322 446 — **(E)** philipallen1982@hotmail.co.uk
**Chairman:** David Johnson
**Ground:** Ron Steel Spts Grd, Lenton Lane, Clifton Bridge, Nottingham NG7 2SA — **(T)** 0115 985 0803
**Capacity:** 1,500 **Seats:** 150 **Covered:** 150 **Midweek Matchday:** Tuesday **Clubhouse:** Yes

**Colours(change):** Red/black/black (All yellow)
**Previous Names:** None
**Previous Leagues:** Notts Amateur 1946-75, Notts Alliance 1975-95, Central Midlands 1995-2008, East Midlands Counties > 2010
**Records:**
**Senior Honours:** Notts Amateur League 1973-75. Central Midlands League Supreme Division 2004-05. East Midlands Counties 2009-10

**10 YEAR RECORD**

| 03-04 | 04-05 | 05-06 | 06-07 | 07-08 | 08-09 | 09-10 | 10-11 | 11-12 | 12-13 |
|---|---|---|---|---|---|---|---|---|---|
| CM Su 6 | CM Su 1 | CM Su 8 | CM Su 6 | CM Su 4 | EMC 5 | EMC 1 | MidAl 8 | MidAl 18 | MidAl 10 |

# GORNAL ATHLETIC

Founded: 1945      Nickname:

**Secretary:** Kevin Williams     **(T)** 07762 585 149      **(E)** gornalathleticfc1@hotmail.co.uk

**Chairman:** N/A

**Ground:**   Garden Walk Stadium, Garden Walk, Lower Gornal, Dudley  DY3 2NR     **(T)** 01384 358 398

**Capacity:**      **Seats:**     **Covered:**     **Midweek Matchday:**      **Clubhouse:**

**Colours(change):**    Yellow/green/green (All royal blue)
**Previous Names:**    Lower Gornal Athletic 1945-72.
**Previous Leagues:** Worcestershire Combination 1951-63. West Midlands (Regional) 1963-2012.
**Records:**
**Senior Honours:**     West Midlands (Regional) Division One South 2003-04, Premier Division 2011-12.

**10 YEAR RECORD**

| 03-04 | 04-05 | 05-06 | 06-07 | 07-08 | 08-09 | 09-10 | 10-11 | 11-12 | 12-13 |
|---|---|---|---|---|---|---|---|---|---|
| WM1S   1 | WMP   10 | WMP   2 | WMP   4 | WMP   16 | WMP   15 | WMP   17 | WMP   2 | WMP   1 | MidAl   3 |

# HEATH HAYES

Founded: 1964      Nickname:

**Secretary:** Kathlyn Davies     **(T)** 07969 203 063      **(E)** kathlyndavies@aol.com

**Chairman:** Craig Brotherton

**Ground:**   Coppice Colliery Grd, Newlands Lane, Heath Hayes, Cannock, WS12 3HH     **(T)** 07969 203 063

**Capacity:**      **Seats:** Yes    **Covered:** Yes    **Midweek Matchday:** Tuesday     **Clubhouse:** Yes

**Colours(change):**    Blue & white stripes/blue/white (Yellow/black/yellow)
**Previous Names:**
**Previous Leagues:** Staffordshire County, West Midlands, Midland Combination 2006-10.
**Records:**
**Senior Honours:**     Staffordshire County League Division 1 1977-78. West Midlands League Division 1 North 1998-99.
                    Midland Combination Premier Division 2009-10.

**10 YEAR RECORD**

| 03-04 | 04-05 | 05-06 | 06-07 | 07-08 | 08-09 | 09-10 | 10-11 | 11-12 | 12-13 |
|---|---|---|---|---|---|---|---|---|---|
| WMP   6 | WMP   6 | WMP   13 | MCmP   8 | MCmP   10 | MCmP   10 | MCmP   1 | MidAl   11 | MidAl   14 | MidAl   18 |

# HEATHER ST. JOHN'S

Founded: 1949      Nickname:

**Secretary:** Adrian Rock     **(T)** 07952 633 331      **(E)** adrianrock@hotmail.co.uk

**Chairman:** Paul Harrison

**Ground:**   St John's Park, Ravenstone Rd, Heather LE67 2QJ.     **(T)** 01530 263 986

**Capacity:**      **Seats:**     **Covered:**     **Midweek Matchday:**      **Clubhouse:**

**Colours(change):**    All royal blue (All red)
**Previous Names:**    Heather Athletic 1949-2007.
**Previous Leagues:** Midland Combination > 2011.
**Records:**
**Senior Honours:**     Midland Combination 2010-11.

**10 YEAR RECORD**

| 03-04 | 04-05 | 05-06 | 06-07 | 07-08 | 08-09 | 09-10 | 10-11 | 11-12 | 12-13 |
|---|---|---|---|---|---|---|---|---|---|
| MCm2   5 | MCm1   13 | MCm1   12 | MCm1   6 | MCmP   7 | MCmP   5 | MCmP   2 | MCmP   1 | MidAl   19 | MidAl   20 |

# HIGHGATE UNITED

Founded: 1948      Nickname: Red or Gate

**Secretary:** Paul Davis     **(T)** 07527 941 993      **(E)** jimmymerry777@gmail.com

**Chairman:** Gary Bishop      **Manager:** Mark Burge

**Ground:**   The Coppice, Tythe Barn Lane, Shirley Solihull B90 1PH     **(T)** 07591 172 318

**Capacity:**      **Seats:**     **Covered:**     **Midweek Matchday:** Tuesday     **Clubhouse:**

**Colours(change):**    All red (White/black/black)
**Previous Names:**    None.
**Previous Leagues:** Worcestershire/Midland Combination.
**Records:**       Not known
**Senior Honours:**     Midland Combination Premier 1972-73, 73-74, 74-75.

**10 YEAR RECORD**

| 03-04 | 04-05 | 05-06 | 06-07 | 07-08 | 08-09 | 09-10 | 10-11 | 11-12 | 12-13 |
|---|---|---|---|---|---|---|---|---|---|
| MCmP   12 | MCmP   18 | MCmP   14 | MCmP   3 | MCmP   2 | MidAl   13 | MidAl   18 | MidAl   18 | MidAl   20 | MidAl   19 |

## KIRKBY MUXLOE

**Founded:** 1910     **Nickname:**

**Secretary:** Philip Moloney     **(T)** 07775 992 778     **(E)** pmoloney1@hotmail.com

**Chairman:** Les Warren

**Ground:** Kirby Muxloe Sports Club, Ratby Lane LE9 2AQ     **(T)** 0116 239 3201

**Capacity:**     **Seats:**     **Covered:**     **Midweek Matchday:** Tuesday     **Clubhouse:** Yes

**Colours(change):** All royal blue (All orange)
**Previous Names:**
**Previous Leagues:** Leicester Mutual. Leicester City. Leicestershire Senior. East Midlands Counties.
**Records:**
**Senior Honours:** Leicestershire Co. Cup 2006-07. Leicestershire Senior Champions 2007-08.
East Midlands Counties Champions 2008-09.

### 10 YEAR RECORD

| 03-04 | | 04-05 | | 05-06 | | 06-07 | | 07-08 | | 08-09 | | 09-10 | | 10-11 | | 11-12 | | 12-13 | |
|---|---|---|---|---|---|---|---|---|---|---|---|---|---|---|---|---|---|---|---|
| LeicS | 2 | LeicS | 4 | LeicS | 8 | LeicS | 2 | LeicS | 1 | EMC | 1 | MidAl | 10 | MidAl | 9 | MidAl | 11 | MidAl | 12 |

## LOUGHBOROUGH UNIVERSITY

**Founded:** 1920     **Nickname:**

**Secretary:** Margaret Folwell     **(T)** 01509 226 127 (Office Hrs)     **(E)** secretary@loughboroughfootball.co.uk

**Chairman:** Stuart McLaren

**Ground:** Loughborough Uni Stadium, Holywell Sports Complex, Holywell Park LE11 3TU     **(T)** 01509 228 774

**Capacity:**     **Seats:**     **Covered:**     **Midweek Matchday:**     **Clubhouse:**

**Colours(change):** Purple/purple/white. (White/white/purple).
**Previous Names:** None
**Previous Leagues:** Leicestershire Senior. Midland Combination.
**Records:**
**Senior Honours:** Midland Combination 2008-09.

### 10 YEAR RECORD

| 03-04 | 04-05 | 05-06 | 06-07 | 07-08 | | 08-09 | | 09-10 | | 10-11 | | 11-12 | | 12-13 | |
|---|---|---|---|---|---|---|---|---|---|---|---|---|---|---|---|
| | | | | MCmP | 4 | MCmP | 1 | MidAl | 13 | MidAl | 4 | MidAl | 5 | MidAl | 4 |

## QUORN

**Founded:** 1924     **Nickname:** Reds

**Secretary:** Reg Molloy     **(T)** 07729 173 333     **(E)** k.molloy@ntlworld.com

**Chairman:** Stuart Turner     **Manager:** Tommy Brookbanks     **Prog Ed:** Malcolm Unwin

**Ground:** Farley Way Stadium, Farley Way, Quorn, Leicestershire LE12 8RB     **(T)** 01509 620 232

**Capacity:** 1,550 **Seats:** 350 **Covered:** 250 **Midweek Matchday:**     **Clubhouse:** Yes

**Colours(change):** All red (Yellow/blue/blue)
**Previous Names:** Quorn Methodists
**Previous Leagues:** Leicestershire Senior, Midland Alliance > 2007. NPL 2007-2012. United Counties 2012-13.
**Records:** Not known
**Senior Honours:** Leicestershire Senior Cup 1940, 1952, 1954.
Leicestershire Senior League 2000-01

### 10 YEAR RECORD

| 03-04 | | 04-05 | | 05-06 | | 06-07 | | 07-08 | | 08-09 | | 09-10 | | 10-11 | | 11-12 | | 12-13 | |
|---|---|---|---|---|---|---|---|---|---|---|---|---|---|---|---|---|---|---|---|
| MidAl | 4 | MidAl | 4 | MidAl | 7 | MidAl | 3 | NP 1 | 12 | NP1S | 12 | NP1S | 20 | NP1S | 15 | NP1S | 21 | UCL | 7 |

## ROCESTER

**Founded:** 1876     **Nickname:** Romans

**Secretary:** Barry Smith     **(T)** 07770 762 825     **(E)** rocesterfc@btinternet.com

**Chairman:** Ian Cruddas     **Prog Ed:** Barry Smith

**Ground:** Hillsfield, Mill Street, Rocester, Uttoxeter ST14 5JX     **(T)** 01889 591 301

**Capacity:** 4,000 **Seats:** 230 **Covered:** 500 **Midweek Matchday:** Tuesday     **Clubhouse:** Yes **Shop:** Yes

**Colours(change):** Amber/black/black. (All royal blue).
**Previous Names:** None.
**Previous Leagues:** Staffs Sen. (Founder Member). W.Mids (Reg). Mid.All (FM) Southern. NPL
**Records:** Apps: Peter Swanwick 1962-82.
**Senior Honours:** Staffordshire Senior 1985-86, 86-87. West Mids (Regional) Div.1 87-88. Midland Alliance 1998-99, 2003-04.

### 10 YEAR RECORD

| 03-04 | | 04-05 | | 05-06 | | 06-07 | | 07-08 | | 08-09 | | 09-10 | | 10-11 | | 11-12 | | 12-13 | |
|---|---|---|---|---|---|---|---|---|---|---|---|---|---|---|---|---|---|---|---|
| MidAl | 1 | NPL 1 | 22 | MidAl | 22 | MidAl | 12 | MidAl | 5 | MidAl | 20 | MidAl | 16 | MidAl | 14 | MidAl | 6 | MidAl | 13 |

# SHEPSHED DYNAMO

Founded: 1994     Nickname: Dynamo

**Secretary:** Danny Pole          **(T)** 07866 500 187          **(E)** secretary@shepsheddynamo.co.uk

**Chairman:** Mick Sloan          **Manager:** Chris White

**Ground:** The Dovecote, Butt Hole Lane, Shepshed, Leicestershire LE12 9BN          **(T)** 01509 650 992

**Capacity:** 2,050  **Seats:** 570  **Covered:** 400  **Midweek Matchday:**          **Clubhouse:** Yes  **Shop:** Yes

| | |
|---|---|
| **Colours(change):** | Black and white stripes/black/black (All claret with sky blue trim) |
| **Previous Names:** | Shepshed Albion/Charterhouse > 1994 |
| **Previous Leagues:** | Leics Sen 1907-16, 19-27, 46-50, 51-81, Mid Co 81-82, N.C.E. 82-83, Sth 83-88, 96-04, N.P.L.88-93 04-12, Mid Com 93-94, Mid All 94-95. UCL 12-13. |
| **Records:** | 2,500 v Leicester City - Friendly 1996-97 |
| **Senior Honours:** | Midland Counties League 1981-82, League Cup 81-82. Northern Counties East 1982-83, League Cup 82-83. Midland Alliance 1995-96. Leicestershire Senior Cup x7 |

**10 YEAR RECORD**

| 03-04 | 04-05 | 05-06 | 06-07 | 07-08 | 08-09 | 09-10 | 10-11 | 11-12 | 12-13 |
|---|---|---|---|---|---|---|---|---|---|
| SthW 21 | NP 1 15 | NP 1 10 | NP 1 20 | NP 1 15 | NP1S 8 | NP1S 17 | NP1S 21 | NP1S 22 | UCL 9 |

# STOURPORT SWIFTS

Founded: 1882     Nickname: Swifts

**Secretary:** Laura McDonald          **(T)** 07793 768 793          **(E)** Lmacca65@hotmail.com

**Chairman:** Chris Reynolds

**Ground:** Walshes Meadow, Harold Davis Drive, Stourport on Severn DY13 0AA          **(T)** 01299 825 188

**Capacity:** 2,000  **Seats:** 250  **Covered:** 150  **Midweek Matchday:**          **Clubhouse:** Yes  **Shop:** Yes

| | |
|---|---|
| **Colours(change):** | Gold & black/black/black (All blue) |
| **Previous Names:** | None |
| **Previous Leagues:** | Kidderminster/Worcestershire/West Midlands (Regional) > 1998, Midland Alliance 1998-2001 |
| **Records:** | 2,000 |
| **Senior Honours:** | Midland Alliance 2000-01 |

**10 YEAR RECORD**

| 03-04 | 04-05 | 05-06 | 06-07 | 07-08 | 08-09 | 09-10 | 10-11 | 11-12 | 12-13 |
|---|---|---|---|---|---|---|---|---|---|
| SthW 18 | SthW 14 | SthW 20 | SthM 22 | SthM 17 | SthM 16 | SthM 17 | Sthsw 17 | Sthsw 21 | MidAl 5 |

# TIPTON TOWN

Founded: 1948     Nickname:

**Secretary:** Ann Wheale          **(T)** 07535 975 142          **(E)** b.wheale@sky.com

**Chairman:** John Cross

**Ground:** Tipton Sports Academy, Wednesbury Oak Road, Tipton DY4 0BS          **(T)** 0121 502 5534

**Capacity:** 1,000  **Seats:** 200  **Covered:** 400  **Midweek Matchday:** Wednesday          **Clubhouse:** Yes

| | |
|---|---|
| **Colours(change):** | Black & white stripes/black/red. (All blue). |
| **Previous Names:** | None. |
| **Previous Leagues:** | West Midlands (Regional). |
| **Records:** | Att: 1,100 v Wolves, 01.08.88. |
| **Senior Honours:** | Wednesbury Senior Cup 1975-76, 76-77, 80-81, 95-96. West Midlands (Regional) Div.1 83-84. Prem 04-05. |

**10 YEAR RECORD**

| 03-04 | 04-05 | 05-06 | 06-07 | 07-08 | 08-09 | 09-10 | 10-11 | 11-12 | 12-13 |
|---|---|---|---|---|---|---|---|---|---|
| WestP 2 | WestP 1 | MidAl 11 | MidAl 5 | MidAl 9 | MidAl 5 | MidAl 4 | MidAl 2 | MidAl 9 | MidAl 6 |

# TIVIDALE

Founded: 1954     Nickname:

**Secretary:** Leon Murray          **(T)** 07939 234 813          **(E)** leon@tividalefc.co.uk

**Chairman:** Chris Dudley          **Manager:** Stuart Scriven & Ian Long

**Ground:** The Beeches, Packwood Road, Tividale, West Mids B69 1UL          **(T)** 01384 211 743

**Capacity:**  **Seats:** Yes  **Covered:** Yes  **Midweek Matchday:**          **Clubhouse:** Yes

| | |
|---|---|
| **Colours(change):** | All yellow (All royal blue) |
| **Previous Names:** | None |
| **Previous Leagues:** | West Midlands (Regional) 1966- 2011. |
| **Records:** | Not known |
| **Senior Honours:** | West Midlands (Regional) League Division One 1972-73, Premier Division 2010-11. |

**10 YEAR RECORD**

| 03-04 | 04-05 | 05-06 | 06-07 | 07-08 | 08-09 | 09-10 | 10-11 | 11-12 | 12-13 |
|---|---|---|---|---|---|---|---|---|---|
| WMP 8 | WMP 16 | WMP 8 | WMP 2 | WMP 11 | WMP 13 | WMP 7 | WMP 1 | MidAl 4 | MidAl 8 |

## WALSALL WOOD

Founded: 1907          Nickname:

**Secretary:** Ivor Osborne          **(T)** 07583 175 664          **(E)** ivorjosborne@talktalk.net

**Chairman:** Andy Roper          **Manager:** Mark Swann

**Ground:**   Oak Park, Lichfield Road, Walsall Wood, Walsall WS9 9NP          **(T)**

**Capacity:**          **Seats:** Yes   **Covered:** Yes   **Midweek Matchday:**          **Clubhouse:** Yes

**Colours(change):**   All red (All sky blue)

**Previous Names:**   Walsall Borough (formed when Walsall Wood & Walsall Sportsco merged) 1982-96.

**Previous Leagues:** Midland Combinataion 1986-92, 2006-13. Staffordshire Senior 1992-93. West Midlands 1993-2006.

**Records:**

**Senior Honours:**   Worcestershire/Midland Combination 1951-52, 2012-13.

**10 YEAR RECORD**

| 03-04 | | 04-05 | | 05-06 | | 06-07 | | 07-08 | | 08-09 | | 09-10 | | 10-11 | | 11-12 | | 12-13 | |
|---|---|---|---|---|---|---|---|---|---|---|---|---|---|---|---|---|---|---|---|
| WM1N | 7 | WM1 | 6 | WM1 | 4 | MidCo | 12 | MidCo | 11 | MidCo | 7 | MidCo | 6 | MidCo | 9 | MidCo | 14 | MidCo | 1 |

## WESTFIELDS

Founded: 1966          Nickname: The Fields

**Secretary:** Andrew Morris          **(T)** 07860 410 548          **(E)** andrew@andrew-morris.co.uk

**Chairman:** John Morgan          **Manager:** Sean Edwards          **Prog Ed:** Andrew Morris

**Ground:**   Allpay Park, Widemarsh Common, Hereford HR4 9NA          **(T)** 07860 410 548

**Capacity:** 2,000 **Seats:** 150   **Covered:** 150   **Midweek Matchday:** Tuesday          **Clubhouse:** Yes   **Shop:** Yes

**Colours(change):**   All Maroon & sky blue/sky blue/sky blue (All white)

**Previous Names:**   None.

**Previous Leagues:** Herefordshire Sunday. Worcester & Dist. West Midlands (Regional).

**Records:**          **Att:** 590 v Hereford United, Hereford Senior Invitation Cup Final 2012. **Goalscorer:** Paul Burton. **Apps:** Jon Pugh.

**Senior Honours:**   Hereford Senior Cup 1985-86, 88-89, 91-92, 95-96, 01-02, 02-03, 04-05, 05-06, 07-08, 11-12, 12-13.
West Midlands (Regional) Premier 2002-03.

**10 YEAR RECORD**

| 03-04 | | 04-05 | | 05-06 | | 06-07 | | 07-08 | | 08-09 | | 09-10 | | 10-11 | | 11-12 | | 12-13 | |
|---|---|---|---|---|---|---|---|---|---|---|---|---|---|---|---|---|---|---|---|
| MidAl | 13 | MidAl | 6 | MidAl | 20 | MidAl | 16 | MidAl | 11 | MidAl | 17 | MidAl | 5 | MidAl | 6 | MidAl | 2 | MidAl | 2 |

# GROUND DIRECTIONS

**AFC WULFRUNIANS - Castlecroft Stadium, Castlecroft Road, Wolverhampton, WV3 8N - 01902-761 410**

Follow A454 (signposted Bridgnorth) and turn left at Mermaid Pub onto Windmill Lane. Turn right onto Castlecroft Avenue. Ground is straight across past Wightwick Cricket Ground.

**ALVECHURCH - Lye Meadow, Redditch Rd., Alvechurch, B48 7RS - 0121-445 2929**

M42 Junction 2. Take A441 towards Redditch. At first roundabout turn right onto A4120 signposted Alvechurch. Ground approx 1km on right. Car park entrance on right before ground.

**BOLDMERE ST. MICHAELS - The Trevor Brown Memorial Ground, Church Road, Boldmere, Sutton Coldfield B73 5RY - 0121-384 7531**

A38(M) from M6 junction 6 and A5127 from Birmingham to Yenton Traffic Lights. Left on A452 Chester Road, then 6th.right into Church Road.

From M6 junction 5 A452 Brownhills to Yenton Traffic Lights. Straight on then 6th right into Church Road.

**CAUSEWAY UNITED - War Memorial Athletic Ground, High Street, Amblecote, Stourbridge, West Midlands, DY8 4HN - 01384-394040**

From Stourbridge Ring Road take A491 towards Wolverhampton. Ground is on left within 300 yards immediately after 1st set of traffic lights and opposite the Royal Oak public house.

**COLESHILL TOWN - Pack Meadow, Packington Lane, Coleshill, B46 3JQ - 01675 463 259**

From M6 Junction 4 take A446 signposted Lichfield. Straight over 1st roundabout then immediately turn right across dual carriageway onto B4117 signposted Coleshill. After school on right, turn right into Packington Lane. Ground is ½ mile on left.

**CONTINENTAL STAR - Rushall Olympic F.C. Dales Lane, Rushall, Walsall, West Midls, WS4 1LJ 1922 641 021**

From M6 Junction 7 head North on Birmingham Road/A34 towards Chapel Lane. At the roundabout take the 2nd exit onto Broadway N/A4148. At the roundabout take the 1st exit onto Birmingham Road. At the roundabout take the 2nd exit onto Springhill Road. At the roundabout take the 1st exit into Ablewell Street. Turn left onto Town Hill. Keep right at the fork. Turn right onto Upper Rushall Street. Continue onto Lower Rushall Street. Continue onto Lichfield Street/A461. Go through 1 roundabout. Turn right onto Daw End Lane/B4154. Continue to follow B4154. Turn right into Rushall Olympic Football Club.

**COVENTRY SPHINX - Sphinx Drive, Off Siddeley Avenue, Coventry, CV3 1WA - 02476 451 361**

From M6. Leave M6 at Junction 3 and take A444 towards Coventry. Continue to Binley Road (6 roundabouts) and turn left on A428 Binley Road towards Binley. Pass a row of shops on left and Bulls Head public house on right. After the Bulls Head, turn 1st right into Biggin Hall Crescent. Then take the 5th left turn into Siddeley Avenue. Take 1st left into Sphinx Drive and the ground is at the end. From M42 & A45. Follow A45 towards Coventry and take A4114 Coventry at Coventry Hill Hotel. At roundabout take 2nd exit to next roundabout and take 3rd exit onto Holyhead Road. After approx 2.5 miles you will come to Coventry Ring Road where you turn left and then get over to your right onto the ring road. Continue on Ring Road and leave at Junction 3 signposted M69 and Football Stadium. Follow signs for A428 Binley until you see Bulls Head public house on your right. Then follow the above instructions.

**DUNKIRK - The Ron Steel Sports Ground, Lenton Lane, Clifton Bridge, Nottingham, NG7 2SA 0115 985 0803**

From M1 Junction 24 take A453 towards Nottingham, through Clifton and join A52 onto Clifton Bridge. Get in middle lane down the slip road onto the island under the flyover signposted Industrial Estate. Take immediate 1st left and 1st left again onto Lenton Lane. Follow the road past Greenwood Meadows and the ground is 200 yards on the right.

**GORNAL ATHLETIC - Garden Walk, Lower Gornal, Dudley, West Midlands, DY3 2NR 01384 358 398**

From Dudley take Himley Road (B4176) to Gornal. Right turn into Central Drive. First left into Bank Road. Beear right at top. Garden Walk.

**HEATH HAYES - Coppice Colliery Ground, Newlands Lane, Heath Hayes, Cannock, Staffordshire, WS12 3HH - 07969 203 063**

From M6 Junction 11 take the A4601 towards Cannock and at the 1st island turn right onto the A460 signposted Rugeley/Cannock Business Parks. At the double island (A5) go straight on still on A460 and over two islands. At the 3rd island, turn right onto A5190 signposted Lichfield. Pass Texaco garage on the right and take the next right turn into Newlands Lane. Entrance to the ground is 50 yards down the lane on the left under the barrier.

**HEATHER ST. JOHN'S - St. John's Park, Ravenstone Road, Heather, Leicestershire, LE67 2QJ - 01530 263 986**

Exit M42 at Junction 11. Take the road towards Measham, pass the Car Auctions and go over the traffic lights. At 2nd mini island take 2nd exit onto Leicester Road. After approximately 3 miles you will enter Heather. At T junction turn left. At mini island take 2nd exit onto Ravenstone Road and go up the hill. Ground is 200 metres on the left.

**HIGHGATE UNITED - The Coppice, Tythe Barn Lane, Shirley, Solihull, B90 1PH - 0121 744 4194**

From M42 Junction 4 take A34 towards Birmingham. Go to far end of Shirley Village and turn left into Haslucks Green Road. Take the left hand fork by the Colebrook pub and go past Shirley Station and the Drawbridge pub. At 'T' junction turn left and go over railway bridge. Turn left into Tythe Barn Lane and the ground is the 2nd entrance on the right approx 200 yards down the lane.

**KIRBY MUXLOE - Kirby Muxloe Sports Club, Ratby Lane, Kirby Muxloe, Leics, LE9 2AQ 0116 239 3201**

Leave M1 at Junction 21a and follow signs to Kirby Muxloe. Road goes round and back over Motorway and down hill to a roundabout. Go straight on to mini roundabout and straight on to Ratby Lane. Entrance is next to last house on the right.

**LOUGHBOROUGH UNIVERSITY - Loughborough University Stadium, Holywell Sports Complex, Holywell Park, Loughborough, Leics, LE11 3TU - 01509 228 774**
From M42/A42 exit at Junction 13 and take the A512 towards Loughborough. After crossing Junction 23 of the M1 travel approx 3/4 mile to first traffic island. Turn right into University (LE11 3QF Red Building is on your right). Keep straight on at both small islands. Bear left into large spectator car park, entrance on left hand side. Please note that there is limited parking at Stadium for Officials/ Team Coach/Cars.

**QUORN - Farley Way, Quorn, Leicestershire, LE12 8RB - 01509 620 232**
Exit Junction 21A of M1 Motorway onto A46. Proceed towards Loughborough on A6. Approx 2 miles from Loughborough turn left at island. After 200 yards turn left at traffic lights. Ground on left.

**ROCESTR - Hillsfield, Mill Street, Rocester, Uttoxeter, Staffordshire ST14 5JX - 01889 591 301**
From Uttoxeter take the B5030, signposted Ashbourne/Alton Towers After 3 miles turn right opposite the JCB factory over humpback bridge into Rocester village. Turn right at mini island into Mill Street, ground is 500 yards on the left immediately past the JCB Academy.

**SHEPSHED DYNAMO - The Dovecote Stadium, Butthole lane, Shepshed, Leicestershire, LE12 9BN - 01509 650 992**
From Junction 23 of M1 motorway take the A512 towards Ashby. Turn right at first set of lights and after approx 1 mile take 2nd exit at mini roundabout (after petrol station). Carry on for half mile over speed humps. Butthole Lane is opposite the Black Swan Public House.

**STOURPORT SWIFTS - Walshes Meadow, Harold Davies Drive, Stourport on Severn, Worcs, DY13 0AA - 01299 825 188**
Follw the one way system through Stourport Town Centre signposted 'Sports Centre'. Go over the river bridge and turn first left into Harold Davies Drive. Ground is at the rear of the Sports Centre.

**STUDLEY - The Beehive, Abbeyfields Drive, Studley, Warks. B80 7BE - 01527 853 817**
Leave M42 at junction 3 ( Redditch A435) and turn towards Redditch. Follow dual carriageway to the end. Stay on A435 and go straight on at island. Pass 'The Boot' public house and after 550 yards turn left into Abbeyfields Drive. The ground is on the right.

**TIPTON TOWN - Tipton Sports Academy, Wednesbury Oak Road, Tipton, West Mids, DY4 0BS - 0121 502 5534**
From M6 junction 9 take A461 through Wednesbury Town Centre to Ockerhill Island. Follow signs taking a full right turn towards Bilston (A4098). In ½ mile turn left at traffic lights (A4037). Ground 100 yards on left. Use 2nd Entrance.
From M5 junction 2 take A4123 for about 3 miles until you reach Burnt Tree Island. Take second exit towards Wolverhampton and continue to next set of traffic lights. Turn right A4037 and continue for 3 miles. Pass ASDA supermarket and ground is 100 yards on the right. Use 1st Entrance.

**TIVIDALE - The Beeches, Packwood Road, Tividale, Oldbury, West Midlands, B69 1UL - 01384 211 743**
From M5 Junction 2 Take A4123 towards Dudley. After approx 1.5 miles and after foot bridge, take left up Trafalgar Road. Take 2nd right into Elm Terrace and then 1st left into Birch Crescent. Take 1st right into Packwood Road and ground is at end of road.

**WALSALL WOOD - Oak Park, Lichfield Road, Walsall Wood, Staffordshire, WS9 9NP- 07583 175 664**
From North- Leave M6 at Junction 12 and take A5 until big island just outside Brownhills (next island after 'The Turn' pub on left). Take A452 Chester Road North through Brownhills High Street to traffic lights at Shire Oak (Pub at junction on right hand side). Turn right onto A461 towards Walsall, go to next set of traffic lights, cross over and turn right immediately onto Oak Park Leisure Centre Car park (rear of Kentucky Fried Chicken). Proceed diagonally over car park and follow road round to ground entrance.
From South using M5/M6 motorways- M5 North past Junction 1 onto M6 North. Leave at Junction 9 (Wednesbury turn off) and take A4148 to Walsall. Proceed for about 2 miles over several islands until going down a hill alongside the Arboretum. At big island at bottom, turn right onto A461 for Lichfield. Take A461 for about 4 miles and go through Walsall Wood village (after Barons Court Hotel on right) up the hill after village, Oak Park is on the left opposite Fitness First. Turn left and go diagonally across Oak Park Leisure Centre car park. Follow road round to ground entrance.

**WESTFIELDS - 'Allpay park', Widemarsh Common, Grandstand Road., Hereford, HR4 9NA 07860 410 548**
On reaching the outskirts of Hereford from Worcester, continue along A4103, over roundabout signposted Holmer and Leisure Centre. Proceed for 1 mile to large roundabout by the "Starting Gate Inn" and turn left towards Hereford. Proceed for ½ mile, past Hereford Leisure Centre and at mini roundabout, turn right. Proceed 150 yards and bear left around the Common, in front of Cricket Pavilion and immediately turn right into the driveway for allpay.park.

# NORTH WEST COUNTIES LEAGUE

**Sponsored by:** Vodkat
**Founded:** 1982
**Recent Champions:**
2008: Trafford.
2009: AFC Fylde.
2010: Newcastle Town.
2011: New Mills.
2012: Ramsbottom United.
nwcfl.com

## LEAGUE CHALLENGE CUP FINAL

**ROUND 1**

| | | | |
|---|---|---|---|
| Abbey Hey | v | Oldham Boro | 2-1 |
| AFC Darwen | v | Leek CSOB | 3-0 |
| Chadderton | v | Atherton Collieries | 2-0 |
| Cheadle Town | v | Ashton Town | 2-2 |
| Ashton Town | v | Cheadle Town | 0-2 |
| Irlam | v | Formby | 0-0 |
| Formby | v | Irlam | 3-0 |
| Nelson | v | Rochdale Town | 1-2 |
| Northwich Villa | v | Daisy Hill | 1-3 |
| West Didsbury & Chorlton | v | Eccleshall | 4-0 |

**ROUND 2**

| | | | |
|---|---|---|---|
| Abbey Hey | v | Colne | 3-1 |
| AFC Liverpool | v | Wigan Robin Park | 4-2 |
| Alsager Town | v | Squires Gate | 3-0 |
| Ashton Athletic | v | Bacup Borough | 1-5 |
| Barnoldswick Town | v | Glossop North End | 4-2 |
| Bootle | v | Runcorn Town | 3-0 |
| Cheadle Town | v | Silsden | 3-2 |
| Congleton Town | v | Atherton LR | 3-2 |
| Padiham | v | Daisy Hill | 2-0 |
| Rochdale Town | v | Formby | 1-6 |
| St Helens Town | v | AFC Blackpool | 0-3 |
| Stockport Sports | v | Runcorn Linnets | 1-2 |
| Stone Dominoes | v | Maine Road | 0-5 |
| West Didsbury & Chorlton | v | Norton United | 3-1 |
| Winsford United | v | Chadderton | 2-0 |
| Holker Old Boys | v | AFC Darwen | 1-5 |

**ROUND 3**

| | | | |
|---|---|---|---|
| Abbey Hey | v | Cheadle Town | 0-1 |
| Alsager Town | v | AFC Liverpool | 0-2 |
| Bacup Borough | v | AFC Darwen | 1-0 |
| Barnoldswick Town | v | Formby | 2-3 |
| Bootle | v | West Didsbury & Chorlton | 2-1 |
| Congleton Town | v | Maine Road | 0-0, 1-3p |
| Padiham | v | AFC Blackpool | 1-0 |
| Runcorn Linnets | v | Winsford United | 3-2 |

**QUARTER FINALS**

| | | | |
|---|---|---|---|
| Cheadle Town | v | AFC Liverpool | 2-1 |
| Runcorn Linnets | v | Bootle | 2-1 |
| Bacup Borough | v | Formby | 1-2 |
| AFC Blackpool | v | Maine Road | 1-3 |

**SEMI-FINALS**

| | | | |
|---|---|---|---|
| Maine Road | v | Formby | 2-2, 5-6p |
| Rurncorn Linnets | v | Cheadle Town | 3-3, 4-2p |

**FINAL**

| | | | |
|---|---|---|---|
| Formby | v | Runcorn Linnets | 0-3 |

| PREMIER DIVISION | P | W | D | L | F | A | Pts |
|---|---|---|---|---|---|---|---|
| (P) Padiham | 42 | 26 | 10 | 6 | 92 | 45 | 88 |
| Maine Road | 42 | 28 | 3 | 11 | 99 | 57 | 87 |
| Bootle | 42 | 26 | 8 | 8 | 79 | 43 | 86 |
| Runcorn Town (-3pts) | 42 | 26 | 9 | 7 | 105 | 45 | 84 |
| Winsford United | 42 | 25 | 8 | 9 | 85 | 45 | 83 |
| Runcorn Linnets | 42 | 21 | 9 | 12 | 82 | 58 | 72 |
| Congleton Town | 42 | 20 | 9 | 13 | 85 | 55 | 69 |
| Colne | 42 | 19 | 10 | 13 | 93 | 60 | 67 |
| Barnoldswick Town | 42 | 19 | 9 | 14 | 77 | 57 | 66 |
| AFC Blackpool | 42 | 19 | 9 | 14 | 60 | 58 | 66 |
| AFC Liverpool | 42 | 18 | 6 | 18 | 69 | 64 | 60 |
| Wigan Robin Park | 42 | 17 | 5 | 20 | 66 | 71 | 56 |
| Glossop North End | 42 | 14 | 11 | 17 | 73 | 71 | 53 |
| Norton United (-3pts) | 42 | 16 | 7 | 19 | 69 | 83 | 52 |
| Alsager Town | 42 | 14 | 8 | 20 | 66 | 78 | 50 |
| Stockport Sports (-6pts) | 42 | 14 | 13 | 15 | 72 | 69 | 49 |
| Bacup Borough | 42 | 13 | 8 | 21 | 51 | 71 | 47 |
| Silsden | 42 | 11 | 6 | 25 | 58 | 98 | 39 |
| St Helens Town | 42 | 9 | 9 | 24 | 54 | 91 | 36 |
| Ashton Athletic | 42 | 10 | 5 | 27 | 58 | 91 | 35 |
| Squires Gate | 42 | 8 | 6 | 28 | 47 | 95 | 30 |
| Stone Dominoes | 42 | 3 | 4 | 35 | 31 | 166 | 13 |

| PREMIER DIVISION | 1 | 2 | 3 | 4 | 5 | 6 | 7 | 8 | 9 | 10 | 11 | 12 | 13 | 14 | 15 | 16 | 17 | 18 | 19 | 20 | 21 | 22 |
|---|---|---|---|---|---|---|---|---|---|---|---|---|---|---|---|---|---|---|---|---|---|---|
| 1 AFC Blackpool | | 2-1 | 3-1 | 2-0 | 0-1 | 0-0 | 3-1 | 0-5 | 2-1 | 1-1 | 2-4 | 1-0 | 0-1 | 1-1 | 1-1 | 3-0 | 1-2 | 0-0 | 3-2 | 2-0 | 2-3 | 1-1 |
| 2 AFC Liverpool | 0-0 | | 3-0 | 1-3 | 2-2 | 1-1 | 2-1 | 3-2 | 3-1 | 1-2 | 2-4 | 2-3 | 2-3 | 2-0 | 0-1 | 2-1 | 1-0 | 3-1 | 1-1 | 4-1 | 1-2 | 0-1 |
| 3 Alsager Town | 1-0 | 0-1 | | 4-1 | 2-1 | 2-3 | 1-3 | 2-0 | 1-0 | 0-0 | 0-2 | 5-2 | 0-1 | 1-2 | 0-2 | 1-2 | 0-3 | 2-0 | 1-2 | 2-0 | 4-2 | 0-4 |
| 4 Ashton Athletic | 2-4 | 1-1 | 4-0 | | 2-1 | 2-0 | 0-3 | 1-3 | 2-3 | 1-0 | 2-3 | 0-2 | 0-3 | 0-6 | 0-1 | 2-2 | 4-0 | 2-2 | 0-4 | 3-0 | 3-1 | 1-2 |
| 5 Bacup Borough | 1-0 | 1-0 | 2-1 | 2-6 | | 1-3 | 2-4 | 2-2 | 1-0 | 0-0 | 2-1 | 2-2 | 1-2 | 4-1 | 1-2 | 3-1 | 0-0 | 0-0 | 2-1 | 4-0 | 0-1 | 1-2 |
| 6 Barnoldswick Town | 0-1 | 1-0 | 1-2 | 2-1 | 1-0 | | 0-0 | 0-4 | 2-3 | 3-1 | 4-0 | 0-1 | 2-2 | 3-5 | 2-0 | 3-2 | 4-2 | 3-0 | 2-1 | 1-1 | 2-3 | 1-3 |
| 7 Bootle | 2-1 | 1-0 | 1-1 | 1-0 | 2-0 | 3-6 | | 2-1 | 3-2 | 2-0 | 1-2 | 1-1 | 2-2 | 2-0 | 1-0 | 2-1 | 2-2 | 2-2 | 2-0 | 7-0 | 2-0 | 3-1 |
| 8 Colne | 4-2 | 0-3 | 2-3 | 3-2 | 6-0 | 0-1 | 2-1 | | 1-0 | 3-1 | 1-2 | 0-0 | 1-1 | 2-0 | 3-5 | 5-0 | 2-0 | 1-2 | 1-1 | 5-1 | 3-3 | 3-2 |
| 9 Congleton Town | 5-1 | 2-2 | 4-4 | 3-0 | 4-2 | 2-1 | 0-2 | 0-1 | | 1-0 | 2-2 | 0-0 | 1-1 | 1-1 | 0-0 | 3-1 | 3-0 | 3-0 | 5-0 | 3-1 | 0-0 | |
| 10 Glossop North End | 4-4 | 6-2 | 1-1 | 3-0 | 2-0 | 1-2 | 0-1 | 1-1 | 3-2 | | 1-4 | 1-2 | 2-3 | 1-2 | 3-2 | 2-0 | 4-0 | 3-4 | 2-2 | 2-2 | 1-0 | 0-3 |
| 11 Maine Road | 4-0 | 1-0 | 6-1 | 2-0 | 2-1 | 1-0 | 0-1 | 3-0 | 2-3 | | 1-1 | 0-1 | 4-1 | 0-2 | 1-2 | 4-0 | 2-1 | 3-0 | 6-1 | 3-1 | 2-1 | |
| 12 Norton United | 0-1 | 2-1 | 1-0 | 1-1 | 1-0 | 3-2 | 2-1 | 1-1 | 2-4 | 5-3 | 3-4 | | 1-2 | 0-3 | 3-9 | 5-3 | 2-0 | 5-2 | 1-3 | 8-0 | 1-2 | 1-2 |
| 13 Padiham | 1-1 | 0-1 | 1-2 | 4-1 | 2-2 | 3-0 | 1-1 | 2-0 | 2-1 | 2-1 | 3-4 | 4-0 | | 2-4 | 1-1 | 6-0 | 5-4 | 4-1 | 4-0 | 4-0 | 2-0 | 3-4 |
| 14 Runcorn Linnets | 0-1 | 2-1 | 2-2 | 3-2 | 5-1 | 1-1 | 3-2 | 2-0 | 2-4 | 0-1 | 1-3 | 1-0 | 0-0 | | 1-1 | 6-1 | 3-2 | 4-2 | 2-1 | 2-2 | 3-0 | 1-3 |
| 15 Runcorn Town | 0-2 | 1-3 | 3-2 | 4-1 | 2-0 | 2-2 | 1-2 | 2-2 | 4-3 | 3-2 | 3-0 | 2-0 | 1-0 | 2-1 | | 3-0 | 5-0 | 1-1 | 8-1 | 10-1 | 2-0 | 0-1 |
| 16 Silsden | 0-2 | 1-3 | 2-1 | 4-0 | 1-0 | 1-1 | 1-2 | 1-1 | 1-5 | 4-2 | 2-0 | 2-1 | 0-5 | | 2-1 | 7-1 | 1-1 | 4-1 | 1-3 | 1-2 | | |
| 17 Squires Gate | 0-2 | 2-3 | 3-3 | 3-2 | 0-2 | 0-2 | 0-4 | 3-1 | 1-3 | 2-2 | 2-1 | 1-2 | 0-2 | 0-1 | 1-4 | 1-1 | | 3-0 | 2-0 | 0-1 | 0-1 | 2-2 |
| 18 St Helens Town | 1-2 | 2-1 | 2-2 | 2-2 | 1-2 | 1-0 | 0-0 | 1-3 | 0-1 | 1-1 | 3-4 | 3-1 | 2-4 | 0-1 | 0-2 | 2-1 | 5-0 | | 0-5 | 1-0 | 1-4 | 0-1 |
| 19 Stockport Sports | 3-0 | 0-1 | 3-3 | 2-0 | 2-0 | 1-4 | 1-2 | 2-2 | 2-0 | 0-0 | 1-3 | 7-0 | 1-1 | 2-2 | 1-1 | 3-1 | 4-0 | 2-1 | | 4-2 | 1-3 | 1-3 |
| 20 Stone Dominoes | 2-4 | 0-6 | 1-4 | 0-4 | 2-3 | 0-9 | 0-1 | 0-7 | 1-6 | 3-2 | 1-4 | 1-2 | 0-1 | 1-3 | 0-3 | 3-2 | 0-3 | 1-3 | 2-2 | | 0-8 | 0-6 |
| 21 Wigan Robin Park | 0-2 | 1-2 | 2-0 | 2-0 | 0-0 | 0-1 | 2-1 | 1-1 | 0-5 | 2-3 | 1-0 | 3-2 | 0-2 | 0-6 | 0-1 | 4-0 | 2-1 | 3-0 | 1-1 | 6-0 | | 1-2 |
| 22 Winsford United | 2-0 | 8-1 | 0-4 | 2-0 | 3-1 | 0-1 | 0-2 | 3-2 | 0-1 | 2-1 | 0-0 | 2-1 | 1-2 | 0-0 | 0-0 | 2-2 | 4-1 | 3-1 | 0-0 | 3-0 | 5-1 | |

| DIVISION ONE | P | W | D | L | F | A | Pts |
|---|---|---|---|---|---|---|---|
| 1 Formby | 34 | 28 | 2 | 4 | 117 | 42 | 86 |
| 2 (P) Abbey Hey | 34 | 26 | 3 | 5 | 88 | 25 | 81 |
| 3 (P) West Didsbury & Chorlton | 34 | 22 | 4 | 8 | 79 | 43 | 70 |
| 4 Atherton Collieries | 34 | 21 | 6 | 7 | 78 | 47 | 69 |
| 5 AFC Darwen | 34 | 20 | 3 | 11 | 79 | 57 | 63 |
| 6 Ashton Town | 34 | 18 | 8 | 8 | 77 | 43 | 62 |
| 7 Cheadle Town | 34 | 14 | 7 | 13 | 61 | 65 | 49 |
| 8 Oldham Boro (-3pts) | 34 | 15 | 5 | 14 | 59 | 50 | 47 |
| 9 Rochdale Town | 34 | 12 | 9 | 13 | 54 | 60 | 45 |
| 10 Nelson | 34 | 11 | 9 | 14 | 64 | 76 | 42 |
| 11 Leek CSOB | 34 | 10 | 9 | 15 | 52 | 68 | 39 |
| 12 Chadderton | 34 | 10 | 9 | 15 | 52 | 69 | 39 |
| 13 Atherton LR | 34 | 8 | 11 | 15 | 37 | 55 | 35 |
| 14 Irlam | 34 | 9 | 6 | 19 | 47 | 72 | 33 |
| 15 Eccleshall | 34 | 7 | 7 | 20 | 44 | 79 | 28 |
| 16 Daisy Hill | 34 | 7 | 6 | 21 | 55 | 81 | 27 |
| 17 Holker Old Boys | 34 | 7 | 2 | 25 | 31 | 74 | 23 |
| 18 Northwich Villa | 34 | 6 | 4 | 24 | 38 | 106 | 22 |

| RESERVE DIVISION | P | W | D | L | F | A | P |
|---|---|---|---|---|---|---|---|
| 1 Padiham Reserves | 24 | 16 | 6 | 2 | 77 | 28 | 5 |
| 2 Irlam Reserves | 24 | 14 | 6 | 4 | 44 | 22 | 4 |
| 3 New Mills Reserves | 24 | 14 | 4 | 6 | 59 | 36 | 4 |
| 4 Wigan Robin Park Reserves | 24 | 13 | 3 | 8 | 68 | 51 | 4 |
| 5 Barnoldswick Town Reserves | 24 | 13 | 3 | 8 | 49 | 43 | 4 |
| 6 Ashton Town Reserves (-1) | 24 | 13 | 1 | 10 | 51 | 43 | 3 |
| 7 Cheadle Town Reserves | 24 | 12 | 2 | 10 | 50 | 50 | 3 |
| 8 Runcorn Linnets Reserves | 24 | 8 | 5 | 11 | 50 | 55 | 2 |
| 9 Glossop North End Reserves | 24 | 8 | 3 | 13 | 40 | 40 | 2 |
| 10 Nelson Reserves | 24 | 7 | 2 | 15 | 36 | 71 | 2 |
| 11 Silsden Reserves | 24 | 5 | 4 | 15 | 27 | 52 | 1 |
| 12 AFC Darwen Reserves | 24 | 5 | 4 | 15 | 39 | 78 | 1 |
| 13 W Didsbury & Chorlton Reserves | 24 | 5 | 3 | 16 | 38 | 59 | 1 |

| DIVISION ONE | 1 | 2 | 3 | 4 | 5 | 6 | 7 | 8 | 9 | 10 | 11 | 12 | 13 | 14 | 15 | 16 | 17 | 18 |
|---|---|---|---|---|---|---|---|---|---|---|---|---|---|---|---|---|---|---|
| 1 Abbey Hey | | 3-0 | 2-1 | 0-1 | 2-1 | 5-1 | 3-1 | 2-0 | 1-0 | 4-0 | 5-0 | 2-1 | 5-2 | 5-1 | 3-0 | 0-1 | 0-2 | 2-1 |
| 2 AFC Darwen | 0-4 | | 3-2 | 1-1 | 2-1 | 2-1 | 2-1 | 3-1 | 1-0 | 1-3 | 3-0 | 0-1 | 3-1 | 3-2 | 6-0 | 0-2 | 1-2 | 2-0 |
| 3 Ashton Town | 0-0 | 4-3 | | 3-1 | 2-2 | 2-0 | 3-3 | 6-0 | 4-3 | 0-3 | 3-1 | 2-0 | 5-2 | 1-0 | 7-1 | 2-0 | 3-1 | 0-4 |
| 4 Atherton Collieries | 2-5 | 4-3 | 3-1 | | 1-1 | 4-1 | 3-0 | 3-1 | 3-0 | 2-3 | 2-0 | 6-1 | 0-0 | 5-2 | 2-0 | 3-1 | 0-0 | 0-1 |
| 5 Atherton LR | 2-3 | 1-0 | 1-1 | 0-1 | | 0-6 | 1-2 | 2-1 | 1-1 | 0-4 | 0-0 | 0-0 | 2-4 | 3-3 | 1-2 | 1-0 | 2-5 | 4-1 |
| 6 Chadderton | 0-2 | 5-3 | 1-0 | 0-2 | 1-1 | | 1-1 | 3-1 | 2-0 | 0-4 | 2-0 | 1-1 | 0-0 | 4-2 | 2-1 | 2-8 | 1-3 | 0-3 |
| 7 Cheadle Town | 2-1 | 2-2 | 1-1 | 4-5 | 1-0 | 0-0 | | 3-0 | 1-2 | 0-3 | 3-0 | 2-2 | 5-3 | 2-3 | 2-1 | 3-1 | 2-1 | 3-2 |
| 8 Daisy Hill | 1-4 | 3-2 | 0-5 | 1-2 | 0-1 | 3-3 | 1-3 | | 2-3 | 1-3 | 3-1 | 1-2 | 5-1 | 2-2 | 7-2 | 0-2 | 2-2 | 0-1 |
| 9 Eccleshall | 0-4 | 1-3 | 2-6 | 5-2 | 1-1 | 2-3 | 0-2 | 2-2 | | 1-7 | 1-0 | 2-3 | 1-1 | 1-1 | 0-1 | 0-7 | 1-4 | 0-1 |
| 10 Formby | 0-2 | 3-3 | 2-1 | 3-2 | 2-0 | 5-0 | 6-0 | 4-3 | 9-3 | | 3-0 | 3-1 | 1-0 | 3-2 | 9-0 | 1-3 | 3-0 | 0-1 |
| 11 Holker Old Boys | 0-7 | 1-4 | 0-1 | 1-5 | 1-0 | 2-0 | 3-0 | 1-4 | 0-2 | 2-3 | | 0-2 | 0-1 | 4-0 | 3-0 | 4-2 | 1-2 | 1-3 |
| 12 Irlam | 0-4 | 2-3 | 1-3 | 0-0 | 0-2 | 2-1 | 3-5 | 2-1 | 1-1 | 2-5 | 0-2 | | 4-1 | 1-3 | 4-1 | 0-3 | 1-2 | 1-1 |
| 13 Leek CSOB | 0-2 | 0-2 | 0-0 | 2-3 | 0-0 | 3-1 | 2-1 | 2-0 | 0-0 | 3-7 | 2-1 | 3-0 | | 2-4 | 6-0 | 1-0 | 4-0 | 1-2 |
| 14 Nelson | 1-3 | 1-2 | 1-1 | 0-3 | 5-2 | 1-1 | 3-1 | 0-2 | 0-4 | 1-6 | 3-0 | 1-5 | 2-1 | | 4-1 | 1-0 | 3-2 | 2-2 |
| 15 Northwich Villa | 1-2 | 2-4 | 0-5 | 1-3 | 1-2 | 2-5 | 0-3 | 2-2 | 2-1 | 0-3 | 4-0 | 0-4 | 1-3 | 2-2 | | 1-2 | 0-3 | 2-0 |
| 16 Oldham Boro | 0-0 | 1-3 | 1-0 | 1-1 | 1-0 | 2-1 | 2-2 | 1-2 | 1-0 | 1-2 | 1-0 | 1-0 | 3-1 | 1-2 | 3-3 | | 3-3 | 2-4 |
| 17 Rochdale Town | 0-3 | 0-6 | 0-1 | 0-2 | 0-0 | 1-1 | 1-0 | 3-3 | 0-3 | 4-0 | 0-4 | 3-2 | 0-0 | 2-2 | 2-3 | 3-1 | | 1-2 |
| 18 West Didsbury & Chorlton | 2-1 | 2-3 | 1-1 | 4-1 | 1-2 | 3-2 | 4-0 | 3-0 | 3-1 | 2-3 | 3-0 | 3-2 | 8-2 | 3-2 | 1-1 | 4-1 | 2-0 | |

## CLUB MOVEMENTS

**Premier Division - In:** Bacup & Rossendale Borough (NC from Bacup Borough). Abbey Hey (P). West Didsbury & Chorlton (P).

**Out:** Padiham (P - Northern Premier Division One North). Stone Dominoes (W).

**Division One - In:** 1874 Northwich (N). Hanley Town (P- Staffordshire County Senior). Northwich Flixton Villa (NC from Northwich Villa). Widnes Vikings (P - West Cheshire).

**Out:** Abbey Hey (P). West Didsbury & Chorlton (P).

## ABBEY HEY
Founded: 1902     Nickname:

**Secretary:** Tony McAllister    **(T)** 0161 231 7147    **(E)**

**Chairman:** James Whittaker    **Manager:** Luke Gibson    **Prog Ed:** Paul Cullen

**Ground:** The Abbey Stadium, Goredale Avenue, Gorton, Manchester M18 7HD    **(T)** 0161 231 7147

**Capacity:**   **Seats:** Yes   **Covered:** Yes   **Midweek Matchday:** Tuesday    **Clubhouse:** Yes

**Colours(change):** Red/black/red (Orange/black/black)
**Previous Names:**
**Previous Leagues:** Manchester Amateur, South East Lancashire, Manchester.
**Records:** 985 v FC United of Manchester, March 2006.
**Senior Honours:** Manchester League 1981-82, 88-89, 88-89, 91-92, 93-94, 94-95.

### 10 YEAR RECORD

| 03-04 | | 04-05 | | 05-06 | | 06-07 | | 07-08 | | 08-09 | | 09-10 | | 10-11 | | 11-12 | | 12-13 | |
|---|---|---|---|---|---|---|---|---|---|---|---|---|---|---|---|---|---|---|---|
| NWC1 | 21 | NWC1 | 14 | NWC1 | 11 | NWC1 | 17 | NWC1 | 17 | NWCP | 21 | NWCP | 22 | NWC1 | 15 | NWC1 | 3 | NWC1 | 2 |

## AFC BLACKPOOL
Founded: 1947     Nickname: Mechs

**Secretary:** William Singleton    **(T)** 01253 761 721    **(E)**

**Chairman:** Henry Baldwin    **Manager:** Stuart Parker    **Prog Ed:** David Tebbett

**Ground:** Mechanics Ground, Jepson Way, Common Edge Road, Blackpool, FY4 5DY    **(T)** 01253 761 721

**Capacity:** 2,000 **Seats:** 250   **Covered:** 1,700   **Midweek Matchday:** Tuesday    **Clubhouse:** Yes   **Shop:** Yes

**Colours(change):** Tangerine/white/tangerine (White/tangerine/tangerine)
**Previous Names:** Blackpool Mechanics. **Previous Ground:** Stanley Park 1947-49.
**Previous Leagues:** Fylde, Blackpool & Fylde Combination, West Lancashire, Lancashire Combination 1962-68.
**Records:** **Att:** 4,300 v FC United of Manchester, 18/02/2006 at Blackpool FC.
**Senior Honours:** Lancashire County FA Shield 1957/58, 1960/61. West Lancashire League 1960/61, 61/62.
North West Counties League Division Three 1985/86, Division One 2010-11.

### 10 YEAR RECORD

| 03-04 | | 04-05 | | 05-06 | | 06-07 | | 07-08 | | 08-09 | | 09-10 | | 10-11 | | 11-12 | | 12-13 | |
|---|---|---|---|---|---|---|---|---|---|---|---|---|---|---|---|---|---|---|---|
| NWC2 | 14 | NWC2 | 10 | NWC2 | 9 | NWC1 | 13 | NWC1 | 9 | NWC1 | 15 | NWC1 | 15 | NWC1 | 1 | NWCP | 9 | NWCP | 10 |

## AFC LIVERPOOL
Founded: 2008     Nickname: Reds

**Secretary:** Pat Cushion    **(T)** 0151 430 0507    **(E)** clubsec@afcliverpool.org.uk

**Chairman:** Chris Stirrup    **Manager:** Paul Moore    **Prog Ed:** Paul Smith

**Ground:** Prescot Cables FC, Valerie Park, Eaton Street, Prescot, Merseyside, L34 6ND    **(T)** 0151 430 0507

**Capacity:** 3,000 **Seats:** 500   **Covered:** 600   **Midweek Matchday:** Wednesday    **Clubhouse:** Yes   **Shop:** Yes

**Colours(change):** All red (Yellow/black/yellow)
**Previous Names:** None
**Previous Leagues:** None
**Records:** **Att:** 604 v Wigan Robin Park 06/09/2008.
**Senior Honours:** North West Counties Trophy 2008-09, 09-10.

### 10 YEAR RECORD

| 03-04 | 04-05 | 05-06 | 06-07 | 07-08 | 08-09 | | 09-10 | | 10-11 | | 11-12 | | 12-13 | |
|---|---|---|---|---|---|---|---|---|---|---|---|---|---|---|
| | | | | | NWC1 | 4 | NWC1 | 5 | NWC1 | 4 | NWCP | 19 | NWCP | 11 |

## ALSAGER TOWN
Founded: 1968     Nickname: The Bullets

**Secretary:** Chris Robinson    **(T)** 07888 750 532    **(E)**

**Chairman:** Terry Greer    **Manager:** Andy Turner    **Prog Ed:** John Shenton

**Ground:** The LAW Training Stadium, Woodland Court, Alsager ST7 2DP    **(T)** 07888 750532

**Capacity:** 3,000 **Seats:** 250   **Covered:** 1,000   **Midweek Matchday:** Tuesday    **Clubhouse:** Yes   **Shop:** Yes

**Colours(change):** White & black/black/black. (All red).
**Previous Names:** Alsager FC (Merger of Alsager Institute & Alsager Utd) in 1965.
**Previous Leagues:** Crewe. Mid Cheshire. Northern Premier.
**Records:** **Att:** 606 v Whitley Bay - 14.11.2009. **Goalscorer:** Gareth Rowe. **Apps:** Wayne Brotherton.
**Senior Honours:** Leek Cup 2002

### 10 YEAR RECORD

| 03-04 | | 04-05 | | 05-06 | | 06-07 | | 07-08 | | 08-09 | | 09-10 | | 10-11 | | 11-12 | | 12-13 | |
|---|---|---|---|---|---|---|---|---|---|---|---|---|---|---|---|---|---|---|---|
| NWC1 | 9 | NWC1 | 7 | NWC1 | 3 | NP1S | 16 | NP1S | 14 | NWCP | 7 | NWCP | 18 | NWCP | 20 | NWCP | 13 | NWCP | 15 |

# ASHTON ATHLETIC

**Founded:** 1968    **Nickname:**

**Secretary:** Alan Greenhalgh    **(T)** 01942 716 360    **(E)**

**Chairman:** Jimmy Whyte    **Manager:** Jay Foulds    **Prog Ed:** Alan Greenhalgh

**Ground:** Brockstedes Park, Downall Green, Ashton in Markerfield WN4 0NR    **(T)** 01942 716 360

**Capacity:** 600   **Seats:** 100   **Covered:** 300   **Midweek Matchday:** Tuesday    **Clubhouse:** Yes

**Colours(change):** All yellow. (All blue).
**Previous Names:** None.
**Previous Leagues:** Lancashire Combination, Manchester Amateur League
**Records:** Att: 165 v Runcorn Linnets 2006-07. Apps: Steve Rothwell - 50+
**Senior Honours:** Atherton Charity Cup 2006-07, 07-08, 08-09.

**10 YEAR RECORD**

| 03-04 | 04-05 | 05-06 | 06-07 | 07-08 | 08-09 | 09-10 | 10-11 | 11-12 | 12-13 |
|---|---|---|---|---|---|---|---|---|---|
| Manc 10 | Manc 10 | Manc 4 | NWC2 16 | NWC2 3 | NWCP 6 | NWCP 21 | NWCP 22 | NWCP 14 | NWCP 20 |

# BACUP & ROSSENDALE BOROUGH

**Founded:** 1878    **Nickname:** The Boro

**Secretary:** Wendy Ennis    **(T)** 01706 878 655    **(E)**

**Chairman:** Frank Manning    **Manager:** Brent Peters    **Prog Ed:** Michael Carr

**Ground:** Brian Boys Stadium, Cowtoot Lane, Blackthorn, Bacup, OL13 8EE    **(T)** 01706 878 655

**Capacity:** 3,000   **Seats:** 500   **Covered:** 1,000   **Midweek Matchday:** Wednesday    **Clubhouse:** Yes

**Colours(change):** White/black/black. (Tangerine/claret/tangerine).
**Previous Names:** Bacup FC. Bacup Borough > 2013.
**Previous Leagues:** Lancashire Combination 1903-82
**Records:** Att: 4,980 v Nelson 1947 Goalscorer: Jimmy Clarke
**Senior Honours:** North West Counties League Division Two 2002-03, Challenge Cup 2003-04.

**10 YEAR RECORD**

| 03-04 | 04-05 | 05-06 | 06-07 | 07-08 | 08-09 | 09-10 | 10-11 | 11-12 | 12-13 |
|---|---|---|---|---|---|---|---|---|---|
| NWC1 14 | NWC1 9 | NWC1 17 | NWC1 15 | NWC1 18 | NWCP 8 | NWCP 12 | NWCP 11 | NWCP 17 | NWCP 17 |

# BARNOLDSWICK TOWN

**Founded:** 1972    **Nickname:**

**Secretary:** Lynn James    **(T)**    **(E)**

**Chairman:** Ian James    **Manager:** Kevin Richardson & Paul Fildes    **Prog Ed:** Peter Naylor

**Ground:** Silentnight Stadium, West Close Road, Barnoldswick, Colne, BB18 5LJ    **(T)** 01282 815 817

**Capacity:**   **Seats:** Yes   **Covered:** Yes   **Midweek Matchday:** Tuesday    **Clubhouse:** Yes

**Colours(change):** Yellow & Royal Blue/royal blue/royal blue socks (All red)
**Previous Names:** Today's club formed after the merger of Barnoldswick United and Barnoldswick Park Rovers in 2003
**Previous Leagues:** Craven, East Lancashire, West Lancashire.
**Records:**
**Senior Honours:** West Lancashire Division 1 1998-99

**10 YEAR RECORD**

| 03-04 | 04-05 | 05-06 | 06-07 | 07-08 | 08-09 | 09-10 | 10-11 | 11-12 | 12-13 |
|---|---|---|---|---|---|---|---|---|---|
| WLaP 12 | WLaP 15 | WLaP 15 | WLaP 13 | WLaP 10 | WLaP 6 | NWC1 2 | NWCP 7 | NWCP 4 | NWCP 9 |

# BOOTLE

**Founded:** 1954    **Nickname:**

**Secretary:** Joe Doran    **(T)** 0151 531 0665    **(E)**

**Chairman:** Frank Doran    **Manager:** Neil Prince    **Prog Ed:** Dave Miley Junior

**Ground:** Delta Taxi Stadium, Vestey Rd, Off Bridle Road, Bootle L30 1NY    **(T)** 0151 525 4796

**Capacity:**   **Seats:**   **Covered:** Yes   **Midweek Matchday:** Tuesday    **Clubhouse:** Yes

**Colours(change):** All blue. (Yellow/black/black).
**Previous Names:** Langton Dock 1953 - 1973.
**Previous Leagues:** Liverpool Shipping. Lancashire Combination. Cheshire. Liverpool County Combination >2006.
**Records:** Att: 1,078 v Everton Reserves, Liverpool Senior Cup Feb 2010.
**Senior Honours:** Liverpool County Champions 1964-65, 65-66, 67-68, 68-69, 69-70, 70-71, 71-72, 72-73, 73-74.
North West Counties Div.1 Champions 2008-09

**10 YEAR RECORD**

| 03-04 | 04-05 | 05-06 | 06-07 | 07-08 | 08-09 | 09-10 | 10-11 | 11-12 | 12-13 |
|---|---|---|---|---|---|---|---|---|---|
| Liv 17 | Liv 12 | Liv 3 | NWC2 10 | NWC2 6 | NWC1 1 | NWCP 3 | NWCP 6 | NWCP 3 | NWCP 3 |

# COLNE
Founded: 1996     Nickname:

**Secretary:** Edward Lambert     **(T)** 01282 862 545     **(E)**
**Chairman:** David Blacklock     **Manager:** Nigel Coates     **Prog Ed:** Ray Davies
**Ground:** The XLCR Stadium, Harrison Drive, Colne, Lancashire. BB8 9SL     **(T)** 01282 862 545
**Capacity:** 1,800  **Seats:** 160  **Covered:** 1,000  **Midweek Matchday:** Tuesday     **Clubhouse:** Yes  **Shop:** Yes

**Colours(change):** All Red. (All sky blue).
**Previous Names:** None
**Previous Leagues:** None
**Records:** Att: 1,742 v AFC Sudbury F.A. Vase SF 2004  **Goalscorer:** Geoff Payton **App:** Richard Walton
**Senior Honours:** BEP Cup Winners 1996-97 North West Counties League Division Two 2003-04.

**10 YEAR RECORD**

| 03-04 | | 04-05 | | 05-06 | | 06-07 | | 07-08 | | 08-09 | | 09-10 | | 10-11 | | 11-12 | | 12-13 | |
|---|---|---|---|---|---|---|---|---|---|---|---|---|---|---|---|---|---|---|---|
| NWC2 | 1 | NWC1 | 10 | NWC1 | 9 | NWC1 | 11 | NWC1 | 5 | NWCP | 18 | NWCP | 8 | NWCP | 5 | NWCP | 8 | NWCP | 8 |

# CONGLETON TOWN
Founded: 1901     Nickname: Bears

**Secretary:** Ken Mead     **(T)** 01260 278 152     **(E)**
**Chairman:** Peter Evans     **Manager:** Jim Vince     **Prog Ed:** Paul Brindley
**Ground:** Ivy Gardens, Booth Street, Crescent Road, Congleton, Cheshire CW12 4DG     **(T)** 01260 274 460
**Capacity:** 5,000  **Seats:** 250  **Covered:** 1,200  **Midweek Matchday:** Tuesday     **Clubhouse:** Yes  **Shop:** Yes

**Colours(change):** Black & white/black/black. (All yellow).
**Previous Names:** Congleton Hornets
**Previous Leagues:** Crew & District, North Staffs, Macclesfield, Cheshire , Mid Cheshire, NW Co, NPL
**Records:** Att: 6,800 v Macclesfield, Cheshire Lge1953-54 **Goalscorer:** Mick Bidde 150+ **App:** Ray Clack 600+ Graham Harrison 600+
**Senior Honours:** Cheshire Senior Cup 1920-21, 37-38.

**10 YEAR RECORD**

| 03-04 | | 04-05 | | 05-06 | | 06-07 | | 07-08 | | 08-09 | | 09-10 | | 10-11 | | 11-12 | | 12-13 | |
|---|---|---|---|---|---|---|---|---|---|---|---|---|---|---|---|---|---|---|---|
| NWC1 | 11 | NWC1 | 19 | NWC1 | 12 | NWC1 | 10 | NWC1 | 9 | NWCP | 4 | NWCP | 5 | NWCP | 8 | NWCP | 11 | NWCP | 7 |

# GLOSSOP NORTH END
Founded: 1886     Nickname: Hillmen

**Secretary:** Stewart Taylor     **(T)**     **(E)**
**Chairman:** David Atkinson     **Manager:** Chris Willcox     Stewart Taylor
**Ground:** Surrey Street, Glossop, Derbys SK13 7AJ     **(T)** 01457 855 469
**Capacity:** 2,374  **Seats:** 209  **Covered:** 509  **Midweek Matchday:** Wednesday     **Clubhouse:** Yes  **Shop:** Yes

**Colours(change):** All blue (Orange/black/orange).
**Previous Names:** Glossop North End1886-1896 and Glossop FC 1898-1992. Reformed in 1992.
**Previous Leagues:** The Football League. Cheshire County. Manchester. Lancashire Comb.
**Records:** Att: 10,736 v Preston North End F.A. Cup 1913-1914
**Senior Honours:** Manchester League 1927-28. Derbyshire Senior Cup 2000-01.

**10 YEAR RECORD**

| 03-04 | | 04-05 | | 05-06 | | 06-07 | | 07-08 | | 08-09 | | 09-10 | | 10-11 | | 11-12 | | 12-13 | |
|---|---|---|---|---|---|---|---|---|---|---|---|---|---|---|---|---|---|---|---|
| NWC1 | 18 | NWC1 | 13 | NWC1 | 16 | NWC1 | 9 | NWC1 | 7 | NWCP | 5 | NWCP | 7 | NWCP | 14 | NWCP | 6 | NWCP | 13 |

# MAINE ROAD
Founded: 1955     Nickname: Blues

**Secretary:** Derek Barber     **(T)** 0161 431 8243     **(E)**
**Chairman:** Ron Meredith     **Manager:** Chris Thomas & John Morrey     **Prog Ed:** Derek Barber
**Ground:** Brantingham Road, Chorlton-cum-Hardy M21 0TT     **(T)** 0161 861 0344
**Capacity:** 2,000  **Seats:** 200  **Covered:** 700  **Midweek Matchday:** Monday     **Clubhouse:** Yes

**Colours(change):** All sky blue. (Red & black stripes/black/black).
**Previous Names:** City Supporters Rusholme 1955-late sixties.
**Previous Leagues:** Rusholme Sunday 1955-66, Manchester Amateur Sunday 1966-72 & Manchester 1972-87.
**Records:** Att: 3,125 v FC United Manchester, NWC Div.1, 04.11.06, at Stalybridge Celtic.
**Senior Honours:** Manchester Premier League 1982-83, 83-84, 84-85, 85-86. North West Counties Division Two 1989-90, Challenge Cup 07-08.

**10 YEAR RECORD**

| 03-04 | | 04-05 | | 05-06 | | 06-07 | | 07-08 | | 08-09 | | 09-10 | | 10-11 | | 11-12 | | 12-13 | |
|---|---|---|---|---|---|---|---|---|---|---|---|---|---|---|---|---|---|---|---|
| NWC2 | 2 | NWC1 | 8 | NWC1 | 10 | NWC1 | 6 | NWC1 | 4 | NWCP | 13 | NWCP | 6 | NWCP | 13 | NWCP | 18 | NWCP | 2 |

## NORTON UNITED
Founded: 1989     Nickname:

**Secretary:** Dennis Vickers          **(T)** 01782 838 290          **(E)**
**Chairman:** Stephen Beaumont     **Manager:** Scott Dundas          **Prog Ed:** Dennis Vickers
**Ground:** Norton CC & MWI Community Drive, Smallthorne, Stoke-on-Trent ST6 1QF     **(T)** 01782 838 290
**Capacity:**     **Seats:**     **Covered:**     **Midweek Matchday:** Tuesday          **Clubhouse:** Yes

**Colours(change):** Red & black/black/black (All yellow)
**Previous Names:** None
**Previous Leagues:** Stafford County Senior. Midland.
**Records:** Att: 1,382 v FC United of Manchester 09/04/2006.
**Senior Honours:** Midland League 1996-97, 98-99, 2000-01. Staffordshire Senior Vase 1998-99, 2003-04.

**10 YEAR RECORD**

| 03-04 | 04-05 | 05-06 | 06-07 | 07-08 | 08-09 | 09-10 | 10-11 | 11-12 | 12-13 |
|---|---|---|---|---|---|---|---|---|---|
| NWC2  15 | NWC2  5 | NWC2  8 | NWC2  17 | NWC2  8 | NWC1  12 | NWC1  3 | NWC1  7 | NWC1  2 | NWCP  14 |

## RUNCORN LINNETS
Founded: 2006     Nickname: Linnets

**Secretary:** Lynn Johnston          **(T)** 01606 43008          **(E)**
**Chairman:** Derek Greenwood     **Manager:** Joey Dunn          **Prog Ed:** Mark Buckley
**Ground:** Millbank Linnets Stadium, Murdishaw Ave, Runcorn, Cheshire WA7 6HP     **(T)** 07050 801733 (Clubline)
**Capacity:**     **Seats:** Yes     **Covered:** Yes     **Midweek Matchday:** Tuesday          **Clubhouse:** Yes

**Colours(change):** Yellow & green hoops/green/yellow & green. (Blue & white/white/blue)
**Previous Names:** None
**Previous Leagues:** None.
**Records:** 1,037 v Witton Albion, pre season friendly July 2010
**Senior Honours:** NWCFL Challenge Cup 2012-13.

**10 YEAR RECORD**

| 03-04 | 04-05 | 05-06 | 06-07 | 07-08 | 08-09 | 09-10 | 10-11 | 11-12 | 12-13 |
|---|---|---|---|---|---|---|---|---|---|
| | | | NWC2  2 | NWC1  12 | NWCP  11 | NWCP  11 | NWCP  12 | NWCP  5 | NWCP  6 |

## RUNCORN TOWN
Founded: 1968     Nickname:

**Secretary:** Martin Fallon          **(T)** 01928 590 508          **(E)**
**Chairman:** Tony Riley     **Manager:** Simon Burton          **Prog Ed:** Alan Bennett
**Ground:** Pavilions Sports Complex, Sandy Lane, Weston Point, Runcorn WA7 4EX     **(T)** 01928 590 508
**Capacity:**     **Seats:** Yes     **Covered:** Yes     **Midweek Matchday:** Monday          **Clubhouse:** Yes

**Colours(change):** Sky & navy/navy/navy (Yellow & black/black/yellow)
**Previous Names:** Mond Rangers 1967-2005 (Amalgamated with ICI Weston 1974-75).
**Previous Leagues:** Runcorn Sunday 1967-73, Warrington & District 1973-84, West Cheshire 1984-10.
**Records:** Att: 665 v Runcorn Linnets, NWCL Premier April 2013.
**Senior Honours:** West Cheshire League Division Two 2006-07. Runcorn Senior Cup 2004-05, 05-06, 07-08.

**10 YEAR RECORD**

| 03-04 | 04-05 | 05-06 | 06-07 | 07-08 | 08-09 | 09-10 | 10-11 | 11-12 | 12-13 |
|---|---|---|---|---|---|---|---|---|---|
| WCh2 | WCh2  2 | WCh1  15 | WCh2  1 | WCh1  3 | WCh1  4 | WCh1  3 | NWC1  2 | NWCP  2 | NWCP  4 |

## SILSDEN
Founded: 1904     Nickname:

**Secretary:** John Barclay          **(T)** 01535 656213          **(E)**
**Chairman:** Sean McNulty     **Manager:** Andy Geary          **Prog Ed:** Peter Hanson
**Ground:** Keighley Road, Keighley Road, Silsden, BD20 0EH     **(T)**
**Capacity:**     **Seats:** Yes     **Covered:** Yes     **Midweek Matchday:** Wednesday          **Clubhouse:** Yes

**Colours(change):** Red/black/red (All yellow).
**Previous Names:** Reformed in 1980.
**Previous Leagues:** Craven & District. West Riding County Amateur.
**Records:** Att:1,564 v FC United of Manchester- March 2007
**Senior Honours:**

**10 YEAR RECORD**

| 03-04 | 04-05 | 05-06 | 06-07 | 07-08 | 08-09 | 09-10 | 10-11 | 11-12 | 12-13 |
|---|---|---|---|---|---|---|---|---|---|
| | NWC2  2 | NWC1  14 | NWC1  14 | NWC1  11 | NWCP  9 | NWCP  14 | NWCP  16 | NWCP  12 | NWCP  18 |

# SQUIRES GATE

Founded: 1948     Nickname:

**Secretary:** John Maguire    **(T)** 01253 348 512    **(E)**

**Chairman:** Stuart Hopwood    **Manager:** Dave McCann    **Prog Ed:** Steve Mclellan & Albert Cooper

**Ground:** School Road, Marton, Blackpool, Lancs FY4 5DS    **(T)** 01253 348 512

**Capacity:** 1,000   **Seats:** 100   **Covered:** Yes   **Midweek Matchday:** Tuesday    **Clubhouse:** Yes

**Colours(change):** All blue. (Red/black/black)
**Previous Names:** Squires Gate British Legion FC >1953.
**Previous Leagues:** Blackpool & District Amateur 1958-61. West Lancashire 1961-91.
**Records:** Att: 600 v Everton, friendly 1995.
**Senior Honours:**

**10 YEAR RECORD**

| 03-04 | 04-05 | 05-06 | 06-07 | 07-08 | 08-09 | 09-10 | 10-11 | 11-12 | 12-13 |
|---|---|---|---|---|---|---|---|---|---|
| NWC1 20 | NWC1 17 | NWC1 13 | NWC1 18 | NWC1 6 | NWCP 10 | NWCP 13 | NWCP 9 | NWCP 16 | NWCP 21 |

# ST HELENS TOWN

Founded: 1946     Nickname: Town

**Secretary:** Jeff Voller    **(T)** 0151 222 2963    **(E)**

**Chairman:** John McKiernan    **Manager:** Ian Granite    **Prog Ed:** Jeff Voller

**Ground:** Ashton Athletic FC, Downall Green, Ashton in Makerfield WN4 0NR    **(T)** 01942 716 360

**Capacity:** 600   **Seats:** 100   **Covered:** 300   **Midweek Matchday:** Tuesday    **Clubhouse:** Yes

**Colours(change):** Red & white/red/red & white. (Sky blue/navy/navy).
**Previous Names:** St Helen's Town formed in 1903 folded in 1923.
**Previous Leagues:** Liverpool Co Comb 1946-49 Lancs Comb 49-75, Chesh Co. 75-82
**Records:** Att: 4,000 v Manchester City 1950. **Goalscorer:** S. Pennington. **App:** Alan Wellens
**Senior Honours:** Lancashire Combination 1971-72 . FA Vase 1986-87.

**10 YEAR RECORD**

| 03-04 | 04-05 | 05-06 | 06-07 | 07-08 | 08-09 | 09-10 | 10-11 | 11-12 | 12-13 |
|---|---|---|---|---|---|---|---|---|---|
| NWC1 19 | NWC1 3 | NWC1 8 | NWC1 19 | NWC1 14 | NWCP 16 | NWCP 9 | NWCP 17 | NWCP 21 | NWCP 19 |

# STOCKPORT SPORTS

Founded: 1970     Nickname: The Saxons

**Secretary:** Chris Culkin    **(T)**    **(E)**

**Chairman:** John Hindley    **Manager:** Darren Finch    **Prog Ed:** Rob Clarke

**Ground:** Stockport Sports Village, Lambeth Grove, Woodley SK6 1QX    **(T)**

**Capacity:** 2,300   **Seats:** 300   **Covered:** Yes   **Midweek Matchday:** Tuesday    **Clubhouse:** Yes

**Colours(change):** All white (All red)
**Previous Names:** Woodley Athletic. Woodley Sports > 2012.
**Previous Leagues:** Lancashire and Cheshire, Manchester, North West Counties
**Records:** 1,500 v Stockport County
**Senior Honours:** North West Counties League Division 2 1999-2000.
Cheshire Senior Cup 2003-04.

**10 YEAR RECORD**

| 03-04 | 04-05 | 05-06 | 06-07 | 07-08 | 08-09 | 09-10 | 10-11 | 11-12 | 12-13 |
|---|---|---|---|---|---|---|---|---|---|
| NWC1 4 | NP 1 11 | NP 1 4 | NP 1 10 | NP1N 17 | NP1N 13 | NP1N 19 | NP1N 11 | NP1N 8 | NWCP 16 |

# WEST DIDSBURY & CHORLTON

Founded: 1908     Nickname: West

**Secretary:** Rob Turley    **(T)** 07891 298 441    **(E)**

**Chairman:** Glyn Meacher    **Manager:** Andy Nelson    **Prog Ed:** John Churchman

**Ground:** The Recreation Ground, End of Brookburn Road, Chorlton, Manchester M21 8FF    **(T)** 07891 298 441

**Capacity:**   **Seats:** Yes   **Covered:** Yes   **Midweek Matchday:** Tuesday    **Clubhouse:** Yes

**Colours(change):** White/black/black (Claret & sky blue or sky blue/Sky blue/sky blue)
**Previous Names:** Christ Church AFC 1908-1920. West Didsbury AFC 1920-2003.
**Previous Leagues:** Manchester Alliance pre 1920. Lancashire & Cheshire Amateur 1920-2006. Manchester 2006-2012.
**Records:** 230 v Altrincham pre-season July 2003.
**Senior Honours:** Manchester League Division One 2010-11. NWCL Division One Trophy 2012-13.

**10 YEAR RECORD**

| 03-04 | 04-05 | 05-06 | 06-07 | 07-08 | 08-09 | 09-10 | 10-11 | 11-12 | 12-13 |
|---|---|---|---|---|---|---|---|---|---|
| | | | | | | | Manc1 1 | MancP 7 | NCE1 3 |

## WIGAN ROBIN PARK

Founded: 2005     Nickname:

**Secretary:** Taffy Roberts    **(T)** 01942 404 950     **(E)**

**Chairman:** Steve Halliwell    **Manager:** John Neafcy     **Prog Ed:** Andrew Vaughan

**Ground:** Robin Park Arena, Loire Drive, Robin Park, Wigan, WN5 0UH    **(T)** 01942 404 950

**Capacity:**    **Seats:** Yes    **Covered:** Yes    **Midweek Matchday:** Tuesday    **Clubhouse:** Yes

**Colours(change):** Red & white/black & red/black & red (Yellow/green/yellow)
**Previous Names:**
**Previous Leagues:** Manchester 2005-08.
**Records:** **Att:** 298 v AFC Liverpool 31/03/09.
**Senior Honours:** Manchester Premier 2007-08. North West Counties Division One 2011-12.
Gilgryst Cup 2007-08.

### 10 YEAR RECORD

| 03-04 | 04-05 | 05-06 | | 06-07 | | 07-08 | | 08-09 | | 09-10 | | 10-11 | | 11-12 | | 12-13 | |
|---|---|---|---|---|---|---|---|---|---|---|---|---|---|---|---|---|---|
| | | Manc1 | 8 | Manc1 | 2 | MancP | 1 | NWC1 | 5 | NWC1 | 12 | NWC1 | 8 | NWC1 | 1 | NWCP | 12 |

## WINSFORD UNITED

Founded: 1883     Nickname: Blues

**Secretary:** Robert Astles    **(T)** 01606 558 447     **(E)**

**Chairman:** Mark Loveless    **Manager:** Lloyd Morrison     **Prog Ed:** Robert Astles

**Ground:** The Barton Stadium, Kingsway, Winsford, Cheshire CW7 3AE    **(T)** 01606 558 447

**Capacity:** 6,000 **Seats:** 250 **Covered:** 5,000 **Midweek Matchday:** Tuesday    **Clubhouse:** Yes **Shop:** Yes

**Colours(change):** All royal blue. (All white).
**Previous Names:** Over Wanderers 1883-1887
**Previous Leagues:** The Combination 1902-04. Cheshire County 1919-40, 47-82. N.P.L. 1987-01
**Records:** **Att:** 8,000 v Witton Albion, 1947. **Goalscorer:** Graham Smith 66 **Apps:** Edward Harrop 400
**Senior Honours:** Cheshire League 1920-21, 76-77. Cheshire Senior Cup 1958-59, 79-80, 92-93.
North West Counties League Division Two 2006-07.

### 10 YEAR RECORD

| 03-04 | | 04-05 | | 05-06 | | 06-07 | | 07-08 | | 08-09 | | 09-10 | | 10-11 | | 11-12 | | 12-13 | |
|---|---|---|---|---|---|---|---|---|---|---|---|---|---|---|---|---|---|---|---|
| NWC2 | 8 | NWC2 | 3 | NWC2 | 4 | NWC2 | 1 | NWC1 | 10 | NWCP | 19 | NWCP | 19 | NWCP | 3 | NWCP | 7 | NWCP | 5 |

# DIVISION ONE

## 1874 NORTHWICH

Founded: 2013    Nickname:

**Secretary:** Vicki England    **(T)**    **(E)**
**Chairman:** Paul Stockton    **Manager:** Ian Street    **Prog Ed:** Andy Dignum
**Ground:** Winsford United FC, Wharton Road, Winsford, Cheshire CW7 3AE    **(T)** 01606 558 447    **Capacity:** 6,000
**Colours(change):** green/black/white (White/white/green)

**ADDITIONAL INFORMATION:**

## AFC DARWEN

Founded: 2009 (reformed)Nickname:

**Secretary:** Sarah Hindle    **(T)**    **(E)**
**Chairman:** Kenny Langford    **Manager:** Kenny Langford    **Prog Ed:** Steve Hart
**Ground:** Anchor Ground, Anchor Road, Darwen, Lancs, BB3 0BB.    **(T)** 01254 776 193
**Colours(change):** All red (All navy)

**ADDITIONAL INFORMATION:** Original club founded in 1875.
**Previous Leagues:** West Lancashire. Football Alliance. Football League. Lancashire Combination. Cheshire League.
**Record Att:** 14,000 v Blackburn Rovers 1882.
**Honours:** Lancashire League 1902. North West Counties League Cup 1983. North West Alliance Cup 1996.

## ASHTON TOWN

Founded: 1962    Nickname:

**Secretary:** Steve Barrett    **(T)** 01942 701 483    **(E)**
**Chairman:** Mark Hayes    **Manager:** John Brownrigg    **Prog Ed:** Ian Promfrett
**Ground:** The AM Property Group Std, Edge Green St, Ashton-in-Makerfield, Wigan, WN4 8SL    **(T)** 01942 701483
**Colours(change):** Red/black/black (White/red/red)

**ADDITIONAL INFORMATION:**
**Record Att:** 1,865 v FC United of Manchester 2007.
**Honours:** Warrington League Guardian Cup.

## ATHERTON COLLIERIES

Founded: 1916    Nickname: The Colts

**Secretary:** Emil Anderson    **(T)**    **(E)**
**Chairman:** Paul Gregory    **Manager:** Steve Pilling    **Prog Ed:** Emil Anderson
**Ground:** Alder Street, Atherton, Greater Manchester. M46 9EY.    **(T)** 07968 548 056
**Colours(change):** Black & white stripes/black/black (All orange)

**ADDITIONAL INFORMATION:**
**Record Att:** 3,300 in Lancashire Combination 1920's.
**Honours:** North West Counties League Division 3 1986-87.

## ATHERTON L.R.

Founded: 1956    Nickname: The Panthers

**Secretary:** Natalie Waldie    **(T)**    **(E)**
**Chairman:** Jane Wilcock    **Manager:** Michael Clegg    **Prog Ed:** Jeff Gorse
**Ground:** Crilly Park, Spa Road, Atherton, Manchester M46 9JX    **(T)** 07873 483 174    3,000
**Colours(change):** Royal blue & yellow/royal blue/yellow. (All white).

**ADDITIONAL INFORMATION: Att:** 2,300 v Aldershot Town F.A. Vase Q-Final replay 93-94. **Goalscorer:** Shaun Parker **App:** Jim Evans
North West Counties League 1992-93, 93-94. Champions Trophy 1992-93, 93-94.

## CHADDERTON

Founded: 1947    Nickname: Chaddy

**Secretary:** David Shepherd    **(T)** 0161 624 9733    **(E)**
**Chairman:** Bob Sopel    **Manager:** Paul Buckley    **Prog Ed:** Bob Sopel
**Ground:** Andrew Street, Chadderton, Oldham, Greater Manchester. OL9 0JT    **(T)** 07506 104 005
**Colours(change):** All red (All orange)

**ADDITIONAL INFORMATION:**
**Record Att:** 2,352 v FC United of Manchester 2006.
**Honours:** Gilgryst Cup 1969-70. Umbro International Cup 1999-00.

## CHEADLE TOWN

Founded: 1961    Nickname:

**Secretary:** Brian Lindon    **(T)** 0161 428 2510    **(E)**
**Chairman:** Chris Davies    **Manager:** Steve Brokenbrow    **Prog Ed:** Stuart Crawford
**Ground:** Park Road Stadium, Cheadle, Cheshire, SK8 2AN    **(T)** 0161 428 2510
**Colours(change):** Green/green/white (White/black/black).

**ADDITIONAL INFORMATION:**
**Record Att:** 3,377 v FC United of Manchester (At Stockport County). **Goalscorer:** Peter Tilley. **Apps:** John McArdle.
**Honours:** Manchester Division One 1979-80.

# DAISY HILL

Founded: 1894          Nickname:

| | | |
|---|---|---|
| **Secretary:** Robert Naylor | **(T)** 01942 818 544 | **(E)** |
| **Chairman:** Graham Follows | **Manager:** Craig Thomas | **Prog Ed:** Robert Naylor |
| **Ground:** New Sirs, St James Street, Westhoughton, Bolton, BL5 2EB | | **(T)** 01942 818 544 |
| **Colours(change):** All royal blue (All red) | | |

**ADDITIONAL INFORMATION:**
Reformed in 1952.
**Record Att:** 2,000 v Horwich RMI, Westhoughton Charity Cup Final 1979-80. **Goalscorer & Apps:** Alan Roscoe 300gls, 450app
**Honours:** Bolton Combination Premier Division 1962-63, 72-73, 75-76, 77-78.

# ECCLESHALL

Founded: 1971          Nickname:

| | | |
|---|---|---|
| **Secretary:** Jim tunney | **(T)** | **(E)** |
| **Chairman:** Andy Mapperson | **Manager:** Dean Sibson | **Prog Ed:** Richard Marsh |
| **Ground:** Pershall Park, Chester Road, Eccleshall, ST21 6NE | | **(T)** 01785 851 351 (MD) |
| **Colours(change):** Blue & black stripes/black/black (All red) | | |

**ADDITIONAL INFORMATION:**
**Record Att:** 2,011 v FC United of Manchester November 2005.
**Honours:** Midland League 1990, 2002-03.

# FORMBY

Founded: 1919          Nickname: Squirrels

| | | |
|---|---|---|
| **Secretary:** Adrian Cook | **(T)** | **(E)** |
| **Chairman:** Frank Smith | **Manager:** Jim Shirley & Kvin Dally | **Prog Ed:** Adrian Cork |
| **Ground:** Burscough FC, Victoria Park, Bobby Langton Way, Mart Lane L40 0SD | | **(T)** 01695 722 123 |
| **Colours(change):** All yellow (All navy) | | |

**ADDITIONAL INFORMATION:**
**Previous Lge:** Liverpool Co. Comb. 1919-68, Lancs Comb. 68-71, Cheshire Co. 71-82.
**Record Att:** At Brows Lane - 2,500 v Oldham Ath. FA Cup 1973. At Altar Road - 603 v Southport Liverpool Senior Cup 2003-04.
**Honours:** NWCL Division One 2012-13.

# HANLEY TOWN

Founded: 1966          Nickname:

| | | |
|---|---|---|
| **Secretary:** Ian Evans | **(T)** | **(E)** |
| **Chairman:** Paul Legge | **Manager:** Dave Price | **Prog Ed:** Andy Drakely |
| **Ground:** Abbey Lane, Bucknall, Stoke-on-Trent, Staffordshire ST2 9AJ | | **(T)** |
| **Colours(change):** All blue (Red & white or black & white or all black) | | |

**ADDITIONAL INFORMATION:**
**Previous Leagues:** Staffordshire County Senior.
**Record: Att:** 1,000.
Honours: Staffordshire County Senior League 2012-13.

# HOLKER OLD BOYS

Founded: 1936          Nickname: Cobs

| | | |
|---|---|---|
| **Secretary:** John Adams | **(T)** 01229 828 176 | **(E)** |
| **Chairman:** Dick John | **Manager:** Dave Smith | **Prog Ed:** Dick John |
| **Ground:** Rakesmoor, Rakesmoor Lane, Hawcoat, Barrow-in-Furness, LA14 4QB | | **(T)** 01229 828 176 |
| **Colours(change):** Green & white/green/green & white (All blue) | | |

**ADDITIONAL INFORMATION:**
**Record Att:** 2,303 v FC United of Manchester FA Cup at Craven Park 2005-06. **Goalscorer:** Dave Conlin.
**Honours:** West Lancashire League 1986-87.

# IRLAM

Founded: 1969          Nickname:

| | | |
|---|---|---|
| **Secretary:** Warren Dodd | **(T)** 07718 756402/07969 946277 | **(E)** |
| **Chairman:** Ron Parker | **Manager:** Steve Nixon | **Prog Ed:** Warren Dodd |
| **Ground:** Silver Street, Irlam, Manchester M44 6HR | | **(T)** 07718756402~07969946277 |
| **Colours(change):** Blue & white/blue/blue (Red/black/black) | | |

**ADDITIONAL INFORMATION:**
**Previous Name:** Mitchell Shackleton. **Previous League:** Manchester Amateur. Manchester.
**Record Att:** 1,600 v Hallam FA Vase.

# LEEK C.S.O.B.

Founded: 1945          Nickname:

| | | |
|---|---|---|
| **Secretary:** Tony Strickson | **(T)** | **(E)** |
| **Chairman:** John Powell | **Manager:** Brett Barlow & Jamie Cullerton | **Prog Ed:** Stan Lockett |
| **Ground:** Leek Town FC, Harrison Park, Macclesfield Road, Leek, Staffs. ST13 8LD | | **(T)** 01538 383 734 |
| **Colours(change):** Red & white stripes/red/red & white hoops (Blue/blue/blue & white hoops) | | |

**ADDITIONAL INFORMATION:**
**Record Att:** 2,590 v FC United of Manchester August 2005.
**Honours:** Midland League 1995-96.

## NELSON
Founded: 1883    Nickname: Blues

**Secretary:** Rauf Abdul Khan    **(T)**    **(E)**
**Chairman:** Fayyaz Ahmed    **Manager:** Mark Fell    **Prog Ed:** Alan Maidment
**Ground:** Little Wembley, Lomeshaye Way, Nelson, Lancs BB9 7BN.    **(T)** 01282 787 752    **Capacity:** 1500
**Colours(change):** All royal blue. (Sky blue & white stripes/white/white).

**ADDITIONAL INFORMATION: Att:** 14,143 v Bradford Park Avenue, Div.3 North, 10.04.26.
**Honours:** Football League Division Three North 1922-23. **Previous Lge:** Lancashire 1889-98,1900-01. Football Lge 1898-1900.
Lancashire Combination 1901-16,46-82. NWC 1982-88. West Lancashire 1988-92.

## NORTHWICH FLIXTON VILLA
Founded: 2005    Nickname:

**Secretary:** Ray Small    **(T)**    **(E)**
**Chairman:** Robert Millington    **Manager:** Wale Ajet    **Prog Ed:** Noel McCourt
**Ground:** Valley Road, Flixton Manchester M41 8RQ    **(T)** 0161 748 2903
**Colours(change):** Green & white/white/green (Yellow/blue/blue).

**ADDITIONAL INFORMATION: Previous Name:** Northwich Villa 2005-13.
**Previous Lge:** Cheshire 2005-11.
**Record Att:** 146 v Northwich Victoria 2009.
**Honours:** Cheshire League Division One 2008-09, Division One Cup 2009-10.

## OLDHAM BORO
Founded: 1964    Nickname:

**Secretary:** Billy O'Neill    **(T)**    **(E)**
**Chairman:** Mark Kilgannon    **Manager:** Tony Mills
**Ground:** Atherton Collieries FC, Alder Street, Atherton M46 9EY    **(T)**
**Colours(change):** Blue/black/white (Cream/royal blue/royal blue)

**ADDITIONAL INFORMATION:**
**Record Att:** 1,767 v FC United of Manchester 2006.
**Honours:** North West Counties Division Two 1997-98.

## ROCHDALE TOWN
Founded: 1924    Nickname:

**Secretary:** Deborah Hibbert    **(T)** 01706 527103    **(E)**
**Chairman:** Mark Canning    **Manager:** Mark Canning    **Prog Ed:** Chris Morgan
**Ground:** Mayfield Sports Centre, Keswick Street, Castleton, Rochdale. OL11 3AG    **(T)** 01706 527 103
**Colours(change):** Black & white stripes/black/black (Blue/white/blue).

**ADDITIONAL INFORMATION:**
**Record Att:** 2,473 v FC United of Manchester (at Radcliffe Borough).
**Honours:** Manchester Division One 1986-87.

## WIDNES VIKINGS
Founded: 2003    Nickname:

**Secretary:** Bill Morley    **(T)**    **(E)**
**Chairman:** Chris Blackett    **Manager:** Steve Hill    **Prog Ed:** Richard Smales
**Ground:** Select Security Stadium, Lower House Lane, Widnes, Cheshire WA8 7DZ    **(T)** 0151 510 6000
**Colours(change):** White/black/white (Royal blue/navy blue/royal blue)

**ADDITIONAL INFORMATION:**
**Previous Leagues:** West Cheshire League.

# GROUND DIRECTIONS

**ABBEY HEY-The Abbey Stadium, Goredale Avenue, Gorton, Manchester M18 7HD. 0161 231 7147**
M60 to junction 24, take A57 to Manchester City Centre for approx 1 mile, at first set of major traffic lights (MacDonalds on right) pass through for approx 300yards, turn left immediatley before overhead railway bridge (A.H.F.C. sign) into Woodland Avenue. Take first right, pass under railway bridge, turn first left into Goredale Avenue.
**AFC BLACKPOOL-Mechanics Ground, Jepson Way, Common Edge Road, Blackpool, Lancashire FY4 5DY. 01253 761721**
M6 to M55, exit at junction 4. At roundabout turn left along A583 to traffic lights, turn right into Whitehill Road, to traffic lights (2 miles). Go straight across the main road into Jepson Way, ground at top.
**AFC LIVERPOOL-Valerie Park, Eaton Street, Prescot, Merseyside, L34 6ND. 0151 430 0507**
From North: M6 to Junction 26, onto M58 to Junction 3. Follow A570 to junction with A580 (East Lancs Road). (Approach junction in right hand lane of the two lanes going straight on). Cross A580 and take first road on right (Bleak Hill Road). Follow this road through to Prescot (2 miles). At traffic lights turn right, straight on at large roundabout (do not follow route onto Prescot by-pass) and right at next lights. 100 yards turn right at Hope and Anchor pub into Hope Street. Club will be in sight at bottom of road. From South: M6 to Junction 21a (M62 junction 10). Follow M62 towards Liverpool, to junction 7. Follow A57 to Rainhill and Prescot. Through traffic lights at Fusilier pub, 100 yards turn right at Hope and Anchor pub (as above). From East: Follow M62 as described in 'From South' or A580 East Lancs Road to Junction with A570 (Rainford by-pass), turn left and take first right. Follow route as 'From North'
**ALSAGER TOWN-The Town Ground, Woodland Court, Alsager, Staffs, ST7 2DP 01270 882336**
M6 to Junction16, A500 towards Stoke, leave A500 at 2nd exit (A34 to Congleton) at 2nd set of traffic lights on A34 turn left for Alsager, turn right opposite Caradon/Twyfords Factory (500 Yards), into Moorhouse Ave, West Grove mile on right. No available parking within the ground.

# NORTH WEST COUNTIES LEAGUE - STEP 5/6

**ASHTON ATHLETIC-Brocstedes Park, Downall Green, Ashton in Makerfield. WN4 0NR. 01942 716360**
M6 northbound to junction 25, follow the slip road to the island and turn right A49, proceed for approx 0.50 mile turning right into Soughers Lane. At the T junction turn right into Downall Green Road and go over the motorway bridge passing a church on your right. Turn 2nd right into Booths Brow Road and turn 2nd right again into Brocstedes Road which is a narrow street. After 200 yards turn right down a shale road into the car park and ground.
From The North: M6 southbound to junction 24, proceed on to the slip road keeping in the right hand lane, turn right go over the motorway bridge and immediately re-enter the M6 Northbound for approximately 100 yards. Leave at junction 25,Follow the slip road to the island and turn right A49, proceed for approx 0.50 mile turning right into Soughers Lane. At the T junction turn right into Downall Green Road and go over the motorway bridge passing a church on your right. Turn 2nd right into Booths Brow Road and turn 2nd right again into Brocstedes Road which is a narrow street. After 200 yards turn right down a shale road into the car park and ground.

**BACUP BOROUGH-Brian Boys Stadium, Cowtoot Lane, Blackthorn, Bacup, Lancashire. OL13 8EE. 01706 878655**
From M62, take M66 onto A681, through Rawtenstall to Bacup Town Centre, turn left onto the A671 towards Burnley, after approx. 300 yards turn right immediately before the Irwell Inn climbing Cooper Street, turn right into Blackthorn Lane, then first left into Cowtoot Lane to ground.

**BARNOLDSWICK TOWN-Silentnight Stadium, West Close Road, Barnoldswick, Colne, BB18 5EW. 01282 815817**
ravelling from Blackburn to Colne on M65 to end, straight on at roundabout onto Vivary Way onto North Valley Road. Through two sets of traffic lights to roundabout, turn left to Barnoldswick. Straight on till you come to roundabout in Kelbrook turn left to Barnoldswick.On entering Barnoldswick straight ahead at traffic lights, straight ahead at mini roundabout. Travel through built up area past Fosters Arms pub on left set back. Take first right onto Greenberfield Lane, travel 50 yards take middle single track (signposted) travel to bottom of track and bare right to car park at rear of ground.
Travelling from Barrow on A59 from Gisburn towards Skipton turn right at Barnoldswick signpost. Travel approx 2 miles taking 1st left onto Greenberfield Lane, travel 50 yards take middle single track (signposted) travel to bottom of track bare right to car park at rear of ground. If using a SatNav use postcode BB18 5LJ.

**BOOTLE-Delta Taxi Stadium, Vestey Road, off Bridle Road, Bootle, L30 4UN. 0151 525 4796 or 07852 742790**
At Liverpool end of M57and M58 follow signs for Liverpool (A59 (S)), for 1 1/2 miles. At Aintree racecourse on left and Aintree Train Station on right ,turn right at lights into Park Lane. Turn left at second set of lights into Bridle Road. After 200 yards turn left at lights into Vestey Estate , ground 200 yards.

**COLNE-The XLCR Stadium, Harrison Drive, Colne, Lancashire. BB8 9SL. 01282 862545**
Follow M65 to end of motorway. Turn left and follow signs for Skipton and Keighley, continue to roundabout, take 1st left up Harrison Drive, across small roundabout, follow road to ground.

**CONGLETON TOWN-Booth Street, off Crescent Road, Congleton, Cheshire, CW12 4DG. 01260 274460**
On approach to Congleton from M6, past Waggon & Horses Pub, at 1st roundabout 2nd exit, past fire station, 2nd right into Booth Street. Ground at top of road.

**GLOSSOP NORTH END-Surrey Street, Glossop, Derbyshire. SK13 7AJ. 01457 855469**
A57 to Glossop, turn left at traffic lights (near Tesco sign), Glossopbrook Road. Follow road to top of hill. Ground on right.

**MAINE ROAD-Brantingham Road, Chorlton-cum-Hardy, Manchester. M21 0TT. 0161 861 0344**
M60 to junction 7, A56 towards Manchester. At traffic island follow signs for Manchester United, Lancs CC, turn right at next set of traffic lights signposted A5145 (Chorlton-cum-Hardy/Stockport), through next set of traffic lights. Take left fork at Y junction (traffic lights) onto A6010 (Wilbraham Road) to Chorlton. Through traffic lights (ignore pedestrian lights) for approx 1 mile. Left at next traffic lights into Withington Road, first left into Brantingham Road. Ground 300 yards on left. From North: M60 clockwise to junction 5 onto A5103 towards Manchester Centre for approx 2 miles, turn left at traffic lights (Wilbraham Road) A6010, then right at 2nd set of lights (Withington Road), first left into Brantingham Road. Ground 300 yards on left.

**NORTON UNITED-Norton CC & MWI-Community Drive, Smallthorne, Stoke-on-Trent ST6 1QF. 01782 838290**
M6 to junction 16, A500 to Burslem/Tunstall, turn off bear right at traffic island to Burslem, through lights to Smallthorne, take 3rd exit on mini-roundabout, turn right by pedestrian crossing into Community Drive, ground 200 metres on left.

**RUNCORN LINNETS-Millbank Linnets Stadium, Murdishaw Ave, Runcorn, Cheshire. WA7 6HP. 07050 801733 (Clubline)**
orth East-M56 junction 12 take A557 Widnes/Northwich. At Roundabout take 1st Exit onto A557 heading Frodsham A56, go through 1 roundabout. Turn left at Chester Rd/A56, turn left at Chester Rd/A533. At the r'about, take the 2nd exit onto Murdishaw Ave. Destination on the Right. Head West on M56 towards Exit 11. At junction 11, take the A56 exit to Preston Brook/Daresbury. At the roundabout take the 1st exit onto Chester Rd/A56 heading to Preston Brook/Daresbury. Continue to follow Chester Rd, go through 2 roundabouts.At the roundabout take the 2nd exit onto Murdishaw Ave. Destination on the right.

**RUNCORN TOWN-Pavilions Sports Complex, Sandy Lane, Weston Point, Runcorn, Cheshire WA7 4EX. 01928 590 508**
M56 J12. Head towards Liverpool. Come off at 4th exit (Runcorn Docks), turn left at the top of slip road, left at T-Junction, then left into Pavilions. M62 J7. Head towards Runcorn. When crossing Runcorn Bridge, stay in the right hand lane. Follow road around and come off at second exit (Runcorn Docks). Turn right at the top of slip road, left at T-Junction, then left into Pavilions.

**SILSDEN-Keighley Road, Silsden, BD20 0EH**
A629 Skipton to Keighley road, take A6034, ground in on the left after the golf driving range.

**SQUIRES GATE-School Road, Marton, Blackpool, FY4 5DS. 01253 798583**
From M55: At the end of the M55 (J4), continue along dual carriageway (A5230), and bear left at major roundabout, staying on A5230. At second traffic lights, turn left onto B5261. After passing Shovels pub on left, turn left at lights, and first car park is on left after approx 50 yards. Parking is also available down the lane leading to the Club, on your left, after another 40 yards. If both these are full, parking is also available on the Shovels car park, or on the car park adjacent to the playing fields (turn right at the lights after passing the pub).

**ST HELENS TOWN - Ashton Athletic FC, Downall Green, Ashton in Makerfield WN4 0NR. 01942 716 360**
From South: M6 to junction 25, turn right onto A49, after 1/2 mile turn right into Soughers Lane, at T junction turn right into Downall Green Road, pass over M6 and turn 2nd right into Boothbrow Road, turn 2nd right in Brocstedes Road.

**STOCKPORT SPORTS-Lambeth Grove, Woodley, Stockport, Cheshire SK6 1QX**
Take exit 25 toward BREDBURY. At the roundabout, take the 2nd exit onto Ashton Rd (A560). Turn slight left-Continue on A560. Turn right at Lower Bents Lane. Continue on School Brow (B6104). Turn slight left at Stockport Rd (B6104). Turn right at Green Lane.

**WEST DIDSBURY & CHORLTON-The Recreation Ground, End of Brookburn Road, Chorlton, Manchester M21 8FF-07891 298441**
From the M60 take junction 5 onto Princess Road towards city centre. Turn left at Christie Fields offices/Premier Inn onto Barlow Moor Road and continue past Chorlton Park to Chorlton bus station. Turn left into Beech Road, then 2nd left into Reynard Road and continue past the Chorltonville sign passing over 5 speed ramps as far as Brookburn Primary School. Turn left into Brookburn Road and continue to the end of the cul de sac, through the gateway and down the tarmac access which leads into the ground. From Stretford follow Edge Lane and turn right into St Clements Road at church. Continue through Chorlton Green and pass graveyard on left and then Bowling Green PH. Go past school and turn immediately right and continue to end of Brookburn Road as above. There is car parking within the grounds of the club, but restricted access for coaches.

*Premier Division continued...*

**WIGAN ROBIN PARK-Robin Park Arena, Loire Drive, Robin Park, Wigan, WN5 0UH. 01942 404 950**
M6 J25 take road into Wigan and follow signs for the DW Stadium (Wigan Athletic) Ground is next to stadium, behind Wickes DIY store on the retail park.

**WINSFORD UNITED-The Barton Stadium, Kingsway, Winsford, Cheshire. CW7 3AE. 01606 558447**
From M6 junction 18, follow A54 through Middlewich for approx 3 miles, bear right at roundabout at Winsford Railway Station, follow road for approx 1 mile, turn right into Kingsway, ground is on the right.

# DIVISION ONE

**1874 NORTHWICH - The Barton Stadium, Kingsway, Winsford, Cheshire. CW7 3AE. 01606 558447**
From M6 junction 18, follow A54 through Middlewich for approx 3 miles, bear right at roundabout at Winsford Railway Station, follow road for approx 1 mile, turn right into Kingsway, ground is on the right.

**AFC DARWEN-Anchor Ground, Anchor Road, Darwen, Lancs, BB3 0BB. 07989-744584**
Leave M65 at Junction 4. At traffic lights turn left onto A666 (signposted Darwen). After approx ? mile turn left between Anchor Car Sales and the Anchor Pub. Bare right and ground 200 yards on left.

**ASHTON TOWN-Edge Green Street, Ashton-in-Makerfield, Wigan, Greater Manchester. WN4 8SL. 01942 701483**
M6 to Junction 23, A49 to Ashton-in-Makerfield. Turn right at the traffic lights onto the A58 towards Bolton. After approx. three quarters of a mile, turn right into Golbourne Road. After 200 yards turn right into Edge Green Street. Ground at bottom of street.

**ATHERTON COLLIERIES-Alder Street, Atherton, Greater Manchester. M46 9EY. 07968 548056**
M61 to junction 5, follow sign for Westhoughton, turn left onto A6, turn right onto A579 (Newbrook Road/Bolton Road) into Atherton. At first set of traffic lights turn left into High Street, then second left into Alder Street to ground.

**ATHERTON L.R.-Crilly Park, Spa Road, Atherton, Greater Manchester. M46 9XG. 01942 883950**
M61 to junction 5, follow signs for Westhoughton, turn left onto A6, turn right at first lights into Newbrook Road, then turn right into Upton Road, passing Atherton Central Station. Turn left into Springfield Road and left again into Hillside Road into Spa Road and ground.

**CHADDERTON-Andrew Street, Chadderton, Oldham, Greater Manchester OL9 0JT. 0161 624 9733**
M62 to junction 20, following A627(M) towards Manchester. Motorway becomes a dual carriageway, turn left at first major traffic lights (A699) Middleton Road, then second left into Burnley Street, Andrew Street at the end.

**CHEADLE TOWN-Park Road Stadium, Cheadle, Cheshire, SK8 2AN. 0161 428 2510**
M60 to junction 2 (formerly M63 junction 11), follow A560 to Cheadle. Go through first main set of traffic lights and then first left after shops into Park Road. Ground at end of road.

**DAISY HILL-New Sirs, St James Street, Westhoughton, Bolton, BL5 2EB. 01942 818 544.**
M61 to junction 5, A58 (Snydale Way/Park Road) for one and a half mile, left into Leigh Road (B5235) for 1 mile to Daisy Hill. Turn right into village 200 yards after mini roundabout, then left between church and school into St James Street. Ground 250 yards on left.

**ECCLESHALL-Pershall Park, Chester Road, Eccleshall, ST21 6NE. 01785-851351 (Match Days Only)**
M6 to junction 14 then A5013 to Eccleshall, right at mini-roundabout and then left at next mini-roundabout into High Street B5026, ground 1 mile on right.
M6 to junction 15, then A519 to Eccleshall right at mini-roundabout to High Street B5026, ground 1 mile on right.

**FORMBY - Burscough FC, Victoria Park, Bobby Langton Way, Mart Lane L40 0SD. 01695 722 123**
M6 to J27. Follow signs for 'Parbold' (A5209), carry on through Newburgh into Burscough passing Briars Hall Hotel on left. Turn right at second mini-roundabout into Junction Lane (signposted 'Burscough & Martin Mere') into village, over canal. Take second left into Mart Lane to ground at end.

**HANLEY TOWN - Abbey Lane, Bucknall, Stoke-on-Trent, Staffordshire ST2 8AJ.**

**HOLKER OLD BOYS-Rakesmoor, Rakesmoor Lane, Hawcoat, Barrow-in-Furness, Cumbria. LA14 4QB. 01229 828176**
M6 to junction 36. Take the A590 all the way to Barrow-in-Furness. At the borough boundary continue along the A590. After 1? miles you will pass the Kimberley Clark paper mill on your right. Immediately after passing the paper mill turn left into Bank Lane, signposted "Barrow Golf Club" on the left hand side of the A590 and "Hawcoat yard" on the right hand side of the A590. Follow this road to the T- junction at the top of the hill outside the Golf Club. Turn left here into Rakesmoor Lane the ground is 200 yds. down the road on the right. *Please be advised that Rakesmoor Lane beyond the ground is a single-track road and as such is unsuitable for coaches. It is not possible to turn a coach into the ground when approaching from that direction.*

**IRLAM-Irlam Football Club, Silver Street, Irlam, Manchester M44 6HR. 07718 756402/07969 946277**
From Peel Green Roundabout (M60 Junction 11), take A57 to Irlam, and then B5320 into Lower Irlam. After passing Morsons Project, turn right into Silver Street, at Nags Head Pub. The ground is situated at the bottom of Silver Street on the right hand side.

**LEEK C.S.O.B.-Harrison Park, Macclesfield Road, Leek, Staffs. ST13 8LD (Leek Town FC). 01538 383 734.**
M6 to junction 17-A534 to Congleton-follow signs for Leek (A54)-carry on A54 until junction with A523-turn right onto A523-this is road direct to Leek and ground (8 miles)-ground on right just into Leek (Macclesfield Road).

**NELSON-Victoria Park, Lomeshaye Way, Nelson, Lancs BB9 7BN. 01282 613 820**
M65 to Junction 13. Take first left (A6068 Fence), 2nd left (B6249 Nelson), the 2nd right, signposted Lomeshaye Village, to ground.

**NORTHWICH VILLA-Valley Road, Flixton, Manchester M41 8RQ-0161 748 2903**
Leave M60 junction 10, take the B5214, signposted Urmston, at the second roundabout take third exit, take right only lane on the exit in Davyhulme Road, follow this road to Valley Road, just after the left hand bend after 1 1/2 miles. The ground is at the other end of the road.

**OLDHAM BORO - Atherton Collieries FC, Alder Street, Atherton M46 9EY**
See Atherton Collieries above.

**ROCHDALE TOWN - Mayfield Sports Centre, Keswick Street, Castleton, Rochdale. OL11 3AG. 01706 527 103**
M62 to junction 20, follow A627M towards Rochdale. Keep right on A627M and turn right at traffic lights at BMW Garage go to next roundabout, take 2nd exit into Queensway towards Castleton and through the Industrial Estate. Turn Right at traffic lights into Manchester Road, A664. Go past Castleton Rail station and turn left at Fairwell Inn, into Keswick St, go through new housing estate to ground --- Rochdale Town FC ground is next to Castlehawk Golf Club.

**WIDNES VIKINGS - Select Security Stadium, Lower House Lane, Widnes, Cheshire WA8 7DZ. 0151 510 6000**
From the M62 - Exit at Junction 7, take A568 dual carriageway towards Widnes (Following brown signs to Halton Stadium). Keep right after junction onto Ashley Way (A562). Take 2nd exit off roundabout (McDonald's on the right). Take 2nd exit off mini-roundabout into Lowerhouse Lane.
From Runcorn & the South: Cross Widnes/Runcorn Bridge (A533). Follow signs to Widnes (A562). At roundabout take 3rd exit towards Widnes Town Centre. Take first left following brown signs to Halton Stadium(McDonald's on the right). Take 2nd exit off mini-roundabout into Lowerhouse Lane.

# NORTHERN COUNTIES EAST LEAGUE

**Sponsored by:** Toolstation
**Founded:** 1982
**Recent Champions:**
2008: Winterton Rangers
2009: Mickleover Sports
2010: Bridlington Town
2011: Farsley
2012: Retford United
ncel.org.uk

## LEAGUE CUP

**PRELIMINARY ROUND**

| | | | |
|---|---|---|---|
| Athersley Recreation | v | Yorkshire Amateur | 3-1 |
| Clipstone | v | Worsbrough Bridge Athletic | 1-3 |

**ROUND 1**

| | | | |
|---|---|---|---|
| Dinnington Town | v | Hemsworth Miners Welfare | 2-1 |
| Knaresborough Town | v | Askern Villa | 6-0 |
| Pontefract Collieries | v | Cleethorpes Town | 3-1 |
| Teversal | v | Rossington Main | 2-1 |
| Appleby Frodingham | v | Ecclesfill United | 2-2 aet 5-4p |
| Bottsford Town | v | Louth Town | 0-1 aet |
| Shirebrook Town | v | Selby Town | 2-1 |
| Athersley Recreation | v | Albion Sports | 2-0 |
| Grimsby Borough | v | Hallam | 4-2 |
| Worsbrough Bridge Ath. | v | AFC Emley | 2-1 |

**ROUND 2**

| | | | |
|---|---|---|---|
| Brighouse Town | v | Tadcaster Albion | 0-2 |
| Glasshoughton Welfare | v | Nostell Miners Welfare | 2-2aet 4-3p |
| Grimsby Borough | v | Armthorpe Welfare | 1-3 |
| Liversedge | v | Scarborough Athletic | 0-2 |
| Parkgate | v | Appleby Frodingham | 5-1 |
| Thackley | v | Pickering Town | 5-1 |
| Worsbrough Bridge Ath. | v | Louth Town | 0-3 |
| Barton Town Old Boys | v | Retford United | 4-2 |
| Lincoln Moorlands Railway | v | Worksop Parramore | 0-1 |
| Maltby Main | v | Winterton Rangers | 2-1 |
| *Maltby removed from the competition Winterton reinstated.* | | | |
| Athersley Recreation | v | Pontefract Collieries | 1-2 aet |
| Dinnington Town | v | Teversal | 3-2 aet |
| Knaresborough Town | v | Shirebrook Town | 1-3 |
| Long Eaton United | v | Arnold Town | 3-2 |
| Staveley Miners Welfare | v | Hall Road Rangers | 4-0 |

**ROUND 3**

| | | | |
|---|---|---|---|
| Shirebrook Town | v | Staveley Miners Welfare | 3-1 |
| *Shirebrook removed from the competition Staveley MW reinstated.* | | | |
| Thackley | v | Barton Town Old Boys | 2-0 |
| Worksop Parramore | v | Bridlington Town | 2-1 |
| Wintertn Rangers | v | Tadcaster Albion | 1-4 |
| Louth Town | v | Pontefract Collieries | 3-2 |
| Armthorpe Welfare | v | Parkgate | 4-6 |
| Nostell Miners Welfare | v | Dinnington Town | 3-2 |
| Long Eaton United | v | Scarborough Athletic | 0-1 |

**QUARTER FINALS**

| | | | |
|---|---|---|---|
| Louth Town | v | Staveley Miners Welfare | 2-0 |
| Tadcaster Albion | v | Nostell Miners Welfare | 0-1 |
| Worksop Parramore | v | Parkgate | 2-0 |
| Thackley | v | Scarborough Athletic | 6-0 |

**SEMI FINALS**

| | | | |
|---|---|---|---|
| Nostell Miners Welfare | v | Louth Town | 3-3 aet 3-4p |
| Thackley | v | Worksop Parramore | 2-0 |

**FINAL**

| | | | |
|---|---|---|---|
| Louth Town | v | Thackley | 1-3 |

## PREMIER DIVISION

| | | P | W | D | L | F | A | Pts |
|---|---|---|---|---|---|---|---|---|
| 1 | (P) Scarborough Athletic | 42 | 30 | 9 | 3 | 129 | 49 | 99 |
| 2 | Brighouse Town | 42 | 30 | 7 | 5 | 106 | 46 | 97 |
| 3 | Bridlington Town | 42 | 30 | 5 | 7 | 137 | 54 | 95 |
| 4 | Retford United | 42 | 24 | 6 | 12 | 78 | 52 | 78 |
| 5 | Pickering Town | 42 | 24 | 5 | 13 | 89 | 49 | 77 |
| 6 | Tadcaster Albion | 42 | 23 | 8 | 11 | 84 | 60 | 77 |
| 7 | Worksop Parramore | 42 | 21 | 9 | 12 | 98 | 78 | 72 |
| 8 | Barton Town Old Boys | 42 | 19 | 12 | 11 | 81 | 68 | 69 |
| 9 | Parkgate | 42 | 20 | 6 | 16 | 87 | 67 | 66 |
| 10 | Thackley | 42 | 17 | 11 | 14 | 77 | 66 | 62 |
| 11 | Heanor Town | 42 | 18 | 4 | 20 | 84 | 84 | 58 |
| 12 | Long Eaton United | 42 | 16 | 9 | 17 | 80 | 84 | 57 |
| 13 | Staveley Miners Welfare | 42 | 15 | 9 | 18 | 71 | 84 | 54 |
| 14 | Maltby Main | 42 | 14 | 6 | 22 | 60 | 73 | 48 |
| 15 | Liversedge | 42 | 11 | 12 | 19 | 68 | 81 | 45 |
| 16 | Glasshoughton Welfare (-1) | 42 | 12 | 10 | 20 | 62 | 84 | 45 |
| 17 | Nostell Miners Welfare | 42 | 10 | 8 | 24 | 51 | 102 | 38 |
| 18 | Winterton Rangers | 42 | 9 | 7 | 26 | 48 | 82 | 34 |
| 19 | Arnold Town (-13) | 42 | 14 | 3 | 25 | 65 | 93 | 32 |
| 20 | Armthorpe Welfare | 42 | 8 | 8 | 26 | 68 | 111 | 32 |
| 21 | Lincoln Moorlands Railway | 42 | 7 | 7 | 28 | 42 | 136 | 28 |
| 22 | (R) Hall Road Rangers | 42 | 7 | 5 | 30 | 52 | 114 | 26 |

| PREMIER DIVISION | 1 | 2 | 3 | 4 | 5 | 6 | 7 | 8 | 9 | 10 | 11 | 12 | 13 | 14 | 15 | 16 | 17 | 18 | 19 | 20 | 21 | 22 |
|---|---|---|---|---|---|---|---|---|---|---|---|---|---|---|---|---|---|---|---|---|---|---|
| 1 Armthorpe Welfare | | 4-0 | 2-3 | 0-3 | 2-5 | 2-1 | 0-4 | 1-7 | 3-3 | 2-1 | 1-2 | 1-2 | 1-1 | 0-2 | 2-2 | 3-2 | 2-3 | 3-3 | 3-3 | 0-2 | 0-0 | 0-3 |
| 2 Arnold Town | 2-1 | | 3-0 | 1-4 | 1-2 | 3-2 | 0-1 | 1-3 | 2-1 | 0-1 | 1-0 | 3-3 | 2-1 | 3-0 | 2-0 | 3-2 | 0-4 | 1-0 | 1-2 | 3-6 | 1-2 | 1-1 | 2-1 | 3-2 |
| 3 Barton Town Old Boys | 6-1 | 2-1 | | 3-2 | 3-3 | 3-1 | 3-1 | 2-0 | 1-2 | 1-1 | 2-2 | 2-0 | 3-0 | 1-1 | 1-0 | 2-2 | 1-1 | 2-2 | 1-4 | 2-3 | 3-0 | 1-2 |
| 4 Bridlington Town | 3-2 | 5-2 | 3-1 | | 2-1 | 1-1 | 4-1 | 4-3 | 9-2 | 1-0 | 2-0 | 1-0 | 11-0 | 4-1 | 4-1 | 4-2 | 3-3 | 3-2 | 1-2 | 4-1 | 5-1 | 2-3 |
| 5 Brighouse Town | 3-1 | 2-1 | 3-1 | 2-1 | | 2-1 | 3-1 | 3-0 | 8-1 | 2-0 | 3-0 | 2-1 | 3-0 | 2-1 | 1-0 | 1-2 | 0-2 | 1-0 | 5-1 | 2-2 | 3-0 | 2-2 |
| 6 Glasshoughton Welfare | 3-2 | 2-2 | 0-3 | 0-1 | 1-1 | | 4-2 | 4-1 | 0-3 | 2-2 | 2-1 | 1-1 | 2-0 | 2-1 | 0-2 | 2-1 | 0-3 | 2-3 | 2-2 | 0-0 | 1-2 |
| 7 Hall Road Rangers | 4-2 | 1-3 | 1-4 | 0-7 | 1-3 | 1-1 | | 0-2 | 6-0 | 2-3 | 4-3 | 2-3 | 0-3 | 3-2 | 0-4 | 1-2 | 1-2 | 0-2 | 0-3 | 1-4 | 0-0 | 4-4 |
| 8 Heanor Town | 3-2 | 1-2 | 0-1 | 3-5 | 2-3 | 3-0 | 3-0 | | 4-1 | 3-0 | 2-4 | 3-2 | 3-2 | 3-2 | 0-3 | 0-2 | 0-3 | 1-2 | 4-1 | 0-5 | 1-2 | 0-2 |
| 9 Lincoln Moorlands Railway | 1-2 | 2-1 | 2-5 | 0-5 | 1-3 | 0-5 | 1-1 | 0-2 | | 0-2 | 0-2 | 5-2 | 0-3 | 0-4 | 1-1 | 0-3 | 0-10 | 0-2 | 0-2 | 0-6 | 3-1 | 0-1 |
| 10 Liversedge | 1-3 | 3-1 | 1-2 | 1-1 | 0-4 | 2-2 | 1-1 | 4-4 | 0-1 | | 1-2 | 3-2 | 3-0 | 1-1 | 0-2 | 1-1 | 2-2 | 8-1 | 1-2 | 0-1 | 2-4 | 1-2 |
| 11 Long Eaton United | 3-3 | 4-2 | 1-1 | 1-1 | 0-4 | 6-1 | 2-2 | 2-3 | 3-3 | 2-2 | | 2-2 | 1-2 | 2-1 | 0-1 | 0-1 | 1-2 | 0-3 | 2-2 | 2-0 | 2-0 |
| 12 Maltby Main | 2-1 | 2-0 | 0-1 | 1-1 | 1-2 | 0-1 | 3-0 | 4-1 | 0-4 | | 3-0 | 3-1 | 0-1 | 0-2 | 2-2 | 3-1 | 2-3 | 2-0 | 1-0 | 1-2 |
| 13 Nostell Miners Welfare | 1-2 | 3-2 | 1-1 | 1-5 | 1-1 | 2-0 | 2-1 | 0-0 | 2-2 | 2-3 | 2-3 | 0-2 | | 0-3 | 1-1 | 1-1 | 3-4 | 3-0 | 2-1 | 1-3 | 3-1 | 2-1 |
| 14 Parkgate | 2-1 | 3-2 | 1-3 | 1-3 | 5-2 | 2-4 | 2-0 | 3-2 | 2-1 | 4-2 | 3-1 | 4-0 | 6-1 | | 2-0 | 0-2 | 2-4 | 2-3 | 4-2 | 0-2 | 3-0 | 1-5 |
| 15 Pickering Town | 6-2 | 3-1 | 3-1 | 3-1 | 1-1 | 3-0 | 4-1 | 2-2 | 7-2 | 3-0 | 2-4 | 2-0 | 5-0 | 0-4 | | 2-3 | 3-2 | 2-1 | 3-1 | 2-1 | 2-0 | 3-0 |
| 16 Retford United | 3-2 | 2-1 | 1-2 | 0-2 | 1-0 | 2-1 | 4-0 | 3-0 | 1-1 | 1-3 | 3-1 | 3-1 | 2-1 | 1-2 | 1-0 | | 2-3 | 2-0 | 4-1 | 2-1 | 3-1 | 1-2 |
| 17 Scarborough Athletic | 2-2 | 3-1 | 2-1 | 2-1 | 3-3 | 3-1 | 7-0 | 4-0 | 5-0 | 3-3 | 7-1 | 4-0 | 5-0 | 1-0 | 2-1 | 2-0 | | 2-1 | 2-0 | 4-1 | 3-0 | 6-0 |
| 18 Staveley Miners Welfare | 5-4 | 1-0 | 3-0 | 1-5 | 0-2 | 0-2 | 3-0 | 1-1 | 2-2 | 1-2 | 1-1 | 3-1 | 4-0 | 0-4 | 2-1 | 2-2 | 1-2 | | 2-2 | 1-4 | 3-0 | 2-1 |
| 19 Tadcaster Albion | 1-0 | 4-1 | 5-1 | 1-0 | 3-4 | 3-1 | 6-1 | 0-2 | 0-1 | 2-2 | 5-2 | 1-0 | 2-0 | 0-0 | 0-2 | 1-0 | 1-1 | 4-0 | | 1-1 | 2-0 | 2-1 |
| 20 Thackley | 3-0 | 1-2 | 2-2 | 2-5 | 0-3 | 0-2 | 1-2 | 3-0 | 3-2 | 4-0 | 2-1 | 3-1 | 1-1 | 1-0 | 0-1 | 1-5 | 1-1 | 1-1 | | 1-0 | 3-5 |
| 21 Winterton Rangers | 1-3 | 1-2 | 4-1 | 1-4 | 0-3 | 1-3 | 2-0 | 1-6 | 7-0 | 3-1 | 2-1 | 3-4 | 0-0 | 2-0 | 1-4 | 0-1 | 3-0 | 1-1 | 1-1 | | 1-2 |
| 22 Worksop Parramore | 4-0 | 5-4 | 2-2 | 0-3 | 0-3 | 7-0 | 4-2 | 2-4 | 5-0 | 4-1 | 4-3 | 1-1 | 1-1 | 1-1 | 0-2 | 3-2 | 4-4 | 2-2 | 1-2 | 3-0 | 2-2 | |

| DIVISION ONE | P | W | D | L | F | A | Pts |
|---|---|---|---|---|---|---|---|
| 1 (P) Albion Sports | 42 | 28 | 8 | 6 | 121 | 42 | 92 |
| 2 (P) Athersley Recreation | 42 | 25 | 10 | 7 | 101 | 52 | 85 |
| 3 Louth Town | 42 | 24 | 8 | 10 | 91 | 62 | 80 |
| 4 Cleethorpes Town | 42 | 23 | 10 | 9 | 108 | 63 | 79 |
| 5 Pontefract Collieries | 42 | 24 | 6 | 12 | 88 | 50 | 78 |
| 6 Shirebrook Town | 42 | 24 | 5 | 13 | 91 | 64 | 77 |
| 7 AFC Emley | 42 | 23 | 6 | 13 | 111 | 56 | 75 |
| 8 Knaresborough Town | 42 | 22 | 9 | 11 | 81 | 55 | 75 |
| 9 Worsbrough Bridge Athletic | 42 | 21 | 9 | 12 | 89 | 61 | 72 |
| 10 Teversal | 42 | 19 | 8 | 15 | 95 | 66 | 65 |
| 11 Clipstone Welfare | 42 | 16 | 9 | 17 | 70 | 71 | 57 |
| 12 Hallam | 42 | 15 | 11 | 16 | 76 | 72 | 56 |
| 13 Hemsworth Miners Welfare | 42 | 17 | 5 | 20 | 69 | 81 | 56 |
| 14 Eccleshill United | 42 | 15 | 10 | 17 | 79 | 67 | 55 |
| 15 Bottesford Town (-1) | 42 | 14 | 9 | 19 | 77 | 88 | 50 |
| 16 Selby Town | 42 | 14 | 4 | 24 | 66 | 91 | 46 |
| 17 Grimsby Borough | 42 | 13 | 6 | 23 | 54 | 74 | 45 |
| 18 Rossington Main | 42 | 11 | 6 | 25 | 57 | 105 | 39 |
| 19 Dinnington Town | 42 | 10 | 7 | 25 | 58 | 102 | 37 |
| 20 Appleby Frodingham | 42 | 9 | 7 | 26 | 56 | 125 | 34 |
| 21 Yorkshire Amateur | 42 | 8 | 5 | 29 | 55 | 120 | 29 |
| 22 (R) Askern Villa | 42 | 7 | 2 | 33 | 47 | 173 | 23 |

| DIVISION ONE | 1 | 2 | 3 | 4 | 5 | 6 | 7 | 8 | 9 | 10 | 11 | 12 | 13 | 14 | 15 | 16 | 17 | 18 | 19 | 20 | 21 | 22 |
|---|---|---|---|---|---|---|---|---|---|---|---|---|---|---|---|---|---|---|---|---|---|---|
| 1 AFC Emley | | 1-3 | 5-1 | 4-0 | 1-2 | 8-0 | 2-3 | 2-1 | 3-0 | 1-1 | 1-2 | 2-1 | 1-2 | 1-2 | 2-2 | 3-1 | 7-1 | 7-0 | 1-2 | 2-2 | 2-1 | 6-0 |
| 2 Albion Sports | 4-1 | | 5-1 | 9-1 | 1-1 | 1-0 | 4-0 | 1-3 | 6-0 | 2-1 | 1-0 | 5-2 | 5-2 | 2-0 | 1-1 | 1-0 | 1-1 | 3-0 | 3-0 | 2-0 | 5-2 | 4-0 |
| 3 Appleby Frodingham | 1-1 | 0-5 | | 0-0 | 3-2 | 1-3 | 0-6 | 0-2 | 0-8 | 3-2 | 1-4 | 1-3 | 3-3 | 3-1 | 0-1 | 0-6 | 1-2 | 1-3 | 0-2 | 1-5 | 1-3 | 3-0 |
| 4 Askern Villa | 2-5 | 0-4 | 2-4 | | 3-1 | 2-3 | 0-6 | 3-7 | 0-1 | 1-5 | 0-2 | 1-7 | 0-4 | 1-4 | 3-1 | 2-10 | 1-3 | 0-4 | 3-1 | 3-5 | 2-0 | 1-2 |
| 5 Athersley Recreation | 1-0 | 4-4 | 4-1 | 8-1 | | 7-1 | 3-3 | 0-0 | 7-1 | 1-3 | 3-0 | 1-1 | 2-1 | 1-0 | 2-0 | 0-1 | 2-2 | 2-1 | 1-2 | 2-1 | 3-0 | 7-1 |
| 6 Bottesford Town | 2-3 | 0-5 | 4-4 | 7-0 | 2-4 | | 1-1 | 1-2 | 3-1 | 1-4 | 0-1 | 3-1 | 0-2 | 1-1 | 5-1 | 1-1 | 4-1 | 1-2 | 1-3 | 1-3 | 1-0 | 1-1 |
| 7 Cleethorpes Town | 3-3 | 1-1 | 2-1 | 5-1 | 4-0 | 3-2 | | 4-2 | 0-1 | 3-2 | 5-2 | 6-2 | 1-0 | 1-1 | 6-1 | 0-3 | 3-2 | 2-1 | 2-3 | 1-1 | 1-0 | 5-0 |
| 8 Clipstone Welfare | 1-2 | 0-5 | 2-2 | 3-1 | 1-2 | 2-2 | 3-1 | | 1-3 | 1-1 | 0-0 | 3-1 | 2-1 | 2-0 | 2-1 | 0-1 | 0-1 | 2-4 | 1-2 | 0-2 | 3-1 | 3-2 |
| 9 Dinnington Town | 0-5 | 2-3 | 1-1 | 3-1 | 0-3 | 1-1 | 0-6 | 2-2 | | 3-1 | 0-2 | 1-4 | 3-4 | 0-2 | 1-4 | 2-3 | 2-2 | 4-2 | 1-4 | 1-6 | 0-0 | 1-2 |
| 10 Eccleshill United | 1-1 | 1-0 | 4-0 | 5-2 | 3-2 | 1-2 | 1-2 | 2-3 | 4-0 | | 2-4 | 1-1 | 1-2 | 1-3 | 0-1 | 0-1 | 6-1 | 2-5 | 4-3 | 4-3 | 2-0 | 1-2 |
| 11 Grimsby Borough | 1-2 | 2-3 | 0-2 | 4-0 | 1-1 | 3-0 | 0-2 | 1-1 | 3-2 | 0-0 | | 1-0 | 1-3 | 0-2 | 1-2 | 1-1 | 3-4 | 1-2 | 0-4 | 1-0 | 0-2 | 3-2 |
| 12 Hallam | 4-1 | 1-0 | 3-4 | 5-0 | 1-2 | 0-5 | 2-2 | 2-0 | 1-1 | 1-1 | 3-1 | | 0-1 | 0-3 | 1-1 | 2-0 | 2-1 | 0-4 | 2-2 | 1-2 | 0-1 | 1-1 |
| 13 Hemsworth Miners Welfare | 0-1 | 0-0 | 2-3 | 1-5 | 2-2 | 3-1 | 1-1 | 0-2 | 2-4 | 1-0 | 1-0 | 1-3 | | 0-4 | 0-2 | 1-2 | 3-4 | 4-0 | 4-2 | 1-3 | 3-4 | 3-0 |
| 14 Knaresborough Town | 2-1 | 1-0 | 3-1 | 0-1 | 2-2 | 3-0 | 2-2 | 2-0 | 1-0 | 1-1 | 4-1 | 1-3 | 1-1 | | 3-2 | 1-3 | 2-1 | 2-1 | 1-4 | 5-2 | 2-4 | 3-3 |
| 15 Louth Town | 1-2 | 2-1 | 3-1 | 11-0 | 1-2 | 3-3 | 2-1 | 2-1 | 2-0 | 0-0 | 4-3 | 2-2 | 5-1 | 1-0 | | 4-2 | 1-0 | 3-1 | 0-3 | 2-0 | 1-0 | 5-1 |
| 16 Pontefract Collieries | 0-2 | 1-3 | 4-0 | 9-0 | 0-3 | 1-2 | 2-1 | 2-1 | 2-0 | 2-1 | 0-0 | 1-2 | 0-1 | 1-1 | 3-1 | | 4-0 | 2-2 | 4-1 | 2-1 | 1-0 | 0-1 |
| 17 Rossington Main | 0-3 | 1-2 | 1-1 | 1-1 | 0-2 | 0-3 | 1-2 | 1-4 | 1-2 | 1-3 | 3-1 | 4-3 | 1-4 | 0-3 | 0-1 | 3-3 | | 2-0 | 0-4 | 0-5 | 1-3 | 5-2 |
| 18 Selby Town | 0-3 | 0-5 | 0-1 | 2-0 | 0-2 | 2-1 | 1-3 | 1-1 | 1-0 | 1-1 | 1-2 | 0-3 | 1-2 | 2-3 | 3-5 | 2-4 | 1-0 | | 2-0 | 2-1 | 2-3 | 4-1 |
| 19 Shirebrook Town | 3-1 | 0-4 | 4-1 | 5-0 | 1-3 | 3-1 | 3-2 | 2-2 | 2-1 | 1-1 | 1-0 | 1-0 | 2-0 | 0-1 | 2-3 | 1-2 | 0-1 | 4-2 | | 2-2 | 3-2 | 2-1 |
| 20 Teversal | 1-4 | 2-2 | 3-1 | 6-0 | 0-1 | 1-3 | 1-1 | 4-1 | 2-0 | 1-2 | 1-0 | 1-1 | 4-0 | 0-4 | 2-2 | 0-1 | 5-0 | 3-2 | 2-2 | | 4-0 | 4-2 |
| 21 Worsbrough Bridge Athletic | 1-0 | 2-2 | 7-2 | 6-0 | 1-1 | 2-2 | 3-2 | 3-0 | 2-2 | 4-0 | 5-1 | 2-2 | 4-0 | 2-2 | 1-1 | 3-0 | 3-1 | 3-0 | 2-1 | 3-2 | | 2-1 |
| 22 Yorkshire Amateur | 1-8 | 5-3 | 4-1 | 0-3 | 1-2 | 0-2 | 2-3 | 1-3 | 1-3 | 0-3 | 3-1 | 1-2 | 1-2 | 3-2 | 0-3 | 0-2 | 1-2 | 2-3 | 2-2 | 0-4 | 1-2 | 2-2 |

## CLUB MOVEMENTS

**Premier Division - In:** Albion Sports (P). Athersley Recreation (P). Basford United (P - East Midlands Counties).
Garforth Town (R - Northern Premier Division One North).
**Out:** Arnold Town (R for breach of NCE rules - East Midlands Counties). Hall Road Rangers (R).
Scarborough Athletic (P - Northern Premier Div.1 South).
**Division One - In:** Dronfield Town (P - Central Midlands North). Hall Road Rangers (R).
Shaw Lane Aquaforce (P - County Senior League).
**Out:** Albion Sports (P). Athersley Recreation (P). Askern Villa (R - Central Midlands North)

# PREMIER DIVISION

## ALBION SPORTS
Founded: 1974     Nickname: Lions

**Secretary:** Jaj Singh     **(T)**     **(E)** info@albionsports.co.uk
**Chairman:** Kultar Singh     **Manager:** Kulwinder Singh Sandhu     **Prog Ed:** Jaj Singh
**Ground:** Throstle Nest, Newlands, Farsley, Leeds, LS28 5BE.     **(T)** 0113 255 7292
**Capacity:** 3,500 **Seats:** 1,750 **Covered:** 1,750 **Midweek Matchday:** Wednesday     **Clubhouse:** n/a

**Colours(change):** Yellow/royal blue/royal blue (All red)
**Previous Names:**
**Previous Leagues:** West Riding County Amateur > 2011.
**Records:**
**Senior Honours:** NCE Division One 2012-13.

**10 YEAR RECORD**

| 03-04 | 04-05 | 05-06 | 06-07 | 07-08 | 08-09 | 09-10 | 10-11 | 11-12 | 12-13 |
|---|---|---|---|---|---|---|---|---|---|
| | | | | | | | | NCE1   4 | NCE1   1 |

## ARMTHORPE WELFARE
Founded: 1926     Nickname: Wellie

**Secretary:** Craig Trewick     **(T)**     **(E)** armthorpe.welfare@hotmail.co.uk
**Chairman:** Steve Taylor     **Manager:** Brian Johnston     **Prog Ed:** Martin Turner
**Ground:** Welfare Ground, Church Street, Armthorpe, Doncaster DN3 3AG     **(T)** 07775 797 013 (Match days only)
**Capacity:** 2,500 **Seats:** 250 **Covered:** 400 **Midweek Matchday:** Tuesday     **Clubhouse:** No **Shop:** No

**Colours(change):** All royal blue (All red)
**Previous Names:**
**Previous Leagues:** Doncaster Senior
**Records:** **Att:** 2,000 v Doncaster R Charity Match 1985-86. **Goalscorer:** Martin Johnson. **App:** Gary Leighton. **Win:** 10-0. **Defeat:** 1-7
**Senior Honours:** West Riding Challenge Cup 1981-82, 82-83. Northern Counties East Division 1 Central 1984-85.

**10 YEAR RECORD**

| 03-04 | 04-05 | 05-06 | 06-07 | 07-08 | 08-09 | 09-10 | 10-11 | 11-12 | 12-13 |
|---|---|---|---|---|---|---|---|---|---|
| NCEP   14 | NCEP   18 | NCEP   10 | NCEP   13 | NCEP   9 | NCEP   15 | NCEP   3 | NCEP   13 | NCEP   13 | NCEP   20 |

## ATHERSLEY RECREATION
Founded: 1979     Nickname: Penguins

**Secretary:** Peter Goodlad     **(T)**     **(E)** petegoodlad@yahoo.co.uk
**Chairman:** Terence Hunt     **Manager:** Peter Goodlad     **Prog Ed:** Jamie Wallman
**Ground:** Sheerien Park, Ollerton Road, Athersley North, Barnsley, S71 3DP     **(T)** 07910 121 070
**Capacity:** 2,000 **Seats:** 150 **Covered:** 420 **Midweek Matchday:** Tuesday     **Clubhouse:** No **Shop:** Yes

**Colours(change):** Black & white/black & white/black & white (Navy & sky quarters/navy/sky)
**Previous Names:**
**Previous Leagues:** Sheffield & Hallamshire County Senior 1997-2012.
**Records:**
**Senior Honours:** Sheffield & Hallamshire County Senior Division Two 1997-98, Premier Division 1999-2000, 03-04, 04-05, 06-07, 08-09, 11-12

**10 YEAR RECORD**

| 03-04 | 04-05 | 05-06 | 06-07 | 07-08 | 08-09 | 09-10 | 10-11 | 11-12 | 12-13 |
|---|---|---|---|---|---|---|---|---|---|
| SHSP   1 | SHSP   1 | SHSP   2 | SHSP   1 | SHSP   2 | SHSP   1 | SHSP   2 | SHSP   2 | SHSP   1 | NCE1   2 |

## BARTON TOWN OLD BOYS
Founded: 1995     Nickname: Swans

**Secretary:** Peter Mitchell     **(T)** 01652 635 838     **(E)** bartontown@gmail.com
**Chairman:** Vacant     **Manager:** Dave Anderson     **Prog Ed:** Phil Hastings
**Ground:** The Euronics Ground, Marsh Lane, Barton-on-Humber     **(T)** 01652 661 871
**Capacity:** 3,000 **Seats:** 240 **Covered:** 540 **Midweek Matchday:** Tuesday     **Clubhouse:** Yes **Shop:** No

**Colours(change):** Sky blue & white stripes/black/sky blue (Red & black stripes/white/red)
**Previous Names:**
**Previous Leagues:** Lincolnshire 1995-00, Humber (Founder member) 2000-01, Central Midlands 2001-07.
**Records:**
**Senior Honours:** Lincolnshire League 1996-97. Central Midlands League Supreme Division 2005-06.

**10 YEAR RECORD**

| 03-04 | 04-05 | 05-06 | 06-07 | 07-08 | 08-09 | 09-10 | 10-11 | 11-12 | 12-13 |
|---|---|---|---|---|---|---|---|---|---|
| CM Su   7 | CM Su   4 | CM Su   1 | CM Su   2 | NCE1   9 | NCE1   5 | NCE1   6 | NCE1   2 | NCEP   11 | NCEP   8 |

# BASFORD UNITED
Founded: 1900    Nickname: None

**Secretary:** Chris Munroe    **(T)** 07803 890 446    **(E)** chrismunroe@me.com
**Chairman:**    **Manager:** Darren Saunders    **Prog Ed:** Chris Munroe
**Ground:** Greenwich Avenue, off Bagnall Road, Basford, Nottingham NG6 0LD    **(T)** 07803 890 446
**Capacity:**    **Seats:**    **Covered:** Yes    **Midweek Matchday:**    **Clubhouse:** Yes

**Colours(change):** Yellow/black/black (All navy)
**Previous Names:** None
**Previous Leagues:** Notts Alliance > 2011. Central Midlands 2011-12. East Midlands Counties 2012-13.
**Records:**
**Senior Honours:** Notts Alliance Division One 1997-98. Central Midlands Southern 2011-12. East Midland Counties 2012-13.

**10 YEAR RECORD**

| 03-04 | 04-05 | 05-06 | 06-07 | 07-08 | 08-09 | 09-10 | 10-11 | 11-12 | 12-13 |
|---|---|---|---|---|---|---|---|---|---|
| NottS 10 | | | NottS 3 | NottS 5 | NottS 3 | NottS 2 | NottS 2 | CMSth 1 | EMC 1 |

# BRIDLINGTON TOWN
Founded: 1918    Nickname: Seasiders

**Secretary:** Gavin Branton    **(T)**    **(E)** gavinbranton@yahoo.co.uk
**Chairman:** Peter Smurthwaite    Gary Allanson    **Prog Ed:** Dom Taylor & Joe Gillott
**Ground:** Neil Hudgell Law Stadium, Queensgate, Bridlington YO16 7LN    **(T)** 01262 606 879
**Capacity:** 3,000 **Seats:** 500 **Covered:** 500    **Midweek Matchday:** Tuesday    **Clubhouse:** Yes **Shop:** Yes

**Colours(change):** All red (All white).
**Previous Names:** Original Bridlington Town folded in 1994. Greyhound FC changed to Bridlington Town.
**Previous Leagues:** Yorkshire 1924-39, 59-82, NCEL 1982-90, 99-2003, Northern Premier 1990-94, 2003-08
**Records:** **Att:** 1,006 v FC Utd of Manchester, NPLD1N, 03.11.07. **Goalscorer:** Neil Grimson. **Apps:** Neil Grimson - 200+ (1987-97).
**Senior Honours:** FA Vase 1992-93. Northern Counties East 2002-03, 2009-10, Division 1 1992-93.
ERCFA Senior Cup 1921,22,23,31,53,57,61,65,67,70,72,89,93,05

**10 YEAR RECORD**

| 03-04 | 04-05 | 05-06 | 06-07 | 07-08 | 08-09 | 09-10 | 10-11 | 11-12 | 12-13 |
|---|---|---|---|---|---|---|---|---|---|
| NP 1 11 | NP P 20 | NP 1 11 | NP 1 24 | NP1N 18 | NCEP 4 | NCEP 1 | NCEP 3 | NCEP 2 | NCEP 3 |

# BRIGHOUSE TOWN
Founded: 1963    Nickname: Town

**Secretary:** Malcolm Taylor    **(T)**    **(E)** malctay@blueyonder.co.uk
**Chairman:** Ray McLaughlin    **Manager:** Paul Quinn    **Prog Ed:** Malcolm Taylor
**Ground:** Dual Seal Stadium, St Giles Rd, Hove Edge, Brighouse, HD6 2PL.    **(T)** 01484 380 088
**Capacity:** 1,000 **Seats:** 100 **Covered:** 200    **Midweek Matchday:** Tuesday    **Clubhouse:** Yes

**Colours(change):** Orange/black/orange. (Yellow/green/yellow).
**Previous Names:**
**Previous Leagues:** Huddersfield Works. 1963-75. West Riding County Amateur 1975-08.
**Records:**
**Senior Honours:** West Riding County Amateur League: Prem Div - 1990/91 1994/95 1995/96 2000/01 2001/02, Prem Cup - 1993/94, 95/96
98/99, 00/01; Div 1 - 1988/89

**10 YEAR RECORD**

| 03-04 | 04-05 | 05-06 | 06-07 | 07-08 | 08-09 | 09-10 | 10-11 | 11-12 | 12-13 |
|---|---|---|---|---|---|---|---|---|---|
| WRCP 3 | WRCP 4 | WRCP 3 | WRCP 3 | WRCP 8 | NCE1 15 | NCE1 2 | NCEP 16 | NCEP 4 | NCEP 2 |

# GARFORTH TOWN
Founded: 1964    Nickname: The Miners

**Secretary:** Paul Bracewell    **(T)**    **(E)**
**Chairman:** Brian Close    **Manager:** Graham Nicholas    **Prog Ed:** Chris Mather
**Ground:** Cedar Ridge, Garforth, Leeds LS25 2PF    **(T)** 0113 287 7145
**Capacity:** 3,000 **Seats:** 278 **Covered:** 200    **Midweek Matchday:** Tuesday    **Clubhouse:** Yes **Shop:** No

**Colours(change):** Yellow & blue/blue/blue
**Previous Names:** Garforth Miners 1964-85
**Previous Leagues:** Leeds Sunday Comb. 1964-72, West Yorkshire 1972-78, Yorkshire 1978-83, NCE 1983-2007. Northern Premier 2007-13.
**Records:** 1,385 v Tadcaster Albion - Socrates debut - Northern Counties East League record
**Senior Honours:** Northern Counties East Division 1 1997-98

**10 YEAR RECORD**

| 03-04 | 04-05 | 05-06 | 06-07 | 07-08 | 08-09 | 09-10 | 10-11 | 11-12 | 12-13 |
|---|---|---|---|---|---|---|---|---|---|
| NCE1 6 | NCE1 2 | NCEP 10 | NCEP 4 | NP1N 10 | NP1N 16 | NP1N 20 | NP1N 13 | NP1N 5 | NP1N 22 |

# GLASSHOUGHTON WELFARE

Founded: 1964     Nickname: Welfare or Blues

**Secretary:** Frank MacLachlan    **(T)** 07710 586 447     **(E)** frank.maclachlan@btinternet.com

**Chairman:** Phil Riding    **Manager:** Rob Hunter     **Prog Ed:** Nigel Lea

**Ground:** Glasshoughton Centre, Leeds Road, Glasshoughton, Castleford WF10 4PF    **(T)** 01977 511 234

**Capacity:** 2,000 **Seats:** 0    **Covered:** 250    **Midweek Matchday:** Tuesday     **Clubhouse:** Yes    **Shop:** Yes

**Colours(change):** Royal blue & white/royal blue/royal blue (All yellow)
**Previous Names:**
**Previous Leagues:** West Yorkshire.
**Records:** **Att:** 350 v Ossett Albion, Presidents Cup 1998. **Win:** 8-1. **Defeat:** 0-8.
**Senior Honours:** West Riding County Cup 1993-94.

**10 YEAR RECORD**

| 03-04 | 04-05 | 05-06 | 06-07 | 07-08 | 08-09 | 09-10 | 10-11 | 11-12 | 12-13 |
|---|---|---|---|---|---|---|---|---|---|
| NCEP 17 | NCEP 11 | NCEP 16 | NCEP 16 | NCEP 20 | NCE1 19 | NCE1 13 | NCE1 7 | NCE1 2 | NCEP 16 |

# HEANOR TOWN

Founded: 1883     Nickname: The Lions

**Secretary:** Amanda Jones    **(T)**     **(E)**

**Chairman:** John McCulloch    **Manager:** Jordan Hall     **Prog Ed:** Stan Wilton

**Ground:** The Town Ground, Mayfield Avenue, Heanor DE75 7EN    **(T)** 01773 713 742

**Capacity:** 2,700 **Seats:** 100    **Covered:** 1,000    **Midweek Matchday:** Wednesday     **Clubhouse:** Yes

**Colours(change):** All white (Orange/black/black)
**Previous Names:** None
**Previous Leagues:** Midland 1961-72. Central Midlands 1986-2008. East Midlands Counties 2008-12.
**Records:**
**Senior Honours:** East Midlands Counties 2011-12.

**10 YEAR RECORD**

| 03-04 | 04-05 | 05-06 | 06-07 | 07-08 | 08-09 | 09-10 | 10-11 | 11-12 | 12-13 |
|---|---|---|---|---|---|---|---|---|---|
| CM Su 3 | CM Su 19 | CM Su 6 | CM Su 14 | CM Su 11 | EMC 12 | EMC 7 | EMC 3 | EMC 1 | NCEP 11 |

# LINCOLN MOORLANDS RAILWAY

Founded: 1989     Nickname: The Moors

**Secretary:** Mark Hodds    **(T)**     **(E)**

**Chairman:** Peter Tute    **Manager:** Mostyn Chester     **Prog Ed:** Mark Hodds

**Ground:** Moorland Sports Ground, Newark Road, Lincoln LN6 8RT    **(T)** 01522 874 111

**Capacity:** 200 **Seats:** 200    **Covered:** 100    **Midweek Matchday:** Wednesday     **Clubhouse:** Yes    **Shop:** No

**Colours(change):** Claret & blue/claret/claret & blue. (Yellow/royal blue/yellow).
**Previous Names:**
**Previous Leagues:** Central Midlands.
**Records:**
**Senior Honours:** Central Midlands Supreme 1999-00. Lincolnshire Senior Cup 2006-07.

**10 YEAR RECORD**

| 03-04 | 04-05 | 05-06 | 06-07 | 07-08 | 08-09 | 09-10 | 10-11 | 11-12 | 12-13 |
|---|---|---|---|---|---|---|---|---|---|
| NCE1 8 | NCE1 4 | NCE1 7 | NCE1 5 | NCEP 19 | NCEP 18 | NCEP 17 | NCEP 6 | NCEP 19 | NCEP 21 |

# LIVERSEDGE

Founded: 1910     Nickname: Sedge

**Secretary:** Bryan Oakes    **(T)** 01274 683 327     **(E)** bryan@bryanoakes.orangehome.co.uk

**Chairman:** Steve Newton    **Manager:** Eric Gilchrist     **Prog Ed:** Alan Dearden

**Ground:** Clayborn Ground, Quaker Lane, Hightown Road, Cleckheaton WF15 8DF    **(T)** 01274 862 108

**Capacity:** 2,000 **Seats:** 250    **Covered:** 750    **Midweek Matchday:** Tuesday     **Clubhouse:** Yes    **Shop:** Yes

**Colours(change):** Sky blue/navy/sky blue. (All red).
**Previous Names:**
**Previous Leagues:** Spen Valley, West Riding Co. Amateur 1922-72, Yorkshire 1972-82
**Records:** **Att:** 986 v Thackley **Goalscorer:** Denis Charlesworth **App:** Barry Palmer
**Senior Honours:** Northern Counties East League Cup 2005-06.

**10 YEAR RECORD**

| 03-04 | 04-05 | 05-06 | 06-07 | 07-08 | 08-09 | 09-10 | 10-11 | 11-12 | 12-13 |
|---|---|---|---|---|---|---|---|---|---|
| NCEP 9 | NCEP 6 | NCEP 2 | NCEP 12 | NCEP 4 | NCEP 14 | NCEP 9 | NCEP 17 | NCEP 14 | NCEP 15 |

# LONG EATON UNITED
Founded: 1956    Nickname: Blues

**Secretary:** Jim Fairley  **(T)**  **(E)** jim@longeatonutd.co.uk

**Chairman:** Jim Fairley    **Manager:** Mick Galloway    **Prog Ed:** Ritchie Woods

**Ground:**   Grange Park, Station Rd, Long Eaton, Derbys NG10 2EG    **(T)** 0115 973 5700

**Capacity:** 1,500  **Seats:** 450    **Covered:** 500    **Midweek Matchday:** Tuesday    **Clubhouse:** Yes    **Shop:** No

**Colours(change):**   All blue. (All red).
**Previous Names:**
**Previous Leagues:**  Central Alliance 1956-61, Mid Co Football Lge 1961-82, NCE 1982-89, Central Midlands 1989-2002
**Records:**       **Att:** 2,019 v Burton Albion FA Cup 1973
**Senior Honours:**   Derbyshire Senior Cup 1964-65, 75-76. Northern Counties East Div1S 1984-85. League Cup 2008-09.

**10 YEAR RECORD**

| 03-04 | | 04-05 | | 05-06 | | 06-07 | | 07-08 | | 08-09 | | 09-10 | | 10-11 | | 11-12 | | 12-13 | |
|---|---|---|---|---|---|---|---|---|---|---|---|---|---|---|---|---|---|---|---|
| NCE1 | 2 | NCEP | 12 | NCEP | 19 | NCEP | 11 | NCEP | 12 | NCEP | 2 | NCEP | 10 | NCEP | 12 | NCEP | 15 | NCEP | 12 |

# MALTBY MAIN
Founded: 1916    Nickname: Miners

**Secretary:** John Mills    **(T)** 01709 813 609    **(E)** john_mills_@hotmail.co.uk

**Chairman:** Graham McCormick    **Prog Ed:** Nick Dunhill

**Ground:**   Muglet Lane, Maltby, Rotherham S66 7JQ.    **(T)** 07795 693 683

**Capacity:** 2,000  **Seats:** 150    **Covered:** 300    **Midweek Matchday:** Wednesday    **Clubhouse:** No    **Shop:** No

**Colours(change):**   Red/black/red (Yellow/white/yellow)
**Previous Names:**   Maltby Miners Welfare 1970-96
**Previous Leagues:** Sheffield Co Senior. Yorkshire League 1973-84
**Records:**       **Att:** 1,500 v Sheffield Weds (friendly) 1991-2
**Senior Honours:**   Sheffield & Hallamshire Senior Cup1977-78

**10 YEAR RECORD**

| 03-04 | | 04-05 | | 05-06 | | 06-07 | | 07-08 | | 08-09 | | 09-10 | | 10-11 | | 11-12 | | 12-13 | |
|---|---|---|---|---|---|---|---|---|---|---|---|---|---|---|---|---|---|---|---|
| NCE1 | 3 | NCEP | 19 | NCEP | 18 | NCEP | 10 | NCEP | 18 | NCEP | 12 | NCEP | 16 | NCEP | 11 | NCEP | 18 | NCEP | 14 |

# NOSTELL MINERS WELFARE
Founded: 1928    Nickname: The Welfare

**Secretary:** Granville Marshall    **(T)** 01924 864 462    **(E)** nostwellmwfc@hotmail.com

**Chairman:** Granville Marshall    **Manager:** Alan Colquhoun    **Prog Ed:** Malcolm Lamb

**Ground:**   The Welfare Grd, Crofton Co. Centre, Middle Lane, New Crofton WF4 1LB    **(T)** 01924  866 010

**Capacity:** 1500  **Seats:** 100    **Covered:** 200    **Midweek Matchday:** Tuesday    **Clubhouse:** Yes

**Colours(change):**   Yellow/black/black. (All blue).
**Previous Names:**
**Previous Leagues:**  Wakefield 1950-66, 69-82, West Yorkshire 1966-68, 82-2006
**Records:**
**Senior Honours:**    West Yorkshire Premier Division 2004-05

**10 YEAR RECORD**

| 03-04 | | 04-05 | | 05-06 | | 06-07 | | 07-08 | | 08-09 | | 09-10 | | 10-11 | | 11-12 | | 12-13 | |
|---|---|---|---|---|---|---|---|---|---|---|---|---|---|---|---|---|---|---|---|
| WYkP | 5 | WYkP | 1 | WYkP | 3 | NCE1 | 4 | NCE1 | 5 | NCEP | 13 | NCEP | 18 | NCEP | 9 | NCEP | 17 | NCEP | 18 |

# PARKGATE
Founded: 1969    Nickname: The Steelmen

**Secretary:** Bruce Bickerdike    **(T)**    **(E)** secretary@parkgatefc.co.uk

**Chairman:** Albert Dudill    **Manager:** Steve Adams    **Prog Ed:** Dave Platts

**Ground:**   Roundwood Sports Complex, Green Lane, Rawmarsh, S62 6LA    **(T)** 01709 826 600

**Capacity:** 1,000  **Seats:** 300    **Covered:** 300    **Midweek Matchday:** Tuesday    **Clubhouse:** Yes    **Shop:** No

**Colours(change):**   All Red & White. (All blue).
**Previous Names:**   BSC Parkgate (1982-86) RES Parkgate (pre 1994)
**Previous Leagues:** BIR County Senior. Yorkshire 1974-82.
**Records:**       **Att:** v Worksop 1982
**Senior Honours:**   N.C.E. Division One 2006-07. Wilkinson Sword Trophy 2006-07.

**10 YEAR RECORD**

| 03-04 | | 04-05 | | 05-06 | | 06-07 | | 07-08 | | 08-09 | | 09-10 | | 10-11 | | 11-12 | | 12-13 | |
|---|---|---|---|---|---|---|---|---|---|---|---|---|---|---|---|---|---|---|---|
| NCE1 | 10 | NCE1 | 12 | NCE1 | 6 | NCE1 | 1 | NCEP | 8 | NCEP | 11 | NCEP | 14 | NCEP | 2 | NCEP | 7 | NCEP | 9 |

## PICKERING TOWN
Founded: 1888     Nickname: Pikes

**Secretary:** Keith Usher    **(T)** 01751 473 317     **(E)** usherso8@btinternet.com

**Chairman:** Keith Usher    **Manager:** Jimmy Reid    **Prog Ed:** Steve Adamson

**Ground:** Recreation Club, off Mill Lane, Malton Road, Pickering YO18 7DB    **(T)** 01751 473 317

**Capacity:** 2,000 **Seats:** 200 **Covered:** 500 **Midweek Matchday:** Tuesday    **Clubhouse:** Yes **Shop:** No

**Colours(change):** All blue. (All yellow).
**Previous Names:**
**Previous Leagues:** Beckett, York & District, Scarborough & District, Yorkshire 1972-1982
**Records:**    **Att:** 1,412 v Notts County (friendly) in August 1991
**Senior Honours:** N.C.E. Div 2 1987-88. North Riding Cup 1990-91. Wilkinson Sword Trophy 2000-01. North Riding Senior Cup 2012-13.

**10 YEAR RECORD**

| 03-04 | 04-05 | 05-06 | 06-07 | 07-08 | 08-09 | 09-10 | 10-11 | 11-12 | 12-13 |
|---|---|---|---|---|---|---|---|---|---|
| NCEP 5 | NCEP 5 | NCEP 6 | NCEP 9 | NCEP 3 | NCEP 9 | NCEP 7 | NCEP 7 | NCEP 12 | NCEP 5 |

## RETFORD UNITED
Founded: 1987     Nickname: The Badgers

**Secretary:** Annie Knight    **(T)**     **(E)** retfordunited@sky.com

**Chairman:** Daniel Keeton    **Manager:** Richard Sennett & Mark Turner    **Prog Ed:** Jon Knight

**Ground:** Cannon Park, Leverton Road, Retford, Notts DN22 6QF    **(T)** 01777 710 300

**Capacity:** 2,000 **Seats:** 150 **Covered:** 200 **Midweek Matchday:** Tuesday    **Clubhouse:** Yes **Shop:** Yes

**Colours(change):** Black and white stripes/black/white (All yellow)
**Previous Names:**
**Previous Leagues:** Gainsborough & Dist, Nottinghamshire Alliance > 2001, Central Midlands 2001-04, Northern Counties East 2004-07
**Records:** 1,527 v Doncaster Rovers - Friendly July 2006
**Senior Honours:** Notts All. Div.1 2000-01. Central Mids Div.1 01-02, Supreme Division 03-04, Lge Cup 01-02, 03-04, Floodlit Cup 03-04. N.C.E. Prem. Division 06-07, 11-12, N.P.L. Div.1S 07-08, 08-09. Notts Sen. Cup 08-09.

**10 YEAR RECORD**

| 03-04 | 04-05 | 05-06 | 06-07 | 07-08 | 08-09 | 09-10 | 10-11 | 11-12 | 12-13 |
|---|---|---|---|---|---|---|---|---|---|
| CM Su 1 | NCE1 8 | NCE1 2 | NCEP 1 | NP1S 1 | NP1S 1 | NP P 6 | NP P 22 | NCEP 1 | NCEP 4 |

## STAVELEY MINERS WELFARE
Founded: 1989     Nickname: The Welfare

**Secretary:** Ele Reaney    **(T)** 01246 471 441     **(E)** staveleyed@hotmail.co.uk

**Chairman:** Terry Damms    **Manager:** Neil Cluxton    **Prog Ed:** Ele Reaney

**Ground:** Inkersall Road, Staveley, Chesterfield, S43 3JL    **(T)** 01246 471 441

**Capacity:** 5,000 **Seats:** 220 **Covered:** 400 **Midweek Matchday:** Wednesday    **Clubhouse:** Yes **Shop:** Yes

**Colours(change):** Blue & white/blue/blue (All orange)
**Previous Names:**
**Previous Leagues:** Chesterfield & District Amateur 1989-91. County Senior 1991-93.
**Records:** 910 v Chesterfield, Friendly, 20/07/2011. **Goalscorer:** Ryan Damms - 102. **Apps:** Shane Turner.
**Senior Honours:** County Senior League Division 3 1991-92, Division 2 1992-93. N.C.E. Division One 2010-11.

**10 YEAR RECORD**

| 03-04 | 04-05 | 05-06 | 06-07 | 07-08 | 08-09 | 09-10 | 10-11 | 11-12 | 12-13 |
|---|---|---|---|---|---|---|---|---|---|
| NCE1 16 | NCE1 9 | NCE1 10 | NCE1 6 | NCE1 8 | NCE1 4 | NCE1 4 | NCE1 1 | NCEP 5 | NCEP 13 |

## TADCASTER ALBION
Founded: 1892     Nickname: The Brewers

**Secretary:** Howard Clarke    **(T)**     **(E)** sandra.clarke1@tiscali.co.uk

**Chairman:** Rob Northfield    **Manager:** Paul Marshall    **Prog Ed:** Kevin Axtell

**Ground:** 2inspire Park, Ings Lane, Tadcaster LS24 9AY    **(T)** 07518 820 730 or 07949 452 054

**Capacity:** 1,500 **Seats:** 150 **Covered:** 400 **Midweek Matchday:** Tuesday    **Clubhouse:** Yes **Shop:** No

**Colours(change):** All yellow (All red)
**Previous Names:** None
**Previous Leagues:** York, Harrogate, Yorkshire 1973-82.
**Records:** **Att:** 1,200 v Winterton FA Vase 4th Round 1996-7
**Senior Honours:** Northern Counties East Division 1 2009-10.

**10 YEAR RECORD**

| 03-04 | 04-05 | 05-06 | 06-07 | 07-08 | 08-09 | 09-10 | 10-11 | 11-12 | 12-13 |
|---|---|---|---|---|---|---|---|---|---|
| NCE1 18 | NCE1 6 | NCE1 3 | NCE1 7 | NCE1 12 | NCE1 17 | NCE1 1 | NCEP 4 | NCEP 8 | NCEP 6 |

# THACKLEY
Founded: 1930          Nickname: Dennyboys

**Secretary:** Mick Lodge          **(T)**          **(E)** mick.lodge@btinternet.com

**Chairman:** Mike Smith          **Manager:** Vince Brockie          **Prog Ed:** John McCreery

**Ground:** Dennyfield, Ainsbury Avenue, Thackley, Bradford  BD10 0TL          **(T)** 01274 615 571

**Capacity:** 3000  **Seats:** 300  **Covered:** 600  **Midweek Matchday:** Tuesday          **Clubhouse:** Yes   **Shop:** No

**Colours(change):** Red/white/red. (White/black/white).
**Previous Names:** Thackley Wesleyians 1930-39
**Previous Leagues:** Bradford Am, W. Riding Co. Am., West Yorks, Yorks 1967-82
**Records:** Att: 1,500 v Leeds United 1983
**Senior Honours:** W. Riding County Cup 1963-64, 66-67, 73-74, 74-75. Bradford & District Senior Cup (x13).

**10 YEAR RECORD**

| 03-04 | | 04-05 | | 05-06 | | 06-07 | | 07-08 | | 08-09 | | 09-10 | | 10-11 | | 11-12 | | 12-13 | |
|---|---|---|---|---|---|---|---|---|---|---|---|---|---|---|---|---|---|---|---|
| NCEP | 11 | NCEP | 8 | NCEP | 9 | NCEP | 18 | NCEP | 16 | NCEP | 7 | NCEP | 4 | NCEP | 8 | NCEP | 10 | NCEP | 10 |

# WINTERTON RANGERS
Founded: 1930          Nickname: Rangers

**Secretary:** Mark Fowler          **(T)** 07775 907 606          **(E)** mark-fowler-68@hotmail.co.uk

**Chairman:** David Crowder          **Manager:** Leigh Herrick          **Prog Ed:** David Paylor

**Ground:** West Street, Winterton, Scunthorpe DN15 9QF.          **(T)** 01724 732 628

**Capacity:** 3,000  **Seats:** 245  **Covered:** 200  **Midweek Matchday:** Wednesday          **Clubhouse:** Yes

**Colours(change):** All royal blue. (All red).
**Previous Names:**
**Previous Leagues:** Scunthorpe & District. 1945-65. Lincolnshire 1965-70. Yorkshire 1970-82.
**Records:** Att: 1,200 v Sheffield United, flood lights switch on, October 1978.
**Senior Honours:** NCE Premier 2007-08.

**10 YEAR RECORD**

| 03-04 | | 04-05 | | 05-06 | | 06-07 | | 07-08 | | 08-09 | | 09-10 | | 10-11 | | 11-12 | | 12-13 | |
|---|---|---|---|---|---|---|---|---|---|---|---|---|---|---|---|---|---|---|---|
| NCE1 | 11 | NCE1 | 10 | NCE1 | 5 | NCE1 | 2 | NCEP | 1 | NCEP | 5 | NCEP | 6 | NCEP | 5 | NCEP | 6 | NCEP | 19 |

# WORKSOP PARRAMORE
Founded: 1936          Nickname: None

**Secretary:** Max Ross          **(T)**          **(E)** max@pandmleisure.co.uk

**Chairman:** Pete Whitehead          **Manager:** Russell Eagle          **Prog Ed:** Paul Hill

**Ground:** The Windsor Foodservice Stadium, Sandy Land, Worksop S80 1TJ          **(T)** 01909 479 955

**Capacity:** 2,500  **Seats:** 200  **Covered:** 750  **Midweek Matchday:** Tuesday          **Clubhouse:** Yes   **Shop:** No

**Colours(change):** Amber & black/black/black
**Previous Names:** Parramore Sports > 2010. Sheffield Parramore 2010-2011.
**Previous Leagues:** Sheffield & Hallam County Senior > 2008. Central Midlands > 2011.
**Records:**
**Senior Honours:** Central Midland League Supreme Division 2010-11.

**10 YEAR RECORD**

| 03-04 | | 04-05 | | 05-06 | | 06-07 | | 07-08 | | 08-09 | | 09-10 | | 10-11 | | 11-12 | | 12-13 | |
|---|---|---|---|---|---|---|---|---|---|---|---|---|---|---|---|---|---|---|---|
| SHS1 | 11 | SHS1 | 12 | SHS1 | 6 | SHS1 | 13 | SHS1 | 5 | CM P | 4 | CM Su | 8 | CM Su | 1 | NCE1 | 3 | NCEP | 7 |

# DIVISION ONE

## A.F.C. EMLEY
Founded: 2005    Nickname: Pewits

**Secretary:** John Whitehead    **(T)**    **(E)** afcemley@tiscali.co.uk
**Chairman:** John Whitehead    **Manager:** Darren Hepworth    **Prog Ed:** Rob Dixon
**Ground:** The Welfare Ground, Off Upper Lane, Emley, nr Huddersfield, HD8 9RE.    **(T)** 01924 849 392    **Capacity:** 2,000
**Colours(change):** Claret & sky blue/sky blue/claret (Sky blue/claret/sky blue)

**ADDITIONAL INFORMATION:**
**Previous League:** West Yorkshire 2005-06.

## APPLEBY FRODINGHAM
Founded: 1990    Nickname: The Steelmen

**Secretary:** Steve Lumley-Holmes    **(T)**    **(E)** lumleyholmes@btinternet.com
**Chairman:** Steve Lumley-Holmes    **Manager:** Martin Blades & Mark Crowston    Dick Drury
**Ground:** Brumby Hall Sports Ground, Ashby Road, Scunthorpe, DN16 1AA    **(T)** 01724 402134 / 843024    **Capacity:** 1,100
**Colours(change):** Red & black/black/black (Blue & white/blue/blue)

**ADDITIONAL INFORMATION:**
**Previous League:** Central Midlands.
**Honours:** Lincolnshire League: 1962-63, 76-77, 77-98, 93-94; Lincolnshire Challenge Cup: 1962-63, 75-76, 76-77, 77-78, 92-93

## BOTTESFORD TOWN
Founded: 1974    Nickname: The Poachers

**Secretary:** Tony Reeve    **(T)**    **(E)** anthony.reeve3@ntlworld.com
**Chairman:** Tony Reeve    **Manager:** John Corbett    **Prog Ed:** Liz Gray
**Ground:** Birch Park, Ontario Road, Bottesford, Scunthorpe, DN17 2TQ    **(T)** 01724 871 883    **Capacity:** 1,000
**Colours(change):** Blue & yellow/blue & yellow/blue (Red & black/black & red/black & red)

**ADDITIONAL INFORMATION:**
**Previous Leagues:** Lincolnshire 1974-2000. Central Midlands 2000-07.
**Honours:** Lincolnshire League 1989-90, 90-91, 91-92. Central Midlands League Supreme Division 2006-07.

## CLEETHORPES TOWN
Founded: 1998    Nickname: None

**Secretary:** Jevon Southam    **(T)**    **(E)** jevon.southam@yahoo.com
**Chairman:** David Patterson    **Manager:** Marcus Newell    **Prog Ed:** Craig Kendall
**Ground:** The Bradley Football Development Centre Bradley Road, Grimsby, DN37 0AG    **(T)**    **Capacity:** 1,000
**Colours(change):** Blue & black stripes/black/blue & black (Red & black stripes/red/red & black)

**ADDITIONAL INFORMATION:**
**Previous Leagues:** Lincolnshire.
**Honours:** Lincolnshire League 2011-12.

## CLIPSTONE
Founded: 1928    Nickname: The Cobras

**Secretary:** Neil Hardwick    **(T)**    **(E)** clipstone.welfare.fc@gmail.com
**Chairman:** Brett Marshall    **Manager:** Lee Tryner    **Prog Ed:** Neil Hardwick
**Ground:** Worksop Van Hire Stad, Clipstone Rd East, Clipstone Village, Mansfield, NG21 9AB.    **(T)** 01623 423 730    **Capacity:** 500
**Colours(change):** White & black/black/black (All red)

**ADDITIONAL INFORMATION:**
**Previous Names:** Clipstone Welfare.
**Honours:** Central Midlands League 1993-94, 96-97.

## DINNINGTON TOWN
Founded: 2000    Nickname: Dinno

**Secretary:** Mark Ramsden    **(T)** 07778 304 836    **(E)** mramsden@baldwinandfrancis.com
**Chairman:** Vacant    **Manager:** Steve Toyne & Mark Ramsden    **Prog Ed:** Wayne Rutledge
**Ground:** Phoenix Park, 131 Laughton Road, Dinnington, Nr Sheffield S25 2PP    **(T)** 07854 722 465    **Capacity:** 2000
**Colours(change):** Yellow & black/black/black. (All white).

**ADDITIONAL INFORMATION:**
**Previous Leagues:** Central Midlands 2000-2006.
**Honours:** Northern Counties East Division One 2007-08, League Cup 2009-10.

## DRONFIELD TOWN
Founded: 1998    Nickname: None

**Secretary:** Darren Bradwell    **(T)**    **(E)**
**Chairman:** Patrick Williams    **Manager:** Craig Butler    **Prog Ed:** Luke Prest
**Ground:** Stonelow Playing Fields, Stonelow Road, Dronfield, S18 2DA    **(T)**
**Colours(change):** Red & black/black/red & black (Royal blue/white/royal blue)

**ADDITIONAL INFORMATION:**
**Previous Leagues:** Central Midlands > 2013.
**Honours:** Central Midlands North 2012-13.

## ECCLESHILL UNITED

Founded: 1948    Nickname: The Eagles

**Secretary:** Adrian Benson    **(T)**    **(E)**
**Chairman:** Adrian Benson    **Manager:** Lee Duxbury    **Prog Ed:** Paul Everett
**Ground:** The Rapid Solicitors Stadium, Kingsway, Wrose, Bradford, BD2 1PN    **(T)** 01274 615 739    **Capacity:** 2,225
**Colours(change):** Blue & white/blue/blue (White & red/red/red).
**ADDITIONAL INFORMATION:**
**Record Att:** 715 v Bradford City 1996-97. **Win:** 10-1. **Defeat:** 0-6.
**Honours:** Bradford Senior Cup 1985-86. Northern Counties East Division 1 1996-97.

## GRIMSBY BOROUGH

Founded: 2003    Nickname: The Wilderness Boys

**Secretary:** Nigel Fanthorpe    **(T)**    **(E)** nigelfanthorpe@hotmail.co.uk
**Chairman:** Kenneth Vincent    **Manager:** Steve Newby & Nigel Fanthorpe    **Prog Ed:** Brian Sylvester
**Ground:** The Bradley Football Development Centre, Bradley Road, Grimsby, DN37 0AG    **(T)** 07890 318 054    **Capacity:** 1,500
**Colours(change):** Royal blue/royal blue/white (Yellow/white/blue)
**ADDITIONAL INFORMATION:**
**Previous League:** Central Midlands 2004-08.

## HALL ROAD RANGERS

Founded: 1959    Nickname: Rangers

**Secretary:** Alan Chaplin    **(T)**    **(E)** hallroadrangers@hotmail.com
**Chairman:** Jason Cox    **Manager:** Andy Foster    **Prog Ed:** Michael Harker
**Ground:** Dene Park, Dene Close, Beverley Road, Dunswell HU6 0AA    **(T)** 01482 850 101    **Capacity:** 1,200
**Colours(change):** Blue & white/blue/blue. (Red & black/black/black)
**ADDITIONAL INFORMATION:** **App:** 1,200 v Manchester City Aug 93 **Goalscorer:** G James **App:** G James
East Riding Senior Cup 1972-73, 93-94. N.C.E. Division Two 1990-91.

## HALLAM (SECOND OLDEST CLUB IN THE WORLD)

Founded: 1860    Nickname: Countrymen

**Secretary:** Kevin Scott    **(T)**    **(E)**
**Chairman:** Chris Taylor    **Manager:** Chris Sellars    **Prog Ed:** Russ Taylor
**Ground:** Sandygate Road, Crosspool, Sheffield S10 5SE    **(T)** 0114 230 9484    **Capacity:** 1,000
**Colours(change):** All blue (All yellow).
**ADDITIONAL INFORMATION:** **Att:** 2,000 v Hendon F.A. Amateur Cup. **Goalscorer:** A Stainrod 46. **App:** P. Ellis 500+. **Win:** 7-0 x2. **Defeat:** 0-7.
**Honours:** Northern Counties East League Cup 2003-04.
**Previous League:** Yorkshire 1952-82.

## HEMSWORTH MINERS WELFARE

Founded: 1981    Nickname: Wells

**Secretary:** Phillip Crapper    **(T)** 01977 614 723    **(E)** acracknell@naue.co.uk
**Chairman:** Tony Benson    **Manager:** Daryl Bowman    **Prog Ed:** Anthony Crapper
**Ground:** Fitzwilliam Stadium, Wakefield Road, Fitzwilliam, Pontefract, WF9 5AJ    **(T)** 01977 614 997    **Capacity:** 2,000
**Colours(change):** All royal blue (All white)
**ADDITIONAL INFORMATION:**
**Previous League:** West Riding County Amateur 1995-2008.

## KNARESBOROUGH TOWN

Founded: 1902    Nickname: None

**Secretary:** Clare Rudzinski    **(T)**    **(E)** clarerudzinski@btinternet.com
**Chairman:** Terry Hewlett    **Manager:** Brian Davey    **Prog Ed:** Ian Pickles
**Ground:** Manse Lane, Knaresborough, HG5 8LF    **(T)** 01423 548 896    **Capacity:** 1,000
**Colours(change):** Red/black/red (Yellow & black stripes/black/black)
**ADDITIONAL INFORMATION:**
**Previous Leagues:** West Yorkshire 1971. Harrogate & District 1971-93. West Yorkshire 1993-2012.
**Honours:** West Yorkshire League Premier Division 2008-09.

## LOUTH TOWN

Founded: 2007    Nickname: The White Wolves

**Secretary:** Richard Hill    **(T)**    **(E)** louthtownfc@gmail.com
**Chairman:** Stephen Clark    **Manager:** Daryl Clare
**Ground:** The Park Avenue Stadium, Park Avenue, Louth, LN11 8BY    **(T)** 01507 601 123    **Capacity:** 1,500
**Colours(change):** White/black/black (All blue)
**ADDITIONAL INFORMATION:**
**Previous League:** Central Midlands 2007-10.
**Honours:** Central Midlands League Premier Division 2008-09, Supreme Division 2009-10.

## PONTEFRACT COLLIERIES

Founded: 1958    Nickname: Colls

**Secretary:** Trevor Waddington    **(T)**    **(E)**
**Chairman:** Guy Nottingham    **Manager:** Nicky Handley & Duncan Bray    **Prog Ed:** Rod Naylor
**Ground:** The Beechnut Lane Stadium, Skinner Lane, Pontefract, WF8 4QE    **(T)** 01977 600 818    **Capacity:** 1,200
**Colours(change):** All blue (All claret)

**ADDITIONAL INFORMATION:**
**Previous League:** Yorkshire 1979-82.
**Honours:** Northern Counties East League Division 1 1983-84, 95-96.

## ROSSINGTON MAIN

Founded: 1919    Nickname: The Colliery

**Secretary:** Gerald Parsons    **(T)**    **(E)** g-parsons2@sky.com
**Chairman:** Carl Stokes    **Manager:** Steve Lodge    **Prog Ed:** Glen Parsons
**Ground:** Welfare Ground, Oxford Street, Rossington, Doncaster, DN11 0TE    **(T)** 01302 865 524 (MD)    **Capacity:** 2,000
**Colours(change):** All blue (All red)

**ADDITIONAL INFORMATION:**
**Record Att:** 1,200 v Leeds United 06/08/1991. **Goalscorer:** Mark Illam. **Apps:** Darren Phipps.
**Honours:** Central Midlands League Premier Division 1984-85, League Cup 1983-84, 84-85.

## SELBY TOWN

Founded: 1919    Nickname: The Robins

**Secretary:** Thomas Arkley    **(T)** 07830 218 657    **(E)** toonarkley@yahoo.co.uk
**Chairman:** Ralph Pearse    **Manager:** Ian Dring    **Prog Ed:** Simon Davies
**Ground:** The Rigid Group Stadium, Richard Street, Scott Road, Selby YO8 0DB    **(T)** 01757 210 900    **Capacity:** 5,000
**Colours(change):** All red (Black & white stripes/white/black).

**ADDITIONAL INFORMATION: Att:** 7,000 v Bradford PA FA Cup1st Round 1953-54
**Honours:** Yorkshire League 1934-35, 35-36, 52-53, 53-54. Northern Counties East Division One 1995-96.

## SHAW LANE AQUAFORCE

Founded: 1991    Nickname: The Ducks

**Secretary:** David Exley    **(T)**    **(E)**
**Chairman:** Craig Wood    **Manager:** Doug O'Connor    **Prog Ed:** Ray Archer
**Ground:** Shaw Lane, Barnsley, S70 6HZ    **(T)** 01226 203 509
**Colours(change):** Blue & white/blue/blue (Orange & black/orange/orange)

**ADDITIONAL INFORMATION:**
**Previous Leagues:** County Senior League > 2013.
**Honours:** County Senior League 2012-13.

## SHIREBROOK TOWN

Founded: 1985    Nickname: None

**Secretary:** Aimee Radford    **(T)** 01623 742 535    **(E)** aimeeradford@yahoo.co.uk
**Chairman:** Dan Marsh    **Manager:** Julian Watts    **Prog Ed:** Paul Harrison
**Ground:** Shirebrook Spts and So C, Langwith Road, Shirebrook, Mansfield, NG20 8TF    **(T)** 01623 742 535    **Capacity:** 2,000
**Colours(change):** Red/black/black (All white)

**ADDITIONAL INFORMATION:**
**Record Goalscorer:** Craig Charlesworth - 345. **Apps:** Martin Rowbottom - 384.
**Honours:** Central Midlands League Supreme Division 2000-01, 01-02, Northern Counties East Division One 2003-04.

## TEVERSAL

Founded: 1918    Nickname: Tevie Boys

**Secretary:** Kevin Newton    **(T)** 07711 358 060    **(E)** enquiries@teversalfc.co.uk
**Chairman:** Peter Cockerill    **Manager:** Jamie Hudson    **Prog Ed:** Kevin Newton
**Ground:** Teversal Grange Spts and So.Centre, Carnarvon St, Teversal, NG17 3HJ    **(T)** 07711 358 060
**Colours(change):** Red/black/black (All royal blue)

**ADDITIONAL INFORMATION:**
**Previous Name:** Teversal Grange. **Previous League:** Central Midlands.
**Honours:** Central Midlands League 2004-05.

## WORSBROUGH BRIDGE ATHLETIC

Founded: 1923    Nickname: The Briggers

**Secretary:** Charlie Wyatt    **(T)** 01226 284 452    **(E)** crw@wyatts.adsl24.co.uk
**Chairman:** John Cooper    **Manager:** Chris Hilton    **Prog Ed:** Charlie Wyatt
**Ground:** Park Road, Worsbrough Bridge, Barnsley, S70 5LJ    **(T)** 01226 284 452    **Capacity:** 2,000
**Colours(change):** Red & white/black/black (Black & white/white/red)

**ADDITIONAL INFORMATION:**
**Record Att:** 1,603 v Blyth Spatans, FA Amateur Cup 1971.
**Honours:** County Senior League Division One 1965-66, 69-70.

# YORKSHIRE AMATEUR
Founded: 1918        Nickname: Ammers

**Secretary:** Keith Huggins        (T)                (E)
**Chairman:** Jeni French        **Manager:** Phil Harding & Lincoln Richards    **Prog Ed:** Jeni French
**Ground:** Bracken Edge, Roxholme Road, Leeds, LS8 4DZ (Sat. Nav. LS7 4JG)        **(T)** 0113 289 2886        **Capacity:** 1,550
**Colours(change):**  White/navy/red (All red)

**ADDITIONAL INFORMATION:**
**Record Att:** 4,000 v Wimbledon, FA Amateur Cup Quarter Final 1932.
**Honours:** Yorkshire League: 1931-32, Div 2 - 1958-59, Div 3 - 1977-78. Leeds & District Senior Cup.

## GROUND DIRECTIONS

**ALBION SPORTS-Throstle Nest, Newlands, Farsley, Leeds, LS28 5BE. Tel: 0113 255 7292**
Come off the M606 at the roundabout. Take fourth exit onto Rooley Lane which is the A6177, continue to follow A6177 through two roundabouts then turn right onto Leeds Road A647. Continue to follow A647, go through roundabout. At next roundabout, take second exit onto Bradford Road B6157. Follow for ½ mile before turning left onto New Street then turn right onto Newlands. Ground on left.

**ARMTHORPE WELFARE-Welfare Ground, Church Street, Armthorpe, Doncaster, DN3 3AG. Tel: (01302) 842795-Match days only**
From the north, turn left at main roundabout in the centre of Doncaster and straight across at next roundabout on to Wheatley Hall Road. Turn right on to Wentworth Road, go to top of hill towards the Hospital on to Armthorpe Road. From the south, take the M18 to J4 on to the A630. At 2nd roundabout, turn left and proceed to next roundabout, then turn right. Ground 400 yards on left behind Netto.

**ATHERSLEY RECREATION-Sheerien Park, Ollerton Road, Athersley North, Barnsley, S71 3DP. Tel: 07910 121070**
From North: M1 J38. Go down slip road, round roundabout and back under motorway. Take first left onto Haigh Lane, go to top of the hill and, at T-junction, turn right. At next T-junction, turn left onto Shaw Lane and go to bottom of hill. At T-junction of A61, turn right to Barnsley, go through first set of traffic lights and take first left onto Newstead Road. Follow to second roundabout and turn right onto Ollerton Road. Follow to second turn on left-do not take it but go past and entrance is between houses 123-125 Ollerton Road. Follow drive into ground.

**BARTON TOWN OLD BOYS-The Euronics Ground, Marsh Lane, Barton-on-Humber. Tel: (01652) 635838**
Approaching from the South on A15, Barton is the last exit before the Humber Bridge. Follow the A1077 into the town. Turn right at the mini roundabout at the bottom of the hill into Holydyke. Take second left onto George Street and then into King Street. Marsh Lane is opposite the junction of King Street and High Street. The ground is at the end of Marsh Lane, on the right, immediately after the cricket ground.

**BASFORD UNITED - Greenwich Avenue, off Bagnall Road, Basford, Nottingham NG6 0LD. Tel: 07803 890 446**
From M1 Junction 26 - Follow A610 to Nottingham for 1.3 miles, passing over one roundabout. Turn left at the second roundabout by the Gateway Hotel onto Cinderhill Road following signpost to Bulwell. After a quarter of mile turn right into Bagnall Road, and a further half a mile turn left into Greenwich Avenue, the entrance to the ground is straight ahead. From the north (A60) - Entering Nottingham via the A60, turn right onto the B6004 Oxclose Lane (signposted to Basford). After 2.2 miles, pass over the level crossing and continue onto David Lane. After a quarter of a mile turn right onto Bagnall Road and a further quarter of a mile turn right into Greenwich Avenue, the entrance to the ground is straight ahead. From the south (A52) - Entering Nottingham via the A52, continue along the Ring Road A6514 following signs to Mansfield for approximately two miles, until the junction with the A610 is reached. Turn left onto the A610 (signposted to M1). After 0.8 miles turn right on to Stockhill Lane (B6004). Continue along Stockhill Lane for a third of a mile, turning left at the mini roundabout into Mill Street and then turning left into Bagnall Road. After a quarter of a mile turn right into Greenwich Avenue, the entrance to the ground is straight ahead.

**BRIDLINGTON TOWN-Queensgate Stadium, Queensgate, Bridlington, East Yorkshire, YO16 7LN. Tel: (01262) 606879**
From South (Hull, Beeford, Barmston): Approach Bridlington on the A165, passing golf course on right and Broadacres Pub, Kingsmead Estate on left. Straight through traffic lights to roundabout by B&Q. Turn right. At traffic lights turn left and over the railway bridge. At roundabout bear left and carry on heading north up Quay Road. After traffic lights turn right into Queensgate. Ground is 300 yards up the road on the right.
From South and West (Driffield, Hull, York): Approach Bridlington on A614. (This was formally the A166). Straight on at traffic lights (Hospital on right) and follow the road round the bend. At roundabout straight across to mini roundabout and bear right (second exit). Follow road around to right and to traffic lights. Straight on. At next traffic lights (just after Kwikfit) turn left into Queensgate. Ground is 800 yards up the road on the right.
From North (Scarborough): Approach Bridlington (Esso garage on right) at roundabout turn left then at mini roundabout second exit. Follow road around to right and to traffic lights. Straight on. At next traffic lights (just after Kwikfit) turn left into Queensgate. Ground is 800 yards up the road on the right.

**BRIGHOUSE TOWN-Dual Seal Stadium, St Giles Road, Hove Edge, Brighouse, West Yorkshire, HD6 2PL.**
M1 to M62 travel westwards to J26 then come off motorway and go on to A58 Halifax to third set of traffic lights at Hipperholme. At lights, turn left onto A644 to Brighouse. Travel approx. one mile passing the Dusty Miller pub, take next left and, within 30-40 metres, turn left on to Spouthouse Lane. Follow this road for approximately 1/4 of a mile until road swings left at this point. Turn right in to car park. Be careful of oncoming traffic on bend.

**GARFORTH TOWN - Cedar Ridge, Garforth, Leeds LS25 2PF. Tel: 0113 287 7145**
From North: travel south on A1 and join M1. Turn off at 1st junc (47). From South: M1 to junc 47. From Leeds area: join M1 at junc 44 or 46 and turn off at junc 47. From West: M62 to junc 29, join M1 and off at junc 47. From junc 47: take turning signe 'Garforth' (A642). Approx. 200 yds turn left into housing estate opposite White House. (Cedar Ridge). Stadium at end of lane. From the South (alternative): A1, turn off on to A63 signposted 'Leeds' immediately after 'Boot & Shoe' Public House. At 1st roundabout turn right on to A656 and follow to next roundabout. Take 1st left on to A642 (Garforth) and follow from M1 junc 47.

**GLASSHOUGHTON WELFARE-The Glasshoughton Centre, Leeds Rd, Glasshoughton, Castleford, WF10 4PF. Tel: (01977) 511234**
Leave the M62 J32, signposted Castleford/Pontefract (A639). At the bottom of the slip road take the A656, taking carer to pick up the middle lane for Castleford. After approx. 1/4 mile, bear left at the first roundabout and, after a further 1/4 mile, left at the next roundabout on to Leeds Road. Ground is then 200 yards on the right.

**HEANOR TOWN-Mayfield Avenue, Heanor DE75 7EN-01773 713 742**
From M1: J26, take A610 Ripley Road to end of dual carriageway then take A608 to Heanor via Langley Mill. At traffic lights at top of long hill take left lane signed Ilkeston. First right into Mundy Street, second left onto Godfrey Street. Ground on left where road forks. From A608 Derby: Enter town and see Tesco on left. Turn right at roundabout to the Market Place. Turn right at end of square and at crossroads right again onto Mundy Street. Then left into Godfrey Street and ground on left where road forks.

**LINCOLN MOORLANDS RAILWAY-Lincoln Moorlands Railway Sports Ground, Newark Road, Lincoln, LN6 8RT. Tel: (01522) 874111**
From North: A1 to Markham Moor. Take A57 until Lincoln by-pass. At Carholme Roundabout take 3rd. exit towards Lincoln South. Travel 1.7 miles to Skellingthorpe Roundabout and take 2nd. Exit towards Lincoln South. Travel 1.6 miles to Doddington Roundabout and take 1st. exit B1190 towards Lincoln South. Travel 2.1 miles until T-junction. Turn left onto A1434 and travel 0.4 mile. Entrance to ground is on left immediately after Chancery Close. From Newark: A46 to Lincoln by-pass. At roundabout take last exit onto A1434 towards Lincoln. Travel for 3.1 miles, entrance to ground on left immediately after Chancery Close signposted 'Moorlands Railway Club'.

**LIVERSEDGE-Clayborn Ground, Quaker Lane, Hightown Road, Cleckheaton, WF15 8DF. Tel: (01274) 682108**
M62 J26, A638 thru Dewsbury and Heckmondwike to Cleckheaton, turn right on corner of Memorial Park, through next lights and under railway bridge, first left (Hightown Rd) and Quaker Lane is approx 1/4 mile on left and leads to ground. From M1 J40, A638 thru Dewsbury and Heckmondwike to Cleckheaton, left at Memorial Park lights then as above. Buses 218 & 220 (Leeds-Huddersfield) pass top of Quaker Lane.

**LONG EATON UNITED-Grange Park, Station Road, Long Eaton, NG10 2EG. Tel: (0115) 973 5700**
From M1 June 25, take A52 towards Nottingham, to island by Bardills Garden Centre, right onto B6003. Approx 2 miles to end of road to T-junction. At traffic lights, turn right again A453 and take 2nd left into Station Road. Entrance on left down un-named road opposite disused car park next to Grange School.

**MALTBY MAIN-Muglet Lane, Maltby, Rotherham, S66 7JQ. Tel: (07795) 693683**
Exit M18 at Junc 1 with A631. Two miles into Maltby, right at traffic lights at Queens Hotel corner on to B6427 Muglet Lane. Ground 3/4 mile on left.

**NOSTELL MINERS WELFARE-The Welfare Ground, Crofton Community Centre, Middle Lane, New Crofton, Wakefield, WF4 1LB. Tel: (01924) 866010**
M1 J39, head towards Wakefield (A638), Denby Dale road. Leave Wakefield on the A638 (Doncaster Rd), towards Wakefield Trinity Ground. Continue on this road for another 2 miles, you will pass the Red Beck Motel on your right. Go under the bridge and turn right opposite the Public house 'Crofton Arms'. Follow road through Crofton village (1 1/4 miles). Turn left at 'Slipper' public house, then right onto Middle Lane, follow road round to reach Crofton Community Centre.

**PARKGATE-Roundwood Sports Complex, Green Lane, Rawmarsh, Rotherham, S62 6LA. Tel: (01709) 826600**
From Rotherham A633 to Rawmarsh. From Doncaster A630 to Conisbrough, then A6023 through Swinton to Rawmarsh. Grd at Green Lane-right from Rotherham, left from Conisbrough at the Crown Inn. Ground 800yds on right.

**PICKERING TOWN-Recreation Club, off Mill Lane, Malton Rd, Pickering, YO18 7DB. Tel: (01751) 473317**
A169 from Malton. On entering Pickering, take 1st left past Police Station and BP garage into Mill Lane, ground 200 yds on right.

NORTHERN COUNTIES EAST LEAGUE - STEP 5/6

**RETFORD-Cannon Park, Leverton Road, Retford, Notts DN22 6QF. Tel: (01777) 869 468 / 710 300**
Leave the A1 at Ranby and follow the A620 towards Retford. Go past Ranby prison and go straight on at the next 2 mini roundabouts. At the 3rd roundabout take the 3rd exit signposted Gainsborough. Passing Morrisons on the left, go through the traffic lights and move into the right hand lane. Turn right at the traffic lights. Turn left at the traffic lights by the Broken Wheel Public House into Leverton Road. Go past the Masons Arms Public House and go over 2 hump backed bridges. The ground is signposted and is on the right.
**STAVELEY MINERS WELFARE-Inkersall Road, Staveley, Chesterfield, S43 3JL. Tel: (01246) 471441**
M1 J30 follow A619 Chesterfield. Staveley is 3 miles from J30. Turn left at GK Garage in Staveley town centre into Inkersall Road. Ground is 200 yards on right at side of Speedwell Rooms.
**TADCASTER ALBION-2inspire Park, Ings Lane, Tadcaster, LS24 9AY**
From West Riding and South Yorks-Turn right off A659 at John Smith's Brewery Clock. From East Riding-Turn left off A659 after passing over river bridge and pelican crossing (New Street).
**THACKLEY-Dennyfield, Ainsbury Avenue, Thackley, Bradford, BD10 0TL. Tel: (01274) 615571**
On main Leeds/Keighley A657 road, turn off at Thackley corner which is 2 miles from Shipley traffic lights and 1 mile from Greengates lights. Ainsbury Avenue bears to the right 200yds down the hill. Ground is 200yds along Ainsbury Avenue on the right.
**WINTERTON RANGERS-West Street, Winterton, Scunthorpe, DN15 9QF. Tel: (01724) 732628**
From Scunthorpe-Take A1077 Barton-on-Humber for 5 miles. On entering Winterton take 3rd right (Eastgate), 3rd left (Northlands Rd) and 1st Right (West St). Ground 200 yards on left.
**WORKSOP PARRAMORE-The Windsor Foodservice Stadium, Sandy Land, Worksop S80 1TJ. Tel: 01909 479 955**
From either the A1 or M1 J31, take the A57 towards Worksop. After approximately 7 miles, look out for the A60/Sandy Lane turnoff at the roundabout. Continue over two mini-roundabouts for ¾mile then turn left into the retail park and left again into the stadium car park.

## DIVISION ONE

**A.F.C. EMLEY-The Welfare Ground, Off Upper Lane, Emley, nr Huddersfield, HD8 9RE. Tel: 01924 849392 or 07702 712287**
From M1 J38: Travel on road signposted to Huddersfield through the village of Bretton to the first roundabout. Take first exit off this roundabout signposted Denby Dale. After approximately one mile turn right at road signposted Emley. After 2 miles enter the village of Emley. Entrance to ground is opposite a white bollard in centre of road. (Narrow entrance).
From M1 J39: Travel on road signposted toward Denby Dale. Travel for approximately 3 miles up hill to first roundabout. Take 2nd exit and follow directions as above.
**APPLEBY FRODINGHAM-Brumby Hall Sports Ground, Ashby Road, Scunthorpe, DN16 1AA. Tel: 01724 402134 or 01724 843024**
From M18, take J5 on to the M180. From M180, take J3 onto the M181 (Scunthorpe West). At the roundabout, turn right onto A18. Straight on at the mini roundabout (McDonalds). At the next large roundabout, take the third exit (A18) up the hill to the next roundabout, turn left and the entrance to the ground is 100 metres on the left.
**BOTTESFORD TOWN-Birch Park, Ontario Road, Bottesford, Scunthorpe, DN17 2TQ. Tel: (01724) 871883**
Exit M180 via M181-Scunthorpe. At circle (Berkeley Hotel), turn right into Scotter Road. At circle (Asda) straight ahead, 2nd left into South Park road then on to Sunningdale Road, turn right into Goodwood Road, Birch Park at end (right turn). Please note that Goodwood Road is not suitable for large vehicles. Instead, take 2nd right off Sunningdale Road which is Quebec Road, then 2nd right which is Ontario Road down to the bottom and ground is on the left.
**CLEETHORPES TOWN-The Bradley Football Development Centre, Bradley Road, Grimsby, DN37 0AG**
Head East along the M180/A180. Exit at the Great Coates Interchange. Travel back over motorway to first Roundabout. Take first exit and follow for two miles to Trawl Pub Roundabout. Take second exit, follow for two miles to Bradley Roundabout. Take second exit on to Bradley Road. The ground is approximately 500 yards on the left.
**CLIPSTONE WELFARE-The Lido Ground, Clipstone Road East, Clipstone Village, Mansfield, NG21 9AB. Tel: 01623 423730**
From M1 J29, take exit signposted A617 Mansfield. At next roundabout, take third exit continuing on the A617. Keep going straight on until you get to the Mansfield ring road with Riley's snooker hall on your right and a miner's statue on your left. Follow the road round underneath a pedestrian bridge and take the next left onto the A6191 (Ratcliffe Gate). After around half a mile, turn left onto the B6030 (Carter Lane). Follow the B6030 for about 3 miles, go straight on at a roundabout and the ground will be on your left.
**DINNINGTON TOWN-Phoenix Park, Dinnington Resource Centre, 131 Laughton Road, Dinnington S25 2PP. Tel: (01909) 518555**
From M1 J31, follow A57 Worksop Road East for 1 mile. At first traffic lights, turn left onto B6463 Todwick Road then Monks Bridge Road for 2 miles. At petrol station roundabout, take third exit signposted Dinnington and travel half-a-mile, then take first left at Morrell Tyres. Cross mini-roundabout at The Squirrel pub and travel on Laughton Road for 300 yards. Ground is on the left.
**DRONFIELD TOWN - Stonelow Playing Fields, Stonelow Road, Dronfield, S18 2DA**
**ECCLESHILL UNITED-The Smith Butler Stadium, Kingsway, Wrose, Bradford, BD2 1PN. Tel: (01274) 615739**
M62 J26 onto M606, right onto Bradford Ring Road A6177, left on to A650 for Bradford at 2nd roundabout. A650 Bradford Inner Ring Road onto Canal Rd, branch right at Staples (Dixons Car showrooms on right), fork left after 30mph sign to junction with Wrose Road, across junction-continuation of Kings Rd, first left onto Kingsway. Ground is 200 yards on right.
**GRIMSBY BOROUGH-Grimsby Community Stadium, Bradley Road, Grimsby, DN37 0AG**
Head South East on the A180 to the Great Coates turn off come back over the A180 and follow for 1/2 mile to the roundabout, take first exit follow over one mini roundabout and through one set of traffic lights until you come to the Trawl Pub roundabout, take the second exit onto Littlecoates road and follow over one mini roundabout to the second roundabout and take the second exit onto Bradley Road. The ground is approx 800 yards on your left with car and coach parking facilities.
**HALL ROAD RANGERS-Dene Park, Dene Close, Beverley Road, Dunswell, nr Hull, HU6 0AA. Tel: (01482) 850101**
M62 to A63, turn left before Humber Bridge onto A164 to Beverley, after approx. 5 miles turn right onto A1079. In 2 miles, turn left at large roundabout to ground 20 yards on right.
**HALLAM-Sandygate, Sandygate Road, Crosspool, Sheffield, S10 5SE. Tel: (0114) 230 9484**
A57 Sheffield to Glossop Rd, left at Crosspool shopping area signed Lodge Moor on to Sandygate Rd. Ground half mile on left opposite Plough Inn. 51 bus from Crucible Theatre.
**HEMSWORTH MINERS WELFARE-Fitzwilliam Stadium, Wakefield Road, Fitzwilliam, Pontefract, WF9 5AJ. Tel: (01977) 614997**
From East/West: M62 to J32 towards Pontefract then follow A628 towards Hemsworth. At Ackworth roundabout (Stoneacre Suzuki Garage), take a right on to the A638 Wakefield Road. Travel half a mile to next roundabout then take first exit. Travel one mile to crossroads and turn left into Fitzwilliam. Pass a row of shops on your right and turn left after the bus shelter before an iron bridge. To ground. **From North**: A1 South to M62 then follow above directions. **From South:** A1(M) North to A638 Wakefield Road. Travel to Ackworth Roundabout (Stoneacre Suzuki Garage) and go straight across and follow the A638 to the next roundabout. Take first exit then to crossroads. Turn left into Fitzwilliam and pass row of shops on your right. Turn left after bus shelter before iron bridge and carry on to the ground. Alternative: M1 to J32 then take M18 to A1(M).
**KNARESBOROUGH TOWN-Manse Lane, Manse Lane, Knaresborough, HG5 8LF. Tel: 01423 548896**
From West/South Leeds Area: A658 or A61 towards Harrogate. Join A658 southern bypass towards York. At roundabout with B6164, turn left to Knaresborough. Turn left at second roundabout and travel over river bridge. Manse Lane is first on right alongside garage; From East Leeds Area: A58 or A1 to Wetherby. Join B6164 to Knaresborough then as above. From East on A59 from A1: Turn right at first roundabout. Manse Lane is first turn left after speed restriction sign.
**LOUTH TOWN-The Park Avenue Stadium, Park Avenue, Louth, LN11 8BY. Tel: 07891 965531**
Enter Louth from the A16 onto North Home Road. Go 1/2 mile and follow the road as it bends to the right to become Newbridge Hill. At the junction, turn right onto Ramsgate. At the mini roundabout next to Morrisons, turn left onto Eastgate. Go 1/2 mile down Eastgate and turn right into Park Avenue just past the fire station.
**PONTEFRACT COLLIERIES-Skinner Lane, Pontefract, WF8 4QE. Tel: (01977) 600818**
M62 jct32 (Xscape) towards Pontefract. Left at lights after roundabout for park entrance and retail park. Traffic through town should follow racecourse signs through lights to roundabout and back to lights.
**ROSSINGTON MAIN-Welfare Ground, Oxford Street, Rossington, Doncaster, DN11 0TE. Tel: (01302) 865524 (Matchdays only)**
Enter Rossington and go over the railway crossings. Passing the Welfare Club, Oxford Street is the next road on the right. The ground is at the bottom of Oxford Street.
**SELBY TOWN-The Selby Times Stadium, Richard St, Scott Rd, Selby, YO8 4BN. Tel: (01757) 210900**
From Leeds, left at main traffic lights in Selby down Scott Rd, then 1st left into Richard St. From Doncaster, go straight across main traffic lights into Scott Rd then 1st left. From York, right at main traffic lights into Scott Rd and 1st left.
**SHAW LANE AQUAFORCE - Shaw Lane, Barnsley, S70 6HZ. Tel: 01226 203 509**
Leave the M1 at J37 and take the A628 (Barnsley). Use left hand lane and proceed through traffic lights. Take second right (Shaw Lane). The ground is 100m on the right.
**SHIREBROOK TOWN-Shirebrook Staff Sports and Social Club, Langwith Road, Shirebrook, Mansfield, Notts, NG20 8TF. Tel: (01623) 742535**
Depart M1 at Junction 29, at roundabout take A617 towards Mansfield (for 3.5 miles), at next roundabout take 2nd Exit B6407 Common Lane towards Shirebrook (or 1.8 miles), go straight on at next roundabout (for 300 yards), at staggered crossroads turn right onto Main Street (for 1.1 miles), at T Junction turn right (for 100 yards), take the first road on your left (Langwith Road). The ground is 400 yards on the right.
**TEVERSAL-Teversal Grange Sports and Social Centre, Carnarvon Street, Teversal, Sutton-in-Ashfield, NG17 3HJ. Tel: (07773) 922539**
From North: Travel South on the M1 to junction 29 take the A6175 to Heath and Holmewood. Travel through Holmewood, and at the roundabout take the B6039 to Hardstaff and Tibshelf. At the T-junction in Tibshelf (pub on your left) turn left onto B6014 travelling over the motorway into Teversal. Follow the road round passing the Carnarvon Arms pub and under a bridge, take 2nd left onto Coppywood Close, travel to the top and following the road round with the ground at the top.
From South: From the M1 junction 28, take the A38 to Mansfield. Travel through a number of sets of traffic lights and after passing the Kings Mill Reservoir you will come to a major junction (King & Miller Pub and McDonalds on your left). Travel straight on taking the A6075 towards Mansfield Woodhouse, at the next set of traffic lights turn left onto the B6014 to Stanton Hill. You will come to a roundabout with a Kwik Save on your left, continue on the B6014 towards Tibshelf. Take the second right onto Coppywood Close, travel to the top and following the road round with the ground at the top.
**WORSBOROUGH BRIDGE ATHLETIC-Park Road, Worsbrough Bridge, Barnsley, S70 5LJ. Tel: (01226) 284452**
On the A61, Barnsley-Sheffield road two miles south of Barnsley, 2 miles from M1 J36 opposite Blackburns Bridge.
**YORKSHIRE AMATEUR-Bracken Edge, Roxholme Road, Leeds, LS8 4DZ. Tel: (0113) 262 4093**
From South-M1 to Leeds, then A58 to Wetherby Road to Fforde Green Hotel, left at lights and proceed to Sycamore Avenue (on right). From East-A1 to Boot & Shoe Inn then to Shaftesbury Hotel, turn right into Harehills Lane, then to Sycamore Avenue.

# NORTHERN LEAGUE

**Sponsored by:** Ebac
**Founded:** 1889
**Recent Champions:**
2008: Durham City
2009: Newcastle Benfield
2010: Spennymoor Town
2011: Spennymoor Town
2012: Spennymoor Town
**northernleague.org**

## LEAGUE CUP

### ROUND 1
| | | | |
|---|---|---|---|
| Celtic Nation FC | v | Brandon United | 5 - 1 |
| Consett | v | Newton Aycliffe | 7 - 2 |
| Crook Town | v | Sunderland RCA | 1-3 |
| Dunston UTS | v | Shildon | 4-1 |
| Bishop Auckland | v | Ashington | 4-1 |
| Guisborough Town | v | Thornaby | 1-0 |
| North Shields | v | Morpeth Town | 4-2 aet |
| Norton & Stockton Ancients | v | Whitley Bay | 1-8 |
| Horden C.W. | v | Darlington RA | 1-4 |
| Stokesley Sports Club | v | Tow Law Town | 5-5 aet 7-8p |
| Washington | v | Esh Winning | 1-2 |
| West Allotment Celtic | v | Chester-Le-Street | 2-1 |
| Penrith | v | Durham City | 1-3 |
| Whitehaven | v | Hebburn Town (@ Hebburn) | 3-4 |

### ROUND 2
| | | | |
|---|---|---|---|
| Billingham Synthonia | v | Esh Winning | 2-1 aet |
| Bishop Auckland | v | Marske United | 3-1 |
| Team Northumbria | v | Guisborough Town | 2-2 aet 8-7p |
| Bedlington Terriers | v | Newcastle Benfield | 1-2 |
| Celtic Nation FC | v | Birtley Town (@ Birtley) | 6-1 |
| Dunston UTS | v | Jarrow Roofing | 4-0 |
| Durham City | v | Seaham Red Star | 5-1 |
| South Shields | v | Alnwick Town | 4-2 |
| Tow Law Town | v | Sunderland RCA | 2-2 aet 2-3 |
| Darlington 1883 | v | Spennymoor Town | 0-2 |
| North Shields | v | Darlington RA | 4-2 |
| Ryton & Crawcrook Albion | v | West Auckland Town | 1-4 |
| West Allotment Celtic | v | Billingham Town | 7-0 |
| Whitley Bay | v | Consett | 3-1 |
| Ryhope CW | v | Hebburn Town | 3-1 |
| Northallerton Town | v | Whickham | 2-1 |

### ROUND 3
| | | | |
|---|---|---|---|
| Celtic Nation FC | v | Spennymoor Town | 1-3 |
| Durham City | v | Sunderland RCA | 2-3 |
| South Shields | v | Newcastle Benfield | 0-1 |
| West Auckland Town | v | Dunston UTS | 0-1 |
| Whitley Bay | v | Ryhope CW | 4-1 |
| West Allotment Celtic | v | Team Northumbria | 3-2 |
| Northallerton Town | v | Billingham Synthonia | 0-3 |
| North Shields | v | Bishop Auckland | 2-3 |

### QUARTER FINALS
| | | | |
|---|---|---|---|
| Sunderland RCA | v | Spennymoor Town | 0-1 |
| West Allotment Celtic | v | Dunston UTS | 0-2 |
| Billingham Synthonia | v | Newcastle Benfield | 0-1 |
| Bishop Auckland | v | Whitley Bay | 0-0 aet 5-4p |

### SEMI FINALS
| | | | |
|---|---|---|---|
| Bishop Auckland | v | Newcastle Benfield | 1-5 aet |
| Dunston UTS | v | Spennymoor Town | 1-2 |

### FINAL
| | | | |
|---|---|---|---|
| Newcastle Benfield | v | Spennymoor Town | 0-1 |

## DIVISION ONE

| | | P | W | D | L | F | A | Pts |
|---|---|---|---|---|---|---|---|---|
| 1 | (P) Darlington 1883 | 46 | 40 | 2 | 4 | 145 | 35 | 122 |
| 2 | Spennymoor Town | 46 | 33 | 10 | 3 | 108 | 34 | 109 |
| 3 | Whitley Bay | 46 | 27 | 7 | 12 | 110 | 62 | 88 |
| 4 | West Auckland Town | 46 | 25 | 9 | 12 | 112 | 75 | 84 |
| 5 | Dunston UTS | 46 | 23 | 10 | 13 | 74 | 50 | 79 |
| 6 | Bishop Auckland | 46 | 24 | 7 | 15 | 95 | 77 | 79 |
| 7 | Ashington | 46 | 21 | 13 | 12 | 106 | 68 | 76 |
| 8 | Shildon | 46 | 19 | 12 | 15 | 83 | 69 | 69 |
| 9 | Consett | 46 | 19 | 11 | 16 | 68 | 63 | 68 |
| 10 | Celtic Nation FC | 46 | 19 | 10 | 17 | 80 | 79 | 67 |
| 11 | Guisborough Town | 46 | 20 | 6 | 20 | 78 | 87 | 66 |
| 12 | Billingham Synthonia | 46 | 17 | 10 | 19 | 79 | 83 | 61 |
| 13 | Penrith | 46 | 17 | 9 | 20 | 92 | 96 | 60 |
| 14 | Durham City | 46 | 17 | 8 | 21 | 90 | 90 | 59 |
| 15 | Bedlington Terriers (-3pts) | 46 | 18 | 7 | 21 | 90 | 83 | 58 |
| 16 | Team Northumbria | 46 | 14 | 14 | 18 | 63 | 80 | 56 |
| 17 | Newton Aycliffe | 46 | 16 | 5 | 25 | 71 | 89 | 53 |
| 18 | Hebburn Town | 46 | 15 | 8 | 23 | 81 | 109 | 53 |
| 19 | Marske United | 46 | 15 | 4 | 27 | 66 | 91 | 49 |
| 20 | Billingham Town | 46 | 13 | 8 | 25 | 84 | 125 | 47 |
| 21 | Newcastle Benfield | 46 | 14 | 4 | 28 | 51 | 88 | 46 |
| 22 | Sunderland RCA (-3pts) | 46 | 12 | 8 | 26 | 62 | 103 | 41 |
| 23 | (R) South Shields | 46 | 11 | 5 | 30 | 54 | 117 | 38 |
| 24 | (R) Norton & Stockton Ancients | 46 | 6 | 7 | 33 | 39 | 128 | 25 |

## DIVISION ONE (results grid)

| DIVISION ONE | 1 | 2 | 3 | 4 | 5 | 6 | 7 | 8 | 9 | 10 | 11 | 12 | 13 | 14 | 15 | 16 | 17 | 18 | 19 | 20 | 21 | 22 | 23 | 24 |
|---|---|---|---|---|---|---|---|---|---|---|---|---|---|---|---|---|---|---|---|---|---|---|---|---|
| 1 Ashington | | 3-3 | 2-1 | 8-1 | 0-1 | 4-1 | 0-0 | 0-1 | 1-1 | 6-2 | 1-2 | 1-1 | 2-2 | 3-0 | 3-1 | 4-1 | 2-2 | 1-2 | 2-0 | 1-2 | 3-1 | 2-0 | 3-3 | 1-2 |
| 2 Bedlington Terriers | 4-0 | | 6-0 | 0-2 | 1-3 | 2-4 | 1-3 | 0-4 | 1-1 | 6-2 | 1-0 | 5-2 | 3-1 | 4-0 | 0-0 | 0-0 | 3-1 | 8-1 | 1-2 | 0-6 | 2-3 | 5-1 | 4-2 | 1-1 |
| 3 Billingham Synthonia | 2-2 | 1-3 | | 0-1 | 3-2 | 1-3 | 1-1 | 1-4 | 0-0 | 1-1 | 0-2 | 1-1 | 4-1 | 3-4 | 0-1 | 2-2 | 1-0 | 1-1 | 4-1 | 0-1 | 2-0 | 3-2 | 2-2 | 2-1 |
| 4 Billingham Town | 2-4 | 4-4 | 1-3 | | 2-5 | 0-0 | 1-0 | 1-7 | 2-5 | 4-2 | 2-5 | 0-4 | 2-1 | 3-2 | 3-0 | 2-1 | 0-0 | 2-1 | 0-3 | 1-1 | 4-0 | 1-4 | 1-2 | |
| 5 Bishop Auckland | 2-1 | 2-1 | 0-8 | 6-2 | | 1-2 | 1-1 | 1-3 | 0-0 | 2-3 | 2-1 | 0-1 | 3-2 | 3-0 | 1-0 | 6-2 | 1-3 | 4-2 | 1-1 | 1-0 | 2-0 | 3-4 | 1-4 | |
| 6 Celtic Nation | 2-0 | 2-0 | 1-4 | 3-1 | 2-2 | | 2-2 | 1-2 | 0-1 | 2-1 | 3-2 | 3-0 | 1-1 | 2-1 | 1-1 | 0-3 | 3-3 | 2-3 | 1-0 | 0-3 | 2-1 | 3-3 | 1-3 | 1-3 |
| 7 Consett | 2-2 | 1-0 | 4-1 | 3-2 | 4-2 | 2-0 | | 0-3 | 1-0 | 0-2 | 1-0 | 2-3 | 1-2 | 1-2 | 1-3 | 2-0 | 0-2 | 1-1 | 1-1 | 2-2 | 3-0 | 0-1 | 3-4 | 0-1 |
| 8 Darlington 1883 | 6-1 | 3-1 | 4-1 | 3-2 | 2-2 | 1-0 | 5-0 | | 4-0 | 3-1 | 3-0 | 1-0 | 3-0 | 5-2 | 1-0 | 6-1 | 1-0 | 4-0 | 2-1 | 0-0 | 7-2 | 3-1 | 2-0 | 3-1 |
| 9 Dunston UTS | 2-2 | 2-1 | 2-0 | 1-1 | 1-1 | 0-0 | 0-2 | 0-3 | | 3-1 | 4-0 | 3-1 | 3-0 | 2-0 | 0-2 | 3-1 | 4-0 | 2-1 | 1-0 | 1-0 | 5-2 | 2-1 | | |
| 10 Durham City | 2-3 | 3-1 | 1-2 | 6-1 | 0-2 | 6-3 | 3-2 | 0-4 | 2-0 | | 1-2 | 4-2 | 0-1 | 4-0 | 5-2 | 1-2 | 4-4 | 1-0 | 6-1 | 2-3 | 1-2 | 0-2 | 3-1 | 0-4 |
| 11 Guisborough Town | 1-0 | 1-2 | 2-4 | 3-7 | 3-2 | 3-1 | 0-2 | 4-1 | 1-1 | 3-0 | | 4-3 | 1-0 | 5-1 | 5-0 | 0-3 | 0-3 | 1-3 | 0-6 | 2-1 | 1-1 | 3-2 | 1-3 | |
| 12 Hebburn Town | 3-5 | 2-3 | 4-0 | 4-3 | 0-0 | 4-3 | 1-1 | 1-7 | 0-3 | 1-3 | 4-3 | | 1-1 | 3-3 | 1-4 | 3-2 | 0-4 | 0-4 | 3-3 | 2-2 | 0-3 | 4-1 | | |
| 13 Marske United | 1-5 | 3-1 | 0-3 | 3-1 | 3-1 | 2-1 | 1-2 | 0-5 | 0-2 | 1-3 | 0-1 | 2-4 | | 2-1 | 1-0 | 1-0 | 2-2 | 1-2 | 2-3 | 1-3 | 4-0 | 1-0 | 0-3 | |
| 14 Newcastle Benfield | 0-2 | 2-0 | 0-2 | 2-1 | 0-1 | 0-4 | 0-1 | 0-4 | 1-2 | 1-0 | 4-4 | 1-3 | 2-1 | | 1-0 | 1-2 | 3-1 | 1-0 | 0-0 | 0-2 | 1-0 | 1-1 | 1-3 | 2-4 |
| 15 Newton Aycliffe | 2-1 | 4-0 | 1-1 | 0-8 | 1-5 | 1-2 | 0-2 | 2-1 | 0-1 | 0-1 | 3-1 | 1-4 | 1-0 | 0-3 | | 4-0 | 1-3 | 3-1 | 2-3 | 1-2 | 2-0 | 5-1 | 2-1 | 2-3 |
| 16 Norton & St'ton Ancients | 0-5 | 1-0 | 1-3 | 3-0 | 3-2 | 1-4 | 0-4 | 2-4 | 0-3 | 0-1 | 1-0 | 0-3 | 0-5 | | 1-2 | | 2-2 | 1-2 | 0-6 | 1-5 | 1-1 | 0-7 | 1-3 | |
| 17 Penrith | 3-4 | 1-4 | 5-0 | 2-2 | 0-2 | 5-1 | 1-2 | 1-4 | 2-2 | 3-2 | 0-1 | 1-2 | 3-1 | 1-3 | 6-0 | | | 2-2 | 3-2 | 3-2 | 2-1 | 0-1 | 0-1 | 2-2 |
| 18 Shildon | 0-2 | 3-0 | 2-1 | 1-3 | 2-1 | 2-2 | 4-1 | 0-2 | 0-2 | 3-1 | 2-0 | 3-2 | 2-3 | 2-0 | 2-1 | 2-0 | 4-1 | | 11-0 | 1-1 | 2-3 | 1-1 | 1-1 | 0-2 |
| 19 South Shields | 0-2 | 1-3 | 0-1 | 3-2 | 0-1 | 2-1 | 1-2 | 0-3 | 0-4 | 1-1 | 3-2 | 0-2 | 0-4 | 0-2 | 3-3 | 3-2 | 5-1 | 0-2 | | 0-4 | 2-4 | 1-3 | 1-1 | 1-6 |
| 20 Spennymoor Town | 0-0 | 0-0 | 4-2 | 3-0 | 4-0 | 1-1 | 3-1 | 1-3 | 2-0 | 3-2 | 2-2 | 3-0 | 1-0 | 2-0 | 2-0 | 0-1 | 2-0 | 1-0 | | | 2-1 | 3-0 | 2-0 | 3-1 |
| 21 Sunderland RCA | 0-6 | 0-1 | 1-3 | 2-0 | 1-5 | 0-2 | 2-2 | 0-4 | 0-1 | 1-1 | 3-3 | 1-0 | 3-2 | 0-3 | 2-2 | 3-4 | 2-0 | 0-3 | 3-2 | 1-1 | | 2-3 | 1-2 | 0-1 |
| 22 Team Northumbria | 1-1 | 2-3 | 2-2 | 3-0 | 3-1 | 1-3 | 0-0 | 2-0 | 2-0 | 0-0 | 1-1 | 0-2 | 3-2 | 2-4 | 3-0 | 2-2 | 1-2 | 1-1 | 2-0 | 0-2 | 5-1 | | 0-1 | 1-2 |
| 23 West Auckland Town | 2-2 | 2-1 | 2-4 | 4-1 | 5-1 | 0-1 | 2-0 | 2-1 | 3-2 | 3-3 | 2-0 | 4-1 | 2-1 | 3-2 | 4-2 | 4-2 | 2-2 | 0-0 | 6-0 | 2-3 | 6-2 | 0-1 | | 3-2 |
| 24 Whitley Bay | 1-3 | 1-0 | 2-1 | 6-0 | 0-2 | 2-2 | 0-2 | 0-3 | 1-0 | 2-2 | 0-3 | 5-0 | 4-0 | 3-1 | 3-0 | 8-3 | 3-1 | 3-0 | 2-3 | 1-1 | 6-0 | 2-2 | | |

## DIVISION TWO

| | | P | W | D | L | F | A | Pts |
|---|---|---|---|---|---|---|---|---|
| 1 | (P) Crook Town | 42 | 32 | 5 | 5 | 123 | 60 | 101 |
| 2 | Ryhope CW | 42 | 30 | 8 | 4 | 147 | 52 | 98 |
| 3 | (P) Morpeth Town | 42 | 25 | 10 | 7 | 108 | 51 | 85 |
| 4 | Jarrow Roofing | 42 | 26 | 7 | 9 | 100 | 46 | 85 |
| 5 | Darlington RA | 42 | 22 | 12 | 8 | 82 | 57 | 78 |
| 6 | Northallerton Town | 42 | 23 | 8 | 11 | 101 | 63 | 77 |
| 7 | West Allotment Celtic | 42 | 23 | 8 | 11 | 95 | 66 | 77 |
| 8 | North Shields | 42 | 21 | 7 | 14 | 72 | 54 | 70 |
| 9 | Whitehaven (-3pts) | 42 | 20 | 8 | 14 | 97 | 74 | 65 |
| 10 | Seaham Red Star | 42 | 19 | 8 | 15 | 86 | 85 | 65 |
| 11 | Tow Law Town | 42 | 19 | 7 | 16 | 83 | 66 | 64 |
| 12 | Washington | 42 | 16 | 4 | 22 | 72 | 93 | 52 |
| 13 | Chester-Le-Street | 42 | 13 | 10 | 19 | 51 | 73 | 49 |
| 14 | Ryton & Crawcrook Albion | 42 | 15 | 4 | 23 | 56 | 82 | 49 |
| 15 | Stokesley Sports Club | 42 | 12 | 8 | 22 | 60 | 93 | 44 |
| 16 | Whickham | 42 | 11 | 8 | 23 | 57 | 86 | 41 |
| 17 | Birtley Town | 42 | 10 | 8 | 24 | 47 | 83 | 38 |
| 18 | Brandon United (-3pts) | 42 | 10 | 11 | 21 | 55 | 93 | 38 |
| 19 | Thornaby | 42 | 9 | 5 | 28 | 59 | 106 | 32 |
| 20 | Esh Winning (-3pts) | 42 | 10 | 3 | 29 | 49 | 108 | 30 |
| 21 | Alnwick Town (-3pts) | 42 | 8 | 8 | 26 | 63 | 100 | 29 |
| 22 | (R) Horden C.W. | 42 | 7 | 5 | 30 | 43 | 115 | 26 |

## ERNSET ARMSTRONG MEMORIAL CUP

### ROUND 1

| | | | |
|---|---|---|---|
| Chester-Le-Street | v | Crook Town | 1-1 aet 4-2p |
| Brandon United | v | Horden C.W. | 4-3 |
| Thornaby | v | Birtley Town | 2-1 |
| Ryton & Crawcrook Albion | v | Washington | 0-2 |
| Jarrow Roofing | v | Tow Law Town | 4-4 aet 5-4p |
| Northallerton Town | v | Alnwick Town | 3-0 |

### ROUND 2

| | | | |
|---|---|---|---|
| Thornaby | v | Chester-Le-Street | 2-2 aet 1-3p |
| Esh Winning | v | Stokesley Sports Club | 7-1 |
| Brandon United | v | Morpeth Town | 3-0 |
| Whickham | v | Darlington RA | 1-4 |
| Northallerton Town | v | Ryhope CW | 5-3 aet |
| Washington | v | North Shields | 1-0 |
| Jarrow Roofing | v | Whitehaven | 4-0 |
| West Allotment Celtic | v | Seaham Red Star | 4-2 |

### QUARTER FINALS

| | | | |
|---|---|---|---|
| Chester-Le-Street | v | Northallerton Town | 2-3 aet |
| Jarrow Roofing | v | Brandon United | 6-4 aet |
| Darlington RA | v | Esh Winning | 4-0 |
| Washington | v | West Allotment Celtic | 1-3 |

### SEMI FINALS

| | | | |
|---|---|---|---|
| West Allotment Celtic | v | Darlington RA | 4-3 aet |
| Northallerton Town | v | Jarrow Roofing | 3-1 |

### FINAL

| | | | |
|---|---|---|---|
| Northallerton Town | v | West Allotment Celtic | 1-3 |

## J.R. CLEATOR CUP
### (League champions v League Cup winners)

| | | | |
|---|---|---|---|
| Spennymoor Town | v | Team Northumbria | 2-0 |

## DIVISION TWO

| DIVISION TWO | 1 | 2 | 3 | 4 | 5 | 6 | 7 | 8 | 9 | 10 | 11 | 12 | 13 | 14 | 15 | 16 | 17 | 18 | 19 | 20 | 21 | 22 |
|---|---|---|---|---|---|---|---|---|---|---|---|---|---|---|---|---|---|---|---|---|---|---|
| 1 Alnwick Town | | 0-1 | 2-2 | 4-1 | 2-3 | 0-2 | 5-1 | 1-1 | 0-0 | 0-4 | 2-2 | 0-4 | 1-1 | 1-3 | 3-4 | 1-1 | 4-1 | 2-0 | 5-2 | 0-4 | 0-1 | 2-1 |
| 2 Birtley Town | 3-3 | | 2-1 | 1-2 | 1-2 | 1-1 | 2-1 | 0-2 | 1-2 | 0-3 | 0-0 | 1-6 | 0-1 | 2-1 | 0-3 | 4-1 | 0-3 | 3-3 | 2-0 | 2-2 | 4-3 | |
| 3 Brandon United | 4-0 | 3-1 | | 1-1 | 1-2 | 1-5 | 2-2 | 3-1 | 1-10 | 1-4 | 2-2 | 2-1 | 1-2 | 0-1 | 6-3 | 2-1 | 0-1 | 0-4 | 1-1 | 0-0 | 1-1 | 1-4 |
| 4 Chester-Le-Street | 2-0 | 2-0 | 2-2 | | 2-3 | 1-1 | 6-1 | 0-0 | 0-1 | 0-2 | 0-2 | 1-5 | 1-2 | 2-0 | 1-2 | 0-1 | 1-0 | 0-5 | 0-0 | 1-1 | 2-0 | 2-1 |
| 5 Crook Town | 3-2 | 5-1 | 2-2 | 6-0 | | 2-2 | 2-0 | 4-1 | 1-1 | 3-2 | 3-1 | 2-0 | 3-2 | 5-0 | 7-1 | 2-0 | 6-1 | 1-3 | 7-1 | 2-0 | 1-1 | 3-1 |
| 6 Darlington RA | 4-2 | 2-1 | 1-1 | 0-0 | 3-2 | | 8-1 | 3-1 | 1-0 | 1-2 | 2-1 | 1-2 | 1-6 | 1-0 | 1-1 | 5-0 | 4-2 | 3-0 | 0-1 | 1-1 | 1-0 | 0-0 |
| 7 Esh Winning | 2-1 | 0-2 | 2-0 | 0-1 | 6-2 | 1-1 | | 1-2 | 2-0 | 1-5 | 1-2 | 3-1 | 0-5 | 0-3 | 4-1 | 2-3 | 0-5 | 0-2 | 0-4 | 0-3 | 4-2 | 2-3 |
| 8 Horden C.W. | 1-2 | 2-2 | 3-0 | 1-2 | 1-2 | 0-1 | 1-0 | | 0-3 | 1-3 | 0-3 | 1-4 | 0-5 | 1-3 | 0-4 | 1-2 | 2-1 | 1-2 | 2-0 | 2-5 | 1-3 | 2-6 |
| 9 Jarrow Roofing | 3-1 | 4-0 | 3-0 | 6-1 | 2-3 | 0-3 | 2-0 | 10-2 | | 3-2 | 1-0 | 0-2 | 2-2 | 0-3 | 3-3 | 3-0 | 1-1 | 3-0 | 1-2 | 5-1 | 2-0 | 3-2 |
| 10 Morpeth Town | 4-1 | 0-0 | 5-2 | 4-2 | 3-1 | 9-1 | 1-0 | 0-0 | 3-2 | | 1-2 | 6-0 | 3-4 | 2-3 | 0-3 | 3-1 | 2-1 | 1-0 | 6-1 | 1-1 | 0-0 | 2-0 |
| 11 North Shields | 1-0 | 1-0 | 1-0 | 0-2 | 2-0 | 3-0 | 2-1 | 2-0 | 0-0 | 1-1 | | 0-2 | 2-2 | 2-1 | 7-2 | 0-1 | 1-2 | 0-2 | 3-0 | 2-3 | 3-0 | 1-1 |
| 12 Northallerton Town | 3-1 | 4-0 | 4-2 | 2-0 | 3-3 | 1-1 | 1-2 | 3-0 | 0-4 | 0-2 | 5-1 | | 2-2 | 1-1 | 5-2 | 4-1 | 7-1 | 2-2 | 3-4 | 0-1 | 1-0 | 4-0 |
| 13 Ryhope CW | 4-3 | 2-0 | 3-0 | 5-0 | 2-5 | 3-0 | 4-0 | 0-5 | 2-2 | 1-3 | 3-1 | | | 5-0 | 2-2 | 5-0 | 5-1 | 1-3 | 1-0 | 7-1 | 3-1 | 5-2 |
| 14 Ryton & Crawcrook Albion | 3-2 | 0-2 | 1-1 | 0-2 | 1-3 | 0-1 | 3-1 | 1-0 | 1-2 | 0-2 | 1-3 | 1-1 | 0-3 | | 4-3 | 3-2 | 0-2 | 0-5 | 1-0 | 0-3 | 1-2 | 3-0 |
| 15 Seaham Red Star | 3-1 | 1-0 | 4-0 | 0-3 | 2-5 | 2-2 | 2-1 | 3-0 | 2-1 | 1-1 | 1-0 | 2-4 | 0-5 | 3-1 | | 6-0 | 2-3 | 2-2 | 2-0 | 3-3 | 0-0 | 1-2 |
| 16 Stokesley Sports Club | 4-0 | 0-0 | 0-1 | 2-2 | 0-1 | 0-3 | 1-1 | 5-1 | 0-0 | 1-1 | 0-1 | 0-2 | 0-7 | 3-4 | 1-0 | | 1-3 | 2-2 | 3-2 | 0-2 | 7-2 | 2-3 |
| 17 Thornaby | 2-3 | 1-1 | 0-2 | 1-3 | 0-1 | 0-2 | 2-3 | 2-0 | 0-1 | 3-3 | 0-6 | 3-5 | 4-4 | 1-2 | 0-2 | 5-2 | | 0-4 | 2-4 | 0-2 | 0-1 | 1-4 |
| 18 Tow Law Town | 0-0 | 2-4 | 1-2 | 3-1 | 2-3 | 1-2 | 0-0 | 3-1 | 5-1 | 2-2 | 2-5 | 1-4 | 1-2 | 2-5 | 0-0 | 3-1 | 1-5 | | 2-0 | 0-1 | | |
| 19 Washington | 4-2 | 1-3 | 3-2 | 1-0 | 0-3 | 1-2 | 2-0 | 5-2 | 2-3 | 1-3 | 2-4 | 2-0 | 0-6 | 2-1 | 1-2 | 6-0 | 1-3 | 1-2 | | 1-4 | 2-2 | |
| 20 West Allotment Celtic | 2-0 | 4-1 | 1-0 | 3-1 | 2-4 | 0-4 | 6-0 | 7-0 | 3-5 | 4-4 | 2-0 | 1-4 | 2-2 | 2-1 | 2-1 | 3-1 | 5-2 | 1-3 | 1-2 | | 2-1 | 1-0 |
| 21 Whickham | 2-3 | 3-2 | 3-1 | 1-1 | 2-3 | 5-3 | 1-2 | 3-2 | 1-2 | 0-3 | 4-0 | 1-2 | 2-5 | 1-0 | 1-2 | 1-3 | 2-0 | 2-2 | 2-2 | 1-4 | | 1-4 |
| 22 Whitehaven | 4-1 | 2-1 | 4-0 | 1-1 | 1-2 | 2-2 | 4-1 | 2-2 | 2-3 | 0-2 | 1-1 | 2-2 | 1-2 | 5-1 | 0-3 | 1-1 | 3-1 | 5-2 | 1-2 | 1-0 | 4-1 | |

## CLUB MOVEMENTS

**Premier Division - In:** Crook Town (P). Morpeth Town (P).

**Out:** Darlington 1883 (P - Northern Premier Div.1 North). Norton & Stockton Ancients (R). South Shields (R).

**Division One - In:** Heaton Stannington (P - Northern Alliance). Norton & Stockton Ancients (R). South Shields (R). Willington (P - Wearside).

**Out:** Crook Town (P). Horden C.W. (R - Wearside). Morpeth Town (P). Ryhope CW (D - Wearside).

# DIVISION ONE

## ASHINGTON
Founded: 1883     Nickname: The Colliers

**Secretary:** Brian Robson    **(T)** 07843 661 686     **(E)** brian.robson@piramal.com

**Chairman:** Ian Lavery      **Prog Ed:** Ian Jobson

**Ground:** Woodhorn Lane, Ashington NE63 9HF    **(T)** 01670 811 991

**Capacity:**   **Seats:**   **Covered:**   **Midweek Matchday:** Tuesday    **Clubhouse:** Yes   **Shop:** Yes

**Colours(change):** Black & White stripes/black/black.
**Previous Names:** None
**Previous Leagues:** Northern Alliance, Football League, N. Eastern, Midland, Northern Counties, Wearside, N.P.L.
**Records:** Att: 13,199 v Rochdale FA Cup 2nd round 1950
**Senior Honours:** Northern League Div.2 Champions 2000-01, 03-04.

### 10 YEAR RECORD
| 03-04 | 04-05 | 05-06 | 06-07 | 07-08 | 08-09 | 09-10 | 10-11 | 11-12 | 12-13 |
|---|---|---|---|---|---|---|---|---|---|
| NL 2   1 | NL 1   10 | NL 1   16 | NL 1   19 | NL 1   17 | NL 1   16 | NL 1   6 | NL 1   8 | NL 1   5 | NL 1   7 |

## BEDLINGTON TERRIERS COMM.
Founded: 1949     Nickname: Terriers

**Secretary:** Shaun Campbell    **(T)** 07815 181 833     **(E)** shauncampbell32@aol.com

**Chairman:** Ronan Liddane

**Ground:** Doctor Pit Welfare Park, Park Road, Bedlington NE22 5DA    **(T)** 07850 268 711

**Capacity:** 3,000 **Seats:** 300   **Covered:** 500   **Midweek Matchday:** Wednesday    **Clubhouse:** Yes

**Colours(change):** Red with white trim/red/red.
**Previous Names:** Bedlington Mechanics 1949-53 Bedlington United 1961-65
**Previous Leagues:** Northern Alliance
**Records:** Att: 2,400 v Colchester United FA Cup 1st round **Goalscorer:** John Milner
**Senior Honours:** Northern Lge Div 1: 97-98, 98-99, 99-00, 2000-01, 01-02. Northumberland Senior Cup 1996-97, 97-98, 2001-02,03-04.

### 10 YEAR RECORD
| 03-04 | 04-05 | 05-06 | 06-07 | 07-08 | 08-09 | 09-10 | 10-11 | 11-12 | 12-13 |
|---|---|---|---|---|---|---|---|---|---|
| NL 1   3 | NL 1   3 | NL 1   2 | NL 1   20 | NL 1   15 | NL 1   14 | NL 1   7 | NL 1   9 | NL 1   7 | NL 1   15 |

## BILLINGHAM SYNTHONIA
Founded: 1923     Nickname: Synners

**Secretary:** Graham Craggs    **(T)** 07702 530 335     **(E)** graham.craggs@gb.abb.com

**Chairman:** Stuart Coleby      **Prog Ed:** Graeme Goodman

**Ground:** The Stadium, Central Ave, Billingham, Cleveland TS23 1LR    **(T)** 01642 532 348

**Capacity:** 1,970 **Seats:** 370   **Covered:** 370   **Midweek Matchday:** Wednesday    **Clubhouse:** Yes   **Shop:** Yes

**Colours(change):** Green & white quarters/white/white
**Previous Names:** Billingham Synthonia Recreation
**Previous Leagues:** Teesside 1923-the war
**Records:** Att: 4,200 v Bishop Auckland 1958 **Goalscorer:** Tony Hetherington **App:** Andy Harbron
**Senior Honours:** Northern Lge 1956-57, 88-89, 89-90, 95-96. Div.2 86-87.

### 10 YEAR RECORD
| 03-04 | 04-05 | 05-06 | 06-07 | 07-08 | 08-09 | 09-10 | 10-11 | 11-12 | 12-13 |
|---|---|---|---|---|---|---|---|---|---|
| NL 1   9 | NL 1   2 | NL 1   7 | NL 1   14 | NL 1   9 | NL 1   15 | NL 1   12 | NL 1   12 | NL 1   11 | NL 1   12 |

## BILLINGHAM TOWN
Founded: 1967     Nickname: Billy Town

**Secretary:** Glenn Youngman    **(T)** 07984 258 608     **(E)** CFS_IFA@hotmail.com

**Chairman:** Glenn Youngman      **Prog Ed:** Peter Martin

**Ground:** Bedford Terrace, Billingham, Cleveland TS23 4AE    **(T)** 01642 560 043

**Capacity:** 3,000 **Seats:** 176   **Covered:** 600   **Midweek Matchday:** Tuesday    **Clubhouse:** Yes   **Shop:** No

**Colours(change):** All blue
**Previous Names:** Billingham Social Club
**Previous Leagues:** Stockton & District 1968-74 Teesside 1974-82
**Records:** Att: 1,500 v Man City FA Youth Cup 1985 **Goalscorer:** Paul Rowntree 396 **App:** Paul Rowntree 505
**Senior Honours:** Durham Cup 1976-77, 77-78, 2003-04

### 10 YEAR RECORD
| 03-04 | 04-05 | 05-06 | 06-07 | 07-08 | 08-09 | 09-10 | 10-11 | 11-12 | 12-13 |
|---|---|---|---|---|---|---|---|---|---|
| NL 1   5 | NL 1   7 | NL 1   4 | NL 1   2 | NL 1   10 | NL 1   17 | NL 1   19 | NL 1   15 | NL 1   17 | NL 1   20 |

# BISHOP AUCKLAND
Founded: 1886      Nickname:

**Secretary:** John Stubbs     **(T)** 07726 694 672     **(E)** johnstubbsuk@btinternet.com

**Chairman:** Terry Jackson     **Prog Ed:** David Ellison

**Ground:** Heritage Park, Bishop Auckland, Co. Durham DL14 9AE     **(T)** 01388 604 605

**Capacity:** 2,004   **Seats:** 250   **Covered:** 722   **Midweek Matchday:** Tuesday    **Clubhouse:** Yes   **Shop:** No

**Colours(change):** Light & dark blue/blue/blue
**Previous Names:** Auckland Town 1889-1893
**Previous Leagues:** Northern Alliance 1890-91, Northern League 1893-1988, Northern Premier 1988-2006
**Records:** **Att:** 17,000 v Coventry City FA Cup 2nd round 1952 **App:** Bob Hardisty
**Senior Honours:** (Post War) Northern League 1949-50, 50-51, 51-52, 53-54, 54-55, 55-56, 66-67, 84-85, 85-86 (18th Nth Lge title). Durham Challenge Cup 2012-13.

**10 YEAR RECORD**

| 03-04 | 04-05 | 05-06 | 06-07 | 07-08 | 08-09 | 09-10 | 10-11 | 11-12 | 12-13 |
|---|---|---|---|---|---|---|---|---|---|
| NP 1 13 | NP P 19 | NP 1 22 | NL 1 16 | NL 1 20 | NL 1 18 | NL 1 13 | NL 1 14 | NL 1 8 | NL 1 6 |

# CELTIC NATION
Founded: 2005      Nickname:

**Secretary:** Michael Linden     **(T)** 07717 103 666     **(E)** linden146@btinternet.com

**Chairman:** Stephen Skinner     **Prog Ed:** Jeff Carr

**Ground:** Gillford Park Railway Club, Off Pettril Bank Rd, Carlisle, Cumbria CA1 3AF     **(T)** 07970 461 749

**Capacity:**   **Seats:** Yes   **Covered:** Yes   **Midweek Matchday:** Tuesday    **Clubhouse:**

**Colours(change):** Green & white hoops/green/green & white hoops
**Previous Names:** Gillford Park Spartans > 2005. Gillford Park 2005-12.
**Previous Leagues:** Northern Alliance 2005-09.
**Records:**
**Senior Honours:** Northern Alliance Division 1 2006-07, Premier Division 2008-09, Challenge Cup 2008-09.

**10 YEAR RECORD**

| 03-04 | 04-05 | 05-06 | 06-07 | 07-08 | 08-09 | 09-10 | 10-11 | 11-12 | 12-13 |
|---|---|---|---|---|---|---|---|---|---|
| | | NAI 2 2 | NAI 1 1 | NAI P 3 | NAI P 2 | NL 2 11 | NL 2 11 | NL 2 2 | NL 1 10 |

# CONSETT
Founded: 1899      Nickname: Steelman

**Secretary:** David Pyke     **(T)** 07889 419 268     **(E)** david_pyke@hotmail .co.uk

**Chairman:** Frank Bell     **Prog Ed:** Gary Welford

**Ground:** Belle Vue Park, Ashdale Road, Consett, DH8 6LZ     **(T)** 01207 503 788

**Capacity:** 4,000   **Seats:** 400   **Covered:** 1000   **Midweek Matchday:** Tuesday    **Clubhouse:** Yes   **Shop:** No

**Colours(change):** All Red
**Previous Names:** None
**Previous Leagues:** N.All 1919-26, 35-37, N.E.C. 26-35, 37-58, 62-64, Midland 58-60, N.Co. 60-62, Wearside 64-70
**Records:** **Att:** 7000 v Sunderland Reserves, first match at Belle Vue 1950
**Senior Honours:** Norh Eastern Lg 39-40 Div 2 26-27, Northern Counties Lg 61-62, Northern Leageu Div.2 1988-89, 05-06.

**10 YEAR RECORD**

| 03-04 | 04-05 | 05-06 | 06-07 | 07-08 | 08-09 | 09-10 | 10-11 | 11-12 | 12-13 |
|---|---|---|---|---|---|---|---|---|---|
| NL 2 3 | NL 1 19 | NL 2 1 | NL 1 4 | NL 1 2 | NL 1 2 | NL 1 10 | NL 1 2 | NL 1 15 | NL 1 9 |

# CROOK TOWN
Founded: 1889      Nickname: Black & Ambers

**Secretary:** Ian Todd     **(T)** 07941 459 755     **(E)** iantodd147@gmail.com

**Chairman:** Kieron Bennett     **Prog Ed:** Ian Todd

**Ground:** The Sir Tom Cowie Millfield, West Road, Crook, Co.Durham DL15 9PW     **(T)** 01388 762 959

**Capacity:**   **Seats:**   **Covered:**   **Midweek Matchday:**    **Clubhouse:**

**Colours(change):** Amber/black/amber
**Previous Names:** Crook C.W.
**Previous Leagues:** Durham Central 1941-45.
**Records:**
**Senior Honours:** FA Amateur Cup 1900-01, 53-54, 58-59, 61-62, 63-64. Northern League x5 Div.2 2012-13, League Cup x3. Durham Challenge Cup x4. Durham Benefit Bowl x6. Ernest Armstrong Memorial Trophy 1997.

**10 YEAR RECORD**

| 03-04 | 04-05 | 05-06 | 06-07 | 07-08 | 08-09 | 09-10 | 10-11 | 11-12 | 12-13 |
|---|---|---|---|---|---|---|---|---|---|
| NL 2 16 | NL 2 7 | NL 2 5 | NL 2 14 | NL 2 14 | NL 2 9 | NL 2 13 | NL 2 12 | NL 2 10 | NL 2 1 |

# DUNSTON UTS

Founded: 1975          Nickname: The Fed

**Secretary:** Bill Montague          **(T)** 07981 194 756          **(E)** w.montague@sky.com

**Chairman:** Malcolm James          **Prog Ed:** Bill Montague

**Ground:**   UTS Stadium, Wellington Rd, Dunston, Gateshead NE11 9LJ          **(T)** 0191 493 2935

**Capacity:** 2,000  **Seats:** 120   **Covered:** 400   **Midweek Matchday:** Wednesday          **Clubhouse:** Yes   **Shop:** No

**Colours(change):**   All Blue with white trim/blue/blue
**Previous Names:**   Dunston Federation Brewery > 2007. Dunston Federation > 2009.
**Previous Leagues:** Northern Amateur & Wearside league
**Records:**        Att: 1,550 v Sunderland Shipowners Cup Final 01.04.88  **Goalscorer:** Paul King  **App:** Paul Dixon
**Senior Honours:**   Wearside League 1988-89, 89-90. Northern League Div.2 92-93. Div.1 2003-04, 04-05. FA Vase 2011-12.

**10 YEAR RECORD**

| 03-04 | | 04-05 | | 05-06 | | 06-07 | | 07-08 | | 08-09 | | 09-10 | | 10-11 | | 11-12 | | 12-13 | |
|---|---|---|---|---|---|---|---|---|---|---|---|---|---|---|---|---|---|---|---|
| NL 1 | 1 | NL 1 | 1 | NL 1 | 3 | NL 1 | 7 | NL 1 | 6 | NL 1 | 6 | NL 1 | 4 | NL 1 | 7 | NL 1 | 3 | NL 1 | 5 |

# DURHAM CITY

Founded: 1949          Nickname: City

**Secretary:** Kevin Hewitt          **(T)** 07897 611 640          **(E)** hewittkd@fsmail.net

**Chairman:** Austin Carney          **Prog Ed:** Gary Hutchinson

**Ground:**   The Durham UTS Arena, New Ferens Park, Belmont Ind.Est. DH1 1GG          **(T)** 0191 386 9616

**Capacity:** 2,700  **Seats:** 270   **Covered:** 750   **Midweek Matchday:** Tuesday          **Clubhouse:** Yes   **Shop:** No

**Colours(change):**   Yellow/blue/blue
**Previous Names:**   Original club founded in 1918 disbanded in 1938 and reformed in 1949
**Previous Leagues:** Victory 1918-19, North Eastern 1919-21, 28-38, Football League 1921-28, Wearside 1938-39, 50-51, Northern 1951-2008. NPL 2008-12.
**Records:**        2,750 v Whitley Bay - FA Vase Semi-final 2001-02
**Senior Honours:**   Northern League 1994-95, 2007-08. Northern Premier League Division 1 North 2008-09, Chairman's Cup 2008-09.

**10 YEAR RECORD**

| 03-04 | | 04-05 | | 05-06 | | 06-07 | | 07-08 | | 08-09 | | 09-10 | | 10-11 | | 11-12 | | 12-13 | |
|---|---|---|---|---|---|---|---|---|---|---|---|---|---|---|---|---|---|---|---|
| NL 1 | 2 | NL 1 | 6 | NL 1 | 11 | NL 1 | 8 | NL 1 | 1 | NP1N | 1 | NP P | 20 | NP1N | 17 | NP1N | 9 | NL 1 | 14 |

# GUISBOROUGH TOWN

Founded: 1973          Nickname: Priorymen

**Secretary:** Keith Smeltzer          **(T)** 07811 850 388          **(E)** keithsmeltzer@hotmail.co.uk

**Chairman:** Dr. Stephen HIll          **Prog Ed:** Danny Clark

**Ground:**   King George V Ground, Howlbeck Road, Guisborough TS14 6LE          **(T)** 01287 636 925

**Capacity:**         **Seats:** Yes   **Covered:** Yes   **Midweek Matchday:** Wednesday          **Clubhouse:** Yes

**Colours(change):**   Red & white stripes/black/red
**Previous Names:**   None
**Previous Leagues:** Northern Counties East 1982-85.
**Records:**        Att: 3,112 v Hungerford FA Vase Semi-final. **Goalscorer:** Mark Davis 341. **Apps:** Mark Davis 587.
**Senior Honours:**   Northern Alliance 1979-80. Northern League Cup 1987-88. Nth Riding Sen Cup 1989-90, 90-91, 91-92, 92-93, 94-95

**10 YEAR RECORD**

| 03-04 | | 04-05 | | 05-06 | | 06-07 | | 07-08 | | 08-09 | | 09-10 | | 10-11 | | 11-12 | | 12-13 | |
|---|---|---|---|---|---|---|---|---|---|---|---|---|---|---|---|---|---|---|---|
| NL 1 | 14 | NL 1 | 21 | NL 1 | 19 | NL 2 | 9 | NL 2 | 12 | NL 2 | 7 | NL 2 | 5 | NL 2 | 2 | NL 1 | 16 | NL 1 | 11 |

# HEBBURN TOWN

Founded: 1912          Nickname: Hornets

**Secretary:** Tom Derrick          **(T)** 07981 456 653          **(E)** tomderrick39@hotmail.com

**Chairman:** Bill Laffey          **Prog Ed:** Richard Bainbridge

**Ground:**   Hebburn Sports & Social, Victoria Rd West, Hebburn, Tyne&Wear NE31 1UN          **(T)** 0191  483 5101

**Capacity:**         **Seats:** Yes   **Covered:** Yes   **Midweek Matchday:** Tuesday          **Clubhouse:** Yes

**Colours(change):**   Yellow & black stripes/black/black
**Previous Names:**   Reyrolles, Hebburn Reyrolles > 1988, Hebburn 1988-2000.
**Previous Leagues:** Wearside 1960-89.
**Records:**        Att: 503 v Darwen FA Cup Prelim replay 07/09/1991, **Win:** 10-1. **Defeat:** 3-10.
**Senior Honours:**   Tyneside League 1938-39, Northern Combination 1943-44, Wearside League 1966-67.

**10 YEAR RECORD**

| 03-04 | | 04-05 | | 05-06 | | 06-07 | | 07-08 | | 08-09 | | 09-10 | | 10-11 | | 11-12 | | 12-13 | |
|---|---|---|---|---|---|---|---|---|---|---|---|---|---|---|---|---|---|---|---|
| NL 2 | 8 | NL 2 | 18 | NL 2 | 15 | NL 2 | 10 | NL 2 | 15 | NL 2 | 10 | NL 2 | 16 | NL 2 | 10 | NL 2 | 3 | NL 1 | 18 |

# MARSKE UNITED
Founded: 1956     Nickname: The Seasiders

**Secretary:** Les Holtby    **(T)** 07804 150 880     **(E)** admin@marskeunitedfc.com
**Chairman:** Peter Collinson     **Prog Ed:** Moss Holtby
**Ground:** GER Stad., Mount Pleasant Avenue, Marske by the Sea, Redcar TS11 7BW    **(T)** 01642 471 091
**Capacity:**    **Seats:** Yes   **Covered:** Yes   **Midweek Matchday:** Tuesday    **Clubhouse:** Yes

**Colours(change):** Yellow/blue/blue
**Previous Names:** None
**Previous Leagues:** Wearside 1985-97.
**Records:** **Defeat:** 3-9. **Goalscorer:** Chris Morgan 169. **Apps:** Mike Kinnair 583.
**Senior Honours:** Teeside League 1980-81, 84-85. Wearside League 1995-96. North Riding Senior Cup 1994-95. North Riding County Cup 1980-81, 85-86.

**10 YEAR RECORD**

| 03-04 | 04-05 | 05-06 | 06-07 | 07-08 | 08-09 | 09-10 | 10-11 | 11-12 | 12-13 |
|---|---|---|---|---|---|---|---|---|---|
| NL 1   20 | NL 2   15 | NL 2   10 | NL 2   5 | NL 2   8 | NL 2   5 | NL 2   4 | NL 2   3 | NL 1   18 | NL 1   19 |

# MORPETH TOWN
Founded: 1909     Nickname: Highwaymen

**Secretary:** David McMeekan    **(T)** 07425 135 301     **(E)** drmcmeekan@yahoo.co.uk
**Chairman:** Ken Beattie     **Prog Ed:** David McMeekan
**Ground:** Craik Park, Morpeth Common, Morpeth, Northumberland, NE61 2YX    **(T)** 07425 135 301
**Capacity:**    **Seats:** Yes   **Covered:** Yes   **Midweek Matchday:** Wednesday    **Clubhouse:** Yes

**Colours(change):** Amber & black stripes/black/black
**Previous Names:** None
**Previous Leagues:** Northern Alliance > 1994.
**Records:**
**Senior Honours:** Northern Alliance 1983-84, 93-94, Northern League Division 2 1995-96. Northumberland Senior Cup 2006-07.

**10 YEAR RECORD**

| 03-04 | 04-05 | 05-06 | 06-07 | 07-08 | 08-09 | 09-10 | 10-11 | 11-12 | 12-13 |
|---|---|---|---|---|---|---|---|---|---|
| NL 1   11 | NL 1   13 | NL 1   6 | NL 1   10 | NL 1   8 | NL 1   12 | NL 1   21 | NL 2   20 | NL 2   4 | NL 2   3 |

# NEWCASTLE BENFIELD
Founded: 1988     Nickname: The Lions

**Secretary:** Mark Hedley    **(T)** 07437 013 929     **(E)** markhedley3@msn.com
**Chairman:** Jimmy Rowe     **Prog Ed:** Jim Clark
**Ground:** Sam Smiths Park, Benfield Road, Walkergate NE6 4NU    **(T)** 0191 265 9357
**Capacity:** 2,000 **Seats:** 150   **Covered:** 250   **Midweek Matchday:** Wednesday    **Clubhouse:** Yes   **Shop:** No

**Colours(change):** Blue & white hoops/blue/blue
**Previous Names:** Heaton Corner House. Newcastle Benfield Saints.
**Previous Leagues:** Northern Alliance 1988-2003
**Records:**
**Senior Honours:** Northern Alliance Div 2 Champions 1989-90, Div 1 1994-95, 2002-03. Northern League Cup 2006-07. Northern League Champions 2008-09.

**10 YEAR RECORD**

| 03-04 | 04-05 | 05-06 | 06-07 | 07-08 | 08-09 | 09-10 | 10-11 | 11-12 | 12-13 |
|---|---|---|---|---|---|---|---|---|---|
| NL 2   2 | NL 1   4 | NL 1   9 | NL 1   5 | NL 1   4 | NL 1   1 | NL 1   5 | NL 1   4 | NL 1   12 | NL 1   21 |

# NEWTON AYCLIFFE
Founded: 1965     Nickname: Aycliffe

**Secretary:** Stephen Cunliffe    **(T)** 07872 985 501     **(E)** stecunliffe@aol.com
**Chairman:** Gary Farley     **Prog Ed:** Glen Robertson
**Ground:** Moore Lane Park, Moore Lane, Newton Aycliffe, Co. Durham DL5 5AG    **(T)** 01325 312 768
**Capacity:**    **Seats:** Yes   **Covered:** Yes   **Midweek Matchday:** Wednesday    **Clubhouse:** Yes

**Colours(change):** All blue
**Previous Names:** None
**Previous Leagues:** Wearside 1984-94, 2008-09. Durham Alliance > 2008.
**Records:** **Att:** 520 v Teeside Athletic (Sunderland Shipwoners Final) 2008-09.
**Senior Honours:** Darlington & District Division 'A' 2004-05. Durham Alliance League 2007-08. Wearside League 2008-09. Northern League Division Two 2010-11.

**10 YEAR RECORD**

| 03-04 | 04-05 | 05-06 | 06-07 | 07-08 | 08-09 | 09-10 | 10-11 | 11-12 | 12-13 |
|---|---|---|---|---|---|---|---|---|---|
| DaD'A' | DaD'A'   1 | | | DuAl   1 | Wear   1 | NL 2   9 | NL 2   1 | NL 1   9 | NL 1   17 |

# PENRITH
Founded: 1894      Nickname: Blues

**Secretary:** Ian White      **(T)** 07960 958 367      **(E)** ianwhite77@hotmail.com

**Chairman:** Mark Forster      **Prog Ed:** Brian Kirkbride

**Ground:** The Stadium, Frenchfield Park, Frenchfield, Penrith CA11 8UA      **(T)** 01768 895 990

**Capacity:** 4,000   **Seats:** 200   **Covered:** 1,000   **Midweek Matchday:** Tuesday    **Clubhouse:** Yes   **Shop:** No

**Colours(change):** Blue/white/blue.
**Previous Names:** Penrith FC. Penrith Town.
**Previous Leagues:** Carlisle & Dist. Northern 1942-82. NWC 1982-87, 90-97. NPL 1987-90.
**Records:** 2,100 v Chester 1981
**Senior Honours:** Northern League Division 2 Champions 2002-03, 07-08.

**10 YEAR RECORD**

| 03-04 | 04-05 | 05-06 | 06-07 | 07-08 | 08-09 | 09-10 | 10-11 | 11-12 | 12-13 |
|---|---|---|---|---|---|---|---|---|---|
| NL 1   21 | NL 2   8 | NL 2   4 | NL 2   7 | NL 2   1 | NL 1   7 | NL 1   14 | NL 1   17 | NL 1   19 | NL 1   13 |

# SHILDON
Founded: 1890      Nickname: Railwaymen

**Secretary:** Gareth Howe      **(T)** 07976 822 453      **(E)** gareth.howe3@btopenworld.com

**Chairman:** Brian Burn      **Prog Ed:** Archie MacKay

**Ground:** Dean Street, Shildon, Co. Durham DL4 1HA      **(T)** 01388 773 877

**Capacity:** 4,000   **Seats:** 480   **Covered:** 1000   **Midweek Matchday:** Wednesday    **Clubhouse:** Yes   **Shop:** No

**Colours(change):** All red
**Previous Names:** Shildon Athletic > 1923.
**Previous Leagues:** Auckland & Dist 1892-86, Wear Valley 1896-97, Northern 1903-07, North Eastern 1907-32
**Records:** **Att:** 11,000 v Ferryhill Athletic, Durham Senior Cup 1922 **Goalscorer:** Jack Downing 61 (1936-7) **App:** Bryan Dale
**Senior Honours:** Durham Amateur Cup 1901-02, 02-03, Durham Challenge Cup 1907-08, 25-26, 71-72,
Northern League Champions 1933-34, 34-35, 35-36,36-37, 39-40, Div 2 2001-02.

**10 YEAR RECORD**

| 03-04 | 04-05 | 05-06 | 06-07 | 07-08 | 08-09 | 09-10 | 10-11 | 11-12 | 12-13 |
|---|---|---|---|---|---|---|---|---|---|
| NL 1   4 | NL 1   11 | NL 1   18 | NL 1   9 | NL 1   5 | NL 1   8 | NL 1   2 | NL 1   5 | NL 1   10 | NL 1   8 |

# SPENNYMOOR TOWN
Founded: 1890      Nickname: Moors

**Secretary:** David Leitch      **(T)** 07530 453 880      **(E)** leitchy1969@btinternet.com

**Chairman:** Bradley Groves      Mike Rowcroft

**Ground:** Brewery Field, Durham Road, Spennymoor DL16 6JN      **(T)**

**Capacity:** 7,500   **Seats:** 300   **Covered:** 2,000   **Midweek Matchday:** Wednesday    **Clubhouse:** Yes   **Shop:** Yes

**Colours(change):** Black & white stripes/black/black
**Previous Names:** Amalgamation of Evenwood Town & Spennymoor Utd in 2005-06.
**Previous Leagues:** None
**Records:**
**Senior Honours:** Northern League Division Two 2006-07, Division One 2009-10, 2010-11, 2011-12.
Durham Challenge Cup 2011-12. FA Vase 2012-13.

**10 YEAR RECORD**

| 03-04 | 04-05 | 05-06 | 06-07 | 07-08 | 08-09 | 09-10 | 10-11 | 11-12 | 12-13 |
|---|---|---|---|---|---|---|---|---|---|
| | | NL 2   8 | NL 2   1 | NL 1   12 | NL 1   4 | NL 1   1 | NL 1   1 | NL 1   1 | NL 1   2 |

# SUNDERLAND RYHOPE C.A.
Founded: 1961      Nickname:

**Secretary:** Rob Jones      **(T)** 07932 951 842      **(E)** Robert-jones10@live.co.uk

**Chairman:** Graham Defty      **Prog Ed:** Colin Wilson

**Ground:** Meadow Park, Beachbrooke, Stockton Rd, Ryhope, Sunderland SR2 0NZ      **(T)** 0191 523 6555

**Capacity:** 2,000   **Seats:** 150   **Covered:** 200   **Midweek Matchday:** Wednesday    **Clubhouse:** Yes

**Colours(change):** Red & white halves/black/red
**Previous Names:** Ryhope Community Ass. FC
**Previous Leagues:** S.C. Vaux: Tyne & Wear, NorthEastern Am a Ryhope CA N Alliance.>82
**Records:** Not Known
**Senior Honours:** Northern Alliance League Cup 1981.

**10 YEAR RECORD**

| 03-04 | 04-05 | 05-06 | 06-07 | 07-08 | 08-09 | 09-10 | 10-11 | 11-12 | 12-13 |
|---|---|---|---|---|---|---|---|---|---|
| NL 2   9 | NL 2   16 | NL 2   17 | NL 2   19 | NL 2   4 | NL 2   4 | NL 2   2 | NL 1   13 | NL 1   4 | NL 1   22 |

# TEAM NORTHUMBRIA
Founded: 1999          Nickname:

**Secretary:** James Hartley          **(T)** 07970 478 723          **(E)** JAMES.HARTLEY@northumbria.ac.uk

**Chairman:** Colin Stromsoy          **Prog Ed:** James Hartley

**Ground:**   Coach Lane, Benton, Newcastle upon Tyne NE7 7XA          **(T)** 0191 215 6575

**Capacity:**          **Seats:** Yes     **Covered:** Yes     **Midweek Matchday:** Monday          **Clubhouse:**

**Colours(change):**   All red
**Previous Names:**   Northumbria University > 2003.
**Previous Leagues:** Northern Alliance 1999-2006.
**Records:**
**Senior Honours:**   Northern Alliance Premier 2005-06. Northern League Division Two 2011-12.

**10 YEAR RECORD**

| 03-04 | | 04-05 | | 05-06 | | 06-07 | | 07-08 | | 08-09 | | 09-10 | | 10-11 | | 11-12 | | 12-13 | |
|---|---|---|---|---|---|---|---|---|---|---|---|---|---|---|---|---|---|---|---|
| NAI P | 2 | NAI P | 3 | NAI P | 1 | NL 2 | 11 | NL 2 | 19 | NL 2 | 12 | NL 2 | 14 | NL 2 | 5 | NL 2 | 1 | NL 1 | 16 |

# WEST AUCKLAND TOWN
Founded: 1893          Nickname: West

**Secretary:** Allen Bayles          **(T)** 07894 329 005          **(E)** allenbayles@hotmail.co.uk

**Chairman:** Jim Palfreyman          **Prog Ed:** Michael Bainbridge

**Ground:**   Darlington Road, West Auckland, Co. Durham DL14 9HU          **(T)** 07800 796 630

**Capacity:** 3,000 **Seats:** 250     **Covered:** 250     **Midweek Matchday:** Tuesday          **Clubhouse:** Yes     **Shop:** No

**Colours(change):**   Yellow/black/yellow
**Previous Names:**   Auckland St Helens. St Helens. West Auckland.
**Previous Leagues:** Auck&D.,Wear Val,Sth D'ham All.Mid D'ham, Nth Lge 1919-20.Palantine 20-24.Sth D'ham 27-28.Gaunless Val 33-34
**Records:**   Att: 6,000 v Dulwich Hamlet FA Amateur Cup 1958-59
**Senior Honours:**   Sir Thomas Lipton Trophy 1909, 1911, Northern League 1959-60, 60-61. Div 2 1990-91. League Cup 1958-59, 62-63,
                      Durham Challenge Cup 1964-65

**10 YEAR RECORD**

| 03-04 | | 04-05 | | 05-06 | | 06-07 | | 07-08 | | 08-09 | | 09-10 | | 10-11 | | 11-12 | | 12-13 | |
|---|---|---|---|---|---|---|---|---|---|---|---|---|---|---|---|---|---|---|---|
| NL 1 | 13 | NL 1 | 17 | NL 1 | 5 | NL 1 | 6 | NL 1 | 16 | NL 1 | 20 | NL 1 | 16 | NL 1 | 6 | NL 1 | 2 | NL 1 | 4 |

# WHITLEY BAY
Founded: 1897          Nickname: The Bay

**Secretary:** Derek Breakwell          **(T)** 07889 888 187          **(E)** dbreakwell@hotmail.co.uk

**Chairman:** Paul McIlduff          **Prog Ed:** Julian Tyley

**Ground:**   Hillheads Park, Rink Way, Whitley Bay, NE25 8HR          **(T)** 0191 291 3637

**Capacity:** 4,500 **Seats:** 450     **Covered:** 650     **Midweek Matchday:** Tuesday          **Clubhouse:** Yes     **Shop:** Yes

**Colours(change):**   Blue & white stripes/blue/blue
**Previous Names:**   Whitley Bay Athletic 1950-58
**Previous Leagues:** Tyneside 1909-10, Northern All. 1950-55, N. Eastern 1955-58, Northern 1958-88 N.P.L. 1988-00
**Records:**   7,301 v Hendon, FA Amateur Cup 1965.
**Senior Honours:**   Northern Alliance 1952-53, 53-54. Northern League 1964-65, 65-66, 06-07. NPL Div 1 1990-91,
                      FA Vase 2001-02, 08-09, 09-10, 10-11.

**10 YEAR RECORD**

| 03-04 | | 04-05 | | 05-06 | | 06-07 | | 07-08 | | 08-09 | | 09-10 | | 10-11 | | 11-12 | | 12-13 | |
|---|---|---|---|---|---|---|---|---|---|---|---|---|---|---|---|---|---|---|---|
| NL 1 | 10 | NL 1 | 5 | NL 1 | 10 | NL 1 | 1 | NL 1 | 3 | NL 1 | 3 | NL 1 | 3 | NL 1 | 3 | NL 1 | 6 | NL 1 | 3 |

Dunston UTS line up before their FA Vase tie at Tunbridge Wells.
Photo: Roger Turner.

# DIVISION TWO

## ALNWICK TOWN

Founded: 1879     Nickname:

**Secretary:** Cyril Cox     **(T)** 07570 834 798
**Chairman:** Tommy McKie
**Ground:** St. Jame's Park, Weavers Way, Alnwick, Northumberland NE66 1BG
**Colours(change):** Black & white stripes/black/black

**(E)** uk2usa@hotmail.com
**Prog Ed:** Michael Cook
**(T)** 01665 603 612

**ADDITIONAL INFORMATION: Previous Names:** Alnwick Utd Services 1879-1900, Alnwick Utd Juniors 1900-1936.
**Previous Lge:** Northern Alliance 1935-82, 2007-11. Northern League 1982-2007.
**Honours:** Nothern Alliance title 9 times.

## BIRTLEY TOWN

Founded: 1993     Nickname: The Hoops

**Secretary:** Trevor Armstrong     **(T)** 07958 540 389
**Chairman:** John Heslington
**Ground:** Birtley Sports Complex, Durham Road, Birtley DH3 2TB
**Colours(change):** Green & white hoops/green/green

**(E)** trevellen1@sky.com
**Prog Ed:** Andrew Walker
**(T)** 07958 540 389

**ADDITIONAL INFORMATION:**
**Previous League:** Wearside 1993-2007.
**Honours:** Wearside League 2002-03, 06-07, Division 2 1994-95, League Cup 1998, 2002, 2006.

## BRANDON UNITED

Founded: 1968     Nickname: United

**Secretary:** Barry Ross     **(T)** 07717 673 090
**Chairman:** David Bussey
**Ground:** Welfare Park, Rear Commercial Street, Brandon DH7 8PR
**Colours(change):** All red

**(E)** barryross430@btinternet.com
**Prog Ed:** Dean Johnson
**(T)** 07949 076 218

**ADDITIONAL INFORMATION: Previous League:** Wearside 1981-83. **Record Att:** 2,500 F.A. Sunday Cup Seim-final.
**Record: Goalscorer:** Tommy Holden. **Apps:** Derek Charlton 1977-86. **Honours:** F.A. Sunday Cup 1975-76.
Northern Alliance Division 2 1977-78, 78-79. Northern League 2002-03, Division 2 1984-85, 99-2000.

## CHESTER-LE-STREET TOWN

Founded: 1972     Nickname: Cestrians

**Secretary:** Lenny Lauchlan     **(T)** 07825 413 237
**Chairman:** Joe Burlison
**Ground:** Moor Park, Chester Moor, Chester-le-Street, Co.Durham DH2 3RW
**Colours(change):** Blue & white hoops/white/white with blue trim

**(E)** l.w.lauchlan@durham.ac.uk
**Prog Ed:** Keith Greener
**(T)** 07972 419 275

**ADDITIONAL INFORMATION: Previous Name:** Garden Farm 1972-78. **Previous League:** Wearside 1977-83.
**Record Att:** 893 v Fleetwood FA Vase 1985 **App:** Colin Wake 361.
**Honours:** Washington League 1975-6 Wearside League1980-81, Northern League Div 2 1983-84, 97-98.

## DARLINGTON R.A.

Founded: 1993     Nickname:

**Secretary:** Alan Hamilton     **(T)** 07872 324 808
**Chairman:** Doug Hawman
**Ground:** Brinkburn Road, Darlington, Co. Durham DL3 9LF
**Colours(change):** All red

**(E)** nobbydarlo@ntlworld.com
**Prog Ed:** Alan Hamilton
**(T)** 01325 468 125

**ADDITIONAL INFORMATION:**
**Previous League:** Darlington & District 1993-99.
**Honours:** Auckland & District League 2000-01. Wearside League 2004-05.

## ESH WINNING

Founded: 1885     Nickname: Stags

**Secretary:** Michael Young     **(T)** 07837 205 732
**Chairman:** Charles Ryan
**Ground:** West Terrace, Waterhouse, Durham DH7 9NQ
**Colours(change):** Yellow/green/green

**(E)** michael.young86@btinternet.com
**Prog Ed:** Michael Young
**(T)** 0191 373 3872     **Capacity:** 3,500

**ADDITIONAL INFORMATION:**
**Record Att:** 5,000 v Newcastle Utd Res. 1910 & Bishop Auckland 1921 **Goalscorer:** Alan Dodsworth 250+ **App:** Neil McLeary - 194.
**Honours:** Northern League Champions 1912-13.

## HEATON STANNINGTON

Founded: 1910     Nickname: The Stan

**Secretary:** Geoff Walker     **(T)** 07932 252 981
**Chairman:** Bill Pitt     **Manager:** Derek Thompson
**Ground:** Grounsell Park, Newton Road, High Heaton, Newcastle upon Tyne NE7 7HP
**Colours(change):** Black & white stripes/black/black & white hoops

**(E)** geoffwalker51@yahoo.com
**Prog Ed:** Ian Cusack
**(T)** 0191 281 9230

**ADDITIONAL INFORMATION:**
**Previous Leagues:** Northern Alliance >2013.
**Honours:** Northern Alliance 2011-12, 12-13.

## JARROW ROOFING BOLDON C.A.

Founded: 1987    Nickname: Roofing

**Secretary:** Bryn Griffiths    **(T)** 07889 279 647    **(E)** bgriffiths94@btinternet.com
**Chairman:** Richard McLoughlin    **Prog Ed:** Ashley Scott
**Ground:** Boldon CA Sports Ground, New Road, Boldon Colliery NE35 9DZ    **(T)** 07714 525 549    **Capacity:** 3,500
**Colours(change):** All blue and yellow

**ADDITIONAL INFORMATION: Att:** 500 v South Shields **Goalscorer:** Mick Hales **App:** Paul Chow

## NORTH SHIELDS

Founded: 1992    Nickname: Robins

**Secretary:** David Thompson    **(T)** 07969 239 476    **(E)** nsfc.dt@gmail.com
**Chairman:** Alan Matthews    **Prog Ed:** Sam Cave
**Ground:** Daren Persson Staduim, Ralph Gardner Park, West Percy Rd, Chirton, North Shields **(T)** 07759 766 732
**Colours(change):** All red

**ADDITIONAL INFORMATION:**
**Previous Names:** Preston Colliery > 1928, North Shields Athletic 1995-99. **Previous League:** Wearside.
**Honours:** FA Amateur Cup 1968-69, N.C.E. Prem Div 91-92, Lge Cup 90-91. Wearside League 1998-99, 01-02, 03-04.

## NORTHALLERTON TOWN

Founded: 1994    Nickname: Town

**Secretary:** Lesley Clark    **(T)** 07891 595 267    **(E)** lesleyclark05@yahoo.co.uk
**Chairman:** Dave Watson    **Prog Ed:** Ricky Butler
**Ground:** The Calvert Stadium, Ainderby Road, Northallerton DL7 8HA    **(T)** 01609 778 337
**Colours(change):** Black & white stripes/black/black

**ADDITIONAL INFORMATION: Previous Name:** Northallerton FC 1994. **Previous League:** Harrogate & District.
**Record Att:** 695 v Farnborough Town FA Trophy 3rd Round 20/02/1993.
**Honours:** Northern League Division 2 1996-97, League Cup 1993-94.

## NORTON & STOCKTON ANCIENTS

Founded: 1959    Nickname: Ancients

**Secretary:** Michael Mulligan    **(T)** 07850 622 544    **(E)** m.mulligan@nasafc.co.uk
**Chairman:** Michael Mulligan    **Prog Ed:** Kevin McGrother
**Ground:** Norton (Teesside) Sports Complex, Station Rd, Norton TS20 1PE    **(T)** 01642 530 203    **Capacity:** 2,000
**Colours(change):** Amber & black/black & amber/black

**ADDITIONAL INFORMATION: Att:** 1,430 v Middlesbrough, Friendly 1988.
Northern League Cup 1982-83.

## RYTON & CRAWCROOK ALBION

Founded: 1970    Nickname:

**Secretary:** Stevie Carter    **(T)** 07939 573 108    **(E)** racafc@outlook.com
**Chairman:** Richard Hands    **Prog Ed:** Chris Holt
**Ground:** Kingsley Park, Stannerford Road, Crawcrook NE40 3SN    **(T)** 0191 413 4448    **Capacity:** 2,000
**Colours(change):** Blue & black stripes/black/blue

**ADDITIONAL INFORMATION: Att:** 1,100 v Newcastle United 1998
Northern Alliance Division 1 Champions 1996-97.

## SEAHAM RED STAR

Founded: 1973    Nickname: The Star

**Secretary:** Kevin Turns    **(T)** 07701 076 848    **(E)** seahamredstarfc@aol.com
**Chairman:** John McBeth    **Prog Ed:** Sue Potts
**Ground:** Seaham Town Park, Stockton Road, Seaham. Co.Durham SR7 0HY    **(T)**
**Colours(change):** Red & white stripes/red/red

**ADDITIONAL INFORMATION: Previous Name:** Seaham Colliery Welfare Red Star 1978-87. **Previous League:** Wearside 1979-83.
**Record Att:** 1,500 v Guisborough. **App:** Michael Whitfield.
**Honours:** Durham Challenge Cup 1979-80, Wearside League & League Cup 1981-82, Norhtern League Cup 1992-93.

## SOUTH SHIELDS

Founded: 1974    Nickname: Mariners

**Secretary:** Philip Reay    **(T)** 07506 641 815    **(E)** philipreay@rocketmail.com
**Chairman:** Gary Crutwell    **Prog Ed:** Philip Reay
**Ground:** Mariners Club, Filtrona Park, Shaftesbury Ave, Jarrow NE32 3UP    **(T)** 0191 427 9839    **Capacity:** 2,500
**Colours(change):** Claret & blue/white/white

**ADDITIONAL INFORMATION: Att:** 1,500 v Spennymoor, Durham Challenge Cup Final 1994-95.
Northern Alliance 1974-75, 75-76, Wearside League 1976-77, 92-93, 94-95.
Monkwearmouth Charity Cup 1986-87.

## STOKESLEY SPORTS CLUB
Founded: 1920    Nickname:

**Secretary:** Peter Grainge    **(T)** 07712 883 874
**Chairman:** Tim Allison
**Ground:** Stokesley Sports Club, Broughton Road, Stokesley TS9 5JQ
**Colours(change):** Black & red/black/black

**(E)** peterssc@hotmail.co.uk
**Prog Ed:** Tim Allison
**(T)** 01642 710 051

**ADDITIONAL INFORMATION:**
Stokesley & District League 1975-76. Northern League Division Two 2009-10.

## THORNABY
Founded: 1980    Nickname:

**Secretary:** Trevor Wing    **(T)** 07860 780 446
**Chairman:** Laurence Lyons
**Ground:** Teesdale Park, Acklam Road, Thornaby, Stockton on Tees TS17 7JU
**Colours(change):** All blue

**(E)** trevor.wing10@btinternet.com
**Prog Ed:** Trevor Wing
**(T)** 01642 672 896

**ADDITIONAL INFORMATION: Previous Names:** Stockton Cricket Club 1965-1980, Stockton 1980-99 and Thornaby-on-Tees 1999-2000
**Previous League:** Wearside 1981-85. **Records Att:** 3,000 v Middlesborough friendly Aug 1986  **App:** Michael Watson
**Honours:** North Riding County Cup, 1985-86, Northern Lge Div 2 1987-88, 91-92

## TOW LAW TOWN
Founded: 1890    Nickname: Lawyers

**Secretary:** Steve Moralee    **(T)** 07810 238 731
**Chairman:** Sandra Gordon
**Ground:** Ironworks Ground, Tow Law, Bishop Auckland DL13 4EQ
**Colours(change):** Black & white stripes/black/black

**(E)** stephen.moralee@btinternet.com
**Prog Ed:** John Dixon
**(T)** 01388 731 443    **Capacity:** 6,000

**ADDITIONAL INFORMATION:** 5,500 v Mansfield Town FA Cup 1967.
Northern League Champions 1923-24, 24-25, 94-95. League Cup 73-74.

## WASHINGTON
Founded: 1949    Nickname: Mechanics

**Secretary:** Barry Spendley    **(T)** 07810 536 964
**Chairman:** Derek Armstrong
**Ground:** Nissan Sports Complex, Washington Road Sunderland SR5 3NS
**Colours(change):** All red

**(E)** Derek.Armstrong1@ntlworld.com
**Prog Ed:** Bob Goodwin
**(T)** 07810530964~07761325797

**ADDITIONAL INFORMATION:**
**Previous Names:** Washington Mechanics, Washington Ikeda Hoover. **Previous League:** Wearside.
**Record Att:** 3,800 v Bradford Park Avenue FA Cup 1970.
**Honours:** Washington Amateur: 1956-57,57-58, 58-59,59-60,61-62,62-63, League Cup: 1955-56, 58-59, 60-61, 64-65.

## WEST ALLOTMENT CELTIC
Founded: 1928    Nickname:

**Secretary:** Ted Ilderton    **(T)** 07795 246 245
**Chairman:** Roland Mather
**Ground:** Whitley Park, Whitley Road, Benton NE12 9FA
**Colours(change):** Green & white hoops/green/green

**(E)** tedilderton@gmail.com
**Prog Ed:** Andrew Cook
**(T)** 0191 270 0885

**ADDITIONAL INFORMATION: Att:** 510 v Cray Wanderers FA Vase 2004
Northern Am. 1956-57, 57-58, 58-59, 59-60, 81-82, 82-83, Div 2: 38-39.
Northern Alliance: 1986-87, 90-91, 91-92, 97-98, 98-99, 99-2000, 01-02, 03-04. Northern League Div 2 2004-05

## WHICKHAM
Founded: 1944    Nickname:

**Secretary:** Les Dixon    **(T)** 07974 308 162
**Chairman:** Brian McCartney
**Ground:** Glebe Sports Club, Rectory Lane, Whickham NE16 4NA
**Colours(change):** Black & white stripes/black/black

**(E)** Whickhamfcsecretary@hotmail.co.uk
**Prog Ed:** Mick Tucker
**(T)** 0191 4200 186

**ADDITIONAL INFORMATION: Record Att:** 3,165 v Windsor & Eton FA Vase SF 1981.
**Honours:** FA Vase 1980-81, Wearside Lge 77-78, 87-88, Sunderland Shipowners Cup 77-78, 80-81,
Northern Comb 69-70, 72-73, 73-74 Lge Cup 60-61, 73-74

## WHITEHAVEN
Founded: 1994    Nickname:

**Secretary:** David Rushforth    **(T)** 07876 612 277
**Chairman:** Dick Stamp
**Ground:** Focus Scaffolding Sports Complex, Coach Road, Whitehaven, CA28 9DB
**Colours(change):** Yellow/blue/yellow

**(E)** secretary@whitehavenafc.co.uk
D J Moors
**(T)** 01946 692 211

**ADDITIONAL INFORMATION: Record Att:** 207 v Workington Reds, Cumberland County Cup 13/12/2007.
**Honours:** Wearside League Division 2 1994-95, Wearside League 2005-06. Monkwearmouth Charity Cup 2006-07.

# WILLINGTON

**Founded:** 1906    **Nickname:**

**Secretary:** Geoff Siddle    **(T)** 07532 341 105    **(E)** siddle403@btinternet.com
**Chairman:** Robert Nichols    **Manager:** Robert Lee    **Prog Ed:** Geoff Siddle
**Ground:** Hall Lane, Willington, Co. Durham DL15 0QG    **(T)** 01388 745 912    **Capacity:** 7,000
**Colours(change):** Blue & white/blue/blue

**ADDITIONAL INFORMATION:**
**Previous Leagues:** Northern League. Wearside > 2013.
**Records (Lge/Cup post 1939): Goalscorer:** Brett Cummings - 150, 1992-08. **Apps:** Brett Cummings - 407, 1992-08.
**Honours:** Northern League 1913-14, 25-26, 29-30. FA Amateur Cup 1949-50.

# GROUND DIRECTIONS

**ALNWICK TOWN-** M1, at exit 32, take slip road left for M18 toward The North / Doncaster / Hull, at exit 2, take slip road left for A1(M) toward the North, keep straight onto A1 / Doncaster by Pass, keep straight onto A1(M), take slip road for A1(M) / Aberford by Pass, road name changes to A1 / Leeming Lane, keep straight onto A1(M), keep left onto A1, take slip road left for A1068 toward Alnwick / Alnmouth, at roundabout, take 1st exit onto Willowburn Avenue, turn left, and then immediately turn left onto St James Estate, ground is on the right.

**ASHINGTON-**Leave the A1 at the junction with the A19 north of Newcastle. Go along the A19 eastwards untio the next roundabout . Here take the second left (A189) signposted to Bedlington and Ashington. Continue along A189 until reach Woodhorn roundabout, turn left onto A197. Turn left at first roundabout. Just before the hospital car park entrance, turn right. Ground is on left.

**BEDLINGTON TERRIERS-**From the A1:- Take the Seaton Burn turn off and at the roundabout take the second turn off (A1088). At the next roundabout, take the first turnoff to pass Aesica on the left. Straight over at the next roundabout.
You will go down a dip, over a bridge and back up the other side, do not turn off, continue on the same road until you come into Bedlington. At the top of the bank there is a roundabout outside the Red Lion pub, go straight over. Down the hill there is another roundabout at the Netto shop, take the second turnoff (turning right). Follow the road past the Police station and Law courts and the road bends sharply to the left. Continue around the corner, take the second right. The ground is at the top of the street.

**BILLINGHAM SYNTHONIA-**Leave A19 onto A1027 sign posted towards Billingham. Continue straight ahead over a couple of roundabouts, and you will be on Central Avenue. The ground is on left opposite an empty office block.

**BILLINGHAM TOWN-**Leave A19 on A1027 signed Billingham. Turn left at third roundabout, into Cowpen Lane. Go over a railway bridge, then first left into Warwick Crescent, then first left again into Bedford Terrace (follow one-way signs) to the ground.

**BIRTLEY TOWN-**Leave A1(M) at Angel of the North and follow signs to Birtley (A167). Continue along main road through town. Go past Komatsu factory on right and then after approx 200 yards turn right into an unmarked side road. Ground is directly in front of you.

**BISHOP AUCKLAND-NORTH:** From junction 60 of the A1 follow the A689 to Bishop Auckland. Go straight across the next 2 roundabouts. At the 3rd roundabout turn left onto the A688 and straight across the next 2 roundabouts. At the following roundabout turn left at Aldi and then go straight across at the next roundabout. The stadium is 200 yards on your right. **SOUTH:** From junction 58 from the A1, take the A68 towards Bishop Auckland. At the West Auckland by-pass, turn right at the roundabout. Go straight across at the next roundabout and the stadium is located 500 yards on your left.

**BRANDON UNITED-**Leave A1 on A690, go through Durham and continue on A690. Once at 'Langley Moor' (you go under a railway bridge), turn right at the "Lord Boyne" pub. After 100 yards take the next left. Go up the road for approx half a mile, and turn right at the newsagents. Take the next left, and Brandon's ground is up a small track.

**CELTIC NATION-**Take junction 42 off the M6 and then the A6 into Carlisle. After 1.75 miles take left turn into Petterill Bank Road (junction is at traffic lights). After half a mile turn right onto track immediately before railway bridge. This leads you to the ground.

**CHESTER LE STREET-**Leave A1M at junction 63 and take the A167 towards Chester le Street and Durtham. Keep going along this road for a couple of miles. You will go under a railway bridge, and as the road begins to climb, you will see the Chester Moor pub on your left. Turn into the pub and the ground is accessed along a track at the rear of the pub car park.

**CONSETT-**Take the A692 from the east into Consett. On the edge of the town, the A692 takes a left at a roundabout. Continue along the A692 for approx 100 yards, before turning right into Leadgate Road. Go along here for approx .25 mile, and turn right into Ashdale Road. There is a road sign for the Leisure Centre pointing into Ashdale Road. The ground is approx 200 yards along Ashdale Road on your right.

**CROOK TOWN-**Leave the A1 at Junction 62, and take the A690 towards Durham. Keep on this road through Durham, Meadowfield, Willington and Helmington Row. When you arrive in Crook town centre keep going straight ahead, as the A690 becomes the A689. The ground is situated on this road on your right, approximately 300 yards from the town centre.

**DARLINGTON RAILWAY ATHLETIC-**Leave A1(M) at junction 58 and follow the A68 into Darlington. Continue along the road until you see the Brown Trout public house on your right. Turn left at this point into Brinkburn Road, and the ground is 100 yards along on the left.

**DUNSTON U.T.S.-**From south take Dunston/Whickham exit off A1M. Turn right at top of slip road into Dunston Road and head down the bank. As the road veers left, the road becomes Wellington Road, and the ground is situated on your left.

**DURHAM CITY-**Leave the A1M at J62 (signed Durham City) At the top of the slip road turn left. After about 1/2 mile bear left (signed Belmont + Dragonville). At the top of the slip road turn left.
At traffic lights turn left then take the 2nd left, the stadium is on your right.

**ESH WINNING-**Leave the A1 at Junction 62, and take the A690 towards Durham. Keep on this road through Durham. Once you start to head down a bank on the A690, you will come to a roundabout. Take the right turn onto the B6302, which will be signposted towards Ushaw Moor. Keep on this road though Ushaw Moor (there is a staggered crossroads to negotiate), and carry on the B6302 into Esh Winning. Keep on going as the ground is not in Esh Winning, but the next village along, Waterhouses. When the road takes a sharp left you will see a track continuing straight ahead. The ground is along this track.

**GUISBOROUGH TOWN-**Turn off the A19 into the A174, then come off at the second junction, turning right onto the A172. Follow this round until roundabout with A1043, take left exit to join the A1043. Take right at next roundabout to join the A171. At second roundabout turn right into Middlesbrough Road (will be signposted towards Guisborough) then take left turning at traffic lights into Park Lane. Take first left into Howlbeck Road, and the ground is at the end of the road.

**HEATON STANNINGTON -** Grounsell Park, Newton Road, High Heaton, Newcastle upon Tyne NE7 7HP. Tel: 0191 281 9230

**HEBBURN TOWN-**Leave A1M on A194(M) (junction 65) and follow signs for Tyne Tunnel. Continue until fourth roundabout and turn left on to B1306 (Hebburn, Mill Lane). Right at traffic lights into Victoria Road. Ground 200 yards long this road on the left.

**HORDEN C.W.-**Take A19 to Peterlee turn off (B1320). Follow main road into Peterlee then through on the same road, following signs to Horden (B1320). At T-junction, turn left into Sunderland Road, at lights, (A1086) and then right into South Terrace. Ground is at bottom of South Terrace.

**JARROW ROOFING-**From south take A19 and follow signs for Tyne Tunnel. Turn right at junction marked Boldon Colliery (Testo Roundabout) on to the A184. Turn left at the next r'about, into the B1293, and head towards Asda. At second r'about, turn right at end of retail park. At the r'about at the entrance to Asda, take the "10 to" exit, and you will pass a large brick building on you right, known as The Shack. Turn right into the car park after this building, and at the far end of the car park there is a small lane that leads off left. Roofers ground is at the end of this track.

**MARSKE UNITED -**Leave A19 and join Parkway (A174) to Marske until Quarry Lane r'about. Take exit (A1085) into Marske. Take the next right after you pass under a railway, into Meadow Rd. Take the next left into Southfield Rd and the entrance is on your left shortly before a T-junc.

**MORPETH TOWN-**From south. Turn off the A1 onto A197, sign posted Morpeth. Turn left at sign pointing Belsay (B6524). Take right turn just before bridge under the A1. Ground is signposted and up a small track is on the right.

**NEWCASTLE BENFIELD-**Take the A1058 from either the Tyne Tunnel or central Newcastle. Turn off this road at the junction with Benfield Road. Turn south at this junction, and the Crosslings building will be on your left. Ground is around 400 metres on left, by taking the first turning after passing railway bridge. The ground is 100 yards along this road.

**NEWTON AYCLIFFE-**From North, leave the A1at junction 60, and travel west along the A689 towards Bishop Auckland. At the roundabout, turn left to join A167. Travel along here for a couple of miles, and at first traffic lights and turn right onto B6443 (Central Avenue). At first roundabout (Tesco's) turn left into Shafto Way then 3rd left into Gunn Way then right into Moore Lane.

**NORTHALLERTON TOWN-**Leave A1 at Leeming Bar (A684) and follow signs to Northallerton. Approaching the town take the left turn B1333, signed Romanby. Ground is on left after 50 yards in Romanby.

**NORTH SHIELDS-**Continue north on the A19 after Tyne Tunnel. Take right exit at roundabout onto the A1058. At next roundabout take third exit at Billy Mill, signed to North Shields. At roundabout with A193, turn right, then take second left into Silkey's Lane. Ground is 100 yards on left.

**NORTON & STOCKTON ANCIENTS -**Leave A19 at Stockton/Norton turn off (A1027) and follow signs to Norton. At the roundabout at the top of the bank take a right turn onto the B1274. Take the next right into Station Road. Ground entrance is on left of road in a large sports complex, the entrance to which is just before the railway crossing. The ground a 200 yards along this track.

**PENRITH-**Turn off M6 at junction 40 then onto dual carriageway to Appleby and Scotch Corner. Take the A686 (signposted Alston), for approximately half a mile. Then take a right turn (opposite Carleton Road), and follow the track running parallel with the A66. Turn left into the sports complex and follow the road to the far end.

**RYTON & CRAWCROOK ALBION-**Leave the A1 at the south side of the River Tyne (A694). At the roundabout take the A695 (sign posted Blaydon). At Blaydon take the B6317 through Ryton to reach Crawcrook. Turn right at the traffic lights (sign posted Ryton/Clara Vale). Kingsley Park is situated approximately 500 meters on the right.

**SEAHAM RED STAR-**Leave A19 on B1404 slip road. Follow signs to Seaham/Ryhope. Turn right at traffic lights on to the B1285. Then left at Red Star social club approximately 200 yards after the traffic lights. There is a car park at the next roundabout behind their social club The ground is a short walk at the top of the park.

**SHILDON-**Leave A1M at junction 58. Follow A68 signed Bishop Auckland, turn right at roundabout onto A6072. At Shildon turn right at second roundabout (onto B6282) , then left into Byerley Rd (still the B6282). Right at Timothy Hackworth pub into Main St., then at the top of the bank, left into Dean Street.

**SOUTH SHIELDS-**From A1 M take A194 (M) to South Shields. Follow signs for town centre. Turn left at traffic lights (TESCO supermarket) into Shaftesbury Avenue. Ground is at the far end of the road

**SPENNYMOOR TOWN-**Turn off A1M at J61. Onto A688 towards Spennymoor, turn right at small roundabout & straight on at Thinford roundabout (Still continuing on the A688). Straight over mini roundabout, and take fourth exit from large roundabout (B6288). Continue for approx. 2 mile and take left into Durham Road. Ground is on Wood Vue, approx 300 yards on right just off Durham Rd.

**STOKESLEY SPORTS CLUB-**Turn off A19 onto A174 (Teesport/Redcar). Take third exit onto A172 (Whitby/Stokesley). Turn right and keep on A172 to Stokesley. In Stokesley bear left at first roundabout, still keeping on the A172. At next roundabout go straight across into Broughton Road (Second exit-B1257). Ground is 100 yards on left-hand side.

**SUNDERLAND R.C.A.-**From the A19, leave at the junction with the A690, but on that roundabout take the B1286 through Doxford Park. Continue along this road for some time (there are number of roundabouts), but there are signposts to Ryhope along this road. You will eventually come to a T-junction at the end of the B1286, and turn right onto the A1018. After 200 yards you will come to another roundabout, here take a right turn. Then take the next right into a new housing estate. There is a board at the entrance pointing you to Meadow Park, the home of R.C.A. The ground is at the far end of the estate.

**TEAM NORTHUMBRIA-**Take the A1058 from either the A19 or central Newcastle. Turn off this road at the junction with Benfield Road. Turn north at large Crosslings warehouse into Red Hall Drive, this then becomes Coach Lane. The ground is on the right just past Newcastle University halls of residence.

**THORNABY-**Turn off A19 onto A1130 and head towards Thornaby. Continue along Acklam Road for about half a mile. Ground is signposted from the main road- on the right up a track between houses after half a mile.

**TOW LAW TOWN-**Leave the A1 at junction 58 and turn on to A68. Follow signs for Tow Law/Corbridge. Ground is at far end of Tow Law on the left side. The ground is situated on Ironworks Road, which is the first left after a sharp left hand bend on the A68 in Tow Law.

**WASHINGTON-**Leave the A19 on slip road marked "Nissan Offices" as you pass Sunderland travelling north. This is the A1290. Continue to follow "Nissan Offices" signs. Left at traffic lights, then right at roundabout into complex. Ground is at far end of the plant.

**WEST ALLOTMENT CELTIC-**Continue on the A19 north after Tyne Tunnel until A191 exit. Take left exit marked Gosforth & Newcastle. A191 for three miles. The ground, The Blue Flames Sports Ground is on left.

**WEST AUCKLAND TOWN-**Leave A1 at junction 58 on to the A68. Follow signs to W. Auckland/Corbridge. On entering village, ground is behind factory on left side. Ground is up a track on the left side of road next to Oakley Grange Farm.

**WHICKHAM-**From A1M take the A692 junction, and travel in the direction signed to Consett. At top of the back the road forks left towards Consett, but you should take the right fork along the B6317 to Whickham. Follow this road for 1.5 miles, left turn into Rectory Lane (B6316). Take first right into Holme Avenue, and then first left. The ground is at top of lane. More car parking can be found further along Rectory Lane, take the next right. Walk past the cricket pitch to access the football club.

**WHITEHAVEN-**From the south, on A595, take the turning into Whitehaven at the top of Inkermann Terrace at traffic lights (A5094). Pass the Chase Hotel on left until reach set of traffic lights next to a garage. Turn left into Coach Lane and travel on until see an access to the left indicating a cycleway. Turn in and follow the path until meet the gates to the ground. From the north, it is easier to travel further down the A595, and follow instructions as above. This way you avoid the town centre.

**WHITLEY BAY-**Leave the A19 on the A191, and turn eastwards towards Whitely Bay. Continue along New York Road (A191) which then becomes Rake Lane (A191). Pass hospital on right & then into Shields Rd. and Hillheads Rd (both A191). Ground is to the right, floodlights can be seen from miles away! It is next to an ice rink.

**WILLINGTON -** Hall Lane, Willington, Co. Durham DL15 0QG. Tel: 01388 745 912

# SOUTH WEST PENINSULA LEAGUE

**Sponsored by:** Carlsberg
**Founded:** 2007
**Recent Champions:**
2008: Bodmin Town
2009: Bodmin Town
2010: Buckland Athletic
2011: Buckland Athletic
2012: Bodmin Town
swpleague.co.uk

| PREMIER DIVISION | P | W | D | L | F | A | Pts |
|---|---|---|---|---|---|---|---|
| 1 Bodmin Town | 36 | 28 | 6 | 2 | 127 | 28 | 90 |
| 2 Plymouth Parkway | 36 | 24 | 6 | 6 | 89 | 45 | 78 |
| 3 Elburton Villa | 36 | 24 | 5 | 7 | 95 | 53 | 77 |
| 4 St Austell | 36 | 23 | 5 | 8 | 89 | 45 | 74 |
| 5 Launceston | 36 | 19 | 4 | 13 | 64 | 46 | 61 |
| 6 Saltash United | 36 | 17 | 9 | 10 | 77 | 43 | 60 |
| 7 Witheridge | 36 | 17 | 6 | 13 | 84 | 58 | 57 |
| 8 St Blazey | 36 | 16 | 8 | 12 | 79 | 57 | 56 |
| 9 Camelford | 36 | 16 | 7 | 13 | 76 | 53 | 55 |
| 10 Tavistock | 36 | 17 | 2 | 17 | 73 | 71 | 53 |
| 11 Liverton United | 36 | 15 | 5 | 16 | 75 | 72 | 50 |
| 12 Newquay | 36 | 15 | 4 | 17 | 68 | 62 | 49 |
| 13 Ivybridge Town | 36 | 14 | 4 | 18 | 65 | 75 | 46 |
| 14 Torpoint Athletic | 36 | 12 | 9 | 15 | 59 | 68 | 45 |
| 15 Bovey tracey | 36 | 11 | 9 | 16 | 49 | 84 | 42 |
| 16 Falmouth Town | 36 | 8 | 6 | 22 | 48 | 87 | 30 |
| 17 Cullompton Rangers | 36 | 8 | 3 | 25 | 44 | 106 | 27 |
| 18 Liskeard Athletic (-1pt) | 36 | 5 | 6 | 25 | 44 | 108 | 20 |
| 19 (R) Penzance | 36 | 0 | 2 | 34 | 22 | 166 | 2 |

## THROGMORTON CUP

**ROUND 1**
| | | |
|---|---|---|
| Alphington | v Bovey Tracey | 2-1 |
| Axminster Town | v Sidmouth Town | 2-1 |
| Crediton United | v Ivybridge Town | 0-4 |
| Cullompton Rangers | v Budleigh Salterton | 5-4 |
| Dobwalls | v Foxhole Stars | 6-2 |
| Galmpton United | v Totnes & Dartington | 3-2 |
| Godolphin Atlantic | v Appledore | Home W/over |
| Hayle | v St Blazey | 2-0 |
| Helston Athletic | v Truro City Reserves | 2-1 |
| Liverton United | v Teignmouth | 2-7 |
| Mousehole | v Penryn Athletic | 1-2 |
| Okehampton Argyle | v Newton Abbot Spurs | 1-5 |
| Perranporth | v Callington Town | 0-2 |
| Plymstock United | v Stoke Gabriel | 2-5 |
| Porthleven | v Penzance | 1-2 |
| Sticker | v Newquay | 0-6 |
| University of Exeter | v Exmouth Town | 1-2 |
| Vospers Oak Villa | v Holsworthy | 2-4 |
| Wadebridge Town | v St Dennis | 2-0 |

**ROUND 2**
| | | |
|---|---|---|
| Alphington | v Cullompton Rangers | 3-1 |
| Bodmin Town | v Ivybridge Town | 4-1 |
| Camelford | v Holsworthy | 4-0 |
| Elburton Villa | v Witheridge | 4-0 |
| Exeter Civil Service | v Newquay | 1-3 |
| Exmouth Town | v Axminster Town | 4-1 |
| Galmpton United | v Torpoint Athletic | 2-5 |
| Hayle | v Penryn Athletic | 1-3 |
| Helston Athletic | v St Austell | 3-1 |
| Launceston | v Callington Town | 2-0 |
| Newton Abbot Spurs | v Dobwalls | 4-5 |
| Penzance | v Falmouth Town | 4-3 |
| Plymouth Parkway | v Liskeard Athletic | 3-4 |
| Saltash United | v Teignmouth | 5-2 |
| Stoke Gabriel | v Godolphin Atlantic | 3-1 |
| Wadebridge Town | v Tavistock | 1-2 |

**Round 3**
| | | |
|---|---|---|
| Bodmin Town | v Torpoint Athletic | 10-0 |
| Camelford | v Stoke Gabriel | 2-3 |
| Elburton Villa | v Alphington | 2-1 |
| Exmouth Town | v Penryn Athletic | 2-0 |
| Launceston | v Saltash United | 1-2 |
| Liskeard Athletic | v Tavistock | 2-5 |
| Newquay | v Dobwalls | 4-1 |
| Penzance | v Helston Athletic | 0-5 |

**QUARTER FINALS**
| | | |
|---|---|---|
| Bodmin Town | v Saltash United | 2-1 |
| Exmouth Town | v Stoke Gabriel | 3-1 |
| Newquay | v Elburton Villa | 1-3 |
| Tavistock | v Helston Athletic | 1-3 |

**SEMI FINALS**
| | | |
|---|---|---|
| Bodmin Town | v Helston Athletic | 2-0 |
| Elburton Villa | v Exmouth Town | 2-1 |

**FINAL**
| | | |
|---|---|---|
| Bodmin Town | v Elburton Villa | 2-0 |

| PREMIER DIVISION | 1 | 2 | 3 | 4 | 5 | 6 | 7 | 8 | 9 | 10 | 11 | 12 | 13 | 14 | 15 | 16 | 17 | 18 | 19 |
|---|---|---|---|---|---|---|---|---|---|---|---|---|---|---|---|---|---|---|---|
| 1 Bodmin Town | | 7-0 | 3-0 | 5-1 | 0-1 | 6-0 | 3-0 | 0-0 | 5-0 | 13-0 | 4-2 | 11-0 | 2-4 | 1-1 | 4-0 | 2-2 | 4-1 | 5-1 | 2-1 |
| 2 Bovey tracey | 2-4 | | 2-0 | 0-1 | 0-0 | 3-2 | 2-3 | 1-2 | 2-1 | 1-4 | 2-4 | 2-2 | 3-0 | 1-1 | 1-3 | 1-1 | 1-5 | 0-0 | 2-1 |
| 3 Camelford | 0-3 | 2-2 | | 3-0 | 2-3 | 6-3 | 2-0 | 2-0 | 3-0 | 2-2 | 2-0 | 4-0 | 3-0 | 3-0 | 0-1 | 6-1 | 1-2 | 2-2 | 1-2 |
| 4 Cullompton Rangers | 0-2 | 1-2 | 0-2 | | 2-3 | 1-2 | 2-3 | 0-3 | 2-2 | 0-5 | 1-2 | 4-1 | 0-4 | 1-8 | 0-7 | 1-3 | 1-4 | 3-0 | 1-2 |
| 5 Elburton Villa | 0-2 | 1-2 | 4-2 | 3-0 | | 5-1 | 1-1 | 2-0 | 5-2 | 2-1 | 3-1 | 8-0 | 2-3 | 1-1 | 2-7 | 2-2 | 5-1 | 4-1 | 0-3 |
| 6 Falmouth Town | 0-3 | 0-2 | 0-0 | 2-2 | 1-4 | | 3-1 | 1-2 | 2-2 | 1-2 | 1-0 | 2-1 | 1-3 | 0-0 | 1-2 | 1-7 | 3-4 | 2-2 | 0-3 |
| 7 Ivybridge Town | 1-3 | 1-2 | 2-0 | 4-2 | 1-2 | 4-3 | | 0-3 | 4-3 | 1-2 | 1-0 | 2-1 | 0-2 | 0-1 | 2-2 | 2-2 | 3-1 | 3-0 | 1-3 |
| 8 Launceston | 1-7 | 1-3 | 1-0 | 3-1 | 2-4 | 3-1 | 3-1 | | 3-1 | 3-1 | 2-1 | 8-0 | 2-3 | 0-0 | 0-3 | 2-0 | 0-1 | 1-2 | 1-0 |
| 9 Liskeard Athletic | 0-4 | 0-0 | 1-1 | 3-1 | 0-4 | 1-4 | 0-6 | 0-2 | | 1-1 | 1-2 | 3-0 | 2-5 | 3-1 | 1-0 | 0-1 | 2-2 | 2-4 | 0-3 |
| 10 Liverton United | 2-2 | 6-0 | 2-0 | 1-2 | 2-1 | 0-2 | 6-0 | 1-1 | 6-2 | | 1-3 | 4-2 | 0-1 | 4-0 | 2-4 | 1-1 | 2-3 | 5-0 | 2-0 |
| 11 Newquay | 1-1 | 1-1 | 4-2 | 11-0 | 1-2 | 2-2 | 0-3 | 2-1 | 6-0 | 3-1 | | 2-1 | 1-4 | 0-4 | 3-2 | 3-2 | 1-2 | 0-2 | 3-3 |
| 12 Penzance | 2-3 | 2-3 | 0-4 | 1-2 | 0-4 | 0-3 | 0-7 | 0-3 | 0-1 | 1-2 | 1-3 | | 1-4 | 0-9 | 1-2 | 0-7 | 0-4 | 0-0 | 0-6 |
| 13 Plymouth Parkway | 1-1 | 3-0 | 2-1 | 3-2 | 1-2 | 1-0 | 4-0 | 0-0 | 7-0 | 0-3 | 1-0 | 5-1 | | 3-3 | 0-1 | 0-0 | 4-3 | 2-2 | 5-0 |
| 14 Saltash United | 0-2 | 2-0 | 2-4 | 3-3 | 4-0 | 1-0 | 2-0 | 2-0 | 4-2 | 2-0 | 0-1 | 9-0 | 2-6 | | 4-0 | 1-2 | 3-0 | 0-0 | 1-0 |
| 15 St Austell | 1-2 | 6-1 | 0-3 | 3-0 | 1-1 | 6-1 | 4-1 | 1-3 | 3-1 | 7-1 | 2-1 | 4-1 | 2-0 | 2-1 | | 4-0 | 3-3 | 1-1 | 0-0 |
| 16 St Blazey | 0-2 | 2-2 | 1-1 | 4-0 | 0-4 | 5-1 | 1-0 | 2-1 | 4-2 | 2-1 | 1-0 | 11-0 | 2-3 | 1-2 | 0-2 | | 4-0 | 1-2 | 1-4 |
| 17 Tavistock | 1-2 | 6-1 | 1-3 | 1-2 | 1-3 | 1-0 | 2-5 | 1-5 | 5-0 | 2-1 | 3-1 | 0-1 | 0-1 | 1-2 | 0-1 | 2-0 | | 2-0 | 0-3 |
| 18 Torpoint Athletic | 0-4 | 3-1 | 3-5 | 0-2 | 3-4 | 1-0 | 3-0 | 1-0 | 4-3 | 2-1 | 0-2 | 12-1 | 1-1 | 1-0 | 0-1 | 1-3 | 1-2 | | 1-1 |
| 19 Witheridge | 2-3 | 6-1 | 4-4 | 1-3 | 2-3 | 1-2 | 5-0 | 1-2 | 2-1 | 4-1 | 5-1 | 2-2 | 2-0 | 3-2 | 1-3 | 4-3 | | | |

## DIVISION ONE EAST

| | P | W | D | L | F | A | Pts |
|---|---|---|---|---|---|---|---|
| (P) Exmouth Town | 30 | 23 | 6 | 1 | 88 | 27 | 75 |
| Stoke Gabriel (+2pts) | 30 | 19 | 7 | 4 | 100 | 49 | 66 |
| Budleigh Salterton | 30 | 18 | 4 | 8 | 73 | 58 | 58 |
| Newton Abbot Spurs | 30 | 17 | 6 | 7 | 80 | 52 | 57 |
| Appledore | 30 | 17 | 5 | 8 | 67 | 42 | 56 |
| Galmpton United (+2pts) | 30 | 14 | 3 | 13 | 58 | 64 | 47 |
| Teignmouth | 30 | 14 | 3 | 13 | 73 | 71 | 45 |
| Exeter Civil Service | 30 | 11 | 10 | 9 | 55 | 56 | 43 |
| Okehampton Argyle | 30 | 11 | 5 | 14 | 59 | 69 | 38 |
| 10 Exeter Unisversity | 30 | 8 | 11 | 11 | 63 | 68 | 35 |
| 11 Axminster Town (-4pts) | 30 | 10 | 7 | 13 | 56 | 59 | 33 |
| 12 Totnes & Dartington | 30 | 9 | 5 | 16 | 62 | 68 | 32 |
| 13 Alphington | 30 | 9 | 5 | 16 | 39 | 65 | 32 |
| 14 Plymstock United | 30 | 7 | 4 | 19 | 50 | 76 | 25 |
| 15 Sidmouth Town | 30 | 3 | 7 | 20 | 33 | 66 | 16 |
| 16 Crediton United (-4pts) | 30 | 4 | 4 | 22 | 29 | 95 | 12 |

## DIVISION ONE WEST

| | P | W | D | L | F | A | Pts |
|---|---|---|---|---|---|---|---|
| 1 (P) Godolphin Atlantic | 30 | 27 | 2 | 1 | 99 | 21 | 83 |
| 2 Helston Athletic | 30 | 21 | 5 | 4 | 135 | 37 | 68 |
| 3 Wadebridge Town | 30 | 21 | 3 | 6 | 112 | 40 | 66 |
| 4 Sticker | 30 | 18 | 4 | 8 | 68 | 45 | 58 |
| 5 Callington Town (+2pts) | 30 | 16 | 7 | 7 | 87 | 32 | 57 |
| 6 St Dennis | 30 | 18 | 2 | 10 | 89 | 62 | 56 |
| 7 Penryn Athletic | 30 | 16 | 5 | 9 | 79 | 55 | 53 |
| 8 Dobwalls | 30 | 16 | 5 | 9 | 75 | 63 | 53 |
| 9 Perranporth | 30 | 13 | 2 | 15 | 64 | 70 | 41 |
| 10 Hayle | 30 | 11 | 7 | 12 | 59 | 49 | 40 |
| 11 Porthleven | 30 | 11 | 3 | 16 | 40 | 65 | 36 |
| 12 Truro City Reserves (-10pts) | 30 | 11 | 1 | 18 | 49 | 68 | 24 |
| 13 Holsworthy | 30 | 7 | 0 | 23 | 40 | 101 | 21 |
| 14 Vospers Oak villa | 30 | 6 | 1 | 23 | 46 | 90 | 19 |
| 15 Mousehole | 30 | 3 | 0 | 27 | 24 | 123 | 9 |
| 16 Foxhole Stars (-4pts) | 30 | 1 | 1 | 28 | 19 | 164 | 0 |

## DIVISION ONE EAST

| | 1 | 2 | 3 | 4 | 5 | 6 | 7 | 8 | 9 | 10 | 11 | 12 | 13 | 14 | 15 | 16 |
|---|---|---|---|---|---|---|---|---|---|---|---|---|---|---|---|---|
| 1 Alphington | | 0-1 | 0-1 | 3-4 | 4-2 | 0-1 | 2-2 | 1-4 | 0-0 | 1-1 | 0-1 | 2-4 | 1-0 | 0-1 | 0-0 | 4-3 |
| 2 Appledore | 0-1 | | 2-3 | 4-1 | 2-0 | 3-0 | 2-0 | 1-2 | 2-1 | 1-3 | 3-2 | 0-0 | 4-0 | 2-3 | 1-0 | 3-2 |
| 3 Axminster Town | 4-1 | 0-4 | | 1-2 | 4-0 | 5-1 | 1-2 | 1-2 | 2-1 | 6-0 | 1-0 | 3-3 | 6-1 | 3-1 | 2-2 | 3-2 |
| 4 Budleigh Salterton | 2-1 | 1-5 | 3-2 | | 5-1 | 1-2 | 1-2 | 2-1 | 6-0 | 2-1 | 4-0 | 2-2 | 1-1 | 3-5 | 3-6 | 3-0 |
| 5 Crediton United | 0-1 | 2-2 | 0-0 | 0-1 | | 0-2 | 1-1 | 2-4 | 0-2 | 3-6 | 0-3 | 1-3 | 1-2 | 1-2 | 3-2 | 3-0 |
| 6 Exeter Civil Service | 1-1 | 1-1 | 3-1 | 3-3 | 6-0 | | 2-2 | 1-3 | 1-2 | 1-2 | 4-2 | 2-2 | 4-1 | 2-2 | 5-3 | 3-2 |
| 7 Exeter Unisversity | 4-1 | 4-2 | 4-3 | 0-1 | 9-0 | 1-1 | | 1-1 | 1-4 | 1-1 | 2-3 | 2-2 | 3-2 | 1-2 | 7-1 | 2-2 |
| 8 Exmouth Town | 5-1 | 1-1 | 4-0 | 2-2 | 7-1 | 3-0 | 6-1 | | 7-1 | 3-2 | 2-0 | 1-0 | 0-0 | 2-1 | 1-1 | 3-0 |
| 9 Galmpton United | 4-5 | 2-3 | 1-0 | 3-5 | 0-0 | 2-2 | 4-0 | 1-3 | | 0-5 | 2-3 | 1-0 | 1-0 | 1-2 | 2-4 | 2-1 |
| 10 Newton Abbot Spurs | 1-3 | 3-2 | 4-2 | 3-2 | 4-1 | 3-1 | 3-1 | 2-3 | 3-1 | | 3-0 | 1-2 | 3-3 | 2-4 | 2-3 | 4-4 |
| 11 Okehampton Argyle | 4-1 | 2-2 | 0-0 | 1-4 | 5-0 | 0-3 | 1-1 | 3-4 | 1-1 | 5-1 | | | 4-1 | 1-5 | 2-1 | 1-1 |
| 12 Plymstock United | 0-2 | 3-4 | 3-2 | 1-2 | 5-0 | 0-2 | 1-1 | 0-3 | 3-4 | 0-4 | 4-6 | | 4-1 | 0-5 | 2-5 | 1-2 |
| 13 Sidmouth Town | 0-1 | 2-3 | 2-0 | 0-1 | 1-2 | 0-1 | 1-1 | 1-2 | 1-2 | 0-1 | 3-2 | 1-2 | | 3-7 | 1-3 | 0-4 |
| 14 Stoke Gabriel | 8-1 | 2-2 | 0-0 | 6-2 | 6-1 | 7-1 | 3-3 | 3-4 | 1-5 | 0-1 | 4-3 | 4-1 | 0-0 | | 6-0 | 4-2 |
| 15 Teignmouth | 3-0 | 1-0 | 6-2 | 1-2 | 1-3 | 2-0 | 7-1 | 1-6 | 2-4 | 1-3 | 4-1 | 2-1 | 5-3 | 3-3 | | 1-0 |
| 16 Totnes & Dartington | 4-1 | 2-3 | 3-0 | 1-2 | 5-1 | 2-2 | 1-4 | 0-4 | 0-2 | 3-5 | 5-2 | 4-2 | 1-1 | 0-2 | 4-2 | |

## DIVISION ONE WEST

| | 1 | 2 | 3 | 4 | 5 | 6 | 7 | 8 | 9 | 10 | 11 | 12 | 13 | 14 | 15 | 16 |
|---|---|---|---|---|---|---|---|---|---|---|---|---|---|---|---|---|
| 1 Callington Town | | 1-0 | 0-1 | 0-2 | 0-2 | 5-2 | 9-1 | 2-2 | 3-1 | 2-2 | 1-3 | 4-0 | 5-1 | 7-0 | 1-2 | |
| 2 Dobwalls | 0-1 | | 5-3 | 3-3 | 1-4 | 4-3 | 2-1 | 1-3 | 5-1 | 4-0 | 6-2 | 0-0 | 4-2 | 3-2 | 0-10 | |
| 3 Foxhole Stars | 0-11 | 1-6 | | 0-7 | 0-1 | 0-13 | 0-3 | 2-1 | 0-6 | 2-6 | 3-5 | 1-7 | 1-5 | 0-3 | 1-3 | 0-12 |
| 4 Godolphin Atlantic | 2-1 | 1-0 | 4-0 | | 7-0 | 5-1 | 2-0 | 8-0 | 1-0 | 1-1 | 5-0 | 6-2 | 2-3 | 3-0 | 6-0 | 5-3 |
| 5 Hayle | 0-0 | 2-2 | 7-0 | 1-2 | | 2-2 | 5-0 | 5-1 | 2-0 | 5-1 | 0-3 | 0-2 | 2-2 | 0-1 | 4-0 | 2-3 |
| 6 Helston Athletic | 2-1 | 2-2 | 8-0 | 2-3 | 4-0 | | 11-0 | 7-0 | 6-2 | 11-0 | 1-2 | 3-0 | 3-1 | 2-0 | 10-0 | 2-2 |
| 7 Holsworthy | 0-2 | 0-2 | 7-0 | 1-4 | 0-2 | 0-8 | | 4-2 | 2-4 | 0-1 | 2-3 | 1-5 | 1-3 | 4-2 | 0-9 | |
| 8 Mousehole | 0-7 | 1-4 | 3-1 | 0-3 | 0-3 | 1-5 | 1-3 | | 0-4 | 0-7 | 1-2 | 2-4 | 1-4 | 1-0 | 3-2 | 1-2 |
| 9 Penryn Athletic | 1-4 | 3-5 | 7-0 | 2-2 | 3-3 | 1-5 | 3-0 | 4-0 | | 2-1 | 4-1 | 3-2 | 4-1 | 3-0 | 2-2 | 2-4 |
| 10 Perranporth | 2-5 | 1-2 | 2-0 | 2-1 | 1-3 | 1-7 | 2-1 | 2-4 | 1-2 | | 0-0 | 3-1 | 3-2 | 3-1 | 3-1 | 0-4 |
| 11 Porthleven | 0-3 | 1-1 | 2-0 | 0-1 | 1-0 | 2-3 | 1-0 | 2-1 | 2-4 | 1-2 | | 2-4 | 1-4 | 1-3 | 1-0 | 0-1 |
| 12 St Dennis | 0-4 | 0-2 | 8-1 | 0-2 | 1-0 | 3-0 | 8-1 | 4-0 | 3-3 | 3-2 | 4-1 | | 1-0 | 1-4 | 6-3 | 0-2 |
| 13 Sticker | 2-1 | 5-2 | 4-1 | 0-2 | 1-1 | 3-3 | 3-1 | 3-0 | 1-2 | 1-0 | 3-0 | 2-3 | | 2-1 | 3-2 | 2-1 |
| 14 Truro City Reserves | 2-2 | 4-1 | 4-1 | 0-2 | 2-1 | 1-4 | 5-2 | 3-1 | 1-0 | 4-2 | 2-5 | 1-2 | 4-2 | | 1-3 | |
| 15 Vospers Oak villa | 0-1 | 2-3 | 4-1 | 0-3 | 3-2 | 1-2 | 1-2 | 6-0 | 0-2 | 4-7 | 0-1 | 1-3 | 1-2 | 1-0 | | 1-2 |
| 16 Wadebridge Town | 1-1 | 5-1 | 10-0 | 0-2 | 4-1 | 1-2 | 2-0 | 7-0 | 2-1 | 1-4 | 5-1 | 4-4 | 0-4 | 4-0 | 6-2 | |

## CLUB MOVEMENTS

**Premier Division - In:** Ellmore (S - Western League Division One). Exmouth Town (P). Godolphin Atlantic (P).

**Out:** Liverton United (R). Penzance (R).

**Division One East - In:** Exwick Villa (NC from Exeter Civil Service). Liverton United (R).

**Out:** Exeter Civil Service (NC to Exwick Villa). Exmouth Town (P).

**Division One West - In:** Bude Town (P - East Cornwall League). Penzance (R).

**Out:** Godolphin Atlantic (P).

# PREMIER DIVISION

## BODMIN TOWN
Founded: 1896    Nickname:

**Secretary:** Nick Giles **(T)** **(E)** nickgiles@live.co.uk
**Chairman:** **Manager:** Darren Gilbert
**Ground:** Priory Park, Bodmin, Cornwall PL31 2AE **(T)** 01208 78165
**Colours(change):** Yellow & black (All white)

**ADDITIONAL INFORMATION:**
**Previous League:** South Western.
**Honours:** South Western League 1990-91, 93-94, 2005-06. South West Peninsula Premier Division 2007-08, 08-09, 11-12, 12-13. Cornwall Senior Cup 2011-12, 12-13.

## BOVEY TRACEY
Founded: 1950    Nickname: Moorlanders

**Secretary:** Steve Cooney **(T)** **(E)** steve.cooney@hotmail.co.uk
**Chairman:** Peter Horrell **Manager:** Micky Hunt & Ryan German
**Ground:** Western Counties Roofing (Mill Marsh Pk), Ashburton Rd, Bovey TQ13 9FF **(T)** 01626 833 896
**Colours(change):** All red (All green)

**ADDITIONAL INFORMATION:**
**Previous League:** South Devon.
**Honours:** Herald Cup 1960-61. South Devon League Premier Division 2007-08.

## CAMELFORD
Founded: 1893    Nickname: Camels

**Secretary:** Hilary Kent **(T)** **(E)** hilarykent@camelfordfc.fsnet.co.uk
**Chairman:** Mark Tapley **Manager:** Reg Hambly
**Ground:** Trefew Park, PL32 9TS **(T)**
**Colours(change):** White & blue (Blue & white)

**ADDITIONAL INFORMATION:**
**Honours:** South West Peninsula Division One West 2010-11.

## CULLOMPTON RANGERS
Founded: 1945    Nickname: The Cully

**Secretary:** Alan Slark **(T)** **(E)** alanslark1@tiscali.co.uk
**Chairman:** Marcus Scott **Manager:** Mike Taylor
**Ground:** Speeds Meadow, Cullompton EX15 1DW **(T)** 01884 33090
**Colours(change):** Red & black (Yellow & blue)

**ADDITIONAL INFORMATION:**
**Previous League:** Devon County 1992-2007.

## ELBURTON VILLA
Founded: 1982    Nickname: The Villa

**Secretary:** Nick Pope **(T)** **(E)** pope.n@sky.com
**Chairman:** Dave Winters **Manager:** Simon Westlake & Mark Bowden
**Ground:** Haye Road, Elburton, Plymouth PL9 8HS **(T)** 01752 480 025
**Colours(change):** Red & white stripes/black (Blue & white)

**ADDITIONAL INFORMATION:**
**Previous League:** Devon County 1992-2007.

## ELMORE
Founded: 1947    Nickname: Eagles

**Secretary:** Keith Humphreys **(T)** 07855 122 683 **(E)** keith_humphreys@sky.com
**Chairman:** Julian (Jed) Hewitt **Manager:** Pete Buckingham
**Ground:** Horsdon Park, Heathcoat Way, Tiverton, Devon EX16 6DB **(T)** 01884 252 341
**Colours(change):** All green (All red)

**ADDITIONAL INFORMATION:**
**Previous League:** Western League > 2013.
**Record Att:** 1,713 v Tiverton Town Friday April 14th 1995. **Apps:** P Webber. **Win:** 17-0. **Defeat:** 2-7.
**Honours:** East Devon Senior Cup 1972-73, 75-76. Devon Senior Cup 1987-88.

## EXMOUTH TOWN
Founded: 1933    Nickname: The Town

**Secretary:** David Richardson **(T)** **(E)** davidrich43@hotmail.com
**Chairman:** Bob Chamberlain **Manager:** Richard Pears
**Ground:** King George V, Exmouth EX8 3EE **(T)** 01395 263 348
**Colours(change):** All royal blue (All red)

**ADDITIONAL INFORMATION:**
**Previous League:** Devon & Exeter League > 2007.
**Honours:** South West Peninsula Division 1 East 2012-13.

# FALMOUTH TOWN
Founded: 1950  Nickname: The Ambers

**Secretary:** Wayne Pascoe **(T)** **(E)** pascoerichard@hotmail.com
**Chairman:** Vacant **Manager:** Robbie Stevens & Les Gilbert
**Ground:** Bickland Park, Bickland Water Road, Falmouth TR11 4PB **(T)** 01326 375 156
**Colours(change):** Amber & black (All blue)

**ADDITIONAL INFORMATION:**
**Honours:** South Western League 1961-62, 65-66, 67-68, 70-71, 71-72, 72-73, 73-74, 85-86, 86-87, 88-89, 89-90, 91-92, 96-97, 99 -2000. Western League 1974-75, 75-76, 76-77, 77-78. Cornwall Combination 1983-84.

# GODOLPHIN ATLANTIC AFC
Founded: 1980  Nickname: G Army

**Secretary:** Margaret Ashwood **(T)** **(E)** godolphin.arms@btconnect.com
**Chairman:** Tania Semmens **Manager:** Derek Martin
**Ground:** Godolphin Way, Cornwall TR7 3BU **(T)**
**Colours(change):** Sky blue & white (Maroon & black)

**ADDITIONAL INFORMATION:**
**Previous League:** East Cornwall Premier > 2008.
**Honours:** South West Peninsula Div.1 West 2012-13.

# IVYBRIDGE TOWN
Founded: 1925  Nickname: The Ivys

**Secretary:** Paul Cocks **(T)** **(E)** secretary@ivybridgefc.com
**Chairman:** Dave Graddon
**Ground:** Erme Valley, Ermington Road, Ivybridge PL21 9ES **(T)** 01752 896 686
**Colours(change):** Green & black (Yellow & blue)

**ADDITIONAL INFORMATION:**
**Previous League:** Devon County.
**Honours:** Devon County League 2005-06.

# LAUNCESTON
Founded: 1891  Nickname: The Clarets

**Secretary:** Keith Ellacott **(T)** **(E)** launcestonfc@aol.com
**Chairman:** Alan Bradley **Manager:** Leigh Cooper
**Ground:** Pennygillam Ind. Est., Launceston PL15 7ED **(T)** 01566 773 279
**Colours(change):** All claret (Sky blue & black)

**ADDITIONAL INFORMATION:**
**Previous League:** South Western.
**Honours:** South Western League 1995-96.

# LISKEARD ATHLETIC
Founded: 1946  Nickname: The Blues

**Secretary:** Brian Olver **(T)** **(E)** brianolver25@yahoo.com
**Chairman:** Roger Williams
**Ground:** Lux Park Sport Association, Coldstyle Rd, Lux Park, Liskeard PL14 2HZ **(T)** 01566 773 279
**Colours(change):** All blue (All yellow)

**ADDITIONAL INFORMATION:**
**Previous League:** South Western 1995-2007.
**Honours:** South Western League 1976-77, 78-79. Western League Premier Division 1987-88.

# NEWQUAY
Founded: 1890  Nickname: The Peppermints

**Secretary:** Bob Steggies **(T)** **(E)** bob@steggies.com
**Chairman:** Peter Butterley **Manager:** Alan Carey
**Ground:** Mount Wise TR7 2BU **(T)** 01637 872 935
**Colours(change):** Red & white (Blue & white)

**ADDITIONAL INFORMATION:**
**Honours:** South West Peninsula Division One West 2011-12.

# PLYMOUTH PARKWAY AFC
Founded: 1988  Nickname: The Parkway

**Secretary:** Genny Turner **(T)** **(E)** genny.woolwell@btinternet.com
**Chairman:** James Parsons **Manager:** Wayne Hillson
**Ground:** Bolitho Park, St Peters Road, Manadon, Plymouth PL5 3JH **(T)**
**Colours(change):** Yellow & blue (Grey & white)

**ADDITIONAL INFORMATION:**
**Previous Name:** Ex-Air Flyers Plymouth.
**Previous League:** South Western 1998-2007.
**Honours:** Throgmorton Cup 2010-11.

## SALTASH UNITED

Founded: 1945     Nickname: The Ashes

**Secretary:** Luke Ranford     **(T)** 07830 299 555     **(E)** luke.ranford@googlemail.com
**Chairman:** Bill Wakeham     **Manager:** Martin Burgess
**Ground:** Kimberley Stadium, Callington Road, Saltash PL12 6DX     **(T)** 01752 845 746
**Colours(change):** Red & white stripes/black (Blue & black)

**ADDITIONAL INFORMATION:**
**Previous League:** South Western 2006-07.
**Honours:** South Western League 1953-54, 75-76. Western League Division 1 1976-77, Premier 1984-85, 86-87, 88-89.

## ST. AUSTELL

Founded: 1890     Nickname: The Lily Whites

**Secretary:** Peter Beard     **(T)**     **(E)** peterbeard45@gmail.com
**Chairman:** James Hutchings     **Manager:** Dan Nancarrow
**Ground:** Poltair Park, Trevarthian Road, St Austell PL25 4LR     **(T)** 01726 66099
**Colours(change):** All white (Yellow & blue)

**ADDITIONAL INFORMATION:**
**Previous League:** South Western 1951-2007.

## ST. BLAZEY

Founded: 1896     Nickname: The Green & Blacks

**Secretary:** Martin Richards (Acting)     **(T)**     **(E)** marty.rich60@talktalk.net
**Chairman:** Martin Richards     **Manager:** Bobby Oaten
**Ground:** Blaise Park, Station Road, St Blazey PL24 2ND     **(T)** 01725 814 110     **Capacity:** 3,000
**Colours(change):** Green & black (Blue & white)

**ADDITIONAL INFORMATION:**
**Previous League:** South Western 1951-2007.
**Honours:** South Western Lge 1954-55, 57-58, 62-63, 63-64, 80-81, 82-83, 98-99, 2000-01, 01-02, 02-03, 03-04, 04-05, 06-07.

## TAVISTOCK

Founded: 1888     Nickname: The Lambs

**Secretary:** Phil Lowe     **(T)** 01822 613 715     **(E)**
**Chairman:** Russell Bartlett     **Manager:** Ian Southcott
**Ground:** Langsford Park, Red & Black Club, Crowndale Road, Tavistock PL19 8DD     **(T)** 01822 614 447
**Colours(change):** Red & black (All blue)

**ADDITIONAL INFORMATION:**
**Previous League:** South Western 1968-2007.

## TORPOINT ATHLETIC

Founded: 1887     Nickname: The Point

**Secretary:** Robbie Morris     **(T)**     **(E)** robbietafc81@live.co.uk
**Chairman:** Paul Whitworth     **Manager:** Bradley Yeo
**Ground:** The Mill, Mill Lane, Carbeile Road, Torpoint PL11 2RE     **(T)** 01752 812 889
**Colours(change):** Yellow & black (All white)

**ADDITIONAL INFORMATION:**
**Previous League:** South Western 1962-2007.
**Honours:** South Western League 1964-65, 66-67.

## WITHERIDGE

Founded: 1920     Nickname: The Withy

**Secretary:** Chris Cole     **(T)**     **(E)** chris.cole@witheridgeafc.co.uk
**Chairman:** Andre Pike     **Manager:** Chris Vinnecombe
**Ground:** Edge Down Park, Fore Street, Witheridge EX16 8AH     **(T)** 01884 861 511
**Colours(change):** All blue (All claret)

**ADDITIONAL INFORMATION:**
**Previous League:** Devon County 2006-07.

## DIVISION ONE EAST CONSTITUTION 2013-14

ALPHINGTON ................................... The Chronicles, Church Road, Alphington, Exeter EX2 8SW.................................01392 279556
APPLEDORE............................................ Marshford, Churchill Way, Appledore EX39 1PA.........................................01237 475015
AXMINSTER TOWN...............2013/14 Home games being played at Colyton Grammar School EX24 6HN ...................................
BUDLEIGH SALTERTON...............................Greenway Lane, Budleigh Salterton EX9 6SG ...............................01395 443850
CREDITON UNITED ............................ Lords Meadow, Commercial Road, Crediton EX17 1ER........................01363 774671
EXWICK VILLA........................................Foxhayes, Exwick, Exter EX4 2BQ .........................................................
GALMPTON UNITED AFC..... War Memorial Playing Field, Greenway Road, Galmpton, Brixham TQ5 0LP .....................
LIVERTON UNITED ...........................................Halford TQ12 6JF....................................................................
NEWTON ABBOT SPURS ................Recreation Ground, Marsh Road, Newton Abbot TQ12 2AR ...............01626 365343
OKEHAMPTON ARGYLE........................Simmons Park, Mill Road, Okehampton EX20 1PR...........................01837 53997
PLYMSTOCK UNITED ...........................Dean Cross, Dean Cross Road, Plymstock PL9 7AZ.........................01752 406776
SIDMOUTH TOWN ....................Manstone Recreation Ground, Manstone Lane, Sidmouth EX10 9TF ...............01395 577087
STOKE GABRIEL............... G J Churchward Mem. Ground, Broadley Lane, Stoke Gabriel, Totnes TQ9 6RR.................01803 782913
TEIGNMOUTH .................................Coombe Valley, Coombe Lane, Teignmouth TQ14 9EX...........................01626 776688
TOTNES & DARTINGTON SC..................... Foxhole Sports Ground, Dartington TQ9 6EB.............................01803 868032
UNIVERSITY OF EXETER .............. University Sports Ground, Topsham Road, Topsham EX3 0LY .........................01392 879542

## DIVISION ONE WEST CONSTITUTION 2013-14

BUDE TOWN....................................................Broadclose Park EX23 8DR ..........................................................
CALLINGTON TOWNGinsters Marshfield Parc, Callington Community College, Launceston Rd, Callington PL17 7DR .....01579 382647
DOBWALLS...............................................Lantoom Park, Duloe Road, Dobwalls PL14 4LU...........................07721 689 380
FOXHOLE STARS.........................Goverseth Park, Goverseth Terrace, Foxhole PL26 7UP.............................01726 824615
HAYLE .................................................. Trevassack Park, Viaduct Hill, Hayle TR27 5HT.....................................01736 757157
HELSTON ATHLETIC..............................Kellaway Park, Clodgy Lane, Helston TR13 8PJ ..............................01326 573742
HOLSWORTHY AFC.............................Upcott Field, North Road, Holsworthy EX22 6HF.............................01409 254295
MOUSEHOLE...............................................Trungle Parc, Paul, Penzance TR19 6UG...................................01736 731518
PENRYN ATHLETIC..............................Kernick, Kernick Road, Penryn TR10 9EW.....................................01326 375182
PENZANCE ............................... Penlee Park, Alexandra Place, Penzance TR18 4NE.....................................01736 361 964
PERRANPORTH ............................... Ponsmere Valley, Budnick Estate, Perranporth TR6 0DB..............................
PORTHLEVEN ....................................Gala Parc, Mill Lane, Porthleven TR13 9LQ....................................01326 569 655
ST DENNIS ............................................Boscawen Park, St Dennis PL26 8DW ......................................01726 822635
STICKER..................................................... Burngullow Park PL26 7EN...............................................01726 71003
TRURO CITY RESERVES.........................Treyew Road, Truro TR1 2TH..............................................01872 225400
VOSPERS OAK VILLA..................Weston Mill, Ferndale Road, Weston Mill, Plymouth PL2 2EL.........................01752 363352
WADEBRIDGE TOWN ...........................Bodieve Park, Bodieve Road, Wadebridge PL27 6EA.........................01208 812537

# GROUND DIRECTIONS-PREMIER DIVISION

**BODMIN TOWN-Priory Park, Bodmin, Cornwall PL31 2AE. Tel: 01208 781 65.**
Situated in Priory Park through main car park. Use football car park on Saturdays.

**BOVEY TRACEY-Western Counties Roofing (Mill Marsh Park), Ashburton Road, Bovey Tracey TQ13 9FF. Tel: 01626 832 780.**
Coming off the A38 East or Westbound at Drumbridges take the Bovey Tracey turn-off, straight through the lights at Heathfield. Next roundabout take 2nd exit, next roundabout take 3rd exit, then left, 35 yards, follow road to bottom of drive then enter through gate.

**CAMELFORD-Trefrew Park PL32 9TS.**
From the South drive into Camelford up Victoria Road for 300 yards, turn left,into Oakwood Rise. Follow road around for approximately 300 yards. Entrance is on the right up the lane. From the North as you enter Camelford turn right into Oakwood Rise then as above.

**CULLOMPTON RANGERS-Speeds Meadow, Cullompton EX15 1DW. Tel: 01884 33090.**
Leave M5 at junction 28, left at Town Centre, at Meadow Lane turn left past Sports Centre, at end of road turn right, then in 100 yards turn left into ground at end of lane.

**ELBURTON VILLA-Haye Road, Elburton, Plymouth PL9 8NS. Tel: 01752 480 025.**
From Plymouth City Centre take A379 Kingsbridge Road. At third roundabout turn left into Haye Road (signposted Saltram House). Ground 50 yards on left.

**ELMORE -Horsdon Park, Heathcoat Way, Tiverton, Devon EX16 6DB. Tel: 01884 252 341.**
From M5 leave at Junction 27 towards Tiverton on the A373. After approx 6 miles take the exit signed "Tiverton & Industrial Estate" Ground is then 350 meters on your right.

**EXMOUTH TOWN -King George V, Exmouth EX8 3EE. Tel: 01395 263348.**
From Junction 30 of M5 take te A376 to Exmouth, on entering the town the ground is on your right, before the railway station.

**FALMOUTH TOWN-Bickland Park, Bickland Water Road, Falmouth TR11 4PB. Tel: 01326 375 156.**
Take Penryn by-pass from Asda roundabout. Leave by-pass at Hillhead roundabout, take first right and follow industrial estate signs. Ground 1/2 mile on the left.

**GODOLPHIN ATLENTIC -Godolphin Way TR7 3BU.**
Off Henver Road turn into Godolphin Way and ground is then first entrance on the left.

## SOUTH WEST PENINSULA LEAGUE - STEP 6/7

**IVYBRIDGE TOWN-Erme Valley, Ermington Road, Ivybridge. Tel: 01752 896 686.**
From Plymouth-leave A38 at Ivybridge and follow signs towards Ermington. Ground is immediately next to South Devon Tennis Centre. From Exeter-leave A38 at Ivybridge. Ground is in front of you at the end of the slip road.

**LAUNCESTON-Pennygillam, Pennygillam Ind. Est., Launceston PL15 7ED. Tel: 01566 773 279.**
Leave A30 onto Pennygillam roundabout, turn into Pennygillam Industrial Estate. Ground is 400 yards on the left.

**LISKEARD ATHLETIC-Lux Park Sport Association, Coldstyle Road, Lux Park, Liskeard PL14 2HZ. Tel: 01579 342 665.**
From the Parade (middle of town) turn left at the monument, then first right following signs for Leisure Centre at Lux Park.

**NEWQUAY AFC-Mount Wise TR7 2BU**
From link road turn right onto Mount Wise, just past traffic lights turn Right into Clevedon Road.

**PLYMOUTH PARKWAY-Bolitho Park, St Peters Road, Manadon, Plymouth PL5 3OZ.**
From Cornwall/Exeter exit at the Manadon/Tavistock junction off the Plymouth Parkway (A38), off roundabout into St Peters Road. Entrance is one mile on the right.

**SALTASH UNITED-Ground: Kimberley Stadium, Callington Road, Saltash PL12 6DX. Tel: 01752 845 746.**
At the top of Town Centre fork right at mini-roundabout. Ground is situated 400m ahead on the left-hand side next to Leisure Centre and Police Station.

**ST AUSTELL-Poltair Park, Trevarthian Road, St Austell PL25 4LR Tel: 07966 130 158**
Near Poltair School and St Austell Brewery (5 minutes from St Austell Rail Station).

**ST BLAZEY-Blaise Park, Station Road, St Blazey PL24 2ND. Tel: 01725 814 110.**
A390 from Lostwithiel to St Austell. At village of St Blazey turn left at traffic lights by Church/Cornish Arms pub into Station Road. Ground is 200 yards on the left.

**TAVISTOCK-Langsford Park, Red & Black Club, Crowndale Road, Tavistock PL19 8DD. Tel: 01822 614 447.**
From Launceston/Okehampton, stay on A386 trhough town signposted Plymouth, past Drake's statue. Over canal turn right, signposted football ground/recycle centre. Ground is 100 metres past Tavistock college. From Plymouth, stay on A386 pass Morrisons and Texaco garage, over River Tavy, turn left signposted football ground/recycle centre. Then as above.

**TORPOINT ATHLETIC-The Mill, Mill Lane, Carbeile Road, Torpoint PL11 2NA. Tel: 01752 812 889.**
Take turning at Carbeile Inn onto Carbeille Road and first turning on the right into Mill Lane.

**WITHERIDGE-Edge Down Park, Fore Street, Witheridge EX16 8AH. Tel: 01884 861 511.**
B3137 Tiverton to Witheridge, on entering the village football pitch is on the right-hand side before the Fire Station and School.

# SOUTHERN COUNTIES LEAGUE

**Founded:** As the Kent League in 1966

### Recent Champions:
2008: Thamesmead Town
2009: VCD Athletic
2010: Faversham Town
2011: Hythe Town
2012: Herne Bay
**scefl.com**

| PREMIER DIVISION | P | W | D | L | F | A | Pts |
|---|---|---|---|---|---|---|---|
| (P) Erith & Belvedere | 32 | 23 | 7 | 2 | 113 | 45 | 76 |
| (P) VCD Athletic | 32 | 23 | 5 | 4 | 97 | 31 | 74 |
| Erith Town | 32 | 19 | 4 | 9 | 74 | 40 | 61 |
| Corinthian | 32 | 17 | 8 | 7 | 74 | 37 | 59 |
| Lordswood | 32 | 17 | 7 | 8 | 60 | 56 | 58 |
| Whyteleafe | 32 | 16 | 6 | 10 | 67 | 49 | 54 |
| Tunbridge Wells | 32 | 15 | 7 | 10 | 82 | 43 | 52 |
| Cray Valley PM | 32 | 13 | 8 | 11 | 63 | 58 | 47 |
| Canterbury City | 32 | 12 | 7 | 13 | 52 | 58 | 43 |
| 0 Woodstock Sports | 32 | 12 | 7 | 13 | 59 | 76 | 43 |
| 1 Beckenham Town | 32 | 11 | 7 | 14 | 63 | 73 | 40 |
| 2 Deal Town | 32 | 11 | 6 | 15 | 58 | 65 | 39 |
| 3 Rochester United | 32 | 12 | 2 | 18 | 52 | 70 | 38 |
| 4 Fisher | 32 | 7 | 7 | 18 | 41 | 71 | 28 |
| 5 Greenwich Borough | 32 | 6 | 5 | 21 | 33 | 93 | 23 |
| 6 Holmesdale | 32 | 5 | 6 | 21 | 34 | 83 | 21 |
| 7 Sevenoaks Town | 32 | 3 | 1 | 28 | 28 | 102 | 10 |

## LEAGUE CUP

**PRELIMINARY ROUND (2 LEGS)**

| | | | |
|---|---|---|---|
| Beckenham Town | v | Erith Town | 2-2 |
| Erith Town | v | Beckenham Town | 2-1 |

**ROUND 1**

| | | | |
|---|---|---|---|
| VCD Athletic | v | Corinthian | 0-1 |
| Corinthian | v | VCD Athletic | 2-1 |
| Fisher | v | Deal Town | 1-1 |
| Deal Town | v | Fisher | 6-0 |
| Tunbridge Wells | v | Woodstock Sports | 2-1 |
| Woodstock Sports | v | Tunbridge Wells | 1-1 |
| Erith & Belvedere | v | Greenwich Borough | 3-0 |
| Greenwich Borough | v | Erith & Belvedere | 1-3 |
| Canterbury City | v | Lordswood | 3-1 |
| Lordswood | v | Canterbury City | 4-0 |
| Holmesdale | v | Rochester United | 1-0 |
| Rochester United | v | Holmesdale | 4-6 |
| Sevenoaks Town | v | Whyteleafe | 3-1 |
| Whyteleafe | v | Sevenoaks Town | 4-0 |
| Cray Valley PM | v | Erith Town | 2-2 |
| Erith Town | v | Cray Valley PM | 1-3 |

**QUARTER FINALS**

| | | | |
|---|---|---|---|
| Corinthian | v | Holmesdale | 1-0 |
| Holmesdale | v | Corinthian | 0-5 |
| Cray Valley PM | v | Deal Town | 1-2 |
| Deal Town | v | Cray Valley PM | 1-0 |
| Lordswood | v | Tunbridge Wells | 4-1 |
| Tunbridge Wells | v | Lordswood | 1-1 |
| Erith & Belvedere | v | Whyteleafe | 1-0 |
| Whyteleafe | v | Erith & Belvedere | 0-1 |

**SEMI FINALS**

| | | | |
|---|---|---|---|
| Erith & Belvedere | v | Lordswood | 3-0 |
| Lordswood | v | Erith & Belvedere | 1-0 |
| Deal Town | v | Corinthian | 0-3 |
| Corinthian | v | Deal Town | 5-0 |

**FINAL**

| | | | |
|---|---|---|---|
| Corinthian | v | Erith & Belvedere | 1-4 |

| PREMIER DIVISION | 1 | 2 | 3 | 4 | 5 | 6 | 7 | 8 | 9 | 10 | 11 | 12 | 13 | 14 | 15 | 16 | 17 |
|---|---|---|---|---|---|---|---|---|---|---|---|---|---|---|---|---|---|
| 1 Beckenham | | 1-3 | 1-0 | 2-0 | 3-0 | 0-6 | 2-2 | 1-2 | 4-3 | 1-1 | 3-1 | 2-3 | 3-5 | 5-4 | 0-7 | 3-1 | 0-1 |
| 2 Canterbury | 1-1 | | 1-0 | 2-2 | 2-1 | 2-2 | 3-0 | 1-0 | 1-0 | 2-0 | 1-2 | 3-1 | 3-0 | 1-3 | 3-0 | 1-3 | 6-1 |
| 3 Corinthian | 3-3 | 4-1 | | 3-1 | 6-0 | 1-1 | 2-1 | 6-1 | 3-1 | 2-3 | 1-2 | 4-1 | 4-0 | 1-0 | 1-1 | 1-2 | 2-2 |
| 4 Cray Valley | 2-2 | 5-0 | 1-1 | | 3-3 | 1-2 | 1-5 | 0-2 | 3-1 | 0-0 | 3-0 | 4-1 | 3-1 | 1-9 | 0-2 | 2-0 | 2-4 |
| 5 Deal Town | 4-3 | 4-1 | 1-2 | 1-0 | | 1-2 | 1-3 | 3-2 | 6-0 | 5-1 | 0-1 | 3-1 | 5-0 | 2-4 | 1-2 | 0-3 | 1-1 |
| 6 Erith & Bel | 3-2 | 3-2 | 4-2 | 4-4 | 5-2 | | 3-1 | 3-2 | 7-0 | 3-3 | 3-3 | 6-1 | 4-0 | 2-0 | 2-2 | 1-2 | 8-5 |
| 7 Erith Town | 3-1 | 3-2 | 0-1 | 0-4 | 2-0 | 4-3 | | 4-3 | 8-0 | 4-0 | 1-2 | 4-1 | 3-0 | 0-0 | 0-2 | 3-0 | 2-3 |
| 8 Fisher | 1-2 | 0-2 | 0-3 | 0-2 | 1-1 | 0-6 | 0-1 | | 1-0 | 2-3 | 2-5 | 1-1 | 1-0 | 1-2 | 0-5 | 0-2 | 3-1 |
| 9 Greenwich | 2-2 | 1-0 | 0-0 | 2-3 | 0-4 | 0-4 | 0-3 | 1-4 | | 2-1 | 0-3 | 1-3 | 1-0 | 2-6 | 1-6 | 0-2 | 2-0 |
| 10 Holmesdale | 1-1 | 2-2 | 0-4 | 3-3 | 3-1 | 0-3 | 0-2 | 0-3 | 2-4 | | 0-3 | 1-2 | 2-1 | 1-2 | 0-1 | 0-5 | 2-0 |
| 11 Lordswood | 1-0 | 1-0 | 1-1 | 4-0 | 3-0 | 0-0 | 0-4 | 1-1 | 2-2 | 4-1 | | 3-1 | 2-1 | 1-4 | 0-0 | 2-4 | 2-2 |
| 12 Rochester Utd | 0-3 | 2-1 | 0-3 | 0-2 | 1-2 | 0-3 | 1-1 | 1-2 | 2-1 | 3-0 | 3-0 | | 4-2 | 1-2 | 1-2 | 3-1 | 2-1 |
| 13 Sevenoaks | 2-6 | 1-1 | 2-4 | 1-6 | 0-1 | 0-5 | 0-3 | 4-0 | 0-1 | 2-3 | 1-3 | 1-4 | | 0-6 | 1-4 | 1-5 | 1-3 |
| 14 Tunbridge W | 3-2 | 6-0 | 1-2 | 0-0 | 2-2 | 2-3 | 1-1 | 1-1 | 5-1 | 5-0 | 2-3 | 3-2 | 0-1 | | 0-2 | 2-3 | 1-1 |
| 15 VCD Athletic | 5-1 | 5-0 | 3-0 | 1-0 | 1-1 | 2-4 | 0-2 | 2-2 | 6-2 | 4-1 | 9-2 | 1-4 | 4-0 | 1-0 | | 2-0 | 6-0 |
| 16 Whyteleafe | 1-2 | 2-2 | 2-2 | 0-2 | 1-1 | 0-3 | 2-3 | 4-1 | 1-1 | 3-1 | 4-0 | 5-1 | 3-0 | 0-0 | 1-4 | | 2-2 |
| 17 Woodstock | 1-0 | 2-2 | 0-5 | 2-3 | 5-0 | 1-4 | 2-1 | 2-2 | 1-0 | 2-1 | 2-3 | 2-1 | 5-0 | 0-6 | 1-5 | 2-3 | |

## SOUTHERN COUNTIES LEAGUE - STEP 5

| DIVISION ONE | P | W | D | L | F | A | Pts |
|---|---|---|---|---|---|---|---|
| 1 Whitstable Town Reserves | 26 | 19 | 3 | 4 | 86 | 28 | 60 |
| 2 Herne Bay Reserves | 26 | 16 | 5 | 5 | 68 | 40 | 53 |
| 3 Maidstone United Reserves | 26 | 15 | 5 | 6 | 80 | 52 | 50 |
| 4 Chatham Town Reserves | 26 | 13 | 7 | 6 | 55 | 32 | 46 |
| 5 Erith Town Reserves | 26 | 13 | 6 | 7 | 56 | 40 | 45 |
| 6 Ramsgate Reserves | 26 | 12 | 4 | 10 | 55 | 54 | 40 |
| 7 Deal Town Reserves | 26 | 10 | 4 | 12 | 49 | 55 | 34 |
| 8 Holmesdale Reserves | 26 | 9 | 6 | 11 | 61 | 60 | 33 |
| 9 VCD Athletic Reserves (-3pts) | 26 | 11 | 0 | 15 | 57 | 60 | 30 |
| 10 Phoenix Sports Reserves | 26 | 9 | 2 | 15 | 60 | 66 | 29 |
| 11 Margate Reserves | 26 | 8 | 5 | 13 | 47 | 57 | 29 |
| 12 Woodstock Sports Reserves | 26 | 8 | 5 | 13 | 41 | 75 | 29 |
| 13 Lordswood Reserves | 26 | 6 | 6 | 14 | 40 | 62 | 24 |
| 14 Rusthall Reserves | 26 | 4 | 0 | 22 | 26 | 100 | 12 |

## CLUB MOVEMENTS

**Premier Division - In:** Ashford United (P - Kent Invicta).

Phoenix Sports (P - Kent Invicta).

**Out:** Erith & Belvedere (P - Isthmian Division One North).

VCD Athletic (P - Isthmian Division One North).

2012-13 - Ashford United.                              Photo: Alan Coomes

2012-13 - Beckenham Town.                              Photo: Alan Coomes

# ASHFORD UNITED
Founded: 1930  Nickname: The Nuts&Bolts

**Secretary:** Elaine Orsbourne  **(T)** 01233 646 713  **(E)** orsbournes@ntlworld.com

**Chairman:** Ernie Warren  **Manager:** Paul Chambers  **Prog Ed:** Sarah Larkin

**Ground:** The Homelands, Ashford Road TN26 1NJ  **(T)** 01233 611 838

**Capacity:**  **Seats:** Yes  **Covered:** Yes  **Midweek Matchday:** Tuesday  **Clubhouse:** Yes

**Colours(change):** Green & white/green/green & white (Yellow & green/yellow/yellow & green)
**Previous Names:** Ashford Town 1930-2010.
**Previous Leagues:** Kent Invicta >2013
**Records:** **Att:** @ Homelands - 3,363 v Fulham, FAC 1st Rnd 1994. **Goalscorer:** Dave Arter - 192. **Apps:** Peter McRobert - 765.
**Senior Honours:** Kent League 1948-49. Kent Senior Cup 1958-59, 62-63, 92-93, 95-96.

**10 YEAR RECORD**

| 03-04 | 04-05 | 05-06 | 06-07 | 07-08 | 08-09 | 09-10 | 10-11 | 11-12 | 12-13 |
|---|---|---|---|---|---|---|---|---|---|
| SthE 12 | Isth1 20 | Isth1 21 | Isth1S 18 | Isth1S 8 | Isth1S 7 | Isth1S 20 | | K_lv 5 | K_lv 3 |

# BECKENHAM TOWN
Founded: 1887  Nickname: Reds

**Secretary:** Peter Palmer  **(T)** 07774 728 758  **(E)** peterpalmer3@sky.com

**Chairman:** Jason Huntley  **Manager:** Jason Huntley  **Prog Ed:** Geoff Ward

**Ground:** Eden Park Avenue, Beckenham Kent BR3 3JL  **(T)** 07774 728 758

**Capacity:** 4,000 **Seats:** 120 **Covered:** 120 **Midweek Matchday:** Tuesday  **Clubhouse:** Yes  **Shop:** Yes

**Colours(change):** All red (All blue).
**Previous Names:** Stanhope Rovers.
**Previous Leagues:** South East London Amateur. Metropolitan. London Spartan.
**Records:** **Att:** 720 v Berkhamsted, FA Cup 1994-95. **Goalscorer:** Ricky Bennett. **Apps:** Lee Fabian - 985.
**Senior Honours:**

**10 YEAR RECORD**

| 03-04 | 04-05 | 05-06 | 06-07 | 07-08 | 08-09 | 09-10 | 10-11 | 11-12 | 12-13 |
|---|---|---|---|---|---|---|---|---|---|
| Kent P 12 | Kent P 10 | Kent P 2 | Kent P 11 | Kent P 3 | Kent P 15 | Kent P 4 | Kent P 10 | Kent P 6 | Kent P 11 |

# CANTERBURY CITY
Founded: 1904  Nickname:

**Secretary:** John Barlow  **(T)** 07852 188 194  **(E)** jonjo@almonry.freeserve.co.uk

**Chairman:** Tim Clarke  **Manager:** Simon Petit  **Prog Ed:** John Fabre

**Ground:** Herne Bay FC, Winch's Field, Standley Gardens, Heren Bay CT6 5SG  **(T)**

**Capacity:** 3,000 **Seats:** 200 **Covered:** 1,500 **Midweek Matchday:** Wednesday  **Clubhouse:** Yes  **Shop:** Yes

**Colours(change):** All burgundy (All green)
**Previous Names:**
**Previous Leagues:** Kent 1947-59, 94-01, Metropolitan 1959-60, Southern 1960-61, 94, Kent County 2007-11.
**Records:**
**Senior Honours:** Kent County League Division One East 2007-08, 08-09.

**10 YEAR RECORD**

| 03-04 | 04-05 | 05-06 | 06-07 | 07-08 | 08-09 | 09-10 | 10-11 | 11-12 | 12-13 |
|---|---|---|---|---|---|---|---|---|---|
| | | | | KC1E 1 | KC1E 1 | KC P 5 | KC P 2 | Kent P 9 | Kent P 9 |

# CORINTHIAN
Founded: 1972  Nickname:

**Secretary:** Sue Billings  **(T)** 07734 855 554  **(E)** corinthians@billingsgroup.com

**Chairman:** R J Billings  **Manager:** Tony Stitford

**Ground:** Gay Dawn Farm, Valley Road, Longfield DA3 8LY  **(T)** 01474 573 118

**Capacity:**  **Seats:**  **Covered:**  **Midweek Matchday:** Tuesday  **Clubhouse:** Yes

**Colours(change):** Green & white hoops/white (Yellow/green/green)
**Previous Names:** Welling United Reserves > 2009.
**Previous Leagues:** Southern 1985-91.
**Records:**
**Senior Honours:**

**10 YEAR RECORD**

| 03-04 | 04-05 | 05-06 | 06-07 | 07-08 | 08-09 | 09-10 | 10-11 | 11-12 | 12-13 |
|---|---|---|---|---|---|---|---|---|---|
| | | | | | Kent 2 6 | Kent P 14 | Kent P 12 | Kent P 7 | Kent P 4 |

2012-13 - Canterbury City. Photo: Alan Coomes

2012-13 - Tunbridge Wells. Photo: Roger Turner.

2012-13 - Eith Town.

Photo: Alan Coomes

# CRAY VALLEY PAPER MILLS
Founded: 1919  Nickname: Millers

**Secretary:** Dave Wilson  **(T)** 07715 961 886  **(E)** wilson433@ntlworld.com

**Chairman:** Frank May  **Manager:** Steve Chapman  **Prog Ed:** Dave Wilson

**Ground:** Badgers Sports, Middle Park Avenue, Eltham SE9 5HT  **(T)**

**Capacity:**  **Seats:**  **Covered:**  **Midweek Matchday:** Tuesday  **Clubhouse:**

**Colours(change):** Green/black/black (Sky blue/white/white).
**Previous Names:** None
**Previous Leagues:** Spartan 1991-97, Spartan South Midlands 1997-98, London Intermediate 1998-01, Kent County 2001-11.
**Records:**
**Senior Honours:** Kent County League Premier Division 2004-05.

### 10 YEAR RECORD

| 03-04 | 04-05 | 05-06 | 06-07 | 07-08 | 08-09 | 09-10 | 10-11 | 11-12 | 12-13 |
|---|---|---|---|---|---|---|---|---|---|
|  | KC P 1 |  | KC P 7 | KC P 9 | KC P 5 | KC P 6 | KC P 3 | Kent P 11 | Kent P 8 |

# DEAL TOWN
Founded: 1908  Nickname: Town

**Secretary:** Gary Rivers  **(T)**  **(E)** dealtownsecretary@hotmail.co.uk

**Chairman:** David Melody  **Manager:** Derek Hares  **Prog Ed:** Colin Adams

**Ground:** Charles Sports Ground, St Leonards Road, Deal. CT14 9BB  **(T)** 01304 375 623

**Capacity:** 2,500 **Seats:** 180 **Covered:** 180 **Midweek Matchday:** Tuesday  **Clubhouse:** Yes **Shop:** Yes

**Colours(change):** Black & white/black. (Claret & blue/blue/claret).
**Previous Names:** Deal Cinque Ports FC > 1920
**Previous Leagues:** Thanet. East Kent. Kent. Aetolian. Southern. Greater London.
**Records:** Att: 2,495 v Newcastle Town, FA Vase S-F, 26.03.2000.
**Senior Honours:**

### 10 YEAR RECORD

| 03-04 | 04-05 | 05-06 | 06-07 | 07-08 | 08-09 | 09-10 | 10-11 | 11-12 | 12-13 |
|---|---|---|---|---|---|---|---|---|---|
| Kent P 16 | Kent P 13 | Kent P 9 | Kent P 8 | Kent P 9 | Kent P 12 | Kent P 9 | Kent P 11 | Kent P 15 | Kent P 12 |

# ERITH TOWN
Founded: 1959  Nickname: The Dockers

**Secretary:** Jim Davie  **(T)** 07831 131 278  **(E)** jamesdavie@ntlworld.com

**Chairman:** Ian Birrell  **Manager:** Mark Tompkins  **Prog Ed:** Ian Birrell

**Ground:** Badger Sports, Middle Park Avenue, Eltham SE9 5HT  **(T)**

**Capacity:** 1,450 **Seats:** 1,006 **Covered:** 1,066 **Midweek Matchday:** Monday  **Clubhouse:** Yes **Shop:** No

**Colours(change):** Red & black/black/black. (Yellow & black/white/white).
**Previous Names:** Woolwich Town 1959-89 and 1990-97.
**Previous Leagues:** London Metropolitan Sunday. London Spartan.
**Records:** Att: 325 v Charlton Athletic, friendly. **Goalscorer:** Dean Bowey.
**Senior Honours:**

### 10 YEAR RECORD

| 03-04 | 04-05 | 05-06 | 06-07 | 07-08 | 08-09 | 09-10 | 10-11 | 11-12 | 12-13 |
|---|---|---|---|---|---|---|---|---|---|
| Kent P 7 | Kent P 15 | Kent P 14 | Kent P 14 | Kent P 5 | Kent P 7 | Kent P 12 | Kent P 8 | Kent P 4 | Kent P 3 |

# FISHER
Founded: 1908  Nickname: The Fish

**Secretary:** Dan York  **(T)** 07719 632 635  **(E)** dan@fisherfc.co.uk

**Chairman:** Ben Westmancott  **Manager:** Billy Walton  **Prog Ed:** Jevon Hall

**Ground:** Dulwich Hamlet FC, Edgar Kail Way, East Dulwich SE22 8BD  **(T)**

**Capacity:** 3,000 **Seats:** 500 **Covered:** 1,000 **Midweek Matchday:** Monday  **Clubhouse:** Yes **Shop:** Yes

**Colours(change):** Black & white/white/white. (Orange/orange/black).
**Previous Names:** Fisher Athletic. Reformed as Fisher F.C. in 2009.
**Previous Leagues:** Parthenon, Kent Amateur, London Spartan, Southern, Isthmian, Conference.
**Records:** Att: 4,283 v Barnet Conference 04/05/1991. **Goalscorer:** Paul Shinners - 205. **Apps:** Dennis Sharp - 720.
**Senior Honours:** Southern League Southern Division 1982-83, Premier 86-87, Eastern 2004-05. Kent Senior Cup 1983-84. Isthmian League Cup 2005-06.

### 10 YEAR RECORD

| 03-04 | 04-05 | 05-06 | 06-07 | 07-08 | 08-09 | 09-10 | 10-11 | 11-12 | 12-13 |
|---|---|---|---|---|---|---|---|---|---|
| SthE 14 | SthE 1 | Isth P 3 | Conf S 10 | Conf S 4 | Conf S 22 | Kent P 13 | Kent P 16 | Kent P 10 | Kent P 14 |

2012-13 - Fisher.                                                    Photo: Alan Coomes

2012-13 - Greenwich Borough.                                        Photo: Alan Coomes

# GREENWICH BOROUGH
Founded: 1928  Nickname: Boro

**Secretary:** Norman Neal  **(T)** 07958 077 958  **(E)** norman.neal@ntlworld.com
**Chairman:** Perry Skinner  **Prog Ed:** Stuart Marlow
**Ground:** Holmesdale FC, 68 Oakley Road, Bromley, Kent BR2 8HQ  **(T)**
**Capacity:**  **Seats:**  **Covered:**  **Midweek Matchday:** Tuesday  **Clubhouse:** Yes  **Shop:** No

**Colours(change):** Red/black/black. (Blue/white/white).
**Previous Names:** Woolwich Borough Council Athletic FC.
**Previous Leagues:** South London Alliance. Kent Amateur. London Spartan.
**Records:** **Att:** 2,000 v Charlton Athletic, turning on of floodlights, 1978.
**Senior Honours:** Kent League 86-87, 87-88.

**10 YEAR RECORD**

| 03-04 | 04-05 | 05-06 | 06-07 | 07-08 | 08-09 | 09-10 | 10-11 | 11-12 | 12-13 |
|---|---|---|---|---|---|---|---|---|---|
| Kent P 8 | Kent P 9 | Kent P 13 | Kent P 5 | Kent P 8 | Kent P 3 | Kent P 5 | Kent P 4 | Kent P 16 | Kent P 15 |

# HOLMESDALE
Founded: 1956  Nickname:

**Secretary:** Ross Mitchell  **(T)** 07875 730 862  **(E)** secretary@holmesdalefc.co.uk
**Chairman:** Mark Harris  **Manager:** Paul Proctor  **Prog Ed:** Mark Harris
**Ground:** Holmesdale Sp.& Soc.Club, 68 Oakley Rd, Bromley BR2 8HQ  **(T)** 020 8462 4440
**Capacity:**  **Seats:**  **Covered:**  **Midweek Matchday:** Wednesday  **Clubhouse:** Yes  **Shop:** Yes

**Colours(change):** Green & yellow/green. (All blue).
**Previous Names:** None.
**Previous Leagues:** Thornton Heath & Dist. Surrey Inter. Surrey South Eastern. Kent County.
**Records:** **Goals:** M Barnett - 410 (in 429 apps).
**Senior Honours:**

**10 YEAR RECORD**

| 03-04 | 04-05 | 05-06 | 06-07 | 07-08 | 08-09 | 09-10 | 10-11 | 11-12 | 12-13 |
|---|---|---|---|---|---|---|---|---|---|
| KC1W 4 | KC1W 8 | KC1W 1 | KC P 1 | Kent P 15 | Kent P 5 | Kent P 10 | Kent P 14 | Kent P 13 | Kent P 16 |

# LORDSWOOD
Founded: 1968  Nickname: Lords

**Secretary:** Steve Lewis  **(T)** 07968 429 941  **(E)** slew1953@hotmail.co.uk
**Chairman:** Ron Constantine  **Manager:** Simon Halsey  **Prog Ed:** John O'Halloran
**Ground:** Martyn Grove, Northdane Way, Walderslade, ME5 8YE  **(T)** 01634 669 138
**Capacity:** 600  **Seats:** 123  **Covered:** 123  **Midweek Matchday:** Tuesday  **Clubhouse:** Yes  **Shop:** No

**Colours(change):** Orange & black/black. (All white).
**Previous Names:** None.
**Previous Leagues:** Rochester & Dist. Kent County.
**Records:**
**Senior Honours:**

**10 YEAR RECORD**

| 03-04 | 04-05 | 05-06 | 06-07 | 07-08 | 08-09 | 09-10 | 10-11 | 11-12 | 12-13 |
|---|---|---|---|---|---|---|---|---|---|
| Kent P 13 | Kent P 16 | Kent P 8 | Kent P 13 | Kent P 16 | Kent P 16 | Kent P 16 | Kent P 13 | Kent P 12 | Kent P 5 |

# PHOENIX SPORTS
Founded: 1935  Nickname:

**Secretary:** Alf Levy  **(T)** 07795 182 927  **(E)** senior@phoenixsportsclub.org
**Chairman:** Andrew Mortlock  **Manager:** Tony Beckingham
**Ground:** Phoenix Sports Ground, Mayplace Road East, Barnehurst, Kent DA7 6JT  **(T)** 01322 526 159
**Capacity:**  **Seats:**  **Covered:**  **Midweek Matchday:** Wednesday  **Clubhouse:**

**Colours(change):** Green/black/black (Red & white/red/red)
**Previous Names:**
**Previous Leagues:** Spartan League. Kent County > 2011. Kent Invicta 2011-13.
**Records:**
**Senior Honours:** Kent County Division Two West 2004-05, Division One West 2007-08. Kent Invicta League 2012-13.

**10 YEAR RECORD**

| 03-04 | 04-05 | 05-06 | 06-07 | 07-08 | 08-09 | 09-10 | 10-11 | 11-12 | 12-13 |
|---|---|---|---|---|---|---|---|---|---|
| KC2W 13 | KC2W 1 | KC1W 3 | KC1W 5 | KC1W 1 | KC P 8 | KC P 4 | KC P 5 | K_Iv 2 | K_Iv 1 |

# ROCHESTER UNITED

**Founded:** 1982    **Nickname:**

**Secretary:** Tony Wheeler    **(T)** 07775 735 543    **(E)** tony.wheelerrufc@yahoo.co.uk

**Chairman:** David Archer    **Manager:** Darren Phillips

**Ground:** Rochester United Sports Ground, Rede Court Road, Strood, Kent ME2 3TU    **(T)** 01634 710577

**Capacity:**    **Seats:**    **Covered:**    **Midweek Matchday:** Tuesday    **Clubhouse:**

**Colours(change):** Red & black
**Previous Names:** Templars. Bly Spartans.
**Previous Leagues:** Kent County > 2011. Founder Members of Kent Invicta 2011-12.
**Records:**
**Senior Honours:** Kent County League Division One West 2007-08. Kent Invicta League 2011-12.

**10 YEAR RECORD**

| 03-04 | | 04-05 | | 05-06 | | 06-07 | | 07-08 | | 08-09 | | 09-10 | | 10-11 | | 11-12 | | 12-13 | |
|---|---|---|---|---|---|---|---|---|---|---|---|---|---|---|---|---|---|---|---|
| KC1W | 2 | KC1W | 3 | KC1W | 10 | KC1W | 2 | KC1W | 1 | KC P | 10 | KC P | 12 | KC P | 15 | K_Iv | 1 | Kent P | 13 |

# SEVENOAKS TOWN

**Founded:** 1883    **Nickname:** Town

**Secretary:** Eddie Diplock    **(T)** 01732 454 280    **(E)**

**Chairman:** Paul Lansdale    **Manager:** Paul Lansdale & Micky Hazard    **Prog Ed:** Ian Murphy

**Ground:** Greatness Park, Seal Road, Sevenoaks TN14 5BL    **(T)** 01732 741 987

**Capacity:** 2,000 **Seats:** 110 **Covered:** 200 **Midweek Matchday:** Tuesday **Clubhouse:**

**Colours(change):** Blue stripes/navy. (Green & white/white).
**Previous Names:** None.
**Previous Leagues:** Sevenoaks League. Kent Amateur/County.
**Records:**
**Senior Honours:**

**10 YEAR RECORD**

| 03-04 | | 04-05 | | 05-06 | | 06-07 | | 07-08 | | 08-09 | | 09-10 | | 10-11 | | 11-12 | | 12-13 | |
|---|---|---|---|---|---|---|---|---|---|---|---|---|---|---|---|---|---|---|---|
| Kent P | 11 | Kent P | 11 | Kent P | 16 | Kent P | 10 | Kent P | 11 | Kent P | 14 | Kent P | 6 | Kent P | 7 | Kent P | 14 | Kent P | 17 |

# TUNBRIDGE WELLS

**Founded:** 1886    **Nickname:** The Wells

**Secretary:** Phill Allcorn    **(T)** 07900 243 508    **(E)** secretary@twfcexec.com

**Chairman:** Clive Maynard    **Manager:** Martin Larkin

**Ground:** Culverden Stadium, Culverden Down, Tunbridge Wells TN4 9SG    **(T)** 01892 520 517

**Capacity:** 3,750 **Seats:** 250 **Covered:** 1,000 **Midweek Matchday:** Tuesday **Clubhouse:** Yes **Shop:** No

**Colours(change):** All red (Blue & black/blue/blue)
**Previous Names:** None.
**Previous Leagues:** Isthminan. London Spartan.
**Records:** Att: 1,754 v Hadleigh United, FA Vase SF 1st Leg 2012-13. **Goalscorer:** John Wingate - 151. **Apps:** Tony Atkins - 410.
**Senior Honours:** Kent Senior Trophy 2012-13.

**10 YEAR RECORD**

| 03-04 | | 04-05 | | 05-06 | | 06-07 | | 07-08 | | 08-09 | | 09-10 | | 10-11 | | 11-12 | | 12-13 | |
|---|---|---|---|---|---|---|---|---|---|---|---|---|---|---|---|---|---|---|---|
| Kent P | 14 | Kent P | 7 | Kent P | 10 | Kent P | 15 | Kent P | 10 | Kent P | 10 | Kent P | 7 | Kent P | 6 | Kent P | 5 | Kent P | 7 |

# WHYTELEAFE

**Founded:** 1946    **Nickname:** Leafe

**Secretary:** Chris Layton    **(T)** 0771 845 7875    **(E)** chris@theleafe.co.uk

**Chairman:** Mark Coote    **Manager:** John Fowler    **Prog Ed:** Chris Layton

**Ground:** 15 Church Road, Whyteleafe, Surrey CR3 0AR    **(T)** 0208 660 5491

**Capacity:** 5,000 **Seats:** 400 **Covered:** 600 **Midweek Matchday:** Tuesday **Clubhouse:** Yes **Shop:** Yes

**Colours(change):** Green/white/white (All maroon)
**Previous Names:** Not known
**Previous Leagues:** Caterham & Ed, Croydon, Thornton Heath & Dist, Surrey Interm. (East) 1954-58, Surrey Sen 58-75, Spartan 75-81, Athenian 81-84, Isthmian 84-2012
**Records:** 2,210 v Chester City - FA Cup 1999-2000
**Senior Honours:** Surrey Senior Cup 1968-69.

**10 YEAR RECORD**

| 03-04 | | 04-05 | | 05-06 | | 06-07 | | 07-08 | | 08-09 | | 09-10 | | 10-11 | | 11-12 | | 12-13 | |
|---|---|---|---|---|---|---|---|---|---|---|---|---|---|---|---|---|---|---|---|
| Isth1S | 17 | Isth1 | 9 | Isth1 | 18 | Isth1S | 20 | Isth1S | 11 | Isth1S | 18 | Isth1S | 15 | Isth1S | 16 | Isth1S | 21 | Kent P | 6 |

# WOODSTOCK SPORTS

Founded: 1927  Nickname: Sports

**Secretary:** David Brown **(T)** **(E)**
**Chairman:** Ron Welling **Manager:** Ben Taylor **Prog Ed:** Mike Wood
**Ground:** The WE Mannin Stadium, Woodstock Park, Broadoak Rd, Sittingbourne ME9 8AG **(T)** 07970 549 355
**Capacity:** 3,000 **Seats:** 200 **Covered:** 1,500 **Midweek Matchday:** Wednesday **Clubhouse:** Yes **Shop:** Yes

**Colours(change):** Blue & white/black. (All red).
**Previous Names:** Amalgamated with Teynham & Lynsted in 1998, Norton Sports 1998-2011.
**Previous Leagues:** Kent County.
**Records:**
**Senior Honours:**

**10 YEAR RECORD**

| 03-04 | 04-05 | 05-06 | 06-07 | 07-08 | 08-09 | 09-10 | 10-11 | 11-12 | 12-13 |
|---|---|---|---|---|---|---|---|---|---|
| | KC1E 1 | | KC P 3 | KC P 1 | Kent P 11 | Kent P 11 | Kent P 9 | Kent P 8 | Kent P 10 |

2012-13 - Holmesdale. Photo: Alan Coomes.

2012-13 - Whyteleafe. Photo: Alan Coomes.

# SPARTAN SOUTH MIDLANDS LEAGUE

**Sponsored by:** Molten
**Founded:** 1998
**Recent Champions:**
2008: Beaconsfield SYCOB
2009: Biggleswade Town
2010: Aylesbury ~~United~~
2011: Chalfont St Peter
2012: Royston Town
ssmfl.org

| PREMIER DIVISION | P | W | D | L | F | A | Pts |
|---|---|---|---|---|---|---|---|
| 1 (P) Dunstable Town | 42 | 36 | 6 | 0 | 143 | 33 | 114 |
| 2 Aylesbury United | 42 | 28 | 10 | 4 | 105 | 42 | 94 |
| 3 Oxhey Jets | 42 | 28 | 7 | 7 | 125 | 50 | 91 |
| 4 St Margaretsbury | 42 | 26 | 5 | 11 | 102 | 72 | 83 |
| 5 Ampthill Town | 42 | 22 | 11 | 9 | 103 | 65 | 77 |
| 6 Hanwell Town | 42 | 22 | 7 | 13 | 89 | 50 | 73 |
| 7 London Colney | 42 | 20 | 9 | 13 | 76 | 73 | 69 |
| 8 AFC Dunstable | 42 | 20 | 5 | 17 | 92 | 70 | 65 |
| 9 Haringey Borough | 42 | 18 | 9 | 15 | 75 | 55 | 63 |
| 10 Harefield United | 42 | 17 | 12 | 13 | 77 | 67 | 63 |
| 11 Berkhamsted | 42 | 16 | 12 | 14 | 76 | 77 | 60 |
| 12 Hadley | 42 | 18 | 5 | 19 | 86 | 84 | 59 |
| 13 Colney Heath | 42 | 16 | 9 | 17 | 75 | 83 | 57 |
| 14 Stotfold | 42 | 14 | 10 | 18 | 80 | 90 | 52 |
| 15 Leverstock Green | 42 | 13 | 5 | 24 | 54 | 95 | 44 |
| 16 Tring Athletic | 42 | 12 | 7 | 23 | 57 | 82 | 43 |
| 17 Hertford Town | 42 | 10 | 10 | 22 | 63 | 93 | 40 |
| 18 Biggleswade United | 42 | 10 | 9 | 23 | 49 | 73 | 39 |
| 19 Hillingdon Borough | 42 | 9 | 11 | 22 | 63 | 102 | 38 |
| 20 London Tigers | 42 | 10 | 5 | 27 | 56 | 111 | 35 |
| 21 Hatfield Town | 42 | 6 | 3 | 33 | 54 | 133 | 21 |
| 22 Holmer Green | 42 | 5 | 5 | 32 | 55 | 155 | 20 |

## PREMIER DIVISION CUP

**ROUND 1**
| | | | |
|---|---|---|---|
| Oxhey Jets | v | Holmer Green | 5-2 |
| Hanwell Town | v | St Margaretsbury | 1-4 |
| Leverstock Green | v | Aylesbury United | 2-2 |

*Aylesbury United won on penalties.*
| | | | |
|---|---|---|---|
| Hillingdon Borough | v | Colney Heath | 1-4 |
| AFC Dunstable | v | Harefield United | 2-1 |
| Biggleswade United | v | Stotfold | 0-2 |

**ROUND 2**
| | | | |
|---|---|---|---|
| Stotfold | v | Haringey Borough | 2-3 |
| Hatfield Town | v | London Tigers | 1-2 |
| Ampthill Town | v | Berkhamsted | 2-1 |
| Colney Heath | v | AFC Dunstable | 2-2 |

*Colney Heath won on penalties.*
| | | | |
|---|---|---|---|
| London Colney | v | Tring Athletic | 1-3 |
| Oxhey Jets | v | Hertford Town | 3-1 |
| Dunstable Town | v | Aylesbury United | 1-3 |
| Hadley | v | St Margaretsbury | 5-4 |

**QUARTER FINALS**
| | | | |
|---|---|---|---|
| Ampthill Town | v | Oxhey Jets | 1-3 |
| Hadley | v | Colney Heath | 5-2 |
| London Tigers | v | Aylesbury United | 1-2 |
| Haringey Borough | v | Tring Athletic | 2-2 |

*Tring Athletic won on penalties.*

**SEMI FINALS**
| | | | |
|---|---|---|---|
| Oxhey Jets | v | Aylesbury United | 3-5 |
| Tring Athletic | v | Hadley | 1-1 |

*Hadley won on penalties.*

**FINAL**
| | | | |
|---|---|---|---|
| Aylesbury United | v | Hadley | 3-2 |

## CHALLENGE TROPHY

**ROUND 1**
| | | | |
|---|---|---|---|
| Ampthill Town | v | St Margaretsbury | 1-3 |
| Aston Clinton | v | Wodson Park | 1-3 |
| London Colney | v | Caddington | 8-0 |
| Bedford | v | Amersham Town | 4-1 |
| Colney Heath | v | Mursley United | 6-0 |
| Harpenden Town | v | Kings Langley | 1-5 |
| Hatfield Town | v | New Bradwell St Peter | 0-2 |
| Sun Postal Sports | v | Biggleswade United | 0-4 |
| Tring Corinthians | v | Stony Stratford Town | 3-5 |
| Langford | v | Cockfosters | 1-3 |
| Hillingdon Borough | v | Harefield United | 1-2 |
| Hale Leys Utd | v | Dunstable Town | 0-6 |
| Chesham United Res. | v | Tring Athletic | 3-2 |
| London Lions | v | Tottenhoe | 4-2 |
| Pitstone & Ivinghoe | v | Broxbourne Borough | 2-1 |
| Berkhamsted | v | Aylesbury United | 2-3 |

| PREMIER DIVISION | 1 | 2 | 3 | 4 | 5 | 6 | 7 | 8 | 9 | 10 | 11 | 12 | 13 | 14 | 15 | 16 | 17 | 18 | 19 | 20 | 21 | 22 |
|---|---|---|---|---|---|---|---|---|---|---|---|---|---|---|---|---|---|---|---|---|---|---|
| 1 AFC Dunstable | | 0-2 | 2- | 1-3 | 0-2 | 1-1 | 1-3 | 3-4 | 3-2 | 0-1 | 1-0 | 5-1 | 2-2 | 6-3 | 4-0 | 6-2 | 1-2 | 1-0 | 2-4 | 0-2 | 1-4 | 2-1 |
| 2 Ampthill Town | 4-6 | | 1-1 | 1-2 | 0-1 | 2-2 | 2-3 | 2-2 | 2-1 | 2-2 | 0-4 | 5-1 | 3-1 | 6-1 | 6-1 | 3-0 | 1-1 | 4-0 | 3-2 | 3-5 | 4-3 | 3-0 |
| 3 Aylesbury United | 2-0 | 4-1 | | 1-1 | 3-1 | 0-1 | 3-1 | 4-3 | 2-0 | 3-2 | 3-0 | 4-1 | 3-0 | 3-0 | 7-0 | 0-0 | 3-1 | 2-0 | 3-1 | 1-2 | 2-0 | 5-0 |
| 4 Berkhamsted | 3-2 | 0-1 | 0-3 | | 1-0 | 3-2 | 1-4 | 4-1 | 1-2 | 2-2 | 1-4 | 1-4 | 2-2 | 1-1 | 2-1 | 2-2 | 1-0 | 5-1 | 0-4 | 2-4 | 2-2 | 1-1 |
| 5 Biggleswade United | 0-2 | 0-3 | 0-2 | 0-1 | | 0-1 | 1-2 | 1-2 | 1-2 | 1-1 | 1-1 | 2-1 | 1-1 | 3-5 | 5-2 | 3-1 | 1-3 | 1-0 | 2-2 | 1-1 | 0-3 | 2-3 |
| 6 Colney Heath | 0-3 | 0-3 | 0-2 | 4-3 | 2-1 | | 0-3 | 3-0 | 1-1 | 4-2 | 3-0 | 4-1 | 3-2 | 0-0 | 7-3 | 1-3 | 6-2 | 2-3 | 0-0 | 6-2 | 1-3 | 2-3 |
| 7 Dunstable Town | 1-0 | 1-1 | 2-2 | 1-0 | 4-0 | 4-0 | | 4-1 | 3-2 | 3-0 | 2-1 | 2-0 | 1-0 | 5-0 | 11-0 | 6-0 | 4-0 | 3-1 | 1-1 | 5-3 | 6-0 | 2-0 |
| 8 Hadley | 0-2 | 1-2 | 4-6 | 1-1 | 3-0 | 1-1 | 0-2 | | 1-1 | 3-2 | 0-2 | 0-1 | 4-0 | 4-1 | 6-4 | 3-0 | 0-2 | 1-2 | 4-2 | 1-2 | 4-2 | 3-2 |
| 9 Hanwell Town | 1-0 | 1-1 | 1-1 | 7-1 | 4-0 | 5-0 | 1-2 | 6-0 | | 0-1 | 1-0 | 3-1 | 3-2 | 2-2 | 3-1 | 0-1 | 0-1 | 4-0 | 0-2 | 0-1 | 2-1 | 4-0 |
| 10 Harefield United | 3-3 | 1-1 | 1-1 | 1-0 | 1-1 | 4-1 | 1-5 | 2-4 | 0-2 | | 2-1 | 4-0 | 3-2 | 3-2 | 3-1 | 1-3 | 0-2 | 6-1 | 0-2 | 0-3 | 2-1 | 1-1 |
| 11 Haringey Borough | 0-0 | 1-1 | 1-2 | 0-0 | 1-2 | 0-0 | 3-3 | 2-1 | 1-1 | 0-1 | | 2-1 | 3-1 | 2-1 | 2-0 | 0-1 | 2-3 | 2-1 | 1-0 | 3-2 | 5-0 | 2-3 |
| 12 Hatfield Town | 1-6 | 3-1 | 0-2 | 1-4 | 1-4 | 3-0 | 1-6 | 2-4 | 2-5 | 0-7 | 2-3 | | 2-3 | 2-2 | 2-3 | 3-4 | 2-2 | 1-3 | 1-6 | 2-3 | 2-3 | 0-1 |
| 13 Hertford Town | 0-1 | 3-3 | 3-1 | 3-3 | 2-1 | 1-1 | 2-5 | 2-1 | 1-2 | 2-3 | 1-2 | 3-0 | | 3-0 | 0-2 | 3-1 | 2-3 | 1-0 | 0-7 | 1-3 | 2-2 | 2-0 |
| 14 Hillingdon Borough | 2-0 | 1-2 | 1-1 | 2-4 | 2-2 | 1-5 | 1-3 | 0-2 | 1-4 | 1-1 | 1-3 | 2-0 | 1-0 | | 0-1 | 2-2 | 2-3 | 3-3 | 1-1 | 2-0 | 5-3 | 4-0 |
| 15 Holmer Green | 0-3 | 2-8 | 3-4 | 0-3 | 0-4 | 1-4 | 3-5 | 1-5 | 2-5 | 2-2 | 2-7 | 1-1 | 0-5 | 0-2 | | 0-4 | 1-5 | 2-3 | 2-4 | 3-0 | 1-1 | 2-0 |
| 16 Leverstock Green | 1-4 | 1-2 | 0-1 | 0-4 | 1-0 | 1-1 | 0-4 | 4-2 | 0-4 | 0-2 | 1-0 | 1-2 | 2-0 | 3-1 | 4-0 | | 1-3 | 0-2 | 1-7 | 1-5 | 1-3 | 2-1 |
| 17 London Colney | 3-2 | 0-3 | 1-2 | 2-2 | 1-0 | 1-2 | 0-3 | 4-2 | 0-0 | 2-2 | 2-1 | 1-0 | 3-1 | 2-2 | 2-0 | 2-1 | | 4-1 | 1-2 | 3-2 | 2-4 | 2-2 |
| 18 London Tigers | 2-4 | 1-3 | 2-6 | 1-4 | 1-1 | 0-1 | 0-3 | 1-6 | 0-1 | 2-0 | 2-0 | 0-4 | 0-5 | 3-3 | 2-0 | 2-3 | | 0-5 | 1-6 | 3-1 | 2-2 | |
| 19 Oxhey Jets | 4-2 | 2-2 | 3-3 | 3-0 | 2-0 | 3-0 | 0-4 | 0-1 | 3-1 | 2-1 | 0-8 | 10-1 | 7-1 | 6-2 | 4-1 | 2-1 | 3-0 | 5-1 | | 0-1 | 3-0 | 3-0 |
| 20 St Margaretsbury | 0-2 | 1-4 | 0-2 | 2-0 | 3-1 | 7-2 | 0-6 | 3-0 | 2-0 | 1-1 | 5-2 | 4-1 | 2-2 | 3-0 | 2-1 | 4-2 | 3-3 | 1-2 | 1-1 | | 4-2 | 2-0 |
| 21 Stotfold | 0-2 | 3-0 | 1-1 | 2-2 | 3-3 | 3-1 | 2-2 | 2-1 | 5-1 | 0-3 | 1-1 | 4-0 | 1-1 | 1-3 | 2-2 | 3-0 | 2-1 | 4-3 | 0-4 | 2-3 | | 1-2 |
| 22 Tring Athletic | 2-6 | 0-2 | 0-4 | 1-3 | 0-1 | 2-0 | 1-1 | 1-3 | 1-4 | 0-2 | 1-2 | 3-0 | 6-0 | 2-0 | 4-1 | 1-1 | 2-0 | 5-1 | 1-4 | 1-2 | 2-0 | |

## DIVISION ONE

| | | P | W | D | L | F | A | Pts |
|---|---|---|---|---|---|---|---|---|
| 1 | (P) London Lions | 40 | 31 | 5 | 4 | 120 | 31 | 98 |
| 2 | (P) Cockfosters | 40 | 28 | 7 | 5 | 124 | 37 | 91 |
| 3 | (P) Hoddesdon Town | 40 | 29 | 4 | 7 | 112 | 51 | 91 |
| 4 | Crawley Green | 40 | 25 | 6 | 9 | 98 | 58 | 81 |
| 5 | Bedford | 40 | 25 | 3 | 12 | 113 | 61 | 78 |
| 6 | Kings Langley | 40 | 22 | 8 | 10 | 109 | 56 | 74 |
| 7 | Harpenden Town | 40 | 21 | 9 | 10 | 83 | 47 | 72 |
| 8 | Codicote | 40 | 20 | 7 | 13 | 100 | 58 | 67 |
| 9 | Southall | 40 | 19 | 7 | 14 | 101 | 55 | 64 |
| 10 | Chesham United Reserves | 40 | 15 | 9 | 16 | 69 | 80 | 54 |
| 11 | Buckingham Athletic | 40 | 15 | 6 | 19 | 71 | 71 | 51 |
| 12 | Stony Stratford Town | 40 | 14 | 7 | 19 | 62 | 93 | 49 |
| 13 | Welwyn Garden City | 40 | 11 | 10 | 19 | 66 | 85 | 43 |
| 14 | Winslow United | 40 | 12 | 7 | 21 | 65 | 113 | 43 |
| 15 | Cranfield United | 40 | 11 | 7 | 22 | 53 | 104 | 40 |
| 16 | Langford | 40 | 9 | 12 | 19 | 68 | 103 | 39 |
| 17 | Sun Postal Sports | 40 | 10 | 8 | 22 | 55 | 110 | 38 |
| 18 | Wodson Park | 40 | 7 | 12 | 21 | 46 | 94 | 33 |
| 19 | Kentish Town | 40 | 9 | 6 | 25 | 46 | 109 | 33 |
| 20 | Amersham Town (-7pts) | 40 | 10 | 8 | 22 | 68 | 99 | 31 |
| 21 | (R) New Bradwell St Peter | 40 | 0 | 6 | 34 | 53 | 167 | 6 |

## DIVISION ONE CUP

**ROUND 1**

| | | |
|---|---|---|
| Crawley Green | v Codicote | 0-2 |
| Welwyn Garden City | v Kentish Town | 3-1 |
| Cranfield United | v Amersham Town | 1-1 |

*Amersham Town won on penalties.*

| | | |
|---|---|---|
| New Bradwell St Peter | v Kings Langley | 1-2 |
| Winslow United | v Hoddesdon Town | 4-4 |

*Hoddesdon Town won on penalties.*

**ROUND 2**

| | | |
|---|---|---|
| Amersham Town | v Kings Langley | 2-6 |
| Codicote | v Buckingham Athletic | 1-0 |
| London Lions | v Bedford | 2-1 |
| Wodson Park | v Chesham United Reserves | 2-3 |
| Harpenden Town | v Hoddesdon Town | 2-3 |
| Sun Postal Sports | v Cockfosters | 2-3 |
| Langford | v Welwyn Garden City | 1-0 |
| Stony Stratford Town | v Southall | 3-3 |

*Stony Stratford Town won on penalties.*

**QUARTER FINALS**

| | | |
|---|---|---|
| Stony Stratford Town | v Langford | 3-1 |
| Hoddesdon Town | v Cockfosters | 0-2 |
| Chesham United Res. | v Codicote | 1-2 |
| Kings Langley | v London Lions | 3-0 |

**SEMI FINALS**

| | | |
|---|---|---|
| Kings Langley | v Cockfosters | 2-1 |
| Codicote | v Stony Stratford Town | 0-1 |

**FINAL**

| | | |
|---|---|---|
| Stony Stratford Town | v Kings Langley | 1-3 |

## CHALLENGE TROPHY continued...

| | | |
|---|---|---|
| Codicote | v Holmer Green | 5-0 |
| Southall | v Cranfield United | 4-0 |
| Aylesbury Reserves | v Buckingham Athletic | 2-3 |
| Leverstock Green | v Old Bradwell United | 5-0 |
| AFC Dunstable | v Hertford Town | 4-2 |
| Risborough Rangers | v Hanwell Town | 0-6 |
| Winslow United | v Kentish Town | 0-1 |
| Welwyn Garden City | v Haringey Borough | 1-5 |
| Oxhey Jets | v Kent Athletic | 9-1 |

**ROUND 2**

| | | |
|---|---|---|
| Chesham United Res. | v Hanwell Town | 3-4 |
| New Bradwell St Peter | v Haringey Borough | 1-6 |
| Wolverton Town | v Buckingham Athletic | 1-2 |
| London Colney | v Cockfosters | 0-1 |
| Dunstable Town | v Stony Stratford Town | 2-0 |
| Aylesbury United | v Oxhey Jets | 1-3 |
| London Lions | v Kentish Town | 4-0 |
| Stottfold | v Pitstone & Ivinghoe | 0-2 |
| Bedford | v Kings Langley | 3-3 |

*Bedford won on penalties.*

| | | |
|---|---|---|
| Codicote | v Hoddesdon Town | 2-2 |

*Codicote won on penalties.*

| | | |
|---|---|---|
| The 61 FC (Luton) | v Hadley | 1-1 |

*Hadley won on penalties.*

| | | |
|---|---|---|
| Crawley Green | v London Tigers | 4-4 |

*Crawley Green won on penalties.*

| | | |
|---|---|---|
| Colney Heath | v Leverstock Green | 2-1 |
| Southall | v AFC Dunstable | 4-1 |
| St Margaretsbury | v Biggleswade United | 2-1 |
| Harefield United | v Wodson Park | 1-0 |

**ROUND 3**

| | | |
|---|---|---|
| Harefield United | v Codicote | 1-2 |
| Colney Heath | v Southall | 2-1 |
| Oxhey Jets | v Hanwell Town | 3-2 |
| Pitstone & Ivinghoe | v Hadley | 0-5 |
| Dunstable Town | v St Margaretsbury | 2-1 |
| Buckingham Athletic | v London Lions | 2-3 |
| Crawley Green | v Haringey Borough | 3-2 |
| Bedford | v Cockfosters | 2-2 |

*Cockfosters won on penalties.*

**QUARTER FINALS**

| | | |
|---|---|---|
| Cockfosters | v Hadley | 1-0 |
| Crawley Green | v Codicote | 1-1 |

*Codicote won on penalties.*

| | | |
|---|---|---|
| London Lions | v Colney Heath | 0-3 |
| Oxhey Jets | v Dunstable Town | 1-4 |

**SEMI FINALS**

| | | |
|---|---|---|
| Colney Heath | v Dunstable Town | 0-5 |
| Codicote | v Cockfosters | 0-0 |

*Codicote won on penalties.*

**FINAL**

| | | |
|---|---|---|
| Codicote | v Dunstable Town | 2-3 |

## DIVISION ONE

| | DIVISION ONE | 1 | 2 | 3 | 4 | 5 | 6 | 7 | 8 | 9 | 10 | 11 | 12 | 13 | 14 | 15 | 16 | 17 | 18 | 19 | 20 | 21 |
|---|---|---|---|---|---|---|---|---|---|---|---|---|---|---|---|---|---|---|---|---|---|---|
| 1 | Amersham Town | | 1-2 | 4-3 | 4-1 | 0-3 | 0-3 | 4-0 | 0-2 | 0-1 | 3-3 | 2-3 | 1-6 | 0-0 | 0-1 | 3-3 | 1-0 | 0-0 | 1-1 | 5-3 | 3-0 | 3-3 |
| 2 | Bedford | 3-1 | | 3-2 | 3-1 | 0-3 | 2-0 | 3-1 | 0-1 | 0-2 | 3-1 | 6-0 | 3-2 | 0-0 | 4-0 | 5-2 | 2-1 | 11-0 | 4-1 | 0-2 | 10-2 | 3-2 |
| 3 | Buckingham Athletic | 2-3 | 0-3 | | 3-0 | 1-6 | 1-0 | 8-2 | 0-3 | 2-2 | 1-2 | 2-0 | 0-0 | 2-0 | 0-1 | 4-1 | 3-3 | 5-1 | 0-2 | 2-2 | 3-4 | 2-0 |
| 4 | Chesham United Reserves | 3-0 | 4-1 | 3-1 | | 0-4 | 3-4 | 1-0 | 2-3 | 3-1 | 1-2 | 5-0 | 0-4 | 1-1 | 1-3 | 3-2 | 2-1 | 3-2 | 6-3 | 2-2 | 0-0 | 4-1 |
| 5 | Cockfosters | 6-3 | 1-1 | 4-1 | 4-0 | | 6-0 | 2-0 | 4-0 | 1-0 | 0-2 | 0-2 | 0-0 | 1-0 | 1-3 | 4-0 | 0-0 | 6-0 | 4-1 | 0-3 | 9-1 | 5-0 |
| 6 | Codicote | 6-1 | 6-1 | 3-1 | 3-0 | 0-0 | | 4-1 | 1-3 | 0-0 | 2-3 | 5-1 | 1-1 | 1-1 | 0-1 | 8-1 | 1-0 | 6-0 | 0-0 | 1-2 | 1-2 | 3-0 |
| 7 | Cranfield United | 2-1 | 2-1 | 1-1 | 2-2 | 1-2 | 1-2 | | 0-3 | 2-2 | 1-0 | 0-9 | 0-5 | 0-6 | 4-2 | 1-3 | 1-0 | 0-2 | 2-1 | 2-2 | 1-2 | 0-0 |
| 8 | Crawley Green | 3-0 | 1-1 | 1-1 | 1-2 | 0-3 | 2-2 | 1-4 | | 0-2 | 3-3 | 6-0 | 4-2 | 5-2 | 3-3 | 5-2 | 2-0 | 2-0 | 2-1 | 4-2 | 2-0 | 5-0 |
| 9 | Harpenden Town | 2-1 | 1-2 | 2-0 | 1-3 | 2-3 | 5-1 | 4-1 | 4-1 | | 0-2 | 4-1 | 2-1 | 0-0 | 0-1 | 4-1 | 1-0 | 2-1 | 3-3 | 0-0 | 3-4 | 2-0 |
| 10 | Hoddesdon Town | 2-0 | 2-1 | 1-0 | 2-1 | 2-3 | 0-5 | 2-0 | 2-3 | 2-1 | | 4-2 | 5-3 | 4-0 | 7-0 | 2-1 | 2-1 | 7-1 | 8-1 | 7-2 | 1-0 | |
| 11 | Kentish Town | 0-1 | 1-6 | 0-3 | 5-1 | 1-4 | 1-5 | 1-2 | 0-2 | 1-3 | 1-5 | | 2-1 | 3-3 | 1-4 | 1-0 | 1-1 | 3-3 | 0-2 | 1-2 | 3-2 | 0-1 |
| 12 | Kings Langley | 1-0 | 4-1 | 7-1 | 1-1 | 3-1 | 3-0 | 3-3 | 1-3 | 2-0 | 3-1 | 2-2 | | 6-0 | 2-4 | 4-1 | 0-2 | 3-0 | 3-3 | 2-1 | 1-2 | 4-1 |
| 13 | Langford | 4-4 | 1-3 | 0-2 | 4-0 | 1-2 | 1-3 | 3-3 | 1-4 | 1-6 | 0-9 | 8-1 | 2-1 | | 0-4 | 5-3 | 2-3 | 2-1 | 4-2 | 0-2 | 2-1 | 1-1 |
| 14 | London Lions | 2-1 | 2-0 | 2-0 | 0-3 | 2-2 | 2-0 | 2-1 | 4-0 | 0-1 | 3-1 | 4-0 | 0-1 | 7-0 | | 12-1 | 2-3 | 3-1 | 3-1 | 5-1 | 2-0 | |
| 15 | New Bradwell St Peter | 1-2 | 1-6 | 1-5 | 1-1 | 0-7 | 2-6 | 1-4 | 0-4 | 1-9 | 1-2 | 2-3 | 1-3 | 4-4 | 1-1 | | 1-5 | 0-4 | 1-2 | 0-6 | 2-2 | 2-3 |
| 16 | Southall | 7-1 | 3-6 | 1-0 | 0-3 | 2-2 | 3-2 | 4-0 | 6-1 | 0-2 | 0-1 | 3-1 | 2-3 | 5-2 | 2-3 | 1-1 | | 3-0 | 4-0 | 3-1 | 9-0 | 2-2 |
| 17 | Stony Stratford Town | 5-4 | 2-0 | 2-1 | 3-2 | 1-2 | 3-3 | 0-0 | 2-1 | 1-2 | 2-5 | 1-2 | 2-2 | 1-0 | 0-0 | 2-1 | 0-5 | | 2-1 | 2-2 | 3-1 | 2-1 |
| 18 | Sun Postal Sports | 1-1 | 0-4 | 0-2 | 0-0 | 1-4 | 2-5 | 4-2 | 1-5 | 1-3 | 0-4 | 2-1 | 1-3 | 4-4 | 1-1 | 3-2 | 0-4 | 0-6 | | 1-0 | 1-2 | 2-1 |
| 19 | Welwyn Garden City | 1-4 | 0-4 | 1-3 | 2-2 | 1-3 | 2-0 | 1-3 | 0-3 | 2-2 | 1-1 | 0-0 | 0-3 | 1-3 | 0-3 | 4-2 | 2-5 | 3-0 | 6-0 | | 3-2 | 1-1 |
| 20 | Winslow United | 5-4 | 4-1 | 0-1 | 0-1 | 0-0 | 0-1 | 2-0 | 0-4 | 0-0 | 1-2 | 2-0 | 1-2 | 2-0 | 0-5 | 4-4 | 0-5 | 2-5 | 5-1 | 5-2 | | 0-4 |
| 21 | Wodson Park | 5-1 | 1-4 | 0-2 | 1-1 | 2-6 | 0-6 | 1-3 | 0-0 | 2-2 | 0-0 | 0-0 | 2-7 | 1-1 | 1-8 | 2-1 | 1-0 | 1-2 | 1-3 | 0-0 | 2-2 | |

# SPARTAN SOUTH MIDLANDS LEAGUE - STEP 5/6/7

## DIVISION TWO

| | | P | W | D | L | F | A | Pts |
|---|---|---|---|---|---|---|---|---|
| 1 | Kent Athletic | 26 | 17 | 4 | 5 | 51 | 24 | 55 |
| 2 | Aston Clinton (-1pt) | 26 | 17 | 4 | 5 | 75 | 38 | 54 |
| 3 | (P) Broxbourne Borough | 26 | 15 | 4 | 7 | 42 | 26 | 49 |
| 4 | (P) Risborough Rangers | 26 | 12 | 8 | 6 | 63 | 36 | 44 |
| 5 | The 61 FC (Luton) | 26 | 12 | 7 | 7 | 62 | 37 | 43 |
| 6 | Tring Corinthians | 26 | 11 | 5 | 10 | 57 | 45 | 38 |
| 7 | Totternhoe | 26 | 11 | 5 | 10 | 55 | 62 | 38 |
| 8 | Hale Leys Utd | 26 | 12 | 1 | 13 | 67 | 76 | 37 |
| 9 | Mursley United | 26 | 9 | 7 | 10 | 46 | 47 | 34 |
| 10 | Old Bradwell United | 26 | 10 | 4 | 12 | 44 | 50 | 34 |
| 11 | Pitstone & Ivinghoe | 26 | 9 | 5 | 12 | 47 | 56 | 32 |
| 12 | Wolverton Town | 26 | 8 | 3 | 15 | 38 | 54 | 27 |
| 13 | Aylesbury Reserves | 26 | 7 | 1 | 18 | 45 | 76 | 22 |
| 14 | Caddington | 26 | 3 | 0 | 23 | 30 | 95 | 9 |

## DIVISION TWO CUP

**ROUND 1**

| | | | |
|---|---|---|---|
| Totternhoe | v | Tring Corinthians | 1-2 |
| Pitstone & Ivinghoe | v | Mursley United | 3-2 |
| Kent Athletic | v | Risborough Rangers | 0-6 |
| Hale Leys Utd | v | Caddington | 8-3 |
| Wolverton Town | v | The 61 FC (Luton) | 2-3 |
| Old Bradwell United | v | Broxbourne Borough | 0-1 |

**QUARTER FINALS**

| | | | |
|---|---|---|---|
| Hale Leys Utd | v | The 61 FC (Luton) | 5-3 |
| Aston Clinton | v | Aylesbury Reserves | 8-1 |
| Pitstone & Ivinghoe | v | Broxbourne Borough | 2-1 |
| Risborough Rangers | v | Tring Corinthians | 4-2 |

**SEMI FINALS**

| | | | |
|---|---|---|---|
| Aston Clinton | v | Hale Leys Utd | 2-1 |
| Pitstone & Ivinghoe | v | Risborough Rangers | 1-2 |

**FINAL**

| | | | |
|---|---|---|---|
| Aston Clinton | v | Risborough Rangers | 2-0 |

## DIVISION TWO

| | | 1 | 2 | 3 | 4 | 5 | 6 | 7 | 8 | 9 | 10 | 11 | 12 | 13 | 14 |
|---|---|---|---|---|---|---|---|---|---|---|---|---|---|---|---|
| 1 | Aston Clinton | | 8-0 | 2-1 | 7-0 | 4-2 | 4-1 | 2-1 | 4-1 | 6-4 | 1-1 | 2-2 | 1-2 | 2-3 | 7-1 |
| 2 | Aylesbury Reserves | 4-0 | | 0-1 | 6-3 | 1-5 | 0-6 | 1-4 | 6-1 | 3-1 | 0-8 | 3-3 | 3-6 | 0-2 | 4-0 |
| 3 | Broxbourne Borough | 1-2 | 3-0 | | 3-0 | 0-5 | 2-0 | 1-0 | 4-3 | 1-0 | 3-1 | 0-0 | 1-1 | 1-1 | 1-2 |
| 4 | Caddington | 1-2 | 1-0 | 0-5 | | 3-4 | 1-3 | 3-5 | 1-3 | 1-3 | 0-2 | 1-0 | 0-4 | 1-4 | 0-3 |
| 5 | Hale Leys Utd | 2-1 | 4-2 | 1-2 | 4-3 | | 0-4 | 2-3 | 1-4 | 3-2 | 2-5 | 1-5 | 4-1 | 4-1 | 3-2 |
| 6 | Kent Athletic | 4-0 | 1-0 | 3-0 | 2-0 | 2-1 | | 0-1 | 0-0 | 2-1 | 1-1 | 2-0 | 2-1 | 2-1 | 2-2 |
| 7 | Mursley United | 0-1 | 2-1 | 1-1 | 6-2 | 4-3 | 0-1 | | 2-1 | 1-1 | 0-4 | 2-2 | 3-4 | 2-3 | 1-2 |
| 8 | Old Bradwell United | 0-2 | 1-0 | 1-2 | 3-4 | 3-2 | 3-2 | 1-0 | | 1-1 | 3-0 | 1-4 | 0-2 | 2-3 | 1-1 |
| 9 | Pitstone & Ivinghoe | 2-4 | 5-3 | 1-0 | 4-1 | 2-7 | 2-4 | 2-2 | 2-2 | | 1-0 | 1-3 | 1-3 | 1-0 | 1-4 |
| 10 | Risborough Rangers | 2-2 | 2-4 | 1-0 | 4-1 | 7-0 | 2-1 | 1-1 | 1-0 | 0-2 | | 2-2 | 11-4 | 1-1 | 2-0 |
| 11 | The 6 FC (Luton) | 2-2 | 1-0 | 0-2 | 8-1 | 2-1 | 1-1 | 5-1 | 2-1 | 1-3 | 3-0 | | 2-3 | 0-2 | 8-0 |
| 12 | Totternhoe | 0-3 | 2-3 | 0-3 | 2-1 | 2-2 | 1-3 | 2-2 | 1-2 | 1-0 | 0-0 | 4-1 | | 5-2 | |
| 13 | Tring Corinthians | 1-5 | 5-1 | 1-3 | 2-0 | 9-0 | 0-1 | 0-0 | 1-3 | 2-2 | 3-3 | 1-3 | 7-1 | | 0-1 |
| 14 | Wolverton Town | 0-1 | 1-0 | 0-1 | 6-1 | 2-4 | 0-1 | 1-2 | 2-3 | 1-2 | 1-2 | 0-2 | 2-2 | 1-2 | |

## RESERVE DIVISION ONE

| | | P | W | D | L | F | A | Pts |
|---|---|---|---|---|---|---|---|---|
| 1 | Hadley Reserves | 28 | 20 | 2 | 6 | 81 | 34 | 62 |
| 2 | Hoddesdon Town Reserves | 28 | 19 | 3 | 6 | 56 | 26 | 60 |
| 3 | London Lions Reserves | 28 | 16 | 6 | 6 | 81 | 40 | 54 |
| 4 | Oxhey Jets Reserves | 28 | 15 | 4 | 9 | 69 | 47 | 49 |
| 5 | Cockfosters Reserves | 28 | 14 | 5 | 9 | 63 | 49 | 47 |
| 6 | Stotfold Reserves | 28 | 13 | 8 | 7 | 54 | 42 | 47 |
| 7 | London Colney Reserves | 28 | 14 | 2 | 12 | 59 | 55 | 44 |
| 8 | AFC Dunstable Reserves | 28 | 10 | 6 | 12 | 72 | 72 | 36 |
| 9 | St Margaretsbury Reserves | 28 | 11 | 3 | 14 | 47 | 53 | 36 |
| 10 | Holmer Green Reserves | 28 | 10 | 4 | 14 | 41 | 71 | 34 |
| 11 | Kings Langley Reserves | 28 | 9 | 5 | 14 | 59 | 62 | 32 |
| 12 | Kent Athletic Reserves | 28 | 8 | 5 | 15 | 57 | 83 | 29 |
| 13 | Risborough Rangers Reserves | 28 | 8 | 4 | 16 | 37 | 43 | 28 |
| 14 | The 61 FC (Luton) Reserves | 28 | 7 | 3 | 18 | 39 | 84 | 24 |
| 15 | Langford Reserves | 28 | 3 | 6 | 19 | 50 | 104 | 15 |

## RESERVE DIVISION TWO

| | | P | W | D | L | F | A | Pts |
|---|---|---|---|---|---|---|---|---|
| 1 | Ampthill Town Reserves | 24 | 21 | 0 | 3 | 91 | 29 | 63 |
| 2 | Harpenden Town Reserves | 24 | 17 | 4 | 3 | 79 | 31 | 55 |
| 3 | Crawley Green Reserves | 24 | 17 | 2 | 5 | 60 | 25 | 53 |
| 4 | Biggleswade United Reserves | 24 | 15 | 2 | 7 | 55 | 43 | 47 |
| 5 | Sun Postal Sports Reserves | 24 | 13 | 4 | 7 | 76 | 37 | 43 |
| 6 | Buckingham Athletic Res(-3pts) | 24 | 12 | 3 | 9 | 42 | 51 | 36 |
| 7 | Wodson Park Reserves | 24 | 9 | 0 | 15 | 29 | 66 | 27 |
| 8 | Totternhoe Reserves | 24 | 7 | 5 | 12 | 45 | 50 | 26 |
| 9 | Stony Stratford Town Reserves | 24 | 7 | 4 | 13 | 47 | 58 | 25 |
| 10 | Welwyn Garden City Reserves | 24 | 7 | 3 | 14 | 30 | 38 | 24 |
| 11 | Winslow United Reserves | 24 | 5 | 5 | 14 | 34 | 51 | 20 |
| 12 | Old Bradwell United Reserves | 24 | 5 | 1 | 18 | 29 | 75 | 16 |
| 13 | Tring Corinthians Reserves | 24 | 4 | 1 | 19 | 18 | 81 | 13 |

## CLUB MOVEMENTS

**Premier Division - In: Cockfosters (P).** Hoddesdon Town (P). London Lions (P).
**Out:** Dunstable Town (P - Southern Division 1 Central). Haringey Borough (S - Essex Senior).

**Division One - In:** Arlesey Town Reserves (Bedfordshire County). Baldock Town (P - Hertfordshire Senior County). Broxbourne Borough (P). Cranfield United (W - Replaced Reserve team in Bedfordshire County Div.2). Risborough Rangers (P).
**Out:** New Bradwell St Peter (R).

**Division Two - In:** Brimsdown (N). Grendon Rangers (P - North Buckinghamshire County). New Bradwell St Peter (R). Willen (P - North Buckinghamshire County).
**Out:** Aylesbury Reserves (W). MK Wanderers (W - now North Bucks & District Premier).

## AFC DUNSTABLE
Founded: 1981       Nickname: Od's

**Secretary:** Craig Renfrew       **(T)** 07976 192 530       **(E)** renfrewcraig@aol.com

**Chairman:** Simon Bullard       **Manager:** Alex Butler       **Prog Ed:** Craig Renfrew

**Ground:** Dunstable Town FC, Creasey Pk, Creasey Pk Dr, Brewers Hill Rd, LU6 1BB       **(T)**
**Capacity:** 3,200   **Seats:** 350   **Covered:** 1,000   **Midweek Matchday:**       **Clubhouse:** Yes   **Shop:** Yes

**Colours(change):** Blue/blue/white (All red)
**Previous Names:** Old Dunstablians 1981- 2004.
**Previous Leagues:**
**Records:**
**Senior Honours:** Spartan South Midlands Division Two 2003-04, 06-07, Premier Division 2012-13.

**10 YEAR RECORD**

| 03-04 | | 04-05 | | 05-06 | | 06-07 | | 07-08 | | 08-09 | | 09-10 | | 10-11 | | 11-12 | | 12-13 | |
|---|---|---|---|---|---|---|---|---|---|---|---|---|---|---|---|---|---|---|---|
| SSM2 | 1 | SSM2 | 6 | SSM2 | 2 | SSM2 | 1 | SSM2 | 4 | SSM2 | 3 | SSM1 | 5 | SSM1 | 2 | SSM P | 3 | SSM P | 8 |

## AMPTHILL TOWN
Founded: 1881       Nickname:

**Secretary:** Eric Turner       **(T)** 07866 336 421       **(E)** ericturner789@btinternet.com

**Chairman:** Manny Garcia       **Manager:** Craig Bicknell       **Prog Ed:** Eric Turner

**Ground:** Ampthill Park, Woburn Street, Ampthill MK45 2HX       **(T)** 01525 404 440
**Capacity:**   **Seats:** Yes   **Covered:** Yes   **Midweek Matchday:**       **Clubhouse:** Yes

**Colours(change):** Yellow/blue/blue (Blue/yellow/blue)
**Previous Names:** None
**Previous Leagues:** United Counties 1965.
**Records:**
**Senior Honours:**

**10 YEAR RECORD**

| 03-04 | | 04-05 | | 05-06 | | 06-07 | | 07-08 | | 08-09 | | 09-10 | | 10-11 | | 11-12 | | 12-13 | |
|---|---|---|---|---|---|---|---|---|---|---|---|---|---|---|---|---|---|---|---|
| SSM1 | 18 | SSM1 | 17 | SSM1 | 16 | SSM1 | 4 | SSM1 | 7 | SSM1 | 15 | SSM1 | 13 | SSM1 | 16 | SSM1 | 2 | SSM P | 5 |

## BERKHAMSTED
Founded: 2009       Nickname: Comrades

**Secretary:** Keith Hicks       **(T)** 07767 430 087       **(E)** keithhicks@btinternet.com

**Chairman:** Steve Davis       **Manager:** Mick Vipond       **Prog Ed:** Grant Hastie

**Ground:** Broadwater, Lower Kings Road, Berkhamsted HP4 2AL       **(T)** 01442 865977
**Capacity:** 2,500   **Seats:** 170   **Covered:** 350   **Midweek Matchday:**       **Clubhouse:** Yes   **Shop:** Yes

**Colours(change):** Yellow/blue/blue (White/black/black)
**Previous Names:** None
**Previous Leagues:**
**Records:**
**Senior Honours:** Spartan South Midlands League Division 1 2009-10, 10-11.

**10 YEAR RECORD**

| 03-04 | 04-05 | 05-06 | 06-07 | 07-08 | 08-09 | 09-10 | | 10-11 | | 11-12 | | 12-13 | |
|---|---|---|---|---|---|---|---|---|---|---|---|---|---|
| | | | | | | SSM1 | 1 | SSM1 | 1 | SSM P | 7 | SSM P | 11 |

## BIGGLESWADE UNITED
Founded: 1929       Nickname:

**Secretary:** Tracey James       **(T)** 07714 661 827       **(E)** tracey.james58@btinternet.com

**Chairman:** Phil Childs       **Manager:** Mick Reardon       **Prog Ed:** Tracey James

**Ground:** Second Meadow, Fairfield Rd, Biggleswade, Beds SG18 0BS       **(T)** 01767 600 408
**Capacity:** 2,000   **Seats:** 30   **Covered:** 130   **Midweek Matchday:** Wednesday       **Clubhouse:** Yes   **Shop:** No

**Colours(change):** Red/navy/red (Yellow/royal blue/yellow)
**Previous Names:** None
**Previous Leagues:** Beds & District and Midland. Herts County.
**Records:** **Att:** 250 v Biggleswade Town
**Senior Honours:** Spartan South Midlands Division One 1996-97, Premier Division 2008-09. Hunts FA Premier Cup 1998-99.
Beds Senior Trophy 2003-04. Beds Senior Cup 2001-02.

**10 YEAR RECORD**

| 03-04 | | 04-05 | | 05-06 | | 06-07 | | 07-08 | | 08-09 | | 09-10 | | 10-11 | | 11-12 | | 12-13 | |
|---|---|---|---|---|---|---|---|---|---|---|---|---|---|---|---|---|---|---|---|
| SSM1 | 8 | SSM1 | 3 | SSM P | 9 | SSM P | 14 | SSM P | 18 | SSM P | 1 | SSM P | 20 | SSM P | 20 | SSM P | 19 | SSM P | 18 |

# COCKFOSTERS

Founded: 1921          Nickname: Fosters

| | | |
|---|---|---|
| **Secretary:** Graham Bint | **(T)** 07729 709 926 | **(E)** graham.bint@ntlworld.com |
| **Chairman:** Roy Syrett | **Manager:** Mick Roche | **Prog Ed:** Alan Simmons |
| **Ground:** Cockfosters Sports Ground, Chalk Lane, Cockfosters, Herts EN4 9JG | | **(T)** 020 8449 5833 |
| **Capacity:** | **Seats:** Yes **Covered:** Yes **Midweek Matchday:** | **Clubhouse:** |

**Colours(change):** All red (White/blue/blue)
**Previous Names:** Cockfosters Athletic 1921-68.
**Previous Leagues:** Barnet 1921-30s. Wood Green 1930s-46. Northern Suburban Int. 1946-66. Hertfordshire County 1966-1991. Spartan 1991-97.
**Records:** 408 v Saffron Walden.
**Senior Honours:** London Interim Cup 1970-71, 89. Herts Sen Co Lge 1978-79, 80-81, 83-84. Aubrey Cup 1978-79, 84-85.
Herts Interm Cup 1978-79.

**10 YEAR RECORD**

| 03-04 | | 04-05 | | 05-06 | | 06-07 | | 07-08 | | 08-09 | | 09-10 | | 10-11 | | 11-12 | | 12-13 | |
|---|---|---|---|---|---|---|---|---|---|---|---|---|---|---|---|---|---|---|---|
| SSM1 | 7 | SSM1 | 8 | SSM1 | 8 | SSM1 | 2 | SSM1 | 17 | SSM1 | 19 | SSM1 | 11 | SSM1 | 15 | SSM1 | 9 | SSM1 | 2 |

# COLNEY HEATH

Founded: 1907          Nickname: Magpies

| | | |
|---|---|---|
| **Secretary:** Martin Marlborough | **(T)** 07960 155 463 | **(E)** m.marlborough@stalbans.gov.uk |
| **Chairman:** Martin Marlborough | **Manager:** Wesley Awad | **Prog Ed:** Martin Marlborough |
| **Ground:** The Recreation Ground, High St, Colney Heath, St Albans AL4 0NS | | **(T)** 01727 826 188 |
| **Capacity:** | **Seats:** **Covered:** **Midweek Matchday:** | **Clubhouse:** Yes |

**Colours(change):** Black & white stripes/black/black & white (Yellow/blue/yellow)
**Previous Names:** None
**Previous Leagues:** Herts Senior County League 1953-2000
**Records:**
**Senior Honours:** Herts County League Div 2 Champions 1953-54 Div 1 A 55-56, Prem 58-99, 99-00, Div 1 88-89,
Spartan South Midlands Div 1 2005-06 , SSML Cup 05-06

**10 YEAR RECORD**

| 03-04 | | 04-05 | | 05-06 | | 06-07 | | 07-08 | | 08-09 | | 09-10 | | 10-11 | | 11-12 | | 12-13 | |
|---|---|---|---|---|---|---|---|---|---|---|---|---|---|---|---|---|---|---|---|
| SSM1 | 6 | SSM1 | 5 | SSM1 | 1 | SSM P | 16 | SSM P | 15 | SSM P | 12 | SSM P | 5 | SSM P | 5 | SSM P | 8 | SSM P | 13 |

# HADLEY

Founded: 1882          Nickname:

| | | |
|---|---|---|
| **Secretary:** Bob Henderson | **(T)** 07748 267 295 | **(E)** gensecretary@hadleyfc.com |
| **Chairman:** Guy Slee | **Manager:** Geoff O'Vell | **Prog Ed:** Guy Slee |
| **Ground:** Potters Bar Town FC, Watkins Rise (off The Walk), Potters Bar EN6 1QB | | **(T)** 01707 654 833 |
| **Capacity:** 2,000 **Seats:** 150 **Covered:** 250 **Midweek Matchday:** | | **Clubhouse:** Yes **Shop:** Yes |

**Colours(change):** Red/black/black (Black & white stripes/white/white)
**Previous Names:** None
**Previous Leagues:** Barnet & Dist. 1922-57, Nth Suburban 57-70, Mid Herts 70-77, Herts Sen. 77-85, 99-2007, Sth Olym. 85-99, W Herts 2007-08.
**Records:**
**Senior Honours:** Hertfordshire Senior County League Division 3 1977-78, Division 1 2001-02, Premier 2003-04, 04-05.
West Hertfordshire League 2007-08. Aubrey Cup 2005-06.

**10 YEAR RECORD**

| 03-04 | | 04-05 | | 05-06 | | 06-07 | | 07-08 | | 08-09 | | 09-10 | | 10-11 | | 11-12 | | 12-13 | |
|---|---|---|---|---|---|---|---|---|---|---|---|---|---|---|---|---|---|---|---|
| HertP | 1 | HertP | 1 | HertP | 3 | HertP | 2 | WHert | 1 | SSM2 | 2 | SSM1 | 2 | SSM P | 14 | SSM P | 15 | SSM P | 12 |

# HANWELL TOWN

Founded: 1948          Nickname: Magpies

| | | |
|---|---|---|
| **Secretary:** Clive Cooke | **(T)** 07791 314 689 | **(E)** clivecooke2@sky.com |
| **Chairman:** Bob Fisher | **Manager:** Ray Duffy | **Prog Ed:** Bob Fisher |
| **Ground:** Reynolds Field, Preivale Lane, Perivale, Greenford, UB6 8TL | | **(T)** 0208 997 1801 |
| **Capacity:** 1,250 **Seats:** 175 **Covered:** 600 **Midweek Matchday:** Tuesday | | **Clubhouse:** Yes **Shop:** No |

**Colours(change):** Black & white stripes/black/black (Sky blue/navy blue/sky blue)
**Previous Names:** None
**Previous Leagues:** Dauntless. Wembley & Dist. Middlesex. London Spartan. Southern.
**Records:** **Att:** 600 v Spurs **Goalscorer:** Keith Rowlands. **App:** Phil Player 617 (20 seasons)
**Senior Honours:** London Spartan Senior Div. 83-84. London Senior Cup 1991-92, 92-93.

**10 YEAR RECORD**

| 03-04 | | 04-05 | | 05-06 | | 06-07 | | 07-08 | | 08-09 | | 09-10 | | 10-11 | | 11-12 | | 12-13 | |
|---|---|---|---|---|---|---|---|---|---|---|---|---|---|---|---|---|---|---|---|
| SSM P | 6 | SSM P | 2 | SSM P | 3 | SthS | 21 | SSM P | 9 | SSM P | 7 | SSM P | 13 | SSM P | 15 | SSM P | 21 | SSM P | 6 |

# HAREFIELD UNITED
Founded: 1868   Nickname: Hares

**Secretary:** Glenn Bellis   **(T)** 07973 563 282   **(E)** glennbellis@btconnect.com
**Chairman:** Dhali Dhaliwal   **Manager:** Phil Granville   **Prog Ed:** Simon Friend
**Ground:** Preston Park, Breakespeare Road North, Harefield, UB9 6NE   **(T)** 01895 823 474
**Capacity:** 1,200 **Seats:** 150 **Covered:** Yes **Midweek Matchday:** Tuesday   **Clubhouse:** Yes **Shop:** No

**Colours(change):** Red/black/black. (Yellow/red/red)
**Previous Names:** None
**Previous Leagues:** Uxbridge & District, Great Western Comb, Panthernon, Middlesex, Athenian & Isthmian.
**Records:** **Att:** 430 v Bashley FA Vase
**Senior Honours:** Middlesex Premier Cup 1985-86

**10 YEAR RECORD**

| 03-04 | 04-05 | 05-06 | 06-07 | 07-08 | 08-09 | 09-10 | 10-11 | 11-12 | 12-13 |
|---|---|---|---|---|---|---|---|---|---|
| SSM P 5 | SSM P 5 | SSM P 4 | SSM P 2 | SSM P 5 | SSM P 2 | SSM P 6 | SSM P 21 | SSM P 18 | SSM P 10 |

# HATFIELD TOWN
Founded: 1886   Nickname: Blueboys

**Secretary:** Joanne Maloney   **(T)** 07725 071 014   **(E)** secretary@hatfieldtownfc.co.uk
**Chairman:** Chris Maloney   **Manager:** Micky Nathan   **Prog Ed:** Tom Bailey
**Ground:** Gosling Sport Park, Stanborough Rd, Welwyn Garden City, Herts AL8 6XE   **(T)** 01707 384 300
**Capacity:** 1,500 **Seats:** 40 **Covered:** 120 **Midweek Matchday:**   **Clubhouse:** Yes **Shop:** Yes

**Colours(change):** All royal blue. (Orange/black/black).
**Previous Names:** Hatfield FC > 1906. Hatfield Utd > 1922. Hatfield Utd Ath. > 1948
**Previous Leagues:** Mid. Hertfordshire. Herts County. Parthenon. London. Metropolitan.
**Records:**
**Senior Honours:** Herts Senior Champions 2007-08

**10 YEAR RECORD**

| 03-04 | 04-05 | 05-06 | 06-07 | 07-08 | 08-09 | 09-10 | 10-11 | 11-12 | 12-13 |
|---|---|---|---|---|---|---|---|---|---|
| HertP 7 | HertP 3 | HertP 2 | HertP 5 | HertP 1 | SSM1 3 | SSM P 12 | SSM P 11 | SSM P 22 | SSM P 21 |

# HERTFORD TOWN
Founded: 1908   Nickname: The Blues

**Secretary:** Ken Williams   **(T)** 07979 251 912   **(E)** kenmwilliams@gmail.com
**Chairman:** Peter Sinclair   **Manager:** Marvin Samuel   **Prog Ed:** Matt Harris
**Ground:** Hertingfordbury Park, West Street, Hertford, SG13 8EZ   **(T)** 01992 583 716
**Capacity:** 6,500 **Seats:** 200 **Covered:** 1,500 **Midweek Matchday:** Tuesday   **Clubhouse:** Yes **Shop:** Yes

**Colours(change):** All blue (Red/black/black)
**Previous Names:** None
**Previous Leagues:** Herts Co. Spartan. Delphian 59-63. Athenian 63-72. Eastern Co 72-73.
**Records:** **Att:** 5,000 v Kingstonian FA Am Cup 2nd Round 55-56 **App:** Robbie Burns
**Senior Honours:** Herts Senior Cup 66-67 East Anglian Cup 62-63, 69-70

**10 YEAR RECORD**

| 03-04 | 04-05 | 05-06 | 06-07 | 07-08 | 08-09 | 09-10 | 10-11 | 11-12 | 12-13 |
|---|---|---|---|---|---|---|---|---|---|
| Isth2 3 | Isth2 4 | Isth2 13 | SSM P 3 | SSM P 4 | SSM P 10 | SSM P 16 | SSM P 9 | SSM P 16 | SSM P 17 |

# HILLINGDON BOROUGH
Founded: 19190   Nickname: Boro

**Secretary:** Graham Smith   **(T)** 01895 673 181   **(E)** jackieandgraham@talktalk.net
**Chairman:** Mick Harris   **Manager:** Jason O'Connor   **Prog Ed:** Oliver Chalk
**Ground:** Middlesex Stadium, Breakspear Rd, Ruislip HA4 7SB   **(T)** 01895 639 544
**Capacity:** 1,500 **Seats:** 150 **Covered:** 150 **Midweek Matchday:**   **Clubhouse:** Yes

**Colours(change):** White/royal blue/royal (Maroon or Navy blue/black or yellow/maroon or navy blue)
**Previous Names:** Yiewsley. Bromley Park Rangers.
**Previous Leagues:** Southern 1964-84, 2006-08. South Midlands 1990-2006. Isthmian 2008-09.
**Records:**
**Senior Honours:** South Midlands Cup 1996-97.

**10 YEAR RECORD**

| 03-04 | 04-05 | 05-06 | 06-07 | 07-08 | 08-09 | 09-10 | 10-11 | 11-12 | 12-13 |
|---|---|---|---|---|---|---|---|---|---|
| SSM P 12 | SSM P 6 | SSM P 2 | SthW 16 | SthW 13 | Isth1N 22 | SSM P 18 | SSM P 16 | SSM P 10 | SSM P 19 |

# HODDESDON TOWN
Founded: 1879          Nickname: Lilywhites

**Secretary:** Jane Sinden          **(T)** 01767 631 297 & fax          **(E)** janedsinden@fsmail.net

**Chairman:** Roger Merton          **Manager:** Andy Crawford          **Prog Ed:** Jane Sinden

**Ground:**   The Stewart Edwards Stadium, Lowfield, Park View Hoddesdon EN11 8PX          **(T)** 01992 463 133

**Capacity:**          **Seats:**          **Covered:**          **Midweek Matchday:**          **Clubhouse:**

**Colours(change):**   White/black/black (All blue)
**Previous Names:**   None
**Previous Leagues:** Hertfordshire County 1920-25. Spartan 1963-75. London Spartan 1975-77. Athenian 1977-84.
**Records:**
**Senior Honours:**   (FA Comps & League): FA Vase 1974-75 (1st Winners).
                      Spartan League Champions 1970-71, Division 1 1935-36, Division 2 'B' 1927-28

**10 YEAR RECORD**

| 03-04 | 04-05 | 05-06 | 06-07 | 07-08 | 08-09 | 09-10 | 10-11 | 11-12 | 12-13 |
|---|---|---|---|---|---|---|---|---|---|
| SSM P  11 | SSM P  20 | SSM1  7 | SSM1  5 | SSM1  3 | SSM1  5 | SSM1  4 | SSM1  9 | SSM1  3 | SSM1  3 |

# HOLMER GREEN
Founded: 1908          Nickname:

**Secretary:** Matt Brades          **(T)** 01494 716 114          **(E)** brades@badgerway.plus.com

**Chairman:** Frank Francies          **Manager:** Chris Allen          **Prog Ed:** John Anderson

**Ground:**   Airedale Park, Watchet Lane, Holmer Green, Bucks HP15 6UF          **(T)** 01494 711 485

**Capacity:** 1,000 **Seats:** 25   **Covered:** yes   **Midweek Matchday:** Tuesday          **Clubhouse:** Yes

**Colours(change):**   Green & white/green/green  (All red)
**Previous Names:**   None
**Previous Leagues:** Chesham 1908-38,  Wycombe Combination 1984-95, Chiltonian 1995-98.
**Records:**
**Senior Honours:**   Spartan South Midlands Senior 1995-96, 98-99, Division 1 2009-10.

**10 YEAR RECORD**

| 03-04 | 04-05 | 05-06 | 06-07 | 07-08 | 08-09 | 09-10 | 10-11 | 11-12 | 12-13 |
|---|---|---|---|---|---|---|---|---|---|
| SSM P  19 | SSM P  13 | SSM P  7 | SSM P  19 | SSM P  20 | SSM P  20 | SSM1  1 | SSM P  17 | SSM P  20 | SSM P  22 |

# LEVERSTOCK GREEN
Founded: 1895          Nickname: The Green

**Secretary:** Brian Barter          **(T)** 07982 072 783          **(E)** b.barter@btopenworld.com

**Chairman:** Brian Barter (Intrim)          **Manager:** Steven Benitez          **Prog Ed:** Brian Barter

**Ground:**   Pancake Lane, Leverstock Green, Hemel Hempstead, Herts  HP2 4NQ          **(T)** 01442 246 280

**Capacity:** 1,500 **Seats:** 50   **Covered:** 100   **Midweek Matchday:** Tuesday          **Clubhouse:** Yes   **Shop:** No

**Colours(change):**   White/green/green. (Yellow/blue/blue or Green & yellow/green/green)
**Previous Names:**   None
**Previous Leagues:** West Herts (pre 1950) & Herts County 50-91
**Records:**          **Att:** 1,000  **App:** Jonnie Wallace
**Senior Honours:**   South Midlands Senior Division 1996-97.

**10 YEAR RECORD**

| 03-04 | 04-05 | 05-06 | 06-07 | 07-08 | 08-09 | 09-10 | 10-11 | 11-12 | 12-13 |
|---|---|---|---|---|---|---|---|---|---|
| SSM P  9 | SSM P  14 | SSM P  6 | SSM P  5 | SSM P  7 | SSM P  6 | SSM P  10 | SSM P  4 | SSM P  11 | SSM P  15 |

# LONDON COLNEY
Founded: 1907          Nickname: Blueboys

**Secretary:** Dave Brock          **(T)** 07508 035 835          **(E)** davebrock42@hotmail.com

**Chairman:** Tony Clafton          **Manager:** Ryan Thompson          **Prog Ed:** Tony Clafton

**Ground:**   Cotlandswick Playing Fields, London Colney, Herts AL2 1DW          **(T)** 01727 822132

**Capacity:**          **Seats:** Yes   **Covered:** Yes   **Midweek Matchday:**          **Clubhouse:** Yes

**Colours(change):**   All royal blue (Red & black or black & white stripes/black/black)
**Previous Names:**
**Previous Leagues:** Herts Senior 1955-93.
**Records:**          300 v St Albans City Hertfordshire Senior Cup 1998-99.
**Senior Honours:**   Herts Senior League 1956-57, 59-60, 86-87, 88-89. 89-90.
                      South Midlands Senior Division 1994-95. Spartan South Midlands Premier Division 2001-02, Division One 2011-12.

**10 YEAR RECORD**

| 03-04 | 04-05 | 05-06 | 06-07 | 07-08 | 08-09 | 09-10 | 10-11 | 11-12 | 12-13 |
|---|---|---|---|---|---|---|---|---|---|
| SSM P  7 | SSM P  11 | SSM P  14 | SSM P  10 | SSM P  22 | SSM1  9 | SSM1  3 | SSM1  5 | SSM1  1 | SSM P  7 |

# LONDON LIONS
Founded: 1995    Nickname: Lions

**Secretary:** Basil Wein    **(T)** 07970 661 990    **(E)** basilw@londonlions.com
**Chairman:** David Pollock    **Manager:** Tony Gold    **Prog Ed:** Dan Jacobs
**Ground:** Rowley Lane Sports Ground, Rowley Lane, Arkley, Barnet, Herts EN5 3HW    **(T)** 020 84441 6051
**Capacity:**    **Seats:**    **Covered:**    **Midweek Matchday:**    **Clubhouse:**

**Colours(change):** All blue (All red or yellow/black/black or all white)
**Previous Names:** MALEX 1995-99. London Maccabi Lions
**Previous Leagues:** Herts Senior County 1995-2010
**Records:**
**Senior Honours:** Hertfordshire Senior County Premier Division 2009-10. Spartan South Midlands Division One 2012-13.

**10 YEAR RECORD**

| 03-04 | 04-05 | 05-06 | 06-07 | 07-08 | 08-09 | 09-10 | 10-11 | 11-12 | 12-13 |
|---|---|---|---|---|---|---|---|---|---|
| HertP 3 | HertP 6 | HertP 11 | HertP 9 | HertP 7 | HertP 2 | HertP 1 | SSM1 8 | SSM1 7 | SSM1 1 |

# LONDON TIGERS
Founded: 2006    Nickname: Tigers

**Secretary:** Mick Wilkins    **(T)** 07802 212 787    **(E)** wilki1@aol.com
**Chairman:** Mesba Ahmed    **Manager:** Armand Kavaja    **Prog Ed:** Sulthana Begum
**Ground:** Avenue Park, Western Avenue, Perivale, Greenford UB6 8GA    **(T)** 020 7289 3395 (10am-6pm)
**Capacity:**    **Seats:**    **Covered:**    **Midweek Matchday:**    **Clubhouse:**

**Colours(change):** Orange/black/black  (Yellow/blue/blue)
**Previous Names:** Kingsbury Town and London Tigers merged in 2006. Kingsbury London Tigers 2006-11.
**Previous Leagues:** None
**Records:**
**Senior Honours:**

**10 YEAR RECORD**

| 03-04 | 04-05 | 05-06 | 06-07 | 07-08 | 08-09 | 09-10 | 10-11 | 11-12 | 12-13 |
|---|---|---|---|---|---|---|---|---|---|
|  |  |  | SSM P 13 | SSM P 14 | SSM P 5 | SSM P 8 | SSM P 12 | SSM P 14 | SSM P 20 |

# OXHEY JETS
Founded:    Nickname: Jets

**Secretary:** David Fuller    **(T)** 07786 627 659    **(E)** d.g.fuller@ntlworld.com
**Chairman:** Phil Andrews    **Manager:** Danny Tilbury    **Prog Ed:** David Fuller
**Ground:** Boundary Stadium, Altham Way, South Oxhey, Watford WD19 6FW    **(T)** 020 8421 6277
**Capacity:** 1,000 **Seats:** 100    **Covered:** 100    **Midweek Matchday:** Wednesday    **Clubhouse:** Yes    **Shop:** No

**Colours(change):** All royal blue (All green)
**Previous Names:** None
**Previous Leagues:** Herts Senior County
**Records:** Att: 257 v Barnet Herts Senior Cup 05-06  **App:** Ian Holdon
**Senior Honours:** Herts Senior County Premier 2000-01, 01-02, 02-03. SSML Div 1 Champions 2004-2005, Herts Senior Centenary Trophy 2004-2005

**10 YEAR RECORD**

| 03-04 | 04-05 | 05-06 | 06-07 | 07-08 | 08-09 | 09-10 | 10-11 | 11-12 | 12-13 |
|---|---|---|---|---|---|---|---|---|---|
| HertP 2 | SSM1 1 | SSM P 13 | SSM P 7 | SSM P 19 | SSM P 13 | SSM P 11 | SSM P 19 | SSM P 17 | SSM P 3 |

# ST MARGARETSBURY
Founded: 1894    Nickname: Athletic

**Secretary:** Richard Palette    **(T)** 07721 679 681    **(E)** SMFCsecretary@aol.com
**Chairman:** Gary Stock    **Manager:** Gavin Kelsey    **Prog Ed:** Steve Green
**Ground:** Recreation Ground, Station Road, St Margarets SG12 8EW    **(T)** 01920 870 473
**Capacity:** 1,000 **Seats:** 60    **Covered:** 60    **Midweek Matchday:** Tuesday    **Clubhouse:** Yes    **Shop:** No

**Colours(change):** Red & black stripes/black/black  (Yellow & blue stripes/blue/yellow)
**Previous Names:** Stanstead Abbots > 1962
**Previous Leagues:** East Herts, Hertford & District, Waltham & District, 47-48 Herts Co. 48-92
**Records:** Att: 450 v Stafford Rangers FA Cup 2001-02
**Senior Honours:** Spartan Lg 95-96 Herts Senior Centenary Trophy 92-93, Herts Charity Shield 97-98

**10 YEAR RECORD**

| 03-04 | 04-05 | 05-06 | 06-07 | 07-08 | 08-09 | 09-10 | 10-11 | 11-12 | 12-13 |
|---|---|---|---|---|---|---|---|---|---|
| SSM P 3 | SSM P 7 | SSM P 12 | SSM P 15 | SSM P 11 | SSM P 14 | SSM P 14 | SSM P 18 | SSM P 12 | SSM P 4 |

# STOTFOLD
Founded: 1946          Nickname: The Eagles

| | | |
|---|---|---|
| **Secretary:** Julie Longhurst | **(T)** 07752 430 493 | **(E)** julie.longhurst46@virginmedia.com |
| **Chairman:** Phil Pateman | **Manager:** Steve Young | **Prog Ed:** Phil Pateman |
| **Ground:** Roker Park, The Green, Stotfold, Hitchin, Herts SG5 4AN | | **(T)** 01462 730 765 |
| **Capacity:** 5,000 **Seats:** 300 **Covered:** 300 **Midweek Matchday:** Tuesday | | **Clubhouse:** Yes |

**Colours(change):** Amber/black/black. (All burgundy).
**Previous Names:** None
**Previous Leagues:** Biggleswade & Dist, Norths Herts & South Midlands, United Counties > 2010
**Records:** **Att:**1,000 **Goalscorer:** Roy Boon **Apps:** Roy Boon & Dave Chellew
**Senior Honours:** S. Midlands League 1980-81. Bedfordshire Senior Cup 1964-65, 93-94. Bedfordshire Premier Cup 1981-82, 98-99. United Counties League 2007-08.

**10 YEAR RECORD**

| 03-04 | 04-05 | 05-06 | 06-07 | 07-08 | 08-09 | 09-10 | 10-11 | 11-12 | 12-13 |
|---|---|---|---|---|---|---|---|---|---|
| UCL P 10 | UCL P 9 | UCL P 11 | UCL P 19 | UCL P 1 | UCL P 2 | UCL P 7 | SSM P 13 | SSM P 9 | SSM P 14 |

# TRING ATHLETIC
Founded: 1958          Nickname: Athletic

| | | |
|---|---|---|
| **Secretary:** Bob Winter | **(T)** 07979 816 528 | **(E)** robert.winter2007@ntlworld.com |
| **Chairman:** Mick Eldridge | **Manager:** Julian Robinson | **Prog Ed:** Barry Simmons |
| **Ground:** Grass Roots Stadium, Pendley Sports Centre, Cow Lane, Tring HP23 5NT | | **(T)** 01442 891 144 |
| **Capacity:** 1,233 **Seats:** 150 **Covered:** 100+ **Midweek Matchday:** Tuesday | | **Clubhouse:** Yes **Shop:** Yes |

**Colours(change):** Red/black/black (Yellow/green/green)
**Previous Names:** None
**Previous Leagues:** West Herts 58-88
**Records:** **Goalscorer:** Andy Humphreys - 209 **App:** Mark Boniface - 642
**Senior Honours:** Spartan South Midlands Senior Division 1999-00

**10 YEAR RECORD**

| 03-04 | 04-05 | 05-06 | 06-07 | 07-08 | 08-09 | 09-10 | 10-11 | 11-12 | 12-13 |
|---|---|---|---|---|---|---|---|---|---|
| SSM1 4 | SSM P 4 | SSM P 10 | SSM P 11 | SSM P 10 | SSM P 8 | SSM P 3 | SSM P 2 | SSM P 6 | SSM P 22 |

# *DIVISION ONE*

## AMERSHAM TOWN
Founded:          Nickname:

| | | |
|---|---|---|
| **Secretary:** Stephen Segal | **(T)** 07889 683 547 | **(E)** ziggysegal51@yahoo.com |
| **Chairman:** Howard Lambert | **Manager:** Chris Martin | **Prog Ed:** Michael Gahagan |
| **Ground:** Spratleys Meadow, School Lane, Amersham, Bucks HP7 0EL | | **(T)** No telephone |
| **Colours(change):** Black & white halves/white/white (All yellow) | | |

**ADDITIONAL INFORMATION:**

## ARLESEY TOWN RESERVES
Founded:          Nickname:

| | | |
|---|---|---|
| **Secretary:** Chris Sterry | **(T)** 07540 201 473 | **(E)** chris.sterry@ntlworld.com |
| **Chairman:** Manny Cohen | **Manager:** Keith Coughlin | **Prog Ed:** Jason Marshall |
| **Ground:** The Armadillo Stadium, Hitchen Road, Arlesey, Beds. SG15 6RS | | **(T)** 01462 734 504 |
| **Colours(change):** Light blue/dark blue/dark blue (Yellow/black/black) | | |

**ADDITIONAL INFORMATION:**
Previous League: Bedfordshire County >2013.

## BALDOCK TOWN
Founded:          Nickname:

| | | |
|---|---|---|
| **Secretary:** Lee Rusbridge | **(T)** 07981 789 037 | **(E)** leeboy0483@hotmail.com |
| **Chairman:** Graham Kingham | **Manager:** Scott Grant | **Prog Ed:** Ross Graham |
| **Ground:** Hitchen Town FC, Top Field, Fishponds Road, Hitchin, SG5 1NU. | | **(T)** 01462 459 028 |
| **Colours(change):** All red (All navy blue) | | |

**ADDITIONAL INFORMATION:**
Previous League: Hertfordshire Senior County > 2013.

## BEDFORD

Founded: 1957    Nickname:

**Secretary:** Paolo Riccio    **(T)** 07868 370 464    **(E)** paolo.riccio@ntlworld.com
**Chairman:** Lui La Mura    **Manager:** Luigi Rocco    **Prog Ed:** Paul Warne
**Ground:** McMullen Park, Meadow Lane, Cardington, Bedford, MK44 3SB    **(T)** 07831 594 444
**Colours(change):** Black & white stripes/black/black (All maroon)

**ADDITIONAL INFORMATION:**
**Previous League:** United Counties 1970-80.
**Record Att:** (at Fairhill) 1,500 v Bedford Town-South Mids Div 1 1992    **Apps:** Simon Fordham - 418
**Honours:** Bedfordshire Senior Trophy 2012-13.

## BROXBOURNE BOROUGH

Founded: 1959    Nickname:

**Secretary:** Tolga Huseyin    **(T)** 07956 470 127    **(E)** tolga.huseyin7@gmail.com
**Chairman:** Inanc Elitok    **Manager:** Kem Kemal    **Prog Ed:** Tolga Huseyin
**Ground:** Broxbourne Borougn V & E Club, Goffs Lane, Cheshunt, Herts EN7 5QN    **(T)** 01992 624 281    **Capacity:** 500
**Colours(change):** All Blue. (All Red)

**ADDITIONAL INFORMATION: Record Att:** 120    **Goalscorer:** Wayne Morris    **App:** Brian Boehmer

## BUCKINGHAM ATHELTIC

Founded:    Nickname:

**Secretary:** Colin Howkins    **(T)** 07751 659 769    **(E)** colin@thehowkins.co.uk
**Chairman:** Stephen Orme    **Manager:** Damien Wiffin    **Prog Ed:** Matt Walker
**Ground:** Stratford Fields, Stratford Road, Buckingham MK18 1NY    **(T)** 01280 816 945 (MD)
**Colours(change):** Sky blue/navy blue/navy blue (Yellow/black/yellow)

**ADDITIONAL INFORMATION:**

## CHESHAM UNITED RESERVES

Founded:    Nickname:

**Secretary:** Alan Lagden    **(T)** 01494 782 022    **(E)** alan.lagden@sky.com
**Chairman:** Brian McCarthy    **Manager:** Paul Burgess    **Prog Ed:** Steve Doman
**Ground:** The Meadow, Amy Lane, Chesham, Bucks HP5 1NE    **(T)** 01494 783 964
**Colours(change):** All claret (Yellow/black/yellow)

**ADDITIONAL INFORMATION:**

## CODICOTE

Founded: 1913    Nickname:

**Secretary:** Ian Moody    **(T)** 07980 920 674    **(E)** codicote.fc@hotmail.co.uk
**Chairman:** James Bundy    **Manager:** Liam Errington    **Prog Ed:** James Bundy
**Ground:** Gosling Sports Park, Stanborough Road, Welwyn Garden City Herts AL8 6XR    **(T)** 01707 331 056
**Colours(change):** Red/black/black & red (Yellow/blue/yellow)

**ADDITIONAL INFORMATION:**
**Previous Leagues:** Hertfordshire County 1913-27, 1993-2012. North Hertfordshire 1927-93.
**Honours:** North Herts League Division One 1929-30, 1974-75, Division Two 1968-69, Premier Division 1977-78.
Herts Senior County League 2011-12.

## CRAWLEY GREEN

Founded: 1988    Nickname:

**Secretary:** Eddie Downey    **(T)** 07956 107 477    **(E)** eddied@thamesideltd.co.uk
**Chairman:** Alan Clark    **Manager:** Mark Smith    **Prog Ed:** Alan Clark
**Ground:** Barton Rovers FC, Sharpenhoe Road, Barton Le Cay, Beds MK45 4SD    **(T)** 01582 882 398
**Colours(change):** All maroon (Sky blue/navy/sky blue)

**ADDITIONAL INFORMATION:**

## HARPENDEN TOWN

Founded: 1891    Nickname: Town

**Secretary:** Paul Newton    **(T)** 07973 264 354    **(E)** pauldgnewton@gmail.com
**Chairman:** Steve Fakes    **Manager:** Simon Andrews    **Prog Ed:** Roman Motyczak
**Ground:** Rothamstead Park, Amenbury Lane, Harpenden AL5 2EF    **(T)** 07734700226/07702 604771
**Colours(change):** Yellow/royal blue/royal blue (Red/red/black)

**ADDITIONAL INFORMATION:**
**Previous Name:** Harpenden FC 1891-1908. **Previous League:** Hertfordshire County.
**Honours:** South Midlands League x2. Hertfordshire Junior Cup x5.

## KENTISH TOWN

Founded: 1994     Nickname: Townies

**Secretary:** Kevin Young    **(T)** 07828 288 238    **(E)** kevin.young63@virginmedia.com
**Chairman:** Catherine Dye    **Manager:** John Creith    **Prog Ed:** Franco Zanre
**Ground:** Middlesex Stadium (Hillingdon B. FC), Breakspear Rd, Ruislip, Middlesex HA4 7SB    **(T)** 01895 639 544
**Colours(change):** Sky & navy/navy/navy (Red & black/black/black)

**ADDITIONAL INFORMATION:**

## KINGS LANGLEY

Founded:     Nickname:

**Secretary:** Andy Mackness    **(T)** 07976 692801    **(E)** andymackness@yahoo.co.uk
**Chairman:** Derry Edgar    **Manager:** Ritchie Hanlon & Paul Hughes    **Prog Ed:** Roy Mitchard
**Ground:** Gaywood Park, Hempstead Road, Kings Langley Herts WD4 8BS    **(T)** 07976 692 801
**Colours(change):** Black & white stripes/white/black (Red/black/white)

**ADDITIONAL INFORMATION:**

## LANGFORD

Founded: 1908     Nickname: Reds

**Secretary:** Ian Chessum    **(T)** 07749 102 060    **(E)** ianchessum@hotmail.com
**Chairman:** Ian Chessum    **Manager:** Tony Lamacraft    **Prog Ed:** Ian Chessum
**Ground:** Forde Park, Langford Road, Henlow, Beds SG16 6AG    **(T)** 01462 816 106    **Capacity:** 2,000
**Colours(change):** All red. (All blue).

**ADDITIONAL INFORMATION: Record Att:** 450 v QPR 75th Anniversary 1985

## RISBOROUGH RANGERS

Founded:     Nickname:

**Secretary:** Nick Bishop    **(T)** 07855 958 236    **(E)** nick@lloydlatchford.co.uk
**Chairman:** Richard Woodward    **Manager:** Bob Rayner    **Prog Ed:** Richard Woodward
**Ground:** " Windsors" Horsenden Lane, Princes Risborough. Bucks HP27 9NE    **(T)** 07849 843632 (MD only)
**Colours(change):** All red (White/black/white)

**ADDITIONAL INFORMATION:**

## SOUTHALL

Founded: 1871     Nickname:

**Secretary:** Aman Jaswal    **(T)** 07957 168 370    **(E)** apnayouth@gmail.com
**Chairman:** Channa Singh    **Manager:** Colin Brown    **Prog Ed:** Emmanuel Asare
**Ground:** Hanwell Town FC, Perivale Lane, Perivale, Greenford, Middlesex UB6 8TL    **(T)** 0208 998 1701
**Colours(change):** Red & white stripes/black/black (White/blue/white)

**ADDITIONAL INFORMATION:**
**Previous Names:** Southall Athletic.

## STONY STRATFORD TOWN

Founded: 1898     Nickname:

**Secretary:** Steve Sartain    **(T)** 07901 664 000    **(E)** steve.sartain456@btinternet.com
**Chairman:** Philip Smith    **Manager:** Sam Callear    **Prog Ed:** Annette Way
**Ground:** Ostlers Lane, Stony Stratford, Milton Keynes MK11 1AR    **(T)** 07914 012 709
**Colours(change):** Sky blue/navy/sky (Yellow/black/yellow)

**ADDITIONAL INFORMATION:**
**Previous League:** Northampton Combination.
**Record Att:** 476 v Aston Villa U21 1996.

## SUN POSTAL SPORTS

Founded:     Nickname:

**Secretary:** Paul Masters    **(T)** 07834 379 034    **(E)** sunpostalsports@btconnect.com
**Chairman:** Martin Sills    **Manager:** Paul Hobbs    **Prog Ed:** Kevin Affleck
**Ground:** Sun Postal Sports Club, Bellmountwood Avenue, Watford, Herts WD17 3BN    **(T)** 01923 227 453
**Colours(change):** Yellow/blue/blue (Orange/black/orange)

**ADDITIONAL INFORMATION:**
**Previous Names:** Sun Postal Sports 2003. Sun Sports 2005.
**Previous League:** Hertfordshire Senior County > 2003.

## WELWYN GARDEN CITY

Founded: 1921    Nickname: Citizens

**Secretary:** Karen Browne      **(T)** 07876 232 670      **(E)** kazzie.browne@gmail.com
**Chairman:** Ray Fiveash      **Manager:** Adam Fisher      **Prog Ed:** Karen Browne
**Ground:** Herns Way, Welwyn Garden City, Herts AL7 1TA      **(T)** 01707 329 358
**Colours(change):** Claret/claret/sky blue (Orange/black/orange)

**ADDITIONAL INFORMATION:**
**Previous League:** Metropolitan & Greater London.
**Honours:** South Midlands League 1973-74, Division 1 1981-82.

## WINSLOW UNITED

Founded: 1891    Nickname:

**Secretary:** David Ward      **(T)** 07944 258 838      **(E)** davden@tesco.net
**Chairman:** Colin O'Dell      **Manager:** Perry Mercer      **Prog Ed:** Gareth Robins
**Ground:** The Recreation Ground, Elmfields Gate, Winslow, Bucks MK18 3JG      **(T)** 01296 713 057
**Colours(change):** Yellow/blue/yellow (Orange/orange/black)

**ADDITIONAL INFORMATION:**

## WODSON PARK

Founded:    Nickname:

**Secretary:** Lucy Bailey      **(T)** 07909 904 454      **(E)** lucy.bailey@wodsonmail.co.uk
**Chairman:** Lee Cook      **Manager:** Simon Riddle      **Prog Ed:** Lee Cook
**Ground:** Ware FC, Wadesmill Road, Herts SG12 0UQ      **(T)** 01920 870 091
**Colours(change):** Sky & navy blue stripes/navy blue/navy blue (Black & red stripes/black/black)

**ADDITIONAL INFORMATION:**

### SPARTAN SOUTH MIDLANDS DIVISION TWO CONSTITUTION 2013-14

ASTON CLINTON ......................... Aston Clinton Park, London Road, Aston Clinton, Bucks. HP22 5HL ................... 01296 631818 or 07707 685 148

BRIMSDOWN ............................... Goldsdown Stadium, Goldsdown Road, Enfield, EN3 7RP .............................................................. 0208 804 5491

CADDINGTON ............................. Caddington Recreation Club, Manor Road, Caddington, Luton, Beds LU1 4HH .................... 01582 450 151

GRENDON RANGERS ................. The Village Hall, Main Street, Grendon Underwood, Aylesbury, Bucks. HP18 0SP ............. 07979 470 734 (Sec)

HALE LEYS UNITED ..................... Fairford Leys Pitch, Andrews Way, Aylesbury, Bucks. HP17 8QQ ................................................ 07731 444 652

KENT ATHLETIC ........................... Kent Social Club, Tenby Drive, Luton, LU4 9BN ............................................................................... 01582 582 723

MURSLEY UNITED ...................... The Playing Field, Station Road, Mursley MK17 0SA ....................................................................... 07852 229 126

NEW BRADWELL ST PETER ....... Recreation Ground, Bradwell Road, Bradville, Milton Keynes MK13 7AD ............................ 01908 313 835

OLD BRADWELL UNITED ............ Abbey Road, Bradwell Village, Milton Keynes, MK13 9AR ............................................................ 07840 583 309

PITSTONE AND IVINGHOE ......... Pitstone Recreation Ground, Vicarage Road, Pitstone LU7 9EY .................... 01296 661 271 (match days)

THE 61 FC (LUTON) ..................... Kingsway Ground, Beverley Road, Luton LU4 8EU ........................................................................ 07749 531 492

TOTTERNHOE ............................. Totternhoe Recreation Ground, Dunstable Road, Totternhoe, Beds LU6 1QP ................... 01582 606 738

TRING CORINTHIANS ................. Tring Corinthians FC, Icknield Way, Tring, Herts HP23 5HJ ...................................................... 07886 528 214

WILLEN ......................................... Willen Playing Fields, Portland Drive, Milton Keynes. MK15 9JP ............................................... 07855 830 229

WOLVERTON TOWN .................... The New Park, Field Lane, Greenleys, Milton Keynes MK12 6AZ ............................................ 01908 226 218

# GROUND DIRECTIONS-PREMIER & DIVISION ONE

**AFC DUNSTABLE - Creasey Park Stadium, Creasey Park Drive, Brewers Hill Road, Dunstable, Beds LU6 1BB Tel 01582 667555**
From the South: When travelling north on the A5, go straight across the lights in the centre of Dunstable. Turn left at the next main set of lights into Brewers Hill Road. You will immediately pass the Fire Station on your left. Carry on until you hit the first roundabout. Go over the roundabout and take the immediate right into Creasey Park Drive. *From North:* When travelling south on the A5, go through the chalk cutting and over the first set of traffic lights. At the next set of lights turn right into Brewers Hill Road. Go over the roundabout and take the immediate right into Creasey Park Drive. Public Transport: Creasey Park is well served by buses. Arriva and Centrebus services from Luton, Houghton Regis Leighton Buzzard and Aylesbury all stop at the bottom of Brewers Hill Road. Some 24 services stop directly opposite Creasey Park Drive in Weatherby.

**AMERSHAM TOWN - Spratleys Meadow, School Lane, Amersham, Bucks HP7 No telephone**
From London, take the A413 towards Aylesbury. At the first roundabout in Amersham where the A413 turns left, keep straight on. Then carry on straight over the next four roundabouts to Amersham Old Town. At the western end of the Old Town turn right into right into Mill Lane. At the top of Mill Lane turn left into School Lane. Ground is 100 yards on the left.

**AMPTHILL TOWN - Ampthill Park, Woburn Street, Ampthill Tel: 01525 404440.**
From the South, leave M1 at junction 12 Toddington. Turn right as signposted until you meet the junction with the Ampthill bypass. Go straight across until you meet a mini-roundabout at the town centre. Turn left into Woburn Street. The ground is about half a mile on the right, just past a lay-by. From the North, leave the M1 at J13 and turn left. At first set of traffic lights, turn right onto A507 Ridgmont bypass. Continue until you see the right-hand turning signposted for Ampthill. Ground is about a mile on the left, opposite the rugby ground.

## SPARTAN SOUTH MIDLANDS LEAGUE - STEP 5/6/7

**ARLESEY TOWN RESERVES - The Armadillo Stadium, Hitchen Road, Arlesey, Beds. SG15 6RS Tel 01462 734 504**
From junction 10 on the A1(M) follow the A507 towards Shefford. At the 3rd roundabout turn left signposted Arlesey station. Follow the road for 1.5 miles through village, ground is on the left.
From M1 North, junction 13 follow A507 to Clophill. Continue straight over roundabout through Shefford & Henlow to roundabout signposted Arlesey station, then as above.
From M1 junction 10, take A1081 Airport Way onto A505 Hitchin Road towards Hitchen. Turn left onto A600 Bedford Road past Hitchin Town FC, turn right at 2nd roundabout to Ickleford. Go through village and bear left to Arlesey, ground is on the right.

**BALDOCK TOWN - Hitchen Town FC, Top Field, Fishponds Road, Hitchen, SG5 1NU. Tel 01462 459 028**
Exit A1(M) at junction 8 ( Stevenage North & Hitchen). Take the A602 towards Hitchen, go over two roundabouts and through the lights on the one-way system following the signs for Bedford (A600). There is a large open green to the right. At the next roundabout, turn right into Fishponds Road and the ground is about 100 yards on the left.
From the M1 junction 10 (Luton South & Airport) follow the A505 signposted Hitchin.On entering Hitchin, turn left at the first large roundabout and follow signs for Bedford A600. At the next roundabout turn right into Fishponds Road and ground is on the left.

**BEDFORD FC - McMullen Park, Meadow Lane, Cardington, Bedford, MK44 3SB. Tel 01234 831024**
From the M1 Junction 13: take the A421 on to the Bedford Bypass, take the third exit onto the A603, the ground is 250 yards on the left.
From the A1 at Sandy: take A603 to Bedford. The ground is on the right just before you reach the Bedford Bypass.

**BERKHAMSTED - Broadwater, Lower Kings Road, Berkhamsted HP4 2AL Tel 01442 865977**
Exit A41 onto A416. Go straight over the town centre traffic lights into Lower Kings Road. Go over the canal bridge and take first left into Broadwater. Follow the road to the left, going parallel to the canal. The ground is on the right hand side, sandwiched between the canal and the railway.

**BIGGLESWADE UNITED - Second Meadow, Fairfield Road, Biggleswade SG18 0BS Tel 01767 316270**
From A1 south take second roundabout (Sainsbury's NOT Homebase). Cross the river bridge and then take second left into Sun Street then take first left into Fairfield Road and travel to the very end and into lane. From A1 north, take first roundabout (Sainsbury's) and follow previous instructions.

**BROXBOURNE BOROUGH - Broxbourne Borough V & E Club, Goffs Lane, Cheshunt, Herts EN7 5QN Tel 01992 624 281**
From M25 junction 25, take A10 north towards Cheshunt. At first roundabout take first exit onto B198 (Cuffey & Goffs Oak) At the second roundabout take third exit into Goffs Lane. Ground is on the immediate right.

**BUCKINGHAM ATHLETIC - Stratford Fields, Stratford Road, Buckingham MK18 1NY Tel: 01280 816945 (match days & opening hours only)**
From Oxford, Aylesbury or Bletchley: take the Buckingham ring road to the roundabout where the A422 from Stony Stratford/Deanshanger meet-turn left, towards town centre. The ground is situated on the left behind fir trees at the bottom of the hill where 30mph begins (opposite a recently-built block of luxury apartments). From Milton Keynes: Up A5 then (A422) to Buckingham-straight across roundabout towards the town centre-ground location as above. From M1: come off at junction 13 and follow A421 straight through, turning right where it meets the Buckingham ring road – then follow as above, turning left at the next-but-one roundabout.

**CHESHAM UNITED RESERVES - The Meadow, Amy Lane, Chesham, Bucks HP5 1NE Tel 01494 783964**
Take J20 off the M25 to the A41 Aylesbury/Hemel follow this road for about 7 miles, your turn off is after the Service Station, the turn off is for Berkhamsted/Chesham, take the right hand lane in the slip road to the A416 to Chesham. Follow this road through Ashley Green (being careful of the speed trap) past the college on your left, when you get to the bottom of the hill take a left turn at the mini roundabout. Follow the road for about 1.5 miles, go straight over the next two roundabouts, then get in to the left lane to take the first exit from the next roundabout, you will pass a pub called the Red Lion on your right shortly after this. Follow the road to a mini roundabout; take the right exit going past two petrol stations either side of the road. Ground is on the third exit off the next roundabout. See club website for other routes.

**COCKFOSTERS - Cockfosters Sports Ground, Chalk Lane, Cockfosters, Herts EN4 9JG Tel: 020 8449 5833**
Leaving the M25 motorway at junction 24 (Potters Bar), take the A111 signposted to Cockfosters. The ground is situated approximately 2 miles from the motorway on the right immediately before Cockfosters Underground Station. VEHICLE DRIVERS PLEASE BE AWARE THAT THE YELLOW LINES & PARKING RESTRICTIONS IN CHALK LANE ARE STRICTLY ENFORCED UP TO 6.30PM INCLUDING SATURDAYS

**CODICOTE - Gosling Sports Park, Stanborough Road, Welwyn Garden City Herts AL8 6XR Tel 01707 331056**
From A1 (M), take A414 towards Hertford/Welwyn Garden City. At the roundabout take the first exit onto the A6129, leading to Stanborough/ Wheathampstead. At the next roundabout take the second exit onto the A6129 Stanborough Road. At the next roundabout take the third exit into Gosling Sports Park.

**COLNEY HEATH - The Recreation Ground, High Street, Colney Heath, St Albans, Herts AL4 0NS Tel 01727 826188**
From the A1, leave at junction 3 and follow A414 St. Albans. At long roundabout take the left into the village and ground is just past the school on left after 400 yards.
From the M25, leave at junction 22 and follow B556 Colney Heath. On entering the village turn left at Queens Head PH (roundabout) and follow High Street for ½ mile. The ground is on the right just before the school.
From M1 going south; leave at junction 7. At Park Street roundabout follow A414 Hatfield. Continue on A414 past London Colney. Enter Colney Heath coming round the long roundabout and into village. The ground is past the school on the left after 400 yards.

**CRANFIELD UNITED - Crawley Road, Cranfield, Beds MK43 0AA Tel: 01234 751444.**
upon entering the village, take the North Crawley/Newport Pagnell road. The ground is on the left hand side just before leaving the speed limit zone.

**CRAWLEY GREEN - Barton Rovers FC, Sharpenhoe Road, Barton Le Cay, Beds MK45 4SD Tel 01582 882398**
From M1 J12, turn right from South turn left from North, onto the A5120. After approximately 1.5 miles, take the second turning on the right signposted Harlington and Barton. Follow the road through Sharpenhoe to Barton. At mini-roundabout turn right and after about 400 yards, turn right into the ground. Ground entrance is in Luton Road.

**HADLEY - Potters Bar Town FC, Parkfield Stadium, Watkins Rise (off The Walk), Potters Bar EN6 1QB Tel 01707 654833**
From M25, exit at junction 24 towards Potters Bar along Southgate Road A111. Turn right at first set of traffic lights into High Street A1000. After the petrol station on the left and pedestrian crossing, take the first left into The Walk. After 200 yards, turn right into Watkins Rise. The ground is at the end on the right. Nearest BR Station: Potters Bar. PLEASE NOTE: do not park in the Mayfair Lodge Home car park opposite the ground. Offenders will be clamped.

**HANWELL TOWN - Reynolds Field, Perivale Lane, Greenford, Middlesex UB6 8TL Tel 020 8998 1701**
From West, junction 16 M25 and follow A40 (M) towards London. Go over the Greenford flyover and get into the nearside lane signposted Ealing & Perivale. Exit and turn right across the A40. The ground is immediately on the left. Turn left into Perivale Lane and the entrance is 200 yards on the left. Nearest railway station is Perivale (London Underground – Central Line).

**HAREFIELD UNITED - Preston Park, Breakspear Road North, Harefield, Middlesex, UB9 6NE Tel: 01895 823474.**
From the M25 at Junction 16 turn left. At the roundabout turn right towards Denham and at the next roundabout turn left then right at the end of the road. Turn left by the Pub and follow the road over the canal and into the village. Go straight across the roundabout into Breakspear Road and the ground is approximately 800 metres on the right.

**HARPENDEN TOWN - Rothamstead Park, Amenbury Lane, Harpenden AL5 2EF Tel: 07968 120032**
Approaching Harpenden from St. Albans, turn left into Leyton Road at mini-roundabout by the Silver Cup and Fire Station. Coming from Luton, go through the town and as you leave (just past The George) turn right into Leyton Road. Turn left in Amenbury Lane and then left into car park after 300 yards. Entrance to the Club is up the pathway, diagonally across the car park in the far corner from the entrance. This is a pay-and-display car park up to 6.30pm.

**HATFIELD TOWN - Gosling Sports Park, Stanborough Road, Welwyn Garden City, Herts AL8 6XE Tel 01707 384300**
From A1 (M) junction 4, take A414 towards Hertford/Welwyn Garden City. At the roundabout take the 1st exit onto the A6129, heading to Stanborough/Wheathampstead. At the next roundabout take the 2nd exit onto the A6129 Stanborough Road. At the next roundabout take the 3rd exit into Gosling Sports Park.

**HERTFORD TOWN - Hertingfordbury Park, West Street, Hertford, Herts SG13 8EZ Tel 01992 583716**
From the A1 follow the A414 to Hertford until you see Gates Ford Dealership on the right. At next roundabout double back and immediately past Gates (now on your left) turn left into West Street. This is a narrow road and when it bears left, turn right and go down the hill and over a bridge to the ground. From the A10 follow the A414 until you see Gates.

**HILLINGDON BOROUGH - Middlesex Stadium, Breakspear Road, Ruislip, Middlesex HA4 7SB Tel 01895 639544**
From M40/A40 eastbound, leave the A40 at the Swakeleys roundabout, exit is sign-posted Ickenham & Ruislip and take the B467. At the second mini-roundabout turn left into Breakspear Road South. After approx 1 mile, turn right into Breakspear Road by the Breakspear Arms PH. The ground is a further 1/2 mile on the left-hand side.

**HODDESDON TOWN - Stewart Edwards Stadium, Lowfield, Park View, Hoddesdon, Herts, EN11 8PU Tel: 01992 463133**
For SatNav users, please key in EN11 8PX, which will take you to Park Road, directly opposite the ground
From the A10, take Hoddesdon turnoff (A1170). Follow the slip road to the roundabout at the bottom of the hill and then turn right into Amwell Street. Take the first right, at the church, into Pauls Lane. Follow the road round to left which becomes Taveners Way. At the mini-roundabout opposite the Iceland store, turn right into Brocket Road. At T junction turn left into Park View and the ground is 200 yards on the right.

**HOLMER GREEN - Airedale Park, Watchet Lane, Holmer Green, Bucks HP15 6UF Tel 01494 711485**
From Amersham on A404 High Wycombe Road. After approx 2 miles turn right into Sheepcote Dell Road. Continue until end of road at Bat & Ball pub. Turn right, then immediately left. Continue approx 1/2 mile until double mini-roundabouts. Turn left in front of the Mandarin Duck restaurant into Airedale Park 150 yards on the right

**KENTISH TOWN - Hillingdon Borough FC, Middlesex Stadium, Breakspear Road, Ruislip, Middlesex HA4 7SB Tel 01895 639544**
See above for directions..

**KINGS LANGLEY - Gaywood Park, Hempstead Road, Kings Langley Herts WD4 8BS Tel: 07976 692801**
From M25 leave at junction 20. Take A4251 to Kings Langley. Go through the village. The ground is approximately 1/2 mile on the right.

**LANGFORD - Forde Park, Langford Road, Henlow, Beds SG16 6AG Tel: 01462 816106.**
From West along A57 to Henlow then north on A6001. Ground at north end of Henlow
From North and East, leave A1 at Langford water tower then into Langford. Turn left at Boot Restaurant. Follow A6001 round to the left. Club is 1/2 mile away.

**LEVERSTOCK GREEN - Pancake Lane, Leverstock Green, Hemel Hempstead, Herts Tel: 01442 246280.**
From M1 at Junction 8, Follow A414 to second roundabout turn left along Leverstock Green Way. Pancake Lane is on the left 300 yards past the Leather Bottle Public House. Ground is 300 yards on left. All visitors are requested to park inside the ground.

**LONDON COLNEY - Cotlandswick Playing Fields, London Colney, Herts AL2 1DW Tel: 01727 822132.**
From M25 J22, follow the A1081 signposted to St Albans. At London Colney roundabout take A414, signposted Hemel Hempstead/Watford. There is a hidden turn into the ground after approximately 500 metres (just after lay-by) signposted Sports Ground and London Colney FC. Follow the ground around between the Rugby and Irish clubs to ground entrance.

**LONDON LIONS - Hemel Hemstead FC, Vauxhall Road, Hemel Hempstead, HP2 4HW Tel 01442 259 777**
From M1 motorway exit at junction 8 onto the A414 towards Hemel Hempstead.After the second roundabout, get into the outside lane and turn right onto Leverstock Green Road. At mini roundabout, turn left into Vauxhall Road, at next mini roundabout, take the second exit into the ground.

## SPARTAN SOUTH MIDLANDS LEAGUE - STEP 5/6/7

**LONDON TIGERS** - Avenue Park, Western Avenue, Perivale, Greenford, Middlesex UB6 8GA Tel 020 7289 3395 (10am-6pm) – out of hours please call 07949 189191

Exit junction 16 of the M25 onto the A40 (M) towards London. After you pass the Target roundabout there will be a sharp left turn at the 200yard marker for the Greenford slip road from the A40 into Avenue Park, just past the overhead footbridge. If coming from Central London or Hangar Lane, drive up to the Target roundabout and do a U-turn onto the eastbound carriageway and turn left into Avenue Park after the footbridge. The nearest Tube station is Greenford on the Central Line, which is a 10-minute walk.

**OXHEY JETS** - Boundary Stadium, Altham Way (off Little Oxhey Lane), South Oxhey, Watford WD19 6FW Tel: 020 8421 6277

From Bushey + Oxhey Station, take Pinner Road (A4008) and continue along Oxhey Lane towards Harrow. At the traffic lights turn right into Little Oxhey Lane. Altham Way is on left just after crossing a narrow railway bridge. Please park in the large swimming pool car park marked "Jets overflow parking" to avoid either blocking in cars, or being blocked in.

**RISBOROUGH RANGERS** - " Windsors" Horsenden Lane, Princes Risborough. Bucks HP27 9NE Tel 07849 843632 (MD only)

On entering Prices Risborough from Aylesbury, turn left at first roundabout. At the second roundabout turn right. Go pass Esso petrol station on left hand side. After approximately 400 yards take the right fork. Take second turn on left (Picts Lane). At junction turn right over the railway bridge and then immediately right again. Ground is approximately 200 yards on the right hand side.

**SOUTHALL** - Hanwell Town FC, Perivale Lane, Perivale, Greenford, Middlesex UB6 8TL Tel 020 8998 1701

See Hanwell Town for directions.

**ST. MARGARETSBURY** - Recreation Ground, Station Road, St. Margarets, Herts SG12 8EH Tel: 01920 870473

A10 to Cambridge. Exit at A414 Harlow & Chelmsford. Proceed 400 yards to Amwell roundabout and take 3rd exit (B181) to Stanstead Abbotts. Ground is 1/2 mile on the right-hand side.

**STONY STRATFORD TOWN** - Ostlers Lane, Stony Stratford, Milton Keynes MK11 1AR Tel: 07914 012709

From Dunstable on the A5 heading north: On approaching Bletchley continue on the main A5 trunk road signposted to Towcester & Hinckley. Continue to the very end of dual carriageway, where you will meet a main roundabout. This is where the main A5 intersects with the A508 to Northampton. At this roundabout take first exit, this is the old (single carriageway) A5. Follow the main road, straight through the traffic lights, over the river bridge and take the second turning right into Ostlers Lane. The ground is approx 200yds on the right.

From Buckingham on the A422: Continue on the A422, straight on at the first roundabout (pedestrian footbridge overhead). Continue on until you meet the next roundabout and take the last exit (the old single carriageway A5). Then proceed as above.

**STOTFOLD** - Roker Park, The Green, Stotfold, Hitchin, Herts SG5 4AN Tel 01462 730765

At A1 junction 10, take the A507 to Stotfold and right into town. Proceed along High Street and at traffic lights turn right (from Hitchin – straight over traffic lights) towards Astwick Turn right at the Crown pub into The Green. The ground is set back from The Green on the left.

**SUN POSTAL SPORTS** - Sun Postal Sports Club, Bellmountwood Avenue, Watford, Herts WD17 3BM Tel: 01923 227453

From Watford town centre take the A411 (Hempstead Road) away from the Town Hall towards Hemel Hempstead. At 2nd set of traffic lights turn left into Langley Way. At the next roundabout, where there is a parade of shops on the left and the "Essex Arms" on the right, take the third exit into Cassiobury Drive. Then take the first turn left into Bellmountwood Avenue then at the left hand bend turn right into the Club entrance.

**TRING ATHLETIC** - The Grass Roots Stadium, Pendley Sports Centre, Cow Lane, Tring, Herts HP23 5NT. Tel: 01442 891144

From M25 take A41 to Aylesbury. At roundabout at junction take last exit sign-posted Berkhamsted. Turn next left into Cow Lane. Stadium is on the right at end of Cow Lane.

**WELWYN GARDEN CITY** - Herns Way, Welwyn Garden City, Herts AL7 1TA Tel: 01707 329358

Best Route to the Ground: From A1 (M) follow Welwyn Garden City signpost A1000. Take second exit off one-way system, sign-posted Panshanger. Ground is 400 yards on left.

**WINSLOW UNITED** - The Recreation Ground, Elmfields Gate, Winslow, Bucks MK18 3JG Tel 01296 713057

Best Route to the Ground: A413 from Aylesbury to Winslow, turn right from High Street into Elmfields Gate. Ground is100 yards on left. A421 Milton Keynes to Buckingham, turn left through Great Horwood to Winslow. Turn left from High Street into Elmfields Gate. PLEASE PARK IN PUBLIC CAR PARK OPPOSITE GROUND IF POSSIBLE.

**WODSON PARK** - Ware FC, Wadesmill Road, Herts SG12 0UQ Tel 01920 463247

From the South: leave the M25 at junction 25 and take the A10 north past Cheshunt and Hoddesdon. After crossing the Lea Valley with Ware below and to your right, leave the A10 at the junction for the A1170 (signposted for Wadesmill and Thundridge). The slip road comes off the A10 onto a roundabout. Turn left (first exit) onto Wadesmill Road (A1170) and come back over the A10 to a second roundabout. Go straight over and take the first turn on the left into Wodson Park Sports Centre. The football ground is on the far left of the car park. From the North: Leave the A10 at the Ware North turn off (A1170). The slip road takes you to a roundabout. Turn right (3rd exit) into Wadesmill Road and take the first left into Wodson Park Sports Centre.

# SUSSEX COUNTY LEAGUE

| Sponsored by: No sponsor |
| --- |

**Founded:** 1920
**Recent Champions:**
2008: Crowborough Athletic
2009: Eastbourne United Association
2010: Whitehawk.  2011: Crawley Down
2012: Three Bridges  **scfl.org.uk**

## LEAGUE CUP

**ROUND 1**

| | | | |
| --- | --- | --- | --- |
| Steyning Town | v | Worthing United | 1-7 |
| Broadbridge Heath | v | Selsey | 1-0 |
| East Grinstead Town | v | Bexhill United | 2-4 |
| Mile Oak | v | Horsham YMCA | 1-3 |
| Newhaven | v | Lancing | 0-2 |
| Peacehaven & Telscombe | v | Eastbourne United AFC | 2-0 |
| Lingfield | v | Saltdean United | 9-2 |
| Westfield | v | Littlehampton Town | 0-2 |

**ROUND 2**

| | | | |
| --- | --- | --- | --- |
| AFC Uckfield | v | Storrington | 3-1 |
| Arundel | v | Wick | 4-0 |
| Hailsham Town | v | Southwick | 2-3 |
| Shoreham | v | Worthing United | 9-0 |
| Hassocks | v | Broadbridge Heath | 3-2 |
| Rustington | v | Bexhill United | 1-2 |
| Oakwood | v | Crowborough Athletic | 0-2 |
| Sidley United | v | Lancing | 4-1 |
| Loxwood | v | Horsham YMCA | 2-3 |
| Redhill | v | Little Common | 4-1 |
| Ringmer | v | Midhurst & Easebourne | 6-0 |
| East Preston | v | Seaford Town | 3-1 |
| Rye United | v | Peacehaven & Telscombe | 0-4 |
| Littlehampton Town | v | Pagham | 3-1 |

**ROUND 3**

| | | | |
| --- | --- | --- | --- |
| AFC Uckfield | v | Shoreham | 0-5 |
| Redhill | v | Hassocks | 0-2 |
| Bexhill United | v | Lingfield | 0-2 |
| Sidley United | v | East Preston | 1-1 aet 5-4p |
| Southwick | v | Littlehampton Town | 1-3 |
| Peacehaven & Telscombe | v | Ringmer | 7-0 |
| St Francis Rangers | v | Arundel | 2-0 |
| Horsham YMCA | v | Crowborough Athletic | 2-1 |

**QUARTER FINALS**

| | | | |
| --- | --- | --- | --- |
| Littlehampton Town | v | Hassocks | 1-0 |
| Peacehaven & Telscombe | v | Bexhill United | 3-2 aet |
| Sidley United | v | Shoreham | 2-0 |

*Sidley removed from the competition, Shoreham reinstated.*

| | | | |
| --- | --- | --- | --- |
| St Francis Rangers | v | Horsham YMCA | 2-1 |

**SEMI FINALS**

| | | | |
| --- | --- | --- | --- |
| Shoreham | v | Peacehaven & Telscombe | 2-4 |
| Littlehampton Town | v | St Francis Rangers | 4-3 |

**FINAL**

| | | | |
| --- | --- | --- | --- |
| Peacehaven & Telscombe | v | Littlehampton Town | 1-0 |

## DIVISION ONE

| | | P | W | D | L | F | A | Pts |
| --- | --- | --- | --- | --- | --- | --- | --- | --- |
| 1 | (P) Peacehaven & Telscombe | 42 | 28 | 10 | 4 | 114 | 35 | 94 |
| 2 | Redhill | 42 | 29 | 6 | 7 | 95 | 42 | 93 |
| 3 | East Preston | 42 | 25 | 10 | 7 | 97 | 50 | 85 |
| 4 | Rye United | 42 | 24 | 11 | 7 | 117 | 57 | 83 |
| 5 | Pagham | 42 | 26 | 5 | 11 | 90 | 52 | 83 |
| 6 | Lingfield | 42 | 23 | 7 | 12 | 102 | 78 | 76 |
| 7 | Hassocks | 42 | 21 | 7 | 14 | 97 | 69 | 70 |
| 8 | East Grinstead Town | 42 | 21 | 6 | 15 | 97 | 65 | 69 |
| 9 | Ringmer | 42 | 20 | 9 | 13 | 76 | 68 | 69 |
| 10 | Horsham YMCA | 42 | 19 | 7 | 16 | 97 | 71 | 64 |
| 11 | St Francis Rangers | 42 | 17 | 8 | 17 | 76 | 73 | 59 |
| 12 | Hailsham Town | 42 | 17 | 2 | 23 | 77 | 90 | 53 |
| 13 | Lancing | 42 | 14 | 10 | 18 | 80 | 75 | 52 |
| 14 | Arundel | 42 | 14 | 8 | 20 | 61 | 86 | 50 |
| 15 | Crowborough Athletic | 42 | 15 | 5 | 22 | 68 | 99 | 50 |
| 16 | Sidley United | 42 | 13 | 7 | 22 | 67 | 87 | 46 |
| 17 | Shoreham | 42 | 14 | 4 | 24 | 69 | 106 | 46 |
| 18 | Selsey | 42 | 11 | 12 | 19 | 53 | 76 | 45 |
| 19 | Chichester City | 42 | 12 | 6 | 24 | 63 | 107 | 42 |
| 20 | Dorking Wanderers | 42 | 10 | 11 | 21 | 62 | 80 | 41 |
| 21 | (R) AFC Uckfield | 42 | 5 | 4 | 33 | 53 | 141 | 19 |
| 22 | Worthing United | 42 | 3 | 7 | 32 | 43 | 147 | 16 |

## DIVISION TWO

| | | P | W | D | L | F | A | Pts |
| --- | --- | --- | --- | --- | --- | --- | --- | --- |
| 1 | (P) Littlehampton Town | 34 | 26 | 4 | 4 | 91 | 27 | 82 |
| 2 | (P) Newhaven | 34 | 22 | 4 | 8 | 90 | 52 | 70 |
| 3 | Little Common | 34 | 21 | 5 | 8 | 94 | 43 | 68 |
| 4 | Eastbourne United AFC | 34 | 20 | 5 | 9 | 97 | 64 | 65 |
| 5 | Westfield | 34 | 17 | 7 | 10 | 67 | 56 | 58 |
| 6 | Broadbridge Heath | 34 | 17 | 4 | 13 | 82 | 62 | 55 |
| 7 | Mile Oak | 34 | 15 | 8 | 11 | 65 | 57 | 53 |
| 8 | Midhurst & Easebourne | 34 | 14 | 9 | 11 | 80 | 73 | 51 |
| 9 | Loxwood | 34 | 14 | 7 | 13 | 57 | 60 | 49 |
| 10 | Steyning Town | 34 | 14 | 6 | 14 | 73 | 61 | 48 |
| 11 | Bexhill United | 34 | 12 | 10 | 12 | 67 | 71 | 46 |
| 12 | Seaford Town | 34 | 12 | 8 | 14 | 64 | 64 | 44 |
| 13 | Storrington | 34 | 12 | 7 | 15 | 50 | 67 | 43 |
| 14 | Southwick | 34 | 9 | 4 | 21 | 58 | 75 | 31 |
| 15 | Oakwood | 34 | 8 | 7 | 19 | 62 | 88 | 31 |
| 16 | Wick | 34 | 8 | 7 | 19 | 44 | 74 | 31 |
| 17 | Rustington | 34 | 7 | 8 | 19 | 53 | 81 | 29 |
| 18 | Saltdean United | 34 | 2 | 2 | 30 | 37 | 156 | 8 |

| DIVISION ONE | | 1 | 2 | 3 | 4 | 5 | 6 | 7 | 8 | 9 | 10 | 11 | 12 | 13 | 14 | 15 | 16 | 17 | 18 | 19 | 20 | 21 | 22 |
| --- | --- | --- | --- | --- | --- | --- | --- | --- | --- | --- | --- | --- | --- | --- | --- | --- | --- | --- | --- | --- | --- | --- | --- |
| 1 | AFC Uckfield | | 3-3 | 4-5 | 3-3 | 4-0 | 2-2 | 0-4 | 1-2 | 1-3 | 0-5 | 4-1 | 0-3 | 0-3 | 1-3 | 1-2 | 1-4 | 2-3 | 4-0 | 0-2 | 2-9 | 1-0 | 2-3 |
| 2 | Arundel | 2-0 | | 2-3 | 3-2 | 3-2 | 0-2 | 1-1 | 0-0 | 2-3 | 1-1 | 2-1 | 1-0 | 0-3 | 1-3 | 0-2 | 1-1 | 2-4 | 3-0 | 2-0 | 2-1 | 1-3 | 1-0 |
| 3 | Chichester City | 0-2 | 0-0 | | 3-2 | 2-2 | 1-4 | 1-4 | 2-3 | 2-2 | 3-6 | 0-0 | 0-3 | 2-4 | 3-1 | 0-2 | 2-1 | 1-4 | 3-1 | 5-4 | 2-2 | 2-1 | 3-0 |
| 4 | Crowborough Athletic | 3-1 | 2-1 | 2-1 | | 0-4 | 0-3 | 2-3 | 2-1 | 1-3 | 2-1 | 0-3 | 2-3 | 0-0 | 1-1 | 1-2 | 2-3 | 0-2 | 2-1 | 1-0 | 2-1 | 3-2 | 6-2 |
| 5 | Dorking Wanderers | 1-1 | 1-2 | 3-1 | 3-0 | | 1-0 | 2-2 | 0-1 | 1-3 | 1-2 | 3-0 | 1-4 | 1-2 | 1-1 | 1-4 | 1-2 | 1-5 | 1-2 | 4-1 | 2-0 | 3-2 | 7-0 |
| 6 | East Grinstead Town | 2-0 | 1-0 | 5-0 | 7-0 | 6-2 | | 0-1 | 7-3 | 0-1 | 1-1 | 1-1 | 1-2 | 0-3 | 1-3 | 0-2 | 2-1 | 4-0 | 6-1 | 1-1 | 3-0 | 2-1 |
| 7 | East Preston | 2-1 | 2-1 | 3-0 | 6-2 | 1-3 | 5-1 | | 2-1 | 0-3 | 2-0 | 2-1 | 6-2 | 1-2 | 2-2 | 0-2 | 2-0 | 1-4 | 1-1 | 4-0 | 3-0 | 3-2 | HW |
| 8 | Hailsham Town | 4-0 | 2-4 | 3-2 | 5-1 | 3-1 | 0-2 | 0-7 | | 3-2 | 0-1 | 2-0 | 1-1 | 0-2 | 2-6 | 0-1 | 4-0 | 2-6 | 3-1 | 3-5 | 0-1 | 1-3 | 6-2 |
| 9 | Hassocks | 6-1 | 2-2 | 3-2 | 6-1 | 0-0 | 6-1 | 3-2 | 2-1 | | 1-3 | 3-1 | 0-1 | 0-2 | 0-1 | 0-5 | 1-2 | 3-1 | 0-2 | 2-1 | 5-0 | 5-0 | 4-0 |
| 10 | Horsham YMCA | 8-0 | 6-1 | 5-2 | 6-1 | 1-1 | 1-4 | 0-1 | 2-1 | 5-0 | | 3-1 | 1-3 | 5-3 | 0-0 | 0-1 | 0-2 | 2-0 | 2-2 | 0-2 | 2-1 | 3-0 | 6-1 |
| 11 | Lancing | 7-1 | 3-1 | 4-0 | 3-2 | 6-1 | 4-2 | 1-3 | 3-1 | 0-0 | 3-1 | | 1-2 | 0-3 | 0-1 | 1-1 | 2-0 | 3-4 | 2-2 | 5-3 | 2-1 | 0-0 | 1-1 |
| 12 | Lingfield | 4-0 | 1-1 | 3-1 | 3-3 | 4-2 | 3-1 | 2-3 | 2-2 | 1-1 | 3-2 | 2-1 | | 2-2 | 0-6 | 2-1 | 2-2 | 5-0 | 2-1 | 2-0 | 4-1 | 8-2 |
| 13 | Pagham | 4-2 | 4-3 | 2-0 | 3-2 | 3-1 | 1-2 | 1-1 | 3-1 | 4-1 | 4-2 | 2-1 | 3-0 | | 2-1 | 0-1 | 1-2 | 0-1 | 3-1 | 2-0 | 2-3 | 1-2 | 4-3 |
| 14 | Peacehaven & Telscombe | 5-2 | 7-0 | 3-1 | 2-0 | 1-1 | 4-1 | 3-3 | 0-1 | 2-1 | 5-0 | 1-3 | 4-2 | 1-0 | | 4-0 | 4-0 | 0-0 | 2-0 | 2-0 | 9-1 | 1-1 | 6-1 |
| 15 | Redhill | 4-1 | 5-1 | 5-2 | 2-0 | 2-2 | 2-0 | 2-2 | HW | 3-1 | 2-1 | 3-3 | 4-1 | 4-0 | 1-2 | | 2-1 | 1-4 | 0-3 | 1-0 | 1-1 | 1-0 | 9-0 |
| 16 | Ringmer | 1-0 | 0-2 | 1-2 | 1-0 | 3-0 | 2-2 | 1-1 | 1-4 | 1-5 | 3-3 | 3-0 | 5-1 | 1-0 | 0-3 | 0-4 | | 2-0 | 2-2 | 5-3 | 4-1 | 1-0 | 8-1 |
| 17 | Rye United | 9-1 | 4-0 | 5-0 | 1-2 | 0-0 | 3-1 | 0-0 | 2-1 | 3-3 | 5-1 | 5-3 | 4-1 | 1-1 | 1-1 | 2-2 | 0-1 | | 3-3 | 5-1 | 6-0 | 6-2 | 3-0 |
| 18 | Selsey | 5-0 | 1-0 | 1-1 | 0-3 | 0-0 | 0-0 | 1-3 | 0-1 | 3-2 | 3-3 | 1-5 | 2-1 | 1-1 | 0-1 | 0-2 | 2-0 | 0-3 | | 2-1 | 1-1 | 1-4 | 3-2 |
| 19 | Shoreham | 4-3 | 1-3 | 3-0 | 1-3 | 2-1 | 0-6 | 0-6 | 4-3 | 2-2 | 2-1 | 1-1 | 2-1 | 0-3 | 1-5 | 0-4 | 1-1 | 1-1 | 3-0 | | 5-1 | 2-0 | 3-1 |
| 20 | Sidley United | 3-0 | 4-2 | 0-1 | 1-3 | 2-0 | 0-2 | 0-1 | 1-2 | 4-1 | 0-3 | 2-1 | 3-4 | 2-0 | 0-0 | 2-0 | 1-3 | 1-2 | 1-1 | 2-1 | | 2-2 | 6-1 |
| 21 | St Francis Rangers | 4-0 | 2-0 | 2-1 | 1-1 | 2-0 | 1-2 | 1-0 | 4-1 | 2-3 | 2-0 | 4-1 | 2-2 | 1-2 | 1-1 | 0-3 | 0-4 | 0-1 | 1-1 | 2-2 | 0-4 | | 8-1 |
| 22 | Worthing United | 3-1 | 3-4 | 0-1 | 1-3 | 0-0 | 3-7 | 1-1 | 1-1 | 0-5 | 1-2 | 1-2 | 1-1 | 2-1 | 0-3 | 0-4 | 0-1 | 1-1 | 2-2 | 0-4 | 0-3 | 1-1 | |

# SUSSEX COUNTY LEAGUE - STEP 5/6/7

## DIVISION THREE

| | | P | W | D | L | F | A | Pts |
|---|---|---|---|---|---|---|---|---|
| 1 | Sidlesham | 22 | 17 | 3 | 2 | 71 | 23 | 54 |
| 2 | (P) Haywards Heath Town | 22 | 16 | 5 | 1 | 59 | 13 | 53 |
| 3 | Barnham | 22 | 14 | 3 | 5 | 73 | 30 | 45 |
| 4 | Billingshurst | 22 | 10 | 5 | 7 | 45 | 37 | 35 |
| 5 | Clymping | 22 | 9 | 5 | 8 | 35 | 29 | 32 |
| 6 | Uckfield Town | 22 | 9 | 5 | 8 | 41 | 43 | 32 |
| 7 | Ferring (-3pts) | 22 | 9 | 7 | 6 | 51 | 45 | 31 |
| 8 | Roffey | 22 | 6 | 4 | 12 | 33 | 50 | 22 |
| 9 | Hurstpierpoint | 22 | 6 | 4 | 12 | 24 | 42 | 22 |
| 10 | Ifield | 22 | 4 | 5 | 13 | 34 | 52 | 17 |
| 11 | Rottingdean Village | 22 | 4 | 2 | 16 | 28 | 76 | 14 |
| 12 | TD Shipley | 22 | 3 | 2 | 17 | 15 | 69 | 11 |

## RESERVE DIVISION PREMIER

| | | P | W | D | L | F | A | Pts |
|---|---|---|---|---|---|---|---|---|
| 1 | Hassocks Reserves | 24 | 17 | 4 | 3 | 76 | 30 | 55 |
| 2 | Eastbourne United AFC Res. | 24 | 17 | 4 | 3 | 69 | 30 | 55 |
| 3 | Eastbourne Town Reserves | 24 | 11 | 5 | 8 | 63 | 41 | 38 |
| 4 | Dorking Wanderers Reserves | 24 | 10 | 4 | 10 | 39 | 47 | 34 |
| 5 | Littlehampton Town Reserves | 24 | 10 | 4 | 10 | 45 | 56 | 34 |
| 6 | Rye United Reserves | 24 | 9 | 4 | 11 | 42 | 29 | 31 |
| 7 | St Francis Rangers Reserves | 24 | 8 | 7 | 9 | 42 | 51 | 31 |
| 8 | Pagham Reserves (-3pts) | 24 | 9 | 5 | 10 | 45 | 44 | 29 |
| 9 | Ringmer Reserves | 24 | 9 | 2 | 13 | 48 | 54 | 29 |
| 10 | Saltdean United Reserves | 24 | 9 | 2 | 13 | 48 | 76 | 29 |
| 11 | Mile Oak Reserves | 24 | 8 | 4 | 12 | 42 | 50 | 28 |
| 12 | East Preston Reserves | 24 | 7 | 4 | 13 | 29 | 62 | 25 |
| 13 | Lancing Reserves (-3pts) | 24 | 4 | 7 | 13 | 31 | 49 | 16 |

## RESERVE DIVISION EAST

| | | P | W | D | L | F | A | Pts |
|---|---|---|---|---|---|---|---|---|
| 1 | Shoreham Reserves | 22 | 18 | 1 | 3 | 78 | 22 | 55 |
| 2 | Peacehaven & Telscombe Res. | 22 | 15 | 3 | 4 | 64 | 29 | 48 |
| 3 | Haywards Heath Town Res. | 22 | 12 | 7 | 3 | 39 | 26 | 43 |
| 4 | Little Common Reserves | 22 | 10 | 4 | 8 | 37 | 40 | 34 |
| 5 | Hailsham Town Reserves | 22 | 9 | 5 | 8 | 28 | 45 | 32 |
| 6 | Southwick Reserves | 22 | 8 | 7 | 7 | 44 | 32 | 31 |
| 7 | Newhaven Reserves | 22 | 9 | 3 | 10 | 39 | 39 | 30 |
| 8 | Westfield Reserves | 22 | 7 | 6 | 9 | 30 | 43 | 27 |
| 9 | Seaford Town Reserves | 22 | 6 | 7 | 9 | 20 | 38 | 25 |
| 10 | Bexhill United Reserves | 22 | 6 | 5 | 11 | 32 | 46 | 23 |
| 11 | Sidley United Reserves | 22 | 3 | 5 | 14 | 41 | 70 | 14 |
| 12 | AFC Uckfield Reserves | 22 | 2 | 1 | 19 | 20 | 42 | 7 |

## RESERVE DIVISION WEST

| | | P | W | D | L | F | A | Pts |
|---|---|---|---|---|---|---|---|---|
| 1 | Selsey Reserves | 18 | 15 | 0 | 3 | 64 | 14 | 45 |
| 2 | Steyning Town Reserves (-1pt) | 18 | 10 | 4 | 4 | 44 | 24 | 33 |
| 3 | Arundel Reserves | 18 | 10 | 2 | 6 | 63 | 38 | 32 |
| 4 | Loxwood Reserves | 18 | 10 | 1 | 7 | 51 | 34 | 31 |
| 5 | Broadbridge Heath Reserves | 18 | 9 | 1 | 8 | 50 | 37 | 28 |
| 6 | Storrington Reserves | 18 | 8 | 2 | 8 | 40 | 43 | 26 |
| 7 | Midhurst & Easebourne Res. | 18 | 6 | 6 | 6 | 49 | 53 | 24 |
| 8 | Hurstpierpoint Reserves | 18 | 6 | 1 | 11 | 28 | 49 | 19 |
| 9 | Rustington Reserves | 18 | 5 | 1 | 12 | 28 | 82 | 16 |
| 10 | Ferring Reserves | 18 | 2 | 0 | 16 | 30 | 73 | 6 |

## DIVISION TWO

| | | 1 | 2 | 3 | 4 | 5 | 6 | 7 | 8 | 9 | 10 | 11 | 12 | 13 | 14 | 15 | 16 | 17 | 18 |
|---|---|---|---|---|---|---|---|---|---|---|---|---|---|---|---|---|---|---|---|
| 1 | Bexhill United | | 1-5 | 1-2 | 2-1 | 2-2 | 1-3 | 2-1 | 2-0 | 2-3 | 1-1 | 1-1 | 9-3 | 3-3 | 5-2 | 1-2 | 2-2 | 2-3 | 2-2 |
| 2 | Broadbridge Heath | 1-1 | | 0-3 | 3-4 | 3-2 | 1-2 | 2-1 | 1-1 | 3-4 | 5-0 | 3-1 | 6-0 | 2-2 | 3-1 | 3-2 | 5-2 | 2-1 | 3-0 |
| 3 | Eastbourne United AFC | 2-2 | 6-1 | | 3-0 | 3-1 | 3-1 | 2-3 | 2-0 | 5-1 | 7-1 | 0-1 | 5-0 | 3-2 | 2-2 | 4-2 | 6-0 | 3-2 | 1-2 |
| 4 | Little Common | 4-1 | 1-1 | 3-2 | | 3-1 | 5-0 | 2-2 | 3-0 | 3-5 | 1-1 | 2-0 | 14-0 | 3-1 | 1-0 | 1-1 | 3-0 | 6-1 | 2-0 |
| 5 | Littlehampton Town | 4-1 | 5-2 | 2-0 | 4-0 | | 1-1 | 5-1 | 2-2 | 1-0 | 5-0 | 3-2 | 3-0 | 2-0 | 2-0 | 3-0 | | 2-0 | 6-0 |
| 6 | Loxwood | 0-1 | 0-2 | 4-2 | 2-5 | 0-4 | | 1-1 | 1-1 | 3-2 | 3-1 | 3-1 | 7-1 | 0-5 | 3-1 | 2-2 | 4-1 | 1-2 | 0-0 |
| 7 | Midhurst & Easebourne | 4-0 | 2-0 | 2-2 | 1-1 | 0-2 | 4-2 | | 1-3 | 6-1 | 1-4 | 6-1 | 6-4 | 0-0 | 4-3 | 1-6 | 2-5 | 2-1 | 6-0 |
| 8 | Mile Oak | 3-1 | 2-1 | 2-2 | 2-4 | 2-0 | 0-3 | 3-5 | | 3-2 | 1-1 | 3-2 | 2-3 | 1-4 | 2-1 | 3-3 | 1-2 | 2-1 | 3-1 |
| 9 | Newhaven | 1-2 | 3-2 | 7-0 | 3-1 | 0-2 | 1-0 | 5-2 | 1-1 | | 2-0 | 2-0 | 3-0 | 1-2 | 5-1 | 1-1 | 3-0 | 2-0 | 2-1 |
| 10 | Oakwood | 4-2 | 2-5 | 2-5 | 1-3 | 1-3 | 1-3 | 3-4 | 1-2 | 1-5 | | 4-1 | 2-1 | 3-3 | 1-1 | 3-2 | 1-1 | 3-5 | 1-2 |
| 11 | Rustington | 1-1 | 2-1 | 3-3 | 0-2 | 1-2 | 4-1 | 1-1 | 0-3 | 2-4 | 1-5 | | 8-1 | 1-3 | 3-0 | 1-3 | 2-1 | 2-2 | 1-1 |
| 12 | Saltdean United | 2-4 | 1-3 | 2-3 | 0-8 | 1-4 | 0-4 | 1-1 | 0-4 | 1-4 | 3-1 | 3-5 | | 0-4 | 1-7 | 1-4 | 0-3 | 1-2 | 2-0 |
| 13 | Seaford Town | 1-3 | 4-3 | 2-3 | 1-2 | 0-4 | 0-0 | 1-2 | 3-2 | 0-3 | 0-4 | 2-2 | 4-1 | | 3-3 | 0-1 | 0-2 | 2-2 | 3-1 |
| 14 | Southwick | 3-4 | 1-2 | 1-2 | 2-1 | 1-2 | 2-0 | 1-5 | 0-1 | 1-4 | 1-4 | 2-0 | 2-1 | 0-2 | | 2-1 | 2-2 | 1-3 | 6-1 |
| 5 | Steyning Town | 0-1 | 0-4 | 4-0 | 2-0 | 0-2 | 4-0 | 5-0 | 1-1 | 3-3 | 3-1 | 7-0 | 4-2 | 2-3 | 0-3 | | 1-0 | 2-4 | 2-0 |
| 16 | Storrington | 2-2 | 2-3 | 3-1 | 1-0 | 0-2 | 0-1 | 0-0 | 2-6 | 1-4 | 2-1 | 2-1 | 2-0 | 3-1 | 1-4 | 4-2 | | 1-2 | 2-1 |
| 17 | Westfield | 3-1 | 2-1 | 3-5 | 0-1 | 0-0 | 1-1 | 1-0 | 1-0 | 2-3 | 2-2 | 1-1 | 8-1 | 2-1 | 1-0 | 3-1 | 0-0 | | 3-2 |
| 18 | Wick | 0-1 | 1-0 | 2-5 | 0-4 | 1-3 | 0-1 | 3-3 | 0-3 | 0-0 | 2-1 | 1-1 | 8-0 | 0-2 | 3-1 | 2-0 | 1-1 | 2-3 | |

## DIVISION THREE

| | | 1 | 2 | 3 | 4 | 5 | 6 | 7 | 8 | 9 | 10 | 11 | 12 |
|---|---|---|---|---|---|---|---|---|---|---|---|---|---|
| 1 | Barnham | | 4-2 | 1-0 | 7-1 | 1-5 | 2-0 | 1-1 | 4-1 | 9-1 | 1-2 | 5-1 | 2-2 |
| 2 | Billingshurst | 2-5 | | 2-0 | 3-2 | 0-5 | 4-0 | 1-1 | 3-1 | 1-1 | 5-0 | 1-3 | |
| 3 | Clymping | 0-4 | 0-3 | | 0-0 | 0-2 | 2-1 | 3-1 | 0-2 | 6-1 | 0-3 | 7-0 | 5-2 |
| 4 | Ferring | 1-3 | 2-2 | 1-1 | | 2-2 | 3-0 | 3-2 | 1-1 | 3-1 | 1-4 | 6-1 | 4-0 |
| 5 | Haywards Heath Town | 1-1 | 1-2 | 1-0 | 1-1 | | 2-1 | 6-0 | 2-2 | 4-0 | 1-0 | 3-0 | 4-0 |
| 6 | Hurstpierpoint | 2-1 | 1-0 | 1-1 | 2-3 | 0-5 | | 0-0 | 0-0 | 4-1 | 0-3 | 3-0 | 0-3 |
| 7 | Ifield | 2-5 | 1-1 | 0-1 | 6-1 | 0-2 | 1-2 | | 1-2 | 2-4 | 0-4 | 1-2 | 2-1 |
| 8 | Roffey | 2-3 | 0-5 | 0-1 | 0-4 | 0-2 | 3-2 | 5-1 | | 3-0 | 2-4 | 0-2 | 2-1 |
| 9 | Rottingdean Village | 0-6 | 5-0 | 1-2 | 1-3 | 0-3 | 2-2 | 1-5 | 4-2 | | 0-4 | 0-3 | 1-0 |
| 10 | Sidlesham | 2-1 | 2-0 | 3-3 | 3-3 | 2-3 | 3-0 | 4-1 | 6-1 | 9-1 | | 2-0 | 5-2 |
| 11 | TD Shipley | 0-7 | 0-0 | 0-3 | 0-1 | 1-1 | 0-3 | 2-5 | 1-4 | 0-3 | 1-3 | | 1-6 |
| 12 | Uckfield Town | 2-0 | 2-5 | 0-0 | 4-1 | 0-3 | 3-0 | 1-1 | 2-0 | 2-0 | 1-2 | 1-0 | |

## CLUB MOVEMENTS

**Division One - In:** Littlehampton Town (P). Newhaven (P).

**Out:** AFC Uckfield (R). Peacehaven & Telscombe (P - Isthmian Div.1 South). Redhill (P - Isthmian Div.1 South). Sidley United (F).

**Division Two - In:** AFC Uckfield R). Haywards Heath Town (P). Wick & Barnham United (NC from Wick).

**Out:** Littlehampton Town (P). Newhaven (P). Southwick (R). Wick (NC to Wick & Barnham United).

**Division Three - In:** Langney Wanderers (P - East Sussex Premier). Southwick (R).

**Out:** Barnham (Merged with Wick). Haywards Heath Town (P). TD Shipley (F).

## ARUNDEL

Founded: 1889     Nickname: Mulletts

**Secretary:** Kathy Wilson    **(T)** 07778 783 294     **(E)** kathymwilson@btinternet.com

**Chairman:** Bob Marchant     **Prog Ed:** Kathy Wilson

**Ground:** Mill Road, Arundel, W. Sussex BN18 9QQ    **(T)** 01903 882 548

**Capacity:** 2,200   **Seats:** 100   **Covered:** 200   **Midweek Matchday:** Tuesday    **Clubhouse:** Yes   **Shop:** No

**Colours(change):** Red/white/red (All Blue)
**Previous Names:**
**Previous Leagues:** West Sussex
**Records:** **Att:** 2,200 v Chichester (League) 1967-68 **Goalscorer:** Paul J Bennett **App:** 537 Paul Bennett (Goalkeeper)
**Senior Honours:** Sussex County Champions 1957-58, 58-59, 86-87.

**10 YEAR RECORD**

| 03-04 | | 04-05 | | 05-06 | | 06-07 | | 07-08 | | 08-09 | | 09-10 | | 10-11 | | 11-12 | | 12-13 | |
|---|---|---|---|---|---|---|---|---|---|---|---|---|---|---|---|---|---|---|---|
| SxC1 | 6 | SxC1 | 9 | SxC1 | 7 | SxC1 | 3 | SxC1 | 3 | SxC1 | 2 | SxC1 | 12 | SxC1 | 9 | SxC1 | 17 | SxC1 | 14 |

## CHICHESTER CITY

Founded: 2000     Nickname: Chi

**Secretary:** Michael Maiden    **(T)** 07971 818 761     **(E)** michael.maiden@virgin.net

**Chairman:** Oliver Adnan

**Ground:** Oaklands Way, Chichester, W Sussex PO19 6AR    **(T)** 01243 533 368

**Capacity:** 2,000   **Seats:** none   **Covered:** 200   **Midweek Matchday:** Tuesday    **Clubhouse:** Yes   **Shop:** Yes

**Colours(change):** White/green/green (Yellow/blue/blue)
**Previous Names:** Chichester FC (pre 1948), Chichester City 1948-2000. Merged with Portfield in 2000, Chicester City Utd 2000-08
**Previous Leagues:**
**Records:**
**Senior Honours:** Sussex County Division One 2003-04.

**10 YEAR RECORD**

| 03-04 | | 04-05 | | 05-06 | | 06-07 | | 07-08 | | 08-09 | | 09-10 | | 10-11 | | 11-12 | | 12-13 | |
|---|---|---|---|---|---|---|---|---|---|---|---|---|---|---|---|---|---|---|---|
| SxC1 | 1 | SxC1 | 16 | SxC1 | 8 | SxC1 | 11 | SxC1 | 16 | SxC1 | 7 | SxC1 | 3 | SxC1 | 14 | SxC1 | 20 | SxC1 | 19 |

## CROWBOROUGH ATHLETIC

Founded: 1894     Nickname: The Crows

**Secretary:** Karen Scott    **(T)** 07788 737 061     **(E)** kes7@talktalk.net

**Chairman:** Julian Head

**Ground:** Crowborough Co. Stadium, Alderbrook Rec, Fermor Rd, TN6 3DJ    **(T)** 01892 661 893

**Capacity:** 2,000   **Seats:**   **Covered:** 150   **Midweek Matchday:**    **Clubhouse:**

**Colours(change):** All blue (All red).
**Previous Names:**
**Previous Leagues:** Sussex County 1974-2008. Isthmian 2008-09
**Records:**
**Senior Honours:** Sussex County Division One 2007-08. League Cup 2006-07.

**10 YEAR RECORD**

| 03-04 | | 04-05 | | 05-06 | | 06-07 | | 07-08 | | 08-09 | | 09-10 | | 10-11 | | 11-12 | | 12-13 | |
|---|---|---|---|---|---|---|---|---|---|---|---|---|---|---|---|---|---|---|---|
| SxC3 | 1 | SxC2 | 1 | SxC1 | 6 | SxC1 | 4 | SxC1 | 1 | Isth1S | 22 | SxC1 | 18 | SxC1 | 12 | SxC1 | 13 | SxC1 | 15 |

## DORKING WANDERERS

Founded:     Nickname:

**Secretary:** Rob Cavallini    **(T)** 07806 590 019     **(E)** rob_cavallini@hotmail.com

**Chairman:** Marc White    **Manager:** Marc White     **Prog Ed:** Rob Cavallini

**Ground:** West Humble Playing Fields, London Road, Dorking, Surrey    **(T)** 07841 671 825

**Capacity:**   **Seats:**   **Covered:**   **Midweek Matchday:**    **Clubhouse:**

**Colours(change):** Blue & black stripes/black/black (All yellow).
**Previous Names:**
**Previous Leagues:**
**Records:**
**Senior Honours:** Sussex County League Division Three 2010-11.

**10 YEAR RECORD**

| 03-04 | 04-05 | 05-06 | 06-07 | 07-08 | 08-09 | 09-10 | 10-11 | | 11-12 | | 12-13 | |
|---|---|---|---|---|---|---|---|---|---|---|---|---|
| | | | | | | | SxC3 | 1 | SxC2 | 3 | SxC1 | 20 |

2012-13 - Hailsham Town. Photo: Roger Turner.

2012-13 - Littlehampton Town before their FA Vase Second Qualifying Round tie with Ringmer. Photo: Roger Turner.

# EAST GRINSTEAD TOWN
Founded: 1890        Nickname: The Wasps

**Secretary:** Brian McCorquodale        **(T)** 07802 528 513        **(E)** brian.mcc@egtfc.co.uk

**Chairman:** Richard Tramontin

**Ground:**  The GAC Stadium, East Court, College Lane, East Grinstead RH19 3LS        **(T)** 01342 325 885
**Capacity:** 3,000  **Seats:** none  **Covered:** 400    **Midweek Matchday:**        **Clubhouse:** Yes    **Shop:** No

**Colours(change):**  Yellow & black/black/yellow & black (Blue & yellow/blue & yellow/blue)
**Previous Names:**  East Grinstead > 1997.
**Previous Leagues:**  Mid Sussex, Sussex County, Souhern Amateur
**Records:**  **Att:** 2,006 v Lancing F A Am Cup  **App:** Guy Hill
**Senior Honours:**  Sussex County League Division Two 2007-08.

**10 YEAR RECORD**

| 03-04 | | 04-05 | | 05-06 | | 06-07 | | 07-08 | | 08-09 | | 09-10 | | 10-11 | | 11-12 | | 12-13 | |
|---|---|---|---|---|---|---|---|---|---|---|---|---|---|---|---|---|---|---|---|
| SxC1 | 9 | SxC1 | 18 | SxC2 | 7 | SxC2 | 11 | SxC2 | 1 | SxC1 | 17 | SxC1 | 15 | SxC1 | 7 | SxC1 | 9 | SxC1 | 8 |

# EAST PRESTON
Founded: 1966        Nickname:

**Secretary:** Keith Freeman        **(T)** 07986 596913        **(E)** keweia@btinternet.com

**Chairman:** Andrew Kinchin

**Ground:**  Roundstone Recreation Ground, Lashmar Road, East Preston BN16 1ES        **(T)** 01903 776 026
**Capacity:**        **Seats:**        **Covered:**        **Midweek Matchday:**        **Clubhouse:**

**Colours(change):**  All white (All blue)
**Previous Names:**
**Previous Leagues:**
**Records:**
**Senior Honours:**  Sussex County League Division Three 1983-84, Division Two 1997-98, 2011-12.

**10 YEAR RECORD**

| 03-04 | | 04-05 | | 05-06 | | 06-07 | | 07-08 | | 08-09 | | 09-10 | | 10-11 | | 11-12 | | 12-13 | |
|---|---|---|---|---|---|---|---|---|---|---|---|---|---|---|---|---|---|---|---|
| SxC1 | 3 | SxC1 | 11 | SxC1 | 16 | SxC1 | 10 | SxC1 | 4 | SxC1 | 18 | SxC2 | 14 | SxC2 | 14 | SxC2 | 1 | SxC1 | 3 |

# HAILSHAM TOWN
Founded: 1885        Nickname: The Stringers

**Secretary:** Sue Williams        **(T)** 07719 590 268        **(E)** williams.susan8@sky.com

**Chairman:** Mervyn Walker

**Ground:**  The Beaconsfield, Western Road, Hailsham BN27 3JF        **(T)** 01323 840 446
**Capacity:** 2,000  **Seats:** none  **Covered:** 100    **Midweek Matchday:** Tuesday        **Clubhouse:** Yes

**Colours(change):**  Yellow/green/green (All light blue)
**Previous Names:**  Hailsham.
**Previous Leagues:**  East Sussex, Southern Combination
**Records:**  **Att:** 1350 v Hungerford T. FA Vase Feb 89  **Goalscorer:** Howard Stephens 51  **App:** Phil Comber 713
**Senior Honours:**

**10 YEAR RECORD**

| 03-04 | | 04-05 | | 05-06 | | 06-07 | | 07-08 | | 08-09 | | 09-10 | | 10-11 | | 11-12 | | 12-13 | |
|---|---|---|---|---|---|---|---|---|---|---|---|---|---|---|---|---|---|---|---|
| SxC1 | 12 | SxC1 | 12 | SxC1 | 10 | SxC1 | 6 | SxC1 | 13 | SxC1 | 15 | SxC1 | 19 | SxC1 | 16 | SxC2 | 2 | SxC1 | 12 |

# HASSOCKS
Founded: 1902        Nickname: The Robins

**Secretary:** Dave Knight        **(T)** 01273 842 023        **(E)** dw.knight45@googlemail.com

**Chairman:** Dave John

**Ground:**  The Beacon, Brighton Road, Hassocks BN6 9NA        **(T)** 01273 846 040
**Capacity:** 1,800  **Seats:** 270  **Covered:** 100    **Midweek Matchday:** Tuesday        **Clubhouse:** Yes    **Shop:** No

**Colours(change):**  All Red. (Yellow/black/yellow)
**Previous Names:**
**Previous Leagues:**  Mid Sussex, Brighton & Hove & Dist and Southern Counties Comb
**Records:**  **Att:** 610 v Burgess Hill Town  **Goalscorer:** Pat Harding 43
**Senior Honours:**

**10 YEAR RECORD**

| 03-04 | | 04-05 | | 05-06 | | 06-07 | | 07-08 | | 08-09 | | 09-10 | | 10-11 | | 11-12 | | 12-13 | |
|---|---|---|---|---|---|---|---|---|---|---|---|---|---|---|---|---|---|---|---|
| SxC1 | 7 | SxC1 | 8 | SxC1 | 9 | SxC1 | 5 | SxC1 | 7 | SxC1 | 16 | SxC1 | 14 | SxC1 | 6 | SxC1 | 4 | SxC1 | 7 |

# HORSHAM YMCA
Founded: 1898    Nickname: YM's

**Secretary:** Andy Flack    **(T)** 0777 585 7392    **(E)** andy.flack@horsham.gov.uk

**Chairman:** Mick Browning

**Ground:** Gorings Mead, Horsham, West Sussex RH13 5BP    **(T)** 01403 252 689

**Capacity:** 1,575  **Seats:** 150    **Covered:** 200    **Midweek Matchday:**    **Clubhouse:** Yes    **Shop:** No

**Colours(change):** White/black/red (Navy & sky blue/navy/navy)
**Previous Names:**
**Previous Leagues:** Horsham & District, Brighton & Hove, Mid Sussex, Sussex County > 2006, Isthmian 2006-11.
**Records:** 950 v Chelmsford City - FA Cup 2000
**Senior Honours:** Sussex League 2004-05, 05-06.
John O'Hara Cup 2001-02.

**10 YEAR RECORD**

| 03-04 | 04-05 | 05-06 | 06-07 | 07-08 | 08-09 | 09-10 | 10-11 | 11-12 | 12-13 |
|---|---|---|---|---|---|---|---|---|---|
| SxC1 13 | SxC1 1 | SxC1 1 | Isth1S 9 | Isth1S 21 | SxC1 3 | Isth1S 11 | Isth1S 22 | SxC1 16 | SxC1 10 |

# LANCING
Founded: 1941    Nickname:

**Secretary:** John Rea    **(T)** 07598 301 296    **(E)** john.rea62@yahoo.com

**Chairman:** Barry Leigh

**Ground:** Culver Road, Lancing, West Sussex BN15 9AX    **(T)** 01903 767 285

**Capacity:**    **Seats:**    **Covered:**    **Midweek Matchday:**    **Clubhouse:** Yes

**Colours(change):** Yellow/blue/yellow (All light blue)
**Previous Names:** Lancing Athletic
**Previous Leagues:** Brighton & Hove & District.
**Records:**
**Senior Honours:** Brighton League 1946-47, 47-48.

**10 YEAR RECORD**

| 03-04 | 04-05 | 05-06 | 06-07 | 07-08 | 08-09 | 09-10 | 10-11 | 11-12 | 12-13 |
|---|---|---|---|---|---|---|---|---|---|
| SxC2 17 | SxC2 13 | SxC2 12 | SxC2 14 | SxC2 12 | SxC2 9 | SxC2 11 | SxC2 2 | SxC1 2 | SxC1 13 |

# LINGFIELD
Founded: 1893    Nickname:

**Secretary:** Pamela Tomsett    **(T)** 07903 428 228    **(E)** pamtomsettlfc@hotmail.co.uk

**Chairman:** Bill Blenkin

**Ground:** Sports Pavillion, Godstone Road, Lingfield, Surrey RH7 6BT    **(T)** 01342 834 269

**Capacity:** 1,000+  **Seats:** Yes    **Covered:** Yes    **Midweek Matchday:** Tuesday    **Clubhouse:** Yes    **Shop:** No

**Colours(change):** Red & Yellow/black/yellow. (Blue & white/blue/blue)
**Previous Names:** None.
**Previous Leagues:** Redhill. Surrey Intermediate. Combined Counties. Mid Sussex.
**Records:**
**Senior Honours:**

**10 YEAR RECORD**

| 03-04 | 04-05 | 05-06 | 06-07 | 07-08 | 08-09 | 09-10 | 10-11 | 11-12 | 12-13 |
|---|---|---|---|---|---|---|---|---|---|
| SxC3 8 | SxC3 3 | SxC3 2 | SxC2 10 | SxC2 2 | SxC1 8 | SxC1 10 | SxC1 11 | SxC1 7 | SxC1 6 |

# LITTLEHAMPTON TOWN
Founded: 1896    Nickname: Golds

**Secretary:** Alan Barnes    **(T)** 07882 460 357    **(E)** truegritagb@aol.com

**Chairman:** Neil Taylor

**Ground:** Sportsfield, St Flora's Road, Littlehampton BN17 6BD    **(T)** 01903 716 390

**Capacity:**    **Seats:**    **Covered:**    **Midweek Matchday:**    **Clubhouse:**

**Colours(change):** Yellow/black/black (All white)
**Previous Names:** Littlehampton 1896-1938.
**Previous Leagues:** None
**Records:** Lost in the FAC Prelim v Tunbridge W. 15-16 on pens after 40 kicks had been taken - At the time a European record and one short of the World record.
**Senior Honours:** Sussex County Division Two 2003-04, 12-13.

**10 YEAR RECORD**

| 03-04 | 04-05 | 05-06 | 06-07 | 07-08 | 08-09 | 09-10 | 10-11 | 11-12 | 12-13 |
|---|---|---|---|---|---|---|---|---|---|
| SxC2 1 | SxC1 4 | SxC1 4 | SxC1 20 | SxC2 8 | SxC2 14 | SxC2 12 | SxC2 11 | SxC2 4 | SxC2 1 |

# NEWHAVEN

Founded: 1887     Nickname:

**Secretary:** John Carpenter     **(T)** 07733 370 398     **(E)** jgcarpenter@cicestra.co.uk

**Chairman:** Andrew Lloyd

**Ground:** Fort Road Newhaven East Sussex BN9 9DA     **(T)** 01273 513 940
**Capacity:**     **Seats:** Yes     **Covered:** Yes     **Midweek Matchday:**     **Clubhouse:** Yes

**Colours(change):** All red & white (All yellow & blue)
**Previous Names:** None
**Previous Leagues:** None
**Records:**
**Senior Honours:** Sussex County League Division One 1953-54, 73-74, Division Two 1971-72, 90-91, Division Three 2011-12.

**10 YEAR RECORD**

| 03-04 | | 04-05 | | 05-06 | | 06-07 | | 07-08 | | 08-09 | | 09-10 | | 10-11 | | 11-12 | | 12-13 | |
|---|---|---|---|---|---|---|---|---|---|---|---|---|---|---|---|---|---|---|---|
| SxC3 | 13 | SxC3 | 11 | SxC3 | 4 | SxC3 | 9 | SxC3 | 5 | SxC3 | 4 | SxC3 | 9 | SxC3 | 7 | SxC3 | 1 | SxC2 | 2 |

# PAGHAM

Founded: 1903     Nickname: The Lions

**Secretary:** Marc Hilton     **(T)** 07771 810 757     **(E)** paghamfc@aol.com

**Chairman:** Brent Williams

**Ground:** Nyetimber Lane, Pagham, W Sussex PO21 3JY     **(T)** 01243 266 112
**Capacity:** 2,000 **Seats:** 200     **Covered:** 200     **Midweek Matchday:**     **Clubhouse:** Yes     **Shop:** No

**Colours(change):** White & black/black/white (Green/white/green & white)
**Previous Names:** None
**Previous Leagues:** Chichester 1903-50, West Sussex 50-69
**Records:** Att: 1,200 v Bognor 1971 **Goalscorer:** Dick De Luca **App:** Graham Peach
**Senior Honours:** Sussex County Division Two 1978-79, 86-87, 2006-07. Division One 80-81, 87-88, 88-89.

**10 YEAR RECORD**

| 03-04 | | 04-05 | | 05-06 | | 06-07 | | 07-08 | | 08-09 | | 09-10 | | 10-11 | | 11-12 | | 12-13 | |
|---|---|---|---|---|---|---|---|---|---|---|---|---|---|---|---|---|---|---|---|
| SxC1 | 17 | SxC1 | 19 | SxC2 | 13 | SxC2 | 1 | SxC1 | 9 | SxC1 | 11 | SxC1 | 17 | SxC1 | 4 | SxC1 | 6 | SxC1 | 5 |

# RINGMER

Founded: 1906     Nickname: Blues

**Secretary:** Sally Crouch     **(T)** 07510 109 509     **(E)** sallycrouch@ringmerfc.co.uk

**Chairman:** Bob Munnery

**Ground:** Caburn Ground, Anchor Field, Ringmer BN8 5QN     **(T)** 01273 812 738
**Capacity:** 1,000 **Seats:** 100     **Covered:** Yes     **Midweek Matchday:** Tuesday     **Clubhouse:** Yes     **Shop:** Yes

**Colours(change):** Navy & light blue/navy/navy. (All orange).
**Previous Names:** None.
**Previous Leagues:** Brighton.
**Records:** 1,350 v Southwick, Sussex County League, 1970-71.
**Senior Honours:** Sussex County Division Two 1968-69. Division One 1970-71. Sussex Senior Cup 1972-73.

**10 YEAR RECORD**

| 03-04 | | 04-05 | | 05-06 | | 06-07 | | 07-08 | | 08-09 | | 09-10 | | 10-11 | | 11-12 | | 12-13 | |
|---|---|---|---|---|---|---|---|---|---|---|---|---|---|---|---|---|---|---|---|
| SxC1 | 10 | SxC1 | 6 | SxC1 | 2 | SxC1 | 9 | SxC1 | 10 | SxC1 | 9 | SxC1 | 13 | SxC1 | 10 | SxC1 | 15 | SxC1 | 9 |

# RYE UNITED

Founded:     Nickname: United

**Secretary:** Roger Bond     **(T)** 07738 154 685     **(E)** e.r.bond@btinternet.com

**Chairman:** Clive Taylor     **Prog Ed:** Roger Bond

**Ground:** Rye Football & Cricket Salts, Fish Market Rd, Rye TN31 7LU     **(T)** 01797 223 855
**Capacity:** 1,500 **Seats:**     **Covered:** 100     **Midweek Matchday:** Tuesday     **Clubhouse:** Yes     **Shop:** No

**Colours(change):** Red & black/black/black (All blue).
**Previous Names:**
**Previous Leagues:** Sussex County & Kent County until 2000
**Records:** Att: 120 **App:** Scott Price
**Senior Honours:** Sussex County League Division Three 2000-01, Division Two 1955-56, 2001-02, 02-03, 09-10.

**10 YEAR RECORD**

| 03-04 | | 04-05 | | 05-06 | | 06-07 | | 07-08 | | 08-09 | | 09-10 | | 10-11 | | 11-12 | | 12-13 | |
|---|---|---|---|---|---|---|---|---|---|---|---|---|---|---|---|---|---|---|---|
| SxC1 | 2 | SxC1 | 2 | SxC1 | 19 | SxC1 | 19 | SxC1 | 19 | SxC2 | 6 | SxC2 | 1 | SxC1 | 2 | SxC1 | 3 | SxC1 | 4 |

# SUSSEX COUNTY LEAGUE - STEP 5/6/7

## SELSEY
Founded: 1903    Nickname: Blues

**Secretary:** Gordon Weller    **(T)** 07852 954 042    **(E)** g.weller1@btinternet.com
**Chairman:** David Lee    **Prog Ed:** Gordon Weller
**Ground:** High Street Ground, Selsey, Chichester, PO20 0QG    **(T)** 01243 603 420
**Capacity:** 1,000 **Seats:** 25 **Covered:** 98 **Midweek Matchday:** Tuesday **Clubhouse:** Yes **Shop:** No

**Colours(change):** All blue (All yellow).
**Previous Names:** None
**Previous Leagues:** Chichester & District, West Sussex.
**Records:** **Att:** 750-800 v Chichester or Portfield 1950's
**Senior Honours:** Sussex County Division Two 1963-64, 75-76.

**10 YEAR RECORD**

| 03-04 | 04-05 | 05-06 | 06-07 | 07-08 | 08-09 | 09-10 | 10-11 | 11-12 | 12-13 |
|---|---|---|---|---|---|---|---|---|---|
| SxC1 18 | SxC2 14 | SxC2 2 | SxC1 8 | SxC1 15 | SxC1 10 | SxC1 11 | SxC1 17 | SxC1 12 | SxC1 18 |

## SHOREHAM
Founded: 1892    Nickname: Musselmen

**Secretary:** Gary Millis    **(T)** 07801 477 979    **(E)** g.millis@sky.com
**Chairman:** Matthew Major    **Prog Ed:** Gary Millis
**Ground:** Middle Road, Shoreham-by-Sea, W Sussex, BN43 6LT    **(T)** 01273 454 261
**Capacity:** 1,500 **Seats:** 150 **Covered:** 700 **Midweek Matchday:** **Clubhouse:** Yes **Shop:** No

**Colours(change):** All blue (All orange).
**Previous Names:** None.
**Previous Leagues:** West Sussex.
**Records:** **Att:** 1,342 v Wimbledon
**Senior Honours:** Sussex County Division One 1951-52, 52-53, 77-78. Division Two 61-62, 76-77, 93-94. John O'Hara League Cup 2007-08.

**10 YEAR RECORD**

| 03-04 | 04-05 | 05-06 | 06-07 | 07-08 | 08-09 | 09-10 | 10-11 | 11-12 | 12-13 |
|---|---|---|---|---|---|---|---|---|---|
| SxC1 19 | SxC2 3 | SxC1 13 | SxC1 13 | SxC1 12 | SxC1 6 | SxC1 9 | SxC1 18 | SxC1 18 | SxC1 17 |

## ST. FRANCIS RANGERS
Founded: 2002    Nickname: Saints/Rangers

**Secretary:** John Goss    **(T)** 07748 785 240    **(E)** j.goss462@btinternet.com
**Chairman:** John Goss    **Prog Ed:** John Goss
**Ground:** Cowell Ground, Princess Royal Hospital, Lewes Rd, Haywards Hth RH16 4EX    **(T)** 01444 474 021
**Capacity:** 1,000 **Seats:** None **Covered:** 100 **Midweek Matchday:** Tuesday **Clubhouse:** Yes **Shop:** No

**Colours(change):** Black & white/black/black (Yellow/black/yellow)
**Previous Names:** Formed when Ansty Rangers & St Francis merged 2002.
**Previous Leagues:** None
**Records:**
**Senior Honours:**

**10 YEAR RECORD**

| 03-04 | 04-05 | 05-06 | 06-07 | 07-08 | 08-09 | 09-10 | 10-11 | 11-12 | 12-13 |
|---|---|---|---|---|---|---|---|---|---|
| SxC3 2 | SxC2 4 | SxC2 3 | SxC2 2 | SxC1 14 | SxC1 12 | SxC1 16 | SxC1 19 | SxC1 19 | SxC1 11 |

## WORTHING UNITED
Founded: 1952    Nickname:

**Secretary:** Malcolm Gamlen    **(T)** 07743 322 571    **(E)** helsnmark@aol.com
**Chairman:** Gary Downie    **Manager:** Martyn Rea
**Ground:** The Robert Albon Memorial Ground, Lyons Way BN14 9JF    **(T)** 01903 234 466
**Capacity:** **Seats:** Yes **Covered:** Yes **Midweek Matchday:** **Clubhouse:** Yes

**Colours(change):** Sky blue & whites/blue/white (Red & white/red/red)
**Previous Names:** Wigmore Athletic 1952-88. Amalgamated with Southdown to form Worthing United in 1988.
**Previous Leagues:**
**Records:**
**Senior Honours:** Sussex County Division 2 1973-74, Division 3 1989-90.

**10 YEAR RECORD**

| 03-04 | 04-05 | 05-06 | 06-07 | 07-08 | 08-09 | 09-10 | 10-11 | 11-12 | 12-13 |
|---|---|---|---|---|---|---|---|---|---|
| SxC2 2 | SxC1 14 | SxC1 16 | SxC1 18 | SxC1 17 | SxC1 20 | SxC2 2 | SxC2 3 | SxC1 14 | SxC1 22 |

# DIVISION TWO

## A.F.C. UCKFIELD    Founded: 1988    Nickname: The Oaks

**Secretary:** Derek York    **(T)** 07847 453 767    **(E)** d-york1@sky.com
**Chairman:** Tom Parker    **Prog Ed:** Anthony Harvey
**Ground:** The Oaks, Old Eastbourne Road, Uckfield TN22 5QL    **(T)** 07847 662 337
**Colours(change):** All light blue (All orange)
**ADDITIONAL INFORMATION:**
Sussex County League Division 2 League Cup 2004-05, Division Two 2010-11.

## BEXHILL UNITED    Founded:    Nickname:

**Secretary:** Mrs Tracy Aston    **(T)** 07791 368 049    **(E)** tracyaston21@aol.com
**Chairman:** Robin Powell    **Prog Ed:** Mrs Tracy Aston
**Ground:** The Polegrove, Brockley Road, Bexhill on Sea TN39 3EX    **(T)** 07791 368 049
**Colours(change):** White & black/black/black (Light blue & yellow/blue/blue)
**ADDITIONAL INFORMATION:**

## BROADBRIDGE HEATH    Founded:    Nickname:

**Secretary:** Andrew Crisp    **(T)** 07501 057 654    **(E)** crispandy@hotmail.com
**Chairman:** Keith Soane    **Manager:** Steve Painter
**Ground:** Broadbridge Leisure Centre, Wickhurst Lane Broadbridge Heath Horsham RH12 3YS **(T)** 01403 211 311
**Colours(change):** All blue (Red & black/red/red)
**ADDITIONAL INFORMATION:**

## EASTBOURNE UNITED ASSOCIATION    Founded: 1894    Nickname: The U's

**Secretary:** Brian Dowling    **(T)** 07507 225 450    **(E)** brian.dowling@btinternet.com
**Chairman:** Les Aisbitt
**Ground:** The Oval, Channel View Road, Eastbourne, BN22 7LN    **(T)** 01323 726 989    **Capacity:** 3,000
**Colours(change):** White/black/white (Claret & blue/claret/claret).
**ADDITIONAL INFORMATION:**
Record Att: 11,000 at Lynchmore

## HAYWARDS HEATH TOWN    Founded: 1888    Nickname:

**Secretary:** Tony Sim    **(T)** 01444 453 754    **(E)**
**Chairman:** Mick Cottingham    **Manager:** Simon Corless
**Ground:** Hanbury Park Stadium, Haywards Heath RH16 4GL    **(T)** 01444 412 837
**Colours(change):** Blue & white
**ADDITIONAL INFORMATION:**
Honours: Sussex County League 1949-50, 69-70. Sussex Senior Cup 1957-58.

## LITTLE COMMON    Founded: 1966    Nickname:

**Secretary:** Mrs Margaret Cherry    **(T)** 01424 217 191    **(E)** danieleldridge11@btinternet.com
**Chairman:** Ken Cherry
**Ground:** Little Common Recreation Ground, Green Lane, Bexhill on Sea TN39 4PH    **(T)** 01424 845 861
**Colours(change):** Claret & blue/claret/claret (Yellow/blue/blue)
**ADDITIONAL INFORMATION:**
Previous Name: Albion United > 1986. Previous League: East Sussex 1994-2005.
Honours: East Sussex League 1975-76, 76-77, 2004-05.

## LOXWOOD    Founded:    Nickname:

**Secretary:** George Read    **(T)** 07791 766 857    **(E)** thomasread00@btinternet.com
**Chairman:** Derek Waterman
**Ground:** Loxwood Sports Ass., Plaistow Road, Loxwood RH14 0RQ    **(T)** 07791 766 857
**Colours(change):** Black & white/black/white (Red & white/white/red)
**ADDITIONAL INFORMATION:**
Previous League: West Sussex.
Honours: Sussex County League Division 3 2007-08.

## MIDHURST & EASEBOURNE

Founded:      Nickname:

**Secretary:** Ted Dummer MBE     **(T)** 01730 813 887     **(E)** TedMBE@gmail.com
**Chairman:** Darren Chiverton     **Prog Ed:** Ted Dummer MBE
**Ground:** Rotherfield, Dodsley Lane, Easebourne, Midhurst GU29 9BE     **(T)** 01730 816 557
**Colours(change):** Blue/black/blue (Orange/blue/orange)

**ADDITIONAL INFORMATION:**
**Previous League:** West Sussex 1999-2002.
**Honours:** Sussex County League Division 2 Cup 1988-89, Division 3 Cup 2002-03.

## MILE OAK

Founded: 1960      Nickname: The Oak

**Secretary:** Colin Brown     **(T)** 07774 754 468     **(E)** colin.d.brown@ntlworld.com
**Chairman:** Leslie Hamilton
**Ground:** Mile Oak Recreation Ground, Chalky Road, Portslade BN41 2YU     **(T)** 01273 423 854
**Colours(change):** Orange & black/black/orange (All green)

**ADDITIONAL INFORMATION:**
**Previous League:** Brighton & Hove District.
**Honours:** Brighton & Hove District 1980-81. Sussex County League Division 2.

## OAKWOOD

Founded: 1962      Nickname:

**Secretary:** Kelly Whittaker     **(T)** 07973 752 761     **(E)** beccakel@hotmail.com
**Chairman:** Stuart Lovegrove
**Ground:** Tinsley Lane, Three Bridges, Crawley RH10 8AJ     **(T)** 01293 515 742
**Colours(change):** Red & black/black/black (Blue & white/white/white)

**ADDITIONAL INFORMATION:**
**Previous League:** Southern Counties Combination 1980-84.
**Honours:** Sussex County Division 2 Cup 1989-90.

## RUSTINGTON

Founded:      Nickname:

**Secretary:** Paul Cox     **(T)** 07771 623 224     **(E)** cox121@yahoo.com
**Chairman:** Frank Sumner
**Ground:** Recreation Ground, Jubilee Avenue, Rustington BN16 3NB     **(T)** 01903 770 495
**Colours(change):** All blue (Red & black/black/red)

**ADDITIONAL INFORMATION:**
**Honours:** Sussex County League Division 3 2006-07.

## SALTDEAN UNITED

Founded: 1966      Nickname:

**Secretary:** Iain Feilding     **(T)** 07880 870 886     **(E)** fieldings@thec.fsnet.co.uk
**Chairman:** Robert Thomas
**Ground:** Hill Park, Coombe Vale Saltdean Brighton East Sussex BN2 8HJ     **(T)** 01273 309 898
**Colours(change):** Red & black/black/black (Green & black/green/green)

**ADDITIONAL INFORMATION:**
**Previous Leagues:** Brighton > 1984.

## SEAFORD TOWN

Founded:      Nickname:

**Secretary:** John Smith     **(T)** 07940 511 504     **(E)** johnsmithn@btinternet.com
**Chairman:** Bob Thomsett
**Ground:** The Crouch, Bramber Road, Seaford BN25 1AG     **(T)** 01323 892 221
**Colours(change):** All red (White/black/black)

**ADDITIONAL INFORMATION:**
**Honours:** Sussex County League Division Two 2005-06.

## STEYNING TOWN

Founded:      Nickname:

**Secretary:** David Kennett     **(T)** 07585 601 213     **(E)** diddy.kennett1@btinternet.com
**Chairman:** Carol Swain
**Ground:** The Shooting Field, Steyning, West Sussex BN44 3RQ     **(T)** 01903 814 601
**Colours(change):** All red (All yellow)

**ADDITIONAL INFORMATION:**
**Honours:** Sussex County League Division 2 1977-78, Division 1 1984-85, 85-86, League Cup 1978-79, 83-84, 85-86.

# STORRINGTON

| | | |
|---|---|---|
| **Secretary:** Keith Dalmon | **(T)** 07889 367 956 | Founded: 1920  Nickname: |
| | | **(E)** keithdalmon@btinternet.com |

**Chairman:** Stan Rhodie
**Ground:** Recreation Ground, Pulborough Road, Storrington RH20 4HJ     **(T)** 01903 745 860
**Colours(change):** All blue (All red)

**ADDITIONAL INFORMATION:**
**Honours:** Sussex County League Division 2 Cup 1979, Division 3 Cup 1998, Division 3 2005.
Vernon Wentworth Cup 1998, 2003.

# WESTFIELD

Founded: 1927  Nickname:

**Secretary:** Gill Attewell     **(T)** 07928 176 658     **(E)** gilljordan@rocketmail.com
**Chairman:** Graham Drinkwater     **Prog Ed:** Gill Attewell
**Ground:** The Parish Field, Main Road, Westfield TN35 4SB     **(T)** 01424 751 011
**Colours(change):** Yellow/green/green (All light blue)

**ADDITIONAL INFORMATION:**
**Previous League:** East Sussex 1971-97.
**Honours:** East Sussex 1977-78, League Cup 77-78. Hastings Senior Cup 2007-08.

# WICK & BARNFIELD UNITED

Founded: 2013  Nickname:

**Secretary:** Terry Gaunt     **(T)** 07880 608 090     **(E)** coxsteven1@aol.com
**Chairman:** Keith Croft     **Manager:** Jon Tucker
**Ground:** Crabtree Park, Coomes Way, Wick, Littlehampton, W Sussex BN17 7LS     **(T)** 01903 713 535     **Capacity:** 1,000
**Colours(change):** Red & black/black & white/red (White/black/black).

**ADDITIONAL INFORMATION:**
**Previous Name:** Barnfield FC merged with Wick June 2013.

## SUSSEX COUNTY DIVISION THREE CONSTITUTION 2013-14

BILLINGHURST ................... Jubilee Field, Three Bridges Road Three Bridges Sussex RH10 1LQ ............................... 01293 442 000

CLYMPING ........................... Clymping Village Hall, Clymping, Littlehampton BN17 5GW................................................ 07951 196 784

FERRING ............................. The Glebelands, Ferring, West Sussex BN12 5JL............................................................. 01903 243 618

HURSTPIERPOINT............... Fairfield Recreation Ground, Cuckfield Road, Hurstpierpoint BN6 9SD ............................ 01273 834 783

IFIELD .................................. Edwards Sports & Social Club, Ifield Green, Rusper Road, Crawley ............................... 01293 420 598

LANGNEY WANDERERS ...... Shinewater Lane Playing Field, off Lavender Close, Milfoil Drive in north Langney, Eastbourne BN23 8DQ

ROFFEY............................... Bartholomew Way, Horsham RH12 5JL ...............................................................................

ROTTINGDEAN VILLAGE ..... Rottingdean Sports Centre, Falmer Road, Rottingdean BN2 7DA...................................... 01273 306 436

SIDLESHAM........................... Recreation Ground, Selsey Road Sidlesham Nr Chichester PO20 7RD ............................. 01243 641538

SOUTHWICK......................... Old Barn Way, Southwick BN42 4NT ................................................................................. 01273 701 010

UCKFIELD TOWN................. Victoria Pleasure Ground, Uckfield TN22 5DJ .......................................................................

2012-13 - Ringmer line up before their FA Vase Second Qualifying Round tie with Littlehampton Town.
Photo: Roger Turner.

# GROUND DIRECTIONS

**ARUNDEL-Mill Road, Arundel, West Sussex BN18 9QQ-01903 882 548**
A27 from Worthing to Arundel over Railway Bridge to roundabout . Second exit into Queen Street to town centre and turn right over bridge. Car park leading to ground 100 yards on right.

**CHICHESTER CITY-Oaklands Park, Oaklands Way, Chichester PO19 6AR-07845 105 822**
Half a mile north of the city centre, adjacent to festival theatre. Turn into Northgate car park and entrance to the ground is next to the Chichester Rackets Club.

**CROWBOROUGH ATHLETIC-Crowborough Community Stadium, Alderbrook Recreation Ground, Fermor Road, TN6 3DJ**
Entering Crowborough from the south on the A26, about half a mile past the Crow and Gate Pub, take the next right into Sheep Plain-This is also signposted for the Railway Station, which meanders into Hurtis Hill. At the mini-roundabout go straight into Fermor Road, take the second turning on the right and turn right immediately into Alderbrook Recreation Ground. The Stadium and parking is ahead of you.

**DORKING WANDERERS- West Humble Playing Fields, London Road, Dorking.**
Take A24 to Dorking at roundabout stay on A24 to Leatherhead. Go past Denbies Vineyard on left. At end of vineyard take 2nd turning on the left straight into the playing field.

**EAST GRINSTEAD TOWN-East Court, East Grinstead RH19 3LS-01342 325885**
A264 Tunbridge Wells road (Moat Road) until mini roundabout at bottom of Blackwell Hollow ,turn immediately right by club sign then 1st left, ground 200 yards down lane past rifle club on right.

**EAST PRESTON - Roundstone Recreation Ground, Lashmar Road, East Preston, West Sussex BN16 1ES - 01903 776026**
From Worthing proceed west for six miles on A259 to The Roundstone PH. From the roundabout, take the first exit, signposted East Preston. Turn left over the railway crossing. Turn left soon afterwards, and then first right into Roundstone Drive. Turn left into Lashmar Road and the approach road to the ground is on the right.

**HAILSHAM TOWN-The Beaconsfield, Western Road, Hailsham, East Sussex BN27 3DN-01323 840446**
A22 to Arlington Road, turn east, then left into South Road- left into Diplocks Way until Daltons. Four miles from Polegate BR (Brighton-Eastbourne line).

**HASSOCKS-The Beacon, Brighton Rd., Hassocks BN6 9NA-01273 846040**
Off A273 Pyecombe Road to Burgess Hill. Ground is 300 yards south of Stonepound crossroads (B2116) to Hurstpeirpoint or Hassocks.

**HORSHAM YMCA-Gorings Mead, Horsham, West Sussex RH13 5BP-01403 252 689**
From the east, take A281 (Brighton Road) and the ground is on the left and sign posted opposite Gorings Mead.

**LANCING-Culver Road, Lancing, West Sussex BN15 9AX. -01903 767 285.**
From A27 turn south at Lancing Manor roundabout into Grinstead Lane, 3rd turning on right North Farm Rd. Turn left then immedlately. right into Culver Rd. From railway station take 3rd turning on left heading north.

**LINGFIELD-Sports Pavilion, Godstone Road, Lingfield, Surrey RH7 6BT-01342 834269**
A22, 4 miles north of East Grinstead, to Mormon Temple roundabout, take exit Lingfield (B2028) Newchapel Road for 1 1/2 miles. Left at T junction into Godstone Road (B2029) and ground is 1/2 mile on left.

**LITTLEHAMPTON TOWN-The Sportsfield, St Flora's Road, Littlehampton BN17 6BD-01903 716 390**
Leave A259 at Waterford Business Park and turn into Horsham Road. After Shell Garage turn left into St. Floras Road. Ground is at the end of road on the left.

**NEWHAVEN-Fort Road Recreation Ground, Newhaven, East Sussex BN9 9EE. -01273 513 940.**
From A259, follow the one way system around the town of Newhaven. Turn left into South Road (pass the Police Station) which becomes Fort Road. The ground is visible on the right just past a small parade of shops and before the approach road to Newhaven Fort. Postcode for Sat-nav users: BN9 9DA

**PAGHAM-Nyetimber Lane, Pagham, West Sussex PO21 3JY-01243 266 112**
Turn off A27 Chichester by-pass (signposted A259 Pagham). Ground in village of Nyetimber. Three miles from Bognor (BR). Buses 260 & 240

**RINGMER-Caburn Ground, Anchor Field, Ringmer-01273 812 738**
From Lewes road turn right into Springett Avenue, opposite Ringmer village

**RYE UNITED-Sydney Allnut Pavilion, Rye Football & Cricket Salts, Fishmarket Road, Rye TN31 7NU-01797 223 855**
Outskirts of Rye on the A268 joins A259 opposite Skinners Rover garage.

**SELSEY-High Street Ground, Selsey, Chichester, West Sussex-01243 603420**
Through Selsey High Street to fire station. Take turning into car park alongside the station. Entrance is in the far corner. Regular buses from Chichester.

**SHOREHAM-Middle Road, Shoreham-by-Sea, West Sussex BN43 6LT-01273 454 261**
From Shoreham (BR) go east over level crossing, up Dolphin Road. Ground is 150 yards on right.

**ST FRANCIS RANGERS-The Princess Royal Hospital, Lewes Road, Haywards Heath, RH16 4EX Tel No: 01444 474 021 and social club 01444 441 881**
Enter through the main hospital entrance on the Lewes Road and follow signs to Sports Complex.

**WORTHING UNITED-The Robert Albion Memorial Ground, Lyons Way, Worthing BN14 9JF. 01903 234 466.**
From the West past Hill Barn roundabout to second set of traffic lights, turn left into Lyons Way. From East first set of traffic lights at end of Sompting bypass, turn right into Lyons Way.

# DIVISION TWO

**AFC UCKFIELD-The Oaks, Old Eastbourne Road, Uckfield, East Sussex TN22 5QL-07847 662 337**
Next to Rajdutt Restaurant on Old Eastbourne Road, south of Uckfield town centre.

**BEXHILL UNITED-The Polegrove, Brockley Road, Bexhill-on-Sea, East Sussex TN39 3EX-07815 425 682.**
A27 to Little Common then fourth exit off roundabout to Cooden Beach. Left and follow to end, turn right into Brockby Road. Ground at bottom of hill on the right.

**BROADBRIDGE HEATH-Wickhurst Lane, Broadbridge Heath, Horsham RH12 3YS-01403 211 311**
Alongside A24, Horsham north/south bypass. From the A24 Horsham Bypass, at the large roundabout/underpass take the Broadbridge Heath Bypass towards Guildford and then at the first roundabout turn left into Wickhurst Lane.

**EASTBOURNE UNITED AFC-The Oval, Channel View Ropad, Eastbourne, East Sussex BN22 7LN-011323 726989**
From A22 follow signs to Eastbourne East seafront. Turn left onto seafront and left again into Channel View Road at Princess Park & ground is first right.

**HAYWARDS HEATH TOWN-Hanbury Park Stadium, Haywards Heath RH16 3PX-01444 412 837.**
A272 to Haywards Heath town centre. At Sussex roundabout, north on B2708 (Hazelgrove Road) take first right into New England Road, then the 4th right (Allen Road) leads to ground.

**LITTLE COMMON-Little Common Spts Pavilion, Little Common Rec., Green Lane, Bexhill-on-Sea, TN39 4PH-01424 845 861.**
From the west take the A259, at Little Common roundabout take second exit into Peartree Lane and then left into Little Common Recreation Ground car park.

**LOXWOOD-Loxwood Sports Association, Plaistow Road, Loxwood RH14 0SX-01404 753 185**
Leave A272 between Billinghurst and Wisborough Green and join the B2133 for 3.4 miles. On entering Loxwood Village take 1st left into Plaistow Road, ground situated 100 yards on the left.

**MIDHURST & EASEBOURNE-Rotherfield, Dodsley Lane, Easebourne, Midhurst, W. Sussex GU29 9BE-01730 816 557.**
Ground one mile out of Midhurst on London Road (A286) opposite Texaco Garage. Ample car parking.

**MILE OAK-Mile Oak Recreation Ground, Chalky Road, Portslade-01273 423 854.**
From A27 (Brighton Bypass) leave at A293 exit. Right at first roundabout. Ground 1 mile on right. Parking in the Sports Centre opposite the ground (park) entrance.

## SUSSEX COUNTY LEAGUE - STEP 5/6/7

**OAKWOOD-Tinsley Lane, Three Bridges, Crawley RH10 8AJ-01293 515 742.**
From the South on M23, take junction 10 exit left onto A2011, next roundabout take fourth exit right, next roundabout second exit, take first right into Tinsley Lane. Ground entrance 100 metres on left.

**RUSTINGTON-Recreation Ground, Jubilee Avenue, Rustington, West Sussex BN16 3NB-01903 770 495.**
From the East follow A259 past Sainsburys. Left at next roundabout on to B2187 over Windmill Bridge. Straight on at roundabout, first right, then first left into Woodlands Avenue. Car park is 80 yards on your right, next to the Village hall. From the West proceed to Watersmead roundabout with Bodyshop on your left. Take B2187 half a mile, past BP garage, take third right into Albert Road, then first right into Woodlands Avenue.

**SALTDEAN UNITED-Hill Park, Coombe Vale, Saltdean, Brighton BN2 8HJ-01273 309 898.**
A259 coast road east from Brighton to Saltdean Lido, left into Arundel Drive West, and Saltdean Vale to bridle path at beginning of Combe Vale. Club 200yds along track.

**SEAFORD TOWN-The Crouch, Bramber Road, Seaford BN25 1AG-01323 892 221.**
A259 to Seaford. At mini roundabout by station, turn left (coming from Newhaven) or RIGHT (from Eastbourne). At end of Church Street, across junction, then left at end. After 500m turn left up Ashurst Road Bramber Road is at the top.

**STEYNING TOWN-The Shooting Field, Steyning, W. Sussex BN44 3RP. -01903 812 228.**
Entering Steyning from the west. Take 1st left in the High St (Tanyard Lane) Follow into Shooting Field estate, ground is 4th turn on the left. Entering Steyning from the east. From the High St., turn right into Church St.. Turn left by Church into Shooting Field estate. NB Coaches MUST park in Church Street Car Park.

**STORRINGTON-Recreation Ground, Pulborough Road, Storrington RH20 4HJ-01903 745 860.**
A24 right at roundabout at Washington. Four miles to Storrington through village. Third exit at roundabout and second right into Spearbridge Road.

**WESTFIELD-The Parish Field, Main Road, Westfield TN35 4SB-01483 751 011.**
From Hastings take the A21, turning right onto the A28 towards Ashford. Travel through Westfield, and the ground is located off Westfield Lane on the left.

**WICK & BARNHAM UNITED -Crabtree Park, Coomes Way, Wick, Littlehampton, West Sussex BN17 7LS Tel No: 01903 713 535**
A27 to Crossbush.A284 towards Littlehampton. After one mile over level crossing left into Coomes Way next to Locomotive pub. Ground at end.

## DIVISION THREE

**BILLINGHURST-Jubilee Field, Three Bridges Road Three Bridges Sussex RH10 1LQ-01293 442 000**
Heading towards Crawley past Three Bridges railway station on the left, take the 2nd right into Three Bridges Road, and then 1st left 75 yards down. The ground is down Jubilee Walk (80 yards)opposite the Plough Inn.

**CLYMPING-Clymping Village Hall, Clymping, Littelhampton BN17 5GW-07951 196 784.**
Follow A259 west of Littlehampton. Just over the Bridge, on the right hand side before the small roundabout.

**FERRING-The Glebelands, Ferring, West Sussex BN12 5JL**
To Ferring main shops, turn right into Greystoke Road.

**HURSTPIERPOINT-Fairfield Rec. Ground, Cuckfield Road, BN6 9SD-01273 834 783.**
At Hurstpierpoint crossroads, go north into Cuckfield Road (B2117) for 1km. Ground entrance between houses nos.158 & 160.

**IFIELD-Edwards Sports & Social Club, Ifield Green, Rusper Road, Crawley. -01293 420 598.**
From A23 Crawley by-pass going north, left at roundabout signed Charlwood. Third left into Ifield Green, first right past Royal Oak (PH) into Rusper Road.

**LANGNEY WANDERERS - Shinewater Lane Playing Field, off Lavender Close, Milfoil Drive in north Langney, Eastbourne, East Sussex BN23 8DQ.**

**ROFFEY-Bartholomew Way, Horsham RH12 5JL.**
A24 heading South, turn left at Rusper roundabout. Take first left into Lemmington Way. Take left at T junction into Bartholomew Way.

**ROTTINGDEAN VILLAGE-Rottingdean Sports Centre, Falmer Road, Rottingdean BN2 7DA. -01273 306 436**
After leaving the Rottingdean Village one way system go past Bazehill Road and the entrance to the ground is next on the right.

**SIDLESHAM**

**SOUTHWICK-Old Barn Way, off Manor Hall Way, Southwick, Brighton BN42 4NT-01273 701 010**
A27 from Brighton take first left after Southwick sign to Leisure Centre. Ground adjacent. Five minutes walk from Fishergate or Southwick stations.

**UCKFIELD TOWN-Victoria Pleasure Ground, Uckfield TN22 5DJ-01825 769 400.**
Take Eastbourne road (old A22) south of Uckfield town centre. Entrance to ground is 1/2 mile on the right (just after the Police station).

# UNITED COUNTIES LEAGUE

**Sponsored by:** ChromaSport & Trophies
**Founded:** 1895
**Recent Champions:**
2008: Stotfold
2009: Stewarts & Lloyds Corby
2010: Daventry Town
2011: St Neots Town
2012: Long Buckby
**nwcfl.co.uk**

## LEAGUE CUP

**PRELIMINARY ROUND**

| | | | |
|---|---|---|---|
| Yaxley | v | Shepshed Dynamo | 3-1 |
| Boston Town | v | Harborough Town | 0-2 |
| Cogenhoe United | v | Buckingham Town | 5-0 |
| Burton Park Wanderers | v | Rothwell Corinthians | 0-2 |
| St Ives Town | v | Blackstones | 4-2 |
| AFC Rushden & Diamonds | v | Wellingborough Whitworth | 5-3 |
| Harrowby United | v | Wootton Blue Cross | 3-0 |
| Oadby Town | v | Raunds Town | 4-4, 4-3p |

**ROUND 1**

| | | | |
|---|---|---|---|
| Eynesbury Rovers | v | Northampton ON Chenecks | 5-0 |
| Holbeach United | v | Deeping Rangers | 4-2 |
| Newport Pagnell Town | v | Yaxley | 2-4 |
| Harborough Town | v | AFC Kempston Rovers | 1-3 |
| Spalding United | v | Northampton Spencer | 1-0 |
| Potton United | v | Cogenhoe United | 2-4 |
| Stewart & Lloyds Corby | v | Peterborough N.S. | 1-1, 2-4p |
| Rothwell Corinthians | v | Northampton Sileby Rangers | 1-0 |
| Olney Town | v | Bugbrooke St Michaels | 0-1 |
| Rushden & Higham United | v | Bourne Town | 2-0 |
| Irchester United | v | St Ives Town | 0-1 |
| Desborough Town | v | Long Buckby | 2-5 |
| *Tie awarded to Desborough Town* | | | |
| Wellingborough Town | v | AFC Rushden & Diamonds | 2-2, 4-3p |
| Thrapston Town | v | Harrowby United | 1-0 |
| Sleaford Town | v | Quorn | 0-1 |
| Huntingdon Town | v | Oadby Town | 1-2 |

**ROUND 2**

| | | | |
|---|---|---|---|
| Eyensbury Rovers | v | Holbeach United | 1-4 |
| Yaxley | v | AFC Kempston Rovers | 2-2, 4-3p |
| Spalding United | v | Cogenhoe United | 3-1 |
| Peterborough Northern Star | v | Rothwell Corinthians | 5-1 |
| Bugbrooke St Michaels | v | Rushden & Higham United | 0-2 |
| St Ives Town | v | Desborough Town | 4-1 |
| Wellingborough Town | v | Thrapston Town | 0-1 |
| Quorn | v | Oadby Town | 1-3 |

## PREMIER DIVISION

| | | P | W | D | L | F | A | Pts |
|---|---|---|---|---|---|---|---|---|
| 1 | Holbeach United | 40 | 31 | 5 | 4 | 114 | 34 | 98 |
| 2 | (P) St Ives Town | 40 | 27 | 9 | 4 | 114 | 42 | 90 |
| 3 | Spalding United (-3pts) | 40 | 29 | 5 | 6 | 117 | 48 | 89 |
| 4 | Huntingdon Town | 40 | 25 | 4 | 11 | 104 | 69 | 79 |
| 5 | Deeping Rangers | 40 | 22 | 10 | 8 | 93 | 47 | 76 |
| 6 | Newport Pagnell Town | 40 | 22 | 7 | 11 | 84 | 58 | 73 |
| 7 | Quorn | 40 | 20 | 8 | 12 | 89 | 57 | 68 |
| 8 | Cogenhoe United | 40 | 18 | 6 | 16 | 81 | 67 | 60 |
| 9 | Shepshed Dynamo | 40 | 16 | 9 | 15 | 82 | 63 | 57 |
| 10 | Boston Town | 40 | 15 | 9 | 16 | 68 | 72 | 54 |
| 11 | Desborough Town | 40 | 15 | 7 | 18 | 67 | 71 | 52 |
| 12 | Yaxley | 40 | 12 | 11 | 17 | 58 | 72 | 47 |
| 13 | Peterborough Northern Star | 40 | 12 | 9 | 19 | 56 | 75 | 45 |
| 14 | Stewarts & Lloyds Corby | 40 | 11 | 11 | 18 | 54 | 84 | 44 |
| 15 | Wellingborough Town | 40 | 12 | 8 | 20 | 55 | 89 | 44 |
| 16 | Long Buckby AFC | 40 | 11 | 9 | 20 | 54 | 82 | 42 |
| 17 | AFC Kempston Rovers | 40 | 10 | 8 | 22 | 56 | 85 | 38 |
| 18 | Sleaford Town | 40 | 10 | 8 | 22 | 47 | 88 | 38 |
| 19 | Harborough Town | 40 | 10 | 8 | 22 | 55 | 101 | 38 |
| 20 | (R) Blackstones FC | 40 | 10 | 6 | 24 | 58 | 94 | 36 |
| 21 | (R) Irchester United | 40 | 2 | 3 | 35 | 37 | 145 | 9 |

## PREMIER DIVISION

| | | 1 | 2 | 3 | 4 | 5 | 6 | 7 | 8 | 9 | 10 | 11 | 12 | 13 | 14 | 15 | 16 | 17 | 18 | 19 | 20 | 21 |
|---|---|---|---|---|---|---|---|---|---|---|---|---|---|---|---|---|---|---|---|---|---|---|
| 1 | AFC Kempston Rovers | | 1-0 | 0-3 | 1-0 | 2-1 | 3-3 | 0-0 | 2-4 | 0-3 | 1-1 | 2-2 | 0-3 | 3-0 | 2-4 | 0-1 | 5-0 | 1-5 | 2-4 | 1-1 | 5-2 | 2-0 |
| 2 | Blackstones FC | 1-1 | | 0-2 | 1-4 | 0-2 | 1-2 | 4-2 | 1-0 | 3-5 | 3-1 | 2-1 | 0-3 | 1-3 | 1-2 | 5-3 | 1-1 | 1-3 | 0-1 | 1-3 | 3-3 | 1-3 |
| 3 | Boston Town | 4-1 | 0-0 | | 2-0 | 1-2 | 1-2 | 0-4 | 0-4 | 1-0 | 4-0 | 3-0 | 1-1 | 3-3 | 4-3 | 0-2 | 0-0 | 3-3 | 0-2 | 2-2 | 1-2 | 2-1 |
| 4 | Cogenhoe United | 0-2 | 3-2 | 4-4 | | 2-2 | 1-2 | 7-1 | 2-0 | 2-1 | 4-0 | 2-1 | 1-2 | 2-1 | 3-0 | 2-1 | 2-3 | 1-2 | 1-3 | 6-1 | 2-1 | 1-2 |
| 5 | Deeping Rangers | 4-2 | 3-0 | 4-1 | 1-1 | | 2-1 | 4-1 | 1-3 | 2-1 | 6-1 | 1-0 | 0-0 | 0-1 | 2-4 | 1-1 | 9-0 | 2-0 | 1-3 | 1-2 | 1-1 | 1-1 |
| 6 | Desborough Town | 2-1 | 0-3 | 3-1 | 2-1 | 0-1 | | 3-0 | 0-1 | 3-4 | 0-1 | 5-0 | 0-2 | 2-0 | 0-3 | 3-1 | 2-2 | 1-2 | 2-6 | 1-1 | 4-0 | 1-2 |
| 7 | Harborough Town | 0-0 | 2-1 | 1-4 | 1-2 | 1-2 | 1-3 | | 1-4 | 2-1 | 5-2 | 1-1 | 1-0 | 1-1 | 1-7 | 0-0 | 1-2 | 1-5 | 1-3 | 2-0 | 0-0 | 1-1 |
| 8 | Holbeach United | 3-1 | 2-1 | 0-0 | 1-0 | 3-3 | 5-1 | 6-1 | | 1-2 | 5-1 | 5-1 | 1-0 | 4-1 | 4-1 | 3-1 | 8-0 | 2-1 | 2-3 | 3-0 | 4-0 | 1-0 |
| 9 | Huntingdon Town | 5-1 | 2-2 | 1-0 | 2-1 | 1-0 | 3-0 | 2-1 | 1-6 | | 4-1 | 4-0 | 4-3 | 2-2 | 1-2 | 4-5 | 4-0 | 1-1 | 0-5 | 5-0 | 8-1 | 4-2 |
| 10 | Irchester United | 1-1 | 1-3 | 4-5 | 1-6 | 1-7 | 2-1 | 1-2 | 0-1 | 2-3 | | 2-3 | 1-4 | 1-2 | 0-5 | 1-4 | 0-4 | 1-11 | 0-7 | 0-2 | 1-3 | 0-2 |
| 11 | Long Buckby AFC | 1-3 | 3-0 | 1-2 | 3-3 | 0-1 | 1-1 | 2-1 | 0-6 | 2-2 | 6-1 | | 1-0 | 1-0 | 0-2 | 0-5 | 1-3 | 2-3 | 1-1 | 1-1 | 2-0 | 3-2 |
| 12 | Newport Pagnell Town | 2-1 | 5-1 | 3-2 | 1-3 | 2-8 | 3-2 | 2-1 | 1-2 | 3-1 | 4-1 | 3-0 | | 1-1 | 1-1 | 2-0 | 1-4 | 1-1 | 4-0 | 2-3 | 3-1 |
| 13 | Peterborough Northern Star | 2-0 | 2-0 | 0-1 | 3-4 | 1-3 | 5-3 | 1-3 | 1-3 | 0-3 | 2-0 | 1-2 | 2-3 | | 3-1 | 1-1 | 2-1 | 0-3 | 2-1 | 2-1 | 4-1 | 1-1 |
| 14 | Quorn | 2-0 | 2-3 | 3-1 | 3-0 | 1-1 | 3-1 | 2-2 | 0-2 | 0-2 | 8-2 | 2-0 | 2-2 | 6-2 | | 0-0 | 5-2 | 1-2 | 2-2 | 4-1 | 1-0 | 1-0 |
| 15 | Shepshed Dynamo | 4-0 | 4-0 | 3-2 | 1-1 | 2-3 | 2-3 | 3-0 | 2-2 | 6-2 | 4-1 | 3-3 | 1-1 | 1-1 | 1-0 | | 2-1 | 1-2 | 0-1 | 1-2 | 3-4 | 5-1 |
| 16 | Sleaford Town | 2-1 | 1-2 | 1-2 | 1-2 | 0-2 | 2-2 | 1-3 | 0-2 | 1-3 | 3-1 | 1-0 | 1-2 | 1-1 | 3-0 | 2-1 | | 1-1 | 0-3 | 2-0 | 0-2 | 1-2 |
| 17 | Spalding United | 4-2 | 5-1 | 4-0 | 5-1 | 1-0 | 2-1 | 7-1 | 1-3 | 4-2 | 2-0 | 2-1 | 4-1 | 1-0 | 3-2 | 3-0 | 5-1 | | 1-3 | 5-0 | 5-2 | 1-0 |
| 18 | St Ives Town | 6-2 | 8-3 | 4-2 | 2-0 | 1-1 | 0-0 | 8-1 | 2-0 | 1-2 | 4-1 | 0-0 | 1-3 | 3-1 | 1-3 | 2-0 | 2-1 | 1-1 | | 4-0 | 5-0 | 2-2 |
| 19 | Stewarts & Lloyds Corby | 2-1 | 0-3 | 3-0 | 1-1 | 1-1 | 3-4 | 1-1 | 2-4 | 1-1 | 2-3 | 3-1 | 1-1 | 0-1 | 1-1 | 2-0 | 3-5 | | | 1-1 | 2-4 | |
| 20 | Wellingborough Town | 2-0 | 2-0 | 0-3 | 2-2 | 2-2 | 1-3 | 2-0 | 1-5 | 1-3 | 1-0 | 2-4 | 0-2 | 3-0 | 0-0 | 0-3 | 3-0 | 1-1 | 2-2 | 0-3 | | 1-2 |
| 21 | Yaxley | 1-3 | 3-3 | 1-1 | 3-1 | 1-4 | 0-1 | 4-3 | 0-2 | 0-2 | 3-2 | 1-4 | 0-0 | 1-1 | 2-2 | 1-1 | | | | 2-3 | 1-1 | |

# UNITED COUNTIES LEAGUE - STEP 5/6

| DIVISION ONE | P | W | D | L | F | A | Pts |
|---|---|---|---|---|---|---|---|
| 1 (P) Northampton Sileby Rangers | 36 | 30 | 2 | 4 | 105 | 31 | 92 |
| 2 (P) AFC Rushden & Diamonds | 36 | 28 | 6 | 2 | 96 | 31 | 90 |
| 3 Eynesbury Rovers | 36 | 26 | 7 | 3 | 109 | 41 | 85 |
| 4 Oadby Town | 36 | 26 | 6 | 4 | 112 | 35 | 84 |
| 5 Northampton Spencer | 36 | 22 | 5 | 9 | 86 | 54 | 71 |
| 6 Harrowby United | 36 | 19 | 4 | 13 | 84 | 58 | 61 |
| 7 Bugbrooke St Michaels | 36 | 18 | 5 | 13 | 77 | 62 | 59 |
| 8 Rushden and Higham United | 36 | 17 | 4 | 15 | 62 | 56 | 55 |
| 9 Olney Town | 36 | 14 | 4 | 18 | 56 | 62 | 46 |
| 10 Bourne Town | 36 | 10 | 11 | 15 | 67 | 71 | 41 |
| 11 Northampton ON Chenecks | 36 | 10 | 8 | 18 | 54 | 75 | 38 |
| 12 Thrapston Town | 36 | 10 | 8 | 18 | 69 | 93 | 38 |
| 13 Wellingborough Whitworth | 36 | 11 | 3 | 22 | 51 | 76 | 36 |
| 14 Raunds Town | 36 | 11 | 3 | 22 | 43 | 87 | 36 |
| 15 Buckingham Town | 36 | 10 | 3 | 23 | 62 | 98 | 33 |
| 16 Potton United | 36 | 9 | 4 | 23 | 44 | 70 | 31 |
| 17 Rothwell Corinthians | 36 | 8 | 6 | 22 | 51 | 98 | 30 |
| 18 Wootton Blue Cross | 36 | 7 | 6 | 23 | 48 | 99 | 27 |
| 19 Burton Park Wanderers | 36 | 6 | 5 | 25 | 33 | 112 | 23 |

## LEAGUE CUP continued...

### QUARTER FINALS

| Holbeach United | v | Yaxley | 0-1 |
|---|---|---|---|
| Spalding United | v | Peterborough Northern Star | 4-0 |
| Rushden & Higham United | v | St Ives Town | 2-4 |
| Thrapston Town | v | Oadby Town | 1-4 |

### SEMI FINALS

| Yaxley | v | Spalding Unted | 1-1, 0-3p |
|---|---|---|---|
| St Ives Town | v | Oadby Town | 3-0 |

### FINAL

| Spalding United | v | St Ives Town | 4-0 |
|---|---|---|---|

| RESERVE DIVISION ONE | P | W | D | L | F | A | Pts |
|---|---|---|---|---|---|---|---|
| 1 Cogenhoe United Reserves | 22 | 16 | 4 | 2 | 59 | 27 | 52 |
| 2 W'borough Whitwth Res. | 22 | 16 | 3 | 3 | 49 | 22 | 51 |
| 3 Bugbrooke St Michaels Res. | 22 | 12 | 4 | 6 | 54 | 36 | 40 |
| 4 Harborough Town Res. | 22 | 12 | 4 | 6 | 52 | 34 | 40 |
| 5 Peterborough Northern Star Res. | 22 | 10 | 5 | 7 | 41 | 37 | 35 |
| 6 Desborough Town Reserves(-3pts) | 22 | 10 | 3 | 9 | 37 | 40 | 30 |
| 7 AFC Kempston Rovers Res. | 22 | 8 | 3 | 11 | 49 | 42 | 27 |
| 8 Huntingdon Town Reserves | 22 | 6 | 6 | 10 | 40 | 53 | 24 |
| 9 Stewart & Lloyds Corby Res. | 22 | 6 | 4 | 12 | 42 | 52 | 22 |
| 10 Thrapston Town Reserves | 22 | 6 | 2 | 14 | 45 | 78 | 20 |
| 11 Blackstones Reserves (-1pt) | 22 | 5 | 5 | 12 | 46 | 46 | 19 |
| 12 Woodford United Reserves | 22 | 1 | 5 | 16 | 16 | 63 | 8 |

| RESERVE DIVISION TWO | P | W | D | L | F | A | Pts |
|---|---|---|---|---|---|---|---|
| 1 Oadby Town Reserves | 20 | 15 | 3 | 2 | 57 | 16 | 48 |
| 2 Raunds Town Reserves | 20 | 13 | 3 | 4 | 46 | 29 | 42 |
| 3 Yaxley Reserves (-3pts) | 20 | 12 | 1 | 7 | 62 | 36 | 34 |
| 4 Bourne Town Reserves | 20 | 7 | 6 | 7 | 42 | 36 | 27 |
| 5 Northampton ON Chenecks Res. | 20 | 8 | 3 | 9 | 49 | 45 | 27 |
| 6 Eynesbury Rovers Reserves | 20 | 7 | 5 | 8 | 39 | 44 | 26 |
| 7 Rothwell Corinthians Reserves | 20 | 6 | 4 | 10 | 40 | 54 | 22 |
| 8 Olney Town Reserves | 20 | 6 | 3 | 11 | 34 | 59 | 21 |
| 9 Burton Park Wanderers Res | 20 | 5 | 5 | 10 | 33 | 53 | 20 |
| 10 Irchester United Reserves | 20 | 5 | 4 | 11 | 27 | 47 | 19 |
| 11 Rushden & H U Res. (-3pts) | 20 | 5 | 5 | 10 | 32 | 42 | 17 |

| DIVISION ONE | 1 | 2 | 3 | 4 | 5 | 6 | 7 | 8 | 9 | 10 | 11 | 12 | 13 | 14 | 15 | 16 | 17 | 18 | 19 |
|---|---|---|---|---|---|---|---|---|---|---|---|---|---|---|---|---|---|---|---|
| 1 AFC Rushden & Diamonds | | 5-2 | 3-0 | 1-1 | 1-1 | 2-2 | 3-2 | 2-0 | 2-2 | 2-1 | 2-2 | 1-0 | 1-0 | 3-0 | 2-1 | 1-0 | 3-0 | 4-1 | 5-0 |
| 2 Bourne Town | 1-2 | | 5-0 | 2-2 | 1-2 | 1-1 | 2-3 | 2-2 | 1-3 | 0-3 | 2-5 | 3-4 | 3-2 | 2-1 | 3-3 | 1-3 | 1-3 | 1-3 | 7-1 |
| 3 Buckingham Town | 0-9 | 3-2 | | 2-4 | 4-0 | 2-5 | 0-6 | 6-1 | 0-2 | 3-2 | 0-3 | 1-1 | 2-5 | 0-3 | 5-1 | 0-2 | 1-3 | 5-3 | 3-1 |
| 4 Bugbrooke St Michaels | 0-3 | 3-2 | 0-5 | | 6-2 | 2-1 | 0-1 | 1-3 | 1-3 | 1-2 | 0-2 | 2-0 | 1-1 | 4-0 | 6-2 | 2-4 | 3-0 | 1-2 | 3-0 |
| 5 Burton Park Wanderers | 0-4 | 1-1 | 1-4 | 0-3 | | 2-3 | 0-6 | 0-5 | 1-3 | 0-3 | 1-4 | 2-1 | 0-2 | 1-2 | 1-0 | 1-7 | 3-4 | 1-1 | 3-3 |
| 6 Eynesbury Rovers | 4-1 | 3-0 | 4-1 | 4-2 | 8-0 | | 1-0 | 3-4 | 3-1 | 4-1 | 0-1 | 3-0 | 1-1 | 0-0 | 4-1 | 1-0 | 3-1 | 2-1 | 5-3 |
| 7 Harrowby United | 0-3 | 2-1 | 3-2 | 1-2 | 5-0 | 2-2 | | 1-0 | 2-3 | 0-2 | 1-2 | 0-0 | 3-2 | 3-0 | 6-0 | 3-0 | 2-2 | 4-1 | 2-0 |
| 8 Northampton ON Chenecks | 1-2 | 0-2 | 1-1 | 3-4 | 3-1 | 0-9 | 4-5 | | 0-2 | 0-1 | 1-2 | 1-1 | 0-2 | 0-1 | 4-1 | 0-0 | 2-2 | 4-1 | 1-1 |
| 9 Northampton Sileby Rangers | 0-1 | 1-0 | 1-0 | 3-2 | 8-0 | 1-2 | 2-0 | 5-0 | | 5-2 | 2-2 | 2-0 | 3-0 | 2-1 | 5-1 | 4-0 | 3-1 | 3-2 | 5-2 |
| 10 Northampton Spencer | 0-3 | 3-0 | 1-1 | 1-0 | 2-1 | 3-3 | 3-4 | 3-0 | 1-0 | | 3-3 | 2-0 | 3-1 | 2-1 | 4-2 | 3-1 | 2-2 | 4-2 | 4-0 |
| 11 Oadby Town | 5-1 | 0-0 | 4-0 | 1-1 | 4-0 | 2-2 | 1-2 | 4-0 | 0-1 | 5-1 | | 3-0 | 8-0 | 4-0 | 5-1 | 2-1 | 4-2 | 3-0 | 4-1 |
| 12 Olney Town | 0-1 | 0-1 | 6-0 | 1-3 | 4-1 | 0-2 | 3-2 | 0-1 | 1-4 | 1-4 | 3-2 | | 4-3 | 6-2 | 0-2 | 1-2 | 2-1 | 1-0 | 3-1 |
| 13 Potton United | 0-2 | 3-3 | 2-1 | 2-1 | 2-0 | 0-1 | 1-3 | 1-0 | 0-1 | 0-2 | 1-3 | 1-2 | | 2-0 | 0-2 | 2-3 | 2-3 | 1-1 | 1-2 |
| 14 Raunds Town | 0-4 | 0-2 | 2-1 | 0-2 | 2-1 | 1-3 | 2-1 | 1-2 | 0-8 | 1-5 | 0-7 | 2-3 | 1-0 | | 3-2 | 0-2 | 3-1 | 0-1 | 6-3 |
| 15 Rothwell Corinthians | 2-4 | 1-1 | 3-2 | 1-1 | 0-1 | 1-4 | 2-0 | 0-3 | 1-3 | 1-7 | 1-3 | 1-1 | 4-3 | 3-3 | | 0-0 | 1-2 | 2-5 | 1-3 |
| 16 Rushden and Higham United | 0-4 | 2-3 | 2-1 | 1-2 | 0-1 | 2-5 | 5-1 | 0-0 | 0-2 | 2-1 | 2-0 | 2-1 | 2-0 | 3-1 | | | 4-3 | 0-1 | 4-1 |
| 17 Thrapston Town | 1-5 | 1-3 | 0-2 | 2-5 | 3-3 | 1-4 | 4-2 | 4-4 | 1-4 | 1-1 | 1-3 | 0-2 | 0-1 | 1-3 | 4-3 | 2-2 | | 3-1 | 1-0 |
| 18 Wellingborough Whitworth | 1-3 | 1-1 | 4-3 | 0-1 | 3-0 | 1-4 | 1-2 | 1-2 | 1-3 | 1-3 | 0-5 | 1-3 | 0-1 | 2-0 | 0-1 | 2-4 | 3-1 | | 2-0 |
| 19 Wootton Blue Cross | 1-1 | 1-1 | 3-1 | 2-5 | 0-1 | 0-3 | 2-2 | 3-2 | 0-5 | 3-1 | 2-4 | 3-1 | 2-0 | 1-1 | 1-2 | 1-2 | 2-6 | 0-1 | |

## CLUB MOVEMENTS

**Premier Division - In:** AFC Rushden & Diamonds (P). Northampton Sileby Rangers (P). Wisbech Town (S - Eastern Counties Premier).
**Out:** Blackstones FC (R). Irchester United (R). Quorn (S - Midland Football Alliance).
Shepshed Dynamo (Midland Football Alliance). St. Ives Town (P - Southern Div.1 Central).

**Division One - In:** Blackstones (R). Irchester United (R). Lutterworth Athletic (S - East Midlands Counties).
Peterborough Sports (P - Peterborough & District). St Neots Town Saints (N).
**Out:** AFC Rushden & Diamonds (P). Northampton Sileby Rangers (P). Wootton Blue Cross (W - Bedfordshire County Premier).

# PREMIER DIVISION

## AFC KEMPSTON ROVERS
Founded: 1884     Nickname: Walnut Boys

**Secretary:** Kevin Howlett    **(T)** 07721 849 671    **(E)** howlett.home@btinternet.com

**Chairman:** Russell Shreeves    **Manager:** Dave Randall    **Prog Ed:** Mark Kennett

**Ground:** Hillgrounds Leisure, Hillgrounds Road, Kempston, Bedford MK42 8SZ    **(T)** 01234 852 346

**Capacity:** 2,000   **Seats:** 100   **Covered:** 250   **Midweek Matchday:** Tuesday    **Clubhouse:** Yes

**Colours(change):** Red & white stripes/black/black (Blue & black stripes/blue/blue or yellow or yellow & black)
**Previous Names:** Kempston Rovers > 2004.
**Previous Leagues:** South Midlands 1927-53
**Records:**
**Senior Honours:** U.C.L. Prem. 1973-74, Div 1 1957-58, 85-86, Div 2 1955-56, KO Cup 1955-56, 57-58, 59-60, 74-75, 76-77. UCL Division One 2010-11. Beds Senior Cup 1908-09, 37-38, 76-77, 91-92. Hinchinbrooke Cup 2010-11.

**10 YEAR RECORD**

| 03-04 | 04-05 | 05-06 | 06-07 | 07-08 | 08-09 | 09-10 | 10-11 | 11-12 | 12-13 |
|---|---|---|---|---|---|---|---|---|---|
| UCL 1 16 | UCL 1 16 | UCL 1 4 | UCL 1 3 | UCL P 12 | UCL 1 5 | UCL 1 5 | UCL 1 1 | UCL P 10 | UCL P 17 |

## AFC RUSHDEN & DIAMONDS
Founded: 2011     Nickname:

**Secretary:** David Albon    **(T)** 07905 451 535    **(E)** secretary@afcdiamonds.com

**Chairman:** Ralph Burditt    **Manager:** Mark Starmer    **Prog Ed:** Miss Stephanie Webb

**Ground:** The Dog and Duck, London Road, Wellingborough, Northants NN8 2DP    **(T)** 01933 441 388

**Capacity:**   **Seats:** Yes   **Covered:** Yes   **Midweek Matchday:**    **Clubhouse:** Yes

**Colours(change):** White/royal blue/white (Yellow/black/yellow or sky blue/royal blue/sky blue)
**Previous Names:** None
**Previous Leagues:** None
**Records:**
**Senior Honours:** None

**10 YEAR RECORD**

| 03-04 | 04-05 | 05-06 | 06-07 | 07-08 | 08-09 | 09-10 | 10-11 | 11-12 | 12-13 |
|---|---|---|---|---|---|---|---|---|---|
| | | | | | | | | | UCL 1 2 |

## BOSTON TOWN
Founded: 1964     Nickname: Poachers

**Secretary:** Edward Graves    **(T)** 07963 418 434    **(E)** btfcsec@hotmail.co.uk

**Chairman:** Mick Vines    **Manager:** Ian Dunn & Matt Hocking    **Prog Ed:** Eddie Graves

**Ground:** Tattershall Road, Boston, Lincs PE21 9LR    **(T)** 01205 365 470

**Capacity:** 6,000   **Seats:** 450   **Covered:** 950   **Midweek Matchday:** Tuesday    **Clubhouse:** Yes

**Colours(change):** Sky blue/navy blue/navy blue (White/red/red)
**Previous Names:** Boston > 1994
**Previous Leagues:** Lincs, Central Alliance, Eastern co, Midland N. Co. E, C. Mids
**Records:** Att: 2,700 v Boston United FA Cup 1970. Goalscorer: Gary Bull 57 during 2006-07 season.
**Senior Honours:** Midland League 1974-75, 78-79, 80-81. Central Midlands 88-89. United Counties League 1994-95, 2000-01.

**10 YEAR RECORD**

| 03-04 | 04-05 | 05-06 | 06-07 | 07-08 | 08-09 | 09-10 | 10-11 | 11-12 | 12-13 |
|---|---|---|---|---|---|---|---|---|---|
| UCL P 5 | UCL P 11 | UCL P 6 | UCL P 2 | UCL P 6 | UCL P 5 | UCL P 5 | UCL P 7 | UCL P 14 | UCL P 10 |

## COGENHOE UNITED
Founded: 1958     Nickname: Cooks

**Secretary:** Phil Wright    **(T)** 07540 380 357    **(E)** secretary@cogenhoeunited.co.uk

**Chairman:** Derek Wright    **Manager:** Andy Marks    **Prog Ed:** Phil Wright

**Ground:** Compton Park, Brafield Road, Cogenhoe NN7 1ND    **(T)** 01604 890 521

**Capacity:** 5,000   **Seats:** 100   **Covered:** 200   **Midweek Matchday:** Tuesday    **Clubhouse:** Yes   **Shop:** No

**Colours(change):** All navy blue (All white)
**Previous Names:**
**Previous Leagues:** Central Northants Comb, prem 67-84
**Records:** Att: 1,000 Charity game 90 **Goalscorer & Appearances:** Tony Smith
**Senior Honours:** United Counties League 2004-05. Buckingham Charity Cup 2010-11.

**10 YEAR RECORD**

| 03-04 | 04-05 | 05-06 | 06-07 | 07-08 | 08-09 | 09-10 | 10-11 | 11-12 | 12-13 |
|---|---|---|---|---|---|---|---|---|---|
| UCL P 6 | UCL P 1 | UCL P 5 | UCL P 5 | UCL P 9 | UCL P 9 | UCL P 8 | UCL P 15 | UCL P 12 | UCL P 8 |

# DEEPING RANGERS

Founded: 1964    Nickname: Rangers

**Secretary:** Haydon Whitham    **(T)** 07736 548 500    **(E)** haydon.whitham@theroegroup.com
**Chairman:** Kevin Davenport    **Manager:** Tuncay Korkmaz    **Prog Ed:** Robin Crowson
**Ground:** Deeping Sports Club, Outgang Road, Market Deeping, PE6 8LQ    **(T)** 01778 344 701
**Capacity:** 1,000 **Seats:** 180    **Covered:** 250    **Midweek Matchday:** Tuesday    **Clubhouse:** Yes

**Colours(change):** Claret & blue/claret/claret. (White/claret/claret)
**Previous Names:** None
**Previous Leagues:** Peterborough & District 1966 - 1999.
**Records:**
**Senior Honours:** Lincs Sen Cup, B Cup, Peterborough FA Cup (3). UCL Premier Champions 2006-07

**10 YEAR RECORD**

| 03-04 | 04-05 | 05-06 | 06-07 | 07-08 | 08-09 | 09-10 | 10-11 | 11-12 | 12-13 |
|---|---|---|---|---|---|---|---|---|---|
| UCL P 17 | UCL P 12 | UCL P 20 | UCL P 1 | UCL P 7 | UCL P 4 | UCL P 4 | UCL P 14 | UCL P 4 | UCL P 5 |

# DESBOROUGH TOWN

Founded: 1896    Nickname: Ar Tam

**Secretary:** John Lee    **(T)** 01536 760 002    **(E)** johnlee@froggerycottage85.fsnet.co.uk
**Chairman:** Ernie Parsons    **Manager:** Steve Walker    **Prog Ed:** John Lee
**Ground:** Waterworks Field, Braybrooke Rd, Desborough NN14 2LJ    **(T)** 01536 761 350
**Capacity:** 8,000 **Seats:** 250    **Covered:** 500    **Midweek Matchday:** Tuesday    **Clubhouse:** Yes

**Colours(change):** All Blue (Yellow/black/black)
**Previous Names:** None
**Previous Leagues:** None
**Records:** Att: 8,000 v Kettering Town
**Senior Honours:** N'hants/Utd Co. Champs 1900-01, 01-02, 06-07, 20-21, 23-24, 24-25, 27-28, 48-49, 66-67. Lge C 77-78, 00-01, 07-08. N'hants Sen C 1910-11, 13-14, 28-29, 51-52. Northants Senior Cup 1910-11, 13-14, 28-29, 51-52.

**10 YEAR RECORD**

| 03-04 | 04-05 | 05-06 | 06-07 | 07-08 | 08-09 | 09-10 | 10-11 | 11-12 | 12-13 |
|---|---|---|---|---|---|---|---|---|---|
| UCL P 16 | UCL P 10 | UCL P 18 | UCL P 14 | UCL P 3 | UCL P 11 | UCL P 18 | UCL P 19 | UCL P 16 | UCL P 11 |

# HARBOROUGH TOWN

Founded: 1976    Nickname:

**Secretary:** Pauline Winston    **(T)** 07446 415 329    **(E)** p.winston2402@btinternet.com
**Chairman:** Andrew Winston    **Manager:** Chris Church    **Prog Ed:** Gary Wainwright
**Ground:** Bowden's Park, Northampton Road, Market Harborough, Leics. LE16 9HF    **(T)** 01858 467 339
**Capacity:**    **Seats:** Yes    **Covered:** Yes    **Midweek Matchday:** Tuesday    **Clubhouse:** Yes

**Colours(change):** Yellow/black/black (All green)
**Previous Names:**
**Previous Leagues:** Northants Combination
**Records:**
**Senior Honours:** Northants Combination 2009-10.

**10 YEAR RECORD**

| 03-04 | 04-05 | 05-06 | 06-07 | 07-08 | 08-09 | 09-10 | 10-11 | 11-12 | 12-13 |
|---|---|---|---|---|---|---|---|---|---|
| | | | | | | NhCo 1 | UCL 1 17 | UCL 1 2 | UCL P 19 |

# HOLBEACH UNITED

Founded: 1929    Nickname: Tigers

**Secretary:** Karl Fawcett    **(T)** 07955 947 606    **(E)** holbeachunitedfc@yahoo.co.uk
**Chairman:** Dave Dougill    **Manager:** Glen Maddison    **Prog Ed:** Jamie Hiller
**Ground:** Carters Park, Park Road, Holbeach, Lincs PE12 7EE    **(T)** 01406 424 761
**Capacity:** 4,000 **Seats:** 200    **Covered:** 450    **Midweek Matchday:** Tuesday    **Clubhouse:** Yes **Shop:** No

**Colours(change):** Yellow & black stripes/black/yellow (Red & white stripes/red/white)
**Previous Names:**
**Previous Leagues:** Peterborough U Co L 46-55, Eastern 55-62, Midland Co 62-63
**Records:** Att: 4,094 v Wisbech 1954
**Senior Honours:** United Counties League 1989-90, 02-03, 12-13. Lincs Sen A Cup (4), Senior Cup B 57-58
Lincolnshire Senior Trophy 2011-12, 12-13.

**10 YEAR RECORD**

| 03-04 | 04-05 | 05-06 | 06-07 | 07-08 | 08-09 | 09-10 | 10-11 | 11-12 | 12-13 |
|---|---|---|---|---|---|---|---|---|---|
| UCL P 7 | UCL P 3 | UCL P 17 | UCL P 11 | UCL P 11 | UCL P 16 | UCL P 16 | UCL P 17 | UCL P 6 | UCL P 1 |

# HUNTINGDON TOWN
Founded: 1995     Nickname:

**Secretary:** Russell Yezek    **(T)** 07974 664818    **(E)** russell.yezek@ntlworld.com

**Chairman:** Paul Hunt    **Manager:** Ricky Marheineke    **Prog Ed:** Russell Yezek

**Ground:** Jubilee Park, Kings Ripton Road,, Huntingdon, Cambridgeshire PE28 2NR    **(T)** 07929 651 226

**Capacity:**   **Seats:**   **Covered:**   **Midweek Matchday:**   **Clubhouse:**

**Colours(change):** Red/red/red & black.(Blue & yellow/blue/blue)
**Previous Names:**
**Previous Leagues:** Cambridgeshire.
**Records:**
**Senior Honours:** Cambridgeshire Div.1B 1999-2000. Hunts. Junior Cup 1999-00, 2000-01, 01-02. Hunts Scott Gatty Cup 2001-02.
United Counties League Division One 2011-12.

**10 YEAR RECORD**

| 03-04 | 04-05 | 05-06 | 06-07 | 07-08 | 08-09 | 09-10 | 10-11 | 11-12 | 12-13 |
|---|---|---|---|---|---|---|---|---|---|
| UCL 1   17 | UCL 1   14 | UCL 1   12 | UCL 1   14 | UCL 1   4 | UCL 1   14 | UCL 1   8 | UCL 1   5 | UCL 1   1 | UCL P   4 |

# LONG BUCKBY AFC
Founded: 1937     Nickname: Bucks

**Secretary:** Dave Austin    **(T)** 07701 723 477    **(E)** lbafc.dja@gmail.com

**Chairman:** Dave Austin    **Manager:** Phil Mason

**Ground:** Station Road, Long Buckby NN6 7QA    **(T)** 01327 842 682

**Capacity:** 1,000 **Seats:** 200 **Covered:** 200 **Midweek Matchday:** Tuesday   **Clubhouse:** Yes   **Shop:** No

**Colours(change):** All claret (All yellow)
**Previous Names:** Long Buckby Nomads
**Previous Leagues:** Rugby & District Central, Northants Combination pre 68
**Records:** Att: 750 v Kettering Town
**Senior Honours:** United Counties League Div.2 1970-71, 71-72, Premier Division 2011-12. Northants Senior Cup 2008-09. Munsell Cup 2009.

**10 YEAR RECORD**

| 03-04 | 04-05 | 05-06 | 06-07 | 07-08 | 08-09 | 09-10 | 10-11 | 11-12 | 12-13 |
|---|---|---|---|---|---|---|---|---|---|
| UCL P   21 | UCL P   8 | UCL P   21 | UCL P   12 | UCL P   2 | UCL P   8 | UCL P   3 | UCL P   4 | UCL P   1 | UCL P   16 |

# NEWPORT PAGNELL TOWN
Founded: 1963     Nickname: Swans

**Secretary:** Mrs Pauline Wooldridge    **(T)** 07966 441 992    **(E)** Pauline.wooldridge@tesco.net

**Chairman:** TBC    **Manager:** Darren Lynch    **Prog Ed:** Wayne Harmes

**Ground:** Willen Road, Newport Pagnell MK16 0DF    **(T)** 01908 611 993

**Capacity:** 2,000 **Seats:** 100 **Covered:** 100 **Midweek Matchday:** Tuesday   **Clubhouse:** Yes   **Shop:** No

**Colours(change):** White & green hoops/white/white (All sky Blue)
**Previous Names:** Newport Pagnell Wanderers > 1972.
**Previous Leagues:** North Bucks 1963-71. South Midlands 1971-73.
**Records:**
**Senior Honours:** United Counties League Div.1 1981-82, 2001-02. Bucks & Berks Intermediate Cup 2001-02.
Berks & Bucks Senior Trophy 2009-10, 10-11.

**10 YEAR RECORD**

| 03-04 | 04-05 | 05-06 | 06-07 | 07-08 | 08-09 | 09-10 | 10-11 | 11-12 | 12-13 |
|---|---|---|---|---|---|---|---|---|---|
| UCL P   13 | UCL P   18 | UCL P   15 | UCL P   7 | UCL P   15 | UCL P   3 | UCL P   6 | UCL P   3 | UCL P   5 | UCL P   6 |

# NORTHAMPTON SILEBY RANGERS
Founded: 1968     Nickname: Sileby

**Secretary:** Dave Battams    **(T)** 07913 909 068    **(E)** david@djbattams.f2s.com

**Chairman:** Robert Clarke    **Manager:** Glenn Botterill    **Prog Ed:** Dave Battams

**Ground:** Fernie Fields Sports Ground, Moulton, Northampton NN3 7BD    **(T)** 01604 670366

**Capacity:**   **Seats:** Yes   **Covered:** Yes   **Midweek Matchday:** Wednesday   **Clubhouse:** Yes

**Colours(change):** Red/black/red (All navy blue)
**Previous Names:** Northampton Vanaid > 2000.
**Previous Leagues:** Northampton League > 1993.
**Records:** Att: 78.
**Senior Honours:** Northampton Town League 1988-89 89-90. UCL Div 1 1993-94, 2002-03, 04-05, 12-13.

**10 YEAR RECORD**

| 03-04 | 04-05 | 05-06 | 06-07 | 07-08 | 08-09 | 09-10 | 10-11 | 11-12 | 12-13 |
|---|---|---|---|---|---|---|---|---|---|
| UCL 1   6 | UCL 1   1 | UCL 1   13 | UCL 1   12 | UCL 1   12 | UCL 1   3 | UCL 1   9 | UCL 1   9 | UCL 1   16 | UCL 1   1 |

# PETERBOROUGH NORTHERN STAR    Founded: 1900    Nickname:

**Secretary:** Glen Harper    **(T)** 07884 288 756    **(E)** ghdjfc@hotmail.com

**Chairman:** Tony Zirpolo    **Manager:** Michael Goode & Darren Jarvis    **Prog Ed:** Rodney Payne

**Ground:** Chestnut Ave, Dogsthorpe, Eye, Peterborough, Cambs PE1 4PE    **(T)** 01733 552 416

**Capacity:** 1,500  **Seats:** none  **Covered:** yes    **Midweek Matchday:** Wednesday    **Clubhouse:** Yes

**Colours(change):** Black & white stripes/black/black (Yellow/navy blue/yellow or sky blue & white stripes/sky blue/sky blue)
**Previous Names:** Eye Utd >2005
**Previous Leagues:** Peterborough Lge >2003
**Records:**
**Senior Honours:** Peterborough League 2002-03. Hinchinbrooke Cup 2009-10. United Counties League Division 1 2008-09. UCL Knock-out Cup 2010-11.

**10 YEAR RECORD**

| 03-04 | | 04-05 | | 05-06 | | 06-07 | | 07-08 | | 08-09 | | 09-10 | | 10-11 | | 11-12 | | 12-13 | |
|---|---|---|---|---|---|---|---|---|---|---|---|---|---|---|---|---|---|---|---|
| UCL 1 | 3 | UCL 1 | 4 | UCL 1 | 9 | UCL 1 | 5 | UCL 1 | 2 | UCL 1 | 1 | UCL 1 | 2 | UCL P | 6 | UCL P | 7 | UCL P | 13 |

# SLEAFORD TOWN    Founded: 1968    Nickname: Town

**Secretary:** Ms Jenny O'Rourke    **(T)** 07777 604 325    **(E)** jennyorourke@btinternet.com

**Chairman:** Ian Clawson    **Manager:** Kris Jones    **Prog Ed:** Steve Thomas

**Ground:** Eslaforde Park, Boston Road, Sleaford, Lincs NG34 7HG    **(T)** 01529 415 951

**Capacity:**    **Seats:** 88    **Covered:** 88    **Midweek Matchday:** Tuesday    **Clubhouse:** Yes

**Colours(change):** Green/black/green (Red/white/red).
**Previous Names:**
**Previous Leagues:** Lincolnshire
**Records:**
**Senior Honours:** United Counties League Division One 2005-06.

**10 YEAR RECORD**

| 03-04 | | 04-05 | | 05-06 | | 06-07 | | 07-08 | | 08-09 | | 09-10 | | 10-11 | | 11-12 | | 12-13 | |
|---|---|---|---|---|---|---|---|---|---|---|---|---|---|---|---|---|---|---|---|
| Lincs | 1 | UCL 1 | 6 | UCL 1 | 1 | UCL 1 | 2 | UCL P | 14 | UCL P | 15 | UCL P | 9 | UCL P | 18 | UCL P | 19 | UCL P | 18 |

# SPALDING UNITED    Founded: 1921    Nickname: Tulips

**Secretary:** Audrey Fletcher    **(T)** 07778 411 916    **(E)** tulips@uk2.net

**Chairman:** Chris Toynton    **Manager:** Pat Rayment    **Prog Ed:** Ray Tucker

**Ground:** Sir Halley Stewart Playing Fields, Winfrey Avenue, Spalding PE11 1DA    **(T)** 01775 713 328

**Capacity:** 2,700  **Seats:** 300    **Covered:** 500    **Midweek Matchday:** Tuesday    **Clubhouse:** Yes    **Shop:** Yes

**Colours(change):** All royal blue (Orange/black/black)
**Previous Names:** Not known
**Previous Leagues:** Peterborough, Utd Co.31-55,68-78,86-88,91-99,03-04, Ea. Co.55-60, Cen. All. 60-61, Midland Co.61-68, N.C.E.82-86, Sth.88-91, 99-03. NPL03-11.
**Records:** 6,972 v Peterborough - FA Cup 1982
**Senior Honours:** United Counties League 1954-55, 75-75, 87-88, 98-99, 2003-04. Northern Counties East 1983-84. Lincolnshire Senior Cup 1952-53.

**10 YEAR RECORD**

| 03-04 | | 04-05 | | 05-06 | | 06-07 | | 07-08 | | 08-09 | | 09-10 | | 10-11 | | 11-12 | | 12-13 | |
|---|---|---|---|---|---|---|---|---|---|---|---|---|---|---|---|---|---|---|---|
| UCL P | 1 | NP 1 | 18 | NP 1 | 20 | SthM | 19 | NP 1 | 18 | NP1S | 17 | NP1S | 21 | NP1S | 22 | UCL P | 13 | UCL P | 3 |

# STEWARTS & LLOYDS CORBY    Founded: 1935    Nickname: The Foundrymen

**Secretary:** Kevin King    **(T)** 07815 907 543    **(E)** kevinking22@hotmail.com

**Chairman:** John Davies    **Manager:** Daren Young    **Prog Ed:** Lee Duffy

**Ground:** Recreation Ground, Occupation Road, Corby NN17 1EH    **(T)** 01536 401 497

**Capacity:** 1,500  **Seats:** 100    **Covered:** 200    **Midweek Matchday:** Tuesday    **Clubhouse:** Yes    **Shop:** No

**Colours(change):** White & grey/grey/grey (All navy blue)
**Previous Names:** Hamlet S & L 1989-92.
**Previous Leagues:** Kettering Amateur
**Records:** Goalscorer: Joey Martin 46
**Senior Honours:** United Counties League Division One 1973-74, 74-75, Premier 85-86, 08-09.

**10 YEAR RECORD**

| 03-04 | | 04-05 | | 05-06 | | 06-07 | | 07-08 | | 08-09 | | 09-10 | | 10-11 | | 11-12 | | 12-13 | |
|---|---|---|---|---|---|---|---|---|---|---|---|---|---|---|---|---|---|---|---|
| UCL P | 19 | UCL P | 21 | UCL P | 16 | UCL P | 16 | UCL P | 12 | UCL P | 1 | UCL P | 12 | UCL P | 8 | UCL P | 9 | UCL P | 14 |

# WELLINGBOROUGH TOWN

Founded: 2004     Nickname: Doughboys

**Secretary:** Mick Walden     **(T)** 07817 841 752     **(E)** mwalden@dsl.pipex.com

**Chairman:** Martin Potton     **Manager:** Craig Adams     **Prog Ed:** Neil Morris

**Ground:** The Dog & Duck, London Road, Wellingborough NN8 2DP     **(T)** 01933 441 388

**Capacity:**     **Seats:** Yes     **Covered:** Yes     **Midweek Matchday:** Tuesday     **Clubhouse:** Yes

**Colours(change):** Yellow/royal blue/royal blue. (Red & black/black/black)
**Previous Names:** Original team (Formed 1867) folded in 2002 reforming in 2004
**Previous Leagues:** Metropolitan. Southern.
**Records:**
**Senior Honours:** United Counties League 1964-65.

**10 YEAR RECORD**

| 03-04 | 04-05 | 05-06 | 06-07 | 07-08 | 08-09 | 09-10 | 10-11 | 11-12 | 12-13 |
|---|---|---|---|---|---|---|---|---|---|
|  |  | UCL 1   2 | UCL P   3 | UCL P   10 | UCL P   18 | UCL P   11 | UCL P   5 | UCL P   8 | UCL P   15 |

# WISBECH TOWN

Founded: 1920     Nickname: Fenmen

**Secretary:** Colin Gant     **(T)** 07803 021 699     **(E)** colin@gant5366.freeserve.co.uk

**Chairman:** Barry Carter     **Manager:** Steve Appleby     **Prog Ed:** Spencer Larham

**Ground:** The Fenland Stadium, Lynn Road, Wisbech PE14 7AM     **(T)** 01945 581 511

**Capacity:**     **Seats:** 118     **Covered:** Yes     **Midweek Matchday:** Tuesday     **Clubhouse:** Yes

**Colours(change):** All red. (Yellow/green/yellow).
**Previous Names:** None
**Previous Leagues:** Peterborough 1920-35. UCL 1935-50. EC 1950-52, 70-97, 2003-13. Midland 1952-58. Southern 1958-70, 97-2002.
**Records:** **Att:** 8,044 v Peterborough Utd, Midland Lge 25/08/1957 **Goalscorer:** Bert Titmarsh - 246 (1931-37) **Apps:** Jamie Brighty - 731
**Senior Honours:** United Counties League Champions 1946-47, 47-48. Southern League Division 1 1961-62.
Eastern Counties League 1971-72, 76-77, 90-91, League Cup 2010-11. East Anglian Cup 1987-88.

**10 YEAR RECORD**

| 03-04 | 04-05 | 05-06 | 06-07 | 07-08 | 08-09 | 09-10 | 10-11 | 11-12 | 12-13 |
|---|---|---|---|---|---|---|---|---|---|
| ECP   14 | ECP   16 | ECP   4 | ECP   11 | ECP   12 | ECP   16 | ECP   11 | ECP   4 | ECP   4 | ECP   2 |

# WOODFORD UNITED

Founded: 1946     Nickname: Reds

**Secretary:** Andrew Worrall     **(T)** 07500 067 734     **(E)** andy.worrall@engel.at

**Chairman:** Mrs Yvonne Worrall     **Manager:** Mark O'Callaghan     **Prog Ed:** Andrew Worrall

**Ground:** Byfield Road, Woodford Halse, Daventry, Northants NN11 3QR     **(T)** 01327 263 734

**Capacity:** 3,000 **Seats:** 252     **Covered:** 252     **Midweek Matchday:** Tuesday     **Clubhouse:** Yes     **Shop:** No

**Colours(change):** All red (All blue)
**Previous Names:** None
**Previous Leagues:** Rugby & District 1946-64. Central Northants Combination 1964-70, United Counties 1971-2006. Southern 2007-13.
**Records:** 1,500 v Stockport County
**Senior Honours:** United Counties League Division 2 1973-74, Premier Division 2005-06.

**10 YEAR RECORD**

| 03-04 | 04-05 | 05-06 | 06-07 | 07-08 | 08-09 | 09-10 | 10-11 | 11-12 | 12-13 |
|---|---|---|---|---|---|---|---|---|---|
| UCL P   12 | UCL P   7 | UCL P   1 | SthM   8 | SthM   19 | SthM   20 | SthM   7 | SthC   9 | SthC   19 | SthC   22 |

# YAXLEY

Founded: 1900     Nickname: The Cuckoos

**Secretary:** Mrs Sandra Cole     **(T)** 07847 123 898     **(E)** sandracole22@ntlworld.com

**Chairman:** Alan Andrews     **Manager:** Brett Whaley     **Prog Ed:** Jeff Lenton

**Ground:** Leading Drove, Holme Road, Yaxley, Peterborough PE7 3NA     **(T)** 01733 244 928

**Capacity:** 1,000 **Seats:** 150     **Covered:** yes     **Midweek Matchday:** Tuesday     **Clubhouse:** Yes     **Shop:** Yes

**Colours(change):** All blue (All red).
**Previous Names:** Yaxley Rovers.
**Previous Leagues:** Peterborough & Dist., Hunts & West Anglia
**Records:** **Goalscorer:** Ricky Hailstone 16
**Senior Honours:** United Counties League Division One 1996-97. Hunts Senior Cup (7), UCL Cup 2005-2006

**10 YEAR RECORD**

| 03-04 | 04-05 | 05-06 | 06-07 | 07-08 | 08-09 | 09-10 | 10-11 | 11-12 | 12-13 |
|---|---|---|---|---|---|---|---|---|---|
| UCL P   8 | UCL P   4 | UCL P   7 | UCL P   15 | UCL P   16 | UCL P   14 | UCL P   19 | UCL P   16 | UCL P   18 | UCL P   12 |

Northampton Sileby Rangers celebrate winning the United Counties Division One title. Photo: Gordon Whittington.

# DIVISION ONE

## BLACKSTONES

Founded: 1920    Nickname: Stones

**Secretary:** Ian MacGillivray    **(T)** 07749 620 825    **(E)** imacgilli@aol.com
**Chairman:** Gary Peace    **Manager:** Dave Stratton    **Prog Ed:** Ian MacGillivray
**Ground:** Lincoln Road, Stamford, Lincs PE9 1SH    **(T)** 01780 757 835    **Capacity:** 1,000
**Colours(change):** Green/black/green. (Orange/black/orange)

**ADDITIONAL INFORMATION: Record Att:** 700 v Glinton
**Honours:** Lincolnshire Senior Cup A 1992-93, 2003-04. Lincolnshire Senior Trophy 2010-11.

## BOURNE TOWN

Founded: 1883    Nickname: Wakes

**Secretary:** Rob Lambert    **(T)** 07443 436 230    **(E)** roblambert51@gmail.com
**Chairman:** Maurice Jesson    **Manager:** Darren Munton    **Prog Ed:** Rob Lambert
**Ground:** Abbey Lawn, Abbey Road, Bourne, Lincs PE10 9EN    **(T)** 07598 815 357
**Colours(change):** Claret & sky blue stripes/claret/claret (All sky blue).

**ADDITIONAL INFORMATION:**
**Record Att:** FA Trophy 1970 **Goalscorer:** David Scotney.
U.C.L. Champions 1968-69, 69-70, 71-72, 90-91. Lincolnshire Senior A Cup 1971-72, 2005-06.

## BUCKINGHAM TOWN

Founded: 1883    Nickname: Robins

**Secretary:** Darren Seaton    **(T)** 07808 792 486    **(E)** djrseaton@hotmail.com
**Chairman:** Vince Hyde    **Manager:** Neil Griffiths    **Prog Ed:** Ms Deb Griffiths
**Ground:** Irish Centre, Manor Fields, Bletchley, Milton Keynes MK2 2HS    **(T)** 01908 375 978
**Colours(change):** All red (Yellow/blue/blue)

**ADDITIONAL INFORMATION:**
Paid: £7,000 to Wealdstone for Steve Jenkins 1992 Received: £1,000 from Kettering Town for Terry Shrieves.
**Honours:** Southern League Southern Division 1990-91. U.C.L. 1983-84, 85-86. Berks & Bucks Senior Cup 1983-84.

## BUGBROOKE ST MICHAELS

Founded: 1929    Nickname: Badgers

**Secretary:** Mrs Debbie Preston    **(T)** 07940 453 883    **(E)** billdebbiepreston@hotmail.com
**Chairman:** William Marriott    **Manager:** Paul Field    **Prog Ed:** Mrs Debbie Preston
**Ground:** Birds Close, Gayton Road, Bugbrooke NN7 3PH    **(T)** 01604 830 707
**Colours(change):** Yellow & blue/royal blue/royal blue (Black & white/black/black)

**ADDITIONAL INFORMATION:**
**Record Att:** 1,156. **Golascorer:** Vince Thomas. **Apps:** Jimmy Nord.
**Honours:** Northants Junior Cup 1989-90, 2011-12, Central Northants Comb. x6. U.C.L. Division 1 Champions 1998-99.

## BURTON PARK WANDERERS

Founded: 1961    Nickname: The Wanderers

**Secretary:** Mrs Sam Gordon    **(T)** 07980 013 506    **(E)** samgordon30@gmail.com
**Chairman:** Kenny Gordon    **Manager:** Joe Smythe    **Prog Ed:** Mrs Sam Gordon
**Ground:** Burton Park, Polwell Lane, Burton Latimer, Northants NN15 5PS    **(T)** 07980 013506
**Colours(change):** Blue & black stripes/black/black (Green/white/green & white)

**ADDITIONAL INFORMATION:**
**Record Att:** 253 v Rothwell, May 1989.

## EYNESBURY ROVERS

Founded: 1897    Nickname: Rovers

**Secretary:** Richard Bissett    **(T)**    **(E)**
**Chairman:**    **Manager:** Dean Shipp    **Prog Ed:** Graham Mills
**Ground:** Alfred Hall Memorial Ground, Hall Road, Eynesbury, St Neots PE19 2SF    **(T)** 01480 477 449
**Colours(change):** Royal & white stripes/royal/royal

**ADDITIONAL INFORMATION:**
**Record Att:** 5,000 v Fulham 1953 (Stanley Matthews guested for Eynesbury). **Honours:** U.C.L. Division 1 1976-77.
Huntingdonshire Senior Cup x11. Huntingdonshire Premier Cup 1950-51, 90-91, 95-96.

## HARROWBY UNITED

Founded: 1949    Nickname: The Arrows

**Secretary:** Michael Atter    **(T)** 07742 077 474    **(E)** mjproperty@fsmail.net
**Chairman:** Ian Weatherstone    **Prog Ed:** Craig Whyley
**Ground:** Harrowby Lane Playing Fields, Harrowby Lane, Grantham, Lincs NG31 9QY    **(T)** 01476 590 822
**Colours(change):** Red/black/black (All blue)

**ADDITIONAL INFORMATION:**
Lincolnshire Junior Cup 2011-12.

## IRCHESTER UNITED
Founded: 1883    Nickname: The Romans

**Secretary:** Glynn Cotter    **(T)** 07802 728 736    **(E)** glynn.cotter@btinternet.com
**Chairman:** Geoff Cotter    **Manager:** Colin Ridgway    **Prog Ed:** Geoff Cotter
**Ground:** Alfred Street, Irchester NN29 7DR    **(T)** 01933 312877    **Capacity:** 1,000
**Colours(change):** All red (All blue)

**ADDITIONAL INFORMATION:**
Northants Lge Div 2 1930-31, 31-32, Rushden & District Lge (9), Northants Jnr Cup 1929-30, 33-34, 48-49, 75-76.
United Counties League Division 1 2009-10.

## LUTTERWORTH ATHLETIC
Founded: 1983    Nickname:

**Secretary:** Mick English    **(T)** 07545 432 200    **(E)** mike622@btinternet.com
**Chairman:** Mick English    **Manager:** Lee English
**Ground:** Hall Park, Hall Lane, Bitteswell, Lutterworth LE17 4LN    **(T)** 07545 432 200
**Colours(change):** Green & white/white/white (All red)

**ADDITIONAL INFORMATION:**
**Previous League:** Leicestershire Senior > 2012. East Midlands Counties 2012-13.

## NORTHAMPTON O.N. CHENECKS
Founded: 1946    Nickname:

**Secretary:** Bryan Lewin    **(T)** 07920 108 300    **(E)** cytringan@tesco.net
**Chairman:** Eddie Slinn    **Manager:** Graham Cottle    **Prog Ed:** Bryan Lewin
**Ground:** Old Northamptonians Sports Ground,Billing Road,Northampton NN1 5RX    **(T)** 01604 634 045
**Colours(change):** White/navy/white (All red or Yellow & blue/blue/yellow)

**ADDITIONAL INFORMATION:**
**Honours:** U.C.L. Div 1 1977-78, 79-80. Northants Junior Cup 2009-10.

## NORTHAMPTON SPENCER
Founded: 1936    Nickname: Millers

**Secretary:** Nick Hillery    **(T)** 07894 150 853    **(E)**
**Chairman:** Graham Wrighting    **Manager:** Ben Stone    **Prog Ed:** Andy Goldsmith
**Ground:** Kingsthorpe Mill, Studand Road, Northampton NN2 6NE    **(T)** 01604 718 898    **Capacity:** 2,000
**Colours(change):** Green & yellow/green/yellow (All royal blue or orange/black/black).

**ADDITIONAL INFORMATION: Record Att:** 800 v Nottingham Forest 1993    **App:** P. Jelley 622 1984-2002
**Honours:** United Counties League Division One 1984-85. Premier 1991-92. Northants Senior Cup Winners 2005-06.

## OADBY TOWN
Founded: 1937    Nickname: The Poachers

**Secretary:** Kev Zupp    **(T)** 07580 004 110    **(E)** zuppy101@hotmail.co.uk
**Chairman:** Brian Fletcher-Warington    **Manager:** Jeff Stocking    **Prog Ed:** Kev Zupp
**Ground:** Freeway Park, Wigston Road, Oadby LE2 5QG    **(T)** 01162 715 728    **Capacity:** 5,000
**Colours(change):** White & red/red/red (All blue or all orange)

**ADDITIONAL INFORMATION:**
**Honours:** Leicestershire Senior Div.2 1951-52. Prem 63-64, 67-68, 68-69, 72-73, 94-95, 96-97, 97-98, 98-99. Midland Alliance 99-00.

## OLNEY TOWN
Founded: 1903    Nickname: The Nurserymen

**Secretary:** Andrew Baldwin    **(T)** 07932 141 623    **(E)** andew@abaldwin.go-plus.net
**Chairman:** Paul Tough    **Manager:** Ed Wheatley    **Prog Ed:** Paul Tough
**Ground:** Recreation Ground, East Street, Olney, Bucks MK46 4DW    **(T)** 01234 712 227
**Colours(change):** Green & white/green/green & white (Yellow/green/yellow)

**ADDITIONAL INFORMATION:**
**Previous League:** Rushden & District.
**Honours:** U.C.L. Div 1 1972-73. Berks & Bucks Intermediate Cup 1992-93.

## PETERBOROUGH SPORTS
Founded: 1908    Nickname:

**Secretary:** Roger Martin    **(T)** 07823 446 983    **(E)** martinroger@virginmedia.com
**Chairman:** Stephen Cooper    **Manager:** Seamus Morgan    **Prog Ed:** Stephen Cooper
**Ground:** 651 Lincoln Road, Peterborough PE1 3HA    **(T)** 01733 567 835
**Colours(change):** All navy blue (All white)

**ADDITIONAL INFORMATION:**
**Previous Names:** Brotherhoods Engineering Works. Bearings Direct during 1990s.
**Previous Leagues:** Peterborough & District >2013.

# POTTON UNITED
Founded: 1943     Nickname: Royals

**Secretary:** Mrs Bev Strong     **(T)** 07703 442 565     **(E)** bev.strong@tiscali.co.uk
**Chairman:** Alan Riley     **Manager:** Darren Staniforth     **Prog Ed:** Mrs Bev Strong
**Ground:** The Hollow, Bigglewade Road, Potton, Beds SG19 2LU     **(T)** 01767 261 100
**Colours(change):** All blue (Red/black/red)

**ADDITIONAL INFORMATION:**
Record Att: 470 v Hastings Town, FA Vase 1989.
Honours: U.C.L. 1986-87, 88-89, Div.1 2003-04. Beds Senior Cup x5. Huntingdonshire Premier Cup x4. E.Anglian Cup 1996-97

# RAUNDS TOWN
Founded: 1946     Nickname: Shopmates

**Secretary:** Dave Jones     **(T)** 07763 492 184     **(E)** david.jones180@ntlworld.com
**Chairman:** Mrs Lesley Jones     **Manager:** Jim Le Masurier & Scott Manning     **Prog Ed:** Dave Jones
**Ground:** Kiln Park, London Rd, Raunds, Northants NN9 6EQ     **(T)** 01933 623 351     **Capacity:** 3,000
**Colours(change):** Red & black stripes/black/black (Blue/white/white).

**ADDITIONAL INFORMATION: Record Att:** 1500 v Crystal Palace 1991     **Goalscorer:** Shaun Keeble. **App:** Martin Lewis - 355
Honours: Northants Senior Cup 1990-91.

# ROTHWELL CORINTHIANS
Founded: 1934     Nickname: Corinthians

**Secretary:** Mark Budworth     **(T)** 07730 416 960     **(E)** mbudworth@budworthhardcastle.com
**Chairman:** Mark Budworth     **Manager:** Ben Watts     **Prog Ed:** Mark Budworth
**Ground:** Sergeants Lawn, Desborough Road, Rothwell, NN14 6JQ     **(T)** 01536 418 688
**Colours(change):** Red & black stripes/red/black. (blue/black/blue).

**ADDITIONAL INFORMATION:**

# RUSHDEN & HIGHAM UNITED
Founded: Formed: 2007 Nickname:

**Secretary:** Ms Jo Griffiths     **(T)** 07792 902 390     **(E)** griffy05@hotmail.co.uk
**Chairman:** Bill Perry     **Manager:** Ady Mann     **Prog Ed:** Ms Jo Griffiths
**Ground:** Hayden Road, Rushden, Northants NN10 0HX     **(T)** 01933 410 036
**Colours(change):** Orange/black/black (All blue)

**ADDITIONAL INFORMATION:**
Club was formed after the merger of Rushden Rangers and Higham Town.

# ST NEOTS TOWN SAINTS
Founded:     Nickname:

**Secretary:** Andrew Armiger     **(T)** 07717 787 493     **(E)** andrewarmiger@hotmail.co.uk
**Chairman:** Colin Parker     **Manager:** Steve Kuhne     **Prog Ed:** Mark Davis
**Ground:** Rowley Park, Kester Way, St Neots, cambridgeshire PE19 6SN     **(T)** 01480 470 012
**Colours(change):** Blue/sky blue/sky blue (Red/black/black)

**ADDITIONAL INFORMATION:**

# THRAPSTON TOWN
Founded: 1960     Nickname: Venturas

**Secretary:** Mrs Cathy Stevens     **(T)** 07972 355 880     **(E)** cathy.stevens@uwclub.net
**Chairman:** Bruce Stevens     **Manager:** Ian Walker     **Prog Ed:** Kevin O'Brien
**Ground:** Chancery Lane, Thrapston, Northants NN14 4JL     **(T)** 01832 732 470     **Capacity:** 1,000
**Colours(change):** All royal blue (Red/black/red)

**ADDITIONAL INFORMATION:**
Honours: Kettering Amateur League 1970-71, 72-73, 73-74, 77-78. Northants Junior Cup 1987-88, 98-99, 03-04.

# WELLINGBOROUGH WHITWORTH
Founded: 1973     Nickname: Flourmen

**Secretary:** Julian Souster     **(T)** 07825 632 545     **(E)** whitworthfc@yahoo.co.uk
**Chairman:** Brian Higgins     **Manager:** James Daldy     **Prog Ed:** Julian Souster
**Ground:** London Road, Wellingborough, Northants NN8 2DP     **(T)**
**Colours(change):** Red & black stripes/black/black (Black & white stripes/black/red)

**ADDITIONAL INFORMATION:**
**Previous Name:** Whitworths. **Previous League:** East Midlands Alliance > 1985.
Honours: Rushden & District League 1976-77. Northants Junior Cup 1996. U.C.L. Division One 2006-07.

# GROUND DIRECTIONS

**AFC KEMPSTON ROVERS** - Take A421 Bedford by pass turning as indicated to Kempston onto A5140 Woburn Road. At roundabout turn left into St John's Street then right into Bedford Road. After the shops and park on the left turn immediately left into Hillgrounds Road. Ground is past the swimming pool on right hand side.

**AFC RUSHDEN & DIAMONDS** - Leave A.45 at Wellingborough turn-off, pass Tesco's Store on left-hand side, up to roundabout. Take first exit to town centre. Ground is 300 yards on right-hand side. Entry just past the Dog & Duck public house adjacent to entry to Whitworths ground.

**BLACKSTONES FC** - From Stamford Centre take A6121 towards Bourne. Turn left into Lincoln Road. Ground on the right hand side. Go into town on A16 from Spalding. Turn left at roundabout into Liquor Pond Street becoming Queen Street over railway crossing along Sleaford Road. Turn right into Carlton Road then right at crossroads into Fydell Street. Over railway crossing and river take 2nd left (sharp turn) into Tattershall Road. Continue over railway crossing, ground on left.

**BOSTON TOWN** - Go into town on A16 from Spalding. Turn left at roundabout into Liquor Pond Street becoming Queen Street over railway crossing along Sleaford Road. Turn right into Carlton Road then right at crossroads into Fydell Street. Over railway crossing an river take 2nd left (sharp turn) into Tattershall Road. Continue over railway crossing, ground on left.

**BOURNE TOWN** - From Town Centre turn east on A151 towards Spalding into Abbey Road. Ground approximately half a mile on right

**BUCKINGHAM TOWN** - Take A413 out of Buckingham and continue on that road until entering Winslow. As you enter Winslow there is a garage on the right hand side. Take the 1st turn right past the garage (Avenue Road) and then the 1st turn right again into Park Road. Entrance at end of road through the blue gates. Bear left into the car park..

**BUGBROOKE ST MICHAELS** - At M1 Junction 16 take A45 to Northampton. At first roundabout follow signs to Bugbrooke. Go straight through village, ground entrance immediately past last house on the left.

**BURTON PARK WANDERERS** - From A14 take J10 towards Burton Latimer, at Alpro roundabout turn right, then straight over roundabout next to Versalift then right at Morrisions. Follow the round around the top of Morrisions continue until you are past the sma Alumasc building on the left.
Entrance to ground is next left.

**COGENHOE UNITED** - From A45 Northampton Ring Road turn as indicated to Billing/Cogenhoe. Go over River Nene and up hill ignoring first turning on left to Cogenhoe. Take next left and ground is on right hand side.

**DEEPING RANGERS** - From Town Centre head north on B1524 towards Bourne. Turn right onto Towngate East at Towngate Tavern Pub. Go straight over mini roundabout onto Outgang Road. Ground 1/4 mile on left. From A16 by pass at roundabout with the A15 Bourne Road turn towards Deeping then left into Northfields Road, then left into Towngate/Outgang Road. Ground 1/4 mile on left.

**DESBOROUGH TOWN** - Take exit 3 marked Desborough off the A14 and follow bypass for 2 miles. At roundabout turn right and ground is 200 yards on the left hand side.

**EYNESBURY ROVERS** - From the A1 take the A428 towards Cambridge. Turn left at the Tesco roundabout and continue on Barford Road for half a mile going straight on at 4 roundabouts. Turn left into Hardwick Road and left into Hall Road. Ground at end of road

**HARBOROUGH TOWN** - Half a mile south of Market Harborough on the A508. 4 miles north of the A14 junction 2 towards Market Harborough turn left towards Leisure Centre, but keep left passed inflatable dome on the right, then through large car park, club house straight in front, with parking area.

**HARROWBY UNITED** - From A1 take B6403, go past roundabout, past Ancaster turn and take road for Harrowby. Follow the road into Grantham, ground on right opposite Cherry Tree public house.

**HOLBEACH UNITED** - Approaching Town Centre traffic lights from Spalding Direction take Second Left, or from Kings Lynn direction take sharp right, into Park Road. Ground is 300 yards on the left.

**HUNTINGDON TOWN** - At the A1 Brampton Hut roundabout, follow signs for A14 East until reaching the Spittals Interchange roundabout, Follow the A141 towards St Ives/March and go over 3 roundabouts. Take next left turn at traffic lights towards Kings Ripton and the ground is on the left.

**IRCHESTER UNITED** - From A509 Wellingborough/Newport Pagnell Road turn into Gidsy Lane to Irchester. Turn left into Wollaston Road B659. Alfred Street is on left hand side with the ground at the end.

**LONG BUCKBY AFC** - From the Village Centre turn into Station Road. Ground on left hand side. Parking is available in South Close adjacent to the Rugby Club (do NOT park "half on half off" the pavement outside the ground)

**NEWPORT PAGNELL TOWN** - From the A422 Newport Pagnell by pass turn into Marsh End Road, then first right into Willen Road.

**NORTHAMPTON ON CHENECKS** - Leave A45 at exit marked Bedford A428 and Town Centre. Take exit into Rushmere Road marked Abington, Kingsthorpe and County Cricket. At first set of lights turn left into Billing Road, sports ground 250 yards on the right.

**NORTHAMPTON SILEBY RANGERS** - Approach from A43 (Kettering): From large roundabout with traffic lights, take the A5076 Talavera Way exit, signpostedto Market Harborough, Moulton Park and Kingsthorpe. The entrance to the ground is about a quarter of a mile on the left. Approach from A45: Take exit to A43 Ring Road / Kettering / Corby. Go straight over 1 roundabout to large roundabout with traffic lights. Then follow directions above.

**NORTHAMPTON SPENCER** - The ground is in Kingsthorpe area of Northampton on A508, Market Harborough road out of Town. Look or W Grose's garage (Vauxhall) and turn left at traffic lights into Thornton Rd, then first right into Studlands Rd. Follow to bottom of hill and onto track between allotments. Ground is after a right turn at end of track.

**OADBY TOWN** - Greene King Park, Wigston Road, Oadby, Leicestershire LE2 5QG - 01162 715728

**OLNEY TOWN** - From the North enter via A509 Warrington Road then turn left into Midland Road and immediately right into East Street. Ground on left hand side after Fire Station. From Milton Keynes: Follow the A509 into Olney, over river bridge, 200 metres past the Swan Bistro and public house and take the first turning right onto the market square immediately before the traffic lights), follow road to the right onto a one way system into East Street. Follow East Street for 500 metres, the ootball Club is on the right hand side, car park entrance being the immediately following right turn.

**PETERBOROUGH NORTHERN STAR** - From A1 turn on to A1139 Fletton Parkway. Follow signs for A47 Wisbech. Exit at Junction 7 near Perkins Engines Site). At top of slip road turn left into Eastfield Road. At Traffic lights turn right into Newark Avenue and then first right in to Eastern Avenue. Take 2nd left in to Chestnut Avenue and the club is on the right behind steel Palisade Fencing

**PETERBOROUGH SPORTS** - From the North - Come in on the A15 Southbound and cross the large A47 Roundabout just past Morrison's on your right.
** Take the left hand slip road at a set of traffic lights after approximately 400 yards and turn right at the T-Junction after 50 yards. The entrance to the ground is approx 400 yards down on your left in front of a church and before a zebra crossing where there is a sign to the health centre. If journeying from the East take the turning from the A47 signposted City Centre and follow instructions from *** above.
* journeying from the South or West come in via the A47 and take the exit signposted City Centre. You go straight on at this roundabout back up alongside A47) and then take the 3rd (right) at the large roundabout with the A15 and follow instructions from *** above.

**POTTON UNITED** - From Sandy, take B1042 into Potton. Head towards Potton Town Centre and take right turn towards Biggleswade 31040). The ground is on left hand side at foot of hill

**RAUNDS TOWN** - From North, East or West, take A14 J13 and follow A45 signs to Raunds. Turn left at roundabout by BP garage. From South follow A45 towards Thrapston. Turn right at roundabout by BP garage. Ground on left.

**ROTHWELL CORINTHIANS** - A14 to Rothwell. Take B669 towards Desborough. Ground on right at rear of cricket field opposite last houses on the left. Parking on verge or in adjacent field if gate open. Access to ground via footpath.

**RUSHDEN AND HIGHAM UNITED** - From A6/A45 Junction take Higham/Rushden bypass. At third roundabout turn right, then turn right immediately after the school. From Bedford (A6) take bypass and turn left at first roundabout then turn right immediately after the school

**SHEPSHED DYNAMO** - The Dovecote Stadium Butt Hole Lane Shepshed Leicestershire LE12 9BN - 01509 650992

**SLEAFORD TOWN** - 15 Sleaford By-pass, roundabout to A17 Holdingham Roundabout third exit towards Boston on A17 Take second exit of A17 towards Sleaford ground is 1 mile on right hand side before you enter Sleaford

**SPALDING UNITED** - Follow signs to Spalding Town Centre. From the north drive south down Pinchbeck Road towards Spalding. At traffic lights turn right into Kings Road. At the next set of lights turn left into Winfrey Avenue. The Ground is on the left. From the south follow signs to the Railway station and Bus Stations. The Ground is opposite the Bus Station on Winfrey Avenue. There is parking outside the ground in a pay and display car park.

**ST NEOTS TOWN SAINTS** - From both the A1 and the Cambridge side of the A428 into Loves Farm St Neots, follow Kester Road until you reach the stadium.

**STEWARTS & LLOYDS CORBY** - From the Oundle/Weldon Road turn at roundabout into A6086 Lloyds Road and continue to roundabout. Take second exit going over railway line along Rockingham Road. Continue over speed bumps then turn left into Occupation Road and first right into Cannock Road. Ground is beyond the British Steel Club and Rugby pitch.

**THRAPSTON TOWN** - Exit A14 at A605 roundabout, travel towards Peterborough till 1st roundabout (approx 700 metres).Take first exit into Thrapston. AT traffic lights turn into Oundle Road adjacent to Masons Arms Pub. Turn left into Devere Road and ground at bottom of hill

**WELLINGBOROUGH TOWN** - Leave A.45 at Wellingborough turn-off, pass Tesco's Store on left-hand side, up to roundabout. Take first exit to town centre. Ground is 300 yards on right-hand side. Entry just past the Dog & Duck public house adjacent to entry to Whitworths ground

**WELLINGBOROUGH WHITWORTH** - Leave A45 by pass and go past Tescos etc. Turn left at roundabout then turn right immediately after Dog and Duck pub and go through 2nd gate down to the ground .

**WOODFORD UNITED** - A361 Daventry to Banbury Road. Turn left in Byfield. Follow road to Woodford Halse. Ground on left just past industrial estate.

**YAXLEY** - Leave A1 at Norman Cross and travel towards Peterborough. Turn off A15 at traffic lights. Bear immediately right and go past cemetery. At bottom of hill turn right into Main Street then left into Holme Road. After short distance go over small bridge and turn left between a bungalow and house into Leading Drove. Ground on left hand side.

# WESSEX LEAGUE

**Sponsored by:** Sydenhams

**Founded:** 1986

**Recent Champions:**
2007: Gosport Borough. 2008: AFC Totton. 2009: Poole Town
2010: Poole Town. 2011: Poole Town. 2012: Winchester City.

**wessexleague.co.uk**

| PREMIER DIVISION | P | W | D | L | F | A | Pts |
|---|---|---|---|---|---|---|---|
| 1 Blackfield & Langley | 40 | 31 | 6 | 3 | 100 | 31 | 99 |
| 2 Alresford Town | 40 | 29 | 2 | 9 | 124 | 51 | 89 |
| 3 Christchurch | 40 | 26 | 6 | 8 | 106 | 49 | 84 |
| 4 Moneyfields | 40 | 22 | 8 | 10 | 85 | 50 | 74 |
| 5 Bemerton Heath Harlequins | 40 | 22 | 8 | 10 | 91 | 57 | 74 |
| 6 Newport (IOW) | 40 | 19 | 11 | 10 | 76 | 63 | 68 |
| 7 GE Hamble | 40 | 19 | 9 | 12 | 87 | 73 | 66 |
| 8 Downton | 40 | 19 | 8 | 13 | 81 | 61 | 65 |
| 9 Fareham Town | 40 | 19 | 5 | 16 | 77 | 72 | 62 |
| 10 Hamworthy United | 40 | 15 | 9 | 16 | 76 | 73 | 54 |
| 11 Horndean | 40 | 15 | 7 | 18 | 79 | 93 | 52 |
| 12 Totton & Eling | 40 | 14 | 8 | 18 | 66 | 81 | 50 |
| 13 Bournemouth | 40 | 14 | 7 | 19 | 72 | 95 | 49 |
| 14 Verwood Town | 40 | 11 | 13 | 16 | 63 | 68 | 46 |
| 15 AFC Portchester | 40 | 13 | 7 | 20 | 69 | 85 | 46 |
| 16 Hayling United | 40 | 13 | 5 | 22 | 74 | 112 | 44 |
| 17 Fawley | 40 | 12 | 5 | 23 | 62 | 91 | 41 |
| 18 Alton Town | 40 | 12 | 4 | 24 | 67 | 92 | 40 |
| 19 Lymington Town | 40 | 9 | 11 | 20 | 47 | 69 | 38 |
| 20 Romsey Town | 40 | 7 | 1 | 32 | 38 | 137 | 22 |
| 21 (R) New Milton Town | 40 | 6 | 6 | 28 | 51 | 88 | 21 |

| DIVISION ONE | P | W | D | L | F | A | Pts |
|---|---|---|---|---|---|---|---|
| 1 (P) Brockenhurst | 30 | 22 | 3 | 5 | 82 | 26 | 69 |
| 2 (P) Whitchurch United | 30 | 22 | 3 | 5 | 76 | 23 | 69 |
| 3 Team Solent | 30 | 20 | 4 | 6 | 65 | 37 | 64 |
| 4 Cowes Sports | 30 | 20 | 2 | 8 | 77 | 36 | 62 |
| 5 Pewsey Vale | 30 | 15 | 8 | 7 | 72 | 41 | 53 |
| 6 Petersfield Town | 30 | 16 | 5 | 9 | 76 | 46 | 53 |
| 7 Tadley Calleva | 30 | 15 | 3 | 12 | 69 | 45 | 48 |
| 8 East Cowes Victoria (-1pt) | 30 | 14 | 7 | 9 | 70 | 55 | 48 |
| 9 Ringwood Town | 30 | 10 | 4 | 16 | 48 | 71 | 34 |
| 10 Fleet Spurs | 30 | 10 | 3 | 17 | 49 | 55 | 33 |
| 11 Stockbridge | 30 | 10 | 2 | 18 | 48 | 80 | 32 |
| 12 United Services Portsmouth | 30 | 9 | 4 | 17 | 56 | 76 | 31 |
| 13 Laverstock & Ford | 30 | 8 | 7 | 15 | 41 | 71 | 31 |
| 14 Amesbury Town | 30 | 7 | 4 | 19 | 31 | 76 | 25 |
| 15 Andover New Street | 30 | 4 | 8 | 18 | 40 | 93 | 20 |
| 16 Hythe & Dibden | 30 | 3 | 3 | 24 | 27 | 96 | 12 |

| PREMIER DIVISION | 1 | 2 | 3 | 4 | 5 | 6 | 7 | 8 | 9 | 10 | 11 | 12 | 13 | 14 | 15 | 16 | 17 | 18 | 19 | 20 | 21 |
|---|---|---|---|---|---|---|---|---|---|---|---|---|---|---|---|---|---|---|---|---|---|
| 1 AFC Portchester | | 3-2 | 2-1 | 0-0 | 1-4 | 4-1 | 3-4 | 0-1 | 2-5 | 4-1 | 1-0 | 3-3 | 2-5 | 3-2 | 1-1 | 1-2 | 3-0 | 1-3 | 1-1 | 0-2 | 0-0 |
| 2 Alresford Town | 3-0 | | 4-1 | 5-1 | 2-4 | 4-2 | 2-0 | 4-2 | 6-0 | 5-0 | 6-0 | 2-0 | 2-1 | 5-3 | 3-0 | 3-2 | 3-1 | 5-1 | 3-0 | 2-4 | 1-1 |
| 3 Alton Town | 1-2 | 0-5 | | 0-3 | 2-3 | 1-4 | 3-3 | 1-5 | 3-0 | 2-0 | 2-4 | 2-5 | 4-0 | 0-1 | 3-2 | 1-2 | 5-1 | 1-3 | 5-1 | 4-0 | 4-4 |
| 4 Bemerton Heath Harlequins | 5-1 | 2-3 | 0-0 | | 1-5 | 5-4 | 1-0 | 3-3 | 3-0 | 4-3 | 0-2 | 4-2 | 4-0 | 1-2 | 2-0 | 2-2 | 4-1 | 2-2 | 3-0 | 2-3 | 4-1 |
| 5 Blackfield & Langley | 3-2 | 2-0 | 4-0 | 1-0 | | 2-2 | 1-0 | 2-0 | 1-1 | 3-0 | 1-1 | 5-1 | 0-1 | 7-1 | 2-0 | 1-0 | 1-1 | 4-1 | 6-1 | 1-0 | 1-1 |
| 6 Bournemouth | 6-2 | 0-5 | 3-4 | 3-3 | 2-4 | | 1-1 | 1-2 | 3-1 | 1-0 | 1-0 | 2-1 | 4-6 | 1-1 | 0-3 | 0-3 | 2-2 | 1-4 | 4-1 | 2-1 | 1-0 |
| 7 Christchurch | 1-2 | 3-0 | 2-1 | 1-2 | 3-0 | 3-0 | | 4-2 | 1-2 | 2-2 | 3-0 | 4-0 | 3-1 | 4-0 | 4-1 | 3-0 | 3-1 | 6-3 | 4-0 | 5-0 | 7-4 |
| 8 Downton | 2-0 | 2-1 | 3-1 | 0-0 | 4-0 | 2-3 | 1-1 | | 0-2 | 0-0 | 7-3 | 1-0 | 1-3 | 3-1 | 1-2 | 0-0 | 2-2 | 1-1 | 1-3 | 4-3 | 1-3 |
| 9 Fareham Town | 3-1 | 1-0 | 4-1 | 1-2 | 1-2 | 7-1 | 1-1 | 3-2 | | 2-1 | 1-5 | 2-3 | 4-2 | 2-1 | 0-2 | 1-3 | 2-0 | 2-3 | 5-2 | 1-2 | 1-1 |
| 10 Fawley | 2-1 | 1-2 | 2-1 | 0-3 | 0-3 | 4-1 | 1-1 | 0-5 | 2-4 | | 2-2 | 3-1 | 2-0 | 1-2 | 2-1 | 1-5 | 2-1 | 3-4 | 4-2 | 0-1 | 2-2 |
| 11 GE Hamble | 1-4 | 2-3 | 0-3 | 3-1 | 1-4 | 3-1 | 1-3 | 2-1 | 1-0 | 2-0 | | 1-1 | 2-3 | 4-2 | 2-1 | 0-4 | 2-1 | 1-1 | 7-1 | 4-0 | 2-2 |
| 12 Hamworthy United | 2-2 | 1-0 | 5-1 | 0-1 | 0-0 | 1-3 | 2-3 | 2-1 | 2-2 | 7-4 | 1-1 | | 8-0 | 0-4 | 1-1 | 0-2 | 2-1 | 2-2 | 3-0 | 3-1 | 2-2 |
| 13 Hayling United | 1-3 | 0-4 | 3-0 | 3-2 | 1-4 | 1-3 | 2-0 | 1-3 | 1-5 | 3-2 | 1-2 | | 2-4 | 2-2 | 0-2 | 2-1 | 1-3 | 3-2 | 1-2 | 5-3 | 3-2 |
| 14 Horndean | 2-0 | 2-4 | 2-0 | 1-3 | 0-1 | 1-1 | 1-3 | 2-3 | 0-2 | 2-1 | 3-3 | 3-2 | 4-4 | | 2-2 | 1-5 | 1-3 | 3-2 | 1-2 | 5-3 | 2-1 |
| 15 Lymington Town | 3-3 | 0-4 | 1-3 | 0-5 | 1-1 | 3-1 | 0-3 | 1-3 | 1-2 | 1-0 | 1-3 | 0-1 | 1-0 | 1-1 | | 1-2 | 0-2 | 1-1 | 3-1 | 1-2 | 0-0 |
| 16 Moneyfields | 5-2 | 2-4 | 2-0 | 2-2 | 0-1 | 4-1 | 0-3 | 3-4 | 4-0 | 2-0 | 1-2 | 3-0 | 3-1 | 3-3 | 1-1 | | 2-2 | 2-2 | 6-2 | 0-3 | 2-0 |
| 17 New Milton Town | 1-3 | 2-4 | 0-1 | 0-1 | 0-5 | 2-0 | 2-3 | 0-3 | 1-4 | 1-2 | 1-3 | 1-3 | 3-4 | 4-1 | 1-1 | 0-1 | | 1-1 | 5-0 | 1-2 | 0-2 |
| 18 Newport (IOW) | 1-0 | 3-2 | 0-3 | 0-2 | 0-1 | 1-0 | 2-3 | 1-0 | 3-0 | 1-2 | 1-1 | 1-0 | 4-3 | 0-4 | 1-0 | 2-0 | HW | | 7-0 | 1-1 | 3-2 |
| 19 Romsey Town | 0-3 | 0-7 | 2-1 | 0-4 | 0-5 | 0-1 | 0-4 | 0-2 | 2-0 | 4-3 | 0-7 | 1-4 | 4-2 | 1-3 | 0-3 | 0-1 | 1-3 | 1-3 | | 1-4 | 1-0 |
| 20 Totton & Eling | 2-1 | 2-2 | 1-1 | 0-3 | 0-2 | 1-1 | 2-3 | 1-2 | 0-2 | 2-5 | 2-5 | 3-2 | 2-3 | 5-3 | 0-2 | 0-0 | 4-1 | 0-0 | 4-1 | | 1-3 |
| 21 Verwood Town | 3-2 | 0-2 | 4-0 | 3-1 | 0-3 | 2-4 | 2-1 | 1-1 | 1-1 | 1-2 | 0-1 | 0-1 | 5-0 | 1-2 | 3-2 | 0-2 | 3-1 | 1-5 | 2-0 | 0-0 | |

## LEAGUE CUP

**ROUND 1**

| | | | |
|---|---|---|---|
| Romsey Town | v | Pewsey Vale | 4-5aet |
| Downton | v | Alresford Town | 2-4 |
| Christchurch | v | Fawley | 2-1 |

**ROUND 2**

| | | | |
|---|---|---|---|
| Amesbury Town | v | Bournemouth | 0-2 |
| Fleet Spurs | v | Ringwood Town | 7-4 |
| Hythe & Dibden | v | East Cowes Victoria | 0-1 |
| Alton Town | v | Pewsey Vale | 7-2 |
| United Services Ports' | v | Cowes Sports | 3-1 |
| Andover New Street | v | Stockbridge | 3-4 |
| New Milton Town | v | Alresford Town | 2-3 aet |
| Laverstock & Ford | v | Team Solent | 1-1 aet 2-3p |
| Christchurch | v | Horndean | 4-0 |
| Blackfield & Langley | v | Bemerton Heath Harlequins | 2-0 |
| Moneyfields | v | Newport (IOW) | 1-3 |
| Fareham Town | v | Hayling United | 0-1 |
| Totton & Eling | v | Tadley Calleva | 4-1 |
| GE Hamble | v | Brockenhurst | 0-1 |
| AFC Portchester | v | Verwood Town | 2-1 |
| Petersfield Town | v | Lymington Town | 2-3 |

**ROUND 3**

| | | | |
|---|---|---|---|
| Bournemouth | v | Fleet Spurs | 2-2 aet 5-3p |
| East Cowes Victoria | v | Alton Town | 2-2 aet 6-5p |
| United Services Ports' | v | Stockbridge | 1-0 |
| Alresford Town | v | Team Solent | 7-1 |
| Christchurch | v | Blackfield & Langley | 1-3 |
| Newport (IOW) | v | Hayling United | 5-1 |
| Totton & Eling | v | Brockenhurst | 0-3 |
| AFC Portchester | v | Lymington Town | 5-1 |

**QUARTER FINALS**

| | | | |
|---|---|---|---|
| Bournemouth | v | East Cowes Victoria | 0-4 |
| United Services Ports' | v | Alresford Town | 0-4 |
| Blackfield & Langley | v | Newport (IOW) | 4-1 |
| Brockenhurst | v | AFC Portchester | 1-0 |

**SEMI FINALS**

| | | | |
|---|---|---|---|
| East Cowes Victoria | v | Alresford Town | 1-2 |
| Blackfield & Langley | v | Brockenhurst | 0-1 |

**FINAL**

| | | | |
|---|---|---|---|
| Alresford Town | v | Brockenhurst | 4-1 |

| DIVISION ONE | 1 | 2 | 3 | 4 | 5 | 6 | 7 | 8 | 9 | 10 | 11 | 12 | 13 | 14 | 15 | 16 |
|---|---|---|---|---|---|---|---|---|---|---|---|---|---|---|---|---|
| 1 Amesbury Town | | 2-1 | 0-3 | 0-2 | 2-2 | 1-0 | 3-1 | 1-1 | 2-1 | 1-3 | 2-3 | 1-0 | 2-1 | 1-2 | 2-1 | 1-4 |
| 2 Andover New Street | 2-2 | | 0-2 | 1-1 | 3-5 | 1-0 | 2-1 | 1-4 | 0-5 | 0-3 | 2-0 | 2-2 | 1-2 | 1-1 | 3-5 | 1-4 |
| 3 Brockenhurst | 5-0 | 0-1 | | 2-0 | 5-0 | 0-0 | 3-0 | 1-0 | 1-3 | 1-0 | 5-1 | 6-1 | 2-1 | 1-0 | 3-0 | 0-2 |
| 4 Cowes Sports | 3-0 | 7-0 | 1-3 | | 2-4 | 1-0 | 3-0 | 4-0 | 2-2 | 4-2 | 8-2 | 2-1 | 2-1 | 1-0 | 2-0 | 0-4 |
| 5 East Cowes Victoria | 1-0 | 6-2 | 0-2 | 1-0 | | 3-1 | 2-1 | 7-2 | 2-1 | 1-1 | 6-0 | 9-0 | 1-2 | 1-1 | 3-0 | 1-3 |
| 6 Fleet Spurs | 4-0 | 4-2 | 0-3 | 1-0 | 5-1 | | 1-1 | 1-3 | 4-3 | 2-6 | 2-3 | 2-3 | 2-3 | 0-1 | 5-2 | 0-0 |
| 7 Hythe & Dibden | 2-1 | 1-1 | 0-6 | 2-6 | 1-3 | 1-0 | | 2-3 | 2-4 | 3-6 | 0-5 | 0-3 | 1-4 | 1-2 | 0-1 | 1-2 |
| 8 Laverstock & Ford | 1-0 | 4-3 | 0-3 | 0-8 | 1-1 | 2-4 | 2-3 | | 1-1 | 2-2 | 0-1 | 1-0 | 2-1 | 1-3 | 1-3 | 0-1 |
| 9 Petersfield Town | 3-0 | 5-1 | 5-4 | 1-2 | 5-0 | 3-0 | 4-0 | 2-1 | | 3-3 | 0-0 | 4-0 | 0-1 | 1-2 | 2-0 | 0-4 |
| 10 Pewsey Vale | 6-2 | 8-0 | 3-0 | 0-1 | 0-0 | 0-1 | 5-1 | 3-3 | 0-0 | | 1-1 | 2-1 | 2-1 | 3-2 | 1-1 | 1-2 |
| 11 Ringwood Town | 0-0 | 3-2 | 2-2 | 3-1 | 0-4 | 2-3 | 4-0 | 0-1 | 2-5 | 2-4 | | 1-2 | 3-2 | 0-1 | 1-6 | 1-0 |
| 12 Stockbridge | 2-1 | 4-1 | 4-5 | 3-4 | 2-2 | 0-3 | 6-1 | 2-0 | 3-4 | 1-0 | 2-1 | | 0-4 | 2-3 | 2-0 | 0-3 |
| 13 Tadley Calleva | 5-2 | 6-0 | 0-0 | 0-2 | 5-2 | 3-1 | 5-0 | 2-2 | 2-4 | 0-1 | 2-1 | 5-0 | | 4-3 | 1-3 | 0-1 |
| 14 Team Solent | 2-1 | 2-2 | 1-4 | 0-4 | 2-0 | 2-1 | 1-1 | 2-0 | 4-3 | 4-1 | 2-1 | 3-1 | 3-0 | | 6-1 | 4-0 |
| 15 United Services Portsmouth | 6-1 | 3-3 | 0-8 | 2-4 | 2-2 | 3-1 | 5-0 | 3-3 | 1-2 | 1-3 | 3-5 | 2-1 | 1-5 | 0-1 | | 1-3 |
| 16 Whitchurch United | 9-0 | 1-1 | 1-2 | 1-0 | 4-0 | 2-1 | 3-0 | 6-0 | 2-0 | 0-2 | 3-0 | 8-0 | 1-1 | 0-5 | 2-0 | |

## CLUB MOVEMENTS

**Premier Division - In:** Brockenhurst (P). Folland Sports (NC from GE Hamble). Sholing (W - Southern Div.1 S&W). Whitchurch United (P). Winchester City (R- Southern Div.1 Central).
**Out:** Alton Town (S - Combined Counties Premier). GE Hamble (NC to Folland Sports). Hayling United (R). New Milton Town (R).

**Division One - In:** Andover Town (N). Hayling United (R).
**Out:** Brockenhurst (P). Whitchurch United (P).

# PREMIER DIVISION

## AFC PORTCHESTER
Founded: 1971          Nickname:

**Secretary:** Jason Brooker          **(T)** 07972 165 077          **(E)** jason.brooker@afcportchester.co.uk
**Chairman:** Paul Kelly          **Prog Ed:** Rob McGinn
**Ground:** Wicor Recreation Ground Cranleigh Road Portchester Hampshire PO16 9DP          **(T)** 01329 233 833 (Clubhouse)
**Capacity:**          **Seats:**          **Covered:**          **Midweek Matchday:** Tuesday          **Clubhouse:** Yes

**Colours(change):** Tangerine/black/tangerine (All grey)
**Previous Names:** Loyds Sports 1971-73. Colourvison Rangers 1973-76. Wilcor Mill 1976-2003.
**Previous Leagues:** City of Portsmouth Sunday. Portsmouth & District >1998. Hampshire 1998-2004.
**Records:**
**Senior Honours:** Hampshire League Division One 2001-02.

**10 YEAR RECORD**

| 03-04 | 04-05 | 05-06 | 06-07 | 07-08 | 08-09 | 09-10 | 10-11 | 11-12 | 12-13 |
|---|---|---|---|---|---|---|---|---|---|
| Hant1 13 | Wex3 14 | Wex3 11 | Wex2 4 | Wex1 14 | Wex1 19 | Wex1 6 | Wex1 3 | Wex1 2 | WexP 15 |

## ALRESFORD TOWN
Founded: 1898          Nickname: The Magpies

**Secretary:** Keith Curtis          **(T)** 07703 346 672          **(E)** secretary.alresfordtownfc@gmail.com
**Chairman:** Trevor Ingram          **Prog Ed:** Gregory Boughton
**Ground:** Arlebury Park, The Avenue, Alresford, Hants SO24 9EP          **(T)** 01962 735 100
**Capacity:**          **Seats:** Yes          **Covered:** Yes          **Midweek Matchday:** Tuesday          **Clubhouse:** Yes

**Colours(change):** Black & white stripes/black/black & white. (Yellow & blue/blue/yellow & blue)
**Previous Names:**
**Previous Leagues:** Winchester League, North Hants league, Hampshire League
**Records:**
**Senior Honours:** Winchester League Division Two & One
          Hampshire Senior Cup 2012-13.

**10 YEAR RECORD**

| 03-04 | 04-05 | 05-06 | 06-07 | 07-08 | 08-09 | 09-10 | 10-11 | 11-12 | 12-13 |
|---|---|---|---|---|---|---|---|---|---|
| Hant1 8 | Wex2 10 | Wex2 20 | Wex1 2 | WexP 21 | WexP 18 | WexP 17 | WexP 15 | WexP 15 | WexP 2 |

## BEMERTON HEATH HARLEQUINS
Founded: 1989          Nickname: Quins

**Secretary:** Andy Hardwick          **(T)** 07561 164 068          **(E)** secretarybhhfc@hotmail.com
**Chairman:** Steve Slade          **Prog Ed:** Steve Brooks
**Ground:** The Clubhouse, Western Way, Bemerton Heath Salisbury SP2 9DT          **(T)** 01722 331925 (Club) 331218 (Office)
**Capacity:** 2,100 **Seats:** 250          **Covered:** 350          **Midweek Matchday:** Monday          **Clubhouse:** Yes          **Shop:** No

**Colours(change):** Black & white quarters/black/black & white (All orange)
**Previous Names:** Bemerton Athletic, Moon FC & Bemerton Boys merged in 1989
**Previous Leagues:** Salisbury & Wilts Comb, Salisbury & Andover Sunday
**Records:** **Att:**1,118 v Aldershot Town          **App:** Keith Richardson
**Senior Honours:** Wiltshire Senior Cup 1992-93. Wessex League Cup 2009-10.

**10 YEAR RECORD**

| 03-04 | 04-05 | 05-06 | 06-07 | 07-08 | 08-09 | 09-10 | 10-11 | 11-12 | 12-13 |
|---|---|---|---|---|---|---|---|---|---|
| Wex 12 | Wex1 14 | Wex1 14 | WexP 11 | WexP 13 | WexP 12 | WexP 3 | WexP 2 | WexP 2 | WexP 5 |

## BLACKFIELD & LANGLEY
Founded: 1935          Nickname:

**Secretary:** Lisa Bray          **(T)** 07870 813 501          **(E)** lee775@btinternet.com
**Chairman:** Owen Lightfoot          **Prog Ed:** Tony Croft
**Ground:** Gang Warily Rec., Newlands Rd, Southampton, SO45 1GA          **(T)** 02380 893 603
**Capacity:** 2,500 **Seats:** 180          **Covered:** nil          **Midweek Matchday:** Tuesday          **Clubhouse:** Yes

**Colours(change):** Green & white/white/green (All maroon).
**Previous Names:**
**Previous Leagues:** Southampton Senior. Hampshire.
**Records:** **Att:** 240
**Senior Honours:** Hampshire League 1987-88, Division Two 1984-85, Southampton Senior Cup (4).
          Wessex League Premier Division 2012-13.

**10 YEAR RECORD**

| 03-04 | 04-05 | 05-06 | 06-07 | 07-08 | 08-09 | 09-10 | 10-11 | 11-12 | 12-13 |
|---|---|---|---|---|---|---|---|---|---|
| Wex 21 | Wex2 7 | Wex2 14 | Wex1 16 | Wex1 10 | Wex1 2 | WexP 8 | WexP 14 | WexP 16 | WexP 1 |

# BOURNEMOUTH
Founded: 1875     Nickname: Poppies

**Secretary:** Mike Robins     **(T)** 07947 687 808     **(E)** bournemouthpoppiesfc@gmail.com

**Chairman:** Bob Corbin     **Prog Ed:** Mike Robins

**Ground:** Victoria Park, Namu Road, Winton, Bournemouth, BH9 2RA     **(T)** 01202 515 123

**Capacity:** 3,000   **Seats:** 205   **Covered:** 205   **Midweek Matchday:** Tuesday    **Clubhouse:** Yes   **Shop:** Yes

**Colours(change):** All Red (All blue)
**Previous Names:** Bournemouth Rovers, Bournemouth Wanderers, Bournemouth Dean Park
**Previous Leagues:** Hampshire
**Records:** Goalscorer (since 1990) Darren McBride 95 (111+26 games) Apps (since 1990) Mark Dancer 358 (318+40 games)
**Senior Honours:** Wessex League Cup Winners: 2011.

### 10 YEAR RECORD

| 03-04 | 04-05 | 05-06 | 06-07 | 07-08 | 08-09 | 09-10 | 10-11 | 11-12 | 12-13 |
|---|---|---|---|---|---|---|---|---|---|
| Wex 20 | Wex1 11 | Wex1 7 | WexP 5 | WexP 5 | WexP 15 | WexP 4 | WexP 5 | WexP 9 | WexP 13 |

# BROCKENHURST
Founded: 1898     Nickname: The Badgers

**Secretary:** Pete Lynes     **(T)** 07908 109 696     **(E)** peter.m.lynes@btopenworld.com

**Chairman:** Pete Lynes     **Prog Ed:** Ian Claxton

**Ground:** Grigg Lane, Brockenhurst, Hants SO42 7RE     **(T)** 01590 623 544

**Capacity:** 2,000   **Seats:** 200   **Covered:** 300   **Midweek Matchday:** Wednesday    **Clubhouse:** Yes

**Colours(change):** Blue & white/blue/blue. (Green & white/green/green).
**Previous Names:**
**Previous Leagues:** Hampshire
**Records:** Att: 1,104 v St Albans City
**Senior Honours:** Hampshire League 1975-76. Wessex League Division One 2012-13.

### 10 YEAR RECORD

| 03-04 | 04-05 | 05-06 | 06-07 | 07-08 | 08-09 | 09-10 | 10-11 | 11-12 | 12-13 |
|---|---|---|---|---|---|---|---|---|---|
| Wex 9 | Wex1 18 | Wex1 21 | WexP 13 | WexP 6 | WexP 5 | WexP 13 | | | Wex1 1 |

# CHRISTCHURCH
Founded: 1885     Nickname: Priory

**Secretary:** Ian Harley     **(T)** 07900 133 954     **(E)** secretary@christchurchfc.co.uk

**Chairman:** Mark Duffy     **Prog Ed:** Mark Duffy

**Ground:** Hurn Bridge S.C, Avon Causeway, Christchurch BH23 6DY     **(T)** 01202 473 792

**Capacity:** 1,200   **Seats:** 215   **Covered:** 265   **Midweek Matchday:** Tuesday    **Clubhouse:** Yes

**Colours(change):** All Blue (Red/black/red)
**Previous Names:**
**Previous Leagues:** Hampshire
**Records:** App: John Haynes
**Senior Honours:** Hants Jnr Cup (3), Hants Intermediate Cup 86-87, Bournemouth Senior Cup (5)

### 10 YEAR RECORD

| 03-04 | 04-05 | 05-06 | 06-07 | 07-08 | 08-09 | 09-10 | 10-11 | 11-12 | 12-13 |
|---|---|---|---|---|---|---|---|---|---|
| Wex 11 | Wex1 17 | Wex1 10 | WexP 14 | WexP 16 | WexP 7 | WexP 5 | WexP 6 | WexP 3 | WexP 3 |

# DOWNTON
Founded: 1905     Nickname: The Robins

**Secretary:** Brian Ford     **(T)** 07743 538984     **(E)** info@downtonfc.com

**Chairman:** Mark Smith     **Prog Ed:** Mark Smith

**Ground:** Brian Whitehead Sports Ground Wick Lane Downton Wiltshire SP5 3NF     **(T)** 01725 512162

**Capacity:**   **Seats:**   **Covered:**   **Midweek Matchday:** Tuesday    **Clubhouse:** Yes

**Colours(change):** Red/white/red (Yellow/blue/yellow)
**Previous Names:** None
**Previous Leagues:** Hampshire > 1993.
**Records:** Att: 55 v AFC Bournemouth - Friendly.
**Senior Honours:** Wiltshire Senior Cup 1979-80, 80-81. Wiltshire Junior Cup 1949-50. Wessex League Cup 1995-96. Wessex League Division One 2010-11.

### 10 YEAR RECORD

| 03-04 | 04-05 | 05-06 | 06-07 | 07-08 | 08-09 | 09-10 | 10-11 | 11-12 | 12-13 |
|---|---|---|---|---|---|---|---|---|---|
| Wex 19 | Wex1 22 | Wex2 4 | WexP 18 | WexP 23 | Wex1 17 | Wex1 4 | Wex1 1 | WexP 6 | WexP 8 |

# FAREHAM TOWN

Founded: 1946     Nickname: The Robins

**Secretary:** Paul Procter     **(T)** 07445 805 122     **(E)** splodge68@gmail.com

**Chairman:** Nick Ralls     **Prog Ed:** Paul Proctor

**Ground:** Cams Alders, Palmerston Drive, Fareham, Hants PO14 1BJ     **(T)** 07930 853 235

**Capacity:** 2,000   **Seats:** 450   **Covered:** 500   **Midweek Matchday:** Tuesday    **Clubhouse:** Yes   **Shop:** Yes

**Colours(change):** Red & black/black/red (All blue)
**Previous Names:** None
**Previous Leagues:** Portsmouth, Hampshire & Southern
**Records:** **Att:** 2,015 v Spurs (friendly 1985)
**Senior Honours:** Hampshire Senior Cup 1957, 1963, 1968, 1993. Hampshire League Champions.

**10 YEAR RECORD**

| 03-04 | | 04-05 | | 05-06 | | 06-07 | | 07-08 | | 08-09 | | 09-10 | | 10-11 | | 11-12 | | 12-13 | |
|---|---|---|---|---|---|---|---|---|---|---|---|---|---|---|---|---|---|---|---|
| Wex | 7 | Wex1 | 16 | Wex1 | 9 | WexP | 8 | WexP | 8 | WexP | 10 | WexP | 6 | WexP | 8 | WexP | 12 | WexP | 9 |

# FAWLEY

Founded: 1923     Nickname:

**Secretary:** Kevin Mitchell     **(T)** 07836 259682     **(E)** fawleysecretary@hotmail.co.uk

**Chairman:** Kevin Mitchell     **Prog Ed:** Kevin Mitchell

**Ground:** Waterside Spts & Soc. club, 179 Long Lane, Holbury, Soto, SO45 2QD     **(T)** 02380 893750 (Club) 896621 (Office)

**Capacity:**   **Seats:**   **Covered:**   **Midweek Matchday:** Wednesday    **Clubhouse:** Yes

**Colours(change):** All Blue (Red/white/red)
**Previous Names:** Esso Fawley > 2002
**Previous Leagues:** Hampshire Premier > 2004.
**Records:**
**Senior Honours:**

**10 YEAR RECORD**

| 03-04 | | 04-05 | | 05-06 | | 06-07 | | 07-08 | | 08-09 | | 09-10 | | 10-11 | | 11-12 | | 12-13 | |
|---|---|---|---|---|---|---|---|---|---|---|---|---|---|---|---|---|---|---|---|
| HantP | 16 | Wex2 | 21 | Wex2 | 7 | Wex1 | 5 | Wex1 | 6 | Wex1 | 9 | Wex1 | 2 | WexP | 20 | WexP | 19 | WexP | 17 |

# FOLLAND SPORTS

Founded: 1938     Nickname:

**Secretary:** Adrian Harris     **(T)** 07774 962813     **(E)** hamble.assc@hotmail.co.uk

**Chairman:** Gilly Bowers     **Prog Ed:** Matthew Newbold

**Ground:** Folland Park, Kings Ave, Hamble, Southampton SO31 4NF     **(T)** 02380 452 173

**Capacity:** 1,000   **Seats:** 150   **Covered:** 150   **Midweek Matchday:** Tuesday    **Clubhouse:** Yes   **Shop:** No

**Colours(change):** Sky blue/maroon/sky blue (White/white/red)
**Previous Names:** Folland Sports (pre 1990), Aerostructures SSC 1990-97, Hamble ASSC 1997-2011. GE Hamble 2011-13.
**Previous Leagues:**
**Records:**
**Senior Honours:** Southampton Senior Cup 1984-85, 86-87, 91-92. Wessex League Division 1 2009-10.

**10 YEAR RECORD**

| 03-04 | | 04-05 | | 05-06 | | 06-07 | | 07-08 | | 08-09 | | 09-10 | | 10-11 | | 11-12 | | 12-13 | |
|---|---|---|---|---|---|---|---|---|---|---|---|---|---|---|---|---|---|---|---|
| Wex | 13 | Wex1 | 21 | Wex1 | 15 | WexP | 20 | WexP | 17 | WexP | 21 | Wex1 | 1 | WexP | 12 | WexP | 5 | WexP | 7 |

# HAMWORTHY UNITED

Founded: 1926     Nickname: The Hammers

**Secretary:** Peter Gallop     **(T)** 07925 062 545     **(E)** ham-utd-fc-secretary@hotmail.co.uk

**Chairman:** Steve Harvey     **Prog Ed:** Stuart Tanner

**Ground:** The County Ground, Blandford Close, Hamworthy, Poole, BH15 4PR     **(T)** 01202 674 974

**Capacity:** 2,000   **Seats:**   **Covered:**   **Midweek Matchday:** Wednesday    **Clubhouse:** Yes   **Shop:** No

**Colours(change):** Maroon & sky blue/maroon/maroon (Yellow & black/black/yellow)
**Previous Names:** Hamworthy St. Michael merged with Trinidad Old Boys 1926
**Previous Leagues:** Dorset Premier
**Records:**
**Senior Honours:** Dorset Premier League 2002-03, 03-04.

**10 YEAR RECORD**

| 03-04 | | 04-05 | | 05-06 | | 06-07 | | 07-08 | | 08-09 | | 09-10 | | 10-11 | | 11-12 | | 12-13 | |
|---|---|---|---|---|---|---|---|---|---|---|---|---|---|---|---|---|---|---|---|
| Dor P | 1 | Wex1 | 15 | Wex1 | 6 | WexP | 15 | WexP | 10 | WexP | 8 | WexP | 16 | WexP | 9 | WexP | 7 | WexP | 10 |

# HORNDEAN
Founded: 1887    Nickname:

**Secretary:** Michael Austin    **(T)** 07983 969 644    **(E)** horndeanfc1887@yahoo.co.uk
**Chairman:** David Sagar    **Prog Ed:** Michael Austin
**Ground:**  Five Heads Park Five Heads Road Horndean Hampshire PO8 9NZ    **(T)** 02392 591 363
**Capacity:**    **Seats:**    **Covered:**    **Midweek Matchday:** Tuesday    **Clubhouse:**

**Colours(change):**  All red (All pale blue)
**Previous Names:**
**Previous Leagues:** Hampshire 1972-86, 1995-2004. Wessex 1986-95
**Records:**    **Att:** 1,560 v Waterlooville, Victory Cup, April 1971. **Goalscorer:** Frank Bryson 348 (including 83 during the 1931-32 season)
**Senior Honours:**

**10 YEAR RECORD**

| 03-04 | | 04-05 | | 05-06 | | 06-07 | | 07-08 | | 08-09 | | 09-10 | | 10-11 | | 11-12 | | 12-13 | |
|---|---|---|---|---|---|---|---|---|---|---|---|---|---|---|---|---|---|---|---|
| HantP | 5 | Wex2 | 9 | Wex2 | 6 | WexP | 16 | WexP | 11 | WexP | 22 | Wex1 | 12 | Wex1 | 2 | WexP | 17 | WexP | 11 |

# LYMINGTON TOWN
Founded: 1876    Nickname:

**Secretary:** Barry Torah    **(T)** 07849 646 234    **(E)** barry.torah@sky.com
**Chairman:** George Shaw    **Prog Ed:** Barry Torah
**Ground:**  The Sports Ground, Southampton Road, Lymington SO41 9ZG    **(T)** 01590 671 305
**Capacity:** 3,000 **Seats:** 200 **Covered:** 300 **Midweek Matchday:** Tuesday    **Clubhouse:** Yes

**Colours(change):**  Red/black/black (Yellow/blue/yellow)
**Previous Names:** None
**Previous Leagues:** Hampshire.
**Records:**
**Senior Honours:**  Wessex League Cup 2006-07.

**10 YEAR RECORD**

| 03-04 | | 04-05 | | 05-06 | | 06-07 | | 07-08 | | 08-09 | | 09-10 | | 10-11 | | 11-12 | | 12-13 | |
|---|---|---|---|---|---|---|---|---|---|---|---|---|---|---|---|---|---|---|---|
| HantP | 7 | Wex2 | 1 | Wex1 | 17 | WexP | 12 | WexP | 20 | WexP | 18 | WexP | 20 | WexP | 11 | WexP | 14 | WexP | 19 |

# MONEYFIELDS
Founded: 1987    Nickname: Moneys

**Secretary:** Wayne Dalton    **(T)** 07766 250 812    **(E)** secretary@moneyfieldsfc.co.uk
**Chairman:** Paul Gregory    **Prog Ed:** David Hayter
**Ground:**  Moneyfields Sports Ground, Moneyfield Ave, Copnor, P'mouth PO3 6LA    **(T)** 02392 665 260
**Capacity:** 1,500 **Seats:** 150 **Covered:** 150 **Midweek Matchday:** Tuesday    **Clubhouse:** Yes **Shop:** Yes

**Colours(change):**  Yellow/navy/navy (All white).
**Previous Names:**  Portsmouth Civil Service
**Previous Leagues:** Portsmouth. Hampshire.
**Records:**    **Att:** 250 v Fareham, WexD1 05-06 **Goalscorer:** Lee Mould 86 **App:** Matt Lafferty - 229 **Win:** 9-0v Blackfield & Langley 01-02.
**Senior Honours:**  Portsmouth Premier Champions 1990-91, 91-92. Senior Cup 1990-91.
    Hampshire Division Three 1991-92, Division Two 1992-93, Division One 1996-97.

**10 YEAR RECORD**

| 03-04 | | 04-05 | | 05-06 | | 06-07 | | 07-08 | | 08-09 | | 09-10 | | 10-11 | | 11-12 | | 12-13 | |
|---|---|---|---|---|---|---|---|---|---|---|---|---|---|---|---|---|---|---|---|
| Wex | 17 | Wex1 | 10 | Wex1 | 11 | WexP | 7 | WexP | 7 | WexP | 3 | WexP | 12 | WexP | 7 | WexP | 4 | WexP | 4 |

# NEWPORT I.O.W.
Founded: 1888    Nickname: The Port

**Secretary:** John Simpkins    **(T)** 07771 964 704    **(E)** simmo123@my-inbox.net
**Chairman:** Paul Phelps
**Ground:**  St George's Park, St George's Way, Newport PO30 2QH    **(T)** 01983 525 027
**Capacity:** 5,000 **Seats:** 300 **Covered:** 1,000 **Midweek Matchday:** Tuesday    **Clubhouse:** Yes **Shop:** Yes

**Colours(change):**  Yellow/blue/yellow. (Navy/navy/lime green)
**Previous Names:**
**Previous Leagues:** I.O.W. 1896-28. Hants 28-86. Wessex 86-90.
**Records:**    **Att:** 2,270 v Portsmouth (friendly) 07.07.2001. **Goalscorer:** Roy Grilfillan - 220 1951-57. **Apps:** Jeff Austin - 540 1969-87.
**Senior Honours:**  Southern League Eastern Division 2000-01. Hants Senior Cup (x8). I.O.W. Cup (34)

**10 YEAR RECORD**

| 03-04 | | 04-05 | | 05-06 | | 06-07 | | 07-08 | | 08-09 | | 09-10 | | 10-11 | | 11-12 | | 12-13 | |
|---|---|---|---|---|---|---|---|---|---|---|---|---|---|---|---|---|---|---|---|
| SthE | 19 | Isth1 | 18 | Isth1 | 22 | SthS | 20 | SthS | 22 | WexP | 6 | WexP | 9 | WexP | 10 | WexP | 13 | WexP | 6 |

# ROMSEY TOWN

Founded: 1886          Nickname:

**Secretary:** Matthew Lock          **(T)** 07817 612 190          **(E)** romseytownfc@gmail.com

**Chairman:** Ken Jacobs          **Prog Ed:** Paul Andrews

**Ground:**   The Bypass Ground, South Front, Romsey, SO51 8GJ          **(T)** 07876 743 651

**Capacity:**          **Seats:**          **Covered:** Yes          **Midweek Matchday:** Tuesday          **Clubhouse:** Yes

**Colours(change):**   White & black/black/black. (Blue & white/white/blue).
**Previous Names:**   None
**Previous Leagues:** Hampshire.
**Records:**
**Senior Honours:**   Wessex League Champions 1989-90.

**10 YEAR RECORD**

| 03-04 | | 04-05 | | 05-06 | | 06-07 | | 07-08 | | 08-09 | | 09-10 | | 10-11 | | 11-12 | | 12-13 | |
|---|---|---|---|---|---|---|---|---|---|---|---|---|---|---|---|---|---|---|---|
| Hant2 | 2 | Wex2 | 4 | Wex2 | 13 | Wex1 | 3 | WexP | 18 | WexP | 11 | WexP | 10 | WexP | 16 | WexP | 8 | WexP | 20 |

# SHOLING

Founded: 1916          Nickname: The Boatmen

**Secretary:** Greg Dickson          **(T)** 07948 832 944          **(E)** secretary.sholingfc@gmail.com

**Chairman:** David Daiper          **Prog Ed:** Greg Dickson

**Ground:**   VT Group Sportsground, Portsmouth Road, Sholing, SO19 9PW          **(T)** 02380 403 829

**Capacity:**          **Seats:** Yes          **Covered:** Yes          **Midweek Matchday:** Tuesday          **Clubhouse:** Yes

**Colours(change):**   Red & white/black/red & white (Yellow & blue/yellow/yellow)
**Previous Names:**   Woolston Works, Thornycrofts (Woolston) 1918-52, Vospers 1960-2003, VT FC 2003-10
**Previous Leagues:** Hampshire 1991-2004, Wessex 2004-09. Southern 2009-13.
**Records:**   **Att:** 150
**Senior Honours:**   Hampshire Premier Division 2000-01, 03-04

**10 YEAR RECORD**

| 03-04 | | 04-05 | | 05-06 | | 06-07 | | 07-08 | | 08-09 | | 09-10 | | 10-11 | | 11-12 | | 12-13 | |
|---|---|---|---|---|---|---|---|---|---|---|---|---|---|---|---|---|---|---|---|
| HantP | 1 | Wex1 | 12 | Wex1 | 13 | WexP | 3 | WexP | 2 | WexP | 2 | Sthsw | 4 | Sthsw | 2 | Sthsw | 4 | Sthsw | 7 |

# TOTTON & ELING

Founded: 1925          Nickname:

**Secretary:** Andrew Tipp          **(T)** 07545 182 379          **(E)** andytipp@ntlworld.com

**Chairman:** Edmond Holmes          **Prog Ed:** Edmund Holmes

**Ground:**   Millers Park,Little Tesrwood Farm Salisbury Road Totton SO40 2RW          **(T)** 07445 523 103

**Capacity:**          **Seats:** Yes          **Covered:** Yes          **Midweek Matchday:** Tuesday          **Clubhouse:** Yes

**Colours(change):**   Red & black/black/black (Yellow/blue/yellow)
**Previous Names:**   BAT Sports > 2007
**Previous Leagues:** Hampshire.
**Records:**   2,763 v AFC Wimbledon, FA Vase (game switched to AFC Wimbedon).
**Senior Honours:**   Hampshire Champions 1987-88, 88-89. Wessex Division 1 2008-09.

**10 YEAR RECORD**

| 03-04 | | 04-05 | | 05-06 | | 06-07 | | 07-08 | | 08-09 | | 09-10 | | 10-11 | | 11-12 | | 12-13 | |
|---|---|---|---|---|---|---|---|---|---|---|---|---|---|---|---|---|---|---|---|
| Wex | 15 | Wex1 | 9 | Wex1 | 18 | Wex2 | 5 | Wex1 | 5 | Wex1 | 1 | WexP | 7 | WexP | 18 | WexP | 11 | WexP | 12 |

# VERWOOD TOWN

Founded: 1920          Nickname:

**Secretary:** Roy Mortimer          **(T)** 07801 713 462          **(E)** secretary@vtfc.co.uk

**Chairman:** Steve Jefferis          **Prog Ed:** Dan Scott

**Ground:**   Potterne Park Potterne Way Verwood Dorset BH21 6RS          **(T)** 01202 814 007

**Capacity:**          **Seats:** Yes          **Covered:** Yes          **Midweek Matchday:** Wednesday          **Clubhouse:**

**Colours(change):**   Red/black/black (Blue & white stripes/blue/yellow)
**Previous Names:**
**Previous Leagues:** Hampshire
**Records:**
**Senior Honours:**   Wessex League Division One 2011-12.

**10 YEAR RECORD**

| 03-04 | | 04-05 | | 05-06 | | 06-07 | | 07-08 | | 08-09 | | 09-10 | | 10-11 | | 11-12 | | 12-13 | |
|---|---|---|---|---|---|---|---|---|---|---|---|---|---|---|---|---|---|---|---|
| Hant1 | 12 | Wex3 | 16 | Wex3 | 3 | Wex1 | 6 | Wex1 | 4 | Wex1 | 13 | Wex1 | 7 | Wex1 | 9 | Wex1 | 1 | WexP | 14 |

# WHITCHURCH UNITED

Founded: 1903          Nickname:

**Secretary:** Phil Cooper          **(T)** 07825 112 677          **(E)** secretarywufc@gmail.com

**Chairman:** Gary Shaughnessy          **Prog Ed:** John Rutledge

**Ground:**   Longmeadow Winchester Road Whitchurch Hampshire RG28 7RB          **(T)** 01256 892 493

**Capacity:**          **Seats:**          **Covered:** Yes          **Midweek Matchday:** Tuesday          **Clubhouse:** Yes

**Colours(change):**   Red & white stripes/black/red (All blue)
**Previous Names:**   None
**Previous Leagues:** Hampshire >1992, 1994-95. Wessex 1992-94.
**Records:**
**Senior Honours:**   Hampshire League Division Two 1989-90.

**10 YEAR RECORD**

| 03-04 | | 04-05 | | 05-06 | | 06-07 | | 07-08 | | 08-09 | | 09-10 | | 10-11 | | 11-12 | | 12-13 | |
|---|---|---|---|---|---|---|---|---|---|---|---|---|---|---|---|---|---|---|---|
| Wex | 22 | Wex2 | 12 | Wex2 | 22 | Wex2 | 12 | Wex1 | 17 | Wex1 | 6 | Wex1 | 10 | Wex1 | 7 | Wex1 | 8 | Wex1 | 2 |

# WINCHESTER CITY

Founded: 1884          Nickname: The Capitals

**Secretary:** Martin Moody          **(T)** 07768 848 905          **(E)** martin.moody@sky.com

**Chairman:** Paul Murray          **Prog Ed:** Andy Hadlington

**Ground:**   The City Ground, Hillier Way, Winchester SO23 7SR          **(T)** 07768 848 905

**Capacity:** 2,500  **Seats:** 200          **Covered:** 275          **Midweek Matchday:** Tuesday          **Clubhouse:** Yes          **Shop:** Yes

**Colours(change):**   Red & black stripes/black/red (White/white/black)
**Previous Names:**   None
**Previous Leagues:** Hampshire 1898-71, 73-03. Southern 1971-73, 2006-09, 2012-13. Wessex 2003-06. 2009-12.
**Records:**   1,818 v Bideford, FA Vase Semi-final.
**Senior Honours:**   Hants Senior Cup 1932, 2005. Southampton Senior Cup 2000-01.
          Hampshire Premier Division 2002-03. Wessex Division One 2003-04, 05-06, Premier Division 2011-12. FA Vase 2004.

**10 YEAR RECORD**

| 03-04 | | 04-05 | | 05-06 | | 06-07 | | 07-08 | | 08-09 | | 09-10 | | 10-11 | | 11-12 | | 12-13 | |
|---|---|---|---|---|---|---|---|---|---|---|---|---|---|---|---|---|---|---|---|
| Wex | 1 | Wex1 | 2 | Wex1 | 1 | SthW | 13 | SthW | 17 | SthW | 22 | WexP | 11 | WexP | 3 | WexP | 1 | SthC | 22 |

2012-13 - Blackfield & Langley line up before their FA Cup Fourth Qualifying tie against Hastings.
Photo: Roger Turner.

# DIVISION ONE

## AMESBURY TOWN
Founded: 1904  ◯ Nickname:

**Secretary:** Arthur Mundy  **(T)** 07791 148 594
**Chairman:** Jason Cameron
**Ground:** Bonnymead Park Recreation Road Amesbury SP4 7BB
**Colours(change):** All blue (All yellow)

**(E)** a.mundy094@virginmedia.com
**Prog Ed:** Mark Hilton
**(T)** 01980 623489

**ADDITIONAL INFORMATION:**
**Previous Name:** Amesbury FC. **Previous League:** Hampshire.
**Record Att:** 625 - 1997.

## ANDOVER NEW STREET
Founded: 1895  Nickname:

**Secretary:** Mick Bugg  **(T)** 07584 562 948
**Chairman:** Martin Tobin
**Ground:** Foxcotte Park Charlton Andover Hampshire SP11 0HS
**Colours(change):** Green & black/black/black (White/blue/blue)

**(E)** andovernewstreetfc@hotmail.co.uk
**Prog Ed:** Jimmy Wilson
**(T)** 01264 358358

**ADDITIONAL INFORMATION:**
**Record Att:** 240.
**Honours:** Trophyman Cup 2003-04.

## ANDOVER TOWN
Founded: 2013  Nickname:

**Secretary:** Barbara Passock  **(T)** 07715 043 869
**Chairman:** Lawrence Blair  **Manager:** Neil Benson
**Ground:** Portway Stadium, West Portway, Portway Industrial Estate, Andover SP10 3LF
**Colours(change):** Blue/white/blue (All orange)

**(E)** barbara.paddock@sparsholt.ac.uk
**Prog Ed:** Lawrence Blair
**(T)**

**ADDITIONAL INFORMATION:**

## COWES SPORTS
Founded: 1881  Nickname: Yachtsmen

**Secretary:** Glynn M Skinner  **(T)** 07854 889 446
**Chairman:** Ian Lee
**Ground:** Westwood Park Reynolds Close off Park Rd Cowes Isle of Wight PO31 7NT
**Colours(change):** Blue & White stripes/black/blue (Red/white/red)

**(E)** csfcsecretary@yahoo.com
**Prog Ed:** Peter Jeffery
**(T)** 01983 718 277

**ADDITIONAL INFORMATION:**
**Previous League:** Hampshire > 1994.
**Honours:** Hampshire League 1993-94.

## EAST COWES VICTORIA ATHLETIC
Founded:  Nickname:

**Secretary:** Darren Dyer  **(T)** 07725 128 701
**Chairman:** Kenny Adams
**Ground:** Beatrice Avenue Whippingham East Cowes Isle of Wight PO32 6PA
**Colours(change):** Red & white/black/black (Orange/white/orange)

**(E)** ecvics@live.co.uk
**Prog Ed:** Darren Dyer
**(T)** 01983 297 165

**ADDITIONAL INFORMATION:**

## FLEET SPURS
Founded:  Nickname:

**Secretary:** Bryan Sheppard  **(T)** 07808 001 014
**Chairman:** Bryan Sheppard
**Ground:** Kennels Lane Southwood Farnborough Hampshire, GU14 0ST
**Colours(change):** Blue with red trim/blue/blue (Yellow/black/yellow)

**(E)** sheppardbryan@virgin.net
**Prog Ed:** Paul Hampshire
**(T)**

**ADDITIONAL INFORMATION:**

## HAYLING UNITED
Founded: 1884  Nickname:

**Secretary:** Ian Gallop  **(T)** 07940 380 524
**Chairman:** Ian Gallop
**Ground:** Hayling College, Church Road, Hayling Island, Hampshire PO11 0NU
**Colours(change):** Black & white/black/black (All red).

**(E)** igollop@yahoo.co.uk
**Prog Ed:** Mark Griffiths
**(T)** 07724 540 916

**ADDITIONAL INFORMATION:**
Hampshire League Division One 2002-03. Wessex Division One 2006-07.

## HYTHE & DIBDEN

Founded:     Nickname:

**Secretary:** Nikki Oakley     **(T)** 07769 951 982     **(E)** hythedibdenfc@aol.com
**Chairman:** Dave Cox     **Prog Ed:** Dee Harvey
**Ground:** Ewart Recreation Ground Jones Lane Hythe Southampton SO45 6AA     **(T)** 02380 845 264 (MD)
**Colours(change):**   Green & white/white/green (All blue)
**ADDITIONAL INFORMATION:**

## LAVERSTOCK & FORD

Founded: 1956     Nickname:

**Secretary:** Matthew McMahon     **(T)** 07795 665 731     **(E)** sec.laverstockandfordfc@gmail.com
**Chairman:** John Pike     Nev Beal     **Prog Ed:** Steve Blackburn
**Ground:** The Dell, Church Road, Laverstock, Salisbury, Wilts SP1 1QX     **(T)** 01722 327 401
**Colours(change):**   Green & white hoops/green/green (Yellow/blue/white)
**ADDITIONAL INFORMATION:**

## NEW MILTON TOWN

Founded: 2007     Nickname: The Linnets

**Secretary:** Ian Claxton     **(T)** 01425 271 865     **(E)** ian.claxton1@btinternet.com
**Chairman:** John Breaker     **Manager:** Callum Brooks     **Prog Ed:** Ian Claxton
**Ground:** Fawcett Fields, Christchurch Road, New Milton, BH25 6QB     **(T)** 01425 628 191     **Capacity:** 3,000
**Colours(change):**   Maroon & blue stripes/blue/blue (Orange/white/orange)
**ADDITIONAL INFORMATION:**
**Honours:** Wessex League 1998-99, 04-05.

## PETERSFIELD TOWN

Founded:     Nickname:

**Secretary:** Mark Nicoll     **(T)** 07949 328 240     **(E)** m.nicoll1@ntlworld.com
**Chairman:** Graeme Moir     **Prog Ed:** Graeme Moir
**Ground:** Love Lane, Petersfield, Hampshire GU31 4BW     **(T)** 01730 233 416
**Colours(change):**   Red & black stripes/black/black (All blue)
**ADDITIONAL INFORMATION:**
**Previous Name:** Petersfield United.
**Previous League:** Isthmian.

## PEWSEY VALE

Founded: 1948     Nickname:

**Secretary:** Julie Wootton     **(T)** 07766 010 419     **(E)** pewseyvalefc@hotmail.co.uk
**Chairman:** Alan Ritchie     **Prog Ed:** Julie Wootton
**Ground:** Recreation Ground, Kings Corne,r Ball Road, Pewsey SN9 5BS     **(T)** 01672 5629 090
**Colours(change):**   White/navy/navy (All yellow)
**ADDITIONAL INFORMATION:**
**Previous League:** Wiltshire.

## RINGWOOD TOWN

Founded: 1879     Nickname:

**Secretary:** Aubrey Hodder     **(T)** 07754 460 501     **(E)** hodder888@btinternet.com
**Chairman:** Phil King     **Prog Ed:** Aubery Hodder
**Ground:** The Canotec Stadium Long Lane Ringwood Hampshire BH24 3BX     **(T)** 07706 903 959
**Colours(change):**   All red (All blue)
**ADDITIONAL INFORMATION:**

## STOCKBRIDGE

Founded: 1894     Nickname:

**Secretary:** Beverley Baker     **(T)** 07917 368 895     **(E)** stockbridgefc@hotmail.co.uk
**Chairman:** Paul Barker     **Prog Ed:** Paul Barker
**Ground:** Stockbridge Recreation Ground High Street Stockbridge SP20 6EU     **(T)**
**Colours(change):**   All red (Blue & yellow/blue/blue & yellow)
**ADDITIONAL INFORMATION:**
**Previous League:** Hampshire.

## TADLEY CALLEVA

Founded:          Nickname:

**Secretary:** Steve Blackburn          **(T)** 07787 501 028
**Chairman:** Sandy Russell
**Ground:** Barlows Park Silchester Road Tadley Hampshire RG26 3PX
**Colours(change):** Yellow & black/black/yellow (Burgundy & blue/burgundy/blue)

**(E)** tadleycallevafc@sky.com
**Prog Ed:** Andy Russell
**(T)** 07787 501 028

**ADDITIONAL INFORMATION:**

## TEAM SOLENT

Founded:          Nickname:

**Secretary:** Barry McGuinness          **(T)** 07917 415 304
**Chairman:** Phil Green
**Ground:** Test Park, Lower Broomhill Road, Southampton SO16 9QZ
**Colours(change):** All red (Yellow/black/black).

**(E)** barry.mcguinness@solent.ac.uk
**Prog Ed:** Joanne Andrews
**(T)**

**ADDITIONAL INFORMATION:**
**Previous Lge:** Hampshire > 2011.

## UNITED SERVICES PORTSMOUTH

Founded: 1962          Nickname:

**Secretary:** Bob Brady          **(T)** 07887 541 782
**Chairman:** Richard Stephenson Lt. RN
**Ground:** Victory Stadium HMS Temeraire Burnaby Road Portsmouth PO1 2HB
**Colours(change):** All royal blue (Red & white/red/red)

**(E)** usportsmouthfc@hotmail.co.uk
**Prog Ed:** Charlie Read
**(T)** 02392 724 235 (Club)

**ADDITIONAL INFORMATION:**
**Previous Name:** Portsmouth Royal Navy 1962-2005.
**Honours:** Hampshire League Division Two 1967-68, 77-78, 80-81. Portsmouth Senior Cup 2011-12.

# GROUND DIRECTIONS

**AFC PORTCHESTER - Wicor Recreation Ground Cranleigh Road Portchester Hampshire PO16 9DP 07798 734678 (M)**
Leave the M27 at Junction 11 and follow the signs to Portchester into Portchester Road. Carry on for approx 1 mile at the large roundabout, take the 3rd exit into Cornaway Lane and at the 'T' junction turn right in Cranleigh Road and follow the road to the end. Postcode for Satellite Navigation systems PO16 9DP
**ALRESFORD TOWN FC - Arlebury Park The Avenue Alresford Hampshire SO24 9EP 01962 735 100**
Alresford is situated on the A31 between Winchester and Alton. Arlebury Park is on the main avenue into Alresford opposite Perins School.
Postcode for Satellite Navigation systems SO24 9EP
**AMESBURY TOWN FC - Bonnymead Park Recreation Road Amesbury SP4 7BB 01980 623489**
From Salisbury take A345 to Amesbury, turn left just past the bus station and proceed through the one way system, when road splits with Friar Tuck Café and Lloyds Bank on left turn left and follow road over the river bridge and when road bears sharp right turn left into Recreation Road.
From A303 at Countess Roundabout go into Amesbury, straight over traffic lights, at mini-roundabout turn right into one way system and follow directions as above.
Postcode for Satellite Navigation systems SP4 7BB
**ANDOVER NEW STREET FC - Foxcotte Park Charlton Andover Hampshire SP11 0HS 01264 358358 Weekends from Midday, Evenings from 1900 hrs**
From Basingstoke follow the A303 to Weyhill roundabout. At roundabout turn right and 2nd roundabout turn left on to A342. Approx 1/2 mile turn right into Short Lane, continue into Harroway Lane to the 'T' junction at the top. Turn right into Foxcotte Lane and continue for about 3/4 mile then turn left, this still Foxcotte Lane, to the top some 3/4 mile to the roundabout straight across into Foxcotte Park. Postcode for Satellite Navigation systems SP11 0TA.
**ANDOVER TOWN - Portway Stadium,Portway Industrial Estate, Andover AP10 3LF**
Leave A303 at Junction for A342 . If from the East cross back over A303. At large roundabout take A342 across the face of the Premier Hotel. First right into the Portway Industrial Estate then follow the one way system and after the road swings right at the bottom of the hill the ground is on the left.
**BEMERTON HEATH HARLEQUINS FC - The Clubhouse Western Way Bemerton Heath Salisbury Wiltshire SP2 9DT 01722 331925 (Club) 331218 (Office)**
Turn off the A36 Salisbury to Bristol road at Skew Bridge (right turn if coming out of Salisbury), 1st left into Pembroke Road for 1/2 mile, 2nd left along Western Way – Ground is 1/4 mile at the end of the road. 40 minutes walk fro Salisbury railway station. Bus service 51 or 52 from the city centre.
Postcode for Satellite Navigation systems SP2 9DP
**BLACKFIELD & LANGLEY FC - Gang Warily Community and Recreation Centre Newlands Road Fawley Southampton SO45 1GA 02380 893 603**
Leave M27 at Junction 2 signposted A326 to Fawley. Head South along A326 through several roundabouts. Pass the Holbury P/H on your right at roundabout take the right fork signposted Lepe and Fawley.At the 1st set of traffic lights turn left then turn left into the ground, approx 200 yards. There is a sign at the traffic lights indicating Blackfield & Langley FC. Postcode for Satellite Navigation systems SO45 1GA
**BOURNEMOUTH FC - Victoria Park Namu Road Winton Bournemouth Dorset BH9 2RA 01202 515 123**
From the North and East – A338 from Ringwood. Take the 3rd exit signed A3060 Wimborne, going under the road you've just left. Stay on this road passing Castlepoint Shopping Centre (on your right), then the Broadway Hotel on your right, keep straight ahead passing the Horse & Jockey on your left, keep to the nearside lane. At roundabout take the 1st exit marked A347, pass Redhill Common on your right and the fire station on your left: continue on the A347 turning left at the filter with the pub – The Ensbury Park Hotel – immediately in front of you. 1st left into Victoria Avenue, and then third right into Namu Road, turning right at the end into the lane for the ground entrance.
From the West – A35 from Poole. Take the A3049 Dorset Way passing Tower Park (which is hidden from view) on your right, at the next roundabout take the second

exit, and then the first exit at the next roundabout, taking up a position in the outside lane. At the next roundabout (with a pub called the Miller and Carter Steakhouse on your right) take the third exit, Wallisdown Road A3049. Go through the shopping area of Wallisdown across two roundabouts and at the third one take the first exit, you will see the ground on your right as you approach the pelican crossing. Turn right into Victoria Avenue, then third right into Namu Road, turning right at the end into the lane for the ground entrance. Postcode for Satellite Navigation systems BH9 2RA

**BROCKENHURST FC - Grigg Lane Brockenhurst Hampshire SO42 7RE  01590 623544**
Leave the M27 at Junction 1 and take the A337 to Lyndhurst. From Lyndhurst take the A337 signposted Brockenhurst, turn right at Careys Manor Hotel into Grigg Lane. Ground situated 200 yards on the right. Postcode for Satellite Navigation systems SO42 7RE

**CHRISTCHURCH FC - Hurn Bridge Sports Club Avon Causeway Hurn Christchurc Dorset BH23 6DY  01202 473 792**
A338 from Ringwood turn off at sign for Bournemouth International Airport (Hurn) on left. At T junction turn right, continue through traffic lights, at the small roundabout in Hurn turn right away from the Airport, exit signed Sopley and 100 yards on the right is Hurn Bridge Sports Ground. Postcode for Sat. Nav. systems BH23 6DY

**COWES SPORTS FC - Westwood Park Reynolds Close off Park Road Cowes Isle of Wight PO31 7NT  01983 293 793**
Turn left out of the Cowes pontoon, 1st right up Park Road approx 1/2 mile take the 4th right into Reynolds Close. Postcode for Sat. Nav. systems PO31 7NT

**DOWNTON FC - Brian Whitehead Sports Ground Wick Lane Downton Wiltshire SP5 3NF  01725 512 162**
The ground is situated 6 miles south of Salisbury on the A338 to Bournemouth. In the village – sign to the Leisure Centre (to west) – this is Wick Lane – football pitch and Club approx 1/4 mile on the left. Postcode for Satellite Navigation systems SP5 3NF

**EAST COWES VICTORIA FC - Beatrice Avenue Whippingham East Cowes Isle of Wight PO32 6PA  01983 297 165**
From East Cowes ferry terminal follow Well Road into York Avenue until reaching Prince of Wells PH, turn at the next right into Crossways Road then turn left into Beatrice Avenue, from Fishbourne follow signs to East Cowes and Whippingham Church, ground is 200 yards from the church on Beatrice Avenue. Postcode for Satellite Navigation systems PO32 6PA

**FAREHAM TOWN FC - Cams Alders Football Stadium Cams Alders Palmerston Drive Fareham Hampshire PO14 1BJ  07930 853 235 (Club)**
Leave the M27 at Junction 11. Follow signs A32 Fareham – Gosport. Pass under the viaduct with Fareham Creek on your left, straight over at the roundabout then fork right – B3385 sign posted Lee-on-Solent. Over the railway bridge, Newgate Lane and turn immediately first right into Palmerston Business Park, follow the road to the ground. Postcode for Satellite Navigation systems PO14 1BJ

**FAWLEY AFC - Waterside Sports and Social Club 179-182 Long Lane Holbury Southampton Hampshire SO45 2PA  02380 893750 (Club) 896621 (Office)**
Leave the M27 at Junction 2 and follow the A326 to Fawley/Beaulieu. Head south for approx 7 miles. The Club is situated on the right hand side 2/3 mile after crossing the Hardley roundabout. The Club is positioned directly behind the service road on the right hand side. Postcode for Satellite Navigation systems SO45 2PA

**FLEET SPURS FC - Kennels Lane Southwood Farnborough Hampshire, GU14 0ST**
From the M3 Junction 4A take the A327 towards Farnborough/Cove. Left at the roundabout, over the railway line, left at the next roundabout Kennels Lane is on the right opposite the Nokia building, entrance is 100 yards on the left.  Postcode for Satellite Navigation systems GU14 0ST

**FOLLAND SPORTS - Folland Park Kings Avenue Hamble-Le-Rice Southampton Hampshire SO31 4NF  02380 452 173**
Leave the M27 at Junction 8 and take the turning for Southampton East At the Windhover roundabout take the exit for Hamble (B3397) Hamble Lane, proceed for 3 miles. Upon entering Hamble the ground is on the right via Kings Avenue, opposite the Harrier P/H. Postcode for Satellite Navigation systems SO31 4NF

**HAMWORTHY UNITED FC - The County Ground Blandford Close Hamworthy Poole Dorset BH15 4BF  01202 674 974**
From M27 to Cadnam – follow A31 to Ringwood – A347/A348 Ferndown - Bearcross – follow on this road until you pass the Mountbatten Arms on your left – turn right at next roundabout onto the A3049 and follow the signs to Dorchester and Poole. Continue on this dual carriageway over the flyover to the next roundabout – straight across and take the 2nd exit left off the dual carriageway to Upton / Hamworthy – go straight across 2 mini roundabouts and continue to Hamworthy passing the Co-op store on your left – then turn left at the 2nd set of traffic lights into Blandford Close.   Postcode for Satellite Navigation systems BH15 4BF

**HAYLING UNITED FC - College Ground The Hayling College Church Road Hayling Island,Hampshire PO11 0NU**
From A27 take the Hayling Island exit, after crossing the Langstone Bridge continue past the Yew Tree P/H. After a mile turn left at the small roundabout into Church Road and after 1/2 mile turn left into Hayling College grounds.
NB All parking must be in front car park. Coaches to be parked in the lay-by outside the college. Postcode for Satellite Navigation systems PO11 0NU

**HORNDEAN FC - Five Heads Park Five Heads Road Horndean Hampshire PO8 9NZ  02392 591 363**
Leave A3(M) at Junction 2 and follow signs to Cowplain. Take the slip road passing Morrisons store on the right crossing over the mini roundabout then continue to the set of traffic lights ensuring you are in the right hand lane signed Horndean. Turn right at these traffic lights and continue on for approximately 400 yards until you reach the Colonial Bar on your left, next junction on your left after the Colonial Bar is Five Heads Road, turn left into Five Heads Road and the ground is approx 1/4 mile along this road. Postcode for Satellite Navigation systems PO8 9NZ

**HYTHE & DIBDEN FC - Ewart Recreation Ground Jones Lane Hythe Southampton SO45 6AA  02380 845264 (Match days only) 07769 951982 (B)**
Travel along the A326 then at the Dibden roundabout take the first left into Southampton Road. Continue for approx. 1 mile and then turn left into Jones Lane just before the Shell Filling Station and the ground is 200 yards on your left. Car parking is available in the Dibden Parish Hall car park at the bottom end of the ground. Postcode for Satellite Navigation systems SO45 6AA

**LAVERSTOCK & FORD FC - The Dell Church Road Laverstock Salisbury Wiltshire SP1 1QX  01722 327 401**
From Southampton – At the end of the carriageway from Southampton (A36) turn right at traffic lights for the Park & Ride by the Tesco store. Turn left at the traffic lights over the narrow bridge then take the next turning into Manor Farm Road. Take the next turning right into Laverstock Road, (do not turn left under the railway bridge). Keep left into Laverstock village, past the Church and the Club is situated on the left hand side directly opposite the Chinese takeaway and shop.
From Bournemouth – Follow the A36 to Southampton past Salisbury College and straight across the Tesco roundabout take left at traffic lights into the Park & Ride take the corner slowly, the road goes back on itself) then follow directions as above. Postcode for Satellite Navigation systems SP1 1QX

**LYMINGTON TOWN FC - The Sports Ground Southampton Road Lymington Hampshire SO41 9ZG  01590 671 305 (Club)**
From the North & East – Leave the M27 at Junction 1 (Cadnam/New Forest) and proceed via Lyndhurst then Brockenhurst on the A337. On the outskirts of Lymington proceed through main set of traffic lights with Royal Quarter Housing Development and the Police Station on your right hand side. Continue for just another 250 metres and turn left immediately into St Thomas's Park with he ground in front of you.
Alternatively, turn left at the traffic lights into Avenue Road then first right, Oberland Court, with the Lymington Bowling Club facing you.
If travelling from the direction of Christchurch & New Milton using the A337 pass the White Hart P/H on the outskirts of Pennington and proceed down and up Stanford Hill. Passing the Waitrose Supermarket on your left hand side, the ground is situated immediately on your right hand side sign posted St Thomas Park. Postcode for Satellite Navigation systems SO41 9ZG

## WESSEX LEAGUE - STEP 5/6

**MONEYFIELDS FC - Moneyfields Sports Ground Moneyfield Avenue Copnor Portsmouth Hampshire PO3 6LA  02392 665 260 (Club) 07766 250 812 (M)**
Leave the A27 from the West and East at the Southsea turn off (A2030). Head down the Eastern Road and turn right into Tangiers Road at the fourth set of traffic lights – continue along this road until you pass the school and shops on your left and take the next right into Folkestone Road carrying on through to Martins Road and the Moneyfields Sports & Social Club is directly in front of you. Postcode for Satellite Navigation systems PO3 6LA

**NEW MILTON TOWN FC - Fawcett Fields Christchurch Road New Milton Hampshire BH25 6QB  01425 628 191**
Leave the M27 at Junction 2 and follow the signs to Lyndhurst. Carry on this road over four roundabouts and take the next slip road.At the traffic lights turn right to Lyndhurst. Go around the one way system and follow the signs to Christchurch (A35). After 10 miles at the Cat and Fiddle Public House turn left and continue towards the Chewton Glen Hotel. First exit at roundabout A337 to New Milton.The ground is one mile on the left. Postcode for Sat. Nav. systems BH25 6QB

**NEWPORT (IOW) FC LTD. - St Georges Park St Georges Way Newport Isle of Wight PO30 2QH  01983 525 027 (Club)**
From the Fishbourne Car Ferry Terminal take the A3054 towards Newport. At the large roundabout in the town centre take the A3020 towards Sandown, under the footbridge then 1st exit off the next roundabout. The ground is 200 yards on the left. Postcode for Satellite Navigation systems PO30 2QH

**PETERSFIELD TOWN FC - Love Lane Petersfield Hampshire GU31 4BW  01730 233 416**
Off circulatory one-way system in the town centre. Approx 10 minutes walk from Petersfield train station. Postcode for Satellite Navigation systems GU31 4BW

**PEWSEY VALE FC - Recreation Ground Kings Corner Ball Road Pewsey  01672 562 900**
From Pewsey's King Alfred statue, take the B3087 Burbage Road for 100 yards and then turn right into the Co-op car park, park in top right hand corner next to the bowls and tennis club and then walk through to the ground. Postcode for Satellite Navigation systems SN9 5BS

**RINGWOOD TOWN FC - The Canotec Stadium Long Lane Ringwood Hampshire BH24 3BX  01425 473 448**
Travel to Ringwood via the A31 (M27). From Ringwood town centre travel 1 mile on the B3347 towards Christchurch. At the Texaco petrol station turn into Moortown Lane and after 200 yards turn right into Long Lane. The ground is situated 250 yards on your left. Postcode for Satellite Navigation systems BH24 3BX

**ROMSEY TOWN FC - The Bypass Ground South Front Romsey Hampshire SO51 8GJ**
The ground is situated on the south of the town on the A27/A3090 roundabout (Romsey by pass), adjacent to the Romsey Rapids and Broadlands Estate. Postcode for Satellite Navigation systems SO51 8GJ

**SHOLING - VT Group Sportsground, Portsmouth Road, Sholing, SO19 9PW  02380 403 829**
Leave the M27 at J8 and follow the signs towards Hamble. As you drive up dual carriageway (remain in the L/H lane), you come to Windover roundabout. Take the second exit towards Hamble. Take the R/H lane and carry on straight across the small roundabout. After 200 yards bear right across a second small roundabout (2nd exit). After about 100 yards turn right into Portsmouth Road. Follow straight on for about half mile. VT ground is on right opposite a lorry entrance.

**STOCKBRIDGE FC - Stockbridge Recreation Ground High Street Stockbridge SP20 6EU  07963 453 162**
From Stockbridge High Street turn right at BT Substation into ground. Postcode for Satellite Navigation systems SP20 6EU

**TADLEY CALLEVA FC - Barlows Park Silchester Road Tadley Hampshire RG26 3PX**
From M3 Basingstoke Junction 6 take the A340 to Tadley, travel through Tadley and at the main traffic lights turn right into Silchester Road, proceed for 0.5 mile then turn left into the car park. Postcode for Satellite Navigation systems RG26 3PX

**TEAM SOLENT - Test Park, Lower Broomhill Road, Southampton SO16 9QZ**
Leave the M27 at junction 3 for M271. Take the first slip road off the M271 and then first exit off the roundabout on to Lower Broomhill Road. Carry on to the next roundabout and take the last exit, (coming back on yourself) into Redbridge lane and the entrance to Test Park is approx. 500m on right.
From City centre take the Millbrook road on the M271, first slip road off on to roundabout, 3rd exit on to Lower Broomhill Way and then as above.
Postcode for Satellite Navigation systems SO16 9QZ

**TOTTON & ELING FC - Millers Park,Little Teswrood Farm Salisbury Road Totton SO40 2RW  07445 523 103**
Leave M27 at Junction.2 and take A326 exit signposted Totton/Fawley. Almost immediately leave A326 onto slip road signposted Totton Town Centre which will meet the A36 (Salisbury Road). Turn left on to A36 and proceed for approx. three quarters of a mile and the ground entrance is on the left just before the Calmore Roundabout

**UNITED SERVICES PORTSMOUTH FC - Victory Stadium HMS Temeraire Burnaby Road Portsmouth Hampshire PO1 2HB 02392 724235 (Clubhouse) 02392 725315 (Office)**
Leave the M27 at Junction 12 and join the M275 to Portsmouth. Follow the signs to Gunwharf, turn right at the traffic lights into Park Road then left at the next set of lights into Burnaby Road and the entrance is at the end of this road on the right.via HMS Temeraire.
NB Car parking in HMS Temeraire is for Senior Club and Match Officials only on the production of a current Sydenhams League (Wessex) pass. Free car parking for players and supporters is at the Portsmouth University Nuffield car park opposite the Registry Public House – follow Anglesea Road and signs for Southsea/Ferry Terminals, go under railway bridge past lights, keeping US Rugby Stadium on your right into Hampshire Terrace and keeping right, LOOP back into Anglesey Road, go through pedestrian lights and then immediately left into the car park. From car park turn right past pedestrian lights into Cambridge Road, then right into Burnaby Road. Postcode for Satellite Navigation systems PO1 2HB

**VERWOOD TOWN FC - POTTERNE PARK POTTERNE WAY VERWOOD DORSET BH21 6RS  01202 814 007**
Turn off the A31 at Verwood/Matchams junctions just West of Ringwood Town centre exit (immediately after garage if coming from the East) to join the B3081. Follow the B3081 through the forest for approximately 4 miles coming into Verwood itself. At the second set of traffic lights turn left into Black Hill. At the roundabout take the 1st exit left into Newtown Road. At the end of Newtown Road turn left and then 1st left into Potterne Way. Note: Along Black Hill on the left you will pass Bradfords Building Merchants and the entrance to the Verwood Sports & Social Club where post match refreshments are made available.
Postcode for Satellite Navigation systems BH21 6RS

**WHITCHURCH UNITED FC - Longmeadow Winchester Road Whitchurch Hampshire RG28 7RB  01256 892 493**
From the South – take the A34 (North), 2 miles north of Bullington Cross take the Whitchurch exit. Head for Whitchurch Town Centre. The ground is 500 yards on your right. Postcode for Satellite Navigation systems RG28 7RB

**WINCHESTER CITY - The City Ground, Hillier Way, Winchester SO23 7SR  07768 848 905**
From Junction 9 on the M3 take the A33/A34 for one mile then follow A33 for a further mile.
Take the first left into Kings Worthy and follow the road for about three miles.  When you enter the 30mph zone take the second left, first right, then left into Hillier Way, Ground is on the right.

# WEST MIDLANDS (REGIONAL) LEAGUE

**Sponsored by:** No sponsor
**Founded:** 1889
**Recent Champions:**
2008: Bridgnorth Town
2009: AFC Wulfrunians
2010: Ellesmere Rangers
2011: Tividale
2012: Gornal Athletic

| DIVISION ONE | P | W | D | L | F | A | Pts |
|---|---|---|---|---|---|---|---|
| 1 (P) AFC Smethwick | 32 | 24 | 2 | 6 | 101 | 39 | 74 |
| 2 Bilston Town (2007) | 32 | 23 | 4 | 5 | 97 | 45 | 73 |
| 3 Wem Town | 32 | 23 | 2 | 7 | 105 | 54 | 71 |
| 4 Haughmond | 32 | 20 | 4 | 8 | 116 | 54 | 64 |
| 5 Hanwood United | 32 | 18 | 4 | 10 | 67 | 54 | 58 |
| 6 AFC Wombourne United | 32 | 17 | 3 | 12 | 78 | 65 | 54 |
| 7 Trysull | 32 | 15 | 7 | 10 | 71 | 52 | 52 |
| 8 Wyrley | 32 | 16 | 3 | 13 | 79 | 71 | 51 |
| 9 Mahal | 32 | 15 | 5 | 12 | 85 | 71 | 50 |
| 10 Stone Old Alleynians | 32 | 13 | 7 | 12 | 66 | 62 | 46 |
| 11 Shenstone Pathfinders | 32 | 10 | 5 | 17 | 65 | 88 | 35 |
| 12 Penncroft | 32 | 8 | 5 | 19 | 71 | 126 | 29 |
| 13 Bridgnorth Town Reserves | 32 | 7 | 4 | 21 | 54 | 88 | 25 |
| 14 Leominster Town | 32 | 6 | 7 | 19 | 72 | 114 | 25 |
| 15 W'Ton United | 32 | 6 | 6 | 20 | 52 | 100 | 24 |
| 16 St Martins | 32 | 6 | 6 | 20 | 62 | 113 | 24 |
| 17 Blackheath Town | 32 | 5 | 6 | 21 | 44 | 89 | 21 |

Warstone Wanderers withdrew

| PREMIER DIVISION | P | W | D | L | F | A | Pts |
|---|---|---|---|---|---|---|---|
| 1 (P) AFC Wulfrunians | 42 | 35 | 1 | 6 | 140 | 42 | 106 |
| 2 Lye Town | 42 | 33 | 6 | 3 | 124 | 43 | 105 |
| 3 Wolverhampton Casuals | 42 | 30 | 7 | 5 | 113 | 48 | 97 |
| 4 Shawbury United | 42 | 29 | 6 | 7 | 146 | 59 | 93 |
| 5 Black Country Rangers | 40 | 29 | 1 | 10 | 144 | 61 | 88 |
| 6 Dudley Town | 42 | 24 | 7 | 11 | 93 | 58 | 79 |
| 7 Pegasus Juniors | 41 | 21 | 8 | 12 | 93 | 65 | 71 |
| 8 Bewdley Town | 42 | 22 | 5 | 15 | 80 | 80 | 71 |
| 9 Cradley Town | 42 | 18 | 6 | 18 | 82 | 77 | 60 |
| 10 W'ton Sporting Community | 42 | 18 | 6 | 18 | 75 | 74 | 60 |
| 11 Sporting Khalsa | 42 | 17 | 6 | 19 | 85 | 89 | 57 |
| 12 Wellington Amateurs | 42 | 16 | 8 | 18 | 79 | 86 | 56 |
| 13 Malvern Town | 42 | 14 | 8 | 20 | 67 | 92 | 50 |
| 14 Bromyard Town | 42 | 15 | 3 | 24 | 76 | 121 | 48 |
| 15 Wellington | 41 | 14 | 5 | 22 | 64 | 93 | 47 |
| 16 Bartley Green | 42 | 14 | 5 | 23 | 69 | 107 | 47 |
| 17 Dudley Sports | 41 | 12 | 9 | 20 | 70 | 84 | 45 |
| 18 Wednesfield | 41 | 12 | 5 | 24 | 58 | 75 | 41 |
| 19 Shifnal Town | 42 | 11 | 5 | 26 | 66 | 107 | 38 |
| 20 Willenhall Town | 42 | 8 | 6 | 28 | 62 | 118 | 30 |
| 21 Darlaston Town | 40 | 6 | 1 | 33 | 42 | 134 | 19 |
| 22 Bustleholme | 42 | 2 | 2 | 38 | 37 | 152 | 8 |

Four matches left unplayed.

| DIVISION TWO | P | W | D | L | F | A | Pts |
|---|---|---|---|---|---|---|---|
| 1 (P) Gornal Athletic Reserves | 28 | 21 | 4 | 3 | 78 | 26 | 67 |
| 2 (P) Ledbury Town | 28 | 18 | 5 | 5 | 109 | 48 | 59 |
| 3 Hereford Lads Club | 27 | 16 | 7 | 4 | 65 | 37 | 55 |
| 4 Bartestree | 28 | 17 | 4 | 7 | 70 | 50 | 55 |
| 5 Penkridge Town | 28 | 14 | 7 | 7 | 69 | 40 | 49 |
| 6 Malvern Rangers | 28 | 12 | 8 | 8 | 59 | 49 | 44 |
| 7 Newport Town | 27 | 12 | 7 | 8 | 68 | 49 | 43 |
| 8 Team Dudley | 28 | 13 | 3 | 12 | 63 | 51 | 42 |
| 9 Sikh Hunters (-3pts) | 27 | 10 | 5 | 12 | 51 | 54 | 32 |
| 10 Wrens Nest | 28 | 10 | 2 | 16 | 64 | 70 | 32 |
| 11 Riverway (-1pt) | 28 | 7 | 10 | 11 | 49 | 57 | 30 |
| 12 Wolv. Sporting Community Res. | 28 | 8 | 2 | 18 | 57 | 96 | 26 |
| 13 Red Star Alma | 28 | 7 | 4 | 17 | 41 | 69 | 25 |
| 14 Tenbury United (-3pts) | 27 | 4 | 3 | 20 | 33 | 101 | 12 |
| 15 (R) Malvern Town Reserves | 28 | 3 | 1 | 24 | 35 | 114 | 10 |

Ettingshall Park Farm - record expunged.
Mahal Reserves - record expunged
Two games were left unplayed

| PREMIER DIVISION | 1 | 2 | 3 | 4 | 5 | 6 | 7 | 8 | 9 | 10 | 11 | 12 | 13 | 14 | 15 | 16 | 17 | 18 | 19 | 20 | 21 | 22 |
|---|---|---|---|---|---|---|---|---|---|---|---|---|---|---|---|---|---|---|---|---|---|---|
| 1 AFC Wulfrunians | | 6-0 | 6-0 | 4-3 | 6-2 | 3-0 | 5-3 | 4-1 | 6-2 | 2-0 | 0-2 | 5-0 | 3-0 | 0-2 | 7-1 | 5-0 | 2-1 | 5-0 | 1-0 | 4-0 | 1-1 | 5-1 |
| 2 Bartley Green | 0-5 | | 5-2 | 1-4 | 1-2 | 5-2 | 1-1 | 4-0 | 1-1 | 1-5 | 2-4 | 1-0 | 1-1 | 1-10 | 1-2 | 2-5 | 1-2 | 1-1 | 0-2 | 1-3 | 2-0 | 2-0 |
| 3 Bewdley Town | 2-3 | 3-2 | | 1-3 | 2-1 | 3-0 | 2-1 | 5-2 | 1-0 | 2-1 | 2-2 | 2-1 | 0-2 | 2-0 | 2-1 | 1-2 | 1-2 | 3-2 | 3-1 | 2-1 | 3-3 | 3-2 |
| 4 Black Country Rangers | 0-1 | 1-3 | 1-3 | | 4-2 | 9-0 | 5-0 | | 9-1 | 4-2 | 0-3 | 3-0 | 2-1 | 2-1 | 3-3 | 3-1 | 1-5 | 0-1 | 3-2 | | 7-1 | 4-1 |
| 5 Bromyard Town | 2-6 | 1-2 | 1-5 | 0-6 | | 2-0 | 2-1 | 2-0 | 3-2 | 1-0 | 1-4 | 3-2 | 0-0 | 1-3 | 1-4 | 4-6 | 0-3 | 0-2 | 2-0 | 2-3 | 3-1 | 3-1 |
| 6 Bustleholme | 0-11 | 1-3 | 1-2 | 2-6 | 1-3 | | 1-5 | 1-2 | 0-3 | 0-6 | 1-5 | 1-2 | 4-3 | 1-4 | 2-3 | 1-2 | 2-3 | 0-1 | 0-6 | 0-4 | 0-4 | 2-4 |
| 7 Cradley Town | 4-2 | 0-2 | 3-0 | 0-5 | 1-5 | 3-1 | | 8-2 | 3-2 | 2-2 | 0-5 | 3-0 | 3-2 | 0-1 | 1-0 | 5-1 | 1-3 | 0-2 | 1-1 | 0-1 | 2-0 | 5-2 |
| 8 Darlaston Town | 0-3 | 2-3 | 0-2 | 1-10 | 6-3 | 1-3 | 0-5 | | 0-1 | 1-3 | 1-3 | 0-1 | 0-7 | 2-2 | 0-3 | 1-4 | 1-0 | 2-1 | 1-0 | 1-3 | 0-5 | |
| 9 Dudley Sports | 1-3 | 3-2 | 0-3 | 0-4 | 3-2 | 1-1 | 1-1 | 3-1 | | 0-2 | 1-3 | 1-3 | 8-0 | 3-3 | 4-2 | 0-0 | 2-2 | 2-1 | 1-1 | 2-2 | 1-3 | 3-3 |
| 10 Dudley Town | 1-3 | 3-1 | 1-1 | 1-6 | 2-2 | 3-1 | 1-0 | 1-0 | | 0-3 | 1-2 | 0-2 | 6-0 | 0-0 | 1-3 | 0-0 | 4-3 | 3-1 | 2-1 | 3-1 | | |
| 11 Lye Town | 1-0 | 5-2 | 4-1 | 0-1 | 11-1 | 3-0 | 4-3 | 6-0 | 2-0 | | 2-2 | 2-2 | 2-2 | 3-1 | 3-2 | 0-0 | 3-2 | 1-1 | 1-2 | 3-1 | 2-0 | |
| 12 Malvern Town | 0-2 | 3-2 | 1-1 | 1-4 | 1-2 | 1-0 | 1-1 | 1-0 | 2-3 | 0-3 | 0-2 | | 1-2 | 0-5 | 5-1 | 4-2 | 3-3 | 1-3 | 4-3 | 1-0 | 3-2 | 2-1 |
| 13 Pegasus Juniors | 2-0 | 2-1 | 2-1 | 2-1 | 5-0 | 4-3 | 2-1 | 8-0 | 2-1 | 0-4 | 0-2 | 5-1 | | 3-4 | 12-0 | 2-0 | 2-2 | 1-2 | | 1-1 | 2-0 | 5-1 |
| 14 Shawbury United | 1-2 | 7-0 | 3-1 | 3-6 | 4-1 | 3-2 | 1-0 | 4-0 | 3-2 | 4-1 | 1-2 | 4-4 | 5-0 | | 3-2 | 2-2 | 3-4 | 1-1 | 4-1 | 8-1 | 4-0 | 3-0 |
| 15 Shifnal Town | 1-2 | 2-3 | 1-3 | 0-3 | 2-4 | 0-0 | 0-1 | 5-3 | 0-1 | 0-3 | 0-4 | 5-0 | 1-2 | | 2-1 | 2-1 | 2-3 | 1-2 | 2-0 | 2-3 | 4-0 | |
| 16 Sporting Khalsa | 1-2 | 2-2 | 4-5 | 2-4 | 8-0 | 1-3 | 8-0 | 2-1 | 3-1 | 1-3 | 0-2 | 1-1 | 1-7 | 3-0 | | 2-4 | 3-1 | 0-2 | 1-0 | 1-0 | 2-2 | |
| 17 Wednesfield | 0-1 | 5-1 | 3-0 | 5-0 | 4-1 | 5-0 | 2-1 | 4-2 | 3-1 | 4-1 | 2-0 | 2-0 | 1-3 | 2-1 | 3-3 | 2-1 | | 3-3 | 3-0 | 1-0 | 4-1 | 6-0 |
| 18 Wellington | 0-1 | 3-1 | 3-0 | 1-3 | 3-2 | 4-0 | 0-1 | 4-0 | 1-0 | 0-2 | 2-3 | 1-4 | 1-1 | 2-3 | 2-1 | 6-4 | 1-0 | | 0-2 | 2-3 | 5-5 | 2-1 |
| 19 Wellington Amateurs | 2-3 | 1-2 | 1-2 | 3-1 | 1-1 | 2-0 | 0-3 | 2-0 | 0-3 | 0-2 | 1-3 | 1-1 | 1-0 | 1-2 | 1-3 | 2-0 | 1-3 | 2-1 | | 2-3 | 0-1 | 2-1 |
| 20 Willenhall Town | 0-4 | 1-0 | 1-0 | 0-2 | 2-5 | 2-1 | 1-2 | 3-1 | 2-1 | 3-6 | 1-4 | 2-2 | 3-3 | 2-7 | 2-3 | 1-2 | 1-2 | 3-3 | 2-1 | | 1-2 | 2-3 |
| 21 Wolverhampton Casuals | 3-5 | 3-0 | 5-1 | 1-6 | 5-1 | 2-0 | 2-2 | 3-2 | 0-1 | 1-1 | 2-3 | 2-2 | 1-4 | 0-2 | 3-1 | 2-1 | 0-2 | 3-1 | 1-0 | 3-0 | | 2-2 |
| 22 Wolverhampton Sporting Com. | 2-1 | 1-3 | 2-2 | 2-5 | 3-1 | 6-2 | 2-3 | 1-4 | 0-4 | 0-3 | 1-0 | 0-3 | 1-7 | 0-0 | 0-4 | 1-2 | 0-2 | 5-3 | 1-2 | 0-0 | | |

# WEST MIDLANDS LEAGUE - STEP 6/7

| DIVISION ONE | 1 | 2 | 3 | 4 | 5 | 6 | 7 | 8 | 9 | 10 | 11 | 12 | 13 | 14 | 15 | 16 | 17 |
|---|---|---|---|---|---|---|---|---|---|---|---|---|---|---|---|---|---|
| 1 AFC Smethwick | | 4-1 | 0-1 | 4-0 | 2-0 | 4-0 | 3-2 | 6-1 | 3-3 | 1-3 | 4-0 | 5-1 | 4-1 | 1-0 | 4-1 | 5-0 | 2-0 |
| 2 AFC Wombourne United | 0-3 | | 2-1 | 5-3 | 4-3 | 5-3 | 2-0 | 2-1 | 1-3 | 4-0 | 2-2 | 3-1 | 3-2 | 4-3 | 4-0 | 2-4 | 0-3 |
| 3 Bilston Town (2007) | 1-3 | 2-1 | | 5-2 | 4-2 | 2-1 | 4-1 | 5-1 | 3-1 | 3-5 | 3-1 | 4-1 | 4-1 | 3-0 | 5-1 | 6-1 | 6-4 |
| 4 Blackheath Town | 1-6 | 1-3 | 0-3 | | 1-0 | 0-0 | 1-1 | 5-2 | 0-5 | 1-1 | 0-2 | 2-0 | 0-2 | 0-0 | 2-2 | 2-7 | 5-1 |
| 5 Bridgnorth Town Reserves | 3-1 | 2-2 | 0-3 | 2-3 | | 1-3 | 3-4 | 1-4 | 1-4 | 2-4 | 4-2 | 2-2 | 2-2 | 3-2 | 5-0 | 1-2 | 1-3 |
| 6 Hanwood United | 5-1 | 3-1 | 0-1 | 2-1 | 2-0 | | 2-1 | 2-1 | 0-0 | 4-1 | 2-1 | 7-3 | 5-2 | 1-4 | 1-0 | 2-0 | 0-2 |
| 7 Haughmond | 2-3 | 2-0 | 2-0 | 2-1 | 6-1 | 2-4 | | 4-4 | 2-1 | 12-0 | 5-2 | 5-0 | 7-0 | 2-2 | 8-1 | 0-2 | 0-2 |
| 8 Leominster Town | 2-9 | 1-1 | 0-5 | 7-2 | 3-0 | 1-3 | 2-2 | | 4-1 | 4-3 | 2-2 | 3-5 | 3-3 | 1-3 | 3-3 | 0-2 | 4-6 |
| 9 Mahal | 0-1 | 3-2 | 1-1 | 4-3 | 7-1 | 2-1 | 0-7 | 5-1 | | 5-1 | 0-5 | 4-4 | 3-3 | 1-0 | 8-2 | 4-1 | 2-4 |
| 10 Penncroft | 1-7 | 3-6 | 1-7 | 5-1 | 2-1 | 1-3 | 3-7 | 2-2 | 0-5 | | 2-4 | 4-4 | 0-8 | 1-2 | 2-7 | 1-4 | 4-1 |
| 11 Shenstone Pathfinders | 4-2 | 1-4 | 1-1 | 3-1 | 2-4 | 2-4 | 2-5 | 5-2 | 3-2 | 0-3 | | 1-0 | 1-3 | 1-4 | 2-1 | 4-7 | 2-4 |
| 12 St Martins | 0-6 | 1-7 | 2-5 | 3-1 | 2-2 | 0-3 | 2-6 | 1-4 | 5-1 | 1-10 | 1-1 | | 1-3 | 2-5 | 8-1 | 2-4 | 3-1 |
| 13 Stone Old Alleynians | 0-1 | 1-3 | 1-2 | 3-2 | 1-0 | 4-0 | 2-5 | 7-4 | 2-0 | 1-1 | 0-0 | 1-0 | | 1-2 | 4-1 | 0-1 | 0-1 |
| 14 Trysull | 1-2 | 1-0 | 2-2 | 2-0 | 1-2 | 1-1 | 2-6 | 6-1 | 4-3 | 2-2 | 4-0 | 6-1 | 2-2 | | 3-0 | 4-2 | 1-2 |
| 15 Wem Town | 2-2 | 1-3 | 0-2 | 1-1 | 3-0 | 3-0 | 2-4 | 2-1 | 1-3 | 4-3 | 2-3 | 3-2 | 1-4 | 1-1 | | 2-2 | 1-2 |
| 16 Wolverhampton United | 3-0 | 5-0 | 5-1 | 3-0 | 4-1 | 2-2 | 0-1 | 6-2 | 3-0 | 8-1 | 4-2 | 2-3 | 3-0 | 4-0 | 4-2 | | 7-2 |
| 17 Wyrley | 0-2 | 2-1 | 2-2 | 3-2 | 3-4 | 5-1 | 1-3 | 5-1 | 2-4 | 5-1 | 6-4 | 1-1 | 1-1 | 0-1 | 4-1 | 2-3 | |

| DIVISION TWO | 1 | 2 | 3 | 4 | 5 | 6 | 7 | 8 | 9 | 10 | 11 | 12 | 13 | 14 | 15 |
|---|---|---|---|---|---|---|---|---|---|---|---|---|---|---|---|
| 1 Bartestree | | 0-5 | 3-3 | 2-1 | 4-3 | 4-1 | 1-6 | 0-4 | 6-2 | 3-3 | 2-1 | 4-1 | 7-1 | 3-2 | 3-2 |
| 2 Gornal Athletic Reserves | 2-1 | | 3-2 | 3-1 | 2-1 | 6-1 | 0-0 | 3-2 | 1-0 | 5-2 | 1-2 | 1-4 | 6-0 | 5-0 | 5-1 |
| 3 Hereford Lads Club | 3-0 | 0-0 | | 2-5 | 0-2 | 6-3 | 2-1 | 2-1 | 1-1 | 3-0 | 3-1 | 2-2 | 7-0 | 3-0 | 2-0 |
| 4 Ledbury Town | 1-2 | 3-3 | 1-1 | | 5-0 | 4-2 | 5-1 | 3-0 | 9-1 | 3-1 | 9-4 | 5-0 | 1-0 | 9-0 | 4-0 |
| 5 Malvern Rangers | 3-1 | 2-2 | 1-3 | 2-4 | | 4-0 | 1-1 | 0-0 | 2-0 | 2-0 | 3-2 | 3-2 | 4-2 | 4-0 | 4-1 |
| 6 Malvern Town Reserves | 1-1 | 0-1 | 1-2 | 2-6 | 0-2 | | 1-7 | 5-1 | 2-5 | 0-5 | 3-1 | 0-1 | 3-2 | 1-5 | 1-3 |
| 7 Newport Town | 3-1 | 0-1 | 3-0 | 4-2 | 3-3 | 8-1 | | 0-3 | 1-1 | 0-0 | 4-3 | 1-4 | P-P | 5-2 | 2-3 |
| 8 Penkridge Town | 1-5 | 1-2 | 1-1 | 4-4 | 1-1 | 5-0 | 2-2 | | 4-0 | 1-1 | 0-0 | 1-2 | 4-1 | 2-1 | 5-2 |
| 9 Red Star Alma | 0-1 | 1-2 | 0-1 | 5-3 | 2-2 | 4-2 | 3-1 | 0-2 | | 0-2 | 1-3 | 0-1 | 1-3 | 0-4 | 1-4 |
| 10 Riverway | 1-1 | 0-3 | 0-4 | 2-2 | 1-1 | 5-1 | 1-3 | 0-4 | 3-0 | | 2-3 | 2-2 | 5-4 | 2-0 | 4-0 |
| 11 Sikh Hunters | 0-2 | 2-0 | P-P | 1-2 | 2-2 | 3-0 | 1-1 | 0-2 | 1-1 | 2-2 | | 0-3 | 3-0 | 4-2 | 0-1 |
| 12 Team Dudley | 0-1 | 0-2 | 2-3 | 2-4 | 2-3 | 3-1 | 2-3 | 0-2 | 1-2 | 3-1 | 3-2 | | 2-0 | 7-0 | 3-3 |
| 13 Tenbury United | 0-9 | 0-3 | 2-3 | 3-3 | 2-1 | 3-2 | 1-2 | 0-8 | 2-6 | 1-1 | 0-3 | 3-2 | | 2-3 | 0-0 |
| 14 Wolverhampton Sporting Community Reserves | 0-2 | 0-8 | 2-2 | 1-4 | 4-2 | 7-1 | 4-1 | 4-5 | 3-1 | 1-1 | 4-5 | 0-6 | 6-0 | | 1-6 |
| 15 Wrens Nest | 0-1 | 0-3 | 2-4 | 0-6 | 3-1 | 10-0 | 1-5 | 1-3 | 2-3 | 1-4 | 1-2 | 2-3 | 6-1 | 5-1 | |

## CLUB MOVEMENTS

**Premier Division - In:** Smethwick Rangers (P & NC from AFC Smethwick).

**Out:** AFC Wulfrunians (P - Midland Football Alliance). Darlaston Town (F).

**Division One - In:** AFC Bridgnorth (N). Gornal Athletic Reserves (P). Ledbury Town (P).

**Out:** AFC Smethwick Rangers (P & NC to Smethwick Rangers). AFC Wombourne United (F). Blackheath Town (W).

Bridgnorth Town Reserves (F). Leominster Town (W - Herefordshire Premier Division). Warstone Wanderers (WN).

**Division Two - In:** AFC Ludlow (P - Mercian Regional Football League Premier). Bilbrook (N). Warstone Wanderers (N).

FC Stafford (N). Worcester Raiders (N). Wyrley Reserves (N).

**Out:** Ettingshall Park Farm (WS). Gornal Athletic Reserves (P). Ledbury Town (P). Mahal Reserves (WS).

Malvern Town Reserves (R - Worcester Premier Division). Riverway (W). Tenbury United (R - Herefordshire Div.1).

## BARTLEY GREEN
Founded: 1948    Nickname:

**Secretary:** John McDermott    **(T)** 07825 576 820
**Chairman:** Pat Goulding
**Ground:** Illey Lane, Halesowen, Birmingham, West Midlands B62 0HF
**Colours(change):** Orange & black/black/black
**(E)** mcdermottjohn47@yahoo.com

**(T)**

**ADDITIONAL INFORMATION:**
**Previous Leagues:** Midland Combination > 2012.
**Honours:** Midland Combination Division 2 2005-06, Division 1 2006-07.

## BEWDLEY TOWN
Founded: 1978    Nickname:

**Secretary:** Steve Godfrey    **(T)** 07739 626 169
**Chairman:** Geoff Edwards
**Ground:** Ribbesford Meadows, Ribbesford, Bewdley, Worcs DY12 2TJ
**Colours(change):** Royal blue with yellow trim/royal blue/royal blue
**(E)** steve_g09@fsmail.net

**(T)** 07739 626 169

**ADDITIONAL INFORMATION:**
**Honours:** Worcestershire Senior Urn 2011-12.

## BLACK COUNTRY RANGERS
Founded: 1996    Nickname:

**Secretary:** Andy Harris    **(T)** 07891 128 896
**Chairman:** Paul Garner
**Ground:** Tividale FC, The Beeches, Packwood Road, Tividale B69 1UL
**Colours(change):** All red.
**(E)** blackcountryrangers@hotmail.co.uk

**(T)** 01384 211 743

**ADDITIONAL INFORMATION:**
**Honours:** West Midlands (Regional) Division One 2010-11.

## BROMYARD TOWN
Founded: 1893    Nickname:

**Secretary:** Richard Haverfield    **(T)** 07885 849 948
**Chairman:** Richard Greenhall
**Ground:** Delahay Meadow, Stourport Road, Bromyard HR7 4NT
**Colours(change):** All blue
**(E)** tony.haverfield@virgin.net

**(T)** 01885 483 974

**ADDITIONAL INFORMATION:**

## BUSTLEHOLME
Founded: 1975    Nickname:

**Secretary:** Geoff Bowden    **(T)** 07805 829 354
**Chairman:** Geoff Benbow
**Ground:** Tipton Town F C, Wednesbury Oak Road, Tipton, West Mid. DY4 0BS
**Colours(change):** Yellow/green/green
**(E)** geoff.benbow@hotmail.co.uk

**(T)** 0121 502 5534

**ADDITIONAL INFORMATION:**

## CRADLEY TOWN
Founded: 1948    Nickname:

**Secretary:** David Attwood    **(T)** 07708 659 636
**Chairman:** Trevor Thomas
**Ground:** The Beeches, Beeches View Avenue, Cradley, Halesowen B63 2HB
**Colours(change):** All red
**(E)** d.attwood@sky.com

**(T)** 07746 231 195

**ADDITIONAL INFORMATION:**

## DUDLEY SPORTS
Founded: 1978    Nickname:

**Secretary:** John Lewis    **(T)** 07737 099 385
**Chairman:** Ashley Forrest
**Ground:** Hillcrest Avenue, Brierley Hill, West Mids DY5 3QH
**Colours(change):** Green & white/green/green & white
**(E)** kath-john.lewis@blueyonder.co.uk

**(T)** 01384 826 420

**ADDITIONAL INFORMATION:**

## DUDLEY TOWN

Founded: 1893     Nickname:

**Secretary:** Pater Evans     **(T)** 07758 460 191     **(E)** peterevans22@hotmail.co.uk
**Chairman:** Stephen Austin
**Ground:** The Dell Stadium, Bryce Road, Brierley Hill, West Mids DY5 4NE     **(T)** 01384 812 943
**Colours(change):** Red/black/red & black

**ADDITIONAL INFORMATION:**

## ELLESMERE RANGERS

Founded: 1969     Nickname: The Rangers

**Secretary:** John Edge     **(T)** 07947 864 357     **(E)** john.edge2@homecall.co.uk
**Chairman:** Neil Williams
**Ground:** Beech Grove, Ellesmere, Shropshire SY12 0BT     **(T)** 07947 864 357     **Capacity:** 1250
**Colours(change):** Sky blue/navy/navy (Yellow/black/yellow)

**ADDITIONAL INFORMATION:**
**Previous Leagues:** West Midlands > 20120. Midland Alliance 2010-2013.
**Honours:** West Midlands League Premier Division 2009-10.

## LYE TOWN

Founded: 1930     Nickname:

**Secretary:** Yvonne Bignell     **(T)** 07921 662 837     **(E)**
**Chairman:** Brian Blakemore
**Ground:** Sports Ground, Stourbridge Road, Lye, Stourbridge, West Mids DY9 7DH     **(T)** 01384 422 672
**Colours(change):** Blue/blue/white

**ADDITIONAL INFORMATION:**

## MALVERN TOWN

Founded: 1947     Nickname:

**Secretary:** Margaret Scott     **(T)** 07944 110 402     **(E)** margscott55@hotmail.com
**Chairman:**
**Ground:** Langland Stadium, Lamgland Avenue, Malvern WR14 2QE     **(T)** 01684 574 068     **Capacity:** 2,500
**Colours(change):** All claret

**ADDITIONAL INFORMATION: Records: Att:** 1,221 v Worcester City FA Cup. **Goals:** Graham Buffery. **Apps:** Nick Clayton.
**Honours:** Worcestershire Senior Urn (x7). Midland Combination Division One 1955-56.

## PEGASUS JUNIORS

Founded: 1955     Nickname: The Redmen

**Secretary:** Nik Marsh     **(T)** 07816 121 248     **(E)** nikmarsh1982@gmail.com
**Chairman:** Chris Wells
**Ground:** Old School Lane, Hereford HR1 1EX     **(T)** 07980 465 995     **Capacity:** 1,000
**Colours(change):** Red & white/white/red

**ADDITIONAL INFORMATION: Att:** 1,400 v Newport AFC, 1989-90.
**Honours:** Worcestershire Senior Urn 85-86. Hellenic Div.1 Champions 84-85, 98-99.
**Previous Lge:** Hellenic > 2011.

## SHAWBURY UNITED

Founded: 1992     Nickname:

**Secretary:** Tracie Howells     **(T)** 07950 740 089     **(E)** traciehowells72@yahoo.co.uk
**Chairman:** David Kirkup
**Ground:** Butler Sports Ground, Bowensfield, Wem, Shrewsbury SY4 5AP     **(T)** 01939 233 287
**Colours(change):** All light blue

**ADDITIONAL INFORMATION:**
**Honours:** Shropshire Challenge Cup 2012-13.

## SHIFNAL TOWN

Founded: 1964     Nickname:

**Secretary:** Derek Groucott     **(T)** 07910 120 512     **(E)** carolderek2@blueyonder.co.uk
**Chairman:**
**Ground:** Phoenix Park, Coppice Green Lane, Shifnal, Shrops TF11 8PB     **(T)** 01952 463 257
**Colours(change):** Red & white stripes/black/black

**ADDITIONAL INFORMATION:**
**Honours:** West Midlands (Regional) League Premier Division 2006-07.

## SMETHWICK RANGERS

Founded: 1977    Nickname:

**Secretary:** Darshan Ram    (T) 07983 625 385    (E) darshan.ram@federalmogul.com
**Chairman:** Ajaib Garcha
**Ground:** Hillcrest Avenue, Brierley Hill, West Mids. DY5 3QH    (T) 01384 826 420
**Colours(change):** All blue

**ADDITIONAL INFORMATION:**
**Previous Name:** AFC Smethwick.
**Honours:** West Midlands Division One 2012-13.

## SPORTING KHALSA

Founded: 1991    Nickname:

**Secretary:** Parmjit Singh Gill    (T) 07976 606 132    (E) Parmjit.gill@globeproperty.co.uk
**Chairman:** Rajinder Singh Gill
**Ground:** Aspray Arena, Noose Lane, Willenhall WV13 3BB    (T) 01902 219 208
**Colours(change):** Yellow/blue/yellow.

**ADDITIONAL INFORMATION:**

## WEDNESFIELD

Founded: 1961    Nickname:

**Secretary:** Ronald Brown    (T) 07528 589 508    (E) rbwedfc@gmail.com
**Chairman:** David Saville
**Ground:** Cottage Ground, Amos Lane, Wednesfield WV11 1ND    (T)
**Colours(change):** Red & white stripes/black/black

**ADDITIONAL INFORMATION:**

## WELLINGTON

Founded: 1968    Nickname:

**Secretary:** Michael Perkins    (T) 07842 186 643    (E) perkins@haworth13.freeserve.co.uk
**Chairman:** Phillip Smith
**Ground:** Wellington Playing Field, Wellington, Hereford HR4 8AZ    (T)
**Colours(change):** All orange

**ADDITIONAL INFORMATION:**

## WELLINGTON AMATEURS

Founded: 1950    Nickname:

**Secretary:** Graeme McDermott    (T) 07837 355 380    (E) Graeme.mcdermott@mercer.com
**Chairman:** Dave Gregory
**Ground:** Wickes Stadium, School grove, Oakengates, telford, Shrops TF2 6BQ    (T)
**Colours(change):** Red/black/black

**ADDITIONAL INFORMATION:**

## WILLENHALL TOWN

Founded: 1953    Nickname: The Lockmen

**Secretary:** Simon Hall    (T) 07901 560 691    (E) sdhwin@aol.com
**Chairman:** Simon Hall
**Ground:** Long Lane Park, Long Lane, Essington, Wolverhampton. WV11 2AA    (T) 01922 406 604
**Colours(change):** All red

**ADDITIONAL INFORMATION:**
**Previous Leagues:** Staffs Co, West Mids 1975-78, 1991-94, Southern 1982-91, 2005-08, Midland All. 1994-2004, 2010-12, N.P.L 2004-05, 2008-10.
**Honours:** Staffs County Premier 1974-75. West Mids Division 1 1975-76, Premier 77-78. Southern League Midland Division 1983-84.

## WOLVERHAMPTON CASUALS

Founded: 1899    Nickname:

**Secretary:** Michael Green    (T) 07870 737 229    (E) wtoncasualsfc@aol.com
**Chairman:** Garth Deacon
**Ground:** Brinsford Stadium, Brinsford Lane, Wolverhampton WS10 7PR    (T) 01902 783 214
**Colours(change):** All green

**ADDITIONAL INFORMATION:**

## WOLVERHAMPTON SPORTING COMMUNITY    Founded: 2001    Nickname:

**Secretary:** Mark Hopson       **(T)** 07966 505 425       **(E)** hopsonma@tiscali.co.uk
**Chairman:** John Quarry
**Ground:** Wednesfield F C, Cottage Ground, Amos Lane, Wednesfield. WV11 1ND     **(T)** 01902 735 506
**Colours(change):** Orange & black/black/black

**ADDITIONAL INFORMATION:**
**Previous Name:** Heath Town Rangers 2001-10.

### WEST MIDLANDS (REGIONAL) LEAGUE DIVISION ONE CONSTITUTION 2013-14

AFC BRIGNORTH....................Crown Meadow, Innage Lane, Bridgnorth. WV16 4HS................ 07748 302 650 (Steve Groome - Sec)

BILSTON TOWN (2007)...........Queen Street, Bilston WV14 7EX .......................................................07949 315 489 (Paul Lloyd - Sec)

GORNAL ATHLETIC RESERVES...Garden Walk Stadium, Garden Walk, Lower Gornal, Dudley. DY3 2NR...........................01384 358398

HANWOOD UNITED.................Hanwood Recreation Ground, Hanwood SY5 8JN...........................01743 343 124 (Gary Evans - Sec)

HAUGHMOND..........................Shrewsbury Sports Village, Sundorne Road, Shrewsbury. SY1 4RG...............................01743 256 260

LEDBURY TOWN....................Ledbury Town FC., New Street, Ledbury. HR8 2ED ..........................................................01531 631 463

MAHAL ......................................Hadley Stadium, Wilson Road, Smethwick B68 9JW ..........................................................0121 434 4848

PENNCROFT ...........................Aldersley Leisure Village, Aldersley Road, Wolverhampton WV6 9NW ...........................01902 556 200

SHENSTONE PATHFINDER.....Shenston Pavilion Club, Birmingham Road, Shenstone WS14 0LR ................................01543 481 658

ST MARTINS............................The Venue, Burma Road, Parkhall, Oswestry, Shrops. SY11 8AS...................................01691 684 840

STONE OLD ALLEYNIANS.......Wellbeing Park, Yarnfield Lane, Yarnfield ST15 0NF..........................................................01785 761 891

TRYSULL...................................Wolverhampton Casuals FC, Brinsford Road, Coven Heath, Wolverhampton WV10 7PR.............01902 783 214

WEM TOWN.............................Butler Sports Centre, Bowens Field, Wem SY4 5AP.........................................................01939 233 287

WOLVERHAMPTON UNITED...Prestwood Road West, Wednesfield WV11 1HN..............................................................01902 730 881

WYRLEY ...................................Wyrley Juniors FC, Long Lane, Essington, Wolverhampton. WS6 6AT ... 07917 191 263 (Candy Ponder - Sec)

### WEST MIDLANDS (REGIONAL) LEAGUE DIVISION TWO CONSTITUTION 2013-14

AFC LUDLOW..........................Showtime Security Stadium, Burway Lane, Bromfield Road, Ludlow SY8 2BN................01584 876 000

BARTESTREE..........................Bartestree Playing Fields, Bartestree, Hereford.................................... 07980 305 118 (Matchdays only)

BILBROOK ...............................Pendeford Lane, off Wobaston Road, Wolverhampton WV9 5HQ ..07910 421 544 (Lorna Painter - Sec)

FC STAFFORD.........................Rowley Park Stadium, (3G surface) Averill, Stafford. ST17 9XX....................................01785 251 060

HEREFORD LADS CLUB ........Hereford Lads Club, Widemarsh Common, Hereford, HR4 9NA....................................01432 267 127

MALVERN RANGERS..............Malvern Vale Community Centre, Swineyard Road, Malvern WR14 1GU .......................01684 592 363

NEWPORT TOWN ..................Shuker Field, Audley Avenue, Newport, Shropshire TF10 7DS.....................................01952 820 280

PENKRIDGE TOWN ...............Monkton Recreation Centre, Pinfold Lane, Penkridge ST19 5QP ..........07833 327 899 (John Partridge - Sec)

RED STAR ALMA.....................Bentley Youth FC, Bentley Road South, Darlaston. WV10 8LN ..... 07703 760 888 (Paul Adshead - Sec)

SIKH HUNTERS.......................Hadley Stadium, Wilson Road, Birmingham B66 4ND ....................................07887 505 491 (MD only)

TEAM DUDLEY........................The Dell Stadium, Bryce Road, Brierley Hill DY5 4NE ...................................................01384 812 943

WARSTONES WANDERERS ...Aldersley Leisure Village, Aldersley Road, Aldersley, Wolverhampton WV6 9NW............01902 556 200

WOLVERHAMPTON SPORTING COM. RES ..Pendeford Lane, off Wobaston Road, Wolverhampton WV9 5HQ ..07966 505 425 (Mark Hopson - Sec)

WORCESTER RAIDERS .........Claines Lane, Worcester. WR3 7SS ................................................................07845 553 400 (MD only)

WRENS NEST...........................Handrahan Sports Stadium, Mile Flat, Wallheath DY6 0AX ..........................07962 397 331 (MD only)

WRLEY RESERVES ................Wyrley Juniors FC, Long Lane, Essington, Wolverhampton. WS6 6AT ... 07917 191 263 (Candy Ponder - Sec)

# GROUND DIRECTIONS - PREMIER DIVISION

**BARTLEY GREEN - Bartley Green FC, Illey Lane, Illey, Halesowen, West Mids. B62 0HF**
From Junction 3 M5 follow the A456 for Halesowen/Kidderminster for approximately 1.5 miles to Grange Island. Turn 1st left along the B4551 Bromsgrove Road for approximately 400 yards and take the 1st turning left into Illey lane. Ground is approximately 1 mile on left hand side.

**BEWDLEY TOWN - Ribbesford Meadows, Ribbesford, Bewdley, Worcs. DY12 2TJ Tel: 07739-626169**
From Kidderminster follow signs to Bewdley on A456 past West Midlands Safari Park and follow signs to Town Centre at next Island. Go over River Bridge into Town and turn left at side of Church (High Street). Stay on this road for 1 ½ miles. Entrance to ground is on left.

**BLACK COUNTRY RANGERS - Tividale F C, The Beeches, Packwood Road, Tividale, B69 1UL Tel: 01384-211743**
Leave M5 at Junction 2. Follow signs to Dudley A4123. Approximately 1 mile past school and playing fields on right, go under Pedestrian walkway to traffic lights. Turn left into Regent Road. Turn left into Elm Terrace. First left into Birch Crescent, second left into Packwood Road. Ground is at the end of the Cul-de-sac.

**BROMYARD TOWN - Delahay Meadow, Stourport Road, Bromyard. HR7 4NT Tel: 01885-483974**
From M5, leave motorway at Junction 7 for Worcester (South) and follow A4440 Southern Link through to last roundabout, and then take A44 signposted Bromyard. Pass through Broadwas and over Bringsty Common to Bromyard. After passing narrow stone bridge on the perimeter of town, turn first right into Sherwood Street and follow signs for Stourport and Kidderminster (B4203). Keep straight on into Church Street, passing Post Office on your right and St Peters Church on your left. Ground is approximately ½ mile on right hand sided through a wide entrance and steel gates, immediately before cottages, next to The Holly Tree Inn.
From Stourport, follow B4203 from Great Witley, up and over Downs, and ground is at bottom of hill, on left, 100 yards after passing the Holly Tree Inn. From Leominster, keep on A44 down by-pass and turn first left after "Ford" garage into Sherwood Street, then as above.

**BUSTLEHOLME - Tipton Town F C, Wednesbury Oak Road, Tipton, West Mids. DY4 0BS Tel: 0121-502-5534**
From M6 Junction 9, take A461 through Wednesbury Town Centre to Ocker Hill island. Follow signpost here taking a full right turn towards Bilston A4098 for half mile, turning left at traffic lights A4037. Ground is 50 yards on left.      From M5 junction 2, take A4123 for about three miles until you reach Burnt Tree island. Take 2nd Exit towards Wolverhampton and continue to next set of traffic lights. Turn right onto A4037 and follow this road for about three miles. After passing Asda on your right, ground is down hill, 200 yards on right.

**CRADLEY TOWN - The Beeches, Beeches View Avenue, Cradley, Halesowen, West Mids. B63 2HB Tel: 07799-363467**
From M5 junction 3 take A456 Manor Way (signposted to Kidderminster) Turn right at second island into Hagley Road pass Foxhunt Inn on left and turn third left into Rosemary Road. Straight on into Landsdowne Road/Dunstall Road and turn left at T Junction into Huntingtree Road/Lutley Mill Road. Left again at next T junction into Stourbridge Road and immediately left again into Beecher Road East, first left into Abbey Road straight up to the end and turn right into Beeches View Avenue. The entrance to ground is 20 yards on the left between houses 50 and 48.

**DUDLEY SPORTS - Hillcrest Avenue, Brierley Hill, West Mids. DY5 3QH Tel: 01384-826420**
The Ground is situated in Brierley Hill, just off A461. It can be approached from Stourbridge off the Ring Road to Amblecote, turning right at third set of traffic lights or from Dudley passing through Brierley Hill Town centre. A – Z ref, 4H, page 67.

**DUDLEY TOWN - The Dell Stadium, Bryce Road, Brierley Hill, West Mids. DY5 4NE Tel: 01384-812943**
From M5 Junction 4 follow signs for Stourbridge. From the Ring Road, take A491 sign posted Wolverhampton. At the second set of lights, turn right onto Brettle Lane A461. After approx 6 miles you will approach Brierley Hill High Street. Turn left at lights onto bank Street. You will see Civic hall and Police Station. Carry on over small bridge and at next set of traffic lights you will see Bryce Road and Stadium is on your left. A-Z Birmingham 5F 93  A-Z West Midlands 5B 88

**ELLESMERE RANGERS - Beech Grove, Ellesmere, Shropshire, SY12 0BT - 07947 864 357**
Follow A5 Wellington and take A495 to Ellesmere. On Approaching Ellesmere, straight over at roundabout, then turn left into housing estate opposite Lakelands School. At crossroads, turn left and the 1st right down the lane to Beech Grove Playing Fields.

**LYE TOWN - Sports Ground, Stourbridge Road, Lye, Stourbridge, West Mids. DY9 7DH Tel: 01384-422672**
Situated on A458 Birmingham to Stourbridge Road.
From M5 Junction 3, take road marked Kidderminster, as far as lights at the bottom of Hagley Hill. Turn right, then take the third turning off the first island. Carry straight on at the next island. Turn left at Lights/Crossroads, onto the A458. Ground approximately 400 yards on the left hand side.

**MALVERN TOWN - Langland Stadium, Langland Avenue, Malvern. WR14 2QE Tel: 01684-574068**
Leave M5 at Junction 7 and turn towards Worcester. Turn left at next roundabout onto A4440 towards Malvern. Straight over next two roundabouts and take left slip road onto A449 at next roundabout. When approaching Malvern, turn left onto B4208 signposted Welland. Straight over three roundabouts and then take the third left into Orford Way. Take the third left into Langland Avenue. Ground is 300 yards on left.

## WEST MIDLANDS LEAGUE - STEP 6/7

**PEGASUS JUNIORS - Old School Lane, Hereford. HR1 1EX Tel: 07980-465995**

Approach City on A4103 from Worcester. At roundabout on outskirts take 2nd exit (A4103) over railway bridge, traffic light controlled. Take 2nd turning on left into Old School Lane. Ground entrance 150 metres on left.

Approach City on A49 from Leominster. On City outskirts take 1st exit at roundabout – Roman Road. First turning on right is Old School Lane. Ground entrance 150 metres on left.

**SHAWBURY UNITED - Butler Sports Ground, Bowensfield, Wem, Shrewsbury. SY4 5AP Tel: 01939-233287**

From the A5 Shrewsbury by-pass, take the A49 heading towards Whitchurch. Go through the villages of Hadnall & Preston Brockhurst and then take a left turn at crossroads onto the B5063 sign posted Wem. At next junction turn right under Railway Bridge on to the B5476 into Mill Street. At next Junction by Church turn right into High Street, take the next left after pedestrian crossing into New Street and then next left by the Public House into Pyms Road. Take the 2nd left into Bowens Field and ground is 100 yards straight ahead.

**SHIFNAL TOWN - Phoenix Park, Coppice Green Lane, Shifnal, Shrops. TF11 8PB Tel: 01952-463257**

From M54 junction 3, take A41 towards Newport and Whitchurch. Take first left signposted Shifnal. As you enter Shifnal, take first turning on right signposted football stadium. The ground is approximately 500 yards on left past Idsall School.

If travelling along A464 Wolverhampton Road to Shifnal. On entering Shifnal, just under the railway bridge and before the traffic lights turn right and sharp right again along Aston Street. Continue along this street until sharp right hand bend. Take left turn and then sharp right along Coppice Green Lane. Ground is approximately 500 yards on left past Idsall School.

**SMETHWICK RANGERS - Hillcrest Avenue, Brierley Hill, West Mids. DY5 3QH Tel: 01384-826420**

The Ground is situated in Brierley Hill, just off A461. It can be approached from Stourbridge off the Ring Road to Amblecote, turning right at third set of traffic lights or from Dudley passing through Brierley Hill Town centre.

A – Z ref, 4H, page 67.

**SPORTING KHALSA - Aspray Arena, Noose Lane, Willenhall. WV13 3BB Tel: 09102-219208**

From M6 junction 10, take 2nd exit onto A454 to Wolverhampton/Dudley A463. Take the A454 exit towards Wolverhampton. At Keyway junction take 2nd exit onto the Keyway A454 and continue on A454 going through one roundabout. At next traffic lights make a u turn at Nechells Lane. Turn left into Noose Lane and over roundabout. Ground is located on your left.

**WEDNESFIELD - Cottage Ground, Amos Lane, Wednesfield. WV11 1ND**

Going south, leave M6 at Junction 11 onto A460 towards Wolverhampton. After approx. 3 miles turn left at the Millhouse Public House into Pear Tree Lane. Continue on across mini-island into Knowle Lane. At Red Lion Public House continue across mini-island into Long Knowle Lane. Continue across mini-island into Amos Lane. Ground is about ½ mile along on left hand side. Going north, leave M6 at Junction 10A onto M54. Leave M54 at Junction 1 onto A460 towards Wolverhampton. Turn left at Millhouse Public House and continue as above.

**WELLINGTON - Wellington Playing Field, Wellington, Hereford. HR4 8AZ**

The Ground is situated in Wellington, behind School and opposite the Church. Wellington is 8 miles South of Leominster or 6 miles North of Hereford on the A49. At the Hereford end of the dual carriageway take the turn for Wellington.

**WELLINGTON AMATEURS - Wickes Stadium, School Grove, Oakengates, Telford, Shrops. TF2 6BQ**

From M54 take Junction 5. At roundabout take first left onto Rampart Way. At traffic lights take the first left onto A442 (Eastern Primary). Leave A442 at next junction. At roundabout (Greyhound Interchange), take the second exit onto B5061 (Holyhead Road). Just after red brick Church on right, turn right onto Vicar Street. Take the next left into School Grove. Continue to the end of the street and proceed up the slope onto the Car Park.

**WILLENHALL TOWN - Long Lane Park, Long Lane, Essington, Wolverhampton. WV11 2AA - Tel: 01922-406604**

From Junction 11 of the M6, take the A462 (Warstones Road) towards Willenhall. Continue straight over the roundabout and then take your second left into Broad Lane. Take your first left into Long Lane. Ground is situated on the left, about halfway down Long Lane.

**WOLVERHAMPTON CASUALS - Brinsford Stadium, Brinsford Lane, Wolverhampton. WV10 7PR Tel: 01902-783214**

Turn onto M54 off M6 Northbound. Take Junction 2 and turn right onto A449 to Stafford. Go to next island and come back on yourself towards M54. Brinsford Lane is approximately ½ mile from island on left.

Ground is 200 yards on left in Brinsford Lane.

**WOLVERHAMPTON SPORTING C. - Wednesfield F C, Cottage Ground, Amos Lane, Wednesfield WV11 1ND Tel: 01902-735506**

Going south, leave M6 at Junction 11 onto A460 towards Wolverhampton. After approx. 3 miles turn left at the Millhouse Public House into Pear Tree Lane. Continue on across mini-island into Knowle Lane. At Red Lion Public House continue across mini-island into Long Knowle Lane. Continue across mini-island into Amos Lane. Ground is about ½ mile along on left hand side. Going north, leave M6 at Junction 10A onto M54. Leave M54 at Junction 1 onto A460 towards Wolverhampton. Turn left at Millhouse Public House and continue as above.

# WESTERN LEAGUE

**Sponsored by:** Toolstation
**Founded:** 1892
**Recent Champions:**
2008: Truro City
2009: Bitton
2010: Bideford
2011: Larkhall Athletic
2012: Merthyr Town
**toolstationleague.com**

## LES PHILLIPS CUP

**PRELIMINARY ROUND**

| | | | |
|---|---|---|---|
| Almondsbury UWE | v | Street | 1-2 |
| Bishop Sutton | v | Barnstaple Town | 10-3 |
| Buckland Athletic | v | Gillingham Town | 3-0 |
| Cribbs Friends Life | v | Sherborne Town | 4-2 |
| Portishead Town | v | Melksham Town | 0-5 |
| Radstock Town | v | Oldland Abbotonians | 0-5 |
| Wells City | v | Ilfracombe Town | 1-2 |
| Welton Rovers | v | Hallen | 1-6 |
| Willand Rovers | v | Shepton Mallet | 4-0 |

**ROUND 1**

| | | | |
|---|---|---|---|
| Bishop Sutton | v | Cadbury Heath | 2-0 |
| Bradford Town | v | Wellington | 3-0 |
| Brislington | v | Bridport | 1-0 |
| Buckland Athletic | v | Devizes Town | 10-0 |
| Calne Town | v | Westbury United | 1-2 |
| Chard Town | v | Melksham Town | 3-5 |
| Cheddar | v | Bitton | 0-1 |
| Hallen | v | Keynsham Town | 3-2 |
| Hengrove Athletic | v | Shrewton United | 0-2 |
| Ilfracombe Town | v | Cribbs Friends Life | 2-0 |
| Larkhall Athletic | v | Oldlands Abbotonians | 1-0 |
| Longwell Green Sports | v | Elmore | 3-2 |
| Odd Down (Bath) | v | Bristol Manor Farm | 4-1 |
| Street | v | Roman Glass St George | 8-1 |
| Willand Rovers | v | Warminster Town | 5-1 |
| Winterbourne Utd | v | Corsham Town | 3-0 |

**ROUND 2**

| | | | |
|---|---|---|---|
| Bitton | v | Melksham Town | 1-2 |
| Bradford Town | v | Odd Down (Bath) | 5-6 |
| Brislington | v | Street | 5-6 |
| Larkhall Athletic | v | Ilfracombe Town | 2-1 |
| Longwell Green Sports | v | Winterbourne Utd | 3-5 |
| Shrewton United | v | Hallen | 1-3 |
| Westbury United | v | Bishop Sutton | 0-3 |
| Willand Rovers | v | Buckland Athletic | 1-0 |

**QUARTER FINALS**

| | | | |
|---|---|---|---|
| Bishop Sutton | v | Street | 1-3 |
| Larkhall Athletic | v | Winterbourne Utd | 2-0 |
| Odd Down (Bath) | v | Hallen | 0-2 |
| Willand Rovers | v | Melksham Town | 4-0 |

**SEMI-FINALS**

| | | | |
|---|---|---|---|
| Street | v | Hallen | 0-3 |
| Willand Rovers | v | Larkhall Athletic | 3-5 |

Larkhall removed from the competition

**FINAL**

| | | | |
|---|---|---|---|
| Hallen | v | Willand Rovers | 0-1 |

## PREMIER DIVISION

| | | P | W | D | L | F | A | Pts |
|---|---|---|---|---|---|---|---|---|
| 1 | Bishop Sutton | 38 | 24 | 10 | 4 | 94 | 34 | 82 |
| 2 | Brislington | 38 | 22 | 10 | 6 | 73 | 42 | 76 |
| 3 | Gillingham Town | 38 | 23 | 4 | 11 | 93 | 59 | 73 |
| 4 | Cadbury Heath | 38 | 22 | 4 | 12 | 85 | 53 | 70 |
| 5 | Larkhall Athletic | 38 | 21 | 6 | 11 | 77 | 50 | 69 |
| 6 | Street | 38 | 18 | 6 | 14 | 74 | 62 | 60 |
| 7 | Bitton | 38 | 17 | 8 | 13 | 60 | 63 | 59 |
| 8 | Odd Down (Bath) | 38 | 16 | 10 | 12 | 84 | 58 | 58 |
| 9 | Hallen | 38 | 17 | 6 | 15 | 78 | 68 | 57 |
| 10 | Buckland Athletic | 38 | 15 | 10 | 13 | 77 | 59 | 55 |
| 11 | Willand Rovers | 38 | 15 | 10 | 13 | 52 | 53 | 55 |
| 12 | Winterbourne Utd | 38 | 15 | 4 | 19 | 66 | 84 | 49 |
| 13 | Melksham Town | 38 | 14 | 6 | 18 | 62 | 74 | 48 |
| 14 | Bridport | 38 | 11 | 14 | 13 | 55 | 63 | 47 |
| 15 | Longwell Green Sports | 38 | 12 | 9 | 17 | 49 | 64 | 45 |
| 16 | Ilfracombe Town | 38 | 13 | 5 | 20 | 52 | 70 | 44 |
| 17 | Radstock Town | 38 | 10 | 10 | 18 | 60 | 85 | 40 |
| 18 | Bristol Manor Farm | 38 | 11 | 6 | 21 | 55 | 72 | 39 |
| 19 | (R) Wells City | 38 | 7 | 6 | 25 | 57 | 90 | 27 |
| 20 | (R) Barnstaple Town | 38 | 3 | 4 | 31 | 23 | 123 | 13 |

## PREMIER DIVISION

| | | 1 | 2 | 3 | 4 | 5 | 6 | 7 | 8 | 9 | 10 | 11 | 12 | 13 | 14 | 15 | 16 | 17 | 18 | 19 | 20 |
|---|---|---|---|---|---|---|---|---|---|---|---|---|---|---|---|---|---|---|---|---|---|
| 1 | Barnstaple Town | | 0-8 | 1-3 | 1-2 | 2-6 | 1-0 | 1-6 | 0-3 | 1-3 | 1-0 | 2-4 | 0-3 | 0-1 | 0-1 | 1-6 | 0-2 | 0-3 | 0-3 | 1-4 | 0-1 |
| 2 | Bishop Sutton | 7-0 | | 4-1 | 0-0 | 1-0 | 2-0 | 2-0 | 2-1 | 3-2 | 1-1 | 4-1 | 1-1 | 3-1 | 3-0 | 1-1 | 3-1 | 4-1 | 3-1 | 1-1 | 5-3 |
| 3 | Bitton | 2-0 | 0-5 | | 3-0 | 0-1 | 3-1 | 2-0 | 1-2 | 3-4 | 2-2 | 2-0 | 2-1 | 0-1 | 2-2 | 1-3 | 3-3 | 2-2 | 0-6 | 3-4 | 0-2 |
| 4 | Bridport | 3-1 | 0-1 | 2-3 | | 0-0 | 1-1 | 1-1 | 0-2 | 0-3 | 4-3 | 3-1 | 2-0 | 3-1 | 1-1 | 4-2 | 4-4 | 2-1 | 2-2 | 2-2 | |
| 5 | Brislington | 2-2 | 1-0 | 0-0 | 1-4 | | 2-0 | 2-1 | 3-2 | 2-0 | 3-0 | 3-0 | 1-3 | 0-2 | 5-2 | 2-0 | 6-5 | 0-0 | 2-2 | 3-1 | 3-1 |
| 6 | Bristol Manor Farm | 4-1 | 1-6 | 1-2 | 0-0 | 2-3 | | 1-3 | 1-3 | 1-3 | 1-0 | 1-0 | 0-1 | 0-1 | 1-2 | 4-7 | 4-4 | 4-3 | 0-3 | 3-0 | 0-1 |
| 7 | Buckland Athletic | 9-1 | 2-2 | 0-1 | 3-2 | 2-2 | 2-2 | | 2-2 | 1-0 | 5-0 | 1-3 | 0-3 | 4-1 | 1-2 | 1-1 | 9-2 | 3-1 | 4-2 | 0-0 | 0-1 |
| 8 | Cadbury Heath | 3-1 | 0-3 | 1-2 | 1-0 | 0-3 | 1-2 | 6-1 | | 1-0 | 1-2 | 0-0 | 1-1 | 3-0 | 9-2 | 4-2 | 2-1 | 4-2 | 2-3 | 0-1 | |
| 9 | Gillingham Town | 1-0 | 4-0 | 2-1 | 1-1 | 1-2 | 3-2 | 4-0 | 4-1 | | 3-5 | 6-0 | 3-0 | 4-2 | 1-0 | 0-3 | 2-1 | 1-5 | 4-5 | 2-3 | 8-3 |
| 10 | Hallen | 1-1 | 0-1 | 0-2 | 4-0 | 0-1 | 3-0 | 2-2 | 0-3 | 0-3 | | 3-2 | 5-3 | 3-0 | 5-2 | 1-1 | 4-0 | 2-4 | 4-2 | 3-1 | 5-2 |
| 11 | Ilfracombe Town | 1-1 | 2-1 | 2-1 | 0-1 | 1-2 | 0-4 | 0-0 | 0-1 | 2-2 | 2-0 | | 1-0 | 1-0 | 3-2 | 1-4 | 2-3 | 4-1 | 2-1 | 0-0 | 0-2 |
| 12 | Larkhall Athletic | 3-0 | 1-1 | 0-3 | 3-3 | 1-1 | 0-1 | 2-0 | 1-0 | 3-4 | 0-3 | 3-2 | | 2-1 | 4-3 | 3-2 | 1-2 | 1-0 | 3-1 | 4-1 | 8-1 |
| 13 | Longwell Green Sports | 3-0 | 2-2 | 1-1 | 2-5 | 1-1 | 1-0 | 0-2 | 0-3 | 1-3 | 2-2 | 4-2 | 0-1 | | 2-0 | 0-2 | 0-0 | 2-4 | 4-2 | 1-1 | 2-1 |
| 14 | Melksham Town | 3-0 | 3-2 | 0-1 | 1-0 | 1-1 | 1-3 | 0-0 | 2-4 | 0-0 | 1-2 | 3-1 | 2-4 | 1-2 | | 3-1 | 2-1 | 0-2 | 4-1 | 0-2 | 3-1 |
| 15 | Odd Down (Bath) | 11-0 | 0-3 | 1-2 | 2-0 | 0-1 | 1-1 | 1-2 | 1-4 | 3-1 | 3-2 | 3-2 | 0-3 | 1-1 | 1-1 | | 1-1 | 2-0 | 3-0 | 0-1 | 4-3 |
| 16 | Radstock Town | 0-1 | 0-0 | 5-0 | 1-1 | 0-1 | 0-4 | 1-3 | 2-1 | 1-3 | 4-2 | 2-1 | 2-2 | 1-1 | 4-3 | 0-4 | | 0-0 | 0-2 | 0-1 | 0-4 |
| 17 | Street | 5-1 | 0-2 | 1-1 | 2-0 | 2-1 | 2-0 | 1-3 | 2-4 | 0-2 | 1-1 | 1-0 | 3-0 | 2-2 | 5-0 | | | | 2-1 | 2-1 | 3-0 |
| 18 | Wells City | 4-0 | 0-4 | 0-1 | 1-1 | 0-4 | 2-3 | 1-4 | 2-1 | 1-1 | 1-3 | 0-2 | 0-4 | 1-1 | 0-3 | 1-3 | 2-2 | 2-3 | | 1-2 | 1-4 |
| 19 | Willand Rovers | 0-0 | 1-1 | 1-2 | 4-0 | 2-1 | 2-2 | 1-0 | 4-1 | 1-3 | 0-2 | 0-2 | 1-0 | 1-3 | 1-2 | 2-2 | 0-2 | 2-0 | 1-1 | | 1-0 |
| 20 | Winterbourne United | 2-1 | 1-2 | 2-2 | 3-0 | 1-1 | 2-0 | 1-2 | 2-2 | 1-2 | 2-3 | 3-1 | 0-3 | 3-2 | 0-4 | 2-1 | 1-5 | 5-2 | 2-1 | 0-2 | |

# WESTERN LEAGUE - STEP 5/6

| DIVISION ONE | P | W | D | L | F | A | Pts |
|---|---|---|---|---|---|---|---|
| 1 (P) Sherborne Town | 40 | 28 | 9 | 3 | 116 | 53 | 93 |
| 2 (P) Hengrove Athletic | 40 | 29 | 4 | 7 | 93 | 34 | 91 |
| 3 Bradford Town | 40 | 26 | 5 | 9 | 103 | 48 | 83 |
| 4 Corsham Town | 40 | 24 | 8 | 8 | 92 | 55 | 80 |
| 5 Oldland Abbotonians | 40 | 24 | 7 | 9 | 77 | 37 | 79 |
| 6 Chard Town | 40 | 24 | 5 | 11 | 94 | 58 | 77 |
| 7 Shepton Mallet | 40 | 21 | 7 | 12 | 85 | 63 | 70 |
| 8 Cribbs Friends Life | 40 | 19 | 8 | 13 | 79 | 55 | 65 |
| 9 Calne Town | 40 | 16 | 11 | 13 | 67 | 59 | 59 |
| 10 Almondsbury UWE | 40 | 15 | 8 | 17 | 67 | 65 | 53 |
| 11 Cheddar | 40 | 15 | 3 | 22 | 76 | 85 | 48 |
| 12 Elmore (-1pt) | 40 | 14 | 7 | 19 | 88 | 100 | 48 |
| 13 Keynsham Town (-3pts) | 40 | 15 | 6 | 19 | 59 | 73 | 48 |
| 14 Portishead Town | 40 | 15 | 3 | 22 | 63 | 82 | 48 |
| 15 Warminster Town | 40 | 10 | 11 | 19 | 60 | 82 | 41 |
| 16 Welton Rovers | 40 | 11 | 7 | 22 | 54 | 88 | 40 |
| 17 Roman Glass St George | 40 | 9 | 10 | 21 | 49 | 76 | 37 |
| 18 Wellington | 40 | 9 | 6 | 25 | 61 | 99 | 33 |
| 19 Westbury United | 40 | 8 | 8 | 24 | 46 | 82 | 32 |
| 20 Shrewton United | 40 | 8 | 6 | 26 | 43 | 105 | 30 |
| 21 Devizes Town | 40 | 8 | 5 | 27 | 65 | 138 | 29 |

| DIVISION ONE | 1 | 2 | 3 | 4 | 5 | 6 | 7 | 8 | 9 | 10 | 11 | 12 | 13 | 14 | 15 | 16 | 17 | 18 | 19 | 20 | 21 |
|---|---|---|---|---|---|---|---|---|---|---|---|---|---|---|---|---|---|---|---|---|---|
| 1 Almondsbury UWE | | 0-3 | 3-0 | 0-4 | 3-1 | 1-2 | 1-0 | 2-3 | 1-2 | 2-1 | 4-1 | 2-0 | 3-4 | 3-1 | 2-1 | 1-2 | 5-0 | 1-1 | 2-0 | 2-1 | 0-0 |
| 2 Bradford Town | 2-1 | | 1-1 | 0-1 | 3-1 | 1-2 | 2-1 | 7-1 | 5-1 | 3-1 | 4-1 | 1-2 | 2-0 | 3-3 | 4-1 | 7-1 | 0-1 | 3-1 | 2-1 | 6-0 | 3-1 |
| 3 Calne Town | 0-0 | 1-1 | | 4-1 | 2-1 | 2-2 | 1-1 | 3-0 | 3-2 | 0-1 | 0-2 | 0-0 | 1-4 | 3-0 | 4-2 | 1-1 | 6-1 | 2-2 | 0-2 | 0-1 | 2-0 |
| 4 Chard Town | 2-1 | 2-1 | 0-0 | | 2-1 | 1-4 | 2-3 | 7-1 | 4-3 | 0-3 | 1-2 | 3-1 | 4-0 | 1-1 | 2-1 | 2-2 | 6-1 | 1-0 | 4-0 | 3-0 | 3-1 |
| 5 Cheddar | 3-1 | 5-3 | 2-3 | 0-2 | | 2-3 | 0-1 | 5-0 | 3-1 | 0-1 | 1-0 | 3-3 | 3-2 | 3-1 | 2-3 | 3-3 | 3-2 | 3-1 | 1-3 | 1-3 | 2-1 |
| 6 Corsham Town | 2-2 | 0-1 | 2-1 | 6-0 | 1-2 | | 2-3 | 5-1 | 5-1 | 3-0 | 3-0 | 1-1 | 2-1 | 3-2 | 1-0 | 0-5 | 1-0 | 4-0 | 3-0 | 3-0 | 3-1 |
| 7 Cribbs Friends Life | 1-5 | 0-2 | 3-2 | 1-1 | 3-2 | 3-1 | | 9-0 | 2-3 | 1-2 | 1-0 | 0-1 | 4-1 | 1-1 | 0-1 | 1-3 | 7-1 | 7-1 | 1-0 | 1-1 | 3-1 |
| 8 Devizes Town | 4-3 | 4-3 | 0-4 | 0-3 | 3-4 | 2-2 | 0-3 | | 4-4 | 2-2 | 1-3 | 0-2 | 1-4 | 3-2 | 1-5 | 2-3 | 3-4 | 2-2 | 5-1 | 2-2 | 2-1 |
| 9 Elmore | 2-1 | 1-4 | 2-2 | 4-1 | 3-2 | 3-1 | 1-4 | 5-4 | | 0-2 | 1-1 | 1-4 | 8-1 | 0-1 | 1-5 | 2-3 | 7-0 | 0-3 | 1-3 | 2-1 | 1-1 |
| 10 Hengrove Athletic | 1-1 | 4-1 | 3-0 | 1-0 | 4-0 | 4-0 | 4-0 | 2-0 | 2-1 | | 3-0 | 1-1 | 2-1 | 3-1 | 1-2 | 1-1 | 5-0 | 3-0 | 3-0 | 2-0 | 2-0 |
| 11 Keynsham Town | 2-1 | 1-4 | 0-1 | 1-4 | 1-0 | 0-2 | 2-2 | 3-2 | 1-3 | 0-3 | | 2-1 | 3-1 | 1-1 | 1-3 | 1-2 | 2-0 | 3-2 | 5-2 | 5-3 | 4-0 |
| 12 Oldland Abbotonians | 2-3 | 3-0 | 1-0 | 4-1 | 3-2 | 1-2 | 3-0 | 6-1 | 0-1 | 2-0 | 1-0 | | 1-1 | 2-0 | 2-0 | 1-0 | 2-0 | 4-1 | 2-1 | 3-0 | 2-1 |
| 13 Portishead Town | 1-1 | 0-1 | 1-2 | 1-4 | 5-2 | 1-6 | 0-1 | 3-2 | 4-1 | 1-3 | 2-1 | 1-0 | | 2-0 | 1-2 | 0-3 | 4-0 | 1-0 | 3-2 | 1-2 | 1-3 |
| 14 Roman Glass St George | 0-0 | 0-1 | 1-2 | 1-4 | 2-1 | 1-2 | 1-1 | 2-0 | 0-2 | 0-2 | 3-1 | 0-2 | 1-1 | | 0-3 | 0-2 | 2-2 | 0-0 | 4-3 | 4-1 | 2-0 |
| 15 Shepton Mallet | 2-0 | 2-4 | 2-2 | 2-0 | 6-3 | 2-0 | 1-1 | 3-0 | 3-2 | 2-5 | 3-3 | 1-1 | 2-3 | 3-2 | | 3-4 | 1-1 | 1-1 | 3-0 | 2-0 | 2-0 |
| 16 Sherborne Town | 5-0 | 2-2 | 4-0 | 2-1 | 2-0 | 2-2 | 2-2 | 6-0 | 4-4 | 3-2 | 2-0 | 3-0 | 2-0 | 4-0 | 1-2 | | 3-0 | 3-2 | 2-0 | 6-1 | 5-2 |
| 17 Shrewton United | 1-2 | 0-0 | 0-1 | 1-4 | 2-1 | 2-3 | 0-3 | 1-2 | 1-1 | 0-1 | 0-1 | 3-2 | 0-2 | 4-1 | 2-3 | 1-5 | | 1-2 | 2-1 | 1-1 | 3-1 |
| 18 Warminster Town | 3-1 | 1-3 | 3-1 | 0-6 | 2-2 | 3-3 | 0-1 | 4-0 | 3-3 | 3-2 | 0-1 | 0-0 | 3-2 | 1-1 | 2-1 | 2-4 | 4-1 | | 0-3 | 0-2 | 2-3 |
| 19 Wellington | 1-1 | 0-1 | 3-3 | 1-3 | 1-3 | 1-3 | 2-1 | 0-4 | 4-3 | 0-1 | 2-2 | 2-7 | 2-0 | 2-3 | 3-3 | 2-5 | 6-1 | 2-5 | | 3-1 | 0-0 |
| 20 Welton Rovers | 3-1 | 0-4 | 2-4 | 2-3 | 0-1 | 1-1 | 2-0 | 3-0 | 3-4 | 2-5 | 3-1 | 0-2 | 2-1 | 3-2 | 0-1 | 2-3 | 1-1 | 1-0 | 2-2 | | 0-3 |
| 21 Westbury United | 1-4 | 0-5 | 1-3 | 2-1 | 0-2 | 1-1 | 0-2 | 5-3 | 4-1 | 1-5 | 1-1 | 0-2 | 0-1 | 1-2 | 1-0 | 1-1 | 0-2 | 1-1 | 4-1 | 2-2 | |

## CLUB MOVEMENTS

**Premier Division - In:** Hengrove Athletic (P). Sherborne Town (P). Slimbridge (S - Hellenic League Premier).
**Out:** Barnstaple Town (R). Wells City (R).

**Division One - In:** Ashton & Backwell United (P - Somerset County). Barnstaple Town (R).
Chippenham Park (P - Wiltshire League Premier Division). Wells City (R). Wincanton Town (P - Dorset Premier).
**Out:** Elmore (S - South West Peninsula Premier). Hengrove Athletic (P). Sherborne Town (P).
Shrewton United (R) Wiltshire League Premier Division).

# PREMIER DIVISION

## BISHOP SUTTON
Founded: 1977     Nickname: Bishops

**Secretary:** Malcolm Hunt     **(T)** 07799 623 901     **(E)** bishopsuttonafcsecretary@hotmail.co.uk

**Chairman:** George Williams     **Manager:** Dave Payne

**Ground:** Lakeview, Wick Road, Bishops Sutton, Bristol BS39 5XN.     **(T)** 01275 333 097

**Capacity:** 1,500  **Seats:** 100  **Covered:** 200  **Midweek Matchday:** Tuesday     **Clubhouse:** Yes  **Shop:** No

**Colours(change):** All blue (All yellow)
**Previous Names:**
**Previous Leagues:** Weston & District (youth), Bristol & Avon, Somerset Senior >1991
**Records:** Att: 400 v Bristol City
**Senior Honours:** Somerset Junior Cup 1980-81. Western League Division One 1997-98, Premier Division 2012-13.

### 10 YEAR RECORD

| 03-04 | 04-05 | 05-06 | 06-07 | 07-08 | 08-09 | 09-10 | 10-11 | 11-12 | 12-13 |
|---|---|---|---|---|---|---|---|---|---|
| WestP 16 | WestP 18 | WestP 16 | WestP 21 | WestP 19 | WestP 15 | WestP 4 | WestP 5 | WestP 6 | WestP 1 |

## BITTON
Founded: 1922     Nickname: The Ton

**Secretary:** Mark Tilling     **(T)**     **(E)** tilling_mark@yahoo.co.uk

**Chairman:** John Langdon     **Manager:** Paul Britton

**Ground:** Rapid Solicitors Ground, Bath Road, Bitton, Bristol BS30 6HX.     **(T)** 01179 323 222

**Capacity:** 1,000  **Seats:** 48  **Covered:** 200  **Midweek Matchday:** Wednesday     **Clubhouse:** Yes  **Shop:** No

**Colours(change):** Red & black/black/black     (Yellow/green/yellow)
**Previous Names:**
**Previous Leagues:** Avon Premier Combination, Gloucestershire County
**Records:** Goalscorer: A. Cole
**Senior Honours:** Somerset Senior Cup 1992-93. Les Phillips Cup 2007-08. Western League Premier Division 2008-09.

### 10 YEAR RECORD

| 03-04 | 04-05 | 05-06 | 06-07 | 07-08 | 08-09 | 09-10 | 10-11 | 11-12 | 12-13 |
|---|---|---|---|---|---|---|---|---|---|
| West1 2 | WestP 8 | WestP 8 | WestP 8 | WestP 7 | WestP 1 | WestP 8 | WestP 2 | WestP 2 | WestP 7 |

## BRIDPORT
Founded: 1885     Nickname: Bees

**Secretary:** Chris Tozer     **(T)** 07500 064 317     **(E)** bridportfc@btconnect.com

**Chairman:** Adrian Scadding     **Manager:** Trevor Senior

**Ground:** St Mary's Field, Bridport, Dorset DT6 5LN     **(T)** 01308 423 834

**Capacity:**     **Seats:**     **Covered:**     **Midweek Matchday:** Tuesday     **Clubhouse:**

**Colours(change):** Red & black/black/black (All blue)
**Previous Names:**
**Previous Leagues:** Dorset Combination 1984-89.
**Records:** Att: 1,150 v Exeter City 1981.
**Senior Honours:** Dorset Senior Cup x8. Dorset Senior Amateur Cup x6.

### 10 YEAR RECORD

| 03-04 | 04-05 | 05-06 | 06-07 | 07-08 | 08-09 | 09-10 | 10-11 | 11-12 | 12-13 |
|---|---|---|---|---|---|---|---|---|---|
| WestP 12 | WestP 19 | West1 6 | West1 11 | West1 18 | West1 13 | West1 10 | West1 3 | WestP 14 | WestP 14 |

## BRISLINGTON
Founded: 1956     Nickname: Bris

**Secretary:** Kevin Jacobs     **(T)** 07976 724 202     **(E)** kevinjacobs919@btinternet.com

**Chairman:** Phil Rex     **Manager:** Jeff Meacham

**Ground:** Ironmould Lane, Brislington, Bristol BS4 4TZ     **(T)** 01179 774 030

**Capacity:** 2,000  **Seats:** 144  **Covered:** 1,500  **Midweek Matchday:** Tuesday     **Clubhouse:** Yes  **Shop:** No

**Colours(change):** Red & black/black/red. (All yellow)
**Previous Names:**
**Previous Leagues:** Somerset Senior until 1991
**Records:**
**Senior Honours:** Somerset Senior League 1988-89. Somerset Premier Cup 1992-93. Western League Division One 1994-95.

### 10 YEAR RECORD

| 03-04 | 04-05 | 05-06 | 06-07 | 07-08 | 08-09 | 09-10 | 10-11 | 11-12 | 12-13 |
|---|---|---|---|---|---|---|---|---|---|
| WestP 7 | WestP 10 | WestP 10 | WestP 17 | WestP 13 | WestP 10 | WestP 9 | WestP 15 | WestP 7 | WestP 2 |

# BRISTOL MANOR FARM
Founded: 1964    Nickname: The Farm

**Secretary:** Andy Radford    **(T)** 07747 038 423    **(E)** andy@bristolmanorfarm.com

**Chairman:** Geoff Sellek    **Manager:** Lee Lashenko

**Ground:** The Creek, Portway, Sea Mills, Bristol BS9 2HS    **(T)** 0117 968 3571

**Capacity:** 2,000 **Seats:** 98    **Covered:** 350    **Midweek Matchday:** Tuesday    **Clubhouse:** Yes    **Shop:** No

**Colours(change):** Red/black (All yellow)
**Previous Names:**
**Previous Leagues:** Bristol Suburban 64-69,  Somerset Senior 69-77
**Records:**    Att; 500 v Portway  **App:** M. Baird
**Senior Honours:** Glos Trophy 1987-88,  Glos Am. Cup 1989-90. Western League Division One 1982-83.

**10 YEAR RECORD**

| 03-04 | | 04-05 | | 05-06 | | 06-07 | | 07-08 | | 08-09 | | 09-10 | | 10-11 | | 11-12 | | 12-13 | |
|---|---|---|---|---|---|---|---|---|---|---|---|---|---|---|---|---|---|---|---|
| WestP | 3 | WestP | 7 | WestP | 3 | WestP | 12 | WestP | 16 | WestP | 5 | WestP | 7 | WestP | 7 | WestP | 8 | WestP | 18 |

# BUCKLAND ATHLETIC
Founded: 1977    Nickname: The Bucks

**Secretary:** Christine Holmes    **(T)** 07856 525 730    **(E)** phardingham@virginmedia.com

**Chairman:** Roy Holmes    **Manager:** Adam Castle

**Ground:** Homers Heath, South Quarry, Kingskerswell Road, Newton Abbot TQ12 5JU    **(T)** 01626 361 020

**Capacity:**    **Seats:** Yes    **Covered:** Yes    **Midweek Matchday:** Wednesday    **Clubhouse:** Yes

**Colours(change):** All yellow (All blue)
**Previous Names:**
**Previous Leagues:** Devon County League 2000-07. South West Pininsula.
**Records:**
**Senior Honours:** South West Peninsula League Premier Division 2009-10, 10-11. Throgmorton Cup 2009-10.

**10 YEAR RECORD**

| 03-04 | | 04-05 | | 05-06 | | 06-07 | | 07-08 | | 08-09 | | 09-10 | | 10-11 | | 11-12 | | 12-13 | |
|---|---|---|---|---|---|---|---|---|---|---|---|---|---|---|---|---|---|---|---|
| Devon | 3 | Devon | 8 | Devon | 7 | Devon | 13 | SWPP | 14 | SWPP | 3 | SWPP | 1 | SWPP | 1 | SWPP | 2 | WestP | 10 |

# CADBURY HEATH
Founded:    Nickname:

**Secretary:** Martin Painter    **(T)** 07971 399 268    **(E)** martinbristol1955@hotmail.com

**Chairman:** Steve Plenty    **Manager:** Andy Black

**Ground:** Springfield, Cadbury Heath Road, Bristol BS30 8BX    **(T)** 07971 399 268

**Capacity:**    **Seats:**    **Covered:**    **Midweek Matchday:** Wednesday    **Clubhouse:** Yes

**Colours(change):** All red (Yellow/blue/blue)
**Previous Names:**
**Previous Leagues:** Gloucestershire County 1968-75, 80-2000. Midland Combination 1975-77.
**Records:**
**Senior Honours:** Gloucestershire County League 1998-99. Western League Division One 2011-12.

**10 YEAR RECORD**

| 03-04 | | 04-05 | | 05-06 | | 06-07 | | 07-08 | | 08-09 | | 09-10 | | 10-11 | | 11-12 | | 12-13 | |
|---|---|---|---|---|---|---|---|---|---|---|---|---|---|---|---|---|---|---|---|
| West1 | 15 | West1 | 13 | West1 | 14 | West1 | 9 | West1 | 5 | West1 | 4 | West1 | 11 | West1 | 4 | West1 | 1 | WestP | 4 |

# GILLINGHAM TOWN
Founded: 1879    Nickname:

**Secretary:** Terry Lucas    **(T)** 07873 587 455    **(E)** terrylucas@sky.com

**Chairman:** Dave Graham    **Manager:** Adrian Foster

**Ground:** Hardings Lane, Gillingham, Dorset SP8 4HX    **(T)** 01747 823 673

**Capacity:**    **Seats:**    **Covered:**    **Midweek Matchday:** Tuesday    **Clubhouse:** Yes

**Colours(change):** All tangerine (Sky blue/navy/sky)
**Previous Names:**
**Previous Leagues:** Dorset Premier 1970-2008.
**Records:**
**Senior Honours:**

**10 YEAR RECORD**

| 03-04 | | 04-05 | | 05-06 | | 06-07 | | 07-08 | | 08-09 | | 09-10 | | 10-11 | | 11-12 | | 12-13 | |
|---|---|---|---|---|---|---|---|---|---|---|---|---|---|---|---|---|---|---|---|
| Dor P | 4 | Dor P | 5 | Dor P | 4 | Dor P | 9 | Dor P | 2 | Dor P | 12 | Dor P | 3 | Dor P | 7 | West1 | 3 | WestP | 3 |

# HALLEN
Founded: 1949     Nickname:

**Secretary:** Richard Stokes     **(T)** 07791 492 640     **(E)** sinbad88@hotmail.co.uk

**Chairman:** Barrie Phillips     **Manager:** Jamie Hillman

**Ground:** Hallen Centre, Moorhouse Lane, Hallen  Bristol  BS10 7RU     **(T)** 01179 505 559

**Capacity:** 2,000  **Seats:** 200   **Covered:** 200   **Midweek Matchday:** Wednesday     **Clubhouse:** Yes

| | |
|---|---|
| **Colours(change):** | Blue & black/black/blue (All maroon) |
| **Previous Names:** | Lawrence Weston Ath, Lawrence Weston Hallen |
| **Previous Leagues:** | Gloucestershire County, Hellenic |
| **Records:** | **Att:** 803 v Bristol Rovers  1997 |
| **Senior Honours:** | Gloucestershire Co. Lge 1988-89, 92-93. Western Division One 2003-04. |

### 10 YEAR RECORD

| 03-04 | | 04-05 | | 05-06 | | 06-07 | | 07-08 | | 08-09 | | 09-10 | | 10-11 | | 11-12 | | 12-13 | |
|---|---|---|---|---|---|---|---|---|---|---|---|---|---|---|---|---|---|---|---|
| West1 | 1 | WestP | 4 | WestP | 9 | WestP | 9 | WestP | 15 | WestP | 9 | WestP | 12 | WestP | 16 | WestP | 4 | WestP | 9 |

# HENGROVE ATHLETIC
Founded: 1948     Nickname: The Grove

**Secretary:** Graham Whitaker     **(T)** 07970 848 285     **(E)** graham.whitaker1@btinternet.com

**Chairman:** Nigel Gray     **Manager:** Nigel Brimble

**Ground:** Norton Lane, Whitchurch, Bristol BS14 0BT     **(T)** 01275 832 894

**Capacity:**   **Seats:**   **Covered:** Yes   **Midweek Matchday:** Wednesday     **Clubhouse:** Yes

| | |
|---|---|
| **Colours(change):** | All green (All blue) |
| **Previous Names:** | |
| **Previous Leagues:** | Somerset County 1974-2006. |
| **Records:** | |
| **Senior Honours:** | Somerset County League Premier Division 2005-06. Somerset Senior Cup 1979-80. |

### 10 YEAR RECORD

| 03-04 | | 04-05 | | 05-06 | | 06-07 | | 07-08 | | 08-09 | | 09-10 | | 10-11 | | 11-12 | | 12-13 | |
|---|---|---|---|---|---|---|---|---|---|---|---|---|---|---|---|---|---|---|---|
| Som1 | 2 | SomP | 5 | SomP | 1 | West1 | 10 | West1 | 6 | West1 | 6 | West1 | 7 | West1 | 10 | West1 | 10 | West1 | 2 |

# ILFRACOMBE TOWN
Founded: 1902     Nickname: Bluebirds

**Secretary:** Tony Alcock     **(T)** 07973 469 673     **(E)** afalcock@aol.com

**Chairman:** M. Hayne & K. Robertson     **Manager:** Ross Middleton

**Ground:** Marlborough Park, Ilfracombe, Devon  EX34 8PD     **(T)** 01271 865 939

**Capacity:** 2,000  **Seats:** 60   **Covered:** 450   **Midweek Matchday:** Tuesday     **Clubhouse:** Yes

| | |
|---|---|
| **Colours(change):** | All blue (Yellow/red/red) |
| **Previous Names:** | |
| **Previous Leagues:** | North Devon, East Devon Premier, Exeter & District, Western, |
| **Records:** | **Att:** 3,000 v Bristol City     **Goalscorer:** Kevin Squire     **App:** Bob Hancock 459 |
| **Senior Honours:** | East Devon Premier League, North Devon Senior League, North Devon Premier League. |

### 10 YEAR RECORD

| 03-04 | | 04-05 | | 05-06 | | 06-07 | | 07-08 | | 08-09 | | 09-10 | | 10-11 | | 11-12 | | 12-13 | |
|---|---|---|---|---|---|---|---|---|---|---|---|---|---|---|---|---|---|---|---|
| West1 | 16 | West1 | 8 | West1 | 4 | West1 | 3 | WestP | 8 | WestP | 14 | WestP | 3 | WestP | 3 | WestP | 11 | WestP | 16 |

# LARKHALL ATHLETIC
Founded: 1914     Nickname: Larks

**Secretary:** Garry Davy     **(T)**     **(E)** garrydvy@aol.com

**Chairman:** Paul Rankin     **Manager:** Wayne Thorne

**Ground:** Plain Ham, Charlcombe Lane, Larkhall, Bath  BA1 8DJ     **(T)** 01225  334 952

**Capacity:** 1,000  **Seats:** Yes   **Covered:** 50   **Midweek Matchday:** Wednesday     **Clubhouse:** Yes

| | |
|---|---|
| **Colours(change):** | All royal blue (All yellow) |
| **Previous Names:** | None |
| **Previous Leagues:** | Somerset Senior |
| **Records:** | |
| **Senior Honours:** | Somerset Senior Cup 1975-76,  Somerset Senior Champions. Western Division One 1988-89, 93-94, 94-95, 08-09. Western Premier Division 2010-11. |

### 10 YEAR RECORD

| 03-04 | | 04-05 | | 05-06 | | 06-07 | | 07-08 | | 08-09 | | 09-10 | | 10-11 | | 11-12 | | 12-13 | |
|---|---|---|---|---|---|---|---|---|---|---|---|---|---|---|---|---|---|---|---|
| West1 | 8 | West1 | 5 | West1 | 7 | West1 | 5 | West1 | 3 | West1 | 1 | WestP | 14 | WestP | 1 | WestP | 3 | WestP | 5 |

# LONGWELL GREEN SPORTS

Founded: 1966    Nickname: The Green

**Secretary:** David Heal    **(T)** 07917 778 463    **(E)** dave@monaghannorthern.co.uk

**Chairman:** Chris Wyrill    Spencer Thomas

**Ground:** Longwell Green Com. Centre, Shellards Road BS30 9AD    **(T)** 01179 323 722

**Capacity:** 1,000 **Seats:** Yes **Covered:** 100 **Midweek Matchday:** Tuesday    **Clubhouse:** Yes **Shop:** Yes

**Colours(change):** Blue & white/black/black (All yellow)
**Previous Names:** None
**Previous Leagues:** Gloucestershire County.
**Records:** **Att:** 500 v Mangotsfield 2005
**Senior Honours:**

**10 YEAR RECORD**

| 03-04 | 04-05 | 05-06 | 06-07 | 07-08 | 08-09 | 09-10 | 10-11 | 11-12 | 12-13 |
|---|---|---|---|---|---|---|---|---|---|
| | GlCo 2 | West1 12 | West1 8 | West1 8 | West1 2 | WestP 11 | WestP 17 | WestP 13 | WestP 15 |

# MELKSHAM TOWN

Founded: 1876    Nickname: Town

**Secretary:** Mark Jeffery    **(T)** 07739 905 575    **(E)** markmtfc@virginmedia.com

**Chairman:** Dave Wiltshire    **Manager:** Dave Clayton

**Ground:** The Conigre, Market Place, Melksham, Wiltshire SN12 6ES    **(T)** 01225 702 843

**Capacity:** **Seats:** Yes **Covered:** Yes **Midweek Matchday:** Monday    **Clubhouse:** Yes

**Colours(change):** Yellow/black/yellow (All red)
**Previous Names:** Melksham > 1951.
**Previous Leagues:**
**Records:** **Att:** 2,821 v Trowbridge Town, FA Cup 1957-58.
**Senior Honours:** Western League Division 1 1979-80, 96-97. Wiltshire Shield x6. Wiltshire Senior Cup x5 Most recently 2012-13.

**10 YEAR RECORD**

| 03-04 | 04-05 | 05-06 | 06-07 | 07-08 | 08-09 | 09-10 | 10-11 | 11-12 | 12-13 |
|---|---|---|---|---|---|---|---|---|---|
| WestP 14 | WestP 14 | WestP 14 | WestP 5 | WestP 11 | WestP 11 | WestP 19 | WestP 8 | West1 2 | WestP 13 |

# ODD DOWN (BATH)

Founded: 1901    Nickname: The Down

**Secretary:** Lorraine Brown    **(T)** 07734 924 435    **(E)** lorainebrown@btinternet.com

**Chairman:** Dave Loxton    **Manager:** Terry Moore

**Ground:** Lew Hill Memorial Ground, Combe Hay Lane, Odd Down BA2 8PA    **(T)** 01225 832 491

**Capacity:** 1,000 **Seats:** 160 **Covered:** 250 **Midweek Matchday:** Tuesday    **Clubhouse:** Yes **Shop:** No

**Colours(change):** All Royal blue (All red)
**Previous Names:**
**Previous Leagues:** Wilts Premier, Bath & District & Somerset Senior
**Records:** **App:** Steve Fuller 475 **Goalscorer:** Joe Matano 104
**Senior Honours:**

**10 YEAR RECORD**

| 03-04 | 04-05 | 05-06 | 06-07 | 07-08 | 08-09 | 09-10 | 10-11 | 11-12 | 12-13 |
|---|---|---|---|---|---|---|---|---|---|
| WestP 9 | WestP 13 | WestP 15 | WestP 11 | WestP 21 | West1 19 | West1 2 | WestP 8 | WestP 9 | WestP 8 |

# RADSTOCK TOWN

Founded: 1895    Nickname:

**Secretary:** Simon Wilkinson    **(T)** 07557 276 619    **(E)** rtfc@hotmail.co.uk

**Chairman:** Jason Holt    **Manager:** Ben Newby

**Ground:** Southfields Recreation Ground, Southfields, Radstock BA3 2NZ    **(T)** 01761 435 004

**Capacity:** 1,250 **Seats:** 80 **Covered:** yes **Midweek Matchday:** Tuesday    **Clubhouse:** Yes **Shop:** No

**Colours(change):** All red (All sky blue)
**Previous Names:** Radstock.
**Previous Leagues:** Somerset Senior League.
**Records:**
**Senior Honours:**

**10 YEAR RECORD**

| 03-04 | 04-05 | 05-06 | 06-07 | 07-08 | 08-09 | 09-10 | 10-11 | 11-12 | 12-13 |
|---|---|---|---|---|---|---|---|---|---|
| SomP 3 | West1 3 | WestP 12 | WestP 16 | WestP 17 | WestP 17 | WestP 16 | WestP 12 | WestP 16 | WestP 17 |

# SHERBORNE TOWN
Founded: 1894          Nickname:

**Secretary:** Colin Goodland     **(T)** 07929 090 612     **(E)** colingoodland@live.co.uk

**Chairman:** Steve Paradise     **Manager:** Jamie Manley

**Ground:** Raleigh Grove, Terrace Playing Field, Sherborne DT9 5NS     **(T)** 01935 816 110

**Capacity:**    **Seats:** Yes    **Covered:** Yes    **Midweek Matchday:** Wednesday    **Clubhouse:** Yes

**Colours(change):** Black & white/black/black (Yellow/white/white).
**Previous Names:**
**Previous Leagues:** Dorset Premier
**Records:** **Att:** 1,000 v Eastleigh, Andy Shephard Memorial match 27.07.03.
**Senior Honours:** Dorset Premier League 1981-82, Dorset Senior Cup 2003-04.
Western League Division One 2012-13.

**10 YEAR RECORD**

| 03-04 | | 04-05 | | 05-06 | | 06-07 | | 07-08 | | 08-09 | | 09-10 | | 10-11 | | 11-12 | | 12-13 | |
|---|---|---|---|---|---|---|---|---|---|---|---|---|---|---|---|---|---|---|---|
| Dor P | 5 | Dor P | 6 | Dor P | 2 | West1 | 4 | West1 | 2 | WestP | 12 | WestP | 18 | WestP | 14 | WestP | 17 | West1 | 1 |

# SLIMBRIDGE
Founded: 1899          Nickname: The Swans

**Secretary:** Colin Gay     **(T)** 07702 070 229     **(E)** colin1956bcfc@o2.co.uk

**Chairman:** John Mack     **Manager:** Leon Sterling     **Prog Ed:** Tim Blake

**Ground:** Wisloe Road, Cambridge, Glos GL2 7AF     **(T)** 07702 070 229

**Capacity:**    **Seats:** Yes    **Covered:** Yes    **Midweek Matchday:** Tuesday    **Clubhouse:** Yes    **Shop:** Yes

**Colours(change):** Blue/blue/white.
**Previous Names:** None
**Previous Leagues:** Stroud & District. Gloucester Northern. Gloucestershire County. Hellenic >2013.
**Records:** Since 2002-03. **Att:** 525 v Shortwood United, Hellenic Prem. 24.08.03. **Goals:** Julian Freeman - 79 (from 122 apps.).
**Senior Honours:** Gloucester Northern League 2007-08. Gloucestershire County League 2008-09.

**10 YEAR RECORD**

| 03-04 | | 04-05 | | 05-06 | | 06-07 | | 07-08 | | 08-09 | | 09-10 | | 10-11 | | 11-12 | | 12-13 | |
|---|---|---|---|---|---|---|---|---|---|---|---|---|---|---|---|---|---|---|---|
| Hel P | 4 | Hel P | 4 | Hel P | 5 | Hel P | 1 | GlN1 | 1 | GlCo | 1 | Hel1W | 1 | Hel P | 5 | Hel P | 5 | Hel P | 6 |

# STREET
Founded: 1880          Nickname: The Cobblers

**Secretary:** Dave Gudge     **(T)**     **(E)** davegudge@ymail.com

**Chairman:** Terry Wolff     **Manager:** Daniel Badman     **Prog Ed:** Phil Norton-Ashley

**Ground:** The Tannery Ground, Middlebrooks, Street BA16 0TA     **(T)** 01458 445 987

**Capacity:** 2,000 **Seats:** 120    **Covered:** 25    **Midweek Matchday:** Tuesday    **Clubhouse:** Yes

**Colours(change):** Green & white/green/white (All red)
**Previous Names:** None
**Previous Leagues:** Somerset Senior.
**Records:** **Att;** 4,300 v Yeovil Town FA Cup 47
**Senior Honours:** Somerset Senior League 1996-97.

**10 YEAR RECORD**

| 03-04 | | 04-05 | | 05-06 | | 06-07 | | 07-08 | | 08-09 | | 09-10 | | 10-11 | | 11-12 | | 12-13 | |
|---|---|---|---|---|---|---|---|---|---|---|---|---|---|---|---|---|---|---|---|
| West1 | 12 | West1 | 7 | West1 | 3 | WLaP | 19 | WestP | 18 | WestP | 13 | WestP | 6 | WestP | 13 | WestP | 10 | WestP | 6 |

# WILLAND ROVERS
Founded: 1946          Nickname: Rovers

**Secretary:** Tony Baker     **(T)** 07887 587 811     **(E)** tonybakerwillandrovers@gmail.com

**Chairman:** Mike Mitchell     **Manager:** Scott Rogers

**Ground:** Silver Street, Willand, Collumpton, Devon EX15 2RG     **(T)** 01884 33885

**Capacity:** 2,000 **Seats:** 75    **Covered:** 150    **Midweek Matchday:** Tuesday    **Clubhouse:** Yes

**Colours(change):** White & black (Yellow/blue/yellow)
**Previous Names:** None.
**Previous Leagues:** Devon County.
**Records:** **Att:** 650 v Newton Abbot 1992-3 **Goalscorer:** Paul Foreman
**Senior Honours:** Devon County League 1998-99, 00-01, Western League Division One 2004-05, Les Phillips Cup 2006-07.

**10 YEAR RECORD**

| 03-04 | | 04-05 | | 05-06 | | 06-07 | | 07-08 | | 08-09 | | 09-10 | | 10-11 | | 11-12 | | 12-13 | |
|---|---|---|---|---|---|---|---|---|---|---|---|---|---|---|---|---|---|---|---|
| West1 | 6 | West1 | 1 | WestP | 6 | WestP | 6 | WestP | 3 | WestP | 3 | WestP | 2 | WestP | 4 | WestP | 5 | WestP | 11 |

# WINTERBOURNE UNITED
Founded: 1911    Nickname: The Bourne

**Secretary:** Geoff Endicott **(T)** 07778 678 823 **(E)** g.endicott@btopenworld.com

**Chairman:** Robyn Maggs **Prog Ed:** Robyn Maggs

**Ground:** Oakland Park, Alomondsbury, Bristol BS32 4AG **(T)** 07976 255 666

**Capacity:** **Seats:** **Covered:** **Midweek Matchday:** Wednesday **Clubhouse:** Yes

**Colours(change):** White & red (Red & black)
**Previous Names:** Winterbourne Wasps 1911-1918
**Previous Leagues:** Bristol & Suburban >1950. Bristol & District 1950-68. Bristol Premier Combination 1968-92. Gloucestershire County 1992-2001. Hellenic 2001-12.
**Records:** **Att:** 229 v Malmesbury Victoria, 29/08/2004.
**Senior Honours:** Gloucestershire County League 2000-01. Hellenic League Division 1 West 2005-06, 07-08.

## 10 YEAR RECORD

| 03-04 | | 04-05 | | 05-06 | | 06-07 | | 07-08 | | 08-09 | | 09-10 | | 10-11 | | 11-12 | | 12-13 | |
|---|---|---|---|---|---|---|---|---|---|---|---|---|---|---|---|---|---|---|---|
| Hel1W | 9 | Hel1W | 9 | Hel1W | 1 | Hel1W | 10 | Hel1W | 1 | Hel1W | 7 | Hel1W | 13 | Hel1W | 10 | Hel1W | 3 | WestP | 12 |

## PREMIER DIVISION GROUND DIRECTIONS

**BISHOP SUTTON - Lakeview, Wick Road, Bishop Sutton BS39 5XN 01275 333097** - On main A368 Bath to Weston-Super-Mare road at rear of Butchers Arms Public House.

**BITTON - Recreation Ground, Bath Road, Bitton, Bristol BS30 6HX 0117 932 3222** - From M4 leave at Junction 18. Take A46 towards Bath, at first roundabout take A420 for Wick / Bridgeyate. On approach to Bridgeyate turn left at mini-roundabout onto A4175 and follow for 2.2 miles, then turn left for Bath on A431. The ground is 100 yards on the right.
From Bath take A431, go through Kelston and Bitton village. Ground is on the left. From Chippenham take A420 to Bristol and turn left at mini-roundabout onto A4175 and follow as above.

**BRIDPORT - St Marys Field, Bridport, Dorset DT6 5LN 01308 423 834** - Follow Bridport by-pass in any direction to the Crown Inn roundabout. Take exit to town centre, at first set of traffic lights (Morrisons) turn left. Ground is 200 yards on the right.

**BRISLINGTON - Ironmould Lane, Brislington, Bristol BS4 4TZ 0117 977 4030** - On A4 Bristol to Bath road, about 500 yards on Bath side of Park & Ride. Opposite the Wyevale Garden Centre.

**BRISTOL MANOR FARM - The Creek, Portway, Sea Mills, Bristol BS9 2HS 0117 968 3571** - Leaving M5 at Junction 18, take A4 marked Bristol. U-turn on dual carriageway by Bristol and West Sports Ground and then ground is half-mile on left hand side

**BUCKLAND ATHLETIC - Homers Heath, Kingskerwell Road, Newton Abbot TQ12 5JU - 01626 361020 - From Plymouth :** Take the exit off the A38 marked Newton Abbot. Travel for approx 5 miles until you come to a roundabout. Turn left and head downhill towards another Roundabout. Turn right & drive for approx 800 yards. Go straight across the B&Q R/bout. Travel along the avenue, and at the top end of this road, turn left and head towards the train Station. Go past the station, go over the railway and get into the right hand lane. At the 2nd set of traffic lights turn right. Go under the railway and follow this road to the next mini roundabout. Go straight across. Go up the hill and down the other side. The ground is situated on the right hand side, opposite Combined linen services. **From Exeter:** Take the A380 signposted Torquay and travel along this road until you reach Penn Inn roundabout. Take the right hand lane and follow the road around which takes you into the left lane and towards the town centre. Take the 1st left and you are now on the main road towards Decoy. The same directions then apply as above. Coaches will not be able to go through the tunnel at Decoy. Please phone for these directions.

**CADBURY HEATH - Springfield, Cadbury Heath Road, Bristol BS30 8BX 0117 967 5731 (social club)** - M5-M4-M32 Exit 1 follow signs for ring road, exit roundabout for Cadbury Heath left, 100m mini roundabout straight across, 400m mini roundabout turn right into Tower Road North, 150m right into Cadbury Heath Road, ground 50m on right via Cadbury Heath Social Club car park.

**GILLINGHAM TOWN - Hardings Lane, Gillingham, Dorset SP8 4HX 01747 823 673** - Proceed to middle of town to the High Street. Hardings Lane is a turning off of the High Street, at the Shaftesbury or Southern end of the High Street.

**HALLEN - Hallen Centre, Moorhouse Lane, Hallen, Bristol BS10 7RU 0117 950 5559** - From Junction 17 M5 follow A4018 towards Bristol. At third roundabout turn right into Crow Lane. Proceed to T junction - turn right and right again at mini roundabout by Henbury Lodge Hotel. At next mini roundabout turn left into Avonmouth Way. Continue for 1.5 miles into Hallen village. At crossroads turn left into Moorhouse Lane

**HENGROVE ATHLETIC - Norton Lane, Whitchurch, Bristol BS14 0BT 01275 832 894** - Take A37 from Bristol through Whitchurch village past Maes Knoll pub, over hump bridge taking next turning on right, which is Norton Lane. Ground is immediately after Garden Centre.

**ILFRACOMBE TOWN - Marlborough Park, Ilfracombe, Devon EX34 8PD 01271 865 939** - Take A361 for Ilfracombe and in town take first right after traffic lights. Follow Marlborough Road to top and ground is on the left.

**LARKHALL ATHLETIC - Plain Ham, Charlcombe Lane, Larkhall, Bath BA1 8DJ 01225 334 952** - Take A4 east from Bath city centre. After approximately 1 mile fork left into St Saviours Road. In Larkhall Square take left exit and turn right at T Junction. Road bears left into Charlcombe Lane where ground is on right as road narrows.

**LONGWELL GREEN SPORTS - Longwell Green Community Centre, Shellards Road, Longwell Green BS30 9DW 0117 932 3722** - Leave Junction 1 M32 follow signs for Ring Road (A4174). At Kingsfield roundabout turn into Marsham Way. At first set of traffic lights turn left into Woodward Drive. Continue to min roundabout and turn right into Parkway Road and continue to Shellards Road. Ground is situated to the rear of the Community Centre.

**MELKSHAM TOWN - The Conigre, Market Place, Melksham, Wiltshire SN12 6ES 01225 702 843** - Turn into Market Place car park and then left into grounds of Cooper Avon Tyres Sports & Social Club (Melksham House) Ground situated at end of drive.

**ODD DOWN - Lew Hill, Memorial Ground, Combe Hay Lane, Odd Down, Bath BA2 8AP 01225 832 491** - Situated behind Odd Down Park & Ride on main A367 Bath to Exeter road.

**RADSTOCK TOWN - Southfields Recreation Ground, Southfields, Radstock BA3 2NZ 01761 435 004** - The town of Radstock is situated 15 miles south east of Bristol and 8 miles southwest of Bath on the A367. At the double roundabout in Radstock town centre take the A362 towards Frome. The ground is on the right hand bend, third turning. Turn right into Southfield, ground is 200 yards ahead.

**SHERBORNE TOWN - Raleigh Grove, The Terrace Playing Field, Sherborne, Dorset DT9 5NS 01935 816 110** - From Yeovil take A30 - marked Sherborne. On entering town turn right at traffic lights, over next traffic lights and at the next junction turn right. Go over bridge, take second left marked 'Terrace Pling Fields'. Turn into car park, football club car park is situated in the far right-hand corner.

**SLIMBRIDGE - Wisloe Road, Cambridge. GL2 7AF 07702 070 229** - From the A38 take the A4135 to Dursley. The ground is 100 yards on the left.

**STREET - The Tannery Field, Middlebrooks, Street, Somerset BA16 0TA 01458 445 987** - Ground is signposted from both ends of A39 and B3151.

**WILLAND ROVERS - Silver Street, Willand, Cullompton, Devon EX15 2RG 01884 33885** - Leave M5 Junction 27 and take first left at roundabout. Follow signs to Willand. After passing Halfway House pub on right, go straight over mini-roundabout (signposted to Cullompton) ground is 400 metres on left hand side.

**WINTERBOURNE UNITED - Oaklands Park, Almondsbury, Bristol BS32 4AG - 01454 612220** - From M4 (West) leave at junction 20 to M5 (Sth West). Leave immediately at junction 16 (A38 Thornbury), turn right onto A38, then first left 100 yards from junction, in front of Motorway Police HQ, Ground next door. Signposted from A38 'Gloucestershire FA HQ'.

# *DIVISION ONE*

## ALMONDSBURY U.W.E.
Founded:     Nickname:

**Secretary:** Douglas Coles     **(T)** 07748 655 399     **(E)** doug2004.coles@blueyonder.co.uk
**Chairman:** Mike Blessing
**Ground:** The Field, Almondsbury, Bristol BS32 4AA     **(T)** 01454 612 240
**Colours(change):** White & green hoops/green/green (All yellow)
**ADDITIONAL INFORMATION:**

## ASHTON & BACKWELL UNITED
Founded: 2010     Nickname:

**Secretary:** Debbie Smith     **(T)**     **(E)** backwellsecretary@yahoo.co.uk
**Chairman:**
**Ground:** Backwell Recreation Ground, West Town Road, Backwell. BS48 3HQ     **(T)** 07916 120 382
**Colours(change):** Claret & sky blue stripes/sky blue (Sky blue/white)
**ADDITIONAL INFORMATION:**
**Previous Names:** Formed when Backwell United merged with the Senior and Youth section of Ashton Boys FC.

## BARNSTAPLE TOWN
Founded: 1906     Nickname: Barum

**Secretary:** Jane Huxtable     **(T)**     **(E)** jane@barnstapletownfc.com
**Chairman:** Warren Crossley
**Ground:** Mill Road, Barnstaple, North Devon EX31 1JQ     **(T)** 01271 411 411     **Capacity:** 5,000
**Colours(change):** All red. (All blue)
**ADDITIONAL INFORMATION: Att:** 6,200 v Bournemouth FA Cup 1st Round 51-52   **App:** Ian Pope
Western Champions 1952-53, 79-80, Devon Pro Cup (12), Devon Senior Cup 1992-93.
Western League Division One 1993-94.

## BRADFORD TOWN
Founded: 1992     Nickname:

**Secretary:** Nikki Akers     **(T)** 07866 693 167     **(E)** bradfordtownfc@gmail.com
**Chairman:**
**Ground:** Bradford Sports & Social Club, Trowbridge Rd, Bradford on Avon BA15 1EE     **(T)** 07801 499 168
**Colours(change):** Navy & white/navy/navy (All yellow)
**ADDITIONAL INFORMATION:**
**Previous League:** Wiltshire Senior.

## CALNE TOWN
Founded: 1886     Nickname: Lilywhites

**Secretary:** Shaun Smith     **(T)** 07817 476 898     **(E)** skevsmith@gmail.com
**Chairman:**     **Manager:** Anthony Brown
**Ground:** Bremhill View, Calne, Wiltshire SN11 9EE     **(T)** 07920 864 879
**Colours(change):** White & black(All blue)
**ADDITIONAL INFORMATION:**
**Record Att:** 1,100 v Swindon, friendly 1987. **Goalscorer:** Robbie Lardner. **Apps:** Gary Swallow - 259.
**Honours:** Wiltshire Senior Cup x4 Most recently 2011-12.

## CHARD TOWN
Founded:     Nickname: The Robins

**Secretary:** Ian Hallett     **(T)**     **(E)** ian.hallett2010@btinternet.com
**Chairman:**     **Manager:** Nik Flory
**Ground:** Denning Sports Field, Zembard Lane, Chard, Somerset TA20 1JL     **(T)** 01460 61402
**Colours(change):** All red (White & blue)
**ADDITIONAL INFORMATION:**
**Honours:** Somerset Senior League 1949-50, 53-54, 59-60, 67-68, 69-70. Somerset Senior Cup 1952-53, 66-67.
South West Counties Cup 1988-89.

## CHEDDAR
Founded: 1892     Nickname: The Cheesemen

**Secretary:** Bruce Harvey     **(T)** 07500 908 538     **(E)** harvs360@hotmail.co.uk
**Chairman:** Steve Bayliss
**Ground:** Bowdens Park, Draycott Road, Cheddar BS27 3RL     **(T)** 01934 707 271
**Colours(change):** Yellow/black/yellow (White/black/white)
**ADDITIONAL INFORMATION:**
**Previous Leagues:** Cheddar Valley. Weston Super Mare & District. Somerset Senior > 2012.
**Honours:** Cheddar Valley League 1910-11. Somerset Senior League Premier Division 2011-12.

## CHIPPENHAM PARK

Founded:     Nickname:

**Secretary:** Jane Blackmore     **(T)**      **(E)** neil@thornburysurfacing.co.uk
**Chairman:**
**Ground:** ardenhuish Park, Bristol Road, Chippenham. SN14 6LR      **(T)** 01249 650 400
**Colours(change):** All blue (All yellow)

**ADDITIONAL INFORMATION:**
**Previous League:** Wiltshire > 2013.

## CORSHAM TOWN

Founded: 1884     Nickname:

**Secretary:** Richard Taylor     **(T)** 07944 183 973      **(E)** richtaylor_ctfc@hotmail.com
**Chairman:** Ken Baldwin
**Ground:** Southbank Ground, Lacock Road, Corsham SN13 9HS      **(T)** 07963 030 652      **Capacity:** 1,500
**Colours(change):** All red (White & black)

**ADDITIONAL INFORMATION: Att:** 550 v Newport Co. FA Cup   **App:** Craig Chaplin
Wiltshire Senior Cup 1975-76, 96-97, 04-05. Western Premier Division 2006-07.

## CRIBBS

Founded: 1958     Nickname:

**Secretary:** Simon Hartley     **(T)** 07970 744 063      **(E)** welshwizard1973@aol.com
**Chairman:** Dave Nelson
**Ground:** The Lawns, Station Road, Henbury, Bristol BS10 7TB      **(T)** 0117 950 2303
**Colours(change):** All blue (All red)

**ADDITIONAL INFORMATION:**
**Previous Leagues:** Gloucestershire County > 2012.
**Honours:** Gloucester County League 2011-12.

## DEVIZES TOWN

Founded: 1885     Nickname:

**Secretary:** Neil Fautley     **(T)** 07891 341 344      **(E)** neil@hallmarkflooring.co.uk
**Chairman:** Shaun Moffat
**Ground:** Nursteed Road, Devizes, Wiltshire SN10 3DX      **(T)** 01380 722 817
**Colours(change):** Red & white stripes/black/red (All blue)

**ADDITIONAL INFORMATION:**
**Honours:** Western League Division One 1999-2000. Wiltshire Senior Cup x14.

## KEYNSHAM TOWN

Founded: 1895     Nickname: K's

**Secretary:** John Peake     **(T)** 07704 340 170      **(E)** helejohn@btinternet.com
**Chairman:** Malcolm Trainer
**Ground:** Crown Fields, Bristol Road, Keynsham BS31 2BE      **(T)** 01179 865 876
**Colours(change):** Gold/black/gold (White & green)

**ADDITIONAL INFORMATION:**
**Previous League:** Somerset Senior.
**Honours:** Somerset Senior Cup 1951-52, 57-58, 2002-03.

## OLDLAND ABBOTONIANS

Founded: 1910     Nickname: The O's

**Secretary:** Derek Jones     **(T)** 07836 648 327      **(E)** avontruckandvan@btconnect.com
**Chairman:** Robert Clarke
**Ground:** Aitchison Playing Field, Castle Road, Oldland Common, Bristol BS30 9PP      **(T)** 01179 328 263
**Colours(change):** Blue & white stripes/blue/blue (All yellow)

**ADDITIONAL INFORMATION:**
**Previous League:** Somerset County.
**Honours:** Les Phillips Cup 2008-09.

## PORTISHEAD TOWN

Founded: 1910     Nickname: Posset

**Secretary:** Brian Hobbs     **(T)** 07791 412 724      **(E)** hobbs.posset@hotmail.co.uk
**Chairman:** Adrian Green
**Ground:** Bristol Road, Portishead, Bristol BS20 6QG      **(T)** 01275 817 600
**Colours(change):** White/black/black (All blue)

**ADDITIONAL INFORMATION:**
**Previous League:** Somerset County.
**Honours:** Somerset County League 2004-05.

## ROMAN GLASS ST GEORGE    Founded:    Nickname:

**Secretary:** Emily Baldwin    **(T)** 07708 277 592    **(E)** emilyjaynebaldwin@blueyonder.co.uk
**Chairman:** Roger Hudd
**Ground:** Oaklands Park, Gloucester Road, Alomndsbury BS32 4AG    **(T)** 01454 612 220
**Colours(change):** White/black/white (All red)

ADDITIONAL INFORMATION:
**Previous League:** Gloucestershire County.
**Honours:** Gloucestershire County League 2006-07.

## SHEPTON MALLET    Founded: 1986    Nickname:

**Secretary:** Gary Banfield    **(T)** 07762 880 705    **(E)** gkrkb@tiscali.co.uk
**Chairman:** John Hugill    **Manager:** Andrew Jones
**Ground:** Playing Fields, Old Wells Road, West Shepton, Shepton Mallet BA4 5XN    **(T)** 01749 344 609
**Colours(change):** Black & white/black/black (Yellow & white)

ADDITIONAL INFORMATION:
**Record Att:** 274 v Chippenham Town FA Cup 2000-01.
**Honours:** Somerset Senior League 2000-01.

## WARMINSTER TOWN    Founded: 1878    Nickname:

**Secretary:** Chris Fenwick    **(T)**    **(E)** warminstertownfc@hotmail.com
**Chairman:** Pete Russell    **Manager:** John Phillips
**Ground:** Weymouth Street, Warminster BA12 9NS    **(T)** 01985 217 828
**Colours(change):** Red & black/black/red (Dark & light blue)

ADDITIONAL INFORMATION:
**Previous Leagues:** Wiltshire County > 1930, 1945-83, 2002-06. Western League 1930-39, 83-2002. Wessex 2006-12.

## WELLINGTON    Founded: 1892    Nickname: Wellie

**Secretary:** David Derrick    **(T)** 07516 482 923    **(E)** david230275@googlemail.com
**Chairman:** Mike Hall    **Manager:** Mike Hawes
**Ground:** Wellington Playing Field, North Street, Wellington TA21 8NE    **(T)** 01823 664 810    3,000
**Colours(change):** All tangerine (Claret/blue/claret)

ADDITIONAL INFORMATION: **Goalscorer:** Ken Jones

## WELLS CITY    Founded: 1890    Nickname:

**Secretary:** Mark Grant    **(T)** 07974 726 607    **(E)** mlgrant62@hotmail.co.uk
**Chairman:** Steve Loxton
**Ground:** Athletic Ground, Rowdens Road, Wells, Somerset BA5 1TU    **(T)** 01749 679 971
**Colours(change):** All blue (All yellow)

ADDITIONAL INFORMATION:
Western League Division One 2009-10.

## WELTON ROVERS    Founded: 1887    Nickname: Rovers

**Secretary:** Malcolm Price    **(T)** 07970 791 644    **(E)** malcolm@weltonr.plus.com
**Chairman:** Stuart Minall    **Manager:** Nick Beaverstock
**Ground:** West Clewes, North Road, Midsomer Norton, Bath BA3 2QD    **(T)** 01761 412 097    **Capacity:** 2,400
**Colours(change):** Green/white/green (Yellow/blue/yellow).

ADDITIONAL INFORMATION: **Att:** 2,000 v Bromley FA Am Cup 1963    **Goalscorer:** Ian Henderson 51
Somerset Senior Cup (10). Somerset Premier Cup 2009-10.

## WESTBURY UNITED    Founded: 1921    Nickname: White Horsemen

**Secretary:** Roger Arnold    **(T)** 07584 318 302    **(E)** rogerarnold33@hotmail.com
**Chairman:** Paul Brickley    **Manager:** Matthew Brown
**Ground:** Meadow Lane, Westbury, Wiltshire BA13 3AF    **(T)** 01373 823 409
**Colours(change):** Green & white/green/green (Orange & blue/blue)

ADDITIONAL INFORMATION:
**Record Att:** 4,000 v Llanelli FA Cup 1st Round 1937 & v Walthamstow Avenue FA Cup 1937.
**Honours:** Wiltshire League 1934-35, 37-38, 38-39, 49-50, 50-51, 55-56. Western League Div.1 1991-92. Wilts Senior Cup x4.

# WINCANTON TOWN

| | Founded: | Nickname: |
|---|---|---|

**Secretary:** Mike Hatcher    **(T)**     **(E)** mike831hatcher@gmail.com
**Chairman:**
**Ground:** Wincanton Sports Ground, Moor Lane, Wincanton. BA9 9EJ     **(T)** 01963 31815
**Colours(change):** Yellow/black (All grey)

**ADDITIONAL INFORMATION:**
**Previous League:** Dorset Premier >2013.

# DIVISION ONE GROUND DIRECTIONS

**ALMONDSBURY UWE - The Field, Almondsbury, Bristol BS34 4AA  01454 612 240** - Exit M5 at Junction 16. Arriving from the south take the left exit lane. Turn left at lights and ground is 150m on right hand side. Arriving from east take right hand lane on slip road. Take 3rd exit and ground is 150m on right hand side.

**ASHTON & BACKWELL UNITED - Backwell Recreation Ground, West Town Road, Backwell. BS48 3HQ - 07916 120 382 -** Off the main A370 in Backwell, travelling from Bristol the entrance is on the right, apprximately 500 metres after the crossroads. Travelling from Weston Super Mare the entrance to the ground is on the left approximately 500 metrs past the New Inn Pub and Restaurant.

**BARNSTAPLE TOWN - Mill Road, Barnstaple, North Devon EX31 1JQ 01271 343469 -** From M5 South, exit junction 27, take A361 to Barnstaple, in town take A361 for Ilfracombe, then first left over bridge is Mill Road.

**BRADFORD TOWN - Bradford Sports & Social Club, Trowbridge Road, Bradford on Avon, Wiltshire BA15 1EW  01225 866 649 -** From Bath or Melksham on entering Bradford on Avon follow the signs for A363 to Trowbridge. The ground is after a mini roundabout and behind a stone wall on the right hand side. From Trowbridge, follow A363 to Bradford-on-Avon. The ground is just past shop on right, behind stone wall on left.

**CALNE TOWN - Bremhill View, Calne, Wiltshire  SN11 9EE -** Take A4 to Calne from Chippenham, on approaching Calne turn left at the first roundabout on to A3102 Calne bypass. At the next roundabout turn right, next left and then right and right again.

**CHARD TOWN - Dening Sports Field, Zembard Lane, Chard, Somerset TA20 1JL  01460 61402 -** From A30 High Street, follow Swimming Pool/Sports Centre signs via Helliers road. Turn right into Crimchard, turn left into Zembard Lane. Ground is on right hand side.

**CHEDDAR - Bowdens Park, Draycott Road, Cheddar BS27 3RL - 01934 707 271 -** FROM WELLS: Take the A371 (Weston Super Mare) through Draycott and Bowdens Park is on your left about half a mile past Cheddar Garden Centre (if you get to the church you've gone too far). FROM WESTON: Head towards Wells on the A371 and go through the village of Cheddar. The church is on your right as you come out of the village and Bowdens Park is 200 yards past the church on your right hand side.

**CORSHAM TOWN - Southbank, Lacock Road, Corsham, Wiltshire SN13 9HS  01249 715609 -** A4 into Corsham, at Hare and Hounds Roundabout take the Melksham Road B3353 until the War Memorial, then Lacock Road. Ground a half a mile on the right side.

**CHIPPENHAM PARK - Hardenhuish Park, Bristol Road, Chippenham. SN14 6LR 01249 650 400 -** Exit 17 from M4. Follow A350 towards Chippenham for three miles to first roundabout, take second exit (A350); follow road to third roundabout (junction with A420). Turn left and follow signs to town centre. Ground is 1km on left hand side adjacent to pedestrian controlled traffic lights. Car/Coach park located adjacent to traffic lights.

**CRIBBS - The Lawns, Station Road, Henbury, Bristol BS10 7TB - 0117 950 2303 -** From M5 J17 follow signs to Bristol West & Clifton on the A4018 dual carriageway cross two roundabouts, at 3rd roundabout take fourth exit and follow signs to M5, take 1st turning left after car dealers, ground straight ahead.

**DEVIZES TOWN - Nursteed Road, Devizes, Wiltshire SN10 3DX  01380 722 817 -** Leave Devizes on A342 for Andover. Ground is on the right hand side opposite Eastleigh Road.

**KEYNSHAM TOWN - Crown Field, Bristol Road, Keynsham BS31 2DZ  0117 986 5876 -** On A4175 off the Bristol to Bath A4. On left immediately after 30mph sign.

**OLDLAND ABBOTONIANS - Aitchison Playing Field, Castle Road, Oldland Common, Bristol BS30 9PP  0117 932 8263 -** Exit M4 at Jct19 to M32. Exit M32 at Jct 1after 400 yds and take 1st exit from roundabout for A4174. Straight over traffic lights to next roundabout continuing on A4174. Go over five roundabouts for approximately 4.8 miles. At next roundabout take 1st exit to Deanery Road (A420) and continue for 0.9 miles to Griffin Public house and turn right into Bath Road (A4175) . Continue for 1.3 miles to Oldland Common High Street and look for Dolphin Public House. Turning for Castle Street is next left between Chinese Chip Shop and Post Office. Ground is at the end of Castle Road.

**PORTISHEAD - Bristol Road, Portishead, Bristol BS20 6QG  01275 817 600 -** Leave M5 at Junction 19 and take road to Portishead. At outskirts of town take 1st exit from small roundabout signposted Clevedon and Police H.Q. Ground is 150 yds along road on left by bus stop.

**ROMAN GLASS ST GEORGE - Oaklands Park, Gloucester Road, Almondsbury BS32 4AG 07708 277592 -** Exit M5 at Junction 16. Arriving from the south take the left exit lane. Turn left at lights and ground is 100m on left hand side. Arriving from east take right hand lane on slip road. Take 3rd exit nd ground is 100m on left hand side.

**SHEPTON MALLET - Playing Fields, Old Wells Road, West Shepton, Shepton Mallet BA4 5XN - 01749 344 609 -** From the town take B3136 (Glastonbury Road) for approximately 1/2 mile. Turn right at junction of Old Wells Road near King William Public House. Approximately 300 yards up the Old Wells Road turn left into the playing fields.

**WARMINSTER TOWN - Weymouth Street, Warminster, BA12 9NS - 01454 612220 -** A36 from Salisbury, head for town centre, turn left at traffic lights in the town centre signposted A350 Shaftesbury. Club is situated approx. 400 yards on left hand side at top of Weymouth Street.

**WELLINGTON - The Playing Field, North Street, Wellington, Somerset TA21 8NA  01749 679 971 -** Leave the M5 motorway at Junction 26 and follow directions to Wellington. At town centre traffic lights take turning into North Street. Take the next left adjacent to the Fire Station and signposted 'Car Park'. The ground is in the corner of the car park.

**WELLS CITY - Athletic Ground, Rowdens Road, Wells, Somerset BA5 1TU  01749 679 971 -** From North & Southwest - Follow A39 to Strawberry Way to roundabout, follow A371 East Somerset Way and take right turn into Rowdens Road. Ground is on left. From East - Follow A371 from Shepton Mallet. After approximately 5 miles on East Somerset Way take left turn into Rowdens Road. Ground is on left.

**WELTON ROVERS - West Clewes, North Road, Midsomer Norton BA3 2QD  01761 412 097 -** The ground is on the main A362 in Midsomer Norton.

**WESTBURY UNITED - Meadow Lane, Westbury, Wiltshire BA13 3AF  01373 823 409 -** From town centre proceed along Station Road towards rail station. At double mini roundabout turn right. Ground is 300 metres on left hand side opposite Fire Station.

**WINCANTON TOWN - Wincanton Sports Ground, Moor Lane, Wincanton. BA9 9EJ -** 01963 31815 - Travelling to Wincanton on the A357 via Sturminster Newton turn right at the roundabout after passing under the A303 into Laurence Hill and follow the road across three further roundabouts into Southgate Road. Traffic from the A303 will also enter Southgate Road when following the signs to the town. At the junction turn right in the direction of Buckhorn Weston going under the A303 again before entering Moor Lane. Wincanton Sports Centre is on the left.

# ANGLIAN COMBINATION LEAGUE

**Sponsored by:** Gleave & Associates
**Founded:** 1964
**Recent Champions:**
2008: Wroxham Reserves
2009: Kirby Muxloe SC
2010: Blofield United
2011: Cromer Town
2012: Cromer Town
**angliancombination.org.uk**

| PREMIER DIVISION | P | W | D | L | F | A | Pts |
|---|---|---|---|---|---|---|---|
| 1 Acle United | 30 | 22 | 6 | 2 | 102 | 28 | 72 |
| 2 Spixworth | 30 | 18 | 11 | 1 | 68 | 24 | 65 |
| 3 Cromer Town | 30 | 19 | 6 | 5 | 93 | 33 | 63 |
| 4 Wroxham Res | 30 | 19 | 4 | 7 | 76 | 39 | 61 |
| 5 Blofield United | 30 | 16 | 8 | 6 | 83 | 38 | 56 |
| 6 Dersingham Rovers | 30 | 16 | 8 | 6 | 64 | 37 | 56 |
| 7 Reepham Town | 30 | 14 | 7 | 9 | 70 | 59 | 49 |
| 8 Beccles Town | 30 | 14 | 6 | 10 | 78 | 60 | 48 |
| 9 Kirkley & Pakefield Res | 30 | 10 | 6 | 14 | 48 | 65 | 36 |
| 10 Loddon United | 30 | 10 | 6 | 14 | 43 | 72 | 36 |
| 11 Mattishall | 30 | 10 | 5 | 15 | 58 | 58 | 35 |
| 12 St Andrews | 30 | 9 | 6 | 15 | 44 | 56 | 33 |
| 13 Wymondham Town | 30 | 8 | 6 | 16 | 43 | 72 | 30 |
| 14 Sheringham | 30 | 5 | 1 | 24 | 37 | 98 | 16 |
| 15 (R) North Walsham Town | 30 | 4 | 2 | 24 | 30 | 95 | 14 |
| 16 (R) Hempnall | 30 | 2 | 0 | 28 | 22 | 125 | 6 |

## DON FROST CUP

(Premier Division champions v Mummery Cup holders)

| Cromer Town | v | Blofield United | 0-0, 5-3p |
|---|---|---|---|

## MUMMERY CUP
(Premier and Division One Clubs)

**ROUND 1**

| St Andrews | v | Corton | 1-1 4-5p |
|---|---|---|---|
| Cromer Town | v | Horsford United | 0-1 |
| Loddon United | v | Kirkley & Pakefield Reserves | 4-5 |
| Reepham Town | v | Brandon Town | 4-2 |
| Bradenham Wanderers | v | Wells Town | HW |
| Wymondham Town | v | Acle United | 0-2 |
| Holt United | v | Caister | 1-2 |
| Blofield United | v | Wroxham Reserves | 3-3 4-5p |
| Norwich CEYMS | v | Hempnall | 4-0 |

**ROUND 2**

| Corton | v | Horsford United | 0-1 |
|---|---|---|---|
| Kirkley & Pakefield Res. | v | Reepham Town | 5-0 |
| Bradenham Wanderers | v | Acle United | 0-4 |
| Caister | v | Wroxham Reserves | 4-2 |
| Norwich CEYMS | v | Long Stratton | 2-1 |
| Harleston Town | v | Dersingham Rovers | 2-1 |
| Stalham Town | v | Watton United | 3-1 aet |
| Mattishall | v | Spixworth | 0-2 |

**QUARTER FINALS**

| Horsford United | v | Kirkley & Pakefield Reserves | 1-3 |
|---|---|---|---|
| Acle United | v | Caister | 5-3 |
| Norwich CEYMS | v | Harleston Town | 2-0 |
| Stalham Town | v | Spixworth | 0-3 |

**SEMI FINALS**

| Kirkley & Pakefield Res. | v | Acle United | 0-2 |
|---|---|---|---|
| Norwich CEYMS | v | Spixworth | 0-3 |

**FINAL**

| Acle United | v | Spixworth | 4-2 |
|---|---|---|---|

## CYRIL BALLYN TROPHY
(Division Two, Three, Four, Five and Six first teams and external league reserve sides)

**FINAL**

| Bungay Town | v | Mulbarton Wanderers | 1-2 |
|---|---|---|---|

## CS MORLEY CUP
(Anglian Combination reserve teams)

**FINAL**

| Earsham | v | Waveney | 1-4 |
|---|---|---|---|

| PREMIER DIVISION | 1 | 2 | 3 | 4 | 5 | 6 | 7 | 8 | 9 | 10 | 11 | 12 | 13 | 14 | 15 | 16 |
|---|---|---|---|---|---|---|---|---|---|---|---|---|---|---|---|---|
| 1 Acle United | | 3-0 | 1-2 | 2-2 | 3-2 | 9-0 | 4-0 | 5-0 | 2-1 | 2-1 | 1-1 | 3-0 | 2-0 | 4-0 | 6-1 | 6-2 |
| 2 Beccles Town | 0-2 | | 1-1 | 2-3 | 0-3 | 4-2 | 3-3 | 5-1 | 2-1 | 3-4 | 5-0 | 6-3 | 1-2 | 3-3 | 6-2 | 6-1 |
| 3 Blofield United | 1-1 | 3-2 | | 2-1 | 0-1 | 5-0 | 3-0 | 7-0 | 0-0 | 0-0 | 9-4 | 1-1 | 1-3 | 2-1 | 3-4 | 8-1 |
| 4 Cromer Town | 2-2 | 3-2 | 2-2 | | 0-0 | 5-0 | 6-2 | 2-3 | 4-3 | 6-2 | 3-1 | 2-0 | 0-1 | 5-0 | 1-0 | 6-2 |
| 5 Dersingham Rovers | 1-4 | 1-1 | 3-1 | 1-5 | | 3-0 | 5-0 | 5-2 | 2-2 | 2-1 | 2-2 | 6-0 | 0-0 | 3-0 | 2-3 | 2-0 |
| 6 Hempnall | 0-6 | 1-3 | 0-7 | 0-11 | 0-4 | | 2-4 | 4-2 | 1-2 | 1-0 | 0-5 | 0-1 | 1-7 | 0-3 | 2-3 | 1-3 |
| 7 Kirkley & Pakefield Reserves | 2-4 | 1-4 | 0-2 | 0-3 | 1-2 | 3-1 | | 2-0 | 2-2 | 2-0 | 1-1 | 4-0 | 0-0 | 2-3 | 0-3 | 0-2 |
| 8 Loddon United | 2-8 | 2-2 | 0-4 | 2-0 | 1-1 | 3-1 | 0-0 | | 1-3 | 2-0 | 1-1 | 3-1 | 1-5 | 1-1 | 0-2 | 2-0 |
| 9 Mattishall | 1-2 | 1-2 | 3-4 | 0-2 | 1-3 | 4-0 | 3-4 | 1-2 | | 5-0 | 2-1 | 3-1 | 1-2 | 3-3 | 0-3 | 2-2 |
| 10 North Walsham Town | 0-5 | 1-3 | 1-6 | 0-8 | 2-1 | 2-0 | 1-4 | 1-4 | 1-2 | | 1-5 | 2-1 | 0-2 | 3-3 | 1-7 | 0-3 |
| 11 Reepham Town | 4-3 | 2-3 | 5-2 | 2-1 | 1-2 | 4-1 | 2-2 | 0-1 | 3-2 | 3-2 | | 5-3 | 0-3 | 3-2 | 0-3 | 3-1 |
| 12 Sheringham | 1-7 | 1-3 | 0-1 | 0-5 | 1-2 | 4-0 | 2-5 | 3-1 | 2-4 | 5-1 | 0-6 | | 2-5 | 0-2 | 0-4 | 2-3 |
| 13 Spixworth | 2-2 | 4-1 | 1-0 | 2-2 | 0-0 | 8-1 | 2-0 | 1-1 | 4-2 | 2-1 | 1-1 | 4-1 | | 1-1 | 2-2 | 1-0 |
| 14 St Andrews | 0-1 | 1-2 | 0-4 | 0-1 | 2-2 | 4-0 | 1-2 | 2-1 | 1-2 | 1-0 | 0-1 | 5-0 | 0-3 | | 1-0 | 2-0 |
| 15 Wroxham Res | 0-2 | 4-1 | 1-1 | 1-1 | 4-0 | 3-2 | 2-0 | 2-0 | 0-1 | 4-2 | 0-2 | 4-0 | 0-0 | 4-2 | | 6-0 |
| 16 Wymondham Town | 0-0 | 2-2 | 1-1 | 0-1 | 0-3 | 3-1 | 2-3 | 3-4 | 2-1 | 3-0 | 2-2 | 1-2 | 0-0 | 3-1 | 1-4 | |

## ANGLIAN COMBINATION PREMIER DIVISION CONSTITUTION 2013-14

|  |  |  |
|---|---|---|
| ACLE UNITED | Bridewell Lane, Acle, Norwich NR13 3RA | 01493 752989 |
| BECCLES TOWN | College Meadow, Common Lane, Beccles NR34 7FA | 07729 782817 |
| BLOFIELD UNITED | Old Yarmouth Road, Blofield, Norwich NR13 4LE | 07748 863203 |
| CAISTER | Caister Playing Fields, off Allendale Road, Caister-on-Sea NR30 5ES | 07852 212210 |
| CROMER TOWN | Cabbell Park, Mill Road, Cromer NR27 0AD | 07940 092131 |
| DERSINGHAM ROVERS | Behind Feathers Hotel, Manor Road, Dersingham, King's Lynn PE31 6LN | 01485 542707 |
| KIRKLEY & PAKEFIELD RESERVES | Kirkley & Pakefield Comm Cnte, Walmer Road, Lowestoft NR33 7LE | 01502 513549 |
| LODDON UNITED | George Lane Playing Field, Loddon, Norwich NR14 6NB | 01508 528497 |
| MATTISHALL | Mattishall Playing Fields, South Green, Mattishall, Norwich NR20 3JY | 01362 850246 |
| NORWICH CEYMS | Hilltops Sports Centre, Main Road, Swardeston, Norwich NR14 8DU | 01508 578826 |
| SHERINGHAM | Recreation Ground, Weybourne Road, Sheringham NR26 8WD | 01263 824804 |
| SPIXWORTH | Spixworth Village Hall, Crostick Lane, Spixworth, Norwich NR10 3NQ | 01603 898092 |
| ST ANDREWS | Thorpe Recreation Ground, Laundry Lane, Thorpe St Andrew, Norwich NR7 0XQ | 01603 300316 |
| WROXHAM RESERVES | Trafford Park, Skinners Lane, Wroxham NR12 8SJ | 01603 783538 |
| WYMONDHAM TOWN | Kings Head Meadow, Back Lane, Wymondham NR18 0LB | 01953 607326 |

**In:** Norwich CEYMS (P), Caister (P).

**Out:** Hempnall (R), North Walsham Town (R).

### DIVISION ONE

| | | P | W | D | L | F | A | Pts |
|---|---|---|---|---|---|---|---|---|
| 1 | (P) Norwich CEYMS | 30 | 24 | 3 | 3 | 105 | 27 | 75 |
| 2 | (P) Caister | 30 | 20 | 4 | 6 | 87 | 38 | 64 |
| 3 | Stalham Town | 30 | 19 | 3 | 8 | 72 | 46 | 60 |
| 4 | Horsford United | 30 | 15 | 7 | 8 | 82 | 57 | 52 |
| 5 | Harleston Town | 30 | 16 | 4 | 10 | 65 | 49 | 52 |
| 6 | Long Stratton | 30 | 16 | 3 | 11 | 61 | 50 | 51 |
| 7 | Bradenham Wanderers | 30 | 14 | 6 | 10 | 64 | 58 | 48 |
| 8 | Corton | 30 | 13 | 8 | 9 | 70 | 55 | 47 |
| 9 | Aylsham | 30 | 14 | 5 | 11 | 74 | 63 | 47 |
| 10 | Watton United | 30 | 9 | 8 | 13 | 67 | 77 | 35 |
| 11 | Holt United | 30 | 11 | 1 | 18 | 56 | 66 | 34 |
| 12 | Poringland Wanderers | 30 | 10 | 4 | 16 | 51 | 66 | 34 |
| 13 | Hindringham (-1pt) | 30 | 10 | 3 | 17 | 44 | 64 | 32 |
| 14 | Hellesdon | 30 | 8 | 2 | 20 | 51 | 96 | 26 |
| 15 | (R) Wells Town (-1pt) | 30 | 6 | 6 | 18 | 40 | 84 | 23 |
| 16 | (R) Brandon Town (-3pts) | 30 | 0 | 3 | 27 | 26 | 119 | 0 |

### DIVISION TWO

| | | P | W | D | L | F | A | Pts |
|---|---|---|---|---|---|---|---|---|
| 1 | (P) Foulsham | 28 | 23 | 4 | 1 | 82 | 30 | 73 |
| 2 | (P) Mundford | 28 | 23 | 0 | 5 | 96 | 26 | 69 |
| 3 | Bungay Town | 28 | 20 | 3 | 5 | 76 | 23 | 63 |
| 4 | Attleborough Town | 28 | 20 | 2 | 6 | 104 | 34 | 62 |
| 5 | Scole United | 28 | 18 | 2 | 8 | 82 | 33 | 56 |
| 6 | Sprowston Athletic | 28 | 16 | 6 | 6 | 76 | 39 | 54 |
| 7 | East Harling | 28 | 14 | 2 | 12 | 61 | 72 | 44 |
| 8 | Sprowston Wanderers | 28 | 13 | 1 | 14 | 57 | 70 | 40 |
| 9 | Beccles Caxton | 28 | 9 | 3 | 16 | 60 | 90 | 30 |
| 10 | Thetford Rovers | 28 | 8 | 3 | 17 | 45 | 62 | 27 |
| 11 | Martham | 28 | 8 | 0 | 20 | 54 | 80 | 24 |
| 12 | Acle United Res (-2pts) | 28 | 7 | 4 | 17 | 31 | 50 | 23 |
| 13 | Hemsby (-1pt) | 28 | 6 | 1 | 21 | 44 | 102 | 18 |
| 14 | (R) Downham Town Res (-1pt) | 28 | 4 | 3 | 21 | 31 | 94 | 14 |
| 15 | (R) Hempnall Res (-5pts) | 28 | 4 | 0 | 24 | 15 | 109 | 7 |

### DIVISION THREE

| | | P | W | D | L | F | A | Pts |
|---|---|---|---|---|---|---|---|---|
| 1 | (P) UEA | 26 | 22 | 3 | 1 | 105 | 25 | 69 |
| 2 | (P) Mulbarton Wanderers | 26 | 20 | 1 | 5 | 101 | 21 | 61 |
| 3 | (P) Hoveton Wherrymen | 26 | 19 | 1 | 6 | 75 | 32 | 58 |
| 4 | Cromer Town Reserves | 26 | 15 | 4 | 7 | 79 | 55 | 49 |
| 5 | Marlingford | 26 | 14 | 6 | 6 | 69 | 37 | 48 |
| 6 | Easton | 26 | 13 | 3 | 10 | 63 | 38 | 42 |
| 7 | Freethorpe | 26 | 13 | 3 | 10 | 64 | 57 | 42 |
| 8 | Swaffham Town Reserves | 26 | 10 | 4 | 12 | 57 | 57 | 34 |
| 9 | Thorpe Village | 26 | 8 | 2 | 16 | 55 | 66 | 26 |
| 10 | North Walsham Town Res (-1pt) | 26 | 8 | 3 | 15 | 48 | 73 | 26 |
| 11 | Loddon United Reserves | 26 | 8 | 0 | 18 | 41 | 86 | 24 |
| 12 | Blofield United Res (-1pt) | 26 | 7 | 3 | 16 | 63 | 85 | 23 |
| 13 | Costessey Sports | 26 | 6 | 1 | 19 | 30 | 152 | 19 |
| 14 | (R) Wymondham Town Res (-2pts) | 26 | 2 | 0 | 24 | 24 | 92 | 4 |

### DIVISION FOUR

| | | P | W | D | L | F | A | Pts |
|---|---|---|---|---|---|---|---|---|
| 1 | (P) Waveney | 28 | 21 | 3 | 4 | 94 | 26 | 66 |
| 2 | (P) South Walsham | 28 | 20 | 4 | 4 | 93 | 26 | 64 |
| 3 | (P) Caister Reserves | 28 | 16 | 4 | 8 | 68 | 46 | 52 |
| 4 | Fakenham Town Reserves | 28 | 14 | 7 | 7 | 82 | 58 | 49 |
| 5 | Long Stratton Reserves | 28 | 13 | 6 | 9 | 55 | 47 | 45 |
| 6 | Norwich CEYMS Reserves | 28 | 13 | 4 | 11 | 69 | 53 | 43 |
| 7 | Saham Toney (-3pts) | 28 | 13 | 5 | 10 | 57 | 59 | 41 |
| 8 | Sprowston Athletic Res (-2pts) | 28 | 13 | 3 | 12 | 46 | 45 | 40 |
| 9 | Redgrave Rangers | 28 | 11 | 2 | 15 | 47 | 60 | 35 |
| 10 | Bungay Town Reserves | 28 | 9 | 7 | 12 | 54 | 58 | 34 |
| 11 | Mattishall Reserves | 28 | 9 | 7 | 12 | 46 | 64 | 34 |
| 12 | Newton Flotman | 28 | 8 | 4 | 16 | 42 | 69 | 28 |
| 13 | Sheringham Res (-1pt) | 28 | 8 | 1 | 19 | 41 | 94 | 24 |
| 14 | (R) St Andrews Reserves | 28 | 6 | 5 | 17 | 36 | 80 | 23 |
| 15 | (R) Beccles Town Res (-4pts) | 28 | 4 | 2 | 22 | 33 | 76 | 10 |

### DIVISION FIVE

| | | P | W | D | L | F | A | Pts |
|---|---|---|---|---|---|---|---|---|
| 1 | (P) Buxton | 24 | 19 | 1 | 4 | 100 | 30 | 58 |
| 2 | (P) Yelverton | 24 | 15 | 6 | 3 | 70 | 35 | 51 |
| 3 | (P) Horsford United Reserves | 24 | 14 | 2 | 8 | 59 | 32 | 44 |
| 4 | (P) Stalham Town Reserves | 24 | 13 | 3 | 8 | 52 | 36 | 42 |
| 5 | Watton United Reserves | 24 | 11 | 6 | 7 | 59 | 39 | 39 |
| 6 | Aylsham Res (-1pt) | 24 | 11 | 3 | 10 | 55 | 47 | 35 |
| 7 | Thorpe Rovers | 24 | 11 | 2 | 11 | 47 | 51 | 35 |
| 8 | Attleborough Town Reserves | 24 | 9 | 4 | 11 | 40 | 72 | 31 |
| 9 | Bradenham Wanderers Res | 24 | 7 | 7 | 10 | 46 | 56 | 28 |
| 10 | Hindringham Reserves | 24 | 7 | 4 | 13 | 39 | 67 | 25 |
| 11 | Poringland Wanderers Res | 24 | 6 | 5 | 13 | 31 | 61 | 23 |
| 12 | Holt United Reserves | 24 | 6 | 1 | 17 | 29 | 54 | 19 |
| 13 | Mundford Res (-1pt) | 24 | 3 | 4 | 17 | 22 | 69 | 11 |

### DIVISION SIX

| | | P | W | D | L | F | A | Pts |
|---|---|---|---|---|---|---|---|---|
| 1 | (P) Redgate Rangers | 26 | 23 | 2 | 1 | 104 | 23 | 71 |
| 2 | (P) Hingham Athletic | 26 | 21 | 3 | 2 | 104 | 40 | 66 |
| 3 | (P) Feltwell United | 26 | 18 | 2 | 6 | 77 | 45 | 56 |
| 4 | (P) Harleston Town Reserves | 26 | 15 | 2 | 9 | 91 | 56 | 47 |
| 5 | Earsham | 26 | 13 | 5 | 8 | 65 | 44 | 44 |
| 6 | Scole United Reserves | 26 | 12 | 3 | 11 | 67 | 70 | 39 |
| 7 | Reepham Town Res (-1pt) | 26 | 9 | 7 | 10 | 50 | 46 | 33 |
| 8 | Freethorpe Res (-1pt) | 26 | 9 | 5 | 12 | 47 | 68 | 31 |
| 9 | Easton Reserves | 26 | 9 | 2 | 15 | 56 | 71 | 29 |
| 10 | Martham Reserves | 26 | 7 | 8 | 11 | 52 | 77 | 29 |
| 11 | East Harling Reserves | 26 | 8 | 3 | 15 | 51 | 62 | 27 |
| 12 | Thorpe Village Res (-1pt) | 26 | 7 | 2 | 17 | 45 | 70 | 22 |
| 13 | Foulsham Res (-1pt) | 26 | 6 | 3 | 17 | 42 | 79 | 20 |
| 14 | (R) Hemsby Reserves (-3pts) | 26 | 1 | 1 | 24 | 33 | 133 | 1 |

**Additional clubs for 2013-14:** Corton Celtic.
Dersingham Rovers Reserves (S - North West Norfolk League).
Mulbarton Wanderers Reserves (P - Central & South Norfolk League). Thetford Town Reserves (N).

**Out:** Hemsby Reserves (Great Yarmouth & District League)

# BEDFORDSHIRE COUNTY LEAGUE

**Sponsored by:** No sponsor
**Founded:** 1904
**Recent Champions:**
2008: Campton
2009: Caldecote
2010: Blunham
2011: Blunham
2012: Shefford Town & Campton
**bedfordshirefootballleague.co.uk**

## BRITANNIA CUP

**ROUND 1**

| | | | |
|---|---|---|---|
| Renhold United | v | Bedford SA | 0-2 |
| AFC Kempston T. & B.C. | v | Bedford Hatters | 1-2 |
| Marston Shelton Rovers | v | Ickwell & Old Warden | 3-2 |
| Shefford Town & Campton | v | Caldecote | 3-1 |
| Flitwick Town | v | Sharnbrook | 4-1 |
| Wilshamstead | v | Lidlington United Sports | 7-1 |
| Oakley Sports M&DH | v | Arlesey Town Reserves | 2-0 |

**QUARTER FINALS**

| | | | |
|---|---|---|---|
| Bedford SA | v | AFC Biggleswade | 2-3 |
| Bedford Hatters | v | Marston Shelton Rovers | 4-2 |
| Shefford Town & Campton | v | Flitwick Town | 1-3 |
| Wilshamstead | v | Oakley Sports M&DH | 1-5 |

**SEMI FINALS**

| | | | |
|---|---|---|---|
| AFC Biggleswade | v | Bedford Hatters | 4-0 |
| Flitwick Town | v | Oakley Sports M&DH | 1-4 |

**FINAL**

| | | | |
|---|---|---|---|
| AFC Biggleswade | v | Oakley Sports M&DH | 0-2 |

## PREMIER DIVISION

| | | P | W | D | L | F | A | Pts |
|---|---|---|---|---|---|---|---|---|
| 1 | Caldecote | 28 | 21 | 3 | 4 | 87 | 42 | 66 |
| 2 | Oakley Sports M&DH | 28 | 20 | 3 | 5 | 95 | 50 | 63 |
| 3 | Renhold United | 28 | 18 | 3 | 7 | 78 | 50 | 57 |
| 4 | (P) Arlesey Town Reserves | 28 | 15 | 3 | 10 | 63 | 46 | 48 |
| 5 | Marston Shelton Rovers | 28 | 13 | 5 | 10 | 50 | 52 | 44 |
| 6 | Ickwell & Old Warden | 28 | 13 | 4 | 11 | 84 | 49 | 43 |
| 7 | Shefford Town & Campton | 28 | 12 | 6 | 10 | 77 | 47 | 42 |
| 8 | Wilshamstead | 28 | 12 | 5 | 11 | 75 | 71 | 41 |
| 9 | Bedford Hatters (-6pts) | 28 | 15 | 2 | 11 | 56 | 56 | 41 |
| 10 | AFC Kempston T. & Bedford Col | 28 | 12 | 4 | 12 | 46 | 49 | 40 |
| 11 | Lidlington United Sports | 28 | 9 | 4 | 15 | 47 | 74 | 31 |
| 12 | Flitwick Town | 28 | 8 | 6 | 14 | 39 | 51 | 30 |
| 13 | AFC Biggleswade | 28 | 7 | 3 | 18 | 44 | 74 | 24 |
| 14 | Sharnbrook | 28 | 7 | 0 | 21 | 45 | 84 | 21 |
| 15 | (R) Bedford SA (-6pts) | 28 | 1 | 3 | 24 | 29 | 120 | 0 |

## DIVISION ONE

| | | P | W | D | L | F | A | Pts |
|---|---|---|---|---|---|---|---|---|
| 1 | (F) Leighton United | 22 | 17 | 3 | 2 | 84 | 35 | 54 |
| 2 | (P) Shillington | 22 | 16 | 3 | 3 | 58 | 25 | 51 |
| 3 | (P) Pavenham | 22 | 12 | 4 | 6 | 61 | 34 | 40 |
| 4 | Luton Boys | 22 | 11 | 3 | 8 | 53 | 47 | 36 |
| 5 | Shefford Town & Campton Res. | 22 | 9 | 5 | 8 | 50 | 52 | 32 |
| 6 | Elstow Abbey | 22 | 9 | 4 | 9 | 56 | 56 | 31 |
| 7 | Sandy | 22 | 9 | 4 | 9 | 38 | 41 | 31 |
| 8 | Caldecote Reserves | 22 | 8 | 6 | 8 | 41 | 35 | 30 |
| 9 | Henlow | 22 | 9 | 2 | 11 | 47 | 53 | 29 |
| 10 | Brickhill Tigers | 22 | 6 | 5 | 11 | 56 | 57 | 23 |
| 11 | Kings AFC | 22 | 2 | 4 | 16 | 32 | 84 | 10 |
| 12 | (R) AFC Kempston T. & Bedford Col Res. | 22 | 1 | 3 | 18 | 19 | 76 | 6 |

## DIVISION TWO

| | | P | W | D | L | F | A | Pts |
|---|---|---|---|---|---|---|---|---|
| 1 | (P) Goldington | 26 | 17 | 6 | 3 | 73 | 39 | 57 |
| 2 | (P) Marabese Ceramics | 26 | 18 | 2 | 6 | 62 | 48 | 56 |
| 3 | (P) Eastcotts AFC | 26 | 16 | 5 | 5 | 46 | 32 | 53 |
| 4 | Sundon Park Rangers Saturday | 26 | 15 | 2 | 9 | 67 | 43 | 47 |
| 5 | (P) Bromham United | 26 | 13 | 6 | 7 | 62 | 43 | 45 |
| 6 | (P) Woburn Athletic | 26 | 12 | 6 | 8 | 72 | 63 | 42 |
| 7 | Queens Park Crescents | 26 | 11 | 6 | 9 | 59 | 51 | 39 |
| 8 | Oakley Sports M&DH Reserves | 26 | 10 | 3 | 13 | 63 | 65 | 33 |
| 9 | Cranfield United Reserves | 26 | 9 | 4 | 13 | 54 | 61 | 31 |
| 10 | St Josephs Saturday Reserves | 26 | 9 | 0 | 17 | 58 | 66 | 27 |
| 11 | Westoning | 26 | 8 | 2 | 16 | 59 | 76 | 26 |
| 12 | Stopsley Park | 26 | 7 | 2 | 17 | 55 | 78 | 23 |
| 13 | Potton United Reserves | 26 | 6 | 4 | 16 | 49 | 69 | 22 |
| 14 | (R) Meltis Albion | 26 | 6 | 2 | 18 | 42 | 87 | 20 |

## PREMIER DIVISION

| | | 1 | 2 | 3 | 4 | 5 | 6 | 7 | 8 | 9 | 10 | 11 | 12 | 13 | 14 | 15 |
|---|---|---|---|---|---|---|---|---|---|---|---|---|---|---|---|---|
| 1 | AFC Biggleswade | | 2-1 | 2-3 | 0-1 | 9-1 | 1-2 | 0-1 | 0-8 | 2-4 | 1-3 | 4-4 | 4-1 | 0-2 | 2-1 | 1-3 |
| 2 | AFC Kempston Town & Bedford College | 4-0 | | 0-2 | 0-1 | 3-2 | 1-3 | 2-2 | 1-6 | 1-3 | 2-0 | 3-0 | 3-0 | 5-2 | 0-2 | 1-4 |
| 3 | Arlesey Town Reserves | 1-1 | 1-2 | | 4-0 | 1-0 | 4-1 | 1-1 | 0-1 | 9-1 | 4-2 | 2-5 | 1-1 | 2-1 | 1-0 | 1-5 |
| 4 | Bedford Hatters | 5-0 | 1-1 | 2-1 | | 4-0 | 2-3 | 1-3 | 3-2 | 1-0 | 2-1 | 2-3 | 4-5 | 3-2 | 3-2 | 9-2 |
| 5 | Bedford SA | 1-1 | 0-1 | 0-9 | 0-2 | | 1-5 | 2-4 | 0-10 | 1-4 | 1-2 | 0-4 | 2-3 | 1-4 | 1-4 | 1-9 |
| 6 | Caldecote | 3-1 | 1-0 | 5-0 | 4-1 | 5-1 | | 3-1 | 3-2 | 5-2 | 1-1 | 4-2 | 0-0 | 2-0 | 4-3 | 1-3 |
| 7 | Flitwick Town | 2-0 | 1-2 | 3-1 | 1-2 | 1-2 | 1-5 | | 1-1 | 2-0 | 2-2 | 2-4 | 3-1 | 1-2 | 0-2 | 1-2 |
| 8 | Ickwell & Old Warden | 1-2 | 2-2 | 0-1 | 8-0 | 4-1 | 2-3 | 1-0 | | 6-0 | 3-1 | 2-5 | 2-4 | 4-0 | 1-1 | 1-5 |
| 9 | Lidlington United Sports | 4-1 | 0-1 | 3-1 | 0-1 | 3-1 | 1-5 | 2-1 | 1-1 | | 2-2 | 1-3 | 1-3 | 0-3 | 2-2 | 5-1 |
| 10 | Marston Shelton Rovers | 2-0 | 0-0 | 1-3 | 0-0 | 5-0 | 0-5 | 1-0 | 0-5 | 2-1 | | 4-3 | 1-2 | 6-3 | 1-0 | 3-1 |
| 11 | Oakley Sports M&DH | 2-1 | 6-2 | 4-1 | 6-0 | 3-2 | 0-4 | 4-0 | 5-0 | 7-0 | 2-1 | | 2-1 | 2-1 | 3-3 | 2-2 |
| 12 | Renhold United | 4-0 | 2-1 | 2-1 | 4-2 | 1-1 | 6-3 | 6-1 | 3-1 | 4-0 | 1-2 | 2-5 | | 3-1 | 1-4 | 7-1 |
| 13 | Sharnbrook | 2-5 | 1-2 | 1-4 | 1-2 | 3-2 | 2-4 | 0-2 | 2-6 | 4-0 | 3-0 | 1-5 | 0-3 | | 1-4 | 0-4 |
| 14 | Shefford Town & Campton | 2-3 | 0-1 | 1-2 | 3-1 | 12-1 | 3-2 | 1-1 | 2-0 | 3-3 | 2-3 | 5-1 | 3-5 | 6-2 | | 4-0 |
| 15 | Wilshamstead | 6-1 | 5-4 | 1-2 | H-W | 4-4 | 1-1 | 1-1 | 3-4 | 1-4 | 3-4 | 0-3 | 1-3 | 5-1 | 2-2 | |

Caldecote celebrate their record breaking ninth Bedfordshire League title. Photo: Gordon Whittington.

## BEDFORDSHIRE COUNTY PREMIER DIVISION CONSTITUTION 2013-14

|  |  |
|---|---|
| AFC BIGGLESWADE | Biggleswade United FC, Fairfield Road, Biggleswade, Bedfordshire SG18 0BS |
| AFC KEMPSTON & BEDFORD COLL. | Hillgrounds Road, Kempston, Bedford MK42 8SZ |
| AFC OAKLEY SPORTS M&DH | Oakley Village Sports Centre, Oakley, Bedford MK43 7RU |
| CALDECOTE | Caldecote Sports Field, Furlong Way, Caldecote, CB23 7ZH |
| FLITWICK TOWN | Flitwick Leisure Centre, Flitwick, Bedford MK45 1TH |
| ICKWELL & OLD WARDEN | Ickwell Green, Ickwell, Bedfordshire SG18 9EE |
| LEIGHTON UNITED SPORTS | Hurst Grove, Lidlington, Bedfordshire MK43 0SB |
| MARSTON SHELTON ROVERS | Bedford Road, Marston Moretaine, Bedford MK43 0LE |
| PAVENHAM | Pavenham Playing Field, Pavenham, Bedfordshire MK43 7PE |
| RENHOLD UNITED | Renhold Playing Fields, Renhold, Bedford MK41 0LR |
| SHARNBROOK | Playing Fields, Lodge Road, Sharnbrook MK44 1JP |
| SHEFFORD TOWN & CAMPTON | Campton Playing Field, Rectory Road, Campton, Bedfordshire SG17 5PF |
| SHILLINGTON | Greenfields, Bury Road, Shillington |
| WILSHAMSTEAD | Jubilee Playing Fields, Bedford Road, Wilshamstead MK45 3HN |
| WOOTTON BLUE CROSS | Weston Park, Bedford Rd., Wootton MK43 9JT |

**In:** AFC Oakley Sports M&DH (NC from Oakley Sports M&DH). Pavenham (P). Shillington (P). Wootton Blue Cross (United Counties Div.1).
**Out:** Arlesey Town Reserves (P - Spartan South Midlands Div.1). Bedford Hatters (F). Bedford SA (R). Oakley Sports M&DH (NC to AFC Oakley Sports M&DH).

| DIVISION THREE | P | W | D | L | F | A | Pts | DIVISION FOUR | P | W | D | L | F | A | Pts |
|---|---|---|---|---|---|---|---|---|---|---|---|---|---|---|---|
| 1 Westoning Reserves | 24 | 15 | 5 | 4 | 75 | 42 | 50 | 1 (P) Bedford Panthers | 24 | 19 | 3 | 2 | 115 | 29 | 60 |
| 2 Renhold United Reserves | 24 | 16 | 2 | 6 | 66 | 49 | 50 | 2 (P) Elstow Abbey Reserves | 24 | 16 | 2 | 6 | 86 | 34 | 50 |
| 3 Great Barford | 24 | 16 | 0 | 8 | 69 | 52 | 48 | 3 (P) Kempston Athletic | 24 | 15 | 5 | 4 | 66 | 39 | 50 |
| 4 Clifton | 24 | 14 | 3 | 7 | 62 | 37 | 45 | 4 (P) Clifton Reserves | 24 | 14 | 4 | 6 | 55 | 53 | 46 |
| 5 Riseley Sports | 24 | 13 | 4 | 7 | 56 | 38 | 43 | 5 (P) Marston Shelton Rovers Reserves | 24 | 14 | 0 | 10 | 64 | 47 | 42 |
| 6 Potton Town | 24 | 13 | 3 | 8 | 67 | 49 | 42 | 6 (P) Kempston Con Club Sports | 24 | 13 | 0 | 11 | 65 | 57 | 39 |
| 7 Stevington | 24 | 10 | 6 | 8 | 72 | 56 | 36 | 7 Dinamo Flitwick | 24 | 9 | 4 | 11 | 58 | 82 | 31 |
| 8 Wilshamstead Reserves | 24 | 9 | 4 | 11 | 62 | 61 | 31 | 8 Flitwick Town Reserves | 24 | 9 | 3 | 12 | 46 | 56 | 30 |
| 9 Ickwell & Old Warden Reserves | 24 | 9 | 2 | 13 | 51 | 58 | 29 | 9 Caldecote A | 24 | 8 | 1 | 15 | 51 | 96 | 25 |
| 10 (F) Dunton | 24 | 9 | 2 | 13 | 34 | 46 | 29 | 10 Sandy Reserves | 24 | 7 | 2 | 15 | 44 | 60 | 23 |
| 11 Kempston Hammers Sports | 24 | 5 | 5 | 14 | 38 | 74 | 20 | 11 Shefford Town & Campton A | 24 | 6 | 3 | 15 | 40 | 67 | 21 |
| 12 (F) Royal Oak Kempston | 24 | 5 | 2 | 17 | 26 | 57 | 17 | 12 (F) Dunton Reserves | 24 | 4 | 5 | 15 | 29 | 69 | 17 |
| 13 (R) Bedford Park Rangers | 24 | 1 | 4 | 19 | 35 | 94 | 7 | 13 Wootton Village | 24 | 4 | 4 | 16 | 43 | 73 | 16 |

### CENTENARY CUP

**FINAL**
Elstow Abbey    v   Henlow     2-2, 1-3p

### JUBILEE CUP

**FINAL**
Marabese Ceramics    v   Oakley Sports M&DH Res.   2-1

### WATSON SHIELD

**FINAL**
Clifton     v   Renhold United Reserves    1-3

# CAMBRIDGESHIRE COUNTY LEAGUE

**Sponsored by:** Kershaw Mechanical Services Ltd

**Founded:** 1891

**Recent Champions:**
2008: Waterbeach
2009: Fulbourn Institute
2010: Fulbourn Institute
2011: Lakenheath
2012: Linton Granta

## PREMIER DIVISION CUP

**ROUND 1**

| | | | |
|---|---|---|---|
| Hardwick | v | Great Shelford | 1-5 |
| Wisbech St Mary | v | West Wratting | 2-3 |

**ROUND 2**

| | | | |
|---|---|---|---|
| Chatteris Town | v | Eaton Socon | 0-4 |
| Brampton | v | Waterbeach | 5-3 |
| Lakenheath | v | Cottenham United | 3-0 |
| Great Shelford | v | West Wratting | 5-0 |
| Linton Granta | v | Sawston United | 3-2 |
| Soham Town Rangers R. | v | Over Sports | 0-3 |
| Littleport Town | v | Ely City Reserves | 3-2 |
| Foxton | v | Fulbourn Institute | 1-2 |

**QUARTER FINALS**

| | | | |
|---|---|---|---|
| Eaton Socon | v | Brampton | 3-1 |
| Lakenheath | v | Great Shelford | 1-5 |
| Linton Granta | v | Over Sports | 4-2 |
| Littleport Town | v | Fulbourn Institute | 3-0 |

**SEMI FINALS**

| | | | |
|---|---|---|---|
| Eaton Socon | v | Great Shelford | 1-2 |
| Linton Granta | v | Littleport Town | 2-0 |

**FINAL**

| | | | |
|---|---|---|---|
| Great Shelford | v | Linton Granta | 2-2, 5-4p |

## PREMIER DIVISION

| | PREMIER DIVISION | P | W | D | L | F | A | Pts |
|---|---|---|---|---|---|---|---|---|
| 1 | Great Shelford | 34 | 24 | 6 | 4 | 87 | 31 | 78 |
| 2 | Linton Granta | 34 | 21 | 7 | 6 | 90 | 39 | 70 |
| 3 | Over Sports | 34 | 21 | 6 | 7 | 86 | 48 | 69 |
| 4 | Foxton | 34 | 18 | 11 | 5 | 68 | 42 | 65 |
| 5 | Fulbourn Institute | 34 | 17 | 8 | 9 | 91 | 54 | 59 |
| 6 | Sawston United | 34 | 17 | 7 | 10 | 76 | 70 | 58 |
| 7 | Wisbech St Mary | 34 | 17 | 4 | 13 | 63 | 57 | 55 |
| 8 | Hardwick | 34 | 16 | 5 | 13 | 71 | 56 | 53 |
| 9 | Lakenheath | 34 | 15 | 8 | 11 | 76 | 64 | 53 |
| 10 | Littleport Town | 34 | 12 | 11 | 11 | 64 | 49 | 47 |
| 11 | Cottenham United | 34 | 12 | 9 | 13 | 69 | 61 | 45 |
| 12 | West Wratting | 34 | 14 | 3 | 17 | 69 | 79 | 45 |
| 13 | Soham Town Rangers Res | 34 | 9 | 5 | 20 | 58 | 81 | 32 |
| 14 | Waterbeach | 34 | 8 | 7 | 19 | 44 | 86 | 31 |
| 15 | Brampton (-3pts) | 34 | 7 | 10 | 17 | 51 | 76 | 28 |
| 16 | Eaton Socon | 34 | 7 | 3 | 24 | 41 | 92 | 24 |
| 17 | (R) Chatteris Town | 34 | 5 | 8 | 21 | 43 | 98 | 23 |
| 18 | (R) Ely City Res (-3pts) | 34 | 5 | 4 | 25 | 40 | 104 | 16 |

| PREMIER DIVISION | 1 | 2 | 3 | 4 | 5 | 6 | 7 | 8 | 9 | 10 | 11 | 12 | 13 | 14 | 15 | 16 | 17 | 18 |
|---|---|---|---|---|---|---|---|---|---|---|---|---|---|---|---|---|---|---|
| 1 Brampton | | 1-1 | 3-4 | 1-0 | 2-2 | 2-3 | 1-0 | 0-3 | 0-6 | 5-2 | 2-3 | 0-5 | 0-4 | 2-2 | 3-1 | 2-2 | 0-1 | 0-2 |
| 2 Chatteris Town | 4-4 | | 1-1 | 1-2 | 1-0 | 0-5 | 3-0 | 2-5 | 0-4 | 1-1 | 2-3 | 1-1 | 1-4 | 3-1 | 2-2 | 4-5 | 1-2 | 1-2 |
| 3 Cottenham United | 4-3 | 11-0 | | 3-1 | 8-0 | 3-2 | 0-1 | 0-3 | 0-5 | 1-1 | 0-2 | 2-5 | 0-3 | 3-1 | 5-0 | 1-1 | 1-0 | 7-0 |
| 4 Eaton Socon | 0-1 | 0-0 | 0-0 | | 0-1 | 2-0 | 3-4 | 0-2 | 1-2 | 0-5 | 0-5 | 0-4 | 3-2 | 1-3 | 3-4 | 4-1 | 1-3 | 0-3 |
| 5 Ely City Reserves | 0-1 | 2-1 | 1-1 | 6-1 | | 2-3 | 0-6 | 0-2 | 0-2 | 2-3 | 2-2 | 0-3 | 1-2 | 2-4 | 1-3 | 4-1 | 1-4 | 1-3 |
| 6 Foxton | 2-1 | 2-1 | 2-2 | 1-1 | 5-1 | | 2-2 | 1-0 | 1-1 | 1-1 | 1-0 | 4-2 | 1-1 | 2-2 | 0-0 | 3-0 | 3-0 | 2-1 |
| 7 Fulbourn Institute | 4-2 | 3-3 | 1-2 | 2-1 | 8-1 | 0-0 | | 1-4 | 6-1 | 4-4 | 1-2 | 2-0 | 0-2 | 4-3 | 3-0 | 4-3 | 1-1 | 1-1 |
| 8 Great Shelford | 1-1 | 3-0 | 2-2 | 6-0 | 4-0 | 1-0 | 1-1 | | 2-0 | 2-1 | 0-1 | 2-0 | 4-1 | 4-5 | 3-0 | 2-1 | 2-0 | 5-2 |
| 9 Hardwick | 2-2 | 2-1 | 3-0 | 4-0 | 0-1 | 1-2 | 2-4 | 0-4 | | 1-3 | 5-2 | 2-2 | 4-2 | 3-2 | 4-2 | 1-2 | 4-0 | 1-1 |
| 10 Lakenheath | 2-0 | 1-2 | 4-1 | 3-0 | 6-1 | 2-3 | 3-2 | 3-4 | 2-1 | | 0-1 | 3-1 | 3-2 | 2-2 | 2-1 | 1-1 | 3-2 | 1-2 |
| 11 Linton Granta | 2-2 | 6-0 | 2-2 | 2-5 | 2-0 | 3-1 | 1-0 | 2-2 | 3-0 | 4-0 | | 1-1 | 0-0 | 7-1 | 4-0 | 5-0 | 4-0 | 4-0 |
| 12 Littleport Town | 2-1 | 4-1 | 1-1 | 1-0 | 8-0 | 1-1 | 1-1 | 1-0 | 3-0 | 2-2 | 1-1 | | 0-1 | 1-3 | 1-4 | 1-0 | 1-3 | 1-0 |
| 13 Over Sports | 3-2 | 4-0 | 4-0 | 4-0 | 3-1 | 2-2 | 0-3 | 0-3 | 3-3 | 5-1 | 4-1 | 4-1 | | 2-2 | 2-1 | 4-2 | 4-1 | 0-2 |
| 14 Sawston United | 3-1 | 0-1 | 2-0 | 3-5 | 4-2 | 0-3 | 1-1 | 3-3 | 2-1 | 2-3 | 3-5 | 2-1 | 2-2 | | 3-1 | 1-3 | 3-1 | 3-0 |
| 15 Soham Town Rangers Reserves | 0-3 | 7-1 | 3-1 | 2-3 | 2-1 | 0-1 | 2-5 | 2-2 | 0-2 | 2-0 | 0-3 | 1-1 | 1-4 | 1-3 | | 0-3 | 6-0 | 1-5 |
| 16 Waterbeach | 1-1 | 3-2 | 0-2 | 3-1 | 3-3 | 0-8 | 0-4 | 1-2 | 0-1 | 3-2 | 1-6 | 3-0 | 0-1 | 1-2 | 0-3 | | 1-1 | 1-3 |
| 17 West Wratting | 1-1 | 4-0 | 0-1 | 7-1 | 3-1 | 7-0 | 0-8 | 0-3 | 2-3 | 2-5 | 2-1 | 3-3 | 1-3 | 0-1 | 5-2 | 4-0 | | 4-1 |
| 18 Wisbech St Mary | 4-1 | 3-1 | 2-1 | 3-2 | 3-0 | 0-1 | 2-3 | 0-1 | 1-0 | 1-1 | 1-0 | 3-1 | 2-4 | 1-2 | 1-4 | 1-1 | 7-1 | |

## CAMBRIDGESHIRE COUNTY PREMIER DIVISION CONSTITUTION 2013-14

| | |
|---|---|
| BRAMPTON | Thrapston Road Playing Fields, Brampton, Huntingdon PE28 4TB |
| CAMBRIDGE CITY RESERVES | Cottenham Village College, High Street, Cottenham, Cambridge, Cambridgeshire CB24 8UA |
| CAMBRIDGE UNIVERSITY PRESS | CUP Sports Ground, Shaftesbury Road, Cambridge CB2 2BS |
| COTTENHAM UNITED | King George V Playing Field, Lamb Lane, Cottenham, Cambridge CB4 8TB |
| EATON SOCON | River Road, Eaton Ford, St Neots PE19 3AU |
| FOXTON | Hardman Road, off High Street, Foxton CB22 6RP |
| FULBOURN INSTITUTE | Fulbourn Recreation, Home End, Fulbourn CB21 5HS |
| GREAT SHELFORD | Recreation Ground, Woollards Lane, Great Shelford CB2 5LZ |
| HARDWICK | Egremont Road, Hardwick, Cambridge CB3 7XR |
| LAKENHEATH | The Pit, Wings Road, Lakenheath IP27 9HN |
| LINTON GRANTA | Recreation Ground, Meadow Lane, Linton, Cambridge CB21 6HX |
| LITTLEPORT TOWN | Sports Centre, Camel Road, Littleport, Ely CB6 1PU |
| OVER SPORTS | Over Recreation Ground, The Doles, Over, Cambridge CB4 5NW |
| SAWSTON UNITED | Spicers Sports Ground, New Road, Sawston CB22 4BW |
| SOHAM TOWN RANGERS RESERVES | Soham Town Rangers FC, Julius Martin Lane, Soham, Ely CB7 5EQ |
| SOHAM UNITED | Qua Fen Common, Qua Fen, Soham, Ely CB7 5DQ |
| WATERBEACH | Waterbeach Reacreation Ground, Cambridge Road, Waterbeach CB5 9NJ |
| WEST WRATTING | Recreation Ground, Bull Lane, West Wratting CB21 5NJ |
| WISBECH ST MARY | Wisbech St Mary Playing Fields , Station Road, Wisbech St Mary, Wisbech PE13 4RT |

**In:** Cambridge City Reserves (P). Cambridge University Press (Eastern counties Div.1). Soham United (P).
**Out:** Chatteris Town (R). Ely City Reserves (R).

# CAMBRIDGESHIRE COUNTY LEAGUE - STEP 7

| SENIOR DIVISION A | P | W | D | L | F | A | Pts |
|---|---|---|---|---|---|---|---|
| 1 (P) Cambridge City Reserves | 26 | 20 | 4 | 2 | 97 | 33 | 64 |
| 2 (P) Soham United | 26 | 19 | 3 | 4 | 74 | 33 | 60 |
| 3 Cambridge University Press Res. | 26 | 19 | 1 | 6 | 71 | 35 | 58 |
| 4 Cherry Hinton | 26 | 17 | 4 | 5 | 57 | 35 | 55 |
| 5 Great Paxton | 26 | 15 | 5 | 6 | 71 | 39 | 50 |
| 6 Fenstanton | 26 | 14 | 5 | 7 | 65 | 45 | 47 |
| 7 Girton United | 26 | 13 | 4 | 9 | 49 | 45 | 43 |
| 8 Hemingfords United | 26 | 11 | 5 | 10 | 59 | 45 | 38 |
| 9 Fulbourn Institute Reserves | 26 | 7 | 5 | 14 | 37 | 58 | 26 |
| 10 Milton | 26 | 5 | 5 | 16 | 36 | 62 | 20 |
| 11 Castle Camps | 26 | 6 | 2 | 18 | 36 | 73 | 20 |
| 12 Hundon | 26 | 3 | 9 | 14 | 40 | 57 | 18 |
| 13 (R) Wimblington | 26 | 3 | 2 | 21 | 31 | 88 | 11 |
| 14 (R) Needingworth United (-3pts) | 26 | 2 | 2 | 22 | 26 | 101 | 5 |

| SENIOR DIVISION B | P | W | D | L | F | A | Pts |
|---|---|---|---|---|---|---|---|
| 1 (P) Gamlingay United | 28 | 22 | 4 | 2 | 89 | 20 | 70 |
| 2 (P) Royston Town A | 28 | 18 | 4 | 6 | 53 | 32 | 58 |
| 3 (P) West Row Gunners | 28 | 17 | 6 | 5 | 65 | 40 | 57 |
| 4 (P) Comberton United | 27 | 17 | 4 | 6 | 68 | 37 | 55 |
| 5 Outwell Swifts | 28 | 16 | 2 | 10 | 61 | 47 | 50 |
| 6 Bluntisham Rangers | 28 | 13 | 4 | 11 | 48 | 40 | 43 |
| 7 Longstanton (-3pts) | 27 | 11 | 7 | 9 | 52 | 56 | 37 |
| 8 Hardwick Res (-3pts) | 28 | 9 | 10 | 9 | 48 | 41 | 34 |
| 9 West Wratting Reserves | 28 | 10 | 4 | 14 | 54 | 68 | 34 |
| 10 Hemingfords United Reserves | 28 | 10 | 3 | 15 | 46 | 73 | 33 |
| 11 St Ives Rangers | 28 | 7 | 7 | 14 | 45 | 55 | 28 |
| 12 Lakenheath Reserves | 28 | 7 | 3 | 18 | 49 | 75 | 24 |
| 13 Swavesey Institute | 28 | 5 | 7 | 16 | 51 | 71 | 22 |
| 14 (R) Duxford United | 28 | 5 | 3 | 20 | 29 | 76 | 18 |
| 15 Littleport Town Res (-6pts) | 28 | 7 | 2 | 19 | 43 | 70 | 17 |

### WILLIAM COCKELL CUP

**FINAL**
| Clifton | v | Renhold United Reserves | 1-3 |
|---|---|---|---|

| DIVISION ONE A | P | W | D | L | F | A | Pts |
|---|---|---|---|---|---|---|---|
| 1 (P) Fowlmere | 24 | 15 | 5 | 4 | 59 | 31 | 50 |
| 2 (P) Sawston Rovers | 24 | 16 | 1 | 7 | 56 | 36 | 49 |
| 3 (P) Glemsford & Cavendish United | 24 | 14 | 4 | 6 | 48 | 36 | 46 |
| 4 Whittlesford United | 24 | 13 | 5 | 6 | 70 | 46 | 44 |
| 5 Sawston United Reserves | 24 | 13 | 3 | 8 | 57 | 37 | 42 |
| 6 Great Chishill | 24 | 12 | 3 | 9 | 66 | 66 | 39 |
| 7 Clare Town | 24 | 11 | 3 | 10 | 51 | 53 | 36 |
| 8 Eaton Socon Reserves | 24 | 9 | 5 | 10 | 61 | 48 | 32 |
| 9 Barrington | 24 | 8 | 5 | 11 | 46 | 52 | 29 |
| 10 Bottisham & Lode | 24 | 8 | 5 | 11 | 40 | 51 | 29 |
| 11 Howden Sports | 24 | 8 | 2 | 14 | 54 | 57 | 26 |
| 12 Bassingbourn | 24 | 7 | 2 | 15 | 36 | 54 | 23 |
| 13 (R) Steeple Bumpstead | 24 | 0 | 1 | 23 | 19 | 96 | 1 |

| DIVISION ONE B | P | W | D | L | F | A | Pts |
|---|---|---|---|---|---|---|---|
| 1 (P) Witchford 96 | 22 | 18 | 3 | 1 | 62 | 16 | 57 |
| 2 (P) Somersham Town | 22 | 13 | 5 | 4 | 51 | 22 | 44 |
| 3 Burwell Swifts | 22 | 13 | 3 | 6 | 66 | 50 | 42 |
| 4 Huntingdon United RGE | 22 | 12 | 2 | 8 | 56 | 48 | 38 |
| 5 Doddington United | 22 | 11 | 1 | 10 | 46 | 37 | 34 |
| 6 Manea United | 22 | 10 | 4 | 8 | 23 | 28 | 34 |
| 7 Earith United | 22 | 10 | 1 | 11 | 52 | 38 | 31 |
| 8 Godmanchester R. Res (-3pts) | 22 | 9 | 4 | 9 | 38 | 34 | 28 |
| 9 Buckden | 22 | 7 | 1 | 14 | 48 | 61 | 22 |
| 10 March Town United Reserves | 22 | 6 | 2 | 14 | 28 | 53 | 20 |
| 11 Chatteris Town Reserves | 22 | 2 | 6 | 14 | 39 | 88 | 12 |
| 12 Cottenham United Res (-3pts) | 22 | 4 | 2 | 16 | 35 | 69 | 11 |

**DIVISION ONE PLAY-OFF**
Witchford 96 3-3, 4-2p Fowlmere

### PERCY OLDHAM CUP

**FINAL**
| Clifton | v | Renhold United Reserves | 1-3 |
|---|---|---|---|

| DIVISION TWO A | P | W | D | L | F | A | Pts |
|---|---|---|---|---|---|---|---|
| 1 (P) Ashdon Villa | 24 | 16 | 6 | 2 | 77 | 19 | 54 |
| 2 (P) Orwell | 24 | 17 | 2 | 5 | 81 | 44 | 53 |
| 3 (P) Balsham | 24 | 15 | 7 | 2 | 62 | 33 | 52 |
| 4 (P) Linton Granta Reserves | 24 | 14 | 4 | 6 | 98 | 42 | 46 |
| 5 Great Chesterford | 24 | 12 | 4 | 8 | 97 | 59 | 40 |
| 6 Papworth | 24 | 11 | 4 | 9 | 74 | 60 | 37 |
| 7 Cambridge University Press A | 24 | 10 | 5 | 9 | 80 | 64 | 35 |
| 8 City Life | 24 | 6 | 5 | 13 | 39 | 53 | 23 |
| 9 Girton United Reserves | 24 | 5 | 7 | 12 | 47 | 67 | 22 |
| 10 Thaxted Rangers | 24 | 6 | 4 | 14 | 35 | 60 | 22 |
| 11 Cambourne Rovers | 24 | 7 | 1 | 16 | 32 | 70 | 22 |
| 12 Great Shelford Reserves | 24 | 5 | 3 | 16 | 46 | 118 | 18 |
| 13 Abington United | 24 | 6 | 0 | 18 | 38 | 117 | 18 |

| DIVISION TWO B | P | W | D | L | F | A | Pts |
|---|---|---|---|---|---|---|---|
| 1 St Ives Town Reserves | 24 | 18 | 5 | 1 | 87 | 25 | 59 |
| 2 (P) Bar Hill Sports & Social | 24 | 14 | 5 | 5 | 71 | 21 | 47 |
| 3 (P) Milton Reserves | 24 | 13 | 8 | 3 | 64 | 39 | 47 |
| 4 Brampton Reserves | 24 | 13 | 6 | 5 | 70 | 43 | 45 |
| 5 Over Sports Reserves | 24 | 12 | 4 | 8 | 45 | 35 | 40 |
| 6 Mepal Sports | 24 | 11 | 5 | 8 | 59 | 36 | 38 |
| 7 March Rangers | 24 | 10 | 4 | 10 | 59 | 54 | 34 |
| 8 Sutton United | 24 | 10 | 0 | 14 | 81 | 69 | 30 |
| 9 Isleham United | 24 | 7 | 9 | 8 | 52 | 43 | 30 |
| 10 Wisbech St Mary Reserves | 24 | 8 | 3 | 13 | 56 | 68 | 27 |
| 11 Fordham | 24 | 8 | 0 | 16 | 49 | 57 | 24 |
| 12 Bluntisham Rangers Reserves | 24 | 6 | 3 | 15 | 46 | 73 | 21 |
| 13 Tydd United (-3pts) | 24 | 0 | 0 | 24 | 22 | 198 | -3 |

**DIVISION TWO PLAY-OFF**
St Ives Town Reserves 1-2 Ashdon Villa

## DIVISION THREE A

| | P | W | D | L | F | A | Pts |
|---|---|---|---|---|---|---|---|
| (P) Saffron Rangers | 24 | 21 | 1 | 2 | 97 | 28 | 64 |
| (P) Fowlmere Reserves | 24 | 18 | 2 | 4 | 80 | 41 | 56 |
| (P) Meldreth | 24 | 16 | 1 | 7 | 75 | 44 | 49 |
| (P) Gransden | 24 | 13 | 4 | 7 | 61 | 37 | 43 |
| Steeple Morden | 24 | 13 | 0 | 11 | 69 | 56 | 39 |
| Eynesbury Rovers A | 24 | 11 | 4 | 9 | 70 | 50 | 37 |
| Hardwick A | 24 | 11 | 4 | 9 | 63 | 54 | 37 |
| Comberton United Res | 24 | 10 | 2 | 12 | 41 | 54 | 32 |
| Hundon Res | 24 | 9 | 2 | 13 | 29 | 56 | 29 |
| Eaton Socon A | 24 | 6 | 4 | 14 | 38 | 63 | 22 |
| Bottisham & Lode Res | 24 | 5 | 2 | 17 | 45 | 90 | 17 |
| Wilbraham (-3pts) | 24 | 5 | 3 | 16 | 22 | 71 | 15 |
| Fulbourn Institute ""A"" (-9pts) | 24 | 2 | 3 | 19 | 35 | 81 | 0 |

## DIVISION THREE B

| | P | W | D | L | F | A | Pts |
|---|---|---|---|---|---|---|---|
| (P) West Row Gunners Res | 24 | 19 | 1 | 4 | 84 | 37 | 58 |
| Wisbech St Mary A | 24 | 18 | 2 | 4 | 90 | 36 | 56 |
| (P) Elsworth Sports | 24 | 15 | 4 | 5 | 84 | 34 | 49 |
| (P) Exning Athletic | 24 | 15 | 2 | 7 | 60 | 31 | 47 |
| Fenstanton Res | 24 | 13 | 3 | 8 | 53 | 43 | 42 |
| Mildenhall United | 24 | 13 | 1 | 10 | 54 | 56 | 40 |
| Little Downham Swifts | 24 | 12 | 3 | 9 | 94 | 85 | 39 |
| Stretham Hotspurs | 24 | 11 | 2 | 11 | 76 | 71 | 35 |
| Estover Park | 24 | 8 | 1 | 15 | 62 | 89 | 25 |
| Benwick Athletic | 24 | 6 | 2 | 16 | 43 | 91 | 20 |
| Longstanton Res | 24 | 4 | 4 | 16 | 54 | 86 | 16 |
| Wimblington Res | 24 | 5 | 0 | 19 | 41 | 82 | 15 |
| Hemingfords United A | 24 | 4 | 1 | 19 | 39 | 93 | 13 |

### DIVISION THREE PLAY-OFF
West Row Gunners Reserves 1-0 Saffron Rangers

## DIVISION FOUR A

| | P | W | D | L | F | A | Pts |
|---|---|---|---|---|---|---|---|
| (P) Thurlow Royal Exchange | 24 | 21 | 1 | 2 | 132 | 35 | 64 |
| (P) Great Paxton Reserves | 24 | 18 | 1 | 5 | 65 | 32 | 55 |
| (P) Cherry Hinton Reserves | 24 | 15 | 3 | 6 | 65 | 41 | 48 |
| (P) Debden | 24 | 15 | 1 | 8 | 76 | 62 | 46 |
| Bar Hill Sports & Social Reserves | 24 | 14 | 1 | 9 | 85 | 66 | 43 |
| Litlington Athletic | 24 | 11 | 3 | 10 | 65 | 65 | 36 |
| West Wratting A | 24 | 10 | 5 | 9 | 54 | 53 | 35 |
| Therfield & Kelshall | 24 | 7 | 4 | 13 | 30 | 62 | 25 |
| Haverhill Rovers A | 24 | 6 | 4 | 14 | 43 | 72 | 22 |
| Foxton Res | 24 | 6 | 3 | 15 | 47 | 80 | 21 |
| Duxford United Reserves | 24 | 4 | 5 | 15 | 35 | 61 | 17 |
| Cambridge Ambassadors (-3pts) | 24 | 5 | 3 | 16 | 31 | 80 | 15 |
| Glemsford & Cav Utd Res (-9pts) | 24 | 6 | 2 | 16 | 40 | 59 | 11 |

## DIVISION FOUR B

| | P | W | D | L | F | A | Pts |
|---|---|---|---|---|---|---|---|
| (P) Red Lodge | 24 | 22 | 1 | 1 | 109 | 20 | 67 |
| Burwell Swifts Reserves | 24 | 19 | 1 | 4 | 86 | 24 | 58 |
| (P) Willingham Wolves (-3pts) | 23 | 17 | 1 | 5 | 73 | 25 | 49 |
| (P) Soham United Reserves | 24 | 15 | 0 | 9 | 77 | 50 | 45 |
| Haddenham Rovers | 24 | 13 | 3 | 8 | 74 | 57 | 42 |
| Waterbeach Reserves | 24 | 9 | 6 | 9 | 54 | 56 | 33 |
| Mepal Sports Reserves | 24 | 10 | 1 | 13 | 47 | 57 | 31 |
| Wisbech St Mary B | 24 | 10 | 1 | 13 | 39 | 52 | 31 |
| Doddington United Reserves | 24 | 9 | 1 | 14 | 43 | 52 | 28 |
| Milton A | 24 | 8 | 3 | 13 | 41 | 78 | 27 |
| Chatteris Town A | 24 | 7 | 2 | 15 | 50 | 86 | 23 |
| (R) Cottenham United "A" (-6pts) | 23 | 2 | 2 | 19 | 32 | 86 | 2 |
| (R) Wicken Amateurs (-6pts) | 24 | 2 | 2 | 20 | 33 | 115 | 2 |

### DIVISION FOUR PLAY-OFF
Red Lodge 2-3 Thurlow

## DIVISION FIVE A

| | | P | W | D | L | F | A | Pts |
|---|---|---|---|---|---|---|---|---|
| 1 | Castle Camps Reserves | 24 | 20 | 2 | 2 | 121 | 26 | 62 |
| 2 | (P) Saffron Crocus | 24 | 17 | 4 | 3 | 98 | 23 | 55 |
| 3 | (P) Linton Granta A | 24 | 17 | 1 | 6 | 67 | 46 | 52 |
| 4 | Whittlesford United Reserves | 24 | 16 | 2 | 6 | 90 | 34 | 50 |
| 5 | Kedington United | 24 | 15 | 3 | 6 | 94 | 47 | 48 |
| 6 | Sawston Rovers Reserves | 24 | 14 | 1 | 9 | 79 | 56 | 43 |
| 7 | Saffron Dynamos | 24 | 12 | 2 | 10 | 74 | 61 | 38 |
| 8 | Saffron Rangers Reserves | 24 | 9 | 3 | 12 | 64 | 67 | 30 |
| 9 | Newport | 24 | 9 | 1 | 14 | 44 | 57 | 28 |
| 10 | Clare Town Res. (-3pts) | 24 | 6 | 2 | 16 | 52 | 82 | 17 |
| 11 | Sawston United A | 24 | 5 | 2 | 17 | 51 | 103 | 17 |
| 12 | Finchingfield (-3pts) | 24 | 3 | 1 | 20 | 44 | 81 | 7 |
| 13 | Bottisham & Lode A | 24 | 1 | 0 | 23 | 33 | 228 | 3 |

## DIVISION FIVE B

| | | P | W | D | L | F | A | Pts |
|---|---|---|---|---|---|---|---|---|
| 1 | (P) Melbourn | 24 | 21 | 0 | 3 | 111 | 26 | 63 |
| 2 | (P) Little Paxton | 24 | 21 | 0 | 3 | 104 | 30 | 63 |
| 3 | (P) Gamlingay United Reserves | 24 | 18 | 2 | 4 | 94 | 32 | 56 |
| 4 | Histon Hornets | 24 | 13 | 4 | 7 | 70 | 58 | 43 |
| 5 | Great Chishill Res (-3pts) | 24 | 13 | 1 | 10 | 69 | 59 | 37 |
| 6 | Papworth Res (-3pts) | 24 | 10 | 2 | 12 | 58 | 54 | 29 |
| 7 | Barrington Reserves | 24 | 9 | 2 | 13 | 43 | 58 | 29 |
| 8 | Mott MacDonald | 24 | 7 | 7 | 10 | 49 | 64 | 28 |
| 9 | Bassingbourn Reserves | 24 | 6 | 6 | 12 | 46 | 56 | 24 |
| 10 | Gransden Reserves | 24 | 7 | 1 | 16 | 47 | 103 | 22 |
| 11 | Steeple Morden Reserves | 24 | 6 | 2 | 16 | 54 | 98 | 20 |
| 12 | Cambourne Rovers Res (-3pts) | 24 | 6 | 2 | 16 | 44 | 74 | 17 |
| 13 | Haslingfield | 24 | 4 | 1 | 19 | 34 | 111 | 13 |

## DIVISION FIVE C

| | | P | W | D | L | F | A | Pts |
|---|---|---|---|---|---|---|---|---|
| 1 | (P) Ely Crusaders | 22 | 20 | 1 | 1 | 93 | 17 | 61 |
| 2 | (P) Houghton & Wyton | 22 | 18 | 1 | 3 | 107 | 20 | 55 |
| 3 | (P) The Eagle | 22 | 17 | 2 | 3 | 86 | 46 | 53 |
| 4 | Witchford 96 Reserves | 22 | 12 | 2 | 8 | 57 | 44 | 38 |
| 5 | Isleham Warriors | 22 | 12 | 1 | 9 | 65 | 62 | 37 |
| 6 | Lakenheath Casuals | 22 | 10 | 3 | 9 | 68 | 39 | 33 |
| 7 | Isleham United Res. (-3pts) | 22 | 11 | 1 | 10 | 54 | 49 | 31 |
| 8 | Swavesey Institute Reserves | 22 | 7 | 3 | 12 | 51 | 75 | 24 |
| 9 | St Ives Rangers Res. (-6pts) | 22 | 6 | 4 | 12 | 47 | 56 | 16 |
| 10 | Red Lodge Res (-3pts) | 22 | 4 | 2 | 16 | 31 | 71 | 11 |
| 11 | Isleham Wanderers | 22 | 2 | 2 | 18 | 37 | 142 | 8 |
| 12 | Burwell Swifts A | 22 | 1 | 2 | 19 | 14 | 89 | 5 |

## DIVISION FIVE D

| | | P | W | D | L | F | A | Pts |
|---|---|---|---|---|---|---|---|---|
| 1 | (P) Gorefield Athletic | 26 | 21 | 2 | 3 | 84 | 23 | 65 |
| 2 | (P) Earith United Reserves | 26 | 18 | 4 | 4 | 84 | 38 | 58 |
| 3 | Wisbech St Mary C | 26 | 15 | 5 | 6 | 63 | 42 | 50 |
| 4 | Littleport United A | 26 | 14 | 5 | 7 | 66 | 47 | 47 |
| 5 | Upwell Town | 26 | 15 | 1 | 10 | 83 | 54 | 46 |
| 6 | Coldham United | 26 | 12 | 3 | 11 | 54 | 57 | 39 |
| 7 | March Saracens | 26 | 12 | 2 | 12 | 55 | 60 | 38 |
| 8 | Chatteris Fen Tigers | 25 | 11 | 4 | 10 | 68 | 50 | 37 |
| 9 | Outwell Swifts Reserves | 26 | 11 | 2 | 13 | 42 | 48 | 35 |
| 10 | Walsoken United | 26 | 11 | 2 | 12 | 55 | 77 | 35 |
| 11 | Wimblington A (-3pts) | 26 | 9 | 5 | 12 | 58 | 65 | 29 |
| 12 | Manea United Reserves | 26 | 5 | 2 | 19 | 40 | 89 | 17 |
| 13 | March Rangers Reserves | 26 | 4 | 2 | 20 | 46 | 84 | 14 |
| 14 | Doddington United A | 26 | 2 | 3 | 21 | 30 | 94 | 9 |

### DIVISION FIVE PLAY-OFFS
**Semi-Finals**
Gorfield Athletic 3-7 Ely Crusaders | Melbourn 4-3 Castle Camps Res.
**Final**
Ely Crusaders 11-0 Melbourn

# CENTRAL MIDLANDS LEAGUE

**Sponsored by:** Windsor Foodservice
**Founded:** 1971
**Recent Champions:**
2008: Askern Welfare
2009: Radcliffe Olympic
2010: Louth Town
2011: Sheffield Parramore
2012: (N) Westella & Willerby. (S) Basford United

## NORTH DIVISION

| | | P | W | D | L | F | A | Pts |
|---|---|---|---|---|---|---|---|---|
| 1 | (P) Dronfield Town | 32 | 30 | 1 | 1 | 132 | 29 | 91 |
| 2 | AFC Mansfield | 32 | 29 | 1 | 2 | 176 | 20 | 88 |
| 3 | Clay Cross Town | 32 | 22 | 2 | 8 | 105 | 65 | 68 |
| 4 | Westella Hanson | 32 | 21 | 3 | 8 | 94 | 43 | 66 |
| 5 | Harworth C I | 32 | 18 | 7 | 7 | 82 | 51 | 61 |
| 6 | Ollerton Town | 32 | 18 | 2 | 12 | 94 | 53 | 56 |
| 7 | Phoenix Sports & Social | 32 | 14 | 6 | 12 | 75 | 65 | 48 |
| 8 | Kiveton Park | 32 | 15 | 2 | 15 | 87 | 74 | 47 |
| 9 | Glapwell | 32 | 13 | 7 | 12 | 68 | 47 | 46 |
| 10 | Thorne Colliery | 32 | 15 | 1 | 16 | 67 | 77 | 46 |
| 11 | Easington United | 32 | 13 | 4 | 15 | 62 | 81 | 43 |
| 12 | Brodsworth Welfare | 32 | 12 | 6 | 14 | 66 | 81 | 42 |
| 13 | Thoresby CW | 32 | 9 | 2 | 21 | 52 | 92 | 29 |
| 14 | Bentley Colliery | 32 | 7 | 3 | 22 | 63 | 113 | 24 |
| 15 | Sherwood Colliery | 32 | 5 | 3 | 24 | 59 | 105 | 18 |
| 16 | Yorkshire Main | 32 | 5 | 0 | 27 | 42 | 158 | 15 |
| 17 | DFS Welbeck | 32 | 1 | 0 | 31 | 24 | 194 | 3 |

## SOUTH DIVISION

| | | P | W | D | L | F | A | Pts |
|---|---|---|---|---|---|---|---|---|
| 1 | (P) Sutton Town AFC (+3pts) | 30 | 22 | 2 | 6 | 87 | 44 | 71 |
| 2 | Pinxton | 30 | 21 | 3 | 6 | 84 | 38 | 66 |
| 3 | Belper United | 30 | 20 | 4 | 6 | 82 | 42 | 64 |
| 4 | Bilborough Pelican | 30 | 18 | 4 | 8 | 72 | 58 | 58 |
| 5 | Clifton All Whites (-3pts) | 30 | 19 | 3 | 8 | 74 | 49 | 57 |
| 6 | Mickleover Royals | 30 | 16 | 5 | 9 | 76 | 47 | 53 |
| 7 | Newark Town | 30 | 17 | 1 | 12 | 78 | 48 | 52 |
| 8 | Real United | 30 | 13 | 5 | 12 | 60 | 58 | 44 |
| 9 | South Normanton Athletic | 30 | 13 | 4 | 13 | 78 | 55 | 43 |
| 10 | Southwell City | 30 | 10 | 8 | 12 | 55 | 51 | 38 |
| 11 | Calverton MW | 30 | 10 | 6 | 14 | 37 | 61 | 36 |
| 12 | Linby Colliery | 30 | 9 | 8 | 13 | 55 | 57 | 35 |
| 13 | Holbrook St Michaels | 30 | 8 | 5 | 17 | 50 | 80 | 29 |
| 14 | Nottingham United | 30 | 5 | 2 | 23 | 38 | 103 | 17 |
| 15 | Hucknall Town AFC | 30 | 3 | 5 | 22 | 24 | 81 | 14 |
| 16 | Blidworth Welfare | 30 | 3 | 1 | 26 | 31 | 109 | 10 |

Blackwell MWFC withdrew - record expunged.

## LEAGUE CHALLENGE CUP

**ROUND 1**

| | | | |
|---|---|---|---|
| Blidworth Welfare | v | Calverton MW | 0-2 |
| Pinxton | v | Blackwell MWFC | 8-1 |

**ROUND 2**

| | | | |
|---|---|---|---|
| Linby Colliery | v | AFC Mansfield | 1-1 |
| AFC Mansfield | v | Linby Colliery | 3-0 |
| Clifton All Whites | v | Kiveton Park | 2-2 |
| Kiveton Park | v | Clifton All Whites | 1-2 |
| Easington United | v | Belper United | 0-4 |
| Pheonix Sports & Social | v | Sutton Town AFC | 1-3 |
| Calverton MW | v | Bentley Colliery | 3-1 |
| Newark Town | v | Harworth CI | 1-0 |
| Mickleover Royals | v | Westella Hanson | 2-3 |
| South Normanton Athletic | v | Real United | 2-2 |
| Real United | v | South Normanton Athletic | 1-2 |
| Glapwell | v | Thoresby CW | 2-2 |
| Thoresby CW | v | Glapwell | 1-2 |
| Hucknall Town AFC | v | Nottingham United | 1-0 |
| Ollerton Town | v | Bilborough Pelican | 6-3 |
| Sherwood Colliery | v | Dronfield Town | 1-4 |
| Southwell City | v | Clay Cross Town | 4-6 |
| Thorne Colliery | v | Holbrook St Michaels | 0-4 |
| Yorkshire Main | v | DFS Welbeck | 3-3 |
| DFS Wellbeck | v | Yorkshire Main | 5-1 |
| Brodsworth Welfare | v | Pinxton | AW |

**ROUND 3**

| | | | |
|---|---|---|---|
| Clifton All Whites | v | Ollerton Town | 2-1 |
| Dronfield Town | v | South Normanton Athletic | 2-1 |
| Glapwell | v | Belper United | 1-1 |
| Belper United | v | Glapwell | 4-1 |
| Calverton MW | v | AFC Mansfield | 0-1 |
| Hucknall Town AFC | v | Sutton Town AFC | 1-3 |
| DFS Wellbeck | v | Holbrook St Michaels | 1-7 |
| Newark Town | v | Westella Hanson | 2-2 |
| Westella Hanson | v | Newark Town | 0-3 |
| Clay Cross Town | v | Pinxton | 4-7 |

**QUARTER FINALS**

| | | | |
|---|---|---|---|
| Newark Town | v | AFC Mansfield | 0-5 |
| Dronfield Town | v | Holbrook St Michaels | 4-1 |
| Clifton All Whites | v | Pinxton | 2-0 |
| Belper United | v | Sutton Town AFC | 3-2 |

**SEMI FINALS**

| | | | |
|---|---|---|---|
| Dronfield Town | v | Clifton All Whites | 1-3 |
| Belper United | v | AFC Mansfield | 0-1 |

**FINAL**

| | | | |
|---|---|---|---|
| Clifton All Whites | v | AFC Mansfield | 1-0 |

## NORTH DIVISION

| | | 1 | 2 | 3 | 4 | 5 | 6 | 7 | 8 | 9 | 10 | 11 | 12 | 13 | 14 | 15 | 16 | 17 |
|---|---|---|---|---|---|---|---|---|---|---|---|---|---|---|---|---|---|---|
| 1 | AFC Mansfield | | 10-0 | 4-0 | 9-0 | 4-0 | 1-5 | 4-0 | 1-0 | 6-1 | 4-0 | 5-0 | 1-0 | 9-0 | 2-0 | 2-0 | 3-1 | 14-0 |
| 2 | Bentley Colliery | 0-6 | | 1-1 | 2-4 | 8-1 | 0-8 | 1-2 | 2-6 | 3-5 | 2-0 | 5-6 | 2-4 | 2-1 | 1-4 | 0-4 | 1-3 | 0-1 |
| 3 | Brodsworth Welfare | 2-6 | 0-5 | | 2-6 | 7-1 | 0-3 | 3-0 | 0-0 | 1-3 | 2-2 | 3-1 | 0-3 | 4-3 | 4-2 | 3-1 | 2-0 | 5-0 |
| 4 | Clay Cross Town | 2-2 | 4-1 | 4-6 | | 8-0 | 2-3 | 4-2 | 3-1 | 1-1 | 2-1 | 4-3 | 7-1 | 3-2 | 7-0 | 4-1 | 5-0 | HW |
| 5 | DFS Welbeck | 0-9 | 1-3 | 1-5 | 2-9 | | 0-3 | 1-4 | 1-7 | 0-9 | 0-10 | 1-5 | 2-0 | 0-4 | 1-2 | 3-2 | 2-9 | 2-6 |
| 6 | Dronfield Town | 5-4 | 7-0 | 6-0 | 5-0 | 9-0 | | 6-0 | 5-2 | 1-4 | 2-1 | 2-1 | 3-1 | 6-1 | 3-0 | 4-2 | 3-1 | 11-3 |
| 7 | Easington United | 1-10 | 8-5 | 2-2 | 1-2 | 8-2 | 0-5 | | 1-1 | 4-3 | HW | 2-3 | 2-3 | 3-1 | 1-0 | 3-1 | 2-0 | 2-1 |
| 8 | Glapwell | 1-3 | 3-0 | 1-1 | 1-2 | 1-0 | 1-4 | 0-2 | | 2-2 | 6-3 | 0-3 | 1-0 | 1-0 | 5-0 | 2-2 | 0-0 | 8-0 |
| 9 | Harworth C I | 0-5 | 3-0 | 1-3 | 3-2 | 4-0 | 0-0 | 1-1 | 2-1 | | 1-2 | 2-2 | 2-2 | 5-2 | 5-1 | 1-0 | 2-2 | 6-0 |
| 10 | Kiveton Park | 0-8 | 4-2 | 1-1 | 4-7 | 10-0 | 1-4 | 2-0 | 2-1 | 1-2 | | 1-4 | 7-1 | 5-1 | 4-1 | 0-3 | 0-1 | 5-1 |
| 11 | Ollerton Town | 0-2 | 2-1 | 4-2 | 4-2 | 10-0 | 0-2 | 7-0 | 2-3 | 1-2 | 1-3 | | 2-1 | 1-0 | 1-0 | 8-0 | 2-1 | 3-2 |
| 12 | Phoenix Sports & Social | 0-9 | 2-2 | 1-2 | 0-1 | 4-2 | 1-2 | 1-0 | 1-1 | 3-0 | 4-0 | 2-2 | | 4-0 | 3-3 | 1-3 | 1-1 | 8-0 |
| 13 | Sherwood Colliery | 0-6 | 1-1 | 2-0 | 0-1 | 8-0 | 2-4 | 1-1 | 0-4 | 1-2 | 4-5 | 0-1 | 0-2 | | 4-4 | 2-3 | 4-8 | 2-5 |
| 14 | Thoresby CW | 1-5 | 3-4 | 3-2 | 1-3 | 6-0 | 1-4 | 1-0 | 0-6 | 1-2 | 0-4 | 1-0 | 2-5 | 3-4 | | 1-2 | 1-2 | HW |
| 15 | Thorne Colliery | 0-2 | 5-4 | 6-2 | 3-2 | 4-1 | 0-2 | 3-2 | 2-0 | 0-5 | 1-2 | 4-1 | 1-2 | 3-2 | 3-7 | | 2-3 | 2-1 |
| 16 | Westella Hanson | 1-4 | 4-1 | 3-0 | 3-1 | 5-0 | 0-1 | 5-0 | 3-1 | 1-0 | 6-0 | 2-0 | 3-2 | 5-1 | 4-1 | 2-0 | | 9-1 |
| 17 | Yorkshire Main | 0-16 | 0-4 | 5-1 | 1-3 | 3-0 | 0-4 | 2-8 | 0-1 | 2-3 | 2-7 | 0-12 | 2-4 | 2-6 | 1-2 | 3-4 | 0-6 | |

# CENTRAL MIDLANDS LEAGUE - STEP 7

| SOUTH DIVISION | 1 | 2 | 3 | 4 | 5 | 6 | 7 | 8 | 9 | 10 | 11 | 12 | 13 | 14 | 15 | 16 |
|---|---|---|---|---|---|---|---|---|---|---|---|---|---|---|---|---|
| 1 Belper United | | 4-4 | 5-2 | 2-0 | 0-0 | 3-0 | 6-0 | 1-0 | 4-0 | 0-3 | 2-0 | 1-3 | 5-1 | 3-1 | 3-3 | 0-3 |
| 2 Bilborough Pelican | 2-3 | | 2-1 | 1-1 | 0-3 | 2-0 | 5-2 | 3-2 | 3-0 | 2-1 | 4-0 | 2-1 | 2-0 | 3-7 | 4-1 | 1-0 |
| 3 Blidworth Welfare | 2-4 | 3-5 | | 1-4 | 1-3 | 0-1 | 1-2 | 3-0 | 1-2 | 1-3 | 2-1 | 0-1 | 1-5 | 0-9 | 0-5 | 0-5 |
| 4 Calverton MW | 0-4 | 0-2 | 4-3 | | 0-1 | 3-0 | 3-0 | 1-1 | 1-1 | 2-6 | 3-1 | 1-4 | 0-2 | 0-5 | 1-1 | 1-1 |
| 5 Clifton All Whites | 2-6 | 1-0 | 5-0 | 2-0 | | 5-3 | 2-1 | 3-2 | 2-2 | 2-3 | 4-2 | 0-1 | 4-0 | 1-3 | 2-1 | 2-4 |
| 6 Holbrook St Michaels | 1-2 | 2-3 | 4-0 | 0-2 | 1-4 | | 1-0 | 2-2 | 1-1 | 0-4 | 1-2 | 1-4 | 3-3 | 2-4 | 2-2 | 1-3 |
| 7 Hucknall Town AFC | 1-5 | 0-0 | 2-2 | 0-1 | 0-4 | 0-3 | | 1-1 | 1-2 | 1-3 | 0-3 | 1-3 | 1-7 | 3-1 | 0-2 | 3-6 |
| 8 Linby Colliery | 1-1 | 1-2 | 5-2 | 3-0 | 1-3 | 2-3 | 0-0 | | 2-0 | 2-2 | 4-1 | 0-1 | 3-2 | 4-2 | 3-1 | 2-5 |
| 9 Mickleover Royals | 2-0 | 3-2 | 1-2 | 7-0 | 7-3 | 4-2 | 6-0 | 2-2 | | 3-0 | 7-0 | 0-1 | 2-1 | 1-2 | 2-2 | 3-0 |
| 10 Newark Town | 1-2 | 6-0 | 5-0 | 2-3 | 0-2 | 1-4 | 4-1 | 6-1 | 1-2 | | 4-2 | 3-1 | 0-2 | 3-0 | 1-4 | 1-3 |
| 11 Nottingham United | 0-6 | 3-3 | 4-0 | 1-2 | 2-7 | 2-2 | 0-3 | 2-4 | 2-3 | 0-5 | | 0-4 | 3-2 | 1-0 | 1-4 | 0-2 |
| 12 Pinxton | 3-1 | 1-4 | 8-0 | 3-2 | 2-2 | 10-1 | 2-1 | 2-0 | 2-0 | 2-3 | 6-1 | | 2-2 | 3-1 | 1-2 | 3-1 |
| 13 Real United | 2-3 | 0-6 | 1-0 | 1-1 | 1-0 | 4-5 | 2-0 | 3-2 | 4-2 | 1-2 | 4-1 | 1-4 | | 2-1 | 0-0 | 1-1 |
| 14 South Normanton Athletic | 2-3 | 2-4 | 6-1 | 2-0 | 2-4 | 1-0 | 3-0 | 2-2 | 4-5 | 1-0 | 6-0 | 1-1 | 2-3 | | 1-1 | 1-3 |
| 15 Southwell City | 1-2 | 5-1 | 2-0 | 0-1 | 4-0 | 2-4 | 0-0 | 1-0 | 0-5 | 0-3 | 3-1 | 1-2 | 1-3 | 1-1 | | 2-3 |
| 16 Sutton Town AFC | 2-1 | 5-0 | 5-2 | 4-0 | 0-1 | 5-0 | 3-0 | 0-3 | 2-1 | 4-2 | 6-2 | 5-3 | 1-0 | 1-5 | 4-3 | |

## CENTRAL MIDLANDS NORTHERN DIVISION CONSTITUTION 2013-14

| | | |
|---|---|---|
| AFC MANSFIELD | Clipstone Road, Mansfield Nottinghamshire NG19 0EE | 01623 623443 |
| ASKERN | Welfare Sports Ground, Manor Way, Doncaster Road, Askern, DN6 0AJ | |
| BENTLEY COLLIERY WELFARE | Bentley Miners Welfare , The Avenue, Bentley , Doncaster DN5 0PN | 01302 874420 |
| BRODSWORTH WELFARE AFC | Welfare Road, Woodlands, Doncaster DN6 | 07967 708430 |
| CLAY CROSS TOWN | Mill Lane, Holmgate, Clay Cross, Chesterfield | 07980 354522 |
| EASINGTON UNITED | Low Farm, Beak Street, Easington, Hull HU12 0TT | None |
| GLAPWELL (2011) | Hall Corner, Glapwell, Chesterfield, Derbyshire S44 5P | 07870 195684 |
| HARWORTH COLLIERY INSTITUTE | Recreation Ground, Scrooby Road, Bircotes, Doncaster DN11 8JT | 01302 750614 |
| KINSLEY BOYS | Kinsley Playing Fields | |
| NEWARK TOWN | Collingham FC, Station Road, Collingham NG23 7RA | 01636 892303 |
| OLLERTON TOWN | The Lane, Walesby Lane, New Ollerton, Newark NG22 9UX | None |
| PHOENIX SPORTS & SOCIAL | Phoenix Sports Complex, Bawtry Road, Brinsworth, Rotherham S60 5PA | 01709 363864 |
| SHERWOOD COLLIERY | Debdale Lane, Mansfield Woodhouse, Mansfield, Nottinghamshire NG19 7N | 07813 718302 |
| THORESBY COLLIERY WELFARE | Thoresby Colliery Spts Ground, Fourth Avenue, Edwinstowe NG21 9NS | 07802 417987 |
| THORNE COLLIERY | Moorends Welfare, Grange Road, Moorends, Thorne, Doncaster DN8 4LU | 07855 545221 |
| WELBECK WELFARE | Elkesley Road, Meden Vale, Mansfield, Nottinghamshire NG20 9P | 07791 155891 |
| WESTELLA HANSON | Blackburn Leisure Social Club, Prescott Avenue, Brough HU15 1BB | 01482 667353 |

In: Askern (R - Northern Counties East Div.1). Kinsley Boys (S - Sheffield & Hallamshire Premier).
Newark Town (S - Central Mids. Southern). Welbeck Welfare (NC from DFS Welbeck Welfare).
Out: DFS Welbeck (NC to Welbeck Welfare). Dronfield (P - Northern Counties East Div.1).
Kiveton Park (W - now Sheffield & Hallamshire Div.2). Yorkshire Main (W - now Doncaster & District Senior Division).

## CENTRAL MIDLANDS SOUTHERN DIVISION CONSTITUTION 2013-14

| | | |
|---|---|---|
| ALLENTON UNITED | Rolls Royce Recreation Ground, (Rifle Range Pitch), Moor Lane, Derby DE24 9HY | |
| BARROWBY | Barrowby Sports Pavilion, Lowfields, Westry Corner, Barrowby NG32 1DJ | |
| BELPER UNITED | Alton Manor, Nailers Way, Belper DE56 0HT | None |
| BILBOROUGH PELICAN | Brian Wakefield Sports Ground, Trentside Lane,Old Lenton Lane, Nottingham NG7 2SA | 0115 929 4728 |
| BLIDWORTH WELFARE | Blidworth Welfare Miners SC, Mansfield Road, Blidworth, Mansfield NG21 0LR | 01623 793361 |
| BULWELL | Mill Street Playing Field, off Greenwich Avenue, Basford, Nottingham NG6 0LD | |
| CALVERTON MINERS WELFARE | Calverton Miners Welfare, Hollinwood Lane, Calverton NG14 6NR | 0115 965 4390 |
| CLIFTON | Green Lane, Clifton, Nottingham NG11 9AY | 0115 921 5401 |
| HOLBROOK ST MICHAELS | Mackney Road, Holbrook, Belper, Derbyshire DE56 0T | 07885 499358 |
| HUCKNALL TOWN AFC | Watnall Road, Hucknall, Nottinghamshire NG15 6E | 07535 124295 |
| LINBY COLLIERY | Church Lane, Linby, Nottinghamshire NG15 8A | 07932 591068 |
| MICKLEOVER ROYAL BRITISH LEGION | Mickleover RBL, Poppyfields Drive, Mickleover, Derby DE3 9GQ | 01332 513548 |
| MICKLEOVER ROYALS | Station Road, Micleover, Derby, Derbyshire DE3 9F | 01332 736356 |
| PINXTON | Welfare Ground, Wharf Road, Pinxton NG16 6LG | 07989 324249 |
| REAL UNITED | Grove Farm, Lenton Lane, Nottingham NG7 2SA | None |
| SOUTH NORMANTON ATHLETIC | ExChem Sports Ground, Lees Lane, South Normanton, Alfreton DE55 2AD | 01773 581491 |
| SOUTHWELL CITY | War Memorial Recreation Ground, Bishop's Drive, Southwell NG25 0JP | 01636 814386 |
| SWANWICK PENTRICH ROAD | Highfield Road, Swanwick, Alfreton, Derbyshire DE55 1BW | |

In: Allenton United (P - Midlands Regional Alliance Premier).Barrowby (P - Grantham Premier).
Bulwell (P - Notts Senior Premier Division). Hucknall Town (NPL Div.1 South).
Mickleover RBL (P - Midlands Regional Alliance Premier).
Swanwick Pentrich Road (P - Midlands Regional Alliance Premier).
Out: Blackwell MWFCS (WS). Nottingham United (S - Notts Senior Premier Division). Sutton Town (P - East Midlands Counties).

# CHESHIRE LEAGUE

**Sponsored by:** No sponsor
**Founded:** 1919
**Recent Champions:**
2008: Styal
2009: Woodley
2010: Club AZ
2011: Greenalls Padgate St Oswalds
2012: Knutsford

## DIVISION ONE

| | | P | W | D | L | F | A | Pts |
|---|---|---|---|---|---|---|---|---|
| 1 | Knutsford | 30 | 23 | 3 | 4 | 77 | 29 | 72 |
| 2 | Eagle Sports | 30 | 20 | 5 | 5 | 68 | 38 | 65 |
| 3 | Whaley Bridge | 30 | 19 | 5 | 6 | 83 | 42 | 62 |
| 4 | Garswood United | 30 | 16 | 5 | 9 | 64 | 47 | 53 |
| 5 | Crewe | 30 | 16 | 4 | 10 | 65 | 45 | 52 |
| 6 | Rylands | 30 | 15 | 4 | 11 | 49 | 42 | 49 |
| 7 | Gamesley | 30 | 12 | 7 | 11 | 76 | 47 | 43 |
| 8 | Middlewich Town | 30 | 12 | 7 | 11 | 52 | 67 | 43 |
| 9 | Greenalls Padgate St Oswalds | 30 | 12 | 4 | 14 | 56 | 47 | 40 |
| 10 | Denton Town FC | 30 | 12 | 1 | 17 | 50 | 76 | 37 |
| 11 | Styal | 30 | 10 | 6 | 14 | 60 | 73 | 36 |
| 12 | Linotype Cheadle HN | 30 | 10 | 5 | 15 | 64 | 61 | 35 |
| 13 | Pilkington | 30 | 10 | 4 | 16 | 44 | 61 | 34 |
| 14 | Billinge FC | 30 | 10 | 1 | 19 | 50 | 68 | 31 |
| 15 | (R) Lostock Gralam | 30 | 8 | 5 | 17 | 47 | 74 | 29 |
| 16 | (R) Grappenhall Sports FC | 30 | 1 | 2 | 27 | 33 | 121 | 5 |

## DIVISION TWO

| | | P | W | D | L | F | A | Pts |
|---|---|---|---|---|---|---|---|---|
| 1 | (P) Barnton | 26 | 21 | 2 | 3 | 101 | 50 | 65 |
| 2 | (P) Rudheath Social | 26 | 21 | 0 | 5 | 83 | 31 | 63 |
| 3 | Poynton | 26 | 18 | 4 | 4 | 76 | 39 | 58 |
| 4 | Runcorn Town Res | 26 | 17 | 4 | 5 | 82 | 47 | 55 |
| 5 | Maine Road Reserves | 26 | 15 | 3 | 8 | 70 | 56 | 48 |
| 6 | Sandbach United | 26 | 12 | 4 | 10 | 69 | 60 | 40 |
| 7 | Golborne Sports | 26 | 10 | 1 | 15 | 53 | 80 | 31 |
| 8 | Penlake | 26 | 9 | 3 | 14 | 58 | 75 | 30 |
| 9 | Tarporley Victoria | 26 | 9 | 2 | 15 | 45 | 59 | 29 |
| 10 | Malpas | 26 | 8 | 4 | 14 | 48 | 69 | 28 |
| 11 | Congleton Vale | 26 | 8 | 3 | 15 | 38 | 61 | 27 |
| 12 | Egerton | 26 | 8 | 2 | 16 | 55 | 79 | 26 |
| 13 | Moore United FC | 26 | 5 | 1 | 20 | 46 | 78 | 16 |
| 14 | Daten | 26 | 3 | 3 | 20 | 42 | 82 | 12 |

**Additional clubs for 2013-14:**
Barnton Wanderers (P - Crewe & District League).
Sale Town (P - Altrincham & District League).

## DIVISION ONE CUP

**ROUND 1**

| | | | | |
|---|---|---|---|---|
| Styal | v | Billinge FC | | 2-3 |
| Lostock Gralam | v | Denton Town | | 3-1 |
| Eagle Sports | v | Crewe | | 6-0 |
| Gamesley | v | Knutsford | | 0-2 |
| Rylands | v | Pilkington | | 3-1 |
| Middlewich Town | v | Garswood United | | 2-1 |
| Greenalls Padgate St Oswa | v | Linotype Cheadle HN | | 2-3 |
| Whaley Bridge | v | grappenhall Sports | | 3-0 |

**QUARTER FINALS**

| | | | |
|---|---|---|---|
| Billinge FC | v | Lostock Gralam | 1-2 |
| Eagle Sports | v | Knutsford | 2-1 |
| Rylands | v | Middlewich Town | 1-0 |
| Linotype Cheadle HN | v | Whaley Bridge | 1-0 |

**SEMI FINALS**

| | | | |
|---|---|---|---|
| Lostock Gralam | v | Eagle Sports | 0-3 |
| Rylands | v | Linotype Cheadle HN | 1-0 |

**FINAL**

| | | | |
|---|---|---|---|
| Eagle Sports | v | Rylands | 1-0 |

## MEMORIAL CUP

**FINAL**

| | | | |
|---|---|---|---|
| Knutsford | v | Eagle Sports | 3-2 |

## DIVISION TWO CHALLENGE CUP

**FINAL**

| | | | |
|---|---|---|---|
| Rudheath Social | v | Sandbach United | 1-3 |

## RESERVES CHALLENGE CUP

**FINAL**

| | | | |
|---|---|---|---|
| Garswood United Res. | v | Styal Reserves | 2-0 |

## RESERVE DIVISION

| | | P | W | D | L | F | A | Pts |
|---|---|---|---|---|---|---|---|---|
| 1 | Greenalls Padgate ST O Res. | 32 | 24 | 4 | 4 | 93 | 43 | 76 |
| 2 | Styal Reserves | 32 | 20 | 7 | 5 | 91 | 45 | 67 |
| 3 | Eagle Sports Reserves | 32 | 20 | 6 | 6 | 116 | 52 | 66 |
| 4 | Middlewich Town Reserves | 32 | 18 | 3 | 11 | 73 | 60 | 57 |
| 5 | Garswood United Reserves | 32 | 17 | 4 | 11 | 68 | 53 | 55 |
| 6 | Whaley Bridge Reserves | 32 | 15 | 7 | 10 | 76 | 44 | 52 |
| 7 | Billinge Reserves | 32 | 15 | 5 | 12 | 77 | 65 | 50 |
| 8 | Linotype Cheadle HN Reserves | 32 | 15 | 5 | 12 | 80 | 71 | 50 |
| 9 | Rylands Reserves | 32 | 11 | 10 | 11 | 66 | 63 | 43 |
| 10 | Barnton Reserves (-3pts) | 32 | 13 | 7 | 12 | 66 | 72 | 43 |
| 11 | Pilkington Reserves | 32 | 12 | 6 | 14 | 55 | 55 | 42 |
| 12 | Grappenhall Sports Reserves | 32 | 11 | 5 | 16 | 60 | 78 | 38 |
| 13 | Poynton Reserves | 32 | 10 | 6 | 16 | 56 | 64 | 36 |
| 14 | Denton Town Reserves | 32 | 8 | 6 | 18 | 54 | 92 | 30 |
| 15 | Gamesley Reserves | 32 | 7 | 4 | 21 | 52 | 91 | 25 |
| 16 | Daten Reserves | 32 | 7 | 4 | 21 | 45 | 97 | 25 |
| 17 | Golborne Sports Reserves | 32 | 4 | 1 | 27 | 34 | 117 | 13 |

## DIVISION ONE

| | | 1 | 2 | 3 | 4 | 5 | 6 | 7 | 8 | 9 | 10 | 11 | 12 | 13 | 14 | 15 | 16 |
|---|---|---|---|---|---|---|---|---|---|---|---|---|---|---|---|---|---|
| 1 | Billinge FC | | 0-0 | 3-4 | 1-1 | 1-0 | 2-4 | 2-0 | 1-3 | 2-0 | 0-2 | 3-2 | 0-1 | 0-1 | 2-0 | 3-0 | 1-2 |
| 2 | Crewe | 2-1 | | 3-0 | 2-4 | 3-4 | 5-1 | 7-2 | 1-2 | 0-1 | 2-0 | 3-1 | 3-0 | 5-1 | 1-1 | 5-0 | 1-1 |
| 3 | Denton Town | 0-3 | 1-2 | | 2-1 | 1-0 | 4-0 | 2-1 | 0-2 | 3-7 | 2-1 | 2-3 | 0-3 | 2-6 | 0-6 | 1-2 | |
| 4 | Eagle Sports | 3-2 | 2-1 | 6-0 | | 1-1 | 1-1 | 3-1 | 2-2 | 0-0 | 5-2 | 0-2 | 7-0 | 2-0 | 1-0 | 2-1 | 1-3 |
| 5 | Gamesley | 6-1 | 1-0 | 0-1 | 0-1 | | 0-1 | 9-1 | 2-2 | 0-1 | 1-2 | 7-0 | 5-0 | 4-1 | 3-2 | 7-2 | 1-1 |
| 6 | Garswood United | 4-1 | 1-0 | 0-1 | 1-2 | 4-3 | | 2-1 | 1-0 | 4-2 | 4-1 | 1-1 | 1-2 | 2-1 | 2-0 | 2-3 | 1-1 |
| 7 | Grappenhall Sports | 3-9 | 1-2 | 1-5 | 1-2 | 4-4 | 2-7 | | 1-6 | 0-2 | 0-6 | 0-1 | 2-2 | 0-2 | 2-7 | 2-1 | 1-8 |
| 8 | Greenalls Padgate St Oswalds | 2-0 | 1-3 | 1-0 | 1-3 | 1-3 | 1-0 | 5-0 | | 0-2 | 1-3 | 1-2 | 1-4 | 0-0 | 5-1 | 3-2 | |
| 9 | Knutsford | 4-0 | 5-1 | 3-1 | 4-2 | 4-0 | 2-1 | 1-0 | 3-2 | | 3-2 | 4-0 | 6-0 | 4-0 | 3-1 | 4-2 | 3-2 |
| 10 | Linotype Cheadle HN | 0-4 | 1-2 | 4-3 | 1-2 | 2-2 | 1-2 | 5-1 | 1-2 | 1-1 | | 5-0 | 2-2 | 2-2 | 0-1 | 7-1 | 1-1 |
| 11 | Lostock Gralam | 6-0 | 1-2 | 0-2 | 1-2 | 1-1 | 2-3 | 3-2 | 4-1 | 2-2 | 0-1 | | 3-3 | 3-3 | 1-0 | 2-3 | 0-4 |
| 12 | Middlewich Town | 3-1 | 1-3 | 3-3 | 1-3 | 3-2 | 2-2 | 2-1 | 4-3 | 0-4 | 3-1 | 6-1 | | 0-2 | 0-0 | 1-2 | 0-2 |
| 13 | Pilkington | 0-1 | 0-0 | 3-0 | 2-3 | 1-1 | 2-0 | 3-2 | 1-2 | 2-1 | 4-2 | 3-4 | 3-2 | | 1-2 | 0-2 | 1-1 |
| 14 | Rylands | 2-1 | 2-0 | 1-2 | 2-1 | 3-1 | 2-4 | 2-0 | 0-3 | 0-3 | 2-1 | 1-0 | 1-3 | 2-0 | | 2-2 | 1-1 |
| 15 | Styal | 3-0 | 2-2 | 2-5 | 2-3 | 2-5 | 3-3 | 3-1 | 0-0 | 1-2 | 3-1 | 3-1 | 1-1 | 4-0 | 1-2 | | 3-4 |
| 16 | Whaley Bridge | 6-2 | 4-0 | 5-2 | 1-2 | 0-3 | 2-1 | 6-1 | 2-1 | 3-1 | 4-0 | 6-2 | 0-2 | 5-2 | 2-4 | 1-1 | |

## CHESHIRE LEAGUE DIVISION ONE CONSTITUTION 2013-14

| | | |
|---|---|---|
| BARNTON | Townfield, Townfield Lane, Barnton, Northwich CW8 4LH | 07597 143886 |
| BILLINGE | Billinge Comm. Spts/Soccer Cte , Carrmill Road , Billinge WN5 7TX | 01744 893533 |
| CREWE | Cumberland Arena, Thomas Street, Crewe CW1 2BD | 01270 537150 |
| DENTON TOWN | Whittles Park, Heather Lea, Denton M34 6EJ | 07951 829551 |
| EAGLE SPORTS | Eagle Sports Club, Thornton Road, Great Sankey, Warrington WA5 2SZ | 01925 632926 |
| GAMESLEY | Melandra Park, Melandra Castle Road, Gamesley, Glossop SK13 0JR | 07590 204594 |
| GARSWOOD UNITED | The Wooders, Simms Lane End, Garswood Road, Garswood, Ashton-in-Makerfield WN4 0XH | |
| | | 01744 893968 |
| GREENALLS PADGATE ST OSWALDS | Carlsberg Tetley Social Club, Long Lane, Warrington WA2 8PU | 01925 634904 |
| KNUTSFORD | Manchester Road, Knutsford WA16 0NT | 07825 843506 |
| LINOTYPE & CHEADLE HN | The Heath, Norbreck Avenue, Cheadle, Stockport SK8 2ET | 0161 282 6574 |
| MIDDLEWICH TOWN | Seddon Street, Middlewich CW10 9DT | 01606 835842 |
| PILKINGTON | Ruskin Drive, Dentons Green, St Helens WA10 6RP | 01744 22893 |
| RUDHEATH SOCIAL | Griffiths Park, Middlewich Road, Rudheath, Northwich, Cheshir CW9 7DR | |
| RYLANDS | Rylands Recreation Club, Gorsey Lane, Warrington WA2 7RZ | 01925 625700 |
| STYAL | Altrincham Road, Styal, Wilmslow SK9 4JE | 01625 529303 |
| WHALEY BRIDGE | Horwich Park, Park Road, Whaley Bridge, High Peak SK23 7DJ | 07759 218399 |

**In:** Barnton (P). Rudheath Social (P).
**Out:** Lostock Gralam (R). Grappenhall Social FC (R).

# Click Back in Time!

Over 36 years of publishing the Non-League Club Directory has filled a room full of information and photographs covering the game we know and love.

What we intend, over time, is to create a website that shares with you everything we have accumulated, which we hope will bring back some fond memories of season's gone by.

# DORSET PREMIER LEAGUE

**Sponsored by:** BeSpoke Teamwear
**Founded:** 1957

**Recent Champions:**
2008: Portland United
2009: Portland United
2010: Hamworthy Recreation
2011: Hamworthy Recreation
2012: Westland Sports

| | | P | W | D | L | F | A | Pts |
|---|---|---|---|---|---|---|---|---|
| 1 | Portland United | 34 | 29 | 2 | 3 | 115 | 32 | 89 |
| 2 | Wincanton Town | 34 | 25 | 5 | 4 | 103 | 33 | 80 |
| 3 | Holt United | 34 | 22 | 3 | 9 | 76 | 46 | 69 |
| 4 | Hamworthy Recreation | 34 | 19 | 5 | 10 | 108 | 57 | 62 |
| 5 | Tintinhull | 34 | 19 | 4 | 11 | 71 | 62 | 61 |
| 6 | Weymouth Reserves | 34 | 15 | 6 | 13 | 52 | 51 | 51 |
| 7 | Bridport Reserves | 34 | 13 | 8 | 13 | 70 | 61 | 47 |
| 8 | Chickerell United | 34 | 13 | 8 | 13 | 61 | 62 | 47 |
| 9 | Parley Sports | 34 | 14 | 4 | 16 | 61 | 67 | 46 |
| 10 | Shaftesbury Town | 34 | 14 | 2 | 18 | 48 | 62 | 44 |
| 11 | Blandford United (-3pts) | 34 | 15 | 1 | 18 | 68 | 85 | 43 |
| 12 | Wareham Rangers (-3pts) | 34 | 12 | 8 | 14 | 70 | 65 | 41 |
| 13 | Hamworthy United Reserves | 34 | 9 | 8 | 17 | 68 | 81 | 35 |
| 14 | Swanage Town & Herston (-6pts) | 34 | 11 | 5 | 18 | 57 | 86 | 32 |
| 15 | Cranborne | 34 | 8 | 8 | 18 | 49 | 92 | 32 |
| 16 | Merley Cobham Sports | 34 | 8 | 5 | 21 | 57 | 97 | 29 |
| 17 | Sherborne Town Reserves | 34 | 7 | 7 | 20 | 43 | 82 | 28 |
| 18 | Poole Borough | 34 | 7 | 3 | 24 | 47 | 103 | 24 |

## LEAGUE CUP

**ROUND 1**

| | | | |
|---|---|---|---|
| Bridport Reserves | v | Hamworthy Utd Reserves | 1-4 |
| Parley Sports | v | Poole Borough | 5-2 |

**Round 2**

| | | | |
|---|---|---|---|
| Holt United | v | Sherborne Town Reserves | 6-1 |
| Shafesbury Town | v | Blandford United | 1-2 |
| Wincanton Town | v | Hamworthy Recreation | 2-2, 5-6p |
| Chickerell United | v | Wareham Rangers | 3-0 |
| Cranborne | v | Merley Cobham Sports | 6-1 |
| Swanage Town & Herston | v | Weymouth Reserves | 0-3 |
| Tintinhull | v | Hamworthy Utd Reserves | 5-5, 5-4p |
| Portland United | v | Parley Sports | 4-2 |

**QUARTER FINALS**

| | | | |
|---|---|---|---|
| Holt United | v | Blandford United | 6-3 |
| Hamworthy Recreation | v | Chickerell United | 2-0 |
| Cranborne | v | Weymouth Reserves | 1-5 |
| Tintinhull | v | Portland United | 1-2 |

**SEMI FINALS**

| | | | |
|---|---|---|---|
| Holt United | v | Hamworthy Recreation | 2-0 |
| Weymouth Reserves | v | Portland United | 4-5 |

**FINAL**

| | | | |
|---|---|---|---|
| Holt United | v | Portland United | 1-0 |

| | | 1 | 2 | 3 | 4 | 5 | 6 | 7 | 8 | 9 | 10 | 11 | 12 | 13 | 14 | 15 | 16 | 17 | 18 |
|---|---|---|---|---|---|---|---|---|---|---|---|---|---|---|---|---|---|---|---|
| 1 | Blandford United | | 2-3 | 2-0 | 3-2 | 3-4 | 4-2 | 3-0 | 3-2 | 3-2 | 3-1 | 0-8 | 1-2 | 0-2 | 3-2 | 0-5 | 2-3 | 5-0 | 0-6 |
| 2 | Bridport Reserves | 2-2 | | 2-2 | 1-0 | 0-1 | 1-1 | 2-1 | 7-0 | 2-1 | 3-3 | 0-5 | 5-1 | 1-1 | 1-2 | 0-1 | 4-1 | 1-1 | 0-6 |
| 3 | Chickerell United | 3-1 | 2-0 | | 0-0 | 1-5 | 3-3 | 1-1 | 3-2 | 1-2 | 2-0 | 0-4 | 0-1 | 3-2 | 4-0 | 1-2 | 3-0 | 1-4 | 1-1 |
| 4 | Cranborne | 1-2 | 0-4 | 1-1 | | 5-3 | 2-2 | 1-2 | 3-3 | 2-1 | 3-2 | 1-2 | 3-2 | 2-2 | 1-2 | 3-1 | 2-2 | 2-2 | 1-1 |
| 5 | Hamworthy Recreation | 4-2 | 2-0 | 4-2 | 12-1 | | 2-2 | 1-5 | 3-1 | 0-1 | 6-0 | 1-1 | 0-2 | 7-1 | 6-1 | 2-2 | 2-2 | 5-2 | 0-4 |
| 6 | Hamworthy United Reserves | 1-5 | 3-3 | 1-1 | 4-0 | 1-6 | | 1-2 | 4-2 | 6-0 | 6-2 | 1-4 | 0-1 | 6-0 | 3-2 | 0-5 | 2-2 | 1-0 | 2-3 |
| 7 | Holt United | 2-1 | 3-2 | 3-1 | 1-0 | 2-1 | 2-1 | | 3-2 | 2-1 | 3-0 | 1-2 | 3-0 | 1-1 | 3-4 | 1-0 | 1-0 | 2-0 | 2-0 |
| 8 | Merley Cobham Sports | 0-3 | 3-1 | 1-6 | 3-1 | 1-3 | 0-0 | 0-3 | | 2-5 | 2-3 | 1-3 | 2-0 | 5-1 | 2-2 | 1-4 | 0-2 | 3-1 | 0-7 |
| 9 | Parley Sports | 1-0 | 3-2 | 2-1 | 7-2 | 2-1 | 4-1 | 1-3 | 2-3 | | 1-0 | 3-2 | 0-1 | 1-1 | 0-2 | 1-2 | 1-2 | 0-0 | 1-5 |
| 10 | Poole Borough | 5-2 | 0-7 | 1-3 | 0-1 | 2-2 | 1-4 | 0-4 | 2-1 | 4-2 | | 1-2 | 4-3 | 0-2 | 3-3 | 0-5 | 1-2 | 1-3 | 1-2 |
| 11 | Portland United | 3-1 | 4-2 | 3-1 | 5-1 | 3-0 | 4-0 | 2-1 | 2-3 | 4-1 | 4-0 | | 5-1 | 6-0 | 7-3 | 6-1 | 1-0 | 2-0 | 2-0 |
| 12 | Shaftesbury Town | 2-3 | 0-0 | 1-5 | 4-1 | 0-3 | 3-2 | 2-0 | 3-1 | 0-2 | 5-0 | 1-4 | | 1-0 | 3-1 | 0-3 | 2-2 | 1-0 | 0-1 |
| 13 | Sherborne Town Reserves | 2-3 | 2-5 | 1-3 | 3-2 | 1-3 | 3-0 | 1-2 | 2-2 | 4-1 | 3-1 | 1-3 | 1-2 | | 0-0 | 3-1 | 1-5 | 0-0 | 1-2 |
| 14 | Swanage Town & Herston | 3-2 | 2-4 | 1-3 | 0-3 | 0-2 | 3-2 | 1-3 | 3-2 | 4-3 | 4-3 | 1-2 | 1-0 | 1-0 | | 2-2 | 1-3 | 0-3 | 2-3 |
| 15 | Tintinhull | 1-2 | 0-1 | 1-1 | 4-0 | 0-13 | 2-1 | 3-2 | 2-1 | 1-5 | 3-0 | 0-4 | 1-0 | 1-1 | 3-1 | | 2-3 | 3-0 | 1-0 |
| 16 | Wareham Rangers | 5-1 | 0-2 | 0-1 | 3-0 | 0-2 | 1-2 | 4-4 | 2-4 | 2-3 | 2-3 | 3-3 | 1-0 | 5-2 | 2-1 | 1-3 | | 0-3 | 5-0 |
| 17 | Weymouth Reserves | 1-0 | 2-0 | 2-1 | 1-2 | 3-0 | 3-2 | 2-1 | 2-2 | 2-0 | 1-3 | 0-2 | 4-3 | 1-0 | 2-3 | 3-2 | 2-1 | | 0-0 |
| 18 | Wincanton Town | 5-1 | 4-2 | 8-0 | 7-0 | 4-2 | 5-1 | 2-2 | 6-0 | 0-0 | 4-0 | 2-1 | 3-1 | 2-0 | 2-1 | 3-2 | 2-0 | 3-2 | |

## DORSET PREMIER LEAGUE CONSTITUTION 2013-14

| | | |
|---|---|---|
| BLANDFORD UNITED | Recreation Ground, Park Road, Blandford Forum DT11 7DB | 07932 414524 (Sec) |
| BRIDPORT RESERVES | St Marys Field, Skilling Hill Road, Bridport DT6 5LA | 01308 423 834 |
| CRANBORNE | Recreation Ground, Penny's Lane, Cranborne, Wimborne BH21 5QE | 01725 517 440 |
| HAMWORTHY RECREATION | Hamworthy Rec. Club, Magna Road, Canford Magna, Wimborne BH21 3AE | 01202 881 922 |
| HAMWORTHY UNITED RESERVES | The County Ground, Blandford Close, Hamworthy, Poole BH15 4BF | 01202 674 974 |
| HOLT UNITED | Petersham Lane, Gaunts Common, Holt, Wimborne BH21 4JR | 01258 840 379 |
| MERE TOWN | Duchy Manor, Springfield Road, Mere, BA12 6EW | 07725 021 587 (Sec) |
| MERLEY COBHAM SPORTS | Cobham Sports & Social Club, Merley House Lane, Wimborne BH21 3AA | 01202 885 773 |
| PARLEY SPORTS | Parley Sports Club, Christchurch Road, West Parley BH22 8SQ | 01202 573 345 |
| POOLE BOROUGH | Turlin Moor Recreation Ground, Hamworthy, Poole BH21 5XX | 07872 167 221 |
| PORTLAND UNITED | New Grove Corner, Grove Road, Portland DT5 1DP | 01305 861 489 |
| SHAFTESBURY TOWN | Cockrams, Coppice Street, Shaftesbury SP7 8PF | 01747 852 990 |
| SHERBORNE TOWN RESERVES | Raleigh Grove, The Terrace Playing Fields, Sherborne DT9 5NS | 01935 816 110 |
| SWANAGE TOWN & HERSTON | Day's Park, off De Moulham Road, Swanage BH19 2JW | 01929 424 673 |
| TINTINHULL | Tintinhull Playing Fields, Montacute Road, Yeovil BA22 8QD | 07525 137759 (Sec) |
| WAREHAM RANGERS | Purbeck Sports Centre, Worgret Road, Wareham, Dorset BH20 4PH | 01929 556 454 |
| WEYMOUTH RESERVES | Bob Lucas Stadium, Radipole Lane, Weymouth DT4 9XJ | 01305 785 558 |

**In:** Mere Town (P - Dorset Football League).
**Out:** Chickerell United (W - now Dorset Football League). Wincanton Town (P - Western League Div.1).

# ESSEX & SUFFOLK BORDER LEAGUE

**Sponsored by:** Kent Blaxill Building Products
**Founded:** 1911
**Recent Champions:**
2008: Gas Recreation
2009: West Bergholt
2010: Gas Recreation
2011: Brightlingsea Regent
2012: West Bergholt

## LEAGUE CUP

**QUARTER FINALS**

| | | | |
|---|---|---|---|
| Tollesbury | v | Little Oakley | 3-1 |
| Gas Recreation | v | Harwich & Parkeston | 4-1 |
| University of Essex | v | Clacton United | 4-1 |
| White Notley | v | Bradfield Rovers | 6-0 |

**SEMI FINALS**

| | | | |
|---|---|---|---|
| Tollesbury | v | White Notley | 2-1 |
| Gas Recreation | v | University of Essex | 1-0 |

**FINAL**

| | | | |
|---|---|---|---|
| Gas Recreation | v | Tollesbury | 2-1 |

### PREMIER DIVISION

| | P | W | D | L | F | A | Pts |
|---|---|---|---|---|---|---|---|
| Gas Recreation | 28 | 26 | 2 | 0 | 118 | 23 | 80 |
| (P) Haverhill Sports Association | 28 | 18 | 6 | 4 | 68 | 35 | 60 |
| West Bergholt | 28 | 16 | 6 | 6 | 71 | 37 | 54 |
| Holland FC | 28 | 16 | 4 | 8 | 69 | 44 | 52 |
| Harwich & Parkeston | 28 | 16 | 4 | 8 | 66 | 45 | 52 |
| Alresford Colne Rangers | 28 | 15 | 6 | 7 | 66 | 32 | 51 |
| Little Oakley | 28 | 13 | 7 | 8 | 64 | 49 | 46 |
| Earls Colne | 28 | 12 | 4 | 12 | 54 | 62 | 40 |
| University of Essex | 28 | 9 | 4 | 15 | 52 | 64 | 31 |
| White Notley (-3pts) | 28 | 9 | 5 | 14 | 45 | 65 | 29 |
| Great Bentley (+3pts) | 28 | 5 | 5 | 18 | 31 | 68 | 23 |
| Hedinghams United | 28 | 6 | 3 | 19 | 43 | 80 | 21 |
| Dedham Old Boys | 28 | 5 | 5 | 18 | 38 | 85 | 20 |
| Lawford Lads | 28 | 5 | 4 | 19 | 49 | 83 | 19 |
| (R) Hatfield Peverel | 28 | 6 | 1 | 21 | 33 | 95 | 19 |

### DIVISION ONE

| | | P | W | D | L | F | A | Pts |
|---|---|---|---|---|---|---|---|---|
| 1 | (P) Tollesbury | 26 | 23 | 0 | 3 | 109 | 26 | 69 |
| 2 | (P) Coggeshall Town | 26 | 22 | 1 | 3 | 88 | 24 | 67 |
| 3 | Colne Engaine & Bell United | 26 | 16 | 5 | 5 | 73 | 36 | 53 |
| 4 | (P) Tiptree Jobserve | 26 | 16 | 4 | 6 | 67 | 35 | 52 |
| 5 | Wormingford Wanderers | 26 | 13 | 6 | 7 | 54 | 41 | 45 |
| 6 | Rayne (+3pts) | 26 | 10 | 6 | 10 | 41 | 46 | 39 |
| 7 | Gosfield United (+3pts) | 26 | 9 | 8 | 9 | 45 | 52 | 38 |
| 8 | Barnston AFC | 26 | 8 | 6 | 12 | 46 | 56 | 30 |
| 9 | Clacton United (-5pts) | 26 | 8 | 6 | 12 | 51 | 70 | 25 |
| 10 | Boxted Lodgers (-3pts) | 26 | 7 | 5 | 14 | 40 | 63 | 23 |
| 11 | Bradfield Rovers (+2pts) | 26 | 4 | 7 | 15 | 50 | 78 | 21 |
| 12 | Mersea Island | 26 | 6 | 3 | 17 | 28 | 59 | 21 |
| 13 | Kirby Athletic | 26 | 4 | 5 | 17 | 35 | 73 | 17 |
| 14 | Foxash Social | 26 | 3 | 4 | 19 | 38 | 106 | 13 |

### PREMIER DIVISION

| | 1 | 2 | 3 | 4 | 5 | 6 | 7 | 8 | 9 | 10 | 11 | 12 | 13 | 14 | 15 |
|---|---|---|---|---|---|---|---|---|---|---|---|---|---|---|---|
| 1 Alresford Colne Rangers | | 4-0 | 1-1 | 2-2 | 1-1 | 0-1 | 8-0 | 0-0 | 7-0 | 3-0 | 4-3 | 1-0 | 2-3 | 0-0 | 4-0 |
| 2 Dedham Old Boys | 0-4 | | 3-1 | 1-7 | 1-1 | 1-2 | 2-3 | 3-3 | 3-2 | 1-2 | 3-2 | 0-4 | 1-4 | 0-6 | 3-2 |
| 3 Earls Colne | 1-1 | 5-1 | | 0-6 | 0-1 | 3-3 | 6-1 | 1-5 | 2-1 | 3-2 | 2-1 | 3-0 | 3-4 | 1-3 | 0-1 |
| 4 Gas Recreation | 4-1 | 5-1 | 4-2 | | 8-1 | 4-3 | 4-0 | 4-1 | 7-0 | 6-0 | 5-2 | 3-0 | 4-0 | 1-1 | 4-0 |
| 5 Great Bentley | 0-3 | 3-3 | 0-2 | 0-2 | | 0-3 | 0-3 | 2-5 | 2-1 | 0-2 | 3-0 | 1-1 | 2-0 | 1-5 | 1-3 |
| 6 Harwich & Parkeston | 1-2 | 3-2 | 3-1 | 2-3 | 1-0 | | 3-1 | 4-0 | 4-2 | 0-1 | 5-0 | 2-2 | 2-0 | 1-1 | 4-3 |
| 7 Hatfield Peverel | 3-4 | 1-2 | 1-3 | 0-5 | 2-1 | 2-4 | | 1-2 | 2-2 | 1-4 | 3-0 | 0-6 | 4-3 | 0-2 | 0-5 |
| 8 Haverhill Sports Association | 2-1 | 4-1 | 4-1 | 0-5 | 1-0 | 2-0 | 5-1 | | 2-1 | 3-0 | 6-2 | 1-0 | 0-0 | 0-0 | 5-1 |
| 9 Hedinghams United | 2-1 | 2-0 | 0-1 | 0-4 | 1-0 | 3-5 | 6-1 | 1-5 | | 3-0 | 2-3 | 2-5 | 2-1 | 0-4 | 1-2 |
| 10 Holland FC | 3-0 | 1-1 | 2-1 | 1-3 | 4-0 | 4-1 | 7-1 | 2-2 | 3-0 | | 7-1 | 4-4 | 4-0 | 3-2 | 2-2 |
| 11 Lawford Lads | 0-1 | 4-1 | 2-4 | 1-5 | 2-4 | 2-2 | 4-0 | 0-0 | 1-1 | 1-6 | | 1-2 | 1-5 | 1-4 | 6-1 |
| 12 Little Oakley | 2-0 | 6-2 | 2-2 | 2-4 | 2-2 | 1-0 | 2-0 | 0-3 | 7-2 | 1-0 | 3-2 | | 1-0 | 3-3 | 2-3 |
| 13 University of Essex | 1-2 | 0-0 | 2-3 | 0-2 | 4-3 | 1-3 | 0-1 | 4-2 | 3-2 | 1-3 | 2-6 | 2-2 | | 6-2 | 3-5 |
| 14 West Bergholt | 1-2 | 2-1 | 8-1 | 0-4 | 6-1 | 4-1 | 3-1 | 0-4 | 3-2 | 2-0 | 2-1 | 4-0 | 0-1 | | 0-0 |
| 15 White Notley | 1-7 | 2-1 | 0-1 | 2-3 | 2-1 | 0-3 | 2-0 | 0-1 | 2-2 | 1-2 | 0-0 | 2-4 | 2-2 | 1-3 | |

### ESSEX & SUFFOLK BORDER LEAGUE PREMIER DIVISION CONSTITUTION 2013-14

| | | |
|---|---|---|
| ALRESFORD COLNE RANGERS | Ford Lane, Alresford, Colchester CO7 8AU | 07896 54 122 |
| COGGESHALL TOWN | The Crops, West Street, Coggeshall CO6 1NS | 01376 562 843 |
| DEDHAM OLD BOYS | Old Grammar School Ground, The Drift, Dedham, Colchester CO7 6AH | None |
| EARLS COLNE | Green Farm Meadow, Halstead Road, Earls Colne, Colchester CO6 2NG | 01787 223 584 |
| GAS RECREATION | Bromley Road, Colchester CO4 3JE | 01206 860 383 |
| GREAT BENTLEY | The Green, Heckfords Road, Great Bentley, Colchester CO7 8LY | 01206 251 532 |
| HARWICH & PARKESTON | The Royal Oak, Main Road, Dovercourt, Harwich CO12 4AA | 01255 503 643 |
| HOLLAND | Eastcliff Sports Ground, Dulwich Road, Holland-on-Sea CO15 5HP | 07833 467 395 |
| HEDINGHAMS UNITED | Lawn Meadow, Yeldham Road, Sible Hedingham, Halstead CO9 3QH | None |
| LAWFORD LADS | School Lane, Lawford, Manningtree CO11 2JA | 01206 397 211 |
| LITTLE OAKLEY | War Memorial Club Ground, Harwich Road, Little Oakley, Harwich CO12 5ED | 01255 880 370 |
| TIPTREE JOBSERVE | Florence Park, Grange Road, Tiptree, Colchester CO5 0UH | None |
| TOLLESBURY | EShrub End Community and Sports Centre, Boadicea Way, Colchester | 01621 869 358 |
| UNIVERSITY OF ESSEX | University Essex Sports Centre, Wivenhoe Park, Colchester CO4 3SQ | 01206 873 250 |
| WEST BERGHOLT | Lorkin Daniel Field, Lexden Road, West Bergholt, Colchester CO6 3BW | 01206 241 525 |
| WHITE NOTLEY | Oak Farm, Faulkbourne, Witham CM8 1SF | 01376 519864 |

In: Coggeshall Town (P). Tiptree Jobserve (P). Tollesbury (P).
Out: Hatfield Peverel R). Haverhill Sports Association (P - Eastern Counties Div.1).

**DIVISION ONE CLUB MOVEMENTS**
In: Alresford Colne Rangers Reserves (N). Little Oakley Reserves (N). West Bergholt Reserves (N). Panfield Bell (NC from Colne Engaine & Bell United after the two sides demerged).
Out: Colne Engaine & Bell United (NC to Panfield Bell, and Colne Engaine now in Div.2). Foxash Social (W).

2012-13 - Division One champions Bishop's Stortford Swifts. Photo: Gordon Whittington.

2012-13 - Division One Runners-up Wadham Lodge. Photo: Gordon Whittington.

# ESSEX OLYMPIAN LEAGUE

**Sponsored by:** ProKit UK
**Founded:** 1966
**Recent Champions:**
2008: White Ensign
2009: Harold Wood Athletic
2010: Harold Wood Athletic
2011: Kelvedon Hatch
2012: Frenford Senior

## SENIOR CUP

**ROUND 1**

| | | | |
|---|---|---|---|
| Buckhurst Hill | v | Forest United | 4-1 |
| Leigh Ramblers | v | Toby | 2-3 |
| Rayliegh Town | v | Chingford Athletic | 7-3 |
| Castle United | v | Forest Glade | 10-1 |
| Galleywood | v | Frenford Senior | 0-2 |
| Southminster St Leonards | v | Epping | 0-1 |
| Bishops Stortford Swifts | v | Sungate | 5-2 |
| Newham United | v | Manford Way | 2-1 |
| M&B club | v | Herongate Athletic | 3-3, 3-4p |
| Hutton | v | White Ensign | 1-3 |
| Broomfield | v | Wadham Lodge | 0-1 |
| Old Chelmsfordians | v | Old Barkabbeyans | 0-2 |
| Springfield | v | Newbury Forest | 2-2, 5-4p |
| Burnham Ramblers Res. | v | Ramsden Scotia | 1-7 |
| Westhamians | v | Canning Town | 3-2 aet |
| Hannakins Farm | v | Ongar Town | 7-3 |
| Runwell Hospital | v | Debden Sports | 3-4 |
| Lakeside | v | LOASS | 3-2 |
| Writtle | v | Leytonstone United | 0-5 |

**ROUND 2**

| | | | |
|---|---|---|---|
| Buckhurst Hill | v | Toby | 5-6 |
| Rayliegh Town | v | Harold Wood Athletic | 3-3, 6-5p |
| Castle United | v | Frenford Senior | 2-8 |
| Ryan FC | v | Epping | 3-3, 6-5p |
| Bishops Stortford Swifts | v | Newham United | 5-4 |

## PREMIER DIVISION

| | Team | P | W | D | L | F | A | Pts |
|---|---|---|---|---|---|---|---|---|
| | Frenford Senior | 26 | 19 | 6 | 1 | 57 | 18 | 63 |
| | Kelvedon Hatch | 26 | 19 | 3 | 4 | 74 | 29 | 60 |
| | Southminster St. Leonards | 26 | 15 | 5 | 6 | 64 | 29 | 50 |
| | Rayleigh Town | 26 | 13 | 6 | 7 | 71 | 46 | 45 |
| | Harold Wood Athletic | 26 | 11 | 8 | 7 | 48 | 45 | 41 |
| | Hannakins Farm | 26 | 11 | 5 | 10 | 49 | 45 | 38 |
| | White Ensign | 26 | 9 | 5 | 12 | 40 | 55 | 32 |
| | M & B Club | 26 | 9 | 4 | 13 | 24 | 43 | 31 |
| | Buckhurst Hill | 26 | 8 | 6 | 12 | 31 | 49 | 30 |
| 0 | Manford Way | 26 | 8 | 4 | 14 | 41 | 53 | 28 |
| 1 | Aldborough Athletic | 26 | 7 | 7 | 12 | 40 | 58 | 28 |
| 2 | Harold Hill | 26 | 7 | 3 | 16 | 30 | 48 | 24 |
| 3 | (R) Westhamians | 26 | 6 | 4 | 16 | 22 | 45 | 22 |
| 4 | (R) Hutton | 26 | 5 | 4 | 17 | 36 | 74 | 19 |

## PREMIER DIVISION

| | | 1 | 2 | 3 | 4 | 5 | 6 | 7 | 8 | 9 | 10 | 11 | 12 | 13 | 14 |
|---|---|---|---|---|---|---|---|---|---|---|---|---|---|---|---|
| 1 | Aldborough Athletic | | 1-1 | 3-3 | 0-2 | 0-0 | 5-2 | 1-2 | 1-3 | 0-0 | 1-3 | 1-0 | 0-2 | 3-2 | 1-3 |
| 2 | Buckhurst Hill | 2-2 | | 0-1 | 3-0 | 2-1 | 2-3 | 3-1 | 1-2 | 1-2 | 1-1 | 0-2 | 0-4 | 1-1 | 1-0 |
| 3 | Frenford Senior | 1-1 | 7-1 | | 2-0 | 1-0 | 1-1 | 4-2 | 0-0 | 1-0 | 2-0 | 2-1 | 2-0 | 1-0 | 4-0 |
| 4 | Hannakins Farm | 6-1 | 0-0 | 1-1 | | 4-0 | 2-3 | 5-0 | 4-3 | 1-2 | 1-4 | 2-3 | 2-3 | 0-1 | 1-0 |
| 5 | Harold Hill | 2-3 | 1-2 | 0-2 | 0-2 | | 0-2 | 4-0 | 0-2 | 0-1 | 2-0 | 0-4 | 2-2 | 1-0 | 4-1 |
| 6 | Harold Wood Athletic | 1-2 | 1-0 | 3-3 | 1-3 | 1-0 | | 4-2 | 2-2 | 1-1 | 4-1 | 0-4 | 2-2 | 1-1 | 3-0 |
| 7 | Hutton | 3-3 | 2-0 | 1-0 | 1-4 | 1-3 | 0-4 | | 3-6 | 1-2 | A-W | 1-9 | 2-5 | 0-0 | 5-2 |
| 8 | Kelvedon Hatch | 2-0 | 10-0 | 0-1 | 0-0 | 5-0 | 4-0 | 3-1 | | 1-0 | 1-5 | 5-2 | 2-1 | 3-0 | 4-0 |
| 9 | M & B Club | 3-2 | 2-0 | 0-1 | 1-0 | 0-1 | 2-5 | 2-6 | 0-3 | | 2-1 | 0-2 | 0-5 | 0-2 | 1-3 |
| 10 | Manford Way | 1-3 | 1-3 | 0-2 | 1-1 | 6-2 | 3-0 | 2-2 | 1-2 | 1-2 | | 1-5 | 1-3 | 3-0 | 2-1 |
| 11 | Rayleigh Town | 6-2 | 3-3 | 2-7 | 1-1 | 3-2 | 2-2 | 2-0 | 0-3 | 1-1 | 2-2 | | 1-1 | 2-0 | 3-4 |
| 12 | Southminster St. Leonards | 5-0 | 1-2 | 0-1 | 3-2 | 3-1 | 2-0 | 3-0 | 1-2 | 0-0 | 5-1 | 2-3 | | 3-1 | 5-0 |
| 13 | Westhamians | 3-1 | 2-0 | 0-2 | 0-3 | 1-4 | 1-2 | 0-1 | 1-2 | 1-0 | 2-0 | 0-5 | 1-2 | | 1-1 |
| 14 | White Ensign | 0-3 | H-W | 2-5 | 1-2 | 0-0 | 0-0 | 1-1 | 5-4 | 3-0 | 4-0 | 4-3 | 1-1 | 4-1 | |

## ESSEX OLYMPIAN LEAGUE PREMIER DIVISION CONSTITUTION 2013-14

| | | |
|---|---|---|
| BISHOP'S STORTFORD SWIFTS | Silver Leys, Hadham Road (A1250), Bishop's Stortford CM23 2QE | 01279 658941 |
| BUCKHURST HILL | Roding Lane, Buckhurst Hill IG9 6BJ | 020 8504 1189 |
| FRENFORD SENIOR | Oakfields Sports Ground, Forest Road, Barkingside IG6 2JL | 020 8500 1998 |
| HANNAKINS FARM | Hannakins Farm Community Centre, Rosebay Avenue, Billericay CM12 0SY | 01277 630851 |
| HAROLD HILL | Brentwood Town FC, The Arena, The Brentwood Centre, Doddinghurst Road, Brentwood CM15 9NN | 07776 232071 |
| HAROLD WOOD ATHLETIC | Harold Wood Recreation Park, Harold View, Harold Wood RM3 0LX | 01708 375698 |
| KELVEDON HATCH | New Hall, School Road, Kelvedon Hatch, Brentwood CM15 0DH | 07774 129867 |
| M & B CLUB | Sanofi-Aventis Spts/Soc. Club, Dagenham Road, Dagenham RM7 0QX | 020 8919 2156 |
| MANFORD WAY | London Marathon Sports Ground, Forest Road, Hainault IG6 3HJ | 020 8500 3486 |
| NEWBURY FOREST | Forest Road, Hainault, Ilford IG6 3H | 07711 073344 |
| RAYLEIGH TOWN | Rayleigh Town Sports/Soc. Club, London Road, Rayleigh SS6 9DT | 01268 784001 |
| SOUTHMINSTER ST LEONARDS | King George V Playing Fields, Station Road, Southminster CM0 7EW | 07718 869883 |
| WADHAM LODGE | Wadham Lodge Sports Ground, Kitchener Road, Walthamstow E17 4JP | 020 8527 2444 |
| WHITE ENSIGN | Borough Football Comb. HQ, Eastwoodbury Lane, Southend-on-Sea SS2 6XG | 01702 520482 |

**In:** Bishops Stortford Swifts (P). Newbury Forest (P). Wadham Lodge (P).
**Out:** Hutton (R). Westhamians (R). Aldborough Athletic (F).

## SENIOR CHALLENGE CUP
### (Premier Champions v Senior Cup Holders)

**FINAL**

| | | | |
|---|---|---|---|
| Frenford Senior | v | Aldborough Athletic | 2-0 |

### DIVISION ONE

| | P | W | D | L | F | A | Pts |
|---|---|---|---|---|---|---|---|
| Bishops Stortford Swifts | 22 | 15 | 1 | 6 | 70 | 40 | 46 |
| Wadham Lodge | 22 | 13 | 4 | 5 | 42 | 26 | 43 |
| Newbury Forest (-1pt) | 22 | 13 | 4 | 5 | 77 | 46 | 42 |
| Springfield | 22 | 11 | 6 | 5 | 52 | 29 | 39 |
| Old Chelmsfordians | 22 | 8 | 7 | 7 | 50 | 53 | 31 |
| Canning Town | 22 | 9 | 2 | 11 | 26 | 43 | 29 |
| Old Southendian | 22 | 7 | 4 | 11 | 39 | 48 | 25 |
| Herongate Athletic | 22 | 6 | 7 | 9 | 36 | 47 | 25 |
| Benfleet | 22 | 7 | 4 | 11 | 39 | 56 | 25 |
| Galleywood (+2pts) | 22 | 5 | 6 | 11 | 32 | 46 | 23 |
| Ongar Town | 22 | 7 | 1 | 14 | 46 | 59 | 22 |
| Runwell Hospital | 22 | 6 | 4 | 12 | 31 | 47 | 22 |

### DIVISION TWO

| | P | W | D | L | F | A | Pts |
|---|---|---|---|---|---|---|---|
| Old Barkabbeyans | 22 | 17 | 5 | 0 | 94 | 20 | 56 |
| Leigh Ramblers | 22 | 16 | 3 | 3 | 63 | 32 | 51 |
| Newham United | 22 | 12 | 5 | 5 | 53 | 46 | 41 |
| Broomfield | 22 | 11 | 3 | 8 | 49 | 42 | 36 |
| Upminster | 21 | 9 | 4 | 8 | 50 | 41 | 31 |
| Ryan F.C. | 22 | 8 | 4 | 10 | 34 | 46 | 28 |
| Lakeside | 22 | 8 | 3 | 11 | 47 | 58 | 27 |
| Roydon | 22 | 7 | 5 | 10 | 45 | 42 | 26 |
| Castle United | 20 | 7 | 5 | 8 | 42 | 47 | 26 |
| (R) Epping | 22 | 5 | 6 | 11 | 51 | 59 | 21 |
| Burnham Ramblers Res | 21 | 6 | 3 | 12 | 41 | 73 | 21 |
| (R) Leytonstone United | 22 | 1 | 0 | 21 | 28 | 91 | 3 |

### DIVISION THREE

| | P | W | D | L | F | A | Pts |
|---|---|---|---|---|---|---|---|
| (P) Debden Sports | 22 | 18 | 1 | 3 | 64 | 17 | 55 |
| (P) Toby | 22 | 16 | 3 | 3 | 48 | 28 | 51 |
| (P) Shenfield A.F.C. | 22 | 16 | 2 | 4 | 75 | 23 | 50 |
| Basildon Town | 22 | 13 | 1 | 8 | 68 | 45 | 40 |
| LOASS | 22 | 11 | 3 | 8 | 50 | 47 | 36 |
| Catholic United | 22 | 10 | 3 | 9 | 48 | 41 | 33 |
| Ramsden Scotia | 22 | 9 | 3 | 10 | 54 | 53 | 30 |
| Stambridge United | 22 | 8 | 2 | 12 | 36 | 43 | 26 |
| Chingford Athletic | 22 | 5 | 3 | 14 | 37 | 65 | 18 |
| Forest United | 22 | 5 | 2 | 15 | 39 | 70 | 17 |
| Sungate | 22 | 5 | 2 | 15 | 46 | 80 | 17 |
| Writtle | 22 | 3 | 1 | 18 | 16 | 69 | 10 |

In: Alemite Athletic (P - Hertford & District League). Forest Glade (N).
Rochford Town (P - Southend Borough Combination).
Maresbrook (P - Essex Business Houses Football League).
Out: Writtle (W - now Mid Essex League).

### RESERVES DIVISION ONE

| | P | W | D | L | F | A | Pts |
|---|---|---|---|---|---|---|---|
| Harold Wood Athletic Res. | 22 | 15 | 4 | 3 | 47 | 22 | 49 |
| Frenford Senior Reserves | 22 | 16 | 0 | 6 | 62 | 26 | 48 |
| Manford Way Reserves | 22 | 14 | 1 | 7 | 55 | 44 | 43 |
| Rayleigh Town Reserves | 22 | 13 | 4 | 5 | 32 | 21 | 43 |
| M & B Club Reserves | 22 | 12 | 4 | 6 | 51 | 34 | 40 |
| Debden Sports Reserves | 22 | 13 | 1 | 8 | 49 | 42 | 40 |
| Kelvedon Hatch Reserves | 22 | 10 | 3 | 9 | 52 | 43 | 33 |
| Canning Town Reserves (-3pts) | 22 | 9 | 1 | 12 | 36 | 52 | 25 |
| Hutton Reserves (+3pts) | 22 | 6 | 1 | 15 | 33 | 63 | 22 |
| Aldborough Athletic Reserves | 22 | 6 | 1 | 15 | 45 | 50 | 19 |
| (R) Buckhurst Hill Reserves | 22 | 5 | 1 | 16 | 45 | 57 | 16 |
| (R) Westhamians Reserves | 22 | 2 | 1 | 19 | 19 | 72 | 7 |

### SENIOR CUP continued...

| | | | |
|---|---|---|---|
| Herongate Athletic | v | Basildon Town | 3-1 |
| White Ensign | v | Wadham Lodge | 2-3 |
| Roydon | v | Old Southendian | 5-6 aet |
| Old Barkabbeyans | v | Springfield | 2-3 |
| Ramsden Scotia | v | Westhamians | 0-2 |
| Hannakins Farm | v | Debden Sports | 1-4 |
| Stambridge United | v | Aldborough Athletic | 1-2 |
| Benfleet | v | Lakeside | 6-1 |
| Kelvedon Hatch | v | Harold Hill | 3-2 |
| Leytonstone United | v | Upminster | 0-3 aet |
| Shenfield AFC | v | Catholic United | 5-2 |

**ROUND 3**

| | | | |
|---|---|---|---|
| Toby | v | Rayleigh Town | 1-4 |
| Frenford Senior | v | Ryan FC | 6-0 |
| Bishops Stortford Swifts | v | Herongate Athletic | 3-0 |
| Wadham Lodge | v | Old Southendian | 3-2 |
| Springfield | v | Westhamians | HW |
| Debden Sports | v | Aldborough Athletic | 2-0 |
| Benfleet | v | Kelvedon Hatch | 3-2 |
| Upminster | v | Shenfield AFC | 2-6 |

**QUARTER FINALS**

| | | | |
|---|---|---|---|
| Rayleigh Town | v | Frenford Senior | 0-1 |
| Bishops Stortford Swifts | v | Wadham Lodge | 5-2 |
| Springfield | v | Debden Sports | 3-0 |
| Benfleet | v | Shenfield AFC | 1-5 |

**SEMI FINALS**

| | | | |
|---|---|---|---|
| Frenford Senior | v | Bishops Stortford Swifts | 0-0, 5-4p |
| Springfield | v | Shenfield AFC | 2-1 |

**FINAL**

| | | | |
|---|---|---|---|
| Frenford Senior | v | Springfield | 1-0 |

### RESERVES DIVISION TWO

| | | P | W | D | L | F | A | Pts |
|---|---|---|---|---|---|---|---|---|
| 1 | (P) White Ensign Reserves | 22 | 17 | 2 | 3 | 74 | 27 | 53 |
| 2 | (P) Old Chelmsfordians Reserves | 22 | 14 | 3 | 5 | 53 | 37 | 45 |
| 3 | (P) Southminster St. L'ds Res. (+3pts) | 22 | 11 | 3 | 8 | 52 | 42 | 39 |
| 4 | Galleywood Reserves | 22 | 11 | 4 | 7 | 51 | 34 | 37 |
| 5 | Runwell Hospital Reserves | 22 | 11 | 4 | 7 | 45 | 38 | 37 |
| 6 | Old Barkabbeyans Reserves | 22 | 10 | 3 | 9 | 58 | 50 | 33 |
| 7 | Herongate Athletic Reserves | 22 | 8 | 4 | 10 | 50 | 49 | 28 |
| 8 | Upminster Reserves | 22 | 8 | 2 | 12 | 44 | 66 | 26 |
| 9 | Springfield Reserves | 22 | 7 | 1 | 14 | 43 | 67 | 22 |
| 10 | Catholic United Reserves (-3pts) | 21 | 7 | 3 | 11 | 42 | 56 | 21 |
| 11 | (R) Newham United Reserves | 21 | 5 | 3 | 13 | 36 | 61 | 18 |
| 12 | (R) Leigh Ramblers Reserves | 22 | 4 | 4 | 14 | 46 | 67 | 163 |

### RESERVES DIVISION THREE

| | | P | W | D | L | F | A | Pts |
|---|---|---|---|---|---|---|---|---|
| 1 | (P) Benfleet Reserves (+3pts) | 20 | 11 | 5 | 4 | 52 | 33 | 41 |
| 2 | (P) Stambridge United Reserves | 20 | 11 | 7 | 2 | 42 | 26 | 40 |
| 3 | (P) Old Southendian Reserves | 20 | 11 | 4 | 5 | 50 | 32 | 37 |
| 4 | Sungate Reserves | 20 | 10 | 5 | 5 | 60 | 38 | 35 |
| 5 | Toby Reserves | 20 | 9 | 5 | 6 | 44 | 31 | 32 |
| 6 | Shenfield A.F.C. Reserves | 20 | 8 | 5 | 7 | 42 | 45 | 29 |
| 7 | Basildon Town Reserves | 20 | 7 | 4 | 9 | 35 | 37 | 25 |
| 8 | Ramsden Scotia Reserves (-3pts) | 20 | 7 | 5 | 8 | 40 | 41 | 23 |
| 9 | Leytonstone United Reserves | 20 | 4 | 5 | 11 | 40 | 76 | 17 |
| 10 | Harold Hill Reserves | 20 | 4 | 1 | 13 | 31 | 51 | 13 |
| 11 | Ryan F.C.Reserves | 20 | 3 | 3 | 14 | 33 | 59 | 12 |

In: Broomfield Reserves (N).

# GLOUCESTERSHIRE COUNTY LEAGUE

**Sponsored by:** David Wilson Homes
**Founded:** 1968
**Recent Champions:**
2008: Hardwicke
2009: Slimbridge
2010: Thornbury Town
2011: Brimscombe and Thrupp
2012: Cribbs Friends Life

| | | P | W | D | L | F | A | Pts |
|---|---|---|---|---|---|---|---|---|
| 1 | Longlevens | 36 | 24 | 5 | 7 | 86 | 44 | 77 |
| 2 | (P) Tuffley Rovers | 36 | 22 | 6 | 8 | 76 | 47 | 72 |
| 3 | Rockleaze Rangers | 36 | 20 | 6 | 10 | 74 | 41 | 66 |
| 4 | Southmead CS Athletic (-3pts) | 36 | 21 | 6 | 9 | 85 | 58 | 66 |
| 5 | Bristol Academy | 36 | 19 | 9 | 8 | 68 | 44 | 66 |
| 6 | Ellwood | 36 | 17 | 9 | 10 | 67 | 45 | 60 |
| 7 | Henbury | 36 | 16 | 6 | 14 | 54 | 57 | 54 |
| 8 | Kings Stanley | 36 | 15 | 8 | 13 | 56 | 46 | 53 |
| 9 | Patchway Town | 36 | 14 | 7 | 15 | 48 | 53 | 49 |
| 10 | Hanham Athletic | 36 | 13 | 9 | 14 | 54 | 58 | 48 |
| 11 | Kingswood | 36 | 13 | 7 | 16 | 42 | 49 | 46 |
| 12 | Bishops Cleeve Res | 36 | 14 | 2 | 20 | 53 | 65 | 44 |
| 13 | Frampton United | 36 | 12 | 8 | 16 | 56 | 75 | 41 |
| 14 | Thornbury Town | 36 | 12 | 4 | 20 | 50 | 66 | 40 |
| 15 | Chipping Sodbury Town | 36 | 11 | 6 | 19 | 52 | 78 | 39 |
| 16 | Yate Town Res | 36 | 9 | 11 | 16 | 53 | 64 | 38 |
| 17 | Berkeley Town | 36 | 8 | 7 | 21 | 45 | 92 | 31 |
| 18 | (R) Taverners | 36 | 7 | 9 | 20 | 35 | 53 | 30 |
| 19 | (R) D.R.G. Frenchay (-3pts) | 36 | 8 | 9 | 19 | 45 | 64 | 30 |

## LES JAMES LEAGUE CUP

**PRELIMINARY ROUND**

| | | | |
|---|---|---|---|
| Yate Town Reserves | v | Bristol Academy | 2-4 |

*Bristol Academy removed for playing an ineligible player.*

| | | | |
|---|---|---|---|
| Patchway Town | v | Ellwood | 2-0 |

**ROUND 1**

| | | | |
|---|---|---|---|
| Yate Town Reserves | v | Patchway Town | 0-4 |
| Southmead CS Athletic | v | Longlevens | 0-4 |
| Berkeley Town | v | Taverners | 0-2 |
| Rockleaze Rangers | v | Tuffley Rovers | 0-2 |
| Chipping Sodbury Town | v | Bishops Cleeve Res. | 0-0, 4-5p |
| Hanham Athletic | v | Frampton United | 0-4 |
| Kings Stanley | v | Henbury | 3-0 |
| Thornbury Town | v | DRG Frenchay | 0-4 |

**QUARTER FINALS**

| | | | |
|---|---|---|---|
| Patchway Town | v | Longlevens | 2-1 |
| Taverners | v | Tuffley Rovers | 1-1, 4-2p |
| Bishops Cleeve Reserves | v | Frampton United | 3-2 |
| Kings Stanley | v | DRG Frenchay | 2-0 |

**SEMI FINALS**

| | | | |
|---|---|---|---|
| Patchway Town | v | Taverners | 1-1, 3-4p |
| Bishops Cleeve Reserves | v | Kings Stanley | 0-0, 2-3ppp |

**FINAL**

| | | | |
|---|---|---|---|
| Taverners | v | Kings Stanley | 0-1 |
| *At Southmead CS Athletic* | | | *Att: 150* |

| | | 1 | 2 | 3 | 4 | 5 | 6 | 7 | 8 | 9 | 10 | 11 | 12 | 13 | 14 | 15 | 16 | 17 | 18 | 19 |
|---|---|---|---|---|---|---|---|---|---|---|---|---|---|---|---|---|---|---|---|---|
| 1 | Berkeley Town | | 2-4 | 0-5 | 0-4 | 2-2 | 2-6 | 4-6 | 2-2 | 0-3 | 0-5 | 0-1 | 2-3 | 0-0 | 3-1 | 2-3 | 2-0 | 1-3 | 1-3 | 2-2 |
| 2 | Bishops Cleeve Reserves | 0-1 | | 2-4 | 4-1 | 1-1 | 4-1 | 3-0 | 1-0 | 1-2 | 0-2 | 2-1 | 0-2 | 0-2 | 3-1 | 1-3 | 1-2 | 0-4 | 1-2 | 1-2 |
| 3 | Bristol Academy | 3-0 | 1-1 | | 4-2 | 1-0 | 3-1 | 3-4 | 0-3 | 3-1 | 0-1 | 0-0 | 2-2 | 2-1 | 0-5 | 1-0 | 0-0 | 1-1 | 2-4 | 1-2 |
| 4 | Chipping Sodbury Town | 2-2 | 2-4 | 1-6 | | 0-2 | 1-2 | 2-3 | 4-3 | 0-2 | 2-0 | 2-2 | 3-2 | 0-3 | 0-5 | 4-1 | 2-1 | 3-1 | 0-1 | 3-1 |
| 5 | D.R.G. Frenchay | 1-2 | 1-3 | 1-1 | 2-2 | | 0-1 | 0-1 | 2-5 | 0-2 | 1-1 | 3-2 | 1-2 | 1-3 | 0-2 | 1-5 | 2-1 | 0-1 | 4-0 | 1-1 |
| 6 | Ellwood | 8-0 | 3-1 | 1-0 | 0-1 | 1-1 | | 5-0 | 2-2 | 2-1 | 1-0 | 3-0 | 2-1 | 2-0 | 2-2 | 2-2 | 3-0 | 2-1 | 0-3 | 0-0 |
| 7 | Frampton United | 1-3 | 1-0 | 1-5 | 3-0 | 3-1 | 2-2 | | 0-2 | 1-2 | 1-1 | 1-4 | 7-0 | 2-2 | 1-1 | 1-1 | 0-4 | 1-2 | 0-1 | 1-1 |
| 8 | Hanham Athletic | 1-2 | 0-1 | 0-0 | 3-2 | 2-1 | 1-0 | 1-2 | | 3-3 | 2-1 | 0-1 | 4-5 | 1-2 | 1-1 | 2-2 | 2-0 | 0-1 | 2-1 | 1-0 |
| 9 | Henbury | 2-0 | 3-2 | 3-5 | 1-1 | 2-1 | 0-3 | 1-3 | 1-2 | | 1-2 | 1-3 | 1-1 | 3-2 | 3-1 | 3-0 | 1-0 | 2-3 | 3-2 | 1-0 |
| 10 | Kings Stanley | 0-0 | 4-1 | 0-1 | 0-2 | 1-1 | 2-1 | 0-1 | 1-1 | 4-1 | | 2-0 | 1-3 | 0-1 | 1-0 | 0-4 | 3-0 | 1-3 | 1-1 | 4-1 |
| 11 | Kingswood | 2-1 | 2-0 | 1-2 | 2-0 | 2-3 | 1-1 | 3-0 | 0-2 | 1-0 | 3-1 | | 2-2 | 0-2 | 1-1 | 0-1 | 1-0 | 1-1 | 0-2 | 0-3 |
| 12 | Longlevens | 2-0 | 4-0 | 1-0 | 2-0 | 1-1 | 3-2 | 3-0 | 4-0 | 4-0 | 2-0 | 2-1 | | 1-0 | 2-1 | 3-4 | 3-2 | 1-2 | 2-4 | 6-1 |
| 13 | Patchway Town | 1-1 | 0-1 | 2-0 | 0-2 | 1-2 | 1-1 | 1-2 | 1-0 | 3-0 | 1-1 | 0-1 | 1-6 | | 0-2 | 2-1 | 3-1 | 5-2 | 1-3 | 0-0 |
| 14 | Rockleaze Rangers | 3-0 | 1-2 | 1-2 | 1-0 | 2-0 | 2-0 | 5-2 | 2-1 | 2-1 | 0-2 | 2-0 | 2-0 | 2-0 | | 3-1 | 2-1 | 2-4 | 0-1 | 5-0 |
| 15 | Southmead CS Athletic | 3-1 | 2-1 | 1-1 | 4-0 | 3-1 | 5-2 | 5-2 | 3-0 | 0-0 | 2-3 | 5-2 | 2-3 | 2-0 | 1-4 | | 4-3 | 4-1 | 1-1 | 1-6 |
| 16 | Taverners | 2-0 | 2-0 | 0-0 | 3-0 | 2-0 | 1-1 | 1-1 | 2-2 | 0-2 | 1-3 | 0-2 | 3-1 | 1-2 | 0-1 | 0-2 | | 0-1 | 0-1 | 1-1 |
| 17 | Thornbury Town | 2-3 | 3-2 | 1-2 | 0-3 | 1-3 | 1-0 | 1-1 | 0-1 | 1-2 | 0-1 | 2-2 | 1-0 | 1-2 | 0-1 | 0-3 | 1-4 | | 1-2 | 2-3 |
| 18 | Tuffley Rovers | 5-1 | 2-3 | 1-4 | 6-1 | 2-2 | 0-1 | 3-1 | 2-0 | 2-0 | 2-1 | 2-2 | 0-2 | 2-2 | 0-3 | 1-2 | 2-0 | 5-0 | | 4-4 |
| 19 | Yate Town Reserves | 1-3 | 1-2 | 0-1 | 1-1 | 1-2 | 1-3 | 1-1 | 5-0 | 1-1 | 2-4 | 2-0 | 2-2 | 1-1 | 1-2 | 1-2 | 0-1 | 2-1 | 0-2 | |

## GLOUCESTERSHIRE COUNTY LEAGUE CONSTITUTION 2013-14

| | | |
|---|---|---|
| BERKELEY TOWN | Station Road, Berkeley GL13 9AJ | 07807 781269 |
| BISHOPS CLEEVE RESERVES | Kayte Lane, Southam, Cheltenham GL52 3PD | 01242 676166 |
| BRISTOL ACADEMY | South Glos & Stroud College, WISE Campus, New Road, Stoke Gifford, Bristol. BS348LP | 0117 919 2601 |
| BRISTOL TELEPHONES | BTRA Sports Ground, Stockwood Lane, Stockwood, Bristol BS14 8SJ | 01275 891 776 |
| CHIPPING SODBURY TOWN | The Ridings, Wickwar Road, Chipping Sodbury, Bristol BS37 6BQ | 07787 522100 |
| ELLWOOD | Bromley Road, Ellwood, Coleford GL16 7LY | 01594 832927 |
| FRAMPTON UNITED | The Bell Field, Bridge Road, Frampton on Severn, Gloucestershire GL2 7HA | 07817 486933 |
| GALA WILTON | The Gala Club, Fairmile Gardens, Tewkesbury Road, Longford, Glou GL2 9EB | 01452 524 447 |
| HANHAM ATHLETIC | The Playing Fields Pavilion, 16 Vicarage Road, Hanham, Bristol BS15 3AH | 0117 9678291 |
| HENBURY | Arnell Drive Playing Field, Lorain Walk, Henbury, Bristol BS10 7AS | 0117 959 0475 |
| KINGS STANLEY | Marling Close, Broad Street, Kings Stanley, Stonehouse GL10 3PN | 01453 828975 |
| KINGSWOOD | Kingswood PF, Wickwar Road, Kingswood, Wotton-under-Edge GL12 8RF | 07971 682091 |
| LONGLEVENS | Sawmills End, Corinium Ave, Gloucester, GL4 3DG | 07717 766720 |
| PATCHWAY TOWN | Scott Park, Coniston Road, Patchway, Bristol BS34 5JR | 0117 949 3952 |
| ROCKLEAZE RANGERS | Coombe Dingle Sport Complex, Coombe Dingle, Bristol BS9 2BJ | 0117 962 6718 |
| SOUTHMEAD CS ATHLETIC | Pen Park Sports Pavillion, Jarratts Road, Bristol BS10 6WF | 0117 9508362 |
| THORNBURY TOWN | Mundy Playing Fields, Kington Lane, Thornbury BS35 1NA | 01454 413645 |
| YATE TOWN RESERVES | Lodge Road, Yate, Bristol BS37 7LE | Club: 01454 228103 |

**In:** Bristol Telephones (P - Bristol & Suburban Lge) Gala Wilton (P - Gloucester Northern Senior Lge).
**Out:** Tuffley Rovers (P - Hellenic Lge Div.1W). Taverners (R - Gloucester Northern Senior Lge). DRG Frenchay (R - Bristol Premier Combination).

**LEAGUE CHAMPIONS - LONGLEVENS FOOTBALL CLUB**
**Back Row – L to R –** James French (Manager), Craig Martin ©, Ellis Sausman, Lee Martin, Brad Martin, Scott Goodhall, Josh Westcarr.
**Middle Row – L to R –** Ryan Dunn, Shaun O'Connor, Dave Rich, Danny Moore, Adam Phillips, Dave Merrick, Andy Davis (Secretary), Bill Davis (President).
**Front Row – L to R –** Adam Hughes, Mark Moore, Ed Smyllie, Luke Kavanagh, Lee Blackmore.

**LES JAMES LEAGUE CUP WINNERS - KINGS STANLEY**
**Back Row: -** Sam Prior (Manager), Nick Humphries, Sean Wager (Coach), Steve Robertson, Tony Oakley, Andy Maryon, Gavin Dean, Luke Barstow, Ryan Stevenson, Jake Davies, Paul Webster, Danny Stephens, Pete Davies, Tom Pass, Ben Carman.
**Front Row: -** James Carman (Physio), Paul Day, Andy Roberts, Liam Gale, Ben Newman, Danny Chandler, Ben Powell (Assist. Manager), Nigel Dean (Goalkeeper Coach).

# HAMPSHIRE PREMIER LEAGUE

**Sponsored by:** Puma Engineering
**Founded:** 2007
**Recent Champions:**
2008: AFC Stoneham. 2009: Colden Common.
2010: Colden Common. 2011: Liphook United
2012: Liphook United

## SENIOR CUP

**ROUND 1**

| | | | |
|---|---|---|---|
| Overton United | v | QK Southampton | 1-2 |
| Paulsgrove | v | Liphook United | 2-3 |

**ROUND 2**

| | | | |
|---|---|---|---|
| AFC Stoneham | v | Sporting Bishops Waltham | 3-0 |
| Bournemouth Sports | v | Locks Heath | 1-2 |
| Otterbourne | v | University of Portsmouth | 1-2 |
| Winchester Castle | v | Liphook United | 1-2 aet |
| AFC Aldermaston | v | QK Southampton | 9-1 |
| Fleetlands | v | Hedge End Rangers | 5-1 |
| Liss Athletic | v | Clanfield | 6-4 |

**QUARTER FINALS**

| | | | |
|---|---|---|---|
| Liphook United | v | Fleetlands | 5-2 |
| Locks Heath | v | University of Portsmouth | 4-1 |
| AFC Aldermaston | v | AFC Stoneham | 0-1 |
| Colden Common | v | Liss Athletic | 3-2 |

**SEMI FINALS**

| | | | |
|---|---|---|---|
| Liphook United | v | Colden Common | 2-3 aet |
| Locks Heath | v | AFC Stoneham | 0-1 |

**FINAL**

| | | | |
|---|---|---|---|
| AFC Stoneham | v | Colden Common | 1-2 |

## SENIOR DIVISION

| | | P | W | D | L | F | A | Pts |
|---|---|---|---|---|---|---|---|---|
| 1 | Locks Heath | 32 | 27 | 4 | 1 | 108 | 42 | 85 |
| 2 | AFC Stoneham | 32 | 23 | 3 | 6 | 98 | 36 | 72 |
| 3 | Colden Common | 32 | 21 | 5 | 6 | 84 | 44 | 68 |
| 4 | Hedge End Rangers | 32 | 20 | 3 | 9 | 87 | 55 | 63 |
| 5 | Clanfield | 32 | 17 | 2 | 13 | 61 | 46 | 53 |
| 6 | Liss Athletic | 32 | 14 | 6 | 12 | 57 | 61 | 48 |
| 7 | Winchester Castle | 32 | 14 | 5 | 13 | 57 | 50 | 47 |
| 8 | AFC Aldermaston | 32 | 11 | 9 | 12 | 59 | 65 | 41 |
| 9 | Bournemouth Sports | 32 | 9 | 9 | 14 | 54 | 65 | 36 |
| 10 | Paulsgrove | 32 | 10 | 6 | 16 | 53 | 67 | 36 |
| 11 | Overton United | 32 | 10 | 4 | 18 | 57 | 76 | 34 |
| 12 | Sporting Bishops Waltham | 32 | 10 | 4 | 18 | 50 | 75 | 34 |
| 13 | Fleetlands | 32 | 10 | 4 | 18 | 43 | 70 | 34 |
| 14 | Liphook United | 32 | 9 | 7 | 16 | 49 | 80 | 34 |
| 15 | QK Southampton | 32 | 10 | 1 | 21 | 60 | 104 | 31 |
| 16 | Otterbourne | 32 | 9 | 4 | 19 | 56 | 76 | 30 |
| 17 | (R) University of Portsmouth | 32 | 10 | 0 | 22 | 53 | 84 | 21 |

| SENIOR DIVISION | 1 | 2 | 3 | 4 | 5 | 6 | 7 | 8 | 9 | 10 | 11 | 12 | 13 | 14 | 15 | 16 | 17 |
|---|---|---|---|---|---|---|---|---|---|---|---|---|---|---|---|---|---|
| 1 AFC Aldermaston | | 0-3 | 1-1 | 1-0 | 3-1 | 3-1 | 0-1 | 1-1 | 0-0 | 1-2 | 2-1 | 2-1 | 2-4 | 2-1 | 1-0 | 2-1 | 4-0 |
| 2 AFC Stoneham | 4-1 | | 3-1 | 2-3 | 3-1 | 3-1 | 2-2 | 6-0 | 4-0 | 3-4 | 2-1 | 1-0 | 6-2 | 4-0 | 1-0 | 12-1 | 0-1 |
| 3 Bournemouth Sports | 4-2 | 0-0 | | 1-1 | 0-1 | 4-0 | 2-3 | 1-2 | 0-2 | 2-3 | 3-1 | 1-0 | 2-2 | 1-1 | 4-1 | 5-1 | 1-1 |
| 4 Clanfield | 2-1 | 1-2 | 4-0 | | 0-1 | 2-1 | 1-2 | 1-0 | 0-2 | 0-1 | 4-3 | 2-1 | 6-1 | 5-2 | 3-0 | 2-1 | 2-3 |
| 5 Colden Common | 4-0 | 5-1 | 2-0 | 2-0 | | 2-4 | 0-0 | 7-0 | 8-1 | 1-2 | 2-1 | 4-2 | 1-1 | 8-1 | 2-1 | 4-2 | 4-0 |
| 6 Fleetlands | 3-3 | 1-3 | 2-4 | 0-1 | 0-1 | | 0-4 | 2-0 | 1-0 | 0-2 | 2-1 | 2-2 | 2-1 | 0-1 | 1-2 | 3-1 | 2-1 |
| 7 Hedge End Range | 3-2 | 2-4 | 7-2 | 0-2 | 0-3 | 1-0 | | 1-1 | 7-1 | 2-3 | 5-2 | 4-1 | 5-1 | 6-0 | 3-0 | 1-0 | 4-1 |
| 8 Liphook United | 3-3 | 1-1 | 2-2 | 1-2 | 2-2 | 0-3 | 4-3 | | 1-4 | 2-5 | 4-1 | 3-1 | 3-1 | 1-2 | 2-0 | 0-3 | 3-1 |
| 9 Liss Athletic | 1-5 | 0-3 | 1-1 | 2-1 | 0-3 | 1-1 | 1-2 | 3-1 | | 3-0 | 1-1 | 1-1 | 1-2 | 3-1 | 0-2 | 4-3 | 3-0 |
| 10 Locks Heath | 3-3 | 2-1 | 5-1 | 3-2 | 3-3 | 3-1 | 5-0 | 8-1 | 2-1 | | 1-0 | 7-0 | 1-1 | 6-2 | 5-2 | 2-1 | 3-1 |
| 11 Otterbourne | 2-2 | 0-2 | 1-4 | 1-1 | 0-4 | 9-2 | 2-3 | 3-1 | 0-3 | 0-4 | | 6-2 | 2-1 | 3-1 | 1-1 | 3-0 | 3-2 |
| 12 Overton United | 1-1 | 1-6 | 1-2 | 2-1 | 3-0 | 4-0 | 4-1 | 2-0 | 1-3 | 3-3 | 4-1 | | 0-1 | 2-3 | 2-0 | 1-4 | 2-3 |
| 13 Paulsgrove | 1-1 | 1-3 | 6-0 | 1-2 | 1-1 | 3-0 | 1-4 | 0-2 | 0-1 | 2-5 | 0-2 | 2-4 | | 3-0 | 2-2 | 4-1 | 1-0 |
| 14 QK Southampton | 3-2 | 1-3 | 4-3 | 2-8 | 0-5 | 4-1 | 0-2 | 1-3 | 3-5 | 1-5 | 8-2 | 4-5 | 2-0 | | 7-5 | 2-3 | 1-3 |
| 15 Sporting Bishop Waltham | 4-3 | 0-8 | 3-1 | 3-1 | 0-1 | 1-3 | 1-4 | 3-1 | 2-2 | 1-5 | 2-1 | 4-1 | 1-3 | 1-2 | | 4-3 | 1-2 |
| 16 University of Portsmouth | 0-5 | 3-1 | 1-0 | 4-0 | 0-1 | 1-2 | 5-4 | 5-2 | 1-5 | 1-3 | 1-2 | 0-3 | 4-1 | 1-0 | 0-3 | | 1-3 |
| 17 Winchester Castle | 9-0 | 0-1 | 1-1 | 0-1 | 3-0 | 2-2 | 4-1 | 2-2 | 4-2 | 0-2 | 2-0 | 4-0 | 1-3 | 3-0 | 0-0 | H-H | |

## HAMPSHIRE PREMIER LEAGUE SENIOR DIVISION CONSTITUTION 2013-14

| | | |
|---|---|---|
| AFC ALDERMASTON | AWE Recreational Society, Aldermaston, Reading RG7 4PR | 07981 004 094 (Secretary) |
| AFC STONEHAM | Jubilee Park, Chestnut Avenue, Eastleigh SO50 9PF | 07765 046 429 (Sec) |
| BAFFINS MILTON ROVERS | Langstone Harbour Sports Ground, Eastern Road, Portsmouth PO3 5LY | 07706 069 957 (Sec) |
| BISHOPS WALTHAM TOWN | Hoe Road Recreation Grd, Hoe Rd, Bishops Waltham, Southampton SO32 1DU | 07966 270 143 (Sec) |
| BOURNEMOUTH SPORTS | Bournemouth Sports Club, Chapel Gate, East Parley, Christchurch BH23 6BD | 07968 497 806 (Sec) |
| CLANFIELD | Peel Park, Chalton Lane, Clanfield, Waterlooville PO8 0PR | 07717 300 905 (Sec) |
| COLDEN COMMON | Colden Common Rec., Main Road, Colden Common, Winchester SO21 1RP | 07506 459 508 (Sec) |
| FLEETLANDS | DARA Fleetlands, Lederle Lane, Gosport PO13 0AA | 023 9223 9723 |
| HEADLEY UNITED | Headley Playing Fields, Mill Lane, Headley, Bordon, GU35 0PD | 07748 901 381 (Sec) |
| HEDGE END RANGERS | Norman Rodaway Rec Ground, Heathouse Lane, Hedge End, Southampton SO30 0LE | 07771 927 886 (Sec) |
| LIPHOOK UNITED | Recreation Ground, London Road, Liphook GU30 7AN | 07979 159012 (Sec) |
| LISS ATHLETIC | Newman Collard Playing Fields Liss (Sat Nav Post Code) GU33 7LH | 07810 865 616 (Sec) |
| LOCKS HEATH | Locksheath Rec, 419 Warsash Rd, Titchfield Common, Fareham PO14 4JX | 01489 600 932 |
| OTTERBOURNE | Oakwood Park, Oakwood Avenue, Otterbourne SO21 2ED | 07748 595 743 (Sec) |
| OVERTON UNITED | Overton Recreation Centre, Bridge Street, Overton RG25 3LZ | 01256 770 561 |
| PAULSGROVE | Paulsgrove Social Club, Marsden Road, Paulsgrove, Portsmouth PO6 4JB | 07901 655485 (Sec) |
| QK SOUTHAMPTON | Lordshill Recreation Centre, Redbridge Lane, Lordshill, Southampton SO16 0XN | 07801 550 337 (Sec) |
| WINCHESTER CASTLE | Hants Co. Council Spts Ground, Petersfield Rd (A31),Chilcombe, Winchester SO23 8ZB | 01962 866 989 |

**In:** Baffins Milton Rovers (P - Portsmouth League Premier Division). Bishops Waltham Town (NC from Sporting Bishops Waltham).
Headley United (P - Aldershot & District Senior Division).
**Out:** Sporting Bishops Waltham (NC to Bishops Waltham Town). University of Portsmouth (R).

# HERTS SENIOR COUNTY LEAGUE

**Sponsored by:** No sponsor
**Founded:** 1898
**Recent Champions:**
2008: Hatfield Town
2009: Metropolitan Police Bushey
2010: London Lions
2011: Hinton
2012: Baldock Town

## AUBERY CUP

**PRELIMINARY ROUND**

| | | | |
|---|---|---|---|
| Bovingdon | v | Lemsford | 0-1 |

**ROUND 1**

| | | | |
|---|---|---|---|
| Standon & Puckeridge | v | Bush Hill Rangers | 1-0 |
| Sarratt | v | Bedmond Sports & S.C. | 1-6 |
| Metropolitan Police Bushey | v | Harvesters 2012 | HW |
| Kimpton Rovers | v | Buntingford Town | AW |
| Hatfield RBL | v | Letchworth Garden City Eagles | 1-4 |
| Chipperfield Corinthians | v | Lemsford | 3-5 |
| Sandridge Rovers | v | Belstone | 1-9 |
| Wormley Rovers | v | Panshanger | 5-0 |
| Old Parmiterians | v | Evergreen | 3-3 |

*Evergreen won on penalties.*

| | | | |
|---|---|---|---|
| Cuffley | v | Hinton | 3-2 |
| Baldock Town | v | St Peters (Colney Heath) | 5-1 |
| AFC Hatfield | v | Whitwell | 1-4 |
| Croxley Guild | v | Hatfield Town Blues | 1-6 |
| Hertford Heath | v | Aslan | 0-4 |
| Knebworth | v | Mill End Sports | 3-1 |
| Bushey Rangers | v | AFC Hertford | 1-0 |

**ROUND 2**

| | | | |
|---|---|---|---|
| Belstone | v | Aslan | 0-3 |
| Buntingford Town | v | Bushey Rangers | 1-3 |
| Hatfield Town Blues | v | Evergreen | 4-1 |
| Letchworth Garden City Eagles | v | Standon & Puckeridge | 1-4 |
| Wormley Rovers | v | Metropolitan Police Bushey | 1-3 |
| Lemsford | v | Bedmond Sports & S.C. | 0-3 |
| Whitwell | v | Baldock Town | 5-1 |
| Knebworth | v | Cuffley | 2-3 |

**QUARTER FINALS**

| | | | |
|---|---|---|---|
| Aslan | v | Bushey Rangers | 4-1 |
| Hatfield Town Blues | v | Metropolitan Police Bushey | 2-4 |
| Bedmond Sports & S.C. | v | Standon & Puckeridge | 2-0 |
| Whitwell | v | Cuffley | 6-2 |

**SEMI FINALS**

| | | | |
|---|---|---|---|
| Bedmond Sports & S.C. | v | Metropolitan Police Bushey | 1-1 |

*Metropolitan Police Bushey won on penalties.*

| | | | |
|---|---|---|---|
| Aslan | v | Whitwell | 5-2 |

**FINAL**

| | | | |
|---|---|---|---|
| Aslan | v | Metropolitan Police Bushey | 5-3 |

### PREMIER DIVISION

| | | P | W | D | L | F | A | Pts |
|---|---|---|---|---|---|---|---|---|
| 1 | Metropolitan Police Bushey | 30 | 23 | 4 | 3 | 104 | 41 | 73 |
| 2 | (P) Baldock Town | 30 | 20 | 3 | 7 | 75 | 36 | 63 |
| 3 | Standon & Puckeridge | 30 | 19 | 6 | 5 | 83 | 50 | 63 |
| 4 | Whitwell | 30 | 16 | 3 | 11 | 90 | 62 | 51 |
| 5 | Bush Hill Rangers | 30 | 16 | 3 | 11 | 72 | 58 | 51 |
| 6 | Cuffley | 30 | 16 | 1 | 13 | 76 | 66 | 49 |
| 7 | Wormley Rovers | 30 | 13 | 4 | 13 | 55 | 46 | 43 |
| 8 | Letchworth Garden City Eagles (-4pts) | 30 | 12 | 7 | 11 | 64 | 55 | 39 |
| 9 | Hinton | 30 | 11 | 4 | 15 | 69 | 81 | 37 |
| 10 | Belstone | 30 | 9 | 9 | 12 | 62 | 63 | 36 |
| 11 | Chipperfield Corinthians | 30 | 11 | 3 | 16 | 61 | 72 | 36 |
| 12 | Sarratt | 30 | 10 | 5 | 15 | 51 | 71 | 35 |
| 13 | Bovingdon | 30 | 10 | 4 | 16 | 48 | 78 | 34 |
| 14 | Mill End Sports | 30 | 9 | 6 | 15 | 41 | 62 | 33 |
| 15 | Knebworth (-1pt) | 30 | 7 | 2 | 21 | 45 | 89 | 22 |
| 16 | Sandridge Rovers | 30 | 4 | 4 | 22 | 37 | 103 | 16 |

### DIVISION ONE

| | | P | W | D | L | F | A | Pts |
|---|---|---|---|---|---|---|---|---|
| 1 | Aslan | 30 | 25 | 3 | 2 | 102 | 27 | 78 |
| 2 | (P) Bedmond Sports & Social Club | 30 | 24 | 3 | 3 | 129 | 34 | 75 |
| 3 | Hatfield RBL | 30 | 22 | 2 | 6 | 99 | 41 | 68 |
| 4 | Hertford Heath (-3pts) | 30 | 19 | 2 | 9 | 85 | 47 | 56 |
| 5 | St Peters (Colney Heath) (-3pts) | 30 | 18 | 2 | 10 | 96 | 63 | 53 |
| 6 | Buntingford Town | 30 | 13 | 6 | 11 | 69 | 56 | 45 |
| 7 | Bushey Rangers | 30 | 13 | 4 | 13 | 71 | 61 | 43 |
| 8 | Croxley Guild | 30 | 12 | 5 | 13 | 85 | 74 | 41 |
| 9 | Hatfield Town Blues | 30 | 12 | 5 | 13 | 65 | 71 | 41 |
| 10 | Old Parmiterians | 30 | 12 | 4 | 14 | 64 | 76 | 40 |
| 11 | Lemsford | 30 | 10 | 6 | 14 | 51 | 73 | 36 |
| 12 | Panshanger | 30 | 8 | 9 | 13 | 59 | 72 | 33 |
| 13 | AFC Hatfield | 30 | 10 | 2 | 18 | 45 | 96 | 32 |
| 14 | Evergreen | 30 | 7 | 5 | 18 | 44 | 91 | 26 |
| 15 | Harvesters 2012 | 30 | 2 | 5 | 23 | 31 | 94 | 11 |
| 16 | Kimpton Rovers (-4pts) | 30 | 1 | 1 | 28 | 28 | 147 | 0 |

### PREMIER DIVISION

| | | 1 | 2 | 3 | 4 | 5 | 6 | 7 | 8 | 9 | 10 | 11 | 12 | 13 | 14 | 15 | 16 |
|---|---|---|---|---|---|---|---|---|---|---|---|---|---|---|---|---|---|
| 1 | Baldock Town | | 1-1 | 5-2 | 5-0 | 5-1 | 5-1 | 4-0 | 4-0 | 1-0 | 0-2 | 3-0 | 2-2 | 2-2 | 2-1 | 1-0 | 2-0 |
| 2 | Belstone | 3-2 | | 3-3 | 1-3 | 2-2 | 3-3 | 2-1 | 6-2 | 4-3 | 1-2 | 1-1 | 1-1 | 6-2 | 1-1 | 3-4 | 0-1 |
| 3 | Bovingdon | 0-2 | 0-3 | | 5-4 | 3-0 | 1-3 | 1-3 | 1-3 | 2-2 | 2-8 | 2-2 | 5-1 | 0-1 | 2-2 | 1-7 | 0-6 |
| 4 | Bush Hill Rangers | 1-2 | 4-2 | 2-4 | | 2-2 | 4-0 | 0-4 | 1-0 | 0-0 | 1-2 | 2-1 | 2-1 | 1-0 | 2-4 | 2-1 | 4-2 |
| 5 | Chipperfield Corinthians | 0-3 | 3-0 | 2-0 | 1-3 | | 1-2 | 2-4 | 7-2 | 2-4 | 1-2 | 4-1 | 1-2 | 2-0 | 2-3 | 2-1 | 4-1 |
| 6 | Cuffley | 0-2 | 2-0 | 4-1 | 2-5 | 6-1 | | 0-5 | 4-0 | 1-2 | 5-1 | 4-1 | 7-1 | 6-2 | 1-2 | 3-1 | 0-2 |
| 7 | Hinton | 1-6 | 2-2 | 2-3 | 1-3 | 1-4 | 3-5 | | 7-2 | 3-4 | 1-4 | 2-2 | 3-4 | 1-1 | 4-3 | 3-2 | 0-5 |
| 8 | Knebworth | 1-3 | 3-2 | 0-2 | 3-1 | 1-4 | 1-2 | 1-2 | | 1-2 | 2-3 | 2-1 | 3-1 | 3-1 | 1-3 | 2-3 | 0-4 |
| 9 | Letchworth Garden City Eagles | 3-1 | 1-0 | 0-1 | 0-1 | 2-3 | 3-2 | 3-3 | 1-3 | | 3-5 | 4-0 | 10-0 | 0-0 | 1-1 | 6-3 | 0-1 |
| 10 | Metropolitan Police Bushey | 3-1 | 1-1 | 5-0 | 4-2 | 6-0 | 3-2 | 3-2 | 4-0 | 5-0 | | 7-0 | 7-0 | 6-2 | 2-2 | 5-1 | 2-2 |
| 11 | Mill End Sports | 2-3 | 2-0 | 1-0 | 0-3 | 2-0 | 2-1 | 4-1 | 5-2 | 3-1 | 0-1 | | 2-2 | 2-0 | 1-4 | 1-2 | 0-1 |
| 12 | Sandridge Rovers | 1-2 | 2-7 | 0-2 | 0-9 | 2-1 | 0-1 | 1-2 | 3-2 | 1-2 | 0-2 | 0-1 | | 0-1 | 1-4 | 1-4 | 3-3 |
| 13 | Sarratt | 3-0 | 2-4 | 0-1 | 3-1 | 0-2 | 3-5 | 1-4 | 6-0 | 1-2 | 3-2 | 1-1 | 4-2 | | 1-6 | 1-7 | 2-1 |
| 14 | Standon & Puckeridge | 2-5 | 4-0 | 4-1 | 5-3 | 4-3 | 4-1 | 1-3 | 1-1 | 3-1 | 3-3 | 3-0 | 4-3 | 2-1 | | 3-1 | 2-1 |
| 15 | Whitwell | 2-0 | 4-1 | 0-3 | 2-2 | 6-5 | 6-1 | 6-1 | 3-3 | 2-2 | 2-3 | 5-2 | 4-1 | 1-2 | 4-0 | | 3-1 |
| 16 | Wormley Rovers | 2-1 | 1-2 | 3-0 | 1-4 | 0-1 | 1-2 | 2-0 | 2-1 | 2-2 | 1-1 | 5-1 | 1-3 | 0-2 | 1-3 | | |

# HERTS SENIOR COUNTY LEAGUE - STEP 7

## RESERVE DIVISION ONE

| | | P | W | D | L | F | A | Pts |
|---|---|---|---|---|---|---|---|---|
| 1 | Sarratt Reserves | 22 | 16 | 1 | 5 | 86 | 40 | 49 |
| 2 | Baldock Town Reserves | 22 | 15 | 3 | 4 | 59 | 35 | 48 |
| 3 | Bush Hill Rangers Reserves | 22 | 13 | 4 | 5 | 65 | 30 | 43 |
| 4 | Cuffley Reserves | 22 | 11 | 6 | 5 | 59 | 41 | 39 |
| 5 | Standon & Puckeridge Reserves | 22 | 9 | 4 | 9 | 61 | 63 | 31 |
| 6 | Letchworth G.C. Eagles Res. (-9pts) | 22 | 10 | 5 | 7 | 63 | 40 | 26 |
| 7 | Metropolitan Police Bushey Res. | 22 | 8 | 2 | 12 | 50 | 63 | 26 |
| 8 | Chipperfield Corinthians Res. | 22 | 8 | 2 | 12 | 45 | 64 | 26 |
| 9 | Hinton Reserves (-1pt) | 22 | 7 | 3 | 12 | 50 | 72 | 23 |
| 10 | Bovingdon Reserves | 22 | 6 | 3 | 13 | 39 | 63 | 21 |
| 11 | Sandridge Rovers Reserves | 22 | 6 | 2 | 14 | 32 | 53 | 20 |
| 12 | Knebworth Reserves | 22 | 4 | 3 | 15 | 28 | 73 | 15 |

## RESERVES CUP

**FINAL**

Sarratt Reserves v Bush Hill Rangers Reserves 1-2

## RESERVE DIVISION TWO

| | | P | W | D | L | F | A | Pts |
|---|---|---|---|---|---|---|---|---|
| 1 | Bedmond Sports & SC Reserves | 15 | 9 | 3 | 3 | 33 | 18 | 30 |
| 2 | Wormley Rovers Reserves | 15 | 9 | 2 | 4 | 49 | 29 | 29 |
| 3 | Buntingford Town Reserves | 15 | 6 | 5 | 4 | 35 | 25 | 23 |
| 4 | Lemsford Reserves | 15 | 5 | 3 | 7 | 26 | 33 | 18 |
| 5 | Croxley Guild Reserves | 15 | 5 | 1 | 9 | 25 | 30 | 16 |
| 6 | Evergreen Reserves (-3pts) | 15 | 4 | 0 | 11 | 23 | 56 | 9 |

## HERTS SENIOR COUNTY PREMIER DIVISION CONSTITUTION 2013-14

| | | |
|---|---|---|
| BEDMOND SPORTS & SOCIAL | Toms Lane Recreation Ground, Toms Lane, Bedmond, Abbots Langley WD5 0RB | 01923 267 991 |
| BELSTONE | The Medburn Ground, Watling Street, Radlett WD6 3AB | 020 8207 2395 |
| BOVINGDON | Green Lane, Bovingdon, Hemel Hempstead HP3 0LA | 01442 832628 |
| BUSHEY SPORTS CLUB | Met Police Sports Club, Aldenham Road, Bushey, Watford WD2 3TR | 01923 243947 |
| BUSH HILL RANGERS | Goldsdown Road, Brimsdown, Enfield, Middlesex EN3 7R | 020 8804 5491 |
| CHIPPERFIELD CORINTHIANS | Queens Street, Chipperfield, Kings Langley WD4 9BT | 01923 269554 |
| CUFFLEY | King George's Playing Fields, Northaw Road East, Cuffley EN6 4LU | 07815 174434 |
| HINTON | Holtwhites Sports & Social, Kirkland Drive, Enfield EN2 0RU | 020 8363 4449 |
| KNEBWORTH | The Recreation Ground, Watton Road, Knebworth, Stevenage SG3 6AH | 07967 140219 |
| LETCHWORTH GARDEN CITY EAGLES | Pixmore Playing Fields, Ledgers Lane, Baldock Road, Letchworth SG6 2EN | 07855 337175 |
| MILL END SPORTS | King George V Playing Fields, Penn Road, Mill End, Rickmansworth WD3 8QX | 01923 776892 |
| SANDRIDGE ROVERS | Spencer Recreation Ground, Sandridge, St Albans AL4 9DD | 01727 835506 |
| SARRATT | King George V Playing Fields, George V Way, Sarratt WD3 6AU | 07711 618028 |
| STANDON & PUCKERIDGE | Station Road, Standon, Ware SG11 1QT | 01920 823460 |
| WHITWELL | King George V Recreation Grnd, Bradway, Whitwell SG4 8BE | 07796 111970 |
| WORMLEY ROVERS | Wormley Sports Club, Church Lane, Wormley EN10 7QF | 01992 460650 |

**In:** Bedmond Sports & Social Club (P).
**Out:** Baldock Town (P - Spartan South Midlands Lge). Met Police Bushey (NC to Bushey Sports Club).

2012-13 - Aslan line up after their 5-3 win over Met Police (Bushey) in the Hertfordshire League's Aubrey Cup.
Inset: Charlie Ledula scores one of his three goals for Aslan. Photos: Gordon Whittington.

# HUMBER PREMIER LEAGUE

**Sponsored by:** No sponsor
**Founded:** 2000
**Recent Champions:**
2008: Sculcoates Amateurs
2009: Chalk Lane
2010: Reckitts
2011: Sculcoates Amateurs
2012: Reckitts AFC

| PREMIER DIVISION | P | W | D | L | F | A | Pts |
|---|---|---|---|---|---|---|---|
| 1 Beverley Town | 24 | 18 | 5 | 1 | 57 | 24 | 59 |
| 2 North Ferriby United Reserves | 24 | 15 | 6 | 3 | 58 | 27 | 51 |
| 3 Sculcoates Amateurs | 24 | 14 | 5 | 5 | 66 | 34 | 47 |
| 4 Crown FC | 24 | 13 | 5 | 6 | 47 | 34 | 44 |
| 5 Reckitts AFC | 24 | 12 | 7 | 5 | 48 | 31 | 43 |
| 6 Hornsea Town | 24 | 10 | 3 | 11 | 43 | 50 | 33 |
| 7 North Cave | 24 | 10 | 2 | 12 | 55 | 50 | 32 |
| 8 Pocklington Town | 24 | 10 | 1 | 13 | 50 | 36 | 31 |
| 9 Hessle Rangers | 24 | 8 | 5 | 11 | 37 | 43 | 29 |
| 10 Chalk Lane | 24 | 7 | 3 | 14 | 40 | 57 | 24 |
| 11 St. Andrews | 24 | 6 | 3 | 15 | 39 | 58 | 21 |
| 12 Bridlington Sports Club | 24 | 5 | 3 | 16 | 39 | 80 | 18 |
| 13 Westella & Willerby | 24 | 3 | 2 | 19 | 22 | 77 | 11 |

Hodgsons FC withdrew - record expunged.
Scarborough Town folded - record expunged.

| DIVISION ONE | P | W | D | L | F | A | Pts |
|---|---|---|---|---|---|---|---|
| 1 (P) Goole United | 30 | 23 | 5 | 2 | 124 | 38 | 74 |
| 2 (P) Scarborough Athletic Reserves | 30 | 22 | 4 | 4 | 93 | 39 | 70 |
| 3 (P) Hedon Rangers | 30 | 20 | 6 | 4 | 88 | 42 | 66 |
| 4 Little Weighton | 30 | 16 | 4 | 10 | 83 | 50 | 52 |
| 5 Hessle Sporting Club | 30 | 13 | 8 | 9 | 68 | 55 | 47 |
| 6 North Ferriby Athletic | 30 | 13 | 5 | 12 | 82 | 78 | 44 |
| 7 Driffield Evening Institute | 30 | 14 | 2 | 14 | 74 | 82 | 44 |
| 8 Malet Lambert YC | 30 | 13 | 3 | 14 | 64 | 69 | 42 |
| 9 Brandesburton | 30 | 13 | 3 | 14 | 73 | 82 | 42 |
| 10 Hessle United | 30 | 13 | 3 | 14 | 55 | 75 | 42 |
| 11 East Riding Rangers | 30 | 11 | 6 | 13 | 71 | 62 | 39 |
| 12 Long Riston | 30 | 12 | 1 | 17 | 54 | 92 | 37 |
| 13 Driffield JFC | 30 | 11 | 1 | 18 | 65 | 80 | 34 |
| 14 Pinefleet Wolfreton | 30 | 7 | 4 | 19 | 68 | 87 | 25 |
| 15 Howden AFC | 30 | 5 | 3 | 22 | 50 | 112 | 18 |
| 16 Withernsea AFC | 30 | 5 | 0 | 25 | 44 | 113 | 15 |

## LEAGUE CUP

### ROUND 1
| | | | |
|---|---|---|---|
| Scarborough Town | v | Hessle Sporting Club | 2-0 |
| Bridlington Sports Club | v | St Andrews | 6-1 |
| Goole United | v | Beverley Town | 1-2 |
| Pinefleet Wolfreton | v | Hessle United | 1-2 |
| Hornsea Town | v | North Ferriby Athletic | 6-2 |
| North Cave | v | Sculcoates Amateurs | 0-2 |
| Hedon Rangers | v | Driffield Eveing Institute | 5-1 |
| Howden AFC | v | Hodgsons FC | 0-4 |
| Brandesburton | v | Withernsea AFC | 4-2 |
| Pocklington Town | v | Little Weighton | 5-3 |
| Hessle Rangers | v | East Riding Rangers | 2-1 |
| Westella & Willerby | v | Chalk Lane | 1-2 |
| Scarborough Athletic Res. | v | Long Riston | 7-2 |
| Driffield JFC | v | Malet Lambert YC | 4-3 |
| Rickitts AFC | v | Crown FC | 3-2 |
| North Ferriby United Res. | v | Bransholme Athletic | 5-2 |

### Round 2
| | | | |
|---|---|---|---|
| Driffield JFC | v | Scarborough Athletic Res. | 2-3 |
| Hornsea Town | v | Reckitts AFC | 1-3 |
| Beverley Town | v | Sculcoates Amateurs | 2-1 |
| Pockington Town | v | Chalk Lane | 2-1 |
| Brandesburton | v | Hodgsons FC | 3-1 |
| Hedon Rangers | v | Hessle Rangers | 1-3 |
| North Ferriby United Res. | v | Bridlington Sports Club | 10-0 |
| Scarborough Town | v | Hessle United | 4-2 |

### QUARTER FINALS
| | | | |
|---|---|---|---|
| Scarborough Athletic Res. | v | Reckitts AFC | 0-3 |
| Beverley Town | v | Pocklington Town | 0-2 |
| Brandesburton | v | Hessle Rangers | 2-3 |
| North Ferriby United Res. | v | Scarborough Town | 3-1 |

### SEMI FINALS
| | | | |
|---|---|---|---|
| Reckitts AFC | v | Pocklington Town | 1-2 |
| Hessle Rangers | v | North Ferriby United Res. | 0-2 |

### FINAL
| | | | |
|---|---|---|---|
| Pocklington Town | v | North Ferriby United Res. | 3-1 |

| PREMIER DIVISION | 1 | 2 | 3 | 4 | 5 | 6 | 7 | 8 | 9 | 10 | 11 | 12 | 13 |
|---|---|---|---|---|---|---|---|---|---|---|---|---|---|
| 1 Beverley Town | | 7-1 | 2-2 | 3-1 | 3-1 | 1-1 | 1-0 | 4-1 | 2-1 | 2-2 | 4-2 | 2-1 | 2-2 |
| 2 Bridlington Sports Club | 2-3 | | 0-3 | 2-3 | 1-6 | 5-4 | 2-7 | 3-3 | 1-4 | 2-3 | 1-3 | 0-4 | 5-1 |
| 3 Chalk Lane | 1-2 | 5-1 | | 1-3 | 0-3 | 2-4 | 3-4 | 1-2 | 2-1 | 0-3 | 1-6 | 0-0 | 4-1 |
| 4 Crown FC | 1-0 | 2-2 | 4-1 | | 0-1 | 0-2 | 3-2 | 0-0 | 2-1 | 1-2 | 2-0 | 3-1 | 4-0 |
| 5 Hessle Rangers | 1-2 | 2-2 | 1-3 | 1-1 | | 1-2 | 0-2 | 2-2 | 0-4 | 2-1 | 1-5 | 1-0 | 2-1 |
| 6 Hornsea Town | 0-2 | 3-0 | 3-3 | 5-3 | 1-3 | | 0-4 | 2-4 | 2-0 | 0-1 | 1-0 | 0-1 | 2-0 |
| 7 North Cave | 1-2 | 1-2 | 1-3 | 3-1 | 3-1 | 2-3 | | 1-1 | 0-6 | 1-3 | 1-2 | 5-1 | 3-0 |
| 8 North Ferriby United Reserves | 0-0 | 2-1 | 5-1 | 0-2 | 2-0 | 7-0 | 3-2 | | 3-0 | 5-1 | 2-2 | 3-0 | 1-0 |
| 9 Pocklington Town | 0-1 | 3-0 | 3-1 | 1-3 | 3-1 | 3-0 | 0-2 | 1-4 | | 1-2 | 2-5 | 7-0 | 0-1 |
| 10 Reckitts AFC | 1-3 | 6-0 | 2-1 | 1-1 | 0-0 | 3-0 | 4-1 | 1-2 | 1-1 | | 0-2 | 2-2 | 4-1 |
| 11 Sculcoates Amateurs | 1-3 | 4-2 | 4-0 | 2-2 | 1-1 | 1-1 | 4-0 | 3-0 | 2-0 | 1-1 | | 1-4 | 5-0 |
| 12 St. Andrews | 1-3 | 0-2 | 0-1 | 2-3 | 4-2 | 4-3 | 4-4 | 0-2 | 1-2 | 0-2 | 2-5 | | 1-2 |
| 13 Westella & Willerby | 0-3 | 1-2 | 2-1 | 1-2 | 0-4 | 0-4 | 1-5 | 0-4 | 0-6 | 2-2 | 3-5 | 3-6 | |

2012-13 - Erith 147 Sports - Runners-up in Division One and promoted to the Premier Division for 2013-14. Photo: Alan Coomes.

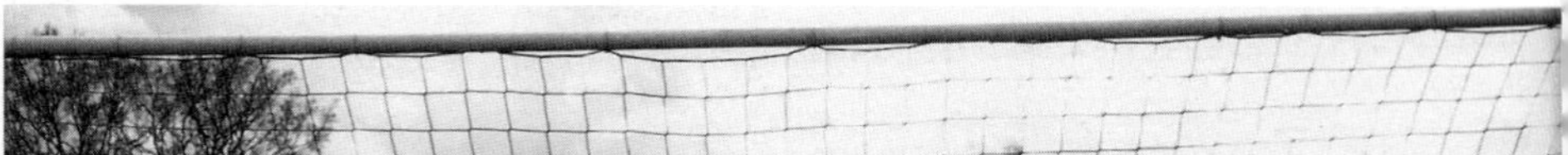

2012-13 - Stansfield Oxford & Bermondsey. Photo: Alan Coomes.

# KENT COUNTY LEAGUE

**Sponsored by:** Haart
**Founded:** 1922
**Recent Champions:**
2008: Norton Sports
2009: Hollands & Blair
2010: Stansfield O & B Club
2011: Hollands & Blair
2012: Bromley Green

## BILL MANKLOW INTER REGIONAL CHALLENGE CUP

**ROUND 1**

| | | | |
|---|---|---|---|
| Chipstead | v | Tonbridge Invicta | 4-6 |
| Stansfeld O&B Club | v | Milton & Fulston United | 5-3 |
| Metrogas | v | Greenways | 6-1 |
| Hildenborough Athletic | v | Fleet Leisure | 3-4 |
| Otford United | v | Kennington | 1-3 |
| Sheerness East | v | AFC Sevenoaks | 3-1 |
| Bromley Green | v | N.K. Aces | 4-0 |
| Erith 147 Sports | v | Sheppey United | HW |
| Coney Hall | v | A.P.M. Contrast | 4-2 |
| Forest Hill Park | v | Farnborough OB Guild | 3-2 |
| Charlton Athletic Comm. | v | Snodland Town | AW |
| Belvedere | v | University of Kent | 0-1 |
| Staplehurst Mon Unted | v | Malgo | 4-0 |
| Fleetdown United | v | Bexlians | 3-4 |

**ROUND 2**

| | | | |
|---|---|---|---|
| Tonbridge Invicta | v | Stansfeld O&B Club | 1-3 |
| Metrogas | v | Fleet Leisure | 3-3, 4-1p |
| Kennington | v | Sheerness East | 4-1 |
| Tudor Sports | v | Bromley Green | 1-3 |
| Bredhurst Juniors | v | Erith 147 Sports | 2-4 |
| Coney Hall | v | Forest Hill Park | 3-4 |
| Snodland Town | v | University of Kent | HW |
| Staplehurst Mon United | v | Bexlians | 2-1 |

**QUARTER FINALS**

| | | | |
|---|---|---|---|
| Stansfeld O&B Club | v | Metrogas | 2-0 |
| Kennington | v | Bromley Green | 3-1 |
| Erith 147 Sports | v | Forest Hill Park | 2-1 |
| Snodland Town | v | Staplehurst Mon United | 0-6 |

**SEMI FINALS**

| | | | |
|---|---|---|---|
| Stansfeld O&B Club | v | Kennington | 1-5 |
| Erith 147 Sports | v | Staplehurst Mon United | 0-4 |

**FINAL**

| | | | |
|---|---|---|---|
| Kennington | v | Staplehurst Mon United | 4-2 |

## PREMIER DIVISION

| | P | W | D | L | F | A | Pts |
|---|---|---|---|---|---|---|---|
| 1 Hildenborough Athletic | 26 | 17 | 5 | 4 | 66 | 42 | 56 |
| 2 Metrogas | 26 | 17 | 4 | 5 | 73 | 39 | 55 |
| 3 Staplehurst Monarchs Utd. | 26 | 16 | 5 | 5 | 68 | 39 | 53 |
| 4 (P) Fleet Leisure | 26 | 13 | 8 | 5 | 57 | 32 | 47 |
| 5 Bromley Green | 26 | 13 | 2 | 11 | 48 | 53 | 41 |
| 6 APM Contrast | 26 | 11 | 7 | 8 | 51 | 38 | 40 |
| 7 Greenways | 26 | 10 | 9 | 7 | 68 | 37 | 39 |
| Tudor Sports | 26 | 9 | 11 | 6 | 51 | 39 | 38 |
| Stansfeld O&B Club | 26 | 10 | 4 | 12 | 53 | 47 | 34 |
| 10 Sheerness East | 26 | 6 | 8 | 12 | 49 | 62 | 26 |
| 11 Snodland Town (-3pts) | 26 | 7 | 5 | 14 | 42 | 72 | 23 |
| 12 Chipstead | 26 | 5 | 4 | 17 | 45 | 82 | 19 |
| 13 Farnborough OB Guild | 26 | 4 | 5 | 17 | 33 | 78 | 17 |
| 14 Bredhurst Juniors | 26 | 4 | 3 | 19 | 37 | 81 | 15 |

## DIVISION ONE

| | P | W | D | L | F | A | Pts |
|---|---|---|---|---|---|---|---|
| 1 (P) Fleetdown United (-1pt) | 24 | 14 | 6 | 4 | 61 | 36 | 47 |
| 2 (P) Erith 147 Sports | 24 | 13 | 4 | 7 | 49 | 36 | 43 |
| 3 Bexlians | 24 | 13 | 1 | 10 | 53 | 44 | 40 |
| 4 Kennington | 24 | 12 | 3 | 9 | 58 | 53 | 39 |
| 5 Otford Utd | 24 | 11 | 5 | 8 | 47 | 51 | 38 |
| 6 Malgo (-1pt) | 24 | 11 | 4 | 9 | 57 | 60 | 36 |
| 7 Forest Hill Park | 24 | 10 | 3 | 11 | 38 | 52 | 33 |
| 8 NK Aces | 23 | 9 | 3 | 11 | 38 | 47 | 30 |
| 9 AFC Sevenoaks | 24 | 9 | 3 | 12 | 48 | 61 | 30 |
| 10 Belvedere (-1pt) | 24 | 9 | 2 | 13 | 60 | 60 | 28 |
| 11 Milton & Fulston United | 24 | 7 | 5 | 12 | 41 | 46 | 26 |
| 12 Coney Hall | 24 | 7 | 3 | 14 | 42 | 48 | 24 |
| 13 University of Kent (-6pts) | 23 | 7 | 4 | 12 | 37 | 35 | 19 |

## PREMIER DIVISION

| | 1 | 2 | 3 | 4 | 5 | 6 | 7 | 8 | 9 | 10 | 11 | 12 | 13 | 14 |
|---|---|---|---|---|---|---|---|---|---|---|---|---|---|---|
| 1 APM Contrast | | 2-0 | 2-1 | 3-1 | 1-1 | 0-2 | 2-1 | 2-2 | 1-4 | 5-1 | 3-0 | 0-1 | 3-3 | 3-0 |
| 2 Bredhurst Juniors | 0-5 | | 1-2 | 7-1 | 1-0 | 1-1 | 3-2 | 1-3 | 1-2 | 0-4 | 0-4 | 3-4 | 0-5 | 1-3 |
| 3 Bromley Green | 2-0 | 3-2 | | 2-1 | 6-0 | 1-2 | 2-1 | 1-4 | 0-2 | 0-2 | 3-2 | 3-1 | 2-0 | 2-1 |
| 4 Chipstead | 2-3 | 5-3 | 6-1 | | 3-3 | 2-1 | 0-9 | 1-5 | 1-3 | 2-3 | 2-2 | 3-2 | 1-4 | 0-2 |
| 5 Farnborough OB Guild | 0-4 | 1-0 | 1-3 | 3-3 | | 0-5 | 2-4 | 1-2 | 1-2 | 4-4 | 2-1 | 2-5 | 4-0 | 0-4 |
| 6 Fleet Leisure | 2-2 | 1-3 | 4-0 | 2-2 | 3-0 | | 2-2 | 7-0 | 1-1 | 2-2 | 3-1 | 2-1 | 0-1 | 1-1 |
| 7 Greenways | 2-0 | 3-3 | 3-1 | 7-0 | 6-0 | 0-3 | | 1-1 | 1-1 | 1-1 | 6-1 | 1-1 | 3-2 | 2-2 |
| 8 Hildenborough Athletic | 2-1 | 3-0 | 4-2 | 3-1 | 4-2 | 3-1 | 0-4 | | 3-1 | 4-0 | 6-2 | 2-1 | 3-4 | 2-2 |
| 9 Metrogas | 2-0 | 9-2 | 6-1 | 4-2 | 6-0 | 1-2 | 1-3 | 2-2 | | 3-2 | 4-2 | 3-1 | 2-2 | 1-4 |
| 10 Sheerness East | 4-1 | 4-2 | 2-2 | 1-3 | 3-1 | 1-2 | 1-1 | 1-3 | 1-3 | | 1-4 | 1-1 | 2-3 | 1-1 |
| 11 Snodland Town | 2-2 | 1-1 | 3-1 | 1-0 | 0-1 | 2-4 | 4-3 | 0-2 | 2-5 | 1-1 | | 2-1 | 1-5 | 0-11 |
| 12 Stansfeld O&B Club | 1-4 | 5-0 | 0-1 | 3-0 | 3-1 | 5-0 | 3-2 | 2-1 | 1-2 | 4-1 | 1-2 | | 1-4 | 2-2 |
| 13 Staplehurst Monarchs United | 1-1 | 5-0 | 0-3 | 4-2 | 3-3 | 1-1 | 1-0 | 0-1 | 3-1 | 6-3 | 3-1 | 3-1 | | 1-0 |
| 14 Tudor Sports | 1-1 | 3-2 | 3-3 | 1-0 | 2-0 | 0-3 | 0-0 | 2-2 | 0-2 | 3-2 | 1-1 | 2-2 | 0-4 | |

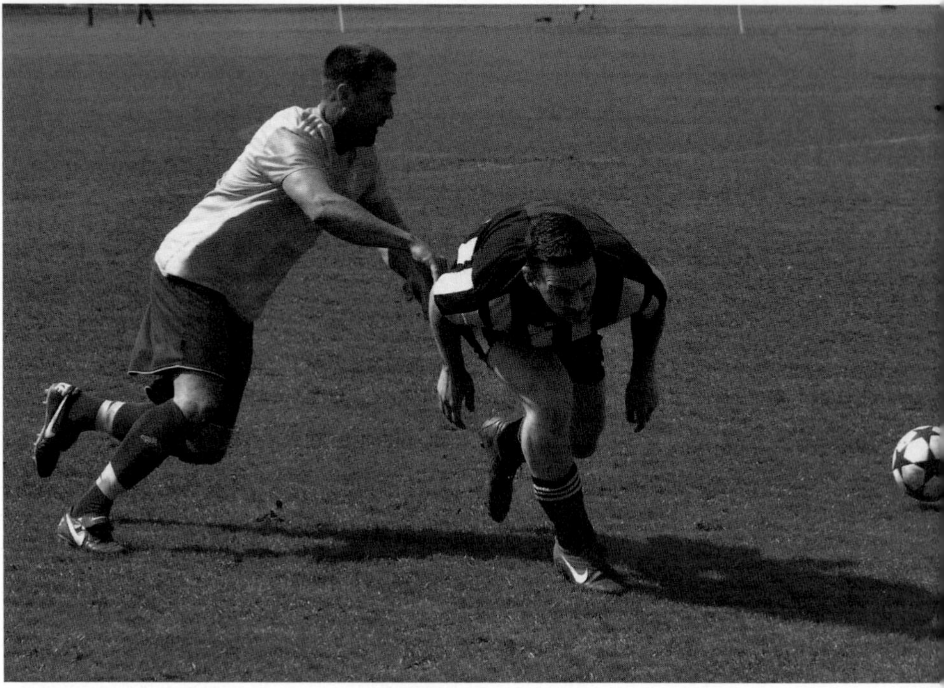

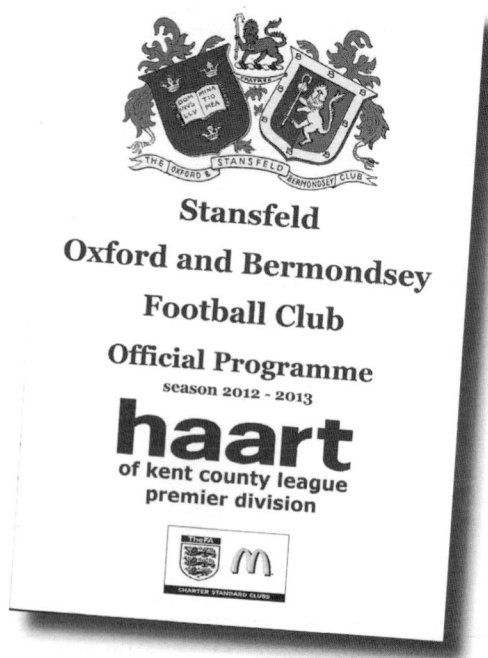

Kent Premier Division action between Stansfield Oxford & Bermondsey and APM Contrast. Photo: Alan Coomes.

THE OXFORD & STANSFELD BERMONDSEY CLUB
Stansfeld
Oxford and Bermondsey
Football Club
Official Programme
season 2012 - 2013
haart
of kent county league
premier division
CHARTER STANDARD CLUBS

## KENT COUNTY LEAGUE PREMIER DIVISION CONSTITUTION 2013-14

| | | |
|---|---|---|
| APM CONTRAST | Otham Sports Club, Honey Lane, Otham, Maidstone, Kent ME15 8RG | 07860 360280 |
| BREDHURST JUNIORS | Upchurch Cricket Club, Hollywell Lane, Upchurch, Kent ME9 7HN | 07939 547353 |
| BROMLEY GREEN | Homelands, Ashford Road, Kingsnorth, Ashford, Kent TN26 1NJ | 01233 611838 |
| CHIPSTEAD | Chipstead Rec, Chevening Road, Chipstead, Sevenoaks TN13 2SA | 07753 603944 |
| ERITH '147 SPORTS | STC Sports Ground, Ivor Grove, New Eltham SE9 2AJ | 020 8858 2057 |
| FARNBOROUGH OLD BOYS GUILD | Farnborough (Kent) Sports Club, High Street, Farnborough BR6 7BA | 01689 862949 |
| FLEETDOWN UNITED | Heath Lane Open Space, Heath Lane (Lower), Dartford DA1 2QE | 01322 273848 |
| GREENWAYS | Elite Venue, (formerly known as the AEI), Dunkirk Close, Gravesend, Kent DA12 5ND | 01474 323817 |
| HILDENBOROUGH ATHLETIC | Racecourse Sports Ground, The Slade, Tonbridge TN9 1DS | 07595 386657 |
| METROGAS | Marathon Playing Fields, Forty Foot Way, Avery Hill Road, New Eltham SE9 2EX | 020 8859 1579 |
| SHEPPEY & SHEERNESS UNITED | Holm Place, Queensborough Road, Sheerness ME12 3DD | 07855 089534 |
| SNODLAND TOWN | Potyn's Field, Paddlesworth Road, Snodland ME6 5DL | 01634 241946 |
| STANSFELD O & B CLUB | Metrogas Sports Grd, Marathon PF, Forty Foot Way, Avery Hill Rd, New Eltham SE9 2EX | 020 8859 1579 |
| STAPLEHURST & MONARCHS UNITED | Jubilee Sports Ground, Headcorn Road, Staplehurst TN12 0DS | 01580 892292 |
| TUDOR SPORTS | STC Sports Ground, Ivor Grove, New Eltham SE9 2AJ | 020 8850 2057 |

**In:** Erith 147 Sports (P). Fleetdown United (P). Sheppey & Sherness United (merger between Sheppey United & Sheerness East).
**Out:** Charlton Athletic Community (WS). Fleet Leisure (P - Kent Invicta).
Sheppey United and Sherness East (merged to form Sheppey & Sherness United).

| DIVISION TWO EAST | P | W | D | L | F | A | Pts | | DIVISION TWO WEST | P | W | D | L | F | A | Pts |
|---|---|---|---|---|---|---|---|---|---|---|---|---|---|---|---|---|
| 1 (P) Sevenoaks | 22 | 20 | 1 | 1 | 77 | 20 | 61 | | 1 (P) Peckham Town (-4pts) | 26 | 21 | 3 | 2 | 75 | 28 | 62 |
| 2 (P) Borden Village | 22 | 18 | 1 | 3 | 81 | 29 | 55 | | 2 (P) Long Lane | 26 | 20 | 0 | 6 | 75 | 45 | 60 |
| 3 (P) Park Regis | 22 | 13 | 3 | 6 | 61 | 38 | 42 | | 3 (P) AFC Mottingham (-1pt) | 26 | 17 | 4 | 5 | 83 | 36 | 54 |
| 4 (P) Guru Nanak (-1pt) | 22 | 11 | 4 | 7 | 47 | 32 | 36 | | 4 (P) Halls AFC | 26 | 14 | 7 | 5 | 55 | 42 | 49 |
| 5 Hadlow Evolution | 22 | 9 | 6 | 7 | 43 | 48 | 33 | | 5 (P) Bexley | 26 | 13 | 5 | 8 | 50 | 44 | 44 |
| 6 (P) Deal Town Rangers | 22 | 8 | 6 | 8 | 54 | 49 | 30 | | 6 (P) Ide Hill | 26 | 11 | 5 | 10 | 59 | 49 | 38 |
| 7 (P) New Romney | 22 | 8 | 4 | 10 | 39 | 50 | 28 | | 7 (P) Holland Sports | 26 | 9 | 7 | 10 | 58 | 57 | 34 |
| 8 Swale Utd. | 22 | 7 | 2 | 13 | 38 | 53 | 23 | | 8 Phoenix Sports Res (-1pt) | 26 | 10 | 3 | 13 | 50 | 65 | 32 |
| 9 Tenterden Town | 22 | 6 | 3 | 13 | 36 | 63 | 21 | | 9 Dulwich Village | 26 | 8 | 6 | 12 | 56 | 62 | 30 |
| 10 Platt United (-1pt) | 22 | 5 | 1 | 16 | 37 | 78 | 15 | | 10 Halstead Utd | 26 | 8 | 4 | 14 | 39 | 36 | 28 |
| 11 Larkfield & New Hythe W (-8pts) | 22 | 5 | 6 | 11 | 47 | 63 | 13 | | 11 Bexley Borough | 26 | 6 | 7 | 13 | 43 | 71 | 25 |
| 12 Hawkenbury (-1pt) | 22 | 3 | 1 | 18 | 36 | 73 | 9 | | 12 Lanes End | 26 | 5 | 4 | 17 | 35 | 53 | 19 |
| | | | | | | | | | 13 Old Bromleians | 26 | 6 | 1 | 19 | 30 | 85 | 19 |
| | | | | | | | | | 14 Blackheath United (-1pt) | 26 | 5 | 2 | 19 | 46 | 81 | 16 |

Clubs promoted to new Division One East.  Clubs promoted to new Division One West.

## LES LECKIE CUP

**SEMI FINALS**
| | | | |
|---|---|---|---|
| Deal Town Rangers | v | New Romney | 3-2 |
| Sevenoaks | v | Ramsgate U24 | HW |

**FINAL**
| | | | |
|---|---|---|---|
| Deal Town Rangers | v | Sevenoaks | 1-3 |

## BARRY BUNDOCK WEST KENT SHIELD

**SEMI FINALS**
| | | | |
|---|---|---|---|
| Halls AFC | v | Holland Sports | 6-4 |
| Long Lane | v | Halstead United | 0-1 |

**FINAL**
| | | | |
|---|---|---|---|
| Halls AFC | v | Halstead United | 1-2 |

| RESERVE DIVISION EAST | P | W | D | L | F | A | Pts |
|---|---|---|---|---|---|---|---|
| 1 (PD1E) Hollands & Blair Res. | 22 | 19 | 2 | 1 | 89 | 16 | 59 |
| 2 (P) Lydd Town Reserves | 22 | 16 | 4 | 2 | 71 | 28 | 52 |
| 3 (P) Bearsted Reserves | 22 | 15 | 1 | 6 | 57 | 38 | 46 |
| 4 (P) APM Contrast Res. (-1pt) | 22 | 13 | 3 | 6 | 52 | 26 | 41 |
| 5 (P) Otford United Reserves | 22 | 12 | 1 | 9 | 59 | 47 | 37 |
| 6 Sheerness (-1pt) | 22 | 9 | 2 | 11 | 51 | 72 | 28 |
| 7 Staplehurst Monarchs. Utd Res | 22 | 6 | 7 | 9 | 30 | 44 | 25 |
| 8 Bromley Green Reserves | 22 | 7 | 3 | 12 | 32 | 51 | 24 |
| 9 Borden Village Res. (-1pt) | 22 | 5 | 3 | 14 | 41 | 78 | 17 |
| 10 New Romney Reserves (-1pt) | 22 | 5 | 1 | 16 | 27 | 46 | 15 |
| 11 Canterbury City (-3pts) | 22 | 5 | 1 | 16 | 38 | 66 | 13 |
| 12 Kennington Reserves (-6pts) | 22 | 5 | 2 | 15 | 28 | 63 | 11 |

| RESERVE DIVISION WEST | P | W | D | L | F | A | PTS |
|---|---|---|---|---|---|---|---|
| 1 (P) Sutton Athletic Reserves | 26 | 21 | 2 | 3 | 84 | 32 | 65 |
| 2 (P) Fleetdown United Reserves | 26 | 19 | 2 | 5 | 81 | 37 | 59 |
| 3 (P) Greenways Reserves | 26 | 15 | 5 | 6 | 85 | 44 | 50 |
| 4 (P) Seven Acre & Sidcup Res. | 26 | 13 | 9 | 4 | 74 | 33 | 48 |
| 5 (P) Crockenhill Reserves | 26 | 12 | 7 | 7 | 62 | 54 | 43 |
| 6 Fleet Leisure Reserves | 26 | 12 | 5 | 9 | 75 | 56 | 41 |
| 7 Bexlians Reserves | 26 | 12 | 5 | 9 | 53 | 52 | 41 |
| 8 Long Lane Reserves (-1pt) | 26 | 9 | 6 | 11 | 59 | 64 | 32 |
| 9 Tudor Sports Reserves (-1pt) | 26 | 8 | 7 | 11 | 61 | 64 | 30 |
| 10 Orpington Reserves | 26 | 8 | 3 | 15 | 40 | 58 | 27 |
| 11 Stansfeld O&B Club Res. (-1pt) | 26 | 7 | 6 | 13 | 61 | 64 | 26 |
| 12 Bridon Ropes (-3pts) | 26 | 6 | 4 | 16 | 46 | 72 | 19 |
| 13 Meridian VP Reserves (-1pt) | 26 | 3 | 4 | 19 | 40 | 105 | 12 |
| 14 Chipstead (-3pts) | 26 | 3 | 3 | 20 | 34 | 120 | 9 |

## RESERVES CUP

**FINAL**
| | | |
|---|---|---|
| Hollands & Blair Reservesv | Tudor Sports Reserves | 3-2 |

2012-13 - Staplehurst Monarchs. Photo: Alan Coomes.

2012-13 - Tudor Sports Reserves. Photo: Alan Coombes.

# haart of kent county league

Halstead United FC
Barry Bundock West Kent Challenge Shield Winners

Danny Hill - Bexlians FC
Secretary of the Year

Hildenborough Athletic FC
Premier Division Champions

Hollands & Blair FC Reserves
Reserve Division East Champions
Reserve Division Cup Winners
Kent FA Intermediate Cup Finalists

Staplehurst Monarchs United FC Reserves
Fair Play Award Winners 2012-13

Kennington FC
Bill Manklow Inter-Regional Challenge Cup Winners

# haart of kent county league

Kennington FC
Bill Manklow Inter-Regional Challenge Cup Winners

Peckham Town FC
Division Two West Champions

haart of kent county league
Representative XI - 2012-13

Phil Knights - Hollands & Blair FC Reserves
Aford Awards Manager of the Year 2012-13

Martyn Staveley
Manager of the Year 2012-13

League Sponsors with Ray Wilkins
Annual Presentation Dinner 2012-13

Sevenoaks FC
Les Leckie Cup Winners

# LEICESTERSHIRE SENIOR LEAGUE

**Sponsored by:** Everards Brewery
**Founded:** 1919
**Recent Champions:**
2008: Kirby Muxloe SC
2009: Anstey Nomads
2010: Thurmaston Town
2011: Ashby Ivanhoe
2012: Rothley Imperial

## BEACON BITTER CUP

### ROUND 1

| | | | |
|---|---|---|---|
| Ashby Ivanhoe | v | Saffron Dynamo | 2-0 |
| Caterpillar | v | Desford | 2-0 |
| Cottesmore Amateurs | v | FC GNG | 6-0 |
| Dunton & Broughton Rangers | v | Kirby Muxloe Reserves | 3-5 |
| Sileby Town | v | Highfield Rangers | 0-1 |
| Stapenhill | v | Sileby Saints | 3-1 |

### ROUND 2

| | | | |
|---|---|---|---|
| Birstall United | v | Cottesmore Amateurs | 6-1 |
| Caterpillar | v | Ashby Ivanhoe | 3-0 |
| Highfield Rangers | v | Stapenhill | 0-2 |
| Rothley Imperial | v | Kirby Muxloe Reserves | 1-3 |

### QUARTER FINALS

| | | | |
|---|---|---|---|
| Earl Shilton Albion | v | Birstall United | 5-0 |
| Stapenhill | v | Kirby Muxloe Reserves | 2-2 |

*Stapenhill won on penalties.*

| | | | |
|---|---|---|---|
| Friar Lane & Epworth | v | Caterpillar | 1-2 |
| Hathern | v | Allexton & New Parks | 1-4 |

### SEMI FINALS

| | | | |
|---|---|---|---|
| Caterpillar | v | Allexton & New Parks | 1-2 |
| Stapenhill | v | Earl Shilton Albion | 4-1 |

### FINAL

| | | | |
|---|---|---|---|
| Stapenhill | v | Allexton & New Parks | 1-3 |

## PREMIER DIVISION

| | P | W | D | L | F | A | Pts |
|---|---|---|---|---|---|---|---|
| Rothley Imperial | 26 | 19 | 2 | 5 | 98 | 45 | 59 |
| Caterpillar | 26 | 18 | 2 | 6 | 86 | 38 | 56 |
| Kirby Muxloe Reserves | 26 | 17 | 4 | 5 | 63 | 27 | 55 |
| Ashby Ivanhoe | 26 | 15 | 4 | 7 | 71 | 51 | 49 |
| Stapenhill | 26 | 15 | 3 | 8 | 66 | 39 | 48 |
| Sileby Town | 26 | 14 | 6 | 6 | 64 | 39 | 48 |
| Highfield Rangers (-3pts) | 26 | 12 | 5 | 9 | 53 | 39 | 38 |
| Cottesmore Amateurs | 26 | 8 | 7 | 11 | 38 | 54 | 31 |
| Dunton & Broughton Rangers | 26 | 9 | 4 | 13 | 33 | 56 | 31 |
| Desford | 26 | 7 | 7 | 12 | 43 | 48 | 28 |
| Birstall United | 26 | 6 | 5 | 15 | 43 | 61 | 23 |
| Sileby Saints | 26 | 6 | 4 | 16 | 45 | 81 | 22 |
| Saffron Dynamo | 26 | 5 | 4 | 17 | 37 | 68 | 19 |
| FC GNG (-3pts) | 26 | 2 | 1 | 23 | 20 | 114 | 4 |

## DIVISION ONE

| | P | W | D | L | F | A | Pts |
|---|---|---|---|---|---|---|---|
| (P) Allexton & New Parks | 24 | 22 | 1 | 1 | 102 | 15 | 67 |
| (P) Melton Mowbray | 24 | 20 | 2 | 2 | 88 | 21 | 62 |
| (P) Friar Lane & Epworth | 24 | 19 | 4 | 1 | 81 | 21 | 61 |
| (P) Shepshed Dynamo Reserves | 24 | 13 | 3 | 8 | 65 | 38 | 42 |
| (P) Earl Shilton Albion | 24 | 12 | 2 | 10 | 69 | 47 | 38 |
| Lutterworth Town | 24 | 11 | 2 | 11 | 59 | 50 | 35 |
| FC Khalsa | 24 | 11 | 1 | 12 | 45 | 47 | 34 |
| Barlestone St Giles | 24 | 10 | 1 | 13 | 53 | 42 | 31 |
| Asfordby Amateurs | 24 | 9 | 0 | 15 | 52 | 66 | 27 |
| Ratby Sports | 24 | 7 | 2 | 15 | 39 | 58 | 23 |
| Hathern | 24 | 7 | 1 | 16 | 48 | 68 | 22 |
| Narborough & Littlethorpe (-3pts) | 24 | 5 | 1 | 18 | 36 | 114 | 13 |
| Castle Donington Town (-3pts) | 24 | 0 | 0 | 24 | 18 | 168 | -3 |

## PREMIER DIVISION

| | | 1 | 2 | 3 | 4 | 5 | 6 | 7 | 8 | 9 | 10 | 11 | 12 | 13 | 14 |
|---|---|---|---|---|---|---|---|---|---|---|---|---|---|---|---|
| 1 | Ashby Ivanhoe | | 3-0 | 0-2 | 3-4 | 4-1 | 3-1 | 6-2 | 2-1 | 2-2 | 0-4 | 4-1 | 3-3 | 5-4 | 3-2 |
| 2 | Birstall United | 3-3 | | 1-1 | 2-2 | 0-2 | 1-2 | 5-1 | 1-2 | 2-3 | 2-3 | 4-2 | 4-0 | 0-3 | 2-1 |
| 3 | Caterpillar | 4-1 | 5-1 | | 3-1 | 3-3 | 5-0 | 8-0 | 2-1 | 0-1 | 2-4 | 4-1 | 7-4 | 1-2 | 4-2 |
| 4 | Cottesmore Amateurs | 3-5 | 0-0 | 2-0 | | 1-4 | 4-1 | 3-0 | 1-0 | 1-0 | 1-3 | 1-1 | 1-5 | 1-2 | 1-1 |
| 5 | Desford | 1-3 | 2-4 | 0-5 | 0-0 | | 1-1 | 7-2 | 0-3 | 0-1 | 3-3 | 2-1 | 0-1 | 1-2 | 1-2 |
| 6 | Dunton & Broughton Rangers | 0-0 | 4-0 | 1-5 | 2-0 | 1-2 | | 4-3 | 1-0 | 1-3 | 0-1 | 0-0 | 0-0 | 0-2 | 2-6 |
| 7 | FC GNG | 0-6 | 1-0 | 2-6 | 2-4 | 1-0 | 1-2 | | 1-1 | 0-4 | 1-6 | 1-4 | 1-7 | 0-6 | 0-6 |
| 8 | Highfield Rangers | 5-2 | 3-0 | 0-7 | 1-1 | 2-1 | 1-2 | 6-1 | | 1-2 | 4-1 | 0-1 | 5-1 | 4-4 | 0-1 |
| 9 | Kirby Muxloe Reserves | 4-0 | 3-1 | 1-2 | 2-2 | 4-1 | 5-4 | 2-0 | 2-2 | | 5-0 | 2-2 | 2-0 | 1-2 | 0-1 |
| 10 | Rothley Imperial | 1-2 | 4-2 | 7-3 | 6-1 | 2-2 | 5-1 | 4-0 | 1-3 | 1-0 | | 6-2 | 10-1 | 3-1 | 3-4 |
| 11 | Saffron Dynamo | 0-3 | 2-3 | 0-1 | 2-0 | 0-2 | 0-1 | 5-0 | 2-3 | 0-5 | 1-6 | | 1-5 | 2-2 | 0-2 |
| 12 | Sileby Saints | 0-4 | 3-3 | 2-1 | 0-3 | 0-5 | 1-2 | 5-0 | 1-3 | 0-4 | 2-7 | 0-3 | | 0-4 | 1-4 |
| 13 | Sileby Town | 3-1 | 4-2 | 1-4 | 2-0 | 0-0 | 2-0 | 6-0 | 1-1 | 0-1 | 1-4 | 5-0 | 2-2 | | 1-1 |
| 14 | Stapenhill | 0-3 | 2-0 | 0-1 | 7-0 | 2-2 | 5-0 | 1-0 | 0-1 | 2-4 | 1-3 | 6-4 | 2-1 | 5-2 | |

# LEICESTERSHIRE SENIOR LEAGUE - STEP 7

## LEICESTERSHIRE SENIOR LEAGUE PREMIER DIVISION CONSTITUTION 2013-14

| | | |
|---|---|---|
| ALLEXTON & NEW PARKS | Glenfield Road, Leicester LE3 6D | 07413 679783 |
| ASHBY IVANHOE | Hood Park, North Street, Ashby-de-la-Zouch LE65 1HU | 01530 412181 |
| BIRSTALL UNITED | Meadow Lane, Birstall LE4 4FN | 0116 267 1230 |
| CATERPILLAR SPORTS | Peckleton Lane, Desford, Leicester LE9 9JT | 07856 179485 |
| COTTESMORE AMATEURS | Rogues Park, Main Street, Cottesmore, Oakham LE15 4DH | 01572 813486 |
| DESFORD | Sport in Desford, Peckleton Lane, Desford, Leicester LE9 9JU | 01455 828736 |
| DUNTON & BROUGHTON RANGERS | Station Road, Dunton Bassett LE17 5LF | 07780 957479 |
| EARL SHILTON ALBION | Stoneycroft Park, New Street, Earl Shilton LE9 7FR | 01455 844271 |
| FC GNG | Nanpantan Sports Ground, Nanpantan Road, Loughborough LE11 3YD | 01509 237148 |
| FRIAR LANE & EPWORTH | Knighton Lane East, Aylestone Park, Leicester LE2 6FT | 0116 283 3629 |
| HIGHFIELD RANGERS | 443 Gleneagles Avenue, Rushey Mead, Leicester LE4 7YJ | 0116 266 0009 |
| KIRBY MUXLOE SC RESERVES | Ratby Lane, Kirby Muxloe, Leicester LE9 9AQ | 0116 239 3201 |
| MELTON MOWBRAY | All England Sports Ground, Saxby Road, Melton Mowbray LE13 1BP | 07977 266729 |
| ROTHLEY IMPERIAL | Loughborough Road, Mountsorrell, Leicester LE7 7NH | 0116 292 0538 |
| SAFFRON DYNAMO | Cambridge Road, Whetstone LE8 3LG | 07957 151630 |
| SHEPSHED DYNAMO RESERVES | The Dovecote, Butt Hole Lane, Shepshed, Loughborough LE12 9BN | 01509 650992 |
| SILEBY SAINTS | Seagrave Road, Sileby LE12 7N | 07810 852670 |
| SILEBY TOWN | Memorial Park, Seagrave Road, Sileby, Loughborough LE12 7TP | 07708 231563/07860 842046 |
| STAPENHILL | Maple Grove, Stapenhill, Burton-on-Trent DE15 1RW | 01283 533133 |

**In:** Allexton & New Parks (P). Earl Shilton Albion (P). Friar Lane & Epworth (P). Melton Mowbray (P).

Shepshed Dynamo Reserves (P).

**Out:** None.

| DIVISION ONE | 1 | 2 | 3 | 4 | 5 | 6 | 7 | 8 | 9 | 10 | 11 | 12 | 13 | 14 | 15 |
|---|---|---|---|---|---|---|---|---|---|---|---|---|---|---|---|
| 1 Asfordby Amateurs | | 0-1 | 1-1 | 3-1 | 0-1 | 1-1 | 3-2 | 0-6 | 0-2 | 1-0 | 1-1 | 3-7 | 0-1 | 2-4 | 1-4 |
| 2 Barlestone St Giles | 10-0 | | 2-3 | 0-1 | 2-4 | 3-1 | 1-2 | 5-1 | 4-3 | 1-1 | 1-1 | 0-2 | 3-0 | 3-2 | 1-0 |
| 3 Belgrave | 5-1 | 3-0 | | 1-1 | 0-2 | 7-0 | 2-0 | 0-4 | 3-1 | 1-2 | 1-5 | 2-2 | 3-1 | 1-1 | 0-2 |
| 4 Castle Donington Town | 5-0 | 5-2 | 2-3 | | 1-5 | 2-1 | 5-3 | 3-2 | 1-3 | 2-0 | 2-0 | 6-1 | 2-1 | 2-2 | 0-1 |
| 5 Caterpillar | 6-1 | 2-1 | 11-2 | 1-2 | | 5-0 | 3-1 | 5-2 | 2-0 | 4-0 | 8-0 | 1-2 | 2-0 | 10-0 | 3-0 |
| 6 Earl Shilton Albion | 2-0 | 1-1 | 2-0 | 2-1 | 2-5 | | 4-0 | 3-1 | 5-0 | 4-0 | 3-2 | 3-4 | 4-1 | 0-3 | 0-3 |
| 7 FC Khalsa | 1-0 | 1-2 | 4-2 | 0-3 | 3-3 | 1-0 | | 0-2 | 2-4 | 0-0 | 0-6 | 0-1 | 0-4 | 3-1 | 1-1 |
| 8 Friar Lane & Epworth | 4-0 | 2-0 | 5-1 | 4-0 | 0-2 | 6-4 | 2-0 | | 0-0 | 3-0 | 0-1 | 2-6 | 3-1 | 5-0 | 0-1 |
| 9 Hathern | 4-1 | 0-2 | 4-1 | 3-2 | 1-5 | 2-0 | 2-3 | 1-1 | | 3-1 | 5-5 | 5-0 | 3-2 | 1-0 | 1-2 |
| 10 Lutterworth Town | 2-1 | 2-3 | 0-3 | 1-0 | 0-5 | 1-0 | 2-2 | 2-4 | 2-1 | | 0-3 | 2-2 | 1-1 | 4-0 | 0-1 |
| 11 Melton Mowbray | 2-0 | 0-1 | 0-1 | 3-1 | 1-3 | 2-2 | 6-0 | 1-6 | 1-2 | 4-2 | | 2-1 | 0-2 | 4-0 | 2-3 |
| 12 Narborough & Littlethorpe | 2-1 | 2-1 | 4-3 | 3-2 | 0-5 | 1-3 | 2-3 | 0-2 | 3-2 | 2-0 | 1-3 | | 1-1 | 1-2 | 1-5 |
| 13 Newhall United | 0-1 | 1-0 | 3-1 | 3-0 | 0-9 | 1-0 | 3-2 | 0-3 | 1-1 | 4-1 | 2-0 | 6-2 | | 5-1 | 6-2 |
| 14 Shepshed Dynamo Reserves | 2-1 | 0-2 | 0-1 | 0-1 | 0-9 | 0-4 | 3-2 | 1-7 | 2-2 | 1-0 | 1-2 | 3-3 | 3-1 | | 1-2 |
| 15 Sileby Saints | 4-3 | 1-1 | 5-1 | 3-2 | 1-3 | 4-1 | 4-2 | 1-2 | 7-1 | 3-0 | 2-2 | 4-1 | 4-2 | 4-1 | |

# LIVERPOOL COUNTY PREMIER LEAGUE

| Sponsored by: No sponsor |
|---|
| **Founded:** 2006 |
| **Recent Champions:** |
| 2008: Waterloo Dock |
| 2009: Waterloo Dock |
| 2010: Waterloo Dock |
| 2011: Waterloo Dock |
| 2012: Aigburth Peoples Hall |

## ZINGARI CUP

**ROUND 1**

| | | | |
|---|---|---|---|
| Liverpool North | v | Page Celtic | 4-5 |
| Red Rum | v | Stoneycroft | 0-4 |
| REMYCA United | v | Old Xavierians | 1-3 |
| South Sefton Borough | v | Ford Motors | 1-0 |
| West Everton Xaviers | v | East Villa | 2-5 |

**QUARTER FINALS**

| | | | |
|---|---|---|---|
| Aigburth PH | v | Stoneycroft | 2-1 |
| East Villa | v | Old Xavierians | 1-0 |
| ROMA | v | Waterloo Dock | 1-2 |
| South Sefton Borough | v | Page Celtic | 1-1, 6-7p |

**SEMI FINALS**

| | | | |
|---|---|---|---|
| Aigburth PH | v | Page Celtic | 1-1, 6-7p |
| Waterloo Dock | v | East Villa | 2-1 |

**FINAL**

| | | | |
|---|---|---|---|
| Page Celtic | v | Waterloo Dock | 0-4 |

## PREMIER DIVISION

| | | P | W | D | L | F | A | Pts |
|---|---|---|---|---|---|---|---|---|
| 1 | West Everton Xaviers | 24 | 15 | 7 | 2 | 49 | 30 | 52 |
| 2 | Waterloo Dock | 24 | 14 | 2 | 8 | 76 | 51 | 44 |
| 3 | South Sefton Borough | 24 | 13 | 3 | 8 | 39 | 33 | 42 |
| 4 | Old Xaverians | 24 | 12 | 5 | 7 | 60 | 41 | 41 |
| 5 | Page Celtic | 24 | 12 | 4 | 8 | 57 | 41 | 40 |
| 6 | East Villa | 24 | 12 | 3 | 9 | 48 | 39 | 39 |
| 7 | Red Rum | 24 | 12 | 2 | 10 | 54 | 37 | 38 |
| 8 | Aigburth PH | 24 | 12 | 1 | 11 | 56 | 48 | 37 |
| 9 | Remyca United | 24 | 10 | 3 | 11 | 40 | 50 | 33 |
| 10 | Liverpool North | 24 | 8 | 0 | 16 | 65 | 83 | 24 |
| 11 | ROMA | 24 | 8 | 0 | 16 | 52 | 78 | 24 |
| 12 | Ford Motors | 24 | 6 | 4 | 14 | 34 | 60 | 22 |
| 13 | Stoneycroft | 24 | 4 | 2 | 18 | 36 | 75 | 14 |

## GEORGE MAHON CUP

**ROUND 1**

| | | | |
|---|---|---|---|
| KCFC | v | Holy Cross | 2-4 |
| Liver Academy | v | Wood Street/MANWEB | 3-2 |
| Waterloo Grammer OB | v | Copperas Hill | 1-3 |

**ROUND 2**

| | | | |
|---|---|---|---|
| Alder | v | Red Rum | 5-8 |
| Allerton | v | Copperas Hill | 4-0 |
| East Villa | v | Holy Cross | 3-1 |
| Eli Lilly | v | Liver Academy | 1-7 |
| Ford Motors | v | Page Celtic | 1-0 |
| Old Xavierians | v | South Sefton Borough | 2-0 |
| Pinewood | v | Liverpool North | 3-2 |

## PREMIER DIVISION

| | | 1 | 2 | 3 | 4 | 5 | 6 | 7 | 8 | 9 | 10 | 11 | 12 | 13 |
|---|---|---|---|---|---|---|---|---|---|---|---|---|---|---|
| 1 | Aigburth PH | | 2-1 | 3-0 | 6-2 | 1-0 | 2-4 | 1-5 | 0-2 | 3-2 | A-W | 5-1 | 2-1 | 1-1 |
| 2 | East Villa | 3-1 | | 5-0 | 4-2 | 2-2 | 1-5 | H-W | 0-1 | 5-1 | 2-0 | 2-1 | 2-1 | 3-3 |
| 3 | Ford Motors | 4-1 | 0-4 | | 4-3 | 0-3 | 0-3 | 1-3 | 1-1 | 1-4 | 0-1 | 4-4 | 1-6 | 2-2 |
| 4 | Liverpool North | 0-4 | 2-1 | 2-3 | | 2-3 | 2-3 | 3-5 | 3-2 | 7-3 | 5-1 | 3-4 | 3-4 | 2-3 |
| 5 | Old Xavierians | 4-2 | 4-0 | 2-1 | 4-5 | | 1-2 | 1-1 | 0-2 | 5-1 | 2-4 | 2-0 | 4-4 | 1-1 |
| 6 | Page Celtic | 0-1 | 1-3 | 2-2 | 5-1 | 1-1 | | 3-0 | 3-3 | 4-3 | 0-3 | 3-0 | 1-5 | 2-2 |
| 7 | Red Rum | 2-4 | 0-1 | 0-2 | 3-1 | 2-5 | 2-0 | | 2-0 | 3-0 | 1-0 | 4-1 | 7-2 | 2-3 |
| 8 | Remyca United | 3-2 | 4-3 | 0-3 | 3-5 | 1-6 | 3-1 | 1-0 | | 2-1 | 0-2 | 2-2 | 1-3 | 1-2 |
| 9 | ROMA | 4-3 | 2-1 | 0-4 | 4-1 | 2-3 | 0-3 | 0-4 | 4-2 | | 2-3 | 4-2 | 3-4 | 0-3 |
| 10 | South Sefton Borough | 1-5 | 1-0 | 2-1 | 3-0 | 2-3 | 1-2 | 2-2 | 4-0 | 4-2 | | 0-1 | 1-1 | 0-1 |
| 11 | Stoneycroft | 5-3 | 0-1 | 5-0 | 3-4 | 1-3 | 0-7 | 0-4 | 0-1 | 3-6 | 1-3 | | 0-4 | 0-2 |
| 12 | Waterloo Dock | 2-4 | 4-2 | 2-0 | 3-5 | 2-0 | 3-2 | 2-1 | 2-3 | 8-1 | 1-2 | 8-2 | | 1-2 |
| 13 | West Everton Xaviers | 1-0 | 2-2 | 2-0 | 5-2 | 2-1 | 2-0 | 4-1 | 3-2 | 0-3 | 1-1 | H-W | 2-3 | |

# LIVERPOOL COUNTY PREMIER LEAGUE - STEP 7

| DIVISION ONE | P | W | D | L | F | A | Pts |
|---|---|---|---|---|---|---|---|
| 1 (P) Kingsley United | 22 | 17 | 4 | 1 | 75 | 27 | 55 |
| 2 (P) Allerton | 22 | 18 | 0 | 4 | 73 | 29 | 54 |
| 3 (P) Pinewoods | 22 | 16 | 1 | 5 | 86 | 44 | 49 |
| 4 Alder | 22 | 15 | 0 | 7 | 64 | 30 | 45 |
| 5 Collegiate OB | 22 | 11 | 2 | 9 | 50 | 53 | 35 |
| 6 Waterloo Grammer OB | 22 | 9 | 6 | 7 | 39 | 35 | 33 |
| 7 BRNESC | 22 | 7 | 3 | 12 | 43 | 67 | 24 |
| 8 Edge Hill BCOB | 22 | 6 | 4 | 12 | 42 | 56 | 22 |
| 9 Alumni | 22 | 6 | 2 | 14 | 31 | 40 | 20 |
| 10 Copperas Hill | 22 | 5 | 4 | 13 | 44 | 74 | 19 |
| 11 Old Holts | 22 | 4 | 5 | 13 | 37 | 64 | 17 |
| 12 Lucas Sports | 22 | 2 | 1 | 19 | 17 | 82 | 7 |

| DIVISION TWO | P | W | D | L | F | A | Pts |
|---|---|---|---|---|---|---|---|
| 1 (P) The Famous Grapes | 24 | 15 | 5 | 4 | 61 | 36 | 50 |
| 2 (P) Old Xaverians Reserves | 24 | 14 | 4 | 6 | 40 | 27 | 46 |
| 3 Woodstreet Manweb | 24 | 14 | 2 | 8 | 75 | 49 | 44 |
| 4 Liver Academy | 24 | 13 | 5 | 6 | 60 | 37 | 44 |
| 5 Old Holts Reserves | 24 | 13 | 5 | 6 | 67 | 49 | 44 |
| 6 (P) Holy Cross | 24 | 12 | 5 | 7 | 82 | 55 | 41 |
| 7 K.C.F.C | 24 | 11 | 3 | 10 | 60 | 56 | 36 |
| 8 Eli Lilly | 24 | 11 | 3 | 10 | 46 | 49 | 36 |
| 9 Quarry Bank OB | 24 | 8 | 3 | 13 | 47 | 62 | 27 |
| 10 REMYCA Utd Reserves | 24 | 7 | 4 | 13 | 41 | 73 | 25 |
| 11 Warbreck | 24 | 7 | 2 | 15 | 60 | 77 | 23 |
| 12 Aintree Villa | 24 | 5 | 3 | 16 | 42 | 76 | 18 |
| 13 Alder Reserves | 24 | 2 | 4 | 18 | 38 | 73 | 10 |

## GEORGE MAHON CUP

**Round 2 continued...**

| | | | |
|---|---|---|---|
| REMYCA United | v | Old Holts | 3-1 |
| Waterloo Dock | v | Kingsley United | 5-0 |
| West Everton Xaviers | v | ROMA | 2-4 |
| The Famous Grapes | v | Aintree Villa | 5-0 |
| Aigburth PH | v | Stoneycroft | |
| Edge Hill BCOB | v | Lucas Sports | 6-2 |
| Quarry Bank OB | v | Alumni | 0-3 |
| Warbeck | v | Collegiate OB | 3-4 |

**ROUND 3**

| | | | |
|---|---|---|---|
| East Villa | v | Copperas Hill | 4-2 |
| Ford Motors | v | Red Rum | 5-3 |
| The Famous Grapes | v | Waterloo Dock | 2-7 |
| Aigburth PH | v | Pinewoods | 7-0 |
| Collegiate OB | v | BRNESC | 4-1 |
| Liver Academy | v | ROMA | 1-2 |
| Old Xaverians | v | Alumni | 1-0 |
| REMYCA united | v | Edge Hill BCOB | 4-2 |

**QUARTER FINALS**

| | | | |
|---|---|---|---|
| Waterloo Dock | v | Ford Motors | 4-0 |
| Aigburth PH | v | Collegiate OB | 4-0 |
| East Villa | v | ROMA | 3-0 |
| REMYCA United | v | Old Xaverians | 0-1 |

**SEMI FINALS**

| | | | |
|---|---|---|---|
| East Villa | v | Old Xaverians | 2-1 |
| Waterloo Dock | v | Aigburth PH | 0-1 |

**FINAL**

| | | | |
|---|---|---|---|
| Aigburth PH | v | East Villa | 2-1 |

## LIVERPOOL COUNTY PREMIER LEAGUE PREMIER DIVISION CONSTITUTION 2013-14

| | | |
|---|---|---|
| AIGBURTH PEOPLE'S HALL | Cheshire Lines FC, Southmead Road, Allerton, Liverpool L19 5NB | 0151 427 7176 |
| ALLERTON | Simpson Ground Menlove Avenue Allerton L18 | 0151 281 1863 |
| EAST VILLA | Litherland Sports Park, Boundary Road, Litherland, Liverpool L21 7NW | 0151 288 6338 |
| KINGSLEY UNITED | Calderstones School Playing Fds, Greenhill Road, Allerton, Liverpool L18 6JJ | 079670 11205 |
| LITHERLAND REMYCA | Litherland Sports Park, Liverpool L21 7L | 07504 096330 |
| LIVERPOOL NORTH | Playfootball.com, Drummond Road, Thornton L20 6DX | 0151 2102417 |
| OLD XAVERIANS | St Francis Xaviers College, Beconsfield Road, Liverpool L25 6EG | 07799 148456 |
| PAGE CELTIC | Huyton Arts & Sports Centre, Seel Road, Huyton, Liverpool L36 6DG | 0151 477 8860 |
| PINEWOODS | JMO Sports Park Skelmesdale WN8 8BX | 0777371 6961 |
| RED RUM | Croxteth Comm. Comp. School, Parkstile Lane, Liverpool L11 0PB | 0151 546 4168 |
| ROMA | Kirkby Sports Centre, Valley Road, Kirkby L20 9PQ | 0151 443 4404 |
| SOUTH SEFTON BOROUGH | Boundary Road, Litherland, Sefton Town L21 7L | 07979 375574 |
| STONEYCROFT | Maiden Lane Playing Fields, Maiden Lane, Liverpool L13 9AN | 07900 915722 |
| WATERLOO DOCK | Edinburgh Park, Townsend Lane, Liverpool L6 0BB | 0151 263 5267 |
| WEST EVERTON XAVERIANS | St Francis Xavier College, Beconsfield Road, Liverpool L25 6EQ | 0151 288 1000 |

**In:** Allerton (P). Kingsley United (P). Pinewoods (P). Litherland REMYCA (NC from REMYCA United).

**Out:** Ford Motors

# MANCHESTER LEAGUE

**Sponsored by:** FBT Europe
**Founded:** 1893
**Recent Champions:**
2008: Wigan Robin Park
2009: Gregorians
2010: AVRO
2011: AVRO
2012: Hindsford

| PREMIER DIVISION | P | W | D | L | F | A | Pts |
|---|---|---|---|---|---|---|---|
| 1  Hindsford (-4pts) | 30 | 22 | 3 | 5 | 84 | 45 | 65 |
| 2  East Manchester | 30 | 20 | 4 | 6 | 74 | 33 | 64 |
| 3  Walshaw Sports | 30 | 19 | 3 | 8 | 92 | 43 | 60 |
| 4  Springhead | 30 | 16 | 4 | 10 | 71 | 46 | 52 |
| 5  AVRO | 30 | 16 | 3 | 11 | 82 | 50 | 51 |
| 6  Manchester Gregorians | 30 | 13 | 7 | 10 | 62 | 53 | 46 |
| 7  Old Alts | 30 | 13 | 7 | 10 | 61 | 53 | 46 |
| 8  Prestwich Heys | 30 | 12 | 7 | 11 | 54 | 54 | 43 |
| 9  Stockport Georgians | 30 | 12 | 5 | 13 | 47 | 58 | 41 |
| 10 Wythenshawe Town | 30 | 10 | 7 | 13 | 73 | 74 | 37 |
| 11 AFC Monton | 30 | 9 | 5 | 16 | 59 | 81 | 32 |
| 12 Royton Town | 30 | 9 | 4 | 17 | 57 | 67 | 31 |
| 13 Wythenshawe Amateurs | 30 | 9 | 3 | 18 | 52 | 65 | 30 |
| 14 (R) Beechfield United | 30 | 8 | 4 | 18 | 46 | 88 | 28 |
| 15 (R) Heywood St James | 30 | 8 | 2 | 20 | 58 | 105 | 26 |
| 16 (R) Leigh Athletic | 30 | 6 | 8 | 16 | 60 | 117 | 26 |

| DIVISION ONE | P | W | D | L | F | A | Pts |
|---|---|---|---|---|---|---|---|
| 1  (P) Rochdale Sacred Heart | 26 | 23 | 0 | 3 | 110 | 20 | 69 |
| 2  (P) Pennington | 26 | 19 | 3 | 4 | 85 | 39 | 60 |
| 3  (P) Dukinfield Town | 26 | 19 | 1 | 6 | 88 | 35 | 58 |
| 4  Atherton Town | 26 | 18 | 2 | 6 | 65 | 28 | 56 |
| 5  Irlam Steel | 26 | 15 | 3 | 8 | 73 | 47 | 48 |
| 6  AFC Bury (-3pts) | 26 | 14 | 1 | 11 | 45 | 41 | 40 |
| 7  Elton Vale | 26 | 12 | 3 | 11 | 67 | 51 | 39 |
| 8  Hollinwood | 26 | 12 | 2 | 12 | 63 | 68 | 38 |
| 9  (WS) Stockport Sports Reserves | 26 | 9 | 2 | 15 | 54 | 83 | 29 |
| 10 Chapel Town | 26 | 8 | 3 | 15 | 30 | 69 | 27 |
| 11 Breightmet United | 26 | 7 | 3 | 16 | 57 | 79 | 24 |
| 12 (WS) Salford Victoria | 26 | 5 | 1 | 20 | 40 | 99 | 16 |
| 13 Chadderton Reserves | 26 | 3 | 4 | 19 | 29 | 93 | 13 |
| 14 Wilmslow Albion | 26 | 3 | 2 | 21 | 48 | 82 | 11 |

Fives Athletic withdrew - record expunged.

## GILGRYST CUP

**ROUND 1**

| | | | |
|---|---|---|---|
| Leigh Athletic | v | AVRO | 1-6 |
| Manchester Gregorians | v | Prestwich Heys | 2-4 |
| Royton Town | v | Walshaw Sports | 1-2 |
| Old Alts | v | East Manchester | 3-1 |
| Wythenshawe Town | v | Stockport Georgians | 1-1, 5-4p |
| Wythenshawe Amateurs | v | AFC Monton | 2-7 |
| Hindsford | v | Beechfield United | 2-0 |
| Springhead | v | Heywood St James | 4-1 |

**QUARTER FINALS**

| | | | |
|---|---|---|---|
| AVRO | v | Prestwich Heys | 2-2, 5-4p |
| Walshaw Sports | v | Old Alts | 8-2 |
| Wythenshawe Town | v | AFC Monton | 6-6, 3-4p |
| Hindsford | v | Springhead | 1-2 |

**SEMI FINALS**

| | | | |
|---|---|---|---|
| AVRO | v | Walshaw Sports | 1-0 |
| AFC Monton | v | Springhead | 1-5 |

**FINAL**

| | | | |
|---|---|---|---|
| AVRO | v | Springhead | 3-0 |

| DIVISION TWO | P | W | D | L | F | A | Pts |
|---|---|---|---|---|---|---|---|
| 1  Springhead Reserves | 26 | 18 | 5 | 3 | 68 | 36 | 59 |
| 2  Old Alts Reserves | 26 | 14 | 7 | 5 | 61 | 39 | 49 |
| 3  Walshaw Reserves | 26 | 13 | 6 | 7 | 64 | 38 | 45 |
| 4  E Manchester Res. (-3pts) | 26 | 11 | 8 | 7 | 55 | 46 | 38 |
| 5  Hindsford Reserves | 26 | 11 | 5 | 10 | 54 | 56 | 38 |
| 6  Wythenshawe Ams Reserves | 26 | 9 | 8 | 9 | 48 | 51 | 35 |
| 7  Wythenshawe T Reserves | 26 | 8 | 9 | 9 | 57 | 60 | 33 |
| 8  Manchester Gregorians Res. | 26 | 10 | 3 | 13 | 55 | 60 | 33 |
| 9  Prestwich Heys Reserves | 26 | 8 | 8 | 10 | 60 | 59 | 32 |
| 10 Stockport G Res. (-3pts) | 26 | 9 | 7 | 10 | 58 | 67 | 31 |
| 11 AVRO Reserves | 26 | 8 | 5 | 13 | 69 | 72 | 29 |
| 12 (R) Dukinfied Town Reserves | 26 | 7 | 7 | 12 | 55 | 62 | 28 |
| 13 (R) AFC Monton Reserves | 26 | 6 | 5 | 15 | 35 | 59 | 23 |
| 14 (R) Leigh Ath Reserves | 26 | 5 | 7 | 14 | 36 | 70 | 22 |

| PREMIER DIVISION | 1 | 2 | 3 | 4 | 5 | 6 | 7 | 8 | 9 | 10 | 11 | 12 | 13 | 14 | 15 | 16 |
|---|---|---|---|---|---|---|---|---|---|---|---|---|---|---|---|---|
| 1  AFC Monton | | 1-4 | 0-1 | 1-2 | 4-1 | 0-2 | 3-2 | 2-1 | 1-4 | 1-1 | 3-1 | 4-5 | 3-3 | 0-4 | 3-2 | 3-1 |
| 2  AVRO | 5-1 | | 1-2 | 2-3 | 4-0 | 1-3 | 7-0 | 2-3 | 2-1 | 0-2 | 6-0 | 4-3 | 5-2 | 1-2 | 3-1 | 4-1 |
| 3  Beechfield United | 2-1 | 4-3 | | 1-2 | 3-2 | 3-5 | 0-1 | 2-0 | 1-2 | 1-1 | 3-0 | 1-3 | 1-3 | 3-4 | 0-3 | 0-5 |
| 4  East Manchester | 3-2 | 1-1 | 7-0 | | 3-0 | 0-2 | 10-1 | 1-0 | 3-0 | 5-1 | 1-2 | 1-0 | 3-2 | 1-1 | 4-0 | 2-2 |
| 5  Heywood St James | 2-7 | 2-3 | 6-2 | 3-1 | | 4-1 | 3-7 | 5-5 | 3-1 | 2-1 | 3-4 | 1-1 | 3-1 | 1-5 | 1-1 | 4-2 |
| 6  Hindsford | 5-1 | 2-0 | 7-2 | 2-1 | 5-1 | | 7-1 | 1-0 | 3-2 | 2-3 | 3-2 | 0-4 | 3-0 | 2-1 | 1-0 | 6-2 |
| 7  Leigh Athletic | 2-1 | 1-10 | 4-4 | 1-7 | 1-4 | 3-3 | | 3-7 | 1-3 | 3-4 | 4-3 | 1-1 | 1-2 | 2-4 | 2-4 | 3-3 |
| 8  Manchester Gregorians | 1-1 | 0-1 | 3-2 | 2-2 | 3-1 | 3-1 | 4-0 | | 0-0 | 3-3 | 1-0 | 2-4 | 2-3 | 0-3 | 5-1 | 3-1 |
| 9  Old Alts | 2-1 | 3-3 | 2-2 | 0-1 | 5-1 | 0-2 | 1-3 | 5-0 | | 3-1 | 2-2 | 3-3 | 4-1 | 1-4 | 3-2 | 2-5 |
| 10 Prestwich Heys | 3-3 | 0-2 | 0-2 | 3-0 | 4-1 | 4-3 | 2-3 | 1-1 | 1-0 | | 3-1 | 0-1 | 1-1 | 2-1 | 2-5 | 2-2 |
| 11 Royton Town | 2-3 | 2-2 | 6-0 | 0-1 | 5-1 | 0-1 | 2-2 | 0-1 | 1-2 | 2-1 | | 3-1 | 2-3 | 5-4 | 2-1 | 2-3 |
| 12 Springhead | 7-0 | 3-1 | 2-1 | 0-3 | 5-1 | 3-3 | 0-0 | 1-2 | 1-2 | 2-1 | 2-1 | | 2-1 | 0-1 | 3-1 | 4-2 |
| 13 Stockport Georgians | 4-1 | 0-2 | 2-1 | 0-2 | 4-0 | 0-1 | 2-2 | 2-2 | 2-2 | 1-0 | 0-3 | 1-0 | | 0-3 | 1-0 | 2-1 |
| 14 Walshaw Sports | 5-1 | 1-2 | 7-0 | 4-1 | 7-0 | 2-2 | 7-4 | 0-2 | 0-1 | 1-2 | 6-2 | 3-2 | 2-0 | | 3-0 | 3-3 |
| 15 Wythenshawe Amateurs | 1-4 | 3-0 | 5-1 | 0-1 | 6-2 | 1-3 | 1-1 | 2-0 | 1-3 | 2-3 | 2-2 | 0-5 | 1-2 | 1-0 | | 1-3 |
| 16 Wythenshawe Town | 3-3 | 3-1 | 1-1 | 0-2 | 2-1 | 1-3 | 8-1 | 3-6 | 2-2 | 0-2 | 3-1 | 2-0 | 5-2 | 2-4 | 2-4 | |

## MANCHESTER LEAGUE - STEP 7

| DIVISION THREE | P | W | D | L | F | A | Pts |
|---|---|---|---|---|---|---|---|
| 1 (P) Irlam Steel Reserves | 26 | 22 | 1 | 3 | 113 | 36 | 67 |
| 2 (P) Rochdale SH Reserves | 25 | 20 | 1 | 4 | 115 | 38 | 61 |
| 3 (P) Hollinwood Reserves | 26 | 16 | 2 | 8 | 105 | 63 | 50 |
| 4 AFC Bury Reserves (-3pts) | 25 | 15 | 3 | 7 | 85 | 43 | 45 |
| 5 Beechfield United Res. (-6pts) | 26 | 15 | 3 | 8 | 99 | 64 | 42 |
| 6 Royton T Reserves | 26 | 13 | 2 | 11 | 68 | 58 | 41 |
| 7 Chapel Town Reserves | 25 | 11 | 4 | 10 | 68 | 54 | 37 |
| 8 Pennington Reserves | 25 | 11 | 1 | 13 | 66 | 71 | 34 |
| 9 Elton Vale Reserves | 26 | 8 | 8 | 10 | 50 | 56 | 32 |
| 10 Breightmet United Reserves | 26 | 8 | 5 | 13 | 49 | 64 | 29 |
| 11 Heywood St James Reserves | 26 | 8 | 1 | 17 | 64 | 118 | 25 |
| 12 Atherton Town Reserves | 26 | 5 | 6 | 15 | 36 | 83 | 21 |
| 13 Wilmslow Alb Reserves | 26 | 4 | 3 | 19 | 51 | 115 | 15 |
| 14 Salford Vic Reserves | 26 | 3 | 2 | 21 | 36 | 142 | 11 |

## MURRAY SHIELD

**ROUND 1**

| | | | |
|---|---|---|---|
| Hollinwood | v | Breightmet United | 6-1 |
| Pennington | v | Chapel Town | 2-3 |
| Atherton Town | v | Wilmslow Albion | 2-0 |
| Elton Vale | v | AFC Bury | 4-1 |
| Irlam Steel | v | Chadderton Reserves | 3-2 |
| Rochdale Sacred Heart | v | Fives Athletic | HW |
| Dukinfield Town | v | Stockport Sports Reserves | 1-0 |

**QUARTER FINALS**

| | | | |
|---|---|---|---|
| Hollinwood | v | Chapel Town | 1-0 |
| Atherton Town | v | Elton Vale | 6-2 |
| Irlam Steel | v | Rochdale Sacred Heart | 1-6 |
| Salford Victoria | v | Dukinfield Town | 0-6 |

**SEMI FINALS**

| | | | |
|---|---|---|---|
| Hollinwood | v | Atherton Town | 2-5 |
| Rochdale Sacred Heart | v | Dukinfield Town | 0-4 |

**FINAL**

| | | | |
|---|---|---|---|
| Atherton Town | v | Dukinfield Town | 3-1 |

## MANCHESTER LEAGUE PREMIER DIVISION CONSTITUTION 2013-14

| | | |
|---|---|---|
| AFC MONTON | Off Worsley Road, Winton, Salford M30 8J | 07836 321193 |
| AVRO | Lancaster Club, Broadway, Failsworth, Oldham M35 0DX | 0161 681 3083 |
| DUKINFIELD TOWN | Woodhams Park, Birch Lane, Dukinfield SK16 5AP | 0161 343 4529 |
| EAST MANCHESTER | Wright Robinson Sports College, Abbey Hey Lane, Gorton M18 8RL | 0161 370 5121 |
| HINDSFORD | Squires Lane, Tyldesley M29 8JF | None |
| MANCHESTER GREGORIANS | MCFC, Platt Lane Complex, Yew Tree Road, Fallowfield M14 7UU | 07740 585459 |
| OLD ALTRINCHAMIANS | Crossford Bridge Sports Ground, Danefield Road, Sale M33 7WR | 0161 767 9233 |
| PENNINGTON | Jubilee Park, Leigh Road, Atherton M46 0PJ | |
| PRESTWICH HEYS | Sandgate Road, Whitefield M45 6WG | 0161 773 8888 |
| ROCHDALE SACRED HEART | Fox Park, Belfield Mill Lane, Rochdale OL16 2UB | |
| ROYTON TOWN | Crompton Cricket Club Complex, Christine Street, Shaw, Oldham OL2 7SF | 01706 847421 |
| SPRINGHEAD | Ashfield Crescent PF, St John Street, Lees, Oldham OL4 4DG | 0161 627 0260 |
| STOCKPORT GEORGIANS | Cromley Road, Woodsmoor, Stockport SK2 7DT | 0161 483 6581 |
| WALSHAW SPORTS CLUB | Walshaw Sports Club, Sycamore Road, Tottington, Bury BL8 3EG | 01204 882448 |
| WEST DIDSBURY & CHORLTON | Brookburn Road, Chorlton-cum-Hardy M21 8EH | 07891 298441 |
| WYTHENSHAWE AMATEUR | Longley Lane, Northenden, Wythenshawe M22 4LA | 0161 998 7268 |

**In:** Dukinfield Town (P). Pennington (P). Rochdale Sacred Heart (P).

**Out:** Beechfield United (R). Heywood St James (R). Leigh Athletic (R).

# MIDDLESEX COUNTY LEAGUE

**Sponsored by:** Cherry Red Books
**Founded:** 1984
**Recent Champions:**
2008: Indian Gymkhana
2009: Bethnal Green United
2010: Interwood
2011: Willesden Constantine
2012: Interwood

| PREMIER DIVISION | P | W | D | L | F | A | Pts |
|---|---|---|---|---|---|---|---|
| 1 British Airways | 30 | 22 | 6 | 2 | 88 | 37 | 72 |
| 2 (P) FC Romania | 30 | 19 | 4 | 7 | 97 | 48 | 61 |
| 3 Interwood | 30 | 17 | 7 | 5 | 77 | 36 | 58 |
| 4 Sporting Hackney | 30 | 17 | 7 | 6 | 65 | 34 | 58 |
| 5 Broadfields United | 30 | 18 | 3 | 8 | 65 | 46 | 57 |
| 6 Sloane | 30 | 14 | 5 | 11 | 46 | 51 | 47 |
| 7 Hillingdon | 30 | 13 | 7 | 10 | 66 | 45 | 46 |
| 8 Indian Gymkhana Club | 30 | 13 | 7 | 10 | 71 | 51 | 46 |
| 9 Kilburn | 30 | 13 | 3 | 14 | 67 | 84 | 42 |
| 10 West Essex | 30 | 12 | 5 | 13 | 53 | 53 | 41 |
| 11 FC Assyria | 30 | 10 | 4 | 16 | 44 | 63 | 34 |
| 12 Singh Sabha Slough | 30 | 9 | 6 | 15 | 45 | 65 | 33 |
| 13 FC Deportivo Galicia | 30 | 9 | 4 | 17 | 51 | 80 | 31 |
| 14 Hounslow Wanderers | 30 | 7 | 3 | 20 | 52 | 87 | 24 |
| 15 (R) Kodak (Harrow) | 30 | 5 | 5 | 20 | 55 | 87 | 20 |
| 16 (R) North Kensington | 30 | 3 | 0 | 27 | 31 | 106 | 9 |

## ALEC SMITH PREMIER DIVISION CUP

**ROUND 1**

| | | | |
|---|---|---|---|
| Sporting Hackney | v | Broadfields United | 1-3 |
| West Essex | v | Sloane | 1-3 |
| FC Deportivo Galicia | v | Interwood | 1-2 |
| FC Assyria | v | North Kensington | 2-0 |
| Kilburn | v | British Airways | 2-4 |
| Indian Gymkhana Club | v | Hounslow Wanderers | 3-1 |
| Hillington | v | Kodak (Harrow) | 1-2 |
| FC Romania | v | Sign Sabha Slough | 3-2 |

**QUARTER FINALS**

| | | | |
|---|---|---|---|
| Indian Gymkhana Club | v | FC Assyria | 3-1 |
| Interwood | v | FC Romania | 2-1 |
| Sloane | v | British Airways | 1-2 |
| Kodak (Harrow) | v | Broadfields United | 1-2 |

**SEMI FINALS**

| | | | |
|---|---|---|---|
| British Airways | v | Indian Gymkhana Club | 4-2 |
| Broadfields United | v | Interwood | 3-2 |

**FINAL**

| | | | |
|---|---|---|---|
| British Airways | v | Broadfields United | 1-2 |

| PREMIER DIVISION | 1 | 2 | 3 | 4 | 5 | 6 | 7 | 8 | 9 | 10 | 11 | 12 | 13 | 14 | 15 | 16 |
|---|---|---|---|---|---|---|---|---|---|---|---|---|---|---|---|---|
| 1 British Airways | | 2-1 | 3-1 | 4-1 | 2-3 | 1-1 | 3-2 | 2-2 | 5-2 | 6-0 | 3-2 | 2-0 | 2-1 | 1-0 | 5-0 | 5-2 |
| 2 Broadfields United | 2-3 | | 2-4 | 4-1 | 1-0 | 1-2 | 2-3 | 2-2 | 4-1 | 3-1 | 3-3 | 0-3 | 2-0 | 1-2 | 2-0 | 3-2 |
| 3 FC Assyria | 0-3 | 3-1 | | 3-0 | 0-6 | 1-2 | 1-0 | 0-5 | 1-1 | 1-2 | 3-0 | 4-2 | 0-1 | 0-1 | 2-2 | 0-6 |
| 4 FC Deportivo Galicia | 2-1 | 3-4 | 1-3 | | 2-4 | 3-2 | 1-0 | 2-0 | 0-7 | 3-2 | 4-3 | 1-2 | 2-2 | 3-3 | 1-2 | 0-3 |
| 5 FC Romania | 2-2 | 1-2 | 4-2 | 4-1 | | 2-2 | 4-3 | 5-1 | 1-3 | 7-3 | 3-1 | 4-2 | 6-0 | 4-0 | 2-1 | 0-0 |
| 6 Hillingdon | 0-1 | AW | 1-1 | 2-1 | 4-1 | | 2-3 | 4-4 | 3-1 | 9-1 | 4-2 | 4-1 | 0-2 | 1-0 | 1-1 | 0-0 |
| 7 Hounslow Wanderers | 1-2 | 1-2 | 1-2 | 4-2 | 2-4 | 0-5 | | 0-4 | 2-3 | 3-4 | 0-6 | 5-0 | 5-1 | 4-3 | 0-2 | 0-3 |
| 8 Indian Gymkhana Club | 1-2 | 3-5 | 0-1 | 0-3 | 0-2 | 4-2 | 5-0 | | 3-3 | 2-3 | 2-2 | HW | 2-1 | 4-1 | 3-3 | 1-0 |
| 9 Interwood | 1-1 | Void | 2-0 | 3-1 | 1-1 | 4-0 | 6-0 | 2-0 | | 5-0 | 5-2 | 5-3 | 2-2 | AW | 1-0 | 3-0 |
| 10 Kilburn | 3-4 | 1-2 | 4-3 | 3-0 | 4-3 | 4-2 | 4-4 | 2-6 | 1-5 | | 5-2 | 3-2 | 5-2 | 3-0 | 5-1 | 1-1 |
| 11 Kodak (Harrow) | 2-3 | 1-3 | 1-0 | 2-3 | 2-5 | 0-3 | 3-3 | 0-1 | 1-1 | 1-1 | | 1-2 | 3-1 | 1-3 | 1-5 | 2-1 |
| 12 North Kensington | 1-8 | 0-2 | 3-5 | 1-2 | 0-6 | 0-6 | 1-3 | 1-5 | 1-4 | AW | 1-7 | | 0-1 | 1-6 | 0-12 | 1-3 |
| 13 Singh Sabha Slough | 1-4 | 0-2 | 3-1 | 3-3 | 1-5 | 1-1 | 3-1 | 2-1 | 1-3 | 2-1 | 4-0 | 3-1 | | 0-0 | 0-3 | 3-5 |
| 14 Sloane | 2-2 | 2-4 | 2-1 | 3-2 | 3-2 | 0-3 | 3-1 | 0-5 | 2-1 | 1-0 | 3-1 | HW | 1-1 | | 0-2 | 3-0 |
| 15 Sporting Hackney | 1-1 | 2-2 | 3-0 | 0-2 | 3-1 | 3-0 | 1-1 | 1-0 | 1-1 | 1-0 | 5-1 | 1-0 | 3-2 | 1-0 | | 1-0 |
| 16 West Essex | 0-5 | 0-3 | 1-1 | 4-1 | 0-5 | 2-0 | 5-0 | 0-3 | 0-1 | 3-1 | 6-2 | 3-2 | 1-0 | 2-2 | 0-4 | |

## MIDDLESEX COUNTY LEAGUE PREMIER DIVISION CONSTITUTION 2013-14

| | | |
|---|---|---|
| AFC HAYES RESERVES | Farm Park, Kingshill Avenue, Hayes UB4 8DD | 020 8845 0110 |
| BRITISH AIRWAYS | Crane Lodge Road, Cranford TW5 9P | 07779 638080 |
| BROADFIELDS UNITED | Hillingdon Borough FC, Breakspear Road, Ruislip, Middlesex HA4 7SB | 01895 639544 |
| CRICKLEWOOD WANDERERS | Ark Academy, Forty Avenue, Wembley, Middlesex HA9 9JR | 020 8385 4391 |
| FC ASSYRIA | Northolt Rugby Club, Cayton Road, Greenford UB6 8B | 020 8813 1701 |
| FC DEPORTIVO GALICIA | Osterley Sports Club, Tentelow Lane, Osterley, Southall UB2 4LW | 020 8574 7055 |
| HILLINGDON | Hillingdon Athletics Stadium, Gatting Way, Park Road, Uxbridge UB8 1ES | 0845 130 7324 |
| HOUNSLOW WANDERERS | Hayes & Yeading FC, The Warren, Beaconsfield Road, Hayes UB4 0SL | 020 8573 2075 |
| INDIAN GYMKHANA | Indian Gymkhana Club, Thornbury Avenue, Osterley TW7 4NQ | 020 8568 4009 |
| INTERWOOD | Wadham Lodge, Kitchener Road, Walthamstow, London E17 4JP | 020 8527 2444 |
| KENSINGTON DRAGONS | Birkbeck Playing Fields, Birkbeck Avenue, Greenford | 07940 858 265 |
| KILBURN | Ark Academy, Forty Avenue, Wembley, Middlesex HA9 9JR | 020 8385 4391 |
| SINGH SABHA SLOUGH | The Falcon Sports Centre, Stoke Poges Centre, Slough SL1 3LW | 07917 773 727 |
| SLOANE | Hackney Marshes, Homerton Road, Hackney, London E9 5PF | 020 8986 7955 |
| SPORTING HACKNEY | Hackney Marshes, Homerton Road, Hackney, London E9 5PF | 020 8986 7955 |
| WEST ESSEX | Rolls Sports Ground, Hickmans Avenue, Hickmans Park E4 9JG | 020 8527 3889 |

In: AFC Hayes Reserves (N). Cricklewood Wanderers (P). Kensington Dragons (P).
Out: FC Romania (P - Essex Senior). Kodak (Harrow) (R). North Kensington (W).

# MIDDLESEX COUNTY LEAGUE - STEP 7

## DIVISION ONE CENTRAL & EAST

| | | P | W | D | L | F | A | Pts |
|---|---|---|---|---|---|---|---|---|
| 1 | (P) Cricklewood Wanderers | 20 | 16 | 1 | 3 | 76 | 32 | 49 |
| 2 | AFC Wembley | 20 | 16 | 0 | 4 | 69 | 25 | 48 |
| 3 | FFC Haringey | 20 | 12 | 4 | 4 | 48 | 36 | 40 |
| 4 | The Lord Sanctuary | 20 | 11 | 1 | 8 | 54 | 42 | 34 |
| 5 | Supreme Athletic | 20 | 10 | 3 | 7 | 40 | 37 | 33 |
| 6 | Stonewall | 20 | 9 | 3 | 8 | 47 | 49 | 30 |
| 7 | West End | 20 | 7 | 3 | 10 | 43 | 43 | 24 |
| 8 | St Lawrence | 20 | 5 | 5 | 10 | 30 | 45 | 20 |
| 9 | Fire United Christian | 20 | 5 | 2 | 13 | 28 | 52 | 17 |
| 10 | The Wilberforce Wanderers | 20 | 3 | 4 | 13 | 29 | 51 | 13 |
| 11 | (R) Vallance | 20 | 2 | 2 | 16 | 23 | 75 | 8 |

Oscar withdrew - record expunged.
Springfield withdrew - record expunged.

## DIVISION ONE WEST

| | | P | W | D | L | F | A | Pts |
|---|---|---|---|---|---|---|---|---|
| 1 | LPOSSA | 22 | 20 | 1 | 1 | 89 | 23 | 61 |
| 2 | (P) Kensington Dragons | 22 | 18 | 0 | 4 | 65 | 26 | 54 |
| 3 | Pitshanger Dynamo | 22 | 16 | 1 | 5 | 72 | 28 | 49 |
| 4 | Sandgate | 22 | 15 | 2 | 5 | 74 | 34 | 47 |
| 5 | Imperial College Old Boys | 22 | 11 | 2 | 9 | 47 | 49 | 35 |
| 6 | West London Saracens | 22 | 11 | 1 | 10 | 55 | 40 | 34 |
| 7 | Brentham | 22 | 9 | 2 | 11 | 40 | 55 | 29 |
| 8 | Marsh Rangers | 22 | 8 | 1 | 13 | 67 | 59 | 25 |
| 9 | Chiswick | 22 | 7 | 1 | 14 | 34 | 51 | 22 |
| 10 | C.B. Hounslow United Social | 22 | 4 | 0 | 18 | 26 | 86 | 12 |
| 11 | Lancaster | 22 | 4 | 0 | 18 | 35 | 99 | 12 |
| 12 | Hillingdon Abbots | 22 | 3 | 1 | 18 | 37 | 91 | 10 |

Bay expelled from the League - record expunged.
Horseed withdrew - record expunged.

## DIVISION TWO

| | | P | W | D | L | F | A | Pts |
|---|---|---|---|---|---|---|---|---|
| 1 | (P) Stedfast | 18 | 13 | 1 | 4 | 50 | 25 | 40 |
| 2 | (P) Wembley Park | 18 | 12 | 2 | 4 | 58 | 23 | 38 |
| 3 | AFC Southall | 18 | 12 | 2 | 4 | 45 | 27 | 38 |
| 4 | Aym Higher | 18 | 11 | 2 | 5 | 62 | 28 | 35 |
| 5 | British Airways 3rds | 18 | 9 | 3 | 6 | 47 | 33 | 30 |
| 6 | Hayes & Hanwell | 18 | 8 | 2 | 8 | 23 | 43 | 26 |
| 7 | All Stars Skills Academy | 18 | 7 | 2 | 9 | 42 | 39 | 23 |
| 8 | AFC Heathrow | 18 | 4 | 2 | 12 | 30 | 60 | 14 |
| 9 | Centenary Park | 18 | 4 | 1 | 13 | 31 | 59 | 13 |
| 10 | C.B. Hounslow United Social 3rds | 18 | 1 | 1 | 16 | 21 | 72 | 4 |

Hearts of Teddlothian withdrew - record expunged.
West London Somaliland Community withdrew - record expunged.

## SENIOR RESERVE DIVISION

| | | P | W | D | L | F | A | Pts |
|---|---|---|---|---|---|---|---|---|
| 1 | Southall Reserves | 20 | 14 | 5 | 1 | 61 | 26 | 47 |
| 2 | Broadfields United Reserves | 20 | 12 | 6 | 2 | 56 | 30 | 42 |
| 3 | Indian Gymkhana Club Reserves | 20 | 12 | 2 | 6 | 48 | 31 | 38 |
| 4 | C.B. Hounslow United Social Res. | 20 | 11 | 4 | 5 | 49 | 27 | 37 |
| 5 | Sporting Hackney Reserves | 20 | 9 | 4 | 7 | 45 | 41 | 31 |
| 6 | Brentham Reserves | 20 | 8 | 1 | 11 | 49 | 66 | 25 |
| 7 | Kensington Dragons Reserves | 20 | 5 | 6 | 9 | 26 | 46 | 21 |
| 8 | British Airways Reserves | 20 | 6 | 2 | 12 | 46 | 46 | 20 |
| 9 | Hillingdon Reserves | 20 | 5 | 3 | 12 | 36 | 51 | 18 |
| 10 | St Lawrence Reserves | 20 | 5 | 2 | 13 | 24 | 62 | 17 |
| 11 | Sloane Reserves | 20 | 5 | 1 | 14 | 34 | 48 | 16 |

## SENIOR OPEN CUP

### ROUND 1

| | | | |
|---|---|---|---|
| Kodak (Harrow) | v | Chiswick | 7-1 |
| LPOSSA | v | Kilburn | 7-1 |
| FFC Haringey | v | The Wilberforce Wanderers | 1-0 |
| Vallance | v | Cricklewood Wanderers | 1-7 |
| AFC Wembley | v | Sporting Hackney | 5-5 |
| *AFC Wembley won on penalties.* | | | |
| Green Island | v | Sloane | AW |
| C.B. Hounslow United Social | v | British Airways | 1-7 |
| Sandgate | v | Horseed | HW |
| Singh Sabha Slough | v | West London Saracens | 3-4 |
| FC Assyria | v | West Essex | 3-2 |
| AFC Diligence | v | The Lord Sanctuary | AW |
| Fire United Christian | v | Oscar (WITHDRAWN) | 5-0 |
| Lancaster | v | Bay (Expelled) | 2-3 |

### ROUND 2

| | | | |
|---|---|---|---|
| Marsh Rangers | v | Indian Gymkhana Club | 5-3 |
| AFC Wembley | v | FC Assyria | 1-3 |
| West End | v | Kensington Dragons | 3-5 |
| Brentham | v | Bay | 0-2 |
| British Airways | v | Springfield | 4-3 |
| Stonewall | v | Interwood | 1-2 |
| North Kensington | v | Hillingdon | 0-3 |
| Cricklewood Wanderers | v | Hillingdon Abbots | 6-1 |
| Supreme Athletic | v | Broadfields United | 3-2 |
| FC Deportivo Galicia | v | Sandgate | 4-3 |
| Hounslow Wanderers | v | Sloane | 0-2 |
| St Lawrence | v | The Lord Sanctuary | 0-5 |
| Pitshanger Dynamo | v | FC Romania | 4-1 |
| Imperial College Old Boys | v | West London Saracens | 3-1 |
| Kodak (Harrow) | v | LPOSSA | 2-5 |
| Fire United Christian | v | FFC Haringey | 4-6 |

### ROUND 3

| | | | |
|---|---|---|---|
| Kensington Dragons | v | Supreme Athletic | 1-0 |
| Imperial College Old Boys | v | FC Deportivo Galicia | 2-5 |
| Interwood | v | FFC Haringey | 2-1 |
| Hillingdon | v | Sloane | 5-4 |
| Bay | v | Pitshanger Dynamo | AW |
| Marsh Rangers | v | British Airways | 1-3 |
| Cricklewood Wanderers | v | LPOSSA | 3-2 |
| FC Assyria | v | The Lord Sanctuary | 3-2 |

### QUARTER FINALS

| | | | |
|---|---|---|---|
| British Airways | v | FC Assyria | 2-1 |
| Interwood | v | Pitshanger Dynamo | 2-3 |
| Hillingdon | v | Kensington Dragons | 5-2 |
| FC Deportivo Galicia | v | Cricklewood Wanderers | 2-1 |

### SEMI FINALS

| | | | |
|---|---|---|---|
| Pitshanger Dynamo | v | British Airways | 4-4 |
| *Pitshanger Dynamo won on penalties.* | | | |
| FC Deportivo Galicia | v | Hillingdon | 1-4 |

### FINAL

| | | | |
|---|---|---|---|
| Pitshanger Dynamo | v | Hillingdon | 1-3 |

# NORTH BERKSHIRE LEAGUE

**Sponsored by:** No sponsor
**Founded:** 1909
**Recent Champions:**
2008: Lambourn Sports
2009: Saxton Rovers
2010: Saxton Rovers
2011: Lambourn Sports
2012: Crowmarsh Gifford
**nbfl.co.uk**

## NORTH BERKS CUP

**ROUND 1**

| | | | |
|---|---|---|---|
| Radley | v | Marcham | 0-2 |

**Round 2**

| | | | |
|---|---|---|---|
| Marcham | v | Warborough United | 2-0 |
| Hanney United | v | Faringdon Town | 0-3 |
| Grove Rangers | v | Benson AFC | 3-9 |
| Hagbourne United | v | Appleton Stars | HW |
| Childrey United | v | Saxton Rovers | 1-9 |
| Sutton Courtenay | v | Dorchester | 2-3 |
| Blewbury | v | Harwell International | 0-5 |
| Crowmarsh Gifford | v | Didcot Casuals | 0-2 |
| Long Wittenham Athletic | v | Coleshill United | 3-1 |
| Wallingford Town | v | Turnpike Sports | 4-2 |
| Drayton | v | Kintbury Rangers | 3-3, 1-2p |
| Challow FC | v | Westminster | 0-7 |
| Ardington & Lockinge | v | Wootton & Dry Sandford | 3-2 |
| Uffington United | v | Steventon | AW |
| Stanford-in-the-Vale | v | Benson Lions | 3-2 |
| Berinsfield | v | East Hendred | 9-1 |

**ROUND 3**

| | | | |
|---|---|---|---|
| Marcham | v | Faringdon Town | 0-4 |
| Benson AFC | v | Hagbourne United | 5-0 |
| Saxton Rovers | v | Dorchester | 1-2 |
| Harwell International | v | Didcot Casuals | 2-4 |
| Long Wittenham Athletic | v | Wallingford Town | 2-1 |
| Kintbury Rangers | v | Westminster | 6-0 |
| Ardington & Lockinge | v | Steventon | 4-2 |
| Stanford-in-the-Vale | v | Berinsfield | 1-4 |

**QUARTER FINALS**

| | | | |
|---|---|---|---|
| Faringdon Town | v | Benson AFC | 6-0 |
| Dorchester | v | Didcot Casuals | 2-3 |
| Long Wittenham Athletic | v | Kintbury Rangers | 1-0 |
| Ardington & Lockinge | v | Berinsfield | 1-5 |

**SEMI FINALS**

| | | | |
|---|---|---|---|
| Faringdon Town | v | Didcot Casuals | 0-1 |
| Long Wittenham Athletic | v | Berinsfield | 1-0 |

**FINAL**

| | | | |
|---|---|---|---|
| Didcot Casuals | v | Long Wittenham Athletic | 2-3 |

## DIVISION ONE

| | DIVISION ONE | P | W | D | L | F | A | Pts |
|---|---|---|---|---|---|---|---|---|
| 1 | Saxton Rovers | 24 | 19 | 2 | 3 | 65 | 22 | 59 |
| 2 | Berinsfield | 24 | 16 | 2 | 6 | 73 | 26 | 50 |
| 3 | (R) Didcot Casuals | 24 | 14 | 3 | 7 | 65 | 29 | 45 |
| 4 | Wootton & Dry Sandford | 24 | 13 | 4 | 7 | 62 | 34 | 43 |
| 5 | Crowmarsh Gifford | 24 | 11 | 7 | 6 | 46 | 38 | 40 |
| 6 | Faringdon Town | 24 | 12 | 4 | 8 | 47 | 43 | 40 |
| 7 | Harwell International | 24 | 10 | 2 | 12 | 39 | 35 | 32 |
| 8 | Long Wittenham Athletic | 24 | 9 | 4 | 11 | 46 | 47 | 31 |
| 9 | Wallingford Town | 24 | 8 | 6 | 10 | 41 | 51 | 30 |
| 10 | Kintbury Rangers | 24 | 8 | 2 | 14 | 50 | 56 | 26 |
| 11 | Childrey United | 24 | 5 | 5 | 14 | 34 | 73 | 20 |
| 12 | (R) Sutton Courtenay | 24 | 6 | 1 | 17 | 36 | 100 | 19 |
| 13 | (R) East Hendred | 24 | 2 | 4 | 18 | 21 | 71 | 10 |

Benson withdrew - record expunged.

| DIVISION ONE | 1 | 2 | 3 | 4 | 5 | 6 | 7 | 8 | 9 | 10 | 11 | 12 | 13 |
|---|---|---|---|---|---|---|---|---|---|---|---|---|---|
| 1 AFC Wallingford | | 0-5 | 2-1 | 1-4 | 1-3 | 1-0 | 3-1 | 4-1 | 3-3 | 2-2 | 0-1 | 5-1 | 0-1 |
| 2 Berinsfield | 1-1 | | H-W | 0-1 | 1-3 | 3-0 | 5-0 | H-W | 3-1 | 7-2 | 1-2 | 13-1 | 4-0 |
| 3 Childrey United | 1-1 | 1-6 | | 3-4 | 2-3 | 2-2 | 1-4 | 1-3 | 3-2 | 1-5 | 2-2 | 3-1 | 1-8 |
| 4 Crowmarsh Gifford | 5-2 | 2-2 | 0-0 | | 1-4 | 4-0 | 4-3 | 2-0 | 1-1 | 1-3 | 0-2 | H-W | 2-1 |
| 5 Didcot Casuals | 5-0 | 2-1 | 6-1 | 1-0 | | 11-0 | 0-2 | 0-3 | 1-0 | 2-2 | 1-1 | 11-0 | 3-3 |
| 6 East Hendred | 2-4 | 0-2 | 1-1 | 2-2 | 0-2 | | 2-3 | 0-7 | 2-1 | 2-3 | 4-1 | 1-7 | |
| 7 Faringdon Town | 2-2 | 2-0 | 1-2 | 3-3 | 1-2 | 0-0 | | H-W | 5-2 | 2-1 | 1-2 | 2-1 | 1-0 |
| 8 Harwell International | 2-1 | 2-1 | 5-1 | 0-1 | 2-1 | 1-0 | 2-2 | | 1-4 | 0-0 | 0-2 | 1-2 | 1-4 |
| 9 Kintbury Rangers | 2-0 | 3-5 | 6-0 | 3-2 | H-W | 2-0 | 1-4 | 2-1 | | 0-2 | 0-1 | 9-1 | 2-3 |
| 10 Long Wittenham Athletic | 3-4 | 1-2 | 4-1 | 1-2 | 3-0 | 4-1 | 1-3 | 1-3 | 3-1 | | 0-3 | 3-1 | 0-1 |
| 11 Saxton Rovers | 2-0 | 2-4 | 0-1 | 1-0 | 0-1 | H-W | 6-2 | 3-2 | 7-2 | 3-0 | | 7-0 | 3-1 |
| 12 Sutton Courtenay | 3-4 | 0-5 | 2-5 | 3-3 | 2-1 | 2-0 | 2-3 | 3-1 | 4-2 | 4-0 | 1-8 | | 0-4 |
| 13 Wootton & Dry Sandford | 0-0 | 0-2 | 5-0 | 2-2 | 3-2 | 5-1 | 1-0 | 0-1 | 4-1 | 2-2 | 1-4 | 6-1 | |

## NORTH BERKSHIRE LEAGUE DIVISION ONE CONSTITUTION 2013-14

| | | |
|---|---|---|
| ARDINGTON & LOCKINGE | White Road (Off Well Street), Ardington, Oxfordshire OX12 8QB | 07989 526959 |
| BERINSFIELD | Lay Avenue, Berinsfield OX10 7N | 07983 399992 |
| CROWMARSH GIFFORD | Crowmarsh Recreation Ground, Crowmarsh Gifford, Wallingford OX10 8EB | 07825 711578 |
| DORCHESTER | Drayton Road, Dorchester | 07800 705516 |
| FARINGDON TOWN | Tucker Park, Park Road, Faringdon SN7 7DP | 01367 241759 |
| HARWELL INTERNATIONAL | Main Gate, Harwell International Bus. Cte, Didcot OX11 0RA | 07947 309120 |
| KINTBURY RANGERS | Inkpen Road, Kintbury, Hungerford RG17 9TY | 07771 636594 |
| LAMBOURN SPORTS | Bockhampton Road Lambourn, Hungerford, Berkshire RG17 8PS | 07838001906 |
| LONG WITTENHAM ATHLETIC | Bodkins Sports Field, East End of Village, Long Wittenham | 01865 407202 |
| SAXTON ROVERS | Recreation Ground, Caldecott Road, Abingdon OX14 5HR | 07752 390039 |
| WALLINGFORD TOWN | Wallingford Sports Park , Hithercroft Road , Wallingford OX10 9RB | 07973 736586 |
| WOOTTON & DRY SANDFORD | Community Centre, Besseleigh Road, Wootton OX13 6DN | 07584 313130 |

**In:** Ardington & Lockinge (P). Dorchester (P). Lambourn Sports (W from Hellenic).
**Out:** Benson (WS). Childrey United (W). Didcot Casuals (R). East Hendred (R). Sutton Courtenay (R).

# NORTH BERKSHRE LEAGUE - STEP 7

## DIVISION TWO

| | | P | W | D | L | F | A | Pts |
|---|---|---|---|---|---|---|---|---|
| 1 | (P) Ardington & Lockinge | 20 | 15 | 3 | 2 | 97 | 39 | 48 |
| 2 | Abingdon United Reserves | 20 | 13 | 4 | 3 | 72 | 31 | 43 |
| 3 | (P) Dorchester | 20 | 11 | 6 | 3 | 66 | 32 | 39 |
| 4 | Coleshill United | 20 | 11 | 2 | 7 | 66 | 52 | 35 |
| 5 | Lambourn Sports Reserves | 20 | 11 | 1 | 8 | 47 | 35 | 34 |
| 6 | Marcham | 20 | 9 | 5 | 6 | 39 | 46 | 32 |
| 7 | Wantage Town 'A' | 20 | 8 | 3 | 9 | 46 | 48 | 27 |
| 8 | Steventon | 20 | 4 | 5 | 11 | 36 | 52 | 17 |
| 9 | Drayton | 20 | 4 | 3 | 13 | 42 | 73 | 15 |
| 10 | Saxton Rovers Reserves | 20 | 4 | 1 | 15 | 29 | 72 | 13 |
| 11 | (R) Benson Lions | 20 | 3 | 1 | 16 | 19 | 79 | 10 |

## DIVISION THREE

| | | P | W | D | L | F | A | Pts |
|---|---|---|---|---|---|---|---|---|
| 1 | (W) Childrey United Reserves | 22 | 16 | 2 | 4 | 71 | 23 | 50 |
| 2 | (P) Faringdon Town Reserves | 22 | 15 | 4 | 3 | 50 | 15 | 49 |
| 3 | (P) Radley | 22 | 13 | 4 | 5 | 60 | 25 | 43 |
| 4 | Harwell Int. Reserves | 22 | 13 | 3 | 6 | 48 | 21 | 42 |
| 5 | Milton United Reserves | 22 | 12 | 2 | 8 | 59 | 36 | 38 |
| 6 | Kintbury Reserves | 22 | 10 | 7 | 5 | 47 | 38 | 37 |
| 7 | Didcot Casuals Reserves | 22 | 8 | 4 | 10 | 30 | 70 | 28 |
| 8 | Stanford-in-the-Vale | 22 | 7 | 5 | 10 | 49 | 47 | 26 |
| 9 | Blewbury | 22 | 7 | 4 | 11 | 40 | 48 | 25 |
| 10 | Marcham Reserves | 22 | 4 | 5 | 13 | 36 | 67 | 17 |
| 11 | (R) Hagbourne United | 22 | 3 | 4 | 15 | 38 | 69 | 13 |
| 12 | (R) East Hendred Reserves | 22 | 1 | 2 | 19 | 11 | 80 | 5 |

## DIVISION FOUR

| | | P | W | D | L | F | A | Pts |
|---|---|---|---|---|---|---|---|---|
| 1 | (P) Hanney United | 22 | 17 | 2 | 3 | 60 | 27 | 53 |
| 2 | (P) Westminster | 22 | 17 | 1 | 4 | 65 | 24 | 52 |
| 3 | Wootton Reserves | 22 | 14 | 3 | 5 | 63 | 33 | 45 |
| 4 | Coleshill United Reserves | 22 | 12 | 1 | 9 | 58 | 37 | 37 |
| 5 | Turnpike Sports | 22 | 12 | 0 | 10 | 77 | 43 | 36 |
| 6 | Grove Rangers | 22 | 11 | 3 | 8 | 48 | 42 | 36 |
| 7 | Long Wittenham Reserves | 22 | 11 | 1 | 10 | 59 | 51 | 34 |
| 8 | Warborough United | 22 | 9 | 1 | 12 | 45 | 36 | 28 |
| 9 | Drayton Reserves | 22 | 8 | 0 | 14 | 40 | 82 | 24 |
| 10 | Ardington Reserves | 22 | 7 | 1 | 14 | 30 | 64 | 22 |
| 11 | (R) Steventon Reserves | 22 | 4 | 5 | 13 | 41 | 75 | 17 |
| 12 | (R) Stanford-in-the-Vale Reserves | 22 | 0 | 2 | 20 | 17 | 89 | 2 |

## DIVISION FIVE

| | | P | W | D | L | F | A | Pts |
|---|---|---|---|---|---|---|---|---|
| 1 | (P) Berinsfield Reserves | 22 | 18 | 1 | 3 | 136 | 44 | 55 |
| 2 | (P) Faringdon Town A | 22 | 17 | 1 | 4 | 89 | 36 | 52 |
| 3 | Crowmarsh Gifford Reserves | 22 | 16 | 2 | 4 | 112 | 31 | 50 |
| 4 | Radley Reserves | 22 | 14 | 2 | 6 | 73 | 48 | 44 |
| 5 | Didcot Casuals 'A' | 22 | 14 | 1 | 7 | 80 | 61 | 43 |
| 6 | (W) Sutton Courtenay Reserves | 22 | 11 | 2 | 9 | 56 | 50 | 35 |
| 7 | Benson Lions Reserves | 22 | 10 | 2 | 10 | 68 | 55 | 32 |
| 8 | Challow FC | 22 | 10 | 1 | 11 | 71 | 63 | 31 |
| 9 | Grove Rangers Reserves | 22 | 6 | 1 | 15 | 51 | 75 | 19 |
| 10 | Uffington United | 22 | 5 | 3 | 14 | 56 | 67 | 18 |
| 11 | Hagbourne Utd. Reserves | 22 | 1 | 3 | 18 | 28 | 116 | 6 |
| 12 | Appleton Stars | 22 | 0 | 1 | 21 | 21 | 195 | 1 |

## NORTH BERKS CHARITY SHIELD

### ROUND 1

| | | | |
|---|---|---|---|
| Challow FC | v | Marcham | 1-3 |
| Turnpike Sports | v | Harwell International | 2-2, 0-2p |
| Crowmarsh Gifford | v | Radley | 3-3, 3-4p |
| Berinsfield | v | Uffington United | HW |
| Faringdon Town | v | Kintbury Rangers | 3-6 |
| Appleton Stars | v | Hanney United | 1-8 |
| Ardington & Lockinge | v | Saxton Rovers | 4-1 |
| Steventon | v | Warborough United | 3-4 |
| Dorchester | v | Childrey United | 4-1 |
| Benson AFC | v | Bension Lions | 3-0 |
| Wootton & Dry Sandford | v | Coleshill United | 4-3 |
| Drayton | v | Stanford-in-the-Vale | 6-3 |
| Long Wittenham Athletic | v | Westminster | 0-2 |
| Grove Rangers | v | Sutton Courtenay | 3-1 |
| Hagbourne United | v | Blewbury | 0-9 |
| Wallingford Town | v | East Hendred | 6-1 |

### ROUND 2

| | | | |
|---|---|---|---|
| Marcham | v | Harwell International | 1-2 |
| Radley | v | Berinsfield | 1-3 |
| Kintbury Rangers | v | Hanney United | 4-0 |
| Ardington & Lockinge | v | Warborough United | 5-1 |
| Dorchester | v | Benson AFC | 1-2 |
| Wootton & Dry Sandford | v | Drayton | 4-0 |
| Westminster | v | Grove Rangers | 3-2 |
| Blewbury | v | Wallingford Town | 2-4 |

### QUARTER FINALS

| | | | |
|---|---|---|---|
| Harwell International | v | Berinsfield | 0-2 |
| Kintbury Rangers | v | Ardington & Lockinge | 4-1 |
| Benson AFC | v | Wootton & Dry Sandford | 1-8 |
| Westminster | v | Wallingford Town | 0-0, 2-3p |

### SEMI FINALS

| | | | |
|---|---|---|---|
| Berinsfield | v | Kintbury Rangers | 3-0 |
| Wootton & Dry Sandford | v | Wallingford Town | 2-3 |

### FINAL

| | | | |
|---|---|---|---|
| Berinsfield | v | Wallingford Town | 1-0 |

## WAR MEMORIAL TROPHY

### FINAL

| | | | |
|---|---|---|---|
| Coleshill United | v | Westminster | 3-1 |

## LEAGUE CUP

### FINAL

| | | | |
|---|---|---|---|
| Radley Reserves | v | Ardington Reserves | 0-3 |

## AG KINGHAM CUP

### FINAL

| | | | |
|---|---|---|---|
| Wantage Town 'A' | v | Coleshill United Reserves | 0-5 |

## NAIRNE PAUL TROPHY

### FINAL

| | | | |
|---|---|---|---|
| Abingdon United Reserves | v | Childrey United Reserves | 2-3 |

# NORTHAMPTONSHIRE COMBINATION

**Sponsored by:** MDH Teamwear
**Founded:** N/K
**Recent Champions:**
2008: Harpole
2009: Harpole
2010: Harborough Town
2011: Brixworth All Saints
2012: Harpole
**northantscombination.co.uk**

| PREMIER DIVISION | P | W | D | L | F | A | Pts |
|---|---|---|---|---|---|---|---|
| 1 Harpole | 26 | 22 | 3 | 1 | 73 | 17 | 69 |
| 2 Welford Victoria | 26 | 18 | 2 | 6 | 74 | 30 | 56 |
| 3 Moulton | 26 | 17 | 5 | 4 | 67 | 27 | 56 |
| 4 Milton | 26 | 17 | 2 | 7 | 57 | 33 | 53 |
| 5 Brixworth All Saints | 26 | 14 | 6 | 6 | 60 | 31 | 48 |
| 6 James King Blisworth | 26 | 14 | 3 | 9 | 72 | 53 | 45 |
| 7 Weldon United | 26 | 11 | 3 | 12 | 55 | 51 | 36 |
| 8 Stanion Quantum Print | 26 | 10 | 5 | 11 | 64 | 61 | 35 |
| 9 Roade | 26 | 9 | 5 | 12 | 57 | 52 | 32 |
| 10 Corby Pegasus | 26 | 8 | 1 | 17 | 54 | 76 | 25 |
| 11 Kettering Nomads | 26 | 7 | 4 | 15 | 44 | 68 | 25 |
| 12 Ringstead Rangers (-3pts) | 26 | 6 | 4 | 16 | 49 | 77 | 19 |
| 13 Corby S& L Khalsa (-3pts) | 26 | 5 | 3 | 18 | 32 | 84 | 15 |
| 14 (R) Heyford Athletic | 26 | 0 | 2 | 24 | 20 | 118 | 2 |

## PREMIER DIVISION CUP

**ROUND 1**

| | | | |
|---|---|---|---|
| Milton | v | Welford Victoria | 1-0 |
| Kettering Nomads | v | Roade | 1-3 |
| Corby S&L Khalsa | v | Brixworth All Saints | 0-3 |
| Heyford Athletic | v | Weldon United | 1-5 |
| James King Blisworth | v | Harpole | 1-2 |
| Moulton | v | Corby Pegasus | 2-0 |

**QUARTER FINALS**

| | | | |
|---|---|---|---|
| Milton | v | Ringstead Rangers | 3-5 |
| Roade | v | Stanion United | 4-0 |
| Brixworth All Saints | v | Weldon United | 2-5 |
| Harpole | v | Moulton | 1-3 |

**SEMI FINALS**

| | | | |
|---|---|---|---|
| Ringstead Rangers | v | Roade | 3-2 |
| Weldon United | v | Moulton | 2-3 |

**FINAL**

| | | | |
|---|---|---|---|
| Ringstead Rangers | v | Moulton | 0-2 |

| PREMIER DIVISION | 1 | 2 | 3 | 4 | 5 | 6 | 7 | 8 | 9 | 10 | 11 | 12 | 13 | 14 |
|---|---|---|---|---|---|---|---|---|---|---|---|---|---|---|
| 1 Brixworth All Saints | | 3-4 | 2-2 | 0-2 | 3-0 | 2-2 | 3-1 | 1-0 | 0-1 | 4-0 | 2-1 | 2-2 | 3-0 | 2-2 |
| 2 Corby Pegasus | 1-3 | | 1-3 | 0-4 | 5-0 | 3-4 | 3-1 | 0-2 | 1-2 | 5-1 | 2-5 | 1-2 | 1-0 | 0-4 |
| 3 Corby S&L Khalsa | A-W | 2-3 | | 1-5 | 5-1 | 1-4 | 0-3 | 1-2 | 1-1 | 3-2 | 1-1 | 1-5 | 2-1 | 0-4 |
| 4 Harpole | 3-0 | 3-1 | 7-0 | | 4-1 | 3-2 | 5-0 | 1-0 | 0-0 | 4-2 | 2-0 | 2-0 | 1-1 | 3-0 |
| 5 Heyford Athletic | 0-9 | 1-9 | 2-3 | 1-3 | | 0-4 | 1-4 | 0-0 | 1-7 | 2-2 | 1-3 | 0-6 | 1-4 | 0-5 |
| 6 James King Blisworth | 2-3 | 3-3 | 5-0 | 1-2 | 5-1 | | 6-1 | 0-5 | 2-1 | 6-2 | 2-2 | 3-0 | 1-2 | 3-2 |
| 7 Kettering Nomads | 0-2 | 3-2 | 3-2 | 0-4 | 6-1 | 3-4 | | 1-2 | 2-4 | 2-2 | 2-1 | 2-2 | 2-2 | 0-1 |
| 8 Milton | 1-0 | 3-1 | 4-0 | 2-5 | 6-0 | 2-1 | 1-0 | | 0-1 | 3-1 | 1-0 | 3-2 | 2-1 | 2-3 |
| 9 Moulton | 2-0 | 5-1 | 4-0 | 2-0 | 4-1 | 3-2 | 2-2 | 4-2 | | 2-2 | 4-2 | 7-0 | 0-1 | 1-2 |
| 10 Ringstead Rangers | 1-3 | 1-0 | 3-2 | 1-1 | 5-2 | 1-2 | 3-1 | 3-6 | 2-3 | | 3-2 | 5-4 | 1-2 | 1-5 |
| 11 Roade | 1-1 | 5-3 | 6-0 | 0-2 | 5-1 | 1-2 | 7-3 | 3-3 | 1-0 | 3-0 | | 0-4 | 2-4 | 0-2 |
| 12 Stanion United | 1-7 | 2-3 | 7-2 | 1-2 | 2-0 | 4-2 | 1-2 | 2-0 | 2-2 | 6-2 | 0-0 | | 3-2 | 0-2 |
| 13 Weldon United | 0-3 | 5-1 | 4-0 | 0-2 | 3-1 | 3-4 | 2-0 | 2-4 | 0-2 | 5-3 | 3-4 | 4-4 | | 3-4 |
| 14 Welford Victoria | 2-2 | 9-0 | 4-0 | 1-3 | 6-1 | 3-0 | 5-0 | 0-1 | 0-3 | H-W | 4-2 | 5-2 | 0-1 | |

## NORTHANTS COMBINATION PREMIER DIVISION CONSTITUTION 2013-14

| | | |
|---|---|---|
| BRIXWORTH ALL SAINTS | St Davids Close, off Froxhill Crescent, Brixworth NN6 9EA | 01604 880073 |
| CORBY DGL LOCOMOTIVES | Cottingham Road, Corby, Northants NN17 1TD | - |
| CORBY PEGASUS | West Glebe South Pavilion, Cottingham Road, Corby NN17 1EL | 01536 402041 |
| CORBY S&L KHALSA | Corby Rugby Club, Rockingham Road, Corby NN17 1AE | 01536 204466 |
| EARLS BARTON UNITED | The Grange, Northampton Road, Earls Barton, Northants NN6 0HA | - |
| HARPOLE | Playing Field, Larkhall Lane, Harpole NN7 4DP | - |
| JAMES KING BLISWORTH | Blisworth Playing Field, Courteenhall Road, Blisworth | 07974 006484 |
| KETTERING NOMADS | Orlingbury Road, Isham, Nr Kettering, Northants. NN14 1HY | - |
| KISLINGBURY | Playing Fields, Beech Lane, Kislingbury, Northampton. NN7 4AL | - |
| MILTON | Collingtree Road, Milton Malsor, Northampton NN7 3AU | - |
| MOULTON | Brunting Road, Moulton, Northampton NN3 7QF | 01604 492675 |
| RINGSTEAD RANGERS | Gladstone Street, Ringstead NN14 4DE | - |
| ROADE | Connolly Way, Hyde Road, Roade NN7 2LU | 01604 862814 |
| STANION QUANTUM PRINT | Village Hall, Brigstock Road, Stanion, Corby | - |
| WELDON UNITED | Oundle Road, Weldon NN17 3JT | - |
| WELFORD VICTORIA | Welford Sports Field, Newlands Road, Welford NN6 6HR | - |

**In:** Corby DGL Locomotives (P). Earls Barton United (P). Kislingbury (P).
**Out:** Heyford Athletic (R).

# NORTHANTS COMBINATION LEAGUE - STEP 7

## DIVISION ONE

| | | P | W | D | L | F | A | Pts |
|---|---|---|---|---|---|---|---|---|
| 1 | (P) Earls Barton United | 22 | 17 | 2 | 3 | 66 | 25 | 53 |
| 2 | (P) Corby Locomotives | 22 | 15 | 3 | 4 | 63 | 29 | 48 |
| 3 | (P) Kislingbury (-3pts) | 22 | 14 | 1 | 7 | 65 | 31 | 40 |
| 4 | Wootton St George | 22 | 12 | 3 | 7 | 69 | 39 | 39 |
| 5 | Corby Everards | 22 | 12 | 3 | 7 | 61 | 40 | 39 |
| 6 | Burton United | 22 | 11 | 2 | 9 | 50 | 40 | 35 |
| 7 | Kettering Ise Lodge | 22 | 9 | 2 | 11 | 44 | 67 | 29 |
| 8 | Stanwick Rovers | 22 | 8 | 2 | 12 | 51 | 47 | 26 |
| 9 | Medbourne | 22 | 6 | 5 | 11 | 36 | 46 | 23 |
| 10 | Kettering Orchard Park | 22 | 6 | 4 | 12 | 38 | 61 | 22 |
| 11 | Gretton | 22 | 3 | 6 | 13 | 42 | 83 | 15 |
| 12 | (R) Finedon Volta | 22 | 1 | 3 | 18 | 24 | 101 | 6 |

## DIVISION TWO

| | | P | W | D | L | F | A | Pts |
|---|---|---|---|---|---|---|---|---|
| 1 | (P) Corby Eagles | 18 | 12 | 6 | 0 | 75 | 27 | 42 |
| 2 | (P) Wollaston Victoria | 18 | 13 | 2 | 3 | 52 | 28 | 41 |
| 3 | (P) Wilby | 18 | 10 | 2 | 6 | 56 | 48 | 32 |
| 4 | Corby Redstar | 18 | 9 | 4 | 5 | 52 | 38 | 31 |
| 5 | (P) Wellingborough Old Grammarians | 18 | 8 | 3 | 7 | 37 | 33 | 27 |
| 6 | Daventry Comms | 18 | 7 | 4 | 7 | 47 | 40 | 25 |
| 7 | (P) Corby Strip Mills | 18 | 6 | 2 | 10 | 40 | 62 | 20 |
| 8 | (P) Clipston | 18 | 5 | 4 | 9 | 32 | 37 | 19 |
| 9 | Spratton | 18 | 3 | 2 | 13 | 27 | 60 | 11 |
| 10 | (R) Wellingborough Rising Sun (-3pts) | 18 | 0 | 5 | 13 | 16 | 61 | 2 |

## DIVISION THREE

| | | P | W | D | L | F | A | Pts |
|---|---|---|---|---|---|---|---|---|
| 1 | Northampton Exiles | 22 | 18 | 4 | 0 | 80 | 14 | 58 |
| 2 | (P) Daventry Drayton Grange | 22 | 14 | 2 | 6 | 56 | 36 | 44 |
| 3 | (P) Weedon | 22 | 13 | 1 | 8 | 57 | 52 | 40 |
| 4 | (P) FC Higham | 22 | 12 | 4 | 6 | 49 | 44 | 40 |
| 5 | (P) Ferrers | 22 | 12 | 2 | 8 | 72 | 51 | 38 |
| 6 | (P) Walgrave Amber | 22 | 12 | 2 | 8 | 58 | 40 | 38 |
| 7 | (P) SPA | 22 | 8 | 1 | 13 | 39 | 55 | 25 |
| 8 | (P) FC Titchmarsh | 22 | 6 | 6 | 10 | 51 | 53 | 24 |
| 9 | (P) Great Doddington | 22 | 7 | 3 | 12 | 39 | 61 | 24 |
| 10 | Grange Park Rangers | 22 | 6 | 5 | 11 | 47 | 60 | 23 |
| 11 | West Haddon | 22 | 6 | 3 | 13 | 48 | 59 | 21 |
| 12 | Wellingborough Gleneagles | 22 | 0 | 3 | 19 | 33 | 104 | 3 |

## DIVISION FOUR

| | | P | W | D | L | F | A | Pts |
|---|---|---|---|---|---|---|---|---|
| 1 | Borough Alliance | 20 | 15 | 4 | 1 | 61 | 18 | 49 |
| 2 | Corby Ravens | 20 | 11 | 5 | 4 | 44 | 34 | 38 |
| 3 | Higham Town | 20 | 12 | 1 | 7 | 51 | 37 | 37 |
| 4 | Kettering Park Rovers | 20 | 12 | 0 | 8 | 64 | 34 | 36 |
| 5 | Corby Albion Vikings (-3pts) | 20 | 10 | 4 | 6 | 51 | 35 | 31 |
| 6 | Desborough & Rothwell United | 20 | 7 | 6 | 7 | 34 | 45 | 27 |
| 7 | Wilbarston | 20 | 6 | 4 | 10 | 38 | 51 | 22 |
| 8 | AFC Rothwell | 20 | 5 | 4 | 11 | 24 | 40 | 19 |
| 9 | Corby United | 20 | 5 | 4 | 11 | 41 | 79 | 19 |
| 10 | Corby Kingswood | 20 | 4 | 5 | 11 | 32 | 55 | 17 |
| 11 | Corby Hellenic Fisher (-9pts) | 20 | 3 | 3 | 14 | 43 | 55 | 3 |

## RESERVE PREMIER DIVISION

| | | P | W | D | L | F | A | Pts |
|---|---|---|---|---|---|---|---|---|
| 1 | James King Blisworth Reserves | 24 | 19 | 2 | 3 | 86 | 31 | 59 |
| 2 | Bugbrooke St Michaels 'A' (-3pts) | 24 | 18 | 1 | 5 | 122 | 54 | 52 |
| 3 | Weldon United Reserves | 24 | 16 | 4 | 4 | 72 | 49 | 52 |
| 4 | Roade Reserves | 24 | 14 | 3 | 7 | 76 | 51 | 45 |
| 5 | Northampton Spencer Reserves | 24 | 12 | 5 | 7 | 54 | 39 | 41 |
| 6 | Harpole Reserves | 24 | 12 | 2 | 10 | 67 | 55 | 38 |
| 7 | Brixworth All Saints Reserves (-3pts) | 24 | 9 | 3 | 12 | 62 | 68 | 27 |
| 8 | Moulton Reserves (-3pts) | 24 | 9 | 2 | 13 | 58 | 63 | 26 |
| 9 | Corby Pegasus Reserves | 24 | 6 | 3 | 15 | 47 | 73 | 21 |
| 10 | Ringstead Rangers Reserves (-3pts) | 24 | 7 | 3 | 14 | 50 | 90 | 21 |
| 11 | ON Chenecks A (-3pts) | 24 | 7 | 1 | 16 | 42 | 99 | 19 |
| 12 | Milton Reserves | 24 | 5 | 3 | 16 | 30 | 64 | 18 |
| 13 | Kettering Nomads Reserves (-3pts) | 24 | 5 | 2 | 17 | 41 | 71 | 14 |

## RESERVE DIVISION ONE

| | | P | W | D | L | F | A | Pts |
|---|---|---|---|---|---|---|---|---|
| 1 | (P) Stanion United Reserves | 24 | 21 | 1 | 2 | 80 | 27 | 64 |
| 2 | (P) Corby Locomotives Reserves | 24 | 13 | 5 | 6 | 59 | 40 | 44 |
| 3 | Wellingborough Old Gram. Res. | 24 | 13 | 1 | 10 | 66 | 46 | 40 |
| 4 | Earls Barton United Reserves | 24 | 12 | 4 | 8 | 56 | 41 | 40 |
| 5 | Welford Victoria Reserves | 24 | 11 | 4 | 9 | 49 | 44 | 37 |
| 6 | Wootton St George Reserves (-3pts) | 24 | 12 | 2 | 10 | 57 | 39 | 35 |
| 7 | Corby Everards Reserves | 24 | 8 | 6 | 10 | 46 | 63 | 30 |
| 8 | Weldon United 'A' (-3pts) | 24 | 10 | 1 | 13 | 43 | 49 | 28 |
| 9 | Heyford Athletic Reserves (-3pts) | 24 | 8 | 5 | 11 | 44 | 55 | 26 |
| 10 | Kislingbury Reserves (-3pts) | 24 | 9 | 2 | 13 | 55 | 84 | 26 |
| 11 | Medbourne Reserves | 24 | 7 | 4 | 13 | 51 | 67 | 25 |
| 12 | Kettering Orchard Park Reserves | 24 | 7 | 3 | 14 | 50 | 77 | 24 |
| 13 | Bugbrooke St Michaels 'B' | 24 | 5 | 2 | 17 | 33 | 57 | 17 |

## RESERVE DIVISION TWO

| | | P | W | D | L | F | A | Pts |
|---|---|---|---|---|---|---|---|---|
| 1 | (P) Wollaston Victoria Reserves | 22 | 18 | 2 | 2 | 80 | 26 | 56 |
| 2 | Corby Redstar Reserves | 22 | 16 | 1 | 5 | 98 | 27 | 49 |
| 3 | (P) Harborough Town 'A' | 22 | 16 | 1 | 5 | 67 | 22 | 49 |
| 4 | (P) Wilby Reserves | 22 | 15 | 2 | 5 | 71 | 31 | 47 |
| 5 | Stanwick Rovers Reserves | 22 | 13 | 3 | 6 | 51 | 41 | 42 |
| 6 | West Haddon Reserves | 22 | 10 | 0 | 9 | 55 | 40 | 39 |
| 7 | Spratton Reserves | 22 | 10 | 0 | 12 | 56 | 55 | 30 |
| 8 | FC Titchmarsh Reserves (-3pts) | 22 | 9 | 1 | 12 | 41 | 41 | 25 |
| 9 | Higham Town Reserves | 22 | 5 | 1 | 16 | 33 | 74 | 16 |
| 10 | Corby Strip Mills Reserves | 22 | 5 | 1 | 16 | 34 | 80 | 16 |
| 11 | Finedon Volta Reserves (-3pts) | 22 | 5 | 2 | 15 | 26 | 68 | 14 |
| 12 | Corby Hellenic (-9pts) | 22 | 0 | 0 | 22 | 23 | 130 | -9 |

# NORTHERN ALLIANCE

| **Sponsored by:** Pin Point Recruitment |
|---|

**Founded:** 1890

**Recent Champions:**
2008: Walker Central
2009: Walker Central
2010: Harraby Catholic Club
2011: Heaton Stannington
2012: Heaton Stannington

| PREMIER DIVISION | P | W | D | L | F | A | Pts |
|---|---|---|---|---|---|---|---|
| 1 (P) Heaton Stannington | 30 | 25 | 2 | 3 | 98 | 33 | 77 |
| 2 Blyth Town | 30 | 21 | 8 | 1 | 92 | 38 | 71 |
| 3 Carlisle City | 30 | 19 | 3 | 8 | 78 | 39 | 60 |
| 4 Amble United | 30 | 18 | 2 | 10 | 81 | 43 | 56 |
| 5 Whitley Bay A | 30 | 15 | 5 | 10 | 75 | 43 | 50 |
| 6 Ashington Colliers | 30 | 15 | 5 | 10 | 65 | 50 | 50 |
| 7 Harraby United (-9pts) | 30 | 17 | 3 | 10 | 72 | 54 | 45 |
| 8 Stocksfield | 30 | 13 | 6 | 11 | 66 | 57 | 45 |
| 9 Seaton Delaval Amateurs | 30 | 12 | 9 | 9 | 52 | 47 | 45 |
| 10 Walker Central | 30 | 10 | 7 | 13 | 41 | 59 | 37 |
| 11 Percy Main Amateurs | 30 | 10 | 5 | 15 | 53 | 80 | 35 |
| 12 Wallsend Town | 30 | 8 | 4 | 18 | 58 | 83 | 28 |
| 13 Killingworth Sporting | 30 | 6 | 8 | 16 | 50 | 65 | 26 |
| 14 Shankhouse | 30 | 8 | 2 | 20 | 51 | 84 | 26 |
| 15 Hebburn Reyrolle | 30 | 5 | 2 | 23 | 37 | 108 | 17 |
| 16 Gateshead Rutherford | 30 | 2 | 1 | 27 | 27 | 113 | 7 |

## CHALLENGE CUP

**ROUND 1**

| | | | |
|---|---|---|---|
| Wallsend Town | v | Stocksfield | 1-4 |
| Seaton Delaval Amateurs | v | Amble United | 1-5 |
| Whitley Bay A | v | Heaton Stannington | 0-4 |
| Gateshead Rutherford | v | Killingworth Sporting YPC | 0-4 |
| Shankhouse | v | Walker Central | 4-3 |
| Harraby United | v | Percy Main Amateurs | 3-0 |
| Carlisle City | v | Hebburn Reyrolle | 10-0 |
| Ashington Colliers | v | Blyth Town | 2-3 |

**QUARTER FINALS**

| | | | |
|---|---|---|---|
| Stockfield | v | Amble United | 3-4 |
| Heaton Stannington | v | Killingworth Sporting YPC | 2-3 |
| Shankhouse | v | Harraby United | 4-1 |
| Carlisle City | v | Blyth Town | 6-4 |

**SEMI FINALS**

| | | | |
|---|---|---|---|
| Amble United | v | Killingworth Sporting YPC | 2-2, 5-4p |
| Shankhouse | v | Carlisle City | 0-5 |

**FINAL**

| | | | |
|---|---|---|---|
| Amble United | v | Carlisle City | 3-2 |

| PREMIER DIVISION | 1 | 2 | 3 | 4 | 5 | 6 | 7 | 8 | 9 | 10 | 11 | 12 | 13 | 14 | 15 | 16 |
|---|---|---|---|---|---|---|---|---|---|---|---|---|---|---|---|---|
| 1 Amble United | | 1-0 | 0-2 | 0-2 | 10-1 | 4-2 | 3-4 | 7-0 | 3-2 | 5-1 | 2-0 | 7-1 | 1-0 | 4-2 | 4-2 | 0-3 |
| 2 Ashington Colliers | 1-0 | | 1-3 | 2-1 | 2-1 | 1-0 | 3-3 | 4-0 | 3-0 | 4-2 | 3-0 | 6-0 | 1-1 | 1-1 | 6-2 | 0-2 |
| 3 Blyth Town | 2-2 | 3-3 | | 3-2 | 4-0 | 6-3 | 0-1 | 3-0 | 3-0 | 3-0 | 1-1 | 2-0 | 3-3 | 2-1 | 2-2 | 0-0 |
| 4 Carlisle City | 2-1 | 2-2 | 2-4 | | 3-0 | 0-2 | 1-1 | 1-0 | 5-1 | 3-1 | 0-2 | 3-0 | 3-1 | 5-2 | 2-0 | 3-2 |
| 5 Gateshead Rutherford | 0-6 | 1-2 | 1-7 | 2-4 | | 2-4 | 2-7 | 1-2 | 1-0 | 2-1 | 1-2 | 1-4 | 0-4 | 2-3 | 1-2 | 1-6 |
| 6 Harraby United | 5-1 | 2-1 | 3-4 | 3-1 | 2-0 | | 1-4 | 4-1 | 2-3 | 1-2 | 1-1 | 4-1 | 3-2 | 1-2 | 5-2 | 2-2 |
| 7 Heaton Stannington | 3-0 | 3-0 | 0-1 | 3-1 | 7-1 | 1-2 | | 7-1 | 3-0 | 5-1 | 2-0 | 3-0 | 2-3 | 2-0 | 3-1 | 2-1 |
| 8 Hebburn Reyrolle | 1-0 | 4-7 | 2-7 | 1-7 | 3-0 | 2-3 | 1-3 | | 2-4 | 4-1 | 2-1 | 1-3 | 0-5 | 0-1 | 2-7 | 0-4 |
| 9 Killingworth Sporting | 0-3 | 1-2 | 3-3 | 1-2 | 4-0 | 1-2 | 1-2 | 2-2 | | 3-3 | 0-1 | 3-1 | 0-3 | 2-2 | 0-0 | 3-2 |
| 10 Percy Main Amateurs | 0-1 | 3-0 | 1-5 | 0-6 | 4-0 | 1-2 | 1-6 | 1-1 | 2-2 | | 3-1 | 3-1 | 3-3 | 0-2 | 5-3 | 1-6 |
| 11 Seaton Delaval Amateurs | 3-3 | 4-2 | 2-2 | 2-2 | 4-1 | 2-1 | 2-3 | 5-0 | 2-1 | 1-1 | | 4-3 | 0-1 | 1-0 | 1-1 | 1-3 |
| 12 Shankhouse | 0-2 | 1-2 | 2-4 | 2-1 | 3-1 | 1-4 | 4-6 | 4-3 | 2-2 | 1-2 | 2-3 | | 3-2 | 2-2 | 3-0 | 1-2 |
| 13 Stocksfield | 1-2 | 1-2 | 2-4 | 0-6 | 4-1 | 1-4 | 1-2 | 2-1 | 2-2 | 3-4 | 1-2 | 2-1 | | 2-2 | 4-3 | 3-1 |
| 14 Walker Central | 2-1 | 2-1 | 1-4 | 0-1 | 2-2 | 0-2 | 0-3 | 2-0 | 0-5 | 3-1 | 1-1 | 2-1 | 0-4 | | 1-1 | 0-3 |
| 15 Wallsend Town | 0-6 | 3-1 | 0-4 | 1-5 | 3-0 | 3-0 | 1-5 | 5-1 | 2-1 | 3-4 | 2-4 | 5-1 | 1-3 | 1-2 | | 1-4 |
| 16 Whitley Bay A | 1-2 | 2-3 | 0-1 | 0-2 | 4-1 | 2-2 | 0-2 | 7-0 | 5-3 | 0-1 | 1-1 | 4-2 | 1-1 | 4-3 | 3-1 | |

## NORTHERN ALLIANCE PREMIER DIVISION CONSTITUTION 2013-14

| | | |
|---|---|---|
| ASHINGTON COLLIERS | Ashington FC, Hirst Welfare, Alexandra Road, Ashington NE63 9HF | 07745 344502 |
| BLYTH TOWN | South Newsham Playing Fields, Blyth NE24 3PP | 07730 058814 |
| CARLISLE CITY | Sheepmount Sports Complex, Sheepmount, Carlisle CA3 8XL | 07739 478547 |
| GATESHEAD RUTHERFORD | Farnacres, Beggarswood Park, Coach Road, Lobley Hill, Gateshead NE11 0HH | 07882 544585 |
| HEBBURN REYROLLE | Hebburn Sports Ground, 16 South Drive, Hebburn NE31 1ZX | 0191 483 5101 |
| KILLINGWORTH SPORTING | West Moor Community Centre, Benton Lane, West Moor, Newcastle NE12 7NP | 07789 900159 |
| NORTHBANK CARLISLE | Sheepmount Sports Complex, Sheepmount, Carlisle CA3 8XL | 07761 416331 |
| PERCY MAIN AMATEURS | Purvis Park, St John's Green, Percy Main, North Shields NE29 6HS | 07960 189667 |
| RED HOUSE FARM | Kingston Park Road, Newcastle-upon-Tyne NE3 2HY | 07809 627368 |
| SEATON DELAVAL AMATEURS | Wheatridge Park, Seaton Delaval, Whitley Bay NE25 0QH | 07527 289744 |
| SHANKHOUSE | Action Park, Dudley NE23 7HY | 07908 969412 |
| STOCKSFIELD | Stocksfield Sports Ground, Main Road, Stocksfield NE43 7NN | 07867 782589 |
| WALKER CENTRAL | Monkchester Green, Walker, Newcastle-upon-Tyne NE6 2LJ | 07449 309210 |
| WALLINGTON | Oakford Park, Scots Gap, Morpeth NE61 4EJ | 07793 596474 |
| WALLSEND TOWN | Langdale School Ground, Mitford Gardens, Wallsend NE28 0HG | 07552 449603 |
| WHITLEY BAY A | Hillheads Park, Rink Way, off Hillheads Road, Whitley Bay NE25 8HR | 0191 291 3636 |

In: Northbank Carlisle (P). Red House Farm (P). Wallington (P).
Out: Amble United (F). Harraby United (W). Heaton Stannington (P - Northern Div.2).

# NORTHERN ALLIANCE - STEP 7

| DIVISION ONE | P | W | D | L | F | A | Pts |
|---|---|---|---|---|---|---|---|
| 1 (P) Wallington | 30 | 22 | 3 | 5 | 94 | 42 | 69 |
| 2 (P) Red House Farm FC | 30 | 21 | 5 | 4 | 94 | 42 | 68 |
| 3 (P) Northbank Carlisle | 30 | 20 | 1 | 9 | 76 | 48 | 61 |
| 4 Heddon | 30 | 17 | 4 | 9 | 62 | 52 | 55 |
| 5 Cramlington Town | 30 | 16 | 4 | 10 | 67 | 54 | 52 |
| 6 Bedlington Terriers Reserves (-4pts) | 30 | 15 | 2 | 13 | 64 | 63 | 43 |
| 7 Gateshead Redheugh 1957 (-6pts) | 30 | 15 | 3 | 12 | 74 | 54 | 42 |
| 8 Hexham (-3pts) | 30 | 13 | 4 | 13 | 71 | 51 | 40 |
| 9 Ponteland United | 30 | 12 | 4 | 14 | 68 | 66 | 40 |
| 10 Gosforth Bohemians | 30 | 9 | 9 | 12 | 56 | 54 | 36 |
| 11 Newcastle Chemfica (Ind) | 30 | 11 | 3 | 16 | 66 | 76 | 36 |
| 12 Newcastle University (-11pts) | 30 | 11 | 5 | 14 | 56 | 67 | 27 |
| 13 Cullercoats (-3pts) | 30 | 9 | 3 | 18 | 55 | 82 | 27 |
| 14 Forest Hall (-3pts) | 30 | 8 | 5 | 17 | 51 | 81 | 26 |
| 15 Willington Quay Saints | 30 | 7 | 4 | 19 | 46 | 76 | 25 |
| 16 (W) Morpeth Town A (-3pts) | 30 | 2 | 5 | 23 | 34 | 126 | 8 |

| DIVISION TWO | P | W | D | L | F | A | Pts |
|---|---|---|---|---|---|---|---|
| 1 (P) North Shields Athletic | 30 | 26 | 2 | 2 | 101 | 36 | 80 |
| 2 (P) Birtley St Josephs | 30 | 22 | 3 | 5 | 119 | 47 | 69 |
| 3 (P) New Fordley | 30 | 21 | 3 | 6 | 96 | 61 | 66 |
| 4 Wooler | 30 | 15 | 8 | 7 | 62 | 42 | 53 |
| 5 Wideopen and District | 30 | 14 | 8 | 8 | 79 | 56 | 50 |
| 6 Blyth Isabella | 30 | 15 | 2 | 13 | 90 | 70 | 47 |
| 7 Seaton Burn | 30 | 13 | 4 | 13 | 65 | 80 | 43 |
| 8 Longbenton | 30 | 10 | 5 | 15 | 69 | 73 | 35 |
| 9 High Howdon Social Club | 30 | 8 | 7 | 15 | 56 | 68 | 31 |
| 10 Alnwick Town Reserves (-6pts) | 30 | 10 | 6 | 14 | 62 | 64 | 30 |
| 11 Wallsend Boys Club (-3pts) | 30 | 9 | 6 | 15 | 61 | 74 | 30 |
| 12 Grainger Park Old Boys (-3pts) | 30 | 10 | 3 | 17 | 64 | 81 | 30 |
| 13 Newcastle Benfield Reserves | 30 | 8 | 5 | 17 | 43 | 79 | 29 |
| 14 Swalwell (-3pts) | 30 | 7 | 8 | 15 | 53 | 96 | 26 |
| 15 Alston (-3pts) | 30 | 6 | 8 | 16 | 49 | 76 | 23 |
| 16 Cramlington United | 30 | 3 | 8 | 19 | 33 | 99 | 17 |

## COMBINATION CUP

### ROUND 1
| | | | |
|---|---|---|---|
| Willington Quay Saints | v | Bedlington Terriers Res. | 0-0, 3-4p |
| Morpeth Town A | v | Heddon | 1-2 aet |
| Ponteland United | v | Wallington | 3-1 |
| Newcastle Chemfica Ind | v | Forest Hall | 3-0 |
| Northbank Carlisle | v | Cramlington Town | 0-1 |
| Gateshead Redheugh 1957 | v | Newcastle Unisversity | 1-0 |
| Cullercoats | v | Gosforth Bohemians | 2-1 |
| Red House Farm | v | Hexham | 4-2 |

### QUARTER FINALS
| | | | |
|---|---|---|---|
| Bedlington Terriers Res. | v | Heddon | 0-1 |
| Ponteland United | v | Newcastle Chemfica Ind | 4-2 |
| Cramlington Town | v | Gateshead Redheugh 1957 | 4-5 |
| Cullercoats | v | Red House Farm | 2-5 |

### SEMI FINALS
| | | | |
|---|---|---|---|
| Heddon | v | Ponteland United | 1-3 |
| Gateshead Redheugh 1957 | v | Red House Farm | 2-3 |

### FINAL
| | | | |
|---|---|---|---|
| Ponteland United | v | Red House Farm | 1-1, 5-4p |

## GEORGE DOBBIN LEAGUE CUP

### ROUND 1
| | | | |
|---|---|---|---|
| Wallsend Town | v | Blyth Isabella | 3-5 |
| High Howdon SC | v | Alston | 5-0 |
| Gosforth Bohemians | v | Killingworth Sporting YPC | 2-4 aet |
| Wideopen and District | v | Amble United | 1-8 |
| Newcastle Benfield Res. | v | Ashington Colliers | 0-2 |
| Birtley St Josephs | v | Swalwell | 7-0 |
| Red House Farm | v | Harraby United | 2-1 |
| Gateshead Redheugh 1957 | v | North Shields Athletic | 4-5 |
| Cullercoats | v | Cramlington Town | 4-1 |
| Grainger Park B C | v | Hexham | 2-6 |
| Carlisle City | v | Longbenton | 8-1 |
| Newcastle University | v | Seaton Burn | 2-3 aet |
| Forest Hall | v | Cramlington Town | 3-0 |
| Walker Central | v | Blyth Town | 1-3 |
| Percy Main Amateurs | v | Morpeth Town A | 3-1 |
| Seaton Delaval Amateurs | v | New Fordley | 10-1 |

### ROUND 2
| | | | |
|---|---|---|---|
| Blyth Isabella | v | High Howdon S C | 4-1 |
| Willington Quay Saints | v | Wooler | 4-3 |
| Killingworth Sporting YPC | v | Amble United | 3-2 |
| Ashington Colliers | v | Wallsend Boys Club | HW |
| Heddon | v | Stocksfield | 1-0 |
| Heaton Stannington | v | Newcastle Chemfica Ind | 4-1 |
| Hebburn Reyrolle | v | Birtley St Josephs | 2-2, 4-1p |
| Red House Farm | v | North Shields Athletic | 4-2 |
| Bedlington Terriers Res. | v | Alnwick Town Reserves | 7-1 |
| Cullercoats | v | Wallington | 2-3 |
| Whitley Bay A | v | Hexham | 1-2 |
| Carlisle City | v | Seaton Burn | 8-0 |
| Gateshead Rutherford | v | Forest Hall | 2-6 |
| Blyth Town | v | Percy Main Amateurs | 5-1 |
| Ponteland United | v | Shankhouse | 3-1 |
| Seaton Delaval Amateurs | v | Northbank Carlisle | 2-1 |

### ROUND 3
| | | | |
|---|---|---|---|
| Blyth Isabella | v | Willington Quay Saints | 3-0 |
| Killingworth Sporting YPC | v | Ashington Colliers | 3-7 |
| Heddon | v | Heaton Stannington | 1-4 |
| Hebburn Reyrolle | v | Red House Farm | HW |
| Bedlington Terriers Res. | v | Wallington | 2-3 |
| Hexham | v | Carlisle City | 1-3 |
| Forest Hall | v | Blyth Town | 1-4 |
| Ponteland United | v | Seaton Delaval Amateurs | 1-0 |

### QUARTER FINALS
| | | | |
|---|---|---|---|
| Blyth Isabella | v | Ashington Colliers | 2-1 |
| Heaton Stannington | v | Hebburn Reyrolle | 3-1 |
| Wallington | v | Carlisle City | 1-0 |
| Blyth Town | v | Ponteland United | 2-3 |

### SEMI FINALS
| | | | |
|---|---|---|---|
| Blyth Isabella | v | Heaton Stannington | 0-2 |
| Wallington | v | Ponteland United | 3-0 |

### FINAL
| | | | |
|---|---|---|---|
| Heaton Stannington | v | Wallington | 6-2 |

# NOTTINGHAMSHIRE SENIOR LEAGUE

**Sponsored by:** Precision
**Founded:** 2004
**Recent Champions:**
2008: Caribbean Cavaliers
2009: Bilborough Pelican
2010: Clifton FC
2011: Boots Athletic
2012: Bulwell FC

| SENIOR DIVISION | P | W | D | L | F | A | Pts |
|---|---|---|---|---|---|---|---|
| 1 (P) Bulwell | 28 | 28 | 0 | 0 | 115 | 29 | 84 |
| 2 Attenborough | 28 | 16 | 4 | 8 | 70 | 53 | 52 |
| 3 Hucknall Rolls Leisure | 28 | 14 | 4 | 10 | 53 | 45 | 46 |
| 4 Ruddington Village | 28 | 15 | 1 | 12 | 64 | 60 | 46 |
| 5 Kimberley Miners Welfare | 28 | 13 | 5 | 10 | 61 | 48 | 44 |
| 6 Magdala Amateurs | 28 | 11 | 10 | 7 | 56 | 45 | 43 |
| 7 Burton Joyce | 28 | 12 | 6 | 10 | 73 | 68 | 42 |
| 8 Awsworth Villa | 28 | 13 | 2 | 13 | 62 | 70 | 41 |
| 9 FC Cavaliers | 28 | 10 | 5 | 13 | 51 | 48 | 35 |
| 10 Bilborough Town | 28 | 10 | 4 | 14 | 64 | 70 | 34 |
| 11 Selston | 28 | 10 | 4 | 14 | 46 | 67 | 34 |
| 12 Cotgrave | 28 | 8 | 6 | 14 | 49 | 64 | 30 |
| 13 Wollaton | 28 | 6 | 9 | 13 | 43 | 68 | 27 |
| 14 Keyworth United | 28 | 6 | 2 | 20 | 39 | 65 | 20 |
| 15 Sandhurst | 28 | 4 | 6 | 18 | 42 | 88 | 18 |

## SENIOR CUP

**ROUND 1**

| | | | |
|---|---|---|---|
| Attenborough | v | Burton Joyce | 8-0 |
| Nottinghamshire | v | Wollaton | 1-3 |
| Cotgrave | v | Gedling Southbank | 7-2 |
| Magdala Amateurs | v | Kirton Brickworks | 5-1 |

Round 2

| | | | |
|---|---|---|---|
| Underwood Villa | v | Bulwell | 0-11 |
| Beeston AFC | v | FC05 | 4-0 |
| Kimberley Miners Welfare | v | West Bridgford | 4-0 |
| Netherfield Albion | v | Ruddington Village | 1-4 |
| Selston | v | Sandhurst | 2-2 5-4p |
| Bilborough Town | v | Keyworth United | 0-3 |
| Attenborough | v | Wollaton | 6-3 |
| Cotgrave | v | Magdala Amateurs | 2-6 |

Quarter Finals

| | | | |
|---|---|---|---|
| Bulwell | v | Beeston AFC | 2-1 |
| Kimberley Miners Welfare | v | Ruddington Village | 2-0 |
| Selston | v | Keyworth United | 0-1 |
| Attenborough | v | Magdala Amateurs | 1-4 |

Semi Finals

| | | | |
|---|---|---|---|
| Bulwell | v | Kimberley Miners Welfare | 4-1 |
| Keyworth United | v | Magdala Amateurs | 3-1 |

Final

| | | | |
|---|---|---|---|
| Bulwell | v | Keyworth United | 4-0 |

| PREMIER DIVISION | 1 | 2 | 3 | 4 | 5 | 6 | 7 | 8 | 9 | 10 | 11 | 12 | 13 | 14 | 15 |
|---|---|---|---|---|---|---|---|---|---|---|---|---|---|---|---|
| 1 Attenborough | | 3-1 | 5-1 | 0-2 | 3-3 | 3-2 | 1-3 | 0-2 | 4-2 | 4-4 | 3-0 | 2-1 | 2-1 | 3-1 | 5-2 |
| 2 Awsworth Villa | 2-1 | | 4-1 | 1-5 | 4-2 | 3-0 | 1-2 | 1-2 | 3-1 | 1-0 | 1-1 | 3-2 | 6-1 | 2-0 | 1-2 |
| 3 Bilborough Town | 2-1 | 2-4 | | 2-4 | 1-3 | 1-4 | 2-2 | 2-2 | 2-1 | 6-2 | 2-2 | 1-2 | 4-2 | 2-3 | 1-1 |
| 4 Bulwell | 4-2 | 5-2 | 6-3 | | 5-1 | 4-1 | 4-0 | 4-1 | 2-1 | 8-0 | 3-2 | 3-0 | 3-1 | 5-3 | 6-1 |
| 5 Burton Joyce | 2-4 | 5-2 | 0-5 | 1-6 | | 6-2 | 3-2 | 2-0 | 3-0 | 0-2 | 2-2 | 3-5 | 7-3 | 6-2 | 6-2 |
| 6 Cotgrave | 1-1 | 8-2 | 1-3 | 0-8 | 1-1 | | 0-3 | 3-0 | 2-1 | 3-3 | 0-0 | 3-4 | 3-2 | 1-2 | 1-2 |
| 7 FC Cavaliers | 1-0 | 1-2 | 1-4 | 2-4 | 2-2 | 4-0 | | 3-4 | 0-1 | 0-0 | 2-3 | 2-1 | 2-4 | 3-0 | 0-1 |
| 8 Hucknall Rolls Leisure | 1-1 | 6-0 | 3-1 | 1-2 | 1-3 | 2-0 | 1-0 | | 2-2 | 2-0 | 1-3 | 0-2 | 4-2 | 1-3 | 2-2 |
| 9 Keyworth United | 1-3 | 2-0 | 3-2 | 0-2 | 1-1 | 0-4 | 1-0 | 1-2 | | 0-3 | 0-1 | 1-2 | 2-3 | 0-1 | 2-6 |
| 10 Kimberley Miners Welfare | 1-2 | 4-1 | 3-0 | 1-2 | 1-1 | 1-4 | 4-1 | 0-1 | 7-0 | | 2-1 | 2-1 | 4-0 | 1-0 | 4-0 |
| 11 Magdala Amateurs | 2-3 | 1-1 | 2-1 | 1-6 | 3-0 | 0-0 | 3-3 | 4-0 | 2-1 | 3-1 | | 1-2 | 4-2 | 5-2 | 1-1 |
| 12 Ruddington Village | 6-3 | 4-3 | 1-3 | 0-3 | 4-0 | 4-0 | 0-6 | 2-4 | 4-1 | 1-6 | | | 1-1 | 4-1 | 2-1 |
| 13 Sandhurst | 3-5 | 0-3 | 4-3 | 0-1 | 0-6 | 3-3 | 1-3 | 1-3 | 0-8 | 0-3 | 1-1 | 2-3 | | 0-0 | 3-3 |
| 14 Selston | 1-2 | 5-3 | 1-3 | 2-4 | 4-2 | 1-0 | 0-0 | 0-5 | 3-2 | 2-6 | 2-0 | 3-2 | 1-2 | | 2-2 |
| 15 Wollaton | 1-4 | 4-5 | 3-4 | 0-4 | 1-2 | 0-2 | 1-3 | 1-0 | 1-4 | 1-1 | 2-2 | 1-0 | 0-0 | 1-1 | |

## NOTTINGHAMSHIRE SENIOR LEAGUE SENIOR DIVISION CONSTITUTION 2013-14

| | | |
|---|---|---|
| ATTENBOROUGH | Nottingham University Grounds, University Boulevard, Nottingham | 07799 105593 |
| AWSWORTH VILLA | The Shilo, Attewell Road, Awsworth, Nottingham NG16 2SY | 07792 509159 |
| BEESTON AFC | Hetley Pearson Rec. Grd, Cartwright Way, Queens Road, Beeston NG9 1RL | 07976 943699 |
| BILBOROUGH TOWN | Basil Russell Park, Maple Drive, Nuthall, Nottingham | 07403 231039 |
| BOOTS ATHLETIC | Trent Vale Road, Beeston Rylands, Nottingham. NG91ND | 07904 409689 |
| BURTON JOYCE | The Poplars, Station Road, Burton Joyce, Nottingham, NG14 5AN | 07738 879266 |
| COTGRAVE | Woodview, Cotgrave Welfare, Woodview, Cotgrave, Nottingham | 07751 114989 |
| FC CAVALIERS | Carrington Sports Ground, Mansfield Road, Carrington, Nottingham | 07527 801634 |
| HUCKNALL ROLLS LEISURE | Hucknall Rolls Royce Leisure, Gate 1, Watnall Road, Hucknall, Nottingham | 07581 227053 |
| KEYWORTH UNITED | Platt Lane Sports Complex, Platt Lane, Keyworth, Nottingham | 07867 676421 |
| KIMBERLEY MINERS WELFARE | Digby Street, Kimberley, Nottingham | 07557 111536 |
| MAGDALA AMATEURS | ROKO Health Club, Wilford Lane, West Bridgford, Nottingham, NG2 7RN | 07816 962429 |
| NOTTINGHAM UNITED | Pavillion Road, Kirkby-in-Ashfield, Nottinghamshire NG17 7L | 07891 380620 |
| RUDDINGTON VILLAGE | Elms Park, Ruddington, Nottingham | 07545 388439 |
| SANDHURST | Walesby Sports & Social Club, Forest Lane, Walesby, Nottingham, NG22 9PF | 07780 661646 |
| SELSTON | Selston Parish Hall, Mansfield Road, Selston, Nottingham, NG16 6EE | 07532 183393 |
| WOLLATON | Wollaton Sports Association, 753 Wollaton Road, Wollaton, NG8 2AN | 07986 584736 |

**In:** Beeston AFC (P). Boots Athletic (P). Nottingham United (S - CML South). **Out:** Bulwell (P - Central Midlands League South).

## NOTTINGHAMSHIRE SENIOR - STEP 7

### DIVISION ONE

| | | P | W | D | L | F | A | Pts |
|---|---|---|---|---|---|---|---|---|
| 1 | (P) Beeston AFC | 24 | 18 | 3 | 3 | 79 | 43 | 57 |
| 2 | (P) Boots Athletic | 24 | 16 | 2 | 6 | 66 | 36 | 50 |
| 3 | Netherfield Albion | 24 | 15 | 4 | 5 | 67 | 37 | 49 |
| 4 | Hucknall Rolls Leisure Reserves | 24 | 15 | 2 | 7 | 72 | 41 | 47 |
| 5 | West Bridgford | 24 | 12 | 4 | 8 | 73 | 40 | 40 |
| 6 | (W) Arnold Town Reserves | 24 | 12 | 3 | 9 | 69 | 39 | 39 |
| 7 | Wollaton Reserves | 24 | 11 | 5 | 8 | 51 | 52 | 38 |
| 8 | Magdala Amateurs Reserves | 24 | 8 | 1 | 15 | 40 | 63 | 25 |
| 9 | Awsworth Villa Reserves | 24 | 7 | 4 | 13 | 42 | 68 | 25 |
| 10 | Radcliffe Olympic Reserves | 24 | 6 | 5 | 13 | 52 | 76 | 23 |
| 11 | Nottinghamshire | 24 | 6 | 3 | 15 | 42 | 66 | 21 |
| 12 | Underwood Villa | 24 | 5 | 4 | 15 | 40 | 72 | 19 |
| 13 | Gedling Southbank | 24 | 3 | 4 | 17 | 18 | 78 | 13 |

### DIVISION TWO

| | | P | W | D | L | F | A | Pts |
|---|---|---|---|---|---|---|---|---|
| 1 | (P) Clifton Reserves | 26 | 18 | 2 | 6 | 85 | 42 | 56 |
| 2 | (P) Linby Colliery Welfare Res. | 26 | 17 | 3 | 6 | 70 | 37 | 54 |
| 3 | (P) Bingham Town | 26 | 16 | 4 | 6 | 70 | 31 | 52 |
| 4 | (P) Ruddington Village Reserves | 26 | 16 | 3 | 7 | 75 | 45 | 51 |
| 5 | (P) Kirton Brickworks | 26 | 16 | 3 | 7 | 66 | 39 | 51 |
| 6 | Calverton Miners Welfare AFC | 26 | 15 | 2 | 9 | 87 | 50 | 47 |
| 7 | FC05 | 26 | 13 | 4 | 9 | 64 | 54 | 43 |
| 8 | Ashland Rovers | 26 | 12 | 5 | 9 | 60 | 49 | 41 |
| 9 | Kimberley Miners Welfare Reserves | 26 | 9 | 4 | 13 | 45 | 55 | 31 |
| 10 | Selston Reserves | 26 | 8 | 4 | 14 | 41 | 54 | 28 |
| 11 | Moorgreen | 26 | 8 | 3 | 15 | 52 | 64 | 27 |
| 12 | Nottinghamshire Reserves | 26 | 5 | 3 | 18 | 45 | 98 | 18 |
| 13 | West Bridgford Reserves | 26 | 5 | 2 | 19 | 32 | 96 | 17 |
| 14 | Sandhurst Reserves | 26 | 1 | 4 | 21 | 27 | 105 | 7 |

**Additional Club Movements**
**Division One In:** Southwell City Reserves (S - Central Midlands Football League Reserve Premier Division).

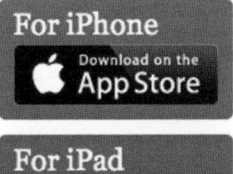

# OXFORDSHIRE SENIOR LEAGUE

**Sponsored by:** No sponsor
**Founded:** N/K
**Recent Champions:**
2008: Rover Cowley
2009: Garsington
2010: Adderbury Park
2011: Hinksey
2012: Oxford University Press

| PREMIER DIVISION | P | W | D | L | F | A | Pts |
|---|---|---|---|---|---|---|---|
| 1 Riverside | 26 | 23 | 1 | 2 | 97 | 26 | 70 |
| 2 Oxford University Press | 26 | 19 | 5 | 2 | 84 | 33 | 62 |
| 3 Bletchingdon | 26 | 14 | 3 | 9 | 74 | 49 | 45 |
| 4 Mansfield Road | 26 | 13 | 4 | 9 | 76 | 53 | 43 |
| 5 Adderbury Park | 26 | 12 | 6 | 8 | 45 | 53 | 42 |
| 6 Stonesfield | 26 | 13 | 2 | 11 | 53 | 51 | 41 |
| 7 Marston Saints | 26 | 10 | 5 | 11 | 52 | 64 | 35 |
| 8 Freeland | 26 | 10 | 2 | 14 | 55 | 52 | 32 |
| 9 Launton Sports | 26 | 10 | 2 | 14 | 48 | 75 | 32 |
| 10 Oxford Irish | 26 | 8 | 6 | 12 | 45 | 65 | 30 |
| 11 Horspath | 26 | 8 | 2 | 16 | 45 | 70 | 26 |
| 12 Kennington United | 26 | 6 | 7 | 13 | 33 | 42 | 25 |
| 13 Garsington | 26 | 6 | 2 | 18 | 38 | 75 | 20 |
| 14 (R) Charlton United | 26 | 6 | 1 | 19 | 43 | 80 | 19 |

## PRESIDENTS CUP

**ROUND 1**

| | | | |
|---|---|---|---|
| Attenborough | v | Burton Joyce | 8-0 |
| Nottinghamshire | v | Wollaton | 1-3 |
| Cotgrave | v | Gedling Southbank | 7-2 |
| Magdala Amateurs | v | Kirton Brickworks | 5-1 |

**ROUND 2**

| | | | |
|---|---|---|---|
| Underwood Villa | v | Bulwell | 0-11 |
| Beeston AFC | v | FC05 | 4-0 |
| Kimberley Miners Welfare | v | West Bridgford | 4-0 |
| Netherfield Albion | v | Ruddington Village | 1-4 |
| Selston | v | Sandhurst | 2-2 5-4p |
| Bilborough Town | v | Keyworth United | 0-3 |
| Attenborough | v | Wollaton | 6-3 |
| Cotgrave | v | Magdala Amateurs | 2-6 |

**QUARTER FINALS**

| | | | |
|---|---|---|---|
| Bulwell | v | Beeston AFC | 2-1 |
| Kimberley Miners Welfare | v | Ruddington Village | 2-0 |
| Selston | v | Keyworth United | 0-1 |
| Attenborough | v | Magdala Amateurs | 1-4 |

**SEMI FINALS**

| | | | |
|---|---|---|---|
| Bulwell | v | Kimberley Miners Welfare | 4-1 |
| Keyworth United | v | Magdala Amateurs | 3-1 |

**FINAL**

| | | | |
|---|---|---|---|
| Bulwell | v | Keyworth United | 4-0 |

| PREMIER DIVISION | 1 | 2 | 3 | 4 | 5 | 6 | 7 | 8 | 9 | 10 | 11 | 12 | 13 | 14 |
|---|---|---|---|---|---|---|---|---|---|---|---|---|---|---|
| 1 Adderbury Park | | 0-3 | 6-2 | 2-3 | 3-1 | 1-0 | HW | 2-1 | 4-2 | 3-1 | 1-4 | 1-0 | 2-7 | 1-2 |
| 2 Bletchingdon | 2-3 | | 6-1 | 0-5 | 8-3 | 2-1 | 1-1 | 4-1 | 6-1 | 1-0 | 0-2 | 8-0 | 2-6 | 1-2 |
| 3 Charlton | 2-2 | 3-6 | | 3-5 | 6-4 | 1-4 | 1-2 | 1-2 | 2-1 | 0-2 | 0-4 | 1-3 | 0-2 | 4-1 |
| 4 Freeland | 1-3 | 3-1 | 3-2 | | HW | 5-1 | 2-3 | 1-4 | 1-1 | 6-0 | 1-1 | 3-4 | 2-3 | 0-1 |
| 5 Garsington | 2-2 | 1-3 | 2-0 | 2-1 | | 1-0 | 1-2 | 0-3 | 2-8 | 1-6 | AW | 2-1 | AW | 1-7 |
| 6 Horspath | 1-2 | 1-3 | 5-1 | 3-2 | 3-2 | | 3-2 | 1-0 | 2-2 | 2-3 | 0-2 | 4-4 | 0-6 | 0-4 |
| 7 Kennington | 0-0 | AW | 1-4 | 0-3 | 2-2 | 6-0 | | 2-4 | 1-2 | 1-1 | 1-1 | 1-1 | 0-4 | 0-1 |
| 8 Launton Sports | 5-1 | 1-5 | 2-0 | 1-0 | 1-4 | 5-4 | 2-1 | | 1-5 | 2-2 | 1-4 | 2-2 | 1-2 | 1-4 |
| 9 Mansfield Rd | 0-0 | 2-6 | 4-0 | 4-3 | 4-2 | 0-2 | 2-3 | 6-1 | | 7-1 | 1-3 | 3-1 | 1-3 | 6-2 |
| 10 Marston Saints | 2-3 | 1-1 | 1-6 | 3-1 | 3-1 | 2-1 | 2-2 | 0-2 | 2-0 | | 4-4 | HW | 1-3 | 6-2 |
| 11 OUP | 6-2 | 2-1 | 2-0 | 6-1 | 6-1 | 4-0 | 3-1 | 9-3 | 0-3 | 4-2 | | 5-0 | 1-1 | 3-0 |
| 12 Oxford Irish | 1-1 | 3-1 | 1-2 | 2-0 | HW | 4-2 | 0-1 | 6-1 | 3-3 | 1-4 | 4-4 | | 1-10 | 1-0 |
| 13 Riverside | 5-0 | 5-2 | 7-0 | HW | 6-0 | 5-2 | HW | 6-0 | 0-5 | 6-1 | 3-0 | 3-0 | | 1-4 |
| 14 Stonesfield | 0-0 | 1-1 | 2-1 | 2-3 | 0-3 | 1-3 | 2-0 | 3-1 | 2-3 | 4-2 | 2-4 | 3-2 | 1-3 | |

## OXFORDSHIRE SENIOR LEAGUE PREMIER DIVISION CONSTITUTION 2013-14

| | | |
|---|---|---|
| ADDERBURY PARK | Lucy Plackett Playing Field, Round Close Road, Adderbury, Banbury OX17 3EE | None |
| BLETCHINGTON | Rover Cowley Sports Ground, Romanway, Cowley, Oxford OX4 6NL | None |
| CHALGROVE | Chalgrove, Oxfordshire OX4 | 07867 972775 |
| FREELAND | The Simon Hole Memorial Ground, Wroslyn Road, Freeland, Witney OX29 8HL | None |
| GARSINGTON | Garsington Sports Club, Denton Lane, Garsington, Oxford OX44 9EL | 01865 361720 |
| HORSPATH | Rover Cowley Sports Ground, Romanway, Cowley, Oxford OX4 6NL | None |
| LAUNTON SPORTS | The Playing Field, Bicester Road, Bicester OX26 5DP | 01869 242007 |
| MANSFIELD ROAD | The University Club, Mansfield Road, Oxford OX1 3SZ | 01865 271044 |
| MARSTON SAINTS | Boults Lane, Old Marston, Oxford OX3 0PW | 01865 203970 |
| OAKLEY UNITED | Playfield Fields, Oxford Road, Oakley, Aylesbury HP18 9RE | None |
| OXFORD IRISH | Rover Cowley Sports Ground, Romanway, Cowley, Oxford OX4 6NL | None |
| OXFORD UNIVERSITY PRESS | Jordan Hill, Banbury Road, Oxford OX2 8EF | None |
| RIVERSIDE | Quarry Recreation Ground, Margaret Road, Headington, Oxford OX3 8AJ | None |
| STONESFIELD SPORTS | Stonesfield Playing Field, Field Close, Longmore, Stonesfield OX29 8HA | None |

In: Chalgrove (P). Oakley United (P).
Out: Charlton United (R). Kennington United (W).

# OXFORDSHIRE SENIOR LEAGUE - STEP 7

| DIVISION ONE | P | W | D | L | F | A | Pts |
|---|---|---|---|---|---|---|---|
| 1 (P) Oakley United | 22 | 21 | 1 | 0 | 114 | 15 | 64 |
| 2 (P) Chalgrove | 22 | 17 | 3 | 2 | 81 | 40 | 54 |
| 3 Middleton Cheney | 22 | 14 | 2 | 6 | 73 | 38 | 44 |
| 4 Eynsham Association | 22 | 11 | 3 | 8 | 59 | 43 | 36 |
| 5 Northway | 22 | 10 | 5 | 7 | 51 | 50 | 35 |
| 6 Kidlington OB | 22 | 9 | 2 | 11 | 51 | 66 | 29 |
| 7 Broughton & NN | 22 | 7 | 4 | 11 | 54 | 53 | 25 |
| 8 Watlington | 22 | 7 | 4 | 11 | 42 | 56 | 25 |
| 9 North Oxford | 22 | 6 | 4 | 12 | 49 | 69 | 22 |
| 10 Yarnton | 22 | 5 | 3 | 14 | 36 | 69 | 18 |
| 11 Long Crendon | 22 | 5 | 2 | 15 | 24 | 76 | 17 |
| 12 Enstone Sports | 22 | 3 | 1 | 18 | 30 | 89 | 10 |

| DIVISION TWO | P | W | D | L | F | A | Pts |
|---|---|---|---|---|---|---|---|
| 1 Bletchingdon Reserves | 18 | 16 | 0 | 2 | 75 | 19 | 48 |
| 2 Garsington Reserves | 18 | 12 | 2 | 4 | 52 | 33 | 38 |
| 3 Middleton Cheney Reserves | 18 | 10 | 1 | 7 | 54 | 37 | 31 |
| 4 Adderbury Park Reserves | 18 | 9 | 0 | 9 | 39 | 33 | 27 |
| 5 Eynsham Reserves | 18 | 8 | 2 | 8 | 39 | 41 | 26 |
| 6 Freeland Reserves | 18 | 7 | 3 | 8 | 47 | 55 | 24 |
| 7 OUP Reserves | 18 | 7 | 1 | 10 | 35 | 39 | 22 |
| 8 Marston Saints Reserves | 18 | 6 | 1 | 11 | 37 | 65 | 19 |
| 9 Yarnton Reserves | 18 | 5 | 1 | 12 | 40 | 67 | 16 |
| 10 Launton Sports Reserves | 18 | 4 | 1 | 13 | 30 | 59 | 13 |

| DIVISION THREE | P | W | D | L | F | A | Pts |
|---|---|---|---|---|---|---|---|
| 1 Mansfield Rd Reserves | 18 | 15 | 2 | 1 | 47 | 24 | 47 |
| 2 Stonesfield Reserves | 18 | 13 | 2 | 3 | 45 | 23 | 41 |
| 3 North Oxford Reserves | 18 | 12 | 2 | 4 | 49 | 22 | 38 |
| 4 Oakley Reserves | 18 | 11 | 4 | 3 | 53 | 20 | 37 |
| 5 Broughton & NN Reserves | 18 | 7 | 3 | 8 | 48 | 31 | 24 |
| 6 Oxford Irish Reserves | 18 | 7 | 1 | 10 | 44 | 44 | 22 |
| 7 Horspath Reserves | 18 | 5 | 2 | 11 | 36 | 45 | 17 |
| 8 Charlton Reserves | 18 | 3 | 3 | 12 | 32 | 60 | 12 |
| 9 Enstone Reserves | 18 | 3 | 2 | 13 | 18 | 65 | 11 |
| 10 Watlington Reserves | 18 | 2 | 3 | 13 | 23 | 61 | 9 |

# NON LEAGUE DAY

## Saturday 7th September

 **Support your local club**

## nonleagueday.co.uk

# PETERBOROUGH & DISTRICT LEAGUE

**Sponsored by:** ChromaSport
**Founded:** 1902
**Recent Champions:**
2008: Perkins Sports
2009: Ramsey Town
2010: Rutland Rangers
2011: Ramsey Town
2012: Pinchbeck United

## SENIOR CUP

**ROUND 1**

| | | | |
|---|---|---|---|
| Ketton | v | Holbeach United Reserves | 5-4 |
| Pinchbeck United | v | Riverside Rovers | 3-5 |
| Kings Cliffe United | v | Moulton Harrox | 0-5 |
| Peterborough ICA Sports | v | Whittlesey Blue Star | 3-1 |
| Whittlesey United | v | Crowland Town | 2-4 |
| Coates Athletic | v | Parson Drove | 4-1 |
| Oakham United | v | Stilton United | 2-2, 4-5p |

**Round 2**

| | | | |
|---|---|---|---|
| Deeping Rangers Res. | v | Leverington Sports | 1-2 |
| Ketton | v | Riverside Rovers | 1-4 |
| Long Sutton Athletic | v | Moulton Harrox | 8-2 |
| Uppingham Town | v | Peterborough Sport Parkway | 2-2, 5-4p |
| Peterborough ICA Sports | v | Kings Lynn Reserves | 2-1 |
| Crowland Town | v | Coates Athletic | 0-3 |
| Ramsey Town | v | Stilton United | 2-0 |
| Netherton United | v | Langtoft United | 6-2 |

**Quarter Finals**

| | | | |
|---|---|---|---|
| Leverington Sports | v | Riverside Rovers | 6-1 |
| Moulton Harrox | v | Uppingham Town | 4-0 |
| Peterborough ICA Sports | v | Coates Athletic | 2-0 |
| Ramsey Town | v | Netherton United | 2-1 |

**Semi Finals**

| | | | |
|---|---|---|---|
| Leverington Sports | v | Moulton Harrox | 2-3 aet |
| Peterborough ICA Sports | v | Ramsey Town | 1-1, 4-3p |

**Final**

| | | | |
|---|---|---|---|
| Moulton Harrox | v | Peterborough ICA Sports | 3-0 |

## PREMIER DIVISION

| | Team | P | W | D | L | F | A | Pts |
|---|---|---|---|---|---|---|---|---|
| 1 | Moulton Harrox | 34 | 27 | 5 | 2 | 96 | 23 | 86 |
| 2 | Netherton United | 34 | 26 | 5 | 3 | 112 | 32 | 83 |
| 3 | Peterborough Sport Parkway | 34 | 26 | 3 | 5 | 120 | 35 | 81 |
| 4 | Peterborough ICA Sports | 34 | 17 | 4 | 13 | 93 | 52 | 55 |
| 5 | Oakham United | 34 | 16 | 7 | 11 | 90 | 79 | 55 |
| 6 | Crowland Town | 34 | 17 | 4 | 13 | 72 | 65 | 55 |
| 7 | Uppingham Town | 34 | 16 | 5 | 13 | 61 | 59 | 53 |
| 8 | Stilton United | 34 | 13 | 7 | 14 | 63 | 65 | 46 |
| 9 | Leverington Sports | 34 | 14 | 4 | 16 | 67 | 79 | 46 |
| 10 | Deeping Rangers Reserves | 34 | 15 | 1 | 18 | 65 | 81 | 46 |
| 11 | Coates Athletic (-1pt) | 34 | 14 | 3 | 17 | 51 | 70 | 44 |
| 12 | Parson Drove (-1pt) | 34 | 12 | 6 | 16 | 58 | 60 | 41 |
| 13 | Ramsey Town | 34 | 12 | 4 | 18 | 44 | 66 | 40 |
| 14 | Whittlesey United | 34 | 11 | 6 | 17 | 74 | 85 | 39 |
| 15 | Pinchbeck United | 34 | 7 | 9 | 18 | 64 | 91 | 30 |
| 16 | Riverside Rovers | 34 | 8 | 4 | 22 | 46 | 102 | 28 |
| 17 | Whittlesey Blue Star | 34 | 6 | 6 | 22 | 57 | 102 | 24 |
| 18 | (R) Kings Cliffe United | 34 | 6 | 3 | 25 | 37 | 124 | 21 |

## PREMIER DIVISION

| | | 1 | 2 | 3 | 4 | 5 | 6 | 7 | 8 | 9 | 10 | 11 | 12 | 13 | 14 | 15 | 16 | 17 | 18 |
|---|---|---|---|---|---|---|---|---|---|---|---|---|---|---|---|---|---|---|---|
| 1 | Coates Athletic | | 1-3 | 1-4 | 4-0 | 1-3 | 1-0 | 0-3 | 2-0 | 2-0 | 2-1 | 0-4 | 1-1 | 1-2 | 5-1 | 1-0 | 2-1 | 3-1 | 1-1 |
| 2 | Crowland Town | 4-3 | | 1-2 | 7-3 | 5-3 | 3-5 | 0-3 | 2-0 | 3-2 | 1-7 | 0-1 | 4-3 | 3-1 | 4-1 | 2-0 | 3-4 | 2-3 | 0-1 |
| 3 | Deeping Rangers Reserves | 2-0 | 1-0 | | 2-1 | 2-4 | 0-2 | 0-3 | 2-4 | 1-2 | 0-3 | 0-3 | 0-2 | 1-0 | 1-0 | 0-4 | 4-6 | 3-2 | 5-4 |
| 4 | Kings Cliffe United | 0-2 | 1-1 | 0-8 | | 2-1 | 0-2 | 0-5 | 1-7 | 2-1 | 1-4 | 1-7 | 2-5 | 1-1 | 2-0 | 0-4 | 1-3 | 1-1 | 2-1 |
| 5 | Leverington Sports | 3-2 | 2-2 | 1-2 | 5-1 | | 0-5 | 0-2 | 2-1 | 2-1 | 1-6 | 2-3 | 5-2 | 4-1 | 2-3 | 3-0 | 0-2 | 1-1 | 4-2 |
| 6 | Moulton Harrox | 5-0 | 6-2 | 1-0 | 3-1 | 6-0 | | 1-1 | 2-1 | 4-0 | 1-1 | 2-0 | 1-1 | 1-0 | 2-0 | 4-0 | 1-0 | 5-0 | 3-2 |
| 7 | Netherton United | 6-0 | 2-1 | 5-1 | 5-0 | 5-1 | 0-2 | | 6-1 | 3-0 | 4-1 | 1-1 | 6-2 | 2-1 | 4-0 | 3-2 | 5-0 | 4-0 | 3-2 |
| 8 | Oakham United | 5-1 | 4-2 | 4-6 | 3-0 | 4-1 | 2-5 | 2-2 | | 2-3 | 3-2 | 3-6 | 3-2 | 4-1 | 2-2 | 1-1 | 1-0 | 3-3 | 3-0 |
| 9 | Parson Drove | 2-0 | 0-1 | 3-2 | 5-0 | 2-2 | 1-1 | 3-2 | 1-1 | | 1-0 | 1-4 | 2-2 | 4-0 | 2-2 | 3-0 | 1-3 | 3-1 | 3-5 |
| 10 | Peterborough ICA Sports | 1-2 | 1-1 | 0-1 | 8-0 | 2-3 | 2-3 | 3-3 | 3-2 | 2-1 | | 5-2 | 4-0 | 1-0 | 10-1 | 6-1 | 1-1 | 8-1 | 1-0 |
| 11 | Peterborough Sport Parkway | 4-1 | 0-1 | 3-1 | 6-0 | 1-5 | 3-4 | 3-0 | 6-1 | 1-0 | 1-0 | | 1-1 | 2-0 | 9-0 | 3-0 | 5-0 | 4-0 | 3-1 |
| 12 | Pinchbeck United | 2-1 | 1-2 | 6-3 | 3-2 | 3-1 | 0-2 | 2-4 | 4-5 | 0-0 | 2-4 | 1-5 | | 1-2 | 5-1 | 2-2 | 1-1 | 1-6 | 1-4 |
| 13 | Ramsey Town | 0-5 | 1-1 | 3-0 | 1-0 | 1-1 | 0-6 | 0-5 | 2-3 | 0-5 | 0-1 | 1-3 | 3-1 | | 2-1 | 1-1 | 3-1 | 2-0 | 1-2 |
| 14 | Riverside Rovers | 6-0 | 0-1 | 2-2 | 0-1 | 2-1 | 1-6 | 1-5 | 1-3 | 2-1 | 4-1 | 1-7 | 3-1 | 0-2 | | 2-4 | 0-6 | 0-1 | 4-4 |
| 15 | Stilton United | 1-0 | 2-1 | 1-3 | 5-2 | 5-1 | 0-3 | 0-0 | 2-2 | 3-1 | 1-0 | 1-5 | 2-2 | 1-4 | 2-0 | | 1-2 | 5-2 | 1-3 |
| 16 | Uppingham Town | 1-1 | 0-2 | 4-2 | 4-0 | 1-0 | 0-0 | 0-2 | 1-4 | 3-1 | 2-1 | 1-1 | 2-1 | 0-1 | 2-1 | 0-5 | | 2-1 | 4-1 |
| 17 | Whittlesey Blue Star | 2-3 | 1-4 | 2-3 | 4-6 | 0-1 | 0-2 | 2-7 | 2-3 | 3-1 | 5-1 | 0-3 | 1-1 | 0-5 | 1-2 | 2-5 | 2-1 | | 4-4 |
| 18 | Whittlesey United | 1-2 | 0-3 | 4-1 | 6-3 | 1-2 | 1-0 | 0-1 | 3-3 | 1-2 | 1-2 | 0-10 | 6-2 | 4-2 | 1-2 | 1-1 | 4-3 | 3-3 | |

# PETERBOROUGH & DISTRICT LEAGUE - STEP 7

## DIVISION ONE

| | | P | W | D | L | F | A | Pts |
|---|---|---|---|---|---|---|---|---|
| 1 | (P) Kings Lynn Town Reserves | 28 | 20 | 6 | 2 | 108 | 26 | 66 |
| 2 | (P) Sawtry | 28 | 18 | 4 | 6 | 80 | 40 | 58 |
| 3 | Long Sutton Athletic | 28 | 17 | 6 | 5 | 88 | 50 | 57 |
| 4 | Thorney | 28 | 14 | 9 | 5 | 53 | 33 | 51 |
| 5 | Langtoft United | 28 | 14 | 5 | 9 | 62 | 44 | 47 |
| 6 | Ketton | 28 | 13 | 6 | 9 | 51 | 50 | 45 |
| 7 | Netherton United Reserves | 28 | 11 | 3 | 14 | 62 | 62 | 36 |
| 8 | Ryhall United | 28 | 9 | 9 | 10 | 45 | 46 | 36 |
| 9 | Moulton Harrox Reserves | 28 | 10 | 6 | 12 | 46 | 48 | 36 |
| 10 | Holbeach United Reserves | 28 | 10 | 5 | 13 | 68 | 75 | 35 |
| 11 | (W) Maccasports  (-2pts) | 28 | 9 | 8 | 11 | 77 | 83 | 34 |
| 12 | Sutton Bridge United | 28 | 8 | 3 | 17 | 61 | 86 | 27 |
| 13 | Farcet United | 28 | 6 | 5 | 17 | 45 | 88 | 23 |
| 14 | Stamford Belvedere | 28 | 6 | 3 | 19 | 39 | 82 | 21 |
| 15 | (R) Hampton Sport | 28 | 4 | 4 | 20 | 37 | 109 | 16 |

## DIVISION TWO

| | | P | W | D | L | F | A | Pts |
|---|---|---|---|---|---|---|---|---|
| 1 | (P) Peterborough S. P. Res. (-2pts) | 24 | 18 | 5 | 1 | 75 | 31 | 55 |
| 2 | (P) Warboys Town  (+2pts) | 24 | 13 | 4 | 7 | 63 | 39 | 45 |
| 3 | Oundle Town  (+2pts) | 24 | 11 | 6 | 7 | 72 | 55 | 41 |
| 4 | Langtoft United Reserves | 24 | 12 | 3 | 9 | 65 | 49 | 39 |
| 5 | (P) Peterborough ICA Sports Res. | 24 | 12 | 2 | 10 | 66 | 59 | 38 |
| 6 | Gedney Hill | 24 | 11 | 4 | 9 | 64 | 70 | 37 |
| 7 | (W) Deeping Rangers 'A' (-6pts) | 24 | 11 | 6 | 7 | 62 | 49 | 33 |
| 8 | Guyhirn | 24 | 9 | 4 | 11 | 49 | 58 | 31 |
| 9 | Crowland Town Reserves (+3pts) | 24 | 9 | 1 | 14 | 49 | 69 | 31 |
| 10 | Leverington Sports Reserves (-1pt) | 24 | 8 | 7 | 9 | 57 | 60 | 30 |
| 11 | Pinchbeck United Reserves | 24 | 8 | 4 | 12 | 67 | 76 | 28 |
| 12 | Oakham United Reserves (+2pts) | 24 | 3 | 6 | 15 | 30 | 62 | 17 |
| 13 | Peterborough Rovers Post Office | 24 | 3 | 4 | 17 | 46 | 88 | 13 |

## DIVISION THREE

| | | P | W | D | L | F | A | Pts |
|---|---|---|---|---|---|---|---|---|
| 1 | (P) Whittlesey United Reserves (+2pts) | 22 | 17 | 3 | 2 | 73 | 28 | 56 |
| 2 | (P) Coates Athletic Reserves | 22 | 16 | 2 | 4 | 74 | 27 | 50 |
| 3 | (P) Baston | 22 | 14 | 2 | 6 | 76 | 32 | 44 |
| 4 | (P) Peterborough ICA Sports 'A' (+2pts) | 22 | 11 | 3 | 8 | 55 | 36 | 38 |
| 5 | (W) Alconbury | 22 | 11 | 4 | 7 | 59 | 45 | 37 |
| 6 | (P) Long Sutton Athletic Reserves | 22 | 10 | 5 | 7 | 50 | 50 | 35 |
| 7 | (P) Ramsey Town Reserves (-3pts) | 22 | 9 | 6 | 7 | 60 | 44 | 32 |
| 8 | Netherton United 'A' | 22 | 9 | 2 | 11 | 71 | 60 | 29 |
| 9 | Kings Cliffe United Reserves | 22 | 6 | 2 | 14 | 45 | 65 | 20 |
| 10 | Uppingham Town Reserves | 22 | 5 | 5 | 12 | 33 | 92 | 20 |
| 11 | Parkside (-4pts) | 22 | 1 | 7 | 14 | 36 | 82 | 6 |
| 12 | (W) Peterborough Rovers PO Res. | 22 | 1 | 3 | 18 | 18 | 89 | 6 |

## DIVISION FOUR

| | | P | W | D | L | F | A | Pts |
|---|---|---|---|---|---|---|---|---|
| 1 | (P) Wittering (-2pts) | 24 | 17 | 5 | 2 | 98 | 40 | 54 |
| 2 | (P) Ketton Reserves | 24 | 15 | 5 | 4 | 76 | 37 | 50 |
| 3 | (P) Sawtry Reserves (+2pts) | 24 | 14 | 4 | 6 | 73 | 45 | 48 |
| 4 | (P) Riverside Rovers Res. (+2pts) | 24 | 12 | 3 | 9 | 76 | 48 | 41 |
| 5 | (P) Thorney Reserves | 24 | 11 | 5 | 8 | 58 | 54 | 38 |
| 6 | (P) Farcet United Reserves | 24 | 10 | 5 | 9 | 65 | 63 | 35 |
| 7 | (W) Oakham United 'A' | 24 | 9 | 7 | 8 | 60 | 51 | 34 |
| 8 | (P) Ryhall United Reserves | 24 | 10 | 4 | 10 | 41 | 63 | 34 |
| 9 | (P) Parkway Eagles  (+2pts) | 24 | 7 | 5 | 12 | 46 | 59 | 28 |
| 10 | (P) Stilton United Reserves (-1pt) | 24 | 8 | 1 | 15 | 59 | 78 | 24 |
| 11 | Leverington Sports 'A' (-6pts) | 24 | 5 | 8 | 11 | 49 | 70 | 17 |
| 12 | Stamford Belvedere Reserves | 24 | 3 | 8 | 13 | 35 | 63 | 17 |
| 13 | Warboys Town Reserves (+2pts) | 24 | 4 | 2 | 18 | 28 | 93 | 16 |

## DIVISION FIVE

| | | P | W | D | L | F | A | Pts |
|---|---|---|---|---|---|---|---|---|
| 1 | (P) Peterborough Sport Parkway 'A' | 20 | 18 | 1 | 1 | 88 | 15 | 55 |
| 2 | (P) Holbeach United 'A' | 20 | 15 | 0 | 5 | 67 | 33 | 45 |
| 3 | (P) Baston Reserves | 20 | 12 | 5 | 3 | 65 | 22 | 41 |
| 4 | (P) Glinton United (+3pts) | 20 | 11 | 0 | 9 | 58 | 44 | 36 |
| 5 | (P) Tydd St Mary | 20 | 11 | 2 | 7 | 100 | 30 | 35 |
| 6 | (P) Ryhall United A | 20 | 9 | 2 | 9 | 42 | 49 | 29 |
| 7 | (P) Sutton Bridge United Res. (-2pts) | 20 | 7 | 4 | 9 | 41 | 44 | 23 |
| 8 | (P) Pinchbeck United 'A' | 20 | 5 | 3 | 12 | 28 | 64 | 18 |
| 9 | (W) Hampton Sport Reserves (+2pts) | 20 | 3 | 3 | 14 | 38 | 64 | 14 |
| 10 | (P) AFC Peterborough (+5pts) | 20 | 2 | 2 | 16 | 26 | 105 | 13 |
| 11 | Gaultree (-12pts) | 20 | 5 | 2 | 13 | 32 | 115 | 5 |

## PETERBOROUGH & DISTRICT LEAGUE PREMIER DIVISION CONSTITUTION 2013-14

| | | |
|---|---|---|
| COATES ATHLETIC | Manor Leisure Centre, Station Road, Whittesey, Peterborough PE17 1UA | 01733 202298 |
| CROWLAND TOWN | Snowden Field, Thorney Road, Crowland PE6 0AL | 01733 211548 |
| DEEPING RANGERS RESERVES | Outgang Road, Towngate East, Market Deeping PE6 8LQ | 01778 344701 |
| KING'S LYNN TOWN RESERVES | The Walks Stadium, Tennyson Road, King's Lynn, Norfolk PE30 5PB | 01553 760060 |
| LEVERINGTON SPORTS | Church Road, Leverington, Wisbech PE12 5ED | 01945 465082 |
| MOULTON HARROX | Broad Lane, Moulton, Spalding PE12 6PN | 01406 371991 |
| NETHERTON UNITED | The Grange, Mayors Walk, Peterborough PE3 6EU | |
| OAKHAM UNITED | Greetham Community Centre, Great Lane, Greetham, Oakham LE15 7NG | 01572 813117 |
| PARSON DROVE | Main Road, Parson Drove, Wisbech PE13 4LA | None |
| PETERBOROUGH ICA SPORTS | Riverside Pavilion, Candy Street, Sugar Way, Woodston, Peterborough PE2 9RE | 01733 567797 |
| PINCHBECK UNITED | Glebe Playing Fields, Knight Street, Pinchbeck, Spalding PE11 3RB | 07966 303275 |
| RAMSEY TOWN | Cricketfield Lane, Ramsey, Huntingdon PE26 1BG | 01487 814218 |
| RIVERSIDE ROVERS | Riverside Pavilion, Candy Street, Sugar Way, Woodston, Peterborough PE2 9RE | 01733 567797 |
| SAWTRY | Greenfields, Straight Drove, Sawtry, Cambridgeshire PE28 5XN | |
| STILTON UNITED | Yaxley FC, Leading Drove, Holme Road, Yaxley PE7 3NA | 01733 244928 |
| UPPINGHAM TOWN | North Street East, Uppingham LE15 9QL | 01572 821446 |
| WHITTLESEY BLUE STAR | Candy Street, Sugar Way, Peterborough Cambridgeshire PE2 9R | 07850 770315 |
| WHITTLESEY UNITED | Manor Leisure Centre, Station Road, Whittlesey, Peterborough PE7 1UA | 01733 202298 |

**In:** King's Lynn Town Reserves (P). Sawtry (P). **Out:** Kings Cliffe United (R).

# READING LEAGUE

| Sponsored by: No sponsor |
|---|
| **Founded:** 1988 |
| **Recent Champions:** |
| 2008: Westwood United |
| 2009: Woodley Town |
| 2010: Reading YMCA |
| 2011: Highmoor Ibis |
| 2012: South Reading |

## SENIOR CUP

**ROUND 1**

| Reading YMCA | v | Cookham Dean | 5-3 |
|---|---|---|---|
| Rotherfield United | v | Woodley Town Reserves | 4-3 |
| AFC Corinthians | v | Barton Rovers | 3-1 |
| Theale | v | Woodcote Stoke Row | 1-0 |
| Newbury FC Reserves | v | Ashridge Park | 2-3 |

**ROUND 2**

| Reading YMCA | v | Frilsham & Yattendon | 6-0 |
|---|---|---|---|
| Mortimer | v | Sandhurst Devels | 2-0 |
| South Reading | v | Goring United | 6-2 |
| Rotherfield United | v | AFC Corinthians | 2-3 |
| Taplow United | v | Unity | 3-1 |
| Westwood United | v | Marlow United | 0-2 |
| Theale | v | Ashbridge Park | 8-0 |
| R.E.M.E. Arborfield | v | Highmoor Ibis Reserves | 3-5 |

**QUARTER FINALS**

| Reading YMCA | v | Mortimer | 3-2 |
|---|---|---|---|
| South Reading | v | AFC Corinthians | 2-1 |
| Taplow United | v | Marlow United | 1-3 |
| Theale | v | Highmoor Ibis Reserves | 3-3, 4-2p |

**SEMI FINALS**

| Reading YMCA | v | South Reading | 0-2 |
|---|---|---|---|
| Marlow United | v | Theale | 6-0 |

**FINAL**

| South Reading | v | Marlow United | 0-2 |
|---|---|---|---|

### SENIOR DIVISION

| | | P | W | D | L | F | A | Pts |
|---|---|---|---|---|---|---|---|---|
| 1 | Reading YMCA | 26 | 19 | 3 | 4 | 71 | 37 | 60 |
| 2 | Woodcote Stoke Row | 26 | 17 | 5 | 4 | 58 | 41 | 56 |
| 3 | Marlow United | 26 | 16 | 3 | 7 | 88 | 55 | 51 |
| 4 | Cookham Dean | 26 | 14 | 6 | 6 | 45 | 39 | 48 |
| 5 | Sandhurst Devels | 26 | 12 | 7 | 7 | 63 | 49 | 43 |
| 6 | South Reading | 26 | 12 | 5 | 9 | 70 | 59 | 41 |
| 7 | Highmoor Ibis Res | 26 | 13 | 1 | 12 | 58 | 43 | 40 |
| 8 | Mortimer | 26 | 11 | 3 | 12 | 48 | 58 | 36 |
| 9 | Theale | 26 | 10 | 2 | 14 | 41 | 56 | 32 |
| 10 | Westwood United | 26 | 8 | 4 | 14 | 48 | 62 | 28 |
| 11 | Taplow United | 26 | 7 | 6 | 13 | 31 | 43 | 27 |
| 12 | Rotherfield United | 26 | 6 | 4 | 16 | 37 | 66 | 22 |
| 13 | (R) Barton Rovers | 26 | 5 | 2 | 19 | 45 | 85 | 17 |
| 14 | (R) Unity (-3pts) | 26 | 4 | 5 | 17 | 38 | 48 | 14 |

| SENIOR DIVISION | | 1 | 2 | 3 | 4 | 5 | 6 | 7 | 8 | 9 | 10 | 11 | 12 | 13 | 14 |
|---|---|---|---|---|---|---|---|---|---|---|---|---|---|---|---|
| 1 | Barton Rovers | | 1-3 | 1-3 | 2-6 | 1-2 | 1-6 | 1-2 | 3-5 | 2-8 | 1-2 | 3-6 | 3-2 | 5-2 | 2-0 |
| 2 | Cookham Dean | 2-1 | | 2-1 | 2-3 | 1-0 | 1-0 | 4-2 | 3-3 | 2-2 | 1-0 | H-W | H-W | 1-4 | 1-3 |
| 3 | Highmoor Ibis Reserves | 4-0 | 2-3 | | 3-2 | 1-3 | 0-1 | 3-1 | 2-0 | 2-2 | 2-3 | 0-1 | H-W | 4-1 | 1-2 |
| 4 | Marlow United | 5-1 | 2-1 | 2-6 | | 6-0 | 3-4 | 4-1 | 2-6 | 6-1 | 1-1 | 6-2 | H-W | 5-1 | 1-2 |
| 5 | Mortimer | 3-1 | 1-3 | 3-2 | 2-5 | | 3-2 | 3-4 | 1-4 | 2-3 | 1-0 | 5-0 | H-W | 1-3 | 2-2 |
| 6 | Reading YMCA | 3-1 | 0-0 | 3-1 | 5-3 | 3-1 | | 3-1 | 3-2 | 1-5 | 2-0 | 4-1 | 0-0 | 5-2 | 0-3 |
| 7 | Rotherfield United | 4-5 | 0-3 | 3-7 | 3-3 | 1-2 | 1-3 | | 2-2 | 1-1 | 2-0 | 1-2 | 1-0 | 0-3 | 0-3 |
| 8 | Sandhurst Devels | 6-2 | 2-2 | 2-1 | 1-4 | 3-3 | 1-2 | 1-1 | | 0-2 | 1-1 | 2-1 | 4-1 | 1-4 | 2-1 |
| 9 | South Reading | H-W | 4-2 | 6-3 | 6-1 | 4-1 | 1-2 | 0-2 | 1-4 | | 3-3 | 3-2 | 1-6 | 4-3 | 2-3 |
| 10 | Taplow United | 1-1 | 2-2 | 0-1 | 1-4 | 1-3 | 1-1 | 3-0 | 1-4 | 3-2 | | 0-1 | 0-1 | 1-0 | 1-3 |
| 11 | Theale | 3-0 | 1-2 | 0-2 | 1-4 | 1-2 | 1-4 | 1-2 | 3-1 | 2-5 | 2-1 | | 2-1 | 2-1 | 3-2 |
| 12 | Unity | 1-2 | 1-2 | 1-4 | 1-3 | 2-1 | 2-4 | 3-0 | 0-2 | 4-4 | 2-3 | 1-1 | | 3-3 | 2-3 |
| 13 | Westwood United | 2-2 | 3-1 | 0-3 | 1-6 | 1-1 | 1-4 | 3-0 | 2-3 | 2-0 | 0-1 | 1-1 | 2-1 | | 1-4 |
| 14 | Woodcote Stoke Row | 4-3 | 1-1 | 1-0 | 1-1 | 4-2 | 1-6 | 3-2 | 1-1 | H-W | 2-1 | 3-1 | 3-3 | 3-2 | |

### READING LEAGUE SENIOR DIVISION CONSTITUTION 2013-14

| BRACKNELL ROVERS | John Nike Stadium, Bagshot Road, Bracknell, Berkshire RG12 9SE | 07584 161621 |
|---|---|---|
| COOKHAM DEAN | Alfred Major Rec Ground, Hillcrest Avenue, Cookham Rise , Maidenhead SL6 9NB | 01628 819423 |
| FRILSHAM & YATTENDON | Frilsham Playing Field, Frilsham Common, Frilsham, near Hermitage | 01635 201847 |
| HIGHMOOR-IBIS RESERVES | Palmer Park Stadium, Wokingham Road, Reading RG6 1LF | 01189 375 080 |
| MARLOW UNITED | Bisham Abbey National Sports Centre, Abbey Way, Marlow, Bucks SL7 1RR | None |
| MORTIMER | Alfred Palmer Memorial PF, West End Road, Mortimer, Reading RG7 3TW | 07770860301 |
| NEWBURY FC RESERVES | Faraday Road, Newbury RG14 2A | 07855 031000 |
| READING YMCA | Padworth Village Hall, Padworth, Reading, Berkshire RG7 4HY | 07917 571835 |
| ROTHERFIELD UNITED | Bishopswood Sports Ground, Horsepond Rd, Gallowstree Common RG4 9BT | 0845 094 1206 |
| SANDHURST DEVELS | Sandhurst Memorial Ground, York Town Road, Sandhurst GU47 9BJ | 07799067751 |
| TAPLOW UNITED | Stanley Jones Field, Berry Hill, Taplow SL6 0DA | 01628 621745 |
| THEALE | Theale Recreation Ground, Englefield Road, Theale, Reading RG7 5AS | None |
| WESTWOOD UNITED | Cotswold Sports Centre, Downs Way, Tilehurst, Reading RG31 6LS | 0118 941 4690 |
| WOODCOTE & STOKE ROW | Woodcote Recreation Ground, Woodcote, Reading RG8 0QY | 0118 9471376 |

**In:** Bracknell Rovers (East Berkshire League Division 2). Frilsham & Yattendon (P). Newbury FC Reserves (P).
**Out:** Barton Rovers (R). South Reading (W). Unity (R).

# READING LEAGUE - STEP 7

| PREMIER DIVISION | P | W | D | L | F | A | Pts |
|---|---|---|---|---|---|---|---|
| 1  (P) Newbury FC Reserves | 20 | 16 | 3 | 1 | 69 | 20 | 51 |
| 2  (P) Frilsham & Yattendon | 20 | 14 | 1 | 5 | 52 | 30 | 43 |
| 3  AFC Corinthians | 20 | 10 | 2 | 8 | 31 | 31 | 32 |
| 4  Cookham Dean Reserves | 20 | 10 | 1 | 9 | 50 | 33 | 31 |
| 5  R.E.M.E Arborfield | 20 | 8 | 6 | 6 | 30 | 28 | 30 |
| 6  Ashridge Park | 20 | 7 | 5 | 8 | 31 | 39 | 26 |
| 7  Westwood United Reserves | 20 | 8 | 0 | 12 | 29 | 50 | 24 |
| 8  Sandhurst Devels Reserves | 20 | 7 | 2 | 11 | 34 | 60 | 23 |
| 9  Woodley Town Reserves | 20 | 6 | 3 | 11 | 27 | 44 | 21 |
| 10 (R) Goring United (-3pts) | 20 | 6 | 3 | 11 | 32 | 36 | 18 |
| 11 (R) Reading YMCA Rapids | 20 | 4 | 2 | 14 | 20 | 34 | 14 |

| DIVISION THREE | P | W | D | L | F | A | Pts |
|---|---|---|---|---|---|---|---|
| 1  (P) Eldon Celtic | 18 | 14 | 1 | 3 | 86 | 35 | 43 |
| 2  (P) Compton | 18 | 12 | 4 | 2 | 94 | 30 | 40 |
| 3  Emmbrook | 18 | 12 | 4 | 2 | 77 | 37 | 40 |
| 4  (P) Marlow United Reserves | 18 | 11 | 2 | 5 | 68 | 33 | 35 |
| 5  AFC Corinthians Reserves | 18 | 9 | 2 | 7 | 47 | 32 | 29 |
| 6  Rotherfield United Reserves | 18 | 7 | 2 | 9 | 39 | 42 | 23 |
| 7  Unity Reserves | 18 | 6 | 1 | 11 | 47 | 80 | 19 |
| 8  "Sonning ""A""" | 18 | 6 | 0 | 12 | 40 | 66 | 18 |
| 9  Sonning Sports | 18 | 1 | 4 | 13 | 29 | 107 | 7 |
| 10 (R) The Hop Leaf | 18 | 1 | 2 | 15 | 22 | 87 | 5 |

| DIVISION ONE | P | W | D | L | F | A | Pts |
|---|---|---|---|---|---|---|---|
| 1  (P) Hurst | 18 | 14 | 2 | 2 | 69 | 26 | 44 |
| 2  (P) Woodley Town "A" | 18 | 10 | 1 | 7 | 34 | 28 | 31 |
| 3  Highmoor Ibis "A" | 17 | 9 | 2 | 6 | 39 | 32 | 29 |
| 4  Sonning (-3pts) | 17 | 9 | 3 | 5 | 36 | 49 | 27 |
| 5  Mortimer Res (-6pts) | 17 | 9 | 3 | 5 | 33 | 21 | 24 |
| 6  Winnersh Rangers | 17 | 6 | 4 | 7 | 43 | 40 | 22 |
| 7  Berkshire United | 18 | 6 | 4 | 8 | 40 | 43 | 22 |
| 8  Wargrave | 18 | 6 | 2 | 10 | 45 | 45 | 20 |
| 9  Reading YMCA Rockets | 18 | 6 | 0 | 12 | 28 | 42 | 18 |
| 10 (R) Woodcote Stoke Row Res. | 18 | 1 | 3 | 14 | 12 | 53 | 6 |

| DIVISION FOUR | P | W | D | L | F | A | Pts |
|---|---|---|---|---|---|---|---|
| 1  (P) White Eagles | 20 | 16 | 1 | 3 | 91 | 29 | 49 |
| 2  (P) FC Winnersh | 20 | 15 | 2 | 3 | 80 | 27 | 47 |
| 3  Royal Oranje | 20 | 14 | 3 | 3 | 93 | 26 | 45 |
| 4  Woodley Hammers Res | 20 | 12 | 3 | 5 | 61 | 36 | 39 |
| 5  S.R.C.C. | 20 | 11 | 3 | 6 | 90 | 40 | 36 |
| 6  AFC Corinthians A | 20 | 7 | 1 | 12 | 41 | 71 | 22 |
| 7  "Taplow United ""A""" | 20 | 5 | 4 | 11 | 27 | 68 | 19 |
| 8  "Highmoor Ibis ""B"" (-3pts)" | 20 | 6 | 3 | 11 | 33 | 68 | 18 |
| 9  Shinfield Village (-3pts) | 20 | 6 | 1 | 13 | 29 | 66 | 16 |
| 10 "Woodley Town ""B"" (-1pt)" | 20 | 2 | 7 | 11 | 22 | 47 | 12 |
| 11 The Hop Leaf Reserves | 20 | 2 | 0 | 18 | 13 | 102 | 6 |

| DIVISION TWO | P | W | D | L | F | A | Pts |
|---|---|---|---|---|---|---|---|
| 1  (P) Woodley Hammers | 18 | 16 | 0 | 2 | 66 | 16 | 48 |
| 2  (P) Pinewood | 18 | 15 | 2 | 1 | 51 | 22 | 47 |
| 3  (P) Taplow United Reserves | 18 | 10 | 2 | 6 | 46 | 34 | 32 |
| 4  Wokingham & Emmbrook ""A"" (-3pts) | 18 | 9 | 4 | 5 | 71 | 37 | 28 |
| 5  Royal Albion (-1pt) | 18 | 6 | 5 | 7 | 31 | 34 | 22 |
| 6  Goring Utd Reserves | 18 | 7 | 1 | 10 | 32 | 41 | 22 |
| 7  Twyford & Ruscombe | 18 | 6 | 2 | 10 | 31 | 44 | 20 |
| 8  Frilsham & Yattendon Res. | 18 | 5 | 0 | 13 | 24 | 56 | 15 |
| 9  Theale Reserves | 18 | 3 | 4 | 11 | 34 | 54 | 13 |
| 10 (R) Hurst Reserves | 18 | 2 | 2 | 14 | 20 | 68 | 8 |

## INTERMEDIATE CUP (FROM THE QUARTER FINALS)

### QUARTER FINALS

| | | | |
|---|---|---|---|
| Royal Albion | v | Cookham Dean Reserves | 0-4 |
| Taplow United Reserves | v | Goring United Reserves | 6-4 |
| Wokingham & Emmbrook A | v | Reading YMCA Rapids | 1-5 |
| Pinewood | v | Hurst | HW |

### SEMI FINALS

| | | | |
|---|---|---|---|
| Cookham Dean Reserves | v | Taplow United Reserves | 8-0 |
| Reading YMCA Rapids | v | Pinewood | 2-2, 2-4p |

### FINAL

| | | | |
|---|---|---|---|
| Cookham Dean Reserves | v | Pinewood | 0-3 |

# SHEFFIELD & HALLAMSHIRE SENIOR LEAGUE

**Sponsored by:** Windsor Food Services
**Founded:** N/K
**Recent Champions:**
2008: Wombwell Main
2009: Athersley Recreation
2010: Sheffield Reserves
2011: Swallownest Miners Welfare
2012: Athersley Recreation

| PREMIER DIVISION | P | W | D | L | F | A | Pts |
|---|---|---|---|---|---|---|---|
| 1 Shaw Lane Aqua Force Barnsley | 28 | 22 | 5 | 1 | 76 | 28 | 71 |
| 2 Millmoor Juniors | 28 | 19 | 5 | 4 | 76 | 39 | 62 |
| 3 Penistone Church | 28 | 17 | 8 | 3 | 61 | 28 | 59 |
| 4 Handsworth | 28 | 17 | 5 | 6 | 80 | 34 | 56 |
| 5 Houghton Main | 28 | 16 | 6 | 6 | 56 | 35 | 54 |
| 6 Swallownest Miners Welfare | 28 | 13 | 8 | 7 | 63 | 50 | 47 |
| 7 Stocksbridge Park Steels Reserves | 28 | 9 | 6 | 13 | 46 | 57 | 33 |
| 8 Everest | 28 | 9 | 5 | 14 | 54 | 57 | 32 |
| 9 Wombwell Main | 28 | 6 | 10 | 12 | 35 | 54 | 28 |
| 10 High Green Villa | 28 | 6 | 9 | 13 | 38 | 57 | 27 |
| 11 Ecclesfield Red Rose | 28 | 7 | 5 | 16 | 42 | 52 | 26 |
| 12 Kinsley Boys (-3pts) | 28 | 8 | 3 | 17 | 57 | 74 | 24 |
| 13 Frecheville CA | 28 | 6 | 6 | 16 | 44 | 75 | 24 |
| 14 Davy FC | 28 | 6 | 3 | 19 | 49 | 96 | 21 |
| 15 South Kirkby Colliery | 28 | 5 | 4 | 19 | 35 | 76 | 19 |

| DIVISION ONE | P | W | D | L | F | A | Pts |
|---|---|---|---|---|---|---|---|
| 1 Oughtibridge WMFC | 26 | 21 | 1 | 4 | 98 | 28 | 64 |
| 2 Athersley Recreation Reserves | 26 | 19 | 6 | 1 | 83 | 25 | 63 |
| 3 Swinton Athletic | 26 | 15 | 6 | 5 | 73 | 41 | 51 |
| 4 Penistone Church Reserves | 26 | 12 | 6 | 8 | 58 | 50 | 42 |
| 5 Thorpe Hesley | 26 | 12 | 5 | 9 | 48 | 51 | 41 |
| 6 Hallam Reserves | 26 | 12 | 4 | 10 | 64 | 64 | 40 |
| 7 Silkstone United | 26 | 11 | 7 | 8 | 51 | 55 | 40 |
| 8 Bramley Sunnyside Juniors | 26 | 10 | 6 | 10 | 53 | 46 | 36 |
| 9 Sheffield Athletic | 26 | 10 | 6 | 10 | 57 | 58 | 36 |
| 10 Sheffield Bankers | 26 | 9 | 4 | 13 | 46 | 69 | 31 |
| 11 Wickersley | 26 | 6 | 5 | 15 | 40 | 60 | 23 |
| 12 Thorncliffe | 26 | 3 | 8 | 15 | 38 | 73 | 17 |
| 13 Worsbrough Bridge Athletic Res. | 26 | 4 | 4 | 18 | 32 | 65 | 16 |
| 14 Caribbean Sports (-1pt) | 26 | 3 | 2 | 21 | 26 | 82 | 10 |

## LEAGUE CUP

**ROUND 1**
| | | | |
|---|---|---|---|
| AFC Dronfield Woodhouse | v | Millmoor Juniors Reserves | AW |
| Ecclesfield Red Rose | v | Kinsley Boys | 2-0 |
| Hare & Hounds MFC | v | Kiveton Park Reserves | 6-1 |
| High Green Villa | v | Hallam Reserves | HW |
| Jubilee Sports | v | Wickersley | 2-0 |
| Penistone Church | v | Oughtibridge WMFC | 0-2 |
| Shaw Lane Aqua Force Barnsley | v | Worsbrough Bridge Ath. Res. | 2-1 |
| Thorpe Hesley | v | Thorncliffe | 3-2 |

**ROUND 2**
| | | | |
|---|---|---|---|
| Athersley Recreation Reserves | v | Davy FC | 3-0 |
| Caribbean Sports | v | Handsworth | 2-3 |
| Everest | v | Millmoor Juniors | 2-6 |
| Frecheville CA | v | Shaw Lane Aqua Force Barnsley | 2-6 |
| Hare & Hounds MFC | v | Silkstone United | 2-0 |
| Houghton Main | v | Swinton Athletic | 2-1 |
| Jubilee Sports | v | Worksop Town Reserves | 5-1 |
| Kingstone United | v | Millmoor Juniors Reserves | 3-1 |
| New Bohemians | v | Boynton Sports | 3-2 |
| Penistone Church Reserves | v | Bramley Sunnyside Juniors | 3-3 |
| Penistone Church Reserves win on penalties. | | | |
| Sheffield Bankers | v | Ecclesfield Red Rose | 3-5 |
| Sheffield Lane Top | v | Frecheville CA Reserves | 1-0 |
| South Kirkby Colliery | v | Thorpe Hesley | 2-1 |
| Swallownest Milners Welfare | v | Oughtibridge WMFC | 2-0 |
| High Green Villa | v | Sheffield Athletic | 6-1 |
| Wombwell Main | v | Stocksbridge Park Steels Res. | 2-1 |

**ROUND 3**
| | | | |
|---|---|---|---|
| Ecclesfield Red Rose | v | Millmoor Juniors | 3-1 |
| Handsworth | v | Athersley Recreation Reserves | 2-0 |
| High Green Villa | v | South Kirkby Colliery | 2-1 |
| Houghton Main | v | Penistone Church Reserves | 2-1 |
| Kingstone United | v | Jubilee Sports | 0-5 |
| New Bohemians | v | Swallownest Miners Welfare | 0-4 |
| Shaw Lane Aqua Force Barnsley | v | Hare & Hounds MFC | 6-1 |
| Wombwell Main | v | Sheffield Lane Top | 3-1 |

**QUARTER FINALS**
| | | | |
|---|---|---|---|
| High Green Villa | v | Ecclesfield Red Rose | 2-1 |
| Houghton Main | v | Wombwell Main | 1-2 |
| Jubilee Sports | v | Shaw Lane Aqua Force Barnsley | 3-2 |
| Swallownest Milners Welfare | v | Handsworth | 2-1 |

**SEMI FINALS**
| | | | |
|---|---|---|---|
| Jubilee Sports | v | Wombwell Main | 2-2 |
| Wombwell Main win on penalties. | | | |
| High Green Villa | v | Swallownest Miners Welfare | 2-1 |

**FINAL**
| | | | |
|---|---|---|---|
| Wombwell Main | v | High Green Villa | 3-0 |

| DIVISION TWO | P | W | D | L | F | A | Pts |
|---|---|---|---|---|---|---|---|
| 1 Jubilee Sports | 18 | 15 | 2 | 1 | 77 | 18 | 47 |
| 2 Millmoor Juniors Reserves | 18 | 11 | 3 | 4 | 41 | 23 | 36 |
| 3 Hare & Hounds MFC | 18 | 11 | 3 | 4 | 42 | 30 | 36 |
| 4 AFC Dronfield Woodhouse | 18 | 10 | 2 | 6 | 39 | 30 | 32 |
| 5 Sheffield Lane Top | 18 | 9 | 2 | 7 | 39 | 40 | 29 |
| 6 New Bohemians | 18 | 6 | 4 | 8 | 36 | 38 | 22 |
| 7 Kiveton Park Reserves | 18 | 6 | 2 | 10 | 32 | 46 | 20 |
| 8 Kingstone United | 18 | 5 | 1 | 12 | 30 | 46 | 16 |
| 9 Boynton Sports | 18 | 4 | 2 | 12 | 36 | 54 | 14 |
| 10 Frecheville CA Reserves | 18 | 2 | 1 | 15 | 29 | 76 | 7 |

| PREMIER DIVISION | 1 | 2 | 3 | 4 | 5 | 6 | 7 | 8 | 9 | 10 | 11 | 12 | 13 | 14 | 15 |
|---|---|---|---|---|---|---|---|---|---|---|---|---|---|---|---|
| 1 Davy FC | | 1-4 | 1-4 | 4-2 | 2-7 | 2-3 | 1-6 | 6-4 | 1-1 | 0-3 | 1-2 | 1-0 | 1-4 | 2-3 | 2-2 |
| 2 Ecclesfield Red Rose | 1-2 | | 1-2 | 3-2 | 1-0 | 3-3 | 1-2 | 2-5 | 1-2 | 1-1 | 1-2 | 1-2 | 1-3 | 2-3 | 5-0 |
| 3 Everest | 2-2 | 1-1 | | 2-2 | 1-2 | 4-0 | 5-0 | 3-2 | 1-3 | 0-2 | 3-5 | 1-4 | 1-0 | 2-2 | 0-1 |
| 4 Frecheville CA | 0-5 | 2-1 | 2-1 | | 0-5 | 3-1 | 1-2 | 3-4 | 3-6 | 0-5 | 0-1 | 3-2 | 2-2 | 0-3 | 2-2 |
| 5 Handsworth | 8-0 | 1-0 | 5-1 | 0-0 | | 3-1 | 0-3 | 5-3 | 4-1 | 2-1 | 1-2 | 6-0 | 6-0 | 6-1 | 3-1 |
| 6 High Green Villa | 2-1 | 2-0 | 2-1 | 1-1 | 2-1 | | 0-0 | 1-1 | 1-3 | 2-2 | 1-1 | 4-0 | 2-3 | 2-3 | 0-1 |
| 7 Houghton Main | 4-1 | 1-1 | 4-1 | 5-1 | 0-3 | 2-1 | | 4-1 | 0-1 | 0-2 | 2-3 | 2-1 | 0-2 | 2-1 | 2-1 |
| 8 Kinsley Boys | 4-1 | 1-1 | 1-2 | 0-3 | 3-0 | 5-0 | 0-1 | | 0-2 | 1-3 | 1-3 | 3-0 | 3-1 | 1-5 | 1-5 |
| 9 Millmoor Juniors | 6-1 | 4-3 | 2-1 | 5-2 | 3-1 | 5-0 | 2-3 | 2-0 | | 1-1 | 1-1 | 1-0 | 1-1 | 3-1 | 2-0 |
| 10 Penistone Church | 6-2 | 1-0 | 3-1 | 4-1 | 1-2 | 1-4 | 7-4 | 0-0 | | 0-2 | 1-0 | 4-1 | 1-1 | 3-1 |
| 11 Shaw Lane Aqua Force Barnsley | 5-0 | 4-1 | 3-3 | 1-0 | 0-0 | 3-0 | 2-2 | 5-1 | 4-1 | 2-2 | | 6-1 | 3-1 | 2-0 | 2-0 |
| 12 South Kirkby Colliery | 2-3 | 1-2 | 1-6 | 1-3 | 1-4 | 3-3 | 0-0 | 1-0 | 3-7 | 0-2 | 1-2 | | 0-1 | 4-4 | 2-2 |
| 13 Stocksbridge Park Steels Reserves | 4-1 | 0-1 | 1-2 | 4-2 | 3-4 | 2-2 | 1-1 | 2-2 | 2-4 | 1-3 | 1-3 | 1-4 | | 3-0 | 0-0 |
| 14 Swallownest Miners Welfare | 4-2 | 3-1 | 3-2 | 3-3 | 2-2 | 1-0 | 0-2 | 5-2 | 2-2 | 0-1 | 2-0 | 5-0 | 3-0 | | 2-2 |
| 15 Wombwell Main | 2-4 | 1-2 | 2-1 | 2-1 | 1-1 | 1-1 | 1-1 | 1-4 | 0-5 | 0-0 | 1-5 | 3-0 | 1-2 | 1-1 | |

# SOMERSET COUNTY LEAGUE

**Sponsored by:** Errea
**Founded:** 1890
**Recent Champions:**
2008: Nailsea United
2009: Bridgwater Town Reserves
2010: Bridgwater Town Reserves
2011: Shirehampton
2012: Nailsea United

## ERREA PREMIER/FIRST DIVISION CUP

**ROUND 1**

| | | | |
|---|---|---|---|
| Brislington Reserves | v | Berrow | 3-2 |
| Odd Down Reserves | v | Westfield | 2-4 |
| Banwell | v | Stockwood Green | 2-1 |
| St George Easton in Gorda | v | Shepton Mallet Reserves | 4-5 |

**ROUND 2**

| | | | |
|---|---|---|---|
| Clutton | v | Bishop Sutton Reserves | 5-1 |
| Street Reserves | v | Ilminster Town | 1-0 |
| Wrington Redhill | v | Keynsham Town Reserves | 3-1 |
| Minehead | v | Shirehampton | 4-2 |
| Watchet Town | v | Brislington Reserves | AW |
| Westfield | v | Burnham United | 3-1 |
| Frome Collegians | v | Purnell Sports | 6-0 |
| Nailsea United | v | Larkhall Athletic Reserves | 1-0 |
| Cleeve West Town | v | Langford Rovers 2000 | 3-1 |
| Banwell | v | Cutters Friday | 3-3, 5-2p |
| Glastonbury FC | v | Yatton Athletic | 3-3, 1-4p |
| Ashton & Backwell United | v | Clevedon United | 0-0, 5-4p |
| Saltford | v | Castle Cary | 2-1 |
| Fry Club | v | Nailsea Town | 4-1 |
| Shepton Mallet Reserves | v | Bridgwater Town Reserves | 1-2 |
| Bishops Lydeard | v | Weston St Johns | 9-0 |

| PREMIER DIVISION | P | W | D | L | F | A | Pts |
|---|---|---|---|---|---|---|---|
| 1 Nailsea United | 34 | 21 | 6 | 7 | 105 | 49 | 69 |
| 2 Minehead | 34 | 20 | 5 | 9 | 63 | 41 | 65 |
| 3 (P) Ashton and Backwell United | 34 | 19 | 8 | 7 | 66 | 51 | 65 |
| 4 Berrow | 34 | 19 | 6 | 9 | 61 | 42 | 63 |
| 5 Shirehampton | 34 | 17 | 10 | 7 | 97 | 57 | 61 |
| 6 Street Res | 34 | 15 | 7 | 12 | 66 | 57 | 52 |
| 7 Cutters Friday | 34 | 16 | 4 | 14 | 74 | 67 | 52 |
| 8 Langford Rovers 2000 | 34 | 15 | 7 | 12 | 91 | 89 | 52 |
| 9 Odd Down Res | 34 | 16 | 4 | 14 | 59 | 59 | 52 |
| 10 Nailsea Town | 34 | 15 | 5 | 14 | 76 | 70 | 50 |
| 11 Watchet Town | 34 | 12 | 7 | 15 | 46 | 46 | 43 |
| 12 Stockwood Green | 34 | 13 | 3 | 18 | 62 | 59 | 42 |
| 13 Bishops Lydeard | 34 | 11 | 9 | 14 | 66 | 73 | 42 |
| 14 Weston St Johns | 34 | 12 | 4 | 18 | 63 | 73 | 40 |
| 15 (R) Clevedon United | 34 | 10 | 6 | 18 | 53 | 71 | 36 |
| 16 Ilminster Town | 34 | 8 | 9 | 17 | 42 | 70 | 33 |
| 17 Bridgwater Town Reserves (-1pt) | 34 | 8 | 9 | 17 | 41 | 61 | 32 |
| 18 (R) St George Easton in Gordano | 34 | 3 | 3 | 28 | 42 | 138 | 12 |

| PREMIER DIVISION | 1 | 2 | 3 | 4 | 5 | 6 | 7 | 8 | 9 | 10 | 11 | 12 | 13 | 14 | 15 | 16 | 17 | 18 |
|---|---|---|---|---|---|---|---|---|---|---|---|---|---|---|---|---|---|---|
| 1 Ashton and Backwell United | | 2-1 | 2-2 | 3-4 | 1-0 | 2-4 | 2-0 | 1-3 | 1-0 | 1-1 | 1-5 | 1-0 | 4-3 | 2-1 | 2-4 | 1-2 | 2-1 | 2-2 |
| 2 Berrow | 0-0 | | 0-0 | 2-0 | 0-1 | 2-0 | 2-3 | 1-3 | 1-4 | 5-3 | 3-2 | 1-0 | 1-1 | 2-2 | 4-1 | 3-1 | 3-1 | 3-1 |
| 3 Bishops Lydeard | 1-2 | 0-4 | | 2-1 | 0-2 | 4-5 | 2-1 | 5-5 | 1-1 | 1-3 | 0-3 | 5-0 | 3-4 | 3-1 | 3-2 | 2-2 | 1-2 | 3-2 |
| 4 Bridgwater Town Reserves | 0-0 | 0-3 | 0-1 | | 1-1 | 1-0 | 2-0 | 2-2 | 4-0 | 1-4 | 1-1 | 0-2 | 1-4 | 3-1 | 1-2 | 0-2 | 1-0 | 2-4 |
| 5 Clevedon United | 1-1 | 3-3 | 2-1 | 0-2 | | 1-5 | 3-2 | 4-5 | 1-2 | 1-3 | 1-4 | 1-2 | 2-5 | 3-1 | 0-2 | 1-3 | 2-0 | 6-2 |
| 6 Cutters Friday | 1-2 | 1-3 | 4-1 | 2-1 | 5-4 | | 3-0 | 1-1 | 4-0 | 3-2 | 0-0 | 3-0 | 5-6 | 8-0 | 5-1 | 0-4 | 0-0 | 1-2 |
| 7 Ilminster Town | 1-1 | 0-2 | 1-0 | 2-2 | 0-0 | 0-1 | | 2-2 | 0-2 | 2-4 | 1-1 | 2-3 | 0-2 | 4-4 | 2-0 | 2-2 | 2-1 | 2-1 |
| 8 Langford Rovers 2000 | 5-4 | 2-1 | 2-4 | 2-2 | 3-3 | 2-3 | 3-1 | | 2-3 | 5-3 | 5-1 | 5-1 | 2-1 | 6-0 | 4-3 | 1-3 | 4-3 | 2-1 |
| 9 Minehead | 0-2 | 2-0 | 4-1 | 1-1 | 4-0 | 1-0 | 0-1 | 2-2 | | 6-1 | 5-2 | 2-0 | 1-1 | 1-1 | 2-0 | 2-0 | 0-1 | 5-0 |
| 10 Nailsea Town | 0-2 | 1-2 | 2-2 | 3-0 | 0-2 | 5-1 | 2-1 | 3-0 | 0-3 | | 1-3 | 2-2 | 2-2 | 6-2 | 1-7 | 2-3 | 1-0 | 3-2 |
| 11 Nailsea United | 2-3 | 3-0 | 5-1 | 2-2 | 4-0 | 10-0 | 6-2 | 7-3 | 3-0 | 2-2 | | 1-1 | 2-1 | 7-1 | 3-1 | 4-1 | 3-2 | 5-2 |
| 12 Odd Down Reserves | 1-3 | 0-1 | 1-5 | 1-0 | 5-2 | 2-0 | 3-1 | 7-1 | 0-1 | 1-0 | 2-1 | | 1-2 | 5-2 | 3-0 | 1-4 | 2-2 | 2-0 |
| 13 Shirehampton | 0-2 | 1-1 | 3-3 | 2-2 | 2-1 | 3-1 | 7-0 | 4-0 | 5-0 | 1-3 | 2-1 | 3-1 | | 8-1 | 2-1 | 1-2 | 2-2 | 7-1 |
| 14 St George Easton in Gordano | 2-7 | 1-2 | 0-3 | 2-1 | 0-4 | 1-3 | 1-3 | 2-1 | 1-2 | 2-8 | 0-4 | 3-4 | 1-2 | | 0-8 | 2-3 | 4-1 | 3-4 |
| 15 Stockwood Green | 1-2 | 0-2 | 0-1 | 4-1 | 0-0 | 3-2 | 1-2 | 3-1 | 2-0 | 0-2 | 3-1 | 0-1 | 2-2 | 3-0 | | 2-2 | 0-2 | 3-2 |
| 16 Street Reserves | 1-2 | 0-1 | 2-2 | 2-1 | 2-0 | 1-1 | 3-0 | 1-3 | 1-3 | 2-1 | 1-4 | 3-5 | 5-1 | 0-1 | | | 1-1 | 3-1 |
| 17 Watchet Town | 1-2 | 3-0 | 1-1 | 0-1 | 0-1 | 1-0 | 1-1 | 3-2 | 1-2 | 1-0 | 0-3 | 0-0 | 3-2 | 5-1 | 2-1 | 4-0 | | 0-1 |
| 18 Weston St Johns | 1-1 | 0-2 | 4-2 | 4-0 | 1-0 | 1-2 | 1-1 | 4-2 | 1-2 | 1-2 | 2-1 | 4-1 | 2-2 | 7-0 | 2-1 | 0-3 | 0-1 | |

## SOMERSET COUNTY LEAGUE PREMIER DIVISION CONSTITUTION 2013-14

| | | |
|---|---|---|
| BERROW | Red Road Playing Fields, Berrow, Burnham-on-Sea TA8 2LY | 07714 122050 |
| BISHOPS LYDEARD | Darby Way, Bishops Lydeard TA4 3BE | 07771 506613 |
| BRIDGWATER TOWN RESEVES | Fairfax Park, College Way, Bath Road, Bridgwater TA6 4TZ | 01278 446899 |
| CLUTTON | Warwick Fields, Upper Bristol Road , Behind Warwick Arms, Clutton, Nr Bristol BS39 5TA | |
| CUTTERS FRIDAY | The Cutters Club, Stockwood Lane, Stockwood, Bristol BS14 8SJ | 01275 839830 |
| FRY CLUB | Cadbury's, Somerdale, Keynsham, Bristol BS31 2AU | 0117 9376500 |
| ILMINSTER TOWN | Recreation Ground, Ilminster TA19 0EF | 07875 378663 |
| LANGFORD ROVERS 2000 | Westland United FC, Winterstoke Road, Weston-super-Mare BS24 9AA | 01934 632037 |
| MINEHEAD | Recreation Ground, Irnham Road, Minehead TA24 5DP | 01643 704989 |
| NAILSEA TOWN | Fryth Way, Pound Lane, Nailsea BS48 2AS | 07763 925811 |
| NAILSEA UNITED | Grove Sports Ground, Old Church, Nailsea BS48 4ND | 01275 856892 |
| ODD DOWN RESERVES | Lew Hill Memorial Ground, Combe Hay Lane, Odd Down, Bath BA2 8PH | 01225 832491 |
| SHIREHAMPTON | Recreation Ground, Penpole Lane, Shirehampton, Bristol BS11 0EA | 0117 923 5461 |
| STOCKWOOD GREEN | Hursley Lane, Woolard Lane, Whitchurch, Bristol BS14 0QY | 01275 891300 |
| STREET RESERVES | The Tannery Ground, Middlebrooks, Street BA16 0TA | 01458 445987 |
| WATCHET TOWN | Memorial Ground, Doniford Road, Watchet TA23 0TG | 01984 631041 |
| WESTON ST JOHNS | Coleridge Road, Bournville Estate, Weston-super-Mare BS23 3UP | 01934 612862 |
| YATTON ATHLETIC | Hangstones Playing Fields, Stowey Road, Yatton, North Somerset BS49 4HS | |

**In:** Clutton (P). Fry Club (P) Yatton Athletic (P).
**Out:** Ashton & Backwell United (P - Western Division One). Clevedon United (R). St George Easton in Godano (R).

## DIVISION ONE

| | | P | W | D | L | F | A | Pts |
|---|---|---|---|---|---|---|---|---|
| 1 | (P) Yatton Athletic | 34 | 23 | 5 | 6 | 101 | 54 | 74 |
| 2 | (P) Clutton | 34 | 21 | 4 | 9 | 80 | 54 | 67 |
| 3 | (P) Fry Club | 34 | 20 | 6 | 8 | 68 | 47 | 66 |
| 4 | Frome Collegians | 34 | 19 | 5 | 10 | 88 | 51 | 62 |
| 5 | Westfield FC (-4pts) | 34 | 20 | 3 | 11 | 81 | 63 | 59 |
| 6 | Banwell | 34 | 17 | 5 | 12 | 80 | 64 | 56 |
| 7 | Wrington Redhill | 34 | 17 | 5 | 12 | 64 | 48 | 56 |
| 8 | Brislington Res | 34 | 15 | 9 | 10 | 57 | 44 | 54 |
| 9 | Keynsham Town Res | 34 | 13 | 10 | 11 | 75 | 61 | 49 |
| 10 | Burnham United | 34 | 14 | 3 | 17 | 65 | 58 | 45 |
| 11 | Shepton Mallet Res | 34 | 11 | 7 | 16 | 53 | 74 | 40 |
| 12 | Castle Cary | 34 | 11 | 6 | 17 | 50 | 59 | 39 |
| 13 | Larkhall Athletic Res | 34 | 10 | 8 | 16 | 55 | 74 | 38 |
| 14 | Purnells Sports FC | 34 | 11 | 3 | 20 | 53 | 79 | 36 |
| 15 | Saltford | 34 | 9 | 4 | 21 | 34 | 79 | 31 |
| 16 | Cleeve West Town | 34 | 7 | 9 | 18 | 33 | 54 | 30 |
| 17 | (R) Glastonbury Town | 34 | 7 | 9 | 18 | 40 | 67 | 30 |
| 18 | (R) Bishop Sutton Reserves (-1pt) | 34 | 9 | 3 | 22 | 51 | 98 | 29 |

## DIVISION TWO EAST

| | | P | W | D | L | F | A | Pts |
|---|---|---|---|---|---|---|---|---|
| 1 | (P) Broad Plain House | 28 | 21 | 4 | 3 | 97 | 34 | 67 |
| 2 | (P) Dundry Athletic | 28 | 21 | 3 | 4 | 88 | 34 | 66 |
| 3 | Peasedown Athletic | 28 | 20 | 3 | 5 | 107 | 33 | 63 |
| 4 | Radstock Town Res | 28 | 19 | 3 | 6 | 70 | 38 | 60 |
| 5 | Long Ashton | 28 | 16 | 4 | 8 | 68 | 49 | 52 |
| 6 | Fry Club Reserves | 28 | 12 | 6 | 10 | 48 | 38 | 42 |
| 7 | Hengrove Athletic Reserves | 28 | 11 | 6 | 11 | 57 | 59 | 39 |
| 8 | Imperial FC | 28 | 9 | 7 | 12 | 44 | 64 | 34 |
| 9 | Cutters Friday Res | 28 | 10 | 3 | 15 | 52 | 69 | 33 |
| 10 | Tunley Athletic | 28 | 7 | 9 | 12 | 44 | 74 | 30 |
| 11 | Welton Rovers Res | 28 | 8 | 3 | 17 | 42 | 64 | 27 |
| 12 | Chew Magna | 28 | 6 | 8 | 14 | 34 | 47 | 26 |
| 13 | Farrington Gurney | 28 | 6 | 4 | 18 | 36 | 76 | 22 |
| 14 | Stockwood Green Reserves | 28 | 6 | 2 | 20 | 33 | 71 | 20 |
| 15 | Timsbury Athletic | 28 | 4 | 3 | 21 | 25 | 95 | 15 |

## PREMIER/FIRST DIVISION CUP continued...

### ROUND 3

| | | | |
|---|---|---|---|
| Clutton | v | Street Reserves | 0-3 |
| Wrington Redhill | v | Minehead | 1-2 |
| Brislington Reserves | v | Westfield | 0-2 |
| Frome Collegians | v | Nailsea United | 4-5 |
| Cleeve West Town | v | Banwell | 2-1 |
| Yatton Athletic | v | Ashton & Backwell United | 2-2, 5-4p |
| Saltford | v | Fry Club | 1-3 |
| Bridgwater Town Reserves | v | Bishops Lydeard | 0-2 |

### QUARTER FINALS

| | | | |
|---|---|---|---|
| Street Reserves | v | Minehead | 0-1 |
| Westfield | v | Nailsea United | 2-3 |
| Cleeve West Town | v | Yatton Athletic | 1-1, 6-7p |
| Fry Club | v | Bishops Lydeard | 3-2 |

### SEMI FINALS

| | | | |
|---|---|---|---|
| Minehead | v | Nailsea United | 1-2 |
| Yatton Athletic | v | Fry Club | 3-6 |

### FINAL

| | | | |
|---|---|---|---|
| Nailsea United | v | Fry Club | 2-1 |

## DIVISION TWO CUP

### FINAL

| | | | |
|---|---|---|---|
| Nailsea Town Reserves | v | Portishead Town Reserves | 2-4 |

## DIVISION TWO WEST

| | | P | W | D | L | F | A | Pts |
|---|---|---|---|---|---|---|---|---|
| 1 | (P) Congresbury | 30 | 22 | 4 | 4 | 89 | 34 | 70 |
| 2 | (P) Middlezoy Rovers | 30 | 20 | 3 | 7 | 80 | 37 | 63 |
| 3 | Winscombe | 30 | 19 | 2 | 9 | 62 | 30 | 59 |
| 4 | Creech North Curry (-3pts) | 30 | 19 | 5 | 6 | 63 | 32 | 59 |
| 5 | Wells City Reserves | 30 | 17 | 3 | 10 | 86 | 49 | 54 |
| 6 | Portishead Town Res | 30 | 13 | 8 | 9 | 65 | 39 | 47 |
| 7 | Nailsea United Reserves | 30 | 15 | 2 | 13 | 63 | 54 | 47 |
| 8 | Combe St Nicholas | 30 | 13 | 4 | 13 | 48 | 46 | 43 |
| 9 | Nailsea Town Reserves | 30 | 11 | 7 | 12 | 54 | 61 | 40 |
| 10 | Weston St Johns Reserves | 30 | 10 | 4 | 16 | 53 | 82 | 34 |
| 11 | Churchill Club 70 | 30 | 9 | 6 | 15 | 59 | 68 | 33 |
| 12 | Cheddar Reserves | 30 | 10 | 2 | 18 | 40 | 73 | 32 |
| 13 | Burnham United Reserves | 30 | 9 | 3 | 18 | 35 | 79 | 30 |
| 14 | Westland United | 30 | 8 | 3 | 19 | 41 | 74 | 27 |
| 15 | Ashton and Backwell United Res. | 30 | 6 | 8 | 16 | 38 | 64 | 26 |
| 16 | Worle | 30 | 4 | 6 | 20 | 34 | 88 | 18 |

# STAFFORDSHIRE COUNTY SENIOR LEAGUE

**Sponsored by:** No sponsor
**Founded:** 1957
**Recent Champions:**
2008: Wolstanton United
2009: Foley
2010: Stretton Eagles
2011: Ball Haye Green
2012: Hanley Town

| PREMIER DIVISION | P | W | D | L | F | A | Pts |
|---|---|---|---|---|---|---|---|
| 1 (P) Hanley Town | 30 | 24 | 5 | 1 | 101 | 29 | 77 |
| 2 Redgate Clayton | 30 | 23 | 4 | 3 | 102 | 27 | 73 |
| 3 Audley | 30 | 20 | 6 | 4 | 69 | 30 | 66 |
| 4 Abbey Hulton United | 30 | 20 | 5 | 5 | 93 | 38 | 65 |
| 5 Cheadle Town | 30 | 16 | 5 | 9 | 64 | 55 | 53 |
| 6 Ball Haye Green | 30 | 16 | 4 | 10 | 74 | 53 | 52 |
| 7 Wolstanton United | 30 | 17 | 2 | 11 | 70 | 53 | 50 |
| 8 Kidsgrove Athletic | 30 | 15 | 4 | 11 | 79 | 49 | 49 |
| 9 Norton FC | 30 | 13 | 4 | 13 | 84 | 83 | 43 |
| 10 Keele University | 30 | 10 | 3 | 17 | 51 | 70 | 33 |
| 11 Alsager Town | 30 | 9 | 5 | 16 | 58 | 71 | 32 |
| 12 Newcastle Town | 30 | 8 | 4 | 18 | 62 | 73 | 28 |
| 13 Eccleshall AFC | 30 | 7 | 5 | 18 | 52 | 106 | 26 |
| 14 Biddulph Town | 30 | 6 | 3 | 21 | 45 | 93 | 21 |
| 15 Florence FC | 30 | 3 | 3 | 24 | 39 | 107 | 9 |
| 16 Stretton FC | 30 | 1 | 2 | 27 | 18 | 124 | 5 |

Stone Dominoes withdrew - record expunged.

## LEAGUE CUP

**ROUND 1**

| Newcastle Town | v | Florence | 3-1 |
|---|---|---|---|

**ROUND 2**

| Wolstanton United | v | Cheadle Town | 2-0 |
|---|---|---|---|
| Stretton | v | Hanley Town | 0-5 |
| Stone Dominoes | v | Biddulph Town | 0-1 |
| Norton | v | Eccleshall AFC | 8-4 |
| Kidsgrove Athletic | v | Redgate Clayton | 0-2 |
| Ball Haye Green | v | Keele University | 4-2 |
| Alsager Town | v | Newcastle Town | 4-2 |
| Abbey Hulton United | v | Audley | 2-1 |

**QUARTER FINALS**

| Abbey Hulton | v | Hanley Town | 2-4 |
|---|---|---|---|
| Biddulph Town | v | Norton | 0-3 |
| Ball Haye Green | v | Redgate Clayton | 2-3 |
| Wolstanton United | v | Alsager Town | 5-0 |

**SEMI FINALS**

| Biddulph Town | v | Hanley Town | 1-3 |
|---|---|---|---|
| Redgate Clayton | v | Wolstanton United | 2-4 |

**FINAL**

| Hanley Town | v | Wolstanton United | 2-1 |
|---|---|---|---|

| DIVISION ONE | P | W | D | L | F | A | Pts |
|---|---|---|---|---|---|---|---|
| 1 (P) Uttoxeter Town | 32 | 29 | 2 | 1 | 148 | 32 | 86 |
| 2 (P) Hilton Harriers | 32 | 26 | 1 | 5 | 88 | 44 | 79 |
| 3 MMU | 32 | 24 | 4 | 4 | 86 | 38 | 76 |
| 4 Hanley Town Reserves | 32 | 21 | 3 | 8 | 75 | 49 | 66 |
| 5 Wolstanton United Reserves | 32 | 20 | 0 | 12 | 100 | 56 | 60 |
| 6 Leek Town | 32 | 19 | 3 | 10 | 84 | 46 | 60 |
| 7 Ashbourne FC | 32 | 18 | 4 | 10 | 89 | 61 | 58 |
| 8 Redgate Clayton Reserves | 32 | 13 | 6 | 13 | 68 | 97 | 45 |
| 9 Congleton Athletic | 32 | 13 | 2 | 17 | 64 | 68 | 41 |
| 10 Abbey Hulton Reserves | 32 | 10 | 7 | 15 | 58 | 71 | 37 |
| 11 Foley | 32 | 9 | 7 | 16 | 59 | 70 | 34 |
| 12 Cheadle SMU | 32 | 8 | 7 | 17 | 44 | 83 | 31 |
| 13 Bradwell FC | 32 | 6 | 8 | 18 | 53 | 94 | 26 |
| 14 Chesterton AFC | 32 | 6 | 6 | 20 | 46 | 88 | 24 |
| 15 (F) Vodafone Stoke | 32 | 7 | 2 | 23 | 54 | 103 | 23 |
| 16 (F) Bradeley Town | 32 | 4 | 7 | 21 | 34 | 90 | 19 |
| 17 Sandbach United Reserves | 32 | 3 | 3 | 26 | 48 | 108 | 12 |

| DIVISION TWO | P | W | D | L | F | A | Pts |
|---|---|---|---|---|---|---|---|
| 1 (P) Silverdale FC | 24 | 19 | 3 | 2 | 85 | 31 | 60 |
| 2 (P) Hall Heath FC | 24 | 17 | 2 | 5 | 117 | 54 | 53 |
| 3 (W) Florence Reserves | 24 | 14 | 4 | 6 | 77 | 50 | 46 |
| 4 (P) Stapenhill FC | 24 | 14 | 3 | 7 | 79 | 50 | 45 |
| 5 (W) Biddulph Town Reserves | 24 | 15 | 0 | 9 | 72 | 53 | 45 |
| 6 Betley FC | 24 | 13 | 3 | 8 | 67 | 36 | 42 |
| 7 (P) Norton FC Reserves | 24 | 12 | 4 | 8 | 77 | 47 | 40 |
| 8 Hawkins Sports | 24 | 10 | 5 | 9 | 52 | 63 | 35 |
| 9 (W) FC Vibromax JCB | 24 | 10 | 2 | 12 | 75 | 69 | 32 |
| 10 Cheadle Town Reserves | 24 | 8 | 3 | 13 | 53 | 52 | 27 |
| 11 Longton FC | 24 | 4 | 2 | 18 | 32 | 91 | 14 |
| 12 Whittington FC | 24 | 3 | 2 | 19 | 38 | 99 | 11 |
| 14 Tunstall Town | 24 | 0 | 1 | 23 | 22 | 151 | 1 |

## STAFFS COUNTY SENIOR LEAGUE PREMIER DIVISION CONSTITUTION 2013-14

| | |
|---|---|
| AFC LEEK TOWN | Ball Haye Green WMC, Ball Haye Green, Leek ST13 6BH |
| AFC HANLEY TOWN | Abbey Lane, Bucknall, Stoke-on-Trent ST2 8AU |
| ABBEY HULTON UNITED | Birches Head Road, Abbey Hulton, Stoke-on-Trent ST2 8DD |
| ALSAGER TOWN RESERVES | Law Training Stadium, Wood Park, Alsager ST7 2DP |
| AUDLEY & DISTRICT | Town Fields, Old Road, Bignall, Stoke-on-Trent ST7 8QH |
| BALL HAYE GREEN | Ball Haye Green WMC, Ball Haye Green, Leek ST13 6BH |
| CHEADLE TOWN | Thorley Drive, Cheadle, Staffordshire. ST10 1SA |
| ECCLESHALL AFC | Pershall Park, Chester Road, Eccleshall ST21 6NE |
| FLORENCE | Florence Sports & Social, Lightwood Road, Longton, Stoke-on-Trent ST3 4JS |
| HILTON HARRIERS ATHLETIC | The Mease, Hilton, Derbyshire, DE65 5LS |
| KEELE UNIVERSITY | Sports Centre, Keele University, Keele ST5 5BD |
| KIDSGROVE ATHLETIC RESERVES | The Seddon Stadium, Hollinwood Road, Kidsgrove, Stoke-on-Trent ST7 1DQ |
| NEWCASTLE TOWN RESERVES | The Aspire Stadium, Buckmaster Avenue, Clayton, Newcastle-under-Lyme ST5 3BX |
| NORTON | The Autonet Insurance Stadium, Community Drive, Smallthorne, Stoke-on-Trent ST6 1QF |
| REDGATE CLAYTON | Clayton Community Centre, Northwood Lane, Clayton, Newcastle-under-Lyme ST5 4BN |
| UTTOXETER TOWN | Oldfields Sports Ground, Springfield Road, Uttoxeter, ST14 7JX |
| WOLSTANTON UNITED | Bradwell Community Centre, Riceyman Road, Bradwell, Newcastle-under-Lyme ST5 8LD |

**In:** AFC Leek Town (N). AFC Hanley Town (N).Hilton Harriers (P). Uttoxeter Town.
**Out:** Biddulph Town (W). Hanley Town (P - North West Counties Div.1). Stretton (W). Stone Dominoes (WS).

# SUFFOLK & IPSWICH LEAGUE

**Sponsored by:** TouchlineSIL
**Founded:** 1896
**Recent Champions:**
2008: Brantham Athletic
2009: Grundisburgh
2010: Old Newton United
2011: Grundisburgh
2012: Woodbridge Athletic

## SENIOR DIVISION

| | | P | W | D | L | F | A | Pts |
|---|---|---|---|---|---|---|---|---|
| 1 | Ipswich Valley Rangers | 29 | 22 | 3 | 4 | 86 | 41 | 69 |
| 2 | Achilles (-1pt) | 29 | 18 | 5 | 6 | 61 | 40 | 58 |
| 3 | Felixstowe United | 30 | 17 | 4 | 9 | 70 | 45 | 55 |
| 4 | Haughley United | 30 | 14 | 8 | 8 | 57 | 37 | 50 |
| 5 | Wickham Market | 30 | 15 | 3 | 12 | 61 | 49 | 48 |
| 6 | Capel Plough | 30 | 14 | 4 | 12 | 48 | 47 | 46 |
| 7 | Coplestonians | 30 | 11 | 8 | 11 | 50 | 44 | 41 |
| 8 | Grundisburgh | 30 | 10 | 9 | 11 | 64 | 57 | 39 |
| 9 | Crane Sports | 30 | 9 | 11 | 10 | 48 | 42 | 38 |
| 10 | Old Newton United | 30 | 9 | 11 | 10 | 49 | 58 | 38 |
| 11 | Leiston St Margarets | 30 | 8 | 9 | 13 | 42 | 51 | 33 |
| 12 | Melton St Audrys | 30 | 8 | 8 | 14 | 41 | 50 | 32 |
| 13 | Stanton | 30 | 8 | 7 | 15 | 63 | 86 | 31 |
| 14 | East Bergholt United | 30 | 8 | 6 | 16 | 45 | 59 | 30 |
| 15 | (R) Ipswich Exiles | 30 | 8 | 6 | 16 | 35 | 67 | 30 |
| 16 | (R) Ipswich Athletic | 30 | 7 | 4 | 19 | 48 | 95 | 25 |

## DIVISION ONE

| | | P | W | D | L | F | A | Pts |
|---|---|---|---|---|---|---|---|---|
| 1 | (P) Westerfield United | 26 | 18 | 2 | 6 | 70 | 31 | 56 |
| 2 | (P) Wenhaston United | 26 | 15 | 5 | 6 | 73 | 31 | 50 |
| 3 | Bramford United | 26 | 16 | 2 | 8 | 70 | 35 | 50 |
| 4 | Henley Athletic | 26 | 16 | 1 | 9 | 59 | 44 | 49 |
| 5 | Saxmundham Sports | 26 | 13 | 4 | 9 | 61 | 42 | 43 |
| 6 | Ransomes Sports | 26 | 12 | 4 | 10 | 45 | 40 | 40 |
| 7 | BT Trimley | 26 | 11 | 6 | 9 | 40 | 37 | 39 |
| 8 | AFC Crowley | 26 | 12 | 2 | 12 | 42 | 47 | 38 |
| 9 | St Johns | 26 | 11 | 4 | 11 | 50 | 45 | 37 |
| 10 | Framlingham Town | 26 | 9 | 8 | 9 | 43 | 49 | 35 |
| 11 | Sporting 87 | 26 | 9 | 5 | 12 | 39 | 46 | 32 |
| 12 | Mendlesham | 26 | 5 | 9 | 12 | 43 | 47 | 24 |
| 13 | (R) Trimley Red Devils (-1pt) | 26 | 6 | 2 | 18 | 39 | 73 | 19 |
| 14 | (R) Cockfield United | 26 | 1 | 2 | 23 | 20 | 127 | 5 |

## BOB COLEMAN CUP

**ROUND 1**

| | | | |
|---|---|---|---|
| AFC Crowley | v | AFC Hoxne | 2-3 |
| AFC Titans | v | Woolverstone United | 2-5 |
| Aldeburgh Town | v | Somersham | 4-3 |
| Benhall St Mary | v | Sizewell Associates | 7-0 |
| Cedars Park | v | Bartons | 1-3 |
| Elmswell | v | Willis | 2-3 |
| Felixstowe Harpers | v | Tacket Street BBOB | 3-0 |
| Great Blakenham | v | Coddenham | 4-2 |
| Halesworth Town | v | Bildeston Rangers | 5-7 |
| Kesgrave Kestrels | v | Tattingstone United | 0-0 |

*Kesgrave Kestrels won on penalties.*

| | | | |
|---|---|---|---|
| Parkside United | v | Waterside | 2-1 |
| Salvation Army | v | Thurston | 2-1 |
| Shotley | v | Walsham Le Willows 'A' | 3-6 |
| Sproughton Sports | v | Bacton United 89 | 3-1 |
| Sporting 87 | v | Claydon | 0-3 |
| St Clements Hospital | v | Sproughton United | 7-1 |
| Stonham Aspal | v | Ufford Sports | 4-2 |
| Stowupland Falcons | v | Chantry Grasshoppers | 12-1 |
| Stradbroke United | v | Adhara | 2-2 |

*Stradbroke United won on penalties.*

| | | | |
|---|---|---|---|
| Witnesham Wasps | v | Bramford Road Old Boys | AW |

**ROUND 2**

| | | | |
|---|---|---|---|
| Bartons | v | Walsham Le Willows 'A' | 3-1 |
| Claydon | v | BT Trimley | 5-3 |
| Kesgrave Kestrels | v | Stonham Aspal | 1-7 |
| Mendlesham | v | Aldeburgh Town | 3-0 |
| Parkside United | v | Felixstowe Harpers | 7-1 |
| Salvation Army | v | Henley Athletic | 0-5 |
| Sproughton Sports | v | Great Blakenham | 7-0 |
| St Clements Hospital | v | Framlingham Town | 3-6 |
| St Johns | v | Bramford Road Old Boys | 11-0 |
| Stowupland Falcons | v | Ransomes Sport | 1-0 |
| Stradbroke United | v | Benhall St Mary | 3-4 |
| Trimley Red Devils | v | AFC Hoxne | 1-3 |
| Wenhaston United | v | Saxmundham Sports | 2-1 |
| Westerfield United | v | Bramford United | 4-1 |
| Willis | v | Bildeston Rangers | 9-3 |
| Woolverstone United | v | Cockfield United | 1-2 |

**ROUND 3**

| | | | |
|---|---|---|---|
| Achilles | v | Sproughton Sports | 6-0 |
| AFC Hoxne | v | Ipswich Exiles | 5-3 |
| Bartons | v | Stowupland Falcons | 2-2 |

*Bartons won on penalties.*

| | | | |
|---|---|---|---|
| Benhall St Mary | v | Grundisburgh | 1-2 |
| Capel Plough | v | Wickham Market | 0-1 |
| Claydon | v | Stonham Aspal | 5-0 |
| Cockfield United | v | Crane Sports | 1-5 |
| Coplestonians | v | Wenhaston United | 2-1 |
| East Bergholt United | v | Henley Athletic | 3-2 |
| Ipswich Athletic | v | Haughley United | 1-2 |
| Ipswich Valley Rangers | v | Felixstowe United | 1-2 |
| Melton St Audrys | v | Old Newton United | 3-2 |
| Mendlesham | v | Leiston St Margarets | 1-4 |
| Parkside United | v | Framlingham Town | 3-2 |
| Westerfield United | v | St Johns | 2-2 |

*Westerfield United won on penalties.*

| | | | |
|---|---|---|---|
| Willis | v | Stanton | 4-6 |

## SENIOR DIVISION

| | | 1 | 2 | 3 | 4 | 5 | 6 | 7 | 8 | 9 | 10 | 11 | 12 | 13 | 14 | 15 | 16 |
|---|---|---|---|---|---|---|---|---|---|---|---|---|---|---|---|---|---|
| 1 | Achilles | | 1-0 | 1-0 | 1-1 | 2-0 | 2-3 | 5-3 | 2-1 | 4-1 | 1-1 | 3-1 | 0-0 | 2-1 | 3-0 | 4-5 | 3-2 |
| 2 | Capel Plough | 1-2 | | 2-1 | 3-2 | 2-0 | 1-1 | 3-0 | 1-2 | 3-1 | 4-0 | 3-2 | 1-1 | 0-2 | 3-0 | 1-1 | 1-2 |
| 3 | Coplestonians | 4-2 | 2-1 | | 0-1 | 2-2 | 0-1 | 2-2 | 0-1 | 1-1 | 2-0 | 0-1 | 1-0 | 1-1 | 4-1 | 0-2 | 0-2 |
| 4 | Crane Sports | 0-3 | 3-0 | 0-1 | | 3-2 | 3-4 | 1-1 | 1-1 | 1-2 | 0-0 | 0-0 | 3-0 | 0-2 | 3-1 | 3-1 | 0-0 |
| 5 | East Bergholt United | 1-0 | 1-1 | 2-0 | 1-1 | | 3-1 | 1-3 | 2-4 | 0-3 | 4-0 | 1-3 | 1-1 | 3-1 | 1-2 | 5-0 | 1-3 |
| 6 | Felixstowe United | 0-3 | 2-0 | 3-2 | 0-0 | 4-1 | | 1-0 | 2-2 | 2-1 | 4-1 | 2-3 | 0-1 | 3-1 | 1-2 | 1-5 | 1-0 |
| 7 | Grundisburgh | 0-1 | 5-0 | 1-1 | 4-2 | 1-0 | 1-4 | | 1-2 | 6-1 | 2-0 | 3-3 | 1-1 | 1-1 | 3-1 | 3-3 | 1-3 |
| 8 | Haughley United | 1-1 | 1-2 | 2-4 | 0-0 | 4-0 | 1-1 | 2-2 | | 3-1 | 2-0 | 1-4 | 2-1 | 1-0 | 0-1 | 5-2 | 0-1 |
| 9 | Ipswich Athletic | 3-5 | 0-2 | 3-4 | 1-2 | 2-3 | 1-8 | 1-4 | 0-5 | | 1-0 | 1-9 | 1-1 | 1-4 | 1-6 | 3-2 | 2-1 |
| 10 | Ipswich Exiles | 3-3 | 2-1 | 2-1 | 2-1 | 3-1 | 2-1 | 1-2 | 0-6 | 1-2 | | 0-3 | 1-3 | 2-2 | 0-0 | 1-0 | 2-1 |
| 11 | Ipswich Valley Rangers | UP | 3-0 | 3-2 | 2-4 | 2-1 | 3-1 | 3-0 | 1-2 | 5-3 | | | 2-1 | 2-1 | 4-2 | 5-0 | 3-1 |
| 12 | Leiston St Margarets | 2-1 | 1-3 | 2-2 | 0-5 | 3-0 | 3-4 | 1-5 | 3-2 | 4-1 | 0-1 | 1-2 | | 1-1 | 1-2 | 3-3 | 0-1 |
| 13 | Melton St Audrys | 1-2 | 1-2 | 1-3 | 1-0 | 2-2 | 0-4 | 2-4 | 1-1 | 2-2 | 4-1 | 0-2 | 2-0 | | 2-2 | 1-3 | 1-0 |
| 14 | Old Newton United | 3-0 | 3-5 | 1-1 | 2-2 | 3-2 | 3-2 | 3-0 | 0-2 | 2-2 | 2-2 | 0-5 | 0-0 | 0-0 | | 3-3 | 0-3 |
| 15 | Stanton | 1-2 | 5-1 | 1-5 | 4-4 | 0-1 | 0-7 | 2-5 | 4-2 | 3-4 | 4-2 | 3-6 | 1-2 | 2-0 | 1-1 | | 2-2 |
| 16 | Wickham Market | 1-2 | 0-1 | 5-2 | 3-2 | 4-3 | 0-2 | 4-1 | 1-0 | 4-1 | 5-2 | 1-2 | 2-5 | 3-1 | 4-3 | 4-0 | |

# SUFFOLK & IPSWICH LEAGUE - STEP 7

| DIVISION TWO | P | W | D | L | F | A | Pts |
|---|---|---|---|---|---|---|---|
| 1 (P) Claydon | 26 | 20 | 4 | 2 | 94 | 33 | 64 |
| 2 (P) Parkside United | 26 | 18 | 4 | 4 | 69 | 36 | 58 |
| 3 Waterside | 26 | 16 | 5 | 5 | 76 | 32 | 53 |
| 4 AFC Hoxne | 26 | 16 | 3 | 7 | 78 | 50 | 51 |
| 5 Bacton United 89 | 26 | 15 | 3 | 8 | 63 | 32 | 48 |
| 6 Stowupland Falcons | 26 | 11 | 7 | 8 | 64 | 42 | 40 |
| 7 Bildeston Rangers | 26 | 11 | 7 | 8 | 80 | 68 | 40 |
| 8 Benhall St Mary | 26 | 9 | 10 | 7 | 58 | 41 | 37 |
| 9 Somersham | 26 | 9 | 5 | 12 | 51 | 46 | 32 |
| 10 Sproughton Sports | 26 | 8 | 4 | 14 | 52 | 68 | 28 |
| 11 Stonham Aspal | 26 | 6 | 2 | 18 | 36 | 71 | 20 |
| 12 Salvation Army | 26 | 5 | 1 | 20 | 26 | 98 | 16 |
| 13 (R) Thurston (-3pts) | 26 | 5 | 3 | 18 | 41 | 79 | 15 |
| 14 (R) Bramford Road Old Boys (-1pt) | 26 | 3 | 2 | 21 | 27 | 119 | 8 |

| INTERMEDIATE A | P | W | D | L | F | A | Pts |
|---|---|---|---|---|---|---|---|
| 1 Crane Sports Reserves | 26 | 19 | 5 | 2 | 66 | 31 | 62 |
| 2 Achilles Reserves | 26 | 13 | 8 | 5 | 66 | 46 | 47 |
| 3 Melton St Audrys Reserves (-1pt) | 26 | 13 | 7 | 6 | 74 | 47 | 45 |
| 4 Coplestonians Reserves (-6pts) | 26 | 14 | 6 | 6 | 59 | 33 | 42 |
| 5 (R) Trimley Red Devils Res. (-1pt) | 26 | 13 | 4 | 9 | 65 | 47 | 42 |
| 6 Old Newton United Reserves | 26 | 13 | 3 | 10 | 64 | 50 | 42 |
| 7 Grundisburgh Reserves (-2pts) | 25 | 12 | 4 | 9 | 56 | 48 | 39 |
| 8 East Bergholt United Reserves | 25 | 10 | 4 | 11 | 49 | 50 | 34 |
| 9 Ipswich Valley Rangers Res. (-1pt) | 26 | 9 | 6 | 11 | 51 | 61 | 32 |
| 10 Wenhaston United Reserves | 26 | 8 | 6 | 12 | 48 | 58 | 30 |
| 11 Haughley United Reserves (-1pt) | 26 | 8 | 4 | 14 | 40 | 44 | 27 |
| 12 Ransomes Sports Reserves | 26 | 5 | 10 | 11 | 49 | 66 | 25 |
| 13 (R) Henley Athletic Res. (-4pts) | 26 | 5 | 5 | 16 | 44 | 95 | 17 |
| 14 (R) Capel Plough Reserves | 26 | 2 | 2 | 22 | 26 | 81 | 8 |

| INTERMEDIATE B | P | W | D | L | F | A | Pts |
|---|---|---|---|---|---|---|---|
| 1 (P) Westerfield United Res. (-3pts) | 26 | 21 | 2 | 3 | 98 | 37 | 62 |
| 2 (P) Felixstowe United Res. (-1pt) | 26 | 19 | 4 | 3 | 103 | 41 | 60 |
| 3 (P) AFC Crowley Reserves | 26 | 17 | 4 | 5 | 79 | 45 | 55 |
| 4 Bramford United Reserves | 26 | 13 | 3 | 10 | 67 | 53 | 42 |
| 5 Stanton Reserves (-9pts) | 25 | 15 | 2 | 8 | 79 | 38 | 38 |
| 6 Wickham Market Reserves | 26 | 11 | 5 | 10 | 57 | 63 | 38 |
| 7 Leiston St Margarets Res. (-2pts) | 24 | 12 | 3 | 9 | 60 | 53 | 37 |
| 8 Sporting 87 Reserves | 26 | 10 | 6 | 10 | 75 | 48 | 36 |
| 9 Saxmundham Sports Reserves | 25 | 9 | 2 | 14 | 47 | 71 | 29 |
| 10 BT Trimley Reserves (-4pts) | 25 | 7 | 3 | 15 | 48 | 91 | 20 |
| 11 Mendlesham Reserves | 24 | 5 | 4 | 15 | 41 | 80 | 19 |
| 12 Ipswich Exiles Reserves (-1pt) | 24 | 5 | 3 | 16 | 42 | 79 | 17 |
| 13 Framlingham Town Reserves (-5pts) | 24 | 6 | 4 | 14 | 43 | 86 | 17 |
| 14 (R) Cockfield United Res. (-3pts) | 25 | 3 | 1 | 21 | 34 | 88 | 7 |

| DIVISION THREE | P | W | D | L | F | A | Pts |
|---|---|---|---|---|---|---|---|
| 1 (P) Aldeburgh Town | 24 | 16 | 4 | 4 | 80 | 33 | 52 |
| 2 (P) Bartons | 24 | 15 | 6 | 3 | 96 | 38 | 51 |
| 3 (P) Cedars Park | 24 | 14 | 4 | 6 | 62 | 30 | 46 |
| 4 Elmswell | 24 | 13 | 3 | 8 | 71 | 46 | 42 |
| 5 Great Blakenham | 24 | 12 | 5 | 7 | 57 | 43 | 41 |
| 6 Tacket Street BBOB | 24 | 11 | 5 | 8 | 52 | 34 | 38 |
| 7 Willis (-1pt) | 24 | 9 | 4 | 11 | 61 | 61 | 30 |
| 8 Walsham Le Willows 'A' | 24 | 8 | 5 | 11 | 43 | 53 | 29 |
| 9 Halesworth Town | 24 | 8 | 5 | 11 | 42 | 57 | 29 |
| 10 Coplestonians 'A' | 24 | 7 | 8 | 9 | 30 | 45 | 29 |
| 11 (R) Bacton United 89 Reserves | 24 | 7 | 4 | 13 | 52 | 66 | 25 |
| 12 (R) Coddenham | 24 | 5 | 1 | 18 | 26 | 100 | 16 |
| 13 (R) Stonham Aspal Reserves | 24 | 3 | 2 | 19 | 20 | 86 | 11 |

## BOB COLEMAN CUP

**ROUND 4**

| | | | |
|---|---|---|---|
| Achilles | v | AFC Hoxne | 7-2 |
| Claydon | v | Leiston St Margarets | 3-2 |
| Crane Sports | v | Bartons | 5-1 |
| East Bergholt United | v | Felixstowe United | 2-3 |
| Grundisburgh | v | Coplestonians | 3-2 |
| Melton St Audrys | v | Stanton | 2-2 |

*Melton St Audrys won on penalties.*

| | | | |
|---|---|---|---|
| Parkside United | v | Westerfield United | 0-5 |
| Wickham Market | v | Haughley United | 4-2 |

**QUARTER FINALS**

| | | | |
|---|---|---|---|
| Achilles | v | Wickham Market | 5-2 |
| Claydon | v | Grundisburgh | 4-0 |
| Melton St Audrys | v | Felixstowe United | 2-1 |
| Westerfield United | v | Crane Sports | 0-2 |

**SEMI FINALS**

| | | | |
|---|---|---|---|
| Achilles | v | Melton St Audrys | 1-2 |
| Crane Sports | v | Claydon | 1-0 |

**FINAL**

| | | | |
|---|---|---|---|
| Crane Sports | v | Melton St Audrys | 4-1 |

| DIVISION FOUR | P | W | D | L | F | A | Pts |
|---|---|---|---|---|---|---|---|
| 1 (P) Adhara (-1pt) | 24 | 21 | 2 | 1 | 102 | 14 | 64 |
| 2 (P) AFC Hoxne Reserves | 24 | 18 | 3 | 3 | 125 | 23 | 57 |
| 3 (P) Ufford Sports | 24 | 18 | 3 | 3 | 108 | 22 | 57 |
| 4 St Clements Hospital | 24 | 17 | 6 | 1 | 74 | 30 | 57 |
| 5 Felixstowe Harpers (+1pt) | 24 | 10 | 5 | 9 | 68 | 51 | 36 |
| 6 (P) Claydon Reserves | 24 | 10 | 2 | 12 | 52 | 58 | 32 |
| 7 Stradbroke United | 24 | 10 | 1 | 13 | 71 | 71 | 31 |
| 8 Cedars Park Reserves | 24 | 10 | 1 | 13 | 64 | 73 | 31 |
| 9 Witnesham Wasps (+2pts) | 24 | 8 | 1 | 15 | 64 | 87 | 27 |
| 10 Tattingstone United | 24 | 7 | 3 | 14 | 51 | 94 | 24 |
| 11 (R) Bramford Road O.B. Res (-1pt) | 24 | 6 | 3 | 15 | 28 | 116 | 20 |
| 12 (R) Benhall St Mary Reserves | 24 | 1 | 6 | 17 | 28 | 87 | 9 |
| 13 (R) Sizewell Associates | 24 | 1 | 2 | 21 | 19 | 128 | 5 |

| DIVISION FIVE | P | W | D | L | F | A | Pts |
|---|---|---|---|---|---|---|---|
| 1 (P) Waterside Reserves | 22 | 15 | 4 | 3 | 79 | 32 | 49 |
| 2 (P) St Johns Reserves | 22 | 14 | 3 | 5 | 81 | 41 | 45 |
| 3 (P) Somersham Reserves | 22 | 14 | 3 | 5 | 57 | 37 | 45 |
| 4 Woolverstone United | 22 | 12 | 3 | 7 | 76 | 49 | 39 |
| 5 Stowupland Falcons Reserves | 22 | 12 | 3 | 7 | 62 | 46 | 3 |
| 6 Sproughton United | 22 | 11 | 3 | 8 | 59 | 47 | 36 |
| 7 Witnesham Wasps Reserves (-3pts) | 22 | 10 | 3 | 9 | 56 | 51 | 36 |
| 8 Aldeburgh Town Reserves | 22 | 9 | 2 | 11 | 54 | 60 | 29 |
| 9 East Bergholt United 'A' (-3pts) | 22 | 8 | 2 | 12 | 30 | 65 | 23 |
| 10 Kesgrave Kestrels (-7pts) | 22 | 6 | 2 | 14 | 40 | 62 | 13 |
| 11 (R) Stonham Aspal 'A' | 22 | 4 | 1 | 17 | 31 | 83 | 13 |
| 12 (R) Salvation Army Res. (-1pt) | 22 | 2 | 1 | 19 | 28 | 80 | 6 |

| DIVISION SIX | P | W | D | L | F | A | Pts |
|---|---|---|---|---|---|---|---|
| 1 (P) Elmswell Reserves | 24 | 18 | 2 | 4 | 95 | 33 | 56 |
| 2 (P) Shotley | 24 | 14 | 4 | 6 | 71 | 38 | 46 |
| 3 (P) Halesworth Town Reserves | 24 | 13 | 1 | 10 | 60 | 44 | 40 |
| 4 (P) Old Newton United 'A' | 24 | 12 | 4 | 8 | 75 | 56 | 40 |
| 5 (P) Tattingstone United Res. | 24 | 12 | 4 | 8 | 59 | 60 | 38 |
| 6 Willis Reserves | 24 | 12 | 7 | 5 | 58 | 39 | 37 |
| 7 AFC Titans | 24 | 9 | 6 | 9 | 46 | 54 | 33 |
| 8 Stowupland Falcons 'A' | 24 | 9 | 4 | 11 | 64 | 58 | 31 |
| 9 Bacton United 89 'A' | 24 | 8 | 4 | 12 | 56 | 77 | 28 |
| 10 Chantry Grasshoppers | 24 | 7 | 5 | 12 | 59 | 68 | 26 |
| 11 Bildeston Rangers Reserves | 24 | 7 | 2 | 15 | 53 | 88 | 23 |
| 12 Sproughton Sports Reserves | 24 | 6 | 4 | 14 | 60 | 82 | 22 |
| 13 Kesgrave Kestrels Reserves | 24 | 4 | 3 | 17 | 42 | 101 | 15 |

## SUFFOLK & IPSWICH LEAGUE SENIOR DIVISION CONSTITUTION 2013-14

| | | |
|---|---|---|
| ACHILLES | Pauls Social Club, Salmet Close, Ipswich IP2 9BA | 01473 604874 |
| CAPEL PLOUGH | Friars, Capel St Mary, Ipswich IP9 2XS | n/a |
| COPLESTONIANS | Woodbridge Town FC, Notcutts Park, Fynn Road, Woodbridge IP12 4DA | 01394 385308 |
| CRANE SPORTS | Gresham Sports & Social Club, Tuddenham Road, Ipswich IP4 3QJ | 01473 250816 |
| EAST BERGHOLT UNITED | Gandish Road, East Bergholt, Colchester CO7 6TP | n/a |
| FELIXSTOWE HARPERS UNITED | Trimley Sports & Social Club, High Road, Trimley St Martin, Felixstowe IP11 0RJ | 01394 275240 |
| GRUNDISBURGH | The Playing Field, Ipswich Road, Grundisburgh, Woodbridge IP13 6TJ | 07974 947221 |
| HAUGHLEY UNITED | King George VI Playing Field, Green Road, Haughley IP14 3RA | 01449 673460 |
| IPSWICH VALLEY RANGERS | Rock Barracks, Sutton Heath, Woodbridge IP12 3LU | n/a |
| LEISTON ST MARGARETS | Junction Meadow, Abbey Road, Leiston IP16 4RD | 01728 831239 |
| MELTON ST AUDRYS | St Audrys Sports & Social Club, Lodge Farm Lane, Melton, Woodbridge IP12 1LX | 01394 389505 |
| OLD NEWTON UNITED | Church Road, Old Newton, Stowmarket IP14 4ED | 01449 770035 |
| STANTON | Stanton Recreation Ground, Old Bury Road, Stanton, Bury St Edmunds IP31 2BX | n/a |
| WENHASTON UNITED | Wenhaston Playing Field, Hall Road, Wenhaston IP19 9EP | n/a |
| WESTERFIELD UNITED | Rushmere Sports Centre, The Street, Rushmere StAndrew, Ipswich IP5 1DE | 01473 272525 |
| WICKHAM MARKET | The Playing Field, Wickham Market IP13 0HE | 01728 747303 |

**In:** Felixstowe Harpers United (NC from Felixstowe United). Wenhaston United (P). Westerfield United (P).
**Out:** Felixstowe United (NC to Felixstowe Harpers United). Ipswich Athletic (R). Ipswich Exiles (R).

# SURREY ELITE INTERMEDIATE LEAGUE

**Sponsored by:** No Sponsor
**Founded:** 2008
**Recent Champions:**
2009: Eversley
2010: Epsom Eagles
2011: Spelthorne Sports
2012: Epsom Athletic

| INTERMEDIATE DIVISION | P | W | D | L | F | A | Pts |
|---|---|---|---|---|---|---|---|
| 1 Yateley Green | 28 | 19 | 6 | 3 | 59 | 26 | 63 |
| 2 Old Farnboronians | 28 | 17 | 4 | 7 | 84 | 40 | 55 |
| 3 Coulsdon Town | 28 | 17 | 3 | 8 | 50 | 32 | 54 |
| 4 Horsley | 28 | 15 | 5 | 8 | 62 | 36 | 50 |
| 5 Bookham | 28 | 13 | 3 | 12 | 51 | 44 | 42 |
| 6 Battersea Ironsides | 28 | 12 | 6 | 10 | 39 | 40 | 42 |
| 7 Abbey Rangers | 28 | 11 | 5 | 12 | 49 | 55 | 38 |
| 8 Weston Green Sports | 28 | 11 | 4 | 13 | 35 | 42 | 37 |
| 9 Tooting Bec | 28 | 11 | 4 | 13 | 48 | 62 | 37 |
| 10 AFC Cubo | 28 | 10 | 3 | 15 | 51 | 55 | 33 |
| 11 Virginia Water | 28 | 9 | 4 | 15 | 44 | 68 | 31 |
| 12 Ripley Village | 28 | 7 | 9 | 12 | 47 | 53 | 30 |
| 13 Reigate Priory | 28 | 7 | 8 | 13 | 53 | 71 | 29 |
| 14 (R) Oxted & District | 28 | 9 | 2 | 17 | 41 | 69 | 29 |
| 15 (R) Crescent Rovers | 28 | 8 | 2 | 18 | 54 | 74 | 26 |

Claygate & Ditton withdrew - record expunged.

## INTERMEDIATE LEAGUE CHALLENGE CUP

**ROUND 1**

| | | | |
|---|---|---|---|
| Abbey Rangers | v | Weston Green Sports | 2-3 |
| Crescent Rovers | v | Horsley | 4-3 |
| Reigate Priory | v | Coulsdon Town | 2-5 |
| AFC Cubo | v | Old Farnboronians | 1-3 |
| Yateley Green | v | Virginia Water | 2-0 |
| Claygate & Ditton | v | Bookham | 1-3 |
| Battersea Ironsides | v | Tooting Bec | 0-1 |
| Ripley Village | v | Oxted & District | 5-0 |

**QUARTER FINALS**

| | | | |
|---|---|---|---|
| Bookham | v | Old Farnboronians | 2-3 |
| Ripley Village | v | Tooting Bec | 2-3 |
| Crescent Rovers | v | Yateley Green | 3-6 |
| Coulsdon Town | v | Weston Green Sports | 3-2 |

**SEMI FINALS**

| | | | |
|---|---|---|---|
| Old Farnboronians | v | Tooting Bec | 3-0 |
| Coulsdon Town | v | Yateley Green | 1-0 |

**FINAL**

| | | | |
|---|---|---|---|
| Old Farnboronians | v | Coulsdon Town | 1-0 |

| INTERMEDIATE DIVISION | 1 | 2 | 3 | 4 | 5 | 6 | 7 | 8 | 9 | 10 | 11 | 12 | 13 | 14 | 15 |
|---|---|---|---|---|---|---|---|---|---|---|---|---|---|---|---|
| 1 Abbey Rangers | | 1-5 | AW | 1-0 | 2-1 | 1-1 | 2-1 | 1-3 | 6-2 | 2-1 | 2-4 | 4-1 | 2-2 | 0-2 | 1-3 |
| 2 AFC Cubo | 4-2 | | 0-2 | 1-4 | 0-1 | 2-4 | 4-4 | 2-3 | 5-0 | 0-1 | 2-2 | 1-3 | 3-0 | 1-3 | 1-0 |
| 3 Battersea Ironsides | 0-0 | 3-2 | | 2-1 | 3-3 | 0-2 | 0-2 | 1-1 | 1-0 | 5-2 | 3-2 | 1-2 | 2-2 | 1-1 | 4-2 |
| 4 Bookham | 2-1 | 3-4 | 3-0 | | 1-0 | 3-2 | 2-1 | 3-0 | 3-1 | 2-1 | 1-2 | 3-2 | 2-1 | 3-0 | 2-3 |
| 5 Coulsdon Town | 0-2 | 2-1 | 1-2 | HW | | 2-1 | 1-4 | 2-1 | 3-1 | 4-1 | 4-0 | 2-0 | 2-0 | 1-2 | 0-1 |
| 6 Crescent Rovers | 1-2 | 0-1 | 1-0 | 2-1 | 1-2 | | 1-4 | 2-1 | 0-2 | 2-3 | 4-4 | 5-3 | 6-2 | 3-4 | 2-4 |
| 7 Horsley | 6-1 | 3-0 | 4-3 | 1-1 | 0-2 | 1-0 | | 1-4 | 4-2 | 2-2 | 3-0 | 6-0 | 3-0 | HW | 1-1 |
| 8 Old Farnboronians | 4-1 | 4-2 | 1-2 | 6-0 | 1-2 | 5-2 | 2-4 | | 4-1 | 2-2 | 3-0 | 3-0 | 4-0 | 1-2 | 3-1 |
| 9 Oxted & District | 2-4 | 3-0 | 4-1 | 2-1 | 1-7 | 3-2 | 1-0 | 3-3 | | 1-0 | 2-2 | 1-3 | 1-2 | 1-2 | 1-2 |
| 10 Reigate Priory | 2-3 | 1-4 | 0-2 | 3-3 | 3-0 | 3-4 | 0-3 | 1-4 | 3-1 | | 4-4 | 1-0 | 3-3 | 2-2 | 4-4 |
| 11 Ripley Village | 2-2 | 1-2 | 0-0 | 3-2 | 0-0 | 5-1 | 0-1 | 1-4 | 1-2 | 3-0 | | 0-2 | 4-1 | 2-0 | 1-1 |
| 12 Tooting Bec | 2-2 | 1-1 | 2-0 | 2-2 | 2-3 | 5-4 | 1-0 | 1-6 | 4-0 | 2-5 | 2-1 | | 1-4 | 1-1 | 1-2 |
| 13 Virginia Water | 0-3 | 4-1 | 1-0 | 2-0 | 0-2 | 4-1 | 3-1 | 2-8 | 3-0 | 2-3 | 3-3 | 0-1 | | 2-0 | 0-2 |
| 14 Weston Green Sports | 2-0 | 0-2 | 0-1 | 1-3 | 2-3 | 5-0 | 1-0 | 0-2 | 1-3 | 1-1 | 1-0 | 0-4 | 2-1 | | 0-1 |
| 15 Yateley Green | 2-1 | HW | 1-0 | HW | 0-0 | 2-0 | 2-2 | 1-1 | 2-0 | 6-1 | 1-0 | 4-0 | 8-0 | 3-0 | |

## SURREY ELITE INTERMEDIATE LEAGUE INTERMEDIATE DIVISION CONSTITUTION 2013-14

| | | |
|---|---|---|
| AFC CUBO | Barn Elms Sports Ground, Queen Elizabeth Walk, Barnes SW13 0DG | 020 8876 9873 |
| ABBEY RANGERS | Addlestone Moor, Addlestone Moor Road, Addlestone KT15 2QH | 01932 442 962 |
| BATTERSEA IRONSIDES | Battersea Ironsides S&S Club, Burntwood Lane, Earlsfield SW17 0AW | 020 8874 9913 |
| BOOKHAM | Christie Recreation Ground, Dorking Road, Bookham KT23 4PA | 01372 459 482 |
| COULSDON TOWN | Woodplace Lane, Coulsdon CR5 1NE | 01737 557 509 |
| HORSLEY | Toms Field, Long Reach, West Horsley KT14 6PG | 01483 282 516 |
| MERROW | The Urnfield, Downside Road, Guildford, Surrey, GU4 8PH | n/a |
| NPL | NPL Sports Club, Queens Road, Teddington, TW11 0LW | n/a |
| OLD FARNBORONIANS | Cody S&S Club, Armstrong Way, The Fairway, Farnborough GU14 0LP | 01252 543 009 |
| PURETOWN | Kingston Uni. Sports Grd, Tolworth Court, Old Kingston Rd, Worcester Park KT4 7QH | n/a |
| REIGATE PRIORY | Reigate Priory Cricket Club, off Park Lane, Reigate RH2 8JX | 01737 240 872 |
| RIPLEY VILLAGE | The Green, Ripley, Woking GU23 6AN | 01483 225 484 |
| TOOTING BEC | Raynes Park Sports Ground, Taunton Avenue SW20 0BH | n/a |
| VIRGINIA WATER | The Timbers, Crown Road, Virginia Water GU25 4HS | 01344 843 811 |
| WARLINGHAM | Verdayne Sports Ground, Warlingham, Surrey | 020 8660 5491 |
| YATELEY UNITED | Chandlers Lane, Yateley, Hampshire GU46 7SZ | n/a |

**In:** Merrow (P - Surrey County Intermediate (Western). NPL (P - Surrey South Eastern Combination).
Puretown (P - Surrey South Eastern Combination). Warlingham (Combined Counties).
Yateley United (N - formed after merger of Yayeley Green and Yateley).
**Out:** Claygate & Ditton (WS). Crescent Rovers (R). Oxted & District (R). Weston Green Sports (W - now Surrey County Intermediate League (Western).

# TEESIDE LEAGUE

| Sponsored by: Jack Hatfield Sports |
|---|
| Founded: 1891 |
| Recent Champions: |
| 2008: BEADS FC |
| 2009: BEADS FC |
| 2010: BEADS FC |
| 2011: Grangetown Boys Club |
| 2012: Richmond Town |

## LOU MOORE TROPHY

**FINAL**
Richmond Mavericks    v    Thornaby Dubliners    0-1

**DIVISION TWO**

| | P | W | D | L | F | A | Pts |
|---|---|---|---|---|---|---|---|
| 1 (P) Lingdale | 24 | 19 | 3 | 2 | 76 | 23 | 60 |
| 2 (P) Northallerton Town Reserves | 24 | 16 | 7 | 1 | 66 | 25 | 55 |
| 3 (P) Redcar Newmarket | 24 | 14 | 4 | 6 | 57 | 33 | 46 |
| 4 Thirsk Falcons | 24 | 14 | 2 | 8 | 81 | 30 | 44 |
| 5 Stockton West End | 24 | 13 | 3 | 8 | 63 | 47 | 42 |
| 6 Guisborough | 24 | 12 | 4 | 8 | 48 | 38 | 40 |
| 7 Grangetown YCC | 24 | 10 | 3 | 11 | 59 | 69 | 33 |
| 8 Billingham Synthonia Res. | 24 | 9 | 3 | 12 | 53 | 58 | 30 |
| 9 Bedale | 24 | 8 | 3 | 13 | 52 | 69 | 27 |
| 10 St Mary's College | 24 | 6 | 7 | 11 | 49 | 53 | 25 |
| 11 New Marske | 24 | 5 | 4 | 15 | 34 | 79 | 19 |
| 12 Yarm | 24 | 4 | 2 | 18 | 29 | 80 | 14 |
| 13 Billingham Town Intermediates | 24 | 3 | 1 | 20 | 23 | 86 | 10 |

**2013-14 In:** Billingham Athletic (Sunday). Cargo Fleet AFC (Youth). Kader FC. (Youth). Loftus Athletic (P- Eskvale & Cleveland Lge). Richmond Town Reserves (N).
**Out:** Grangetown YCC (W). Redcar Athletic Reserves (W).

**DIVISION ONE**

| | P | W | D | L | F | A | Pts |
|---|---|---|---|---|---|---|---|
| 1 Endeavour | 24 | 18 | 2 | 4 | 93 | 34 | 56 |
| 2 Thornaby Dubliners | 24 | 18 | 2 | 4 | 75 | 34 | 56 |
| 3 Beechwood, Eastside & CC | 24 | 16 | 3 | 5 | 65 | 43 | 51 |
| 4 Whinney Banks Youth & CC | 24 | 15 | 4 | 5 | 98 | 40 | 49 |
| 5 Grangetown Boys Club | 24 | 13 | 1 | 10 | 69 | 57 | 40 |
| 6 North Ormesby (-3pts) | 24 | 13 | 2 | 9 | 57 | 49 | 38 |
| 7 Richmond Mavericks | 24 | 11 | 3 | 10 | 48 | 67 | 36 |
| 8 (R) Redcar Athletic Reserves | 24 | 8 | 3 | 13 | 34 | 43 | 27 |
| 9 Darlington Rugby Club | 24 | 8 | 1 | 15 | 49 | 83 | 25 |
| 10 Great Ayton United | 24 | 6 | 3 | 15 | 41 | 64 | 21 |
| 11 Fishburn Park | 24 | 6 | 3 | 15 | 43 | 68 | 21 |
| 12 Hemlington Sports Club (-3pts) | 24 | 5 | 2 | 17 | 51 | 89 | 14 |
| 13 Nunthorpe Athletic (-3pts) | 24 | 3 | 3 | 18 | 28 | 80 | 9 |

**DIVISION ONE**

| | 1 | 2 | 3 | 4 | 5 | 6 | 7 | 8 | 9 | 10 | 11 | 12 | 13 |
|---|---|---|---|---|---|---|---|---|---|---|---|---|---|
| 1 BEADS | | 4-1 | 2-1 | 5-1 | 1-5 | 3-2 | 5-0 | 3-2 | 2-1 | 1-0 | 2-3 | 2-4 | 2-2 |
| 2 Darlington Rugby Club | 0-6 | | 2-0 | 4-3 | 4-10 | 2-0 | 4-5 | 1-4 | 1-2 | 3-2 | 5-3 | 1-8 | 1-2 |
| 3 Endeavour | 7-1 | 4-2 | | 2-1 | 3-1 | 3-1 | 7-3 | 2-4 | 4-1 | 2-0 | 12-0 | 0-1 | 0-0 |
| 4 Fishburn Park | 2-5 | 3-3 | 1-3 | | 2-3 | 3-2 | 2-3 | 1-2 | 3-1 | 1-4 | 5-0 | 0-1 | 0-5 |
| 5 Grangetown BC | 2-0 | 3-0 | 1-5 | 1-3 | | 3-1 | 2-5 | 4-1 | 7-1 | 0-0 | 1-3 | 1-5 | 2-0 |
| 6 Great Ayton United | 2-2 | 0-5 | 1-5 | 1-1 | 1-5 | | 3-2 | 1-2 | 1-0 | 3-1 | 2-2 | 3-4 | 2-4 |
| 7 Hemlington Smithy | 2-2 | 1-2 | 0-5 | 1-1 | 3-7 | 2-4 | | 2-3 | 6-1 | 3-1 | 0-1 | 3-5 | 1-10 |
| 8 North Ormesby | 0-2 | 5-1 | 2-2 | 3-2 | 1-3 | 4-1 | 3-2 | | 1-1 | 3-2 | 3-1 | 1-2 | 2-4 |
| 9 Nunthorpe Athletic | 2-5 | 0-2 | 1-6 | 0-3 | 3-1 | 1-3 | 3-1 | 1-5 | | 0-1 | 2-2 | 0-3 | 3-6 |
| 10 Redcar Athletic Reserves | 0-1 | 3-1 | 2-4 | 3-0 | 3-2 | 0-2 | 3-2 | 0-1 | 3-0 | | 2-1 | 2-2 | 2-2 |
| 11 Richmond Mavericks | 0-3 | 1-0 | 1-8 | 6-0 | 1-4 | 3-2 | 6-2 | 3-1 | 2-2 | 3-0 | | 1-0 | 1-0 |
| 12 Thornaby Dubliners | 2-3 | 3-2 | 3-4 | 2-3 | 2-0 | 4-2 | 5-1 | 3-2 | 6-1 | 1-0 | 6-0 | | 2-2 |
| 13 Whinney Banks YCC | 2-3 | 11-2 | 3-4 | 8-2 | 9-1 | 3-1 | 4-1 | 5-2 | 6-1 | 5-0 | 5-4 | 0-1 | |

## TEESIDE LEAGUE DIVISION ONE CONSTITUTION 2013-14

| | |
|---|---|
| ACKLAM STEELWORKS | Prissick Base, Marton Road, Middlesbrough TS7 8AE |
| BEADS FC | Marton Road, Middlesbrough TS4 3PP |
| FISHBURN PARK | Eskdale School, Broomfield Park, Whitby, N Yorkshire YO22 4HS |
| GRANGETOWN BOYS CLUB | Trunk Road, Grangetown, Middlesbrough TS6 7HP |
| GREAT AYTON UNITED | Leven Park, Easby Lane, Great Ayton, Middlesbrough TS9 6JJ |
| HEMLINGTON SMITHY FC | Hemlington Recreation Centre, Cass House Road, Hemlington, Middlesbrough TS8 9QW |
| LINGDALE FC | The Track, Lingdale Playing Field, Lingdale TS12 3DW |
| NORTHALLERTON TOWN | Calvert Stadium, Ainderby Road, Romanby, Northallerton DL7 8HA |
| NORTH ORMESBY | The Vicarage Field, Ormesby Road, Middlesbrough TS3 7AL |
| NUNTHORPE ATHLETIC | Guisborough Road, Nunthorpe, Middlesbrough TS7 0LE |
| REDCAR NEWMARKET | Ryehills School, Redcar Lane, Redcar TS10 2HN |
| RICHMOND MAVERICKS | Richmond School, Darlington Road, Richmond DL10 7BQ |
| THORNABY DUBLINERS | Harold Wilson Sports Complex, Bader Avenue, Thornaby TS17 0EX |
| WHINNEY BANKS YCC | Sandy Flatts, Oakfield School, Hall Drive, Middlesbrough TS5 7JX |

**In:** Acklam Steelworks (NC from Edeavour). Lingdale (P). Northallerton Town Reserves (P), Redcar Newmarket (P).
**Out:** Claygate & Ditton (WS). Darlington Rugby Club (W). Redcar Athletic Reserves (R).

# WEARSIDE LEAGUE

**Sponsored by:** No Sponsor
**Founded:** 1892
**Recent Champions:**
2008: New Marske Sports Club
2009: Newton Aycliffe
2010: Ryhope Colliery Welfare
2011: Ryhope Colliery Welfare
2012: Stockton Town

| | | P | W | D | L | F | A | Pts |
|---|---|---|---|---|---|---|---|---|
| 1 | Stockton Town | 42 | 34 | 1 | 7 | 112 | 33 | 103 |
| 2 | (P) Willington | 42 | 32 | 5 | 5 | 89 | 40 | 101 |
| 3 | Richmond Town | 42 | 28 | 10 | 4 | 122 | 47 | 94 |
| 4 | Cleator Moor Celtic | 42 | 26 | 5 | 11 | 105 | 68 | 83 |
| 5 | Redcar Athletic | 42 | 21 | 8 | 13 | 71 | 59 | 71 |
| 6 | Ashbrooke Belford House | 42 | 22 | 5 | 15 | 84 | 74 | 71 |
| 7 | Prudhoe Town | 42 | 20 | 10 | 12 | 81 | 58 | 70 |
| 8 | Sunderland West End | 42 | 20 | 9 | 13 | 75 | 61 | 69 |
| 9 | Jarrow FC | 42 | 19 | 10 | 13 | 87 | 56 | 67 |
| 10 | Seaton Carew | 42 | 18 | 7 | 17 | 90 | 92 | 61 |
| 11 | Peterlee Town | 42 | 19 | 3 | 20 | 88 | 74 | 60 |
| 12 | Harton & Westoe | 42 | 16 | 5 | 21 | 79 | 110 | 53 |
| 13 | Gateshead Leam Rangers | 42 | 13 | 10 | 19 | 67 | 88 | 49 |
| 14 | Hartlepool FC | 42 | 13 | 8 | 21 | 84 | 95 | 47 |
| 15 | Darlington Cleveland Bridge | 42 | 14 | 4 | 24 | 79 | 118 | 46 |
| 16 | Boldon CA | 42 | 14 | 3 | 25 | 71 | 102 | 45 |
| 17 | Wolviston | 42 | 11 | 9 | 22 | 61 | 78 | 42 |
| 18 | Annfield Plain | 42 | 13 | 2 | 27 | 53 | 103 | 41 |
| 19 | Coxhoe Athletic | 42 | 12 | 4 | 26 | 67 | 88 | 40 |
| 20 | Kirkbymoorside | 42 | 12 | 4 | 26 | 64 | 91 | 40 |
| 21 | Easington Colliery | 42 | 12 | 3 | 27 | 55 | 87 | 39 |
| 22 | Silksworth Rangers | 42 | 9 | 3 | 30 | 51 | 113 | 30 |

## LEAGUE CUP

**FINAL**
Richmond Town v Prudhoe Town    1-1, 4-5p

## MONKWEARMOUTH CHARITY CUP

**FINAL**
Prudhoe Town v Darlington Cleveland Bridge    2-1

## SUNDERLAND SHIPOWNERS CUP

**FINAL**
Willington v Cleator Moor Celtic    0-4

| | 1 | 2 | 3 | 4 | 5 | 6 | 7 | 8 | 9 | 10 | 11 | 12 | 13 | 14 | 15 | 16 | 17 | 18 | 19 | 20 | 21 | 22 |
|---|---|---|---|---|---|---|---|---|---|---|---|---|---|---|---|---|---|---|---|---|---|---|
| 1 Annfield Plain | | 1-4 | 1-3 | 0-4 | 0-2 | 1-2 | 5-2 | 1-1 | 2-0 | 2-3 | 1-10 | 2-1 | 2-3 | 0-1 | 0-2 | 2-6 | 1-1 | 0-2 | 0-3 | 3-2 | 2-3 | 1-3 |
| 2 Ashbrooke Belford House | 0-1 | | 3-2 | 3-3 | 2-1 | 5-0 | 1-2 | 3-1 | 2-1 | 6-2 | 2-2 | 3-0 | 5-2 | 1-1 | 3-2 | 0-6 | 1-2 | 3-2 | 0-2 | 2-0 | 2-3 | 3-1 |
| 3 Boldon CA | 0-1 | 1-1 | | 3-2 | 1-3 | 5-3 | 1-2 | 3-2 | 1-4 | 1-2 | 2-4 | 4-1 | 2-1 | 1-3 | 1-2 | 0-1 | 1-4 | 3-1 | 2-3 | 3-1 | 2-5 | 1-0 |
| 4 Cleator Moor Celtic | 3-2 | 2-3 | 4-2 | | 1-0 | 7-1 | 5-2 | 4-0 | 6-1 | 3-0 | 2-0 | 1-0 | 0-9 | 2-0 | 0-2 | 1-2 | 3-0 | 2-1 | 2-1 | 2-1 | 3-0 | 3-0 |
| 5 Coxhoe Athletic | 0-2 | 0-1 | 3-0 | 2-5 | | 1-2 | 0-1 | 2-3 | 1-4 | 4-0 | 0-0 | 3-0 | 1-2 | 2-4 | 1-2 | 1-4 | 3-3 | 6-0 | 0-2 | 2-0 | 0-2 | 3-0 |
| 6 Darlington Cleveland Bridge | 0-1 | 3-4 | 2-1 | 1-4 | 1-2 | | 3-1 | 2-1 | 3-3 | 2-2 | 0-1 | 3-2 | 0-2 | 3-4 | 1-3 | 0-5 | 4-1 | 6-2 | 2-3 | 0-0 | 0-4 | 4-7 |
| 7 Easington Colliery AFC | 1-4 | 0-1 | 3-1 | 0-2 | 4-2 | 2-5 | | 1-2 | 1-4 | 3-3 | 0-3 | 3-2 | 0-2 | 1-3 | 1-1 | 3-5 | 3-4 | 3-0 | 1-2 | 0-3 | 0-1 | 2-0 |
| 8 Gateshead Leam Rangers | 0-2 | 2-0 | 1-1 | 2-1 | 1-2 | 1-0 | 2-1 | | 1-1 | 0-4 | 2-2 | 0-3 | 1-3 | 4-2 | 0-0 | 1-1 | 4-3 | 3-2 | 0-3 | 2-3 | 1-3 | 3-2 |
| 9 Hartlepool | 1-3 | 2-4 | 3-1 | 1-0 | 5-2 | 0-4 | 0-3 | 2-2 | | 3-0 | 3-2 | 0-3 | 7-4 | 4-1 | 0-5 | 2-2 | 0-3 | 8-1 | 1-2 | 1-1 | 1-3 | 0-3 |
| 10 Harton and Westoe CW | 1-2 | 3-1 | 2-3 | 5-3 | 1-0 | 5-5 | 0-2 | 5-4 | 5-3 | | 2-3 | 2-0 | 0-4 | 1-0 | 0-1 | 0-5 | 6-4 | 3-1 | 0-6 | 2-3 | 1-3 | 2-3 |
| 11 Jarrow | 0-2 | 2-1 | 1-3 | 3-3 | 3-1 | 5-0 | 1-0 | 1-1 | 2-3 | 4-0 | | 3-0 | 4-6 | 1-0 | 3-1 | 0-0 | 7-0 | 6-1 | 0-3 | 3-1 | 1-1 | 1-2 |
| 12 Kirkbymoorside | 4-1 | 6-2 | 3-1 | 0-1 | 1-1 | 1-4 | 1-3 | 3-2 | 4-2 | 1-2 | 2-2 | | 1-4 | 3-2 | 1-0 | 2-4 | 1-4 | 4-2 | 0-2 | 2-1 | 0-1 | 5-2 |
| 13 Peterlee Town | 2-0 | 1-2 | 2-0 | 1-3 | 7-0 | 1-3 | 4-0 | 1-2 | 4-1 | 0-3 | 0-1 | 1-0 | | 0-3 | 0-3 | 1-4 | 2-2 | 2-1 | 2-1 | 2-3 | 1-2 | 3-2 |
| 14 Prudhoe Town | 2-0 | 1-0 | 5-1 | 2-2 | 4-2 | 3-0 | 1-0 | 3-3 | 1-0 | 5-2 | 1-0 | 6-2 | 1-1 | | 1-1 | 2-2 | 0-2 | 3-0 | 1-5 | 1-2 | 0-0 | 1-1 |
| 15 Redcar Athletic | 2-0 | 2-0 | 1-4 | 1-5 | 2-3 | 0-1 | 3-1 | 3-3 | 2-1 | 0-1 | 3-1 | 5-0 | 1-0 | 1-1 | | 1-1 | 1-5 | 4-0 | 2-1 | 1-1 | 1-2 | 4-1 |
| 16 Richmond Town | 7-1 | 3-2 | 4-1 | 4-3 | 1-1 | 5-2 | 3-0 | 5-2 | 1-1 | 2-1 | 2-1 | 2-0 | 3-4 | 3-2 | | | 3-2 | 0-0 | 4-2 | 3-0 | 0-1 | 2-1 |
| 17 Seaton Carew | 5-3 | 2-3 | 4-1 | 1-3 | 2-1 | 3-1 | 1-1 | 2-1 | 1-1 | 4-2 | 0-1 | 1-0 | 2-0 | 0-2 | 0-3 | 2-1 | | 5-2 | 2-4 | 2-2 | 3-5 | 3-0 |
| 18 Silksworth Colliery Welfare | 4-0 | 4-0 | 1-2 | 1-1 | 0-1 | 1-2 | 2-0 | 2-4 | 1-6 | 2-3 | 1-2 | 1-1 | 0-5 | 1-0 | 0-1 | 0-2 | 3-0 | | 1-6 | 2-1 | 1-6 | 1-0 |
| 19 Stockton Town | 6-0 | 0-1 | 5-0 | 2-1 | 4-1 | 3-1 | 1-2 | 2-0 | 1-0 | 2-1 | 4-0 | 1-1 | 3-0 | 1-0 | 4-2 | 5-1 | | | | 4-0 | 1-0 | 0-1 |
| 20 Sunderland West End | 1-0 | 1-1 | 3-0 | 3-0 | 6-4 | 9-0 | 1-0 | 3-1 | 1-1 | 1-1 | 2-0 | 3-1 | 2-1 | 0-4 | 1-1 | 1-1 | 3-0 | 1-0 | 0-3 | | 2-0 | 3-2 |
| 21 Willington | 3-1 | 2-1 | 2-2 | 5-0 | 3-2 | 5-2 | 1-0 | 1-0 | 2-0 | 1-0 | 1-0 | 2-0 | 2-1 | 2-1 | 0-1 | 2-0 | 2-0 | 2-1 | 1-2 | 3-2 | | 1-1 |
| 22 Wolviston | 3-0 | 0-2 | 3-4 | 2-3 | 2-1 | 2-1 | 1-0 | 0-1 | 1-3 | 2-2 | 1-1 | 1-1 | 1-1 | 1-3 | 3-0 | 1-1 | 3-3 | 1-2 | 0-1 | 0-1 | 1-1 | |

## WEARSIDE LEAGUE CONSTITUTION 2013-14

| Club | Ground | Contact |
|---|---|---|
| ANNFIELD PLAIN | Derwent Park , West Road , Annfield Plain DH9 8PZ | 07833 366 056 |
| ASHBROOKE BELFORD HOUSE | Silksworth Park, Blind Lane, Silksworth, Sunderland SR3 1AX | 07505 503873 |
| BOLDON COMMUNITY ASSOCIATION | Boldon Welfare, New Road, Boldon Colliery NE35 9DS | 0191 536 4180 (Cricket Club) |
| CLEATOR MOOR CELTIC | Celtic Club, Birks Road, Cleator Moor CA25 5HR | 01946 812476 |
| COXHOE ATHLETIC | Beechfield Park, Coxhoe DH6 4SD | 07956 159916 |
| DARLINGTON CLEVELAND BRIDGE | Eastbourne Sports Complex, Bourne Avenue, Darlington DL1 1LJ | 01325 243177/243188 |
| EASINGTON COLLIERY AFC | Easington Welfare Park SR8 3JJ | 07720 611905 |
| GATESHEAD LEAM RANGERS | Dawdon Welfare Park, Green Drive, Dawdon, Seaham SR7 7XL | 07859 0066432 |
| HARTLEPOOL | Grayfields Enclose, Jesmond Gardens, Hartlepool TS24 8QS | 01429 299428 |
| HARTON AND WESTOE | Harton Colliery Welfare, Boldon Lane. NE34 ONA | 07847 271495 |
| JARROW | Perth Green Community Assoc., Inverness Road, Jarrow NE32 4AQ | 0191 489 3743 |
| PRUDHOE TOWN | Kimberley Park, Broomhouse Road, Prudhoe NE42 5EH | 01661 835900 |
| REDCAR ATHLETIC | Green Lane, Redcar TS10 3RW | 07854 935380 |
| RICHMOND TOWN | Earls Orchard Playing Field. DL10 4RH | 07970 789526 |
| RYHOPE COLLIERY WELFARE | Ryhope Recreation Park, Ryhope Street, Ryhope, Sunderland SR2 0AS | n/a |
| SEATON CAREW | Hornby Park, Elizabeth Way, Seaton Carew. TS25 2AZ | 07877 077515 |
| SILKSWORTH RANGERS | Silksworth Park, Blind Lane, Silksworth, Sunderland SR3 1AX | 07423 014566 |
| STOCKTON TOWN | Bishopton Road West, Stockton-on-Tees TS19 0QD | 07832 967008 |
| SUNDERLAND WEST END | Ford Quarry, Keelmans Lane, Pennywell, Sunderland | 07812 439248 |
| WOLVISTON | Metcalfe Park, Wynyard Road, Wolviston, Billingham TS22 5NE | 07768 321651 |

**In:** Ryhope C.W. (R - Northern League Div.2) **Out:** Peterlee Town (W). Kirbymoorside (W). Willington (P - Northern League Div.2).

# WEST CHESHIRE LEAGUE

| Sponsored by: Carlsberg<br>Founded: 1892<br>Recent Champions:<br>2008: West Kirby<br>2009: West Kirby<br>2010: Cammell Laird Reserves<br>2011: West Kirby<br>2012: Ashville |
| --- |

## PYKE CUP

**ROUND 1**

| | | |
| --- | --- | --- |
| Blacon Youth Club | v Mossley Hill Athletic | 1-2 |
| Southport Trinity | v Ashville | 0-5 |
| Newton | v Ellesmere Port | 5-3 |
| Christleton | v Maghull | 3-1 |
| Cammell Laird Reserves | v Chester Nomads | 1-2 |
| Upton A.A. | v West Kirby | 0-4 |
| Vauxhall Motors Reserves | v Marine Reserves | 3-0 |
| Heswall | v Hale | 3-2 aet |

**QUARTER FINALS**

| | | |
| --- | --- | --- |
| Mossley Hill Athletic | v Ashville | 3-0 |
| Newton | v Christleton | 2-0 |
| Chester Nomads | v West Kirby | 1-4 |
| Vauxhall Motors Reserves | v Heswell | 1-2 |

**SEMI FINALS**

| | | |
| --- | --- | --- |
| Mossley Hill Athletic | v Newton | 3-2 |
| West Kirby | v Heswall | 3-0 |

**FINAL**

| | | |
| --- | --- | --- |
| Mossley Hill Athletic | v West Kirby | 0-1 |

| DIVISION ONE | P | W | D | L | F | A | Pts |
| --- | --- | --- | --- | --- | --- | --- | --- |
| 1 Heswell | 28 | 20 | 7 | 1 | 68 | 23 | 67 |
| 2 Cammell Laird Reserves | 28 | 17 | 4 | 7 | 78 | 42 | 55 |
| 3 West Kirby | 28 | 16 | 5 | 7 | 63 | 38 | 53 |
| 4 Vauxhall Motors Reserves | 28 | 12 | 8 | 8 | 52 | 42 | 44 |
| 5 Chester Nomads | 28 | 11 | 9 | 8 | 59 | 50 | 42 |
| 6 Christleton | 28 | 10 | 6 | 12 | 41 | 46 | 36 |
| 7 Marine Reserves (-3pts) | 28 | 12 | 2 | 14 | 64 | 58 | 35 |
| 8 Hale | 28 | 10 | 5 | 13 | 71 | 71 | 35 |
| 9 Ashville | 28 | 10 | 5 | 13 | 48 | 56 | 35 |
| 10 Blacon Youth Club | 28 | 10 | 3 | 15 | 51 | 62 | 33 |
| 11 Newton (-3pts) | 28 | 11 | 3 | 14 | 47 | 68 | 33 |
| 12 Maghull | 28 | 8 | 6 | 14 | 41 | 63 | 30 |
| 13 Mossley Hill Athletic | 28 | 8 | 5 | 15 | 48 | 66 | 29 |
| 14 Southport Trinity | 28 | 8 | 5 | 15 | 44 | 62 | 29 |
| 15 Upton A.A. (-3pts) | 28 | 9 | 3 | 16 | 43 | 71 | 27 |

Ellesmere Port withdrew - record expunged.

| DIVISION ONE | 1 | 2 | 3 | 4 | 5 | 6 | 7 | 8 | 9 | 10 | 11 | 12 | 13 | 14 | 15 |
| --- | --- | --- | --- | --- | --- | --- | --- | --- | --- | --- | --- | --- | --- | --- | --- |
| Ashville | | 0-4 | 2-1 | 1-1 | 2-2 | 0-0 | 1-3 | 2-1 | 2-5 | 6-1 | 4-2 | 1-1 | 2-1 | 3-1 | 0-2 |
| Blacon Youth Club | 2-4 | | 1-1 | 3-2 | 3-1 | 0-0 | 0-4 | 2-1 | 4-3 | 1-3 | 7-2 | 0-2 | 2-0 | 1-2 | 1-0 |
| Cammell Laird Reserves | 3-1 | 2-0 | | 4-4 | 2-1 | 7-2 | 2-3 | 10-0 | 4-3 | 4-0 | 6-0 | 1-0 | 2-3 | 6-1 | 5-3 |
| Chester Nomads | 1-0 | 4-1 | 0-3 | | 2-0 | 3-3 | 2-2 | 3-2 | 0-3 | 1-2 | 1-2 | 4-1 | 4-3 | 2-2 | 2-2 |
| Christleton | 2-1 | 0-2 | 3-0 | 1-7 | | 4-0 | 0-0 | 2-1 | 3-0 | 2-2 | 1-2 | 1-1 | 3-0 | 0-1 | 0-3 |
| Hale | 2-4 | 5-0 | 2-2 | 2-3 | 0-3 | | 0-3 | 1-2 | 8-5 | 5-0 | 4-1 | 0-1 | 8-0 | 3-3 | 2-4 |
| Heswall | 3-2 | 3-2 | 2-0 | 2-0 | 4-0 | 4-1 | | 1-1 | 1-0 | 5-1 | 3-2 | 3-1 | 5-0 | 2-0 | 0-0 |
| Maghull | 2-1 | 2-4 | 0-1 | 0-2 | 4-4 | 4-2 | 1-1 | | 0-1 | 1-0 | 2-0 | 1-3 | 2-2 | 3-2 | 0-5 |
| Marine Reserves | 5-3 | 1-0 | 1-2 | 5-1 | 0-2 | 2-3 | 3-2 | 3-0 | | 0-2 | 1-4 | 2-0 | 2-3 | 2-1 | 1-3 |
| Mossley Hill Athletic | 1-1 | 3-1 | 3-3 | 2-2 | 0-2 | 3-4 | 0-1 | 3-3 | 3-0 | | 4-2 | 5-1 | 1-3 | 1-2 | 1-3 |
| Newton | 3-1 | 2-2 | 0-1 | 1-0 | 2-1 | 3-5 | 0-5 | 2-0 | 3-3 | 4-3 | | 1-3 | 2-1 | 1-1 | 3-1 |
| Southport Trinity | 5-1 | 5-4 | 0-2 | 1-4 | 2-2 | 1-4 | 2-2 | 1-2 | 0-7 | 0-2 | 1-2 | | 3-4 | 0-1 | 1-3 |
| Upton AA | 0-1 | 4-2 | 0-1 | 0-0 | 0-1 | 6-2 | 2-2 | 2-4 | 1-5 | 2-0 | 1-0 | 1-4 | | 0-6 | 1-0 |
| Vauxhall Motors Reserves | 0-1 | 5-2 | 3-1 | 0-2 | 2-0 | 1-0 | 0-1 | 1-1 | 1-1 | 2-1 | 4-0 | 1-1 | 4-2 | | 2-2 |
| West Kirby | 2-1 | 1-0 | 4-2 | 2-2 | 3-0 | 2-3 | 0-1 | 2-1 | 2-0 | 5-1 | 2-1 | 1-3 | 3-1 | 3-3 | |

## WEST CHESHIRE LEAGUE DIVISION ONE CONSTITUTION 2013-14

| | | |
| --- | --- | --- |
| ASHVILLE | Villa Park, Cross Lane, Wallasey Village, Wallasey CH45 8RH | 0151 638 2127 |
| BLACON YOUTH CLUB | Cairns Crescent Playing Fields, Blacon, Chester CH1 5JF | None |
| CAMMELL LAIRD RESERVES | Kirklands, St Peters Road, Rock Ferry, Birkenhead CH42 1PY | 0151 645 312 |
| CHESTER NOMADS | Boughton Hall Cricket Club, Boughton, Chester, CH3 5EL | 01244 326 072 |
| CHRISTLETON | Little Heath Road, Christleton, Chester CH3 7AH | 01244 336589 |
| ELLESMERE PORT | Whitby Sports & Social Club, Chester Road, Whitby, Ellesmere Port CH66 2NX | 0151 200 7080/7054 |
| HALE | Hale Park, The High Street, Hale Village, Liverpool L24 4AF | None |
| HESWALL | Gayton Park, Brimstage Road, Heswall CH60 1XG | 0151 342 8172 |
| MAGHULL | Old Hall Field, Hall Lane, Maghull L31 7BB | 0151 526 7320 |
| MALLABY | Unilever Sports Ground, Bromborough CH62 3PU | |
| MOSSLEY HILL ATHLETIC | Mossley Hill Athletic Club, Mossley Hill Road, Liverpool L18 8BX | 0151 724 4377 |
| NEWTON | Millcroft, Frankby Road, Greasby CH47 0NB | 0151 677 8282 |
| SOUTH LIVERPOOL | North Field, Jericho Lane, Aigburth, Liverpool L17 4JR | None |
| SOUTHPORT TRINITY | Netherpool Sports Ground, Ellesmere Port CH66 1TP | |
| UPTON ATHLETIC ASSOCIATION | Cheshire County S & S Club, Plas Newton Lane, Chester CH2 1PR | 01244 318161 |
| VAUXHALL MOTORS RESERVES | Vauxhall Sports Ground, Rivacre Road, Hooton, Ellesmere Port CH66 1NJ | 0151 328 1114 Clubhouse: 0151 327 2294 |
| WEST KIRBY | Marine Park, Greenbank Road, West Kirby CH48 5HL | 0151 625 7734 |

**In:** Mallaby (P). South Liverpool (P). **Out:** Ellesmere Port (WS). Marine Reserves (W).

| DIVISION TWO | P | W | D | L | F | A | Pts |
|---|---|---|---|---|---|---|---|
| (P) South Liverpool | 30 | 25 | 3 | 2 | 111 | 35 | 78 |
| (P) Mallaby | 30 | 23 | 5 | 2 | 93 | 35 | 74 |
| Maghull Reserves | 30 | 14 | 9 | 7 | 68 | 52 | 51 |
| Heswell Reserves (-3pts) | 30 | 16 | 6 | 8 | 58 | 44 | 51 |
| Capenhurst Villa | 30 | 15 | 5 | 10 | 63 | 49 | 50 |
| Richmond Raith Rovers | 30 | 14 | 7 | 9 | 66 | 59 | 49 |
| Ashville Reserves | 30 | 12 | 5 | 13 | 59 | 58 | 41 |
| AFC Bebington Athletic | 30 | 11 | 6 | 13 | 55 | 53 | 39 |
| Prescot Cables Reserves | 30 | 9 | 8 | 13 | 59 | 70 | 35 |
| 0 Marshalls | 30 | 9 | 7 | 14 | 49 | 62 | 34 |
| 1 Manor Athletic | 30 | 8 | 9 | 13 | 54 | 68 | 33 |
| 2 West Kirby Reserves | 30 | 9 | 6 | 15 | 43 | 71 | 33 |
| 3 Helsby | 30 | 9 | 5 | 16 | 58 | 61 | 32 |
| 4 Willaston | 30 | 9 | 4 | 17 | 45 | 68 | 31 |
| 5 Mossley Hill Athletic Reserves | 30 | 9 | 3 | 18 | 41 | 74 | 30 |
| 6 Mersey Royal | 30 | 2 | 4 | 24 | 40 | 103 | 10 |

| DIVISION THREE | P | W | D | L | F | A | Pts |
|---|---|---|---|---|---|---|---|
| 1 (P) Redgate Rovers | 28 | 19 | 1 | 8 | 97 | 47 | 58 |
| 2 (P) Gateacre Village | 28 | 17 | 7 | 4 | 69 | 33 | 58 |
| 3 Marshalls Reserves (-3pts) | 27 | 19 | 3 | 5 | 75 | 42 | 57 |
| 4 Widnes Vikings Reserves | 28 | 15 | 3 | 10 | 76 | 45 | 48 |
| 5 Belfry | 28 | 14 | 4 | 10 | 73 | 60 | 46 |
| 6 South Liverpool Reserves | 28 | 11 | 8 | 9 | 52 | 41 | 41 |
| 7 Neston Nomads | 28 | 13 | 2 | 13 | 64 | 73 | 41 |
| 8 Chester Nomads Reserves | 28 | 11 | 7 | 10 | 52 | 54 | 40 |
| 9 Capenhurst Villa Reserves | 28 | 12 | 3 | 13 | 53 | 54 | 39 |
| 10 Christleton Reserves | 28 | 11 | 5 | 12 | 64 | 62 | 38 |
| 11 (W) AFC Bebington Athletic Res. | 28 | 9 | 5 | 14 | 43 | 71 | 32 |
| 12 Merseyside Police | 28 | 6 | 9 | 13 | 47 | 66 | 27 |
| 13 Hale Reserves | 28 | 6 | 7 | 15 | 57 | 69 | 25 |
| 14 Upton A.A. Reserves | 28 | 3 | 6 | 19 | 39 | 99 | 15 |
| 15 (W) Ellesmere Port Res.(-13pts) | 27 | 6 | 4 | 17 | 36 | 81 | 9 |

# Click Back in Time!

Over 36 years of publishing the Non-League Club Directory has filled a room full of information and photographs covering the game we know and love.

What we intend, over time, is to create a website that shares with you everything we have accumulated, which we hope will bring back some fond memories of season's gone by.

A unique look back at how the game has evolved since the 1940s will also make for interesting reading, including league tables from season's gone by.

Log on to **www.non-leagueclubdirectory.co.uk** today and see how many faces from teams gone by you recognise

# WEST LANCASHIRE LEAGUE

**Sponsored by:** Bay Radio

**Founded:** 1904

**Recent Champions:**

2008: Garstang

2009: Charnock Richard

2010: Blackpool Wren Rovers

2011: Blackpool Wren Rovers

2012: Charnock Richard

## RICHARDSON CUP

**SEMI FINALS**

| Eagley | v | Euxton Villa | 0-0, 4-2p |
| Longridge Town | v | Blackpool Wren Rovers | 1-1, 4-5p |

**FINAL**

| Eagley | v | Blackpool Wren Rovers | 4-2 |

| PREMIER DIVISION | P | W | D | L | F | A | Pts |
|---|---|---|---|---|---|---|---|
| 1 Charnock Richard | 30 | 22 | 7 | 1 | 107 | 31 | 73 |
| 2 Blackpool Wren Rovers | 30 | 20 | 5 | 5 | 53 | 30 | 65 |
| 3 Longridge Town | 30 | 18 | 6 | 6 | 74 | 36 | 60 |
| 4 Eagley | 30 | 16 | 6 | 8 | 82 | 52 | 54 |
| 5 Fleetwood Hesketh | 30 | 15 | 6 | 9 | 62 | 40 | 51 |
| 6 Coppull United | 30 | 14 | 7 | 9 | 46 | 35 | 49 |
| 7 Slyne With Hest | 30 | 11 | 9 | 10 | 52 | 56 | 42 |
| 8 Thornton Cleveleys | 30 | 11 | 8 | 11 | 44 | 45 | 41 |
| 9 Euxton Villa | 30 | 10 | 9 | 11 | 43 | 47 | 39 |
| 10 Vickerstown Ccfc | 30 | 10 | 3 | 17 | 49 | 70 | 33 |
| 11 Crooklands Casuals | 30 | 9 | 6 | 15 | 55 | 81 | 33 |
| 12 Tempest United (-3pts) | 30 | 8 | 8 | 14 | 50 | 65 | 29 |
| 13 Fulwood Amateurs | 30 | 7 | 7 | 16 | 41 | 60 | 28 |
| 14 Burnley United (-3pts) | 30 | 8 | 4 | 18 | 40 | 70 | 25 |
| 15 (R) Lostock St. Gerards | 30 | 4 | 9 | 17 | 44 | 69 | 21 |
| 16 (R) Poulton Town | 30 | 5 | 4 | 21 | 23 | 78 | 19 |

| PREMIER DIVISION | 1 | 2 | 3 | 4 | 5 | 6 | 7 | 8 | 9 | 10 | 11 | 12 | 13 | 14 | 15 | 16 |
|---|---|---|---|---|---|---|---|---|---|---|---|---|---|---|---|---|
| 1 Blackpool Wren Rovers | | 4-0 | 1-1 | 2-0 | 2-1 | 0-3 | 1-1 | 2-1 | 1-0 | 2-1 | 2-1 | 1-0 | 1-0 | 0-0 | 2-1 | 1-0 |
| 2 Burnley United | 0-2 | | 2-9 | 2-0 | 0-1 | 1-1 | 2-1 | 1-3 | 1-2 | 0-1 | 1-0 | 6-0 | 1-3 | 1-0 | 2-1 | 4-0 |
| 3 Charnock Richard | 3-1 | 6-0 | | 1-1 | 4-0 | 2-2 | 4-3 | 2-3 | 3-2 | 4-3 | 3-2 | 3-0 | 4-1 | 4-0 | 3-1 | 8-1 |
| 4 Coppull United | 4-1 | 2-1 | 0-0 | | 3-0 | 1-5 | 2-0 | 0-2 | 1-2 | 1-1 | 0-0 | 1-0 | 2-1 | 4-1 | 3-0 | 2-2 |
| 5 Crooklands Casuals | 0-2 | 3-2 | 2-5 | 1-4 | | 1-2 | 5-1 | 1-2 | 3-1 | 0-2 | 2-2 | 3-0 | 3-3 | 3-3 | 2-1 | 6-1 |
| 6 Eagley | 2-1 | 3-3 | 0-3 | 2-1 | 8-1 | | 2-1 | 2-3 | 3-3 | 2-3 | 4-3 | 4-0 | 4-0 | 3-2 | 0-0 | 3-1 |
| 7 Euxton Villa | 3-0 | 1-0 | 0-0 | 0-2 | 4-3 | 2-5 | | 2-0 | 1-1 | 0-1 | 1-1 | 1-1 | 3-4 | 3-0 | 1-0 | 2-1 |
| 8 Fleetwood Hesketh | 0-3 | 2-1 | 2-2 | 1-3 | 2-0 | 2-1 | 0-0 | | 1-0 | 1-1 | 6-0 | 12-1 | 0-2 | 0-1 | 2-3 | 2-3 |
| 9 Fulwood Amateurs | 1-1 | 3-1 | 0-3 | 1-0 | 1-2 | 3-5 | 3-2 | 0-2 | | 0-2 | 1-1 | 1-2 | 0-3 | 2-4 | 2-2 | 1-4 |
| 10 Longridge Town | 0-3 | 8-0 | 2-2 | 4-0 | 2-2 | 4-1 | 3-0 | 1-2 | 3-0 | | 4-2 | 3-0 | 0-2 | 3-1 | 2-0 | 4-1 |
| 11 Lostock St. Gerards | 3-5 | 1-1 | 0-5 | 0-0 | 5-0 | 2-6 | 3-3 | 2-2 | 1-3 | 1-3 | | 0-1 | 0-1 | 2-1 | 1-3 | 2-3 |
| 12 Poulton Town | 0-1 | 1-2 | 1-3 | 0-2 | 1-3 | 0-5 | 0-2 | 0-1 | 3-2 | 0-4 | 2-2 | | 0-2 | 2-2 | 1-2 | 2-1 |
| 13 Slyne With Hest | 1-3 | 4-2 | 1-3 | 2-2 | 4-4 | 2-0 | 1-1 | 1-1 | 1-4 | 2-2 | 0-3 | 2-1 | | 2-0 | 3-3 | 2-4 |
| 14 Tempest United | 1-5 | 3-0 | 0-10 | 0-1 | 8-0 | 2-2 | 2-3 | 2-2 | 0-0 | 4-4 | 1-2 | 4-0 | 1-1 | | 2-6 | 1-0 |
| 15 Thornton Cleveleys | 1-1 | 3-1 | 0-3 | 3-2 | 2-2 | 2-1 | 0-1 | 2-1 | 0-0 | 0-1 | 2-1 | 1-1 | 1-1 | 0-2 | | 2-0 |
| 16 Vickerstown Ccfc | 1-2 | 2-2 | 0-4 | 0-2 | 4-1 | 3-1 | 0-0 | 1-4 | 4-2 | 3-2 | 3-1 | 2-3 | 3-0 | 0-2 | 1-2 | |

| IVISION ONE | P | W | D | L | F | A | Pts |
|---|---|---|---|---|---|---|---|
| (P) Norcross & Warbreck | 30 | 26 | 1 | 3 | 111 | 41 | 79 |
| (P) Garstang | 30 | 21 | 6 | 3 | 84 | 37 | 69 |
| Hesketh Bank | 30 | 17 | 6 | 7 | 63 | 42 | 57 |
| Burscough Richmond | 30 | 15 | 8 | 7 | 61 | 37 | 53 |
| Wyre Villa | 30 | 17 | 2 | 11 | 77 | 57 | 53 |
| Turton | 30 | 11 | 9 | 10 | 71 | 62 | 42 |
| Dalton United | 30 | 13 | 2 | 15 | 64 | 78 | 41 |
| Mill Hill St. Peters | 30 | 12 | 4 | 14 | 51 | 61 | 40 |
| Furness Rovers | 30 | 11 | 6 | 13 | 56 | 59 | 39 |
| Bac/Ee Preston | 30 | 11 | 5 | 14 | 73 | 81 | 38 |
| Lytham Town | 30 | 10 | 3 | 17 | 56 | 78 | 33 |
| Hawcoat Park | 30 | 8 | 8 | 14 | 61 | 84 | 32 |
| Millom | 30 | 9 | 5 | 16 | 57 | 82 | 32 |
| Ambleside United (-3pts) | 30 | 10 | 4 | 16 | 72 | 78 | 31 |
| (R) Haslingden St.Mary`s | 30 | 7 | 6 | 17 | 48 | 68 | 27 |
| (R) Stoneclough | 30 | 2 | 5 | 23 | 36 | 96 | 11 |

| DIVISION TWO | | P | W | D | L | F | A | Pts |
|---|---|---|---|---|---|---|---|---|
| 1 | (P) Hurst Green | 28 | 19 | 6 | 3 | 92 | 33 | 63 |
| 2 | (P) Bolton County | 28 | 19 | 4 | 5 | 79 | 47 | 61 |
| 3 | Leyland United (-6pts) | 28 | 20 | 5 | 3 | 101 | 28 | 59 |
| 4 | Askam United | 28 | 15 | 5 | 8 | 82 | 53 | 50 |
| 5 | Walney Island | 28 | 15 | 3 | 10 | 64 | 61 | 48 |
| 6 | Kendal County | 28 | 14 | 3 | 11 | 56 | 55 | 45 |
| 7 | Todmorden Borough | 28 | 12 | 4 | 12 | 63 | 49 | 40 |
| 8 | (W) Whinney Hill | 28 | 9 | 9 | 10 | 50 | 59 | 36 |
| 9 | Gsk Ulverston Rangers | 28 | 11 | 3 | 14 | 40 | 49 | 36 |
| 10 | Ladybridge | 28 | 11 | 2 | 15 | 58 | 72 | 35 |
| 11 | CMB (-3pts) | 28 | 10 | 4 | 14 | 52 | 63 | 31 |
| 12 | Croston Sports | 28 | 8 | 5 | 15 | 34 | 46 | 29 |
| 13 | Furness Cavaliers | 28 | 8 | 3 | 17 | 46 | 63 | 27 |
| 14 | Barrow Wanderers | 28 | 6 | 3 | 19 | 33 | 76 | 21 |
| 15 | Milnthorpe Corinthians | 28 | 3 | 1 | 24 | 28 | 124 | 10 |

## WEST LANCASHIRE LEAGUE PREMIER DIVISION CONSTITUTION 2013-14

| BLACKPOOL WREN ROVERS | Bruce Park, School Road, Marton, Blackpool FY4 5DX | 07876 013181 |
|---|---|---|
| BURNLEY UNITED | Barden Sports Ground, Barden Lane, Burnley BB10 1JQ | 01282 437943 / 07961 604412 |
| CHARNOCK RICHARD | Mossie Park, Charter Lane, Charnock Richard, Chorley PR7 5LZ | 07507 608887 |
| COPPULL UNITED | Springfield Road, Coppull PR7 5EJ | 07747 606358 |
| CROOKLANDS CASUALS | Longlands Park, Greystone Lane, Dalton-in-Furness LA15 8JF | 07792417609 |
| EAGLEY | Eagley Sports Complex, Dunscar Bridge, Bolton BL7 9PQ | 01204 306178 / 07706 192923 |
| EUXTON VILLA | Jim Fowler Memorial Ground, Runshaw Hall Lane, Euxton, Chorley PR7 6HH | 07778 678221 |
| FLEETWOOD HESKETH | Fylde Road, Southport PR9 9XH | 07927 325585 |
| FULWOOD AMATEURS | Lightfoot Lane, Fulwood, Preston PR2 3LP | 0774 464601 |
| GARSTANG | The Riverside, High Street, Garstang PR3 1EB | 07870 325388 |
| LONGRIDGE TOWN | Inglewhite Road, Longridge, Preston PR3 2NA | 07530 819305 |
| NORCROSS & WARBRECK | Anchorsholme Lane, Thornton Cleveleys, Blackpool FY5 3DA | 01253 859836 |
| SLYNE-WITH-HEST | Bottomdale Road, Slyne, Lancaster LA2 6BG | 01524 417193 / 07770 851787 |
| TEMPEST UNITED | Tempest Road, Chew Moor Village, Lostock, Bolton BL6 4HP | 01942 811938 |
| THORNTON CLEVELEYS | Bourne Road, Cleveleys, Thornton Cleveleys FY5 4QA | 01253 859907 / 07940 179502 |
| VICKERSTOWN CC | Park Vale, Mill Lane, Walney, Barrow-in-Furness LA14 3NB | 07446 112716 |

In: Garstang (P). Norcross & Warbeck (P).

Out: Lostock St Gerards (R). Poulton Town (R).

| ESERVE DIVISION ONE | P | W | D | L | F | A | Pts |
|---|---|---|---|---|---|---|---|
| Eagley Reserves | 30 | 26 | 2 | 2 | 119 | 32 | 80 |
| (W) Norcross & Warbreck Res. | 30 | 22 | 1 | 7 | 91 | 43 | 67 |
| Charnock Richard Reserves | 30 | 16 | 6 | 8 | 86 | 56 | 54 |
| Lostock St. Gerards Reserves | 30 | 18 | 5 | 7 | 75 | 50 | 53 |
| Thornton Cleveleys Reserves | 30 | 14 | 7 | 9 | 70 | 56 | 49 |
| (W) Fleetwood Hesketh Res. | 30 | 14 | 7 | 9 | 61 | 47 | 49 |
| Garstang Reserves | 30 | 14 | 6 | 10 | 68 | 42 | 48 |
| Euxton Villa Reserves | 30 | 13 | 8 | 9 | 53 | 51 | 47 |
| Tempest United Reserves | 30 | 10 | 7 | 13 | 58 | 61 | 37 |
| Coppull United Reserves | 30 | 11 | 4 | 15 | 51 | 67 | 37 |
| Haslingden St.Mary`s Reserves | 30 | 7 | 10 | 13 | 51 | 57 | 31 |
| Fulwood Amateurs Reserves | 30 | 8 | 4 | 18 | 52 | 100 | 28 |
| Burnley United Reserves (-3pts) | 30 | 8 | 5 | 17 | 72 | 78 | 26 |
| Bac/Ee Preston Reserves (-12pts) | 30 | 10 | 3 | 17 | 60 | 87 | 21 |
| (R) Poulton Town Reserves | 30 | 6 | 3 | 21 | 42 | 89 | 21 |
| (R) Mill Hill St. Peters Reserves | 30 | 3 | 2 | 25 | 39 | 132 | 11 |

| RESERVE DIVISION TWO | | P | W | D | L | F | A | Pts |
|---|---|---|---|---|---|---|---|---|
| 1 | (P) Blackpool Wren Rovers Reserves | 26 | 20 | 4 | 2 | 103 | 16 | 64 |
| 2 | (P) Wyre Villa Reserves | 26 | 19 | 4 | 3 | 85 | 29 | 61 |
| 3 | Lytham Town Reserves | 26 | 19 | 2 | 5 | 103 | 33 | 59 |
| 4 | Slyne With Hest Reserves | 26 | 16 | 2 | 8 | 82 | 45 | 50 |
| 5 | Bolton County Reserves | 26 | 15 | 1 | 10 | 73 | 61 | 46 |
| 6 | Burscough Richmond Reserves | 26 | 12 | 5 | 9 | 61 | 38 | 41 |
| 7 | Todmorden Borough Reserves | 26 | 12 | 4 | 10 | 73 | 63 | 40 |
| 8 | Longridge Town Reserves (-3pts) | 26 | 12 | 1 | 13 | 56 | 63 | 34 |
| 9 | Hesketh Bank Reserves | 26 | 10 | 3 | 13 | 61 | 68 | 33 |
| 10 | Whinney Hill Reserves | 26 | 9 | 3 | 14 | 60 | 69 | 30 |
| 11 | Croston Sports Reserves | 26 | 9 | 2 | 15 | 64 | 76 | 29 |
| 12 | (W) Stoneclough Res. (-3pts) | 26 | 6 | 3 | 17 | 43 | 75 | 18 |
| 13 | Turton Reserves | 26 | 3 | 3 | 20 | 28 | 99 | 12 |
| 14 | Milnthorpe Corinthians Res. (-6pts) | 26 | 1 | 1 | 24 | 22 | 179 | -2 |

# WEST YORKSHIRE LEAGUE

**Sponsored by:** Active 8
**Founded:** 1928
**Recent Champions:**
**2008:** Carlton Athletic
**2009:** Knaresborough Town **2010:** Bardsey
**2011:** Bardsey **2012:** Beeston St Anthony's

## PREMIER DIVISION

| | | P | W | D | L | F | A | Pts |
|---|---|---|---|---|---|---|---|---|
| 1 | Bardsey | 30 | 22 | 5 | 3 | 93 | 35 | 71 |
| 2 | Leeds City | 30 | 21 | 5 | 4 | 72 | 31 | 68 |
| 3 | Oxenhope Recreation | 30 | 21 | 4 | 5 | 119 | 52 | 67 |
| 4 | Beeston St Anthony's | 30 | 19 | 8 | 3 | 93 | 31 | 65 |
| 5 | Ripon City | 30 | 15 | 7 | 8 | 61 | 45 | 52 |
| 6 | Rothwell | 30 | 12 | 2 | 16 | 67 | 69 | 38 |
| 7 | Field | 30 | 10 | 7 | 13 | 58 | 66 | 37 |
| 8 | Brighouse Old Boys (-3pts) | 30 | 11 | 6 | 13 | 58 | 54 | 36 |
| 9 | Otley Town | 30 | 10 | 6 | 14 | 60 | 71 | 36 |
| 10 | East End Park | 30 | 10 | 5 | 15 | 65 | 74 | 35 |
| 11 | Wetherby Athletic | 30 | 11 | 2 | 17 | 51 | 65 | 35 |
| 12 | Boroughbridge | 30 | 10 | 3 | 17 | 55 | 90 | 33 |
| 13 | Kippax | 30 | 9 | 2 | 19 | 51 | 104 | 29 |
| 14 | Whitkirk Wanderers (-1pt) | 30 | 7 | 6 | 17 | 63 | 87 | 26 |
| 15 | (R) Carlton Athletic (-6pts) | 30 | 10 | 1 | 19 | 48 | 85 | 25 |
| 16 | (R) Pool | 30 | 6 | 3 | 21 | 40 | 95 | 21 |

## DIVISION ONE

| | | P | W | D | L | F | A | Pts |
|---|---|---|---|---|---|---|---|---|
| 1 | (P) Hunslet Club | 28 | 19 | 6 | 3 | 78 | 34 | 63 |
| 2 | (P) Shelley | 28 | 19 | 5 | 4 | 74 | 34 | 62 |
| 3 | (P) Horbury Town | 28 | 18 | 5 | 5 | 66 | 31 | 59 |
| 4 | Robin Hood Athletic | 28 | 17 | 6 | 5 | 64 | 34 | 57 |
| 5 | Old Modernians | 28 | 16 | 5 | 7 | 66 | 43 | 53 |
| 6 | Old Headingley | 28 | 12 | 8 | 8 | 52 | 38 | 44 |
| 7 | Ilkley Town | 28 | 11 | 5 | 12 | 44 | 40 | 38 |
| 8 | Wyke Wanderers | 28 | 10 | 7 | 11 | 38 | 43 | 37 |
| 9 | Stanley United (-3pts) | 28 | 10 | 5 | 13 | 48 | 47 | 32 |
| 10 | Altofts | 28 | 8 | 8 | 12 | 48 | 50 | 32 |
| 11 | Sherburn White Rose | 28 | 8 | 7 | 13 | 35 | 41 | 31 |
| 12 | Baildon Trinity Athletic | 28 | 9 | 3 | 16 | 33 | 74 | 30 |
| 13 | Old Centralians | 28 | 7 | 6 | 15 | 46 | 56 | 27 |
| 14 | (R) Swillington Saints | 28 | 4 | 2 | 22 | 34 | 88 | 14 |
| 15 | (W) FC RIASA | 28 | 1 | 4 | 23 | 24 | 97 | 7 |

## DIVISION TWO

| | | P | W | D | L | F | A | Pts |
|---|---|---|---|---|---|---|---|---|
| 1 | (P) Featherstone Colliery | 30 | 23 | 3 | 4 | 107 | 38 | 72 |
| 2 | (P) Aberford Albion | 30 | 23 | 3 | 4 | 85 | 41 | 72 |
| 3 | (P) Kellingley Welfare | 30 | 20 | 5 | 5 | 110 | 45 | 65 |
| 4 | (P) Knaresborough Town | 30 | 20 | 5 | 5 | 98 | 43 | 65 |
| 5 | Howden Clough | 30 | 15 | 7 | 8 | 72 | 65 | 52 |
| 6 | Glasshoughton Welfare | 30 | 16 | 3 | 11 | 78 | 54 | 51 |
| 7 | Mount St. Mary's | 30 | 13 | 3 | 14 | 57 | 70 | 42 |
| 8 | Yorkshire Amateur (-3pts) | 30 | 13 | 5 | 12 | 50 | 52 | 41 |
| 9 | Woodhouse Hill WMC | 30 | 11 | 3 | 16 | 88 | 80 | 36 |
| 10 | Ossett Common Rovers | 30 | 11 | 3 | 16 | 50 | 63 | 36 |
| 11 | Barwick (-4pts) | 30 | 10 | 5 | 15 | 73 | 82 | 31 |
| 12 | Rothwell Town | 30 | 8 | 7 | 15 | 49 | 64 | 31 |
| 13 | Garforth Rangers | 30 | 8 | 4 | 18 | 46 | 74 | 28 |
| 14 | Hartshead | 30 | 8 | 3 | 19 | 52 | 97 | 27 |
| 15 | Nostell Miners Welfare | 30 | 7 | 2 | 21 | 54 | 93 | 23 |
| 16 | Great Preston (-3pts) | 30 | 2 | 3 | 25 | 41 | 149 | 6 |

## LEAGUE CUP

**ROUND 1**

| | | | |
|---|---|---|---|
| Kellingley Welfare | v | Horbury Town | 1-2 |
| Knaresborough Town | v | Old Centralians | 1-0 |
| Ilkley Town | v | Nostell Miners Welfare | 5-1 |
| Rothwell Town | v | Old Modernians | 1-2 |
| Yorkshire Amateur | v | Old Headingley | 1-3 |
| Swillington Saints | v | Altofts | 2-1 |
| Garforth Rangers | v | Hartshead | 0-4 |
| Stanley United | v | Hunslet Club | 0-4 |
| Howden Clough | v | FC RIASA | 4-4, 3-4p |
| Sherburn White Rosev | v | Robin Hood Athletic | 0-2 |
| Featherstone Colliery | v | Shelley | 3-2 |
| Barwick | v | Glasshoughton Welfare | 3-2 |
| Rothwell Athletic | v | Wyke Wanderers | AW |
| Woodhouse Hill WMC | v | Ossett Common Rovers | 2-1 |
| Mount St. Mary's | v | Great Preston | 3-5 |
| Baildon Trinity Athletic | v | Aberford Albion | 3-1 |

**ROUND 2**

| | | | |
|---|---|---|---|
| Horbury Town | v | Knaresborough Town | 5-0 |
| East End Park | v | Kippax | 1-2 |
| Otley Town | v | Rothwell | 2-3 |
| Ilkley Town | v | Wetherby Athletic | 2-1 |
| Old Modernians | v | Brighouse Old Boys | 2-0 |
| Leeds City | v | Old Headingley | 1-0 |
| Field | v | Oxenhope Recreation | 2-5 |
| Swillington Saints | v | Pool | 2-3 |
| Hartshead | v | Hunslet Club | 0-4 |
| FC RIASA | v | Ripon City | 0-3 |
| Robin Hood Athletic | v | Featherstone Colliery | 5-1 |
| Boroughbridge | v | Barwick | 8-1 |
| Wyke Wanderers | v | Woodhouse Hill WMC | 4-2 |
| Beeston St Anthony's | v | Great Preston | 11-1 |
| Whitkirk Wanderers | v | Baildon Trinity Athletic | 1-4 |
| Carlton Athletic | v | Bardsey | 0-2 |

**ROUND 3**

| | | | |
|---|---|---|---|
| Horbury Town | v | Kippax | 3-0 |
| Rothwell | v | Ilkley Town | 0-2 |
| Old Modernians | v | Leeds City | 0-1 |
| Oxenhope Recreation | v | Pool | 3-0 |
| Hunslet Club | v | Ripon City | 1-2 |
| Robin Hood Athletic | v | Boroughbridge | 1-1, 3-4p |
| Wyke Wanderers | v | Beeston St Anthony's | 2-1 |
| Baildon Trinity Athletic | v | Bardsey | 1-6 |

**QUARTER FINALS**

| | | | |
|---|---|---|---|
| Horbury Town | v | Ilkley Town | 3-1 |
| Leeds City | v | Oxenhope Recreation | 0-0, 2-4p |
| Ripon City | v | Boroughbridge | 2-0 |
| Wyke Wanderers | v | Bardsey | 1-5 |

**SEMI FINALS**

| | | | |
|---|---|---|---|
| Horbury Town | v | Oxenhope Recreation | 3-0 |
| Ripon City | v | Bardsey | 2-1 |

**FINAL**

| | | | |
|---|---|---|---|
| Horbury Town | v | Ripon City | 0-1 |

## PREMIER DIVISION

| | | 1 | 2 | 3 | 4 | 5 | 6 | 7 | 8 | 9 | 10 | 11 | 12 | 13 | 14 | 15 | 16 |
|---|---|---|---|---|---|---|---|---|---|---|---|---|---|---|---|---|---|
| 1 | Bardsey | | 1-1 | 6-1 | 3-1 | 5-1 | 3-1 | 3-1 | 6-4 | 4-1 | 2-3 | 2-2 | 3-0 | 2-0 | 6-0 | 3-1 | 1-1 |
| 2 | Beeston St Anthony's | 1-1 | | 5-0 | 0-0 | 2-1 | 7-1 | 0-2 | 6-0 | 1-1 | 4-2 | 3-0 | 5-0 | 2-1 | 3-1 | 6-0 | 4-4 |
| 3 | Boroughbridge | 1-3 | 1-7 | | 3-1 | 6-1 | 4-4 | 4-2 | 1-1 | 0-3 | 0-0 | 2-6 | 1-2 | 1-2 | H-W | 1-6 | 4-5 |
| 4 | Brighouse Old Boys | 5-2 | 2-2 | 2-3 | | 3-0 | 3-2 | 2-2 | 1-4 | 1-4 | 1-1 | 0-1 | 1-1 | 5-0 | 0-1 | 1-1 | |
| 5 | Carlton Athletic | 0-2 | 1-8 | 3-1 | 1-4 | | 3-2 | 3-7 | 3-0 | 2-1 | 2-1 | 1-4 | 4-0 | 1-2 | 0-3 | 0-3 | 4-2 |
| 6 | East End Park | 1-2 | 1-4 | 1-2 | 2-0 | 1-1 | | 2-2 | 4-0 | 0-4 | 1-2 | 1-2 | 4-0 | 2-0 | 1-0 | 2-1 | 3-2 |
| 7 | Field | 1-6 | 0-0 | 3-2 | 2-0 | 2-1 | 2-4 | | 1-2 | 1-3 | 4-1 | 1-4 | 1-3 | 1-2 | 4-4 | 1-1 | 2-2 |
| 8 | Kippax | 0-7 | 0-6 | 1-4 | 4-1 | 3-7 | 5-4 | 2-4 | | 3-2 | 4-1 | 2-9 | 3-1 | 0-2 | 0-2 | 1-2 | 0-3 |
| 9 | Leeds City | 2-0 | 2-0 | 3-4 | 2-1 | 5-0 | 1-1 | 2-0 | 5-3 | | 2-0 | 2-2 | 2-1 | 3-1 | 3-0 | 1-1 | 3-1 |
| 10 | Otley Town | 0-4 | 1-2 | 4-0 | 3-5 | 2-1 | 1-5 | 2-2 | 1-1 | 0-1 | | 2-6 | 4-3 | 2-4 | 2-3 | 3-1 | 3-1 |
| 11 | Oxenhope Recreation | 1-2 | 2-3 | 5-0 | 5-3 | 6-1 | 2-1 | 2-0 | 7-0 | 0-4 | 3-3 | | 12-2 | 4-2 | 3-5 | 2-1 | 9-1 |
| 12 | Pool | 0-4 | 1-4 | 2-4 | 0-3 | 1-2 | 2-2 | 3-1 | 0-3 | 4-2 | 2-1 | 1-5 | | 0-4 | 1-4 | 1-3 | |
| 13 | Ripon City | 2-2 | 3-1 | 4-1 | 1-2 | 2-0 | 1-4 | 4-1 | 6-0 | 2-2 | 1-1 | 1-1 | 2-2 | | 3-3 | 1-0 | 4-3 |
| 14 | Rothwell | 2-3 | 2-4 | 0-2 | 1-2 | 3-0 | 7-3 | 1-4 | 2-0 | 0-1 | 3-4 | 2-3 | 5-3 | 0-1 | | 3-0 | 2-5 |
| 15 | Wetherby Athletic | 0-2 | 0-2 | 3-0 | 3-2 | 2-3 | 5-3 | 0-2 | 1-4 | 0-2 | 1-2 | 1-6 | 1-3 | 2-1 | 1-4 | | 5-2 |
| 16 | Whitkirk Wanderers | 1-3 | 0-0 | 5-2 | 0-4 | 2-1 | 6-2 | 2-3 | 2-1 | 1-2 | 0-7 | 2-5 | 0-0 | A-W | 3-5 | 2-4 | |

## WEST YORKSHIRE LEAGUE PREMIER DIVISION CONSTITUTION 2013-14

| | |
|---|---|
| BARDSEY | The Sportsfield, Keswick Lane, Bardsey LS17 9AQ |
| BEESTON ST ANTHONY'S | St Antony's Road, Beeston, Leeds LS11 8DT |
| BOROUGHBRIDGE | Aldborough Road, Boroughbridge YO51 9EA |
| BRIGHOUSE OLD BOYS | Hipperholme & Lightcliffe School, Stoney Lane, Lightcliffe, Halifax HX3 8TL |
| EAST END PARK | East End Park, Skelton Road, Leeds LS9 9EP |
| FIELD | Field Sports & Social Club, Hollingwood Lane, Bradford BD7 2RE |
| HORBURY TOWN | Slazengers Sports Complex, Southfields, Horbury WF4 5BH |
| HUNSLET CLUB | Hunslet Green Community Sports Club, The Oval, Anchor Street, Hunslet, Leeds LS10 2AU |
| KIPPAX | Kippax Welfare Sports & Social Club, Longdike Lane, Kippax LS25 7BP |
| LEEDS CITY | Adel War Memorial Association, Church Lane, Adel, Leeds LS16 8DE |
| OTLEY TOWN | Old Showground, Pool Road, Otley LS21 1DY |
| OXENHOPE RECREATION | The Recreation ground, Hebden Bridge Road, Oxenhope BD22 9LY |
| RIPON CITY | Mallorie Park, Mallorie Park Drive, Ripon |
| SHELLEY | Storthes Hall, Huddersfield HD8 0WA |
| WETHERBY ATHLETIC | The Ings, Wetherby LS22 5HA |
| WHITKIRK WANDERERS | Whitkirk Social & Sports Club, Selby Road, Whitkirk, Leeds LS15 0AA |

**In:** Horbury Town (P). Hunslet Club (P). Shelley (P). **Out:** Carlton Athletic (R). Pool (R).

| ALLIANCE DIVISION ONE | P | W | D | L | F | A | Pts |
|---|---|---|---|---|---|---|---|
| Leeds City Reserves | 26 | 19 | 5 | 2 | 79 | 35 | 62 |
| Beeston St. Anthony's Res. | 26 | 18 | 3 | 5 | 78 | 35 | 57 |
| East End Park Reserves | 26 | 15 | 4 | 7 | 66 | 56 | 49 |
| Oxenhope Recreation Reserves | 25 | 12 | 4 | 9 | 73 | 52 | 40 |
| Wetherby Athletic Reserves | 26 | 12 | 4 | 10 | 56 | 48 | 40 |
| Rothwell Reserves | 26 | 12 | 3 | 11 | 64 | 56 | 39 |
| Bardsey Reserves (-3pts) | 25 | 12 | 6 | 7 | 57 | 49 | 39 |
| Robin Hood Athletic Reserves | 26 | 12 | 2 | 12 | 52 | 60 | 38 |
| Brighouse Old Boys Reserves | 26 | 11 | 3 | 12 | 57 | 56 | 36 |
| 0 Old Headingley Reserves | 26 | 7 | 7 | 12 | 47 | 55 | 28 |
| 1 Field Reserves | 26 | 7 | 5 | 14 | 48 | 66 | 26 |
| 2 Ripon City Reserves | 26 | 8 | 0 | 18 | 40 | 87 | 24 |
| 3 (R) Whitkirk Wanderers Res. (-3pts) | 26 | 5 | 5 | 16 | 37 | 60 | 17 |
| 4 (R) Boroughbridge Reserves | 26 | 4 | 3 | 19 | 36 | 75 | 15 |

**Out:** Rothwell Reserves (W).

| | ALLIANCE DIVISION TWO | P | W | D | L | F | A | Pts |
|---|---|---|---|---|---|---|---|---|
| 1 | (P) Hunslet Club Reserves | 24 | 22 | 0 | 2 | 121 | 23 | 66 |
| 2 | (P) Kippax Reserves | 24 | 15 | 4 | 5 | 80 | 45 | 49 |
| 3 | Pool Reserves | 24 | 14 | 3 | 7 | 76 | 57 | 45 |
| 4 | Ilkley Town Reserves | 24 | 14 | 2 | 8 | 80 | 47 | 44 |
| 5 | Sherburn White Rose Reserves | 23 | 12 | 2 | 9 | 60 | 39 | 38 |
| 6 | Hartshead Reserves | 24 | 12 | 1 | 11 | 58 | 69 | 37 |
| 7 | Baildon Trinity Athletic Reserves | 24 | 11 | 2 | 11 | 56 | 70 | 35 |
| 8 | Aberford Albion Reserves | 24 | 8 | 7 | 9 | 60 | 56 | 31 |
| 9 | Otley Town Reserves | 23 | 8 | 3 | 12 | 55 | 77 | 27 |
| 10 | Howden Clough Reserves | 24 | 8 | 1 | 15 | 51 | 78 | 25 |
| 11 | Rothwell Town Reserves | 24 | 7 | 2 | 15 | 62 | 117 | 23 |
| 12 | Garforth Rangers Reserves | 24 | 6 | 2 | 16 | 43 | 70 | 20 |
| 13 | Barwick Reserves | 24 | 2 | 3 | 19 | 40 | 94 | 9 |

**Out:** Hartshead Reserves (W).

# WILTSHIRE LEAGUE

**Sponsored by:** No sponsor
**Founded:** 1928
**Recent Champions:**
2010: New College - Swindon
2011: Corsham Town Reserves
2012: FC Sanford

## SENIOR CUP

**ROUND 1**

| | | | |
|---|---|---|---|
| Wroughton | v | Chippenham Park | 2-6 |
| Chiseldon | v | Marlborough Town | AW |
| Corsham Town Reserves | v | Wilts Calne Town | 0-2 |
| Trowbridge Town | v | RGV Shrewton | 3-2 |
| Beversbrook | v | Southbrook | 1-2 |
| Devizes Town Reserves | v | Purton Reserves | 4-7 |
| Bradford Town Reserves | v | Ludgershall Sports | 7-1 |
| SKS Blyskawica | v | Vale of Pewsey | 3-3, 3-4p |

**QUARTER FINALS**

| | | | |
|---|---|---|---|
| Chippenham Park | v | Marlborough Town | 4-0 |
| Wilts Calne Town | v | Trowbridge Town | 4-2 |
| Southbrook | v | Purton Reserves | 2-4 |
| Bradford Town Reserves | v | Vale of Pewsey | 1-0 |

**SEMI FINALS**

| | | | |
|---|---|---|---|
| Chippenham Park | v | Wilts Calne Town | 1-2 |
| Purton Reserves | v | Bradford Town Reserves | 4-3 |

**FINAL**

| | | | |
|---|---|---|---|
| Wilts Calne Town | v | Purton Reserves | 1-0 |

## PREMIER DIVISION

| | | P | W | D | L | F | A | Pts |
|---|---|---|---|---|---|---|---|---|
| 1 | Wilts Calne Town | 26 | 19 | 5 | 2 | 83 | 32 | 62 |
| 2 | Purton FC Reserves | 26 | 19 | 2 | 5 | 85 | 40 | 59 |
| 3 | (P) Chippenham Park | 26 | 16 | 7 | 3 | 74 | 27 | 55 |
| 4 | Bradford Town Reserves (-1pt) | 26 | 13 | 8 | 5 | 63 | 36 | 46 |
| 5 | Corsham Town Reserves (-1pt) | 26 | 10 | 9 | 7 | 39 | 42 | 38 |
| 6 | Trowbridge Town | 26 | 10 | 6 | 10 | 46 | 49 | 36 |
| 7 | Ludgershall Sports | 26 | 8 | 9 | 9 | 49 | 61 | 33 |
| 8 | RGV Shrewton (-1pt) | 26 | 10 | 3 | 13 | 57 | 66 | 32 |
| 9 | Devizes Town Reserves | 26 | 9 | 4 | 13 | 44 | 62 | 31 |
| 10 | Vale of Pewsey (-1pt) | 26 | 8 | 2 | 16 | 39 | 61 | 25 |
| 11 | Southbrook | 26 | 6 | 6 | 14 | 44 | 60 | 24 |
| 12 | Marlborough Town | 26 | 7 | 3 | 16 | 38 | 62 | 24 |
| 13 | SKS Blyskawica | 26 | 5 | 7 | 14 | 39 | 54 | 22 |
| 14 | Beversbrook | 26 | 5 | 3 | 18 | 36 | 84 | 18 |

Wroughton withdrew - record expunged.

## DIVISION ONE

| | | P | W | D | L | F | A | Pts |
|---|---|---|---|---|---|---|---|---|
| 1 | Madames | 20 | 16 | 1 | 3 | 81 | 20 | 49 |
| 2 | Ashton Keynes (-1pt) | 20 | 13 | 2 | 5 | 75 | 40 | 40 |
| 3 | Wootton Bassett Town Dev. | 20 | 11 | 1 | 8 | 62 | 45 | 34 |
| 4 | NALGO Wanderers | 20 | 10 | 4 | 6 | 47 | 42 | 34 |
| 5 | Chippenham Park Reserves | 20 | 8 | 6 | 6 | 51 | 38 | 30 |
| 6 | Malmesbury Victoria Res. (-2pts) | 20 | 8 | 7 | 5 | 53 | 41 | 29 |
| 7 | Intel | 20 | 9 | 1 | 10 | 32 | 38 | 28 |
| 8 | Marshfield | 20 | 7 | 5 | 8 | 46 | 71 | 26 |
| 9 | Wilton Town (-1pt) | 20 | 5 | 2 | 13 | 20 | 48 | 16 |
| 10 | AFC Wroughton | 20 | 3 | 5 | 12 | 41 | 68 | 14 |
| 11 | Marlborough Town Res. (-5pts) | 20 | 3 | 0 | 17 | 23 | 80 | 4 |

## PREMIER DIVISION

| | | 1 | 2 | 3 | 4 | 5 | 6 | 7 | 8 | 9 | 10 | 11 | 12 | 13 | 14 |
|---|---|---|---|---|---|---|---|---|---|---|---|---|---|---|---|
| 1 | Beversbrook | | 1-2 | 0-8 | 0-4 | 1-5 | 2-3 | 2-2 | 1-5 | 2-5 | 2-1 | 2-1 | 0-3 | 1-2 | A-W |
| 2 | Bradford Town Reserves | 5-1 | | 4-0 | 1-3 | 0-1 | 7-2 | 2-0 | 4-2 | 2-5 | 1-0 | 1-0 | 1-0 | 3-3 | 1-3 |
| 3 | Chippenham Park | 5-0 | 2-2 | | 1-1 | 5-0 | 4-0 | 6-1 | 3-0 | 1-0 | 2-0 | 1-1 | 3-1 | 2-1 | 1-2 |
| 4 | Corsham Town Reserves | 0-0 | 0-0 | 1-1 | | 0-0 | 3-2 | 2-1 | 0-3 | 4-3 | 2-1 | 3-0 | 2-2 | 4-1 | 1-1 |
| 5 | Devizes Town Reserves | 5-0 | 1-1 | 0-2 | 4-0 | | 2-2 | 0-4 | 1-6 | 6-1 | 1-2 | 2-1 | 3-1 | 2-1 | 1-3 |
| 6 | Ludgershall Sports | 2-1 | 0-0 | 2-2 | 2-1 | 7-1 | | 2-2 | 2-5 | 2-6 | 0-3 | 2-1 | 1-1 | 1-0 | 2-3 |
| 7 | Marlborough Town | 1-2 | 1-3 | 1-5 | 1-2 | 2-1 | 2-2 | | 0-6 | 2-1 | 3-1 | 0-1 | 1-4 | 2-0 | 2-3 |
| 8 | Purton Reserves | 4-2 | 3-3 | 2-1 | 2-0 | 7-0 | 2-3 | 4-1 | | 3-4 | 3-1 | 3-2 | 4-0 | 3-1 | 6-2 |
| 9 | RGV Shrewton | 4-2 | 1-1 | 2-3 | 1-1 | 1-1 | 0-3 | 2-0 | 2-3 | | 2-0 | 5-4 | 1-2 | 2-0 | 0-8 |
| 10 | SKS Blyskawica | 1-1 | 2-7 | 3-3 | 5-0 | 2-3 | 2-2 | 2-1 | 0-1 | 2-6 | | 1-4 | 0-3 | 2-3 | 1-2 |
| 11 | Southbrook | 0-7 | 2-2 | 1-4 | 0-0 | 3-0 | 3-0 | 2-3 | 2-2 | 6-3 | 2-2 | | 0-2 | 0-2 | 0-4 |
| 12 | Trowbridge Town | 3-4 | 1-6 | 1-4 | 2-0 | 2-0 | 3-3 | 3-2 | 0-2 | 3-0 | 0-0 | 2-4 | | 2-2 | 2-2 |
| 13 | Vale of Pewsey | 3-0 | 2-1 | 0-4 | 2-4 | 3-2 | 1-2 | 2-3 | 2-4 | 3-0 | 0-4 | 2-1 | 1-2 | | 1-6 |
| 14 | Wilts Calne Town | 10-2 | 0-3 | 1-1 | 6-1 | 5-2 | 3-0 | 2-0 | 3-0 | 3-0 | 2-0 | 0-0 | 5-2 | 3-1 | 4-1 |

## WILTSHIRE LEAGUE PREMIER DIVISION CONSTITUTION 2013-14

| | | |
|---|---|---|
| CORSHAM TOWN RESERVES | Southbank Ground, Lacock Road, Corsham | 07963 030652 |
| DEVIZES TOWN RESERVES | Nursteed Road, Devizes SN10 3DX | 01380 722817 |
| FC CHIPPENHAM YOUTH | Hardenhuish Park, Bristol Road, Chippenham, Wiltshire SN14 6LR | 07768 353558 |
| LUDGERSHALL SPORTS | Astor Crescent, Ludgershall SP11 9QE | |
| MARLBOROUGH TOWN | Elcot Lane, Marlborough, SN8 2BG | 01672 513340 |
| PURTON RESERVES | Red House, Church Street, Purton SN5 4DY | 01793 770262 |
| SKS BLYSKAWICA | Hooper's Field, Wanborough SN4 0AN | |
| SHREWTON UNITED | Shrewton Recreation Ground, Mill Lane, Shrewton SP3 4JY | |
| SOUTHBROOK | Southbrook Recreation Ground, Pinehurst Road, Swindon | |
| SUPERMARINE SPORTS CLUB | | |
| TROWBRIDGE TOWN | Woodmarsh, Bradley Road, Trowbridge BA14 0SB | |
| VALE OF PEWSEY | Recreation Ground, Ball Road, Pewsey SN9 5BS | 01672 562990 |
| WILTS CALNE TOWN | Bremhill View, Calne SN11 9EE | |
| WROUGHTON | The Weir Field Ground, Devizes Road, Wroughton, Wiltshire | |

**In:** FC Chippenham Youth (P - formerly Chippenham Park Res.). Shrewton United (NC from RGV Shrewton). Wroughton (reformed).
**Out:** Beversbrook (S - Hellenic League Div.2 West). Bradford Town Reserves (W). Chippenham Park (P - Western Div.1).
RGV Shrewton (NC to Shrewton United). Wroughton (WS).

# LEAGUE TABLES 2012-13

ACCRINGTON COMBINATION
ALDERSHOT & DISTRICT LEAGUE
ALTRINCHAM & DISTRICT LEAGUE
AMATEUR COMBINATION
ANDOVER & DISTRICT LEAGUE
ARMY FOOTBALL ASSOCIATION
ARTHURIAN LEAGUE
AYLESBURY & DISTRICT LEAGUE
BANBURY & LORD JERSEY FA
BASINGSTOKE & DISTRICT LEAGUE
BATH & DISTRICT LEAGUE
BIRMINGHAM AFA
BISHOP'S STORTFORD, STANSTED & DISTRICT LEAGUE
BLACKBURN & DISTRICT COMBINATION
BOURNEMOUTH LEAGUE
BRIGHTON, HOVE & DISTRICT LEAGUE
BRISTOL & AVON FOOTBALL LEAGUE
BRISTOL & DISTRICT LEAGUE
BRISTOL DOWNS LEAGUE
BRISTOL PREMIER COMBINATION
BRISTOL SUBURBAN LEAGUE
BURTON & DISTRICT FOOTBALL ASSOCIATION
CENTRAL & SOUTH NORFOLK LEAGUE
CHELTENHAM ASSOCIATION LEAGUE
CHESTER & DISTRICT LEAGUE
CHORLEY & DISTRICT ALLIANCE
CIRENCESTER & DISTRICT LEAGUE
COLCHESTER & EAST ESSEX LEAGUE
CORNWALL COMBINATION
CRAVEN & DISTRICT LEAGUE
CREWE & DISTRICT LEAGUE
CROOK & DISTRICT LEAGUE
CUMBERLAND COUNTY LEAGUE
DEVON & EXETER LEAGUE
DONCASTER & DISTRICT SENIOR LEAGUE
DORSET FOOTBALL LEAGUE
DRIFFIELD & DISTRICT LEAGUE
DUCHY LEAGUE
DURHAM FOOTBALL ALLIANCE
EAST BERKSHIRE LEAGUE
EAST CHESHIRE LEAGUE
EAST CORNWALL LEAGUE
EAST LANCASHIRE LEAGUE
EAST RIDING AMATEUR LEAGUE
EAST RIDING COUNTY LEAGUE
ENFIELD ALLIANCE
ESKVALE & CLEVELAND LEAGUE
ESSEX BUSINESS HOUSES LEAGUE

FURNESS PREMIER LEAGUE
GAINSBOROUGH & DISTRICT LEAGUE
GLOUCESTERSHIRE NORTHERN SENIOR LEAGUE
GRANTHAM & DISTRICT LEAGUE
GREAT YARMOUTH & DISTRICT LEAGUE
GUERNSEY LEAGUE
GUILDFORD & WOKING ALLIANCE
HALIFAX & DISTRICT LEAGUE
HALSTEAD & DISTRICT LEAGUE
HARROGATE & DISTRICT LEAGUE
HEREFORDSHIRE LEAGUE
HOPE VALLEY AMATEUR LEAGUE
HUDDERSFIELD & DISTRICT LEAGUE
HUDDERSFIELD & DISTRICT WORKS & COMBINATION LEAGUE
I ZINGARI COMBINATION
ILFORD & DISTRICT LEAGUE
ISLE OF MAN SENIOR LEAGUE
ISLE OF WIGHT LEAGUE
JERSEY FOOTBALL COMBINATION
KIDDERMINSTER & DISTRICT LEAGUE
KINGSTON & DISTRICT LEAGUE
LANCASHIRE & CHESHIRE LEAGUE
LANCASHIRE AMATEUR LEAGUE
LANCASHIRE LEAGUE
LEEDS RED TRIANLE LEAGUE
LEICESTER & DISTRICT LEAGUE
LINCOLN & DISTRICT LEAGUE
LINCOLNSHIRE LEAGUE
LIVERPOOL CMS LEAGUE
LONDON COMMERCIAL LEAGUE
LOWESTOFT & DISTRICT LEAGUE
LUTON DISTRICT & SOUTH BEDS LEAGUE
MAIDSTONE & DISTRICT LEAGUE
MERCIAN REGIONAL LEAGUE
MID-ESSEX LEAGUE
MID-LANCASHIRE LEAGUE
MID-SOMERSET LEAGUE
MID-SUSSEX LEAGUE
MIDLAND REGIONAL ALLIANCE
NORTH & MID-HERTS LEAGUE
NORTH BUCKS & DISTRICT LEAGUE
NORTH DEVON LEAGUE
NORTH EAST NORFOLK LEAGUE
NORTH GLOUSCESTERSHIRE LEAGUE
NORTH LANCS & DISTRICT LEAGUE
NORTH LEICS LEAGUE
NORTH NORTHUMBERLAND LEAGUE
NORWICH & DISTRICT LEAGUE
NOTTS AMATEUR ALLIANCE
NOTTS SENIOR LEAGUE
PERRY STREET & DISTRICT
PLYMOUTH & WEST DEVON COMBINATION

PORTSMOUTH LEAGUE
REDDITCH & SOUTH WARWICKSHIRE COMBINATION
REDHILL & DISTRICT LEAGUE
ROCHDALE ALLIANCE
SALISBURY & DISTRICT LEAGUE
SCUNTHORPE & DISTRICT
SELBY & DISTRICT LEAGUE
SOUTH DEVON LEAGUE
SOUTH LONDON ALLIANCE
SOUTH WEST GLOUCESTERSHIRE NORTHERN SENIOR LEAGUE
SOUTH YORKSHIRE AMATEUR LEAGUE
SOUTHAMPTON FOOTBALL LEAGUE
SOUTHEND BOROUGH COMBINATION
SOUTHERN AMATEUR LEAGUE
SOUTHPORT & DISTRICT LEAGUE
SPEN VALLEY & DISTRICT
STRATFORD ALLIANCE
STROUD & DISTRICT LEAGUE
SUBURBAN LEAGUE
SURREY ELITE INTERMEDIATE LEAGUE
SURREY INTERMEDIATE (WEST)
SURREY SOUTH EASTERN COMBINATION
SWINDON & DISTRICT LEAGUE
TAUNTON & DISTRICT LEAGUE
TEESSIDE LEAGUE
THANET & DISTRICT LEAGUE
TONBRIDGE & DISTRICT
TYNESIDE AMATEUR LEAGUE
WAKEFIELD & DISTRICT LEAGUE
WEARSIDE
WEARSIDE COMBINATION
WENSLEYDALE LEAGUE
WEST END LEAGUE
WEST RIDING COUNTY AMATEUR LEAGUE
WEST SUSSEX LEAGUE
WESTMORLAND
WIGAN & DISTRICT LEAGUE
WILTSHIRE LEAGUE
WIMBLEDON & DISTRICT LEAGUE
WITNEY & DISTRICT LEAGUE
WORCESTER & DISTRICT LEAGUE
WORTHING & DISTRICT LEAGUE
WYCOMBE & DISTRICT LEAGUE
YEOVIL & DISTRICT LEAGUE
YORK LEAGUE

# LEAGUE TABLES

## ACCRINGTON COMBINATION

### Division One

| | P | W | D | L | F | A | Pts |
|---|---|---|---|---|---|---|---|
| 1 Park | 18 | 14 | 0 | 4 | 69 | 29 | 42 |
| 2 Edenfield | 17 | 13 | 2 | 2 | 61 | 33 | 41 |
| 3 Victoria | 18 | 11 | 4 | 3 | 52 | 25 | 37 |
| 4 Oswaldtwistle St Mary's 'A' | 18 | 9 | 2 | 7 | 58 | 35 | 29 |
| 5 Great Harwood Town F.C. | 17 | 7 | 4 | 6 | 59 | 47 | 25 |
| 6 Hapton | 18 | 7 | 2 | 9 | 39 | 44 | 23 |
| 7 Crown Rovers | 18 | 6 | 1 | 11 | 31 | 53 | 19 |
| 8 Arden Athletic F.C. | 18 | 5 | 1 | 12 | 37 | 75 | 16 |
| 9 St Mary's Coll. OB | 18 | 4 | 1 | 13 | 24 | 64 | 13 |
| 10 Whinney Hill Reserves | 18 | 3 | 3 | 12 | 30 | 55 | 12 |

Calderstones Utd record expunged.

### Division Two

| | P | W | D | L | F | A | Pts |
|---|---|---|---|---|---|---|---|
| 1 Burnley Road | 16 | 13 | 2 | 1 | 67 | 25 | 41 |
| 2 Blue Bell United F.C.. (-3pts) | 16 | 12 | 4 | 0 | 61 | 21 | 37 |
| 3 Sydney Street WMC | 16 | 9 | 4 | 3 | 46 | 30 | 31 |
| 4 The Commercial F.C. | 16 | 7 | 2 | 7 | 49 | 36 | 23 |
| 5 Lowmoor | 16 | 6 | 2 | 8 | 37 | 55 | 20 |
| 6 Globe Bullough Park | 16 | 4 | 5 | 7 | 46 | 56 | 17 |
| 7 Hyndburn Athletic F.C. | 16 | 4 | 2 | 10 | 31 | 49 | 14 |
| 8 Rishton Rovers | 16 | 2 | 4 | 10 | 26 | 52 | 10 |
| 9 AFC Burnley (-4pts) | 16 | 2 | 1 | 13 | 20 | 59 | 3 |

Accrington Town record expunged.

## ALDERSHOT & DISTRICT LEAGUE

### Senior Division

| | P | W | D | L | F | A | Pts |
|---|---|---|---|---|---|---|---|
| 1 Bagshot | 22 | 18 | 1 | 3 | 76 | 23 | 55 |
| 2 Headley United | 22 | 15 | 3 | 4 | 62 | 33 | 48 |
| 3 Old Farboronians Reserves | 22 | 15 | 2 | 5 | 64 | 36 | 47 |
| 4 West End Village | 22 | 13 | 4 | 5 | 58 | 37 | 43 |
| 5 Tongham Spartans (-3pts) | 22 | 12 | 2 | 8 | 55 | 53 | 35 |
| 6 Hale Rovers | 22 | 10 | 3 | 9 | 58 | 55 | 33 |
| 7 Alton Athletic | 22 | 8 | 1 | 13 | 43 | 46 | 25 |
| 8 Frimley Select | 22 | 6 | 5 | 11 | 39 | 59 | 23 |
| 9 Fleet Spurs Reserves | 22 | 6 | 5 | 11 | 36 | 56 | 23 |
| 10 Yateley Green Reserves | 22 | 6 | 1 | 15 | 35 | 56 | 19 |
| 11 Eversley & California A | 22 | 5 | 1 | 16 | 44 | 92 | 16 |
| 12 Shalford Social | 22 | 3 | 2 | 17 | 20 | 44 | 11 |

### Division One

| | P | W | D | L | F | A | Pts |
|---|---|---|---|---|---|---|---|
| 1 West Meon & Warnford (-1pt) | 20 | 15 | 3 | 2 | 70 | 25 | 47 |
| 2 Sandhurst Sports | 20 | 15 | 1 | 4 | 52 | 19 | 46 |
| 3 Headley Utd Reserves | 20 | 13 | 3 | 4 | 46 | 28 | 42 |
| 4 Wey Valley | 20 | 12 | 4 | 4 | 63 | 34 | 40 |
| 5 Fleet Spurs A | 20 | 11 | 0 | 9 | 48 | 46 | 33 |
| 6 Courtmoor | 20 | 9 | 3 | 8 | 50 | 37 | 30 |
| 7 South Farnborough | 20 | 7 | 1 | 12 | 35 | 60 | 22 |
| 8 Hindhead Athletic | 20 | 5 | 5 | 10 | 28 | 55 | 20 |
| 9 Letef Select | 20 | 4 | 3 | 13 | 43 | 44 | 15 |
| 10 Hartley Wintney A (-3pts) | 20 | 4 | 3 | 13 | 34 | 52 | 12 |
| 11 Farnham United | 20 | 1 | 2 | 17 | 16 | 85 | 5 |

### Division Two

| | P | W | D | L | F | A | Pts |
|---|---|---|---|---|---|---|---|
| 1 Wrecclesham | 16 | 15 | 0 | 0 | 75 | 12 | 45 |
| 2 Lindford | 16 | 9 | 1 | 5 | 43 | 34 | 28 |
| 3 Alton United | 16 | 8 | 2 | 6 | 41 | 40 | 26 |
| 4 Rushmoor Community | 16 | 7 | 2 | 7 | 35 | 31 | 23 |
| 5 Four Marks Reserves (+2pts) | 16 | 6 | 2 | 8 | 36 | 53 | 22 |
| 6 BOSC United | 16 | 6 | 2 | 8 | 31 | 40 | 20 |
| 7 Normandy | 16 | 4 | 4 | 8 | 27 | 49 | 16 |
| 8 Freedom Spartans Ath. (-4pts) | 16 | 5 | 2 | 9 | 36 | 40 | 13 |
| 9 Hawley | 16 | 3 | 1 | 12 | 28 | 53 | 10 |

### Division Three

| | P | W | D | L | F | A | Pts |
|---|---|---|---|---|---|---|---|
| 1 Headley United Academy | 16 | 15 | 0 | 1 | 67 | 19 | 45 |
| 2 Ropley | 16 | 12 | 2 | 2 | 57 | 21 | 38 |
| 3 Shalford Social Reserves | 16 | 7 | 3 | 6 | 37 | 43 | 24 |
| 4 Fleet Spurs Vet | 16 | 7 | 1 | 8 | 40 | 44 | 22 |
| 5 Yateley A | 16 | 5 | 5 | 6 | 35 | 32 | 20 |
| 6 West End Village Reserves | 16 | 6 | 2 | 8 | 33 | 31 | 20 |
| 7 Hindhead Athletic Reserves | 16 | 5 | 4 | 7 | 28 | 36 | 19 |
| 8 South Farnborough Reserves | 16 | 4 | 2 | 10 | 34 | 49 | 14 |
| 9 Normandy Reserves | 16 | 0 | 3 | 13 | 15 | 71 | 3 |

Rushmoor Community Res record expunged.

## AMATEUR COMBINATION

### Premier Division

| | P | W | D | L | F | A | PTS |
|---|---|---|---|---|---|---|---|
| 1 Old Minchendenians | 18 | 11 | 4 | 3 | 51 | 26 | 37 |
| 2 Honorable Artillery Company | 18 | 11 | 3 | 4 | 49 | 29 | 36 |
| 3 Bealonians | 18 | 10 | 1 | 7 | 38 | 34 | 31 |
| 4 Old Suttonians | 18 | 8 | 3 | 7 | 30 | 31 | 27 |
| 5 Old Parmiterians | 18 | 7 | 5 | 6 | 40 | 41 | 26 |
| 6 Old Meadonians | 18 | 7 | 4 | 7 | 31 | 34 | 25 |
| 7 Old Hamptonians | 18 | 6 | 5 | 7 | 44 | 42 | 23 |
| 8 Parkfield | 18 | 4 | 6 | 8 | 24 | 38 | 18 |
| 9 Old Aloysians | 18 | 4 | 3 | 11 | 26 | 43 | 15 |
| 10 Albanian | 18 | 4 | 2 | 12 | 28 | 43 | 14 |

### Senior One

| | P | W | D | L | F | A | PTS |
|---|---|---|---|---|---|---|---|
| 1 Enfield Old Grammarians | 18 | 9 | 7 | 2 | 44 | 26 | 34 |
| 2 Old Salvatorians | 18 | 8 | 7 | 3 | 45 | 23 | 31 |
| 3 Dorkinians | 18 | 8 | 5 | 5 | 31 | 28 | 29 |
| 4 Honorable Artillery Company II | 18 | 9 | 2 | 7 | 37 | 39 | 29 |
| 5 UCL Academicals | 18 | 7 | 5 | 6 | 33 | 34 | 26 |
| 6 Old Ignatians | 18 | 7 | 4 | 7 | 45 | 35 | 25 |
| 7 Hale End Athletic | 18 | 7 | 2 | 9 | 42 | 48 | 23 |
| 8 Old Thorntonians | 18 | 7 | 2 | 9 | 34 | 40 | 23 |
| 9 Old Belgravians | 18 | 7 | 2 | 9 | 30 | 36 | 23 |
| 10 Economicals | 18 | 2 | 2 | 14 | 23 | 55 | 8 |

### Senior Two

| | P | W | D | L | F | A | PTS |
|---|---|---|---|---|---|---|---|
| 1 Shene Old Grammarians | 20 | 17 | 1 | 2 | 53 | 22 | 52 |
| 2 Kings Old Boys | 20 | 13 | 6 | 1 | 53 | 29 | 45 |
| 3 Latymer Old Boys | 20 | 11 | 2 | 7 | 49 | 41 | 35 |
| 4 Old Tenisonians | 20 | 8 | 7 | 5 | 44 | 34 | 31 |
| 5 Old Suttonians II | 20 | 8 | 3 | 9 | 37 | 35 | 27 |
| 6 Old Parmiterians II | 20 | 6 | 6 | 8 | 34 | 35 | 24 |
| 7 Clapham Old Xaverians (-3pts) | 20 | 6 | 7 | 7 | 53 | 54 | 22 |
| 8 Albanian II (-3pts) | 20 | 7 | 3 | 10 | 43 | 57 | 21 |
| 9 UCL Academicals II | 20 | 4 | 3 | 13 | 32 | 48 | 15 |
| 10 Sinjuns Grammarians | 20 | 3 | 4 | 13 | 30 | 55 | 13 |
| 11 Old Uffingtonians (-3pts) | 20 | 3 | 6 | 11 | 32 | 50 | 12 |

| Senior Three North | P | W | D | L | F | A | PTS |
|---|---|---|---|---|---|---|---|
| 1 Mayfield Athletic | 20 | 16 | 2 | 2 | 55 | 23 | 50 |
| 2 Old Danes | 20 | 12 | 4 | 4 | 79 | 41 | 40 |
| 3 Globe Rangers | 20 | 13 | 1 | 6 | 47 | 32 | 40 |
| 4 Lea Valley | 20 | 11 | 1 | 8 | 65 | 52 | 34 |
| 5 Old Woodhouseians | 20 | 9 | 4 | 7 | 37 | 33 | 31 |
| 6 Old Manorians | 20 | 10 | 1 | 9 | 41 | 41 | 31 |
| 7 Bealonians II | 20 | 9 | 0 | 11 | 37 | 39 | 27 |
| 8 Birkbeck College | 20 | 6 | 3 | 11 | 28 | 56 | 21 |
| 9 Albanian III (-7pts) | 20 | 6 | 3 | 11 | 36 | 48 | 14 |
| 10 Old Salvatorians II (-3pts) | 20 | 5 | 1 | 14 | 28 | 63 | 13 |
| 11 Old Magdalenians | 20 | 3 | 0 | 17 | 26 | 51 | 9 |

| Senior Three South | P | W | D | L | F | A | PTS |
|---|---|---|---|---|---|---|---|
| 1 Old Wokingians | 20 | 16 | 2 | 2 | 69 | 20 | 50 |
| 2 Old Pauline | 20 | 12 | 2 | 6 | 47 | 32 | 38 |
| 3 Old Meadonians II | 20 | 11 | 4 | 5 | 46 | 31 | 37 |
| 4 Royal Bank of Scotland | 20 | 9 | 2 | 9 | 57 | 49 | 29 |
| 5 John Fisher Old Boys | 20 | 8 | 4 | 8 | 31 | 30 | 28 |
| 6 Old Vaughanians | 20 | 8 | 4 | 8 | 46 | 49 | 28 |
| 7 Old Hamptonians II | 20 | 8 | 1 | 11 | 31 | 40 | 25 |
| 8 Wandsworth Borough | 20 | 7 | 2 | 11 | 40 | 41 | 23 |
| 9 Old Isleworthians (-3pts) | 20 | 8 | 2 | 10 | 46 | 58 | 23 |
| 10 Old St Marys | 20 | 6 | 2 | 12 | 25 | 40 | 20 |
| 11 Old Tiffinians | 20 | 4 | 1 | 15 | 30 | 78 | 13 |

| Intermediate North | P | W | D | L | F | A | PTS |
|---|---|---|---|---|---|---|---|
| 1 Old Minchendenians II | 20 | 15 | 3 | 2 | 62 | 24 | 48 |
| 2 Old Parmiterians III | 20 | 12 | 2 | 6 | 54 | 42 | 38 |
| 3 Leyton County Old Boys | 20 | 11 | 4 | 5 | 58 | 42 | 37 |
| 4 Old Ignatians II | 20 | 9 | 4 | 7 | 45 | 34 | 31 |
| 5 Old Aloysians II | 20 | 9 | 3 | 8 | 37 | 37 | 30 |
| 6 Old Tollingtonians | 20 | 8 | 5 | 7 | 34 | 36 | 29 |
| 7 Oakhill Tigers | 20 | 8 | 2 | 10 | 41 | 43 | 26 |
| 8 UCL Academicals III | 20 | 7 | 3 | 10 | 33 | 36 | 24 |
| 9 Old Buckwellians | 20 | 6 | 5 | 9 | 29 | 42 | 23 |
| 10 Enfield Old Grammarians II | 20 | 5 | 3 | 12 | 36 | 65 | 18 |
| 11 Old Salvatorians III (-3pts) | 20 | 2 | 2 | 16 | 27 | 55 | 5 |

| Intermediate South | P | W | D | L | F | A | PTS |
|---|---|---|---|---|---|---|---|
| 1 Reigatians | 18 | 16 | 0 | 2 | 73 | 26 | 48 |
| 2 Economicals II | 18 | 13 | 2 | 3 | 54 | 22 | 41 |
| 3 Fulham Compton Old Boys | 18 | 12 | 3 | 3 | 39 | 25 | 39 |
| 4 National Westminster Bank | 18 | 9 | 4 | 5 | 42 | 27 | 31 |
| 5 Fitzwilliam Old Boys | 18 | 6 | 5 | 7 | 32 | 43 | 23 |
| 6 Hampstead Heathens | 18 | 6 | 4 | 8 | 28 | 38 | 22 |
| 7 Old Meadonians III | 18 | 5 | 4 | 9 | 26 | 31 | 19 |
| 8 Old Vaughanians II | 18 | 5 | 1 | 12 | 35 | 59 | 16 |
| 9 Brent | 18 | 3 | 3 | 12 | 20 | 44 | 12 |
| 10 Old Pauline II | 18 | 1 | 2 | 15 | 26 | 60 | 5 |

| Division One North | P | W | D | L | F | A | PTS |
|---|---|---|---|---|---|---|---|
| 1 Queen Mary College Old Boys | 18 | 15 | 1 | 2 | 70 | 19 | 46 |
| 2 Hale End Athletic II | 18 | 10 | 6 | 2 | 43 | 24 | 36 |
| 3 Globe Rangers II | 18 | 10 | 5 | 3 | 50 | 35 | 35 |
| 4 University of Hertfordshire | 18 | 10 | 1 | 7 | 55 | 39 | 31 |
| 5 Old Salvatorians IV (-3pts) | 18 | 8 | 3 | 7 | 53 | 50 | 24 |
| 6 Wood Green Old Boys II | 18 | 7 | 3 | 8 | 50 | 49 | 24 |
| 7 Old Edmontonians | 18 | 7 | 1 | 10 | 43 | 46 | 22 |
| 8 Parkfield II | 18 | 5 | 2 | 11 | 34 | 64 | 17 |
| 9 Old Aloysians III | 18 | 4 | 0 | 14 | 34 | 70 | 12 |
| 10 Bealonians III | 18 | 1 | 4 | 13 | 31 | 67 | 7 |

| Division Two North | P | W | D | L | F | A | PTS |
|---|---|---|---|---|---|---|---|
| 1 Hale End Athletic III | 18 | 10 | 5 | 3 | 56 | 29 | 35 |
| 2 Albanian IV | 18 | 9 | 3 | 6 | 49 | 29 | 30 |
| 3 Southgate County | 18 | 9 | 3 | 6 | 44 | 40 | 30 |
| 4 Old Manorians II | 18 | 9 | 2 | 7 | 49 | 42 | 29 |
| 5 Old Parmiterians IV | 18 | 9 | 1 | 8 | 54 | 45 | 28 |
| 6 Latymer Old Boys II | 18 | 7 | 2 | 9 | 38 | 62 | 23 |
| 7 Mill Hill County Old Boys | 18 | 6 | 4 | 8 | 48 | 58 | 22 |
| 8 Enfield Old Grammarians III | 18 | 5 | 5 | 8 | 45 | 46 | 20 |
| 9 Phoenix Old Boys | 18 | 6 | 2 | 10 | 38 | 47 | 20 |
| 10 Leyton County Old Boys II | 18 | 5 | 3 | 10 | 31 | 54 | 18 |

| Division Three North | P | W | D | L | F | A | PTS |
|---|---|---|---|---|---|---|---|
| 1 Old Parmiterians V | 18 | 15 | 1 | 2 | 80 | 15 | 46 |
| 2 Old Minchendenians III | 18 | 14 | 3 | 1 | 75 | 37 | 45 |
| 3 Old Woodhouseians II | 18 | 12 | 0 | 6 | 51 | 39 | 36 |
| 4 Egbertian | 18 | 11 | 2 | 5 | 42 | 26 | 35 |
| 5 Old Aloysians IV | 18 | 7 | 2 | 9 | 44 | 41 | 23 |
| 6 Old Ignatians III | 18 | 5 | 5 | 8 | 34 | 54 | 20 |
| 7 Queen Mary College O.B. II | 18 | 6 | 1 | 11 | 46 | 54 | 19 |
| 8 Old Manorians III | 18 | 3 | 4 | 11 | 25 | 69 | 13 |
| 9 Old Magdalenians II | 18 | 3 | 2 | 13 | 30 | 70 | 11 |
| 10 Old Uffingtonians II (-3pts) | 18 | 3 | 2 | 13 | 31 | 53 | 8 |

| Division Four North | P | W | D | L | F | A | PTS |
|---|---|---|---|---|---|---|---|
| 1 Parkfield III | 18 | 16 | 1 | 1 | 78 | 26 | 49 |
| 2 Oakhill Tigers II | 18 | 16 | 1 | 1 | 74 | 25 | 49 |
| 3 Old Parmiterians VI | 18 | 9 | 1 | 8 | 43 | 45 | 28 |
| 4 Old Minchendenians IV | 18 | 9 | 0 | 9 | 51 | 54 | 27 |
| 5 UCL Academicals IV | 18 | 7 | 4 | 7 | 41 | 46 | 25 |
| 6 Latymer Old Boys III | 18 | 6 | 2 | 10 | 39 | 47 | 20 |
| 7 Egbertian II | 18 | 5 | 4 | 9 | 35 | 40 | 19 |
| 8 Old Salvatorians V (-3pts) | 18 | 5 | 2 | 11 | 30 | 47 | 14 |
| 9 Hale End Athletic IV (-3pts) | 18 | 4 | 3 | 11 | 42 | 64 | 12 |
| 10 Albanian V | 18 | 3 | 2 | 13 | 26 | 65 | 11 |

| Division Five North | P | W | D | L | F | A | PTS |
|---|---|---|---|---|---|---|---|
| 1 UCL Academicals V | 20 | 16 | 2 | 2 | 88 | 19 | 50 |
| 2 Old Manorians IV | 20 | 16 | 0 | 4 | 97 | 29 | 48 |
| 3 Old Buckwellians II | 20 | 8 | 6 | 6 | 45 | 53 | 30 |
| 4 Bealonians IV | 20 | 9 | 3 | 8 | 48 | 65 | 30 |
| 5 Comets MPSSA | 20 | 9 | 1 | 10 | 39 | 58 | 28 |
| 6 Old Edmontonians II | 20 | 8 | 2 | 10 | 50 | 54 | 26 |
| 7 Ravenscroft Old Boys II | 20 | 7 | 4 | 9 | 54 | 63 | 25 |
| 8 Southgate County II | 20 | 5 | 4 | 11 | 34 | 65 | 19 |
| 9 Wood Green O.B. III (-6pts) | 20 | 7 | 2 | 11 | 50 | 67 | 17 |
| 10 Egbertian III | 20 | 4 | 5 | 11 | 26 | 47 | 17 |
| 11 London Hospital O.B. (-1pt) | 20 | 4 | 5 | 11 | 40 | 51 | 16 |

# LEAGUE TABLES

## Division Six North

| | | P | W | D | L | F | A | PTS |
|---|---|---|---|---|---|---|---|---|
| 1 | Old Edmontonians III | 18 | 14 | 2 | 2 | 74 | 31 | 44 |
| 2 | Albanian VI (-7pts) | 18 | 15 | 1 | 2 | 68 | 24 | 39 |
| 3 | Enfield Old Grammarians IV | 18 | 12 | 1 | 5 | 68 | 49 | 37 |
| 4 | Mayfield Athletic II | 18 | 10 | 3 | 5 | 69 | 36 | 33 |
| 5 | Old Tollingtonians II | 18 | 9 | 3 | 6 | 51 | 35 | 30 |
| 6 | Old Woodhouseians III | 18 | 6 | 2 | 10 | 45 | 47 | 20 |
| 7 | Old Minchendenians V | 18 | 4 | 1 | 13 | 45 | 80 | 13 |
| 8 | Old Parmiterians VII (-3pts) | 18 | 4 | 3 | 11 | 35 | 65 | 12 |
| 9 | Old Aloysians V | 18 | 3 | 3 | 12 | 35 | 83 | 12 |
| 10 | Egbertian IV | 18 | 3 | 1 | 14 | 35 | 75 | 10 |

## Division Seven North

| | | P | W | D | L | F | A | PTS |
|---|---|---|---|---|---|---|---|---|
| 1 | UCL Academicals VI | 20 | 17 | 1 | 2 | 77 | 26 | 52 |
| 2 | Mill Hill Village | 20 | 13 | 4 | 3 | 76 | 35 | 43 |
| 3 | Oakhill Tigers III | 20 | 10 | 4 | 6 | 63 | 45 | 34 |
| 4 | Queen Mary College O.B. III | 20 | 9 | 2 | 9 | 67 | 51 | 29 |
| 5 | Lea Valley II | 20 | 8 | 3 | 9 | 53 | 50 | 27 |
| 6 | Wood Green Old Boys IV | 20 | 8 | 3 | 9 | 44 | 46 | 27 |
| 7 | Ravenscroft Old Boys III | 20 | 7 | 3 | 10 | 59 | 76 | 24 |
| 8 | Latymer Old Boys IV | 20 | 7 | 2 | 11 | 51 | 60 | 23 |
| 9 | Old Parmiterians VIII (-3pts) | 20 | 6 | 7 | 7 | 49 | 48 | 22 |
| 10 | Bealonians V | 20 | 5 | 1 | 14 | 21 | 77 | 16 |
| 11 | Parkfield IV | 20 | 4 | 2 | 14 | 36 | 82 | 14 |

## Division Eight North

| | | P | W | D | L | F | A | PTS |
|---|---|---|---|---|---|---|---|---|
| 1 | Old Kingsburians II | 18 | 13 | 4 | 1 | 60 | 21 | 43 |
| 2 | Old Salvatorians VI (-3pts) | 18 | 12 | 4 | 2 | 53 | 24 | 37 |
| 3 | Old Parmiterians IX | 18 | 12 | 1 | 5 | 55 | 35 | 37 |
| 4 | Old Woodhouseians IV | 18 | 8 | 2 | 8 | 54 | 51 | 26 |
| 5 | Mill Hill Village II | 18 | 8 | 2 | 8 | 58 | 57 | 26 |
| 6 | Old Edmontonians IV | 18 | 6 | 3 | 9 | 45 | 63 | 21 |
| 7 | Old Ignatians IV | 18 | 5 | 2 | 11 | 44 | 70 | 17 |
| 8 | Bealonians VI | 18 | 4 | 4 | 10 | 37 | 61 | 16 |
| 9 | Albanian VII (-3pts) | 18 | 5 | 2 | 11 | 45 | 56 | 14 |
| 10 | Old Manorians V | 18 | 4 | 2 | 12 | 34 | 47 | 14 |

## Division Nine North

| | | P | W | D | L | F | A | PTS |
|---|---|---|---|---|---|---|---|---|
| 1 | Mayfield Athletic III | 20 | 12 | 5 | 3 | 66 | 31 | 41 |
| 2 | Latymer Old Boys V | 20 | 11 | 6 | 3 | 45 | 37 | 39 |
| 3 | Southgate County III | 20 | 11 | 4 | 5 | 62 | 50 | 37 |
| 4 | Old Kingsburians III | 20 | 11 | 2 | 7 | 64 | 46 | 35 |
| 5 | Mill Hill Village III | 20 | 8 | 5 | 7 | 52 | 49 | 29 |
| 6 | Old Salvatorians VII (-3pts) | 20 | 8 | 5 | 7 | 62 | 51 | 26 |
| 7 | Old Minchendenians VI | 20 | 6 | 3 | 11 | 37 | 48 | 21 |
| 8 | Davenant Wanderers Old Boys | 20 | 4 | 6 | 10 | 41 | 59 | 18 |
| 9 | Old Parmiterians X (-3pts) | 20 | 5 | 6 | 9 | 33 | 55 | 18 |
| 10 | Leyton County Old Boys III | 20 | 3 | 7 | 10 | 48 | 66 | 16 |
| 11 | Enfield Old Grammarians V | 20 | 3 | 7 | 10 | 47 | 65 | 16 |

## Division Ten North

| | | P | W | D | L | F | A | PTS |
|---|---|---|---|---|---|---|---|---|
| 1 | Old Manorians VI | 16 | 13 | 2 | 1 | 93 | 21 | 41 |
| 2 | Old Woodhouseians V | 16 | 9 | 3 | 4 | 56 | 43 | 30 |
| 3 | Goffs Old Boys | 16 | 8 | 5 | 3 | 49 | 41 | 29 |
| 4 | Latymer Old Boys VI | 16 | 8 | 4 | 4 | 51 | 31 | 28 |
| 5 | Old Kingsburians IV | 16 | 6 | 3 | 7 | 51 | 61 | 21 |
| 6 | Old Minchendenians VII | 16 | 6 | 2 | 8 | 60 | 66 | 20 |
| 7 | Old Parmiterians XI (-3pts) | 16 | 5 | 3 | 8 | 45 | 63 | 15 |
| 8 | Old Ignatians V | 16 | 3 | 2 | 11 | 48 | 73 | 11 |
| 9 | Bealonians VII | 16 | 1 | 2 | 13 | 18 | 72 | 5 |

## Division One South

| | | P | W | D | L | F | A | PTS |
|---|---|---|---|---|---|---|---|---|
| 1 | Citigroup | 20 | 14 | 3 | 3 | 58 | 30 | 45 |
| 2 | Glyn Old Boys | 20 | 14 | 1 | 5 | 51 | 26 | 43 |
| 3 | Economicals III | 20 | 11 | 3 | 6 | 37 | 28 | 36 |
| 4 | Royal Bank of Scotland II | 20 | 9 | 3 | 8 | 53 | 51 | 30 |
| 5 | Mickleham Old Boxhillians | 20 | 9 | 2 | 9 | 46 | 30 | 29 |
| 6 | Old Meadonians IV | 20 | 7 | 5 | 8 | 35 | 42 | 26 |
| 7 | Witan | 20 | 7 | 5 | 8 | 33 | 40 | 26 |
| 8 | National Westminster Bank II | 20 | 7 | 3 | 10 | 28 | 45 | 24 |
| 9 | Dorkinians II | 20 | 7 | 2 | 11 | 46 | 57 | 23 |
| 10 | Old Sedcopians | 20 | 6 | 3 | 11 | 35 | 36 | 21 |
| 11 | Old Guildfordians | 20 | 3 | 2 | 15 | 21 | 58 | 11 |

## Division Two South

| | | P | W | D | L | F | A | PTS |
|---|---|---|---|---|---|---|---|---|
| 1 | Old Suttonians III | 20 | 15 | 2 | 3 | 69 | 24 | 47 |
| 2 | Old Thorntonians II | 20 | 11 | 5 | 4 | 57 | 32 | 38 |
| 3 | Economicals IV | 20 | 11 | 4 | 5 | 61 | 32 | 37 |
| 4 | Standard Chargers | 20 | 10 | 4 | 6 | 44 | 35 | 34 |
| 5 | Tilburg Regents | 20 | 9 | 5 | 6 | 53 | 44 | 32 |
| 6 | Clapham Old Xaverians II (-3pts) | 20 | 10 | 4 | 6 | 64 | 43 | 31 |
| 7 | City of London | 20 | 6 | 5 | 9 | 39 | 40 | 23 |
| 8 | Sinjuns Grammarians II | 20 | 5 | 5 | 10 | 31 | 68 | 20 |
| 9 | Shene Old Grammarians II | 20 | 5 | 2 | 13 | 39 | 63 | 17 |
| 10 | Old Meadonians V | 20 | 4 | 4 | 12 | 32 | 59 | 16 |
| 11 | Old Grantonians | 20 | 2 | 4 | 14 | 30 | 79 | 10 |

## Division Three South

| | | P | W | D | L | F | A | PTS |
|---|---|---|---|---|---|---|---|---|
| 1 | Glyn Old Boys II | 20 | 16 | 1 | 3 | 81 | 40 | 49 |
| 2 | Economicals V | 20 | 12 | 2 | 6 | 70 | 42 | 38 |
| 3 | Old Sedcopians II | 20 | 12 | 2 | 6 | 60 | 40 | 38 |
| 4 | Old Crosbeians | 20 | 10 | 1 | 9 | 65 | 56 | 31 |
| 5 | Old Wokingians II | 20 | 9 | 3 | 8 | 53 | 51 | 30 |
| 6 | Wandsworth Borough II | 20 | 8 | 3 | 9 | 50 | 47 | 27 |
| 7 | Nat West Bank III (-3pts) | 20 | 8 | 4 | 8 | 47 | 39 | 25 |
| 8 | Kings Old Boys II | 20 | 6 | 3 | 11 | 39 | 49 | 21 |
| 9 | Old St Marys II | 20 | 6 | 3 | 11 | 36 | 56 | 21 |
| 10 | Clapham Old Xaverians III (-3pts) | 20 | 6 | 5 | 9 | 38 | 56 | 20 |
| 11 | Old Whitgiftian | 20 | 3 | 1 | 16 | 36 | 99 | 10 |

## Division Four South

| | | P | W | D | L | F | A | PTS |
|---|---|---|---|---|---|---|---|---|
| 1 | Old Suttonians IV | 18 | 15 | 0 | 3 | 75 | 24 | 45 |
| 2 | Glyn Old Boys III | 18 | 11 | 0 | 7 | 68 | 36 | 33 |
| 3 | Wandgas | 18 | 10 | 2 | 6 | 61 | 44 | 32 |
| 4 | Witan II | 18 | 10 | 1 | 7 | 54 | 41 | 31 |
| 5 | Phoenix Old Boys II | 18 | 9 | 3 | 6 | 41 | 35 | 30 |
| 6 | Reigatians II | 18 | 8 | 3 | 7 | 50 | 39 | 27 |
| 7 | Old Meadonians VI | 18 | 7 | 1 | 10 | 48 | 55 | 22 |
| 8 | Fulham Compton Old Boys II | 18 | 5 | 2 | 11 | 31 | 74 | 17 |
| 9 | John Fisher Old Boys II | 18 | 4 | 2 | 12 | 33 | 57 | 14 |
| 10 | City of London II | 18 | 4 | 0 | 14 | 29 | 85 | 12 |

## Division Five South

| | | P | W | D | L | F | A | PTS |
|---|---|---|---|---|---|---|---|---|
| 1 | Old Pauline III | 18 | 11 | 3 | 4 | 48 | 27 | 36 |
| 2 | Old Meadonians VII | 18 | 9 | 4 | 5 | 34 | 27 | 31 |
| 3 | Old Tenisonians III | 18 | 9 | 4 | 5 | 38 | 42 | 31 |
| 4 | Old Thorntonians III | 18 | 6 | 6 | 6 | 52 | 43 | 24 |
| 5 | Fulham Compton Old Boys III | 18 | 7 | 3 | 8 | 41 | 44 | 24 |
| 6 | Old Suttonians V | 18 | 6 | 5 | 7 | 46 | 39 | 23 |
| 7 | Glyn Old Boys IV | 18 | 7 | 2 | 9 | 38 | 48 | 23 |
| 8 | Old Josephians | 18 | 7 | 2 | 9 | 31 | 45 | 23 |
| 9 | Royal Sun Alliance | 18 | 6 | 3 | 9 | 45 | 55 | 21 |
| 10 | John Fisher Old Boys III | 18 | 4 | 4 | 10 | 45 | 48 | 16 |

| Division Six South | P | W | D | L | F | A | PTS |
|---|---|---|---|---|---|---|---|
| John Fisher Old Boys IV (-3pts) | 18 | 12 | 6 | 0 | 47 | 21 | 39 |
| Dorkinians III | 18 | 11 | 4 | 3 | 73 | 29 | 37 |
| Old Sedcopians III | 18 | 11 | 4 | 3 | 56 | 32 | 37 |
| Old Wokingians III | 18 | 11 | 3 | 4 | 52 | 36 | 36 |
| Glyn Old Boys V | 18 | 8 | 1 | 9 | 33 | 34 | 25 |
| Old St Marys III | 18 | 6 | 1 | 11 | 32 | 54 | 19 |
| Old Tiffinians II | 18 | 5 | 2 | 11 | 32 | 49 | 17 |
| Fulham Compton Old Boys IV | 18 | 4 | 3 | 11 | 40 | 61 | 15 |
| Old Tenisonians IV | 18 | 3 | 5 | 10 | 28 | 45 | 14 |
| Old Guildfordians II | 18 | 3 | 3 | 12 | 22 | 54 | 12 |

| Division Seven South | P | W | D | L | F | A | PTS |
|---|---|---|---|---|---|---|---|
| Shene Old Grammarians III | 20 | 14 | 4 | 2 | 64 | 26 | 46 |
| John Fisher Old Boys V (-3pts) | 20 | 15 | 2 | 3 | 90 | 34 | 44 |
| Heathrow Seniors | 20 | 13 | 3 | 4 | 56 | 21 | 42 |
| Wandsworth Borough III | 20 | 12 | 0 | 8 | 61 | 52 | 36 |
| Old Guildfordians III | 20 | 10 | 1 | 9 | 54 | 48 | 31 |
| Mickleham Old Boxhillians II | 20 | 9 | 0 | 11 | 46 | 67 | 27 |
| Old Suttonians VI | 20 | 7 | 2 | 11 | 41 | 62 | 23 |
| Old Thorntonians IV | 20 | 7 | 1 | 12 | 49 | 55 | 22 |
| Old Tiffinians III | 20 | 6 | 3 | 11 | 43 | 58 | 21 |
| Old Wokingians IV | 20 | 5 | 0 | 15 | 40 | 77 | 15 |
| Reigatians III | 20 | 3 | 2 | 15 | 34 | 78 | 11 |

| Division Eight South | P | W | D | L | F | A | PTS |
|---|---|---|---|---|---|---|---|
| Reigatians IV | 20 | 13 | 3 | 4 | 62 | 35 | 42 |
| Old Suttonians VII | 20 | 13 | 1 | 6 | 56 | 33 | 40 |
| Shene Old Grammarians IV | 20 | 10 | 4 | 6 | 65 | 49 | 34 |
| Dorkinians IV | 20 | 11 | 1 | 8 | 60 | 47 | 34 |
| Old Meadonians VIII | 20 | 10 | 2 | 8 | 52 | 48 | 32 |
| Old Whitgiftian II | 20 | 9 | 3 | 8 | 60 | 56 | 30 |
| Clapham Old Xaverians IV (-3pts) | 20 | 9 | 1 | 10 | 55 | 44 | 25 |
| City of London III | 20 | 7 | 4 | 9 | 36 | 50 | 25 |
| Wandgas II | 20 | 6 | 4 | 10 | 49 | 65 | 22 |
| Old Wokingians V | 20 | 5 | 2 | 13 | 40 | 78 | 17 |
| Old St Marys IV | 20 | 3 | 3 | 14 | 32 | 62 | 12 |

| Division Nine South | P | W | D | L | F | A | PTS |
|---|---|---|---|---|---|---|---|
| Sinjuns Grammarians III | 16 | 13 | 2 | 1 | 61 | 22 | 41 |
| Reigatians V | 16 | 10 | 4 | 2 | 53 | 31 | 34 |
| Wandsworth Borough IV | 16 | 7 | 3 | 6 | 43 | 37 | 24 |
| Old Sedcopians IV | 16 | 7 | 1 | 8 | 47 | 38 | 22 |
| Old Pauline IV | 16 | 6 | 4 | 6 | 35 | 34 | 22 |
| Old Grantonians II (-3pts) | 16 | 8 | 1 | 7 | 41 | 46 | 22 |
| Old Suttonians VIII | 16 | 5 | 4 | 7 | 40 | 47 | 19 |
| Tilburg Regents II | 16 | 2 | 3 | 11 | 25 | 53 | 9 |
| Old Wokingians VI | 16 | 3 | 0 | 13 | 24 | 61 | 9 |

| Division Ten South | P | W | D | L | F | A | PTS |
|---|---|---|---|---|---|---|---|
| Wandsworth Borough V | 14 | 10 | 1 | 3 | 47 | 24 | 31 |
| Old Suttonians IX | 14 | 9 | 1 | 4 | 49 | 26 | 28 |
| Old Guildfordians IV | 14 | 7 | 3 | 4 | 39 | 28 | 24 |
| Dorkinians V | 14 | 6 | 3 | 5 | 44 | 30 | 21 |
| Reigatians VI | 14 | 5 | 5 | 4 | 30 | 32 | 20 |
| Old Meadonians IX | 14 | 5 | 2 | 7 | 28 | 35 | 17 |
| Old Sedcopians V | 14 | 3 | 3 | 8 | 34 | 43 | 12 |
| Old Wokingians VII | 14 | 1 | 2 | 11 | 27 | 80 | 5 |

| Division One West | | P | W | D | L | F | A | PTS |
|---|---|---|---|---|---|---|---|---|
| 1 | Cardinal Manning Old Boys | 18 | 12 | 3 | 3 | 56 | 19 | 39 |
| 2 | Old Hamptonians III | 18 | 11 | 3 | 4 | 51 | 37 | 36 |
| 3 | Birkbeck College II | 18 | 10 | 4 | 4 | 47 | 26 | 34 |
| 4 | Old Isleworthians II (-3pts) | 18 | 12 | 1 | 5 | 53 | 34 | 34 |
| 5 | Old Challoners | 18 | 8 | 3 | 7 | 54 | 42 | 27 |
| 6 | London Welsh | 18 | 7 | 4 | 7 | 36 | 29 | 25 |
| 7 | Old Pegasonians | 18 | 7 | 3 | 8 | 49 | 45 | 24 |
| 8 | Phoenix Old Boys III | 18 | 5 | 3 | 10 | 42 | 59 | 18 |
| 9 | Brent II | 18 | 2 | 2 | 14 | 32 | 69 | 8 |
| 10 | Old Vaughanians III | 18 | 2 | 2 | 14 | 27 | 87 | 8 |

| Division Two West | | P | W | D | L | F | A | PTS |
|---|---|---|---|---|---|---|---|---|
| 1 | Hampstead Heathens II | 14 | 12 | 1 | 1 | 75 | 28 | 37 |
| 2 | Somerville Old Boys | 14 | 12 | 0 | 2 | 76 | 13 | 36 |
| 3 | London Welsh II | 14 | 9 | 0 | 5 | 59 | 34 | 27 |
| 4 | Old Isleworthians III (-3pts) | 14 | 9 | 0 | 5 | 68 | 40 | 24 |
| 5 | Old Uxonians | 14 | 4 | 2 | 8 | 43 | 66 | 14 |
| 6 | Old Challoners II | 14 | 4 | 2 | 8 | 26 | 54 | 14 |
| 7 | Brent III | 14 | 2 | 2 | 10 | 21 | 66 | 8 |
| 8 | Old Vaughanians IV | 14 | 0 | 1 | 13 | 32 | 99 | 1 |

## ANDOVER & DISTRICT LEAGUE

| | | P | W | D | L | F | A | Pts |
|---|---|---|---|---|---|---|---|---|
| 1 | Kings Somborne | 24 | 21 | 3 | 0 | 90 | 14 | 66 |
| 2 | Andover New Street Swifts | 24 | 18 | 3 | 3 | 96 | 22 | 57 |
| 3 | Sutton Scotney | 24 | 16 | 2 | 6 | 60 | 24 | 50 |
| 4 | Broughton Reserves | 24 | 13 | 5 | 6 | 53 | 37 | 44 |
| 5 | Spartan | 24 | 13 | 4 | 7 | 48 | 37 | 43 |
| 6 | South Wonston Swifts | 24 | 12 | 4 | 8 | 64 | 42 | 40 |
| 7 | Ludgershall Sports Reserves | 24 | 9 | 3 | 12 | 43 | 50 | 30 |
| 8 | ABC United | 24 | 8 | 5 | 11 | 45 | 55 | 29 |
| 9 | Andover Lions Reserves | 24 | 6 | 5 | 13 | 39 | 72 | 23 |
| 10 | CO-OP FC | 24 | 7 | 2 | 15 | 51 | 85 | 23 |
| 11 | AFC White Hart | 24 | 6 | 2 | 16 | 46 | 61 | 20 |
| 12 | The Arms | 24 | 4 | 2 | 18 | 24 | 95 | 14 |
| 13 | Railway Club | 24 | 2 | 2 | 20 | 21 | 86 | 8 |

## ARTHURIAN LEAGUE

| Premier Division | | P | W | D | L | F | A | Pts |
|---|---|---|---|---|---|---|---|---|
| 1 | Old Carthusians | 17 | 14 | 3 | 0 | 56 | 20 | 45 |
| 2 | Lancing Old Boys | 18 | 12 | 4 | 2 | 39 | 13 | 40 |
| 3 | Old Cholmeleians | 18 | 8 | 4 | 6 | 38 | 32 | 28 |
| 4 | Old Harrovians | 18 | 9 | 0 | 9 | 47 | 47 | 27 |
| 5 | Old Foresters | 18 | 7 | 4 | 7 | 36 | 42 | 25 |
| 6 | Old Chigwellians | 18 | 7 | 3 | 8 | 26 | 23 | 24 |
| 7 | Old Brentwoods | 17 | 7 | 1 | 9 | 40 | 44 | 22 |
| 8 | Old Etonians (-1pt) | 18 | 6 | 2 | 10 | 33 | 39 | 19 |
| 9 | Old King's (Wimbledon) | 18 | 3 | 5 | 10 | 26 | 44 | 14 |
| 10 | Old Tonbridgians | 18 | 2 | 2 | 14 | 28 | 65 | 8 |

| Division One | | P | W | D | L | F | A | Pts |
|---|---|---|---|---|---|---|---|---|
| 1 | Old Salopians | 15 | 13 | 1 | 1 | 56 | 14 | 40 |
| 2 | Old Malvernians | 16 | 10 | 0 | 6 | 39 | 34 | 30 |
| 3 | Old Aldenhamians | 16 | 9 | 0 | 7 | 34 | 35 | 27 |
| 4 | Old Bradfieldians | 14 | 7 | 3 | 4 | 39 | 33 | 24 |
| 5 | Old Wykehamists | 15 | 6 | 3 | 6 | 33 | 24 | 21 |
| 6 | Old Westminsters | 15 | 6 | 2 | 7 | 28 | 32 | 20 |
| 7 | Old Radleians | 16 | 6 | 1 | 9 | 37 | 35 | 19 |
| 8 | Old King's Scholars | 16 | 3 | 1 | 12 | 17 | 53 | 10 |
| 9 | Old Haileyburians | 15 | 2 | 3 | 10 | 22 | 45 | 9 |

# LEAGUE TABLES

## Division Two

| | | P | W | D | L | F | A | Pts |
|---|---|---|---|---|---|---|---|---|
| 1 | Old Carthusians III | 14 | 10 | 3 | 1 | 46 | 21 | 33 |
| 2 | Old Carthusians II | 15 | 9 | 3 | 3 | 31 | 22 | 30 |
| 3 | Old Reptonians | 16 | 6 | 7 | 3 | 48 | 27 | 25 |
| 4 | Old Salopians II | 15 | 7 | 3 | 5 | 33 | 29 | 24 |
| 5 | Old Chigwellians II | 16 | 5 | 4 | 7 | 28 | 36 | 19 |
| 6 | Lancing Old Boys II | 16 | 5 | 2 | 9 | 20 | 26 | 17 |
| 7 | Old Haberdashers | 16 | 5 | 2 | 9 | 39 | 53 | 17 |
| 8 | Old Cholmeleians II | 16 | 4 | 3 | 9 | 25 | 31 | 15 |
| 9 | Old Wellingtonians | 16 | 4 | 3 | 9 | 22 | 47 | 15 |

## Division Three

| | | P | W | D | L | F | A | Pts |
|---|---|---|---|---|---|---|---|---|
| 1 | Old Marlburians | 14 | 12 | 0 | 2 | 48 | 23 | 36 |
| 2 | Old Aldenhamians II | 14 | 11 | 1 | 2 | 43 | 19 | 34 |
| 3 | Old Etonians II | 14 | 6 | 3 | 5 | 36 | 28 | 21 |
| 4 | Old Brentwoods II | 14 | 6 | 0 | 8 | 29 | 38 | 18 |
| 5 | Old Foresters II | 14 | 5 | 2 | 7 | 27 | 37 | 17 |
| 6 | Old King's (Wimbledon) II | 14 | 5 | 1 | 8 | 33 | 35 | 16 |
| 7 | Old Harrovians II | 14 | 5 | 1 | 8 | 24 | 35 | 16 |
| 8 | Old Wykehamists II | 14 | 1 | 2 | 11 | 17 | 42 | 5 |

## Division Four

| | | P | W | D | L | F | A | Pts |
|---|---|---|---|---|---|---|---|---|
| 1 | Old Cholmeleians III | 13 | 9 | 0 | 4 | 31 | 15 | 27 |
| 2 | Old Berkhamstedians | 13 | 7 | 3 | 3 | 25 | 18 | 24 |
| 3 | Old Epsomians (-3pts) | 13 | 8 | 1 | 4 | 36 | 25 | 22 |
| 4 | Old Chigwellians III | 14 | 6 | 2 | 6 | 29 | 25 | 20 |
| 5 | Old Westminsters II | 13 | 5 | 3 | 5 | 31 | 28 | 18 |
| 6 | Old Eastbournians | 14 | 4 | 4 | 6 | 22 | 27 | 16 |
| 7 | Old Harrovians III | 9 | 2 | 3 | 4 | 10 | 22 | 9 |
| 8 | Old Amplefordians | 13 | 1 | 2 | 10 | 19 | 43 | 5 |

## Division Five

| | | P | W | D | L | F | A | Pts |
|---|---|---|---|---|---|---|---|---|
| 1 | Old Citizens | 12 | 10 | 1 | 1 | 66 | 16 | 31 |
| 2 | Old Malvernians II | 12 | 10 | 1 | 1 | 60 | 12 | 31 |
| 3 | Old Brentwoods IV | 14 | 8 | 0 | 6 | 37 | 32 | 24 |
| 4 | Old Brentwoods III | 14 | 5 | 2 | 7 | 30 | 47 | 17 |
| 5 | Old Foresters IV | 12 | 4 | 3 | 5 | 22 | 36 | 15 |
| 6 | Old Cholmeleians IV | 13 | 4 | 0 | 9 | 27 | 49 | 12 |
| 7 | Old Foresters III | 14 | 3 | 2 | 9 | 24 | 50 | 11 |
| 8 | Old Chigwellians IV | 13 | 3 | 1 | 9 | 15 | 39 | 10 |

# ARMY FOOTBALL ASSOCIATION

## Massey Trophy Division One

| | | P | W | D | L | F | A | Pts |
|---|---|---|---|---|---|---|---|---|
| 1 | Royal Signals | 12 | 9 | 1 | 2 | 43 | 18 | 28 |
| 2 | Royal Artillery | 12 | 9 | 0 | 3 | 31 | 22 | 27 |
| 3 | Royal Engineers | 12 | 7 | 2 | 3 | 31 | 22 | 23 |
| 4 | Infantry | 12 | 4 | 2 | 6 | 22 | 28 | 14 |
| 5 | Royal Electrical & Mech. Eng. | 12 | 3 | 2 | 7 | 14 | 31 | 11 |
| 6 | Royal Logistic Corps | 12 | 2 | 4 | 6 | 31 | 35 | 10 |
| 7 | Royal Army Physical Training Corps | 12 | 1 | 3 | 8 | 22 | 38 | 6 |

## Massey Trophy Division Two

| | | P | W | D | L | F | A | Pts |
|---|---|---|---|---|---|---|---|---|
| 1 | Army Air Corps | 8 | 5 | 1 | 2 | 20 | 12 | 16 |
| 2 | Adjutants General's Corps | 8 | 4 | 3 | 1 | 19 | 11 | 15 |
| 3 | Intelligence Corps | 8 | 4 | 3 | 1 | 23 | 18 | 15 |
| 4 | Royal Armoured Corps | 8 | 1 | 2 | 5 | 12 | 17 | 5 |
| 5 | Army Medical Services | 8 | 1 | 1 | 6 | 8 | 24 | 4 |

# AYLESBURY & DISTRICT LEAGUE

## Premier Division

| | | P | W | D | L | F | A | Pt |
|---|---|---|---|---|---|---|---|---|
| 1 | Bucks CC | 18 | 14 | 3 | 1 | 67 | 18 | 4 |
| 2 | Walton Court Wanderers | 18 | 12 | 3 | 3 | 69 | 25 | 3 |
| 3 | Aylesbury Dynamos | 18 | 10 | 2 | 6 | 56 | 34 | 3 |
| 4 | Berkhamsted Sports | 18 | 9 | 1 | 8 | 42 | 43 | 2 |
| 5 | Downley Albion | 17 | 8 | 3 | 6 | 50 | 39 | 2 |
| 6 | Aston Park | 17 | 8 | 3 | 6 | 39 | 35 | 2 |
| 7 | Bedgrove Dynamos | 18 | 7 | 2 | 9 | 42 | 42 | 2 |
| 8 | FC Spandits | 18 | 5 | 4 | 9 | 50 | 69 | 1 |
| 9 | Bedgrove United | 18 | 2 | 5 | 11 | 24 | 66 | 1 |
| 10 | P & IC United | 18 | 1 | 0 | 17 | 18 | 86 | |

## Division One

| | | P | W | D | L | F | A | Pt |
|---|---|---|---|---|---|---|---|---|
| 1 | Bierton FC Wanderers | 20 | 16 | 1 | 3 | 61 | 20 | 4 |
| 2 | Haddenham United | 20 | 13 | 2 | 5 | 59 | 39 | 4 |
| 3 | Britannia | 20 | 13 | 1 | 6 | 61 | 33 | 4 |
| 4 | AFC Victoria | 20 | 11 | 6 | 3 | 60 | 37 | 3 |
| 5 | Long Marston | 20 | 11 | 2 | 7 | 47 | 35 | 3 |
| 6 | FC Mandeville | 20 | 8 | 3 | 9 | 35 | 44 | 2 |
| 7 | Elmhurst | 20 | 7 | 4 | 9 | 37 | 48 | 2 |
| 8 | Cheddington | 20 | 5 | 4 | 11 | 28 | 58 | 1 |
| 9 | Wendover | 20 | 4 | 4 | 12 | 24 | 50 | 1 |
| 10 | Aston Clinton | 20 | 5 | 0 | 15 | 31 | 50 | 1 |
| 11 | Wingrave | 20 | 2 | 3 | 15 | 34 | 63 | |

## Division Two

| | | P | W | D | L | F | A | Pt |
|---|---|---|---|---|---|---|---|---|
| 1 | Great Milton | 20 | 16 | 2 | 2 | 81 | 24 | 5 |
| 2 | Oving | 20 | 13 | 3 | 4 | 76 | 42 | 4 |
| 3 | Haydon United | 20 | 12 | 3 | 5 | 68 | 41 | 3 |
| 4 | Ludgershall | 20 | 13 | 0 | 7 | 58 | 37 | 3 |
| 5 | Aylesbury Sports | 20 | 6 | 6 | 8 | 43 | 58 | 2 |
| 6 | Downley Albion Reserves | 20 | 7 | 2 | 11 | 34 | 44 | 2 |
| 7 | MDM United | 20 | 7 | 2 | 11 | 41 | 71 | 2 |
| 8 | Haddenham United Reserves | 20 | 7 | 1 | 12 | 47 | 69 | 2 |
| 9 | Bierton FC Wanderers Reserves | 20 | 6 | 2 | 12 | 36 | 46 | 2 |
| 10 | Bucks CC Reserves | 20 | 6 | 1 | 13 | 45 | 73 | 1 |
| 11 | Stone Magnets / St Johns | 20 | 5 | 2 | 13 | 37 | 61 | 1 |

## Division Three

| | | P | W | D | L | F | A | Pt |
|---|---|---|---|---|---|---|---|---|
| 1 | Tring Titans | 20 | 15 | 4 | 1 | 85 | 21 | 4 |
| 2 | Northchurch | 20 | 15 | 3 | 2 | 73 | 32 | 4 |
| 3 | Aylesbury Park Rangers | 20 | 11 | 5 | 4 | 70 | 35 | 3 |
| 4 | Quainton | 20 | 9 | 6 | 5 | 50 | 35 | 3 |
| 5 | Aylesbury Wanderers | 20 | 8 | 5 | 7 | 48 | 36 | 2 |
| 6 | Tetsworth | 20 | 6 | 4 | 10 | 57 | 64 | 2 |
| 7 | Haydon United Reserves | 20 | 6 | 3 | 11 | 35 | 51 | 2 |
| 8 | Wendover Reserves | 20 | 6 | 3 | 11 | 32 | 64 | 2 |
| 9 | Wingrave Reserves | 20 | 4 | 6 | 10 | 49 | 59 | 1 |
| 10 | Long Marston Reserves | 20 | 3 | 5 | 12 | 37 | 88 | 1 |
| 11 | P & IC United Reserves | 20 | 4 | 2 | 14 | 32 | 83 | 1 |

### Division Four

| | | P | W | D | L | F | A | Pts |
|---|---|---|---|---|---|---|---|---|
| 1 | MDM United Reserves | 20 | 16 | 1 | 3 | 105 | 18 | 49 |
| 2 | Ludgershall Reserves | 20 | 12 | 4 | 4 | 63 | 44 | 40 |
| 3 | FC Spandits Reserves | 20 | 12 | 3 | 5 | 83 | 50 | 39 |
| 4 | Waddesdon | 20 | 12 | 3 | 5 | 76 | 49 | 39 |
| 5 | Brill United | 20 | 11 | 1 | 8 | 71 | 43 | 34 |
| 6 | AC Meadowcroft | 20 | 9 | 3 | 8 | 66 | 59 | 30 |
| 7 | Bedgrove Dynamos Reserves | 20 | 10 | 0 | 10 | 44 | 57 | 30 |
| 8 | Bedgrove United Reserves | 20 | 8 | 2 | 10 | 36 | 42 | 26 |
| 9 | Tring Titans Reserves | 20 | 5 | 1 | 14 | 48 | 81 | 16 |
| 10 | Oving Reserves | 20 | 4 | 1 | 15 | 23 | 82 | 13 |
| 11 | Tetsworth Reserves | 20 | 1 | 1 | 18 | 37 | 127 | 4 |

## BANBURY & LORD JERSEY LEAGUE

### Premier Division

| | | P | W | D | L | F | A | Pts |
|---|---|---|---|---|---|---|---|---|
| 1 | Deddington Town | 20 | 15 | 2 | 3 | 67 | 24 | 47 |
| 2 | Bodicote Sports | 20 | 10 | 6 | 4 | 54 | 29 | 36 |
| 3 | Sinclair United | 20 | 11 | 3 | 6 | 53 | 47 | 36 |
| 4 | Woodford United | 20 | 11 | 2 | 7 | 53 | 47 | 35 |
| 5 | Hanwell United | 20 | 8 | 4 | 8 | 54 | 55 | 28 |
| 6 | ABBA Athletic | 20 | 8 | 4 | 8 | 40 | 44 | 28 |
| 7 | Highfield Old Boys | 20 | 8 | 3 | 9 | 38 | 55 | 27 |
| 8 | Cropredy | 20 | 8 | 1 | 11 | 57 | 48 | 25 |
| 9 | KEA | 20 | 5 | 4 | 11 | 40 | 62 | 19 |
| 10 | Steeple Aston | 20 | 4 | 3 | 13 | 38 | 57 | 15 |
| 11 | Heyford Athletic (-3pts) | 20 | 5 | 2 | 13 | 50 | 76 | 14 |

Star Bicester withdrew - record expunged.

### Division One

| | | P | W | D | L | F | A | Pts |
|---|---|---|---|---|---|---|---|---|
| 1 | Bishops Itchington | 16 | 13 | 2 | 1 | 72 | 23 | 41 |
| 2 | Heyford United | 16 | 13 | 1 | 2 | 50 | 23 | 40 |
| 3 | Bloxham | 16 | 10 | 2 | 4 | 50 | 29 | 32 |
| 4 | Highfield Old Boys Reserves | 16 | 7 | 1 | 8 | 58 | 63 | 22 |
| 5 | Hornton | 16 | 7 | 0 | 9 | 42 | 40 | 21 |
| 6 | Fenny Compton | 16 | 6 | 2 | 8 | 43 | 45 | 20 |
| 7 | Deddington Town Reserves | 16 | 4 | 2 | 10 | 29 | 54 | 14 |
| 8 | Sinclair United Reserves | 16 | 3 | 2 | 11 | 21 | 48 | 11 |
| 9 | Kings Sutton | 16 | 3 | 0 | 13 | 25 | 65 | 9 |

### Division Two

| | | P | W | D | L | F | A | Pts |
|---|---|---|---|---|---|---|---|---|
| 1 | Slade Farm United | 20 | 17 | 1 | 2 | 97 | 14 | 52 |
| 2 | Chesterton | 20 | 14 | 2 | 4 | 66 | 31 | 44 |
| 3 | Middleton Cheney | 20 | 14 | 2 | 4 | 58 | 31 | 44 |
| 4 | FC Langford | 20 | 13 | 1 | 6 | 53 | 33 | 40 |
| 5 | Banbury Rangers | 20 | 10 | 6 | 4 | 49 | 39 | 36 |
| 6 | Finmere | 20 | 10 | 1 | 9 | 45 | 39 | 31 |
| 7 | Wroxton Heath | 20 | 8 | 2 | 10 | 46 | 50 | 26 |
| 8 | Banbury Town | 20 | 6 | 4 | 10 | 39 | 50 | 22 |
| 9 | Souldern | 20 | 4 | 1 | 15 | 30 | 72 | 13 |
| 10 | Hardwick Old Boys | 20 | 2 | 1 | 17 | 24 | 63 | 7 |
| 11 | Kings Sutton Reserves | 20 | 1 | 1 | 18 | 19 | 104 | 4 |

### Division Three

| | | P | W | D | L | F | A | Pts |
|---|---|---|---|---|---|---|---|---|
| 1 | Woodford United Reserves | 18 | 12 | 4 | 2 | 51 | 35 | 40 |
| 2 | Swis FC | 18 | 11 | 3 | 4 | 58 | 39 | 36 |
| 3 | Chasewell Park | 18 | 10 | 3 | 5 | 68 | 40 | 33 |
| 4 | Diverse | 18 | 10 | 3 | 5 | 45 | 39 | 33 |
| 5 | Banbury Galaxy | 18 | 9 | 5 | 4 | 65 | 37 | 32 |
| 6 | Bloxham Reserves | 18 | 10 | 2 | 6 | 50 | 46 | 32 |
| 7 | Heyford Park | 18 | 5 | 1 | 12 | 42 | 56 | 16 |
| 8 | Chacombe | 18 | 4 | 2 | 12 | 31 | 53 | 14 |
| 9 | Merton FC | 18 | 3 | 2 | 13 | 31 | 67 | 11 |
| 10 | Wroxton Heath | 18 | 2 | 3 | 13 | 31 | 60 | 9 |

### Division Four

| | | P | W | D | L | F | A | Pts |
|---|---|---|---|---|---|---|---|---|
| 1 | Heyford Athletic Reserves | 18 | 12 | 3 | 3 | 58 | 19 | 39 |
| 2 | Bodicote Sports Reserves | 18 | 12 | 2 | 4 | 88 | 35 | 38 |
| 3 | KEA Reserves | 18 | 12 | 2 | 4 | 68 | 35 | 38 |
| 4 | Gyftid | 18 | 12 | 1 | 5 | 78 | 37 | 37 |
| 5 | Bishops Itchington Reserves | 18 | 11 | 3 | 4 | 67 | 35 | 36 |
| 6 | Steeple Aston Reserves | 18 | 10 | 2 | 6 | 63 | 57 | 32 |
| 7 | Finmere Reserves | 18 | 6 | 0 | 12 | 25 | 72 | 18 |
| 8 | Wroxton Sports Reserves | 18 | 3 | 2 | 13 | 40 | 73 | 11 |
| 9 | Swis FC Reserves | 18 | 2 | 2 | 14 | 24 | 74 | 8 |
| 10 | Woodford United A | 18 | 1 | 1 | 16 | 16 | 90 | 4 |

## BASINGSTOKE & DISTRICT LEAGUE

### Premier Division

| | | P | W | D | L | F | A | Pts |
|---|---|---|---|---|---|---|---|---|
| 1 | FC Censo | 20 | 18 | 2 | 0 | 71 | 16 | 56 |
| 2 | Basingstoke Royals | 20 | 15 | 3 | 2 | 69 | 24 | 48 |
| 3 | Welly Old Boys | 20 | 13 | 4 | 3 | 81 | 35 | 43 |
| 4 | Kingsclere | 20 | 11 | 2 | 7 | 67 | 38 | 35 |
| 5 | Tron | 20 | 10 | 1 | 9 | 72 | 38 | 31 |
| 6 | Poison | 20 | 10 | 1 | 9 | 30 | 40 | 31 |
| 7 | Sherborne St John | 20 | 9 | 2 | 9 | 48 | 39 | 29 |
| 8 | Old Basing Rangers | 20 | 4 | 5 | 11 | 53 | 57 | 17 |
| 9 | Hook | 20 | 5 | 1 | 14 | 50 | 72 | 16 |
| 10 | Bramley United | 20 | 4 | 1 | 15 | 46 | 63 | 13 |
| 11 | Heathpark | 20 | 0 | 0 | 20 | 10 | 175 | 0 |

### Division One

| | | P | W | D | L | F | A | Pts |
|---|---|---|---|---|---|---|---|---|
| 1 | North Warnborough | 20 | 18 | 1 | 1 | 65 | 11 | 55 |
| 2 | MFC Popley | 20 | 16 | 2 | 2 | 62 | 31 | 50 |
| 3 | Sherfield | 20 | 11 | 1 | 8 | 44 | 48 | 34 |
| 4 | Tadley Calleva (A) | 20 | 10 | 3 | 7 | 50 | 43 | 33 |
| 5 | Welly Old Boys Reserves | 20 | 9 | 3 | 8 | 41 | 27 | 30 |
| 6 | Herriard Sports | 20 | 9 | 2 | 9 | 50 | 52 | 29 |
| 7 | FC Burghclere | 20 | 5 | 5 | 10 | 37 | 36 | 20 |
| 8 | Baughurst AFC | 20 | 6 | 2 | 12 | 38 | 52 | 20 |
| 9 | Kingsclere Reserves | 20 | 5 | 3 | 12 | 39 | 70 | 18 |
| 10 | Chineham Albion | 20 | 5 | 1 | 14 | 48 | 68 | 16 |
| 11 | Bounty United | 20 | 4 | 1 | 15 | 24 | 60 | 13 |

# LEAGUE TABLES

## Division Two

| | | P | W | D | L | F | A | Pts |
|---|---|---|---|---|---|---|---|---|
| 1 | Skewers | 22 | 19 | 3 | 0 | 109 | 29 | 60 |
| 2 | Pure Spartan | 22 | 19 | 2 | 1 | 101 | 28 | 59 |
| 3 | Tron FC Reserves | 22 | 15 | 3 | 4 | 82 | 42 | 48 |
| 4 | AFC Berg | 22 | 12 | 1 | 9 | 70 | 58 | 37 |
| 5 | Basingstoke Athletic | 22 | 9 | 5 | 8 | 51 | 45 | 32 |
| 6 | Basingstoke Labour Club | 22 | 9 | 2 | 11 | 57 | 59 | 29 |
| 7 | Bengal Brasserie | 22 | 9 | 1 | 12 | 60 | 63 | 28 |
| 8 | Chineham Albion Reserves | 22 | 9 | 1 | 12 | 52 | 59 | 28 |
| 9 | Overton Utd (A) | 22 | 7 | 1 | 14 | 49 | 79 | 22 |
| 10 | AFC Aldermaston (A) | 22 | 6 | 1 | 15 | 43 | 68 | 19 |
| 11 | Baughurst Reserves | 22 | 4 | 2 | 16 | 33 | 100 | 14 |
| 12 | Sherborne St John Reserves | 22 | 3 | 0 | 19 | 30 | 107 | 9 |

# BATH & DISTRICT LEAGUE

## Division One

| | | P | W | D | L | F | A | Pts |
|---|---|---|---|---|---|---|---|---|
| 1 | Odd Down | 18 | 14 | 1 | 3 | 87 | 37 | 43 |
| 2 | Trowbridge House | 18 | 12 | 2 | 4 | 60 | 40 | 38 |
| 3 | AFC Durbin United | 18 | 11 | 3 | 4 | 64 | 29 | 36 |
| 4 | Stothert & Pitt | 18 | 9 | 1 | 8 | 48 | 54 | 28 |
| 5 | Old Crown Weston | 18 | 5 | 3 | 10 | 42 | 63 | 18 |
| 6 | Full Moon | 18 | 3 | 1 | 14 | 29 | 71 | 10 |
| 7 | Aces | 18 | 2 | 3 | 13 | 23 | 59 | 9 |

## Division Two

| | | P | W | D | L | F | A | Pts |
|---|---|---|---|---|---|---|---|---|
| 1 | Newbridge | 12 | 11 | 0 | 1 | 51 | 8 | 33 |
| 2 | Saltford Reserves | 11 | 8 | 0 | 3 | 31 | 21 | 24 |
| 3 | Larkhall Inn FC | 12 | 7 | 0 | 5 | 35 | 16 | 21 |
| 4 | Aces Reserves | 11 | 3 | 0 | 8 | 14 | 36 | 9 |
| 5 | Westfield 'A' | 12 | 0 | 0 | 12 | 14 | 64 | 0 |

AFC Spartans record expunged.
Marc Warman Wanderers record expunged.

# BIRMINGHAM AFA

## Premier Division

| | | P | W | D | L | F | A | Pts |
|---|---|---|---|---|---|---|---|---|
| 1 | Village A | 24 | 17 | 3 | 4 | 63 | 26 | 54 |
| 2 | Crusaders A | 24 | 14 | 4 | 6 | 54 | 32 | 46 |
| 3 | Boldmere Sports & Social A (-3pts) | 24 | 14 | 4 | 6 | 61 | 37 | 43 |
| 4 | Silhill A | 24 | 14 | 1 | 9 | 58 | 46 | 43 |
| 5 | Old Wulfrunians A | 24 | 13 | 3 | 8 | 54 | 27 | 42 |
| 6 | Kingstanding Warriors | 24 | 13 | 3 | 8 | 54 | 38 | 42 |
| 7 | AFC Somers | 24 | 12 | 2 | 10 | 41 | 40 | 38 |
| 8 | Shirley Athletic A | 24 | 12 | 0 | 12 | 47 | 54 | 36 |
| 9 | Athletic Sparkhill | 24 | 9 | 3 | 12 | 55 | 55 | 30 |
| 10 | Wake Green Amateurs A | 24 | 7 | 4 | 13 | 40 | 45 | 25 |
| 11 | Handsworth GSOBs A (-1pt) | 24 | 7 | 3 | 14 | 47 | 65 | 23 |
| 12 | St Francis | 24 | 4 | 3 | 17 | 22 | 63 | 15 |
| 13 | Cresconians A | 24 | 2 | 3 | 19 | 34 | 102 | 9 |

## Division One

| | | P | W | D | L | F | A | Pts |
|---|---|---|---|---|---|---|---|---|
| 1 | Smithswood Colts | 20 | 13 | 2 | 5 | 62 | 38 | 41 |
| 2 | Walsall Phoenix A | 20 | 12 | 5 | 3 | 47 | 25 | 41 |
| 3 | CPA | 20 | 13 | 2 | 5 | 44 | 30 | 41 |
| 4 | Flamengo | 20 | 11 | 3 | 6 | 44 | 38 | 36 |
| 5 | Old Hill | 20 | 10 | 2 | 8 | 43 | 38 | 32 |
| 6 | Sutton United A | 20 | 9 | 2 | 9 | 47 | 38 | 29 |
| 7 | Parkfield Amateurs A | 20 | 8 | 4 | 8 | 53 | 38 | 28 |
| 8 | Village B | 20 | 7 | 3 | 10 | 45 | 43 | 24 |
| 9 | Shirley Athletic B | 20 | 7 | 2 | 11 | 40 | 58 | 23 |
| 10 | Shere Punjab | 20 | 3 | 4 | 13 | 40 | 65 | 13 |
| 11 | St Pauls | 20 | 2 | 1 | 17 | 22 | 76 | 7 |

## Division Two

| | | P | W | D | L | F | A | Pts |
|---|---|---|---|---|---|---|---|---|
| 1 | Paget Rangers | 22 | 18 | 2 | 2 | 80 | 22 | 5 |
| 2 | Aston A | 22 | 18 | 0 | 4 | 78 | 32 | 5 |
| 3 | Bentley Heath United | 22 | 12 | 2 | 8 | 68 | 68 | 3 |
| 4 | Sutton United B | 22 | 11 | 3 | 8 | 60 | 51 | 3 |
| 5 | Silhill B | 22 | 11 | 3 | 8 | 60 | 55 | 3 |
| 6 | Rossi & Rossi A | 22 | 10 | 3 | 9 | 58 | 41 | 3 |
| 7 | Bearwood Athletic | 22 | 8 | 3 | 11 | 60 | 67 | 2 |
| 8 | Desi A | 22 | 8 | 3 | 11 | 48 | 78 | 2 |
| 9 | Wake Green Amateurs B | 22 | 7 | 2 | 13 | 40 | 50 | 2 |
| 10 | Malremo Rangers (-3pts) | 22 | 7 | 4 | 11 | 46 | 47 | 2 |
| 11 | Village C | 22 | 5 | 3 | 14 | 41 | 61 | 1 |
| 12 | Britannia OBs | 22 | 2 | 2 | 18 | 38 | 105 | |

## Division Three

| | | P | W | D | L | F | A | Pts |
|---|---|---|---|---|---|---|---|---|
| 1 | Premier FC 2008 | 22 | 18 | 1 | 3 | 63 | 21 | 5 |
| 2 | Bournville Colts | 22 | 13 | 4 | 5 | 49 | 25 | 4 |
| 3 | Coldlands | 22 | 13 | 3 | 6 | 66 | 38 | 4 |
| 4 | Old Wulfrunians B | 22 | 14 | 0 | 8 | 66 | 49 | 4 |
| 5 | Wake Green Amateurs C | 22 | 9 | 3 | 10 | 36 | 50 | 3 |
| 6 | Pathfinder | 22 | 8 | 5 | 9 | 47 | 43 | 2 |
| 7 | Wednesbury Athletic | 22 | 8 | 4 | 10 | 60 | 60 | 2 |
| 8 | Aston B | 22 | 8 | 2 | 12 | 41 | 50 | 2 |
| 9 | St Georges Warriors | 22 | 6 | 7 | 9 | 37 | 39 | 2 |
| 10 | Cresconians B (-3pts) | 22 | 8 | 3 | 11 | 48 | 69 | 2 |
| 11 | Walsall Phoenix B | 22 | 4 | 8 | 10 | 32 | 49 | 2 |
| 12 | Great Barr | 22 | 1 | 4 | 17 | 20 | 72 | |

## Division Four

| | | P | W | D | L | F | A | Pts |
|---|---|---|---|---|---|---|---|---|
| 1 | Kingstanding Celtic | 22 | 18 | 3 | 1 | 108 | 36 | 5 |
| 2 | Triumph Meriden | 22 | 15 | 3 | 4 | 57 | 29 | 4 |
| 3 | BT (-3pts) | 22 | 14 | 1 | 7 | 64 | 45 | 4 |
| 4 | Maypole AFC | 21 | 11 | 3 | 7 | 78 | 54 | 3 |
| 5 | Birmingham Irish | 21 | 9 | 5 | 7 | 55 | 42 | 3 |
| 6 | Shuttington Town (-6pts) | 19 | 10 | 2 | 7 | 53 | 39 | 2 |
| 7 | Birmingham Medics | 22 | 7 | 5 | 10 | 45 | 41 | 2 |
| 8 | Boldmere Sports & Social B | 21 | 8 | 2 | 11 | 45 | 76 | 2 |
| 9 | Parkfield Amateurs B | 22 | 6 | 2 | 14 | 42 | 65 | 2 |
| 10 | Sportsco (-6pts) | 22 | 7 | 1 | 14 | 44 | 61 | 1 |
| 11 | Meriden Athletic | 22 | 5 | 2 | 15 | 33 | 73 | 1 |
| 12 | Old Wulfrunians C (-3pts) | 22 | 4 | 1 | 17 | 28 | 91 | |

## Division Five

| | | P | W | D | L | F | A | Pts |
|---|---|---|---|---|---|---|---|---|
| 1 | Urban Athletic C | 26 | 19 | 3 | 4 | 72 | 38 | 6 |
| 2 | Fairfax Sport | 26 | 17 | 5 | 4 | 85 | 41 | 5 |
| 3 | Olympia 808 | 26 | 16 | 3 | 7 | 75 | 48 | 5 |
| 4 | Rossi & Rossi B | 26 | 16 | 2 | 8 | 51 | 34 | 5 |
| 5 | Real Riverside A | 26 | 13 | 7 | 6 | 83 | 40 | 4 |
| 6 | Amanah A | 26 | 14 | 4 | 8 | 71 | 53 | 4 |
| 7 | Birmingham Citadel | 26 | 13 | 3 | 10 | 62 | 49 | 4 |
| 8 | Premier FC 2008 B (-1pt) | 26 | 10 | 2 | 14 | 54 | 72 | 3 |
| 9 | Silhill C | 26 | 8 | 4 | 14 | 63 | 74 | 2 |
| 10 | Village D | 26 | 7 | 5 | 14 | 45 | 65 | 2 |
| 11 | Sutton United C | 26 | 6 | 6 | 14 | 53 | 71 | 2 |
| 12 | Wake Green Amateurs D | 26 | 6 | 4 | 16 | 43 | 62 | 2 |
| 13 | Red Star Galaxy | 26 | 6 | 4 | 16 | 54 | 86 | 2 |
| 14 | Crusaders B | 26 | 4 | 2 | 20 | 31 | 109 | 1 |

| Division Six | P | W | D | L | F | A | Pts |
|---|---|---|---|---|---|---|---|
| 1 Coldfield Rangers | 26 | 21 | 2 | 3 | 105 | 30 | 65 |
| 2 Castle Brom United | 26 | 19 | 4 | 3 | 112 | 45 | 61 |
| 3 Wood Wanderers | 26 | 18 | 2 | 6 | 92 | 50 | 56 |
| 4 Castlecroft Rangers | 26 | 17 | 1 | 8 | 78 | 51 | 52 |
| 5 Walsall Allstar (-6pts) | 26 | 18 | 2 | 6 | 99 | 38 | 50 |
| 6 Village E | 26 | 11 | 8 | 7 | 65 | 44 | 41 |
| 7 Garden House Rangers | 26 | 8 | 7 | 11 | 67 | 63 | 31 |
| 8 Boldmere Sports & Social C | 26 | 9 | 2 | 15 | 48 | 56 | 29 |
| 9 Railway Hockley (-3pts) | 26 | 9 | 4 | 13 | 58 | 84 | 28 |
| 10 Dudley Athletic | 26 | 8 | 3 | 15 | 56 | 78 | 27 |
| 11 Amanah B (-1pt) | 26 | 8 | 1 | 17 | 59 | 92 | 24 |
| 12 Coton Green | 26 | 6 | 4 | 16 | 51 | 75 | 22 |
| 13 Dosthill Boys Club | 26 | 6 | 4 | 16 | 54 | 88 | 22 |
| 14 Sporting | 26 | 2 | 0 | 24 | 40 | 190 | 6 |

| Division Seven | P | W | D | L | F | A | Pts |
|---|---|---|---|---|---|---|---|
| 1 Hall Green United | 30 | 24 | 1 | 5 | 102 | 41 | 73 |
| 2 Desi B | 30 | 23 | 3 | 4 | 127 | 42 | 72 |
| 3 Round Oak Rangers | 30 | 18 | 7 | 5 | 95 | 59 | 61 |
| 4 Silhill D | 30 | 16 | 4 | 10 | 87 | 62 | 52 |
| 5 Handsworth GSOBs B | 30 | 16 | 4 | 10 | 85 | 66 | 52 |
| 6 Sutton United D | 30 | 14 | 6 | 10 | 83 | 73 | 48 |
| 7 Parkfield Amateurs C | 30 | 13 | 8 | 9 | 78 | 63 | 47 |
| 8 Manchester Wanderers | 30 | 14 | 3 | 13 | 77 | 67 | 45 |
| 9 Real Riverside B | 30 | 13 | 5 | 12 | 73 | 75 | 44 |
| 10 Walsall Phoenix C | 30 | 12 | 5 | 13 | 66 | 58 | 41 |
| 11 Small Heath Tigers | 30 | 10 | 5 | 15 | 62 | 84 | 35 |
| 12 Amanah C | 30 | 10 | 2 | 18 | 85 | 104 | 32 |
| 13 Village F | 30 | 6 | 8 | 16 | 60 | 96 | 26 |
| 14 Smethwick Raiders | 30 | 6 | 5 | 19 | 53 | 125 | 23 |
| 15 Wake Green Amateurs E | 30 | 5 | 4 | 21 | 51 | 104 | 19 |
| 16 Steelhouse Lane | 30 | 3 | 4 | 23 | 49 | 114 | 13 |

## BISHOP'S STORTFORD, STANSTED & DISTRICT LEAGUE

| Premier Division | P | W | D | L | F | A | Pts |
|---|---|---|---|---|---|---|---|
| 1 Sheering | 14 | 12 | 1 | 1 | 32 | 13 | 37 |
| 2 Northolt | 14 | 7 | 4 | 3 | 45 | 30 | 25 |
| 3 Heath Rovers | 14 | 6 | 5 | 3 | 34 | 24 | 23 |
| 4 Parsloe Athletic | 14 | 7 | 2 | 5 | 26 | 27 | 23 |
| 5 Hertfordshire Rangers | 14 | 4 | 5 | 5 | 26 | 31 | 17 |
| 6 Avondale Rangers | 14 | 4 | 2 | 8 | 28 | 33 | 14 |
| 7 Frontiers | 14 | 2 | 4 | 8 | 17 | 37 | 10 |
| 8 Harbridge Athletic | 14 | 2 | 1 | 11 | 15 | 28 | 7 |

| Division One | P | W | D | L | F | A | Pts |
|---|---|---|---|---|---|---|---|
| 1 Hatfield Heath | 18 | 16 | 1 | 1 | 84 | 22 | 49 |
| 2 North Weald | 18 | 12 | 2 | 4 | 44 | 27 | 38 |
| 3 Lower Street | 18 | 11 | 2 | 5 | 66 | 30 | 35 |
| 4 Fairways Corinthians | 18 | 9 | 2 | 7 | 51 | 39 | 29 |
| 5 Avondale Rangers Reserves | 18 | 8 | 4 | 6 | 54 | 37 | 28 |
| 6 Birchanger | 18 | 7 | 2 | 9 | 53 | 44 | 23 |
| 7 E F Lakers | 18 | 5 | 4 | 9 | 32 | 62 | 19 |
| 8 Albury | 18 | 5 | 3 | 10 | 27 | 54 | 18 |
| 9 Potter Street | 18 | 4 | 0 | 14 | 23 | 54 | 12 |
| 10 Sheering Reserves | 18 | 2 | 2 | 14 | 23 | 88 | 8 |

## BLACKBURN & DISTRICT COMBINATION

| Premier Division | P | W | D | L | F | A | Pts |
|---|---|---|---|---|---|---|---|
| 1 Hole Ith Wall | 18 | 11 | 3 | 4 | 43 | 35 | 36 |
| 2 Blackburn Olympic | 18 | 9 | 3 | 6 | 51 | 37 | 30 |
| 3 Clifton | 18 | 9 | 2 | 7 | 51 | 44 | 29 |
| 4 Blackmoor Inn | 18 | 9 | 2 | 7 | 50 | 48 | 29 |
| 5 Blackburn United | 18 | 7 | 4 | 6 | 40 | 32 | 25 |
| 6 Rishton United | 18 | 7 | 3 | 8 | 50 | 50 | 24 |
| 7 Islington | 18 | 7 | 2 | 9 | 41 | 44 | 23 |
| 8 Feildens Arms | 18 | 6 | 4 | 8 | 38 | 43 | 22 |
| 9 Greenfield | 18 | 5 | 4 | 9 | 33 | 43 | 19 |
| 10 Feniscowles & Pleasington Res. | 18 | 3 | 5 | 9 | 29 | 50 | 14 |

Tricky FC record expunged.

Blackburn United v Feniscowles & Pleasington Reserves game was declared a VOID game and all goals and points from this game have been removed from the records.

| Division One | P | W | D | L | F | A | Pts |
|---|---|---|---|---|---|---|---|
| 1 Rishton United Reserves | 16 | 14 | 0 | 2 | 71 | 26 | 42 |
| 2 Wellington Inn | 16 | 13 | 1 | 2 | 77 | 32 | 40 |
| 3 Vauxhall Inn | 16 | 10 | 1 | 5 | 44 | 36 | 31 |
| 4 Alexandra Hotel | 16 | 9 | 1 | 6 | 63 | 57 | 28 |
| 5 I.M.O. | 16 | 5 | 2 | 8 | 32 | 32 | 17 |
| 6 Whalley Range | 16 | 5 | 2 | 8 | 52 | 60 | 17 |
| 7 The Lion | 16 | 5 | 2 | 9 | 40 | 64 | 17 |
| 8 Worth Avenue | 16 | 2 | 2 | 12 | 27 | 60 | 8 |
| 9 Blackburn United Reserves | 16 | 1 | 3 | 12 | 28 | 67 | 6 |

Whalley Range v I.M.O. game was declared a VOID game and all goals and points from this game have been removed from the records.

## BOURNEMOUTH LEAGUE

| Premier Division | P | W | D | L | F | A | Pts |
|---|---|---|---|---|---|---|---|
| 1 Sway | 22 | 18 | 1 | 3 | 65 | 32 | 55 |
| 2 Bournemouth Manor | 22 | 16 | 3 | 3 | 50 | 25 | 51 |
| 3 Portcastrian | 22 | 14 | 3 | 5 | 61 | 36 | 45 |
| 4 Hamworthy Recreation | 22 | 14 | 2 | 6 | 55 | 31 | 44 |
| 5 Bournemouth Electric | 22 | 12 | 5 | 5 | 66 | 45 | 41 |
| 6 Westover Bournemouth | 22 | 9 | 4 | 9 | 34 | 38 | 31 |
| 7 Mudeford Mens Club | 22 | 6 | 8 | 8 | 50 | 51 | 26 |
| 8 Parley Sports | 22 | 7 | 5 | 10 | 44 | 53 | 26 |
| 9 Bournemouth Poppies Res | 22 | 7 | 2 | 13 | 65 | 70 | 23 |
| 10 Old Oakmeadians | 22 | 5 | 4 | 13 | 34 | 50 | 19 |
| 11 Allendale | 22 | 3 | 2 | 17 | 41 | 74 | 11 |
| 12 Redlynch and Woodfalls | 22 | 1 | 1 | 20 | 25 | 85 | 4 |

| Division One | P | W | D | L | F | A | Pts |
|---|---|---|---|---|---|---|---|
| 1 Richmond Park Con Club | 18 | 16 | 0 | 2 | 82 | 19 | 48 |
| 2 Ferndown Sports | 18 | 12 | 4 | 2 | 51 | 27 | 40 |
| 3 Alderholt | 18 | 8 | 4 | 6 | 39 | 29 | 28 |
| 4 Harrington Utd | 18 | 8 | 2 | 8 | 41 | 38 | 26 |
| 5 Holt | 18 | 6 | 2 | 10 | 30 | 47 | 20 |
| 6 Queens Park Athletic | 18 | 3 | 3 | 12 | 30 | 55 | 12 |
| 7 Bournemouth Electric Reserves | 18 | 2 | 1 | 15 | 19 | 77 | 7 |

# Soccer Books Limited

## 72 ST. PETERS AVENUE (Dept. NLD)
## CLEETHORPES
## N.E. LINCOLNSHIRE
## DN35 8HU
## ENGLAND

### Tel. 01472 696226    Fax 01472 698546

Web site    www.soccer-books.co.uk
e-mail    info@soccer-books.co.uk

## Division Two

| | P | W | D | L | F | A | Pts |
|---|---|---|---|---|---|---|---|
| Bournemouth Electric A (-3pts) | 18 | 17 | 1 | 0 | 77 | 18 | 49 |
| Sway Reserves (+3pts) | 18 | 15 | 0 | 3 | 63 | 21 | 48 |
| Walkford | 18 | 7 | 4 | 7 | 41 | 35 | 25 |
| Mploy | 18 | 7 | 2 | 9 | 45 | 37 | 23 |
| New Milton Linnets | 18 | 7 | 1 | 10 | 49 | 55 | 22 |
| Bisterne Rangers | 18 | 6 | 2 | 10 | 41 | 56 | 20 |
| St Marys | 18 | 6 | 2 | 10 | 32 | 60 | 20 |
| Westover Bournemouth Reserves | 18 | 6 | 1 | 11 | 28 | 42 | 19 |
| Bournemouth Manor Reserves | 18 | 5 | 4 | 9 | 32 | 51 | 19 |
| Fordingbridge Turks | 18 | 4 | 3 | 11 | 17 | 50 | 15 |

## Division Three

| | P | W | D | L | F | A | Pts |
|---|---|---|---|---|---|---|---|
| BU Staff | 20 | 14 | 4 | 2 | 51 | 22 | 46 |
| AFC Pennington | 20 | 14 | 4 | 2 | 61 | 36 | 46 |
| Mudeford Mens Club Reserves | 20 | 10 | 5 | 5 | 57 | 32 | 35 |
| Ferndown Sports Reserves | 20 | 10 | 5 | 5 | 50 | 41 | 35 |
| AFC Burton | 20 | 10 | 1 | 9 | 54 | 44 | 31 |
| Old Oakmeadians Reserves | 20 | 8 | 4 | 8 | 46 | 50 | 28 |
| Queens Park Athletic Reserves | 20 | 6 | 5 | 9 | 37 | 49 | 23 |
| Seyward Windows | 20 | 6 | 3 | 11 | 55 | 48 | 21 |
| Redhill Rangers | 20 | 6 | 3 | 11 | 53 | 56 | 21 |
| FC Athletico | 20 | 6 | 1 | 13 | 35 | 57 | 19 |
| Redlynch and Woodfalls Reserves | 20 | 2 | 1 | 17 | 13 | 77 | 7 |

## Division Four

| | P | W | D | L | F | A | Pts |
|---|---|---|---|---|---|---|---|
| New Milton Eagles | 18 | 13 | 2 | 3 | 64 | 30 | 41 |
| Bisterne Blue Sox | 18 | 12 | 2 | 4 | 45 | 35 | 38 |
| Fifa Standards | 18 | 10 | 2 | 6 | 47 | 38 | 32 |
| Seabournes | 18 | 9 | 1 | 8 | 40 | 43 | 28 |
| AFC Bransgore | 18 | 8 | 3 | 7 | 59 | 36 | 27 |
| Richmond Park Con Club Res. | 18 | 6 | 5 | 7 | 32 | 35 | 23 |
| Pig & Whistle | 18 | 7 | 2 | 9 | 40 | 48 | 23 |
| Magpies | 18 | 4 | 5 | 9 | 30 | 49 | 17 |
| Allendale Reserves | 18 | 5 | 2 | 11 | 32 | 52 | 17 |
| Burley | 18 | 3 | 2 | 13 | 32 | 55 | 11 |

## Division Five

| | P | W | D | L | F | A | Pts |
|---|---|---|---|---|---|---|---|
| A & T Athletic | 18 | 13 | 2 | 3 | 69 | 24 | 41 |
| West Howe | 18 | 12 | 3 | 3 | 69 | 36 | 39 |
| Lower Parkstone CFC | 18 | 10 | 4 | 4 | 60 | 23 | 34 |
| Witchampton Reserves | 18 | 9 | 0 | 9 | 37 | 65 | 27 |
| Portcastrian Reserves | 18 | 8 | 2 | 8 | 41 | 45 | 26 |
| Shoulder of Mutton United | 18 | 7 | 2 | 9 | 54 | 51 | 23 |
| Milford | 18 | 6 | 4 | 8 | 50 | 57 | 22 |
| Rounders | 18 | 6 | 3 | 9 | 43 | 45 | 21 |
| Bournemouth Poppies A | 18 | 5 | 0 | 13 | 34 | 65 | 15 |
| Bransgore Utd | 18 | 3 | 2 | 13 | 28 | 74 | 11 |

## Division Six

| | P | W | D | L | F | A | Pts |
|---|---|---|---|---|---|---|---|
| AFC Burton Reserves | 18 | 14 | 1 | 3 | 69 | 24 | 43 |
| Alderholt Reserves | 18 | 14 | 1 | 3 | 57 | 29 | 43 |
| Ringwood Athletic | 18 | 12 | 1 | 5 | 71 | 32 | 37 |
| Redhill Rangers Reserves | 18 | 9 | 3 | 6 | 50 | 43 | 30 |
| Boldre Royals | 18 | 7 | 3 | 8 | 62 | 49 | 24 |
| Everton & Lymington Argyle | 18 | 5 | 4 | 9 | 33 | 46 | 19 |
| Ferndown Sports A | 18 | 6 | 1 | 11 | 46 | 66 | 19 |
| Parkstone Athletic | 18 | 5 | 2 | 11 | 33 | 49 | 17 |
| Milford Reserves | 18 | 5 | 1 | 12 | 27 | 83 | 16 |
| Fordingbridge Turks Reserves | 18 | 3 | 3 | 12 | 25 | 52 | 12 |

# BRIGHTON, HOVE & DISTRICT LEAGUE

## Premier Division

| | | P | W | D | L | F | A | Pts |
|---|---|---|---|---|---|---|---|---|
| 1 | Hair Razors | 18 | 16 | 2 | 0 | 60 | 12 | 50 |
| 2 | Brighton Electricity | 18 | 9 | 6 | 3 | 50 | 36 | 33 |
| 3 | AFC Stanley | 18 | 10 | 2 | 6 | 37 | 38 | 32 |
| 4 | Peacehaven Academicals | 18 | 9 | 1 | 8 | 45 | 31 | 28 |
| 5 | Hurren & Glynn | 18 | 7 | 5 | 6 | 35 | 28 | 26 |
| 6 | BSM08 | 18 | 5 | 5 | 8 | 47 | 62 | 20 |
| 7 | C.C.K. | 18 | 5 | 2 | 11 | 39 | 49 | 17 |
| 8 | Montpelier Villa | 18 | 5 | 2 | 11 | 31 | 47 | 17 |
| 9 | Royal Hove | 18 | 4 | 4 | 10 | 25 | 40 | 16 |
| 10 | Ovingdean | 18 | 4 | 3 | 11 | 25 | 51 | 15 |

Whitehawk Vets record expunged.

## Division One

| | | P | W | D | L | F | A | Pts |
|---|---|---|---|---|---|---|---|---|
| 1 | TMG | 22 | 20 | 1 | 1 | 94 | 30 | 61 |
| 2 | Midway | 22 | 12 | 7 | 3 | 90 | 56 | 43 |
| 3 | Hobgoblin | 22 | 13 | 2 | 7 | 87 | 46 | 41 |
| 4 | South Coast City | 22 | 13 | 1 | 8 | 68 | 50 | 40 |
| 5 | Boys Brigade Old Boys | 22 | 12 | 1 | 9 | 61 | 38 | 37 |
| 6 | The View | 22 | 11 | 1 | 10 | 48 | 58 | 34 |
| 7 | Peacehaven Academicals II | 22 | 9 | 4 | 9 | 53 | 53 | 31 |
| 8 | Rottingdean Village Reserves | 22 | 6 | 4 | 12 | 52 | 62 | 22 |
| 9 | Southwick Rangers | 22 | 6 | 3 | 13 | 34 | 78 | 21 |
| 10 | Deans Dynamos | 22 | 5 | 3 | 14 | 43 | 82 | 18 |
| 11 | Royal Hove II | 22 | 5 | 1 | 16 | 34 | 71 | 16 |
| 12 | ATS Southern | 22 | 4 | 4 | 14 | 38 | 78 | 16 |

Ovingdean II withdrawn from League

## Division Two

| | | P | W | D | L | F | A | PTS |
|---|---|---|---|---|---|---|---|---|
| 1 | Racing Palmeria | 22 | 17 | 3 | 2 | 73 | 30 | 54 |
| 2 | Bishop & Light | 22 | 16 | 1 | 5 | 85 | 41 | 49 |
| 3 | Hardly Athletic | 22 | 15 | 1 | 6 | 80 | 38 | 46 |
| 4 | Millhouse | 22 | 11 | 2 | 9 | 60 | 54 | 35 |
| 5 | Portslade Athletic Reserves (-1pt) | 22 | 11 | 2 | 9 | 58 | 44 | 34 |
| 6 | Boys Brigade Old Boys II | 22 | 10 | 4 | 8 | 53 | 46 | 34 |
| 7 | Southwick Rangers II (-3pts) | 22 | 11 | 1 | 10 | 62 | 67 | 31 |
| 8 | Midway II | 22 | 8 | 3 | 11 | 70 | 73 | 27 |
| 9 | Montpelier Villa II | 22 | 7 | 2 | 13 | 35 | 39 | 23 |
| 10 | C.C.K. II (+2pts) | 22 | 6 | 3 | 13 | 33 | 61 | 23 |
| 11 | Unity | 22 | 6 | 3 | 13 | 44 | 66 | 21 |
| 12 | Hove Park Tavern (+3pts) | 22 | 1 | 1 | 20 | 29 | 123 | 7 |

FC Shepherds Withdrawn from League

# BRISTOL & AVON FOOTBALL LEAGUE

## Premier Division

| | | P | W | D | L | F | A | Pts |
|---|---|---|---|---|---|---|---|---|
| 1 | Stapleton AFC | 16 | 16 | 0 | 0 | 62 | 7 | 48 |
| 2 | AFC Whitchurch | 16 | 12 | 0 | 4 | 44 | 38 | 36 |
| 3 | De-Veys Reserves | 16 | 10 | 1 | 5 | 47 | 23 | 31 |
| 4 | Broad Plain 'A' | 16 | 8 | 2 | 6 | 36 | 46 | 26 |
| 5 | Imperial 'A' | 16 | 4 | 6 | 6 | 29 | 36 | 18 |
| 6 | Cutters Friday 'A' (-3pts) | 16 | 6 | 2 | 8 | 38 | 31 | 17 |
| 7 | Long Ashton 'A' | 16 | 3 | 3 | 10 | 29 | 59 | 12 |
| 8 | AFC Hartcliffe Reserves | 16 | 3 | 1 | 12 | 40 | 56 | 10 |
| 9 | Sea Mills Park 'A' | 16 | 1 | 3 | 12 | 29 | 58 | 6 |

# LEAGUE TABLES

## Division One

| | | P | W | D | L | F | A | Pts |
|---|---|---|---|---|---|---|---|---|
| 1 | Dodington | 16 | 13 | 0 | 3 | 62 | 28 | 39 |
| 2 | Golden Hill Sports 'A' | 16 | 12 | 0 | 4 | 60 | 37 | 36 |
| 3 | Wessex Wanderers 'A' | 16 | 9 | 1 | 6 | 37 | 31 | 28 |
| 4 | Iron Acton 'B' | 16 | 7 | 2 | 7 | 38 | 43 | 23 |
| 5 | Broadwalk Athletic (-3pts) | 16 | 8 | 1 | 7 | 38 | 37 | 22 |
| 6 | Westerleigh Sports Reserves | 16 | 6 | 0 | 10 | 55 | 60 | 18 |
| 7 | Wanderers Reserves | 16 | 5 | 2 | 9 | 39 | 59 | 17 |
| 8 | Warmley United Reserves | 16 | 5 | 1 | 10 | 34 | 48 | 16 |
| 9 | Bradley Stoke Town 'B' (-6pts) | 16 | 3 | 1 | 12 | 19 | 39 | 4 |

# BRISTOL & DISTRICT LEAGUE

## Senior Division

| | | P | W | D | L | F | A | Pts |
|---|---|---|---|---|---|---|---|---|
| 1 | Sea Mills Park | 26 | 18 | 3 | 5 | 69 | 30 | 57 |
| 2 | Warmley Saints | 26 | 17 | 4 | 5 | 71 | 36 | 55 |
| 3 | Crosscourt United | 26 | 17 | 4 | 5 | 60 | 29 | 55 |
| 4 | Iron Acton | 26 | 15 | 5 | 6 | 64 | 32 | 50 |
| 5 | Stockwood Wanderers (-3pts) | 25 | 15 | 2 | 8 | 60 | 39 | 44 |
| 6 | Roman Glass St George 'A' | 26 | 10 | 9 | 7 | 45 | 33 | 39 |
| 7 | Bristol Barcelona | 26 | 10 | 4 | 12 | 53 | 51 | 34 |
| 8 | Wick Reserves | 26 | 10 | 4 | 12 | 52 | 68 | 34 |
| 9 | Nicholas Wanderers Res | 26 | 9 | 6 | 11 | 49 | 54 | 33 |
| 10 | Longwell Green Sports 'A' | 26 | 9 | 5 | 12 | 41 | 43 | 32 |
| 11 | Hallen 'A' | 26 | 9 | 3 | 14 | 52 | 63 | 30 |
| 12 | Shirehampton Reserves | 26 | 8 | 3 | 15 | 50 | 77 | 27 |
| 13 | Chipping Sodbury Town Reserves | 26 | 3 | 4 | 19 | 17 | 72 | 13 |
| 14 | Hanham Athletic Reserves (-3pts) | 25 | 2 | 2 | 21 | 21 | 77 | 5 |

## Division One

| | | P | W | D | L | F | A | Pts |
|---|---|---|---|---|---|---|---|---|
| 1 | AEK Boco Reserves | 24 | 17 | 4 | 3 | 61 | 21 | 55 |
| 2 | Pucklechurch Sports | 24 | 16 | 6 | 2 | 85 | 29 | 54 |
| 3 | Portville Warriors | 24 | 14 | 5 | 5 | 70 | 38 | 47 |
| 4 | De Veys | 24 | 14 | 4 | 6 | 70 | 47 | 46 |
| 5 | Talbot Knowle United | 24 | 12 | 4 | 8 | 76 | 48 | 40 |
| 6 | Rangeworthy | 24 | 11 | 4 | 9 | 57 | 69 | 37 |
| 7 | Mendip United Reserves | 24 | 10 | 4 | 10 | 33 | 49 | 34 |
| 8 | Stanton Drew | 24 | 9 | 3 | 12 | 53 | 53 | 30 |
| 9 | Bradley Stoke Town | 24 | 7 | 8 | 9 | 47 | 42 | 29 |
| 10 | St Pancras | 24 | 8 | 4 | 12 | 60 | 57 | 28 |
| 11 | Hambrook | 24 | 4 | 3 | 17 | 39 | 79 | 15 |
| 12 | Seymour United Reserves | 24 | 2 | 6 | 16 | 26 | 78 | 12 |
| 13 | Miners | 24 | 3 | 3 | 18 | 26 | 93 | 12 |

## Division Two

| | | P | W | D | L | F | A | Pts |
|---|---|---|---|---|---|---|---|---|
| 1 | Totterdown United Reserves | 24 | 20 | 3 | 1 | 86 | 26 | 63 |
| 2 | Wnterbourne United 'A' | 24 | 16 | 4 | 4 | 75 | 27 | 52 |
| 3 | Soundwell Victoria | 24 | 15 | 3 | 6 | 83 | 49 | 48 |
| 4 | Lebeq (Saturday) FC.Res | 24 | 15 | 3 | 6 | 84 | 54 | 48 |
| 5 | Hartcliffe | 24 | 12 | 3 | 9 | 62 | 52 | 39 |
| 6 | DRG Frenchay Reserves (-4pts) | 24 | 13 | 1 | 10 | 62 | 45 | 36 |
| 7 | Iron Acton Res | 24 | 10 | 6 | 8 | 42 | 49 | 36 |
| 8 | Bendix | 24 | 9 | 6 | 9 | 62 | 59 | 33 |
| 9 | Chipping Sodbury Town 'A' | 24 | 7 | 3 | 14 | 44 | 74 | 24 |
| 10 | Bitton 'A' | 24 | 5 | 4 | 15 | 43 | 71 | 19 |
| 11 | Frys Club 'A' | 24 | 5 | 2 | 17 | 37 | 78 | 17 |
| 12 | Nicholas Wanderers 'A' | 24 | 5 | 1 | 18 | 33 | 72 | 16 |
| 13 | Lloyd Coalpit Heath | 24 | 3 | 3 | 18 | 27 | 84 | 12 |

## Division Three

| | | P | W | D | L | F | A | Pt |
|---|---|---|---|---|---|---|---|---|
| 1 | Real Thornbury | 26 | 20 | 3 | 3 | 87 | 26 | 6 |
| 2 | Cribbs Friends Life 'A' | 26 | 18 | 3 | 5 | 105 | 45 | 5 |
| 3 | AEK Boco 'A' | 26 | 16 | 3 | 7 | 73 | 44 | 5 |
| 4 | Greyfriars Athletic Reserves | 26 | 14 | 3 | 9 | 63 | 46 | 4 |
| 5 | Frampton Athletic Reserves | 26 | 15 | 0 | 11 | 73 | 59 | 4 |
| 6 | Roman Glass St George 'A' | 26 | 13 | 3 | 10 | 60 | 50 | 4 |
| 7 | Yate Athletic | 26 | 12 | 6 | 8 | 64 | 55 | 4 |
| 8 | Patchway North End | 26 | 11 | 2 | 13 | 58 | 56 | 3 |
| 9 | Hambrook Reserves (-3pts) | 26 | 11 | 3 | 12 | 66 | 75 | 3 |
| 10 | Horfield United | 26 | 9 | 4 | 13 | 50 | 50 | 3 |
| 11 | Bristol Barcelona Reserves | 26 | 9 | 4 | 13 | 45 | 57 | 3 |
| 12 | Olveston United Reserves | 26 | 8 | 2 | 16 | 36 | 60 | 2 |
| 13 | Henbury F C 'A' | 26 | 3 | 5 | 18 | 30 | 81 | 1 |
| 14 | Lawrence Rovers Res | 26 | 2 | 1 | 23 | 23 | 129 | |

## Division Four

| | | P | W | D | L | F | A | Pt |
|---|---|---|---|---|---|---|---|---|
| 1 | South Bristol Central | 24 | 23 | 0 | 1 | 75 | 28 | 6 |
| 2 | Pucklechurch Sports Reserves | 24 | 15 | 3 | 6 | 50 | 34 | 4 |
| 3 | Hallen 'B' | 24 | 13 | 5 | 6 | 89 | 44 | 4 |
| 4 | Hillfields Old Boys | 24 | 13 | 4 | 7 | 76 | 64 | 4 |
| 5 | Made for Ever Reserves | 24 | 13 | 4 | 7 | 54 | 45 | 4 |
| 6 | Shaftesbury Crusade Reserves | 24 | 11 | 3 | 10 | 59 | 37 | 3 |
| 7 | Wick 'A' | 24 | 9 | 5 | 10 | 44 | 55 | 3 |
| 8 | Bishopsworth United | 24 | 8 | 4 | 12 | 56 | 55 | 2 |
| 9 | Sea Mills Park Res | 24 | 8 | 4 | 12 | 51 | 64 | 2 |
| 10 | Bradley Stoke Town Reserves | 24 | 6 | 6 | 12 | 40 | 49 | 2 |
| 11 | Talbot Knowle United | 24 | 8 | 0 | 16 | 39 | 85 | 2 |
| 12 | Soundwell Victoria Res | 24 | 5 | 4 | 15 | 37 | 74 | 1 |
| 13 | Brislington Cricketers Reserves | 24 | 3 | 0 | 21 | 31 | 67 | |

## Division Five

| | | P | W | D | L | F | A | Pt |
|---|---|---|---|---|---|---|---|---|
| 1 | Old Sodbury Res | 22 | 21 | 0 | 1 | 112 | 34 | 6 |
| 2 | Westerleigh Sports | 22 | 19 | 0 | 3 | 107 | 38 | 5 |
| 3 | Fishponds Athletic | 22 | 14 | 2 | 6 | 69 | 41 | 4 |
| 4 | Bendix Reserves | 22 | 12 | 1 | 9 | 47 | 59 | 3 |
| 5 | Frys Club 'B' | 22 | 10 | 2 | 10 | 51 | 53 | 3 |
| 6 | Greyfriars Athletic 'A' | 22 | 9 | 1 | 12 | 42 | 74 | 2 |
| 7 | Highridge United 'A' | 22 | 8 | 3 | 11 | 51 | 49 | 2 |
| 8 | Crosscourt United Reserves | 22 | 8 | 3 | 11 | 55 | 54 | 2 |
| 9 | Warmley Saints Res | 22 | 8 | 3 | 11 | 40 | 56 | 2 |
| 10 | Iron Acton 'A' | 22 | 6 | 1 | 15 | 34 | 71 | 1 |
| 11 | Oldland Abbotonians 'A' (-3pts) | 22 | 6 | 1 | 15 | 49 | 64 | 1 |
| 12 | Seymour United 'A' | 22 | 2 | 1 | 19 | 25 | 89 | |

## Division Six

| | | P | W | D | L | F | A | Pt |
|---|---|---|---|---|---|---|---|---|
| 1 | Rangeworthy Reserves | 22 | 18 | 4 | 0 | 91 | 29 | 5 |
| 2 | Stockwood Wanderers Reserves | 22 | 15 | 3 | 4 | 81 | 48 | |
| 3 | Stanton Drew Res | 22 | 12 | 6 | 4 | 68 | 47 | 4 |
| 4 | Cesson | 22 | 12 | 5 | 5 | 63 | 28 | 4 |
| 5 | Mendip United 'A' | 22 | 11 | 2 | 9 | 51 | 55 | 3 |
| 6 | Patchway North End Res | 22 | 9 | 4 | 9 | 52 | 38 | 3 |
| 7 | Winford PH 'A' | 22 | 10 | 1 | 11 | 61 | 72 | 3 |
| 8 | Cribbs Friends Life 'B' | 22 | 8 | 2 | 12 | 51 | 77 | 2 |
| 9 | Bradley Stoke Town 'A' | 22 | 7 | 4 | 11 | 55 | 59 | 2 |
| 10 | Greyfriars Athletic 'B' | 22 | 7 | 3 | 12 | 50 | 70 | 2 |
| 11 | Yate Athletic | 22 | 3 | 1 | 18 | 33 | 65 | 1 |
| 12 | Bristol Deaf | 22 | 2 | 1 | 19 | 28 | 99 | |

## BRISTOL DOWNS LEAGUE

| Division One | P | W | D | L | F | A | Pts |
|---|---|---|---|---|---|---|---|
| 1 Sneyd Park | 26 | 22 | 3 | 1 | 83 | 17 | 69 |
| 2 Clifton St Vincents | 26 | 21 | 2 | 3 | 91 | 28 | 65 |
| 3 Torpedo | 26 | 20 | 4 | 2 | 103 | 28 | 64 |
| 4 Sporting Greyhound | 26 | 13 | 6 | 7 | 48 | 36 | 45 |
| 5 Saints Old Boys | 26 | 12 | 1 | 13 | 57 | 68 | 37 |
| 6 Ashley | 26 | 10 | 5 | 11 | 48 | 48 | 35 |
| 7 Jamaica Bell | 26 | 8 | 7 | 11 | 44 | 57 | 31 |
| 8 Lawes Juniors | 26 | 8 | 6 | 12 | 38 | 41 | 30 |
| 9 AFC Bohemia | 26 | 7 | 6 | 13 | 38 | 55 | 27 |
| 10 Retainers | 26 | 8 | 3 | 15 | 47 | 68 | 27 |
| 11 Cotswool | 26 | 7 | 5 | 14 | 47 | 83 | 26 |
| 12 DAC Beachcroft | 26 | 7 | 4 | 15 | 55 | 78 | 25 |
| 13 Easton Cowboys | 26 | 6 | 5 | 15 | 51 | 78 | 23 |
| 14 Clifton Rockets | 26 | 3 | 3 | 20 | 33 | 98 | 12 |

| Division Two | P | W | D | L | F | A | Pts |
|---|---|---|---|---|---|---|---|
| 1 Portland Old Boys | 26 | 18 | 7 | 1 | 78 | 28 | 61 |
| 2 Torpedo Reserves | 26 | 18 | 6 | 2 | 77 | 24 | 60 |
| 3 Jersey Rangers | 26 | 14 | 8 | 4 | 62 | 41 | 50 |
| 4 Sneyd Park Reserves | 26 | 15 | 4 | 7 | 61 | 35 | 49 |
| 5 Clifton St Vincents Reserves | 26 | 14 | 2 | 10 | 54 | 39 | 44 |
| 6 St Andrews | 26 | 10 | 5 | 11 | 54 | 63 | 35 |
| 7 Saints Old Boys Reserves | 26 | 10 | 2 | 14 | 50 | 64 | 32 |
| 8 Lion FC | 26 | 9 | 4 | 13 | 48 | 62 | 31 |
| 9 Sporting Greyhound Reserves | 26 | 8 | 5 | 13 | 50 | 59 | 29 |
| 10 Ashley Res | 26 | 8 | 4 | 14 | 38 | 65 | 28 |
| 11 Hare on the Hill | 26 | 7 | 4 | 15 | 47 | 62 | 25 |
| 12 Tebby AFC | 26 | 7 | 3 | 16 | 30 | 78 | 24 |
| 13 Evergreen | 26 | 6 | 5 | 15 | 39 | 62 | 23 |
| 14 Greens Park Rangers (-3pts) | 26 | 5 | 7 | 14 | 44 | 50 | 19 |

| Division Three | P | W | D | L | F | A | Pts |
|---|---|---|---|---|---|---|---|
| 1 Old Cliftonians | 24 | 17 | 3 | 4 | 61 | 32 | 54 |
| 2 Corinthians | 24 | 15 | 3 | 6 | 63 | 37 | 48 |
| 3 Clifton St Vincents A | 24 | 14 | 5 | 5 | 58 | 41 | 47 |
| 4 Torpedo A | 24 | 13 | 5 | 6 | 57 | 39 | 44 |
| 5 Easton Cowboys Reserves | 24 | 9 | 7 | 8 | 57 | 52 | 34 |
| 6 Wellington Wanderers | 24 | 10 | 3 | 11 | 76 | 63 | 33 |
| 7 Sneyd Park A | 24 | 9 | 5 | 10 | 54 | 46 | 32 |
| 8 Helios FC | 24 | 9 | 5 | 10 | 51 | 54 | 32 |
| 9 Cotham Old Boys (-3pts) | 24 | 9 | 2 | 13 | 43 | 52 | 26 |
| 10 Bengal Tigers | 24 | 7 | 4 | 13 | 45 | 67 | 25 |
| 11 Retainers Reserves (-3pts) | 24 | 7 | 5 | 12 | 47 | 52 | 23 |
| 12 Portland Old Boys Reserves | 24 | 4 | 7 | 13 | 33 | 65 | 19 |
| 13 Clifton Rockets Reserves | 24 | 3 | 6 | 15 | 40 | 85 | 15 |

| Division Four | P | W | D | L | F | A | Pts |
|---|---|---|---|---|---|---|---|
| 1 Luccombe Garage | 26 | 21 | 4 | 1 | 89 | 31 | 67 |
| 2 Old Elizabethans AFC | 26 | 21 | 1 | 4 | 95 | 30 | 64 |
| 3 Durdham Down Adult School | 26 | 13 | 5 | 8 | 55 | 37 | 44 |
| 4 Conham Rangers | 26 | 11 | 5 | 10 | 64 | 55 | 38 |
| 5 Torpedo B | 26 | 12 | 2 | 12 | 47 | 50 | 38 |
| 6 West Town United | 26 | 11 | 4 | 11 | 50 | 49 | 37 |
| 7 Tebby AFC Reserves | 26 | 10 | 6 | 10 | 71 | 68 | 36 |
| 8 NCSF United | 26 | 10 | 5 | 11 | 50 | 57 | 35 |
| 9 Clifton St Vincents B | 26 | 10 | 4 | 12 | 61 | 56 | 34 |
| 10 Sneyd Park B | 26 | 8 | 5 | 13 | 40 | 56 | 29 |
| 11 Jersey Rangers Reserves | 26 | 7 | 6 | 13 | 50 | 74 | 27 |
| 12 Retainers A | 26 | 6 | 5 | 15 | 40 | 69 | 23 |
| 13 Lion FC Reserves | 26 | 6 | 5 | 15 | 32 | 70 | 23 |
| 14 Cosmos UK FC | 26 | 6 | 3 | 17 | 39 | 81 | 21 |

## BRISTOL PREMIER COMBINATION

| Premier Division | P | W | D | L | F | A | Pts |
|---|---|---|---|---|---|---|---|
| 1 Longwell Green Reserves | 26 | 20 | 2 | 4 | 79 | 33 | 62 |
| 2 Winterbourne United Reserves | 26 | 17 | 3 | 6 | 92 | 44 | 54 |
| 3 Mendip United | 26 | 17 | 3 | 6 | 74 | 33 | 54 |
| 4 Lebeq (Saturday) FC | 26 | 16 | 4 | 6 | 95 | 44 | 52 |
| 5 Totterdown United | 26 | 14 | 6 | 6 | 54 | 34 | 48 |
| 6 Old Sodbury | 26 | 12 | 5 | 9 | 52 | 50 | 41 |
| 7 A.E.K. Boco | 26 | 11 | 2 | 13 | 56 | 47 | 35 |
| 8 Hallen Reserves | 26 | 9 | 5 | 12 | 51 | 55 | 32 |
| 9 Nicholas Wanderers | 26 | 7 | 9 | 10 | 45 | 48 | 30 |
| 10 Shaftesbury Crusade | 26 | 8 | 6 | 12 | 51 | 61 | 30 |
| 11 Wick | 26 | 9 | 3 | 14 | 42 | 66 | 30 |
| 12 Bitton Reserves | 26 | 7 | 1 | 18 | 40 | 84 | 22 |
| 13 Lawrence Rovers | 26 | 4 | 4 | 18 | 34 | 98 | 16 |
| 14 Roman Glass/St George Reserves | 26 | 3 | 3 | 20 | 27 | 95 | 12 |

| Premier One | P | W | D | L | F | A | Pts |
|---|---|---|---|---|---|---|---|
| 1 Highridge United | 26 | 19 | 4 | 3 | 81 | 30 | 61 |
| 2 Cribbs Friends Life Reserves | 26 | 16 | 5 | 5 | 61 | 33 | 53 |
| 3 Eden Grove | 26 | 14 | 3 | 9 | 76 | 57 | 45 |
| 4 Seymour United | 26 | 11 | 9 | 6 | 49 | 44 | 42 |
| 5 Greyfriars Athletic | 26 | 12 | 5 | 9 | 55 | 53 | 41 |
| 6 Oldland Abbotonians Reserves | 26 | 10 | 7 | 9 | 64 | 60 | 37 |
| 7 Frampton Athletic | 26 | 10 | 6 | 10 | 54 | 52 | 36 |
| 8 Bristol Manor Farm Reserves | 26 | 11 | 3 | 12 | 53 | 53 | 36 |
| 9 Olveston United | 26 | 10 | 5 | 11 | 48 | 46 | 35 |
| 10 Brislington Cricketers | 26 | 10 | 3 | 13 | 46 | 47 | 33 |
| 11 Patchway Town Reserves | 26 | 9 | 5 | 12 | 40 | 51 | 32 |
| 12 Made for Ever | 26 | 6 | 6 | 14 | 48 | 79 | 24 |
| 13 Brimsham Green | 26 | 5 | 4 | 17 | 25 | 57 | 19 |
| 14 Henbury AFC Reserves (-3pts) | 26 | 5 | 3 | 18 | 36 | 74 | 15 |

## BRISTOL SUBURBAN LEAGUE

| Premier Division One | P | W | D | L | F | A | Pts |
|---|---|---|---|---|---|---|---|
| 1 Bristol Telephones | 24 | 19 | 3 | 2 | 96 | 33 | 60 |
| 2 Avonmouth | 24 | 15 | 3 | 6 | 69 | 48 | 48 |
| 3 Lawrence Weston | 24 | 13 | 5 | 6 | 61 | 43 | 44 |
| 4 Little Stoke | 24 | 15 | 2 | 7 | 77 | 45 | 43 |
| 5 Stoke Gifford United | 24 | 13 | 3 | 8 | 75 | 48 | 42 |
| 6 Ashton United | 24 | 8 | 7 | 9 | 46 | 51 | 31 |
| 7 Fishponds Old Boys | 24 | 9 | 2 | 13 | 60 | 57 | 29 |
| 8 Easton Cowboys Suburbia | 24 | 8 | 5 | 11 | 54 | 53 | 29 |
| 9 Winford PH | 24 | 9 | 2 | 13 | 56 | 72 | 29 |
| 10 Severn Beach | 24 | 8 | 3 | 13 | 42 | 56 | 27 |
| 11 St Aldhelms | 24 | 7 | 5 | 12 | 39 | 62 | 26 |
| 12 Old Georgians | 24 | 5 | 6 | 13 | 31 | 61 | 21 |
| 13 Cadbury Heath Reserves | 24 | 2 | 4 | 18 | 31 | 108 | 10 |

| Premier Division Two | P | W | D | L | F | A | Pts |
|---|---|---|---|---|---|---|---|
| 1 Ridings High | 20 | 14 | 4 | 2 | 81 | 29 | 46 |
| 2 Tytherington Rocks Reserves | 20 | 14 | 3 | 3 | 72 | 21 | 45 |
| 3 Mangotsfield Sports | 20 | 11 | 4 | 5 | 51 | 37 | 37 |
| 4 Almondsbury UWE Reserves | 20 | 9 | 6 | 5 | 44 | 39 | 33 |
| 5 Bristol Athletic | 20 | 10 | 3 | 7 | 46 | 42 | 33 |
| 6 Rockleaze Rangers Reserves | 20 | 8 | 5 | 7 | 43 | 39 | 29 |
| 7 Southmead CS United | 20 | 7 | 5 | 8 | 45 | 55 | 26 |
| 8 Brislington A | 20 | 5 | 8 | 7 | 36 | 46 | 23 |
| 9 Wessex Wanderers | 20 | 6 | 2 | 12 | 34 | 59 | 20 |
| 10 Glenside 5 Old Boys | 20 | 3 | 3 | 14 | 23 | 52 | 12 |
| 11 Totterdown POB | 20 | 1 | 1 | 18 | 21 | 77 | 4 |

# LEAGUE TABLES

## Division One

| | | P | W | D | L | F | A | Pts |
|---|---|---|---|---|---|---|---|---|
| 1 | AFC Mangotsfield | 22 | 20 | 1 | 1 | 84 | 22 | 61 |
| 2 | Downend Foresters | 22 | 20 | 1 | 1 | 81 | 19 | 61 |
| 3 | CAB Olympic SC | 22 | 13 | 1 | 8 | 61 | 32 | 40 |
| 4 | Lebeq United | 22 | 9 | 4 | 9 | 62 | 49 | 31 |
| 5 | Tyndalls Park Rangers | 22 | 10 | 0 | 12 | 43 | 43 | 30 |
| 6 | Cleeve Colts | 22 | 9 | 3 | 10 | 40 | 50 | 30 |
| 7 | Parson Street Old Boys | 22 | 9 | 3 | 10 | 55 | 68 | 30 |
| 8 | Filton Athletic | 22 | 7 | 4 | 11 | 44 | 66 | 25 |
| 9 | Avonmouth Reserves | 22 | 7 | 1 | 14 | 49 | 71 | 22 |
| 10 | Golden Hill Sports | 22 | 5 | 5 | 12 | 32 | 53 | 20 |
| 11 | Ashton Backwell Colts | 22 | 6 | 2 | 14 | 37 | 68 | 20 |
| 12 | Ridings High Reserves | 22 | 4 | 1 | 17 | 25 | 72 | 13 |

## Division Two

| | | P | W | D | L | F | A | Pts |
|---|---|---|---|---|---|---|---|---|
| 1 | Stoke Rangers | 22 | 19 | 0 | 3 | 94 | 23 | 57 |
| 2 | Stoke Gifford United Reserves | 22 | 15 | 3 | 4 | 67 | 27 | 48 |
| 3 | Broad Plain House Reserves | 22 | 15 | 2 | 5 | 61 | 31 | 47 |
| 4 | Oldbury FC | 22 | 12 | 2 | 8 | 51 | 40 | 38 |
| 5 | St Aldhelms Reserves | 22 | 10 | 5 | 7 | 46 | 47 | 35 |
| 6 | Old Cothamians | 22 | 10 | 4 | 8 | 71 | 50 | 34 |
| 7 | Lawrence Weston Reserves | 22 | 8 | 2 | 12 | 43 | 62 | 26 |
| 8 | Wanderers | 22 | 7 | 4 | 11 | 46 | 52 | 25 |
| 9 | Little Stoke Reserves | 22 | 7 | 4 | 11 | 34 | 57 | 25 |
| 10 | Almondsbury UWE A | 22 | 3 | 7 | 12 | 48 | 78 | 16 |
| 11 | Corinthian Sports | 22 | 4 | 3 | 15 | 38 | 83 | 15 |
| 12 | Fishponds Old Boys Reserves | 22 | 3 | 2 | 17 | 27 | 76 | 11 |

## Division Three

| | | P | W | D | L | F | A | Pts |
|---|---|---|---|---|---|---|---|---|
| 1 | AFC Hartcliffe | 22 | 20 | 0 | 2 | 115 | 17 | 60 |
| 2 | Hanham Athletic Suburbia | 22 | 16 | 1 | 5 | 64 | 36 | 49 |
| 3 | Ashton United Reserves | 22 | 13 | 3 | 6 | 60 | 43 | 42 |
| 4 | Bristol Telephones Reserves | 22 | 12 | 0 | 10 | 62 | 49 | 36 |
| 5 | Fry's Club OB | 22 | 10 | 4 | 8 | 39 | 39 | 34 |
| 6 | Emersons Green | 22 | 10 | 3 | 9 | 76 | 54 | 33 |
| 7 | Keynsham Town A | 22 | 9 | 5 | 8 | 50 | 47 | 32 |
| 8 | Hydez Futebol Clube | 22 | 8 | 4 | 10 | 52 | 59 | 28 |
| 9 | St Annes Town | 22 | 7 | 5 | 10 | 43 | 63 | 26 |
| 10 | Old Cothamians Reserves | 22 | 6 | 3 | 13 | 34 | 60 | 21 |
| 11 | Filton Athletic Reserves | 22 | 3 | 3 | 16 | 21 | 89 | 12 |
| 12 | Glenside 5 Old Boys Reserves | 22 | 2 | 1 | 19 | 30 | 90 | 7 |

## Division Four

| | | P | W | D | L | F | A | Pts |
|---|---|---|---|---|---|---|---|---|
| 1 | Downend Foresters Reserves | 20 | 18 | 2 | 0 | 87 | 15 | 56 |
| 2 | Broadwalk | 20 | 16 | 2 | 2 | 92 | 33 | 50 |
| 3 | Rockleaze Rangers 'A' | 20 | 14 | 2 | 4 | 81 | 29 | 44 |
| 4 | Long Ashton Reserves | 20 | 10 | 3 | 7 | 45 | 37 | 33 |
| 5 | Coupland Insulation | 20 | 10 | 0 | 10 | 50 | 59 | 30 |
| 6 | AEK Boco Colts | 20 | 9 | 1 | 10 | 44 | 58 | 28 |
| 7 | Severn Beach Reserves | 20 | 5 | 6 | 9 | 48 | 57 | 21 |
| 8 | Winford PH Reserves | 20 | 5 | 4 | 11 | 44 | 68 | 19 |
| 9 | AFC Keynsham | 20 | 5 | 3 | 12 | 43 | 63 | 18 |
| 10 | Old Georgians Reserves | 20 | 4 | 4 | 12 | 35 | 69 | 16 |
| 11 | Fishponds Old Boys A | 20 | 0 | 1 | 19 | 30 | 111 | 1 |

## Division Five

| | | P | W | D | L | F | A | Pts |
|---|---|---|---|---|---|---|---|---|
| 1 | Cadbury Heath 'A' | 18 | 15 | 2 | 1 | 86 | 22 | 47 |
| 2 | Severnside | 18 | 13 | 3 | 2 | 70 | 28 | 42 |
| 3 | Rockleaze Rangers B | 18 | 12 | 2 | 4 | 52 | 29 | 38 |
| 4 | Oldbury FC Reserves | 18 | 10 | 1 | 7 | 50 | 35 | 31 |
| 5 | The Park - Knowle | 18 | 8 | 3 | 7 | 63 | 54 | 27 |
| 6 | Stoke Gifford United A | 18 | 8 | 2 | 8 | 44 | 47 | 26 |
| 7 | Brandon Sports | 18 | 4 | 4 | 10 | 41 | 67 | 16 |
| 8 | Wessex Wanderers Reserves | 18 | 3 | 3 | 12 | 34 | 56 | 12 |
| 9 | AFC Mangotsfield Reserves | 18 | 3 | 2 | 13 | 29 | 77 | 11 |
| 10 | Lawrence Weston A | 18 | 2 | 2 | 14 | 21 | 75 | 8 |

## Division Six

| | | P | W | D | L | F | A | Pts |
|---|---|---|---|---|---|---|---|---|
| 1 | Bristol Bilbao | 22 | 20 | 0 | 2 | 154 | 15 | 60 |
| 2 | Sartan United | 22 | 19 | 1 | 2 | 135 | 33 | 58 |
| 3 | North Bristol Catalans | 22 | 17 | 2 | 3 | 103 | 50 | 53 |
| 4 | Staple Hill | 22 | 13 | 1 | 8 | 75 | 42 | 40 |
| 5 | Whitchurch Sports | 22 | 10 | 2 | 10 | 82 | 96 | 32 |
| 6 | Rolls Royce | 22 | 9 | 2 | 11 | 68 | 88 | 29 |
| 7 | Lockleaze and Horfield | 22 | 7 | 3 | 12 | 52 | 79 | 24 |
| 8 | Avonmouth 'A' | 22 | 7 | 2 | 13 | 62 | 74 | 22 |
| 9 | Golden Hill Sports Reserves | 22 | 6 | 3 | 13 | 48 | 77 | 21 |
| 10 | Fry's OB Reserves | 22 | 6 | 2 | 14 | 50 | 88 | 20 |
| 11 | AFC Mangotsfield 'A' | 22 | 4 | 2 | 16 | 26 | 104 | 14 |
| 12 | Bristol Spartak | 22 | 4 | 0 | 18 | 36 | 145 | 12 |

## BURTON & DISTRICT FA

### Premier League

| | | P | W | D | L | F | A | Pts |
|---|---|---|---|---|---|---|---|---|
| 1 | Real Medina FC | 15 | 11 | 1 | 3 | 59 | 38 | 34 |
| 2 | Stretton Spartans | 15 | 11 | 1 | 3 | 57 | 38 | 34 |
| 3 | Ashbourne FC Reserves | 15 | 8 | 2 | 5 | 57 | 35 | 26 |
| 4 | Navi FC | 15 | 8 | 1 | 6 | 51 | 50 | 25 |
| 5 | Gresley | 15 | 3 | 1 | 11 | 37 | 52 | 10 |
| 6 | Overseal Saint Matthews | 15 | 1 | 0 | 14 | 18 | 66 | 3 |

### Championship

| | | P | W | D | L | F | A | Pts |
|---|---|---|---|---|---|---|---|---|
| 1 | TL Darby | 18 | 13 | 3 | 2 | 74 | 26 | 42 |
| 2 | Rec FC | 18 | 13 | 1 | 4 | 54 | 23 | 40 |
| 3 | Barton United | 18 | 13 | 0 | 5 | 63 | 22 | 39 |
| 4 | Tamworth United | 18 | 11 | 1 | 6 | 40 | 39 | 34 |
| 5 | Blacksmiths Arms | 18 | 8 | 5 | 5 | 45 | 28 | 29 |
| 6 | Overseal Saint Matthews Reserves | 18 | 6 | 4 | 8 | 44 | 44 | 22 |
| 7 | Athletico Princess | 18 | 6 | 3 | 9 | 40 | 40 | 21 |
| 8 | Whittington | 18 | 4 | 3 | 11 | 20 | 78 | 15 |
| 9 | The Sump | 18 | 2 | 3 | 13 | 21 | 45 | 9 |
| 10 | Brewers Bar | 18 | 2 | 1 | 15 | 27 | 83 | 7 |

## CENTRAL & SOUTH NORFOLK LEAGUE

### Division One

| | | P | W | D | L | F | A | Pts |
|---|---|---|---|---|---|---|---|---|
| 1 | Castle Acre Swifts | 26 | 20 | 4 | 2 | 107 | 46 | 64 |
| 2 | Dereham Town A | 26 | 16 | 5 | 5 | 82 | 53 | 53 |
| 3 | Morley Village | 26 | 14 | 5 | 7 | 71 | 54 | 47 |
| 4 | North Elmham | 26 | 14 | 2 | 10 | 83 | 60 | 44 |
| 5 | Yaxham | 26 | 13 | 4 | 9 | 87 | 69 | 43 |
| 6 | Tacolneston | 26 | 13 | 3 | 10 | 78 | 57 | 42 |
| 7 | Swaffham Town A | 26 | 11 | 7 | 8 | 69 | 61 | 40 |
| 8 | Shipdham | 26 | 11 | 4 | 11 | 52 | 57 | 37 |
| 9 | Thetford Rovers Reserves | 26 | 10 | 3 | 13 | 63 | 83 | 33 |
| 10 | Bridgham United | 26 | 7 | 7 | 12 | 64 | 82 | 28 |
| 11 | Northwold S&SC | 26 | 8 | 4 | 14 | 55 | 84 | 28 |
| 12 | Gressenhall | 26 | 7 | 5 | 14 | 47 | 64 | 26 |
| 13 | Rockland United | 26 | 7 | 3 | 16 | 39 | 63 | 24 |
| 14 | Narborough | 26 | 3 | 0 | 23 | 26 | 90 | 9 |

## Division Two

| | | P | W | D | L | F | A | Pts |
|---|---|---|---|---|---|---|---|---|
| 1 | West End | 18 | 14 | 1 | 3 | 61 | 21 | 43 |
| 2 | Mulbarton Wanderers Res. | 18 | 14 | 0 | 4 | 67 | 21 | 42 |
| 3 | Scarning United | 18 | 11 | 4 | 3 | 57 | 38 | 37 |
| 4 | Nostro | 18 | 9 | 3 | 6 | 54 | 52 | 30 |
| 5 | Necton | 18 | 9 | 2 | 7 | 50 | 42 | 29 |
| 6 | Rampant Horse | 18 | 6 | 3 | 9 | 39 | 42 | 21 |
| 7 | Hethersett Athletic | 18 | 5 | 4 | 9 | 38 | 57 | 19 |
| 8 | Sporle | 18 | 4 | 4 | 10 | 34 | 47 | 16 |
| 9 | Cockers | 18 | 5 | 0 | 13 | 34 | 63 | 15 |
| 10 | Saham Toney Reserves | 18 | 1 | 3 | 14 | 24 | 75 | 6 |

# CHELTENHAM ASSOCIATION LEAGUE

## Division One

| | | P | W | D | L | F | A | Pts |
|---|---|---|---|---|---|---|---|---|
| 1 | Bibury | 24 | 18 | 2 | 4 | 112 | 35 | 56 |
| 2 | Charlton Rovers | 24 | 16 | 3 | 5 | 72 | 25 | 51 |
| 3 | Whaddon United | 24 | 15 | 5 | 4 | 81 | 35 | 50 |
| 4 | Butlers FC | 24 | 15 | 3 | 6 | 90 | 49 | 48 |
| 5 | AC Olympia | 24 | 15 | 2 | 7 | 71 | 31 | 47 |
| 6 | Falcons | 24 | 11 | 8 | 5 | 71 | 47 | 41 |
| 7 | Kings AFC | 24 | 10 | 4 | 10 | 50 | 60 | 34 |
| 8 | Star FC Reserves | 24 | 10 | 3 | 11 | 47 | 63 | 33 |
| 9 | Gloucester Elmleaze | 24 | 9 | 3 | 12 | 43 | 68 | 30 |
| 10 | Bishops Cleeve III | 24 | 5 | 3 | 16 | 37 | 78 | 18 |
| 11 | Northway (-6pts) | 24 | 7 | 2 | 15 | 41 | 60 | 17 |
| 12 | Tewkesbury Town (-3pts) | 24 | 4 | 3 | 17 | 34 | 89 | 12 |
| 13 | Apperley & Tewkesbury Dynamos Res. | 24 | 0 | 1 | 23 | 20 | 129 | 1 |

## Division Two

| | | P | W | D | L | F | A | Pts |
|---|---|---|---|---|---|---|---|---|
| 1 | Gala Wilton Reserves | 26 | 19 | 7 | 0 | 73 | 17 | 64 |
| 2 | Hanley Swan | 26 | 17 | 5 | 4 | 70 | 37 | 56 |
| 3 | R.S.G. | 26 | 16 | 4 | 6 | 81 | 31 | 52 |
| 4 | Newton FC | 26 | 15 | 4 | 7 | 91 | 40 | 49 |
| 5 | Upton Town | 26 | 12 | 6 | 8 | 55 | 41 | 42 |
| 6 | Churchdown Panthers | 26 | 10 | 5 | 11 | 65 | 55 | 35 |
| 7 | Southside FC | 26 | 9 | 6 | 11 | 50 | 54 | 33 |
| 8 | Staunton & Corse | 26 | 9 | 6 | 11 | 34 | 43 | 33 |
| 9 | Bredon Reserves | 26 | 9 | 5 | 12 | 51 | 68 | 32 |
| 10 | FC Barometrics Reserves | 26 | 8 | 6 | 12 | 36 | 51 | 30 |
| 11 | Northleach Town | 26 | 8 | 4 | 14 | 39 | 77 | 28 |
| 12 | Shurdington Rovers | 26 | 7 | 3 | 16 | 50 | 84 | 24 |
| 13 | Brockworth Albion Reserves | 26 | 3 | 8 | 15 | 33 | 60 | 17 |
| 14 | Winchcombe Town Reserves | 26 | 4 | 3 | 19 | 28 | 98 | 15 |

## Division Three

| | | P | W | D | L | F | A | Pts |
|---|---|---|---|---|---|---|---|---|
| 1 | FC Lakeside | 26 | 22 | 4 | 0 | 110 | 24 | 70 |
| 2 | Villagereal | 26 | 17 | 3 | 6 | 104 | 47 | 54 |
| 3 | Andoversford | 26 | 17 | 1 | 8 | 90 | 61 | 52 |
| 4 | Chelt Civil Service Reserves | 26 | 14 | 6 | 6 | 66 | 45 | 48 |
| 5 | Prestbury Rovers | 26 | 15 | 2 | 9 | 74 | 62 | 47 |
| 6 | Whaddon United Reserves | 26 | 14 | 3 | 9 | 88 | 73 | 45 |
| 7 | W.M.K. | 26 | 13 | 2 | 11 | 77 | 60 | 41 |
| 8 | Belmore | 26 | 12 | 2 | 12 | 57 | 62 | 38 |
| 9 | Naunton Park Rovers | 26 | 9 | 2 | 15 | 61 | 78 | 29 |
| 10 | Falcons Reserves (-3pts) | 26 | 9 | 4 | 13 | 60 | 70 | 28 |
| 11 | Tivoli Rovers | 26 | 9 | 1 | 16 | 51 | 77 | 28 |
| 12 | Hatherley Rangers | 26 | 7 | 2 | 17 | 46 | 95 | 23 |
| 13 | Kings AFC Reserves | 26 | 6 | 1 | 19 | 37 | 73 | 19 |
| 14 | Elmbridge OB | 26 | 1 | 1 | 24 | 43 | 131 | 4 |

## Division Four

| | | P | W | D | L | F | A | Pts |
|---|---|---|---|---|---|---|---|---|
| 1 | Priors (-1pt) | 24 | 20 | 4 | 0 | 97 | 29 | 63 |
| 2 | Charlton Rovers Reserves | 24 | 17 | 2 | 5 | 81 | 36 | 53 |
| 3 | Leckhampton Rovers | 24 | 17 | 2 | 5 | 71 | 29 | 53 |
| 4 | Welland FC (-1pt) | 24 | 16 | 5 | 3 | 97 | 29 | 52 |
| 5 | Cheltonians | 24 | 14 | 2 | 8 | 90 | 53 | 44 |
| 6 | Gala Wilton III | 24 | 9 | 9 | 6 | 65 | 41 | 36 |
| 7 | Fintan | 24 | 11 | 2 | 11 | 64 | 45 | 35 |
| 8 | Montpellier (-3pts) | 24 | 9 | 5 | 10 | 36 | 46 | 29 |
| 9 | Bredon III | 24 | 5 | 2 | 17 | 33 | 104 | 17 |
| 10 | Chelt Civil Service III | 24 | 3 | 6 | 15 | 30 | 76 | 15 |
| 11 | Sherborne Harriers | 24 | 5 | 0 | 19 | 30 | 81 | 15 |
| 12 | Tewkesbury Town Reserves | 24 | 3 | 2 | 19 | 21 | 107 | 11 |
| 13 | Bourton Rovers III (-52pts) | 24 | 6 | 1 | 17 | 42 | 81 | -33 |

## Division Five

| | | P | W | D | L | F | A | Pts |
|---|---|---|---|---|---|---|---|---|
| 1 | Pittville United (+2pts) | 24 | 16 | 4 | 4 | 89 | 53 | 54 |
| 2 | Dowty Dynamos | 24 | 16 | 2 | 6 | 97 | 51 | 50 |
| 3 | Newlands Athletic (-16pts) | 24 | 20 | 2 | 2 | 148 | 32 | 46 |
| 4 | Shurdington Rovers Res. (+3pts) | 24 | 12 | 5 | 7 | 89 | 57 | 44 |
| 5 | Apperley & Tewkesbury Dynamos Res. | 24 | 12 | 3 | 9 | 61 | 77 | 39 |
| 6 | Southside Reserves FC (+3pts) | 24 | 10 | 3 | 11 | 54 | 62 | 36 |
| 7 | Star FC III (+3pts) | 24 | 8 | 5 | 11 | 71 | 73 | 32 |
| 8 | Staunton & Corse Reserves | 24 | 9 | 2 | 13 | 60 | 60 | 29 |
| 9 | Smiths Athletic Reserves | 24 | 8 | 5 | 11 | 67 | 86 | 29 |
| 10 | Hesters Way United (-18pts) | 24 | 13 | 3 | 8 | 89 | 62 | 24 |
| 11 | Northway Reserves (-9pts) | 24 | 6 | 4 | 14 | 52 | 81 | 13 |
| 12 | Chelt Saracens III | 24 | 3 | 3 | 18 | 46 | 133 | 12 |
| 13 | Winchcombe Town III (-7pts) | 24 | 2 | 1 | 21 | 24 | 120 | 0 |

## Division Six

| | | P | W | D | L | F | A | Pts |
|---|---|---|---|---|---|---|---|---|
| 1 | Hatherley FC | 20 | 15 | 2 | 3 | 91 | 35 | 47 |
| 2 | Tewkesbury Town III | 20 | 13 | 3 | 4 | 90 | 35 | 42 |
| 3 | FC Barometrics III | 20 | 13 | 3 | 4 | 67 | 35 | 42 |
| 4 | Cheltenham United | 20 | 13 | 3 | 4 | 64 | 36 | 42 |
| 5 | Prestbury Rovers Reserves | 20 | 10 | 3 | 7 | 61 | 42 | 33 |
| 6 | Chelt Civil Service IV | 20 | 9 | 5 | 6 | 50 | 58 | 32 |
| 7 | Leckhampton Rovers Res. (-7pts) | 20 | 12 | 1 | 7 | 67 | 35 | 30 |
| 8 | Kingshill Sports Reserves | 20 | 7 | 1 | 12 | 59 | 90 | 22 |
| 9 | Fintan Reserves | 20 | 3 | 0 | 17 | 28 | 81 | 9 |
| 10 | Andoversford Reserves | 20 | 2 | 2 | 16 | 20 | 83 | 8 |
| 11 | Regency Town (-1pt) | 20 | 1 | 1 | 18 | 25 | 92 | 3 |

# CHESTER & DISTRICT LEAGUE

## Premier

| | | P | W | D | L | F | A | Pts |
|---|---|---|---|---|---|---|---|---|
| 1 | Kelsall | 22 | 15 | 5 | 2 | 64 | 33 | 50 |
| 2 | Whitby Athletic | 22 | 14 | 4 | 4 | 66 | 42 | 46 |
| 3 | Shaftsbury Youth | 22 | 14 | 4 | 4 | 54 | 34 | 46 |
| 4 | Kelma | 22 | 12 | 4 | 6 | 53 | 40 | 40 |
| 5 | Ellesmere Port | 22 | 9 | 3 | 10 | 46 | 42 | 30 |
| 6 | Lever | 22 | 7 | 6 | 9 | 38 | 44 | 27 |
| 7 | Hoole Rangers | 22 | 7 | 6 | 9 | 38 | 48 | 27 |
| 8 | Newton Athletic | 22 | 7 | 6 | 9 | 42 | 54 | 27 |
| 9 | Greyhound | 22 | 7 | 4 | 11 | 49 | 46 | 25 |
| 10 | Waggon & Horses | 22 | 7 | 2 | 13 | 48 | 65 | 23 |
| 11 | Raby Villa | 22 | 4 | 4 | 14 | 50 | 62 | 16 |
| 12 | Crossway | 22 | 3 | 4 | 15 | 41 | 79 | 13 |

# LEAGUE TABLES

## Division One

| | | P | W | D | L | F | A | Pts |
|---|---|---|---|---|---|---|---|---|
| 1 | Lache | 20 | 18 | 2 | 0 | 91 | 24 | 56 |
| 2 | Woodlands Santos | 20 | 14 | 2 | 4 | 74 | 34 | 44 |
| 3 | Uberlube | 20 | 13 | 3 | 4 | 76 | 50 | 42 |
| 4 | Halfwayhouse Celtic | 20 | 8 | 5 | 7 | 51 | 47 | 29 |
| 5 | Chester Celtic | 20 | 8 | 4 | 8 | 56 | 44 | 28 |
| 6 | Ashton | 20 | 8 | 1 | 11 | 47 | 57 | 25 |
| 7 | Pensby Athletic | 20 | 6 | 6 | 8 | 31 | 46 | 24 |
| 8 | Orange Athletic Chester | 20 | 7 | 2 | 11 | 36 | 46 | 23 |
| 9 | Chester Nomads III | 20 | 7 | 1 | 12 | 28 | 57 | 22 |
| 10 | Cestrian Alex | 20 | 4 | 4 | 12 | 39 | 62 | 16 |
| 11 | Hoole Rangers Reserves | 20 | 1 | 2 | 17 | 21 | 83 | 5 |

## Division Two

| | | P | W | D | L | F | A | Pts |
|---|---|---|---|---|---|---|---|---|
| 1 | Helsby Res | 20 | 19 | 0 | 1 | 155 | 25 | 57 |
| 2 | Birkenhead Town | 20 | 19 | 0 | 1 | 131 | 21 | 57 |
| 3 | Ellesmere Port Town | 20 | 14 | 0 | 6 | 71 | 37 | 42 |
| 4 | Shippons Athletic | 20 | 12 | 2 | 6 | 43 | 44 | 38 |
| 5 | Lodge Bar | 20 | 9 | 2 | 9 | 33 | 55 | 29 |
| 6 | Neston Nomads | 20 | 7 | 3 | 10 | 52 | 78 | 24 |
| 7 | Peacock 09 | 20 | 7 | 2 | 11 | 51 | 55 | 23 |
| 8 | Boughton Athletic | 20 | 7 | 1 | 12 | 47 | 76 | 22 |
| 9 | Rangers Breaks | 20 | 3 | 4 | 13 | 22 | 67 | 13 |
| 10 | Crossway Reserves | 20 | 3 | 2 | 15 | 34 | 101 | 11 |
| 11 | Orange Athletic Chester Res. | 20 | 2 | 0 | 18 | 15 | 95 | 6 |

## Division Three

| | | P | W | D | L | F | A | Pts |
|---|---|---|---|---|---|---|---|---|
| 1 | Deva Athletic | 18 | 13 | 3 | 2 | 75 | 17 | 42 |
| 2 | Wirral Villa | 18 | 13 | 3 | 2 | 64 | 21 | 42 |
| 3 | Blacon Youth Reserves | 18 | 12 | 5 | 1 | 46 | 14 | 41 |
| 4 | Porky's Pantry | 18 | 11 | 2 | 5 | 55 | 28 | 35 |
| 5 | Hooton | 18 | 10 | 1 | 7 | 46 | 28 | 31 |
| 6 | Bronze Social | 18 | 7 | 0 | 11 | 54 | 46 | 21 |
| 7 | Avenue Vets | 18 | 6 | 3 | 9 | 44 | 45 | 21 |
| 8 | Springview | 18 | 5 | 0 | 13 | 31 | 70 | 15 |
| 9 | Oldershaw Athletic | 18 | 4 | 1 | 13 | 44 | 83 | 13 |
| 10 | Clubbies AFC | 18 | 0 | 0 | 18 | 6 | 113 | 0 |

## CHORLEY & DISTRICT ALLIANCE

| | | P | W | D | L | F | A | Pts |
|---|---|---|---|---|---|---|---|---|
| 1 | Whittle | 16 | 13 | 2 | 1 | 66 | 24 | 41 |
| 2 | Eagle | 16 | 12 | 2 | 2 | 86 | 32 | 38 |
| 3 | Little Eagle | 16 | 11 | 2 | 3 | 73 | 38 | 35 |
| 4 | Bolton Sixth Form College | 16 | 11 | 1 | 4 | 51 | 35 | 34 |
| 5 | International Allstars | 16 | 6 | 3 | 7 | 47 | 42 | 21 |
| 6 | Chorley Athletic | 16 | 5 | 3 | 8 | 53 | 60 | 18 |
| 7 | Spinners | 16 | 4 | 1 | 11 | 31 | 60 | 13 |
| 8 | AFC Mawdsley | 16 | 2 | 0 | 14 | 23 | 64 | 6 |
| 9 | FC Clayton Brook | 16 | 0 | 2 | 14 | 27 | 84 | 2 |

Gillibrand Arms record expunged.

## CIRENCESTER & DISTRICT LEAGUE

### Division One

| | | P | W | D | L | F | A | Pts |
|---|---|---|---|---|---|---|---|---|
| 1 | CHQ United | 18 | 14 | 3 | 1 | 75 | 24 | 45 |
| 2 | South Cerney | 18 | 12 | 4 | 2 | 52 | 37 | 40 |
| 3 | Lechlade FC 87 | 18 | 9 | 4 | 5 | 76 | 54 | 31 |
| 4 | Bibury Reserves | 18 | 9 | 4 | 5 | 53 | 32 | 31 |
| 5 | The Beeches | 18 | 8 | 2 | 8 | 52 | 38 | 26 |
| 6 | Real Fairford | 18 | 8 | 3 | 7 | 55 | 47 | 26 |
| 7 | Poulton | 18 | 6 | 5 | 7 | 52 | 46 | 23 |
| 8 | Oaksey | 18 | 4 | 0 | 14 | 36 | 67 | 12 |
| 9 | Down Ampney (-3pts) | 18 | 4 | 3 | 11 | 31 | 62 | 12 |
| 10 | Sherston | 18 | 1 | 2 | 15 | 28 | 103 | 5 |

## Division Two

| | | P | W | D | L | F | A | Pts |
|---|---|---|---|---|---|---|---|---|
| 1 | Corinium Sports | 18 | 16 | 2 | 0 | 71 | 26 | 50 |
| 2 | Stratton United | 18 | 11 | 4 | 3 | 67 | 34 | 37 |
| 3 | Sherston Reserves (-1pt) | 18 | 11 | 2 | 5 | 65 | 42 | 34 |
| 4 | Kingshill Sports | 18 | 11 | 1 | 6 | 62 | 41 | 34 |
| 5 | The Beeches Reserves (-4pts) | 18 | 10 | 2 | 6 | 44 | 38 | 28 |
| 6 | Ashton Keynes Reserves (-9pts) | 18 | 5 | 5 | 8 | 46 | 59 | 11 |
| 7 | Lechlade FC 87 Reserves (-3pts) | 18 | 3 | 5 | 10 | 56 | 83 | 11 |
| 8 | South Cerney Reserves | 18 | 3 | 2 | 13 | 38 | 71 | 11 |
| 9 | Down Ampney Reserves (-3pts) | 18 | 2 | 5 | 11 | 36 | 64 | 8 |
| 10 | Oaksey Reserves (-3pts) | 18 | 1 | 6 | 11 | 28 | 55 | 6 |

## COLCHESTER & EAST ESSEX LEAGUE

### Premier Division

| | | P | W | D | L | F | A | Pts |
|---|---|---|---|---|---|---|---|---|
| 1 | Stoke-by-Nayland | 20 | 15 | 2 | 3 | 98 | 32 | 47 |
| 2 | Oyster | 20 | 15 | 2 | 3 | 56 | 32 | 47 |
| 3 | Boxford Rovers | 20 | 13 | 2 | 5 | 55 | 18 | 41 |
| 4 | Kelvedon Social | 20 | 12 | 1 | 7 | 50 | 41 | 37 |
| 5 | Cinque Port | 20 | 11 | 1 | 8 | 42 | 27 | 34 |
| 6 | University of Essex 3rd XI | 20 | 9 | 2 | 9 | 39 | 51 | 29 |
| 7 | Castle | 20 | 7 | 2 | 11 | 46 | 62 | 23 |
| 8 | Colchester Athletic | 20 | 6 | 3 | 11 | 41 | 55 | 21 |
| 9 | Horkesley | 20 | 4 | 2 | 14 | 21 | 53 | 14 |
| 10 | Brightlingsea Regent 'A' | 20 | 4 | 2 | 14 | 24 | 59 | 14 |
| 11 | Witchfinders | 20 | 3 | 3 | 14 | 30 | 72 | 12 |

### Division One

| | | P | W | D | L | F | A | Pts |
|---|---|---|---|---|---|---|---|---|
| 1 | Bures United | 18 | 13 | 2 | 3 | 52 | 22 | 41 |
| 2 | St Osyth Social | 18 | 12 | 3 | 3 | 52 | 20 | 39 |
| 3 | New Field | 18 | 12 | 1 | 5 | 44 | 24 | 37 |
| 4 | Feering United | 18 | 11 | 1 | 6 | 51 | 34 | 34 |
| 5 | Brantham Athletic 'A' | 18 | 10 | 2 | 6 | 43 | 38 | 32 |
| 6 | Harwich Rangers | 18 | 9 | 3 | 6 | 47 | 33 | 30 |
| 7 | University of Essex 4th XI | 18 | 6 | 2 | 10 | 44 | 42 | 20 |
| 8 | Sporting Rebels | 18 | 5 | 2 | 11 | 30 | 41 | 17 |
| 9 | Great Bentley 'A' | 18 | 4 | 0 | 14 | 41 | 65 | 12 |
| 10 | Wimpole 2000 | 18 | 0 | 0 | 18 | 9 | 94 | 0 |

### Division Two

| | | P | W | D | L | F | A | Pts |
|---|---|---|---|---|---|---|---|---|
| 1 | Belle Vue Social | 14 | 12 | 2 | 0 | 49 | 11 | 38 |
| 2 | Marks Tey | 14 | 7 | 3 | 4 | 33 | 21 | 24 |
| 3 | Langham Lodgers | 14 | 8 | 0 | 6 | 40 | 35 | 24 |
| 4 | Belchamps | 14 | 6 | 2 | 6 | 30 | 30 | 20 |
| 5 | Abbey Fields | 14 | 6 | 1 | 7 | 32 | 38 | 19 |
| 6 | AFC Sudbury 'A' | 14 | 5 | 2 | 7 | 29 | 37 | 17 |
| 7 | Nayland Rangers | 14 | 4 | 2 | 8 | 32 | 42 | 14 |
| 8 | Stoke-by-Nayland Reserves | 14 | 1 | 2 | 11 | 31 | 62 | 5 |

### Division Three

| | | P | W | D | L | F | A | Pts |
|---|---|---|---|---|---|---|---|---|
| 1 | Lexden Allstars | 22 | 15 | 3 | 4 | 86 | 37 | 48 |
| 2 | Acton Crown | 22 | 15 | 2 | 5 | 63 | 39 | 47 |
| 3 | Tollesbury Reserves | 22 | 14 | 2 | 6 | 54 | 36 | 44 |
| 4 | Colchester Athletic Reserves | 22 | 14 | 1 | 7 | 97 | 62 | 43 |
| 5 | Bures United Reserves | 22 | 13 | 3 | 6 | 64 | 39 | 42 |
| 6 | Brightlingsea Regent 'B' | 22 | 11 | 2 | 9 | 74 | 51 | 35 |
| 7 | Kelvedon Social Reserves | 22 | 10 | 4 | 8 | 68 | 54 | 34 |
| 8 | Little Clacton | 22 | 10 | 2 | 10 | 63 | 77 | 32 |
| 9 | Riverbank Athletic | 22 | 7 | 2 | 13 | 69 | 83 | 23 |
| 10 | University of Essex 5th XI | 22 | 6 | 1 | 15 | 44 | 83 | 19 |
| 11 | New Field Reserves | 22 | 4 | 0 | 18 | 36 | 98 | 12 |
| 12 | Foxash Social 'A' | 22 | 2 | 0 | 20 | 31 | 90 | 6 |

## CORNWALL COMBINATION

| | P | W | D | L | F | A | Pts |
|---|---|---|---|---|---|---|---|
| Illogan RBL | 38 | 31 | 3 | 4 | 117 | 43 | 96 |
| St Day | 38 | 27 | 3 | 8 | 144 | 64 | 84 |
| Perranwell | 38 | 26 | 4 | 8 | 106 | 44 | 82 |
| Ludgvan | 38 | 26 | 2 | 10 | 141 | 65 | 80 |
| Pendeen Rovers | 38 | 23 | 8 | 7 | 103 | 56 | 77 |
| St Ives Town | 38 | 19 | 11 | 8 | 98 | 67 | 68 |
| Penryn Athletic | 38 | 20 | 3 | 15 | 90 | 83 | 63 |
| Mullion | 38 | 18 | 7 | 13 | 101 | 91 | 61 |
| St Just | 38 | 18 | 4 | 16 | 84 | 78 | 58 |
| Goonhavern | 38 | 17 | 5 | 16 | 78 | 68 | 56 |
| St Agnes (+3pts) | 38 | 15 | 6 | 17 | 65 | 71 | 54 |
| Wendron United | 38 | 13 | 7 | 18 | 68 | 73 | 46 |
| RNAS Culdrose | 38 | 11 | 10 | 17 | 81 | 91 | 43 |
| Falmouth Town (-3pts) | 38 | 13 | 6 | 19 | 79 | 105 | 42 |
| Troon | 38 | 13 | 2 | 23 | 79 | 104 | 41 |
| Falmouth Athletic DC | 38 | 10 | 3 | 25 | 72 | 151 | 33 |
| Porthleven | 38 | 9 | 4 | 25 | 61 | 116 | 31 |
| Newquay | 38 | 7 | 6 | 25 | 59 | 108 | 27 |
| Hayle | 38 | 7 | 6 | 25 | 50 | 112 | 27 |
| Holman Sports Club | 38 | 5 | 4 | 29 | 51 | 137 | 19 |

## CRAVEN & DISTRICT LEAGUE

### Premier Division

| | P | W | D | L | F | A | Pts |
|---|---|---|---|---|---|---|---|
| Skipton LMS | 18 | 13 | 3 | 2 | 75 | 31 | 42 |
| Rolls | 18 | 11 | 5 | 2 | 54 | 30 | 38 |
| Grindleton | 18 | 10 | 4 | 4 | 46 | 28 | 34 |
| Trawden Celtic | 18 | 9 | 3 | 6 | 33 | 33 | 30 |
| Cowling | 18 | 7 | 4 | 7 | 40 | 36 | 25 |
| Cross Hills | 18 | 7 | 2 | 9 | 46 | 62 | 23 |
| Embsay | 18 | 6 | 1 | 11 | 37 | 59 | 19 |
| Carleton | 18 | 5 | 1 | 12 | 34 | 54 | 16 |
| Pendle Athletic | 18 | 4 | 3 | 11 | 43 | 58 | 15 |
| Grassington Utd | 18 | 4 | 2 | 12 | 28 | 45 | 14 |

### Division One

| | P | W | D | L | F | A | Pts |
|---|---|---|---|---|---|---|---|
| Wilsden Athletic | 20 | 15 | 2 | 3 | 64 | 30 | 47 |
| Cononley Sports | 20 | 14 | 3 | 3 | 81 | 28 | 45 |
| Gargrave | 20 | 13 | 3 | 4 | 55 | 33 | 42 |
| Earby Town | 20 | 9 | 4 | 7 | 67 | 60 | 31 |
| Oakworth | 20 | 10 | 1 | 9 | 48 | 46 | 31 |
| Pendle | 20 | 8 | 4 | 8 | 50 | 55 | 28 |
| Chatburn | 20 | 7 | 3 | 10 | 49 | 55 | 24 |
| Settle Utd | 20 | 6 | 6 | 8 | 34 | 41 | 24 |
| Hellifield Sports | 20 | 7 | 1 | 12 | 45 | 64 | 22 |
| Silsden Whitestar | 20 | 6 | 1 | 13 | 38 | 57 | 19 |
| Rolls Reserves | 20 | 1 | 0 | 19 | 24 | 86 | 3 |

### Division Two

| | P | W | D | L | F | A | Pts |
|---|---|---|---|---|---|---|---|
| Embsay Reserves | 20 | 12 | 3 | 5 | 50 | 38 | 39 |
| Pendle Renegades | 20 | 11 | 5 | 4 | 44 | 30 | 38 |
| Skipton Town | 20 | 10 | 3 | 7 | 56 | 43 | 33 |
| AFC Colne | 19 | 10 | 2 | 7 | 46 | 39 | 32 |
| Barnoldswick Barons | 20 | 9 | 3 | 8 | 54 | 54 | 30 |
| Earby Town Reserves | 20 | 9 | 2 | 9 | 59 | 46 | 29 |
| Bingley Town | 20 | 9 | 2 | 9 | 34 | 42 | 29 |
| Ingrow and Worth Valley | 20 | 6 | 5 | 9 | 56 | 57 | 23 |
| Skipton LMS Reserves | 19 | 6 | 2 | 11 | 33 | 48 | 20 |
| Silsden Whitestar Reserves | 20 | 5 | 4 | 11 | 41 | 55 | 19 |
| Gargrave Reserves | 20 | 5 | 3 | 12 | 33 | 54 | 18 |

## Division Three

| | P | W | D | L | F | A | Pts |
|---|---|---|---|---|---|---|---|
| 1 Cononley Sports Reserves | 20 | 13 | 5 | 2 | 67 | 45 | 44 |
| 2 Cross Hills Reserves | 20 | 11 | 5 | 4 | 63 | 40 | 38 |
| 3 Bradley | 20 | 9 | 4 | 7 | 43 | 34 | 31 |
| 4 Oxenhope Recreation | 20 | 9 | 3 | 8 | 45 | 24 | 30 |
| 5 Grindleton Reserves | 20 | 9 | 3 | 8 | 60 | 55 | 30 |
| 6 Sutton | 20 | 8 | 5 | 7 | 45 | 42 | 29 |
| 7 Oakworth Reserves | 20 | 9 | 0 | 11 | 38 | 42 | 27 |
| 8 Grassington Utd Reserves | 20 | 7 | 5 | 8 | 27 | 29 | 26 |
| 9 Cowling Reserves | 20 | 7 | 4 | 9 | 43 | 51 | 25 |
| 10 Settle Utd Reserves | 20 | 6 | 3 | 11 | 35 | 57 | 21 |
| 11 Ingrow and Worth Valley Reserves | 20 | 2 | 3 | 15 | 32 | 79 | 9 |

## Division Four

| | P | W | D | L | F | A | Pts |
|---|---|---|---|---|---|---|---|
| 1 FC Sporting Keighley | 19 | 18 | 0 | 1 | 86 | 27 | 54 |
| 2 Padiham Town | 19 | 17 | 0 | 2 | 106 | 25 | 51 |
| 3 Horton | 20 | 14 | 0 | 6 | 57 | 35 | 42 |
| 4 Manningham All Stars | 20 | 12 | 0 | 8 | 76 | 20 | 36 |
| 5 Skipton Town Reserves | 20 | 9 | 3 | 8 | 41 | 46 | 30 |
| 6 Pendle Renegades Reserves | 20 | 7 | 1 | 12 | 51 | 45 | 22 |
| 7 Sutton Reserves | 20 | 6 | 2 | 12 | 39 | 74 | 20 |
| 8 Bradley Reserves | 20 | 6 | 1 | 13 | 42 | 72 | 19 |
| 9 Barnoldswick Barons Reserves | 20 | 6 | 1 | 13 | 28 | 90 | 19 |
| 10 Addingham | 20 | 5 | 1 | 14 | 30 | 81 | 16 |
| 11 Carleton Reserves | 20 | 3 | 3 | 14 | 29 | 70 | 12 |

## CREWE & DISTRICT LEAGUE

### Premier Division

| | P | W | D | L | F | A | Pts |
|---|---|---|---|---|---|---|---|
| 1 Winnington Avenue | 14 | 10 | 2 | 2 | 39 | 25 | 32 |
| 2 Cuddington | 14 | 9 | 2 | 3 | 47 | 24 | 29 |
| 3 Barnton Wanderers | 14 | 7 | 2 | 5 | 49 | 33 | 23 |
| 4 Sandbach Town | 14 | 7 | 1 | 6 | 41 | 39 | 22 |
| 5 Rudheath Social Reserves | 14 | 6 | 3 | 5 | 38 | 22 | 21 |
| 6 Curshaws | 14 | 4 | 3 | 7 | 35 | 37 | 15 |
| 7 MMU Cheshire | 14 | 3 | 3 | 8 | 28 | 42 | 12 |
| 8 Malpas Reserves | 14 | 2 | 0 | 12 | 24 | 79 | 6 |

### Division One

| | P | W | D | L | F | A | Pts |
|---|---|---|---|---|---|---|---|
| 1 Tarporley Victoria Reserves | 12 | 9 | 1 | 2 | 36 | 20 | 28 |
| 2 Crewe FC Reserves | 12 | 7 | 0 | 5 | 48 | 35 | 21 |
| 3 Duddon United | 12 | 6 | 1 | 5 | 27 | 25 | 19 |
| 4 Cuddington Reserves | 12 | 5 | 3 | 4 | 28 | 27 | 18 |
| 5 Sandbach United 3rds | 12 | 5 | 1 | 6 | 31 | 29 | 16 |
| 6 Barnton Wanderers Reserves | 12 | 3 | 3 | 6 | 26 | 41 | 12 |
| 7 Winnington Reserves | 12 | 2 | 1 | 9 | 16 | 35 | 7 |

## CROOK & DISTRICT LEAGUE

### Division One

| | P | W | D | L | F | A | Pts |
|---|---|---|---|---|---|---|---|
| 1 Witton Park | 18 | 15 | 3 | 0 | 70 | 24 | 48 |
| 2 Middlestone Moor Masons Arms | 18 | 13 | 1 | 4 | 59 | 38 | 40 |
| 3 West Auckland Prince of Wales | 18 | 13 | 0 | 5 | 55 | 29 | 39 |
| 4 Bowes | 18 | 11 | 1 | 6 | 70 | 31 | 34 |
| 5 Darlington D.S.R.M. Social Club | 18 | 8 | 3 | 7 | 38 | 33 | 27 |
| 6 Shildon Three Tuns | 18 | 5 | 1 | 12 | 29 | 48 | 16 |
| 7 Bishop Auckland The Bay Horse | 18 | 5 | 1 | 12 | 21 | 59 | 16 |
| 8 Heighington | 18 | 4 | 3 | 11 | 25 | 56 | 15 |
| 9 Willington W.M.C. | 18 | 4 | 2 | 12 | 41 | 65 | 14 |
| 10 Evenwood Town | 18 | 2 | 5 | 11 | 27 | 52 | 11 |

## LEAGUE TABLES

| Division Two | P | W | D | L | F | A | Pts |
|---|---|---|---|---|---|---|---|
| 1 Coundon Forester's Blue Star | 20 | 18 | 0 | 2 | 82 | 20 | 54 |
| 2 Bishop Auckland Green Tree | 20 | 17 | 1 | 2 | 107 | 26 | 52 |
| 3 Crook Town Wanderers | 20 | 11 | 4 | 5 | 79 | 44 | 37 |
| 4 Wearhead United | 20 | 12 | 1 | 7 | 50 | 44 | 37 |
| 5 Wolsingham | 20 | 10 | 2 | 8 | 70 | 40 | 32 |
| 6 Stanhope Town Sports & Social Club | 20 | 7 | 5 | 8 | 57 | 52 | 26 |
| 7 Darlington Shuttle & Loom | 20 | 8 | 2 | 10 | 61 | 70 | 26 |
| 8 Howden-Le-Wear Australian | 20 | 4 | 6 | 10 | 42 | 52 | 18 |
| 9 Middleton Rangers | 20 | 5 | 1 | 14 | 39 | 73 | 16 |
| 10 Darlington Hole in the Wall | 20 | 4 | 3 | 13 | 35 | 67 | 15 |
| 11 Crook Albion | 20 | 1 | 1 | 18 | 25 | 159 | 4 |

## CUMBERLAND COUNTY LEAGUE

| Premier Division | P | W | D | L | F | A | Pts |
|---|---|---|---|---|---|---|---|
| 1 Netherhall | 22 | 17 | 2 | 3 | 75 | 23 | 53 |
| 2 Carlisle City Reserves | 22 | 14 | 4 | 4 | 60 | 31 | 46 |
| 3 Windscale | 22 | 12 | 4 | 6 | 60 | 41 | 40 |
| 4 Workington Red House | 22 | 11 | 2 | 9 | 54 | 51 | 35 |
| 5 Longtown | 22 | 9 | 2 | 11 | 34 | 37 | 29 |
| 6 Aspatria | 22 | 8 | 4 | 10 | 40 | 40 | 28 |
| 7 Cleator Moor Celtic Reserves | 22 | 8 | 3 | 11 | 41 | 66 | 27 |
| 8 Wigton Harriers | 22 | 6 | 8 | 8 | 46 | 38 | 26 |
| 9 Mirehouse | 22 | 8 | 5 | 9 | 49 | 64 | 26 |
| 10 Silloth | 22 | 8 | 4 | 10 | 61 | 67 | 25 |
| 11 Warwick Wanderers | 22 | 6 | 3 | 13 | 31 | 53 | 18 |
| 12 Borough | 22 | 3 | 3 | 16 | 31 | 71 | 12 |

| Division One | P | W | D | L | F | A | Pts |
|---|---|---|---|---|---|---|---|
| 1 Whitehaven Miners | 20 | 14 | 1 | 5 | 68 | 30 | 43 |
| 2 Workington Red Star | 20 | 13 | 2 | 5 | 72 | 28 | 41 |
| 3 St Bees | 20 | 12 | 2 | 6 | 70 | 39 | 38 |
| 4 Wigton Athletic | 20 | 12 | 2 | 6 | 68 | 37 | 38 |
| 5 Whitehaven AFC Reserves | 20 | 12 | 2 | 6 | 67 | 37 | 38 |
| 6 Cockermouth (-3pts) | 20 | 13 | 1 | 6 | 64 | 35 | 37 |
| 7 Frizington WS | 20 | 9 | 1 | 10 | 39 | 51 | 28 |
| 8 Hensingham | 20 | 7 | 1 | 12 | 43 | 90 | 22 |
| 9 Windscale Reserves | 20 | 3 | 3 | 14 | 27 | 68 | 12 |
| 10 Parton United (-3pts) | 20 | 4 | 1 | 15 | 32 | 73 | 10 |
| 11 St Bees Reserves | 20 | 3 | 0 | 17 | 26 | 88 | 9 |

## DEVON & EXETER LEAGUE

| Premier Division | P | W | D | L | F | A | PTS |
|---|---|---|---|---|---|---|---|
| 1 Feniton | 28 | 23 | 3 | 2 | 116 | 39 | 72 |
| 2 Hatherleigh Town | 28 | 21 | 4 | 3 | 75 | 31 | 67 |
| 3 St Martins | 28 | 17 | 8 | 3 | 84 | 42 | 59 |
| 4 Heavitree United | 28 | 13 | 9 | 6 | 63 | 39 | 48 |
| 5 Seaton Town | 28 | 14 | 6 | 8 | 65 | 58 | 48 |
| 6 Morchard Bishop | 28 | 14 | 5 | 9 | 64 | 55 | 47 |
| 7 Newtown | 28 | 11 | 7 | 10 | 68 | 56 | 40 |
| 8 University 2nds | 28 | 10 | 4 | 14 | 56 | 76 | 34 |
| 9 Topsham Town | 28 | 9 | 6 | 13 | 46 | 52 | 33 |
| 10 Thorverton | 28 | 8 | 7 | 13 | 55 | 67 | 31 |
| 11 Beer Albion | 28 | 8 | 5 | 15 | 61 | 89 | 29 |
| 12 Clyst Valley | 28 | 6 | 7 | 15 | 38 | 67 | 25 |
| 13 Willand Rovers 2nds | 28 | 5 | 8 | 15 | 43 | 68 | 23 |
| 14 Budleigh Salterton 2nds | 28 | 3 | 6 | 19 | 39 | 103 | 15 |
| 15 Exmouth Amateurs | 28 | 3 | 5 | 20 | 39 | 70 | 14 |

| Division One | P | W | D | L | F | A | PTS |
|---|---|---|---|---|---|---|---|
| 1 Bow AAC | 26 | 20 | 4 | 2 | 67 | 20 | 6 |
| 2 Tiverton Town 2nds | 26 | 18 | 7 | 1 | 79 | 12 | 6 |
| 3 Chard Town 2nds | 26 | 19 | 4 | 3 | 75 | 21 | 6 |
| 4 Sidbury United | 26 | 14 | 7 | 5 | 58 | 29 | 4 |
| 5 Wellington Town 2nds | 26 | 14 | 5 | 7 | 47 | 31 | 4 |
| 6 Heavitree United 2nds | 26 | 14 | 4 | 8 | 50 | 47 | 4 |
| 7 University 3rds | 26 | 11 | 2 | 13 | 52 | 50 | 3 |
| 8 Witheridge 2nds | 26 | 11 | 0 | 15 | 52 | 49 | 3 |
| 9 Alphington 2nds | 26 | 8 | 6 | 12 | 29 | 54 | 3 |
| 10 East Budleigh | 26 | 7 | 4 | 15 | 31 | 60 | 2 |
| 11 Cullompton Rangers 2nds | 26 | 6 | 4 | 16 | 37 | 61 | 2 |
| 12 Tipton St John | 26 | 5 | 7 | 14 | 35 | 70 | 2 |
| 13 Colyton | 26 | 2 | 5 | 19 | 32 | 78 | 1 |
| 14 Culm United | 26 | 2 | 3 | 21 | 17 | 79 | |

| Division Two | P | W | D | L | F | A | PTS |
|---|---|---|---|---|---|---|---|
| 1 Elmore 2nds | 26 | 21 | 1 | 4 | 90 | 24 | 6 |
| 2 Beacon Knights | 26 | 17 | 3 | 6 | 73 | 47 | 5 |
| 3 Bickleigh | 26 | 16 | 3 | 7 | 64 | 42 | 5 |
| 4 Newton Poppleford | 26 | 14 | 0 | 12 | 69 | 64 | 4 |
| 5 Honiton Town | 26 | 13 | 3 | 10 | 59 | 61 | 4 |
| 6 Dawlish United | 26 | 12 | 4 | 10 | 64 | 56 | 4 |
| 7 Pinhoe | 26 | 12 | 2 | 12 | 48 | 59 | 3 |
| 8 Topsham Town 2nds | 26 | 11 | 4 | 11 | 51 | 41 | 3 |
| 9 Halwill | 26 | 11 | 2 | 13 | 50 | 48 | 3 |
| 10 Clyst Valley 2nds | 26 | 10 | 2 | 14 | 39 | 72 | 3 |
| 11 Exwick Villa 2nds | 26 | 8 | 2 | 16 | 50 | 73 | 2 |
| 12 Westexe Rovers | 26 | 7 | 3 | 16 | 32 | 58 | 2 |
| 13 Sidmouth Town 2nds (-2pts) | 26 | 6 | 5 | 15 | 33 | 53 | 2 |
| 14 Chagford | 26 | 6 | 2 | 18 | 42 | 66 | 2 |

| Division Three | P | W | D | L | F | A | PT |
|---|---|---|---|---|---|---|---|
| 1 Dolphin | 30 | 23 | 4 | 3 | 111 | 39 | 7 |
| 2 Crediton United 2nds | 30 | 21 | 5 | 4 | 120 | 32 | 6 |
| 3 Newton St Cyres | 30 | 20 | 4 | 6 | 76 | 34 | 6 |
| 4 South Zeal United | 30 | 15 | 6 | 9 | 83 | 51 | 5 |
| 5 Lympstone | 30 | 16 | 2 | 12 | 64 | 60 | 5 |
| 6 Newtown 2nds | 30 | 15 | 4 | 11 | 70 | 60 | 4 |
| 7 University 4ths | 30 | 15 | 3 | 12 | 63 | 54 | 4 |
| 8 Upottery | 30 | 14 | 4 | 12 | 75 | 53 | 4 |
| 9 Hemyock | 30 | 13 | 3 | 14 | 70 | 67 | 4 |
| 10 Tedburn St Mary | 30 | 12 | 5 | 13 | 67 | 62 | 4 |
| 11 Ottery St Mary | 30 | 11 | 6 | 13 | 51 | 51 | 3 |
| 12 Offwell Rangers | 30 | 10 | 7 | 13 | 83 | 94 | 3 |
| 13 Winkleigh | 30 | 8 | 2 | 20 | 52 | 127 | 2 |
| 14 Thorverton 2nds | 30 | 7 | 3 | 20 | 46 | 104 | 2 |
| 15 North Tawton | 30 | 6 | 2 | 22 | 46 | 110 | 2 |
| 16 Sandford | 30 | 3 | 2 | 25 | 30 | 109 | 1 |

| Division Four | P | W | D | L | F | A | PT |
|---|---|---|---|---|---|---|---|
| 1 Heavitree United 3rds | 24 | 16 | 3 | 5 | 74 | 40 | 5 |
| 2 Woodbury | 24 | 16 | 2 | 6 | 66 | 50 | 5 |
| 3 Chulmleigh | 24 | 15 | 3 | 6 | 87 | 35 | 4 |
| 4 University 5ths | 24 | 13 | 4 | 7 | 81 | 47 | 4 |
| 5 Axminster Town 2nds | 24 | 12 | 1 | 11 | 58 | 49 | 3 |
| 6 Exmouth Amateurs 2nds | 24 | 11 | 4 | 9 | 63 | 58 | 3 |
| 7 Bampton (-4pts) | 24 | 11 | 3 | 10 | 54 | 50 | 3 |
| 8 Axmouth United | 24 | 9 | 4 | 11 | 64 | 65 | 3 |
| 9 Newtown 3rds | 24 | 9 | 2 | 13 | 53 | 74 | 2 |
| 10 Lord's XI | 24 | 8 | 3 | 13 | 56 | 57 | 2 |
| 11 Exmouth Town 2nds | 24 | 7 | 5 | 12 | 50 | 68 | 2 |
| 12 Okehampton Argyle 2nds (-2pts) | 24 | 4 | 4 | 16 | 44 | 92 | 1 |
| 13 Seaton Town 2nds (-2pts) | 24 | 3 | 6 | 15 | 32 | 97 | 1 |

| Division Five | P | W | D | L | F | A | PTS |
|---|---|---|---|---|---|---|---|
| Culm United 2nds | 24 | 18 | 3 | 3 | 75 | 32 | 57 |
| Cheriton Fitzpaine | 24 | 19 | 0 | 5 | 78 | 36 | 57 |
| Awliscombe United | 24 | 13 | 2 | 9 | 43 | 28 | 41 |
| Topsham Town 3rds | 24 | 10 | 6 | 8 | 55 | 42 | 36 |
| Hatherleigh Town 2nds | 24 | 9 | 7 | 8 | 42 | 42 | 34 |
| Countess Wear Dynamoes | 24 | 10 | 2 | 12 | 53 | 54 | 32 |
| Westex Rovers 2nds | 24 | 9 | 3 | 12 | 41 | 44 | 30 |
| Bow AAC 2nds | 24 | 9 | 3 | 12 | 43 | 48 | 30 |
| St Martins 2nds | 24 | 9 | 2 | 13 | 46 | 47 | 29 |
| Beer Albion 2nds | 24 | 8 | 5 | 11 | 39 | 60 | 29 |
| Sampford Peverell | 24 | 8 | 4 | 12 | 45 | 57 | 28 |
| Lapford | 24 | 7 | 5 | 12 | 36 | 57 | 26 |
| Uplowman Athletic (-1pt) | 24 | 5 | 2 | 17 | 38 | 87 | 16 |

Clyst Valley 3rds record expunged.

| Division Six | P | W | D | L | F | A | PTS |
|---|---|---|---|---|---|---|---|
| Feniton 2nds | 28 | 21 | 4 | 3 | 105 | 38 | 67 |
| Amory Park Rangers | 28 | 20 | 3 | 5 | 103 | 35 | 63 |
| Dawlish United 2nds | 28 | 19 | 2 | 7 | 65 | 31 | 59 |
| Morchard Bishop 2nds | 28 | 19 | 1 | 8 | 90 | 61 | 58 |
| Langdon | 28 | 18 | 3 | 7 | 113 | 52 | 57 |
| Dunkeswell Rovers | 28 | 13 | 4 | 11 | 77 | 68 | 43 |
| Silverton | 28 | 11 | 5 | 12 | 55 | 77 | 38 |
| Amory Green Rovers | 28 | 12 | 1 | 15 | 63 | 73 | 37 |
| Stoke Hill | 28 | 10 | 5 | 13 | 84 | 77 | 35 |
| East Budleigh 2nds (-1pt) | 28 | 10 | 5 | 13 | 64 | 55 | 34 |
| Topsham Town 4ths | 28 | 9 | 5 | 14 | 59 | 90 | 32 |
| Exwick Village | 28 | 10 | 0 | 18 | 62 | 80 | 30 |
| Priory | 28 | 8 | 4 | 16 | 54 | 81 | 28 |
| Chagford 2nds | 28 | 6 | 0 | 22 | 39 | 97 | 18 |
| North Tawton 2nds (-3pts) | 28 | 3 | 0 | 25 | 35 | 153 | 6 |

| Division Seven | P | W | D | L | F | A | PTS |
|---|---|---|---|---|---|---|---|
| Halwill 2nds | 26 | 21 | 0 | 5 | 96 | 49 | 63 |
| Fluxton | 26 | 20 | 2 | 4 | 97 | 41 | 62 |
| Newton St Cyres 2nds | 26 | 17 | 2 | 7 | 95 | 51 | 53 |
| Starcross Generals | 26 | 15 | 3 | 8 | 93 | 64 | 48 |
| Honiton Town 2nds | 26 | 14 | 3 | 9 | 69 | 60 | 45 |
| Tipton St John 2nds | 26 | 12 | 6 | 8 | 70 | 55 | 42 |
| Otterton | 26 | 12 | 3 | 11 | 60 | 48 | 39 |
| Ottery St Mary 2nds | 26 | 10 | 5 | 11 | 65 | 77 | 35 |
| Met Office | 26 | 10 | 4 | 12 | 38 | 55 | 34 |
| Lympstone 2nds | 26 | 9 | 2 | 15 | 48 | 67 | 29 |
| Tedburn St Mary 2nds | 26 | 8 | 1 | 17 | 60 | 83 | 25 |
| Colaton Raleigh 2nds (-2pts) | 26 | 7 | 2 | 17 | 46 | 74 | 21 |
| Space International | 26 | 4 | 3 | 19 | 47 | 117 | 15 |
| Cheriton Fitzpaine 2nds | 26 | 3 | 4 | 19 | 41 | 84 | 13 |

| Division Eight | P | W | D | L | F | A | PTS |
|---|---|---|---|---|---|---|---|
| Alphington 3rds | 28 | 18 | 5 | 5 | 92 | 48 | 59 |
| Woodbury 2nds | 28 | 16 | 9 | 3 | 77 | 41 | 57 |
| Sidbury United 2nds (-11pts) | 28 | 21 | 2 | 5 | 93 | 40 | 56 |
| Pinhoe 2nds | 28 | 17 | 5 | 6 | 87 | 55 | 56 |
| Langdon 2nds | 28 | 15 | 3 | 10 | 70 | 59 | 48 |
| Offwell Rangers 2nds | 28 | 12 | 9 | 7 | 88 | 57 | 45 |
| Newtown 4ths | 28 | 13 | 4 | 11 | 66 | 59 | 43 |
| Bampton 2nds | 28 | 12 | 5 | 11 | 59 | 57 | 41 |
| Bickleigh 2nds | 28 | 11 | 4 | 13 | 81 | 58 | 37 |
| Hemyock 2nds (-1pt) | 28 | 11 | 3 | 14 | 68 | 64 | 35 |
| Colyton 2nds | 28 | 10 | 4 | 14 | 60 | 82 | 34 |
| Lapford 2nds | 28 | 10 | 4 | 14 | 48 | 73 | 34 |
| Folly Gate & Inwardleigh | 28 | 5 | 2 | 21 | 56 | 135 | 17 |
| Winkleigh 2nds (-1pt) | 28 | 4 | 3 | 21 | 27 | 96 | 14 |
| Sandford 2nds | 28 | 3 | 2 | 23 | 40 | 88 | 11 |

# DONCASTER & DISTRICT LEAGUE

| Premier Division | P | W | D | L | F | A | Pts |
|---|---|---|---|---|---|---|---|
| 1 Denaby United | 18 | 14 | 1 | 3 | 81 | 26 | 43 |
| 2 Sutton Rovers | 18 | 12 | 3 | 3 | 64 | 28 | 39 |
| 3 Bramley Sunnyside | 18 | 11 | 0 | 7 | 54 | 44 | 33 |
| 4 Shafton Villa | 18 | 10 | 2 | 6 | 52 | 17 | 32 |
| 5 Rossington MW (-3pts) | 18 | 8 | 3 | 7 | 46 | 28 | 24 |
| 6 South Elmsall United Services | 18 | 6 | 5 | 7 | 26 | 32 | 23 |
| 7 Bawtry Town (-3pts) | 18 | 8 | 1 | 9 | 46 | 55 | 22 |
| 8 Hemsworth Town Terriers | 18 | 5 | 2 | 11 | 28 | 41 | 17 |
| 9 Kinsley Boys | 18 | 4 | 3 | 11 | 25 | 38 | 15 |
| 10 South Kirkby Colliery | 18 | 2 | 0 | 16 | 11 | 124 | 6 |

| Division One | P | W | D | L | F | A | Pts |
|---|---|---|---|---|---|---|---|
| 1 Denaby Main | 26 | 23 | 3 | 0 | 91 | 19 | 72 |
| 2 Hemsworth MW | 26 | 23 | 1 | 2 | 119 | 22 | 70 |
| 3 Ackworth United | 26 | 17 | 2 | 7 | 74 | 34 | 53 |
| 4 Dunscroft United | 26 | 15 | 1 | 10 | 70 | 65 | 46 |
| 5 South Kirkby Town | 26 | 14 | 2 | 10 | 86 | 56 | 44 |
| 6 Rovers Foundation | 25 | 13 | 1 | 11 | 54 | 54 | 40 |
| 7 Swinton Athletic | 26 | 12 | 4 | 10 | 47 | 47 | 40 |
| 8 Bawtry Town | 26 | 8 | 2 | 16 | 48 | 74 | 26 |
| 9 Newton Arms | 26 | 6 | 6 | 14 | 44 | 67 | 24 |
| 10 Harworth Colliery | 26 | 7 | 3 | 16 | 44 | 80 | 24 |
| 11 Westwoodside Rangers | 26 | 7 | 2 | 17 | 44 | 120 | 23 |
| 12 F.C. Central | 25 | 6 | 4 | 15 | 54 | 73 | 22 |
| 13 Scawthorpe Scorpions | 26 | 5 | 7 | 14 | 48 | 69 | 22 |
| 14 ISG Doncaster | 26 | 4 | 4 | 18 | 28 | 71 | 16 |

# DORSET FOOTBALL LEAGUE

| Senior Division | P | W | D | L | F | A | Pts |
|---|---|---|---|---|---|---|---|
| 1 Mere Town | 26 | 23 | 2 | 1 | 88 | 26 | 71 |
| 2 Upwey and Broadway | 26 | 18 | 0 | 8 | 79 | 33 | 54 |
| 3 Gillingham Town Reserves | 26 | 17 | 2 | 7 | 70 | 38 | 53 |
| 4 Witchampton United | 26 | 16 | 3 | 7 | 65 | 50 | 51 |
| 5 Kingston Lacey | 26 | 14 | 4 | 8 | 59 | 42 | 46 |
| 6 Westland Sports | 26 | 13 | 2 | 11 | 47 | 31 | 41 |
| 7 Sturminster Newton United | 26 | 10 | 6 | 10 | 47 | 36 | 36 |
| 8 Piddletrenthide United | 26 | 9 | 4 | 13 | 56 | 71 | 31 |
| 9 Stourpaine | 26 | 8 | 5 | 13 | 41 | 59 | 29 |
| 10 Blandford United Reserves | 26 | 8 | 3 | 15 | 33 | 63 | 27 |
| 11 Portland United Reserves | 26 | 6 | 4 | 16 | 30 | 57 | 22 |
| 12 Okeford United | 26 | 6 | 4 | 16 | 32 | 68 | 22 |
| 13 Sturminster Marshall | 26 | 6 | 2 | 18 | 37 | 71 | 20 |
| 14 Weymouth Sports | 26 | 4 | 7 | 15 | 34 | 73 | 19 |

| Division One | P | W | D | L | F | A | Pts |
|---|---|---|---|---|---|---|---|
| 1 Corfe Mullen United | 22 | 20 | 2 | 0 | 65 | 7 | 62 |
| 2 South Cheriton | 22 | 17 | 1 | 4 | 77 | 30 | 52 |
| 3 Milborne Sports | 22 | 12 | 4 | 6 | 63 | 34 | 40 |
| 4 Wincanton Town Reserves | 22 | 10 | 4 | 8 | 38 | 40 | 34 |
| 5 Kangaroos | 22 | 9 | 5 | 8 | 70 | 44 | 32 |
| 6 Bere Regis | 22 | 9 | 3 | 10 | 50 | 45 | 30 |
| 7 Swanage Town & Herston Reserves | 22 | 9 | 0 | 13 | 38 | 56 | 27 |
| 8 Poundbury Rovers | 22 | 7 | 4 | 11 | 34 | 50 | 25 |
| 9 Bridport A | 22 | 7 | 3 | 12 | 34 | 65 | 24 |
| 10 Poole Borough Reserves | 22 | 6 | 3 | 13 | 50 | 68 | 21 |
| 11 Chickerell United Reserves | 22 | 5 | 1 | 16 | 32 | 66 | 16 |
| 12 Merley Cobham Sports Reserves | 22 | 4 | 4 | 14 | 35 | 81 | 16 |

# LEAGUE TABLES

| Division Two | P | W | D | L | F | A | Pts |
|---|---|---|---|---|---|---|---|
| 1 The Balti House | 24 | 17 | 2 | 5 | 88 | 47 | 53 |
| 2 Dorchester Sports | 24 | 16 | 5 | 3 | 81 | 44 | 53 |
| 3 Weymouth Spartans | 24 | 16 | 3 | 5 | 79 | 44 | 51 |
| 4 AFC Cobham | 24 | 15 | 2 | 7 | 77 | 44 | 47 |
| 5 Shaftesbury Town Reserves | 24 | 10 | 4 | 10 | 61 | 51 | 34 |
| 6 Gillingham Town A | 24 | 10 | 4 | 10 | 56 | 48 | 34 |
| 7 Portland Town B | 24 | 9 | 6 | 9 | 63 | 58 | 33 |
| 8 Corfe Castle | 24 | 10 | 2 | 12 | 53 | 62 | 32 |
| 9 Wyke Regis Social Club | 24 | 8 | 4 | 12 | 57 | 79 | 28 |
| 10 Wareham Rangers Reserves | 24 | 6 | 6 | 12 | 39 | 64 | 24 |
| 11 Ship Inn, Wool | 24 | 5 | 5 | 14 | 45 | 72 | 20 |
| 12 Sturminster Newton United Reserves | 24 | 6 | 1 | 17 | 35 | 77 | 19 |
| 13 Donhead Utd | 24 | 5 | 2 | 17 | 41 | 85 | 17 |

| Division Three | P | W | D | L | F | A | Pts |
|---|---|---|---|---|---|---|---|
| 1 Lytchett Red Triangle | 20 | 18 | 1 | 1 | 95 | 13 | 55 |
| 2 Piddlehinton United | 20 | 13 | 4 | 3 | 51 | 18 | 43 |
| 3 Portesham United | 20 | 10 | 3 | 7 | 45 | 39 | 33 |
| 4 Maiden Newton & Cattistock | 20 | 9 | 3 | 8 | 50 | 59 | 30 |
| 5 The Belvedere Inn (-3pts) | 20 | 9 | 5 | 6 | 49 | 44 | 29 |
| 6 Handley Sports | 20 | 8 | 4 | 8 | 49 | 54 | 28 |
| 7 Stalbridge | 20 | 7 | 5 | 8 | 36 | 46 | 26 |
| 8 Sturminster Marshall Reserves (-3pts) | 20 | 8 | 2 | 10 | 41 | 50 | 23 |
| 9 Stickland United | 20 | 4 | 6 | 10 | 39 | 50 | 18 |
| 10 Bere Regis Reserves | 20 | 2 | 5 | 13 | 27 | 62 | 11 |
| 11 Owermoigne | 20 | 2 | 2 | 16 | 26 | 73 | 8 |

| Division Four | P | W | D | L | F | A | Pts |
|---|---|---|---|---|---|---|---|
| 1 Mere Town Reserves | 18 | 13 | 1 | 4 | 70 | 26 | 40 |
| 2 Broadstone FC Seniors | 18 | 12 | 3 | 3 | 72 | 21 | 39 |
| 3 AFC Blandford | 18 | 11 | 4 | 3 | 64 | 26 | 37 |
| 4 Puddletown | 18 | 11 | 3 | 4 | 59 | 39 | 36 |
| 5 Cranborne Reserves | 18 | 8 | 3 | 7 | 48 | 60 | 27 |
| 6 Uniited Football Club of Poundbury | 18 | 6 | 6 | 6 | 46 | 50 | 24 |
| 7 Bishops Caundle | 18 | 6 | 3 | 9 | 49 | 51 | 21 |
| 8 Portland Town Reserves | 18 | 4 | 6 | 8 | 34 | 48 | 18 |
| 9 Corfe Mullen Utd Reserves | 18 | 2 | 0 | 16 | 22 | 78 | 6 |
| 10 Weymouth Spartans Reserves (-6pts) | 18 | 2 | 1 | 15 | 19 | 84 | 1 |

| Division Five | P | W | D | L | F | A | Pts |
|---|---|---|---|---|---|---|---|
| 1 Pimperne Sports Society | 20 | 16 | 0 | 4 | 97 | 37 | 48 |
| 2 Swanage Town & Herston A (-3pts) | 20 | 12 | 5 | 3 | 71 | 31 | 38 |
| 3 Kangaroos Reserves | 20 | 11 | 5 | 4 | 67 | 42 | 38 |
| 4 Milborne Sports Reserves (-3pts) | 20 | 11 | 4 | 5 | 69 | 41 | 34 |
| 5 Wellworthys (-1pt) | 20 | 11 | 3 | 6 | 76 | 51 | 33 |
| 6 Lytchett Red Triangle Youth | 20 | 6 | 4 | 10 | 50 | 75 | 22 |
| 7 Marnhull | 20 | 6 | 3 | 11 | 36 | 50 | 21 |
| 8 Broadstone FC Seniors Reserves | 20 | 6 | 2 | 12 | 44 | 59 | 20 |
| 9 Maiden Newton & Cattistock Reserves | 20 | 5 | 3 | 12 | 33 | 59 | 18 |
| 10 Portland Town A | 20 | 5 | 2 | 13 | 40 | 72 | 17 |
| 11 Handley Sports Reserves | 20 | 4 | 3 | 13 | 33 | 99 | 15 |

# DRIFFIELD & DISTRICT LEAGUE

| Premier Division | P | W | D | L | F | A | Pt |
|---|---|---|---|---|---|---|---|
| 1 Bridlington Excelsior | 22 | 16 | 2 | 4 | 77 | 33 | 5 |
| 2 Sports Club utd | 22 | 15 | 4 | 3 | 75 | 40 | 4 |
| 3 Bridlington Snooker Centre | 22 | 15 | 3 | 4 | 55 | 26 | 4 |
| 4 Bridlington Tigers | 22 | 12 | 6 | 4 | 69 | 31 | 4 |
| 5 Bridlington Rovers | 22 | 10 | 6 | 6 | 57 | 43 | 3 |
| 6 Stirling Wanderers | 22 | 9 | 5 | 8 | 68 | 52 | 3 |
| 7 Flamborough | 22 | 8 | 2 | 12 | 67 | 83 | 2 |
| 8 Northcote FC | 22 | 7 | 3 | 12 | 40 | 76 | 2 |
| 9 Driffield JFC 2nds | 22 | 5 | 4 | 13 | 42 | 68 | 1 |
| 10 Foresters Athletic | 22 | 5 | 2 | 15 | 35 | 66 | 1 |
| 11 Driffield Star | 22 | 4 | 4 | 14 | 38 | 84 | 1 |
| 12 Driffield Red Lion | 22 | 4 | 3 | 15 | 49 | 70 | 1 |

| Division One | P | W | D | L | F | A | Pt |
|---|---|---|---|---|---|---|---|
| 1 Mermaid United Old Boys | 22 | 16 | 1 | 5 | 86 | 34 | 4 |
| 2 Flamborough 2nds | 22 | 16 | 1 | 5 | 88 | 45 | 4 |
| 3 Afc Lounge Bar | 22 | 14 | 2 | 6 | 65 | 43 | 4 |
| 4 Bridlington Snooker Centre 2nd | 22 | 11 | 4 | 7 | 72 | 55 | 3 |
| 5 Little Driffield | 22 | 11 | 3 | 8 | 49 | 41 | 3 |
| 6 Pocklington 4th | 22 | 10 | 3 | 9 | 45 | 47 | 3 |
| 7 Stirling Wanderers Res | 22 | 10 | 1 | 11 | 49 | 61 | 3 |
| 8 Driffield Town | 22 | 8 | 3 | 11 | 62 | 67 | 2 |
| 9 Hilderthorpe | 22 | 9 | 0 | 13 | 50 | 58 | 2 |
| 10 North Frodingham | 22 | 7 | 3 | 12 | 52 | 84 | 2 |
| 11 Driffield JFC 3rds | 22 | 4 | 4 | 14 | 34 | 66 | 1 |
| 12 Forester Athletic 2nds | 22 | 0 | 7 | 15 | 33 | 84 | |

# DUCHY LEAGUE

| Premier Division | P | W | D | L | F | A | Pt |
|---|---|---|---|---|---|---|---|
| 1 AFC St Austell | 24 | 19 | 2 | 3 | 78 | 23 | 5 |
| 2 Fowey United | 24 | 15 | 4 | 5 | 95 | 32 | 4 |
| 3 Mevagissey | 24 | 14 | 5 | 5 | 82 | 43 | 4 |
| 4 Saltash United | 24 | 14 | 4 | 6 | 84 | 44 | 4 |
| 5 Torpoint Athletic (-3pts) | 24 | 15 | 3 | 6 | 85 | 37 | 4 |
| 6 Lamerton | 24 | 12 | 2 | 10 | 50 | 43 | 3 |
| 7 St Newlyn East | 24 | 12 | 1 | 11 | 58 | 74 | 3 |
| 8 St Cleer | 24 | 7 | 6 | 11 | 37 | 69 | 2 |
| 9 St Columb Major | 24 | 6 | 6 | 12 | 44 | 71 | 2 |
| 10 Probus (-3pts) | 24 | 7 | 3 | 14 | 50 | 55 | 2 |
| 11 Bodmin Saints | 24 | 7 | 0 | 17 | 60 | 108 | 2 |
| 12 St Mawgan | 24 | 5 | 4 | 15 | 41 | 71 | 1 |
| 13 Calstock (-3pts) | 24 | 2 | 2 | 20 | 30 | 124 | |

| Division One | P | W | D | L | F | A | Pt |
|---|---|---|---|---|---|---|---|
| 1 Pensilva | 24 | 14 | 8 | 2 | 69 | 36 | 5 |
| 2 Biscovey (-3pts) | 24 | 17 | 1 | 6 | 63 | 39 | 4 |
| 3 Pelynt | 24 | 13 | 4 | 7 | 69 | 43 | 4 |
| 4 Looe Town | 24 | 12 | 5 | 7 | 71 | 55 | 4 |
| 5 Altarnun | 24 | 11 | 8 | 5 | 39 | 25 | 4 |
| 6 Godolphin Atlantic (-1pt) | 24 | 11 | 9 | 4 | 47 | 35 | 4 |
| 7 St Dominick | 24 | 11 | 3 | 10 | 47 | 43 | 3 |
| 8 Polperro | 24 | 10 | 3 | 11 | 48 | 46 | 3 |
| 9 Grampound | 24 | 8 | 3 | 13 | 37 | 38 | 2 |
| 10 Maker with Rame (-6pts) | 24 | 7 | 5 | 12 | 48 | 62 | 2 |
| 11 St Dennis | 24 | 6 | 1 | 17 | 39 | 83 | 1 |
| 12 Week St Mary | 24 | 3 | 6 | 15 | 39 | 67 | 1 |
| 13 Gunnislake | 24 | 4 | 2 | 18 | 45 | 89 | 1 |

| Division Two | P | W | D | L | F | A | Pts |
|---|---|---|---|---|---|---|---|
| 1 Padstow United | 22 | 17 | 2 | 3 | 80 | 24 | 53 |
| 2 Lostwithiel | 22 | 16 | 1 | 5 | 54 | 29 | 49 |
| 3 North Petherwin | 22 | 15 | 2 | 5 | 78 | 28 | 47 |
| 4 Foxhole Stars (+3pts) | 22 | 12 | 1 | 9 | 59 | 47 | 40 |
| 5 Sticker | 22 | 12 | 3 | 7 | 41 | 30 | 39 |
| 6 Premier Sixes | 22 | 11 | 3 | 8 | 69 | 64 | 36 |
| 7 AFC Bodmin | 22 | 11 | 3 | 8 | 43 | 40 | 36 |
| 8 Boscastle | 22 | 7 | 3 | 12 | 39 | 56 | 24 |
| 9 Gerrans & St Mawes Utd | 22 | 6 | 3 | 13 | 33 | 55 | 21 |
| 10 St Breward (-3pts) | 22 | 4 | 4 | 14 | 26 | 65 | 13 |
| 11 Lanreath | 22 | 2 | 3 | 17 | 24 | 82 | 9 |
| 12 Queens Rangers (-6pts) | 22 | 4 | 2 | 16 | 27 | 53 | 8 |

| Division Three | P | W | D | L | F | A | Pts |
|---|---|---|---|---|---|---|---|
| 1 St Minver | 22 | 20 | 2 | 0 | 99 | 17 | 62 |
| 2 LC Phoenix | 22 | 18 | 2 | 2 | 105 | 23 | 56 |
| 3 Holywell and Cubert | 22 | 13 | 4 | 5 | 87 | 37 | 43 |
| 4 St Stephen | 22 | 12 | 5 | 5 | 61 | 46 | 41 |
| 5 Stoke Climsland | 22 | 12 | 1 | 9 | 54 | 42 | 37 |
| 6 Welcome Inn | 22 | 10 | 4 | 8 | 54 | 52 | 34 |
| 7 Lanivet Inn | 22 | 8 | 1 | 13 | 39 | 69 | 25 |
| 8 Camelford | 22 | 6 | 2 | 14 | 40 | 72 | 20 |
| 9 Callington Town | 22 | 5 | 5 | 12 | 48 | 86 | 20 |
| 10 Delabole United (-1pt) | 22 | 6 | 2 | 14 | 43 | 79 | 19 |
| 11 Tregony | 22 | 4 | 1 | 17 | 36 | 87 | 13 |
| 12 Roche | 22 | 2 | 3 | 17 | 33 | 89 | 9 |

| Division Four | P | W | D | L | F | A | Pts |
|---|---|---|---|---|---|---|---|
| 1 North Hill | 24 | 18 | 3 | 3 | 71 | 28 | 57 |
| 2 St Neot | 24 | 15 | 4 | 5 | 64 | 46 | 49 |
| 3 Lifton | 24 | 13 | 4 | 7 | 54 | 38 | 43 |
| 4 Pensilva Reserves | 24 | 13 | 4 | 7 | 57 | 57 | 43 |
| 5 Mevagissey Reserves | 24 | 12 | 4 | 8 | 73 | 51 | 40 |
| 6 Tintagel | 24 | 11 | 6 | 7 | 63 | 64 | 39 |
| 7 Wadebridge Town | 24 | 10 | 3 | 11 | 54 | 55 | 33 |
| 8 Gorran (-6pts) | 24 | 11 | 3 | 10 | 59 | 58 | 30 |
| 9 Grampound Reserves (+3pts) | 24 | 8 | 2 | 14 | 50 | 58 | 29 |
| 10 Torpoint Comrades | 24 | 5 | 6 | 13 | 47 | 54 | 21 |
| 11 Gunnislake Reserves | 24 | 6 | 3 | 15 | 53 | 78 | 21 |
| 12 St Cleer Reserves | 24 | 5 | 4 | 14 | 42 | 56 | 20 |
| 13 St Teath (-3pts) | 24 | 3 | 5 | 16 | 33 | 77 | 11 |

| Division Five | P | W | D | L | F | A | Pts |
|---|---|---|---|---|---|---|---|
| 1 Veryan | 22 | 20 | 2 | 0 | 123 | 19 | 62 |
| 2 St Columb Major Reserves | 22 | 13 | 4 | 5 | 69 | 33 | 43 |
| 3 North Petherwin Reserves | 22 | 12 | 5 | 5 | 84 | 44 | 41 |
| 4 St Merryn | 22 | 12 | 5 | 5 | 79 | 42 | 41 |
| 5 Southgate Seniors | 22 | 12 | 5 | 5 | 70 | 35 | 41 |
| 6 St Minver Reserves | 22 | 9 | 6 | 7 | 45 | 52 | 33 |
| 7 Tregrehan Mills | 22 | 9 | 1 | 12 | 53 | 71 | 28 |
| 8 Boscastle Reserves | 22 | 7 | 3 | 12 | 38 | 61 | 24 |
| 9 Pelynt Reserves | 22 | 6 | 5 | 11 | 53 | 66 | 23 |
| 10 St Mawgan Reserves | 22 | 4 | 5 | 13 | 40 | 64 | 17 |
| 11 St Newlyn East Reserves | 22 | 4 | 0 | 18 | 25 | 129 | 12 |
| 12 Royal Par FC | 22 | 2 | 3 | 17 | 40 | 103 | 9 |

# DURHAM FOOTBALL ALLIANCE

| | P | W | D | L | F | A | Pts |
|---|---|---|---|---|---|---|---|
| 1 Coundon and Leeholm | 26 | 21 | 0 | 5 | 80 | 36 | 63 |
| 2 Whitehill | 26 | 18 | 2 | 6 | 81 | 38 | 56 |
| 3 Sunderland Hylton CW | 26 | 17 | 2 | 7 | 84 | 51 | 53 |
| 4 Murton AFC | 26 | 15 | 3 | 8 | 78 | 37 | 48 |
| 5 Durham Garden House | 26 | 15 | 3 | 8 | 75 | 52 | 48 |
| 6 Gateshead Leam Rangers | 26 | 12 | 3 | 11 | 58 | 46 | 39 |
| 7 Brandon British Legion | 26 | 10 | 7 | 9 | 82 | 68 | 37 |
| 8 Ebchester Consett Reserves | 26 | 11 | 4 | 11 | 64 | 64 | 37 |
| 9 Wheatley Hill WMC | 26 | 9 | 5 | 12 | 56 | 66 | 32 |
| 10 Sherburn Village WMC | 26 | 7 | 8 | 11 | 50 | 67 | 29 |
| 11 Dunston Holmside Amateurs (-3pts) | 26 | 8 | 4 | 14 | 65 | 69 | 25 |
| 12 Brandon United Reserves (-3pts) | 26 | 7 | 2 | 17 | 33 | 95 | 20 |
| 13 Washington Town (-3pts) | 26 | 5 | 6 | 15 | 43 | 82 | 18 |
| 14 Coxhole United (-3pts) | 26 | 1 | 3 | 22 | 36 | 114 | 3 |

# EAST BERKSHIRE LEAGUE

| Premier Division | P | W | D | L | F | A | Pts |
|---|---|---|---|---|---|---|---|
| 1 Iver | 20 | 15 | 2 | 3 | 58 | 40 | 47 |
| 2 Orchard Park Rangers (+6pts) | 20 | 10 | 3 | 7 | 56 | 36 | 39 |
| 3 Wraysbury Village FC (-6pts) | 20 | 14 | 2 | 4 | 65 | 41 | 38 |
| 4 FC Beaconsfield (+3pts) | 20 | 9 | 4 | 7 | 61 | 52 | 34 |
| 5 Stoke Green Rovers | 20 | 7 | 10 | 3 | 45 | 35 | 31 |
| 6 Chalvey (WMC) Sports (+3pts) | 20 | 7 | 5 | 8 | 48 | 55 | 29 |
| 7 Alpha Arms Academicals (-3pts) | 20 | 8 | 5 | 7 | 53 | 50 | 26 |
| 8 Slough Irish Society | 20 | 7 | 2 | 11 | 43 | 47 | 23 |
| 9 Slough Laurencians | 20 | 6 | 2 | 12 | 54 | 68 | 20 |
| 10 Slough Heating (+3pts) | 20 | 3 | 3 | 14 | 33 | 57 | 15 |
| 11 Farnham Park (-6pts) | 20 | 4 | 2 | 14 | 32 | 67 | 8 |

| Division One | P | W | D | L | F | A | Pts |
|---|---|---|---|---|---|---|---|
| 1 Langley Wanderers | 16 | 12 | 0 | 4 | 57 | 28 | 36 |
| 2 Swinley Forest | 16 | 10 | 2 | 4 | 54 | 24 | 32 |
| 3 Upton Lea | 16 | 8 | 3 | 5 | 29 | 29 | 27 |
| 4 Old Windsor | 16 | 7 | 3 | 6 | 35 | 28 | 24 |
| 5 Slough Heating Res. (+3pts) | 16 | 6 | 2 | 8 | 38 | 55 | 23 |
| 6 KS Gryf | 16 | 6 | 3 | 7 | 26 | 19 | 21 |
| 7 Richings Park | 16 | 6 | 1 | 9 | 32 | 38 | 19 |
| 8 Falcons (-3pts) | 16 | 4 | 4 | 8 | 28 | 46 | 13 |
| 9 Admiral Cunningham | 16 | 3 | 2 | 11 | 30 | 62 | 11 |
| Delaford record expunged. | | | | | | | |

| Division Two | P | W | D | L | F | A | Pts |
|---|---|---|---|---|---|---|---|
| 1 Windsor Great Park | 20 | 17 | 1 | 2 | 68 | 33 | 52 |
| 2 Langley | 20 | 16 | 2 | 2 | 84 | 37 | 50 |
| 3 Bracknell Rovers | 20 | 16 | 1 | 3 | 64 | 24 | 49 |
| 4 Maidenhead Magpies | 20 | 12 | 1 | 7 | 63 | 49 | 37 |
| 5 AFC Ascot | 20 | 10 | 1 | 9 | 62 | 47 | 31 |
| 6 Cippenham Sports | 20 | 8 | 2 | 10 | 56 | 63 | 26 |
| 7 Stoke Green Rovers Res. | 20 | 8 | 1 | 11 | 48 | 57 | 25 |
| 8 Maidenhead Town | 20 | 4 | 3 | 13 | 35 | 42 | 15 |
| 9 Frontline (+3pts) | 20 | 3 | 3 | 14 | 47 | 79 | 15 |
| 10 Britwell (-3pts) | 20 | 5 | 2 | 13 | 40 | 77 | 14 |
| 11 Red Lion | 20 | 2 | 1 | 17 | 36 | 95 | 7 |

# LEAGUE TABLES

## Division Three

| | | P | W | D | L | F | A | Pts |
|---|---|---|---|---|---|---|---|---|
| 1 | Iver Heath Rovers | 20 | 17 | 1 | 2 | 71 | 15 | 52 |
| 2 | Sandgate | 19 | 14 | 0 | 5 | 41 | 24 | 42 |
| 3 | Robertswood | 20 | 12 | 2 | 6 | 45 | 35 | 38 |
| 4 | Old Windsor Reserves | 20 | 11 | 1 | 8 | 60 | 39 | 34 |
| 5 | Hurley | 20 | 11 | 1 | 8 | 54 | 43 | 34 |
| 6 | Real Saracens | 20 | 9 | 2 | 9 | 42 | 45 | 29 |
| 7 | Burnham Beeches Seniors | 20 | 8 | 3 | 9 | 41 | 44 | 27 |
| 8 | Braybrooke | 20 | 8 | 3 | 9 | 42 | 60 | 27 |
| 9 | Colne Valley Datchet | 20 | 6 | 3 | 11 | 33 | 48 | 21 |
| 10 | Windsor Great Park Res. | 19 | 2 | 4 | 13 | 26 | 58 | 10 |
| 11 | Stanwell | 20 | 1 | 0 | 19 | 15 | 59 | 3 |

## Division Four

| | | P | W | D | L | F | A | Pts |
|---|---|---|---|---|---|---|---|---|
| 1 | Iver Heath Rovers Reserves | 18 | 14 | 3 | 1 | 67 | 24 | 45 |
| 2 | Willow Wanderers | 18 | 11 | 3 | 4 | 52 | 32 | 36 |
| 3 | Britwell Reserves | 18 | 9 | 4 | 5 | 56 | 43 | 31 |
| 4 | Fulmer | 18 | 8 | 5 | 5 | 55 | 38 | 29 |
| 5 | Upton Park Rangers | 18 | 6 | 5 | 7 | 36 | 32 | 23 |
| 6 | St Peters Iver | 18 | 7 | 2 | 9 | 45 | 54 | 23 |
| 7 | Chalvey (WMC) Sports Vets | 18 | 7 | 1 | 10 | 31 | 47 | 22 |
| 8 | The Wolfpack (-3pts) | 18 | 6 | 3 | 9 | 47 | 47 | 18 |
| 9 | Bracknell Cavaliers | 18 | 3 | 3 | 12 | 36 | 65 | 15 |
| 10 | Upton Lea Reserves | 18 | 2 | 5 | 11 | 21 | 64 | 11 |

## Division Five

| | | P | W | D | L | F | A | Pts |
|---|---|---|---|---|---|---|---|---|
| 1 | Brackburn Rovers | 20 | 16 | 2 | 2 | 62 | 18 | 50 |
| 2 | Langley Reserves | 20 | 14 | 3 | 3 | 67 | 35 | 45 |
| 3 | SL Dons (+2pts) | 20 | 13 | 2 | 5 | 50 | 23 | 43 |
| 4 | FC Beaconsfield Reserves | 20 | 12 | 4 | 4 | 59 | 30 | 40 |
| 5 | Richings Park Reserves | 20 | 9 | 4 | 7 | 58 | 49 | 31 |
| 6 | Real Saracens Res (-1pt) | 20 | 9 | 5 | 6 | 40 | 43 | 31 |
| 7 | Slough Town Rebels | 20 | 7 | 3 | 10 | 47 | 47 | 24 |
| 8 | New Park United | 20 | 5 | 3 | 12 | 36 | 73 | 18 |
| 9 | Langley Hornets | 20 | 4 | 4 | 12 | 44 | 54 | 16 |
| 10 | Bracknell Rovers Reserves | 20 | 4 | 4 | 12 | 40 | 62 | 16 |
| 11 | Mercian United | 20 | 0 | 0 | 20 | 19 | 88 | 0 |

## EAST CHESHIRE LEAGUE

### Division One

| | | P | W | D | L | F | A | Pts |
|---|---|---|---|---|---|---|---|---|
| 1 | FC Woodford | 16 | 14 | 1 | 1 | 73 | 25 | 43 |
| 2 | FC Flyers | 16 | 13 | 0 | 3 | 74 | 28 | 39 |
| 3 | Prestbury FC | 16 | 8 | 3 | 5 | 45 | 33 | 27 |
| 4 | High Lane | 16 | 8 | 2 | 6 | 38 | 45 | 26 |
| 5 | Club AZ | 16 | 8 | 1 | 7 | 41 | 43 | 25 |
| 6 | Old Alts | 16 | 5 | 3 | 8 | 35 | 44 | 18 |
| 7 | Mary Dendy | 16 | 4 | 2 | 10 | 31 | 63 | 14 |
| 8 | Bulls Head Poynton | 16 | 2 | 4 | 10 | 24 | 66 | 10 |
| 9 | Poynton Nomads | 16 | 1 | 2 | 13 | 30 | 44 | 5 |

## EAST CORNWALL LEAGUE

### Premier Division

| | | P | W | D | L | F | A | Pts |
|---|---|---|---|---|---|---|---|---|
| 1 | Plymouth Parkway | 28 | 21 | 4 | 3 | 90 | 36 | 67 |
| 2 | Bude Town | 28 | 18 | 5 | 5 | 102 | 40 | 59 |
| 3 | Tavistock | 28 | 16 | 7 | 5 | 52 | 32 | 55 |
| 4 | Torpoint Athletic | 28 | 15 | 7 | 6 | 77 | 36 | 52 |
| 5 | Saltash United | 28 | 14 | 8 | 6 | 49 | 32 | 50 |
| 6 | Millbrook | 28 | 15 | 4 | 9 | 56 | 44 | 49 |
| 7 | Liskeard Athletic | 28 | 11 | 9 | 8 | 56 | 52 | 42 |
| 8 | Launceston | 28 | 9 | 8 | 11 | 35 | 45 | 35 |
| 9 | Probus | 28 | 7 | 10 | 11 | 38 | 54 | 31 |
| 10 | Elburton Villa | 28 | 7 | 9 | 12 | 49 | 58 | 30 |
| 11 | Bere Alston United | 28 | 8 | 4 | 16 | 37 | 61 | 28 |
| 12 | St Dominick | 28 | 7 | 3 | 18 | 43 | 81 | 24 |
| 13 | Morwenstow | 28 | 6 | 4 | 18 | 42 | 80 | 22 |
| 14 | Wadebridge Town (-3pts) | 28 | 7 | 3 | 18 | 48 | 70 | 21 |
| 15 | Lanreath | 28 | 4 | 5 | 19 | 34 | 87 | 17 |

## Division One

| | | P | W | D | L | F | A | Pts |
|---|---|---|---|---|---|---|---|---|
| 1 | Polperro | 26 | 17 | 4 | 5 | 81 | 39 | 55 |
| 2 | Kilkhampton | 26 | 17 | 4 | 5 | 76 | 42 | 55 |
| 3 | St Teath | 26 | 16 | 3 | 7 | 54 | 38 | 51 |
| 4 | Roche | 26 | 15 | 5 | 6 | 63 | 36 | 50 |
| 5 | Callington Town | 26 | 15 | 4 | 7 | 60 | 38 | 49 |
| 6 | Bodmin Town (-3pts) | 26 | 13 | 3 | 10 | 57 | 44 | 39 |
| 7 | Plymstock United | 26 | 10 | 8 | 8 | 62 | 52 | 38 |
| 8 | St Stephen | 26 | 10 | 5 | 11 | 76 | 74 | 35 |
| 9 | Camelford | 26 | 11 | 1 | 14 | 59 | 82 | 34 |
| 10 | St Stephens Borough | 26 | 9 | 2 | 15 | 44 | 65 | 29 |
| 11 | Edgcumbe | 26 | 7 | 5 | 14 | 59 | 70 | 26 |
| 12 | St Blazey FC | 26 | 8 | 2 | 16 | 42 | 69 | 26 |
| 13 | St Blazey Gate | 26 | 5 | 3 | 18 | 39 | 81 | 18 |
| 14 | Nanpean Rovers | 26 | 3 | 3 | 20 | 32 | 74 | 12 |

## EAST LANCASHIRE LEAGUE

### Division One

| | | P | W | D | L | F | A | Pts |
|---|---|---|---|---|---|---|---|---|
| 1 | Rimington | 22 | 16 | 3 | 3 | 75 | 22 | 51 |
| 2 | Enfield | 22 | 14 | 5 | 3 | 67 | 38 | 47 |
| 3 | Mill Hill | 22 | 14 | 3 | 5 | 61 | 43 | 45 |
| 4 | Worsthorne | 22 | 11 | 5 | 6 | 60 | 43 | 38 |
| 5 | Feniscowles & Pleasington | 22 | 10 | 5 | 7 | 52 | 51 | 35 |
| 6 | Oswaldtwistle SM | 22 | 9 | 4 | 9 | 38 | 38 | 31 |
| 7 | Read United | 22 | 8 | 3 | 11 | 36 | 54 | 27 |
| 8 | Langho | 22 | 7 | 5 | 10 | 64 | 64 | 26 |
| 9 | Calder Vale FC | 22 | 6 | 2 | 14 | 35 | 48 | 20 |
| 10 | Rock Rovers | 22 | 5 | 4 | 13 | 34 | 58 | 19 |
| 11 | Stackstead SJ | 22 | 3 | 7 | 12 | 28 | 56 | 16 |
| 12 | Colne United | 22 | 4 | 4 | 14 | 34 | 69 | 16 |

Burnley Athletic record expunged.
The Ivy record expunged.

### Division Two

| | | P | W | D | L | F | A | Pts |
|---|---|---|---|---|---|---|---|---|
| 1 | Barrowford Celtic | 16 | 12 | 1 | 3 | 56 | 19 | 37 |
| 2 | Burnley Belvedere | 16 | 11 | 2 | 3 | 51 | 21 | 35 |
| 3 | Canberra FC | 16 | 9 | 3 | 4 | 44 | 31 | 30 |
| 4 | Clitheroe RBL | 16 | 7 | 2 | 7 | 26 | 37 | 23 |
| 5 | Borrowdale United | 16 | 7 | 1 | 8 | 32 | 28 | 22 |
| 6 | Barnoldswick Town United | 16 | 5 | 5 | 6 | 21 | 25 | 20 |
| 7 | Prairie United | 16 | 5 | 3 | 8 | 47 | 47 | 18 |
| 8 | Waddington | 16 | 3 | 4 | 9 | 25 | 49 | 13 |
| 9 | Peel Park | 16 | 2 | 1 | 13 | 17 | 62 | 7 |

Pendle Forest record expunged.
Whinney Hill record expunged.

## EAST RIDING AMATEUR LEAGUE

### Premier Division

| | | P | W | D | L | F | A | Pts |
|---|---|---|---|---|---|---|---|---|
| 1 | Rapid Solicitors FC | 20 | 19 | 0 | 1 | 97 | 26 | 57 |
| 2 | Queens County FC | 20 | 13 | 2 | 5 | 64 | 39 | 41 |
| 3 | Quaddy Rangers | 20 | 11 | 4 | 5 | 45 | 41 | 37 |
| 4 | Kingburn Athletic | 20 | 10 | 2 | 8 | 46 | 66 | 32 |
| 5 | West Hull Utd | 20 | 9 | 3 | 8 | 48 | 39 | 30 |
| 6 | Pinefleet Wolf Res | 20 | 8 | 1 | 11 | 46 | 54 | 25 |
| 7 | AFC Preston | 20 | 7 | 3 | 10 | 42 | 50 | 24 |
| 8 | St Andrews Res | 20 | 6 | 5 | 9 | 50 | 56 | 23 |
| 9 | Hall Rd Rang Res | 20 | 6 | 3 | 11 | 46 | 53 | 21 |
| 10 | Bev Road Rangers | 20 | 2 | 13 | 32 | 68 | | 17 |
| 11 | Inter Charter FC | 20 | 3 | 1 | 16 | 34 | 58 | 10 |

| Division One | P | W | D | L | F | A | Pts |
|---|---|---|---|---|---|---|---|
| 1 Eddie Beedle FC | 16 | 12 | 2 | 2 | 61 | 21 | 38 |
| 2 Cross Keys Cott'm | 16 | 12 | 2 | 2 | 43 | 13 | 38 |
| 3 Queens County Res | 16 | 11 | 1 | 4 | 63 | 29 | 34 |
| 4 Longhill Ravens FC | 16 | 11 | 0 | 5 | 65 | 41 | 33 |
| 5 Rapid Solrs Res | 16 | 7 | 1 | 8 | 46 | 51 | 22 |
| 6 Drum Athletic | 16 | 6 | 1 | 9 | 54 | 56 | 19 |
| 7 Orchard Park Utd | 16 | 6 | 0 | 10 | 59 | 54 | 18 |
| 8 Swiss Cottage FC | 16 | 1 | 2 | 13 | 34 | 84 | 5 |
| 9 Abusua FC | 16 | 0 | 3 | 13 | 21 | 97 | 3 |

| Division Two | P | W | D | L | F | A | Pts |
|---|---|---|---|---|---|---|---|
| 1 AFC Northfield | 18 | 17 | 1 | 0 | 125 | 24 | 52 |
| 2 DJM Athletic | 18 | 12 | 0 | 6 | 52 | 49 | 36 |
| 3 AFC North | 18 | 10 | 4 | 4 | 66 | 36 | 34 |
| 4 AFC Hawthorn | 18 | 8 | 4 | 6 | 49 | 42 | 28 |
| 5 Waterloo FC | 18 | 8 | 2 | 8 | 48 | 33 | 26 |
| 6 Cott Road Rangers | 18 | 8 | 1 | 9 | 55 | 65 | 25 |
| 7 Fiveways Rangers | 18 | 7 | 2 | 9 | 39 | 51 | 23 |
| 8 AFC Hull Academy | 18 | 6 | 0 | 12 | 44 | 80 | 18 |
| 9 Cross Keys Cott 2nd | 18 | 4 | 0 | 14 | 29 | 75 | 12 |
| 10 C-Force Utd | 18 | 3 | 0 | 15 | 23 | 75 | 9 |

# EAST RIDING COUNTY LEAGUE

| Premier Division | P | W | D | L | F | A | Pts |
|---|---|---|---|---|---|---|---|
| 1 Wawne United | 22 | 19 | 2 | 1 | 74 | 19 | 59 |
| 2 South Cave Sporting Club | 22 | 17 | 2 | 3 | 58 | 26 | 53 |
| 3 Beverley Town Reserves | 22 | 15 | 2 | 5 | 54 | 36 | 47 |
| 4 AFC Rovers | 22 | 14 | 1 | 7 | 53 | 44 | 43 |
| 5 Park Athletic | 22 | 10 | 5 | 7 | 50 | 38 | 35 |
| 6 Bridlington Town Reserves | 22 | 11 | 1 | 10 | 48 | 44 | 34 |
| 7 St George's FC (-3pts) | 22 | 9 | 3 | 10 | 57 | 59 | 27 |
| 8 Sculcoates Amateurs Reserves (+3pts) | 22 | 6 | 1 | 15 | 32 | 42 | 22 |
| 9 Holme Rovers | 22 | 6 | 4 | 12 | 35 | 54 | 22 |
| 10 Driffield Rangers | 22 | 5 | 3 | 14 | 17 | 47 | 18 |
| 11 Goole United Reserves | 22 | 5 | 3 | 14 | 32 | 64 | 18 |
| 12 Reckitts Reserves | 22 | 1 | 1 | 20 | 26 | 63 | 4 |

| Division One | P | W | D | L | F | A | Pts |
|---|---|---|---|---|---|---|---|
| 1 Wawne United Reserves | 22 | 20 | 0 | 2 | 91 | 30 | 60 |
| 2 Walkington | 22 | 17 | 2 | 3 | 64 | 28 | 53 |
| 3 Easington United Reserves | 22 | 15 | 2 | 5 | 67 | 38 | 47 |
| 4 Haltemprice Rangers | 22 | 12 | 1 | 9 | 73 | 48 | 37 |
| 5 Hodgsons Reserves | 22 | 11 | 1 | 10 | 54 | 59 | 34 |
| 6 Gilberdyke Phoenix | 22 | 10 | 4 | 8 | 43 | 54 | 34 |
| 7 Hedon Rangers Reserves | 22 | 10 | 2 | 10 | 59 | 48 | 32 |
| 8 Hornsea Town Reserves | 22 | 7 | 5 | 10 | 43 | 58 | 26 |
| 9 North Ferriby United Academy | 22 | 5 | 4 | 13 | 42 | 60 | 19 |
| 10 Molescroft Rangers | 22 | 4 | 4 | 14 | 38 | 62 | 16 |
| 11 Haltemprice | 22 | 4 | 4 | 14 | 41 | 67 | 16 |
| 12 Driffield Evening Institute Reserves | 22 | 2 | 1 | 19 | 29 | 92 | 7 |

| Division Two | P | W | D | L | F | A | Pts |
|---|---|---|---|---|---|---|---|
| 1 Leven Members Club | 24 | 19 | 2 | 3 | 83 | 40 | 59 |
| 2 Eastern Raiders | 24 | 15 | 3 | 6 | 58 | 47 | 48 |
| 3 Skirlaugh | 24 | 15 | 2 | 7 | 69 | 49 | 47 |
| 4 West Hull Amateurs | 24 | 13 | 3 | 8 | 53 | 54 | 42 |
| 5 Aldbrough United | 24 | 11 | 2 | 11 | 42 | 32 | 35 |
| 6 Westella and Willerby Juniors | 24 | 10 | 3 | 11 | 45 | 37 | 33 |
| 7 Full Measure | 24 | 9 | 4 | 11 | 60 | 65 | 31 |
| 8 Goole United Academy | 24 | 8 | 6 | 10 | 46 | 54 | 30 |
| 9 Skidby Millers | 24 | 9 | 2 | 13 | 39 | 63 | 29 |
| 10 Lord Nelson | 24 | 8 | 3 | 13 | 49 | 59 | 27 |
| 11 Malet Lambert Youth Club Res. | 24 | 8 | 3 | 13 | 53 | 66 | 27 |
| 12 Beverley Town Beavers | 24 | 7 | 5 | 12 | 46 | 50 | 26 |
| 13 Shiptonthorpe United | 24 | 3 | 4 | 17 | 41 | 68 | 13 |

| Division Three | P | W | D | L | F | A | Pts |
|---|---|---|---|---|---|---|---|
| 1 Middleton Rovers | 22 | 19 | 1 | 2 | 114 | 39 | 58 |
| 2 Priory Athletic | 22 | 16 | 3 | 3 | 97 | 49 | 51 |
| 3 Langtoft | 22 | 16 | 1 | 5 | 95 | 49 | 49 |
| 4 South Cave Sporting Club Reserves | 22 | 13 | 2 | 7 | 85 | 56 | 41 |
| 5 Skirlaugh Reserves | 22 | 9 | 4 | 9 | 71 | 61 | 31 |
| 6 Howden Reserves | 22 | 9 | 4 | 9 | 62 | 58 | 31 |
| 7 Roos | 22 | 9 | 3 | 10 | 54 | 53 | 30 |
| 8 Old Zoological | 22 | 9 | 1 | 12 | 54 | 74 | 28 |
| 9 Long Riston Reserves (-3pts) | 22 | 8 | 0 | 14 | 56 | 84 | 21 |
| 10 Withernsea Reserves (+3pts) | 22 | 5 | 1 | 16 | 48 | 97 | 19 |
| 11 Brandesburton Reserves | 22 | 3 | 6 | 13 | 29 | 95 | 15 |
| 12 Market Weighton United | 22 | 2 | 2 | 18 | 26 | 76 | 8 |

| Division Four | P | W | D | L | F | A | Pts |
|---|---|---|---|---|---|---|---|
| 1 FC Ridings | 20 | 16 | 3 | 1 | 55 | 28 | 51 |
| 2 Hutton Cranswick SRA | 20 | 13 | 5 | 2 | 46 | 20 | 44 |
| 3 Newland Young Boys | 20 | 12 | 3 | 5 | 60 | 28 | 39 |
| 4 Mill Lane United | 20 | 10 | 5 | 5 | 51 | 33 | 35 |
| 5 Eastrington Village | 20 | 9 | 4 | 7 | 33 | 37 | 31 |
| 6 Easington United Casuals | 20 | 9 | 2 | 9 | 34 | 56 | 29 |
| 7 Gilberdyke Phoenix Reserves | 20 | 7 | 2 | 11 | 38 | 46 | 23 |
| 8 Shiptonthorpe United Reserves | 20 | 5 | 4 | 11 | 35 | 45 | 19 |
| 9 Leven Members Club Reserves | 20 | 6 | 1 | 13 | 32 | 48 | 19 |
| 10 Newbald United | 20 | 3 | 3 | 14 | 31 | 51 | 12 |
| 11 East Hull Athletic | 20 | 3 | 2 | 15 | 24 | 47 | 11 |

| Division Five | P | W | D | L | F | A | Pts |
|---|---|---|---|---|---|---|---|
| 1 Bluebell Nafferton | 20 | 15 | 0 | 5 | 87 | 41 | 45 |
| 2 East Riding Rangers Reserves | 20 | 14 | 3 | 3 | 82 | 39 | 45 |
| 3 Holme Rovers Reserves | 20 | 14 | 1 | 5 | 63 | 31 | 43 |
| 4 Hornsea Town 3rd Team | 20 | 10 | 2 | 8 | 52 | 55 | 32 |
| 5 Hedon Rangers Juniors | 20 | 9 | 2 | 9 | 58 | 60 | 29 |
| 6 Cottingham Forest | 20 | 8 | 4 | 8 | 56 | 51 | 28 |
| 7 Cottingham Rangers | 20 | 7 | 3 | 10 | 36 | 38 | 24 |
| 8 Withernsea 3rd Team | 20 | 6 | 6 | 8 | 20 | 58 | 24 |
| 9 Molescroft Rangers Reserves | 20 | 4 | 6 | 10 | 41 | 62 | 18 |
| 10 Haltemprice Reserves | 20 | 5 | 2 | 13 | 45 | 68 | 17 |
| 11 Market Weighton United Reserves | 20 | 3 | 1 | 16 | 27 | 64 | 10 |

## LEAGUE TABLES

### Division Six

| | | P | W | D | L | F | A | Pts |
|---|---|---|---|---|---|---|---|---|
| 1 | Cottingham Rangers Reserves | 18 | 16 | 1 | 1 | 96 | 23 | 49 |
| 2 | South Park Rangers | 18 | 14 | 1 | 3 | 62 | 21 | 43 |
| 3 | Wawne United 3rd Team | 18 | 13 | 2 | 3 | 62 | 28 | 41 |
| 4 | West Hull Amateurs Reserves | 18 | 9 | 2 | 7 | 55 | 51 | 29 |
| 5 | Hornsea Town 4th Team | 18 | 8 | 3 | 7 | 42 | 46 | 27 |
| 6 | Bilton Athletic FC | 18 | 7 | 3 | 8 | 38 | 69 | 24 |
| 7 | Howden 3rd Team | 18 | 4 | 4 | 10 | 36 | 68 | 16 |
| 8 | Leven Members Club 3rd Team | 18 | 4 | 2 | 12 | 24 | 47 | 14 |
| 9 | Eastrington Village Reserves | 18 | 2 | 2 | 14 | 32 | 46 | 8 |
| 10 | Withernsea 4th Team | 18 | 1 | 4 | 13 | 20 | 68 | 7 |

## ENFIELD ALLIANCE

### Premier Division

| | | P | W | D | L | F | A | Pts |
|---|---|---|---|---|---|---|---|---|
| 1 | Broadwater Utd. | 15 | 9 | 3 | 3 | 36 | 19 | 30 |
| 2 | Origin | 15 | 9 | 2 | 4 | 39 | 31 | 29 |
| 3 | Brimsdown Rvrs. | 15 | 7 | 4 | 4 | 38 | 34 | 25 |
| 4 | Persian | 15 | 7 | 3 | 5 | 47 | 30 | 24 |
| 5 | Crescent Rngrs. | 15 | 3 | 1 | 11 | 25 | 49 | 10 |
| 6 | F.F.London | 15 | 2 | 3 | 10 | 24 | 46 | 9 |

## ESKVALE & CLEVELAND LEAGUE

### Division One

| | | P | W | D | L | F | A | Pts |
|---|---|---|---|---|---|---|---|---|
| 1 | Lingdale United | 20 | 17 | 1 | 2 | 121 | 33 | 52 |
| 2 | Lealholm FC | 20 | 15 | 3 | 2 | 66 | 33 | 48 |
| 3 | Staithes Athletic | 20 | 13 | 3 | 4 | 68 | 28 | 42 |
| 4 | Loftus Athletic | 20 | 13 | 1 | 6 | 78 | 33 | 40 |
| 5 | Stokesley SC | 20 | 12 | 3 | 5 | 67 | 45 | 39 |
| 6 | Boosbeck Utd AFC (-3pts) | 20 | 8 | 2 | 10 | 55 | 58 | 23 |
| 7 | Brotton Railway Arms FC (-3pts) | 20 | 7 | 2 | 11 | 34 | 71 | 20 |
| 8 | Goldsborough United | 20 | 5 | 3 | 12 | 37 | 67 | 18 |
| 9 | Hinderwell F.C. | 20 | 3 | 2 | 15 | 24 | 72 | 11 |
| 10 | Hollybush United | 20 | 3 | 2 | 15 | 30 | 81 | 11 |
| 11 | Great Ayton Utd (-3pts) | 20 | 2 | 2 | 16 | 35 | 94 | 5 |

## ESSEX BUSINESS HOMES LEAGUE

### Premier Division

| | | P | W | D | L | F | A | Pts |
|---|---|---|---|---|---|---|---|---|
| 1 | Snaresbrook | 20 | 14 | 5 | 1 | 53 | 28 | 47 |
| 2 | FC Hamlets | 18 | 13 | 2 | 3 | 44 | 29 | 41 |
| 3 | Newtown Wesley | 19 | 10 | 3 | 6 | 63 | 44 | 33 |
| 4 | Essex United | 15 | 8 | 2 | 5 | 43 | 31 | 26 |
| 5 | Flanders | 18 | 7 | 4 | 7 | 29 | 32 | 25 |
| 6 | R.W.M.C. | 20 | 7 | 3 | 10 | 32 | 45 | 24 |
| 7 | Switch Bar | 18 | 7 | 2 | 9 | 23 | 30 | 23 |
| 8 | St Johns Deaf | 17 | 6 | 4 | 7 | 40 | 45 | 22 |
| 9 | Blue Marlin | 17 | 4 | 3 | 10 | 42 | 45 | 15 |
| 10 | Silk | 16 | 4 | 1 | 11 | 22 | 32 | 13 |
| 11 | Singh Sabha Barking | 20 | 3 | 3 | 14 | 28 | 58 | 12 |

## FURNESS PREMIER LEAGUE

### Premier Division

| | | P | W | D | L | F | A | Pts |
|---|---|---|---|---|---|---|---|---|
| 1 | Vickerstown Reserves | 24 | 19 | 3 | 2 | 94 | 27 | 60 |
| 2 | Bootle | 24 | 16 | 4 | 4 | 92 | 39 | 52 |
| 3 | Haverigg United | 24 | 15 | 2 | 7 | 54 | 30 | 47 |
| 4 | Holker Old Boys Reserves | 24 | 13 | 6 | 5 | 59 | 45 | 45 |
| 5 | Furness Rovers Reserves | 24 | 10 | 6 | 8 | 49 | 44 | 36 |
| 6 | Kirkby United | 24 | 12 | 0 | 12 | 64 | 64 | 36 |
| 7 | Millom Reserves | 24 | 9 | 3 | 12 | 43 | 53 | 30 |
| 8 | Britannia | 24 | 8 | 3 | 13 | 56 | 63 | 27 |
| 9 | Hawcoat Park Reserves | 24 | 8 | 1 | 15 | 62 | 67 | 25 |
| 10 | Crooklands Casuals Reserves (-3pts) | 24 | 9 | 1 | 14 | 52 | 70 | 25 |
| 11 | Barrow Celtic | 24 | 7 | 4 | 13 | 50 | 73 | 25 |
| 12 | Dalton United Reserves | 24 | 7 | 3 | 14 | 33 | 65 | 24 |
| 13 | Barrow Wanderers Reserves | 24 | 3 | 4 | 17 | 41 | 109 | 13 |

### Division One

| | | P | W | D | L | F | A | Pts |
|---|---|---|---|---|---|---|---|---|
| 1 | Barrow Island | 18 | 12 | 2 | 4 | 42 | 31 | 38 |
| 2 | Furness Cavaliers Reserves | 18 | 9 | 5 | 4 | 37 | 21 | 32 |
| 3 | Walney Island Reserves | 18 | 8 | 5 | 5 | 30 | 22 | 29 |
| 4 | Holker Old Boys 'A' | 18 | 8 | 4 | 6 | 35 | 30 | 28 |
| 5 | Swarthmoor Social Reserves | 18 | 8 | 4 | 6 | 30 | 30 | 28 |
| 6 | Askam United Reserves | 18 | 8 | 3 | 7 | 54 | 34 | 27 |
| 7 | GSK Ulverston Rangers Reserves | 18 | 7 | 6 | 5 | 34 | 30 | 27 |
| 8 | Vickerstown 'A' | 18 | 7 | 3 | 8 | 38 | 35 | 24 |
| 9 | Millom 'A' | 18 | 6 | 0 | 12 | 40 | 65 | 18 |
| 10 | Dalton United 'A' | 18 | 1 | 0 | 17 | 23 | 65 | 3 |

### Division Two

| | | P | W | D | L | F | A | Pts |
|---|---|---|---|---|---|---|---|---|
| 1 | Britannia Reserves | 16 | 11 | 2 | 3 | 38 | 21 | 35 |
| 2 | Haverigg United Reserves | 16 | 11 | 1 | 4 | 45 | 20 | 34 |
| 3 | Furness Rovers 'A' | 16 | 8 | 2 | 6 | 55 | 36 | 26 |
| 4 | Bootle Reserves | 16 | 7 | 1 | 8 | 39 | 41 | 22 |
| 5 | Barrow Wanderers 'A' | 16 | 7 | 1 | 8 | 48 | 55 | 22 |
| 6 | Walney Island 'A' (-3pts) | 16 | 7 | 1 | 8 | 46 | 56 | 19 |
| 7 | Hawcoat Park 'A' | 16 | 5 | 2 | 9 | 43 | 46 | 17 |
| 8 | Askam United 'A' (-3pts) | 16 | 5 | 3 | 8 | 30 | 40 | 15 |
| 9 | Barrow Celtic Reserves | 16 | 3 | 3 | 10 | 33 | 62 | 12 |

## GLOUCESTERSHIRE NORTHERN LEAGUE

### Division One

| | | P | W | D | L | F | A | Pts |
|---|---|---|---|---|---|---|---|---|
| 1 | Gala Wilton | 30 | 25 | 1 | 4 | 84 | 26 | 76 |
| 2 | Cheltenham Civil Service | 30 | 20 | 3 | 7 | 61 | 29 | 63 |
| 3 | Cam Bulldogs | 30 | 18 | 5 | 7 | 63 | 37 | 59 |
| 4 | Harrow Hill | 30 | 14 | 7 | 9 | 55 | 51 | 49 |
| 5 | Sharpness | 30 | 14 | 5 | 11 | 72 | 48 | 47 |
| 6 | Broadwell Amateurs | 30 | 12 | 9 | 9 | 54 | 44 | 45 |
| 7 | Star FC | 30 | 12 | 5 | 13 | 63 | 58 | 41 |
| 8 | Stonehouse Town | 30 | 13 | 1 | 16 | 53 | 55 | 40 |
| 9 | Bredon (-1pt) | 30 | 10 | 7 | 13 | 71 | 70 | 36 |
| 10 | Dursley Town | 30 | 9 | 9 | 12 | 61 | 67 | 36 |
| 11 | Brockworth Albion | 30 | 9 | 9 | 12 | 47 | 55 | 36 |
| 12 | Ramblers | 30 | 10 | 3 | 17 | 46 | 79 | 33 |
| 13 | Lydbrook Athletic | 30 | 8 | 7 | 15 | 31 | 55 | 31 |
| 14 | Leonard Stanley | 30 | 8 | 6 | 16 | 43 | 70 | 30 |
| 15 | Smiths Athletic | 30 | 8 | 5 | 17 | 35 | 66 | 29 |
| 16 | Winchcombe Town | 30 | 6 | 6 | 18 | 42 | 73 | 24 |

### Division Two

| | | P | W | D | L | F | A | Pts |
|---|---|---|---|---|---|---|---|---|
| 1 | Ruardean Hill Rangers | 30 | 26 | 0 | 4 | 106 | 43 | 78 |
| 2 | Minsterworth | 30 | 24 | 3 | 3 | 103 | 33 | 75 |
| 3 | Hardwicke | 30 | 22 | 4 | 4 | 92 | 42 | 70 |
| 4 | Moreton Rangers | 30 | 21 | 2 | 7 | 92 | 41 | 65 |
| 5 | Abbeymead Rovers | 30 | 20 | 3 | 7 | 65 | 47 | 63 |
| 6 | FC Barometrics | 30 | 17 | 4 | 9 | 88 | 46 | 55 |
| 7 | Real Whaddon | 30 | 11 | 5 | 14 | 79 | 76 | 38 |
| 8 | Longford | 30 | 11 | 4 | 15 | 52 | 62 | 37 |
| 9 | Tuffley Rovers Res | 30 | 9 | 4 | 17 | 48 | 63 | 31 |
| 10 | Viney St Swithins | 30 | 8 | 6 | 16 | 61 | 71 | 30 |
| 11 | Chalford | 30 | 8 | 6 | 16 | 43 | 82 | 30 |
| 12 | Soudley | 30 | 8 | 2 | 20 | 44 | 90 | 26 |
| 13 | Stroud F.C. | 30 | 6 | 7 | 17 | 47 | 87 | 25 |
| 14 | Bourton Rovers | 30 | 6 | 6 | 18 | 49 | 82 | 24 |
| 15 | Wotton Rovers | 30 | 5 | 9 | 16 | 53 | 76 | 24 |
| 16 | Barnwood United | 30 | 3 | 5 | 22 | 42 | 104 | 14 |

## GRANTHAM & DISTRICT LEAGUE

| Premier Division | P | W | D | L | F | A | Pts |
|---|---|---|---|---|---|---|---|
| 1 White Swan Barrowby | 16 | 12 | 2 | 2 | 61 | 18 | 38 |
| 2 Buckminster United | 16 | 10 | 3 | 3 | 54 | 27 | 33 |
| 3 Harrowby Reserves | 16 | 9 | 2 | 5 | 43 | 26 | 29 |
| 4 Bottesford | 16 | 7 | 5 | 4 | 38 | 29 | 26 |
| 5 Greyhounders | 16 | 7 | 2 | 7 | 26 | 34 | 23 |
| 6 White Horse Sleaford | 16 | 5 | 4 | 7 | 36 | 35 | 19 |
| 7 Ancaster | 16 | 4 | 3 | 9 | 36 | 60 | 15 |
| 8 Heckington Millers | 16 | 2 | 4 | 10 | 32 | 60 | 10 |
| 9 Cranmer Arms | 16 | 2 | 3 | 11 | 29 | 66 | 9 |

| Division One | P | W | D | L | F | A | Pts |
|---|---|---|---|---|---|---|---|
| 1 CK Dons | 10 | 9 | 0 | 1 | 29 | 10 | 27 |
| 2 AFC Three Gables | 10 | 7 | 0 | 3 | 32 | 13 | 21 |
| 3 Croxton AFC | 10 | 6 | 1 | 3 | 23 | 20 | 19 |
| 4 Bottesford Reserves | 10 | 3 | 0 | 7 | 14 | 37 | 9 |
| 5 Rippingale & Folkingham | 10 | 2 | 2 | 6 | 16 | 30 | 8 |
| 6 Caythorpe | 10 | 1 | 1 | 8 | 14 | 18 | 4 |

| Division Two | P | W | D | L | F | A | Pts |
|---|---|---|---|---|---|---|---|
| 1 AFC Three Gables | 6 | 4 | 1 | 1 | 27 | 7 | 13 |
| 2 Croxton AFC | 6 | 3 | 0 | 3 | 9 | 19 | 9 |
| 3 Bottesford Reserves | 6 | 2 | 1 | 3 | 7 | 13 | 7 |
| 4 Rippingale & Folkingham | 6 | 1 | 2 | 3 | 15 | 19 | 5 |

## GREAT YARMOUTH & DISTRICT LEAGUE

| Division One | P | W | D | L | F | A | Pts |
|---|---|---|---|---|---|---|---|
| 1 Haven Bridge United | 14 | 13 | 0 | 1 | 60 | 18 | 39 |
| 2 Catfield | 14 | 12 | 1 | 1 | 63 | 13 | 37 |
| 3 MK Shrubs | 14 | 7 | 3 | 4 | 40 | 26 | 24 |
| 4 Albion Tramway | 14 | 6 | 2 | 6 | 38 | 30 | 20 |
| 5 Caister Roma | 14 | 6 | 1 | 7 | 46 | 40 | 19 |
| 6 Great Yarmouth International | 14 | 3 | 1 | 10 | 17 | 44 | 10 |
| 7 South Yarmouth | 14 | 3 | 1 | 10 | 22 | 65 | 10 |
| 8 Bohemians | 14 | 1 | 1 | 12 | 20 | 70 | 4 |

| Division Two | P | W | D | L | F | A | Pts |
|---|---|---|---|---|---|---|---|
| 1 Wanderers | 16 | 11 | 2 | 3 | 67 | 23 | 35 |
| 2 Great Yarmouth Peelers | 16 | 11 | 2 | 3 | 60 | 30 | 35 |
| 3 Caister FC A | 16 | 10 | 3 | 3 | 52 | 29 | 33 |
| 4 Prostar Windows | 16 | 9 | 3 | 4 | 39 | 29 | 30 |
| 5 MK Shrubs Reserves | 16 | 8 | 2 | 6 | 38 | 30 | 26 |
| 6 Caister Roma Reserves | 16 | 5 | 3 | 8 | 44 | 40 | 18 |
| 7 Filby and Runham | 16 | 6 | 0 | 10 | 50 | 47 | 18 |
| 8 Grosvenor Casino | 16 | 3 | 2 | 11 | 34 | 59 | 11 |
| 9 Martham A | 16 | 0 | 1 | 15 | 10 | 107 | 1 |

## GUERNSEY LEAGUE

| Priaulx League | P | W | D | L | F | A | Pts |
|---|---|---|---|---|---|---|---|
| 1 Belgrave Wanderers | 24 | 19 | 4 | 1 | 87 | 21 | 61 |
| 2 Vale Rec | 24 | 17 | 3 | 4 | 58 | 28 | 54 |
| 3 St Martins | 24 | 13 | 5 | 6 | 74 | 43 | 44 |
| 4 North | 24 | 11 | 5 | 8 | 62 | 36 | 38 |
| 5 Sylvans | 24 | 7 | 2 | 15 | 35 | 58 | 23 |
| 6 Rangers | 24 | 6 | 3 | 15 | 44 | 76 | 21 |
| 7 Rovers | 24 | 0 | 0 | 24 | 15 | 113 | 0 |

| Jackson League | P | W | D | L | F | A | Pts |
|---|---|---|---|---|---|---|---|
| 1 Belgrave Wanderers Reserves | 14 | 12 | 1 | 1 | 65 | 18 | 37 |
| 2 North Reserves | 14 | 9 | 2 | 3 | 41 | 22 | 29 |
| 3 Sylvans Reserves | 14 | 9 | 0 | 5 | 44 | 32 | 27 |
| 4 Bavaria Nomads | 14 | 6 | 1 | 7 | 34 | 45 | 19 |
| 5 Centrals Reserves | 14 | 6 | 0 | 8 | 38 | 43 | 18 |
| 6 St Martins Reserves | 14 | 5 | 2 | 7 | 29 | 42 | 17 |
| 7 Vale Rec Reserves | 14 | 3 | 1 | 10 | 21 | 49 | 10 |
| 8 Rangers Reserves | 14 | 2 | 1 | 11 | 25 | 46 | 7 |

## GUILDFORD & WOKING ALLIANCE

| Premier Division | P | W | D | L | F | A | Pts |
|---|---|---|---|---|---|---|---|
| 1 Chertsey Old Salesians | 16 | 10 | 1 | 5 | 44 | 18 | 31 |
| 2 Lyne | 16 | 9 | 4 | 3 | 44 | 19 | 31 |
| 3 Laleham | 16 | 9 | 3 | 4 | 49 | 17 | 30 |
| 4 Keens Park Rangers | 16 | 8 | 4 | 4 | 45 | 30 | 28 |
| 5 Hambledon | 16 | 5 | 5 | 6 | 21 | 20 | 20 |
| 6 N.L.U. | 16 | 5 | 3 | 8 | 30 | 38 | 18 |
| 7 Puttenham United | 16 | 4 | 3 | 9 | 25 | 67 | 15 |
| 8 Burpham | 16 | 3 | 5 | 8 | 18 | 30 | 14 |
| 9 West Byfleet Albion | 16 | 3 | 4 | 9 | 26 | 53 | 13 |

| Division One | P | W | D | L | F | A | Pts |
|---|---|---|---|---|---|---|---|
| 1 Guildford United | 22 | 15 | 3 | 4 | 71 | 41 | 48 |
| 2 FC Shepperton | 22 | 13 | 4 | 5 | 66 | 31 | 43 |
| 3 Dunsfold | 22 | 14 | 1 | 7 | 58 | 40 | 43 |
| 4 Guildford Rangers | 22 | 12 | 4 | 6 | 64 | 40 | 40 |
| 5 Merrow 'A' | 22 | 11 | 3 | 8 | 70 | 43 | 36 |
| 6 Holmbury St Mary Reserves | 22 | 11 | 2 | 9 | 47 | 41 | 35 |
| 7 Hersham | 22 | 9 | 3 | 10 | 54 | 67 | 30 |
| 8 University of Surrey 'A' | 22 | 7 | 4 | 11 | 45 | 63 | 25 |
| 9 Elstead | 22 | 7 | 3 | 12 | 48 | 50 | 24 |
| 10 AFC Bedfont Green | 22 | 6 | 2 | 14 | 36 | 76 | 20 |
| 11 Abbey Rangers 'A' | 22 | 5 | 3 | 14 | 31 | 71 | 18 |
| 12 Guildford City Weysiders | 22 | 4 | 4 | 14 | 32 | 59 | 16 |

| Division Two | P | W | D | L | F | A | Pts |
|---|---|---|---|---|---|---|---|
| 1 AFC Bedfont Green Reserves | 20 | 16 | 2 | 2 | 72 | 23 | 50 |
| 2 Guildford Park | 20 | 15 | 2 | 3 | 66 | 21 | 47 |
| 3 Manorcroft United | 20 | 15 | 2 | 3 | 61 | 26 | 47 |
| 4 The Bourne | 20 | 13 | 2 | 5 | 60 | 39 | 41 |
| 5 AFC Gomshall | 20 | 8 | 2 | 10 | 48 | 57 | 26 |
| 6 Staines Lammas Reserves | 20 | 7 | 4 | 9 | 55 | 47 | 25 |
| 7 AFC Crown & Anchor | 20 | 6 | 1 | 13 | 34 | 50 | 19 |
| 8 Guildford United Reserves | 20 | 5 | 2 | 13 | 36 | 64 | 17 |
| 9 Knaphill Athletic 'A' | 20 | 4 | 4 | 12 | 43 | 72 | 16 |
| 10 Blackwater Royals | 20 | 4 | 3 | 13 | 34 | 76 | 15 |
| 11 Ripley Village 'A' | 20 | 4 | 2 | 14 | 34 | 68 | 14 |

| Division Three | P | W | D | L | F | A | Pts |
|---|---|---|---|---|---|---|---|
| 1 Astolat Athletic | 16 | 16 | 0 | 0 | 94 | 10 | 48 |
| 2 AFC Brooklands Seniors | 16 | 11 | 0 | 5 | 53 | 25 | 33 |
| 3 Worplesdon Phoenix 'A' | 16 | 9 | 1 | 6 | 60 | 38 | 28 |
| 4 Chertsey Old Salesians Reserves | 16 | 7 | 3 | 6 | 41 | 30 | 24 |
| 5 Allianz | 16 | 7 | 2 | 7 | 37 | 41 | 23 |
| 6 Burpham Reserves | 16 | 7 | 1 | 8 | 42 | 51 | 22 |
| 7 Cranleigh 'A' | 16 | 6 | 2 | 8 | 32 | 44 | 20 |
| 8 Chobham Burymead 'A' | 16 | 3 | 2 | 11 | 23 | 59 | 11 |
| 9 Hambledon Reserves | 16 | 0 | 1 | 15 | 14 | 98 | 1 |

# LEAGUE TABLES

| Division Four North | P | W | D | L | F | A | Pts |
|---|---|---|---|---|---|---|---|
| 1 Addlestone | 18 | 13 | 3 | 2 | 58 | 20 | 42 |
| 2 Christian Club Woking | 18 | 12 | 3 | 3 | 51 | 29 | 39 |
| 3 Woking United Sports Club | 18 | 12 | 1 | 5 | 67 | 31 | 37 |
| 4 AFC Watermans | 18 | 10 | 2 | 6 | 37 | 28 | 32 |
| 5 University of Surrey 'B' | 18 | 10 | 1 | 7 | 40 | 39 | 31 |
| 6 Woking Tigers | 18 | 7 | 1 | 10 | 47 | 54 | 22 |
| 7 Lyne Reserves | 18 | 6 | 1 | 11 | 43 | 55 | 19 |
| 8 Surrey Athletic | 18 | 5 | 2 | 11 | 49 | 62 | 17 |
| 9 Byfleet | 18 | 4 | 1 | 13 | 27 | 54 | 13 |
| 10 Knaphill Athletic 'B' | 18 | 3 | 1 | 14 | 33 | 80 | 10 |

| Division Four South | P | W | D | L | F | A | Pts |
|---|---|---|---|---|---|---|---|
| 1 Worplesdon Phoenix 'B' | 18 | 13 | 3 | 2 | 59 | 34 | 42 |
| 2 Dunsfold Reserves | 18 | 13 | 1 | 4 | 90 | 32 | 40 |
| 3 Shottermill & Haslemere 'A' | 18 | 9 | 5 | 4 | 34 | 37 | 32 |
| 4 Guildford Park Reserves | 18 | 9 | 3 | 6 | 57 | 48 | 30 |
| 5 Milford & Witley 'A' | 18 | 8 | 2 | 8 | 39 | 44 | 26 |
| 6 Elstead Reserves | 18 | 7 | 4 | 7 | 54 | 48 | 25 |
| 7 Guildford City Weysiders Reserves | 18 | 7 | 4 | 7 | 33 | 33 | 25 |
| 8 Guildford Vapors | 18 | 5 | 2 | 11 | 52 | 70 | 17 |
| 9 Guildford Rangers Reserves | 18 | 4 | 1 | 13 | 42 | 59 | 13 |
| 10 Guildford United 'A' | 18 | 2 | 1 | 15 | 23 | 78 | 7 |

| Division Two | P | W | D | L | F | A | Pts |
|---|---|---|---|---|---|---|---|
| 1 Sowerby Bridge Reserves | 18 | 14 | 2 | 2 | 85 | 35 | 44 |
| 2 Greetland AFC Reserves | 18 | 10 | 3 | 5 | 53 | 34 | 33 |
| 3 Warley Rangers Reserves | 18 | 9 | 5 | 4 | 44 | 30 | 32 |
| 4 AFC Crossleys | 18 | 9 | 2 | 7 | 65 | 69 | 29 |
| 5 Shelf United Reserves | 18 | 8 | 4 | 6 | 62 | 58 | 28 |
| 6 Halifax Athletic | 18 | 8 | 2 | 8 | 46 | 49 | 26 |
| 7 Hebden Royd RS Reserves | 18 | 7 | 4 | 7 | 37 | 48 | 25 |
| 8 Midgley United Reserves | 18 | 5 | 2 | 11 | 41 | 45 | 17 |
| 9 Sowerby United Reserves | 18 | 3 | 2 | 13 | 39 | 63 | 11 |
| 10 Halifax Irish Centre Reserves | 18 | 3 | 2 | 13 | 39 | 80 | 11 |

| Division Three | P | W | D | L | F | A | Pts |
|---|---|---|---|---|---|---|---|
| 1 Denholme United Reserves | 18 | 12 | 3 | 3 | 39 | 24 | 39 |
| 2 Spring Hall Celtic | 18 | 12 | 2 | 4 | 87 | 26 | 38 |
| 3 Calder 76 Reserves | 18 | 12 | 2 | 4 | 74 | 31 | 38 |
| 4 Shelf FC | 18 | 12 | 2 | 4 | 70 | 34 | 38 |
| 5 Savile Arms FC | 18 | 9 | 3 | 6 | 55 | 48 | 30 |
| 6 Brighouse Sports AFC | 18 | 7 | 3 | 8 | 49 | 44 | 24 |
| 7 Elland Allstars Reserves | 18 | 5 | 2 | 11 | 48 | 76 | 17 |
| 8 West Central FC | 18 | 4 | 4 | 10 | 34 | 63 | 16 |
| 9 Volunteer Arms Reserves | 18 | 3 | 3 | 12 | 31 | 80 | 12 |
| 10 Salem Reserves | 18 | 1 | 2 | 15 | 15 | 76 | 5 |

## HALIFAX & DISTRICT LEAGUE

| Premier Division | P | W | D | L | F | A | Pts |
|---|---|---|---|---|---|---|---|
| 1 Midgley United | 20 | 17 | 2 | 1 | 75 | 30 | 53 |
| 2 Stump Cross | 20 | 14 | 3 | 3 | 64 | 30 | 45 |
| 3 Elland United | 20 | 10 | 3 | 7 | 47 | 46 | 33 |
| 4 Ryburn United | 20 | 9 | 4 | 7 | 59 | 44 | 31 |
| 5 Warley Rangers | 20 | 6 | 8 | 6 | 38 | 44 | 26 |
| 6 Holmfield | 20 | 6 | 6 | 8 | 49 | 52 | 24 |
| 7 Greetland AFC | 20 | 7 | 3 | 10 | 42 | 50 | 24 |
| 8 Calder 76 | 20 | 6 | 3 | 11 | 45 | 52 | 21 |
| 9 Copley United | 20 | 6 | 1 | 13 | 39 | 68 | 19 |
| 10 Sowerby United | 20 | 4 | 6 | 10 | 42 | 55 | 18 |
| 11 Shelf United | 20 | 4 | 3 | 13 | 40 | 69 | 15 |

| Division One | P | W | D | L | F | A | Pts |
|---|---|---|---|---|---|---|---|
| 1 Hebden Royd RS | 22 | 18 | 3 | 1 | 66 | 29 | 57 |
| 2 Sowerby Bridge | 22 | 17 | 3 | 2 | 87 | 50 | 54 |
| 3 Wadsworth United | 22 | 11 | 5 | 6 | 56 | 36 | 38 |
| 4 Elland Allstars | 22 | 11 | 3 | 8 | 56 | 58 | 36 |
| 5 Salem | 22 | 11 | 1 | 10 | 63 | 68 | 34 |
| 6 Northowram | 22 | 10 | 2 | 10 | 64 | 55 | 32 |
| 7 Volunteer Arms | 22 | 9 | 1 | 12 | 62 | 86 | 28 |
| 8 Denholme United | 22 | 7 | 5 | 10 | 79 | 74 | 26 |
| 9 Halifax Irish Centre | 22 | 7 | 1 | 14 | 68 | 84 | 22 |
| 10 Ryburn United Reserves | 22 | 6 | 3 | 13 | 48 | 65 | 21 |
| 11 Stainland United | 22 | 6 | 2 | 14 | 51 | 73 | 20 |
| 12 Mixenden United | 22 | 2 | 5 | 15 | 41 | 63 | 11 |

## HALSTEAD & DISTRICT LEAGUE

| Premier Division | P | W | D | L | F | A | Pts |
|---|---|---|---|---|---|---|---|
| 1 Belchamps | 24 | 17 | 3 | 4 | 79 | 30 | 54 |
| 2 Halstead Wanderers | 24 | 16 | 3 | 5 | 81 | 36 | 51 |
| 3 Pebmarsh | 22 | 17 | 0 | 5 | 80 | 36 | 51 |
| 4 Punch 68 | 24 | 16 | 3 | 5 | 58 | 29 | 51 |
| 5 Helions Bumpstead | 24 | 13 | 4 | 7 | 62 | 31 | 43 |
| 6 Acton Crown | 24 | 11 | 4 | 9 | 47 | 41 | 37 |
| 7 Kedington | 23 | 10 | 3 | 10 | 60 | 56 | 33 |
| 8 Sporting 77 | 24 | 9 | 5 | 10 | 51 | 52 | 32 |
| 9 Bures Res | 24 | 9 | 2 | 13 | 46 | 61 | 29 |
| 10 Rayne Res | 24 | 6 | 2 | 16 | 30 | 70 | 20 |
| 11 Clare Reserves | 24 | 5 | 2 | 17 | 50 | 75 | 17 |
| 12 Glemsford Gladiators | 23 | 4 | 4 | 15 | 35 | 79 | 16 |
| 13 Finchingfield | 24 | 3 | 1 | 20 | 30 | 113 | 10 |

## HARROGATE & DISTRICT LEAGUE

| Premier Division | P | W | D | L | F | A | Pts |
|---|---|---|---|---|---|---|---|
| 1 Beckwithshaw Saints | 18 | 13 | 2 | 3 | 65 | 23 | 41 |
| 2 Kirk Deighton Rangers | 18 | 12 | 4 | 2 | 53 | 32 | 40 |
| 3 Harlow Hill | 18 | 8 | 4 | 6 | 43 | 47 | 28 |
| 4 Knaresborough Celtic | 18 | 7 | 5 | 6 | 40 | 38 | 26 |
| 5 Pannal Sports | 18 | 7 | 4 | 7 | 38 | 36 | 25 |
| 6 Killinghall Nomads | 18 | 7 | 4 | 7 | 43 | 45 | 25 |
| 7 Pateley Bridge | 18 | 5 | 5 | 8 | 46 | 51 | 20 |
| 8 Ripon Red Arrows | 18 | 6 | 2 | 10 | 51 | 63 | 20 |
| 9 Kirkby Malzeard | 18 | 4 | 2 | 12 | 32 | 49 | 14 |
| 10 Clifford | 18 | 3 | 4 | 11 | 25 | 52 | 13 |

| Division One | P | W | D | L | F | A | Pts |
|---|---|---|---|---|---|---|---|
| 1 Rawdon Old Boys | 20 | 17 | 2 | 1 | 82 | 17 | 53 |
| 2 Otley Rovers | 20 | 16 | 0 | 4 | 92 | 28 | 48 |
| 3 Kirk Deighton Rangers Reserves | 20 | 12 | 2 | 6 | 45 | 44 | 38 |
| 4 Wetherby Athletic A | 20 | 12 | 1 | 7 | 50 | 33 | 37 |
| 5 Burley Trojans | 20 | 10 | 3 | 7 | 64 | 48 | 33 |
| 6 Thirsk Falcons Reserves | 20 | 10 | 0 | 10 | 52 | 43 | 30 |
| 7 Bedale Reserves | 20 | 7 | 1 | 12 | 45 | 65 | 22 |
| 8 Harlow Hill Reserves | 20 | 6 | 2 | 12 | 42 | 57 | 20 |
| 9 Hillside | 20 | 6 | 2 | 12 | 34 | 59 | 20 |
| 10 Westbrook YMCA Res | 20 | 5 | 2 | 13 | 35 | 54 | 17 |
| 11 Kirkby Malzeard Reserves | 20 | 0 | 3 | 17 | 21 | 114 | 3 |

| Division Two | P | W | D | L | F | A | Pts |
|---|---|---|---|---|---|---|---|
| 1 Hampsthwaite United | 20 | 16 | 1 | 3 | 79 | 37 | 49 |
| 2 Leyburn United | 20 | 15 | 1 | 4 | 88 | 43 | 46 |
| 3 Beckwithshaw Saints Reserves | 20 | 10 | 6 | 4 | 41 | 28 | 36 |
| 4 Dalton Athletic | 20 | 11 | 3 | 6 | 60 | 49 | 36 |
| 5 Boroughbridge A | 20 | 8 | 3 | 9 | 45 | 48 | 27 |
| 6 Bramham | 20 | 7 | 4 | 9 | 48 | 47 | 25 |
| 7 Pannal Sports Reserves | 20 | 7 | 3 | 10 | 40 | 50 | 24 |
| 8 Wetheby Athletic `B` | 20 | 6 | 5 | 9 | 47 | 56 | 23 |
| 9 Albert Sport Yeadon | 20 | 6 | 3 | 11 | 44 | 54 | 21 |
| 10 Bramhope | 20 | 4 | 4 | 12 | 25 | 56 | 16 |
| 11 Pateley Bridge Reserves | 20 | 2 | 3 | 15 | 28 | 77 | 9 |

| Division Three | P | W | D | L | F | A | Pts |
|---|---|---|---|---|---|---|---|
| 1 Hillside Reserves | 20 | 17 | 0 | 3 | 79 | 42 | 51 |
| 2 Addingham | 20 | 14 | 2 | 4 | 90 | 37 | 44 |
| 3 Hampsthwaite HC | 20 | 14 | 1 | 5 | 86 | 44 | 43 |
| 4 Knaresborough Celtic Res | 20 | 13 | 2 | 5 | 63 | 33 | 41 |
| 5 Hampsthwaite United Res | 20 | 9 | 0 | 11 | 51 | 69 | 27 |
| 6 Helperby United | 20 | 8 | 2 | 10 | 78 | 85 | 26 |
| 7 Pool A | 20 | 8 | 1 | 11 | 41 | 64 | 25 |
| 8 Ripon Red Arrows Reserves | 20 | 5 | 3 | 12 | 44 | 66 | 18 |
| 9 Catterick Village | 20 | 5 | 2 | 13 | 38 | 71 | 17 |
| 10 Ilkley Town 'A' | 20 | 5 | 1 | 14 | 26 | 42 | 16 |
| 11 Pannal Sports A | 20 | 4 | 2 | 14 | 37 | 80 | 14 |

## HEREFORDSHIRE LEAGUE

| Premier Division | P | W | D | L | F | A | Pts |
|---|---|---|---|---|---|---|---|
| 1 Wellington Reserves | 16 | 10 | 5 | 1 | 43 | 20 | 35 |
| 2 Ewyas Harold | 16 | 10 | 3 | 3 | 38 | 20 | 33 |
| 3 Fownhope | 16 | 8 | 3 | 5 | 34 | 22 | 27 |
| 4 Sinkum | 16 | 8 | 2 | 6 | 36 | 25 | 26 |
| 5 Westfields Reserves | 16 | 6 | 5 | 5 | 31 | 25 | 23 |
| 6 Mercia Athletic | 16 | 5 | 4 | 7 | 35 | 41 | 19 |
| 7 Hinton | 16 | 6 | 1 | 9 | 24 | 34 | 19 |
| 8 Pegasus Reserves | 16 | 4 | 2 | 10 | 27 | 38 | 14 |
| 9 Kington Town | 16 | 2 | 1 | 13 | 28 | 71 | 7 |

| Division One | P | W | D | L | F | A | Pts |
|---|---|---|---|---|---|---|---|
| 1 Weobley | 18 | 13 | 4 | 1 | 41 | 18 | 43 |
| 2 Shobdon | 18 | 9 | 7 | 2 | 43 | 32 | 34 |
| 3 Wellington Colts | 18 | 11 | 0 | 7 | 52 | 32 | 33 |
| 4 Kingstone Rovers | 18 | 10 | 2 | 6 | 48 | 27 | 32 |
| 5 Ross Juniors | 18 | 9 | 2 | 7 | 41 | 28 | 29 |
| 6 Woofferton | 18 | 6 | 3 | 9 | 38 | 44 | 21 |
| 7 Ewyas Harold Reserves | 18 | 6 | 2 | 10 | 25 | 39 | 20 |
| 8 Ledbury Town Reserves | 18 | 6 | 1 | 11 | 23 | 35 | 19 |
| 9 Hinton Reserves | 18 | 4 | 2 | 12 | 26 | 58 | 14 |
| 10 Holme Lacy | 18 | 4 | 1 | 13 | 36 | 60 | 13 |

| Division Two | P | W | D | L | F | A | Pts |
|---|---|---|---|---|---|---|---|
| 1 Woofferton Colts | 20 | 19 | 0 | 1 | 113 | 22 | 57 |
| 2 Orleton Colts | 20 | 16 | 1 | 3 | 71 | 33 | 49 |
| 3 Pencombe | 20 | 13 | 3 | 4 | 55 | 34 | 42 |
| 4 Civil Service | 20 | 10 | 2 | 8 | 58 | 40 | 32 |
| 5 Fownhope Res | 20 | 9 | 4 | 7 | 43 | 39 | 31 |
| 6 Mercia Athletic Colts | 20 | 9 | 0 | 11 | 57 | 57 | 27 |
| 7 Toros | 20 | 7 | 2 | 11 | 52 | 59 | 23 |
| 8 Weston | 20 | 6 | 1 | 13 | 31 | 53 | 19 |
| 9 Kingstone Harriers | 20 | 5 | 4 | 11 | 34 | 59 | 19 |
| 10 Hereford City (-3pts) | 20 | 5 | 2 | 13 | 35 | 67 | 14 |
| 11 Burghill (-3pts) | 20 | 1 | 1 | 18 | 23 | 109 | 1 |

| Division Three | P | W | D | L | F | A | Pts |
|---|---|---|---|---|---|---|---|
| 1 Bromyard FC | 16 | 16 | 0 | 0 | 91 | 14 | 48 |
| 2 Tenbury Town | 16 | 13 | 1 | 2 | 74 | 14 | 40 |
| 3 Sinkum Colts | 16 | 8 | 5 | 3 | 46 | 22 | 29 |
| 4 Relentless | 16 | 8 | 2 | 6 | 54 | 33 | 26 |
| 5 Orleton Colts Reserves | 16 | 6 | 2 | 8 | 46 | 49 | 20 |
| 6 Kington Town Res | 16 | 4 | 2 | 10 | 32 | 66 | 14 |
| 7 Ross Juniors Reserves | 16 | 4 | 2 | 10 | 28 | 71 | 14 |
| 8 Tenbury Colts | 16 | 3 | 0 | 13 | 21 | 96 | 9 |
| 9 Leintwardine | 16 | 2 | 2 | 12 | 29 | 56 | 8 |

## HOPE VALLEY AMATEUR LEAGUE

| Premier Division | P | W | D | L | F | A | Pts |
|---|---|---|---|---|---|---|---|
| 1 Bradwell | 24 | 21 | 2 | 1 | 96 | 22 | 65 |
| 2 Dove Holes | 24 | 18 | 1 | 5 | 80 | 29 | 55 |
| 3 Tintwistle Villa | 24 | 17 | 2 | 5 | 74 | 45 | 53 |
| 4 Holmesfield | 24 | 15 | 3 | 6 | 65 | 51 | 48 |
| 5 Tideswell United | 24 | 15 | 2 | 7 | 60 | 37 | 47 |
| 6 Dronfield Woodhouse | 24 | 10 | 6 | 8 | 45 | 47 | 36 |
| 7 Brampton | 24 | 9 | 5 | 10 | 48 | 55 | 32 |
| 8 Bakewell Town | 24 | 9 | 4 | 11 | 52 | 66 | 31 |
| 9 Furness Vale | 24 | 6 | 5 | 13 | 46 | 56 | 23 |
| 10 AFC Dronfield Woodhouse | 24 | 6 | 3 | 15 | 42 | 66 | 21 |
| 11 Hunters Bar | 24 | 5 | 3 | 16 | 25 | 65 | 18 |
| 12 Hathersage | 24 | 3 | 3 | 18 | 24 | 65 | 12 |
| 13 Buxton Town | 24 | 0 | 5 | 19 | 27 | 80 | 5 |

# LEAGUE TABLES

## A Division

| | | P | W | D | L | F | A | Pts |
|---|---|---|---|---|---|---|---|---|
| 1 | Peak Dale | 26 | 23 | 2 | 1 | 98 | 27 | 71 |
| 2 | Youlgrave United | 26 | 18 | 2 | 6 | 91 | 48 | 56 |
| 3 | Blazing Rag | 26 | 15 | 5 | 6 | 83 | 39 | 50 |
| 4 | Chinley | 26 | 15 | 4 | 7 | 92 | 51 | 49 |
| 5 | Totley Sports | 26 | 13 | 3 | 10 | 84 | 67 | 42 |
| 6 | Dove Holes Reserves | 26 | 11 | 7 | 8 | 59 | 56 | 40 |
| 7 | Cote Heath | 26 | 12 | 3 | 11 | 70 | 46 | 39 |
| 8 | Buxworth | 26 | 10 | 7 | 9 | 69 | 63 | 37 |
| 9 | Baslow | 26 | 10 | 5 | 11 | 62 | 78 | 35 |
| 10 | Grindleford | 26 | 10 | 1 | 15 | 53 | 68 | 31 |
| 11 | FC United of Tideswell | 26 | 9 | 3 | 14 | 58 | 88 | 30 |
| 12 | Red Lion | 26 | 9 | 2 | 15 | 46 | 76 | 29 |
| 13 | Bamford | 26 | 2 | 1 | 23 | 46 | 133 | 7 |
| 14 | Calver | 26 | 1 | 3 | 22 | 31 | 102 | 6 |

## B Division

| | | P | W | D | L | F | A | Pts |
|---|---|---|---|---|---|---|---|---|
| 1 | Tideswell Blue Star | 26 | 21 | 0 | 5 | 80 | 42 | 63 |
| 2 | Hope Sports | 26 | 19 | 1 | 6 | 132 | 49 | 58 |
| 3 | Chesterfield Town Reserves | 26 | 16 | 2 | 8 | 62 | 44 | 50 |
| 4 | Bradwell Reserves | 26 | 14 | 5 | 7 | 85 | 51 | 47 |
| 5 | Darley Dale Lions | 26 | 11 | 7 | 8 | 64 | 53 | 40 |
| 6 | Eyam | 26 | 11 | 4 | 11 | 51 | 74 | 37 |
| 7 | Dronfield Town B | 26 | 11 | 3 | 12 | 58 | 53 | 36 |
| 8 | Edale | 26 | 9 | 7 | 10 | 49 | 60 | 34 |
| 9 | Furness Vale Reserves | 26 | 9 | 5 | 12 | 71 | 73 | 32 |
| 10 | Winster Wasps | 26 | 7 | 8 | 11 | 39 | 65 | 29 |
| 11 | Buxworth Reserves | 26 | 7 | 4 | 15 | 59 | 91 | 25 |
| 12 | Railway FC | 26 | 7 | 3 | 16 | 62 | 93 | 24 |
| 13 | Stoney Middleton | 26 | 5 | 7 | 14 | 37 | 67 | 22 |
| 14 | Bakewell Town Reserves | 26 | 5 | 4 | 17 | 34 | 68 | 19 |

## HUDDERSFIELD & DISTRICT LEAGUE

### Division One

| | | P | W | D | L | F | A | Pts |
|---|---|---|---|---|---|---|---|---|
| 1 | Uppermill | 20 | 17 | 2 | 1 | 48 | 17 | 53 |
| 2 | Newsome | 20 | 15 | 1 | 4 | 76 | 34 | 46 |
| 3 | Hepworth Utd | 20 | 14 | 3 | 3 | 53 | 18 | 45 |
| 4 | Diggle | 20 | 8 | 4 | 8 | 50 | 45 | 28 |
| 5 | Netherton | 20 | 8 | 3 | 9 | 50 | 45 | 27 |
| 6 | Holmbridge | 20 | 6 | 5 | 9 | 43 | 51 | 23 |
| 7 | Scholes | 20 | 6 | 4 | 10 | 37 | 52 | 22 |
| 8 | Berry Brow | 20 | 6 | 2 | 12 | 28 | 45 | 20 |
| 9 | Lepton Highlanders | 20 | 4 | 5 | 11 | 41 | 68 | 17 |
| 10 | Shepley | 20 | 3 | 7 | 10 | 30 | 63 | 16 |
| 11 | Moldgreen | 20 | 4 | 2 | 14 | 35 | 53 | 14 |

### Division Two

| | | P | W | D | L | F | A | Pts |
|---|---|---|---|---|---|---|---|---|
| 1 | Britannia Sports | 22 | 14 | 5 | 3 | 72 | 42 | 47 |
| 2 | Heywood Irish Centre FC | 22 | 14 | 2 | 6 | 64 | 51 | 44 |
| 3 | Heyside FC | 22 | 12 | 6 | 4 | 57 | 29 | 42 |
| 4 | Shelley | 22 | 11 | 3 | 8 | 45 | 41 | 36 |
| 5 | Skelmanthorpe | 22 | 10 | 5 | 7 | 60 | 54 | 35 |
| 6 | Meltham Athletic | 22 | 10 | 3 | 9 | 43 | 33 | 33 |
| 7 | Holmfirth Town | 22 | 9 | 4 | 9 | 61 | 46 | 31 |
| 8 | Kirkheaton Rovers | 22 | 8 | 3 | 11 | 45 | 51 | 27 |
| 9 | Slaithwaite Utd | 22 | 6 | 8 | 8 | 42 | 48 | 26 |
| 10 | Cumberworth | 22 | 7 | 1 | 14 | 40 | 54 | 22 |
| 11 | Dalton Crusaders (-3pts) | 22 | 5 | 7 | 10 | 56 | 64 | 19 |
| 12 | Westend | 22 | 2 | 1 | 19 | 35 | 107 | 7 |

## Division Three

| | | P | W | D | L | F | A | Pts |
|---|---|---|---|---|---|---|---|---|
| 1 | Honley | 26 | 22 | 3 | 1 | 121 | 21 | 69 |
| 2 | H.V.Academicals | 26 | 18 | 6 | 2 | 58 | 38 | 60 |
| 3 | Linthwaite Athletic | 26 | 17 | 3 | 6 | 86 | 45 | 54 |
| 4 | Moldgreen Con | 26 | 15 | 5 | 6 | 59 | 45 | 50 |
| 5 | KKS Spartans | 26 | 14 | 4 | 8 | 92 | 47 | 46 |
| 6 | Scissett | 26 | 11 | 6 | 9 | 68 | 64 | 39 |
| 7 | Upperthong SC | 26 | 11 | 6 | 9 | 50 | 53 | 39 |
| 8 | Grange Moor | 26 | 10 | 5 | 11 | 55 | 54 | 35 |
| 9 | Dewsbury Town OB (-1pt) | 26 | 8 | 6 | 12 | 65 | 65 | 31 |
| 10 | AFC Waterloo | 26 | 8 | 4 | 14 | 53 | 76 | 28 |
| 11 | Wooldale Wanderers | 26 | 6 | 5 | 15 | 53 | 77 | 23 |
| 12 | Brook Motors (-1pt) | 26 | 4 | 8 | 14 | 40 | 56 | 19 |
| 13 | Flockton FC | 26 | 4 | 2 | 20 | 42 | 114 | 14 |
| 14 | Paddock Rangers | 26 | 1 | 3 | 22 | 30 | 117 | 6 |

## Division Four

| | | P | W | D | L | F | A | Pts |
|---|---|---|---|---|---|---|---|---|
| 1 | AFC Lindley | 24 | 24 | 0 | 0 | 122 | 20 | 72 |
| 2 | Aimbry | 24 | 18 | 2 | 4 | 79 | 30 | 56 |
| 3 | Hade Edge | 24 | 16 | 1 | 7 | 77 | 47 | 49 |
| 4 | Huddersfield United | 24 | 14 | 1 | 9 | 84 | 59 | 43 |
| 5 | Brighouse Old Boys | 24 | 13 | 2 | 9 | 62 | 50 | 41 |
| 6 | Moorside | 24 | 12 | 3 | 9 | 70 | 52 | 39 |
| 7 | Thornhill United | 24 | 12 | 2 | 10 | 48 | 49 | 38 |
| 8 | 3D Dynamos | 24 | 8 | 3 | 13 | 54 | 61 | 27 |
| 9 | Almondbury Woolpack | 24 | 7 | 2 | 15 | 48 | 52 | 23 |
| 10 | Mount | 24 | 6 | 5 | 13 | 58 | 79 | 23 |
| 11 | FC Lockwood | 24 | 6 | 3 | 15 | 38 | 77 | 21 |
| 12 | Lokomotiv Cowcliffe | 24 | 6 | 1 | 17 | 50 | 93 | 19 |
| 13 | Cartworth Moor | 24 | 1 | 1 | 22 | 29 | 150 | 4 |

## HUDDERSFIELD & DISTRICT WORKS & COMBINATION LEAGUE

### Division One

| | | P | W | D | L | F | A | Pts |
|---|---|---|---|---|---|---|---|---|
| 1 | Lindley Saddle | 12 | 9 | 0 | 3 | 31 | 26 | 27 |
| 2 | Mac Athletic | 12 | 8 | 2 | 2 | 47 | 24 | 26 |
| 3 | Aimbry F.C. (+2pts) | 12 | 7 | 1 | 4 | 37 | 22 | 24 |
| 4 | Coach & Horses | 12 | 8 | 0 | 4 | 35 | 25 | 24 |
| 5 | Lepton Highlanders (-1pt) | 12 | 3 | 1 | 8 | 21 | 33 | 9 |
| 6 | "Uppermill ""A""" | 12 | 2 | 2 | 8 | 16 | 34 | 8 |
| 7 | Sovereign Sports | 12 | 2 | 0 | 10 | 13 | 36 | 6 |

### Division Two

| | | P | W | D | L | F | A | Pts |
|---|---|---|---|---|---|---|---|---|
| 1 | Golcar United | 16 | 15 | 1 | 0 | 70 | 20 | 46 |
| 2 | Yetton Cask | 16 | 9 | 3 | 4 | 47 | 37 | 30 |
| 3 | Scissett (+6pts) | 16 | 8 | 0 | 8 | 62 | 54 | 30 |
| 4 | Force United (-1pt) | 16 | 9 | 2 | 5 | 37 | 33 | 28 |
| 5 | Lindley Saddle Reserves | 16 | 7 | 0 | 9 | 50 | 49 | 21 |
| 6 | Grange Moor | 16 | 5 | 1 | 10 | 30 | 42 | 16 |
| 7 | Marsden (-4pts) | 16 | 6 | 1 | 9 | 39 | 54 | 15 |
| 8 | Phoenix Knights | 16 | 4 | 3 | 9 | 28 | 55 | 15 |
| 9 | F C Lockwood (-3pts) | 16 | 3 | 1 | 12 | 32 | 51 | 7 |

## I ZINGARI COMBINATION

### Division One

| | P | W | D | L | F | A | Pts |
|---|---|---|---|---|---|---|---|
| 1 Jaymc | 18 | 14 | 2 | 2 | 50 | 19 | 44 |
| 2 Walton CTC | 18 | 12 | 2 | 4 | 58 | 29 | 38 |
| 3 Essemmay OB | 18 | 11 | 3 | 4 | 46 | 29 | 36 |
| 4 Liverpool Cavaliers | 18 | 11 | 2 | 5 | 44 | 30 | 35 |
| 5 Alder | 18 | 7 | 2 | 9 | 31 | 42 | 23 |
| 6 BRNESC | 18 | 6 | 3 | 9 | 30 | 48 | 21 |
| 7 Leyfield | 18 | 6 | 2 | 10 | 47 | 48 | 20 |
| 8 Woodstreet - | 18 | 6 | 2 | 10 | 33 | 44 | 20 |
| 9 Old Xaverians | 18 | 5 | 2 | 11 | 35 | 40 | 17 |
| 10 Orrell Park Ballroom | 18 | 1 | 2 | 15 | 29 | 74 | 5 |

### Division Two

| | P | W | D | L | F | A | Pts |
|---|---|---|---|---|---|---|---|
| 1 The First Dock | 18 | 11 | 4 | 3 | 64 | 35 | 37 |
| 2 Liobians | 18 | 10 | 4 | 4 | 55 | 32 | 34 |
| 3 Mount Athletic | 18 | 10 | 1 | 7 | 51 | 41 | 31 |
| 4 St Michaels | 18 | 9 | 2 | 7 | 45 | 36 | 29 |
| 5 Huyton CSC | 18 | 9 | 1 | 8 | 52 | 29 | 28 |
| 6 Liver V FC | 18 | 8 | 3 | 7 | 44 | 39 | 27 |
| 7 Rockville (Wallasey) | 18 | 8 | 0 | 10 | 40 | 60 | 24 |
| 8 Mersey Harps | 18 | 6 | 1 | 11 | 30 | 63 | 19 |
| 9 Woodstreet | 18 | 5 | 2 | 11 | 29 | 56 | 17 |
| 10 The Castle | 18 | 4 | 2 | 12 | 31 | 50 | 14 |

## ILFORD & DISTRICT LEAGUE

### Premier Division

| | P | W | D | L | F | A | Pts |
|---|---|---|---|---|---|---|---|
| 1 East London Academy | 20 | 14 | 4 | 1 | 97 | 34 | 46 |
| 2 St Francis | 20 | 13 | 2 | 5 | 72 | 38 | 41 |
| 3 Melbourne Sports | 20 | 11 | 6 | 3 | 66 | 40 | 39 |
| 4 Wanstead Hippos | 20 | 11 | 3 | 5 | 52 | 42 | 36 |
| 5 AAH Romford | 20 | 10 | 3 | 6 | 47 | 38 | 33 |
| 6 East Londoners | 20 | 7 | 3 | 8 | 52 | 40 | 24 |
| 7 DM United | 20 | 7 | 2 | 11 | 63 | 70 | 23 |
| 8 Chingford Harriers | 20 | 6 | 5 | 8 | 36 | 52 | 23 |
| 9 Glendale | 20 | 5 | 2 | 13 | 45 | 73 | 17 |
| 10 William Fitt | 20 | 3 | 4 | 11 | 32 | 59 | 13 |
| 11 Eastfield | 20 | 1 | 2 | 17 | 33 | 109 | 5 |

### Division One

| | P | W | D | L | F | A | Pts |
|---|---|---|---|---|---|---|---|
| 1 AFC Kings | 20 | 13 | 3 | 1 | 57 | 21 | 42 |
| 2 Trelawny | 20 | 13 | 0 | 6 | 61 | 47 | 39 |
| 3 Eastside Rangers | 20 | 10 | 4 | 5 | 53 | 38 | 34 |
| 4 Chingford Athletic Reserves | 20 | 10 | 3 | 7 | 50 | 32 | 33 |
| 5 LA Raiders | 20 | 9 | 4 | 6 | 39 | 31 | 31 |
| 6 Hackney | 20 | 9 | 4 | 6 | 48 | 44 | 31 |
| 7 Melbourne Sports Reserves | 20 | 8 | 3 | 9 | 56 | 61 | 27 |
| 8 Ryan A | 20 | 7 | 2 | 10 | 31 | 38 | 23 |
| 9 Forest United Reserves | 20 | 4 | 3 | 10 | 36 | 50 | 15 |
| 10 Lansbury | 20 | 4 | 1 | 14 | 36 | 59 | 13 |
| 11 Akhi United | 20 | 3 | 1 | 16 | 23 | 69 | 10 |

### Division Three

| | P | W | D | L | F | A | Pts |
|---|---|---|---|---|---|---|---|
| 1 Custom House | 18 | 12 | 2 | 4 | 48 | 22 | 38 |
| 2 St Francis Reserves | 18 | 11 | 3 | 4 | 61 | 37 | 36 |
| 3 Leyton United | 18 | 12 | 2 | 4 | 61 | 43 | 35 |
| 4 West Essex Reserves | 18 | 10 | 3 | 5 | 40 | 29 | 33 |
| 5 Euro Dagenham Reserves | 18 | 7 | 3 | 8 | 43 | 40 | 24 |
| 6 Ascot United | 18 | 7 | 3 | 7 | 32 | 30 | 24 |
| 7 Leyton Green | 18 | 7 | 0 | 10 | 43 | 49 | 21 |
| 8 Lucky Strikes | 18 | 6 | 2 | 10 | 33 | 38 | 20 |
| 9 Newham Royals | 18 | 3 | 2 | 11 | 31 | 52 | 11 |
| 10 AC Meridian | 18 | 3 | 0 | 15 | 27 | 79 | 9 |

## ISLE OF MAN SENIOR LEAGUE

### Premier League

| | P | W | D | L | F | A | Pts |
|---|---|---|---|---|---|---|---|
| 1 St Georges | 24 | 21 | 2 | 1 | 120 | 16 | 65 |
| 2 Laxey | 24 | 16 | 4 | 4 | 81 | 38 | 52 |
| 3 DHSOB | 24 | 16 | 2 | 6 | 73 | 36 | 50 |
| 4 St Marys | 24 | 15 | 3 | 6 | 84 | 34 | 48 |
| 5 Rushen Utd | 24 | 13 | 3 | 8 | 73 | 45 | 42 |
| 6 St Johns Utd | 24 | 13 | 3 | 8 | 61 | 47 | 42 |
| 7 Peel | 24 | 10 | 8 | 6 | 78 | 54 | 38 |
| 8 Corinthians | 24 | 9 | 3 | 12 | 43 | 54 | 30 |
| 9 Ramsey | 24 | 7 | 2 | 15 | 45 | 70 | 23 |
| 10 Union Mills | 24 | 5 | 4 | 15 | 40 | 81 | 19 |
| 11 Castletown | 24 | 5 | 3 | 16 | 30 | 102 | 18 |
| 12 Gymnasium | 24 | 3 | 4 | 17 | 27 | 90 | 13 |
| 13 Marown | 24 | 2 | 1 | 21 | 17 | 105 | 7 |

### Division Two

| | P | W | D | L | F | A | Pts |
|---|---|---|---|---|---|---|---|
| 1 Michael United | 24 | 17 | 4 | 3 | 98 | 38 | 55 |
| 2 RYCOB | 24 | 17 | 4 | 3 | 69 | 24 | 55 |
| 3 Colby | 24 | 17 | 4 | 3 | 59 | 24 | 55 |
| 4 Ayre United | 24 | 14 | 5 | 5 | 80 | 42 | 47 |
| 5 Douglas Royal | 24 | 13 | 5 | 6 | 84 | 46 | 44 |
| 6 Braddan | 24 | 11 | 2 | 11 | 49 | 62 | 35 |
| 7 Onchan | 24 | 9 | 1 | 14 | 47 | 73 | 28 |
| 8 Pulrose United | 24 | 8 | 3 | 13 | 52 | 70 | 27 |
| 9 Foxdale | 24 | 8 | 2 | 14 | 64 | 73 | 26 |
| 10 Douglas & District | 24 | 8 | 1 | 15 | 44 | 70 | 25 |
| 11 Malew | 24 | 5 | 3 | 16 | 38 | 89 | 18 |
| 12 Ronaldsway | 24 | 5 | 2 | 17 | 40 | 84 | 17 |
| 13 Douglas Athletic | 24 | 4 | 4 | 16 | 36 | 65 | 16 |

## ISLE OF WIGHT LEAGUE

### Division One

| | P | W | D | L | F | A | Pts |
|---|---|---|---|---|---|---|---|
| 1 West Wight | 22 | 18 | 3 | 1 | 55 | 15 | 57 |
| 2 Northwood St Johns | 22 | 17 | 2 | 3 | 87 | 23 | 53 |
| 3 Brading Town | 22 | 17 | 2 | 3 | 69 | 25 | 53 |
| 4 Cowes Sports Reserves | 22 | 12 | 5 | 5 | 45 | 33 | 41 |
| 5 Oakfield | 22 | 8 | 3 | 11 | 57 | 45 | 27 |
| 6 Pan Sports | 22 | 8 | 3 | 11 | 43 | 47 | 27 |
| 7 Ryde Saints | 22 | 8 | 2 | 12 | 63 | 66 | 26 |
| 8 Shanklin | 22 | 7 | 4 | 11 | 26 | 43 | 25 |
| 9 Osborne Coburg | 22 | 7 | 3 | 12 | 42 | 71 | 24 |
| 10 E.C.S.F.C. | 22 | 5 | 4 | 13 | 35 | 68 | 19 |
| 11 Niton | 22 | 6 | 1 | 15 | 34 | 67 | 19 |
| 12 Ventnor | 22 | 3 | 0 | 19 | 19 | 72 | 9 |

# NON LEAGUE DAY

## Saturday
## 7th September

 **Support your local club**

# nonleagueday.co.uk

## Division Two

| | | P | W | D | L | F | A | Pts |
|---|---|---|---|---|---|---|---|---|
| 1 | Vectis Nomads | 20 | 15 | 3 | 2 | 74 | 21 | 48 |
| 2 | Binstead & COB | 20 | 15 | 3 | 2 | 59 | 32 | 48 |
| 3 | Sandown | 20 | 12 | 3 | 5 | 51 | 30 | 39 |
| 4 | St Helens Blue Star | 20 | 11 | 5 | 4 | 62 | 31 | 38 |
| 5 | Carisbrooke United | 20 | 7 | 4 | 9 | 39 | 52 | 25 |
| 6 | Brighstone | 20 | 8 | 1 | 11 | 26 | 48 | 25 |
| 7 | Shanklin VYCC | 20 | 7 | 3 | 10 | 46 | 46 | 24 |
| 8 | Whitecroft & Barton Sports | 20 | 7 | 2 | 11 | 46 | 56 | 23 |
| 9 | Yarmouth & Calbourne | 20 | 6 | 1 | 13 | 40 | 43 | 19 |
| 10 | Seaview | 20 | 4 | 3 | 13 | 35 | 77 | 15 |
| 11 | Newchurch | 20 | 3 | 2 | 15 | 31 | 73 | 11 |

## Division Three

| | | P | W | D | L | F | A | Pts |
|---|---|---|---|---|---|---|---|---|
| 1 | Rookley (+3pts) | 19 | 16 | 0 | 3 | 106 | 25 | 51 |
| 2 | Newport IOW | 20 | 15 | 1 | 4 | 71 | 25 | 46 |
| 3 | AFC Wootton | 20 | 13 | 2 | 5 | 51 | 40 | 41 |
| 4 | AFC Bournemouth | 20 | 11 | 2 | 7 | 47 | 24 | 35 |
| 5 | Kyngs Towne (+3pts) | 20 | 8 | 3 | 9 | 53 | 48 | 30 |
| 6 | Wroxall (+3pts) | 20 | 9 | 0 | 11 | 61 | 57 | 30 |
| 7 | East Cowes Vics A (+3pts) | 19 | 7 | 0 | 12 | 32 | 46 | 24 |
| 8 | Shanklin A (+3pts) | 20 | 3 | 5 | 12 | 25 | 67 | 17 |
| 9 | Ryde Saints A (+5pts) | 20 | 3 | 3 | 14 | 28 | 78 | 17 |
| 10 | Holmwood Athletic (-25pts) | 20 | 13 | 2 | 5 | 63 | 42 | 16 |
| 11 | Seaclose (+6pts) | 20 | 1 | 2 | 17 | 16 | 101 | 11 |

## JERSEY FOOTBALL COMBINATION

### Premiership

| | | P | W | D | L | F | A | Pts |
|---|---|---|---|---|---|---|---|---|
| 1 | Jersey Scottish | 16 | 14 | 1 | 1 | 55 | 11 | 43 |
| 2 | St Paul's | 16 | 11 | 3 | 2 | 50 | 17 | 36 |
| 3 | Jersey Wanderers | 16 | 11 | 1 | 4 | 35 | 22 | 34 |
| 4 | St Peter | 16 | 4 | 7 | 5 | 26 | 27 | 19 |
| 5 | St Brelade | 16 | 4 | 6 | 6 | 15 | 19 | 18 |
| 6 | Grouville | 16 | 4 | 4 | 8 | 18 | 36 | 16 |
| 7 | St Ouen (-1pt) | 16 | 4 | 4 | 8 | 19 | 30 | 15 |
| 8 | Rozel Rovers | 16 | 2 | 3 | 11 | 13 | 31 | 9 |
| 9 | St Lawrence | 16 | 2 | 3 | 11 | 17 | 55 | 9 |

### Championship

| | | P | W | D | L | F | A | Pts |
|---|---|---|---|---|---|---|---|---|
| 1 | Trinity | 16 | 16 | 0 | 0 | 86 | 10 | 48 |
| 2 | St Clement | 16 | 11 | 3 | 2 | 45 | 18 | 36 |
| 3 | First Tower Utd | 16 | 8 | 2 | 6 | 49 | 28 | 26 |
| 4 | St John | 16 | 7 | 0 | 9 | 37 | 54 | 21 |
| 5 | Jersey Portuguese (-2pt) | 16 | 6 | 3 | 7 | 41 | 34 | 19 |
| 6 | Beeches OB | 16 | 5 | 2 | 9 | 33 | 35 | 17 |
| 7 | Magpies | 16 | 4 | 2 | 10 | 19 | 44 | 14 |
| 8 | Sporting Academics | 16 | 4 | 2 | 10 | 29 | 69 | 14 |
| 9 | St Martin | 16 | 3 | 2 | 11 | 27 | 74 | 11 |

## KIDDERMINSTER & DISTRICT LEAGUE

### Premier Division

| | | P | W | D | L | F | A | Pts |
|---|---|---|---|---|---|---|---|---|
| 1 | Netherton Athletic | 13 | 9 | 2 | 2 | 53 | 15 | 29 |
| 2 | Wyre Forest | 11 | 8 | 0 | 3 | 48 | 20 | 24 |
| 3 | Dudley Villa | 11 | 7 | 0 | 4 | 36 | 14 | 21 |
| 4 | Areley Kings | 14 | 6 | 2 | 6 | 36 | 41 | 20 |
| 5 | Kings Heath Old Boys | 9 | 5 | 3 | 1 | 28 | 14 | 18 |
| 6 | Dudley Wood Athletic | 12 | 5 | 2 | 5 | 32 | 36 | 17 |
| 7 | Two Gates | 12 | 5 | 2 | 5 | 23 | 32 | 17 |
| 8 | Fairfield Villa | 12 | 3 | 2 | 7 | 24 | 27 | 11 |
| 9 | Lodgefield Park | 14 | 3 | 1 | 10 | 24 | 55 | 10 |
| 10 | Kinver | 12 | 2 | 0 | 10 | 7 | 57 | 6 |

## KINGSTON & DISTRICT LEAGUE

### Premier Division

| | | P | W | D | L | F | A | Pts |
|---|---|---|---|---|---|---|---|---|
| 1 | Chessington K.C. | 14 | 10 | 3 | 1 | 45 | 15 | 33 |
| 2 | Summerstown | 14 | 9 | 2 | 3 | 41 | 19 | 29 |
| 3 | AFC Watermans | 14 | 8 | 2 | 4 | 50 | 27 | 26 |
| 4 | Parkside | 14 | 6 | 3 | 5 | 30 | 26 | 21 |
| 5 | A.C.Malden | 14 | 6 | 1 | 7 | 27 | 39 | 19 |
| 6 | Darkside | 14 | 4 | 4 | 6 | 23 | 26 | 16 |
| 7 | SHFC London | 14 | 2 | 3 | 9 | 13 | 53 | 9 |
| 8 | AFC Westend | 14 | 0 | 4 | 10 | 16 | 40 | 4 |
| | Robin Hood Withdrawn | | | | | | | |

### Division One

| | | P | W | D | L | F | A | Pts |
|---|---|---|---|---|---|---|---|---|
| 1 | Wandle | 16 | 11 | 3 | 2 | 42 | 26 | 36 |
| 2 | Sunbury Galaxy | 16 | 10 | 1 | 5 | 33 | 22 | 31 |
| 3 | Kingston Albion | 16 | 8 | 2 | 6 | 30 | 34 | 26 |
| 4 | Old Roehamptonians | 16 | 7 | 4 | 5 | 29 | 23 | 25 |
| 5 | Richmond & Kingston O.B. | 16 | 6 | 4 | 6 | 36 | 34 | 22 |
| 6 | Esher United | 16 | 6 | 3 | 7 | 30 | 29 | 21 |
| 7 | L.M.United | 16 | 5 | 5 | 6 | 38 | 37 | 20 |
| 8 | N.P.L. | 16 | 4 | 4 | 8 | 40 | 37 | 16 |
| 9 | Repton | 16 | 2 | 0 | 14 | 18 | 54 | 6 |

### Division Two

| | | P | W | D | L | F | A | Pts |
|---|---|---|---|---|---|---|---|---|
| 1 | Kingsbrook | 18 | 12 | 3 | 2 | 35 | 16 | 39 |
| 2 | Hanworth Sports | 18 | 11 | 4 | 23 | 44 | 19 | 37 |
| 3 | Chessington K.C.Reserves | 18 | 9 | 3 | 6 | 49 | 32 | 30 |
| 4 | Esher | 18 | 9 | 2 | 7 | 33 | 29 | 29 |
| 5 | Maori Park | 18 | 6 | 7 | 5 | 35 | 31 | 25 |
| 6 | Thornton Heath | 18 | 6 | 4 | 8 | 31 | 50 | 22 |
| 7 | St Martins | 18 | 6 | 3 | 9 | 32 | 35 | 21 |
| 8 | Oxshott Royals | 18 | 4 | 5 | 8 | 28 | 37 | 17 |
| 9 | Lower Green | 18 | 4 | 3 | 11 | 34 | 51 | 15 |
| 10 | Surbiton Eagles | 18 | 2 | 6 | 10 | 18 | 39 | 12 |

### Division Three

| | | P | W | D | L | F | A | Pts |
|---|---|---|---|---|---|---|---|---|
| 1 | Monkey Tennis | 16 | 16 | 0 | 0 | 67 | 10 | 48 |
| 2 | AFC Molesey | 16 | 11 | 1 | 4 | 50 | 25 | 34 |
| 3 | Surrey Fire | 16 | 9 | 2 | 5 | 44 | 28 | 29 |
| 4 | Barnslake | 16 | 9 | 2 | 5 | 40 | 33 | 29 |
| 5 | N.P.L. Reserves | 16 | 9 | 0 | 7 | 48 | 39 | 27 |
| 6 | Twickenham Athletic | 16 | 5 | 0 | 11 | 36 | 54 | 15 |
| 7 | Claygate & Ditton | 16 | 4 | 1 | 11 | 22 | 59 | 13 |
| 8 | Epsom Casuals | 16 | 2 | 2 | 12 | 14 | 36 | 8 |
| 9 | Dynamo Kingston | 16 | 2 | 2 | 12 | 15 | 52 | 8 |

## LEAGUE TABLES

### Division Four

| | | P | W | D | L | F | A | Pts |
|---|---|---|---|---|---|---|---|---|
| 1 | Lennox | 18 | 15 | 1 | 2 | 71 | 27 | 46 |
| 2 | FC Carlisle | 18 | 10 | 4 | 4 | 45 | 30 | 34 |
| 3 | AFC Watermans Reserves | 18 | 10 | 2 | 6 | 42 | 24 | 32 |
| 4 | Darkside Reserves | 18 | 8 | 2 | 8 | 47 | 38 | 26 |
| 5 | Parkside Reserves | 18 | 7 | 5 | 6 | 43 | 38 | 26 |
| 6 | AFC Kingston | 18 | 8 | 1 | 9 | 31 | 31 | 25 |
| 7 | Merton Social | 18 | 7 | 4 | 7 | 36 | 40 | 25 |
| 8 | Hook Venturers | 18 | 6 | 4 | 8 | 38 | 46 | 22 |
| 9 | AFC Hampton | 18 | 5 | 3 | 10 | 29 | 38 | 18 |
| 10 | Westside | 18 | 0 | 2 | 16 | 18 | 88 | 2 |

### Division Five

| | | P | W | D | L | F | A | Pts |
|---|---|---|---|---|---|---|---|---|
| 1 | Kingston Tigers | 16 | 13 | 1 | 2 | 69 | 23 | 40 |
| 2 | Chessington K.C. 111 | 16 | 10 | 2 | 4 | 48 | 21 | 32 |
| 3 | AFC Kingston Reserves | 16 | 10 | 2 | 4 | 37 | 30 | 32 |
| 4 | St Martins Reserves | 16 | 8 | 3 | 5 | 43 | 23 | 27 |
| 5 | Ewell Saxons Seniors | 16 | 8 | 1 | 7 | 42 | 30 | 25 |
| 6 | Merton Social Reserves | 16 | 7 | 1 | 8 | 23 | 43 | 22 |
| 7 | North Leatherhead | 16 | 4 | 1 | 11 | 12 | 34 | 13 |
| 8 | Lennox Reserves | 16 | 3 | 1 | 12 | 19 | 59 | 10 |
| 9 | Lower Green Reserves | 16 | 3 | 0 | 13 | 15 | 45 | 9 |

### Division Two

| | | P | W | D | L | F | A | Pts |
|---|---|---|---|---|---|---|---|---|
| 1 | Castleton FC First | 20 | 15 | 3 | 2 | 60 | 31 | 48 |
| 2 | Boothstown FC 1st | 20 | 13 | 3 | 4 | 48 | 29 | 42 |
| 3 | Whalley Range Reserves | 20 | 11 | 3 | 6 | 63 | 37 | 36 |
| 4 | Tintwistle Athletic FC | 20 | 9 | 4 | 7 | 56 | 38 | 31 |
| 5 | Moorside Rangers FC | 20 | 9 | 4 | 7 | 35 | 33 | 31 |
| 6 | Chorltonians Reserves | 20 | 9 | 4 | 7 | 38 | 38 | 31 |
| 7 | Eagle (-3pts) | 20 | 10 | 1 | 9 | 57 | 45 | 28 |
| 8 | Rochdalians Reserves | 20 | 5 | 4 | 11 | 31 | 39 | 19 |
| 9 | Mellor Reserves | 20 | 4 | 3 | 13 | 28 | 64 | 15 |
| 10 | Old Trafford | 20 | 4 | 2 | 14 | 40 | 84 | 14 |
| 11 | Hollingworth O.B. | 20 | 2 | 7 | 11 | 26 | 44 | 13 |

### Division Three

| | | P | W | D | L | F | A | Pts |
|---|---|---|---|---|---|---|---|---|
| 1 | Spurley Hey Reserves | 22 | 19 | 0 | 3 | 79 | 40 | 57 |
| 2 | Bury Amateur AFC 1st | 22 | 14 | 4 | 4 | 60 | 28 | 46 |
| 3 | Signol Athletic FC First | 22 | 15 | 1 | 6 | 57 | 31 | 46 |
| 4 | Urmston Town 1st | 22 | 8 | 6 | 8 | 50 | 50 | 30 |
| 5 | Hooley Bridge Celtic Reserves | 22 | 8 | 5 | 9 | 41 | 45 | 29 |
| 6 | Manchester Valiant 1st (-3pts) | 22 | 9 | 3 | 10 | 52 | 48 | 27 |
| 7 | Oldham Victoria | 22 | 7 | 4 | 11 | 50 | 58 | 25 |
| 8 | Trafford United 1st | 22 | 7 | 3 | 12 | 49 | 55 | 24 |
| 9 | Bedians Reserves | 22 | 7 | 3 | 12 | 38 | 59 | 24 |
| 10 | Burnage Metro Reserves | 22 | 7 | 2 | 13 | 39 | 63 | 23 |
| 11 | Cheadle Hulme Villa Res. (-6pts) | 22 | 8 | 4 | 10 | 45 | 50 | 22 |

## LANCASHIRE & CHESHIRE LEAGUE

### Premier Division

| | | P | W | D | L | F | A | Pts |
|---|---|---|---|---|---|---|---|---|
| 1 | Whalley Range | 26 | 18 | 3 | 5 | 82 | 37 | 57 |
| 2 | Cheadle Hulme Villa | 26 | 17 | 4 | 5 | 58 | 37 | 55 |
| 3 | Spurley Hey | 26 | 15 | 5 | 6 | 73 | 52 | 50 |
| 4 | Rochdalians | 26 | 15 | 4 | 7 | 74 | 36 | 49 |
| 5 | Newton 1st | 26 | 14 | 5 | 7 | 62 | 39 | 47 |
| 6 | Mellor | 26 | 14 | 4 | 8 | 64 | 46 | 46 |
| 7 | AFC Oldham 2005 | 26 | 11 | 8 | 7 | 80 | 56 | 41 |
| 8 | Old Ashtonians | 26 | 12 | 3 | 11 | 83 | 65 | 39 |
| 9 | Chorltonians | 26 | 10 | 4 | 12 | 58 | 58 | 34 |
| 10 | South Manchester | 26 | 9 | 3 | 14 | 40 | 65 | 30 |
| 11 | Hazel Grove (-3pts) | 26 | 8 | 1 | 17 | 41 | 89 | 22 |
| 12 | Bedians | 26 | 6 | 1 | 19 | 47 | 93 | 19 |
| 13 | Hooley Bridge Celtic | 26 | 5 | 3 | 18 | 34 | 68 | 18 |
| 14 | Old Stretfordians | 26 | 3 | 2 | 21 | 40 | 95 | 11 |

### Division One

| | | P | W | D | L | F | A | Pts |
|---|---|---|---|---|---|---|---|---|
| 1 | Gorse Hill | 24 | 19 | 2 | 3 | 81 | 33 | 59 |
| 2 | Moston Brook | 24 | 16 | 4 | 4 | 109 | 45 | 52 |
| 3 | Parrswood Celtic | 24 | 15 | 3 | 6 | 63 | 38 | 48 |
| 4 | Ardwick FC 1st | 24 | 14 | 3 | 7 | 86 | 50 | 45 |
| 5 | Newton Heath | 24 | 12 | 4 | 8 | 82 | 60 | 40 |
| 6 | Govan Athletic | 24 | 12 | 1 | 11 | 65 | 59 | 37 |
| 7 | Abacus Media | 24 | 11 | 3 | 10 | 68 | 70 | 36 |
| 8 | Milton FC | 24 | 11 | 1 | 12 | 61 | 62 | 34 |
| 9 | Alkrington Dynamos FC | 24 | 8 | 5 | 11 | 47 | 62 | 29 |
| 10 | Burnage Metro | 24 | 7 | 2 | 15 | 41 | 68 | 23 |
| 11 | Santos FC (-3pts) | 24 | 7 | 0 | 17 | 60 | 97 | 18 |
| 12 | Heaton Mersey | 24 | 4 | 2 | 18 | 46 | 99 | 14 |
| 13 | Stoconians 1st | 24 | 4 | 2 | 18 | 36 | 102 | 14 |

## LANCASHIRE AMATEUR LEAGUE

### Premier Division

| | | P | W | D | L | F | A | Pts |
|---|---|---|---|---|---|---|---|---|
| 1 | Prestwich | 26 | 19 | 3 | 4 | 71 | 31 | 60 |
| 2 | Old Boltonians | 26 | 18 | 5 | 3 | 71 | 28 | 59 |
| 3 | Horwich Victoria | 26 | 17 | 2 | 7 | 92 | 52 | 53 |
| 4 | Rochdale St Clements | 26 | 16 | 3 | 7 | 69 | 44 | 51 |
| 5 | Old Mancunians | 26 | 14 | 8 | 4 | 55 | 28 | 50 |
| 6 | Bury GSOB | 26 | 14 | 3 | 9 | 67 | 47 | 45 |
| 7 | Failsworth Dynamos | 26 | 12 | 6 | 8 | 68 | 49 | 42 |
| 8 | Little Lever SC | 26 | 13 | 3 | 10 | 67 | 57 | 42 |
| 9 | Howe Bridge Mills | 26 | 8 | 7 | 11 | 42 | 51 | 31 |
| 10 | Old Blackburnians | 26 | 8 | 5 | 13 | 46 | 74 | 29 |
| 11 | Castle Hill | 26 | 5 | 5 | 16 | 34 | 70 | 20 |
| 12 | Rossendale Amateurs | 26 | 4 | 3 | 19 | 36 | 75 | 15 |
| 13 | Hindley Juniors | 26 | 3 | 3 | 20 | 43 | 96 | 12 |
| 14 | Chaddertonians | 26 | 1 | 4 | 21 | 35 | 94 | 7 |

### Division One

| | | P | W | D | L | F | A | Pts |
|---|---|---|---|---|---|---|---|---|
| 1 | Tottington United | 26 | 20 | 3 | 3 | 108 | 38 | 63 |
| 2 | Hesketh Casuals | 26 | 17 | 2 | 7 | 94 | 59 | 53 |
| 3 | Roach Dynamos (-4pts) | 26 | 18 | 3 | 5 | 68 | 47 | 53 |
| 4 | Old Boltonians Reserves | 26 | 14 | 4 | 8 | 77 | 55 | 46 |
| 5 | Horwich RMI | 26 | 13 | 6 | 7 | 77 | 56 | 45 |
| 6 | Mostonians | 26 | 10 | 6 | 10 | 60 | 56 | 36 |
| 7 | Rochdale St Clements Reserves | 26 | 11 | 2 | 13 | 62 | 63 | 35 |
| 8 | Bolton Wyresdale | 26 | 9 | 5 | 12 | 32 | 44 | 32 |
| 9 | North Walkden -3pts) | 26 | 10 | 4 | 12 | 83 | 66 | 30 |
| 10 | Tyldesley United | 26 | 9 | 2 | 15 | 54 | 75 | 29 |
| 11 | Ainsworth | 26 | 7 | 7 | 12 | 53 | 88 | 28 |
| 12 | Thornleigh | 26 | 7 | 3 | 16 | 53 | 77 | 24 |
| 13 | Radcliffe Town | 26 | 4 | 5 | 17 | 40 | 90 | 17 |
| 14 | Rossendale Amateurs Res. (-4pts) | 26 | 6 | 2 | 18 | 45 | 92 | 16 |

| Division Two | P | W | D | L | F | A | Pts |
|---|---|---|---|---|---|---|---|
| 1 Oldham Hulmeians | 24 | 18 | 2 | 4 | 75 | 41 | 56 |
| 2 Blackrod Town | 24 | 17 | 2 | 5 | 113 | 49 | 53 |
| 3 Farnworth Town | 24 | 16 | 4 | 4 | 57 | 29 | 52 |
| 4 Accrington Amateurs | 24 | 17 | 0 | 7 | 101 | 66 | 51 |
| 5 Littleborough Juniors | 24 | 13 | 2 | 9 | 65 | 52 | 41 |
| 6 Old Mancunians Reserves | 24 | 11 | 3 | 10 | 63 | 69 | 36 |
| 7 Bury GSOB Reserves | 24 | 9 | 6 | 9 | 44 | 51 | 33 |
| 8 Old Blackburnians Reserves | 24 | 8 | 7 | 9 | 38 | 44 | 31 |
| 9 Ashtonians | 24 | 8 | 5 | 11 | 60 | 60 | 29 |
| 10 Little Lever SC Reserves | 24 | 6 | 5 | 13 | 62 | 78 | 23 |
| 11 Stand AFC (-4pts) | 24 | 6 | 1 | 17 | 45 | 84 | 15 |
| 12 Chaddertonians Reserves | 24 | 3 | 4 | 17 | 38 | 93 | 13 |
| 13 Radcliffe Boys | 24 | 2 | 3 | 19 | 38 | 83 | 9 |

| Division Three | P | W | D | L | F | A | Pts |
|---|---|---|---|---|---|---|---|
| 1 Failsworth Dynamos Reserves | 22 | 17 | 4 | 1 | 91 | 32 | 55 |
| 2 Oldham Hulmeians Reserves | 22 | 17 | 2 | 3 | 91 | 25 | 53 |
| 3 Hesketh Casuals Reserves | 22 | 13 | 3 | 6 | 65 | 43 | 42 |
| 4 Westhoughton Town (-8pts) | 22 | 14 | 3 | 5 | 85 | 33 | 37 |
| 5 Old Boltonians A | 22 | 11 | 1 | 10 | 68 | 57 | 34 |
| 6 Radcliffe Town Reserves | 22 | 10 | 3 | 9 | 48 | 66 | 33 |
| 7 Prestwich Reserves | 22 | 6 | 5 | 11 | 40 | 60 | 23 |
| 8 Bacup United (-4pts) | 22 | 8 | 2 | 12 | 47 | 58 | 22 |
| 9 Castle Hill Reserves | 22 | 7 | 1 | 14 | 60 | 90 | 22 |
| 10 Bolton Lads Club | 22 | 7 | 1 | 14 | 40 | 77 | 22 |
| 11 Rossendale Amateurs A | 22 | 4 | 2 | 16 | 48 | 80 | 14 |
| 12 Lymm | 22 | 4 | 1 | 17 | 19 | 81 | 13 |

| Division Four | P | W | D | L | F | A | Pts |
|---|---|---|---|---|---|---|---|
| 1 Mostonians Reserves | 18 | 12 | 3 | 3 | 66 | 35 | 39 |
| 2 Rochdale St Clements A | 18 | 12 | 3 | 3 | 61 | 35 | 39 |
| 3 AFC Dobbies | 18 | 10 | 3 | 5 | 43 | 30 | 33 |
| 4 Roach Dynamos Reserves (-3pts) | 18 | 11 | 3 | 4 | 67 | 38 | 32 |
| 5 Horwich Victoria Reserves | 18 | 9 | 3 | 6 | 63 | 40 | 30 |
| 6 Bolton Wyresdale Reserves | 18 | 7 | 7 | 4 | 54 | 55 | 28 |
| 7 Old Blackburnians A | 18 | 5 | 3 | 10 | 23 | 44 | 18 |
| 8 Horwich RMI Reserves | 18 | 3 | 6 | 9 | 29 | 52 | 15 |
| 9 Accrington Amateurs Reserves | 18 | 3 | 4 | 11 | 35 | 64 | 13 |
| 10 Chaddertonians A | 18 | 0 | 1 | 17 | 24 | 72 | 1 |

| Division Five | P | W | D | L | F | A | Pts |
|---|---|---|---|---|---|---|---|
| 1 Thornleigh Reserves | 20 | 16 | 1 | 3 | 80 | 24 | 49 |
| 2 Howe Bridge Mills Reserves | 20 | 12 | 5 | 3 | 49 | 42 | 41 |
| 3 Ashtonians Reserves | 20 | 10 | 5 | 5 | 58 | 35 | 35 |
| 4 Bury GSOB A | 20 | 11 | 2 | 7 | 58 | 50 | 35 |
| 5 Old Boltonians B | 20 | 9 | 4 | 7 | 34 | 34 | 31 |
| 6 Ainsworth Reserves | 20 | 9 | 2 | 9 | 48 | 44 | 29 |
| 7 Rochdale St Clements B | 20 | 9 | 1 | 10 | 45 | 49 | 28 |
| 8 Old Mancunians A | 20 | 7 | 4 | 9 | 41 | 37 | 25 |
| 9 Lymm Reserves | 20 | 6 | 1 | 13 | 38 | 56 | 19 |
| 10 Hesketh Casuals A | 20 | 4 | 1 | 15 | 36 | 75 | 13 |
| 11 Radcliffe Town A | 20 | 2 | 4 | 14 | 31 | 72 | 10 |

| Division Six | P | W | D | L | F | A | Pts |
|---|---|---|---|---|---|---|---|
| 1 Thornleigh A | 20 | 15 | 4 | 1 | 79 | 31 | 49 |
| 2 Farnworth Town Reserves | 20 | 14 | 2 | 4 | 63 | 28 | 44 |
| 3 Horwich Victoria A | 20 | 13 | 2 | 5 | 76 | 30 | 41 |
| 4 Bolton Wyresdale A | 20 | 12 | 1 | 7 | 58 | 40 | 37 |
| 5 Tottington United Reserves | 20 | 9 | 2 | 9 | 48 | 52 | 29 |
| 6 Mostonians A (-4pts) | 20 | 9 | 3 | 8 | 51 | 44 | 26 |
| 7 Oldham Hulmeians A | 20 | 8 | 0 | 12 | 44 | 62 | 24 |
| 8 Old Mancunians B | 20 | 7 | 1 | 12 | 40 | 51 | 22 |
| 9 AFC Dobbies Reserves | 20 | 5 | 2 | 13 | 44 | 60 | 17 |
| 10 Old Blackburnians B | 20 | 5 | 2 | 13 | 35 | 86 | 17 |
| 11 Radcliffe Boys Reserves (-4pts) | 20 | 3 | 1 | 16 | 33 | 87 | 6 |

| Division Seven | P | W | D | L | F | A | Pts |
|---|---|---|---|---|---|---|---|
| 1 Howe Bridge Mills A | 18 | 14 | 3 | 1 | 66 | 23 | 45 |
| 2 Little Lever SC A | 18 | 13 | 3 | 2 | 68 | 29 | 42 |
| 3 Thornleigh B | 18 | 10 | 3 | 5 | 57 | 42 | 33 |
| 4 Tyldesley United Reserves | 18 | 6 | 7 | 5 | 43 | 39 | 25 |
| 5 Hesketh Casuals B | 18 | 5 | 7 | 6 | 34 | 44 | 22 |
| 6 Bury GSOB B | 18 | 5 | 6 | 7 | 32 | 52 | 21 |
| 7 Bolton Wyresdale B | 18 | 5 | 4 | 9 | 34 | 41 | 19 |
| 8 Radcliffe Town B | 18 | 5 | 2 | 11 | 51 | 73 | 17 |
| 9 Oldham Hulmeians B | 18 | 3 | 6 | 9 | 42 | 59 | 15 |
| 10 Horwich RMI A | 18 | 3 | 1 | 14 | 32 | 57 | 10 |

## LANCASHIRE LEAGUE

| East Division | P | W | D | L | F | A | Pts |
|---|---|---|---|---|---|---|---|
| 1 Ossett Albion | 24 | 16 | 4 | 4 | 67 | 32 | 52 |
| 2 Hyde | 24 | 15 | 4 | 5 | 65 | 27 | 49 |
| 3 Brighouse Town | 24 | 13 | 2 | 9 | 67 | 54 | 41 |
| 4 Harrogate Rail | 24 | 10 | 4 | 10 | 55 | 58 | 34 |
| 5 Eccleshill United | 24 | 11 | 1 | 12 | 57 | 65 | 34 |
| 6 Stalybridge Celtic A | 24 | 9 | 4 | 11 | 52 | 41 | 31 |
| 7 Farsley AFC | 24 | 8 | 3 | 13 | 49 | 66 | 27 |
| 8 Liversedge | 24 | 6 | 5 | 13 | 48 | 74 | 23 |
| 9 Thackley | 24 | 5 | 3 | 16 | 37 | 80 | 18 |

| West Division | P | W | D | L | F | A | Pts |
|---|---|---|---|---|---|---|---|
| 1 Lancaster City | 20 | 14 | 3 | 3 | 59 | 34 | 45 |
| 2 AFC Fylde | 20 | 12 | 2 | 6 | 59 | 27 | 38 |
| 3 Burscough | 20 | 11 | 4 | 5 | 51 | 35 | 37 |
| 4 Colne | 20 | 10 | 5 | 5 | 53 | 35 | 35 |
| 5 Curzon Ashton | 20 | 10 | 3 | 7 | 59 | 37 | 33 |
| 6 Bootle | 20 | 8 | 2 | 10 | 40 | 53 | 26 |
| 7 Ashton Athletic | 20 | 8 | 1 | 11 | 47 | 45 | 25 |
| 8 Workington | 20 | 6 | 5 | 9 | 37 | 48 | 23 |
| 9 Witton Albion | 20 | 7 | 2 | 11 | 37 | 62 | 23 |
| 10 Droylsden | 20 | 3 | 5 | 12 | 37 | 56 | 14 |
| 11 Stalybridge Celtic B | 20 | 4 | 2 | 14 | 26 | 73 | 14 |

# LEAGUE TABLES

## LEEDS RED TRIANGLE INVITATION LEAGUE

| Premier Division | P | W | D | L | F | A | Pts |
|---|---|---|---|---|---|---|---|
| 1 Halton Moor | 13 | 12 | 0 | 1 | 59 | 16 | 36 |
| 2 Seacroft W.M.C. | 14 | 11 | 0 | 3 | 48 | 18 | 33 |
| 3 FC Corpus Christi | 14 | 7 | 2 | 5 | 42 | 34 | 23 |
| 4 C.F.Y.D. Chance | 14 | 6 | 3 | 5 | 31 | 33 | 21 |
| 5 Drighlington Adwalton | 14 | 5 | 3 | 6 | 26 | 17 | 18 |
| 6 Kirkstall Crusaders 11S | 13 | 4 | 1 | 8 | 22 | 36 | 13 |
| 7 Drighlington Malt Shovel | 14 | 3 | 0 | 11 | 24 | 51 | 9 |
| 8 Old Headingley Academy | 14 | 2 | 1 | 11 | 22 | 69 | 7 |

| | P | W | D | L | F | A | Pts |
|---|---|---|---|---|---|---|---|
| 1 Kirkstall Crusaders 22S | 14 | 11 | 2 | 1 | 67 | 28 | 35 |
| 2 Parkfield | 14 | 11 | 1 | 2 | 61 | 24 | 34 |
| 3 Churwell | 14 | 6 | 2 | 6 | 45 | 45 | 20 |
| 4 South Leeds Independents | 14 | 6 | 2 | 6 | 33 | 33 | 20 |
| 5 Seacroft W.M.C. | 14 | 6 | 2 | 6 | 33 | 35 | 20 |
| 6 Seacroft Green | 15 | 5 | 2 | 7 | 39 | 45 | 17 |
| 7 Swarcliffe W.M.C. | 14 | 3 | 1 | 10 | 26 | 52 | 10 |
| 8 Merlins | 14 | 1 | 2 | 11 | 25 | 67 | 5 |

## LEICESTER & DISTRICT LEAGUE

| Premier Division | P | W | D | L | F | A | Pts |
|---|---|---|---|---|---|---|---|
| 1 Houghton Rangers | 24 | 20 | 3 | 1 | 83 | 18 | 63 |
| 2 Braders | 24 | 18 | 2 | 4 | 93 | 39 | 56 |
| 3 County Hall | 24 | 14 | 3 | 7 | 67 | 48 | 45 |
| 4 Mountsorrel Amateurs | 24 | 13 | 5 | 6 | 56 | 36 | 44 |
| 5 Birstall RBL | 24 | 13 | 4 | 7 | 58 | 37 | 43 |
| 6 Magna 73 | 24 | 11 | 6 | 7 | 72 | 49 | 39 |
| 7 North Kilworth | 24 | 10 | 5 | 9 | 52 | 57 | 35 |
| 8 Glen Villa | 24 | 9 | 3 | 12 | 62 | 74 | 30 |
| 9 Huncote | 24 | 6 | 4 | 14 | 40 | 63 | 22 |
| 10 Kibworth Town | 24 | 6 | 3 | 15 | 45 | 85 | 21 |
| 11 Cosby United | 24 | 4 | 5 | 15 | 54 | 89 | 17 |
| 12 Glenfield Town | 24 | 3 | 7 | 14 | 46 | 80 | 16 |
| 13 Kingsway Celtic | 24 | 2 | 4 | 18 | 43 | 96 | 10 |

| Division One | P | W | D | L | F | A | Pts |
|---|---|---|---|---|---|---|---|
| 1 Beaumont Town | 22 | 14 | 3 | 5 | 61 | 27 | 45 |
| 2 Belgrave | 22 | 13 | 2 | 7 | 68 | 39 | 41 |
| 3 Northfield Emerald | 22 | 13 | 0 | 9 | 59 | 44 | 39 |
| 4 Burbage Old Boys | 22 | 11 | 3 | 8 | 59 | 45 | 36 |
| 5 Braunstone Trinity | 22 | 10 | 2 | 10 | 61 | 53 | 32 |
| 6 Royal Anglians | 22 | 8 | 6 | 8 | 44 | 50 | 30 |
| 7 NKF Burbage | 22 | 9 | 3 | 10 | 37 | 48 | 30 |
| 8 Fleckney Athletic | 22 | 8 | 4 | 10 | 35 | 55 | 28 |
| 9 Saffron Lounge | 22 | 8 | 2 | 12 | 53 | 65 | 26 |
| 10 Queniborough | 22 | 7 | 4 | 11 | 62 | 69 | 25 |
| 11 Leicester Three Lions | 22 | 7 | 3 | 12 | 47 | 78 | 24 |
| 12 Ashby Road | 22 | 7 | 2 | 13 | 49 | 62 | 23 |

| Division Two | P | W | D | L | F | A | Pts |
|---|---|---|---|---|---|---|---|
| 1 Oadby Boys Club 93 | 24 | 18 | 2 | 4 | 79 | 29 | 56 |
| 2 Thurlaston Magpies | 24 | 16 | 2 | 6 | 62 | 42 | 50 |
| 3 Birstall RBL Reserves | 24 | 14 | 3 | 7 | 82 | 42 | 45 |
| 4 The New Joiners | 24 | 14 | 3 | 7 | 73 | 57 | 45 |
| 5 Thurnby Valley | 24 | 14 | 2 | 8 | 82 | 46 | 44 |
| 6 Shoemakers Ath | 24 | 11 | 3 | 10 | 59 | 64 | 36 |
| 7 Guru Nanak Gurdwara (GNG) | 24 | 11 | 2 | 11 | 66 | 68 | 35 |
| 8 Magna 73 Reserves | 24 | 11 | 2 | 11 | 56 | 63 | 35 |
| 9 Houghton Rangers Reserves | 24 | 8 | 3 | 13 | 38 | 53 | 27 |
| 10 North Kilworth Reserves | 24 | 6 | 5 | 13 | 51 | 66 | 23 |
| 11 St Patricks (-6pts) | 24 | 8 | 4 | 12 | 42 | 53 | 22 |
| 12 Broughton Astley | 24 | 5 | 5 | 14 | 54 | 86 | 20 |
| 13 Cosby United Reserves | 24 | 2 | 0 | 22 | 32 | 107 | 6 |

| Division Three | P | W | D | L | F | A | Pts |
|---|---|---|---|---|---|---|---|
| 1 Glenfield Town Reserves | 24 | 20 | 2 | 2 | 105 | 25 | 62 |
| 2 Beaumont Town Reserves | 24 | 18 | 2 | 4 | 83 | 37 | 56 |
| 3 Thurlaston Magpies Reserves | 24 | 18 | 1 | 5 | 91 | 36 | 55 |
| 4 Belgrave Reserves | 24 | 15 | 2 | 7 | 63 | 43 | 47 |
| 5 Queniborough Reserves | 24 | 12 | 2 | 10 | 79 | 53 | 38 |
| 6 County Hall Reserves | 24 | 10 | 4 | 10 | 64 | 72 | 34 |
| 7 Glen Villa Reserves | 24 | 9 | 5 | 10 | 52 | 50 | 32 |
| 8 Mountsorrel Amateurs Reserves | 24 | 10 | 1 | 13 | 52 | 44 | 31 |
| 9 Earl of Stamford | 24 | 7 | 2 | 15 | 51 | 86 | 23 |
| 10 Huncote Reserves | 24 | 6 | 4 | 14 | 59 | 100 | 22 |
| 11 Park End 74 | 24 | 6 | 1 | 17 | 55 | 91 | 19 |
| 12 NKF Burbage Reserves | 24 | 5 | 2 | 17 | 30 | 82 | 17 |
| 13 Kibworth Town Reserves | 24 | 5 | 2 | 17 | 31 | 96 | 17 |
| Old Aylestone record expunged | | | | | | | |

## LINCOLN & DISTRICT LEAGUE

| | P | W | D | L | F | A | Pts |
|---|---|---|---|---|---|---|---|
| 1 AFC Rustons | 12 | 10 | 0 | 2 | 48 | 27 | 30 |
| 2 RM Imps | 12 | 9 | 2 | 1 | 35 | 17 | 29 |
| 3 Ivy Tavern CSA | 12 | 6 | 1 | 5 | 32 | 27 | 19 |
| 4 Nettleham Reserves | 12 | 5 | 1 | 6 | 32 | 28 | 16 |
| 5 Metheringham | 12 | 3 | 2 | 7 | 22 | 32 | 11 |
| 6 Fulbeck United | 12 | 3 | 1 | 8 | 28 | 30 | 10 |
| 7 Cherry Willingham | 12 | 2 | 1 | 9 | 27 | 63 | 7 |

## LINCOLNSHIRE LEAGUE

| Premier Division | P | W | D | L | F | A | Pts |
|---|---|---|---|---|---|---|---|
| 1 Skegness United | 32 | 26 | 4 | 2 | 111 | 33 | 82 |
| 2 Gainsborough Town (-3pts) | 32 | 22 | 4 | 6 | 101 | 43 | 67 |
| 3 Ruston Sports | 32 | 21 | 4 | 7 | 92 | 54 | 67 |
| 4 Cleethorpes Town Reserves | 32 | 20 | 6 | 6 | 84 | 28 | 66 |
| 5 Hykeham Town (+3pts) | 32 | 20 | 0 | 12 | 87 | 48 | 63 |
| 6 Boston United Reserves (-3pts) | 32 | 18 | 4 | 10 | 80 | 46 | 55 |
| 7 Nettleham | 32 | 17 | 4 | 11 | 70 | 64 | 55 |
| 8 Skegness Town | 32 | 17 | 3 | 12 | 78 | 61 | 54 |
| 9 Horncastle Town | 32 | 15 | 3 | 14 | 70 | 63 | 48 |
| 10 Sleaford Town Reserves (+3pts) | 32 | 11 | 7 | 14 | 48 | 63 | 43 |
| 11 CGB Humbertherm | 32 | 13 | 0 | 19 | 51 | 70 | 39 |
| 12 Louth Town Reserves | 32 | 11 | 3 | 18 | 49 | 73 | 36 |
| 13 Lincoln United Reserves (+2pts) | 32 | 8 | 6 | 18 | 42 | 69 | 32 |
| 14 Grimsby Borough Reserves | 32 | 8 | 3 | 21 | 41 | 73 | 27 |
| 15 Market Rasen Town | 32 | 8 | 0 | 24 | 39 | 99 | 24 |
| 16 Heckington United | 32 | 7 | 2 | 23 | 38 | 92 | 23 |
| 17 Boston Town Reserves (-1pt) | 32 | 2 | 3 | 27 | 25 | 127 | 8 |

## LIVERPOOL CMS LEAGUE

### Premier Division

| | | P | W | D | L | F | A | Pts |
|---|---|---|---|---|---|---|---|---|
| 1 | Railway | 18 | 17 | 1 | 0 | 79 | 20 | 52 |
| 2 | Northpark United | 18 | 13 | 2 | 3 | 66 | 28 | 41 |
| 3 | Mosslane | 18 | 9 | 3 | 6 | 64 | 54 | 30 |
| 3 | Speke ACSIL RCU | 18 | 9 | 3 | 6 | 66 | 60 | 30 |
| 5 | Rose & Crown | 18 | 9 | 1 | 8 | 50 | 49 | 28 |
| 6 | AFC Kirkby | 18 | 8 | 2 | 8 | 60 | 48 | 26 |
| 7 | Western Speke | 18 | 8 | 0 | 10 | 41 | 50 | 24 |
| 8 | Mandela | 18 | 3 | 2 | 13 | 38 | 71 | 11 |
| 8 | The Derby Mills | 18 | 3 | 2 | 13 | 48 | 82 | 11 |
| 10 | Polonia Camps | 18 | 3 | 0 | 15 | 22 | 72 | 9 |

### Division One

| | | P | W | D | L | F | A | Pts |
|---|---|---|---|---|---|---|---|---|
| 1 | The Abbey | 22 | 18 | 3 | 1 | 95 | 32 | 57 |
| 2 | Pipes | 22 | 17 | 3 | 2 | 80 | 25 | 54 |
| 3 | Elmoore | 22 | 14 | 3 | 5 | 77 | 35 | 45 |
| 4 | Western Speke Reserves | 22 | 13 | 4 | 5 | 70 | 44 | 43 |
| 5 | East Liverpool (-1pt) | 22 | 13 | 4 | 5 | 74 | 37 | 42 |
| 6 | The Claremont | 22 | 10 | 1 | 11 | 54 | 51 | 31 |
| 7 | The Botanic | 22 | 9 | 1 | 12 | 50 | 64 | 28 |
| 8 | Everton P.L.H. (-1pt) | 22 | 8 | 3 | 11 | 71 | 84 | 26 |
| 9 | Dunnings Bridge | 22 | 7 | 3 | 12 | 47 | 53 | 24 |
| 10 | Stuart Road | 22 | 4 | 2 | 16 | 40 | 84 | 14 |
| 11 | Leighbridge | 22 | 3 | 3 | 16 | 35 | 91 | 12 |
| 12 | Walton Athletic | 22 | 0 | 2 | 20 | 13 | 106 | 2 |

## LONDON COMMERCIAL LEAGUE

### Division One

| | | P | W | D | L | F | A | Pts |
|---|---|---|---|---|---|---|---|---|
| 1 | New Hanford | 16 | 13 | 2 | 1 | 52 | 27 | 41 |
| 2 | Fulham Dynamo Sports | 16 | 8 | 2 | 6 | 48 | 33 | 26 |
| 3 | Northwood III | 16 | 7 | 5 | 4 | 40 | 32 | 26 |
| 4 | Paddington Vale | 16 | 7 | 4 | 5 | 36 | 23 | 25 |
| 5 | Ealing Old Boys | 16 | 7 | 3 | 6 | 39 | 43 | 24 |
| 6 | North Greenford United III | 16 | 7 | 2 | 7 | 38 | 39 | 23 |
| 7 | Park View | 16 | 5 | 1 | 10 | 20 | 14 | 16 |
| 8 | Old Alpertonians | 16 | 3 | 3 | 10 | 18 | 47 | 12 |
| 9 | Abbey National Sports & Social Club | 16 | 2 | 4 | 10 | 34 | 67 | 10 |
| | Pearcroft United - record expunged | | | | | | | |

### Division Two

| | | P | W | D | L | F | A | Pts |
|---|---|---|---|---|---|---|---|---|
| 1 | British Airways IV | 14 | 10 | 1 | 3 | 64 | 29 | 31 |
| 2 | New Hanford II | 14 | 10 | 1 | 3 | 54 | 19 | 31 |
| 3 | Travaux Saints | 14 | 7 | 2 | 5 | 34 | 31 | 23 |
| 4 | Hounslow Wanderers II | 14 | 7 | 1 | 6 | 36 | 30 | 22 |
| 5 | Greenford Celtic | 14 | 7 | 1 | 6 | 29 | 27 | 22 |
| 6 | Charing Cross Association | 14 | 4 | 1 | 9 | 20 | 40 | 13 |
| 7 | Sudbury Court | 14 | 3 | 2 | 9 | 26 | 43 | 11 |
| 8 | Old Alpertonians II | 14 | 3 | 1 | 10 | 21 | 65 | 10 |

### Division Three

| | | P | W | D | L | F | A | Pts |
|---|---|---|---|---|---|---|---|---|
| 1 | Barnet Municipal Officers | 14 | 11 | 2 | 1 | 41 | 15 | 35 |
| 2 | AFC Angel Hayes | 14 | 8 | 2 | 4 | 57 | 29 | 26 |
| 3 | Hillingdon III | 14 | 7 | 3 | 4 | 43 | 35 | 24 |
| 4 | Lampton Park | 14 | 6 | 2 | 6 | 36 | 32 | 20 |
| 5 | Fulham Dynamo Sports II | 14 | 5 | 2 | 7 | 30 | 36 | 17 |
| 6 | Chiswick Homefields | 14 | 5 | 2 | 7 | 29 | 39 | 17 |
| 7 | Harrow Lyons | 14 | 2 | 4 | 8 | 26 | 49 | 10 |
| 8 | LPOSSA II | 14 | 3 | 1 | 10 | 23 | 50 | 10 |

## LOWESTOFT & DISTRICT LEAGUE

### Division One

| | | P | W | D | L | F | A | Pts |
|---|---|---|---|---|---|---|---|---|
| 1 | Oulton Broad | 18 | 18 | 0 | 0 | 78 | 16 | 54 |
| 2 | Barsham | 18 | 14 | 0 | 4 | 68 | 25 | 42 |
| 3 | Spexhall | 18 | 10 | 3 | 5 | 49 | 37 | 33 |
| 4 | DK Consultants | 18 | 7 | 4 | 7 | 43 | 42 | 25 |
| 5 | Gt Yarmouth Town Hall | 18 | 7 | 2 | 9 | 40 | 52 | 23 |
| 6 | Waveney Reserves | 18 | 6 | 3 | 9 | 41 | 44 | 21 |
| 7 | Corton Seltic | 18 | 6 | 2 | 10 | 35 | 63 | 20 |
| 8 | Norton Athletic | 18 | 5 | 4 | 9 | 55 | 57 | 19 |
| 9 | Oxford Arms | 18 | 5 | 1 | 12 | 39 | 81 | 16 |
| 10 | Kirkley & Pakefield A | 18 | 1 | 3 | 14 | 34 | 65 | 6 |

### Division Two

| | | P | W | D | L | F | A | Pts |
|---|---|---|---|---|---|---|---|---|
| 1 | Mutford & Wrentham | 26 | 20 | 3 | 3 | 91 | 35 | 63 |
| 2 | Kirkley & Pakefield B (-4pts) | 26 | 17 | 5 | 4 | 84 | 41 | 52 |
| 3 | Norton Athletic Reserves | 26 | 15 | 5 | 6 | 59 | 39 | 50 |
| 4 | Waveney Gunners | 26 | 15 | 4 | 7 | 71 | 56 | 49 |
| 5 | Carlton Rangers | 26 | 12 | 6 | 8 | 72 | 55 | 42 |
| 6 | Oxford Arms Reserves | 26 | 12 | 3 | 11 | 87 | 54 | 39 |
| 7 | Telecom Rovers | 26 | 12 | 2 | 12 | 78 | 79 | 38 |
| 8 | Beccles Caxton Reserves | 26 | 10 | 4 | 12 | 76 | 80 | 34 |
| 9 | Waveney A | 26 | 8 | 6 | 12 | 58 | 81 | 30 |
| 10 | FC Eastport (-3pts) | 26 | 10 | 2 | 14 | 66 | 77 | 29 |
| 11 | Crusaders | 26 | 8 | 1 | 17 | 57 | 98 | 25 |
| 12 | Spexhall Reserves | 26 | 7 | 3 | 16 | 46 | 76 | 24 |
| 13 | Bungay Town A | 26 | 6 | 3 | 17 | 42 | 80 | 21 |
| 14 | Factory Arms | 26 | 5 | 3 | 18 | 52 | 88 | 18 |

### Division Three

| | | P | W | D | L | F | A | Pts |
|---|---|---|---|---|---|---|---|---|
| 1 | Earsham Reserves | 24 | 19 | 1 | 4 | 74 | 43 | 58 |
| 2 | W.E.M.P | 24 | 18 | 3 | 3 | 110 | 45 | 57 |
| 3 | Payton | 24 | 17 | 3 | 4 | 108 | 32 | 54 |
| 4 | DK Consultants Res | 24 | 17 | 2 | 5 | 84 | 35 | 53 |
| 5 | Ellingham | 24 | 15 | 3 | 6 | 93 | 34 | 48 |
| 6 | Southwold Town | 24 | 14 | 2 | 8 | 82 | 56 | 44 |
| 7 | Stanford Arms | 24 | 9 | 4 | 11 | 71 | 79 | 31 |
| 8 | Corton Seltic Reserves | 24 | 8 | 4 | 12 | 47 | 64 | 28 |
| 9 | Carlton Rangers Res | 24 | 7 | 2 | 15 | 40 | 71 | 23 |
| 10 | Gunton United | 24 | 6 | 3 | 15 | 39 | 75 | 21 |
| 11 | Carlton Colville Town | 24 | 5 | 4 | 15 | 45 | 65 | 19 |
| 12 | Westhall | 24 | 4 | 3 | 17 | 36 | 91 | 15 |
| 13 | Electro Tec | 24 | 0 | 0 | 24 | 12 | 151 | 0 |

## LUTON DISTRICT & SOUTH BEDS LEAGUE

### Premier Division

| | | P | W | D | L | F | A | Pts |
|---|---|---|---|---|---|---|---|---|
| 1 | Christians in Sport | 14 | 10 | 2 | 2 | 39 | 18 | 32 |
| 2 | Farley Boys | 14 | 10 | 1 | 3 | 40 | 26 | 31 |
| 3 | Offley Cab | 14 | 9 | 2 | 3 | 41 | 21 | 29 |
| 4 | Lewsey Park | 14 | 5 | 2 | 7 | 21 | 27 | 17 |
| 5 | Dunstable Rangers | 14 | 5 | 1 | 8 | 24 | 27 | 16 |
| 6 | CO OP Sports | 14 | 5 | 1 | 8 | 26 | 50 | 16 |
| 7 | St Josephs | 14 | 4 | 3 | 7 | 23 | 28 | 15 |
| 8 | FC Wisla Luton | 14 | 2 | 0 | 12 | 20 | 37 | 6 |

## LEAGUE TABLES

### Division One

| | | P | W | D | L | F | A | Pts |
|---|---|---|---|---|---|---|---|---|
| 1 | Offley Cab 2nd XI | 18 | 17 | 1 | 0 | 88 | 12 | 52 |
| 2 | Luton Leagrave | 18 | 11 | 4 | 3 | 65 | 29 | 37 |
| 3 | Four Model | 18 | 12 | 1 | 5 | 52 | 24 | 37 |
| 4 | Jedenastka | 18 | 11 | 4 | 3 | 44 | 26 | 37 |
| 5 | Square Rangers | 18 | 8 | 3 | 7 | 43 | 31 | 27 |
| 6 | Caddington 2nd XI | 18 | 8 | 2 | 8 | 66 | 43 | 26 |
| 7 | FC Wisla Luton 2nd XI | 18 | 8 | 2 | 8 | 40 | 37 | 26 |
| 8 | North Sundon Wanderers | 18 | 2 | 2 | 14 | 24 | 86 | 8 |
| 9 | Luton Deaf | 18 | 2 | 1 | 15 | 23 | 95 | 7 |
| 10 | Multi Channel | 18 | 0 | 2 | 16 | 13 | 75 | 2 |

## MAIDSTONE & DISTRICT LEAGUE

### Premier Division

| | | P | W | D | L | F | A | Pts |
|---|---|---|---|---|---|---|---|---|
| 1 | Leeds SV | 20 | 18 | 1 | 1 | 102 | 36 | 55 |
| 2 | Eccles | 20 | 13 | 4 | 3 | 74 | 32 | 43 |
| 3 | Three Suttons | 20 | 13 | 3 | 4 | 65 | 35 | 42 |
| 4 | Lenham Wanderers | 20 | 10 | 3 | 7 | 53 | 54 | 33 |
| 5 | West Farleigh | 20 | 8 | 5 | 7 | 49 | 27 | 29 |
| 6 | Aylesford | 20 | 8 | 2 | 10 | 42 | 56 | 26 |
| 7 | Wateringbury Colts | 20 | 8 | 1 | 11 | 38 | 48 | 25 |
| 8 | Headcorn | 20 | 5 | 3 | 12 | 31 | 55 | 18 |
| 9 | Kingsley Chief | 20 | 5 | 3 | 12 | 29 | 55 | 18 |
| 10 | AFC Biddenden | 20 | 5 | 0 | 15 | 39 | 77 | 15 |
| 11 | Hunton | 20 | 4 | 1 | 15 | 25 | 72 | 13 |

### Division One

| | | P | W | D | L | F | A | Pts |
|---|---|---|---|---|---|---|---|---|
| 1 | Leybourne Athletic | 22 | 15 | 3 | 4 | 89 | 27 | 48 |
| 2 | Aylesford Reserves | 22 | 14 | 3 | 5 | 88 | 43 | 45 |
| 3 | Hunton Res | 22 | 13 | 4 | 5 | 56 | 31 | 43 |
| 4 | Sutton Saints | 22 | 13 | 2 | 7 | 56 | 37 | 41 |
| 5 | Kings Hill FC | 22 | 12 | 3 | 7 | 53 | 33 | 39 |
| 6 | Lenham Wanderers Res | 22 | 12 | 3 | 7 | 66 | 49 | 39 |
| 7 | Marden Minors | 22 | 11 | 4 | 7 | 67 | 43 | 37 |
| 8 | Eccles Reserves | 22 | 10 | 5 | 7 | 62 | 40 | 35 |
| 9 | West Farleigh Res | 22 | 6 | 2 | 14 | 43 | 69 | 20 |
| 10 | Lashings FC | 22 | 3 | 5 | 14 | 26 | 90 | 14 |
| 11 | Headcorn Res | 22 | 3 | 2 | 17 | 28 | 100 | 11 |
| 12 | Staplehurst Mon A | 22 | 1 | 2 | 19 | 23 | 95 | 5 |

### Division Two

| | | P | W | D | L | F | A | Pts |
|---|---|---|---|---|---|---|---|---|
| 1 | Maidstone Kestrels | 20 | 16 | 1 | 3 | 90 | 22 | 49 |
| 2 | Burham | 20 | 14 | 1 | 5 | 79 | 34 | 43 |
| 3 | Town Malling Club | 20 | 14 | 0 | 6 | 60 | 39 | 42 |
| 4 | Leybourne Athletic Reserves | 20 | 13 | 2 | 5 | 59 | 29 | 41 |
| 5 | Parkwood Jupitors | 20 | 9 | 1 | 10 | 50 | 51 | 28 |
| 6 | FC Ditton | 20 | 8 | 2 | 10 | 41 | 72 | 26 |
| 7 | Trisports | 20 | 8 | 1 | 11 | 49 | 55 | 25 |
| 8 | Maidstone Athletic | 20 | 7 | 3 | 10 | 41 | 48 | 24 |
| 9 | Phoenix United | 20 | 5 | 3 | 12 | 55 | 62 | 18 |
| 10 | The Early Bird | 20 | 5 | 3 | 12 | 42 | 65 | 18 |
| 11 | Hollingbourne | 20 | 2 | 1 | 17 | 30 | 119 | 7 |

## MERCIAN REGIONAL LEAGUE

### Premier Division

| | | P | W | D | L | F | A | Pts |
|---|---|---|---|---|---|---|---|---|
| 1 | AFC Ludlow | 24 | 18 | 3 | 3 | 81 | 21 | 57 |
| 2 | Telford Juniors | 24 | 14 | 6 | 4 | 45 | 27 | 48 |
| 3 | Morda United | 24 | 14 | 4 | 6 | 59 | 43 | 46 |
| 4 | Church Stretton | 24 | 14 | 4 | 6 | 50 | 41 | 46 |
| 5 | Wellington Amateurs Reserves | 24 | 12 | 2 | 10 | 49 | 40 | 38 |
| 6 | FC Hodnet | 24 | 11 | 3 | 10 | 38 | 32 | 36 |
| 7 | Shifnal United 97 | 24 | 10 | 3 | 11 | 37 | 36 | 33 |
| 8 | Oakengates Athletic | 24 | 8 | 4 | 12 | 44 | 49 | 28 |
| 9 | Allscott | 24 | 8 | 2 | 14 | 45 | 61 | 26 |
| 10 | Ketley Bank United | 24 | 7 | 4 | 13 | 32 | 53 | 25 |
| 11 | Whitchurch Alport | 24 | 6 | 5 | 13 | 35 | 55 | 23 |
| 12 | Weston Rhyn | 24 | 6 | 2 | 16 | 28 | 53 | 20 |
| 13 | Dawley Town | 24 | 5 | 4 | 15 | 32 | 64 | 19 |

### Division One

| | | P | W | D | L | F | A | Pts |
|---|---|---|---|---|---|---|---|---|
| 1 | Madeley Sports | 28 | 21 | 3 | 4 | 99 | 35 | 66 |
| 2 | Wroxeter Rovers | 28 | 21 | 1 | 6 | 111 | 42 | 64 |
| 3 | Prees (+3pts) | 28 | 20 | 1 | 7 | 104 | 48 | 64 |
| 4 | Ketley Town | 28 | 19 | 5 | 4 | 128 | 43 | 62 |
| 5 | Rock Rovers | 28 | 19 | 5 | 4 | 116 | 42 | 62 |
| 6 | Bishops Castle Town | 28 | 16 | 4 | 8 | 77 | 53 | 52 |
| 7 | Oswestry Lions | 28 | 15 | 3 | 10 | 87 | 59 | 48 |
| 8 | Brown Clee | 28 | 13 | 2 | 13 | 58 | 67 | 41 |
| 9 | Oswestry BG Club (-3pts) | 28 | 11 | 6 | 11 | 51 | 52 | 36 |
| 10 | Clee Hill United | 28 | 10 | 4 | 14 | 55 | 72 | 34 |
| 11 | Meole Brace | 28 | 7 | 3 | 18 | 51 | 96 | 24 |
| 12 | Hopesgate United | 28 | 6 | 2 | 20 | 60 | 100 | 20 |
| 13 | Shawbury United Reserves | 28 | 3 | 4 | 21 | 26 | 114 | 13 |
| 14 | Morda United Reserves | 28 | 4 | 1 | 23 | 37 | 130 | 13 |
| 15 | Wrockwardine Wood Juniors | 28 | 2 | 2 | 24 | 35 | 142 | 8 |

### Division Two

| | | P | W | D | L | F | A | Pts |
|---|---|---|---|---|---|---|---|---|
| 1 | Childs Ercall | 30 | 27 | 1 | 2 | 145 | 35 | 82 |
| 2 | Oakengates Rangers | 30 | 21 | 5 | 4 | 104 | 45 | 68 |
| 3 | Claverley | 30 | 21 | 0 | 9 | 123 | 65 | 63 |
| 4 | AFC Wellington | 30 | 20 | 2 | 8 | 148 | 61 | 62 |
| 5 | Market Drayton Tigers | 30 | 19 | 4 | 7 | 75 | 48 | 61 |
| 6 | Athletico Broseley | 30 | 19 | 3 | 8 | 124 | 61 | 60 |
| 7 | Randlay 2012 | 30 | 16 | 4 | 10 | 102 | 67 | 52 |
| 8 | Wrockwardine Wood | 30 | 15 | 4 | 11 | 97 | 50 | 49 |
| 9 | Donnington Sports & Social (-3pts) | 28 | 14 | 4 | 10 | 84 | 64 | 43 |
| 10 | Edgmond Rangers (+3pts) | 29 | 11 | 6 | 12 | 73 | 58 | 42 |
| 11 | Impact United | 30 | 13 | 2 | 15 | 68 | 79 | 41 |
| 12 | Highley Miners Welfare | 30 | 9 | 1 | 20 | 68 | 107 | 28 |
| 13 | Madeley Sports Reserves | 29 | 6 | 3 | 20 | 43 | 99 | 21 |
| 14 | Albrighton Juniors | 30 | 3 | 1 | 26 | 41 | 116 | 10 |
| 15 | Spalaig Britannia | 30 | 3 | 0 | 27 | 36 | 186 | 9 |
| 16 | Denso | 30 | 1 | 0 | 29 | 13 | 203 | 3 |

# MID ESSEX LEAGUE

| Premier Division | P | W | D | L | F | A | Pts |
|---|---|---|---|---|---|---|---|
| 1 Great Baddow | 18 | 14 | 2 | 2 | 59 | 24 | 44 |
| 2 Silver End United (+3pts) | 18 | 11 | 1 | 6 | 48 | 26 | 37 |
| 3 Debden Sports | 18 | 10 | 2 | 6 | 48 | 42 | 32 |
| 4 AFC Cranham | 18 | 10 | 2 | 6 | 35 | 31 | 32 |
| 5 Braintree and Bocking United | 18 | 7 | 4 | 7 | 31 | 37 | 25 |
| 6 Writtle Manor (+3pts) | 18 | 6 | 2 | 10 | 31 | 31 | 23 |
| 7 St.Clere's (-12pts) | 18 | 10 | 4 | 4 | 44 | 24 | 22 |
| 8 SFC Billericay | 18 | 5 | 5 | 8 | 23 | 29 | 20 |
| 9 United Chelmsford Churches | 18 | 3 | 3 | 12 | 28 | 50 | 12 |
| 10 Harold Wood Athletic | 18 | 1 | 1 | 16 | 17 | 70 | 4 |

| Division One | P | W | D | L | F | A | Pts |
|---|---|---|---|---|---|---|---|
| 1 Tillingham Hotspur | 18 | 17 | 1 | 0 | 86 | 22 | 52 |
| 2 Hutton | 18 | 10 | 3 | 5 | 54 | 28 | 33 |
| 3 Beacon Hill Rovers (+2pts) | 18 | 9 | 3 | 6 | 37 | 31 | 32 |
| 4 Stifford Town (-1pt) | 18 | 8 | 4 | 6 | 35 | 26 | 27 |
| 5 Sparta Basildon | 18 | 7 | 4 | 7 | 30 | 33 | 25 |
| 6 White Hart United | 18 | 6 | 3 | 9 | 36 | 44 | 21 |
| 7 Battlesbridge | 18 | 5 | 4 | 9 | 36 | 53 | 19 |
| 8 Academy Soccer | 18 | 5 | 4 | 9 | 28 | 53 | 19 |
| 9 Frenford Senior A | 18 | 5 | 2 | 11 | 29 | 54 | 17 |
| 10 Dunton Rangers | 18 | 3 | 2 | 13 | 26 | 53 | 11 |

| Division Two | P | W | D | L | F | A | Pts |
|---|---|---|---|---|---|---|---|
| 1 CT 66 | 24 | 18 | 3 | 3 | 98 | 49 | 57 |
| 2 Focus Ferrers | 24 | 18 | 3 | 3 | 81 | 36 | 57 |
| 3 Laindon Orient | 24 | 16 | 4 | 4 | 60 | 37 | 52 |
| 4 Flitch United | 24 | 13 | 4 | 7 | 78 | 48 | 43 |
| 5 Boreham | 24 | 11 | 3 | 10 | 46 | 53 | 36 |
| 6 Sandon Royals | 24 | 10 | 5 | 9 | 63 | 52 | 35 |
| 7 Stags Head (-1pt) | 24 | 10 | 5 | 9 | 52 | 47 | 34 |
| 8 Silver End United Reserves | 24 | 8 | 3 | 13 | 45 | 80 | 27 |
| 9 St.Clere's Reserves | 24 | 7 | 3 | 14 | 57 | 60 | 24 |
| 10 Old Chelmsfordians | 24 | 7 | 3 | 14 | 54 | 81 | 24 |
| 11 Manford Way | 24 | 6 | 3 | 15 | 41 | 57 | 21 |
| 12 St.Margarets | 24 | 5 | 4 | 15 | 45 | 63 | 19 |
| 13 Brendans (+2pts) | 24 | 3 | 5 | 16 | 25 | 82 | 16 |

| Division Three | P | W | D | L | F | A | Pts |
|---|---|---|---|---|---|---|---|
| 1 Dunmow Rhodes | 22 | 17 | 3 | 2 | 69 | 23 | 54 |
| 2 White Hart United Reserves | 22 | 14 | 2 | 6 | 69 | 32 | 44 |
| 3 Basildon Athletic | 22 | 12 | 3 | 7 | 53 | 29 | 39 |
| 4 Shelley Royals | 22 | 10 | 6 | 6 | 48 | 33 | 36 |
| 5 Stock United | 22 | 11 | 3 | 8 | 36 | 37 | 36 |
| 6 Runwell Hospital | 22 | 9 | 7 | 6 | 47 | 42 | 34 |
| 7 Mundon Vics | 22 | 11 | 1 | 10 | 46 | 43 | 34 |
| 8 Felsted Rovers | 22 | 10 | 3 | 9 | 38 | 46 | 33 |
| 9 Benfleet | 22 | 5 | 4 | 13 | 43 | 84 | 19 |
| 10 Latchingdon | 22 | 5 | 3 | 14 | 38 | 58 | 18 |
| 11 Harold Wood Athletic Reserves | 22 | 3 | 7 | 12 | 23 | 46 | 16 |
| 12 E2V Technologies | 22 | 2 | 4 | 16 | 29 | 66 | 10 |

| Division Four | P | W | D | L | F | A | Pts |
|---|---|---|---|---|---|---|---|
| 1 Great Baddow Reserves | 22 | 15 | 2 | 5 | 80 | 21 | 47 |
| 2 Hutton Reserves | 22 | 14 | 4 | 4 | 50 | 25 | 46 |
| 3 Durning (+3pts) | 22 | 13 | 2 | 7 | 53 | 29 | 44 |
| 4 Mayland Village | 22 | 13 | 3 | 6 | 49 | 32 | 42 |
| 5 Rayleigh Town | 22 | 12 | 2 | 8 | 56 | 40 | 38 |
| 6 Writtle | 22 | 9 | 5 | 8 | 37 | 47 | 32 |
| 7 Sparta Basildon Reserves | 22 | 9 | 4 | 9 | 41 | 47 | 31 |
| 8 Extreme United | 22 | 8 | 4 | 10 | 49 | 50 | 28 |
| 9 United Churches Brentwood (-6pts) | 22 | 8 | 3 | 11 | 36 | 44 | 21 |
| 10 Beacon Hill Rovers Reserves | 22 | 6 | 1 | 15 | 36 | 82 | 19 |
| 11 City Colts | 22 | 4 | 2 | 16 | 34 | 71 | 14 |
| 12 Braintree & Bocking Utd Reserves | 22 | 3 | 4 | 15 | 27 | 60 | 13 |

| Division Five | P | W | D | L | F | A | Pts |
|---|---|---|---|---|---|---|---|
| 1 Real Maldon | 22 | 16 | 4 | 2 | 65 | 23 | 52 |
| 2 Beacon Hill Rovers A | 22 | 12 | 4 | 6 | 63 | 58 | 40 |
| 3 St.Clere's A | 22 | 12 | 3 | 7 | 70 | 46 | 39 |
| 4 Kenson | 22 | 11 | 3 | 8 | 62 | 38 | 36 |
| 5 Battlesbridge Reserves | 22 | 11 | 3 | 8 | 47 | 45 | 36 |
| 6 Laindon Orient Reserves | 22 | 10 | 5 | 7 | 58 | 58 | 35 |
| 7 Burnham Athletic | 22 | 9 | 4 | 9 | 32 | 35 | 31 |
| 8 Teagan Athletic | 22 | 9 | 3 | 10 | 62 | 53 | 30 |
| 9 Frenford Senior B | 22 | 7 | 5 | 10 | 40 | 51 | 26 |
| 10 Focus Ferrers Reserves | 22 | 6 | 3 | 13 | 39 | 65 | 21 |
| 11 Halstead Wanderers | 22 | 6 | 1 | 15 | 48 | 61 | 19 |
| 12 Mundon Vics Reserves | 22 | 3 | 2 | 17 | 37 | 90 | 11 |

| Division Six | P | W | D | L | F | A | Pts |
|---|---|---|---|---|---|---|---|
| 1 Haver Town | 20 | 18 | 1 | 1 | 77 | 13 | 55 |
| 2 Latchingdon Reserves | 20 | 14 | 1 | 5 | 73 | 26 | 43 |
| 3 Moulsham | 20 | 13 | 1 | 6 | 49 | 36 | 40 |
| 4 Battlesbridge A | 20 | 12 | 1 | 7 | 70 | 39 | 37 |
| 5 United Chelsmford Churches Res | 20 | 10 | 2 | 8 | 41 | 33 | 32 |
| 6 Rayne United | 19 | 9 | 1 | 9 | 39 | 44 | 28 |
| 7 Parkway Sports (-3pts) | 19 | 10 | 0 | 9 | 42 | 47 | 27 |
| 8 Maldon Saints (-3pts) | 20 | 7 | 1 | 12 | 38 | 65 | 19 |
| 9 E2V Technologies Reserves | 20 | 5 | 1 | 14 | 32 | 66 | 16 |
| 10 Dengie Athletic | 20 | 5 | 1 | 14 | 30 | 71 | 16 |
| 11 Marconi Athletic (+6pts) | 20 | 0 | 2 | 18 | 21 | 72 | 8 |

# MID LANCASHIRE LEAGUE
(Formerly Preston & District)

| Premier Division | P | W | D | L | F | A | Pts |
|---|---|---|---|---|---|---|---|
| 1 Green Town | 22 | 18 | 1 | 3 | 90 | 32 | 55 |
| 2 Preston Wanderers | 22 | 18 | 0 | 4 | 110 | 36 | 54 |
| 3 Blessed Sacrament | 22 | 16 | 3 | 3 | 95 | 31 | 51 |
| 4 Southport & Ainsdale Amateurs | 22 | 13 | 5 | 4 | 59 | 38 | 44 |
| 5 Preston GSA | 22 | 12 | 0 | 10 | 50 | 50 | 33 |
| 6 Penwortham Town | 22 | 8 | 3 | 11 | 51 | 67 | 27 |
| 7 Hoole United | 22 | 8 | 1 | 13 | 51 | 63 | 25 |
| 8 Eccleston & Heskin | 22 | 6 | 6 | 10 | 40 | 42 | 24 |
| 9 Appley Bridge | 22 | 6 | 3 | 13 | 41 | 72 | 21 |
| 10 Deepdale | 22 | 5 | 2 | 15 | 46 | 80 | 17 |
| 11 Leyland United Reserves | 22 | 4 | 4 | 14 | 44 | 90 | 16 |
| 12 Charnock Richard | 22 | 3 | 2 | 17 | 36 | 112 | 11 |

# LEAGUE TABLES

## Division One

| | | P | W | D | L | F | A | Pts |
|---|---|---|---|---|---|---|---|---|
| 1 | Bolton United | 20 | 17 | 3 | 0 | 68 | 23 | 54 |
| 2 | Highcross | 20 | 15 | 0 | 5 | 55 | 29 | 45 |
| 3 | Adelphi | 20 | 13 | 1 | 6 | 60 | 41 | 40 |
| 4 | Walmer Bridge | 20 | 10 | 3 | 7 | 49 | 36 | 33 |
| 5 | Southport & Ainsdale Amateurs Res. | 19 | 8 | 2 | 9 | 44 | 47 | 26 |
| 6 | Broughton Amateurs | 20 | 7 | 3 | 10 | 39 | 48 | 24 |
| 7 | Southport Trinity | 20 | 6 | 5 | 9 | 55 | 50 | 23 |
| 8 | Walton Le Dale | 20 | 6 | 2 | 12 | 43 | 66 | 20 |
| 9 | Baxters | 20 | 4 | 7 | 9 | 38 | 58 | 19 |
| 10 | Leyland Athletic | 19 | 4 | 2 | 13 | 47 | 78 | 14 |
| 11 | New Longton Rovers | 20 | 3 | 4 | 13 | 33 | 55 | 13 |

## Division Two

| | | P | W | D | L | F | A | Pts |
|---|---|---|---|---|---|---|---|---|
| 1 | Burscough Bridge | 18 | 15 | 1 | 2 | 57 | 31 | 46 |
| 2 | Wilbraham | 18 | 12 | 3 | 3 | 70 | 37 | 39 |
| 3 | Leyland Utd 'A' | 18 | 11 | 2 | 5 | 77 | 51 | 35 |
| 4 | Springfields | 18 | 9 | 3 | 6 | 51 | 49 | 30 |
| 5 | Goosnargh | 18 | 7 | 2 | 9 | 40 | 44 | 23 |
| 6 | Newman College | 18 | 5 | 5 | 8 | 34 | 46 | 20 |
| 7 | Broughton Amateurs Res. | 18 | 5 | 3 | 10 | 40 | 61 | 18 |
| 8 | Eccleston & Heskin Res. | 18 | 4 | 4 | 10 | 45 | 55 | 16 |
| 9 | Chipping | 18 | 4 | 3 | 11 | 25 | 43 | 15 |
| 10 | Ribbleton Rovers | 18 | 4 | 2 | 12 | 42 | 64 | 14 |

## Division Three

| | | P | W | D | L | F | A | Pts |
|---|---|---|---|---|---|---|---|---|
| 1 | Lostock St.Gerards A | 20 | 16 | 3 | 1 | 86 | 28 | 51 |
| 2 | Ribble Wanderers | 20 | 15 | 2 | 3 | 68 | 29 | 47 |
| 3 | Fulwood Garrison | 20 | 14 | 2 | 4 | 52 | 28 | 44 |
| 4 | Greenlands FC | 20 | 10 | 3 | 7 | 62 | 37 | 33 |
| 5 | Farington Villa FC | 20 | 9 | 6 | 5 | 48 | 32 | 33 |
| 6 | Ribchester FC | 20 | 8 | 4 | 8 | 39 | 45 | 28 |
| 7 | Broughton Amateurs A | 20 | 8 | 0 | 12 | 30 | 50 | 24 |
| 8 | Tarleton Corinthians FC | 20 | 5 | 3 | 12 | 32 | 38 | 18 |
| 9 | Hoole United Reserves | 20 | 5 | 2 | 13 | 32 | 64 | 17 |
| 10 | Walmer Bridge Reserves | 20 | 4 | 2 | 14 | 30 | 69 | 14 |
| 11 | New Longton Rovers Res. | 20 | 2 | 1 | 17 | 15 | 74 | 7 |

## Division Four

| | | P | W | D | L | F | A | Pts |
|---|---|---|---|---|---|---|---|---|
| 1 | Penwortham Town Res | 18 | 15 | 2 | 1 | 75 | 23 | 47 |
| 2 | PLCC Nomads | 18 | 14 | 1 | 3 | 47 | 15 | 43 |
| 3 | AFC Preston FC | 18 | 11 | 2 | 5 | 53 | 32 | 35 |
| 4 | Broughton Amateurs B | 18 | 10 | 3 | 5 | 47 | 42 | 33 |
| 5 | FC Ribbleton | 18 | 8 | 2 | 8 | 51 | 46 | 26 |
| 6 | Cottam Corinthians | 18 | 8 | 0 | 10 | 40 | 42 | 24 |
| 7 | Southport Trinity B | 18 | 8 | 0 | 10 | 43 | 46 | 18 |
| 8 | Leyland Athletic Res | 18 | 5 | 0 | 13 | 42 | 62 | 15 |
| 9 | Tarleton Corinthians Res | 18 | 4 | 1 | 13 | 27 | 48 | 13 |
| 10 | Newman College Res | 18 | 1 | 1 | 16 | 17 | 86 | 4 |

# MID SOMERSET LEAGUE

## Premier League

| | | P | W | D | L | F | A | Pts |
|---|---|---|---|---|---|---|---|---|
| 1 | Chilcompton Sports | 20 | 15 | 2 | 3 | 69 | 23 | 47 |
| 2 | Welton Arsenal | 20 | 13 | 4 | 3 | 73 | 38 | 43 |
| 3 | Mells & Vobster United | 20 | 13 | 2 | 5 | 53 | 25 | 41 |
| 4 | Frome Town Sports | 20 | 13 | 2 | 5 | 56 | 29 | 41 |
| 5 | Meadow Rangers | 20 | 10 | 3 | 7 | 42 | 39 | 33 |
| 6 | Westfield Reserves | 20 | 10 | 2 | 8 | 57 | 46 | 32 |
| 7 | Coleford Athletic (-3pts) | 20 | 10 | 1 | 9 | 59 | 47 | 28 |
| 8 | Belrose | 20 | 6 | 2 | 12 | 38 | 58 | 20 |
| 9 | Wells City A | 20 | 3 | 3 | 14 | 35 | 53 | 12 |
| 10 | Oakhill | 20 | 2 | 1 | 17 | 27 | 81 | 7 |
| 11 | Evercreech Rovers (-8pts) | 20 | 4 | 0 | 16 | 27 | 97 | 4 |

## Division One

| | | P | W | D | L | F | A | Pts |
|---|---|---|---|---|---|---|---|---|
| 1 | Pensford FC | 20 | 17 | 3 | 0 | 93 | 16 | 54 |
| 2 | Interhound | 20 | 15 | 2 | 3 | 82 | 29 | 47 |
| 3 | Shepton Mallet Town A | 20 | 10 | 5 | 5 | 37 | 26 | 35 |
| 4 | Stoke Rovers | 20 | 8 | 5 | 7 | 70 | 45 | 29 |
| 5 | Purnells Sports A | 20 | 9 | 2 | 9 | 39 | 39 | 29 |
| 6 | Temple Cloud (-1pt) | 20 | 7 | 4 | 9 | 38 | 46 | 24 |
| 7 | Frome Collegians Reserves | 20 | 7 | 3 | 10 | 27 | 47 | 24 |
| 8 | Pilton United | 20 | 5 | 5 | 10 | 31 | 53 | 20 |
| 9 | Coleford Athletic Reserves | 20 | 6 | 2 | 12 | 29 | 73 | 20 |
| 10 | Glastonbury Reserves (-3pts) | 20 | 6 | 3 | 11 | 42 | 57 | 18 |
| 11 | Timsbury Athletic Res. (-4pts) | 20 | 1 | 4 | 15 | 19 | 76 | 3 |

## Division Two

| | | P | W | D | L | F | A | Pts |
|---|---|---|---|---|---|---|---|---|
| 1 | Westfield A | 20 | 15 | 3 | 2 | 70 | 32 | 48 |
| 2 | Clutton Reserves | 20 | 14 | 4 | 2 | 80 | 26 | 46 |
| 3 | Camerton Athletic (-4pts) | 20 | 15 | 2 | 3 | 76 | 38 | 43 |
| 4 | Peasedown Athletic Reserves | 20 | 8 | 3 | 9 | 38 | 39 | 27 |
| 5 | Chilcompton Sports Reserves | 20 | 7 | 4 | 9 | 58 | 68 | 25 |
| 6 | Radstock Town A | 20 | 7 | 2 | 11 | 45 | 65 | 23 |
| 7 | Mells & Vobster United Reserves | 20 | 7 | 1 | 12 | 50 | 61 | 22 |
| 8 | High Littleton FC | 20 | 5 | 5 | 10 | 28 | 54 | 20 |
| 9 | Farrington Gurney Reserves(-3pts) | 20 | 7 | 1 | 12 | 68 | 69 | 19 |
| 10 | Meadow Rangers Reserve | 20 | 6 | 1 | 13 | 32 | 77 | 19 |
| 11 | Frome Town Sports Reserves | 20 | 5 | 2 | 13 | 39 | 55 | 17 |

## Division Three

| | | P | W | D | L | F | A | Pts |
|---|---|---|---|---|---|---|---|---|
| 1 | Westhill Sports FC | 20 | 20 | 0 | 0 | 86 | 18 | 60 |
| 2 | Tunley Athletic Reserve | 20 | 15 | 1 | 4 | 67 | 23 | 46 |
| 3 | Pensford Reserves | 20 | 10 | 3 | 7 | 64 | 50 | 33 |
| 4 | Chew Magna Reserves | 20 | 10 | 2 | 8 | 36 | 40 | 32 |
| 5 | Wells City B | 20 | 9 | 4 | 7 | 60 | 35 | 31 |
| 6 | Tor Leisure | 20 | 10 | 0 | 10 | 46 | 53 | 30 |
| 7 | Purnells Sports B | 20 | 8 | 2 | 10 | 44 | 51 | 26 |
| 8 | Chilcompton United | 20 | 7 | 3 | 10 | 36 | 53 | 24 |
| 9 | Temple Cloud Reserves (-6pts) | 20 | 7 | 1 | 12 | 42 | 57 | 16 |
| 10 | Stoke Rovers Reserves (-3pts) | 20 | 4 | 1 | 15 | 31 | 77 | 10 |
| 11 | Belrose Reserves (-9pts) | 20 | 1 | 1 | 18 | 26 | 81 | -5 |

# MID SUSSEX LEAGUE

## Premier Division

| | P | W | D | L | F | A | Pts |
|---|---|---|---|---|---|---|---|
| 1 Dormansland Rockets | 24 | 18 | 1 | 5 | 91 | 43 | 55 |
| 2 Cuckfield Town | 24 | 16 | 4 | 4 | 79 | 40 | 52 |
| 3 Balcombe | 24 | 16 | 4 | 4 | 76 | 37 | 52 |
| 4 Willingdon Athletic (+2pts) | 24 | 14 | 4 | 6 | 53 | 34 | 48 |
| 5 Cuckfield Rangers | 24 | 15 | 1 | 8 | 65 | 42 | 46 |
| 6 Lindfield | 24 | 12 | 4 | 8 | 58 | 43 | 40 |
| 7 Old Varndeanians (-1pt) | 24 | 11 | 5 | 8 | 71 | 44 | 37 |
| 8 East Grinstead United (+1pt) | 24 | 8 | 4 | 12 | 30 | 41 | 29 |
| 9 Rotherfield | 24 | 7 | 5 | 12 | 57 | 70 | 26 |
| 10 Phoenix United (+1pt) | 24 | 6 | 2 | 16 | 46 | 72 | 21 |
| 11 Jarvis Brook | 24 | 6 | 1 | 17 | 19 | 67 | 19 |
| 12 Maresfield Village | 24 | 4 | 2 | 18 | 25 | 90 | 14 |
| 13 Furnace Green Galaxy | 24 | 4 | 1 | 19 | 22 | 69 | 13 |

## Championship

| | P | W | D | L | F | A | Pts |
|---|---|---|---|---|---|---|---|
| 1 Burgess Hill Albion | 20 | 16 | 1 | 3 | 63 | 26 | 49 |
| 2 Peacehaven United | 20 | 15 | 3 | 2 | 54 | 13 | 48 |
| 3 Montpelier Villa | 20 | 12 | 2 | 6 | 57 | 31 | 38 |
| 4 Portslade Athletic | 20 | 12 | 1 | 7 | 71 | 47 | 37 |
| 5 Polegate Town | 20 | 10 | 3 | 7 | 55 | 26 | 33 |
| 6 Saint Hill | 20 | 10 | 1 | 9 | 48 | 44 | 31 |
| 7 AFC Ringmer | 20 | 8 | 1 | 11 | 32 | 46 | 25 |
| 8 Buxted | 20 | 6 | 4 | 10 | 33 | 45 | 22 |
| 9 Old Varndeanians II | 20 | 5 | 2 | 13 | 28 | 54 | 17 |
| 10 Turners Hill (+3pts) | 20 | 3 | 1 | 16 | 23 | 59 | 13 |
| 11 Uckfield Town II (-3pts) | 20 | 2 | 3 | 15 | 19 | 92 | 6 |

## Division One

| | P | W | D | L | F | A | Pts |
|---|---|---|---|---|---|---|---|
| 1 Smallfield | 20 | 18 | 2 | 0 | 63 | 19 | 56 |
| 2 Copthorne | 20 | 14 | 2 | 4 | 56 | 23 | 44 |
| 3 Felbridge | 20 | 10 | 3 | 7 | 39 | 32 | 33 |
| 4 Ditchling | 20 | 10 | 1 | 9 | 40 | 38 | 31 |
| 5 Forest Row | 20 | 7 | 8 | 5 | 36 | 29 | 29 |
| 6 Framfield & Blackboys United | 20 | 9 | 2 | 9 | 30 | 36 | 29 |
| 7 Keymer & Hassocks | 20 | 7 | 4 | 9 | 30 | 28 | 25 |
| 8 Crawley Portuguese SC (-3pts) | 20 | 6 | 8 | 6 | 41 | 34 | 23 |
| 9 Ifield II | 20 | 4 | 6 | 10 | 33 | 48 | 18 |
| 10 Lindfield II | 20 | 3 | 5 | 12 | 32 | 60 | 14 |
| 11 Ardingly | 20 | 0 | 3 | 17 | 14 | 67 | 3 |

## Division Two

| | P | W | D | L | F | A | Pts |
|---|---|---|---|---|---|---|---|
| 1 East Court | 20 | 12 | 5 | 3 | 43 | 27 | 41 |
| 2 Furnace Green Rovers | 20 | 12 | 4 | 4 | 62 | 33 | 40 |
| 3 Ashurst Wood (+2pts) | 20 | 11 | 3 | 6 | 68 | 41 | 38 |
| 4 Hydraquip | 20 | 10 | 6 | 4 | 49 | 29 | 36 |
| 5 Village of Ditchling | 20 | 8 | 4 | 8 | 49 | 42 | 28 |
| 6 Barcombe (+3pts) | 20 | 7 | 3 | 10 | 34 | 43 | 27 |
| 7 East Grinstead Town III | 20 | 7 | 4 | 9 | 50 | 53 | 25 |
| 8 Sporting Elite (-1pt) | 20 | 8 | 2 | 10 | 39 | 63 | 25 |
| 9 Newick (-3pts) | 20 | 8 | 1 | 11 | 34 | 39 | 22 |
| 10 Hartfield | 20 | 6 | 1 | 13 | 30 | 66 | 19 |
| 11 Cuckfield Town II | 20 | 2 | 5 | 13 | 34 | 56 | 11 |

## Division Three

| | P | W | D | L | F | A | Pts |
|---|---|---|---|---|---|---|---|
| 1 Roffey II | 20 | 16 | 1 | 3 | 59 | 29 | 49 |
| 2 Willingdon Athletic II | 20 | 15 | 1 | 4 | 47 | 23 | 46 |
| 3 Wivelsfield Green (+3pts) | 20 | 14 | 1 | 5 | 60 | 38 | 46 |
| 4 Balcombe II | 20 | 11 | 3 | 6 | 49 | 32 | 36 |
| 5 Ansty Sports & Social (-3pts) | 20 | 11 | 3 | 6 | 62 | 40 | 33 |
| 6 Plumpton Athletic | 20 | 8 | 3 | 9 | 44 | 39 | 27 |
| 7 West Hoathly | 20 | 8 | 2 | 10 | 50 | 45 | 26 |
| 8 Sporting Lindfield | 20 | 5 | 3 | 12 | 43 | 52 | 18 |
| 9 Wingspan | 20 | 5 | 3 | 12 | 40 | 67 | 18 |
| 10 Scaynes Hill | 20 | 5 | 2 | 13 | 35 | 62 | 17 |
| 11 Maresfield Village II | 20 | 1 | 0 | 19 | 10 | 72 | 3 |

## Division Four

| | P | W | D | L | F | A | Pts |
|---|---|---|---|---|---|---|---|
| 1 Copthorne II | 20 | 14 | 3 | 3 | 57 | 23 | 45 |
| 2 North Chailey Lions (+5pts) | 20 | 12 | 3 | 5 | 48 | 44 | 44 |
| 3 Burgess Hill Albion II | 20 | 13 | 2 | 5 | 50 | 30 | 41 |
| 4 Fairwarp | 20 | 10 | 5 | 5 | 47 | 47 | 35 |
| 5 Phoenix United II (+3pts) | 20 | 7 | 7 | 6 | 49 | 43 | 31 |
| 6 Dormansland Rockets II | 20 | 10 | 0 | 10 | 52 | 40 | 30 |
| 7 Furnace Green Galaxy II | 20 | 8 | 2 | 10 | 39 | 35 | 26 |
| 8 Fletching | 20 | 7 | 5 | 8 | 45 | 43 | 26 |
| 9 Old Varndeanians III (-6pts) | 20 | 8 | 1 | 11 | 43 | 53 | 19 |
| 10 Wisdom Sports | 20 | 4 | 2 | 14 | 41 | 68 | 14 |
| 11 Turners Hill II (-1pt) | 20 | 1 | 2 | 17 | 20 | 65 | 4 |

## Division Five

| | P | W | D | L | F | A | Pts |
|---|---|---|---|---|---|---|---|
| 1 DCK Copthorne | 20 | 19 | 0 | 1 | 77 | 18 | 57 |
| 2 Horsted Keynes (+2pts) | 20 | 12 | 5 | 3 | 48 | 28 | 43 |
| 3 Buxted II | 20 | 13 | 1 | 6 | 57 | 26 | 40 |
| 4 United Services | 20 | 9 | 3 | 8 | 41 | 33 | 30 |
| 5 East Grinstead Mavericks | 20 | 8 | 5 | 7 | 50 | 44 | 29 |
| 6 Handcross Village | 20 | 8 | 3 | 9 | 36 | 30 | 27 |
| 7 Cuckfield Rangers II | 20 | 6 | 6 | 8 | 37 | 35 | 24 |
| 8 East Grinstead United II (-1pt) | 20 | 7 | 4 | 9 | 25 | 31 | 24 |
| 9 Polegate Town II | 20 | 5 | 3 | 12 | 31 | 58 | 18 |
| 10 Ardingly II | 20 | 3 | 4 | 13 | 27 | 72 | 13 |
| 11 Sporting Elite II | 20 | 2 | 2 | 16 | 21 | 75 | 8 |

## Division Six

| | P | W | D | L | F | A | Pts |
|---|---|---|---|---|---|---|---|
| 1 Nutley | 20 | 18 | 1 | 1 | 100 | 16 | 55 |
| 2 Lindfield III | 20 | 15 | 2 | 3 | 69 | 32 | 47 |
| 3 Ifield III | 20 | 10 | 3 | 7 | 49 | 46 | 33 |
| 4 Felbridge II | 20 | 10 | 1 | 9 | 45 | 38 | 31 |
| 5 Copthorne III | 20 | 9 | 3 | 8 | 62 | 45 | 30 |
| 6 Rottingdean Village Veterans | 20 | 9 | 2 | 9 | 45 | 60 | 29 |
| 7 Jarvis Brook II | 20 | 7 | 3 | 10 | 32 | 37 | 24 |
| 8 Rotherfield II | 20 | 6 | 3 | 11 | 35 | 53 | 21 |
| 9 Horley Wanderers | 20 | 6 | 3 | 11 | 31 | 56 | 21 |
| 10 Danehill | 20 | 5 | 2 | 13 | 35 | 73 | 17 |
| 11 Ditchling II | 20 | 3 | 1 | 16 | 19 | 66 | 10 |

# LEAGUE TABLES

| Division Seven | P | W | D | L | F | A | Pts |
|---|---|---|---|---|---|---|---|
| 1 Hydraquip II | 20 | 14 | 3 | 3 | 50 | 28 | 45 |
| 2 Peacehaven United II | 20 | 13 | 5 | 2 | 58 | 17 | 44 |
| 3 Cherry Lane | 20 | 12 | 5 | 3 | 68 | 38 | 41 |
| 4 Crawley Athletic | 20 | 11 | 2 | 7 | 77 | 36 | 35 |
| 5 Copthorne IV | 20 | 11 | 2 | 7 | 58 | 33 | 35 |
| 6 Ashurst Wood II | 20 | 6 | 7 | 7 | 49 | 58 | 25 |
| 7 Forest Row II | 20 | 7 | 2 | 11 | 45 | 64 | 23 |
| 8 Fairwarp II | 20 | 5 | 4 | 11 | 43 | 66 | 19 |
| 9 Bolney Rovers | 20 | 4 | 6 | 10 | 36 | 52 | 18 |
| 10 Newick II | 20 | 5 | 3 | 12 | 27 | 64 | 18 |
| 11 Cuckfield Town III | 20 | 1 | 3 | 16 | 35 | 90 | 6 |

| Division Eight | P | W | D | L | F | A | Pts |
|---|---|---|---|---|---|---|---|
| 1 Framfield & Blackboys United II | 20 | 17 | 2 | 1 | 91 | 13 | 53 |
| 2 Wivelsfield Green II | 20 | 13 | 4 | 3 | 66 | 31 | 43 |
| 3 Ansty Sports & Social II | 20 | 11 | 3 | 6 | 48 | 36 | 36 |
| 4 Willingdon Athletic III | 20 | 11 | 2 | 7 | 61 | 39 | 35 |
| 5 Plumpton Athletic II (+1pt) | 20 | 9 | 4 | 7 | 50 | 42 | 34 |
| 6 Fletching II | 20 | 8 | 1 | 11 | 46 | 54 | 25 |
| 7 East Grinstead Town IV | 20 | 7 | 4 | 9 | 32 | 47 | 25 |
| 8 Hartfield II | 20 | 6 | 2 | 12 | 40 | 79 | 20 |
| 9 Maresfield Village III (-3pts) | 20 | 5 | 4 | 11 | 31 | 58 | 16 |
| 10 Pilgrims | 20 | 4 | 2 | 14 | 39 | 51 | 14 |
| 11 Fairfield | 20 | 4 | 2 | 14 | 29 | 83 | 14 |

| Division Nine | P | W | D | L | F | A | Pts |
|---|---|---|---|---|---|---|---|
| 1 AFC Haywards | 18 | 14 | 2 | 2 | 66 | 27 | 44 |
| 2 Keymer & Hassocks II | 18 | 13 | 3 | 2 | 52 | 22 | 42 |
| 3 Stones (+6pts) | 18 | 10 | 2 | 6 | 57 | 47 | 38 |
| 4 Wingspan II (-6pts) | 18 | 12 | 2 | 4 | 74 | 32 | 32 |
| 5 Cuckfield Rangers III | 18 | 10 | 1 | 7 | 40 | 38 | 31 |
| 6 Heath Rangers | 18 | 6 | 2 | 10 | 37 | 52 | 20 |
| 7 West Hoathly II (+3pts) | 18 | 4 | 3 | 11 | 22 | 64 | 18 |
| 8 Handcross Village II | 18 | 5 | 1 | 12 | 35 | 52 | 16 |
| 9 Lindfield IV | 18 | 3 | 1 | 14 | 36 | 50 | 10 |
| 10 Uckfield Town III (-3pts) | 18 | 4 | 1 | 13 | 24 | 59 | 10 |

| Division Ten | P | W | D | L | F | A | Pts |
|---|---|---|---|---|---|---|---|
| 1 Ridgewood | 22 | 15 | 3 | 4 | 66 | 21 | 48 |
| 2 Burgess Hill Albion III (+2pts) | 22 | 14 | 3 | 5 | 57 | 40 | 47 |
| 3 Roffey III | 22 | 14 | 4 | 4 | 53 | 19 | 46 |
| 4 Barcombe II | 22 | 12 | 3 | 7 | 54 | 44 | 39 |
| 5 Sporting Devils | 22 | 9 | 6 | 7 | 52 | 39 | 33 |
| 6 Buxted III (+3pts) | 22 | 9 | 3 | 10 | 43 | 50 | 33 |
| 7 Lindfield V (-3pts) | 22 | 10 | 1 | 11 | 46 | 52 | 28 |
| 8 Cherry Lane II (-3pts) | 22 | 8 | 4 | 10 | 44 | 46 | 25 |
| 9 Copthorne V (+3pts) | 22 | 6 | 1 | 15 | 42 | 60 | 22 |
| 10 Scaynes Hill II | 22 | 6 | 3 | 13 | 40 | 68 | 21 |
| 11 Hydraquip III (-1pt) | 22 | 6 | 3 | 13 | 47 | 67 | 20 |
| 12 Brighton & Hove Albion Disability | 22 | 5 | 2 | 15 | 44 | 82 | 17 |

| Division Eleven A | P | W | D | L | F | A | Pts |
|---|---|---|---|---|---|---|---|
| 1 Burgess Hill Wanderers | 21 | 18 | 3 | 0 | 60 | 24 | 57 |
| 2 Hassocks Hornets | 21 | 15 | 1 | 5 | 84 | 38 | 46 |
| 3 Rotherfield III | 21 | 13 | 2 | 6 | 65 | 26 | 41 |
| 4 Crawley United | 21 | 11 | 2 | 8 | 57 | 42 | 35 |
| 5 Ashurst Wood III | 21 | 5 | 6 | 10 | 35 | 57 | 21 |
| 6 Danehill II (-3pts) | 21 | 7 | 0 | 14 | 42 | 59 | 18 |
| 7 Hartfield III | 21 | 2 | 6 | 13 | 21 | 65 | 12 |
| 8 Scaynes Hill III (+3pts) | 21 | 1 | 4 | 16 | 18 | 71 | 10 |

| Division Eleven B | P | W | D | L | F | A | Pts |
|---|---|---|---|---|---|---|---|
| 1 Burgess Hill Athletic | 21 | 15 | 3 | 3 | 49 | 30 | 48 |
| 2 Furngate (-3pts) | 21 | 15 | 3 | 3 | 79 | 42 | 45 |
| 3 East Grinstead Meads (+3pts) | 21 | 10 | 3 | 8 | 52 | 59 | 36 |
| 4 Saint Hill II (-2pts) | 21 | 8 | 2 | 11 | 54 | 63 | 24 |
| 5 AFC Haywards II | 21 | 7 | 2 | 12 | 40 | 46 | 23 |
| 6 Wivelsfield Wanderers | 21 | 7 | 1 | 13 | 56 | 51 | 22 |
| 7 Stones II (+2pts) | 21 | 5 | 5 | 11 | 49 | 68 | 22 |
| 8 Nutley II (+2pts) | 21 | 4 | 7 | 10 | 43 | 63 | 21 |

# MIDLAND REGIONAL ALLIANCE

| Premier Division | P | W | D | L | F | A | Pts |
|---|---|---|---|---|---|---|---|
| 1 Allenton United | 30 | 22 | 5 | 3 | 122 | 31 | 71 |
| 2 Rowsley 86 | 30 | 21 | 4 | 5 | 103 | 44 | 67 |
| 3 Derby Rolls Royce Leisure | 30 | 20 | 1 | 9 | 100 | 61 | 61 |
| 4 Melbourne Dynamo | 30 | 18 | 5 | 7 | 83 | 48 | 59 |
| 5 Swanwick Pentrich Road | 30 | 16 | 8 | 6 | 63 | 45 | 56 |
| 6 Mickleover Royal British Legion | 30 | 16 | 7 | 7 | 69 | 44 | 55 |
| 7 Willington | 30 | 17 | 3 | 10 | 94 | 55 | 54 |
| 8 Wirksworth Town | 30 | 14 | 4 | 12 | 67 | 55 | 46 |
| 9 Cromford | 30 | 13 | 7 | 10 | 72 | 62 | 46 |
| 10 Newhall United | 30 | 12 | 7 | 11 | 63 | 53 | 43 |
| 11 Allestree | 30 | 11 | 5 | 14 | 52 | 67 | 38 |
| 12 Matlock Sports | 30 | 8 | 2 | 20 | 46 | 94 | 26 |
| 13 Chellaston | 30 | 6 | 3 | 21 | 39 | 88 | 21 |
| 14 Newmount | 30 | 4 | 4 | 22 | 43 | 91 | 16 |
| 15 Punjab United | 30 | 3 | 5 | 22 | 47 | 110 | 14 |
| 16 Sandiacre Town | 30 | 3 | 2 | 25 | 27 | 142 | 11 |

| Division One | P | W | D | L | F | A | Pts |
|---|---|---|---|---|---|---|---|
| 1 Woolley Moor United | 26 | 21 | 3 | 2 | 110 | 48 | 66 |
| 2 Derby Rolls Royce Leisure Res. | 26 | 16 | 3 | 7 | 79 | 48 | 51 |
| 3 Little Eaton | 26 | 16 | 3 | 7 | 60 | 37 | 51 |
| 4 Mackworth St. Francis | 26 | 16 | 2 | 8 | 78 | 45 | 50 |
| 5 Allenton United Reserves | 26 | 12 | 4 | 10 | 66 | 63 | 40 |
| 6 Derby Singh Brothers | 26 | 12 | 3 | 11 | 49 | 56 | 39 |
| 7 Rowsley 86 Reserves | 26 | 11 | 5 | 10 | 62 | 47 | 38 |
| 8 Ripley Town | 26 | 10 | 4 | 12 | 67 | 53 | 34 |
| 9 Pastures (-3pts) | 26 | 11 | 3 | 12 | 75 | 75 | 33 |
| 10 Tibshelf | 26 | 8 | 5 | 13 | 64 | 74 | 29 |
| 11 Bargate Rovers | 26 | 8 | 2 | 16 | 52 | 76 | 26 |
| 12 Swanwick Pentrich Road Res. | 26 | 7 | 2 | 17 | 54 | 78 | 23 |
| 13 Wirksworth Ivanhoe | 26 | 5 | 6 | 15 | 44 | 73 | 21 |
| 14 Stanton Ilkeston | 26 | 5 | 3 | 18 | 38 | 125 | 14 |

| Division Two | P | W | D | L | F | A | Pts |
|---|---|---|---|---|---|---|---|
| 1 Shardlow St. James | 26 | 21 | 0 | 5 | 109 | 36 | 63 |
| 2 Pastures Reserves | 26 | 18 | 2 | 6 | 89 | 53 | 56 |
| 3 Ambergate (-3pts) | 26 | 18 | 4 | 4 | 83 | 34 | 55 |
| 4 Newhall United Reserves | 26 | 15 | 4 | 7 | 87 | 53 | 49 |
| 5 Mackworth St. Francis Res. | 26 | 14 | 5 | 7 | 70 | 46 | 47 |
| 6 Little Eaton Reserves | 26 | 15 | 2 | 9 | 70 | 48 | 47 |
| 7 Melbourne Dynamo Reserves | 26 | 14 | 4 | 8 | 69 | 54 | 46 |
| 8 Willington Sports | 26 | 8 | 4 | 14 | 47 | 84 | 28 |
| 9 Newton (-3pts) | 26 | 9 | 2 | 15 | 48 | 59 | 26 |
| 10 Hilton Harriers | 26 | 7 | 3 | 16 | 40 | 68 | 24 |
| 11 Bargate Rovers Reserves | 26 | 7 | 2 | 17 | 44 | 87 | 23 |
| 12 Wirksworth Town Reserves | 26 | 5 | 7 | 14 | 44 | 63 | 22 |
| 13 Punjab United Reserves (-5pts) | 26 | 7 | 5 | 14 | 44 | 83 | 21 |
| 14 Roe Farm | 26 | 1 | 2 | 23 | 31 | 107 | 5 |

## NORTH & MID HERTS LEAGUE

### Premier Division

| | P | W | D | L | F | A | Pts |
|---|---|---|---|---|---|---|---|
| Tansley | 16 | 14 | 1 | 1 | 68 | 16 | 43 |
| St Ippolyts | 16 | 13 | 0 | 3 | 61 | 29 | 39 |
| FC Cornerstone | 16 | 12 | 1 | 3 | 93 | 23 | 37 |
| AFC Baldock | 16 | 9 | 0 | 7 | 57 | 30 | 27 |
| FC Letchworth | 16 | 7 | 1 | 8 | 40 | 40 | 22 |
| Warriors XI | 16 | 7 | 0 | 9 | 41 | 29 | 21 |
| London Colney Blues | 16 | 5 | 1 | 10 | 37 | 45 | 16 |
| Barmond United | 16 | 2 | 1 | 13 | 16 | 100 | 7 |
| Buntingford Cougars | 16 | 0 | 1 | 15 | 8 | 109 | 1 |

## NORTH BUCKS & DISTRICT LEAGUE

### Premier Division

| | P | W | D | L | F | A | Pts |
|---|---|---|---|---|---|---|---|
| Potterspury | 24 | 17 | 4 | 3 | 73 | 38 | 55 |
| Grendon Rangers | 24 | 16 | 4 | 4 | 59 | 35 | 52 |
| Loughton Manor | 24 | 14 | 5 | 5 | 72 | 38 | 47 |
| Great Horwood | 24 | 14 | 2 | 8 | 57 | 45 | 44 |
| City Colts | 24 | 13 | 4 | 7 | 70 | 34 | 43 |
| Silverstone | 24 | 10 | 2 | 12 | 51 | 55 | 32 |
| Stewkley | 23 | 9 | 3 | 11 | 51 | 45 | 30 |
| Brackley Sports | 24 | 8 | 5 | 11 | 58 | 50 | 29 |
| Thornborough Athletic | 23 | 7 | 6 | 10 | 42 | 49 | 27 |
| Southcott Village R.A. | 24 | 6 | 5 | 13 | 44 | 63 | 23 |
| MK Titans | 24 | 7 | 2 | 15 | 33 | 95 | 23 |
| Great Linford | 24 | 6 | 4 | 14 | 32 | 56 | 22 |
| Yardley Gobion | 24 | 3 | 4 | 17 | 39 | 78 | 13 |

### Intermediate

| | P | W | D | L | F | A | Pts |
|---|---|---|---|---|---|---|---|
| Buckingham Town Res. | 25 | 20 | 3 | 2 | 76 | 25 | 63 |
| Woburn Sands Wanderers | 25 | 20 | 2 | 3 | 96 | 43 | 62 |
| Bow Brickhill | 25 | 16 | 1 | 8 | 91 | 65 | 49 |
| Wicken Sports | 25 | 14 | 5 | 6 | 80 | 48 | 47 |
| Syresham | 24 | 12 | 3 | 9 | 71 | 50 | 39 |
| City Colts Res. | 24 | 9 | 7 | 8 | 59 | 50 | 34 |
| Brackley Sports Res. | 26 | 9 | 1 | 16 | 51 | 77 | 28 |
| Hanslope | 24 | 8 | 4 | 12 | 51 | 78 | 28 |
| AFC Santander | 23 | 8 | 3 | 12 | 41 | 52 | 27 |
| Grendon Rangers Res. | 24 | 8 | 3 | 13 | 37 | 58 | 27 |
| Denbigh Hall Sports & Social | 24 | 8 | 2 | 14 | 47 | 59 | 26 |
| Deanshanger Athletic | 26 | 6 | 6 | 14 | 41 | 76 | 24 |
| Wolverton Town Res. | 24 | 6 | 4 | 14 | 43 | 64 | 22 |
| Potterspury Res. | 25 | 5 | 2 | 18 | 41 | 80 | 17 |

### Division One

| | P | W | D | L | F | A | Pts |
|---|---|---|---|---|---|---|---|
| Bow Brickhill Res. | 27 | 20 | 2 | 5 | 89 | 44 | 62 |
| Stoke Hammond Wanderers | 28 | 18 | 3 | 7 | 88 | 58 | 57 |
| Marsh Gibbon | 27 | 17 | 5 | 5 | 76 | 40 | 56 |
| University of Buckingham | 27 | 15 | 3 | 9 | 76 | 74 | 48 |
| Charlton & District | 27 | 13 | 8 | 6 | 64 | 40 | 47 |
| Olney | 28 | 13 | 6 | 9 | 54 | 55 | 45 |
| Southcott Village R.A. Res. | 27 | 13 | 5 | 9 | 71 | 56 | 44 |
| Great Linford Res. | 28 | 12 | 6 | 10 | 81 | 76 | 42 |
| Padbury Village | 27 | 9 | 6 | 12 | 60 | 59 | 33 |
| Wicken Sports Res. | 28 | 8 | 5 | 15 | 51 | 69 | 29 |
| Stewkley Res. | 27 | 9 | 2 | 16 | 46 | 78 | 29 |
| Woughton | 27 | 8 | 4 | 15 | 73 | 95 | 28 |
| Cage Athletic | 27 | 7 | 3 | 17 | 45 | 78 | 24 |
| Deanshanger Athletic Res. | 27 | 7 | 2 | 18 | 41 | 83 | 23 |
| Syresham Res. | 26 | 4 | 2 | 20 | 48 | 58 | 14 |

### Division Two

| | P | W | D | L | F | A | Pts |
|---|---|---|---|---|---|---|---|
| 1 Comet MK | 26 | 25 | 1 | 0 | 114 | 26 | 76 |
| 2 Scot | 25 | 22 | 1 | 2 | 92 | 31 | 67 |
| 3 M.K. Wanderers Res. | 27 | 17 | 3 | 7 | 73 | 34 | 54 |
| 4 Steeple Claydon | 28 | 16 | 4 | 8 | 85 | 54 | 52 |
| 5 Stantonbury Sports | 27 | 16 | 2 | 9 | 68 | 51 | 50 |
| 6 Twyford United | 27 | 15 | 4 | 8 | 63 | 53 | 49 |
| 7 Wing Village | 26 | 15 | 1 | 10 | 94 | 65 | 46 |
| 8 Great Horwood Res. | 26 | 15 | 1 | 10 | 63 | 60 | 46 |
| 9 St. George's MK | 27 | 8 | 4 | 15 | 58 | 66 | 28 |
| 10 Hanslope Res. | 28 | 7 | 5 | 16 | 53 | 80 | 26 |
| 11 Westbury | 28 | 7 | 1 | 20 | 41 | 95 | 22 |
| 12 Yardley Gobion Res. | 26 | 6 | 3 | 17 | 58 | 82 | 21 |
| 13 Marsh Gibbon Res. | 27 | 5 | 5 | 17 | 45 | 78 | 20 |
| 14 Silverstone Res. | 27 | 5 | 5 | 17 | 51 | 90 | 20 |
| 15 Padbury Village Res. | 27 | 1 | 2 | 24 | 40 | 133 | 5 |

## NORTH DEVON LEAGUE

### Premier Division

| | P | W | D | L | F | A | Pts |
|---|---|---|---|---|---|---|---|
| 1 Torridgeside | 28 | 24 | 3 | 1 | 105 | 21 | 75 |
| 2 Bideford Reserves | 28 | 24 | 3 | 1 | 112 | 33 | 75 |
| 3 Boca Seniors | 28 | 21 | 1 | 6 | 124 | 39 | 64 |
| 4 Braunton | 28 | 20 | 4 | 4 | 83 | 47 | 64 |
| 5 North Molton Sports Club | 28 | 20 | 2 | 6 | 102 | 38 | 62 |
| 6 Shamwickshire Rovers | 28 | 13 | 3 | 12 | 63 | 65 | 42 |
| 7 Chittlehampton | 28 | 9 | 4 | 15 | 58 | 76 | 31 |
| 8 Appledore Reserves | 28 | 9 | 4 | 15 | 51 | 70 | 31 |
| 9 Bradworthy | 28 | 9 | 3 | 16 | 40 | 73 | 30 |
| 10 Ilfracombe Town Reserves | 28 | 8 | 2 | 18 | 32 | 66 | 26 |
| 11 Dolton | 28 | 8 | 1 | 19 | 47 | 74 | 25 |
| 12 Shebbear United | 28 | 7 | 4 | 17 | 42 | 102 | 25 |
| 13 Georgeham & Croyde | 28 | 6 | 5 | 17 | 37 | 83 | 23 |
| 14 Barnstaple AAC | 28 | 6 | 1 | 21 | 38 | 93 | 19 |
| 15 Putford | 28 | 4 | 4 | 20 | 25 | 79 | 16 |

### Senior Division

| | P | W | D | L | F | A | Pts |
|---|---|---|---|---|---|---|---|
| 1 Fremington | 28 | 25 | 2 | 1 | 111 | 15 | 77 |
| 2 Torrington | 28 | 24 | 1 | 3 | 117 | 21 | 73 |
| 3 Combe Martin | 28 | 20 | 4 | 4 | 103 | 46 | 64 |
| 4 Braunton Reserves | 28 | 15 | 4 | 9 | 79 | 43 | 49 |
| 5 Woolsery | 28 | 14 | 7 | 7 | 69 | 56 | 49 |
| 6 Park United | 28 | 13 | 6 | 9 | 71 | 70 | 45 |
| 7 Ashwater | 28 | 11 | 4 | 13 | 75 | 77 | 37 |
| 8 Bude Town | 28 | 11 | 4 | 13 | 71 | 80 | 37 |
| 9 Merton | 28 | 10 | 3 | 15 | 69 | 63 | 33 |
| 10 Lynton & Lynmouth (-3pts) | 28 | 10 | 3 | 15 | 54 | 64 | 30 |
| 11 North Molton Sports Club Res. | 28 | 7 | 4 | 17 | 42 | 92 | 25 |
| 12 Northam Lions | 28 | 7 | 1 | 20 | 46 | 88 | 22 |
| 13 Shamwickshire Rovers Reserves | 28 | 7 | 1 | 20 | 54 | 106 | 22 |
| 14 South Molton | 28 | 6 | 4 | 18 | 52 | 121 | 22 |
| 15 Pilton Academicals | 28 | 4 | 4 | 20 | 42 | 113 | 16 |

# LEAGUE TABLES

| Intermediate One | P | W | D | L | F | A | Pts |
|---|---|---|---|---|---|---|---|
| 1 Barnstaple FC | 30 | 26 | 2 | 2 | 138 | 40 | 80 |
| 2 Torridgeside Reserves | 30 | 20 | 4 | 6 | 83 | 40 | 64 |
| 3 Landkey Town | 30 | 18 | 5 | 7 | 86 | 58 | 59 |
| 4 Hartland | 30 | 17 | 3 | 10 | 90 | 55 | 54 |
| 5 Woolacombe & Mortehoe | 30 | 17 | 1 | 12 | 106 | 63 | 52 |
| 6 Anchor Chiefs | 30 | 15 | 6 | 9 | 75 | 52 | 51 |
| 7 Ilfracombe Town Thirds | 30 | 13 | 7 | 10 | 72 | 54 | 46 |
| 8 Northside Atlantic (-3pts) | 30 | 14 | 3 | 13 | 76 | 67 | 42 |
| 9 Braunton Thirds | 30 | 11 | 6 | 13 | 57 | 73 | 39 |
| 10 Equalizers | 30 | 10 | 6 | 14 | 78 | 94 | 36 |
| 11 Barnstaple AAC Reserves | 30 | 10 | 5 | 15 | 68 | 85 | 35 |
| 12 Clovelly | 30 | 8 | 8 | 14 | 68 | 86 | 32 |
| 13 High Bickington | 30 | 8 | 6 | 16 | 49 | 84 | 30 |
| 14 Torrington Reserves | 30 | 9 | 1 | 20 | 51 | 101 | 28 |
| 15 Northam Lions Reserves (-3pts) | 30 | 5 | 4 | 21 | 49 | 110 | 16 |
| 16 Sporting Barum | 30 | 5 | 1 | 24 | 46 | 130 | 16 |

| Intermediate Two | P | W | D | L | F | A | Pts |
|---|---|---|---|---|---|---|---|
| 1 Braunton Fourths | 24 | 20 | 2 | 2 | 105 | 21 | 62 |
| 2 Barnstaple FC Reserves | 24 | 16 | 3 | 5 | 81 | 23 | 51 |
| 3 Buckland Brewer | 24 | 16 | 2 | 6 | 63 | 51 | 50 |
| 4 Fremington Reserves | 24 | 16 | 1 | 7 | 71 | 37 | 49 |
| 5 Georgeham & Croyde Reserves | 24 | 14 | 3 | 7 | 73 | 56 | 45 |
| 6 Putford Reserves | 24 | 12 | 3 | 9 | 76 | 34 | 39 |
| 7 Anchor Chiefs Reserves | 24 | 11 | 3 | 10 | 57 | 50 | 36 |
| 8 Hartland Reserves | 24 | 10 | 2 | 12 | 42 | 45 | 32 |
| 9 Chittlehampton Reserves | 24 | 10 | 0 | 14 | 53 | 71 | 30 |
| 10 North Molton Sports Club Thirds (-3pts) | 24 | 6 | 3 | 15 | 33 | 72 | 18 |
| 11 South Molton Reserves | 24 | 4 | 3 | 17 | 37 | 116 | 15 |
| 12 Woolsery Reserves | 24 | 3 | 4 | 17 | 31 | 91 | 13 |
| 13 Lynton & Lynmouth Reserves | 24 | 3 | 1 | 20 | 26 | 81 | 10 |

## NORTH EAST NORFOLK LEAGUE

| Division One | P | W | D | L | F | A | Pts |
|---|---|---|---|---|---|---|---|
| 1 Runton | 20 | 17 | 2 | 1 | 96 | 21 | 53 |
| 2 Haisboro Atheltic | 20 | 14 | 4 | 2 | 84 | 45 | 46 |
| 3 Gimingham | 20 | 13 | 3 | 4 | 83 | 41 | 42 |
| 4 Ludham | 20 | 11 | 2 | 7 | 58 | 51 | 35 |
| 5 East Ruston | 20 | 9 | 2 | 9 | 45 | 50 | 29 |
| 6 North Walsham A | 20 | 8 | 4 | 8 | 49 | 39 | 28 |
| 7 Mundesley (-2pts) | 20 | 9 | 1 | 10 | 40 | 42 | 26 |
| 8 Aylsham 'A' | 20 | 7 | 4 | 9 | 41 | 61 | 25 |
| 9 Horning (-3pts) | 20 | 4 | 1 | 15 | 26 | 69 | 10 |
| 10 Worstead | 20 | 3 | 0 | 17 | 37 | 79 | 9 |
| 11 Corpusty (-2pts) | 20 | 3 | 1 | 16 | 31 | 92 | 8 |

| Division Two | P | W | D | L | F | A | Pts |
|---|---|---|---|---|---|---|---|
| 1 Cromer Y O B | 18 | 15 | 1 | 2 | 80 | 25 | 46 |
| 2 Aldborough Lions (-1pt) | 18 | 13 | 1 | 4 | 70 | 36 | 39 |
| 3 Plumstead Rangers | 18 | 11 | 1 | 6 | 72 | 43 | 34 |
| 4 Erpingham | 18 | 10 | 1 | 7 | 66 | 33 | 31 |
| 5 Holt 'A' | 18 | 9 | 2 | 7 | 62 | 29 | 29 |
| 6 Hickling | 18 | 6 | 4 | 8 | 34 | 50 | 22 |
| 7 Blakeney | 18 | 6 | 2 | 10 | 42 | 55 | 20 |
| 8 Cawston (-3pts) | 18 | 6 | 3 | 9 | 40 | 46 | 18 |
| 9 Corpusty Res (-1pt) | 18 | 4 | 1 | 13 | 22 | 78 | 12 |
| 10 Gimingham Res (-1pt) | 18 | 2 | 0 | 16 | 27 | 120 | 5 |

| Division Three | P | W | D | L | F | A | Pts |
|---|---|---|---|---|---|---|---|
| 1 Trunch | 18 | 15 | 1 | 2 | 68 | 25 | 46 |
| 2 Southrepps | 18 | 14 | 0 | 4 | 61 | 36 | 42 |
| 3 Felmingham (-1pt) | 18 | 11 | 4 | 3 | 62 | 30 | 36 |
| 4 Holt Colts | 18 | 11 | 1 | 6 | 57 | 39 | 34 |
| 5 Mundesley Res | 18 | 7 | 1 | 10 | 51 | 44 | 22 |
| 6 Plumstead Rangers Res | 18 | 6 | 2 | 10 | 39 | 54 | 20 |
| 7 Erpingham Res (-1pt) | 18 | 6 | 2 | 10 | 39 | 63 | 19 |
| 8 East Ruston Res (-1pt) | 18 | 6 | 0 | 12 | 50 | 65 | 17 |
| 9 Worstead Res (-1pt) | 18 | 4 | 2 | 12 | 37 | 68 | 13 |
| 10 Aldborough Lions Res (-1pt) | 18 | 3 | 1 | 14 | 25 | 65 | 9 |

## NORTH GLOUCESTERSHIRE LEAGUE

| Premier Division | P | W | D | L | F | A | Pts |
|---|---|---|---|---|---|---|---|
| 1 Newent Town | 26 | 20 | 3 | 3 | 80 | 24 | 63 |
| 2 Milkwall | 26 | 19 | 4 | 3 | 85 | 29 | 61 |
| 3 Woolaston | 26 | 16 | 6 | 4 | 72 | 39 | 54 |
| 4 Mitcheldean | 26 | 13 | 4 | 9 | 50 | 50 | 43 |
| 5 Whitecroft | 26 | 11 | 6 | 9 | 34 | 33 | 39 |
| 6 English Bicknor | 26 | 10 | 7 | 9 | 51 | 57 | 37 |
| 7 Huntley | 26 | 9 | 8 | 9 | 61 | 61 | 35 |
| 8 Sedbury Utd | 26 | 9 | 5 | 12 | 47 | 63 | 32 |
| 9 Lydney Town Res | 26 | 9 | 4 | 13 | 45 | 58 | 31 |
| 10 St Briavels | 26 | 8 | 6 | 12 | 47 | 72 | 30 |
| 11 Broadwell Res | 26 | 8 | 3 | 15 | 49 | 51 | 27 |
| 12 Westbury Utd | 26 | 8 | 2 | 16 | 48 | 67 | 26 |
| 13 Bream Amts | 26 | 6 | 7 | 13 | 47 | 62 | 25 |
| 14 Redbrook Rovers | 26 | 3 | 1 | 22 | 39 | 89 | 10 |

| Division One | P | W | D | L | F | A | Pts |
|---|---|---|---|---|---|---|---|
| 1 Lydbrook Athletic Res | 26 | 22 | 2 | 2 | 94 | 22 | 68 |
| 2 Coleford Utd | 26 | 22 | 0 | 4 | 101 | 23 | 66 |
| 3 Ruardean Hill Rangers Res | 26 | 15 | 3 | 8 | 66 | 37 | 48 |
| 4 Newent Town Res | 26 | 15 | 3 | 8 | 56 | 46 | 48 |
| 5 Yorkley | 26 | 14 | 4 | 8 | 47 | 42 | 46 |
| 6 Whitecroft Res | 26 | 12 | 6 | 12 | 55 | 57 | 34 |
| 7 Newnham Utd | 26 | 11 | 4 | 11 | 55 | 64 | 37 |
| 8 Puma FC | 26 | 10 | 3 | 13 | 58 | 60 | 33 |
| 9 Mushet & Coalway Utd | 26 | 9 | 4 | 13 | 36 | 63 | 31 |
| 10 Worrall Hill | 26 | 8 | 4 | 14 | 46 | 53 | 28 |
| 11 Ellwood Res | 26 | 7 | 7 | 12 | 41 | 48 | 28 |
| 12 Lydney Town A | 26 | 7 | 5 | 14 | 44 | 65 | 26 |
| 13 Mitcheldean Res | 26 | 7 | 3 | 16 | 37 | 59 | 24 |
| 14 White Horse | 26 | 0 | 2 | 24 | 28 | 125 | 2 |

| Division Two | P | W | D | L | F | A | Pts |
|---|---|---|---|---|---|---|---|
| 1 English Bicknor Res | 24 | 20 | 3 | 1 | 61 | 20 | 63 |
| 2 Blakeney | 24 | 18 | 1 | 5 | 81 | 33 | 55 |
| 3 Utd Longhope | 24 | 18 | 1 | 5 | 65 | 34 | 55 |
| 4 Howle Hill | 24 | 17 | 3 | 4 | 80 | 36 | 54 |
| 5 Woolaston Res | 24 | 8 | 6 | 10 | 51 | 60 | 30 |
| 6 Lydbrook Athletic A | 24 | 9 | 3 | 12 | 35 | 52 | 30 |
| 7 Milkwall Res | 24 | 8 | 5 | 11 | 50 | 58 | 29 |
| 8 Puma FC Res | 24 | 8 | 4 | 12 | 51 | 63 | 28 |
| 9 Westbury Utd Res | 24 | 8 | 3 | 13 | 47 | 64 | 27 |
| 10 Soudley Res | 24 | 7 | 3 | 14 | 40 | 54 | 24 |
| 11 Viney St Swithins Res | 24 | 5 | 5 | 14 | 44 | 69 | 20 |
| 12 Bream Amts Res | 24 | 4 | 4 | 16 | 27 | 51 | 16 |
| 13 Rank Outsiders | 24 | 5 | 1 | 18 | 29 | 67 | 16 |

## Division Three

| | P | W | D | L | F | A | Pts |
|---|---|---|---|---|---|---|---|
| Tidenham | 20 | 17 | 2 | 1 | 80 | 19 | 53 |
| Redmarley | 20 | 16 | 3 | 1 | 78 | 15 | 51 |
| Newent Town A | 20 | 14 | 2 | 4 | 68 | 31 | 44 |
| Ruardean Utd | 20 | 10 | 4 | 6 | 48 | 40 | 34 |
| Minsterworth Res | 20 | 8 | 3 | 9 | 38 | 52 | 27 |
| Harrow Hill Res | 20 | 7 | 4 | 9 | 39 | 56 | 25 |
| Ruspidge Utd | 20 | 7 | 1 | 12 | 60 | 64 | 22 |
| Whitecroft A | 20 | 5 | 4 | 11 | 33 | 50 | 19 |
| Redside | 20 | 5 | 3 | 12 | 37 | 62 | 18 |
| Blakeney Res | 20 | 3 | 2 | 15 | 31 | 78 | 11 |
| Mushet & Coalway Utd Res | 20 | 2 | 4 | 14 | 30 | 75 | 10 |

## Division Four

| | P | W | D | L | F | A | Pts |
|---|---|---|---|---|---|---|---|
| Aylburton Rovers | 24 | 24 | 0 | 0 | 143 | 13 | 72 |
| Ruardean Hill Rangers A | 24 | 17 | 2 | 5 | 86 | 27 | 53 |
| Hilldene Athletic | 24 | 17 | 2 | 5 | 73 | 23 | 53 |
| Yorkley Res | 24 | 14 | 3 | 7 | 67 | 42 | 45 |
| Littledean | 24 | 14 | 1 | 9 | 77 | 43 | 43 |
| Broadwell A | 24 | 12 | 3 | 9 | 52 | 39 | 39 |
| Harrow Hill A | 24 | 11 | 3 | 10 | 43 | 73 | 36 |
| Redbrook Rovers Res | 24 | 9 | 1 | 14 | 59 | 51 | 28 |
| St Briavels Res | 24 | 8 | 4 | 12 | 48 | 83 | 28 |
| Coleford Utd Res | 24 | 8 | 3 | 13 | 65 | 59 | 27 |
| Lydney Town B | 24 | 7 | 1 | 16 | 39 | 102 | 22 |
| Rank Outsiders Res | 24 | 2 | 1 | 21 | 26 | 113 | 7 |
| Puma FC A | 24 | 0 | 2 | 22 | 19 | 129 | 2 |

# NORTH LANCS & DISTRICT LEAGUE

## Premier Division

| | P | W | D | L | F | A | Pts |
|---|---|---|---|---|---|---|---|
| TIC Dynamos of Overton & Middleton | 26 | 17 | 4 | 5 | 46 | 28 | 55 |
| Galgate | 26 | 14 | 3 | 9 | 47 | 43 | 45 |
| Morecambe Royals | 26 | 13 | 5 | 8 | 59 | 45 | 44 |
| Bowerham | 26 | 14 | 2 | 10 | 55 | 44 | 44 |
| Caton United | 26 | 12 | 5 | 9 | 58 | 50 | 41 |
| Carnforth Rangers (-3pts) | 26 | 12 | 5 | 9 | 48 | 34 | 38 |
| Ingleton | 26 | 10 | 6 | 10 | 44 | 49 | 36 |
| Bentham | 26 | 9 | 7 | 10 | 40 | 40 | 34 |
| Cartmel & District | 26 | 10 | 4 | 12 | 44 | 48 | 34 |
| Highgrove | 26 | 9 | 4 | 13 | 29 | 45 | 31 |
| College AFC | 26 | 7 | 9 | 10 | 48 | 45 | 30 |
| Marsh United | 26 | 8 | 6 | 12 | 43 | 48 | 30 |
| Storeys | 26 | 6 | 9 | 11 | 44 | 53 | 27 |
| Arnside (-4pts) | 26 | 5 | 3 | 18 | 34 | 67 | 14 |

## Division One

| | P | W | D | L | F | A | Pts |
|---|---|---|---|---|---|---|---|
| Trimpell | 22 | 18 | 2 | 2 | 79 | 26 | 56 |
| Swarthmoor Social Club | 22 | 12 | 4 | 6 | 61 | 34 | 40 |
| Carnforth Rangers Reserves (-3pts) | 22 | 13 | 2 | 7 | 58 | 41 | 38 |
| TIC Dynamos of Overton & Middleton Res. | 22 | 10 | 3 | 9 | 41 | 47 | 33 |
| Freehold (-4pts) | 22 | 10 | 6 | 6 | 49 | 41 | 32 |
| Heysham | 22 | 10 | 2 | 10 | 52 | 71 | 32 |
| Bolton Le Sands | 22 | 9 | 4 | 9 | 60 | 45 | 31 |
| Cartmel & District Reserves | 22 | 8 | 6 | 8 | 35 | 38 | 30 |
| Millhead | 22 | 8 | 4 | 10 | 58 | 56 | 28 |
| Kirkby Lonsdale | 22 | 6 | 4 | 12 | 35 | 48 | 22 |
| Boys Club | 22 | 6 | 3 | 13 | 38 | 41 | 21 |
| Marsh United Reserves (-3pts) | 22 | 1 | 2 | 19 | 31 | 109 | 2 |

## Division Two

| | P | W | D | L | F | A | Pts |
|---|---|---|---|---|---|---|---|
| 1 Moor Lane FC | 22 | 19 | 0 | 3 | 93 | 20 | 57 |
| 2 Westgate Wanderers | 22 | 16 | 1 | 5 | 79 | 49 | 49 |
| 3 Boys Club Reserves | 22 | 11 | 5 | 6 | 34 | 29 | 38 |
| 4 Grange | 22 | 11 | 4 | 7 | 69 | 51 | 37 |
| 5 Lancaster Rovers | 22 | 10 | 5 | 7 | 59 | 35 | 35 |
| 6 Morecambe Gold | 22 | 10 | 4 | 8 | 41 | 49 | 34 |
| 7 Morecambe Royals Reserves | 22 | 10 | 3 | 9 | 46 | 46 | 33 |
| 8 Highgrove Reserves | 22 | 6 | 3 | 13 | 34 | 58 | 21 |
| 9 Trimpell Reserves | 22 | 6 | 2 | 14 | 50 | 90 | 20 |
| 10 Ingleton Reserves | 22 | 5 | 4 | 13 | 35 | 64 | 19 |
| 11 Galgate Reserves | 22 | 5 | 3 | 14 | 45 | 63 | 18 |
| 12 Storeys Reserves (-3pts) | 22 | 5 | 2 | 15 | 36 | 67 | 14 |

## Division Three

| | P | W | D | L | F | A | Pts |
|---|---|---|---|---|---|---|---|
| 1 Mayfield United | 18 | 15 | 0 | 3 | 70 | 16 | 45 |
| 2 Burton Thistle | 18 | 12 | 1 | 5 | 54 | 28 | 37 |
| 3 AFC Moorlands | 18 | 9 | 2 | 7 | 65 | 47 | 29 |
| 4 Preesall & Pilling (-3pts) | 18 | 9 | 4 | 5 | 36 | 33 | 28 |
| 5 Caton United Reserves | 18 | 7 | 3 | 8 | 40 | 48 | 24 |
| 6 Moghuls (-3pts) | 18 | 8 | 2 | 8 | 59 | 36 | 23 |
| 7 Torrisholme | 18 | 6 | 3 | 9 | 32 | 49 | 21 |
| 8 College AFC Reserves (-6pts) | 18 | 8 | 1 | 9 | 37 | 56 | 19 |
| 9 Bentham Reserves (-3pts) | 18 | 5 | 3 | 10 | 24 | 40 | 15 |
| 10 Kirkby Lonsdale Reserves | 18 | 1 | 1 | 16 | 10 | 74 | 4 |

## Division Four

| | P | W | D | L | F | A | Pts |
|---|---|---|---|---|---|---|---|
| 1 Lancaster Rovers Reserves | 20 | 13 | 3 | 4 | 49 | 30 | 42 |
| 2 CC Wanderers (-4pts) | 20 | 13 | 4 | 3 | 61 | 25 | 39 |
| 3 Freehold F.C. Reserves | 20 | 12 | 3 | 5 | 35 | 23 | 39 |
| 4 Carnforth Rangers A (-3pts) | 20 | 12 | 4 | 4 | 52 | 25 | 37 |
| 5 FC Britannia | 20 | 6 | 5 | 9 | 37 | 39 | 23 |
| 6 Bolton Le Sands Reserves (+3pts) | 20 | 5 | 5 | 10 | 30 | 53 | 23 |
| 7 Heysham Reserves | 20 | 6 | 2 | 12 | 35 | 65 | 20 |
| 8 Arnside Reserves | 20 | 4 | 6 | 10 | 37 | 43 | 18 |
| 9 TIC Dynamos of Over. & Midd. A (-9pts) | 20 | 8 | 1 | 11 | 39 | 51 | 16 |
| 10 Westgate Wanderers Reserves | 20 | 4 | 4 | 12 | 35 | 57 | 16 |
| 11 FC International (-15pts) | 20 | 7 | 3 | 10 | 54 | 53 | 9 |

# NORTH LEICESTERSHIRE LEAGUE

## Premier Division

| | P | W | D | L | F | A | Pts |
|---|---|---|---|---|---|---|---|
| 1 Anstey Town | 20 | 15 | 1 | 4 | 65 | 27 | 46 |
| 2 Greenhill YC | 20 | 14 | 2 | 4 | 69 | 44 | 44 |
| 3 Whitwick FC | 20 | 11 | 5 | 4 | 57 | 29 | 38 |
| 4 East Leake Athletic | 20 | 11 | 5 | 4 | 42 | 28 | 38 |
| 5 Genesis FC | 20 | 9 | 5 | 6 | 49 | 34 | 32 |
| 6 Sileby Victoria | 20 | 9 | 2 | 9 | 40 | 37 | 29 |
| 7 Falcons FC | 20 | 5 | 9 | 6 | 44 | 42 | 24 |
| 8 Anstey Crown | 20 | 5 | 4 | 11 | 33 | 57 | 19 |
| 9 Ingles FC | 20 | 4 | 5 | 11 | 40 | 48 | 17 |
| 10 Kegworth Imperial | 20 | 5 | 2 | 13 | 44 | 61 | 17 |
| 11 Birstall Old Boys | 20 | 1 | 2 | 17 | 23 | 99 | 5 |

## LEAGUE TABLES

### Division One

| | P | W | D | L | F | A | Pts |
|---|---|---|---|---|---|---|---|
| 1 Loughborough FC | 20 | 19 | 1 | 0 | 108 | 12 | 58 |
| 2 Whitwick United | 20 | 14 | 1 | 5 | 79 | 33 | 43 |
| 3 Ingles Reserves FC | 20 | 13 | 0 | 7 | 67 | 45 | 39 |
| 4 Ravenstone United | 20 | 12 | 1 | 7 | 58 | 53 | 37 |
| 5 Sutton Bonington Academicals | 20 | 11 | 1 | 8 | 46 | 46 | 34 |
| 6 Thringstone MW | 20 | 9 | 2 | 9 | 38 | 38 | 29 |
| 7 Loughborough Athletic | 20 | 8 | 3 | 9 | 45 | 47 | 27 |
| 8 Markfield FC | 20 | 8 | 1 | 11 | 49 | 62 | 25 |
| 9 Woodhouse Imperial | 20 | 5 | 3 | 12 | 37 | 69 | 18 |
| 10 Shepshed Amateurs | 20 | 3 | 3 | 14 | 24 | 69 | 12 |
| 11 Sutton Bonington | 20 | 0 | 0 | 20 | 28 | 105 | 0 |

### Division Two

| | P | W | D | L | F | A | Pts |
|---|---|---|---|---|---|---|---|
| 1 Whitwick White Horse | 16 | 11 | 3 | 2 | 40 | 14 | 36 |
| 2 Ferrari FC | 16 | 11 | 2 | 3 | 54 | 24 | 35 |
| 3 Thurmaston Rangers | 16 | 8 | 2 | 6 | 35 | 29 | 26 |
| 4 Belton Villa | 16 | 7 | 4 | 5 | 35 | 29 | 25 |
| 5 East Leake Athletic Reserves | 16 | 5 | 2 | 9 | 22 | 25 | 17 |
| 6 Victoria FC (-11pts) | 16 | 7 | 4 | 5 | 32 | 25 | 14 |
| 7 Ravenstone United Res. (-6pts) | 16 | 5 | 4 | 7 | 29 | 40 | 13 |
| 8 Sileby Saints | 16 | 3 | 1 | 12 | 29 | 59 | 10 |
| 9 Loughborough FC Reserves (-1pt) | 16 | 2 | 4 | 10 | 19 | 50 | 9 |

### Division Three

| | P | W | D | L | F | A | Pts |
|---|---|---|---|---|---|---|---|
| 1 Loughborough United | 16 | 15 | 1 | 0 | 84 | 16 | 46 |
| 2 Greenhill YC Reserves | 16 | 12 | 2 | 2 | 48 | 21 | 38 |
| 3 Forest Road Rangers | 16 | 8 | 3 | 5 | 47 | 50 | 27 |
| 4 Measham Imperial | 16 | 6 | 4 | 6 | 37 | 36 | 22 |
| 5 Sileby Victoria Reserves | 16 | 5 | 4 | 7 | 36 | 37 | 19 |
| 6 Loughborough Galaxy | 16 | 4 | 6 | 6 | 31 | 35 | 18 |
| 7 Anstey Crown Reserves | 16 | 5 | 2 | 9 | 35 | 57 | 17 |
| 8 Genesis FC Reserves | 16 | 4 | 2 | 10 | 30 | 47 | 14 |
| 9 Loughborough Emmanuel (-1pt) | 16 | 0 | 2 | 14 | 18 | 67 | 1 |

### Division Four

| | P | W | D | L | F | A | Pts |
|---|---|---|---|---|---|---|---|
| 1 Shelthorpe FC | 18 | 17 | 0 | 1 | 129 | 17 | 51 |
| 2 ATI Garryson | 18 | 12 | 2 | 4 | 71 | 45 | 38 |
| 3 Loughborough United Reserves | 18 | 10 | 2 | 6 | 52 | 38 | 32 |
| 4 FC Coalville | 18 | 9 | 0 | 9 | 36 | 43 | 27 |
| 5 Kegworth Imperial Reserves | 18 | 6 | 6 | 6 | 53 | 54 | 24 |
| 6 Birstall Old Boys Reserves (-1pt) | 18 | 6 | 3 | 9 | 40 | 65 | 20 |
| 7 Nags Head Harby FC | 18 | 5 | 3 | 10 | 48 | 75 | 18 |
| 8 Woodhouse Imperial Reserves | 18 | 5 | 2 | 11 | 43 | 69 | 17 |
| 9 Shepshed Amateurs Res. (-3pts) | 18 | 6 | 2 | 10 | 38 | 65 | 17 |
| 10 Mountsorrel FC | 18 | 3 | 2 | 13 | 23 | 62 | 11 |

## NORTH NORTHUMBERLAND LEAGUE

### Division One

| | P | W | D | L | F | A | Pts |
|---|---|---|---|---|---|---|---|
| 1 AFC Newbiggin | 16 | 13 | 1 | 2 | 57 | 24 | 40 |
| 2 Red Row Welfare | 16 | 11 | 1 | 4 | 56 | 23 | 34 |
| 3 Shilbottle C.W. | 16 | 9 | 3 | 4 | 50 | 27 | 30 |
| 4 Springhill | 16 | 9 | 1 | 6 | 43 | 35 | 28 |
| 5 Belford (-3pts) | 16 | 8 | 2 | 6 | 35 | 35 | 23 |
| 6 North Sunderland (-3pts) | 16 | 6 | 3 | 7 | 32 | 32 | 18 |
| 7 Rothbury | 16 | 4 | 2 | 10 | 36 | 56 | 14 |
| 8 Tweedmouth Harrow (-3pts) | 16 | 3 | 2 | 11 | 29 | 58 | 8 |
| 9 Berwick United (-3pts) | 16 | 1 | 1 | 14 | 17 | 65 | 1 |

### Division Two

| | P | W | D | L | F | A | Pt |
|---|---|---|---|---|---|---|---|
| 1 Tweedmouth Rangers | 16 | 13 | 1 | 2 | 78 | 22 | 4 |
| 2 Bamburgh Castle | 16 | 13 | 0 | 3 | 83 | 23 | 3 |
| 3 Lowick United | 16 | 8 | 3 | 5 | 49 | 41 | 2 |
| 4 Boulmer (-3pts) | 16 | 7 | 4 | 5 | 48 | 42 | 2 |
| 5 Craster Rovers | 16 | 7 | 1 | 8 | 35 | 47 | 2 |
| 6 Amble St Cuthbert | 16 | 5 | 2 | 9 | 29 | 77 | 1 |
| 7 Shilbottle C.W. Reserves | 16 | 3 | 3 | 10 | 25 | 50 | 1 |
| 8 Wooler Reserves (-3pts) | 16 | 4 | 2 | 10 | 28 | 52 | 1 |
| 9 Alnmouth United (-3pts) | 16 | 3 | 2 | 11 | 25 | 46 | |

## NORTH NORFOLK & DISTRICT LEAGUE

### Division One

| | P | W | D | L | F | A | Pt |
|---|---|---|---|---|---|---|---|
| 1 Jubilee Rangers | 16 | 11 | 1 | 4 | 54 | 30 | 3 |
| 2 Circle Anglia | 16 | 9 | 3 | 4 | 49 | 24 | 3 |
| 3 Eaton Beehive | 16 | 9 | 2 | 5 | 36 | 38 | 2 |
| 4 UEA Reserves | 16 | 9 | 1 | 6 | 55 | 28 | 2 |
| 5 Norwich Medics | 16 | 8 | 1 | 7 | 45 | 43 | 2 |
| 6 Mousehold Athletic | 16 | 6 | 2 | 8 | 36 | 41 | 2 |
| 7 Drayton | 16 | 6 | 0 | 10 | 30 | 63 | 1 |
| 8 Marlborough OB (-2pts) | 16 | 5 | 4 | 7 | 34 | 33 | 1 |
| 9 Jarrolds | 16 | 1 | 2 | 13 | 23 | 62 | |

### Division Two

| | P | W | D | L | F | A | Pt |
|---|---|---|---|---|---|---|---|
| 1 UEA A | 20 | 14 | 4 | 2 | 65 | 30 | 4 |
| 2 Homecare United | 20 | 12 | 1 | 7 | 57 | 55 | 3 |
| 3 Drayton Res | 20 | 11 | 0 | 9 | 56 | 45 | 3 |
| 4 Old Catton Rovers | 20 | 10 | 1 | 9 | 44 | 35 | 3 |
| 5 Wensum Albion | 20 | 9 | 3 | 8 | 56 | 50 | 3 |
| 6 Hockering FC | 20 | 8 | 4 | 8 | 61 | 49 | 2 |
| 7 Newton Flotman Reserves | 20 | 8 | 4 | 8 | 39 | 40 | 2 |
| 8 Yelverton Reserves | 20 | 7 | 2 | 11 | 38 | 50 | 2 |
| 9 Taverham (-2pts) | 20 | 8 | 1 | 11 | 42 | 63 | 2 |
| 10 Blofield United A | 20 | 6 | 2 | 12 | 41 | 60 | 2 |
| 11 Dyers Arms (-2pts) | 20 | 5 | 2 | 13 | 41 | 63 | 1 |

### Division Three

| | P | W | D | L | F | A | Pt |
|---|---|---|---|---|---|---|---|
| 1 One Love United | 18 | 13 | 2 | 3 | 64 | 30 | 4 |
| 2 Tiger FC | 18 | 11 | 5 | 2 | 64 | 35 | 3 |
| 3 Frettenham United | 18 | 12 | 1 | 5 | 61 | 42 | 3 |
| 4 CNSOB | 18 | 11 | 3 | 4 | 60 | 29 | 3 |
| 5 Hellesdon Reserves | 18 | 9 | 0 | 9 | 56 | 46 | 2 |
| 6 Norman Wanderers | 18 | 7 | 1 | 10 | 46 | 51 | 2 |
| 7 South Walsham Reserves | 18 | 6 | 1 | 11 | 49 | 44 | 1 |
| 8 Anglian Knights | 18 | 5 | 3 | 10 | 42 | 78 | 1 |
| 9 Mousehold Athletic Reserves | 18 | 5 | 2 | 11 | 37 | 61 | 1 |
| 10 Ketts Tavern Toucans | 18 | 1 | 2 | 15 | 26 | 89 | |

## NOTTS AMATEUR ALLIANCE

### Premier Division

| | P | W | D | L | F | A | Pts |
|---|---|---|---|---|---|---|---|
| Kashmir | 24 | 19 | 4 | 1 | 88 | 29 | 61 |
| Bilborough United | 24 | 17 | 2 | 5 | 86 | 47 | 53 |
| Nottingham Sikh Lions | 24 | 13 | 5 | 6 | 71 | 49 | 44 |
| Gedling Southbank A | 24 | 14 | 2 | 8 | 54 | 54 | 44 |
| Kimberley MW A | 24 | 13 | 3 | 8 | 51 | 37 | 42 |
| Fox & Crown | 24 | 10 | 1 | 13 | 45 | 57 | 31 |
| AFC Bridgford | 24 | 9 | 3 | 12 | 42 | 51 | 30 |
| FC Samba | 24 | 9 | 3 | 12 | 51 | 65 | 30 |
| Santos (-6pts) | 24 | 10 | 3 | 11 | 65 | 67 | 27 |
| FC Dynamo | 24 | 7 | 3 | 14 | 49 | 60 | 24 |
| Beeston Rovers | 24 | 6 | 4 | 14 | 44 | 54 | 22 |
| Netherfield Town | 24 | 5 | 4 | 15 | 56 | 88 | 19 |
| Nuthall | 24 | 5 | 1 | 18 | 38 | 82 | 16 |

### Division One

| | P | W | D | L | F | A | Pts |
|---|---|---|---|---|---|---|---|
| Basford United Reserves | 22 | 17 | 4 | 1 | 104 | 38 | 55 |
| Strelley Rose | 22 | 16 | 3 | 3 | 77 | 39 | 51 |
| Kimberley MW B | 22 | 13 | 5 | 4 | 65 | 49 | 44 |
| Aspley | 22 | 14 | 1 | 7 | 56 | 40 | 43 |
| Crusader | 22 | 14 | 0 | 8 | 74 | 57 | 42 |
| Vernon Villa | 22 | 9 | 3 | 10 | 49 | 53 | 30 |
| Birchover Park | 22 | 6 | 4 | 12 | 48 | 56 | 22 |
| Netherfield Albion Reserves | 22 | 7 | 1 | 14 | 57 | 78 | 22 |
| Bold Forester | 22 | 5 | 5 | 12 | 43 | 70 | 20 |
| AFC Bridgford Reserves | 22 | 6 | 2 | 14 | 47 | 77 | 20 |
| Nottingham United A | 22 | 5 | 4 | 13 | 57 | 72 | 19 |
| Ashfield Athletic | 22 | 2 | 4 | 16 | 28 | 76 | 10 |

### Division Two

| | P | W | D | L | F | A | Pts |
|---|---|---|---|---|---|---|---|
| Crown Inn Selston | 28 | 22 | 2 | 4 | 152 | 36 | 68 |
| FC Geordie | 28 | 20 | 2 | 6 | 80 | 36 | 62 |
| Trent Bridge | 28 | 17 | 2 | 9 | 71 | 60 | 53 |
| Hyson Green Cavaliers A | 28 | 16 | 3 | 9 | 82 | 71 | 51 |
| Ali Islam | 28 | 13 | 4 | 11 | 95 | 89 | 43 |
| Rushcliffe Dynamo | 28 | 12 | 5 | 11 | 63 | 67 | 41 |
| West 8 | 28 | 11 | 6 | 11 | 69 | 63 | 39 |
| Arnold Celtic | 28 | 12 | 3 | 13 | 48 | 59 | 39 |
| Bestwood AFC | 28 | 12 | 2 | 14 | 80 | 74 | 38 |
| Beeston Rylands | 28 | 11 | 4 | 13 | 59 | 87 | 37 |
| Skegby United | 28 | 10 | 6 | 12 | 52 | 54 | 36 |
| Netherfield Seniors | 28 | 10 | 1 | 17 | 75 | 97 | 31 |
| Premier | 28 | 8 | 4 | 16 | 57 | 95 | 28 |
| Boots Athletic Reserves | 28 | 8 | 2 | 18 | 65 | 90 | 26 |
| Forest Green | 28 | 4 | 2 | 22 | 52 | 122 | 14 |

### Division Three

| | P | W | D | L | F | A | Pts |
|---|---|---|---|---|---|---|---|
| Netherfield Town Pumas | 24 | 21 | 0 | 3 | 130 | 32 | 63 |
| Highbury | 24 | 19 | 3 | 2 | 111 | 44 | 60 |
| Crusader Reserves | 24 | 16 | 2 | 6 | 84 | 55 | 50 |
| Bingham Town Reserves | 24 | 15 | 1 | 8 | 63 | 54 | 46 |
| Robin Hood Colts | 24 | 13 | 4 | 7 | 70 | 51 | 43 |
| ASC Ilkeston | 24 | 12 | 0 | 12 | 59 | 74 | 36 |
| Gedling Town | 24 | 8 | 5 | 11 | 55 | 68 | 29 |
| Gedling Southbank Colts | 24 | 8 | 1 | 15 | 57 | 67 | 25 |
| Hyson Green Cavaliers B | 24 | 8 | 1 | 15 | 58 | 76 | 25 |
| FC Samba Reserves | 24 | 7 | 4 | 13 | 39 | 66 | 25 |
| Jiberah | 24 | 6 | 2 | 16 | 37 | 109 | 20 |
| Mapperley | 24 | 6 | 1 | 17 | 43 | 76 | 19 |
| Nottingham Albion | 24 | 4 | 2 | 18 | 39 | 73 | 14 |

## NOTTINGHAM SENIOR LEAGUE

### Senior

| | P | W | D | L | F | A | Pts |
|---|---|---|---|---|---|---|---|
| 1 Bulwell | 28 | 28 | 0 | 0 | 115 | 29 | 84 |
| 2 Attenborough | 28 | 16 | 4 | 8 | 70 | 53 | 52 |
| 3 Hucknall Rolls Leisure | 28 | 14 | 4 | 10 | 53 | 45 | 46 |
| 4 Ruddington Village | 28 | 15 | 1 | 12 | 64 | 60 | 46 |
| 5 Kimberley Miners Welfare | 28 | 13 | 5 | 10 | 61 | 48 | 44 |
| 6 Magdala Amateurs | 28 | 11 | 10 | 7 | 56 | 45 | 43 |
| 7 Burton Joyce | 28 | 12 | 6 | 10 | 73 | 68 | 42 |
| 8 Awsworth Villa | 28 | 13 | 2 | 13 | 62 | 70 | 41 |
| 9 FC Cavaliers | 28 | 10 | 5 | 13 | 51 | 48 | 35 |
| 10 Bilborough Town | 28 | 10 | 4 | 14 | 64 | 70 | 34 |
| 11 Selston | 28 | 10 | 4 | 14 | 46 | 67 | 34 |
| 12 Cotgrave | 28 | 8 | 6 | 14 | 49 | 64 | 30 |
| 13 Wollaton | 28 | 6 | 9 | 13 | 43 | 68 | 27 |
| 14 Keyworth United | 28 | 6 | 2 | 20 | 39 | 65 | 20 |
| 15 Sandhurst | 28 | 4 | 6 | 18 | 42 | 88 | 18 |

### Division One

| | P | W | D | L | F | A | Pts |
|---|---|---|---|---|---|---|---|
| 1 Beeston AFC | 24 | 18 | 3 | 3 | 79 | 43 | 57 |
| 2 Boots Athletic | 24 | 16 | 2 | 6 | 66 | 36 | 50 |
| 3 Netherfield Albion | 24 | 15 | 4 | 5 | 67 | 37 | 49 |
| 4 Hucknall Rolls Leisure Reserves | 24 | 15 | 2 | 7 | 72 | 41 | 47 |
| 5 West Bridgford | 24 | 12 | 4 | 8 | 73 | 40 | 40 |
| 6 Arnold Town Reserves | 24 | 12 | 3 | 9 | 69 | 39 | 39 |
| 7 Wollaton Reserves | 24 | 11 | 5 | 8 | 51 | 52 | 38 |
| 8 Magdala Amateurs Reserves | 24 | 8 | 1 | 15 | 40 | 63 | 25 |
| 9 Awsworth Villa Reserves | 24 | 7 | 4 | 13 | 42 | 68 | 25 |
| 10 Radcliffe Olympic Reserves | 24 | 6 | 5 | 13 | 52 | 76 | 23 |
| 11 Nottinghamshire | 24 | 6 | 3 | 15 | 42 | 66 | 21 |
| 12 Underwood Villa | 24 | 5 | 4 | 15 | 40 | 72 | 19 |
| 13 Gedling Southbank | 24 | 3 | 4 | 17 | 18 | 78 | 13 |

### Division Two

| | P | W | D | L | F | A | Pts |
|---|---|---|---|---|---|---|---|
| 1 Clifton Reserves | 26 | 18 | 2 | 6 | 85 | 42 | 56 |
| 2 Linby Colliery Welfare Reserves | 26 | 17 | 3 | 6 | 70 | 37 | 54 |
| 3 Bingham Town | 26 | 16 | 4 | 6 | 70 | 31 | 52 |
| 4 Ruddington Village Reserves | 26 | 16 | 3 | 7 | 75 | 45 | 51 |
| 5 Kirton Brickworks | 26 | 16 | 3 | 7 | 66 | 39 | 51 |
| 6 Calverton Miners Welfare AFC | 26 | 15 | 2 | 9 | 87 | 50 | 47 |
| 7 FC05 | 26 | 13 | 4 | 9 | 64 | 54 | 43 |
| 8 Ashland Rovers | 26 | 12 | 5 | 9 | 60 | 49 | 41 |
| 9 Kimberley Miners Welfare Reserves | 26 | 9 | 4 | 13 | 45 | 55 | 31 |
| 10 Selston Reserves | 26 | 8 | 4 | 14 | 41 | 54 | 28 |
| 11 Moorgreen | 26 | 8 | 3 | 15 | 52 | 64 | 27 |
| 12 Nottinghamshire Reserves | 26 | 5 | 3 | 18 | 45 | 98 | 18 |
| 13 West Bridgford Reserves | 26 | 5 | 2 | 19 | 32 | 96 | 17 |
| 14 Sandhurst Reserves | 26 | 1 | 4 | 21 | 27 | 105 | 7 |

# LEAGUE TABLES
## PERRY STREET & DISTRICT LEAGUE

| Premier Division | P | W | D | L | F | A | Pts |
|---|---|---|---|---|---|---|---|
| 1 Winsham | 20 | 15 | 5 | 0 | 60 | 25 | 50 |
| 2 Lyme Regis | 20 | 12 | 4 | 4 | 54 | 30 | 40 |
| 3 Crewkerne Town | 20 | 11 | 3 | 6 | 54 | 37 | 36 |
| 4 Beaminster | 20 | 10 | 4 | 6 | 48 | 42 | 34 |
| 5 Combe Reserves | 20 | 9 | 4 | 7 | 43 | 35 | 31 |
| 6 Millwey Rise | 20 | 8 | 2 | 10 | 53 | 51 | 26 |
| 7 Ilminster Reserves | 20 | 5 | 7 | 8 | 42 | 45 | 22 |
| 8 Perry Street (-3pts) | 20 | 7 | 4 | 9 | 54 | 59 | 22 |
| 9 Shepton Beauchamp | 20 | 5 | 6 | 9 | 35 | 50 | 21 |
| 10 South Petherton | 20 | 5 | 3 | 12 | 38 | 55 | 18 |
| 11 Farway United | 20 | 0 | 4 | 16 | 32 | 84 | 4 |

| Division One | P | W | D | L | F | A | Pts |
|---|---|---|---|---|---|---|---|
| 1 West & Middle Chinnock | 18 | 15 | 1 | 2 | 55 | 23 | 46 |
| 2 Misterton | 18 | 13 | 4 | 1 | 61 | 26 | 43 |
| 3 Netherbury | 18 | 13 | 2 | 3 | 60 | 29 | 41 |
| 4 Barrington | 18 | 12 | 2 | 4 | 58 | 23 | 38 |
| 5 Forton Rangers | 18 | 7 | 1 | 10 | 38 | 39 | 22 |
| 6 Lyme Regis Reserves | 18 | 4 | 6 | 8 | 27 | 37 | 18 |
| 7 Perry Street Reserves | 18 | 4 | 4 | 10 | 26 | 46 | 16 |
| 8 Beaminster Reserves (-1pt) | 18 | 3 | 4 | 11 | 19 | 41 | 12 |
| 9 Crewkerne Reserves | 18 | 2 | 5 | 11 | 35 | 56 | 11 |
| 10 South Petherton Reserves (-3pts) | 18 | 2 | 1 | 15 | 17 | 76 | 4 |

| Division Two | P | W | D | L | F | A | Pts |
|---|---|---|---|---|---|---|---|
| 1 Uplyme | 18 | 11 | 4 | 3 | 58 | 29 | 37 |
| 2 Pymore | 18 | 10 | 4 | 4 | 60 | 25 | 34 |
| 3 Chard United. (-3pts) | 18 | 11 | 3 | 4 | 47 | 28 | 33 |
| 4 Thorncombe | 18 | 9 | 4 | 5 | 61 | 49 | 31 |
| 5 Dowlish & Donyatt | 18 | 9 | 1 | 8 | 43 | 38 | 28 |
| 6 Waytown Hounds | 18 | 8 | 4 | 6 | 40 | 45 | 28 |
| 7 Crewkerne Rangers | 18 | 7 | 1 | 10 | 45 | 55 | 22 |
| 8 Charmouth | 18 | 6 | 3 | 9 | 36 | 50 | 21 |
| 9 Ilminster Colts | 18 | 4 | 2 | 12 | 39 | 69 | 14 |
| 10 Chard Rangers | 18 | 2 | 0 | 16 | 32 | 73 | 6 |

| Division Two | P | W | D | L | F | A | Pts |
|---|---|---|---|---|---|---|---|
| 1 Luso-Chard (-3pts) | 20 | 16 | 2 | 2 | 71 | 29 | 47 |
| 2 Combe A | 20 | 15 | 1 | 4 | 71 | 30 | 46 |
| 3 Drimpton | 20 | 14 | 3 | 3 | 68 | 31 | 45 |
| 4 Winsham Reserves | 20 | 13 | 2 | 5 | 68 | 44 | 41 |
| 5 Lyme Bantams (-1pt) | 20 | 8 | 4 | 8 | 57 | 54 | 27 |
| 6 Millwey Rise Reserves | 20 | 8 | 2 | 10 | 55 | 30 | 26 |
| 7 Ilminster Town A | 20 | 8 | 2 | 10 | 49 | 46 | 26 |
| 8 Hawkchurch | 20 | 7 | 1 | 12 | 43 | 66 | 22 |
| 9 Chard Utd. Reserves (+1pt) | 20 | 4 | 3 | 13 | 32 | 58 | 16 |
| 10 Hinton St George | 20 | 4 | 2 | 14 | 35 | 88 | 14 |
| 11 Misterton Reserves | 20 | 1 | 2 | 17 | 28 | 101 | 5 |

| Division Three | P | W | D | L | F | A | Pt |
|---|---|---|---|---|---|---|---|
| 1 Shepton Reserves (-3pts) | 18 | 17 | 1 | 0 | 75 | 14 | 4 |
| 2 Barrington Reserves | 18 | 9 | 4 | 5 | 54 | 40 | 3 |
| 3 Thorncombe Reserves (-3pts) | 18 | 10 | 3 | 5 | 53 | 31 | 3 |
| 4 Combe B | 18 | 7 | 6 | 5 | 26 | 23 | 2 |
| 5 Kingsbury | 18 | 7 | 3 | 8 | 49 | 43 | 2 |
| 6 Crewkerne Rangers Reserves | 18 | 7 | 3 | 8 | 45 | 45 | 2 |
| 7 Forton Rangers Reserves | 18 | 7 | 3 | 8 | 40 | 42 | 2 |
| 8 Farway Reserves | 18 | 5 | 3 | 10 | 36 | 62 | 1 |
| 9 Uplyme Reserves | 18 | 4 | 3 | 11 | 29 | 60 | 1 |
| 10 Chard Rangers Reserves | 18 | 1 | 3 | 14 | 12 | 59 | |

## PLYMOUTH & WEST DEVON COMBINATION

| Division One | P | W | D | L | F | A | Pt |
|---|---|---|---|---|---|---|---|
| 1 Mount Gould | 24 | 20 | 2 | 2 | 94 | 29 | 6 |
| 2 Vospers Oak Villa | 24 | 19 | 3 | 2 | 91 | 30 | 6 |
| 3 Roborough | 24 | 10 | 9 | 5 | 48 | 43 | 3 |
| 4 Plymouth Marjon | 24 | 10 | 7 | 7 | 54 | 46 | 3 |
| 5 FC Manadon | 24 | 10 | 4 | 10 | 47 | 47 | 3 |
| 6 Lee Moor 'A' | 24 | 10 | 2 | 12 | 57 | 48 | 3 |
| 7 Tavistock Community 'A' | 24 | 10 | 2 | 12 | 58 | 62 | 3 |
| 8 University of Plymouth 'A' | 24 | 10 | 2 | 12 | 52 | 68 | 3 |
| 9 Plympton RBL | 24 | 9 | 3 | 12 | 44 | 58 | 3 |
| 10 Chaddlewood Miners OB | 24 | 7 | 5 | 12 | 49 | 70 | 2 |
| 11 Efford United Bluebird | 24 | 5 | 7 | 12 | 32 | 61 | 2 |
| 12 Shakespeare | 24 | 5 | 4 | 15 | 41 | 68 | 1 |
| 13 Millbrook AFC Reserves | 24 | 4 | 4 | 16 | 27 | 64 | 1 |

| Division Two | P | W | D | L | F | A | Pt |
|---|---|---|---|---|---|---|---|
| 1 The Windmill (Sat) | 20 | 14 | 5 | 1 | 83 | 22 | 4 |
| 2 Hideaway Cafe | 20 | 14 | 4 | 2 | 72 | 25 | 4 |
| 3 Steam Packet | 20 | 10 | 6 | 4 | 51 | 39 | 3 |
| 4 Morley Rangers 'A' | 20 | 9 | 4 | 7 | 58 | 41 | 3 |
| 5 Roborough Reserves | 20 | 8 | 3 | 9 | 49 | 45 | 2 |
| 6 Wembury Rovers | 20 | 7 | 4 | 9 | 46 | 65 | 2 |
| 7 Horrabridge Rangers SA | 20 | 6 | 5 | 9 | 49 | 55 | 2 |
| 8 University of Plymouth 'B' (-3pts) | 20 | 7 | 4 | 9 | 32 | 39 | 2 |
| 9 Hooe Rovers | 20 | 6 | 4 | 10 | 46 | 54 | 2 |
| 10 Windsor Car Sales | 20 | 5 | 4 | 11 | 38 | 61 | 1 |
| 11 Yelverton FC | 20 | 1 | 3 | 16 | 27 | 105 | |

| Division Three | P | W | D | L | F | A | Pt |
|---|---|---|---|---|---|---|---|
| 1 Plymouth Hope | 18 | 12 | 3 | 2 | 67 | 33 | 3 |
| 2 Tavistock Hire Centre | 18 | 11 | 2 | 5 | 44 | 24 | 3 |
| 3 Lee Moor 'B' | 18 | 11 | 1 | 5 | 48 | 31 | 3 |
| 4 Plymouth Falcons | 18 | 10 | 3 | 5 | 64 | 50 | 3 |
| 5 Star Garage | 18 | 8 | 2 | 8 | 40 | 43 | 2 |
| 6 Chaddlewood Miners OB 'A' | 18 | 5 | 4 | 9 | 32 | 40 | 1 |
| 7 Staddiscombe Colts (-3pts) | 18 | 6 | 2 | 10 | 33 | 52 | 1 |
| 8 University of Plymouth 'C' (-6pts) | 18 | 6 | 4 | 8 | 54 | 37 | 1 |
| 9 Morley Rangers 'B' | 18 | 4 | 4 | 10 | 43 | 57 | 1 |
| 10 Shakespeare Reserves | 18 | 3 | 1 | 14 | 32 | 90 | 1 |

## Division Four

| | P | W | D | L | F | A | Pts |
|---|---|---|---|---|---|---|---|
| 1 Sporting Plymouth | 22 | 18 | 3 | 1 | 90 | 19 | 57 |
| 2 Plymouth Spurs | 22 | 16 | 0 | 6 | 86 | 41 | 48 |
| 3 Chaddlewood Miners OB 'B' | 22 | 15 | 3 | 4 | 67 | 31 | 48 |
| 4 Novahomes | 22 | 11 | 3 | 8 | 59 | 46 | 36 |
| 5 Plymstock United | 22 | 11 | 2 | 9 | 56 | 54 | 35 |
| 6 The Edgcombe Hotel | 22 | 8 | 7 | 7 | 59 | 53 | 31 |
| 7 Tavistock Community 'B' | 22 | 8 | 2 | 12 | 52 | 73 | 26 |
| 8 Plymouth Rangers (-3pts) | 22 | 7 | 4 | 11 | 42 | 59 | 22 |
| 9 Yelverton Villa | 22 | 7 | 1 | 14 | 46 | 74 | 22 |
| 10 Harveys Garage Services | 22 | 6 | 4 | 12 | 38 | 69 | 22 |
| 11 Princetown | 22 | 6 | 0 | 16 | 58 | 85 | 18 |
| 12 Woodford | 22 | 4 | 1 | 17 | 38 | 87 | 13 |

## PORTSMOUTH LEAGUE

### Premier Division

| | P | W | D | L | F | A | Pts |
|---|---|---|---|---|---|---|---|
| 1 Waterlooville Social Club | 12 | 10 | 1 | 1 | 46 | 14 | 31 |
| 2 Baffins Milton Rovers (-3pts) | 12 | 9 | 0 | 3 | 60 | 14 | 24 |
| 3 Wymering | 12 | 5 | 2 | 5 | 38 | 31 | 17 |
| 4 AFC Hereford | 12 | 4 | 3 | 5 | 17 | 21 | 15 |
| 5 St Helena Bobs (-3pts) | 12 | 6 | 0 | 6 | 23 | 32 | 15 |
| 6 Meon United | 12 | 3 | 2 | 7 | 26 | 46 | 11 |
| 7 Horndean Utd | 12 | 0 | 2 | 10 | 16 | 68 | 2 |

### Division One

| | P | W | D | L | F | A | Pts |
|---|---|---|---|---|---|---|---|
| 1 Horndean Hawks (-3pts) | 16 | 13 | 1 | 2 | 45 | 13 | 37 |
| 2 Swan FC | 16 | 11 | 0 | 5 | 49 | 27 | 33 |
| 3 Carberry | 16 | 9 | 3 | 4 | 54 | 31 | 30 |
| 4 Horndean Utd Reserves | 16 | 8 | 1 | 7 | 37 | 43 | 25 |
| 5 Cosham Park Rangers | 16 | 6 | 4 | 6 | 37 | 31 | 22 |
| 6 Portchester (-6pts) | 16 | 7 | 3 | 6 | 28 | 31 | 18 |
| 7 Rovers United | 16 | 5 | 2 | 9 | 33 | 37 | 17 |
| 8 Valley FC | 16 | 5 | 2 | 9 | 37 | 51 | 17 |
| 9 Compass Rose | 0 | 0 | 0 | 0 | 0 | 0 | 0 |
| 10 AFC Ventora | 16 | 0 | 0 | 16 | 16 | 72 | 0 |

### Division Two

| | P | W | D | L | F | A | Pts |
|---|---|---|---|---|---|---|---|
| 1 Segensworth FC | 18 | 13 | 1 | 4 | 59 | 27 | 40 |
| 2 Southsea Utd | 18 | 12 | 1 | 5 | 69 | 32 | 37 |
| 3 Uplands Utd | 18 | 12 | 1 | 5 | 49 | 35 | 37 |
| 4 Cosham Dynamos (-3pts) | 18 | 11 | 2 | 5 | 51 | 40 | 32 |
| 5 Budd AFC | 18 | 9 | 1 | 8 | 52 | 47 | 28 |
| 6 Horndean Hawks Reserves | 18 | 7 | 2 | 9 | 38 | 43 | 23 |
| 7 Fareport Town | 18 | 7 | 0 | 11 | 45 | 44 | 21 |
| 8 DCP Utd | 18 | 6 | 2 | 10 | 31 | 48 | 20 |
| 9 Tempest Crusaders | 18 | 4 | 3 | 11 | 24 | 47 | 15 |
| 10 Lee Rangers | 18 | 2 | 1 | 15 | 34 | 93 | 7 |

## REDDITCH & SOUTH WARWICKSHIRE COMBINATION

### Premier Division

| | P | W | D | L | F | A | PTS |
|---|---|---|---|---|---|---|---|
| 1 Church Hill | 22 | 19 | 1 | 2 | 82 | 35 | 58 |
| 2 Black Horse | 22 | 17 | 1 | 4 | 78 | 25 | 52 |
| 3 Austin Ex Apprentices | 22 | 14 | 2 | 6 | 64 | 32 | 44 |
| 4 Bartley Green Sunday | 22 | 14 | 2 | 6 | 58 | 34 | 44 |
| 5 Athletico | 22 | 10 | 3 | 9 | 49 | 55 | 33 |
| 6 Rubery Bridge | 22 | 9 | 2 | 11 | 45 | 55 | 29 |
| 7 Alcester Town | 22 | 9 | 2 | 11 | 40 | 60 | 29 |
| 8 Hizza United | 22 | 7 | 4 | 11 | 32 | 41 | 25 |
| 9 Fairfield General La Coruna | 22 | 7 | 2 | 13 | 44 | 56 | 23 |
| 10 Wychbold RBL | 22 | 6 | 2 | 14 | 37 | 62 | 20 |
| 11 Webheath (-1pt) | 22 | 5 | 5 | 12 | 37 | 56 | 19 |
| 12 Studley Sporting (+2pts) | 22 | 1 | 2 | 19 | 30 | 85 | 7 |

### Division One

| | P | W | D | L | F | A | PTS |
|---|---|---|---|---|---|---|---|
| 1 Redditch Cricket Club | 14 | 9 | 3 | 2 | 53 | 20 | 30 |
| 2 South Redditch | 14 | 9 | 0 | 5 | 36 | 36 | 27 |
| 3 CBH Fasteners (+3pts) | 14 | 7 | 2 | 5 | 32 | 27 | 26 |
| 4 Kings Heath Concorde FC (-3pts) | 14 | 8 | 3 | 3 | 38 | 25 | 24 |
| 5 Thomas Brothers | 14 | 6 | 0 | 8 | 26 | 34 | 18 |
| 6 Translift Bendi | 14 | 3 | 4 | 7 | 34 | 40 | 13 |
| 7 Fleece | 14 | 3 | 3 | 8 | 32 | 47 | 12 |
| 8 JMC United | 14 | 2 | 3 | 9 | 27 | 49 | 9 |

### Division Two

| | P | W | D | L | F | A | PTS |
|---|---|---|---|---|---|---|---|
| 1 Washford Lions | 16 | 13 | 2 | 1 | 57 | 15 | 41 |
| 2 Millfield Rovers (-1pt) | 16 | 10 | 3 | 3 | 54 | 28 | 32 |
| 3 Woodland | 16 | 10 | 2 | 4 | 41 | 18 | 32 |
| 4 Beoley Village | 16 | 7 | 3 | 6 | 32 | 31 | 24 |
| 5 Merchants FC (+2pts) | 16 | 7 | 1 | 8 | 29 | 37 | 24 |
| 6 Rocklands | 16 | 6 | 2 | 8 | 25 | 34 | 20 |
| 7 Royal Oak Studley (+3pts) | 16 | 3 | 2 | 11 | 18 | 34 | 14 |
| 8 Kingswood Town | 16 | 3 | 2 | 11 | 15 | 44 | 11 |
| 9 Mayfly (-3pts) | 16 | 3 | 3 | 10 | 23 | 53 | 9 |

### Division Three

| | P | W | D | L | F | A | PTS |
|---|---|---|---|---|---|---|---|
| 1 Bell Studley | 18 | 15 | 1 | 2 | 79 | 20 | 46 |
| 2 Wythall Wanderers | 18 | 13 | 2 | 3 | 68 | 35 | 41 |
| 3 SHTP FC | 18 | 10 | 4 | 4 | 50 | 27 | 34 |
| 4 Dagnell End Rovers | 18 | 11 | 1 | 6 | 57 | 36 | 34 |
| 5 Sporting Club Redditch | 18 | 10 | 2 | 6 | 53 | 35 | 32 |
| 6 Peter Simpson XI | 18 | 7 | 4 | 7 | 46 | 53 | 25 |
| 7 Park FC | 18 | 4 | 2 | 12 | 23 | 45 | 14 |
| 8 Winyates Wanderers | 18 | 2 | 5 | 11 | 32 | 65 | 11 |
| 9 Shakespeare (-1pt) | 18 | 3 | 3 | 12 | 33 | 79 | 11 |
| 10 Washford Lions Reserves (+2pts) | 18 | 1 | 4 | 13 | 21 | 67 | 9 |

## LEAGUE TABLES

### REDHILL & DISTRICT LEAGUE

| Premier Division | P | W | D | L | F | A | Pts |
|---|---|---|---|---|---|---|---|
| 1 Caterham Old Boys | 14 | 11 | 1 | 2 | 47 | 18 | 34 |
| 2 Limpsfield Blues | 14 | 9 | 4 | 1 | 40 | 19 | 31 |
| 3 Frenches Athletic | 14 | 7 | 2 | 5 | 29 | 29 | 23 |
| 4 South Park 'A' | 14 | 6 | 3 | 5 | 32 | 32 | 21 |
| 5 Racing Epsom | 14 | 5 | 1 | 8 | 30 | 32 | 16 |
| 6 AFC Reigate | 14 | 4 | 4 | 6 | 25 | 33 | 16 |
| 7 Merstham Newton | 14 | 2 | 4 | 8 | 27 | 37 | 10 |
| 8 Warlingham 'A' | 14 | 2 | 1 | 11 | 19 | 49 | 7 |

| Division One | P | W | D | L | F | A | Pts |
|---|---|---|---|---|---|---|---|
| 1 Godstone | 18 | 15 | 1 | 2 | 55 | 19 | 46 |
| 2 RH Athletic | 18 | 12 | 2 | 4 | 59 | 29 | 38 |
| 3 South Godstone | 18 | 9 | 1 | 8 | 41 | 34 | 28 |
| 4 Real Holmesdale Reserves | 18 | 9 | 1 | 8 | 47 | 44 | 28 |
| 5 Woodmansterne Hyde | 18 | 7 | 4 | 7 | 30 | 32 | 25 |
| 6 Westcott 35 | 18 | 6 | 6 | 6 | 33 | 44 | 24 |
| 7 Edenbridge United | 18 | 7 | 2 | 9 | 45 | 46 | 23 |
| 8 Warlingham 'B' | 18 | 6 | 4 | 8 | 31 | 47 | 22 |
| 9 Nutfield | 18 | 6 | 3 | 9 | 44 | 41 | 21 |
| 10 Heath Old Boys | 18 | 0 | 2 | 16 | 23 | 72 | 2 |

| Division Two | P | W | D | L | F | A | Pts |
|---|---|---|---|---|---|---|---|
| 1 New Nork Dynamos | 18 | 15 | 2 | 1 | 84 | 23 | 47 |
| 2 Woodmansterne Hyde Reserves | 18 | 12 | 3 | 3 | 72 | 29 | 39 |
| 3 Tatsfield Rovers | 18 | 11 | 3 | 4 | 73 | 29 | 36 |
| 4 Smallfield Reserves | 18 | 8 | 2 | 8 | 40 | 44 | 26 |
| 5 Wallington | 18 | 8 | 1 | 9 | 38 | 49 | 25 |
| 6 Charlwood | 18 | 7 | 3 | 8 | 35 | 41 | 24 |
| 7 Merstham Newton Reserves | 18 | 5 | 5 | 8 | 38 | 42 | 20 |
| 8 FC Earlswood 212 | 18 | 5 | 2 | 11 | 36 | 81 | 17 |
| 9 Reigate Priory 'A' | 18 | 4 | 2 | 12 | 38 | 63 | 14 |
| 10 RH Athletic Reserves | 18 | 3 | 1 | 14 | 27 | 80 | 10 |

| Division Three | P | W | D | L | F | A | Pts |
|---|---|---|---|---|---|---|---|
| 1 Overton Athletic | 20 | 17 | 2 | 1 | 58 | 15 | 53 |
| 2 Horley AFC | 20 | 15 | 1 | 4 | 82 | 23 | 46 |
| 3 Real Holmesdale 'A' | 20 | 15 | 1 | 4 | 98 | 44 | 46 |
| 4 South Park 'B' | 20 | 12 | 2 | 6 | 47 | 34 | 38 |
| 5 AFC Redhill | 20 | 9 | 1 | 10 | 54 | 64 | 28 |
| 6 Limpsfield Blues Reserves | 20 | 7 | 3 | 10 | 39 | 50 | 24 |
| 7 AFC Reigate Reserves | 20 | 7 | 2 | 11 | 43 | 61 | 23 |
| 8 RH Athletic 'A' | 20 | 7 | 1 | 12 | 35 | 69 | 22 |
| 9 South Godstone Reserves | 20 | 6 | 1 | 13 | 49 | 60 | 19 |
| 10 Reigate Priory 'B' | 20 | 3 | 3 | 14 | 39 | 86 | 12 |
| 11 Brockham Reserves | 20 | 3 | 1 | 16 | 34 | 72 | 10 |

| Division Four | P | W | D | L | F | A | Pts |
|---|---|---|---|---|---|---|---|
| 1 Holland Sports Reserves | 22 | 20 | 1 | 1 | 102 | 19 | 61 |
| 2 AFC Sporting Horley | 22 | 18 | 1 | 3 | 114 | 28 | 55 |
| 3 Tatsfield Rovers Reserves | 22 | 14 | 2 | 6 | 74 | 52 | 44 |
| 4 Westcott 35 Reserves | 22 | 14 | 0 | 8 | 81 | 54 | 42 |
| 5 Oxted & District 'A' | 22 | 12 | 1 | 9 | 58 | 49 | 37 |
| 6 Frenches Athletic Reserves | 22 | 11 | 1 | 10 | 59 | 69 | 34 |
| 7 Nutfield Reserves | 22 | 10 | 1 | 11 | 66 | 60 | 31 |
| 8 Horley AFC Reserves | 22 | 8 | 1 | 13 | 50 | 72 | 25 |
| 9 RH Athletic 'B' | 22 | 7 | 2 | 13 | 47 | 56 | 23 |
| 10 Monotype Senior | 22 | 6 | 0 | 16 | 48 | 59 | 18 |
| 11 Walton Heath | 22 | 5 | 2 | 15 | 39 | 86 | 17 |
| 12 Reigate Priory 'C' | 22 | 1 | 0 | 21 | 15 | 149 | 3 |

### ROCHDALE ALLIANCE

| Premier Division | P | W | D | L | F | A | Pts |
|---|---|---|---|---|---|---|---|
| 1 Wardle 1st | 21 | 17 | 2 | 2 | 78 | 25 | 53 |
| 2 Fothergill & Whittles 1st | 21 | 10 | 5 | 6 | 68 | 46 | 35 |
| 3 Balderstone 1st | 21 | 10 | 3 | 8 | 74 | 58 | 33 |
| 4 FC Bury Town | 21 | 10 | 2 | 9 | 65 | 78 | 32 |
| 5 Whitworth Valley 1st | 21 | 9 | 4 | 8 | 52 | 50 | 31 |
| 6 Moorcock Inn | 21 | 8 | 6 | 7 | 65 | 74 | 30 |
| 7 Asia | 21 | 5 | 5 | 11 | 29 | 40 | 20 |
| 8 Rochdale Asia (-1pt) | 21 | 0 | 3 | 18 | 39 | 99 | 2 |

| Division One | P | W | D | L | F | A | Pts |
|---|---|---|---|---|---|---|---|
| 1 Westdene (-1pt) | 18 | 13 | 1 | 4 | 71 | 23 | 39 |
| 2 Wardle 2nd | 18 | 10 | 2 | 6 | 50 | 38 | 32 |
| 3 Fothergill & Whittles 2nd | 18 | 8 | 3 | 7 | 53 | 54 | 27 |
| 4 Balderstone 2nd | 17 | 7 | 3 | 7 | 39 | 40 | 24 |
| 5 Whitworth Valley 2nd (-2pts) | 17 | 8 | 2 | 7 | 35 | 42 | 24 |
| 6 Rochdale Sacred Heart | 18 | 6 | 3 | 9 | 30 | 45 | 21 |
| 7 Hargreaves | 18 | 2 | 2 | 14 | 28 | 64 | 8 |
| 8 Jacks House | 0 | 0 | 0 | 0 | 0 | 0 | 0 |

| Division Two | P | W | D | L | F | A | Pts |
|---|---|---|---|---|---|---|---|
| 1 Woodbank | 21 | 15 | 4 | 2 | 80 | 27 | 49 |
| 2 White Lion | 21 | 14 | 3 | 4 | 85 | 42 | 45 |
| 3 Sudden | 21 | 14 | 3 | 4 | 75 | 34 | 45 |
| 4 Fothergill & Whittles 3rd | 21 | 10 | 2 | 9 | 48 | 32 | 32 |
| 5 AFC Royton | 21 | 10 | 2 | 9 | 52 | 38 | 32 |
| 6 Wardle 3rd | 21 | 5 | 4 | 12 | 45 | 67 | 19 |
| 7 Rochdale Galaxy | 21 | 5 | 2 | 14 | 37 | 68 | 17 |
| 8 Horse & Farrier | 21 | 1 | 0 | 20 | 23 | 137 | 3 |

### SALISBURY & DISTRICT LEAGUE

| Premier Division | P | W | D | L | F | A | PTS |
|---|---|---|---|---|---|---|---|
| 1 Durrington Dynamoes | 18 | 16 | 0 | 2 | 50 | 22 | 48 |
| 2 The Wanderers | 18 | 14 | 2 | 2 | 57 | 18 | 44 |
| 3 Alderbury (-1pt) | 18 | 10 | 4 | 4 | 40 | 21 | 33 |
| 4 South Newton & Wishford | 18 | 10 | 2 | 6 | 41 | 28 | 32 |
| 5 Porton Sports | 18 | 8 | 4 | 6 | 41 | 31 | 28 |
| 6 Stockton & Codford | 18 | 8 | 3 | 7 | 32 | 29 | 27 |
| 7 Halfway House (-1pt) | 18 | 7 | 0 | 11 | 33 | 43 | 20 |
| 8 Tisbury United | 18 | 2 | 5 | 11 | 18 | 43 | 11 |
| 9 Deacon Alms FC | 18 | 2 | 3 | 13 | 22 | 57 | 9 |
| 10 Whiteparish (-1pt) | 18 | 0 | 3 | 15 | 23 | 65 | 2 |

Nomansland & Landford record expunged.

| Division One | P | W | D | L | F | A | PTS |
|---|---|---|---|---|---|---|---|
| 1 Stockton & Codford Reserves | 24 | 24 | 0 | 0 | 127 | 22 | 72 |
| 2 Halfway House Reserves | 24 | 16 | 3 | 5 | 81 | 41 | 51 |
| 3 Devizes Inn | 24 | 15 | 3 | 6 | 72 | 44 | 48 |
| 4 Nomansland & Landford | 24 | 14 | 3 | 7 | 94 | 40 | 45 |
| 5 Deacon Alms FC Reserves | 24 | 13 | 3 | 8 | 57 | 55 | 42 |
| 6 Winterslow | 24 | 10 | 4 | 10 | 47 | 67 | 34 |
| 7 Boscombe Down Rec Club | 24 | 10 | 3 | 11 | 75 | 52 | 33 |
| 8 Chalke Valley (-2pts) | 24 | 9 | 6 | 9 | 69 | 71 | 31 |
| 9 Durrington WMC | 24 | 7 | 6 | 11 | 53 | 43 | 27 |
| 10 Alderbury Reserves (-2pts) | 24 | 7 | 1 | 16 | 43 | 82 | 20 |
| 11 West Harnham (-1pt) | 24 | 6 | 1 | 17 | 29 | 96 | 18 |
| 12 Value Cars | 24 | 3 | 3 | 18 | 44 | 91 | 12 |
| 13 Enford (-1pt) | 24 | 3 | 2 | 19 | 38 | 125 | 10 |

South Newton & Wishford Reserves record expunged.
Wilton Club record expunged.

## SCUNTHORPE & DISTRICT LEAGUE

| Division One | P | W | D | L | F | A | Pts |
|---|---|---|---|---|---|---|---|
| 1 College Wanderers | 18 | 14 | 2 | 2 | 65 | 22 | 44 |
| 2 Epworth Town | 18 | 13 | 2 | 3 | 50 | 24 | 41 |
| 3 Swinefleet Juniors | 18 | 13 | 0 | 5 | 49 | 29 | 39 |
| 4 Barnetby United | 18 | 9 | 4 | 5 | 34 | 33 | 31 |
| 5 Limestone Rangers | 18 | 8 | 3 | 7 | 42 | 35 | 27 |
| 6 B.B.M. | 18 | 8 | 1 | 9 | 51 | 45 | 25 |
| 7 Crosby Colts | 18 | 6 | 1 | 11 | 32 | 44 | 19 |
| 8 Scotter United | 18 | 5 | 2 | 11 | 33 | 51 | 17 |
| 9 Crowle Town Colts | 18 | 2 | 3 | 13 | 17 | 55 | 9 |
| 10 Scunthonians | 18 | 2 | 2 | 14 | 32 | 67 | 8 |

| Division Two | P | W | D | L | F | A | Pts |
|---|---|---|---|---|---|---|---|
| 1 New Holland Villa | 18 | 13 | 2 | 3 | 75 | 26 | 41 |
| 2 Scunthonians Reserves (-3pts) | 18 | 14 | 1 | 3 | 82 | 39 | 40 |
| 3 Bottesford Town Reserves | 18 | 12 | 1 | 5 | 72 | 37 | 37 |
| 4 Barrow Wanderers (+3pts) | 18 | 8 | 3 | 7 | 47 | 50 | 30 |
| 5 Sherpa | 18 | 9 | 2 | 7 | 47 | 40 | 29 |
| 6 Scotter United Reserves | 18 | 8 | 4 | 6 | 46 | 40 | 28 |
| 7 Crosby Colts Reserves | 18 | 8 | 0 | 10 | 58 | 54 | 24 |
| 8 Limestone Rangers Reserves | 18 | 5 | 1 | 12 | 38 | 57 | 16 |
| 9 Briggensians | 18 | 3 | 0 | 15 | 24 | 77 | 9 |
| 10 Barnetby United Reserves | 18 | 3 | 0 | 15 | 19 | 88 | 9 |

| Division Three | P | W | D | L | F | A | Pts |
|---|---|---|---|---|---|---|---|
| 1 Brumby | 20 | 20 | 0 | 0 | 116 | 9 | 60 |
| 2 Crosby Colts Juniors | 20 | 14 | 1 | 5 | 94 | 50 | 43 |
| 3 Keadby Club | 20 | 13 | 0 | 7 | 86 | 33 | 39 |
| 4 College Wanderers Reserves | 20 | 9 | 4 | 7 | 50 | 46 | 31 |
| 5 Broughton Colts (+3pts) | 20 | 8 | 3 | 9 | 50 | 64 | 30 |
| 6 Epworth Town Reserves | 20 | 9 | 2 | 9 | 51 | 51 | 29 |
| 7 Santon | 20 | 9 | 1 | 10 | 58 | 66 | 28 |
| 8 Six Bells | 20 | 6 | 3 | 11 | 37 | 60 | 21 |
| 9 Leggott's (-3pts) | 20 | 7 | 2 | 11 | 68 | 99 | 20 |
| 10 Harsco Metals | 20 | 4 | 1 | 15 | 33 | 89 | 13 |
| 11 Crowle Town Colts Reserves | 20 | 1 | 3 | 16 | 30 | 106 | 6 |

## SELBY & DISTRICT LEAGUE

| Division One | P | W | D | L | F | A | Pts |
|---|---|---|---|---|---|---|---|
| 1 Chequerfield United | 18 | 14 | 2 | 2 | 65 | 37 | 44 |
| 2 Garforth Rangers | 18 | 13 | 2 | 3 | 64 | 30 | 41 |
| 3 Pontefract Town | 18 | 12 | 1 | 5 | 61 | 41 | 37 |
| 4 South Milford | 18 | 10 | 4 | 4 | 54 | 45 | 34 |
| 5 Drax | 18 | 8 | 4 | 6 | 46 | 46 | 28 |
| 6 Moorends Comrades | 18 | 6 | 4 | 8 | 47 | 57 | 22 |
| 7 Knottingley Albion | 18 | 5 | 4 | 9 | 33 | 49 | 19 |
| 8 Pontefract SSC | 18 | 4 | 0 | 14 | 42 | 57 | 12 |
| 9 Airedale Celtics | 18 | 3 | 2 | 13 | 33 | 62 | 11 |
| 10 Garforth Crusaders | 18 | 2 | 3 | 13 | 30 | 51 | 9 |

| Division Two | P | W | D | L | F | A | Pts |
|---|---|---|---|---|---|---|---|
| 1 Carleton South Ponte | 12 | 9 | 1 | 2 | 40 | 16 | 28 |
| 2 Leodis | 12 | 8 | 2 | 2 | 33 | 16 | 26 |
| 3 Pollington | 12 | 7 | 3 | 2 | 42 | 28 | 24 |
| 4 Hensall & Kellington | 12 | 6 | 1 | 5 | 32 | 30 | 19 |
| 5 Kippax Athletic | 12 | 2 | 5 | 5 | 30 | 28 | 11 |
| 6 Eggborough Eagles | 12 | 1 | 3 | 9 | 16 | 58 | 6 |
| 7 Swillington Saints | 12 | 1 | 1 | 10 | 13 | 31 | 4 |

Great Preston withdrew - record expunged.

## SOUTH DEVON LEAGUE

| Premier Division | P | W | D | L | F | A | Pts |
|---|---|---|---|---|---|---|---|
| 1 Buckland Athletic 2nd | 26 | 22 | 1 | 3 | 114 | 22 | 67 |
| 2 Kingskerswell & Chelston | 26 | 17 | 5 | 4 | 65 | 39 | 56 |
| 3 Watts Blake & Bearne | 26 | 14 | 7 | 5 | 64 | 44 | 49 |
| 4 Brixham AFC | 26 | 15 | 3 | 8 | 65 | 40 | 48 |
| 5 Loddiswell Athletic | 26 | 13 | 6 | 7 | 70 | 46 | 45 |
| 6 Stoke Gabriel 2nd | 26 | 13 | 2 | 11 | 55 | 46 | 41 |
| 7 Upton Athletic | 26 | 11 | 6 | 9 | 51 | 44 | 39 |
| 8 Ivybridge Town 2nd | 26 | 9 | 3 | 14 | 40 | 57 | 30 |
| 9 Kingsteignton Athletic | 26 | 8 | 3 | 15 | 59 | 69 | 27 |
| 10 Galmpton United 2nd (-3pts) | 26 | 8 | 5 | 13 | 30 | 58 | 26 |
| 11 Ipplepen Athletic | 26 | 8 | 2 | 16 | 51 | 89 | 26 |
| 12 Newton Abbot Spurs 2nd | 26 | 7 | 4 | 15 | 46 | 65 | 25 |
| 13 Abbotskerswell | 26 | 7 | 3 | 16 | 40 | 89 | 24 |
| 14 Teignmouth 2nd | 26 | 3 | 4 | 19 | 50 | 92 | 13 |

| Division One | P | W | D | L | F | A | Pts |
|---|---|---|---|---|---|---|---|
| 1 Watcombe Wanderers | 24 | 21 | 1 | 2 | 128 | 33 | 64 |
| 2 Waldon Athletic | 24 | 18 | 2 | 4 | 67 | 25 | 56 |
| 3 East Allington United | 24 | 16 | 3 | 5 | 73 | 39 | 51 |
| 4 Dartmouth AFC | 24 | 12 | 3 | 9 | 55 | 37 | 39 |
| 5 Newton Abbot 66 | 24 | 9 | 5 | 10 | 40 | 47 | 32 |
| 6 Buckfastleigh Rangers | 24 | 9 | 3 | 12 | 49 | 60 | 30 |
| 7 Brixham AFC 2nds | 24 | 9 | 3 | 12 | 42 | 55 | 30 |
| 8 Langdon FC (-6pts) | 24 | 10 | 3 | 11 | 46 | 63 | 27 |
| 9 Chudleigh Athletic (-3pts) | 24 | 8 | 5 | 11 | 44 | 60 | 26 |
| 10 Totnes & Dartington 2nds | 24 | 8 | 2 | 14 | 52 | 84 | 26 |
| 11 Riviera Spurs | 24 | 5 | 5 | 14 | 47 | 69 | 20 |
| 12 Kingskerswell & Chelston 2nd | 24 | 5 | 4 | 15 | 31 | 61 | 19 |
| 13 Hele Rovers (-3pts) | 24 | 6 | 1 | 17 | 37 | 78 | 16 |

| Division Two | P | W | D | L | F | A | Pts |
|---|---|---|---|---|---|---|---|
| 1 Bovey Tracey 2nds | 24 | 21 | 1 | 2 | 88 | 22 | 64 |
| 2 Broadhempston United | 24 | 17 | 4 | 3 | 84 | 34 | 55 |
| 3 Buckland Athletic 3rd | 24 | 16 | 4 | 4 | 84 | 39 | 52 |
| 4 Hookhills United | 24 | 16 | 2 | 6 | 79 | 42 | 50 |
| 5 Beesands Rovers | 24 | 13 | 4 | 7 | 50 | 29 | 43 |
| 6 Paignton Villa | 24 | 12 | 4 | 8 | 68 | 55 | 40 |
| 7 Harbertonford | 24 | 12 | 3 | 9 | 70 | 59 | 39 |
| 8 Kingsteignton Athletic 2nds (-3pts) | 24 | 9 | 5 | 10 | 52 | 69 | 29 |
| 9 Newton United | 24 | 8 | 3 | 13 | 40 | 70 | 27 |
| 10 Brixham Town | 24 | 5 | 4 | 15 | 47 | 77 | 19 |
| 11 Brixham AFC 3rds | 24 | 4 | 1 | 19 | 36 | 89 | 13 |
| 12 Paignton Saints | 24 | 2 | 2 | 20 | 28 | 80 | 8 |
| 13 Ashburton | 24 | 1 | 3 | 20 | 22 | 83 | 6 |

| Division Three | P | W | D | L | F | A | Pts |
|---|---|---|---|---|---|---|---|
| 1 Upton Athletic 2nds | 26 | 20 | 0 | 6 | 113 | 42 | 60 |
| 2 Babbacombe Corinthians (-3pts) | 26 | 19 | 5 | 2 | 100 | 27 | 59 |
| 3 Stoke Gabriel 3rds | 26 | 18 | 2 | 6 | 95 | 39 | 56 |
| 4 Foxhole United | 26 | 16 | 3 | 7 | 106 | 59 | 51 |
| 5 Ipplepen Athletic 2nds | 26 | 13 | 2 | 11 | 58 | 68 | 41 |
| 6 South Brent | 26 | 12 | 4 | 10 | 62 | 41 | 40 |
| 7 Liverton United 2nd | 26 | 11 | 5 | 10 | 66 | 60 | 38 |
| 8 Newton Abbot Spurs 3rd (-3pts) | 26 | 12 | 3 | 11 | 64 | 69 | 36 |
| 9 Waldon Athletic 2nd | 26 | 9 | 2 | 15 | 54 | 78 | 29 |
| 10 Watts Blake & Bearne 2nd | 26 | 9 | 2 | 15 | 51 | 83 | 29 |
| 11 Teign Village | 26 | 8 | 1 | 17 | 53 | 74 | 25 |
| 12 East Allington United 2nd | 26 | 6 | 4 | 16 | 57 | 85 | 22 |
| 13 Dartmouth AFC 2nd (-3pts) | 26 | 7 | 3 | 16 | 43 | 88 | 21 |
| 14 Meadowbrook Athletic | 26 | 4 | 0 | 22 | 31 | 140 | 12 |

# Click Back in Time!

Over 36 years of publishing the Non-League Club Directory has filled a room full of information and photographs covering the game we know and love.

What we intend, over time, is to create a website that shares with you everything we have accumulated, which we hope will bring back some fond memories of season's gone by.

A unique look back at how the game has evolved since the 1940s will also make for interesting reading, including league tables from season's gone by.

Log on to **www.non-leagueclubdirectory.co.uk** today and see how many faces from teams gone by you recognise

## Division Four

| | | P | W | D | L | F | A | Pts |
|---|---|---|---|---|---|---|---|---|
| 1 | Bishopsteignton United | 24 | 20 | 2 | 2 | 111 | 28 | 62 |
| 2 | Buckland & Milber | 24 | 18 | 4 | 2 | 113 | 43 | 58 |
| 3 | Chudleigh Athletic 2nds | 24 | 17 | 2 | 5 | 122 | 46 | 53 |
| 4 | Loddiswell Athletic 2nd | 24 | 17 | 1 | 6 | 95 | 41 | 52 |
| 5 | Totnes & Dartington 3rd (-3pts) | 24 | 17 | 1 | 6 | 72 | 31 | 49 |
| 6 | Kingskerswell & Chelston 3rd (-3pts) | 24 | 13 | 2 | 9 | 89 | 50 | 38 |
| 7 | Ilsington Villa | 24 | 12 | 0 | 12 | 69 | 61 | 36 |
| 8 | South Brent 2nd | 24 | 9 | 0 | 15 | 78 | 79 | 27 |
| 9 | Paignton Villa 2nds | 24 | 8 | 0 | 16 | 65 | 114 | 24 |
| 10 | Waldon Athletic 3rds (-3pts) | 24 | 7 | 1 | 16 | 81 | 105 | 19 |
| 11 | Brixham AFC 4ths (-3pts) | 24 | 4 | 5 | 15 | 62 | 82 | 14 |
| 12 | Paignton Saints 2nds | 24 | 4 | 2 | 18 | 40 | 112 | 14 |
| 13 | Moretonhampstead (-12pts) | 24 | 0 | 0 | 24 | 10 | 215 | -12 |

Marldon withdrew - record expunged.

## Division Five

| | | P | W | D | L | F | A | Pts |
|---|---|---|---|---|---|---|---|---|
| 1 | Roselands | 26 | 25 | 1 | 0 | 118 | 27 | 76 |
| 2 | Dittisham United | 26 | 18 | 4 | 4 | 108 | 39 | 58 |
| 3 | Watcombe Wanderers 2nds | 26 | 17 | 4 | 5 | 84 | 27 | 55 |
| 4 | Bovey Tracey 3rds | 26 | 14 | 3 | 9 | 68 | 65 | 45 |
| 5 | Harbertonford 2nd (-3pts) | 26 | 14 | 4 | 8 | 89 | 53 | 43 |
| 6 | Riviera Spurs 2nds | 26 | 12 | 6 | 8 | 79 | 62 | 42 |
| 7 | Salcombe Town (-6pts) | 26 | 12 | 4 | 10 | 68 | 49 | 34 |
| 8 | Newton Rovers | 26 | 10 | 3 | 13 | 54 | 69 | 33 |
| 9 | Newton United 2nd | 26 | 9 | 5 | 12 | 60 | 70 | 32 |
| 10 | Babbacombe Corinthians 2nd | 26 | 6 | 4 | 16 | 44 | 63 | 22 |
| 11 | Newton Abbot 66 2nd | 26 | 6 | 4 | 16 | 60 | 95 | 22 |
| 12 | Broadhempston United 2nd | 26 | 6 | 4 | 16 | 40 | 92 | 22 |
| 13 | Malborough United (-3pts) | 26 | 4 | 2 | 20 | 47 | 119 | 11 |
| 14 | Ashburton 2nd (-6pts) | 26 | 4 | 2 | 20 | 38 | 127 | 8 |

## Division Six

| | | P | W | D | L | F | A | Pts |
|---|---|---|---|---|---|---|---|---|
| 1 | Preston South End | 22 | 17 | 1 | 4 | 99 | 32 | 52 |
| 2 | Polonia Torbay | 22 | 15 | 5 | 2 | 103 | 40 | 50 |
| 3 | AFC Staverton | 22 | 16 | 2 | 4 | 85 | 28 | 50 |
| 4 | Buckfastleigh Rangers 2nds | 22 | 13 | 1 | 8 | 67 | 40 | 40 |
| 5 | Buckland & Milber 2nds | 22 | 11 | 6 | 5 | 70 | 46 | 39 |
| 6 | Torbay Police | 22 | 12 | 2 | 8 | 57 | 48 | 38 |
| 7 | Riviera United | 22 | 8 | 6 | 8 | 47 | 59 | 30 |
| 8 | Roselands 2nds | 22 | 6 | 5 | 11 | 41 | 73 | 23 |
| 9 | Teign Village 2nd | 22 | 6 | 1 | 15 | 49 | 67 | 19 |
| 10 | Newton Abbot 66 3rds | 22 | 6 | 0 | 16 | 33 | 97 | 18 |
| 11 | Kingsbridge & Kellaton United | 22 | 4 | 2 | 16 | 33 | 65 | 14 |
| 12 | Ipplepen Athletic 3rd (-6pts) | 22 | 2 | 1 | 19 | 20 | 109 | 1 |

## SOUTH LONDON ALLIANCE

### Premier Division

| | | P | W | D | L | F | A | Pts |
|---|---|---|---|---|---|---|---|---|
| 1 | Johnson & Phillips | 20 | 15 | 3 | 2 | 66 | 26 | 48 |
| 2 | Metrogas Reserves | 20 | 12 | 1 | 7 | 61 | 44 | 37 |
| 3 | Tudor Sports 'A' | 20 | 11 | 3 | 6 | 46 | 39 | 36 |
| 4 | House of Praise | 20 | 9 | 6 | 5 | 55 | 34 | 33 |
| 5 | Wickham Park | 20 | 9 | 5 | 6 | 54 | 32 | 32 |
| 6 | Old Roan | 20 | 10 | 1 | 9 | 41 | 42 | 31 |
| 7 | Chislehurst Dynamoes | 20 | 9 | 2 | 9 | 54 | 50 | 29 |
| 8 | Long Lane | 20 | 8 | 0 | 12 | 39 | 51 | 24 |
| 9 | Southwark Borough | 20 | 6 | 2 | 12 | 22 | 46 | 20 |
| 10 | Parkhurst Rangers | 20 | 4 | 3 | 13 | 32 | 66 | 15 |
| 11 | Drummond Athletic | 20 | 3 | 2 | 15 | 29 | 69 | 11 |

Dulwich Village Reserves withdrew.

## Division One

| | | P | W | D | L | F | A | Pts |
|---|---|---|---|---|---|---|---|---|
| 1 | Lewisham Athletic | 16 | 13 | 2 | 1 | 65 | 27 | 41 |
| 2 | West Bromley Albion | 16 | 9 | 1 | 6 | 40 | 26 | 28 |
| 3 | Red Velvet | 16 | 9 | 1 | 6 | 39 | 33 | 28 |
| 4 | Old Roan Reserves | 16 | 8 | 1 | 7 | 40 | 38 | 25 |
| 5 | Farnborough Old Boys Guild Res. | 16 | 6 | 4 | 6 | 43 | 34 | 22 |
| 6 | Long Lane Blue | 16 | 5 | 5 | 6 | 28 | 31 | 20 |
| 7 | Blackheath Wanderers | 16 | 5 | 3 | 8 | 35 | 42 | 18 |
| 8 | Old Bromleians Reserves | 16 | 5 | 0 | 11 | 34 | 57 | 15 |
| 9 | Beaverwood | 16 | 3 | 1 | 12 | 31 | 67 | 10 |
| | Thames Borough withdrew | | | | | | | |

## Division Two

| | | P | W | D | L | F | A | Pts |
|---|---|---|---|---|---|---|---|---|
| 1 | Beehive | 18 | 15 | 2 | 1 | 60 | 18 | 47 |
| 2 | Southmere | 18 | 11 | 2 | 5 | 55 | 29 | 35 |
| 3 | Fleetdown United 'A' | 18 | 10 | 2 | 6 | 33 | 29 | 32 |
| 4 | Oldsmiths | 18 | 9 | 3 | 6 | 51 | 36 | 30 |
| 5 | Old Roan 'A' | 18 | 8 | 1 | 9 | 52 | 56 | 25 |
| 6 | Heathfield | 18 | 7 | 2 | 9 | 34 | 34 | 23 |
| 7 | Forest Hill Park Reserves | 18 | 6 | 4 | 8 | 31 | 45 | 22 |
| 8 | Seven Acre Sports | 18 | 5 | 4 | 9 | 48 | 64 | 19 |
| 9 | Avery Hill College | 18 | 5 | 2 | 11 | 34 | 54 | 17 |
| 10 | Johnson & Phillips Reserves | 18 | 2 | 2 | 14 | 32 | 65 | 8 |

## Division Three

| | | P | W | D | L | F | A | Pts |
|---|---|---|---|---|---|---|---|---|
| 1 | New Park | 20 | 17 | 2 | 1 | 70 | 26 | 53 |
| 2 | Elite | 20 | 14 | 1 | 5 | 69 | 44 | 43 |
| 3 | Crayford Arrows | 20 | 14 | 1 | 5 | 59 | 34 | 43 |
| 4 | Our Lady Seniors | 20 | 11 | 3 | 6 | 54 | 32 | 36 |
| 5 | Crown AFC Academy | 20 | 9 | 1 | 10 | 60 | 45 | 28 |
| 6 | Chislehurst Sports | 20 | 8 | 4 | 8 | 60 | 53 | 28 |
| 7 | Old Colfeians | 20 | 8 | 2 | 10 | 48 | 49 | 26 |
| 8 | Oakfield | 20 | 8 | 1 | 11 | 60 | 60 | 25 |
| 9 | Downham Town | 20 | 5 | 2 | 13 | 38 | 68 | 17 |
| 10 | Iron Tugboat City | 20 | 5 | 2 | 13 | 27 | 58 | 17 |
| 11 | Old Bromleians 'A' | 20 | 1 | 1 | 18 | 26 | 102 | 4 |
| | State Street withdrew | | | | | | | |

## Division Four

| | | P | W | D | L | F | A | Pts |
|---|---|---|---|---|---|---|---|---|
| 1 | Hope & Glory | 20 | 18 | 0 | 2 | 85 | 25 | 54 |
| 2 | Lewisham Athletic Reserves | 20 | 14 | 1 | 5 | 67 | 39 | 43 |
| 3 | Meridian Sports | 20 | 12 | 1 | 7 | 61 | 23 | 37 |
| 4 | Old Colfeians 'B' | 20 | 11 | 3 | 6 | 51 | 41 | 36 |
| 5 | New Saints | 20 | 11 | 1 | 8 | 56 | 60 | 34 |
| 6 | Farnborough Old Boys Guild 'A' | 20 | 10 | 2 | 8 | 49 | 47 | 32 |
| 7 | Bexley Sports | 20 | 5 | 5 | 10 | 35 | 46 | 20 |
| 8 | Seven Acre Sports Reserves | 20 | 5 | 5 | 10 | 45 | 59 | 20 |
| 9 | Chatterton Town | 20 | 4 | 7 | 9 | 44 | 60 | 19 |
| 10 | Windmill | 20 | 4 | 2 | 14 | 27 | 60 | 14 |
| 11 | Crayford Athletic | 20 | 2 | 1 | 17 | 16 | 76 | 7 |

# LEAGUE TABLES

## SOUTH YORKSHIRE AMATEUR LEAGUE

### Premier Division

| | | P | W | D | L | F | A | Pts |
|---|---|---|---|---|---|---|---|---|
| 1 | North Gawber Colliery | 21 | 20 | 1 | 0 | 91 | 14 | 61 |
| 2 | Byron House | 21 | 13 | 1 | 7 | 64 | 29 | 40 |
| 3 | Sheffield Medics | 21 | 13 | 0 | 8 | 83 | 38 | 39 |
| 4 | Beighton Albion | 21 | 9 | 1 | 11 | 55 | 74 | 28 |
| 5 | Shaw Lane Aquaforce Reserves | 21 | 9 | 1 | 11 | 37 | 61 | 28 |
| 6 | Swallownest MW | 21 | 4 | 1 | 12 | 50 | 43 | 25 |
| 7 | Sheffield West End | 21 | 6 | 1 | 14 | 36 | 76 | 19 |
| 8 | Sheffield Bankers | 21 | 2 | 2 | 17 | 24 | 105 | 8 |

### Division One

| | | P | W | D | L | F | A | Pts |
|---|---|---|---|---|---|---|---|---|
| 1 | Dodworth M.W. | 18 | 15 | 1 | 2 | 103 | 26 | 46 |
| 2 | North Gawber Colliery Reserves | 18 | 15 | 0 | 3 | 75 | 29 | 45 |
| 3 | Millmoor Juniors | 18 | 13 | 0 | 5 | 86 | 40 | 39 |
| 4 | Dale Dynamos | 18 | 8 | 1 | 9 | 42 | 70 | 25 |
| 5 | Horse & Groom | 18 | 4 | 2 | 12 | 46 | 75 | 14 |
| 6 | Sheffield Bankers Pavilion | 18 | 3 | 1 | 14 | 20 | 84 | 10 |
| 7 | New Bohemians | 18 | 2 | 1 | 15 | 20 | 68 | 7 |

## SOUTHAMPTON FOOTBALL LEAGUE

### Premier Division

| | | P | W | D | L | F | A | Pts |
|---|---|---|---|---|---|---|---|---|
| 1 | Bush Hill | 18 | 16 | 1 | 1 | 55 | 16 | 49 |
| 2 | Netley Central Sports | 18 | 14 | 1 | 3 | 39 | 21 | 43 |
| 3 | Comrades | 18 | 13 | 2 | 3 | 65 | 27 | 41 |
| 4 | Cadnam United | 18 | 10 | 2 | 6 | 40 | 30 | 32 |
| 5 | BTC Southampton | 18 | 6 | 2 | 10 | 40 | 55 | 20 |
| 6 | Bishopstoke WMC | 18 | 6 | 2 | 10 | 30 | 55 | 20 |
| 7 | Questmap (-3pts) | 18 | 7 | 1 | 10 | 58 | 33 | 19 |
| 8 | Nursling | 18 | 5 | 1 | 12 | 24 | 45 | 16 |
| 9 | AFC Hiltingbury | 18 | 4 | 2 | 12 | 28 | 45 | 14 |
| 10 | White Star Wombles FC | 18 | 1 | 2 | 15 | 7 | 59 | 5 |

### Senior One

| | | P | W | D | L | F | A | Pts |
|---|---|---|---|---|---|---|---|---|
| 1 | Hedge End Town | 16 | 13 | 1 | 2 | 63 | 21 | 40 |
| 2 | East Boldre (-3pts) | 16 | 12 | 1 | 3 | 52 | 24 | 34 |
| 3 | Park Sports | 16 | 11 | 0 | 5 | 42 | 19 | 33 |
| 4 | Soton Energy | 16 | 10 | 0 | 6 | 66 | 27 | 30 |
| 5 | Comrades Reserves (-3pts) | 16 | 7 | 2 | 7 | 39 | 37 | 20 |
| 6 | BTC Southampton Reserves | 16 | 6 | 1 | 9 | 34 | 56 | 19 |
| 7 | Durley Reserves | 16 | 5 | 1 | 10 | 28 | 54 | 16 |
| 8 | Burridge AFC | 16 | 4 | 1 | 11 | 46 | 59 | 13 |
| 9 | Michelmersh & Timsbury Reserves | 16 | 0 | 1 | 15 | 17 | 90 | 1 |

## SOUTHEND BOROUGH COMBINATION

### Premier Division

| | | P | W | D | L | F | A | Pts |
|---|---|---|---|---|---|---|---|---|
| 1 | Rochford Town 1st | 16 | 15 | 0 | 1 | 45 | 19 | 45 |
| 2 | Railway Academicals 1st | 16 | 14 | 1 | 1 | 70 | 17 | 43 |
| 3 | F.C. Toro | 16 | 8 | 1 | 7 | 30 | 36 | 25 |
| 4 | Shoebury Town 1st | 15 | 7 | 1 | 7 | 35 | 28 | 22 |
| 5 | Leigh Town 1st | 16 | 7 | 1 | 8 | 22 | 36 | 22 |
| 6 | Borough Rovers 1st | 16 | 7 | 0 | 9 | 26 | 30 | 21 |
| 7 | Corinthians 1st | 16 | 6 | 0 | 10 | 38 | 33 | 18 |
| 8 | Heathfield | 16 | 4 | 0 | 12 | 15 | 54 | 12 |
| 9 | Ensign | 15 | 1 | 0 | 14 | 14 | 42 | 3 |

### Division One

| | | P | W | D | L | F | A | Pts |
|---|---|---|---|---|---|---|---|---|
| 1 | AFC Horndon | 20 | 14 | 3 | 3 | 61 | 46 | 45 |
| 2 | Thundersley United 1st | 20 | 13 | 4 | 3 | 61 | 34 | 43 |
| 3 | Club Sirrus | 20 | 12 | 2 | 6 | 66 | 42 | 38 |
| 4 | Wakering Wanderers | 19 | 11 | 4 | 4 | 54 | 23 | 37 |
| 5 | Cupids Country Club 1st | 20 | 9 | 5 | 6 | 49 | 40 | 29 |
| 6 | Thorpe Athletic | 19 | 9 | 2 | 8 | 54 | 52 | 29 |
| 7 | Earls Hall United 1st | 20 | 9 | 2 | 9 | 55 | 58 | 29 |
| 8 | Ashingdon 1st | 20 | 7 | 3 | 10 | 37 | 44 | 24 |
| 9 | Elmwood | 20 | 4 | 4 | 12 | 40 | 55 | 16 |
| 10 | Leigh Town 2nd | 20 | 3 | 4 | 13 | 29 | 54 | 13 |
| 11 | Weir Sports 1st | 20 | 1 | 1 | 18 | 32 | 90 | 4 |

### Division Two

| | | P | W | D | L | F | A | Pts |
|---|---|---|---|---|---|---|---|---|
| 1 | Stambridge United 3rd | 18 | 12 | 4 | 2 | 70 | 26 | 40 |
| 2 | Railway Academicals 2nd | 18 | 12 | 3 | 3 | 39 | 27 | 39 |
| 3 | Rayleigh & Rawreth Sports | 18 | 11 | 3 | 4 | 47 | 36 | 36 |
| 4 | Barnsford Hurricanes | 18 | 7 | 5 | 6 | 52 | 44 | 26 |
| 5 | Corinthians 2nd | 18 | 7 | 5 | 6 | 45 | 39 | 26 |
| 6 | Old Southendian 3rd | 18 | 6 | 6 | 6 | 36 | 29 | 24 |
| 7 | Torch | 18 | 7 | 3 | 8 | 49 | 54 | 24 |
| 8 | Rochford Town 2nd | 18 | 5 | 1 | 12 | 39 | 40 | 16 |
| 9 | Southend Collegians 1st | 18 | 4 | 1 | 13 | 24 | 79 | 13 |
| 10 | Ashingdon 2nd | 18 | 2 | 3 | 13 | 29 | 56 | 9 |

### Division Three

| | | P | W | D | L | F | A | Pts |
|---|---|---|---|---|---|---|---|---|
| 1 | Christchurch | 18 | 18 | 0 | 0 | 76 | 14 | 54 |
| 2 | Thundersley Rovers | 18 | 12 | 0 | 6 | 44 | 19 | 36 |
| 3 | Southend Collegians 2nd | 18 | 10 | 2 | 6 | 51 | 36 | 32 |
| 4 | Sceptre Elite 1st | 18 | 10 | 1 | 7 | 44 | 34 | 31 |
| 5 | Shoebury Town 2nd | 18 | 8 | 3 | 7 | 41 | 37 | 27 |
| 6 | Sporting Hadleigh | 18 | 6 | 4 | 8 | 29 | 37 | 22 |
| 7 | Earls Hall United 2nd | 18 | 4 | 4 | 10 | 29 | 54 | 16 |
| 8 | Little Theatre Club 1st | 18 | 4 | 3 | 11 | 30 | 51 | 15 |
| 9 | Leigh Ramblers 3rd | 18 | 3 | 4 | 11 | 28 | 57 | 13 |
| 10 | Catholic United 3rd | 18 | 3 | 3 | 12 | 25 | 58 | 12 |

### Division Four

| | | P | W | D | L | F | A | Pts |
|---|---|---|---|---|---|---|---|---|
| 1 | Rayford Athletic 1st | 18 | 14 | 4 | 0 | 70 | 21 | 46 |
| 2 | Corinthians 3rd | 18 | 14 | 2 | 2 | 62 | 25 | 44 |
| 3 | Landwick | 18 | 10 | 3 | 5 | 42 | 36 | 33 |
| 4 | B.K.S. Sports | 18 | 8 | 4 | 6 | 40 | 30 | 28 |
| 5 | Southend Collegians 3rd | 18 | 7 | 6 | 5 | 52 | 45 | 27 |
| 6 | Cupids Country Club 2nd | 18 | 6 | 2 | 10 | 38 | 56 | 20 |
| 7 | Leigh Town 3rd | 18 | 4 | 6 | 8 | 42 | 50 | 18 |
| 8 | Old Southendian 4th | 18 | 4 | 4 | 10 | 39 | 47 | 16 |
| 9 | Southend Rangers | 18 | 2 | 5 | 11 | 28 | 66 | 11 |
| 10 | Ashingdon 3rd | 18 | 1 | 4 | 13 | 23 | 60 | 7 |

## Division Five

| | P | W | D | L | F | A | Pts |
|---|---|---|---|---|---|---|---|
| Dunton United | 16 | 13 | 0 | 3 | 64 | 20 | 39 |
| Southend E.M.T. | 16 | 12 | 1 | 3 | 57 | 29 | 37 |
| Weir Sports 2nd | 16 | 9 | 1 | 6 | 83 | 24 | 28 |
| Playfootball Elite | 16 | 8 | 3 | 5 | 54 | 49 | 27 |
| Hawkwell Athletic | 16 | 8 | 2 | 6 | 40 | 50 | 26 |
| Stambridge United 4th | 16 | 6 | 2 | 8 | 44 | 35 | 20 |
| Trinity (S) | 16 | 5 | 2 | 9 | 25 | 46 | 17 |
| Southend Collegians 4th | 16 | 3 | 0 | 13 | 16 | 75 | 9 |
| Old Southendian 5th | 16 | 2 | 1 | 13 | 20 | 75 | 7 |

## SOUTHERN AMATEUR LEAGUE

### Senior Division One

| | P | W | D | L | F | A | Pts |
|---|---|---|---|---|---|---|---|
| Nottsborough | 20 | 14 | 2 | 4 | 43 | 18 | 44 |
| Winchmore Hill | 20 | 13 | 3 | 4 | 54 | 27 | 42 |
| Old Wilsonians | 20 | 11 | 4 | 5 | 36 | 25 | 37 |
| Old Owens | 20 | 10 | 4 | 6 | 29 | 24 | 34 |
| West Wickham | 20 | 9 | 4 | 7 | 44 | 29 | 31 |
| Old Salesians | 20 | 9 | 4 | 7 | 31 | 33 | 31 |
| Civil Service | 20 | 6 | 5 | 9 | 26 | 33 | 23 |
| Alleyn Old Boys | 20 | 7 | 1 | 12 | 30 | 43 | 22 |
| Old Parkonians | 20 | 6 | 3 | 11 | 31 | 41 | 21 |
| East Barnet Old Grammarians | 20 | 4 | 4 | 12 | 19 | 47 | 16 |
| Broomfield | 20 | 3 | 2 | 15 | 26 | 49 | 11 |

### Senior Division Two

| | P | W | D | L | F | A | Pts |
|---|---|---|---|---|---|---|---|
| Polytechnic | 20 | 14 | 3 | 3 | 61 | 25 | 45 |
| Alexandra Park | 20 | 13 | 5 | 2 | 53 | 22 | 44 |
| Crouch End Vampires | 20 | 11 | 4 | 5 | 40 | 26 | 37 |
| BB Eagles | 20 | 9 | 6 | 5 | 48 | 43 | 33 |
| Old Actonians Association | 20 | 9 | 3 | 8 | 38 | 40 | 30 |
| Merton | 20 | 7 | 7 | 6 | 37 | 37 | 28 |
| Norsemen | 20 | 5 | 5 | 10 | 35 | 45 | 20 |
| Old Finchleians | 20 | 5 | 5 | 10 | 28 | 42 | 20 |
| Carshalton | 20 | 5 | 2 | 13 | 26 | 50 | 17 |
| HSBC | 20 | 4 | 4 | 12 | 28 | 49 | 16 |
| Old Esthameians | 20 | 3 | 6 | 11 | 30 | 45 | 15 |

### Senior Division Three

| | P | W | D | L | F | A | Pts |
|---|---|---|---|---|---|---|---|
| Old Garchonians | 20 | 18 | 2 | 0 | 75 | 18 | 56 |
| Weirside Rangers | 20 | 14 | 4 | 2 | 71 | 28 | 46 |
| Bank of England | 20 | 12 | 3 | 5 | 50 | 24 | 39 |
| South Bank Cuaco | 20 | 10 | 2 | 8 | 43 | 43 | 32 |
| Old Latymerians | 20 | 7 | 6 | 7 | 34 | 39 | 27 |
| Old Westminster Citizens | 20 | 8 | 3 | 9 | 45 | 55 | 27 |
| Lloyds AFC | 20 | 6 | 6 | 8 | 32 | 37 | 24 |
| Ibis | 20 | 7 | 3 | 10 | 33 | 52 | 24 |
| Old Lyonians | 20 | 4 | 3 | 13 | 31 | 54 | 15 |
| Old Stationers | 20 | 4 | 2 | 14 | 28 | 44 | 14 |
| Southgate Olympic | 20 | 3 | 0 | 17 | 22 | 70 | 9 |

### Intermediate Division One

| | | P | W | D | L | F | A | Pts |
|---|---|---|---|---|---|---|---|---|
| 1 | Nottsborough Reserves | 20 | 14 | 2 | 4 | 75 | 26 | 44 |
| 2 | Winchmore Hill Reserves | 20 | 12 | 1 | 7 | 44 | 25 | 37 |
| 3 | Civil Service Reserves | 20 | 10 | 4 | 6 | 34 | 32 | 34 |
| 4 | Polytechnic Reserves | 20 | 9 | 5 | 6 | 32 | 31 | 32 |
| 5 | West Wickham Reserves | 20 | 9 | 4 | 7 | 41 | 24 | 31 |
| 6 | Old Salesians Reserves (-3pts) | 20 | 8 | 5 | 7 | 42 | 41 | 26 |
| 7 | Alleyn Old Boys Reserves | 20 | 7 | 5 | 8 | 40 | 42 | 26 |
| 8 | Old Wilsonians Reserves | 20 | 6 | 8 | 6 | 36 | 40 | 26 |
| 9 | Old Owens Reserves | 20 | 6 | 4 | 10 | 28 | 36 | 22 |
| 10 | Old Actonians Association Reserves | 20 | 4 | 5 | 11 | 30 | 60 | 17 |
| 11 | Norsemen Reserves | 20 | 3 | 1 | 16 | 28 | 73 | 10 |

### Intermediate Division Two

| | | P | W | D | L | F | A | Pts |
|---|---|---|---|---|---|---|---|---|
| 1 | Merton Reserves | 22 | 15 | 4 | 3 | 52 | 28 | 49 |
| 2 | Old Parkonians Reserves | 22 | 15 | 2 | 5 | 65 | 24 | 47 |
| 3 | BB Eagles Reserves | 22 | 13 | 2 | 7 | 63 | 49 | 41 |
| 4 | Crouch End Vampiresres Reserves | 22 | 13 | 0 | 9 | 61 | 41 | 39 |
| 5 | Carshalton Reserves | 22 | 11 | 3 | 8 | 54 | 44 | 36 |
| 6 | Alexandra Park Reserves | 22 | 10 | 5 | 7 | 54 | 46 | 35 |
| 7 | East Barnet Old Grammarians Res. | 22 | 9 | 2 | 11 | 55 | 50 | 29 |
| 8 | Old Stationers Reserves | 22 | 8 | 1 | 13 | 46 | 58 | 25 |
| 9 | Bank of England Reserves | 22 | 7 | 4 | 11 | 38 | 57 | 25 |
| 10 | Lloyds AFC Reserves | 22 | 7 | 3 | 12 | 27 | 46 | 24 |
| 11 | Old Westminster Citizens Reserves | 22 | 6 | 3 | 13 | 50 | 67 | 21 |
| 12 | Weirside Rangers Reserves (-3pts) | 22 | 3 | 1 | 18 | 29 | 84 | 7 |

### Intermediate Division Three

| | | P | W | D | L | F | A | Pts |
|---|---|---|---|---|---|---|---|---|
| 1 | Old Esthameians Reserves | 22 | 16 | 3 | 3 | 86 | 35 | 51 |
| 2 | Old Garchonians Reserves | 22 | 16 | 2 | 4 | 80 | 23 | 50 |
| 3 | Kew Association Reserves | 22 | 13 | 3 | 6 | 79 | 46 | 42 |
| 4 | Ibis Reserves | 22 | 13 | 2 | 7 | 67 | 54 | 41 |
| 5 | South Bank Cuaco Reserves | 22 | 12 | 3 | 7 | 72 | 64 | 39 |
| 6 | Broomfield Reserves | 22 | 10 | 1 | 11 | 54 | 54 | 31 |
| 7 | Old Finchleians Reserves (-3pts) | 22 | 9 | 3 | 10 | 71 | 60 | 27 |
| 8 | Old Latymerians Reserves | 22 | 8 | 3 | 11 | 52 | 66 | 27 |
| 9 | HSBC Reserves | 22 | 8 | 3 | 11 | 38 | 62 | 27 |
| 10 | Old Blues | 22 | 7 | 3 | 12 | 39 | 54 | 24 |
| 11 | Old Lyonians Reserves | 22 | 4 | 2 | 16 | 43 | 84 | 14 |
| 12 | Southgate Olympic Reserves | 22 | 1 | 2 | 19 | 25 | 104 | 5 |

## SOUTHPORT & DISTRICT LEAGUE

### Division One

| | | P | W | D | L | F | A | Pts |
|---|---|---|---|---|---|---|---|---|
| 1 | Devonshire FC | 18 | 15 | 0 | 3 | 74 | 34 | 45 |
| 2 | St Pauls | 18 | 13 | 1 | 4 | 83 | 47 | 40 |
| 3 | FC De Corona | 18 | 11 | 3 | 4 | 62 | 33 | 36 |
| 4 | Sandy Lane | 18 | 11 | 1 | 6 | 63 | 38 | 34 |
| 5 | Trojan Security | 18 | 9 | 3 | 6 | 59 | 47 | 30 |
| 6 | Formby Dons | 18 | 6 | 3 | 9 | 57 | 66 | 21 |
| 7 | Jubilee FC | 18 | 5 | 4 | 9 | 44 | 53 | 19 |
| 8 | FC Chivas | 18 | 4 | 3 | 11 | 34 | 67 | 15 |
| 9 | Poulton Wanderers | 18 | 4 | 1 | 13 | 33 | 71 | 13 |
| 10 | Banks Saturday | 18 | 2 | 1 | 15 | 34 | 87 | 7 |

# LEAGUE TABLES

## SPEN VALLEY & DISTRICT LEAGUE

| Premier Division | P | W | D | L | F | A | Pts |
|---|---|---|---|---|---|---|---|
| 1 Bradford | 16 | 13 | 1 | 2 | 51 | 26 | 40 |
| 2 BD3 United | 16 | 11 | 1 | 4 | 53 | 33 | 34 |
| 3 Fairbank United | 16 | 10 | 0 | 6 | 40 | 31 | 30 |
| 4 Savile Youth | 16 | 7 | 1 | 8 | 42 | 49 | 22 |
| 5 T.V.R United | 16 | 7 | 1 | 8 | 40 | 56 | 22 |
| 6 Girlington | 16 | 5 | 4 | 7 | 29 | 33 | 19 |
| 7 Marsh | 16 | 5 | 3 | 8 | 45 | 51 | 18 |
| 8 Vision | 16 | 4 | 3 | 9 | 53 | 56 | 15 |
| 9 Ravensthorpe Rangers | 16 | 2 | 2 | 12 | 33 | 51 | 8 |

| Division One | P | W | D | L | F | A | Pts |
|---|---|---|---|---|---|---|---|
| 1 Soothill | 22 | 17 | 1 | 4 | 124 | 43 | 52 |
| 2 Fairbank United Reserves | 22 | 17 | 1 | 4 | 76 | 36 | 52 |
| 3 Ravensthorpe Bulls (-1pt) | 22 | 15 | 2 | 5 | 104 | 56 | 46 |
| 4 Abundant Life Church | 22 | 15 | 0 | 7 | 116 | 46 | 45 |
| 5 Savile United | 22 | 13 | 4 | 5 | 59 | 55 | 43 |
| 6 BD3 United Reserves | 22 | 12 | 2 | 8 | 73 | 56 | 38 |
| 7 Norfolk | 22 | 7 | 4 | 11 | 54 | 85 | 25 |
| 8 Howden Clough | 22 | 6 | 2 | 14 | 51 | 83 | 20 |
| 9 Inter Batley | 22 | 5 | 4 | 13 | 35 | 63 | 19 |
| 10 Bulls Head Dewsbury | 22 | 5 | 3 | 14 | 48 | 80 | 18 |
| 11 Heckmondwike Sports | 22 | 3 | 4 | 15 | 38 | 90 | 13 |
| 12 Cleckheaton Sporting | 22 | 2 | 3 | 17 | 34 | 119 | 9 |

## STRATFORD-UPON-AVON ALLIANCE

| Division One | P | W | D | L | F | A | Pts |
|---|---|---|---|---|---|---|---|
| 1 Washford Lions | 20 | 14 | 2 | 4 | 55 | 30 | 44 |
| 2 FISSC | 20 | 14 | 1 | 5 | 54 | 26 | 43 |
| 3 Badsey Rangers | 20 | 12 | 5 | 3 | 74 | 29 | 41 |
| 4 Shipston Excelsior | 20 | 12 | 5 | 3 | 64 | 28 | 41 |
| 5 Broadway United | 20 | 10 | 2 | 8 | 50 | 37 | 32 |
| 6 South Redditch Athletic | 20 | 10 | 2 | 8 | 51 | 43 | 32 |
| 7 Redditch United (-6pts) | 20 | 10 | 5 | 5 | 58 | 33 | 29 |
| 8 Kenilworth Town | 20 | 6 | 2 | 12 | 32 | 69 | 20 |
| 9 Quinton | 20 | 3 | 5 | 12 | 25 | 63 | 14 |
| 10 Alveston | 20 | 2 | 1 | 17 | 25 | 68 | 7 |
| 11 Coventry Spires | 20 | 2 | 0 | 18 | 20 | 82 | 6 |

| Division Two | P | W | D | L | F | A | Pts |
|---|---|---|---|---|---|---|---|
| 1 Bidford Boys Club | 18 | 14 | 1 | 3 | 71 | 36 | 43 |
| 2 Badsey United (-3pts) | 18 | 15 | 0 | 3 | 75 | 26 | 42 |
| 3 Welford On Avon (-3pts) | 18 | 8 | 5 | 5 | 69 | 46 | 26 |
| 4 AFC Solihull Harriers | 18 | 8 | 2 | 8 | 46 | 36 | 26 |
| 5 Snitterfield Snipers | 18 | 7 | 1 | 10 | 47 | 89 | 22 |
| 6 Coventry Amateurs (-3pts) | 18 | 7 | 2 | 9 | 55 | 50 | 20 |
| 7 Henley Forest | 18 | 5 | 5 | 8 | 32 | 43 | 20 |
| 8 Tysoe United | 18 | 6 | 2 | 10 | 43 | 55 | 20 |
| 9 Studley Swan | 18 | 6 | 1 | 11 | 39 | 60 | 19 |
| 10 Shipston Excelsior Reserves | 18 | 4 | 1 | 13 | 31 | 67 | 13 |

| Division Three | P | W | D | L | F | A | Pts |
|---|---|---|---|---|---|---|---|
| 1 Moreton Rangers | 16 | 12 | 1 | 3 | 59 | 22 | 37 |
| 2 Inkberrow | 16 | 12 | 0 | 4 | 61 | 43 | 36 |
| 3 Badsey Rangers Reserves | 16 | 9 | 4 | 3 | 49 | 30 | 31 |
| 4 Wellesbourne | 16 | 8 | 4 | 4 | 55 | 34 | 28 |
| 5 International Football Club | 16 | 7 | 3 | 6 | 37 | 46 | 24 |
| 6 Blockley Sports | 16 | 6 | 0 | 10 | 55 | 67 | 18 |
| 7 The Badgers | 16 | 3 | 6 | 7 | 32 | 39 | 15 |
| 8 Claverdon AFC (-9pts) | 16 | 4 | 2 | 10 | 34 | 55 | 5 |
| 9 Henley Forest Reserves | 16 | 0 | 2 | 14 | 23 | 69 | 2 |

| Division Four | P | W | D | L | F | A | Pts |
|---|---|---|---|---|---|---|---|
| 1 Red Alert | 14 | 12 | 2 | 0 | 69 | 23 | 38 |
| 2 Astwood Bank | 14 | 9 | 4 | 1 | 66 | 18 | 31 |
| 3 AFC Solihull Harriers Res (-3pts) | 14 | 8 | 1 | 5 | 37 | 38 | 22 |
| 4 FISSC Reserves | 14 | 5 | 2 | 7 | 27 | 36 | 17 |
| 5 Quinton Reserves | 14 | 3 | 2 | 9 | 25 | 42 | 11 |
| 6 Shipston Excelsior Colts (-3pts) | 14 | 4 | 2 | 8 | 16 | 34 | 11 |
| 7 Needlemakers (-3pts) | 14 | 4 | 1 | 9 | 29 | 39 | 10 |
| 8 Tysoe Colts (-3pts) | 14 | 3 | 2 | 9 | 27 | 66 | 8 |

## STROUD & DISTRICT LEAGUE

| Division One | P | W | D | L | F | A | Pts |
|---|---|---|---|---|---|---|---|
| 1 Quedgeley Wanderers | 24 | 15 | 5 | 4 | 46 | 25 | 50 |
| 2 Randwick | 24 | 15 | 4 | 5 | 63 | 32 | 49 |
| 3 Whitminster | 24 | 13 | 7 | 4 | 54 | 33 | 46 |
| 4 Old Richians | 24 | 13 | 6 | 5 | 67 | 43 | 45 |
| 5 Cashes Green | 24 | 11 | 4 | 9 | 54 | 48 | 37 |
| 6 Upton St Leonards | 24 | 11 | 4 | 9 | 40 | 44 | 37 |
| 7 Kings Stanley Reserves | 24 | 9 | 5 | 10 | 59 | 58 | 32 |
| 8 Matson | 24 | 8 | 5 | 11 | 55 | 57 | 29 |
| 9 Tetbury Town | 24 | 7 | 6 | 11 | 50 | 63 | 27 |
| 10 Slimbridge Reserves | 24 | 6 | 6 | 12 | 50 | 60 | 24 |
| 11 Dursley Town Reserves | 24 | 5 | 9 | 10 | 37 | 54 | 24 |
| 12 Horsley United | 24 | 7 | 2 | 15 | 54 | 74 | 23 |
| 13 Stonehouse Town Reserves | 24 | 3 | 3 | 18 | 27 | 65 | 12 |

| Division Two | P | W | D | L | F | A | Pts |
|---|---|---|---|---|---|---|---|
| 1 Avonvale United | 24 | 21 | 1 | 2 | 100 | 20 | 64 |
| 2 Didmarton | 24 | 18 | 2 | 4 | 59 | 33 | 56 |
| 3 Longlevens Reserves | 24 | 18 | 0 | 6 | 78 | 42 | 54 |
| 4 Frampton United Reserves | 24 | 17 | 2 | 5 | 96 | 38 | 53 |
| 5 Taverners Reserves | 24 | 14 | 3 | 7 | 52 | 36 | 45 |
| 6 AC Royals | 24 | 12 | 2 | 10 | 61 | 48 | 38 |
| 7 Kingswood Reserves | 24 | 10 | 4 | 10 | 50 | 58 | 34 |
| 8 Uley | 24 | 8 | 2 | 14 | 41 | 65 | 26 |
| 9 Tibberton United | 24 | 7 | 3 | 14 | 55 | 71 | 24 |
| 10 Minchinhampton/RDS | 24 | 5 | 3 | 16 | 45 | 83 | 18 |
| 11 Ramblers Reserves | 24 | 6 | 0 | 18 | 31 | 74 | 18 |
| 12 Tetbury Town Reserves | 24 | 3 | 5 | 16 | 33 | 82 | 14 |
| 13 Charfield | 24 | 3 | 1 | 20 | 27 | 78 | 10 |

| Division Three | P | W | D | L | F | A | Pts |
|---|---|---|---|---|---|---|---|
| 1 AFC Phoenix | 24 | 18 | 3 | 3 | 53 | 26 | 57 |
| 2 Quedgeley Wanderers Reserves | 24 | 17 | 1 | 6 | 75 | 25 | 52 |
| 3 Tredworth Tigers (-1pt) | 24 | 13 | 6 | 5 | 65 | 35 | 44 |
| 4 Abbeymead Rovers Res. (-6pts) | 24 | 14 | 3 | 7 | 54 | 34 | 39 |
| 5 Sharpness Reserves | 24 | 11 | 3 | 10 | 63 | 69 | 36 |
| 6 Wickwar Wanderers (-3pts) | 24 | 10 | 5 | 9 | 38 | 42 | 32 |
| 7 Eastcombe | 24 | 8 | 7 | 9 | 41 | 42 | 31 |
| 8 Cam Bulldogs Reserves | 24 | 9 | 3 | 12 | 51 | 58 | 30 |
| 9 Thornbury Town Reserves (-4pts) | 24 | 10 | 2 | 12 | 38 | 22 | 28 |
| 10 Wotton Rovers Reserves | 24 | 9 | 1 | 14 | 32 | 63 | 28 |
| 11 Berkeley Town Reserves | 24 | 7 | 3 | 14 | 35 | 55 | 24 |
| 12 Coaley Rovers | 24 | 5 | 5 | 14 | 34 | 48 | 20 |
| 13 Chalford Reserves (-6pts) | 24 | 3 | 2 | 19 | 22 | 89 | 5 |

| Division Four | P | W | D | L | F | A | Pts |
|---|---|---|---|---|---|---|---|
| 1 Stroud Harriers | 24 | 19 | 2 | 3 | 111 | 49 | 59 |
| 2 Stroud Imperial | 24 | 19 | 1 | 4 | 87 | 33 | 58 |
| 3 Leonard Stanley Reserves | 24 | 18 | 0 | 6 | 70 | 31 | 54 |
| 4 Bush FC | 24 | 12 | 4 | 8 | 65 | 53 | 40 |
| 5 Randwick Reserves | 24 | 12 | 3 | 9 | 62 | 52 | 39 |
| 6 Arlingham | 24 | 12 | 3 | 9 | 76 | 72 | 39 |
| 7 Longlevens 3rds | 24 | 8 | 4 | 12 | 45 | 54 | 28 |
| 8 Nympsfield | 24 | 7 | 4 | 13 | 64 | 72 | 25 |
| 9 Ramblers 3rds (-3pts) | 24 | 6 | 7 | 11 | 43 | 51 | 22 |
| 10 Whitminster Reserves (-9pts) | 24 | 9 | 4 | 11 | 49 | 65 | 22 |
| 11 Barnwood United Reserves | 24 | 5 | 5 | 14 | 48 | 80 | 20 |
| 12 Matchplay | 24 | 5 | 5 | 14 | 38 | 72 | 20 |
| 13 Glevum United (-3pts) | 24 | 2 | 2 | 20 | 36 | 110 | 5 |

| Division Five | P | W | D | L | F | A | Pts |
|---|---|---|---|---|---|---|---|
| 1 Avonvale United Reserves | 22 | 17 | 3 | 2 | 86 | 24 | 54 |
| 2 Hardwicke Reserves | 22 | 16 | 1 | 5 | 70 | 31 | 49 |
| 3 Tuffley Rovers 3rds | 22 | 15 | 1 | 6 | 86 | 35 | 46 |
| 4 Old Richians Reserves | 22 | 11 | 4 | 7 | 52 | 31 | 37 |
| 5 McCadam | 22 | 11 | 2 | 9 | 51 | 42 | 35 |
| 6 Minchinhampton/RDS Reserves | 22 | 10 | 4 | 8 | 50 | 44 | 34 |
| 7 Longford Reserves | 22 | 9 | 2 | 11 | 42 | 41 | 29 |
| 8 Dursley Town 3rds (-3pts) | 22 | 9 | 4 | 9 | 59 | 38 | 28 |
| 9 Upton St Leonards Res. (-3pts) | 22 | 7 | 6 | 9 | 56 | 58 | 24 |
| 10 Stonehouse Town 3rds | 22 | 6 | 5 | 11 | 47 | 60 | 23 |
| 11 Brockworth Albion 3rds (-6pts) | 22 | 3 | 2 | 17 | 22 | 72 | 5 |
| 12 Alkerton Rangers | 22 | 0 | 2 | 20 | 19 | 164 | 2 |

| Division Six | P | W | D | L | F | A | Pts |
|---|---|---|---|---|---|---|---|
| 1 St Nicholas Old Boys | 22 | 18 | 3 | 1 | 100 | 14 | 57 |
| 2 Cotswold Rangers | 22 | 15 | 3 | 4 | 96 | 35 | 48 |
| 3 Uley Reserves | 22 | 15 | 1 | 6 | 58 | 42 | 46 |
| 4 Quedgeley Wanderers 3rds | 22 | 12 | 5 | 5 | 69 | 42 | 41 |
| 5 Cashes Green Reserves | 22 | 12 | 1 | 9 | 55 | 53 | 37 |
| 6 Horsley United Reserves | 22 | 9 | 2 | 11 | 57 | 74 | 29 |
| 7 Tetbury Town 3rds | 22 | 7 | 4 | 11 | 49 | 78 | 25 |
| 8 Eastcombe Reserves (-3pts) | 22 | 7 | 6 | 9 | 49 | 55 | 24 |
| 9 Slimbridge 3rds | 22 | 5 | 4 | 13 | 33 | 82 | 19 |
| 10 Wotton Rovers 3rds (-9pts) | 22 | 7 | 6 | 9 | 51 | 48 | 18 |
| 11 Coaley Rovers Reserves | 22 | 4 | 2 | 16 | 38 | 68 | 14 |
| 12 Charfield Reserves | 22 | 1 | 3 | 18 | 25 | 89 | 6 |

| Division Seven | P | W | D | L | F | A | Pts |
|---|---|---|---|---|---|---|---|
| 1 Trident | 20 | 17 | 2 | 1 | 87 | 19 | 53 |
| 2 Hardwicke 3rds | 20 | 12 | 3 | 5 | 92 | 50 | 39 |
| 3 The Village FC | 20 | 12 | 3 | 5 | 68 | 38 | 39 |
| 4 Rodborough Old Boys | 20 | 11 | 3 | 6 | 83 | 34 | 36 |
| 5 Hawkesbury Stallions | 20 | 11 | 3 | 6 | 61 | 33 | 36 |
| 6 Wickwar Wanderers Reserves | 20 | 9 | 3 | 8 | 62 | 51 | 30 |
| 7 North Nibley | 20 | 6 | 0 | 14 | 31 | 82 | 18 |
| 8 Avonvale United 3rds | 20 | 5 | 2 | 13 | 31 | 83 | 17 |
| 9 Cam Bulldogs 3rds (-3pts) | 20 | 5 | 4 | 11 | 35 | 78 | 16 |
| 10 Sharpness 3rds (-3pts) | 20 | 4 | 4 | 12 | 42 | 63 | 13 |
| 11 Woodchester (-6pts) | 20 | 4 | 1 | 15 | 43 | 106 | 7 |

| Division Eight | P | W | D | L | F | A | Pts |
|---|---|---|---|---|---|---|---|
| 1 Tuffley Rovers 4ths | 20 | 17 | 2 | 1 | 74 | 27 | 53 |
| 2 Frampton United 3rds | 20 | 16 | 0 | 4 | 81 | 25 | 48 |
| 3 Randwick 3rds | 20 | 15 | 2 | 3 | 113 | 30 | 47 |
| 4 Cotswold Rangers Reserves | 20 | 13 | 2 | 5 | 72 | 40 | 41 |
| 5 Stroud Imperial Reserves | 20 | 11 | 2 | 7 | 71 | 56 | 35 |
| 6 Old Richians 3rds | 20 | 7 | 2 | 11 | 46 | 58 | 23 |
| 7 Longlevens 4ths | 20 | 6 | 3 | 11 | 47 | 54 | 21 |
| 8 Rodborough Old Boys Reserves | 20 | 5 | 1 | 14 | 47 | 81 | 16 |
| 9 Stonehouse Town 4ths (-3pts) | 20 | 4 | 2 | 14 | 35 | 74 | 11 |
| 10 Uley 3rds | 20 | 3 | 2 | 15 | 36 | 112 | 11 |
| 11 Alkerton Rangers Reserves (-3pts) | 20 | 4 | 0 | 16 | 26 | 91 | 9 |

## SUBURBAN LEAGUE

| Premier Division A | P | W | D | L | F | A | Pts |
|---|---|---|---|---|---|---|---|
| 1 Sutton United Reserves | 20 | 17 | 3 | 0 | 58 | 22 | 54 |
| 2 Eastleigh Reserves | 20 | 11 | 5 | 4 | 47 | 28 | 38 |
| 3 Woking Reserves | 20 | 11 | 2 | 7 | 48 | 38 | 35 |
| 4 Metropolitan Police Reserves | 20 | 11 | 0 | 9 | 52 | 43 | 33 |
| 5 Farnborough Reserves | 20 | 9 | 4 | 7 | 42 | 32 | 31 |
| 6 Tonbridge Angels Reserves | 20 | 8 | 5 | 7 | 43 | 34 | 29 |
| 7 Eastbourne Borough Reserves | 20 | 7 | 1 | 12 | 33 | 54 | 22 |
| 8 Bromley Reserves | 20 | 5 | 6 | 9 | 37 | 39 | 21 |
| 9 Carshalton Athletic Reserves | 20 | 5 | 4 | 11 | 32 | 46 | 19 |
| 10 Hampton & Richmond Borough Res. | 20 | 5 | 3 | 12 | 38 | 56 | 18 |
| 11 Tooting & Mitcham United Reserves | 20 | 3 | 3 | 14 | 29 | 67 | 12 |

| Premier Division B | P | W | D | L | F | A | Pts |
|---|---|---|---|---|---|---|---|
| 1 Walton Casuals Reserves | 24 | 18 | 5 | 1 | 60 | 23 | 59 |
| 2 Corinthian-Casuals Reserves | 24 | 15 | 2 | 7 | 56 | 34 | 47 |
| 3 Leatherhead Reserves | 24 | 13 | 4 | 7 | 53 | 39 | 43 |
| 4 Walton & Hersham Reserves | 24 | 13 | 2 | 9 | 54 | 45 | 41 |
| 5 Thamesmead Town Reserves | 24 | 12 | 5 | 7 | 39 | 32 | 41 |
| 6 Chalfont St. Peter Reserves | 24 | 11 | 6 | 7 | 39 | 26 | 39 |
| 7 North Greenford United Reserves | 24 | 9 | 5 | 10 | 53 | 55 | 32 |
| 8 Hanworth Villa Reserves | 24 | 8 | 5 | 11 | 35 | 51 | 29 |
| 9 Uxbridge Reserves | 24 | 8 | 3 | 13 | 41 | 50 | 27 |
| 10 Northwood Reserves | 24 | 8 | 2 | 14 | 41 | 49 | 26 |
| 11 Hastings United Reserves | 24 | 7 | 5 | 12 | 35 | 52 | 26 |
| 12 Camberley Town Reserves | 24 | 6 | 3 | 15 | 34 | 55 | 21 |
| 13 Colliers Wood United Reserves | 24 | 2 | 5 | 17 | 20 | 49 | 11 |

## LEAGUE TABLES

### Northern Division

| | | P | W | D | L | F | A | Pts |
|---|---|---|---|---|---|---|---|---|
| 1 | Royston Town Reserves | 22 | 16 | 2 | 4 | 64 | 18 | 50 |
| 2 | Ashford Town (Middlesex) Res. | 22 | 15 | 4 | 3 | 66 | 31 | 49 |
| 3 | Leighton Town Reserves | 22 | 14 | 3 | 5 | 62 | 31 | 45 |
| 4 | Harefield United Reserves | 22 | 12 | 5 | 5 | 58 | 41 | 41 |
| 5 | Barton Rovers Reserves | 22 | 12 | 3 | 7 | 64 | 36 | 39 |
| 6 | Tring Athletic Reserves | 22 | 10 | 4 | 8 | 34 | 31 | 34 |
| 7 | Bedfont Sports Reserves | 22 | 10 | 1 | 11 | 47 | 40 | 31 |
| 8 | Newport Pagnell Town Reserves | 22 | 7 | 5 | 10 | 35 | 46 | 26 |
| 9 | Berkhamsted Reserves | 22 | 5 | 8 | 9 | 29 | 55 | 23 |
| 10 | Dunstable Town Reserves | 22 | 4 | 2 | 16 | 41 | 74 | 14 |
| 11 | Hartley Wintney Reserves | 22 | 4 | 1 | 17 | 30 | 71 | 13 |
| 12 | Leverstock Green Reserves | 22 | 2 | 4 | 16 | 30 | 86 | 10 |

### Southern Division

| | | P | W | D | L | F | A | Pts |
|---|---|---|---|---|---|---|---|---|
| 1 | East Grinstead Town Reserves | 22 | 14 | 4 | 4 | 64 | 30 | 46 |
| 2 | Corinthian Reserves | 22 | 12 | 6 | 4 | 57 | 31 | 42 |
| 3 | Horley Town Reserves | 22 | 11 | 7 | 4 | 54 | 35 | 40 |
| 4 | Horsham YMCA Reserves | 22 | 11 | 6 | 5 | 60 | 43 | 39 |
| 5 | Molesey Reserves | 22 | 12 | 2 | 8 | 44 | 36 | 38 |
| 6 | Chessington & Hook United Res. | 22 | 10 | 4 | 8 | 47 | 49 | 34 |
| 7 | South Park Reserves | 22 | 8 | 6 | 8 | 59 | 50 | 30 |
| 8 | Redhill Reserves | 22 | 7 | 2 | 13 | 45 | 60 | 23 |
| 9 | Cobham Reserves | 22 | 5 | 6 | 11 | 39 | 61 | 21 |
| 10 | Crowborough Athletic Reserves | 22 | 5 | 5 | 12 | 33 | 57 | 20 |
| 11 | Chichester City Reserves | 22 | 5 | 3 | 14 | 41 | 65 | 18 |
| 12 | Lingfield Reserves | 22 | 5 | 3 | 14 | 45 | 71 | 18 |

## SURREY INTERMEDIATE LEAGUE (WESTERN)

### Premier Division

| | | P | W | D | L | F | A | Pts |
|---|---|---|---|---|---|---|---|---|
| 1 | Merrow | 26 | 20 | 4 | 2 | 61 | 24 | 64 |
| 2 | Shottermill & Haslemere | 26 | 18 | 3 | 5 | 68 | 24 | 57 |
| 3 | AFC Spelthorne Sports | 26 | 17 | 4 | 5 | 58 | 37 | 55 |
| 4 | Godalming & Farncombe Athletic | 26 | 13 | 3 | 10 | 52 | 37 | 42 |
| 5 | Bedfont Town | 26 | 12 | 5 | 9 | 57 | 53 | 41 |
| 6 | Cranleigh | 26 | 12 | 5 | 9 | 44 | 58 | 41 |
| 7 | Milford & Witley | 26 | 12 | 3 | 11 | 52 | 43 | 39 |
| 8 | Worplesdon Phoenix | 26 | 12 | 1 | 13 | 59 | 46 | 37 |
| 9 | University of Surrey | 26 | 9 | 4 | 13 | 57 | 59 | 31 |
| 10 | Royal Holloway Old Boys | 26 | 9 | 4 | 13 | 41 | 60 | 31 |
| 11 | Chiddingfold | 26 | 7 | 6 | 13 | 40 | 50 | 27 |
| 12 | Lightwater United | 26 | 7 | 3 | 16 | 43 | 64 | 24 |
| 13 | Yateley | 26 | 6 | 5 | 15 | 36 | 54 | 23 |
| 14 | Farnborough North End | 26 | 2 | 2 | 22 | 17 | 76 | 8 |

### Division One

| | | P | W | D | L | F | A | Pts |
|---|---|---|---|---|---|---|---|---|
| 1 | Tongham | 22 | 16 | 3 | 3 | 55 | 27 | 51 |
| 2 | Chobham Burymead | 22 | 14 | 6 | 2 | 58 | 28 | 48 |
| 3 | AFC Molesey | 22 | 12 | 4 | 6 | 59 | 27 | 40 |
| 4 | Knaphill Athletic | 22 | 12 | 4 | 6 | 58 | 37 | 40 |
| 5 | Millmead | 22 | 12 | 1 | 9 | 58 | 51 | 37 |
| 6 | Shalford | 22 | 9 | 1 | 12 | 45 | 49 | 28 |
| 7 | Old Salesians | 22 | 7 | 4 | 11 | 62 | 59 | 25 |
| 8 | Pyrford | 22 | 7 | 4 | 11 | 35 | 51 | 25 |
| 9 | Windlesham United | 22 | 8 | 1 | 13 | 33 | 60 | 25 |
| 10 | Elm Grove Seniors | 22 | 7 | 2 | 13 | 48 | 63 | 23 |
| 11 | Woking & Horsell | 22 | 5 | 4 | 13 | 32 | 63 | 19 |
| 12 | Ockham | 22 | 5 | 2 | 15 | 28 | 56 | 17 |

## SURREY SOUTH EASTERN COMBINATION

### Intermediate Division One

| | | P | W | D | L | F | A | Pts |
|---|---|---|---|---|---|---|---|---|
| 1 | N P L | 18 | 13 | 4 | 1 | 54 | 28 | 43 |
| 2 | Puretown | 18 | 12 | 4 | 2 | 43 | 17 | 4 |
| 3 | Westminster Casuals | 18 | 11 | 3 | 4 | 33 | 22 | 3 |
| 4 | Project Clapham | 18 | 9 | 0 | 9 | 41 | 41 | 2 |
| 5 | Real Holmesdale | 18 | 7 | 1 | 10 | 30 | 30 | 2 |
| 6 | Battersea (+3pts) | 18 | 6 | 1 | 11 | 28 | 37 | 2 |
| 7 | Cheam Village Warriors | 18 | 6 | 2 | 10 | 35 | 40 | 2 |
| 8 | Old Plymouthians | 18 | 5 | 2 | 11 | 30 | 46 | 1 |
| 9 | South East London (-10pts) | 18 | 7 | 2 | 9 | 39 | 55 | 1 |
| 10 | Old Rutlishians | 18 | 2 | 5 | 11 | 31 | 48 | 1 |

### Intermediate Division Two

| | | P | W | D | L | F | A | Pts |
|---|---|---|---|---|---|---|---|---|
| 1 | Old Boys Clapham | 20 | 16 | 1 | 3 | 54 | 17 | 4 |
| 2 | Trinity | 20 | 14 | 4 | 2 | 70 | 28 | 4 |
| 3 | Balham | 20 | 14 | 2 | 4 | 70 | 25 | 4 |
| 4 | Fulham Deaf | 20 | 10 | 2 | 8 | 47 | 52 | 3 |
| 5 | Tolworth Athletic | 20 | 9 | 4 | 7 | 34 | 41 | 3 |
| 6 | Westside | 20 | 8 | 5 | 7 | 46 | 43 | 2 |
| 7 | Brockham | 20 | 8 | 2 | 10 | 39 | 46 | 2 |
| 8 | AC Malden | 20 | 5 | 2 | 13 | 37 | 58 | 1 |
| 9 | Sutton High | 20 | 3 | 7 | 10 | 29 | 55 | 1 |
| 10 | Ashtead | 20 | 4 | 4 | 12 | 30 | 64 | 1 |
| 11 | Kerria Knights | 20 | 1 | 3 | 16 | 22 | 49 | |

## SWINDON & DISTRICT LEAGUE

### Premier Division

| | | P | W | D | L | F | A | Pts |
|---|---|---|---|---|---|---|---|---|
| 1 | Fratellos | 16 | 14 | 2 | 0 | 54 | 13 | 4 |
| 2 | Queensfield United | 16 | 10 | 3 | 3 | 52 | 30 | 3 |
| 3 | Swiss Chalet Rangers | 16 | 9 | 2 | 5 | 47 | 44 | 2 |
| 4 | AFC Globe | 16 | 8 | 1 | 7 | 37 | 28 | 2 |
| 5 | DJC Marlborough | 16 | 5 | 4 | 7 | 30 | 46 | 1 |
| 6 | Spectrum | 16 | 5 | 2 | 9 | 41 | 39 | 1 |
| 7 | Village Inn | 16 | 5 | 2 | 9 | 24 | 31 | 1 |
| 8 | Auto Engine Tune | 16 | 3 | 3 | 10 | 43 | 57 | 1 |
| 9 | Lower Stratton | 16 | 3 | 1 | 12 | 29 | 69 | 1 |
| 10 | Highworth Town | 0 | 0 | 0 | 0 | 0 | 0 | 0 |

### Division One

| | | P | W | D | L | F | A | Pts |
|---|---|---|---|---|---|---|---|---|
| 1 | Old Town United | 18 | 15 | 3 | 0 | 75 | 23 | 4 |
| 2 | Sportz Central | 18 | 10 | 3 | 5 | 48 | 36 | 3 |
| 3 | Fox and Hound | 18 | 9 | 4 | 5 | 52 | 50 | 3 |
| 4 | Bassett Bulldogs | 18 | 9 | 2 | 7 | 47 | 41 | 2 |
| 5 | Tap and Barrel | 18 | 8 | 0 | 10 | 39 | 21 | 2 |
| 6 | Ramsbury | 18 | 6 | 5 | 7 | 41 | 42 | 2 |
| 7 | Ferndale WMC | 18 | 5 | 5 | 8 | 43 | 62 | 2 |
| 8 | Swindon Spitfires | 18 | 5 | 2 | 11 | 46 | 59 | 1 |
| 9 | Chiseldon | 18 | 4 | 3 | 11 | 39 | 62 | 1 |
| 10 | Larry's Plaice | 18 | 3 | 5 | 10 | 33 | 67 | 1 |

# TAUNTON & DISTRICT LEAGUE

| Division One | P | W | D | L | F | A | Pts |
|---|---|---|---|---|---|---|---|
| 1 Locomotives | 16 | 12 | 3 | 1 | 61 | 18 | 39 |
| 2 Staplegrove | 16 | 11 | 3 | 2 | 49 | 23 | 36 |
| 3 Bridgwater Sports (-3pts) | 16 | 8 | 2 | 6 | 41 | 27 | 23 |
| 4 North Petherton | 16 | 6 | 3 | 7 | 32 | 40 | 21 |
| 5 Sampford Blues | 16 | 5 | 5 | 6 | 34 | 36 | 20 |
| 6 Alcombe Rovers | 16 | 5 | 3 | 8 | 25 | 33 | 18 |
| 7 Highbridge Town | 16 | 4 | 4 | 8 | 28 | 48 | 16 |
| 8 Bishops Lydeard Reserves (-3pts) | 16 | 4 | 5 | 7 | 23 | 29 | 14 |
| 9 Dulverton Town | 16 | 3 | 0 | 13 | 18 | 57 | 9 |

| Division Two | P | W | D | L | F | A | Pts |
|---|---|---|---|---|---|---|---|
| 1 Middlezoy Rovers Reserves | 20 | 15 | 1 | 4 | 42 | 21 | 46 |
| 2 Hamilton Hawks | 20 | 12 | 3 | 5 | 56 | 28 | 39 |
| 3 Staplegrove Reserves | 20 | 11 | 3 | 6 | 62 | 45 | 36 |
| 4 Porlock | 20 | 8 | 7 | 5 | 33 | 27 | 31 |
| 5 Westonzoyland | 20 | 8 | 6 | 6 | 35 | 33 | 30 |
| 6 Wyvern Rangers | 20 | 7 | 4 | 9 | 39 | 52 | 25 |
| 7 Wembdon Saints (-3pts) | 20 | 7 | 6 | 7 | 45 | 39 | 24 |
| 8 Nether Stowey | 20 | 7 | 2 | 11 | 43 | 47 | 23 |
| 9 Bishops Lydeard Colts | 20 | 6 | 5 | 9 | 40 | 54 | 23 |
| 10 Appletree | 20 | 5 | 1 | 14 | 41 | 70 | 16 |
| 11 Watchet Town Reserves | 20 | 3 | 4 | 13 | 25 | 45 | 13 |

| Division Three | P | W | D | L | F | A | Pts |
|---|---|---|---|---|---|---|---|
| 1 Blagdon Hill | 20 | 18 | 1 | 1 | 119 | 22 | 55 |
| 2 Stogursey | 20 | 13 | 4 | 3 | 63 | 23 | 43 |
| 3 The Merry Monk | 20 | 13 | 3 | 4 | 89 | 46 | 42 |
| 4 Wembdon | 20 | 12 | 3 | 5 | 50 | 28 | 39 |
| 5 Minehead Reserves | 20 | 10 | 6 | 4 | 79 | 39 | 36 |
| 6 Bishops Hull | 20 | 9 | 2 | 9 | 77 | 56 | 29 |
| 7 Sydenham Rangers | 20 | 8 | 2 | 10 | 63 | 68 | 26 |
| 8 Redgate | 20 | 7 | 0 | 13 | 35 | 64 | 21 |
| 9 Bridgwater Sports Reserves | 20 | 6 | 2 | 12 | 46 | 62 | 20 |
| 10 Highbridge Town Reserves | 20 | 0 | 3 | 17 | 19 | 105 | 3 |
| 11 Williton (-3pts) | 20 | 0 | 2 | 18 | 20 | 147 | -1 |

| Division Four | P | W | D | L | F | A | Pts |
|---|---|---|---|---|---|---|---|
| 1 Milverton Rangers | 20 | 17 | 1 | 2 | 83 | 29 | 52 |
| 2 Alcombe Rovers Reserves | 20 | 13 | 2 | 5 | 46 | 28 | 41 |
| 3 The Gallery | 20 | 12 | 3 | 5 | 58 | 20 | 39 |
| 4 Galmington Dragons | 20 | 12 | 2 | 6 | 54 | 32 | 38 |
| 5 Morganians | 20 | 9 | 3 | 8 | 52 | 44 | 30 |
| 6 Rhode Lane Wanderers | 20 | 10 | 0 | 10 | 57 | 60 | 30 |
| 7 North Petherton Reserves | 20 | 9 | 3 | 8 | 29 | 41 | 30 |
| 8 Norton Fitzwarren | 20 | 7 | 2 | 11 | 31 | 48 | 23 |
| 9 Dulverton Town Reserves | 20 | 5 | 2 | 13 | 33 | 55 | 17 |
| 10 Porlock Reserves | 20 | 3 | 1 | 16 | 27 | 68 | 10 |
| 11 Bridgwater Sports Colts (-3pts) | 20 | 3 | 1 | 16 | 30 | 75 | 7 |

| Division Five | P | W | D | L | F | A | Pts |
|---|---|---|---|---|---|---|---|
| 1 Tone Youth | 22 | 18 | 4 | 0 | 121 | 39 | 58 |
| 2 Woolavington F.C | 22 | 16 | 1 | 5 | 108 | 37 | 49 |
| 3 Sampford Blues Reserves | 22 | 15 | 2 | 5 | 86 | 43 | 47 |
| 4 Nether Stowey Reserves | 22 | 10 | 4 | 8 | 53 | 52 | 34 |
| 5 Staplegrove Colts | 22 | 11 | 1 | 10 | 60 | 73 | 34 |
| 6 Exmoor Rangers | 22 | 10 | 3 | 9 | 72 | 45 | 33 |
| 7 Creech Coogars | 22 | 9 | 5 | 8 | 68 | 70 | 32 |
| 8 Middlezoy Athletic | 22 | 8 | 3 | 11 | 47 | 59 | 27 |
| 9 East Bower | 22 | 8 | 2 | 12 | 63 | 75 | 26 |
| 10 Galmington Dragons Res | 22 | 7 | 2 | 13 | 41 | 83 | 23 |
| 11 Wembdon Saints Reserves | 22 | 3 | 1 | 18 | 54 | 116 | 10 |
| 12 Bridgwater Grasshoppers | 22 | 2 | 2 | 18 | 35 | 116 | 8 |

# THANET & DISTRICT LEAGUE

| Division One | P | W | D | L | F | A | Pts |
|---|---|---|---|---|---|---|---|
| 1 St Lukes | 14 | 12 | 2 | 0 | 61 | 20 | 38 |
| 2 Social Team United | 14 | 11 | 3 | 0 | 62 | 20 | 36 |
| 3 AFC Margate | 14 | 7 | 2 | 5 | 37 | 29 | 23 |
| 4 S.I. United | 14 | 6 | 2 | 6 | 41 | 35 | 20 |
| 5 Ramsgate | 14 | 4 | 3 | 7 | 42 | 37 | 15 |
| 6 Westcliff United | 14 | 3 | 2 | 9 | 25 | 57 | 11 |
| 7 Trinity | 14 | 3 | 1 | 10 | 18 | 44 | 10 |
| 8 Minster | 14 | 2 | 1 | 11 | 18 | 62 | 7 |

# TONBRIDGE & DISTRICT LEAGUE

| Premier Division | P | W | D | L | F | A | Pts |
|---|---|---|---|---|---|---|---|
| 1 Southborough | 14 | 11 | 2 | 1 | 73 | 22 | 35 |
| 2 Blackham & Ashurst | 14 | 10 | 3 | 1 | 32 | 20 | 33 |
| 3 Pembury | 14 | 10 | 1 | 3 | 52 | 29 | 31 |
| 4 High Brooms Casuals | 14 | 6 | 1 | 7 | 43 | 43 | 19 |
| 5 Woodlands | 14 | 5 | 2 | 7 | 41 | 45 | 17 |
| 6 Swan (Edenbridge) | 14 | 5 | 0 | 9 | 35 | 40 | 15 |
| 7 Rusthall III | 14 | 1 | 3 | 10 | 22 | 56 | 6 |
| 8 Penshurst Park | 14 | 2 | 0 | 12 | 31 | 74 | 6 |

| Division One | P | W | D | L | F | A | Pts |
|---|---|---|---|---|---|---|---|
| 1 Paddock Wood | 22 | 16 | 3 | 3 | 74 | 23 | 51 |
| 2 Dowgate | 22 | 15 | 4 | 3 | 65 | 21 | 49 |
| 3 AFC Valour | 22 | 13 | 2 | 7 | 62 | 42 | 41 |
| 4 High Brooms Casuals Reserves | 22 | 12 | 5 | 5 | 47 | 40 | 41 |
| 5 Roselands | 22 | 13 | 2 | 7 | 70 | 64 | 41 |
| 6 Capel Sports and Social | 22 | 12 | 3 | 7 | 77 | 63 | 39 |
| 7 Southborough Reserves | 22 | 11 | 0 | 11 | 58 | 65 | 33 |
| 8 Pembury Reserves | 22 | 8 | 3 | 11 | 46 | 47 | 27 |
| 9 Frant | 22 | 4 | 3 | 15 | 40 | 67 | 18 |
| 10 Hadlow Harrow | 22 | 5 | 3 | 14 | 34 | 68 | 18 |
| 11 Swan (Edenbridge) Reserves | 22 | 3 | 3 | 16 | 44 | 74 | 12 |
| 12 Hawkenbury Reserves | 22 | 3 | 3 | 16 | 32 | 75 | 9 |

# LEAGUE TABLES

| Division Two | P | W | D | L | F | A | Pts |
|---|---|---|---|---|---|---|---|
| 1 Woodlands Reserves | 18 | 14 | 0 | 4 | 70 | 33 | 42 |
| 2 Yalding & Laddingford | 18 | 12 | 2 | 4 | 76 | 29 | 38 |
| 3 Leigh | 18 | 12 | 2 | 4 | 76 | 41 | 38 |
| 4 FC Revolution | 18 | 9 | 3 | 6 | 68 | 52 | 30 |
| 5 Ashton Prime | 18 | 8 | 4 | 6 | 43 | 37 | 28 |
| 6 Rusthall IV | 18 | 7 | 4 | 7 | 68 | 52 | 25 |
| 7 AFC Valour Reserves | 18 | 8 | 1 | 9 | 52 | 43 | 25 |
| 8 Hawkenbury III | 18 | 7 | 3 | 8 | 34 | 49 | 24 |
| 9 Brenchley Wanderers | 18 | 2 | 0 | 16 | 18 | 62 | 6 |
| 10 Roselands Reserves | 18 | 1 | 1 | 16 | 20 | 127 | 4 |

| Division One | P | W | D | L | F | A | Pts |
|---|---|---|---|---|---|---|---|
| 1 FC Gawthorpe | 18 | 17 | 1 | 0 | 98 | 26 | 52 |
| 2 Prince of Wales (OCR) FC | 18 | 11 | 3 | 4 | 76 | 34 | 36 |
| 3 Black Swan Normanton FC | 18 | 11 | 2 | 5 | 48 | 47 | 35 |
| 4 Dewsbury Rangers OB | 18 | 9 | 3 | 6 | 52 | 35 | 30 |
| 5 Inns of Court FC | 18 | 6 | 4 | 8 | 49 | 57 | 22 |
| 6 Morley Town AFC | 18 | 6 | 3 | 9 | 48 | 57 | 21 |
| 7 Ossett Two Brewers FC | 18 | 6 | 2 | 10 | 48 | 80 | 20 |
| 8 Wortley FC Res | 18 | 5 | 1 | 12 | 40 | 54 | 16 |
| 9 Weavers Arms FC (-3pts) | 18 | 5 | 3 | 10 | 37 | 63 | 15 |
| 10 Woodhouse Hill (Normanton) | 18 | 1 | 4 | 13 | 35 | 78 | 7 |

## TYNESIDE AMATEUR LEAGUE

| Division One | P | W | D | L | F | A | Pts |
|---|---|---|---|---|---|---|---|
| 1 New York | 20 | 14 | 3 | 3 | 65 | 35 | 45 |
| 2 West Jesmond | 20 | 11 | 3 | 6 | 64 | 36 | 36 |
| 3 Cullercoats Reserves | 20 | 10 | 5 | 5 | 50 | 33 | 35 |
| 4 Heaton Rifles | 20 | 9 | 5 | 6 | 52 | 46 | 32 |
| 5 Gosforth Bohemians Reserves | 20 | 9 | 3 | 8 | 42 | 36 | 30 |
| 6 Walker Central Reserves | 20 | 9 | 3 | 8 | 51 | 53 | 30 |
| 7 Lindisfarne Athletic | 20 | 8 | 4 | 8 | 55 | 53 | 28 |
| 8 Wardley | 20 | 8 | 2 | 10 | 44 | 53 | 26 |
| 9 Newcastle Chemfica Ind. Res. | 20 | 7 | 3 | 10 | 34 | 54 | 24 |
| 10 (FoWS) Diggers | 20 | 3 | 5 | 12 | 49 | 76 | 14 |
| 11 Winlaton The Queens Head (-6pts) | 20 | 3 | 2 | 15 | 44 | 75 | 5 |

| Division Two | P | W | D | L | F | A | Pts |
|---|---|---|---|---|---|---|---|
| 1 Chopwell | 16 | 14 | 2 | 0 | 70 | 16 | 44 |
| 2 North Shields Athletic Reserves | 16 | 10 | 0 | 6 | 47 | 41 | 30 |
| 3 Kenton Bar Community | 16 | 9 | 2 | 5 | 44 | 32 | 29 |
| 4 Newcastle Medicals | 16 | 8 | 3 | 5 | 33 | 33 | 27 |
| 5 Ponteland United Reserves | 16 | 6 | 3 | 7 | 44 | 40 | 21 |
| 6 Gosforth Bohemians 'A' | 16 | 6 | 2 | 8 | 31 | 45 | 20 |
| 7 Stobswood Welfare | 16 | 5 | 1 | 10 | 29 | 35 | 13 |
| 8 Newcastle East End | 16 | 3 | 3 | 10 | 22 | 47 | 12 |
| 9 North Shields Town | 16 | 2 | 2 | 12 | 22 | 53 | 8 |

## WAKEFIELD & DISTRICT LEAGUE

| Premier Division | P | W | D | L | F | A | Pts |
|---|---|---|---|---|---|---|---|
| 1 Gate FC | 20 | 15 | 3 | 2 | 87 | 27 | 48 |
| 2 Crofton Sports FC | 20 | 12 | 4 | 4 | 53 | 26 | 40 |
| 3 Fieldhead Hospital (-3pts) | 20 | 13 | 3 | 4 | 75 | 30 | 39 |
| 4 Garforth WMC FC | 20 | 10 | 2 | 8 | 55 | 43 | 32 |
| 5 Walton FC | 20 | 9 | 5 | 6 | 65 | 56 | 32 |
| 6 Thornes FC | 20 | 9 | 3 | 8 | 55 | 59 | 30 |
| 7 Thornhill FC | 20 | 9 | 2 | 9 | 67 | 80 | 29 |
| 8 Wortley FC | 20 | 8 | 4 | 8 | 67 | 62 | 28 |
| 9 Eastmoor FC | 20 | 7 | 4 | 9 | 55 | 59 | 25 |
| 10 Rose & Crown (Darton) FC | 20 | 1 | 3 | 16 | 34 | 74 | 6 |
| 11 Ossett Dynamos (-3pts) | 20 | 0 | 1 | 19 | 20 | 117 | -2 |

| Division Two | P | W | D | L | F | A | Pts |
|---|---|---|---|---|---|---|---|
| 1 Horbury Town | 22 | 15 | 3 | 4 | 69 | 35 | 48 |
| 2 Snydale Athletic | 22 | 15 | 2 | 5 | 71 | 51 | 47 |
| 3 Old Bank WMC (-3pts) | 22 | 15 | 4 | 3 | 77 | 37 | 46 |
| 4 Altofts AFC | 22 | 10 | 4 | 8 | 66 | 43 | 34 |
| 5 Wakefield City (-3pts) | 22 | 12 | 1 | 9 | 72 | 57 | 34 |
| 6 Featherstone Colliery FC | 22 | 10 | 3 | 9 | 64 | 45 | 33 |
| 7 Nostell Miners Welfare (-6pts) | 22 | 11 | 2 | 9 | 48 | 41 | 29 |
| 8 Red Lion Alverthorpe FC | 22 | 8 | 3 | 11 | 41 | 58 | 27 |
| 9 White Hart FC | 22 | 7 | 5 | 10 | 58 | 66 | 26 |
| 10 Wagon FC (-3pts) | 22 | 6 | 3 | 13 | 68 | 75 | 18 |
| 11 Stanley United (-15pts) | 22 | 7 | 2 | 13 | 59 | 63 | 8 |
| 12 College FC (-6pts) | 22 | 0 | 0 | 22 | 28 | 150 | -6 |

| Division Three | P | W | D | L | F | A | Pts |
|---|---|---|---|---|---|---|---|
| 1 New Wheel FC | 24 | 18 | 3 | 3 | 95 | 36 | 57 |
| 2 Durkar FC | 24 | 17 | 2 | 5 | 83 | 35 | 53 |
| 3 Junction Featherstone FC (-3pts) | 24 | 16 | 6 | 2 | 74 | 36 | 51 |
| 4 AFC Kettlethorpe | 24 | 15 | 3 | 6 | 81 | 45 | 48 |
| 5 Waterloo FC | 24 | 13 | 5 | 6 | 91 | 53 | 44 |
| 6 Horbury Athletic | 24 | 14 | 2 | 8 | 60 | 48 | 44 |
| 7 Garforth WMC FC Reserves | 24 | 11 | 5 | 8 | 89 | 51 | 38 |
| 8 Railway FC (-3pts) | 24 | 11 | 1 | 12 | 72 | 69 | 31 |
| 9 Crofton Sports FC Reserves | 24 | 7 | 3 | 14 | 44 | 73 | 24 |
| 10 Snydale Athletic Reserves (-3pts) | 24 | 6 | 4 | 14 | 41 | 82 | 19 |
| 11 Inns of Court FC Reserves | 24 | 4 | 2 | 18 | 45 | 104 | 14 |
| 12 Dewsbury Rangers OB Res | 24 | 3 | 1 | 20 | 29 | 114 | 10 |
| 13 Wrenthorpe FC (-3pts) | 24 | 2 | 1 | 21 | 44 | 102 | 4 |

## WEARSIDE COMBINATION

| Division One | P | W | D | L | F | A | Pts |
|---|---|---|---|---|---|---|---|
| 1 Sunderland Blue Stone Construction | 12 | 10 | 1 | 1 | 67 | 22 | 31 |
| 2 Sunderland Alexandra | 12 | 10 | 1 | 1 | 60 | 18 | 31 |
| 3 FC Whitburn | 12 | 8 | 0 | 4 | 42 | 27 | 24 |
| 4 Sunderland Times Inn | 12 | 6 | 1 | 5 | 49 | 48 | 19 |
| 5 East Durham Spartans | 12 | 1 | 4 | 7 | 23 | 47 | 7 |
| 6 University of Sunderland B | 12 | 2 | 1 | 9 | 19 | 51 | 7 |
| 7 Sunderland Park View | 12 | 0 | 2 | 10 | 18 | 65 | 2 |

## WENSLEYDALE LEAGUE

### WEST RIDING COUNTY AMATEUR LEAGUE

| Division One | P | W | D | L | F | A | Pts |
|---|---|---|---|---|---|---|---|
| Unicorn FC | 26 | 19 | 5 | 2 | 110 | 25 | 62 |
| Colburn Town | 26 | 20 | 0 | 6 | 104 | 31 | 60 |
| Hawes United | 26 | 17 | 4 | 5 | 81 | 40 | 55 |
| Richmond Buck Inn | 26 | 18 | 1 | 7 | 95 | 55 | 55 |
| Richmond Academy | 26 | 15 | 5 | 6 | 85 | 30 | 50 |
| Richmond Mavericks | 26 | 15 | 4 | 7 | 84 | 44 | 49 |
| Spennithorne & Harmby (-3pts) | 26 | 13 | 4 | 9 | 73 | 49 | 40 |
| Reeth & District Athletic Club | 26 | 12 | 2 | 12 | 82 | 66 | 38 |
| Catterick Garrison Football Centre (-9pts) | 26 | 11 | 5 | 10 | 55 | 45 | 29 |
| Catterick Rovers | 26 | 7 | 2 | 17 | 62 | 79 | 23 |
| Redmire United | 26 | 5 | 4 | 17 | 46 | 74 | 19 |
| Carperby Rovers | 26 | 4 | 4 | 18 | 41 | 84 | 16 |
| Askrigg United | 26 | 4 | 3 | 19 | 48 | 91 | 15 |
| Hawes Gayle | 26 | 0 | 1 | 25 | 15 | 268 | 1 |

| Premier Division | P | W | D | L | F | A | Pts |
|---|---|---|---|---|---|---|---|
| 1 Bay Athletic | 26 | 21 | 0 | 5 | 87 | 34 | 63 |
| 2 Steeton | 26 | 17 | 5 | 4 | 69 | 37 | 56 |
| 3 Ovenden West Riding | 25 | 17 | 2 | 6 | 78 | 36 | 53 |
| 4 Tyersal | 26 | 14 | 3 | 9 | 80 | 58 | 45 |
| 5 Storthes Hall | 26 | 11 | 7 | 8 | 65 | 54 | 40 |
| 6 Golcar United | 26 | 10 | 8 | 8 | 67 | 63 | 38 |
| 7 Hall Green United | 26 | 11 | 5 | 10 | 44 | 45 | 38 |
| 8 Marsden | 25 | 9 | 7 | 9 | 64 | 61 | 34 |
| 9 Salts | 26 | 9 | 5 | 12 | 56 | 63 | 32 |
| 10 Kirkburton | 26 | 9 | 4 | 13 | 56 | 67 | 31 |
| 11 Littletown | 26 | 7 | 6 | 13 | 50 | 72 | 27 |
| 12 Campion | 26 | 7 | 4 | 15 | 58 | 64 | 25 |
| 13 Lepton Highlanders | 26 | 5 | 5 | 16 | 45 | 72 | 20 |
| 14 Overthorpe Sports Club | 26 | 1 | 5 | 20 | 37 | 130 | 8 |

## WEST END (LONDON) AFA LEAGUE

| Premier Division | P | W | D | L | F | A | Pts |
|---|---|---|---|---|---|---|---|
| IB Albion | 18 | 14 | 1 | 3 | 68 | 32 | 43 |
| Cambridge Heath | 18 | 12 | 3 | 3 | 53 | 27 | 39 |
| North Acton 'A' | 18 | 10 | 1 | 7 | 43 | 39 | 31 |
| Earlsberg Eagles | 17 | 9 | 2 | 6 | 53 | 36 | 29 |
| Arian | 17 | 8 | 2 | 7 | 44 | 47 | 26 |
| Primrose Hill | 18 | 7 | 1 | 10 | 39 | 56 | 22 |
| Bishops Park | 18 | 7 | 1 | 10 | 34 | 52 | 22 |
| Racing Chiswick | 18 | 5 | 3 | 10 | 29 | 35 | 18 |
| Mavericks | 18 | 4 | 2 | 12 | 35 | 45 | 14 |
| Clissold Park Rangers | 18 | 4 | 2 | 12 | 31 | 60 | 14 |

| Division One | P | W | D | L | F | A | Pts |
|---|---|---|---|---|---|---|---|
| 1 Huddersfield YMCA | 22 | 17 | 3 | 2 | 53 | 25 | 54 |
| 2 Hunsworth | 22 | 16 | 1 | 5 | 67 | 34 | 49 |
| 3 Wakefield City | 22 | 14 | 3 | 5 | 62 | 39 | 45 |
| 4 Halifax Irish | 22 | 10 | 3 | 9 | 54 | 49 | 33 |
| 5 Lower Hopton | 22 | 9 | 4 | 9 | 44 | 42 | 31 |
| 6 AFC Emley . | 22 | 7 | 8 | 7 | 45 | 41 | 29 |
| 7 Wibsey | 22 | 7 | 6 | 9 | 57 | 65 | 27 |
| 8 Ventus/Yeadon Celtic | 22 | 8 | 1 | 13 | 61 | 66 | 25 |
| 9 Campion Reserves | 22 | 7 | 3 | 12 | 31 | 55 | 24 |
| 10 Westbrook YMCA | 22 | 7 | 2 | 13 | 29 | 45 | 23 |
| 11 Tingley Athletic | 22 | 5 | 7 | 10 | 47 | 57 | 22 |
| 12 Storthes Hall Reserves | 22 | 3 | 3 | 16 | 33 | 65 | 12 |

| Division One | P | W | D | L | F | A | Pts |
|---|---|---|---|---|---|---|---|
| AFC NUFC Oilers | 18 | 16 | 0 | 2 | 90 | 13 | 48 |
| BUOB | 18 | 14 | 2 | 2 | 40 | 22 | 44 |
| Real | 18 | 13 | 0 | 5 | 57 | 35 | 39 |
| Greenhouse Bethwin SEFC | 18 | 11 | 1 | 6 | 54 | 41 | 34 |
| West London | 16 | 8 | 1 | 7 | 36 | 30 | 25 |
| Spaniards | 18 | 7 | 3 | 8 | 24 | 44 | 24 |
| Primrose Hill 'A' | 18 | 3 | 4 | 11 | 25 | 45 | 13 |
| Atholl 1965 | 17 | 3 | 2 | 12 | 24 | 62 | 11 |
| Racing Chiswick Legends | 17 | 3 | 1 | 13 | 22 | 51 | 10 |
| Olympic Waterloo | 18 | 2 | 2 | 14 | 20 | 49 | 8 |

| Division Two | P | W | D | L | F | A | Pts |
|---|---|---|---|---|---|---|---|
| 1 Bay Athletic Reserves | 24 | 20 | 2 | 2 | 89 | 25 | 62 |
| 2 Steeton Reserves | 24 | 17 | 3 | 4 | 55 | 40 | 54 |
| 3 Salts Reserves | 24 | 16 | 0 | 8 | 63 | 42 | 48 |
| 4 West Horton | 24 | 13 | 3 | 8 | 64 | 43 | 42 |
| 5 Dudley Hill Rangers | 24 | 13 | 2 | 9 | 56 | 49 | 41 |
| 6 Ovenden West Riding Reserves | 24 | 11 | 4 | 9 | 63 | 42 | 37 |
| 7 Hall Green United Reserves | 24 | 11 | 3 | 10 | 49 | 57 | 36 |
| 8 Tyersal Reserves | 24 | 6 | 5 | 13 | 52 | 71 | 23 |
| 9 Tingley Athletic Reserves | 24 | 6 | 5 | 13 | 44 | 85 | 23 |
| 10 Littletown Reserves | 24 | 5 | 6 | 13 | 51 | 57 | 21 |
| 11 Golcar United Reserves | 24 | 6 | 3 | 15 | 49 | 66 | 21 |
| 12 Lower Hopton Reserves | 24 | 6 | 3 | 15 | 33 | 58 | 21 |
| 13 Kirkburton Reserves | 24 | 5 | 3 | 16 | 38 | 71 | 18 |

| Division Two | P | W | D | L | F | A | Pts |
|---|---|---|---|---|---|---|---|
| Viva Capri | 18 | 12 | 2 | 4 | 68 | 39 | 38 |
| Manor Boys | 18 | 10 | 4 | 4 | 44 | 28 | 34 |
| Spiders from Mars | 18 | 11 | 1 | 6 | 43 | 35 | 34 |
| Milton Rovers | 18 | 10 | 2 | 6 | 47 | 36 | 32 |
| Cambridge Heath 'A' | 18 | 9 | 2 | 7 | 43 | 32 | 29 |
| Hub Athletic | 18 | 7 | 3 | 8 | 44 | 46 | 24 |
| Clissold Park Rangers 'A' | 18 | 6 | 2 | 10 | 28 | 59 | 20 |
| St Marks | 18 | 5 | 2 | 11 | 36 | 42 | 17 |
| Iranian Association Football Club | 18 | 4 | 5 | 9 | 32 | 46 | 17 |
| Park Stars | 18 | 3 | 3 | 12 | 27 | 49 | 12 |

# LEAGUE TABLES
## WEST SUSSEX LEAGUE

**Premier Division**

| | | P | W | D | L | F | A | Pts |
|---|---|---|---|---|---|---|---|---|
| 1 | COWFOLD | 22 | 15 | 3 | 4 | 71 | 30 | 48 |
| 2 | WEST CHILTINGTON | 22 | 14 | 4 | 4 | 74 | 41 | 46 |
| 3 | BOSHAM | 22 | 12 | 5 | 5 | 45 | 25 | 41 |
| 4 | HUNSTON COMMUNITY CLUB | 22 | 11 | 4 | 7 | 53 | 42 | 37 |
| 5 | FAYGATE UTD | 22 | 11 | 4 | 7 | 39 | 30 | 37 |
| 6 | LAVANT | 22 | 11 | 1 | 10 | 41 | 40 | 34 |
| 7 | NEWTOWN VILLA | 22 | 10 | 3 | 9 | 31 | 38 | 33 |
| 8 | UPPER BEEDING | 22 | 9 | 2 | 11 | 40 | 39 | 29 |
| 9 | LANCING UTD | 22 | 7 | 3 | 12 | 39 | 63 | 24 |
| 10 | HOLBROOK | 22 | 6 | 4 | 12 | 40 | 55 | 22 |
| 11 | BARNHAM RESERVES | 22 | 3 | 4 | 15 | 22 | 62 | 13 |
| 12 | WATERSFIELD | 22 | 2 | 5 | 15 | 18 | 48 | 11 |

**Division One**

| | | P | W | D | L | F | A | Pts |
|---|---|---|---|---|---|---|---|---|
| 1 | WITTERING UTD | 20 | 15 | 3 | 2 | 53 | 21 | 48 |
| 2 | HENFIELD | 20 | 15 | 3 | 2 | 65 | 37 | 48 |
| 3 | YAPTON | 20 | 15 | 0 | 5 | 77 | 28 | 45 |
| 4 | PETWORTH | 20 | 10 | 4 | 6 | 41 | 29 | 34 |
| 5 | PULBOROUGH | 20 | 10 | 3 | 7 | 60 | 32 | 33 |
| 6 | COWFOLD RESERVES | 20 | 8 | 5 | 7 | 33 | 35 | 29 |
| 7 | BARNS GREEN | 20 | 8 | 3 | 9 | 41 | 39 | 27 |
| 8 | EAST DEAN | 20 | 6 | 2 | 12 | 42 | 49 | 20 |
| 9 | SOUTHWATER | 20 | 5 | 3 | 12 | 41 | 55 | 18 |
| 10 | SELSEY 'A' | 20 | 3 | 1 | 16 | 22 | 89 | 10 |
| 11 | CLYMPING RESERVES | 20 | 0 | 3 | 17 | 22 | 83 | 3 |

**Division Two North**

| | | P | W | D | L | F | A | Pts |
|---|---|---|---|---|---|---|---|---|
| 1 | OCKLEY | 20 | 15 | 3 | 2 | 60 | 27 | 48 |
| 2 | ALFOLD | 20 | 12 | 6 | 2 | 36 | 15 | 42 |
| 3 | RUDGWICK | 20 | 12 | 2 | 6 | 52 | 31 | 38 |
| 4 | FAYGATE UTD RESERVES | 20 | 11 | 5 | 4 | 40 | 24 | 38 |
| 5 | PARTRIDGE GREEN | 20 | 11 | 4 | 5 | 45 | 36 | 37 |
| 6 | CAPEL | 20 | 10 | 0 | 10 | 56 | 54 | 30 |
| 7 | NEWDIGATE | 20 | 5 | 6 | 9 | 40 | 53 | 21 |
| 8 | BILLINGSHURST RESERVES | 20 | 6 | 2 | 12 | 43 | 46 | 20 |
| 9 | HOLBROOK RESERVES | 20 | 5 | 3 | 12 | 38 | 54 | 18 |
| 10 | UPPER BEEDING RESERVES | 20 | 3 | 1 | 16 | 18 | 50 | 10 |
| 11 | HORSHAM TRINITY | 20 | 2 | 4 | 14 | 29 | 67 | 10 |

**Division Two South**

| | | P | W | D | L | F | A | Pts |
|---|---|---|---|---|---|---|---|---|
| 1 | NEWTOWN VILLA RESERVES | 20 | 15 | 2 | 3 | 70 | 31 | 47 |
| 2 | TANGMERE | 20 | 15 | 2 | 3 | 69 | 32 | 47 |
| 3 | PREDATORS (-3PTS) | 20 | 12 | 3 | 5 | 72 | 28 | 36 |
| 4 | ROGATE 08 FC | 20 | 11 | 3 | 6 | 66 | 35 | 36 |
| 5 | FITTLEWORTH | 20 | 10 | 4 | 6 | 51 | 46 | 34 |
| 6 | FERNHURST SPORTS | 20 | 8 | 3 | 9 | 55 | 47 | 27 |
| 7 | BOXGROVE | 20 | 7 | 4 | 9 | 47 | 47 | 25 |
| 8 | LODSWORTH | 20 | 6 | 3 | 11 | 46 | 74 | 21 |
| 9 | GRAFFHAM | 20 | 6 | 1 | 13 | 31 | 75 | 19 |
| 10 | ATHLETICO ARUNDEL | 20 | 5 | 2 | 13 | 31 | 52 | 17 |
| 11 | HUNSTON C.C. RESERVES | 20 | 1 | 1 | 18 | 27 | 98 | 4 |

**Division Three North**

| | | P | W | D | L | F | A | Pts |
|---|---|---|---|---|---|---|---|---|
| 1 | FOREST FC | 20 | 18 | 2 | 0 | 78 | 18 | 5 |
| 2 | SLINFOLD | 20 | 11 | 3 | 6 | 61 | 28 | 3 |
| 3 | WISBOROUGH GREEN | 20 | 10 | 6 | 4 | 47 | 29 | 3 |
| 4 | HENFIELD RESERVES | 20 | 10 | 4 | 6 | 58 | 50 | 3 |
| 5 | ASHINGTON ROVERS | 20 | 8 | 5 | 7 | 55 | 48 | 2 |
| 6 | T D SHIPLEY RESERVES | 20 | 8 | 3 | 9 | 46 | 46 | 2 |
| 7 | EWHURST | 20 | 7 | 6 | 7 | 37 | 42 | 2 |
| 8 | ALFOLD RESERVES | 20 | 8 | 2 | 10 | 38 | 45 | 2 |
| 9 | COWFOLD THIRDS | 20 | 6 | 5 | 9 | 38 | 33 | 2 |
| 10 | HORSHAM CRUSADERS | 20 | 3 | 0 | 17 | 26 | 119 | |
| 11 | SOUTHWATER RESERVES | 20 | 1 | 4 | 15 | 33 | 59 | |

**Division Three South**

| | | P | W | D | L | F | A | Pts |
|---|---|---|---|---|---|---|---|---|
| 1 | THE VARDAR VIP FC | 18 | 14 | 1 | 3 | 60 | 29 | 4 |
| 2 | WITTERING UTD RES | 18 | 12 | 2 | 4 | 43 | 25 | 3 |
| 3 | STEDHAM UTD | 18 | 11 | 3 | 4 | 48 | 30 | 3 |
| 4 | NYETIMBER PIRATES | 18 | 11 | 2 | 5 | 61 | 46 | 3 |
| 5 | HARTING | 18 | 6 | 7 | 5 | 41 | 37 | 2 |
| 6 | YAPTON RESERVES | 18 | 6 | 3 | 9 | 39 | 52 | 2 |
| 7 | RUSTINGTON PARK SENIORS | 18 | 5 | 4 | 9 | 48 | 60 | 1 |
| 8 | WHYKE UTD | 18 | 5 | 3 | 10 | 38 | 49 | 1 |
| 9 | LAVANT RESERVES | 18 | 5 | 2 | 11 | 34 | 56 | 1 |
| 10 | BOSHAM RESERVES | 18 | 0 | 3 | 15 | 27 | 55 | |

**Division Four North**

| | | P | W | D | L | F | A | Pts |
|---|---|---|---|---|---|---|---|---|
| 1 | BORDER WANDERERS | 20 | 19 | 0 | 1 | 99 | 26 | 5 |
| 2 | BILLINGSHURST THIRDS | 20 | 13 | 2 | 5 | 63 | 40 | 4 |
| 3 | HORSHAM OLYMPIC | 20 | 11 | 5 | 4 | 62 | 40 | 3 |
| 4 | PULBOROUGH RESERVES | 20 | 8 | 4 | 8 | 49 | 49 | 2 |
| 5 | HENFIELD THIRDS | 20 | 9 | 1 | 10 | 47 | 47 | 2 |
| 6 | HORSHAM BAP & AM | 20 | 9 | 1 | 10 | 39 | 40 | 2 |
| 7 | HOLBROOK THIRDS | 20 | 9 | 0 | 11 | 56 | 57 | 2 |
| 8 | ROWFANT VILLAGE | 20 | 7 | 1 | 12 | 34 | 57 | 2 |
| 9 | HORSHAM TRINITY RESERVES | 20 | 6 | 4 | 10 | 48 | 72 | 2 |
| 10 | RUDGWICK RESERVES | 20 | 5 | 3 | 12 | 42 | 56 | 1 |
| 11 | CAPEL RESERVES | 20 | 2 | 3 | 15 | 26 | 81 | |

**Division Four South**

| | | P | W | D | L | F | A | Pts |
|---|---|---|---|---|---|---|---|---|
| 1 | HAMMER UTD | 20 | 16 | 2 | 2 | 69 | 26 | 5 |
| 2 | FELPHAM COLTS | 20 | 12 | 3 | 5 | 45 | 33 | 3 |
| 3 | LANCING UTD RESERVES | 20 | 10 | 3 | 7 | 49 | 42 | 3 |
| 4 | AMBASSADORS | 20 | 10 | 2 | 8 | 65 | 32 | 3 |
| 5 | THE SPORTSMAN | 20 | 8 | 5 | 7 | 38 | 36 | 2 |
| 6 | LAKE ROAD RANGERS | 20 | 8 | 4 | 8 | 54 | 47 | 2 |
| 7 | BRACKLESHAM | 20 | 8 | 2 | 10 | 39 | 56 | 2 |
| 8 | WHYKE UTD RES | 20 | 8 | 1 | 11 | 44 | 50 | 2 |
| 9 | COAL EXCHANGE | 20 | 8 | 1 | 11 | 52 | 61 | 2 |
| 10 | PREDATORS RES | 20 | 5 | 5 | 10 | 30 | 35 | 2 |
| 11 | ELMER FC | 20 | 3 | 0 | 17 | 22 | 89 | |

## Division Five North

| | P | W | D | L | F | A | Pts |
|---|---|---|---|---|---|---|---|
| 1 FAYGATE UTD THIRDS | 20 | 15 | 1 | 4 | 66 | 30 | 46 |
| 2 HORSHAM SPARROWS MENS FC | 20 | 14 | 3 | 3 | 52 | 29 | 45 |
| 3 OCKLEY RESERVES | 20 | 14 | 1 | 5 | 65 | 23 | 43 |
| 4 NEWDIGATE RESERVES | 20 | 11 | 1 | 8 | 54 | 45 | 34 |
| 5 HOLBROOK FOURTHS | 20 | 9 | 3 | 8 | 56 | 44 | 30 |
| 6 EWHURST RESERVES (-3PTS) | 20 | 9 | 5 | 6 | 35 | 32 | 29 |
| 7 BARNS GREEN RESERVES | 20 | 8 | 1 | 11 | 36 | 44 | 25 |
| 8 HORSHAM BAP & AM RESERVES | 20 | 6 | 4 | 10 | 34 | 51 | 22 |
| 9 HORSHAM OLYMPIC RESERVES | 20 | 6 | 3 | 11 | 38 | 47 | 21 |
| 10 HORSHAM TRINITY THIRDS | 20 | 6 | 1 | 13 | 38 | 49 | 19 |
| 11 HORSHAM CRUSADERS RES. | 20 | 0 | 1 | 19 | 18 | 98 | 1 |

## Division Five Central

| | P | W | D | L | F | A | Pts |
|---|---|---|---|---|---|---|---|
| 1 AMBERLEY | 20 | 18 | 0 | 2 | 94 | 13 | 54 |
| 2 PLAISTOW | 20 | 13 | 1 | 6 | 68 | 35 | 40 |
| 3 WATERSFIELD RESERVES | 20 | 13 | 1 | 6 | 66 | 42 | 40 |
| 4 WEST CHILTINGTON RESERVES | 20 | 10 | 2 | 8 | 63 | 60 | 32 |
| 5 WISBOROUGH GREEN RESERVES | 20 | 10 | 0 | 10 | 35 | 47 | 30 |
| 6 PETWORTH RESERVES | 20 | 9 | 2 | 9 | 43 | 63 | 29 |
| 7 FITTLEWORTH RESERVES | 20 | 7 | 2 | 11 | 30 | 42 | 23 |
| 8 PARTRIDGE GREEN RESERVES | 20 | 6 | 3 | 11 | 45 | 61 | 21 |
| 9 BILLINGSHURST ATHLETIC | 20 | 6 | 2 | 12 | 42 | 67 | 20 |
| 10 SLINFOLD RESERVES | 20 | 5 | 3 | 12 | 30 | 45 | 18 |
| 11 SOUTHWATER THIRDS | 20 | 4 | 2 | 14 | 29 | 70 | 14 |

## Division Five South

| | P | W | D | L | F | A | Pts |
|---|---|---|---|---|---|---|---|
| 1 THE CROWN FC | 18 | 14 | 2 | 2 | 57 | 23 | 44 |
| 2 HARTING RES | 18 | 12 | 4 | 2 | 62 | 29 | 40 |
| 3 TANGMERE RES | 18 | 11 | 3 | 4 | 66 | 28 | 36 |
| 4 MILLAND | 18 | 11 | 2 | 5 | 62 | 33 | 35 |
| 5 HAMMER UTD RES | 18 | 11 | 1 | 6 | 41 | 37 | 34 |
| 6 WHEATSHEAF BOGNOR REGIS | 18 | 8 | 0 | 10 | 29 | 31 | 24 |
| 7 STEDHAM UTD RESERVES | 18 | 6 | 0 | 12 | 35 | 51 | 18 |
| 8 FELPHAM COLTS RES | 18 | 5 | 2 | 11 | 33 | 53 | 17 |
| 9 CHAPEL | 18 | 3 | 0 | 15 | 29 | 73 | 9 |
| 10 LODSWORTH RESERVES | 18 | 2 | 0 | 16 | 14 | 70 | 6 |

## WESTMORLAND ASSOCIATION FOOTBALL LEAGUE

### Division One

| | P | W | D | L | F | A | Pts |
|---|---|---|---|---|---|---|---|
| 1 Wetheriggs Utd | 22 | 18 | 2 | 2 | 90 | 23 | 56 |
| 2 Appleby | 22 | 16 | 5 | 1 | 77 | 27 | 53 |
| 3 Keswick | 22 | 17 | 2 | 3 | 71 | 27 | 53 |
| 4 Kirkoswald | 22 | 14 | 0 | 8 | 64 | 44 | 42 |
| 5 Kendal Utd | 22 | 11 | 0 | 11 | 55 | 57 | 33 |
| 6 Ambleside Utd Res.(-3pts) | 22 | 10 | 0 | 12 | 43 | 60 | 27 |
| 7 Burneside | 22 | 6 | 5 | 11 | 37 | 60 | 23 |
| 8 Staveley Utd | 22 | 6 | 3 | 13 | 33 | 60 | 21 |
| 9 Lunesdale Utd | 22 | 6 | 3 | 13 | 46 | 79 | 21 |
| 10 Sedbergh Wanderers | 22 | 6 | 1 | 15 | 53 | 81 | 19 |
| 11 Penrith Rangers (-3pts) | 22 | 4 | 5 | 13 | 46 | 69 | 14 |
| 12 Kendal Celtic | 22 | 2 | 6 | 14 | 26 | 54 | 12 |

## Division Two

| | P | W | D | L | F | A | Pts |
|---|---|---|---|---|---|---|---|
| 1 Carvetii Utd | 20 | 14 | 4 | 2 | 75 | 25 | 46 |
| 2 Penrith Reserves | 20 | 14 | 2 | 4 | 58 | 33 | 44 |
| 3 Langwathby Utd | 20 | 13 | 3 | 4 | 57 | 34 | 42 |
| 4 Endmoor KGR | 20 | 11 | 2 | 7 | 50 | 47 | 35 |
| 5 Ibis | 20 | 9 | 4 | 7 | 47 | 41 | 31 |
| 6 Kendal County Reserves | 20 | 6 | 4 | 10 | 37 | 50 | 22 |
| 7 Keswick Reserves | 20 | 5 | 6 | 9 | 36 | 45 | 21 |
| 8 Windermere SC | 20 | 5 | 5 | 10 | 39 | 50 | 20 |
| 9 Shap | 20 | 4 | 6 | 10 | 37 | 54 | 18 |
| 10 Eden Thistle | 20 | 4 | 4 | 12 | 32 | 57 | 16 |
| 11 Wetheriggs Utd Reserves | 20 | 3 | 4 | 13 | 28 | 60 | 13 |

## Division Three

| | P | W | D | L | F | A | Pts |
|---|---|---|---|---|---|---|---|
| 1 Unisun Athletic | 20 | 18 | 2 | 0 | 95 | 13 | 56 |
| 2 Kirkby Thore Rangers | 20 | 12 | 4 | 4 | 42 | 29 | 40 |
| 3 Kendal Utd Reserves | 20 | 12 | 1 | 7 | 56 | 46 | 37 |
| 4 Endmoor KGR Reserves | 20 | 10 | 1 | 9 | 52 | 68 | 31 |
| 5 Greystoke | 20 | 9 | 1 | 10 | 64 | 58 | 28 |
| 6 Coniston | 20 | 8 | 3 | 9 | 50 | 54 | 27 |
| 7 Wetheriggs Utd 'A' | 20 | 7 | 1 | 12 | 37 | 55 | 22 |
| 8 Braithwaite | 20 | 6 | 2 | 12 | 39 | 56 | 20 |
| 9 Burneside Reserves | 20 | 5 | 4 | 11 | 41 | 59 | 19 |
| 10 Windermere SC Reserves | 20 | 5 | 3 | 12 | 26 | 57 | 18 |
| 11 Kendal Celtic Reserves (-3pts) | 20 | 5 | 4 | 11 | 49 | 56 | 16 |

## Division Four

| | P | W | D | L | F | A | Pts |
|---|---|---|---|---|---|---|---|
| 1 Greystoke Reserves | 18 | 12 | 2 | 4 | 50 | 23 | 38 |
| 2 Esthwaite Vale | 18 | 11 | 3 | 4 | 65 | 33 | 36 |
| 3 Dent | 18 | 11 | 2 | 5 | 58 | 34 | 35 |
| 4 Carvetii Utd Reserves | 18 | 10 | 1 | 7 | 39 | 37 | 31 |
| 5 Ibis Res | 18 | 8 | 2 | 8 | 41 | 47 | 26 |
| 6 Penrith Academy | 18 | 8 | 0 | 10 | 33 | 42 | 24 |
| 7 Lunesdale Utd Reserves | 18 | 6 | 2 | 10 | 49 | 52 | 20 |
| 8 Penrith Saints | 18 | 6 | 2 | 10 | 46 | 58 | 20 |
| 9 Ullswater Utd | 18 | 6 | 0 | 12 | 26 | 54 | 18 |
| 10 Burneside 'A' | 18 | 3 | 4 | 11 | 30 | 57 | 13 |

## WIGAN & DISTRICT AMATEUR LEAGUE

### Premier Division

| | P | W | D | L | F | A | Pts |
|---|---|---|---|---|---|---|---|
| 1 Winstanley St.Aidans | 24 | 15 | 6 | 3 | 85 | 27 | 51 |
| 2 Bickerstaffe | 24 | 16 | 1 | 7 | 57 | 35 | 49 |
| 3 Hindley Town (-1pt) | 24 | 15 | 2 | 7 | 59 | 34 | 46 |
| 4 Standish St.Wilfrid's | 24 | 14 | 2 | 8 | 61 | 38 | 44 |
| 5 Pemberton | 24 | 12 | 3 | 9 | 61 | 37 | 39 |
| 6 Newburgh Harrock United | 24 | 11 | 6 | 7 | 43 | 44 | 39 |
| 7 Digmoor | 24 | 10 | 5 | 9 | 52 | 56 | 35 |
| 8 Leigh Rangers | 24 | 10 | 4 | 10 | 45 | 43 | 34 |
| 9 Shevington | 24 | 8 | 8 | 8 | 27 | 39 | 32 |
| 10 AFC Scholes | 24 | 8 | 2 | 14 | 42 | 65 | 26 |
| 11 Ince Central | 24 | 6 | 3 | 15 | 22 | 68 | 21 |
| 12 Atherton Royal (-1pt) | 24 | 4 | 5 | 15 | 29 | 63 | 16 |
| 13 Gidlow Athletic (-2pts) | 24 | 2 | 3 | 19 | 20 | 54 | 7 |

## LEAGUE TABLES

### Division One

| | | P | W | D | L | F | A | Pts |
|---|---|---|---|---|---|---|---|---|
| 1 | Bel Air | 24 | 17 | 3 | 4 | 89 | 41 | 54 |
| 2 | Leigh Phoenix | 24 | 15 | 6 | 3 | 91 | 54 | 51 |
| 3 | Winstanley St.Aidans Res | 24 | 15 | 3 | 6 | 62 | 45 | 48 |
| 4 | Aspull | 24 | 13 | 5 | 6 | 60 | 51 | 44 |
| 5 | Ince FC | 24 | 13 | 3 | 8 | 57 | 46 | 42 |
| 6 | St.Judes | 24 | 11 | 4 | 9 | 64 | 41 | 37 |
| 7 | Leigh Legion | 24 | 10 | 3 | 11 | 49 | 50 | 33 |
| 8 | Foundry | 24 | 10 | 3 | 11 | 54 | 71 | 33 |
| 9 | Wigan Rovers | 24 | 8 | 4 | 12 | 43 | 56 | 28 |
| 10 | AFC Tyldesley | 24 | 8 | 3 | 13 | 46 | 58 | 27 |
| 11 | Standish St.Wilfrid's Res | 24 | 7 | 2 | 15 | 49 | 63 | 23 |
| 12 | Goose Green United | 24 | 4 | 3 | 17 | 39 | 90 | 15 |
| 13 | Ormskirk | 24 | 3 | 2 | 19 | 47 | 84 | 11 |

### Division Two

| | | P | W | D | L | F | A | Pts |
|---|---|---|---|---|---|---|---|---|
| 1 | Bickerstaffe Res | 24 | 15 | 7 | 2 | 74 | 27 | 52 |
| 2 | Boars Head | 24 | 15 | 5 | 4 | 57 | 37 | 50 |
| 3 | UpHolland | 24 | 15 | 4 | 5 | 81 | 56 | 49 |
| 4 | Digmoor Reserves | 24 | 15 | 1 | 8 | 66 | 46 | 46 |
| 5 | Lowton Rams (-3pts) | 24 | 11 | 6 | 7 | 67 | 46 | 36 |
| 6 | Punchbowl | 24 | 11 | 3 | 10 | 67 | 55 | 36 |
| 7 | Pemberton Reserves | 24 | 10 | 4 | 10 | 47 | 49 | 34 |
| 8 | Leigh Rangers Reserves | 24 | 9 | 6 | 9 | 46 | 49 | 33 |
| 9 | Foundry Reserves | 24 | 8 | 6 | 10 | 52 | 58 | 30 |
| 10 | A H Leisure (-2pts) | 24 | 8 | 3 | 13 | 48 | 57 | 25 |
| 11 | Hindley Town Reserves | 24 | 5 | 4 | 15 | 36 | 65 | 19 |
| 12 | Wigan Rovers Reserves | 24 | 5 | 0 | 19 | 34 | 89 | 15 |
| 13 | Cart and Horses | 24 | 3 | 3 | 18 | 38 | 79 | 12 |

### Division Three

| | | P | W | D | L | F | A | Pts |
|---|---|---|---|---|---|---|---|---|
| 1 | Ashton Villa | 22 | 19 | 2 | 1 | 127 | 33 | 59 |
| 2 | Black Bull | 22 | 17 | 1 | 4 | 97 | 38 | 52 |
| 3 | Ince Central Reserves | 22 | 13 | 2 | 7 | 58 | 52 | 41 |
| 4 | Atherton George | 22 | 12 | 3 | 7 | 61 | 37 | 39 |
| 5 | Winstanley Warriors | 22 | 11 | 5 | 6 | 57 | 44 | 38 |
| 6 | Gidlow Athletic Reserves | 22 | 9 | 3 | 10 | 68 | 72 | 30 |
| 7 | Farnworth Town | 22 | 7 | 5 | 10 | 50 | 56 | 26 |
| 8 | Sporting Leigh | 22 | 7 | 5 | 10 | 43 | 70 | 26 |
| 9 | Billinge Community | 22 | 7 | 4 | 11 | 40 | 71 | 25 |
| 10 | AFC Waterside | 22 | 6 | 4 | 12 | 51 | 54 | 22 |
| 11 | Hurlston Hall | 22 | 4 | 4 | 14 | 60 | 94 | 16 |
| 12 | Landgate Springs | 22 | 0 | 2 | 20 | 22 | 113 | 2 |

## WIMBLEDON & DISTRICT LEAGUE

### Premier Division

| | | P | W | D | L | F | A | Pts |
|---|---|---|---|---|---|---|---|---|
| 1 | Peckham United | 22 | 17 | 2 | 3 | 65 | 25 | 53 |
| 2 | Brentnal | 22 | 15 | 2 | 5 | 51 | 32 | 47 |
| 3 | UCC Diaspora 1st XI | 22 | 15 | 1 | 6 | 51 | 28 | 46 |
| 4 | Union | 22 | 14 | 1 | 7 | 50 | 43 | 43 |
| 5 | Sporting Duet | 22 | 13 | 1 | 8 | 66 | 48 | 40 |
| 6 | PWCA Wimbledon | 22 | 10 | 2 | 10 | 44 | 51 | 32 |
| 7 | Barn Elms United | 22 | 9 | 4 | 9 | 53 | 51 | 31 |
| 8 | AFC Battersea | 22 | 7 | 4 | 11 | 40 | 41 | 25 |
| 9 | Partizan Wandsworth | 22 | 7 | 2 | 13 | 42 | 53 | 23 |
| 10 | AFC Cubo 2nd XI | 22 | 5 | 6 | 11 | 27 | 47 | 21 |
| 11 | Goldfingers | 22 | 5 | 4 | 13 | 26 | 41 | 19 |
| 12 | Claremont | 22 | 0 | 1 | 21 | 15 | 70 | 1 |

### Division One

| | | P | W | D | L | F | A | Pts |
|---|---|---|---|---|---|---|---|---|
| 1 | Brentside | 20 | 12 | 6 | 2 | 46 | 22 | 42 |
| 2 | Durban United | 20 | 11 | 3 | 6 | 41 | 26 | 36 |
| 3 | South Wimbledon Dazzlers | 20 | 10 | 5 | 5 | 51 | 34 | 35 |
| 4 | Northern Town | 20 | 9 | 4 | 7 | 27 | 27 | 31 |
| 5 | Mint Green Army Veterans | 20 | 9 | 3 | 8 | 38 | 35 | 30 |
| 6 | Croydon Red Star | 20 | 8 | 5 | 7 | 46 | 46 | 29 |
| 7 | Kiwi | 20 | 8 | 4 | 8 | 40 | 31 | 28 |
| 8 | Wadham College Old Boys | 20 | 9 | 1 | 10 | 36 | 45 | 28 |
| 9 | London XI | 20 | 7 | 4 | 9 | 50 | 57 | 25 |
| 10 | AFC Cubo 3rd XI | 20 | 4 | 3 | 13 | 27 | 46 | 15 |
| 11 | Sporting Duet Reserves | 20 | 3 | 2 | 15 | 28 | 61 | 11 |

### Division Two

| | | P | W | D | L | F | A | Pts |
|---|---|---|---|---|---|---|---|---|
| 1 | Merchant | 16 | 12 | 4 | 0 | 49 | 16 | 40 |
| 2 | Imperial College Old Boys Reserves | 16 | 12 | 2 | 2 | 58 | 27 | 38 |
| 3 | Inter Old Boys | 16 | 9 | 4 | 3 | 39 | 19 | 31 |
| 4 | Boca Seniors | 16 | 9 | 3 | 4 | 40 | 23 | 30 |
| 5 | Merton Orient | 16 | 4 | 4 | 8 | 16 | 35 | 16 |
| 6 | Balham Rangers | 16 | 4 | 2 | 10 | 23 | 45 | 14 |
| 7 | London Lionhearts | 16 | 4 | 1 | 11 | 14 | 36 | 13 |
| 8 | Rivelino City | 16 | 3 | 2 | 11 | 20 | 38 | 11 |
| 9 | South East London 2nd XI | 16 | 2 | 4 | 10 | 18 | 38 | 10 |

### Division Three

| | | P | W | D | L | F | A | Pts |
|---|---|---|---|---|---|---|---|---|
| 1 | UCC Diaspora 2nd XI | 14 | 11 | 0 | 3 | 36 | 19 | 33 |
| 2 | FC Porto of London | 14 | 9 | 1 | 4 | 40 | 22 | 28 |
| 3 | South London Football Network FC | 14 | 8 | 0 | 6 | 37 | 29 | 24 |
| 4 | Ocean | 14 | 7 | 2 | 5 | 46 | 25 | 23 |
| 5 | Putney Ferrets | 14 | 7 | 2 | 5 | 16 | 19 | 23 |
| 6 | FC Lokomotiv Lavender | 14 | 6 | 1 | 7 | 34 | 28 | 19 |
| 7 | Eagles 2012 | 14 | 3 | 1 | 10 | 22 | 45 | 10 |
| 8 | Sporting Duet Lycee | 14 | 0 | 3 | 11 | 10 | 54 | |

## WITNEY & DISTRICT LEAGUE

### Premier Divison

| | P | W | D | L | F | A | Pts |
|---|---|---|---|---|---|---|---|
| 1 Hailey, | 20 | 15 | 1 | 4 | 58 | 23 | 46 |
| 2 Hanborough, | 20 | 13 | 1 | 6 | 41 | 22 | 40 |
| 3 Northleigh A, | 20 | 11 | 5 | 4 | 48 | 34 | 38 |
| 4 Ducklington, | 20 | 10 | 4 | 6 | 48 | 29 | 34 |
| 5 Witney Royals, | 20 | 10 | 4 | 6 | 47 | 29 | 34 |
| 6 Spartan Rangers, | 20 | 7 | 7 | 6 | 36 | 38 | 28 |
| 7 Charlbury Town, | 20 | 7 | 4 | 9 | 38 | 40 | 25 |
| 8 Carterton FC A, | 20 | 7 | 3 | 10 | 42 | 37 | 24 |
| 9 Combe, | 20 | 5 | 3 | 12 | 20 | 45 | 18 |
| 10 FC Chequers, | 20 | 3 | 5 | 12 | 20 | 47 | 14 |
| 11 Kingham All Blacks, | 20 | 1 | 5 | 14 | 15 | 69 | 8 |

### Division One

| | P | W | D | L | F | A | Pts |
|---|---|---|---|---|---|---|---|
| 1 West Witney, | 22 | 20 | 1 | 1 | 104 | 26 | 61 |
| 2 Chipping Norton Town | 22 | 14 | 5 | 3 | 73 | 33 | 47 |
| 3 Brize Norton, | 22 | 13 | 3 | 6 | 55 | 29 | 42 |
| 4 Minster Lovell, | 22 | 11 | 6 | 5 | 46 | 41 | 39 |
| 5 Aston FC, | 22 | 8 | 6 | 8 | 40 | 46 | 30 |
| 6 Stanton Harcourt, | 22 | 7 | 5 | 10 | 40 | 51 | 26 |
| 7 AC Finstock, | 22 | 6 | 6 | 10 | 46 | 61 | 24 |
| 8 FC Nomads, | 22 | 6 | 5 | 11 | 30 | 48 | 23 |
| 9 Hanborough Reserves, | 22 | 5 | 7 | 10 | 31 | 48 | 22 |
| 10 FC Mills, | 22 | 4 | 9 | 9 | 32 | 49 | 21 |
| 11 Ducklington Reserves, | 22 | 4 | 5 | 13 | 20 | 50 | 17 |
| 12 Witney Royals Reserves, | 22 | 2 | 6 | 14 | 38 | 73 | 12 |

### Division Two

| | P | W | D | L | F | A | Pts |
|---|---|---|---|---|---|---|---|
| 1 Freeland FC A | 20 | 15 | 0 | 5 | 70 | 30 | 45 |
| 2 Ducklington A | 20 | 14 | 2 | 4 | 67 | 40 | 44 |
| 3 Hailey Reserves | 20 | 12 | 2 | 6 | 48 | 33 | 38 |
| 4 FC Chequers Reserves | 20 | 10 | 5 | 5 | 67 | 31 | 35 |
| 5 Milton | 20 | 10 | 0 | 10 | 35 | 43 | 30 |
| 6 Middle Barton | 20 | 8 | 4 | 8 | 51 | 41 | 28 |
| 7 Bampton Town | 20 | 7 | 5 | 8 | 46 | 44 | 26 |
| 8 Witney Wanderers | 20 | 7 | 3 | 10 | 41 | 43 | 24 |
| 9 Charlbury Town Reserves | 20 | 6 | 2 | 12 | 39 | 77 | 20 |
| 10 Brize Norton Reserves | 20 | 5 | 3 | 12 | 39 | 72 | 18 |
| 11 Wootton Sports | 20 | 2 | 2 | 16 | 16 | 65 | 8 |

### Division Three

| | P | W | D | L | F | A | Pts |
|---|---|---|---|---|---|---|---|
| 1 Carterton Pumas | 24 | 20 | 2 | 2 | 82 | 19 | 62 |
| 2 Eynsham Sports and Social Club | 24 | 17 | 3 | 4 | 90 | 33 | 54 |
| 3 North Leigh B | 24 | 16 | 2 | 6 | 64 | 29 | 50 |
| 4 West Witney Reserves | 24 | 14 | 5 | 5 | 64 | 39 | 47 |
| 5 AFC Marlborough | 24 | 12 | 5 | 7 | 67 | 40 | 41 |
| 6 Spartan Rangers Reserves | 24 | 10 | 6 | 8 | 58 | 55 | 36 |
| 7 FC Hollybush | 24 | 11 | 2 | 11 | 44 | 51 | 35 |
| 8 Chipping Norton Town Reserves | 24 | 10 | 3 | 11 | 57 | 57 | 33 |
| 9 Minster Lovell Reserves | 24 | 4 | 9 | 11 | 39 | 64 | 21 |
| 10 Aston FC Reserves | 24 | 6 | 2 | 16 | 24 | 78 | 20 |
| 11 Tackley | 24 | 5 | 4 | 15 | 26 | 53 | 19 |
| 12 Kingham All Blacks Reserves | 24 | 2 | 7 | 15 | 34 | 81 | 13 |
| 13 Witney Royals A | 24 | 2 | 4 | 18 | 23 | 73 | 10 |

### Division Four

| | P | W | D | L | F | A | Pts |
|---|---|---|---|---|---|---|---|
| 1 Carterton Rangers | 20 | 16 | 4 | 0 | 101 | 26 | 52 |
| 2 Carterton FC B | 20 | 15 | 4 | 1 | 72 | 18 | 49 |
| 3 Freeland FC B | 20 | 14 | 2 | 4 | 80 | 35 | 44 |
| 4 Corinthians | 20 | 12 | 3 | 5 | 70 | 40 | 39 |
| 5 FC Mills Reserves (-3pts) | 20 | 11 | 1 | 8 | 62 | 58 | 31 |
| 6 Ducklington B | 20 | 9 | 1 | 10 | 52 | 64 | 28 |
| 7 Graystones | 20 | 8 | 3 | 9 | 51 | 58 | 27 |
| 8 Wychwood Foresters FC | 20 | 6 | 2 | 12 | 37 | 54 | 20 |
| 9 Spartan Rangers A | 20 | 3 | 3 | 14 | 32 | 64 | 12 |
| 10 Combe Reserves | 20 | 2 | 2 | 16 | 24 | 52 | 8 |
| 11 Eynsham S & S C Reserves | 20 | 1 | 1 | 18 | 20 | 132 | 4 |

## WORCESTER & DISTRICT LEAGUE

### Division One

| | P | W | D | L | F | A | Pts |
|---|---|---|---|---|---|---|---|
| 1 Worcester Raiders | 18 | 14 | 0 | 4 | 91 | 45 | 42 |
| 2 Powick FC | 18 | 11 | 2 | 5 | 68 | 41 | 35 |
| 3 Arrow 2000 | 18 | 11 | 2 | 5 | 71 | 46 | 35 |
| 4 Hallow | 18 | 8 | 4 | 6 | 71 | 49 | 28 |
| 5 Newtown Sports | 18 | 6 | 3 | 9 | 38 | 51 | 21 |
| 6 University of Worcester | 18 | 3 | 3 | 12 | 41 | 70 | 12 |
| 7 The Red Lion FC | 18 | 2 | 2 | 14 | 42 | 120 | 8 |

### Division Two

| | P | W | D | L | F | A | Pts |
|---|---|---|---|---|---|---|---|
| 1 Worcester Anchors | 18 | 11 | 3 | 4 | 82 | 50 | 36 |
| 2 Malvern Hills | 18 | 10 | 3 | 5 | 49 | 45 | 33 |
| 3 Katy O'Ryans | 18 | 10 | 1 | 7 | 61 | 46 | 31 |
| 4 Sylla F.C. | 18 | 9 | 3 | 6 | 56 | 55 | 30 |
| 5 West Malvern 2012 | 18 | 8 | 1 | 9 | 49 | 48 | 25 |
| 6 Foregate | 18 | 7 | 0 | 11 | 49 | 63 | 21 |
| 7 Leigh & Bransford Badgers | 18 | 2 | 1 | 15 | 30 | 69 | 7 |

## WORTHING & DISTRICT LEAGUE

### Premier Division

| | P | W | D | L | F | A | Pts |
|---|---|---|---|---|---|---|---|
| 1 L&S Athletic | 18 | 15 | 2 | 1 | 79 | 30 | 47 |
| 2 KSG Chaplain Ahtletic | 18 | 13 | 3 | 2 | 78 | 27 | 42 |
| 3 Worthing Leisure | 18 | 13 | 1 | 4 | 62 | 22 | 40 |
| 4 Worthing BCOB | 18 | 12 | 1 | 5 | 69 | 41 | 37 |
| 5 Sompting | 18 | 11 | 2 | 5 | 72 | 30 | 35 |
| 6 Broadwater Athletic | 18 | 7 | 0 | 11 | 37 | 52 | 21 |
| 7 Worthing Dynamos | 18 | 6 | 1 | 11 | 34 | 64 | 19 |
| 8 AFC Boundstone | 18 | 4 | 2 | 12 | 44 | 69 | 14 |
| 9 Northbrook | 18 | 2 | 0 | 16 | 17 | 82 | 6 |
| 10 Real Rustington | 18 | 1 | 0 | 17 | 17 | 92 | 3 |

# LEAGUE TABLES

## Division One

| | | P | W | D | L | F | A | Pts |
|---|---|---|---|---|---|---|---|---|
| 1 | Goring | 22 | 18 | 4 | 0 | 95 | 23 | 58 |
| 2 | Worthing Town | 22 | 15 | 5 | 2 | 78 | 34 | 50 |
| 3 | KSG Chaplain Ahtletic Reserves | 22 | 15 | 1 | 6 | 80 | 55 | 46 |
| 4 | Worthing Leisure Res | 22 | 14 | 2 | 6 | 60 | 43 | 44 |
| 5 | AFC Broadwater | 22 | 11 | 2 | 9 | 63 | 46 | 35 |
| 6 | AFC Forest | 22 | 10 | 1 | 11 | 55 | 58 | 31 |
| 7 | George & Dragon | 22 | 8 | 3 | 11 | 56 | 59 | 27 |
| 8 | Angmering | 22 | 7 | 2 | 13 | 48 | 73 | 23 |
| 9 | Del United | 22 | 7 | 0 | 15 | 47 | 84 | 21 |
| 10 | Worthing Albion | 22 | 6 | 2 | 14 | 42 | 79 | 20 |
| 11 | Worthing BCOB Reserves | 22 | 5 | 2 | 15 | 43 | 67 | 17 |
| 12 | Adur Athletic | 22 | 4 | 0 | 18 | 40 | 86 | 12 |

## Division Two

| | | P | W | D | L | F | A | Pts |
|---|---|---|---|---|---|---|---|---|
| 1 | Sompting Reserves | 18 | 12 | 2 | 4 | 75 | 23 | 38 |
| 2 | St Marys | 18 | 11 | 4 | 3 | 54 | 26 | 37 |
| 3 | Maybridge | 18 | 11 | 4 | 3 | 42 | 25 | 37 |
| 4 | Goring Res | 18 | 10 | 2 | 6 | 64 | 45 | 32 |
| 5 | Northbrook Reserves | 18 | 8 | 4 | 6 | 39 | 41 | 28 |
| 6 | West Tarring | 18 | 6 | 3 | 9 | 38 | 44 | 21 |
| 7 | "GSK Sports ""B""" | 18 | 6 | 3 | 9 | 46 | 55 | 21 |
| 8 | Worthing Town Res | 18 | 4 | 2 | 12 | 35 | 64 | 14 |
| 9 | MBS United | 18 | 3 | 5 | 10 | 21 | 50 | 14 |
| 10 | Goring St Theresa's | 18 | 3 | 3 | 12 | 40 | 81 | 12 |

## WYCOMBE & DISTRICT LEAGUE

### Senior Division

| | | P | W | D | L | F | A | Pts |
|---|---|---|---|---|---|---|---|---|
| 1 | AFC Spartans | 14 | 11 | 1 | 2 | 39 | 19 | 34 |
| 2 | Hambleden | 14 | 9 | 2 | 3 | 30 | 18 | 29 |
| 3 | Prestwood | 14 | 8 | 3 | 3 | 41 | 15 | 27 |
| 4 | Walters Leisure | 14 | 7 | 2 | 5 | 36 | 17 | 23 |
| 5 | Great Missenden | 14 | 5 | 2 | 7 | 31 | 33 | 17 |
| 6 | Lane End | 14 | 5 | 1 | 8 | 27 | 31 | 16 |
| 7 | Hazlemere Sports | 14 | 4 | 2 | 8 | 22 | 27 | 14 |
| 8 | Stokenchurch | 14 | 0 | 1 | 13 | 3 | 69 | 1 |

### Premier Division

| | | P | W | D | L | F | A | Pts |
|---|---|---|---|---|---|---|---|---|
| 1 | FC Titans | 16 | 14 | 0 | 2 | 63 | 14 | 42 |
| 2 | Penn & Tylers Green 'A' | 16 | 12 | 2 | 2 | 58 | 27 | 38 |
| 3 | AFC Amersham | 16 | 9 | 1 | 6 | 41 | 36 | 28 |
| 4 | Hazlemere Sports Reserves | 16 | 8 | 2 | 6 | 31 | 25 | 26 |
| 5 | Wycombe Athletic | 16 | 8 | 1 | 7 | 40 | 46 | 25 |
| 6 | Winchmore Hill | 16 | 5 | 1 | 10 | 35 | 38 | 16 |
| 7 | Chinnor 'A' | 16 | 4 | 2 | 10 | 22 | 51 | 14 |
| 8 | Wizards | 16 | 3 | 3 | 10 | 24 | 36 | 12 |
| 9 | Walters Leisure Reserves | 16 | 2 | 2 | 12 | 20 | 61 | 8 |

### Division One

| | | P | W | D | L | F | A | Pts |
|---|---|---|---|---|---|---|---|---|
| 1 | Winchmore Hill Reserves | 16 | 12 | 2 | 2 | 63 | 33 | 38 |
| 2 | Lane End Reserves | 16 | 11 | 1 | 4 | 60 | 29 | 34 |
| 3 | Prestwood Reserves | 16 | 11 | 0 | 5 | 61 | 38 | 33 |
| 4 | APMG Oakridge | 16 | 8 | 2 | 6 | 46 | 28 | 26 |
| 5 | FC Leisure | 16 | 7 | 4 | 5 | 47 | 49 | 25 |
| 6 | Hambleden Reserves | 16 | 7 | 0 | 9 | 47 | 46 | 21 |
| 7 | Hazlemere Sports 'A' | 16 | 4 | 2 | 10 | 26 | 52 | 14 |
| 8 | Wycombe Athletic Reserves | 16 | 4 | 1 | 11 | 24 | 62 | 13 |
| 9 | Chinnor 'B' | 16 | 1 | 2 | 13 | 28 | 65 | 5 |

## YEOVIL & DISTRICT LEAGUE

### Premier Division

| | | P | W | D | L | F | A | Pts |
|---|---|---|---|---|---|---|---|---|
| 1 | Waggy Athletic | 22 | 17 | 4 | 1 | 84 | 25 | 55 |
| 2 | Victoria Sports | 22 | 17 | 2 | 3 | 56 | 23 | 53 |
| 3 | Ilchester (-3pts) | 22 | 15 | 1 | 6 | 69 | 30 | 43 |
| 4 | Aller Park Rangers | 22 | 12 | 4 | 6 | 67 | 52 | 40 |
| 5 | Normalair | 22 | 11 | 1 | 10 | 44 | 48 | 34 |
| 6 | Somerton Sports | 22 | 10 | 1 | 11 | 57 | 50 | 31 |
| 7 | Tor FC (-5pts) | 22 | 10 | 3 | 9 | 47 | 33 | 28 |
| 8 | Baltonsborough | 22 | 8 | 1 | 13 | 52 | 70 | 25 |
| 9 | Henstridge (-1pt) | 22 | 6 | 2 | 14 | 31 | 62 | 19 |
| 10 | Odcombe | 22 | 5 | 2 | 15 | 33 | 72 | 17 |
| 11 | Barwick & Stoford (-4pts) | 22 | 6 | 2 | 14 | 52 | 57 | 16 |
| 12 | Templecombe Rovers (-2pt) | 22 | 3 | 1 | 18 | 30 | 100 | 8 |

### Division One

| | | P | W | D | L | F | A | Pts |
|---|---|---|---|---|---|---|---|---|
| 1 | Brhoden | 22 | 22 | 0 | 0 | 83 | 14 | 66 |
| 2 | Pen Mill | 22 | 15 | 2 | 5 | 67 | 43 | 47 |
| 3 | Milborne Port | 22 | 14 | 1 | 7 | 74 | 37 | 43 |
| 4 | AFC Huish | 22 | 14 | 1 | 7 | 65 | 38 | 43 |
| 5 | Abbey Moor | 22 | 9 | 4 | 9 | 61 | 55 | 31 |
| 6 | Martock United | 22 | 7 | 5 | 10 | 45 | 64 | 26 |
| 7 | Normalair Reserves (-1pt) | 22 | 8 | 1 | 13 | 48 | 54 | 24 |
| 8 | Stoke (--3pts) | 22 | 8 | 3 | 11 | 34 | 55 | 24 |
| 9 | Butleigh Dynamos | 22 | 6 | 3 | 13 | 41 | 76 | 21 |
| 10 | Castle Cary (-7pts) | 22 | 6 | 5 | 11 | 27 | 40 | 16 |
| 11 | Ilchester Reserves (-3pts) | 22 | 6 | 1 | 15 | 33 | 57 | 16 |
| 12 | AFC Wessex | 22 | 2 | 4 | 16 | 32 | 77 | 10 |

### Division Two

| | | P | W | D | L | F | A | Pts |
|---|---|---|---|---|---|---|---|---|
| 1 | Bradford Abbas | 22 | 15 | 3 | 4 | 59 | 34 | 48 |
| 2 | FC Barton Leverkusen | 22 | 12 | 4 | 6 | 52 | 44 | 40 |
| 3 | Mudford | 22 | 12 | 3 | 7 | 58 | 41 | 39 |
| 4 | Milborne Port Reserves | 22 | 12 | 3 | 7 | 51 | 38 | 39 |
| 5 | Waggy Athletic | 22 | 11 | 4 | 7 | 73 | 55 | 37 |
| 6 | Wincanton Town (-3pts) | 22 | 11 | 3 | 8 | 72 | 43 | 33 |
| 7 | Montacute (-3pts) | 22 | 9 | 6 | 7 | 56 | 43 | 30 |
| 8 | Somerton Sports Reserves | 22 | 9 | 1 | 12 | 64 | 68 | 28 |
| 9 | Zeals Development | 22 | 7 | 5 | 10 | 61 | 64 | 26 |
| 10 | Barwick & Stoford Reserves | 22 | 7 | 3 | 12 | 41 | 64 | 24 |
| 11 | Pen Mill Reserves (-1pt) | 22 | 3 | 5 | 14 | 41 | 95 | 13 |
| 12 | Bruton United | 22 | 3 | 2 | 17 | 32 | 71 | 11 |

### Division Three

| | | P | W | D | L | F | A | Pts |
|---|---|---|---|---|---|---|---|---|
| 1 | East Coker | 24 | 16 | 3 | 5 | 90 | 38 | 51 |
| 2 | Manor Athletic | 24 | 15 | 4 | 5 | 59 | 32 | 49 |
| 3 | AFC Huish Reserves | 24 | 15 | 4 | 5 | 67 | 45 | 49 |
| 4 | Aller Park Rangers Reserves (-1pt) | 24 | 12 | 4 | 8 | 85 | 57 | 39 |
| 5 | Milborne Port A | 24 | 11 | 6 | 7 | 59 | 44 | 39 |
| 6 | Martock United Reserves | 24 | 12 | 3 | 9 | 57 | 51 | 39 |
| 7 | Stoke Reserves | 24 | 11 | 4 | 9 | 70 | 57 | 37 |
| 8 | AFC Camel | 24 | 9 | 4 | 11 | 59 | 72 | 31 |
| 9 | Victoria Sports Reserves | 24 | 9 | 2 | 13 | 43 | 49 | 29 |
| 10 | Somerton Sports A (-7pts) | 24 | 8 | 5 | 11 | 47 | 59 | 22 |
| 11 | Tor Sports (-1pt) | 24 | 6 | 4 | 14 | 60 | 75 | 21 |
| 12 | Odcombe Reserves | 24 | 5 | 4 | 15 | 41 | 84 | 19 |
| 13 | Baltonsborough Res. (-1pt) | 24 | 1 | 5 | 18 | 39 | 113 | 7 |

# NORTHERN IRISH TABLES 2012-13

## IRELAND FOOTBALL ASSOCIATION

### Premiership

| | P | W | D | L | F | A | Pts |
|---|---|---|---|---|---|---|---|
| Cliftonville | 38 | 29 | 4 | 5 | 95 | 38 | 91 |
| Crusaders | 38 | 26 | 5 | 7 | 82 | 41 | 83 |
| Linfield | 38 | 17 | 11 | 10 | 69 | 48 | 62 |
| Glentoran | 38 | 15 | 12 | 11 | 63 | 44 | 57 |
| Portadown | 38 | 15 | 10 | 13 | 55 | 55 | 55 |
| Ballinamallard United | 38 | 15 | 8 | 15 | 49 | 43 | 53 |
| Coleraine | 38 | 13 | 14 | 11 | 50 | 57 | 53 |
| Ballymena United | 38 | 11 | 13 | 14 | 54 | 68 | 46 |
| Glenavon | 38 | 12 | 6 | 20 | 64 | 62 | 42 |
| Dungannon Swifts | 38 | 9 | 13 | 16 | 42 | 58 | 40 |
| Donegal Celtic | 38 | 6 | 9 | 23 | 32 | 80 | 27 |
| Lisburn Distillery | 38 | 4 | 7 | 27 | 29 | 90 | 19 |

### Championship One

| | P | W | D | L | F | A | Pts |
|---|---|---|---|---|---|---|---|
| Ards | 24 | 18 | 5 | 1 | 56 | 19 | 59 |
| Warrenpoint Town | 24 | 15 | 5 | 4 | 46 | 23 | 50 |
| Institute | 24 | 14 | 5 | 5 | 50 | 23 | 47 |
| Dundela | 24 | 13 | 4 | 7 | 62 | 51 | 43 |
| Carrick Rangers | 24 | 11 | 6 | 7 | 48 | 32 | 39 |
| HW Welders | 24 | 10 | 4 | 10 | 37 | 35 | 34 |
| Dergview | 24 | 7 | 6 | 11 | 27 | 39 | 27 |
| Larne | 24 | 5 | 9 | 10 | 24 | 40 | 24 |
| Coagh United | 24 | 6 | 5 | 13 | 35 | 51 | 23 |
| Bangor | 24 | 6 | 5 | 13 | 23 | 42 | 23 |
| Loughgall | 24 | 6 | 5 | 13 | 27 | 48 | 23 |
| Limavady United | 24 | 5 | 6 | 13 | 34 | 49 | 21 |
| Tobermore United | 24 | 6 | 3 | 15 | 38 | 55 | 21 |

### Championship Two

| | P | W | D | L | F | A | Pts |
|---|---|---|---|---|---|---|---|
| Knockbreda | 30 | 25 | 2 | 3 | 106 | 25 | 77 |
| Ballyclare Comrades | 30 | 23 | 2 | 5 | 77 | 28 | 71 |
| Armagh City | 30 | 21 | 3 | 6 | 81 | 34 | 66 |
| Lurgan Celtic | 30 | 20 | 3 | 7 | 71 | 43 | 63 |
| Glebe Rangers | 30 | 15 | 7 | 8 | 58 | 41 | 52 |
| Wakehurst | 30 | 16 | 4 | 10 | 61 | 50 | 52 |
| Queens University | 30 | 13 | 6 | 11 | 65 | 43 | 45 |
| PSNI | 30 | 14 | 1 | 15 | 60 | 48 | 43 |
| Banbridge Town | 30 | 11 | 7 | 12 | 57 | 58 | 40 |
| Ballymoney United | 30 | 10 | 7 | 13 | 53 | 67 | 37 |
| Annagh United | 30 | 9 | 7 | 14 | 39 | 53 | 34 |
| Moyola Park | 30 | 6 | 10 | 14 | 35 | 51 | 28 |
| Portstewart | 30 | 5 | 7 | 18 | 37 | 70 | 22 |
| Sports & Leisure Swifts | 30 | 5 | 5 | 20 | 41 | 101 | 20 |
| Killymoon Rangers | 30 | 4 | 7 | 19 | 38 | 85 | 19 |
| Chimney Corner | 30 | 3 | 2 | 25 | 26 | 108 | 11 |

## BALLYMENA & PROVINCIAL LEAGUE

### Intermediate Division

| | | P | W | D | L | F | A | Pts |
|---|---|---|---|---|---|---|---|---|
| 1 | Newtowne FC | 18 | 16 | 2 | 0 | 60 | 13 | 50 |
| 2 | Brantwood FC | 18 | 12 | 2 | 4 | 44 | 23 | 38 |
| 3 | Desertmartin | 18 | 11 | 4 | 3 | 40 | 21 | 37 |
| 4 | Magherafelt Sky Blues | 18 | 9 | 3 | 6 | 38 | 30 | 30 |
| 5 | Ballynure OB | 18 | 9 | 3 | 6 | 36 | 43 | 30 |
| 6 | Dunloy | 18 | 8 | 3 | 7 | 44 | 41 | 27 |
| 7 | Raceview | 18 | 5 | 3 | 10 | 34 | 42 | 18 |
| 8 | FC Ballynure | 18 | 3 | 2 | 13 | 25 | 56 | 11 |
| 9 | Carniny Amateurs | 18 | 2 | 2 | 14 | 25 | 50 | 8 |
| 10 | Clough Rangers Athletic | 18 | 0 | 6 | 12 | 26 | 53 | 6 |

### Junior Division One

| | | P | W | D | L | F | A | Pts |
|---|---|---|---|---|---|---|---|---|
| 1 | Ballyclare Comrades Res. | 20 | 16 | 2 | 2 | 77 | 14 | 50 |
| 2 | Tobermore Utd Reserves | 20 | 15 | 1 | 4 | 49 | 22 | 46 |
| 3 | Desertmartin Swifts | 20 | 10 | 5 | 5 | 38 | 31 | 35 |
| 4 | Antrim Rovers | 20 | 10 | 1 | 7 | 43 | 37 | 31 |
| 5 | Mallusk Athletic | 20 | 8 | 1 | 11 | 36 | 36 | 25 |
| 6 | Cookstown Olympic | 20 | 7 | 3 | 10 | 52 | 60 | 24 |
| 7 | Ballymoney Utd Reserves | 20 | 6 | 5 | 9 | 38 | 52 | 23 |
| 8 | 3rd Ballyclare OB | 20 | 6 | 2 | 12 | 28 | 53 | 20 |
| 9 | Magherafelt Sky Blue Res. | 20 | 5 | 4 | 11 | 41 | 56 | 19 |
| 10 | Killymoon Rangers Res. | 20 | 5 | 4 | 11 | 36 | 65 | 19 |
| 11 | Glebe Rangers Reserves | 20 | 4 | 5 | 11 | 33 | 56 | 17 |

Larne Olympic record expunged.

### Junior Division Two

| | | P | W | D | L | F | A | Pts |
|---|---|---|---|---|---|---|---|---|
| 1 | York Road Loughside 'A' | 24 | 18 | 2 | 4 | 127 | 22 | 56 |
| 2 | Woodlands | 24 | 15 | 2 | 7 | 67 | 40 | 47 |
| 3 | Chimney Corner Reserves | 24 | 14 | 4 | 6 | 66 | 42 | 46 |
| 4 | 1st Mossley YM | 24 | 11 | 9 | 4 | 60 | 45 | 42 |
| 5 | Carnmoney FC | 24 | 12 | 6 | 6 | 55 | 47 | 42 |
| 6 | Castle Star | 24 | 13 | 2 | 9 | 75 | 49 | 41 |
| 7 | Ballynure OB 'B' | 24 | 12 | 2 | 10 | 69 | 67 | 38 |
| 8 | Carniny Amateurs II | 24 | 9 | 7 | 8 | 53 | 78 | 34 |
| 9 | Ballyclare North End | 24 | 7 | 4 | 13 | 38 | 67 | 25 |
| 10 | Moyola Park Olympic | 24 | 7 | 3 | 14 | 46 | 72 | 24 |
| 11 | FC Larne | 24 | 4 | 8 | 12 | 37 | 55 | 20 |
| 12 | Wakehurst Strollers | 24 | 4 | 5 | 15 | 35 | 72 | 17 |
| 13 | Red Star | 24 | 0 | 6 | 18 | 25 | 97 | 6 |

## Junior Division Three

| | P | W | D | L | F | A | Pts |
|---|---|---|---|---|---|---|---|
| Rathcoole FC | 24 | 22 | 1 | 1 | 134 | 23 | 67 |
| Cookstown RBL | 24 | 20 | 1 | 3 | 78 | 32 | 61 |
| Ballysillan Swifts | 24 | 14 | 3 | 7 | 92 | 42 | 45 |
| FC Whiteabbey | 24 | 14 | 1 | 9 | 83 | 52 | 43 |
| Remo FC | 24 | 13 | 3 | 8 | 69 | 47 | 42 |
| Sport & Leisure Swifts Res | 24 | 14 | 0 | 10 | 72 | 57 | 42 |
| AFC Carrickfergus | 24 | 13 | 2 | 9 | 85 | 48 | 41 |
| FC Ballynure Reserves | 24 | 10 | 5 | 9 | 77 | 69 | 35 |
| 14th Newtownabbey | 24 | 5 | 4 | 15 | 47 | 89 | 19 |
| 10 Encore FC | 24 | 5 | 3 | 16 | 42 | 96 | 18 |
| 11 Carnlough Swifts | 24 | 5 | 2 | 17 | 34 | 105 | 17 |
| 12 1st Carrickfergus OB | 24 | 3 | 3 | 18 | 31 | 120 | 12 |
| 13 Carrickfergus YC | 24 | 3 | 2 | 19 | 35 | 99 | 11 |

York Road Loughside 'B' record expunged.

## MID ULSTER LEAGUE

### Intermediate A

| | P | W | D | L | F | A | Pts |
|---|---|---|---|---|---|---|---|
| Dollingstown | 22 | 18 | 2 | 2 | 74 | 22 | 56 |
| Tandragee Rovers | 22 | 17 | 0 | 5 | 70 | 27 | 51 |
| Camlough Rovers | 22 | 15 | 3 | 4 | 49 | 25 | 48 |
| Crewe United | 22 | 12 | 2 | 8 | 50 | 45 | 38 |
| Banbridge Rangers | 22 | 10 | 1 | 11 | 40 | 51 | 31 |
| Broomhill | 22 | 9 | 3 | 10 | 48 | 60 | 30 |
| Seapatrick | 22 | 7 | 4 | 11 | 39 | 51 | 25 |
| Fivemiletown United | 22 | 7 | 2 | 13 | 41 | 49 | 23 |
| Markethill Swifts | 22 | 6 | 5 | 11 | 37 | 61 | 23 |
| 10 Lower Maze | 22 | 6 | 4 | 12 | 56 | 59 | 22 |
| 11 Lisanally Rangers | 22 | 6 | 4 | 12 | 43 | 56 | 22 |
| 12 Blackers Mill | 22 | 2 | 4 | 16 | 26 | 67 | 10 |

### Intermediate B

| | P | W | D | L | F | A | Pts |
|---|---|---|---|---|---|---|---|
| Ballymacash Rangers | 24 | 19 | 2 | 3 | 91 | 28 | 59 |
| AFC Craigavon | 24 | 18 | 4 | 2 | 52 | 25 | 58 |
| Valley Rangers | 24 | 18 | 3 | 3 | 89 | 21 | 57 |
| Hanover | 24 | 14 | 4 | 6 | 71 | 43 | 46 |
| Moneyslane | 24 | 12 | 6 | 6 | 54 | 35 | 42 |
| Bourneview YM | 24 | 10 | 3 | 11 | 52 | 55 | 33 |
| Seagoe | 24 | 9 | 6 | 9 | 43 | 50 | 33 |
| Oxford Sunnyside | 24 | 8 | 5 | 11 | 39 | 50 | 29 |
| Richill | 24 | 8 | 3 | 13 | 41 | 61 | 27 |
| 10 Lurgan Town | 24 | 7 | 5 | 12 | 34 | 44 | 26 |
| 11 Laurelvale | 24 | 4 | 2 | 18 | 31 | 73 | 14 |
| 12 Broomhedge | 24 | 3 | 2 | 19 | 36 | 74 | 11 |
| 13 Banbridge AFC | 24 | 3 | 1 | 20 | 28 | 102 | 10 |

## Division One

| | | P | W | D | L | F | A | Pts |
|---|---|---|---|---|---|---|---|---|
| 1 | Coalisland Athletic | 22 | 17 | 3 | 2 | 60 | 19 | 54 |
| 2 | Silverwood United | 22 | 16 | 2 | 4 | 75 | 25 | 50 |
| 3 | Ambassadors | 22 | 15 | 2 | 5 | 70 | 39 | 47 |
| 4 | St Marys | 22 | 13 | 4 | 5 | 70 | 41 | 43 |
| 5 | Armagh Rovers | 22 | 12 | 2 | 8 | 72 | 54 | 38 |
| 6 | Hill Street | 22 | 10 | 3 | 9 | 56 | 40 | 33 |
| 7 | Gilford Crusaders | 22 | 10 | 0 | 12 | 36 | 63 | 30 |
| 8 | Dungannon Tigers | 22 | 8 | 3 | 11 | 53 | 51 | 27 |
| 9 | Dungannon Rovers | 22 | 5 | 3 | 14 | 36 | 55 | 18 |
| 10 | Riverdale | 22 | 4 | 3 | 15 | 39 | 78 | 15 |
| 11 | Derryhirk United | 22 | 4 | 2 | 16 | 30 | 79 | 14 |
| 12 | Lurgan Institute | 22 | 4 | 1 | 17 | 22 | 75 | 13 |

## Division Two

| | | P | W | D | L | F | A | Pts |
|---|---|---|---|---|---|---|---|---|
| 1 | Scarva Rangers | 20 | 16 | 2 | 2 | 69 | 22 | 50 |
| 2 | Ballyoran | 20 | 12 | 5 | 3 | 62 | 35 | 41 |
| 3 | Armagh Celtic | 20 | 9 | 5 | 6 | 46 | 53 | 32 |
| 4 | Tullyvallen | 20 | 8 | 6 | 6 | 58 | 56 | 30 |
| 5 | Lurgan BBOB | 20 | 9 | 2 | 9 | 50 | 39 | 29 |
| 6 | Portadown BBOB | 20 | 8 | 4 | 8 | 47 | 45 | 28 |
| 7 | Glenavy | 20 | 7 | 5 | 8 | 40 | 37 | 26 |
| 8 | Keady Celtic | 20 | 7 | 4 | 9 | 40 | 42 | 25 |
| 9 | Craigavon City | 20 | 5 | 4 | 11 | 39 | 47 | 19 |
| 10 | Stranmillis | 20 | 4 | 5 | 11 | 34 | 54 | 17 |
| 11 | Tullygally | 20 | 2 | 4 | 14 | 29 | 84 | 10 |

## Division Three

| | | P | W | D | L | F | A | Pts |
|---|---|---|---|---|---|---|---|---|
| 1 | Celtic Club (Lurgan No.1) | 22 | 22 | 0 | 0 | 71 | 16 | 66 |
| 2 | Donaghmore | 22 | 16 | 3 | 3 | 62 | 19 | 51 |
| 3 | Red Star | 22 | 15 | 1 | 6 | 74 | 42 | 46 |
| 4 | Caledon Rovers | 22 | 12 | 3 | 7 | 69 | 44 | 39 |
| 5 | Lurgan United | 22 | 10 | 4 | 8 | 44 | 33 | 34 |
| 6 | Donacloney | 22 | 10 | 3 | 9 | 47 | 55 | 33 |
| 7 | Santos FC | 22 | 8 | 5 | 9 | 33 | 53 | 29 |
| 8 | Rectory Rangers | 22 | 7 | 4 | 11 | 59 | 62 | 25 |
| 9 | Corinthians | 22 | 6 | 6 | 10 | 34 | 40 | 24 |
| 10 | Armagh Blues | 22 | 3 | 5 | 14 | 35 | 66 | 14 |
| 11 | Glenanne United | 22 | 3 | 1 | 18 | 42 | 76 | 10 |
| 12 | Moira Albion | 22 | 1 | 3 | 18 | 22 | 86 | 6 |

## Division Four

| | | P | W | D | L | F | A | Pts |
|---|---|---|---|---|---|---|---|---|
| 1 | Mowhan United | 20 | 16 | 3 | 1 | 83 | 29 | 51 |
| 2 | Sandy Hill | 20 | 16 | 3 | 1 | 61 | 20 | 51 |
| 3 | Cookstown Celtic | 20 | 14 | 4 | 2 | 74 | 20 | 46 |
| 4 | White City | 20 | 10 | 3 | 7 | 68 | 55 | 33 |
| 5 | Union Lusa FC | 20 | 8 | 4 | 8 | 40 | 42 | 28 |
| 6 | The Dons | 20 | 8 | 2 | 10 | 45 | 45 | 26 |
| 7 | Lurgan Thistle | 20 | 7 | 3 | 10 | 47 | 52 | 24 |
| 8 | CTA Athletic | 20 | 6 | 1 | 13 | 34 | 52 | 19 |
| 9 | Castlecaulfield | 20 | 3 | 8 | 9 | 33 | 47 | 17 |
| 10 | Milford Swifts | 20 | 4 | 3 | 13 | 36 | 50 | 15 |
| 11 | Aghalee Village | 20 | 0 | 2 | 18 | 26 | 135 | 2 |

# LEAGUE TABLES
## NORTHERN AMATEUR LEAGUE

### Intermediate Football
### Premier Division

| | | P | W | D | L | F | A | Pts |
|---|---|---|---|---|---|---|---|---|
| 1 | Newington Y.C. | 26 | 20 | 3 | 3 | 66 | 32 | 63 |
| 2 | Albert Foundry F.C. | 26 | 15 | 6 | 5 | 67 | 41 | 51 |
| 3 | Kilmore Rec | 26 | 14 | 5 | 7 | 60 | 43 | 47 |
| 4 | Comber Rec F.C. | 26 | 13 | 4 | 9 | 55 | 37 | 43 |
| 5 | Ards Rangers | 26 | 13 | 3 | 10 | 55 | 49 | 42 |
| 6 | Dunmurry Rec | 26 | 10 | 3 | 13 | 46 | 57 | 33 |
| 7 | Ardglass | 26 | 8 | 8 | 10 | 49 | 48 | 32 |
| 8 | Dromara Village | 26 | 9 | 5 | 12 | 50 | 53 | 32 |
| 9 | Malachians | 26 | 8 | 8 | 10 | 43 | 55 | 32 |
| 10 | Nortel | 26 | 8 | 7 | 11 | 46 | 52 | 31 |
| 11 | Islandmagee | 26 | 9 | 3 | 14 | 38 | 46 | 30 |
| 12 | Killyleagh Y.C | 26 | 7 | 9 | 10 | 42 | 53 | 30 |
| 13 | Shankill United | 26 | 7 | 6 | 13 | 31 | 47 | 27 |
| 14 | Larne Tech O.B. | 26 | 4 | 4 | 18 | 36 | 71 | 16 |

### Division 1A

| | | P | W | D | L | F | A | Pts |
|---|---|---|---|---|---|---|---|---|
| 1 | Crumlin Star | 26 | 21 | 2 | 3 | 82 | 23 | 65 |
| 2 | Drumaness Mills | 26 | 17 | 4 | 5 | 60 | 33 | 55 |
| 3 | University of Ulster at Jordanstown | 26 | 14 | 2 | 10 | 57 | 36 | 44 |
| 4 | Derriaghy C C | 26 | 13 | 5 | 8 | 53 | 39 | 44 |
| 5 | Orangefield Old Boys | 26 | 12 | 3 | 11 | 51 | 45 | 39 |
| 6 | Abbey Villa | 26 | 10 | 7 | 9 | 43 | 43 | 37 |
| 7 | Downpatrick F.C. | 26 | 10 | 5 | 11 | 58 | 54 | 35 |
| 8 | Wellington Rec (-3pts) | 26 | 10 | 6 | 10 | 38 | 47 | 33 |
| 9 | East Belfast | 26 | 9 | 5 | 12 | 46 | 53 | 32 |
| 10 | Rosario Y.C. | 26 | 8 | 5 | 13 | 36 | 54 | 29 |
| 11 | Crumlin United (-3pts) | 25 | 9 | 4 | 12 | 40 | 51 | 28 |
| 12 | Dundonald | 26 | 8 | 4 | 14 | 37 | 52 | 28 |
| 13 | Barn United (-3pts) | 25 | 7 | 3 | 15 | 52 | 70 | 21 |
| 14 | Grove United | 26 | 4 | 3 | 19 | 23 | 76 | 15 |

### Division 1B

| | | P | W | D | L | F | A | Pts |
|---|---|---|---|---|---|---|---|---|
| 1 | Immaculata F.C. | 26 | 22 | 0 | 4 | 82 | 30 | 66 |
| 2 | Rathfriland Rangers | 26 | 21 | 2 | 3 | 84 | 31 | 65 |
| 3 | Dunmurry Y. M. | 26 | 15 | 4 | 7 | 64 | 40 | 49 |
| 4 | Bloomfield F.C. | 26 | 13 | 6 | 7 | 60 | 50 | 45 |
| 5 | Sirocco Wks | 26 | 12 | 5 | 9 | 52 | 49 | 41 |
| 6 | Lisburn Rangers | 26 | 11 | 4 | 11 | 54 | 44 | 37 |
| 7 | Rathfern Rangers | 26 | 11 | 4 | 11 | 52 | 62 | 37 |
| 8 | Ballynahinch United | 26 | 9 | 8 | 9 | 35 | 35 | 35 |
| 9 | Newcastle | 26 | 8 | 8 | 10 | 50 | 54 | 32 |
| 10 | Ballywalter Rec. F.C. | 26 | 7 | 3 | 16 | 30 | 58 | 24 |
| 11 | Holywood F.C. | 26 | 6 | 4 | 16 | 42 | 67 | 22 |
| 12 | Bangor Rangers | 26 | 6 | 4 | 16 | 39 | 65 | 22 |
| 13 | Saintfield United | 26 | 5 | 6 | 15 | 40 | 76 | 21 |
| 14 | Downshire YM | 26 | 3 | 8 | 15 | 24 | 47 | 17 |

### Division 1C

| | | P | W | D | L | F | A | Pt |
|---|---|---|---|---|---|---|---|---|
| 1 | St Patricks Y.M. F.C. | 26 | 23 | 3 | 0 | 119 | 27 | 7 |
| 2 | 1st Bangor Old Boys | 26 | 18 | 5 | 3 | 88 | 38 | 5 |
| 3 | Bryansburn Rangers | 26 | 16 | 3 | 7 | 69 | 45 | 5 |
| 4 | 18th Newtownabbey O.B. | 26 | 15 | 5 | 6 | 63 | 39 | 5 |
| 5 | Bangor Swifts | 26 | 13 | 5 | 8 | 73 | 49 | 4 |
| 6 | Bangor Amateurs F.C. | 26 | 14 | 2 | 10 | 63 | 53 | 4 |
| 7 | Iveagh United | 26 | 11 | 1 | 14 | 59 | 58 | 3 |
| 8 | Mossley F.C. | 26 | 10 | 2 | 14 | 44 | 57 | 3 |
| 9 | Newington Rangers | 26 | 9 | 4 | 13 | 44 | 53 | 3 |
| 10 | Shorts FC | 26 | 9 | 4 | 13 | 50 | 62 | 3 |
| 11 | Dromore Amateurs | 26 | 7 | 5 | 14 | 41 | 73 | 2 |
| 12 | Donard Hospital | 26 | 7 | 4 | 15 | 36 | 70 | 2 |
| 13 | Groomsport | 26 | 8 | 0 | 18 | 42 | 64 | 2 |
| 14 | Kilroot Recreation | 26 | 0 | 1 | 25 | 24 | 127 | |

### Junior Football
### Division 2A

| | | P | W | D | L | F | A | Pt |
|---|---|---|---|---|---|---|---|---|
| 1 | Portaferry Rovers | 22 | 16 | 4 | 2 | 68 | 35 | 5 |
| 2 | Ballynahinch Olympic (-3pts) | 21 | 17 | 3 | 1 | 83 | 19 | 5 |
| 3 | Woodvale F.C. | 22 | 12 | 4 | 6 | 58 | 40 | 4 |
| 4 | Ford | 22 | 11 | 3 | 8 | 48 | 41 | 3 |
| 5 | Colin Valley F.C. | 22 | 9 | 6 | 7 | 47 | 50 | 3 |
| 6 | Kircubbin F.C. | 22 | 10 | 2 | 10 | 57 | 47 | 3 |
| 7 | Kelvin Old Boys | 22 | 9 | 3 | 10 | 59 | 64 | 3 |
| 8 | St Oliver Plunkett F.C. (-3pts) | 21 | 10 | 2 | 9 | 52 | 44 | 2 |
| 9 | Suffolk F.C. | 22 | 8 | 3 | 11 | 50 | 52 | 2 |
| 10 | Queens Grads. | 22 | 6 | 3 | 13 | 45 | 66 | 2 |
| 11 | Queens University 11's | 22 | 2 | 5 | 15 | 37 | 73 | 1 |
| 12 | Civil Service | 22 | 2 | 0 | 20 | 24 | 97 | 1 |

### Division 2B

| | | P | W | D | L | F | A | Pt |
|---|---|---|---|---|---|---|---|---|
| 1 | Rosemount Rec | 22 | 17 | 3 | 2 | 66 | 31 | 5 |
| 2 | Greencastle Rovers F.C. | 22 | 16 | 2 | 4 | 66 | 32 | 5 |
| 3 | St Lukes F.C. | 22 | 14 | 3 | 5 | 68 | 38 | 4 |
| 4 | Temple Rangers F.C. | 22 | 11 | 4 | 7 | 58 | 43 | 3 |
| 5 | Newtownbreda F C | 22 | 8 | 3 | 11 | 50 | 56 | 2 |
| 6 | Portavogie Rangers F.C. | 22 | 7 | 5 | 10 | 48 | 58 | 2 |
| 7 | Grange Rangers | 22 | 7 | 5 | 10 | 38 | 54 | 2 |
| 8 | Ardoyne WMC (-3pts) | 22 | 7 | 6 | 9 | 40 | 51 | 2 |
| 9 | Rooftop | 22 | 7 | 3 | 12 | 45 | 58 | 2 |
| 10 | Whitehead Eagles | 22 | 6 | 1 | 15 | 38 | 56 | 1 |
| 11 | Bangor Y.M. | 22 | 4 | 7 | 11 | 37 | 61 | 1 |
| 12 | Suffolk Swifts | 22 | 4 | 6 | 12 | 41 | 57 | 1 |

### Division 2C

| | | P | W | D | L | F | A | Pt |
|---|---|---|---|---|---|---|---|---|
| 1 | Tullycarnet FC | 20 | 18 | 0 | 2 | 68 | 25 | 5 |
| 2 | Drumbo F.C. | 20 | 14 | 2 | 4 | 72 | 24 | 4 |
| 3 | Greenisland F.C. | 20 | 13 | 3 | 4 | 46 | 16 | 4 |
| 4 | Lower Shankill FC | 20 | 13 | 2 | 5 | 56 | 27 | 4 |
| 5 | Basement FC | 20 | 9 | 5 | 6 | 50 | 42 | 3 |
| 6 | Finaghy F.C. | 20 | 9 | 3 | 8 | 36 | 31 | 3 |
| 7 | St Teresas Y.C. | 20 | 7 | 4 | 9 | 37 | 43 | 2 |
| 8 | Wesley F.C. | 20 | 8 | 0 | 12 | 39 | 54 | 2 |
| 9 | Donaghadee F.C. | 20 | 4 | 3 | 13 | 25 | 55 | 1 |
| 10 | 4th Newtownabbey F.C. | 20 | 3 | 0 | 17 | 28 | 67 | |
| 11 | Carryduff F.C. | 20 | 1 | 0 | 19 | 18 | 91 | |

## Division 3A

| Division 3A | P | W | D | L | F | A | Pts |
|---|---|---|---|---|---|---|---|
| 1 Newington Y.C. 11's | 26 | 21 | 3 | 2 | 80 | 28 | 66 |
| 2 Albert Foundry F.C.11's | 26 | 21 | 1 | 4 | 101 | 35 | 64 |
| 3 Crumlin Star 11's | 26 | 15 | 6 | 5 | 80 | 44 | 51 |
| 4 Derriaghy CC 11's | 26 | 14 | 3 | 9 | 69 | 45 | 45 |
| 5 U.U.Jordanstown 11's | 26 | 10 | 9 | 7 | 65 | 43 | 39 |
| 6 Malachians 11's | 26 | 10 | 7 | 9 | 65 | 60 | 37 |
| 7 Rosario Y.C. 11's | 25 | 9 | 7 | 9 | 67 | 65 | 34 |
| 8 Ards Rangers 11's | 25 | 9 | 4 | 13 | 55 | 66 | 30 |
| 9 Orangefield O.B. 11's | 26 | 8 | 5 | 13 | 56 | 70 | 29 |
| 10 Dunmurry Rec 11's | 26 | 7 | 7 | 12 | 50 | 52 | 28 |
| 11 Comber Rec F.C.11's | 26 | 7 | 6 | 13 | 52 | 81 | 27 |
| 12 Rathfern Rgs 11's | 26 | 7 | 5 | 14 | 52 | 89 | 26 |
| 13 Killyleagh Y.C. 11's | 26 | 7 | 4 | 15 | 42 | 63 | 25 |
| 14 Holywood F.C. 11's | 26 | 1 | 4 | 21 | 29 | 122 | 7 |

## Division 3B

| Division 3B | P | W | D | L | F | A | Pts |
|---|---|---|---|---|---|---|---|
| 1 Immaculata F.C.11's | 26 | 18 | 4 | 4 | 90 | 42 | 58 |
| 2 East Belfast 11's | 26 | 15 | 6 | 5 | 68 | 50 | 51 |
| 3 Crumlin Utd 11's | 26 | 14 | 6 | 6 | 72 | 51 | 48 |
| 4 Lisburn Rgs 11's | 26 | 14 | 3 | 9 | 58 | 48 | 45 |
| 5 Barn Utd 11's | 26 | 13 | 3 | 10 | 54 | 42 | 42 |
| 6 Shankill Utd. 11's (-3pts) | 26 | 14 | 3 | 9 | 64 | 57 | 42 |
| 7 Islandmagee 11's | 26 | 12 | 5 | 9 | 67 | 54 | 41 |
| 8 Nortel 11's | 26 | 9 | 7 | 10 | 56 | 58 | 34 |
| 9 Sirocco Wks 11's | 26 | 10 | 4 | 12 | 49 | 51 | 34 |
| 10 Bloomfield F.C.11's | 26 | 9 | 7 | 10 | 48 | 61 | 34 |
| 11 Larne Tech O.B. 11's | 26 | 6 | 7 | 13 | 51 | 63 | 25 |
| 12 Grove Utd 11's | 26 | 6 | 5 | 15 | 44 | 71 | 23 |
| 13 Dromara Village 11's | 26 | 6 | 5 | 15 | 39 | 68 | 23 |
| 14 Abbey Villa II | 26 | 2 | 3 | 21 | 33 | 77 | 9 |

## Division 3C

| Division 3C | P | W | D | L | F | A | Pts |
|---|---|---|---|---|---|---|---|
| 1 St Patricks YM 11's (-3pts) | 26 | 24 | 0 | 2 | 109 | 25 | 69 |
| 2 Woodvale F.C.11's | 26 | 23 | 0 | 3 | 97 | 34 | 69 |
| 3 Bangor Rgs 11's | 26 | 20 | 1 | 5 | 92 | 35 | 61 |
| 4 Dundonald 11's | 26 | 13 | 2 | 11 | 74 | 50 | 41 |
| 5 Shorts 11's | 26 | 13 | 2 | 11 | 42 | 58 | 41 |
| 6 Iveagh Utd 11's | 26 | 12 | 2 | 12 | 63 | 62 | 38 |
| 7 Ford F.C. 11's | 26 | 12 | 1 | 13 | 43 | 43 | 37 |
| 8 Dunmurry Y.M.11's | 26 | 11 | 2 | 13 | 58 | 75 | 35 |
| 9 Wellington Rec 11's | 26 | 11 | 1 | 14 | 46 | 62 | 34 |
| 10 Bangor Swifts 11's | 26 | 9 | 4 | 13 | 54 | 65 | 31 |
| 11 Queens Grads 11's | 26 | 8 | 3 | 15 | 42 | 73 | 27 |
| 12 Downshire YM. 11's | 26 | 7 | 1 | 18 | 52 | 69 | 22 |
| 13 Mossley FC 11's | 26 | 5 | 1 | 20 | 36 | 93 | 16 |
| 14 Newington Rgs 11's | 26 | 3 | 2 | 21 | 28 | 92 | 11 |

## Division 3D

| Division 3D | P | W | D | L | F | A | Pts |
|---|---|---|---|---|---|---|---|
| 1 St Lukes F.C. 11's | 26 | 20 | 5 | 1 | 95 | 22 | 65 |
| 2 Colin Valley F.C.11's | 26 | 17 | 5 | 4 | 87 | 35 | 56 |
| 3 Greencastle Rovers F.C.11's (-3pts) | 25 | 18 | 3 | 4 | 77 | 30 | 54 |
| 4 Suffolk FC 11's | 26 | 14 | 3 | 9 | 65 | 55 | 45 |
| 5 Bangor YM 11's | 26 | 11 | 11 | 4 | 58 | 39 | 44 |
| 6 1st Bangor Old Boys 11's | 26 | 12 | 5 | 9 | 74 | 50 | 41 |
| 7 Bryansburn Rgs. 11's | 26 | 12 | 5 | 9 | 71 | 58 | 41 |
| 8 Ballynahinch Utd 11's | 26 | 10 | 7 | 9 | 59 | 69 | 37 |
| 9 Saintfield Utd 11's | 26 | 10 | 4 | 12 | 50 | 52 | 34 |
| 10 Ballywalter Rec. F.C.11's | 26 | 7 | 6 | 13 | 45 | 67 | 27 |
| 11 St Teresas Y.C.11's | 26 | 6 | 5 | 15 | 37 | 57 | 23 |
| 12 Groomsport 11's | 26 | 7 | 0 | 19 | 48 | 94 | 21 |
| 13 Kilroot Rec 11's | 26 | 3 | 3 | 20 | 43 | 122 | 12 |
| 14 Civil Service 11's (-3pts) | 25 | 3 | 0 | 22 | 28 | 87 | 6 |

## Division 3E

| Division 3E | P | W | D | L | F | A | Pts |
|---|---|---|---|---|---|---|---|
| 1 Portaferry Rovers 11's | 24 | 18 | 3 | 3 | 63 | 30 | 57 |
| 2 18th Newtownabbey O.B. 11's | 24 | 16 | 3 | 5 | 66 | 28 | 51 |
| 3 St Oliver Plunkett F.C.11's | 24 | 15 | 6 | 3 | 79 | 45 | 51 |
| 4 Ardoyne WMC 11's | 24 | 14 | 4 | 6 | 70 | 50 | 46 |
| 5 Kelvin OB 11's | 24 | 12 | 5 | 7 | 56 | 46 | 41 |
| 6 Drumbo F.C.11's | 24 | 10 | 5 | 9 | 52 | 40 | 35 |
| 7 Newtownbreda 11's | 24 | 10 | 4 | 10 | 47 | 65 | 34 |
| 8 Lower Shankill 11's | 24 | 10 | 2 | 12 | 47 | 45 | 32 |
| 9 Portavogie Rangers F.C.11's | 24 | 7 | 4 | 13 | 43 | 58 | 25 |
| 10 Rooftop 11's | 24 | 7 | 3 | 14 | 60 | 71 | 24 |
| 11 4th Newtownabbey O.B. 11's | 24 | 7 | 0 | 17 | 46 | 75 | 21 |
| 12 Dromore Amateurs 11's | 24 | 4 | 5 | 15 | 32 | 59 | 17 |
| 13 Donard Hospital 11's | 24 | 3 | 2 | 19 | 33 | 82 | 11 |

## Division 3F

| Division 3F | P | W | D | L | F | A | Pts |
|---|---|---|---|---|---|---|---|
| 1 Tullycarnet FC 11's | 22 | 17 | 4 | 1 | 106 | 34 | 55 |
| 2 Rosemount Rec 11's | 22 | 17 | 2 | 3 | 70 | 32 | 53 |
| 3 Temple Rgs 11's | 22 | 14 | 4 | 4 | 66 | 37 | 46 |
| 4 Queens Colts | 22 | 14 | 1 | 7 | 91 | 46 | 43 |
| 5 Suffolk Swifts 11"s | 22 | 12 | 2 | 8 | 48 | 39 | 38 |
| 6 Greenisland F.C.11's | 22 | 12 | 0 | 10 | 62 | 47 | 36 |
| 7 Basement 11's | 22 | 8 | 1 | 13 | 52 | 69 | 25 |
| 8 Bangor Amateurs 11's | 22 | 6 | 4 | 12 | 47 | 67 | 22 |
| 9 Grange Rgs11s | 22 | 5 | 5 | 12 | 47 | 73 | 20 |
| 10 Donaghadee FC 11's | 22 | 6 | 1 | 15 | 47 | 74 | 19 |
| 11 Wesley FC 11's (-3pts) | 22 | 3 | 5 | 14 | 39 | 93 | 11 |
| 12 Carryduff 11's | 22 | 1 | 5 | 16 | 28 | 93 | 8 |

# LEAGUE TABLES

## NORTHERN IRELAND INTERMEDIATE LEAGUE

### Intermediate Division

| | | P | W | D | L | F | A | Pts |
|---|---|---|---|---|---|---|---|---|
| 1 | Newbuildings United | 14 | 11 | 3 | 0 | 41 | 14 | 36 |
| 2 | Strabane Athletic | 14 | 8 | 3 | 3 | 39 | 19 | 27 |
| 3 | Ardstraw | 14 | 8 | 0 | 6 | 32 | 20 | 24 |
| 4 | Oxford United Stars | 14 | 7 | 3 | 4 | 26 | 19 | 24 |
| 5 | Dungiven | 14 | 7 | 2 | 5 | 28 | 21 | 23 |
| 6 | Roe Rovers | 14 | 3 | 2 | 9 | 17 | 43 | 11 |
| 7 | Mountjoy United | 14 | 2 | 2 | 10 | 25 | 46 | 8 |
| 8 | Draperstown Celtic | 14 | 1 | 3 | 10 | 17 | 43 | 6 |

## BELFAST & DISTRICT LEAGUE

### Premier Division

| | | P | W | D | L | F | A | Pts |
|---|---|---|---|---|---|---|---|---|
| 1 | St Matthews | 16 | 13 | 1 | 2 | 51 | 17 | 40 |
| 2 | Tollymore Swifts | 16 | 12 | 2 | 2 | 47 | 20 | 38 |
| 3 | Cumann Spoirt an Phobail | 16 | 12 | 0 | 4 | 68 | 19 | 36 |
| 4 | St Pauls | 16 | 9 | 1 | 6 | 37 | 28 | 28 |
| 5 | Shamrock | 16 | 7 | 4 | 5 | 37 | 31 | 25 |
| 6 | Clifton Athletic | 16 | 4 | 3 | 9 | 33 | 54 | 15 |
| 7 | Willowbank | 16 | 4 | 1 | 11 | 19 | 48 | 13 |
| 8 | West Belfast | 16 | 2 | 5 | 9 | 20 | 46 | 11 |
| 9 | St Malachys OB | 16 | 0 | 1 | 15 | 16 | 65 | 1 |

### Division One

| | | P | W | D | L | F | A | Pts |
|---|---|---|---|---|---|---|---|---|
| 1 | Aquinas | 22 | 19 | 2 | 1 | 66 | 18 | 59 |
| 2 | Bheann Mhadigan | 22 | 15 | 5 | 2 | 74 | 35 | 50 |
| 3 | Colin Bhoys | 22 | 13 | 4 | 5 | 56 | 30 | 43 |
| 4 | Belfast City | 22 | 9 | 7 | 6 | 42 | 42 | 34 |
| 5 | New Santos | 21 | 9 | 5 | 7 | 43 | 37 | 32 |
| 6 | St Pauls II | 22 | 9 | 4 | 9 | 54 | 60 | 31 |
| 7 | Kashmir Bilbao | 21 | 7 | 4 | 10 | 36 | 48 | 25 |
| 8 | Cumann Spoirt an Phobail II | 22 | 6 | 5 | 11 | 42 | 50 | 23 |
| 9 | Tollymore Swifts II | 22 | 6 | 4 | 12 | 49 | 56 | 22 |
| 10 | Glanville Rec. | 22 | 5 | 3 | 14 | 39 | 65 | 18 |
| 11 | Sparta Belfast | 22 | 5 | 2 | 15 | 32 | 69 | 17 |
| 12 | Glenpark | 22 | 4 | 3 | 15 | 40 | 63 | 15 |

### Division Two

| | | P | W | D | L | F | A | Pts |
|---|---|---|---|---|---|---|---|---|
| 1 | Ballysillan YM | 22 | 21 | 1 | 0 | 106 | 29 | 64 |
| 2 | St James Swifts | 22 | 11 | 6 | 5 | 61 | 34 | 39 |
| 3 | St Patricks YM III | 22 | 11 | 5 | 6 | 60 | 43 | 38 |
| 4 | Glenbryn YM A | 22 | 11 | 3 | 8 | 59 | 54 | 36 |
| 5 | Aquinas II | 22 | 11 | 1 | 10 | 63 | 50 | 34 |
| 6 | St Lukes III | 22 | 9 | 6 | 7 | 58 | 50 | 33 |
| 7 | Ligoniel WMC | 22 | 8 | 6 | 8 | 46 | 43 | 30 |
| 8 | St Matthews II | 22 | 6 | 11 | 5 | 47 | 43 | 29 |
| 9 | Belfast United | 22 | 7 | 5 | 10 | 54 | 69 | 26 |
| 10 | Clonard Hibs | 22 | 7 | 3 | 12 | 50 | 63 | 24 |
| 11 | Clifton Athletic II | 22 | 3 | 3 | 17 | 35 | 84 | 12 |
| 12 | Hibernians | 22 | 3 | 0 | 20 | 36 | 113 | 9 |

### Division Three

| | | P | W | D | L | F | A | Pts |
|---|---|---|---|---|---|---|---|---|
| 1 | Ballysillan Elim | 18 | 15 | 1 | 2 | 75 | 19 | 46 |
| 2 | Holylands | 18 | 13 | 3 | 2 | 69 | 30 | 42 |
| 3 | Glenbawn Celtic | 18 | 13 | 2 | 3 | 76 | 37 | 41 |
| 4 | Shamrock II | 18 | 13 | 1 | 4 | 85 | 47 | 40 |
| 5 | Colin Bhoys II | 18 | 9 | 2 | 7 | 49 | 46 | 29 |
| 6 | Bheann Mhadigan II | 18 | 7 | 1 | 10 | 40 | 54 | 22 |
| 7 | Rock Athletic | 18 | 4 | 2 | 12 | 41 | 69 | 14 |
| 8 | New Santos II | 18 | 4 | 2 | 12 | 30 | 59 | 14 |
| 9 | Kashmir Bilbao II | 18 | 3 | 0 | 15 | 26 | 86 | 9 |
| 10 | St Malachys OB II | 18 | 1 | 2 | 15 | 26 | 70 | 5 |

# SCOTTISH TABLES 2012-13

## EAST OF SCOTLAND LEAGUE

| Premier Division | P | W | D | L | F | A | Pts |
|---|---|---|---|---|---|---|---|
| 1 Whitehill Welfare | 22 | 18 | 1 | 3 | 53 | 21 | 55 |
| 2 Stirling University | 22 | 15 | 2 | 5 | 54 | 22 | 47 |
| 3 Spartans | 22 | 14 | 4 | 4 | 44 | 23 | 46 |
| 4 Gretna 2008 | 22 | 9 | 7 | 6 | 34 | 25 | 34 |
| 5 Edinburgh City | 22 | 9 | 3 | 10 | 31 | 32 | 30 |
| 6 Lothian Thistle H Vale | 22 | 8 | 3 | 11 | 35 | 38 | 27 |
| 7 Preston Athletic | 22 | 7 | 3 | 12 | 41 | 55 | 24 |
| 8 Civil Service Strollers | 22 | 7 | 3 | 12 | 30 | 56 | 24 |
| 9 Vale of Leithen | 22 | 5 | 8 | 9 | 41 | 49 | 23 |
| 10 Heriot-Watt University | 22 | 6 | 5 | 11 | 21 | 37 | 23 |
| 11 Edinburgh University | 22 | 4 | 8 | 10 | 26 | 40 | 20 |
| 12 Tynecastle | 22 | 5 | 3 | 14 | 41 | 53 | 18 |

| Division One | P | W | D | L | F | A | Pts |
|---|---|---|---|---|---|---|---|
| 1 Craigroyston | 26 | 21 | 2 | 3 | 77 | 29 | 65 |
| 2 Coldstream | 26 | 18 | 5 | 3 | 80 | 25 | 59 |
| 3 Leith Athletic | 26 | 18 | 3 | 5 | 88 | 38 | 57 |
| 4 Berwick Rangers | 26 | 15 | 4 | 7 | 74 | 46 | 49 |
| 5 Eyemouth United | 26 | 15 | 3 | 8 | 70 | 59 | 48 |
| 6 Easthouses Lily | 26 | 14 | 3 | 9 | 69 | 63 | 45 |
| 7 Gala Fairydean | 26 | 12 | 3 | 11 | 56 | 69 | 39 |
| 8 Kelso United | 26 | 9 | 6 | 11 | 59 | 62 | 33 |
| 9 Selkirk | 26 | 8 | 4 | 14 | 34 | 49 | 28 |
| 10 Duns | 26 | 6 | 6 | 14 | 43 | 56 | 24 |
| 11 Ormiston | 26 | 6 | 5 | 15 | 46 | 53 | 23 |
| 12 Peebles | 26 | 6 | 5 | 15 | 36 | 76 | 23 |
| 13 Burntisland Shipyard | 26 | 3 | 5 | 18 | 34 | 84 | 14 |
| 14 Hawick Royal Albert | 26 | 2 | 4 | 20 | 32 | 89 | 10 |

## HIGHLAND LEAGUE

| | P | W | D | L | F | A | Pts |
|---|---|---|---|---|---|---|---|
| 1 Cove Rangers | 34 | 25 | 5 | 4 | 101 | 26 | 80 |
| 2 Formartine United | 34 | 25 | 3 | 6 | 106 | 39 | 78 |
| 3 Wick Academy | 34 | 25 | 1 | 8 | 101 | 48 | 76 |
| 4 Nairn County | 34 | 22 | 5 | 7 | 80 | 43 | 71 |
| 5 Clachnacuddin | 34 | 21 | 3 | 10 | 68 | 49 | 66 |
| 6 Fraserburgh | 34 | 18 | 5 | 11 | 83 | 47 | 59 |
| 7 Deveronvale | 34 | 17 | 7 | 10 | 66 | 45 | 58 |
| 8 Brora Rangers | 34 | 17 | 4 | 13 | 83 | 52 | 55 |
| 9 Forres Mechanics | 34 | 16 | 7 | 11 | 78 | 49 | 55 |
| 10 Inverurie Loco Works | 34 | 16 | 5 | 13 | 71 | 60 | 53 |
| 11 Turriff United | 34 | 16 | 4 | 14 | 68 | 67 | 52 |
| 12 Buckie Thistle | 34 | 13 | 7 | 14 | 58 | 62 | 46 |
| 13 Huntly | 34 | 14 | 3 | 17 | 66 | 68 | 45 |
| 14 Keith | 34 | 12 | 7 | 15 | 56 | 65 | 43 |
| 15 Strathspey Thistle | 34 | 5 | 0 | 29 | 23 | 112 | 15 |
| 16 Rothes | 34 | 4 | 2 | 28 | 29 | 126 | 14 |
| 17 Lossiemouth | 34 | 3 | 1 | 30 | 35 | 108 | 10 |
| 18 Fort William | 34 | 1 | 3 | 30 | 20 | 126 | 6 |

## NORTH CALEDONIAN LEAGUE

| | P | W | D | L | F | A | Pts |
|---|---|---|---|---|---|---|---|
| 1 Thurso | 18 | 15 | 2 | 1 | 50 | 11 | 47 |
| 2 Golspie Sutherland | 18 | 11 | 4 | 3 | 58 | 26 | 37 |
| 3 Muir of Ord Rovers | 18 | 8 | 6 | 4 | 47 | 41 | 30 |
| 4 Halkirk United | 18 | 5 | 3 | 8 | 39 | 56 | 22 |
| 5 Clachnacuddin | 16 | 6 | 1 | 11 | 29 | 38 | 18 |
| 6 Alness United | 18 | 5 | 2 | 8 | 23 | 27 | 14 |
| 7 Invergordon | 18 | 2 | 3 | 13 | 20 | 69 | 9 |

## SJFA EAST REGION

| Superleague | P | W | D | L | F | A | Pts |
|---|---|---|---|---|---|---|---|
| 1 Linlithgow Rose | 22 | 19 | 3 | 0 | 59 | 15 | 60 |
| 2 Bonnyrigg Rose | 22 | 12 | 5 | 5 | 58 | 36 | 41 |
| 3 Camelon Juniors | 22 | 12 | 3 | 7 | 50 | 39 | 39 |
| 4 Boness United | 22 | 11 | 5 | 6 | 44 | 32 | 38 |
| 5 Kelty Hearts | 22 | 8 | 4 | 10 | 33 | 33 | 28 |
| 6 Broxburn Athletic | 22 | 8 | 4 | 10 | 31 | 32 | 28 |
| 7 Musselburgh Athletic | 22 | 8 | 3 | 11 | 32 | 37 | 27 |
| 8 Hill of Beath Hawthorn | 22 | 7 | 5 | 10 | 38 | 38 | 26 |
| 9 Carnoustie Panmure | 22 | 8 | 2 | 12 | 33 | 52 | 26 |
| 10 Lochee United | 22 | 7 | 4 | 11 | 33 | 51 | 25 |
| 11 Sauchie Juniors | 22 | 6 | 6 | 10 | 28 | 32 | 24 |
| 12 St Andrews United | 22 | 3 | 2 | 17 | 24 | 66 | 11 |

| Premier League | P | W | D | L | F | A | Pts |
|---|---|---|---|---|---|---|---|
| 1 Newtongrange Star (+3pts) | 22 | 14 | 3 | 4 | 57 | 27 | 48 |
| 2 Ballingry Rovers | 22 | 14 | 2 | 6 | 58 | 31 | 44 |
| 3 Tayport | 22 | 12 | 6 | 4 | 50 | 24 | 42 |
| 4 Armadale Thistle | 22 | 11 | 5 | 6 | 42 | 27 | 38 |
| 5 Penicuik Athletic | 22 | 11 | 4 | 7 | 43 | 31 | 37 |
| 6 Bathgate Thistle | 22 | 10 | 5 | 7 | 38 | 33 | 35 |
| 7 Dalkeith Thistle | 22 | 8 | 7 | 7 | 43 | 57 | 31 |
| 8 Jeanfield Swifts | 22 | 8 | 5 | 9 | 43 | 40 | 29 |
| 9 Oakley United | 22 | 6 | 5 | 11 | 45 | 73 | 23 |
| 10 Dundee Violet (-3pts) | 22 | 8 | 1 | 12 | 34 | 38 | 22 |
| 11 Glenrothes | 22 | 3 | 3 | 16 | 23 | 46 | 12 |
| 12 Broughty Athletic | 22 | 1 | 4 | 17 | 21 | 70 | 7 |

| Central Division | P | W | D | L | F | A | Pts |
|---|---|---|---|---|---|---|---|
| 1 Kinnoull | 24 | 21 | 1 | 2 | 66 | 16 | 64 |
| 2 Kirkcaldy YM | 24 | 20 | 1 | 3 | 86 | 27 | 61 |
| 3 Dundonald Bluebell | 24 | 20 | 0 | 4 | 114 | 27 | 60 |
| 4 Newburgh | 24 | 13 | 5 | 6 | 63 | 37 | 44 |
| 5 Lochore Welfare | 24 | 13 | 4 | 7 | 60 | 47 | 43 |
| 6 Rosyth | 24 | 13 | 3 | 8 | 48 | 40 | 42 |
| 7 Thornton Hibs | 24 | 9 | 4 | 11 | 46 | 63 | 31 |
| 8 Lochgelly Albert | 24 | 9 | 3 | 12 | 56 | 54 | 30 |
| 9 Steelend Vics | 24 | 7 | 4 | 13 | 42 | 71 | 25 |
| 10 Crossgates Primrose | 24 | 5 | 1 | 18 | 37 | 75 | 16 |
| 11 Scone Thistle | 24 | 3 | 5 | 16 | 28 | 60 | 14 |
| 12 Bankfoot | 24 | 3 | 3 | 18 | 31 | 78 | 12 |
| 13 Luncarty | 24 | 2 | 2 | 20 | 14 | 96 | 8 |

# SCOTTISH FOOTBALL

| North Division | P | W | D | L | F | A | Pts |
|---|---|---|---|---|---|---|---|
| 1 Kirriemuir Thistle | 22 | 15 | 5 | 2 | 75 | 28 | 50 |
| 2 Montrose Roselea | 22 | 15 | 2 | 5 | 68 | 23 | 47 |
| 3 East Craigie | 22 | 15 | 2 | 5 | 60 | 32 | 47 |
| 4 Forfar West End (-6pts) | 22 | 17 | 0 | 5 | 71 | 33 | 45 |
| 5 Dundee North End | 22 | 12 | 4 | 6 | 59 | 32 | 40 |
| 6 Arbroath Vics | 22 | 11 | 4 | 7 | 51 | 37 | 37 |
| 7 Downfield | 22 | 11 | 3 | 8 | 57 | 41 | 36 |
| 8 Blairgowrie | 22 | 10 | 2 | 10 | 49 | 40 | 32 |
| 9 Lochee Harp | 22 | 6 | 3 | 13 | 28 | 53 | 21 |
| 10 Brechin Vics | 22 | 3 | 1 | 18 | 31 | 73 | 10 |
| 11 Forfar Albion | 22 | 2 | 1 | 19 | 24 | 98 | 7 |
| 12 Coupar Angus | 22 | 1 | 1 | 20 | 19 | 102 | 4 |

| South Division | P | W | D | L | F | A | Pts |
|---|---|---|---|---|---|---|---|
| 1 Fauldhouse United | 28 | 21 | 4 | 3 | 98 | 30 | 67 |
| 2 Pumpherston Juniors | 28 | 17 | 4 | 7 | 73 | 58 | 55 |
| 3 Livingston United | 28 | 16 | 6 | 6 | 61 | 41 | 54 |
| 4 Arniston Rangers | 28 | 14 | 10 | 4 | 62 | 34 | 52 |
| 5 Haddington Athletic | 28 | 16 | 3 | 9 | 75 | 45 | 51 |
| 6 Dunbar United | 28 | 15 | 3 | 10 | 58 | 52 | 48 |
| 7 Tranent Juniors | 28 | 11 | 8 | 9 | 51 | 40 | 41 |
| 8 Whitburn Juniors | 28 | 12 | 4 | 12 | 49 | 38 | 40 |
| 9 Spartans | 28 | 11 | 5 | 12 | 50 | 54 | 38 |
| 10 Blackburn United | 28 | 10 | 6 | 12 | 43 | 46 | 36 |
| 11 West Calder United | 28 | 9 | 3 | 16 | 35 | 55 | 30 |
| 12 Stoneyburn Juniors | 28 | 8 | 6 | 14 | 52 | 75 | 30 |
| 13 Falkirk JFC | 28 | 6 | 4 | 18 | 36 | 69 | 22 |
| 14 Harthill Royal | 28 | 3 | 6 | 19 | 33 | 99 | 15 |
| 15 Edinburgh United | 28 | 2 | 6 | 20 | 27 | 67 | 12 |

## SJFA NORTH REGION

| Superleague | P | W | D | L | F | A | Pts |
|---|---|---|---|---|---|---|---|
| 1 Culter | 26 | 21 | 1 | 4 | 92 | 29 | 64 |
| 2 Dyce Juniors | 26 | 17 | 3 | 6 | 60 | 38 | 54 |
| 3 Hermes | 26 | 15 | 2 | 9 | 63 | 43 | 47 |
| 4 Banks o' Dee | 26 | 13 | 5 | 8 | 58 | 38 | 44 |
| 5 Deveronside | 26 | 13 | 3 | 10 | 42 | 50 | 42 |
| 6 FC Stoneywood | 26 | 12 | 5 | 9 | 63 | 44 | 41 |
| 7 Stonehaven | 26 | 10 | 7 | 9 | 64 | 47 | 37 |
| 8 Maud | 26 | 11 | 4 | 11 | 55 | 52 | 37 |
| 9 Ellon United | 26 | 9 | 8 | 9 | 39 | 40 | 35 |
| 10 Banchory St Ternan | 26 | 10 | 2 | 14 | 43 | 69 | 32 |
| 11 Longside | 26 | 9 | 2 | 15 | 46 | 61 | 29 |
| 12 Hall Russell United | 26 | 6 | 9 | 11 | 36 | 50 | 27 |
| 13 Lewis United | 26 | 5 | 3 | 18 | 35 | 73 | 18 |
| 14 Fraserburgh United | 26 | 4 | 0 | 22 | 24 | 86 | 12 |

| Division One | P | W | D | L | F | A | Pts |
|---|---|---|---|---|---|---|---|
| 1 New Elgin | 26 | 22 | 1 | 3 | 78 | 31 | 67 |
| 2 East End | 26 | 17 | 3 | 6 | 67 | 39 | 54 |
| 3 Inverness City | 26 | 16 | 4 | 6 | 75 | 40 | 52 |
| 4 Glentanar | 26 | 13 | 7 | 6 | 68 | 49 | 46 |
| 5 Islavale | 26 | 13 | 4 | 9 | 61 | 58 | 43 |
| 6 Parkvale | 26 | 13 | 2 | 11 | 74 | 47 | 41 |
| 7 Portgordon Victoria | 26 | 11 | 3 | 12 | 55 | 73 | 36 |
| 8 Sunnybank | 26 | 9 | 6 | 11 | 50 | 63 | 33 |
| 9 Nairn St Ninian | 26 | 9 | 3 | 14 | 47 | 68 | 30 |
| 10 Forres Thistle | 26 | 7 | 8 | 11 | 51 | 62 | 29 |
| 11 Burghead Thistle | 26 | 9 | 1 | 16 | 52 | 59 | 28 |
| 12 Bridge of Don Thistle | 26 | 6 | 6 | 14 | 48 | 68 | 24 |
| 13 Buchanhaven Hearts | 26 | 3 | 8 | 15 | 44 | 75 | 17 |
| 14 Lossiemouth United | 26 | 3 | 6 | 17 | 39 | 77 | 15 |

| Division Two | P | W | D | L | F | A | Pts |
|---|---|---|---|---|---|---|---|
| 1 Colony Park | 20 | 14 | 2 | 4 | 65 | 21 | 44 |
| 2 Buckie Rovers | 20 | 14 | 2 | 4 | 70 | 29 | 44 |
| 3 Newmachar United | 20 | 8 | 5 | 7 | 47 | 36 | 29 |
| 4 Cruden Bay | 20 | 8 | 4 | 8 | 45 | 42 | 28 |
| 5 Fochabers | 20 | 4 | 3 | 13 | 24 | 81 | 15 |
| 6 Whitehills | 20 | 3 | 2 | 15 | 24 | 66 | 11 |

## SJFA WESTERN REGION

| Superleague Premier | P | W | D | L | F | A | Pts |
|---|---|---|---|---|---|---|---|
| 1 Auchinleck Talbot | 22 | 20 | 2 | 0 | 62 | 14 | 62 |
| 2 Petershill | 22 | 11 | 6 | 5 | 41 | 23 | 39 |
| 3 Clydebank | 22 | 11 | 3 | 8 | 34 | 32 | 36 |
| 4 Glenafton Athletic | 22 | 10 | 2 | 10 | 26 | 37 | 32 |
| 5 Irvine Meadow | 22 | 9 | 3 | 10 | 36 | 37 | 30 |
| 6 Arthurlie | 22 | 8 | 5 | 9 | 40 | 40 | 29 |
| 7 Kirkintilloch Rob Roy | 22 | 8 | 5 | 9 | 49 | 50 | 29 |
| 8 Pollok | 22 | 7 | 6 | 9 | 25 | 35 | 27 |
| 9 Cumnock Juniors | 22 | 7 | 4 | 11 | 36 | 40 | 25 |
| 10 Ashfield | 22 | 7 | 4 | 11 | 35 | 40 | 25 |
| 11 Beith Juniors | 22 | 7 | 3 | 12 | 36 | 50 | 24 |
| 12 Shotts Bon Accord | 22 | 2 | 7 | 13 | 23 | 45 | 13 |

| Superleague Division One | P | W | D | L | F | A | Pts |
|---|---|---|---|---|---|---|---|
| 1 Hurlford United | 26 | 16 | 3 | 7 | 52 | 43 | 51 |
| 2 Kilbirnie Ladeside | 26 | 15 | 5 | 6 | 58 | 37 | 50 |
| 3 Largs Thistle | 26 | 14 | 3 | 9 | 59 | 39 | 45 |
| 4 Thorniewood United | 26 | 13 | 5 | 8 | 44 | 31 | 44 |
| 5 Yoker Athletic | 26 | 11 | 7 | 8 | 67 | 49 | 40 |
| 6 Rutherglen Glencairn | 26 | 12 | 4 | 10 | 51 | 42 | 40 |
| 7 Renfrew | 26 | 11 | 4 | 11 | 48 | 40 | 37 |
| 8 Cumbernauld United | 26 | 11 | 4 | 11 | 53 | 63 | 37 |
| 9 Kilsyth Rangers | 26 | 10 | 6 | 10 | 44 | 42 | 36 |
| 10 Maybole Juniors | 26 | 9 | 8 | 9 | 43 | 48 | 35 |
| 11 Glasgow Perthshire | 26 | 10 | 4 | 12 | 57 | 48 | 34 |
| 12 Kello Rovers | 26 | 9 | 2 | 15 | 43 | 69 | 29 |
| 13 Ardrossan Winton Rovers | 26 | 5 | 7 | 14 | 52 | 80 | 22 |
| 14 Whitletts Victoria | 26 | 3 | 4 | 19 | 30 | 70 | 13 |

| Central District Div. One | P | W | D | L | F | A | Pts |
|---|---|---|---|---|---|---|---|
| 1 Greenock Juniors | 26 | 17 | 5 | 4 | 66 | 33 | 56 |
| 2 Lesmahagow Juniors | 26 | 15 | 6 | 5 | 73 | 37 | 51 |
| 3 Larkhall Thistle | 26 | 16 | 2 | 8 | 80 | 52 | 50 |
| 4 Shettleston | 26 | 15 | 4 | 7 | 57 | 34 | 49 |
| 5 St. Anthony's | 26 | 14 | 7 | 5 | 49 | 28 | 49 |
| 6 Lanark United | 26 | 14 | 3 | 9 | 56 | 41 | 45 |
| 7 Carluke Rovers | 26 | 13 | 4 | 9 | 58 | 47 | 43 |
| 8 Benburb | 26 | 11 | 4 | 11 | 57 | 51 | 37 |
| 9 Bellshill Athletic | 26 | 10 | 6 | 10 | 56 | 50 | 36 |
| 10 Dunipace | 26 | 11 | 3 | 12 | 51 | 46 | 36 |
| 11 Neilston Juniors | 26 | 10 | 4 | 12 | 51 | 51 | 34 |
| 12 Port Glasgow Juniors | 26 | 6 | 2 | 18 | 39 | 65 | 20 |
| 13 St. Roch's | 26 | 3 | 1 | 22 | 21 | 96 | 10 |
| 14 East Kilbride Thistle | 26 | 1 | 1 | 24 | 20 | 103 | 4 |

## Central District Div. Two

| | P | W | D | L | F | A | Pts |
|---|---|---|---|---|---|---|---|
| 1 Cambuslang Rangers | 20 | 15 | 1 | 4 | 65 | 20 | 46 |
| 2 Maryhill | 20 | 14 | 2 | 4 | 52 | 32 | 44 |
| 3 Johnstone Burgh | 20 | 11 | 2 | 7 | 55 | 40 | 35 |
| 4 Wishaw Juniors | 20 | 10 | 4 | 6 | 42 | 36 | 34 |
| 5 Rossvale | 20 | 9 | 4 | 7 | 34 | 35 | 31 |
| 6 Vale of Clyde | 20 | 8 | 4 | 8 | 39 | 30 | 28 |
| 7 Vale of Leven | 20 | 8 | 4 | 8 | 37 | 38 | 28 |
| 8 Blantyre Victoria | 20 | 8 | 2 | 10 | 32 | 32 | 26 |
| 9 Forth Wanderers | 20 | 4 | 6 | 10 | 26 | 38 | 18 |
| 10 Royal Albert | 20 | 5 | 2 | 13 | 32 | 62 | 17 |
| 11 Newmains United | 20 | 2 | 1 | 17 | 13 | 64 | 7 |

## Ayrshire District League

| | P | W | D | L | F | A | Pts |
|---|---|---|---|---|---|---|---|
| 1 Kilwinning Rangers | 22 | 18 | 2 | 2 | 76 | 22 | 56 |
| 2 Troon | 22 | 16 | 3 | 3 | 66 | 23 | 51 |
| 3 Lugar Boswell Thistle | 22 | 16 | 2 | 4 | 60 | 27 | 50 |
| 4 Ardeer Thistle | 22 | 12 | 2 | 8 | 55 | 26 | 38 |
| 5 Irvine Victoria | 22 | 11 | 3 | 8 | 37 | 38 | 36 |
| 6 Saltcoats Victoria | 22 | 9 | 3 | 10 | 43 | 44 | 30 |
| 7 Girvan | 22 | 8 | 3 | 11 | 52 | 43 | 27 |
| 8 Annbank United | 22 | 8 | 2 | 12 | 41 | 45 | 26 |
| 9 Darvel Juniors | 22 | 7 | 4 | 11 | 43 | 57 | 25 |
| 10 Dalry Thistle | 22 | 6 | 2 | 14 | 39 | 76 | 20 |
| 11 Craigmark Burntonians | 22 | 6 | 1 | 15 | 39 | 69 | 19 |
| 12 Muirkirk Juniors | 22 | 1 | 1 | 20 | 16 | 97 | 4 |

## SOUTH OF SCOTLAND LEAGUE

| | P | W | D | L | F | A | Pts |
|---|---|---|---|---|---|---|---|
| 1 Dalbeattie Star | 22 | 18 | 2 | 2 | 93 | 17 | 56 |
| 2 St Cuthbert Wanderers | 22 | 16 | 2 | 4 | 67 | 30 | 50 |
| 3 Wigtown and Bladnoch | 22 | 15 | 2 | 5 | 62 | 30 | 47 |
| 4 Threave Rovers | 22 | 15 | 1 | 6 | 76 | 27 | 46 |
| 5 Heston Rovers | 22 | 12 | 1 | 9 | 59 | 42 | 37 |
| 6 Newton Stewart | 22 | 11 | 1 | 10 | 62 | 44 | 34 |
| 7 Abbey Vale | 22 | 10 | 1 | 11 | 48 | 52 | 31 |
| 8 Nithsdale Wanderers | 22 | 10 | 1 | 11 | 52 | 57 | 31 |
| 9 Crichton | 22 | 8 | 2 | 12 | 52 | 56 | 26 |
| 10 Mid Annandale | 22 | 7 | 0 | 15 | 36 | 59 | 21 |
| 11 Creetown | 22 | 2 | 1 | 19 | 21 | 80 | 7 |
| 12 Fleet Star | 22 | 1 | 0 | 21 | 13 | 147 | 3 |

## SCOTTISH AMATEUR FOOTBALL LEAGUE

### Premier Division

| | P | W | D | L | F | A | Pts |
|---|---|---|---|---|---|---|---|
| 1 Postal United | 18 | 13 | 2 | 3 | 48 | 22 | 41 |
| 2 Oban Saints | 17 | 10 | 3 | 4 | 34 | 16 | 33 |
| 3 Aikenhead Thistle | 17 | 9 | 4 | 4 | 36 | 22 | 31 |
| 4 Castlemilk | 18 | 10 | 1 | 7 | 39 | 27 | 31 |
| 5 St. Josephs | 18 | 7 | 4 | 7 | 31 | 32 | 25 |
| 6 Inverclyde | 18 | 6 | 2 | 10 | 27 | 52 | 20 |
| 7 Finnart (-3pts) | 18 | 6 | 4 | 8 | 37 | 42 | 19 |
| 8 Thorn Athletic | 18 | 6 | 1 | 11 | 26 | 37 | 19 |
| 9 Rolls Royce (EK) | 18 | 5 | 4 | 9 | 32 | 44 | 19 |
| 10 Eaglesham | 18 | 4 | 1 | 13 | 20 | 36 | 13 |

## Premier Division One

| | P | W | D | L | F | A | Pts |
|---|---|---|---|---|---|---|---|
| 1 Alba Thistle (+3pts) | 16 | 13 | 1 | 1 | 41 | 11 | 43 |
| 2 Haldane United | 16 | 10 | 3 | 3 | 48 | 18 | 33 |
| 3 Kilbowie Union | 16 | 9 | 2 | 5 | 49 | 35 | 29 |
| 4 Busby | 16 | 8 | 2 | 6 | 43 | 23 | 26 |
| 5 Auldhouse (+3pts & -9) | 16 | 7 | 3 | 5 | 30 | 28 | 18 |
| 6 Arkleston | 16 | 4 | 4 | 6 | 28 | 36 | 16 |
| 7 Kings Park Rangers | 16 | 4 | 3 | 9 | 21 | 41 | 15 |
| 8 Shawlands F.P | 16 | 2 | 3 | 11 | 25 | 55 | 9 |
| 9 Duncanrig FP | 16 | 1 | 3 | 12 | 15 | 53 | 6 |

## Premier Division Two

| | P | W | D | L | F | A | Pts |
|---|---|---|---|---|---|---|---|
| 1 Campbeltown Pupils | 18 | 13 | 5 | 0 | 67 | 15 | 44 |
| 2 Hillington AFC | 18 | 12 | 4 | 2 | 59 | 24 | 40 |
| 3 Rutherglen | 18 | 12 | 3 | 3 | 51 | 26 | 39 |
| 4 Centre | 18 | 10 | 3 | 5 | 46 | 35 | 33 |
| 5 Paisley | 18 | 8 | 7 | 3 | 46 | 30 | 31 |
| 6 Dunoon (+3pts) | 18 | 5 | 5 | 7 | 35 | 39 | 23 |
| 7 Clydebank | 18 | 4 | 6 | 8 | 36 | 45 | 18 |
| 8 Glencastle Sparta | 18 | 4 | 1 | 13 | 31 | 61 | 13 |
| 9 Port Glasgow O.B. Union | 18 | 2 | 2 | 14 | 25 | 57 | 8 |
| 10 Carlton YM | 18 | 1 | 0 | 16 | 17 | 76 | 3 |

## Division One A

| | P | W | D | L | F | A | Pts |
|---|---|---|---|---|---|---|---|
| 1 East Kilbride AFC (+3pts) | 16 | 11 | 2 | 3 | 47 | 19 | 38 |
| 2 Port Glasgow United | 16 | 11 | 1 | 4 | 51 | 25 | 34 |
| 3 Dunoon Athletic | 16 | 8 | 4 | 4 | 70 | 47 | 28 |
| 4 Port Glasgow Hibs | 16 | 8 | 2 | 6 | 54 | 38 | 26 |
| 5 East Kilbride Y.M.C.A (-3pts) | 16 | 6 | 6 | 4 | 40 | 51 | 21 |
| 6 Tarbert | 16 | 5 | 3 | 8 | 35 | 47 | 18 |
| 7 Eaglesham AFC (B) | 16 | 4 | 3 | 9 | 31 | 53 | 15 |
| 8 Strathaven Dynamo | 16 | 4 | 1 | 11 | 44 | 49 | 13 |
| 9 Millbeg | 16 | 2 | 4 | 10 | 34 | 77 | 10 |

## Division One B

| | P | W | D | L | F | A | Pts |
|---|---|---|---|---|---|---|---|
| 1 Easthall Star | 20 | 17 | 2 | 1 | 101 | 35 | 53 |
| 2 Goldenhill AFC | 20 | 17 | 1 | 2 | 106 | 34 | 52 |
| 3 Jamestown | 20 | 13 | 3 | 4 | 75 | 43 | 42 |
| 4 Lochgilphead Red Star | 20 | 12 | 1 | 7 | 65 | 37 | 37 |
| 5 Rosehill Star | 20 | 11 | 2 | 7 | 61 | 43 | 35 |
| 6 Whitehill F.P | 20 | 10 | 0 | 10 | 53 | 59 | 30 |
| 7 Millerston Thistle | 20 | 7 | 1 | 12 | 32 | 61 | 22 |
| 8 Inverkip Thistle | 20 | 5 | 0 | 15 | 28 | 84 | 15 |
| 9 Kings Park Rangers (B) | 20 | 4 | 1 | 15 | 26 | 74 | 13 |
| 10 Bothwell and Uddingston Albion | 20 | 3 | 3 | 14 | 32 | 61 | 12 |
| 11 Shawlands F.P (B) | 20 | 3 | 2 | 15 | 33 | 81 | 11 |

# SCOTTISH FOOTBALL
## ABERDEENSHIRE AMATEUR FOOTBALL ASSOCIATION

### Premier Division

| | P | W | D | L | F | A | Pts |
|---|---|---|---|---|---|---|---|
| Woodside | 26 | 18 | 5 | 3 | 70 | 23 | 59 |
| University | 26 | 17 | 7 | 2 | 93 | 38 | 58 |
| Sportsmans Club | 26 | 15 | 4 | 7 | 89 | 42 | 49 |
| Kincorth | 26 | 15 | 4 | 7 | 85 | 55 | 49 |
| Echt | 26 | 14 | 3 | 9 | 69 | 59 | 45 |
| Westdyke | 26 | 12 | 6 | 8 | 53 | 44 | 42 |
| Blackburn | 26 | 11 | 3 | 12 | 64 | 69 | 36 |
| Cove Thistle | 26 | 9 | 6 | 11 | 80 | 73 | 33 |
| Cowie Thistle | 26 | 8 | 8 | 10 | 46 | 59 | 32 |
| Great Western United | 26 | 10 | 1 | 15 | 62 | 73 | 31 |
| Mearns United | 26 | 8 | 7 | 11 | 65 | 84 | 31 |
| Bon Accord City | 26 | 7 | 4 | 15 | 50 | 63 | 25 |
| Dyce ITC Hydraulics | 26 | 6 | 2 | 18 | 45 | 96 | 20 |
| Kintore | 26 | 1 | 2 | 23 | 28 | 121 | 5 |

### Division One (North)

| | P | W | D | L | F | A | Pts |
|---|---|---|---|---|---|---|---|
| 1 MS United | 24 | 16 | 2 | 6 | 74 | 51 | 50 |
| 2 Feughside | 24 | 14 | 3 | 7 | 73 | 46 | 45 |
| 3 Dyce ITC Hydraulics | 24 | 12 | 6 | 6 | 50 | 43 | 42 |
| 4 Kaimhill United | 24 | 11 | 5 | 8 | 54 | 46 | 38 |
| 5 Stoneywood Amateurs | 24 | 12 | 1 | 11 | 56 | 64 | 37 |
| 6 Ellon Amateurs | 24 | 11 | 2 | 11 | 62 | 44 | 35 |
| 7 Rothie Rovers | 24 | 10 | 4 | 10 | 64 | 59 | 34 |
| 8 Bervie Caledonian | 24 | 9 | 6 | 9 | 47 | 45 | 33 |
| 9 Halliburton | 24 | 9 | 6 | 9 | 47 | 55 | 33 |
| 10 Rattrays XI | 24 | 9 | 4 | 11 | 44 | 45 | 31 |
| 11 Glendale | 24 | 9 | 3 | 12 | 48 | 56 | 30 |
| 12 Lads Club Amateurs | 24 | 8 | 4 | 12 | 39 | 47 | 28 |
| 13 Kemnay Youth | 24 | 2 | 2 | 20 | 30 | 87 | 8 |

### Division One (East)

| | P | W | D | L | F | A | Pts |
|---|---|---|---|---|---|---|---|
| 1 Beacon Rangers | 26 | 20 | 0 | 6 | 90 | 53 | 60 |
| 2 Hazlehead United | 26 | 18 | 4 | 4 | 118 | 57 | 58 |
| 3 RGU | 26 | 17 | 4 | 5 | 82 | 35 | 55 |
| 4 Johnshaven Athletic | 26 | 16 | 3 | 7 | 67 | 44 | 51 |
| 5 Newtonhill | 26 | 13 | 3 | 10 | 84 | 77 | 42 |
| 6 Alford | 26 | 11 | 3 | 12 | 62 | 69 | 36 |
| 7 Nicolls | 26 | 10 | 5 | 11 | 66 | 65 | 35 |
| 8 Glendale XI | 26 | 10 | 4 | 12 | 59 | 63 | 34 |
| 9 Old Aberdonians | 26 | 9 | 5 | 12 | 52 | 63 | 32 |
| 10 Bon Accord City | 26 | 8 | 3 | 15 | 51 | 79 | 27 |
| 11 Don Athletic | 26 | 7 | 6 | 13 | 50 | 72 | 27 |
| 12 West End | 26 | 6 | 9 | 13 | 57 | 69 | 27 |
| 13 Scotstown Rovers | 26 | 4 | 6 | 16 | 51 | 90 | 18 |
| 14 Kintore | 26 | 2 | 8 | 16 | 36 | 89 | 14 |

### Division Two (North)

| | P | W | D | L | F | A | Pts |
|---|---|---|---|---|---|---|---|
| 1 Dee Amateurs | 24 | 21 | 2 | 1 | 131 | 17 | 65 |
| 2 Northern United | 24 | 21 | 0 | 3 | 84 | 36 | 63 |
| 3 Turriff Thistle | 24 | 16 | 2 | 6 | 95 | 42 | 50 |
| 4 Stonehaven Athletic | 24 | 15 | 2 | 7 | 62 | 47 | 47 |
| 5 University Colts | 24 | 13 | 2 | 9 | 74 | 60 | 41 |
| 6 St Laurence | 24 | 10 | 3 | 11 | 74 | 79 | 33 |
| 7 Ferryhill | 24 | 10 | 1 | 13 | 51 | 54 | 31 |
| 8 Torry United | 24 | 10 | 1 | 13 | 56 | 66 | 31 |
| 9 University Strollers | 24 | 10 | 0 | 14 | 58 | 65 | 30 |
| 10 Torphins | 24 | 9 | 3 | 12 | 68 | 79 | 30 |
| 11 Westhill | 24 | 7 | 2 | 15 | 50 | 76 | 23 |
| 12 Glendale Youth | 24 | 3 | 0 | 21 | 36 | 116 | 9 |
| 13 McTeagle | 24 | 1 | 2 | 21 | 8 | 110 | 5 |

Mintlaw withdrew.

### Division Two (East)

| | P | W | D | L | F | A | Pts |
|---|---|---|---|---|---|---|---|
| 1 AC Mill Inn | 26 | 21 | 3 | 2 | 107 | 37 | 66 |
| 2 Great Northern Athletic | 26 | 20 | 1 | 5 | 87 | 37 | 61 |
| 3 Highland Hotel | 26 | 13 | 5 | 8 | 86 | 65 | 44 |
| 4 Burghmuir | 26 | 11 | 7 | 8 | 64 | 56 | 40 |
| 5 Banchory Amateurs | 26 | 11 | 4 | 11 | 54 | 63 | 37 |
| 6 Glentanar Reflex | 26 | 9 | 6 | 11 | 53 | 58 | 33 |
| 7 Ellon Thistle | 26 | 9 | 5 | 12 | 52 | 59 | 32 |
| 8 JS XI | 26 | 8 | 7 | 11 | 58 | 61 | 31 |
| 9 Newburgh Thistle | 26 | 8 | 6 | 12 | 52 | 77 | 30 |
| 10 Trophies International | 26 | 8 | 5 | 13 | 53 | 71 | 29 |
| 11 Cammachmore | 26 | 8 | 5 | 13 | 71 | 82 | 29 |
| 12 Theologians NE | 26 | 8 | 5 | 13 | 58 | 76 | 29 |
| 13 Monymusk | 26 | 7 | 6 | 13 | 41 | 66 | 27 |
| 14 Auchnagatt Barons | 26 | 6 | 5 | 15 | 50 | 78 | 23 |

Relegation Play-Offs

Trophies International 3-1 Cammachmore

Cammachmore 3-0 Theologians

Theologians 1-1 Trophies International

### Division Three

| | P | W | D | L | F | A | Pts |
|---|---|---|---|---|---|---|---|
| 1 Granite City | 32 | 28 | 3 | 1 | 142 | 28 | 87 |
| 2 Bankhead | 32 | 26 | 2 | 4 | 148 | 58 | 80 |
| 3 Torry Select | 32 | 22 | 4 | 6 | 119 | 51 | 70 |
| 4 Summerhill | 32 | 21 | 4 | 7 | 118 | 53 | 67 |
| 5 FC Polska | 32 | 21 | 4 | 7 | 96 | 68 | 67 |
| 6 Grammar FPs | 32 | 20 | 2 | 10 | 103 | 68 | 62 |
| 7 Continental | 32 | 17 | 4 | 11 | 77 | 54 | 55 |
| 8 Byron | 32 | 15 | 4 | 13 | 84 | 89 | 49 |
| 9 Huntly Amateurs | 32 | 15 | 3 | 14 | 80 | 77 | 48 |
| 10 Fintray Thistle | 32 | 12 | 5 | 15 | 84 | 106 | 41 |
| 11 Bridge of Don | 32 | 11 | 4 | 17 | 74 | 81 | 37 |
| 12 BSFC | 32 | 11 | 3 | 18 | 74 | 88 | 36 |
| 13 Postal ALC | 32 | 7 | 7 | 18 | 72 | 108 | 28 |
| 14 ARI Thistle | 32 | 7 | 4 | 21 | 58 | 103 | 25 |
| 15 Kaiser Dons (-3pts) | 32 | 5 | 1 | 26 | 42 | 119 | 13 |
| 16 RAM | 32 | 3 | 4 | 25 | 42 | 115 | 13 |
| 17 Mugiemoss Youth (-3pts) | 32 | 2 | 0 | 30 | 41 | 188 | 3 |

# BORDER AMATEUR LEAGUE

## CALADONIAN LEAGUE

| A League | P | W | D | L | F | A | Pts |
|---|---|---|---|---|---|---|---|
| 1 Gala Rovers | 22 | 15 | 3 | 4 | 74 | 40 | 48 |
| 2 Newtown | 22 | 13 | 3 | 6 | 54 | 44 | 42 |
| 3 Leithen Rovers | 22 | 12 | 2 | 8 | 62 | 44 | 38 |
| 4 Pencaitland (-3pts) | 22 | 12 | 3 | 7 | 88 | 55 | 36 |
| 5 Chirnside Utd | 22 | 10 | 4 | 8 | 64 | 60 | 34 |
| 6 Tweeddale Rovers | 22 | 9 | 5 | 8 | 50 | 50 | 32 |
| 7 Hawick Waverley | 22 | 9 | 4 | 9 | 59 | 56 | 31 |
| 8 Hearts of Liddesdale (-3pts) | 22 | 10 | 2 | 10 | 63 | 68 | 29 |
| 9 Greenlaw | 22 | 8 | 2 | 12 | 41 | 56 | 26 |
| 10 West Barns Star | 22 | 6 | 6 | 10 | 58 | 70 | 24 |
| 11 Langholm Legion (-3pts) | 22 | 6 | 5 | 11 | 49 | 69 | 20 |
| 12 Duns Ams | 22 | 2 | 1 | 19 | 33 | 83 | 7 |

| B League | P | W | D | L | F | A | Pts |
|---|---|---|---|---|---|---|---|
| 1 Ancrum | 20 | 15 | 1 | 4 | 58 | 32 | 46 |
| 2 Stow | 20 | 14 | 1 | 5 | 72 | 28 | 43 |
| 3 Eyemouth Ams (-3pts) | 20 | 13 | 2 | 5 | 61 | 48 | 38 |
| 4 Hawick Utd (-3pts) | 20 | 11 | 5 | 4 | 63 | 40 | 35 |
| 5 Selkirk Victoria | 20 | 10 | 3 | 7 | 45 | 43 | 33 |
| 6 Jed Legion (+2pts) | 20 | 8 | 4 | 8 | 41 | 36 | 30 |
| 7 Linton Hotspur (-3pts) | 20 | 7 | 3 | 10 | 36 | 50 | 21 |
| 8 Gala Hotspur | 20 | 6 | 2 | 12 | 36 | 49 | 20 |
| 9 Coldstream Ams (-3pts) | 20 | 7 | 1 | 12 | 46 | 56 | 19 |
| 10 Hawick Legion | 20 | 5 | 3 | 12 | 42 | 56 | 18 |
| 11 CFC Bowholm | 20 | 1 | 1 | 18 | 22 | 84 | 4 |

| C League | P | W | D | L | F | A | Pts |
|---|---|---|---|---|---|---|---|
| 1 Biggar (-3pts) | 20 | 16 | 2 | 2 | 65 | 20 | 47 |
| 2 Gordon | 20 | 13 | 4 | 3 | 59 | 30 | 43 |
| 3 Tweedmouth Ams Colts | 20 | 12 | 3 | 5 | 62 | 40 | 39 |
| 4 Lauder (-3pts) | 20 | 11 | 6 | 3 | 41 | 21 | 36 |
| 5 Chirnside Utd Colts | 20 | 10 | 3 | 7 | 53 | 39 | 33 |
| 6 Kelso Thistle | 20 | 6 | 7 | 7 | 49 | 45 | 25 |
| 7 St.Boswells | 20 | 7 | 3 | 10 | 38 | 55 | 24 |
| 8 Earlston Rhymers | 20 | 6 | 4 | 10 | 35 | 43 | 22 |
| 9 Hawick Legion Rovers | 20 | 5 | 2 | 13 | 37 | 72 | 17 |
| 10 Peebles Ams | 20 | 3 | 3 | 14 | 32 | 62 | 12 |
| 11 Abbotsford Albion | 20 | 2 | 1 | 17 | 23 | 67 | 4 |

| Premier Division | P | W | D | L | F | A | Pts |
|---|---|---|---|---|---|---|---|
| 1 Giffnock North | 22 | 14 | 4 | 4 | 40 | 28 | 46 |
| 2 Westerlands | 22 | 14 | 3 | 5 | 62 | 30 | 45 |
| 3 Glasgow Harp | 22 | 14 | 3 | 5 | 51 | 22 | 45 |
| 4 Doune Castle | 22 | 10 | 4 | 8 | 41 | 50 | 34 |
| 5 St Mungo's | 22 | 9 | 6 | 7 | 39 | 37 | 33 |
| 6 Milton | 22 | 9 | 4 | 9 | 53 | 45 | 31 |
| 7 Dumbarton | 22 | 7 | 6 | 9 | 31 | 34 | 27 |
| 8 Gartcosh | 22 | 8 | 2 | 12 | 30 | 39 | 26 |
| 9 Glasgow University | 22 | 7 | 4 | 11 | 43 | 48 | 25 |
| 10 Cambusbarron | 22 | 6 | 6 | 10 | 40 | 54 | 24 |
| 11 Dalzielhsfp | 22 | 5 | 6 | 11 | 36 | 48 | 21 |
| 12 Crumchapel FP | 22 | 3 | 4 | 15 | 32 | 63 | 13 |

| Division One | P | W | D | L | F | A | Pts |
|---|---|---|---|---|---|---|---|
| 1 Ekfcwhitehills | 26 | 21 | 3 | 2 | 92 | 26 | 63 |
| 2 Cambria | 26 | 17 | 3 | 6 | 70 | 40 | 54 |
| 3 Strathclyde University | 26 | 16 | 4 | 6 | 89 | 49 | 52 |
| 4 Stirling University | 26 | 15 | 5 | 6 | 80 | 39 | 50 |
| 5 Milngavie | 26 | 14 | 6 | 6 | 70 | 50 | 45 |
| 6 East Kilbride YM | 26 | 13 | 4 | 9 | 70 | 55 | 43 |
| 7 Viewfield | 26 | 12 | 1 | 13 | 74 | 84 | 37 |
| 8 Hamilton FP | 26 | 12 | 3 | 11 | 53 | 48 | 36 |
| 9 Bearsden | 26 | 9 | 5 | 12 | 56 | 49 | 32 |
| 10 RHU | 26 | 10 | 2 | 14 | 65 | 82 | 32 |
| 11 Balmore | 26 | 7 | 4 | 15 | 42 | 57 | 22 |
| 12 Rothesay | 26 | 6 | 3 | 17 | 45 | 79 | 18 |
| 13 Weirs | 26 | 4 | 5 | 17 | 39 | 97 | 17 |
| 14 Symington | 26 | 2 | 0 | 24 | 30 | 119 | 6 |

## Central Scottish Amateur League

| Premier Division | P | W | D | L | F | A | Pts |
|---|---|---|---|---|---|---|---|
| 1 Colville Park | 22 | 16 | 6 | 0 | 60 | 21 | 54 |
| 2 Wellhouse | 22 | 17 | 2 | 3 | 69 | 24 | 53 |
| 3 Bannockburn | 22 | 15 | 4 | 3 | 62 | 35 | 49 |
| 4 Campsie Minerva | 22 | 12 | 4 | 6 | 56 | 44 | 40 |
| 5 St Patricks FP | 22 | 8 | 7 | 7 | 47 | 49 | 31 |
| 6 Drumchapel United | 22 | 9 | 3 | 10 | 51 | 46 | 30 |
| 7 Ashvale Victoria | 22 | 9 | 2 | 11 | 33 | 38 | 29 |
| 8 Harestanes | 22 | 8 | 2 | 12 | 35 | 38 | 26 |
| 9 Uddingston Anvil | 22 | 5 | 4 | 13 | 49 | 57 | 19 |
| 10 Steins Thistle | 22 | 4 | 6 | 12 | 34 | 59 | 18 |
| 11 Kilsyth | 22 | 4 | 1 | 17 | 33 | 69 | 13 |
| 12 Wishaw HSFP | 22 | 2 | 5 | 15 | 25 | 74 | 11 |

| Division One A | P | W | D | L | F | A | Pts |
|---|---|---|---|---|---|---|---|
| 1 Greenock HSFP | 20 | 16 | 3 | 1 | 83 | 24 | 51 |
| 2 Eastfield | 20 | 14 | 1 | 5 | 64 | 32 | 43 |
| 3 Stirling City | 20 | 11 | 3 | 6 | 45 | 42 | 36 |
| 4 Condorrat Club | 20 | 10 | 3 | 7 | 30 | 27 | 33 |
| 5 Arthurlie United | 20 | 10 | 2 | 8 | 46 | 42 | 32 |
| 6 Mill United | 20 | 9 | 2 | 9 | 47 | 53 | 29 |
| 7 Cambusnethan Talbot | 20 | 8 | 4 | 8 | 47 | 46 | 28 |
| 8 East Kilbride | 20 | 7 | 3 | 10 | 53 | 56 | 24 |
| 9 Redbrae | 20 | 6 | 2 | 12 | 40 | 59 | 20 |
| 10 Chryston | 20 | 5 | 2 | 13 | 35 | 61 | 17 |
| 11 Stedfast | 20 | 0 | 3 | 17 | 33 | 81 | 3 |

## SCOTTISH FOOTBALL

| Division One B | P | W | D | L | F | A | Pts |
|---|---|---|---|---|---|---|---|
| 1 Drumchapel | 20 | 17 | 3 | 0 | 80 | 19 | 54 |
| 2 Garrowhill Thistle | 20 | 14 | 1 | 5 | 68 | 32 | 43 |
| 3 Pollok | 20 | 10 | 6 | 4 | 61 | 40 | 36 |
| 4 Waterside | 20 | 11 | 2 | 7 | 70 | 47 | 35 |
| 5 Linwood | 20 | 10 | 5 | 5 | 47 | 32 | 35 |
| 6 Mearns | 20 | 10 | 3 | 7 | 55 | 41 | 33 |
| 7 Gourock Athletic | 20 | 6 | 8 | 6 | 30 | 35 | 26 |
| 8 Scotia Athletic | 20 | 5 | 3 | 12 | 32 | 78 | 18 |
| 9 Brightons | 20 | 3 | 3 | 14 | 26 | 69 | 12 |
| 10 Cumbernauld Clyde | 20 | 2 | 3 | 15 | 31 | 78 | 9 |
| 11 Grangemouth | 20 | 1 | 5 | 14 | 23 | 52 | 8 |

## DUMFRIES & DISTRICT AMATEUR LEAGUE

| | P | W | D | L | F | A | Pts |
|---|---|---|---|---|---|---|---|
| 1 Lochmaben | 21 | 19 | 0 | 2 | 93 | 25 | 57 |
| 2 Lochar Thistle | 21 | 15 | 2 | 4 | 70 | 30 | 47 |
| 3 Dynamo Star | 21 | 10 | 2 | 9 | 53 | 65 | 32 |
| 4 Upper Annandale | 21 | 10 | 0 | 11 | 59 | 54 | 30 |
| 5 Maxwelltown Thistle | 21 | 7 | 4 | 10 | 46 | 50 | 25 |
| 6 Terregles Athletic | 21 | 7 | 2 | 12 | 49 | 63 | 23 |
| 7 Morton Thistle | 21 | 6 | 2 | 13 | 47 | 75 | 20 |
| 8 YMCA | 21 | 4 | 0 | 17 | 37 | 92 | 12 |

## SCOTTISH JUNIOR CUP

**ROUND 1**

| | | | |
|---|---|---|---|
| Crossgates Primrose | v | Cumnock Juniors | 0-5 |
| Muirkirk Juniors | v | Yoker Athletic | 0-6 |
| Lesmahagow Juniors | v | Bellshill Athletic | 0-1 |
| Dunbar United | v | Penicuik Athletic | 4-4 |
| Penicuik Athletic | v | Dunbar United | 3-1 |
| Port Glasgow Juniors | v | Aberdeen East End | 7-1 |
| Sunnybank | v | Lossiemouth United | 2-2 |
| Lossiemouth United | v | Sunnybank | 3-1 |
| Fochabers | v | Larkhall Thistle | 4-9 |
| Troon | v | Kilwinning Rangers | 0-4 |
| Bo'ness United | v | Whitletts Victoria | 5-2 |
| Colony Park | v | Fauldhouse United | 1-6 |
| Fraserburgh United | v | Lochgelly Albert | 1-4 |
| Arbroath Victoria | v | Kelty Hearts | 1-4 |
| Tayport | v | West Calder United | 1-0 |
| Broughty Athletic | v | Armadale Thistle | 0-3 |
| Harthill Royal | v | Whitburn Juniors | 0-8 |
| Cambuslang Rangers | v | Pollok | 0-6 |
| Kirkcaldy Y.M.C.A. | v | Thorniewood United | 2-6 |
| Bishopmill United | v | Longside | 2-7 |
| F C Stoneywood | v | Tranent Juniors | 4-2 |
| Glasgow Perthshire | v | Petershill | 0-2 |
| St. Roch's | v | Jeanfield Swifts | 0-6 |
| St. Andrew's United | v | Spartans | 3-2 |
| Vale of Clyde | v | Ashfield | 0-2 |
| Newmachars | v | Lugar Boswell Thistle | 0-1 |
| Oakley United | v | Darvel Juniors | 7-3 |
| Blantyre Victoria | v | Lochee United | 1-1 |
| Lochee United | v | Blantyre Victoria | 2-0 |
| Renfrew | v | Lewis United | 2-0 |
| Burghead Thistle | v | Maybole Juniors | 2-0 |
| Buckie Rovers | v | New Elgin | 3-0 |
| Beith Juniors | v | Bankfoot Athletic | 8-0 |
| Craigmark Burntonians | v | St. Anthony's | 1-3 |
| Kello Rovers | v | Hill of Beath Hawthorn | 1-7 |
| Lochore Welfare | v | Newburgh | 2-0 |
| Bathgate Thistle | v | Clydebank | 0-4 |
| Newmains United | v | Dundee East Craigie F.C | 2-1 |

# DOWNLOAD THE DIRECTORY FOR FREE!

The Non-League Club Directory is also avaialble as a download on the platforms listed to the right. As a reader of the Directory we'd like to offer you the chance to sample it for FREE until the season ends.

Including all that's in the this paperback edition, the download will have the added benefit of being updated as the season progresses. Including photos, previews and reports the Directory will grow as the season goes on.

If you would like to take us up on this offer please send your request for a FREE subsription to tw.publications@btinternet.com
Please quote: NLD14APP

For iPhone

For iPad

## ROUND 2

| | | |
|---|---|---|
| Bo'ness United | v Port Gordon Victoria | 11-1 |
| Musselburgh Athletic | v Bridge of Don | 5-0 |
| Glentanar | v Blackburn United | 3-6 |
| Culter | v Thornton Hibs | 4-0 |
| Kilsyth Rangers | v Irvine Victoria | 2-1 |
| Whitburn Juniors | v Newtongrange Star | 1-6 |
| Ellon United | v East Kilbride Thistle | 1-2 |
| Kirriemuir Thistle | v Banks O'Dee | 4-2 |
| Carnoustie Panmure | v Dundonald Bluebell | 0-2 |
| Blairgowrie Juniors | v Nairn St. Ninian | 5-1 |
| Fauldhouse United | v Lochee Harp | 8-0 |
| Lugar Boswell Thistle | v Yoker Athletic | 1-3 |
| Inverness City | v Dundee Downfield | 3-2 |
| Bellshill Athletic | v Largs Thistle | 2-0 |
| Hurlford United | v Rutherglen Glencairn | 1-3 |
| Deveronside | v Lochore Welfare | 3-1 |
| Jeanfield Swifts | v Port Glasgow Juniors | 0-0 |
| Port Glasgow Juniors | v Jeanfield Swifts | 1-6 |
| Ashfield | v Arniston Rangers | 3-0 |
| Dyce | v Hill of Beath Hawthorn | 1-0 |
| Dundee Violet | v Kilbirnie Ladeside | 5-3 |
| Carluke Rovers | v Kinnoull | 1-1 |
| Kinnoull | v Carluke Rovers | 1-0 |
| Lanark United | v Forth Wanderers | 0-3 |
| Ballingry Rovers | v Sauchie Juniors | 0-0 |
| Sauchie Juniors | v Ballingry Rovers | 2-1 |
| R.A.F. Lossiemouth | v Camelon Juniors | 0-13 |
| Forfar West End | v Buckie Rovers | 2-1 |
| Buchanhaven Hearts | v F C Stoneywood | 2-1 |
| Ardrossan Winton Rovers | v Linlithgow Rose | 0-9 |
| Lochee United | v Kilwinning Rangers | 4-1 |
| Glenafton Athletic | v Clydebank | 3-2 |
| Greenock Juniors | v Forres Thistle | 6-1 |
| Cumnock Juniors | v Larkhall Thistle | 5-0 |
| Oakley United | v Stonehaven | 3-1 |
| Brechin Victoria | v Coupar Angus | 4-3 |
| Longside | v St. Anthony's | 1-1 |
| St. Anthony's | v Longside | 3-1 |
| Vale of Leven | v Irvine Meadow X1 F.C. | 0-2 |
| Haddington Athletic | v Shotts Bon Accord | 0-4 |
| Islavale | v Luncarty | 4-0 |
| Tayport | v Annbank United | 1-0 |
| Burghead Thistle | v Kirkintilloch Rob Roy | 1-11 |
| Parkvale | v St. Andrew's United | 1-2 |
| Forfar Albion | v Saltcoats Victoria | 1-5 |
| Pollok | v Neilston Juniors | 2-1 |
| Auchinleck Talbot | v Dalkeith Thistle | 6-1 |
| Banchory St. Ternan | v Rosyth Recreation | 4-5 |
| Petershill | v Newmains United | 3-0 |
| Rossvale | v Ardeer Thistle | 0-2 |
| Thorniewood United | v Dundee North End | 4-1 |
| Dalry Thistle | v Cumbernauld United | 0-4 |
| Falkirk Juniors | v Hermes | 1-4 |
| Kelty Hearts | v Renfrew | 4-0 |
| Wishaw Juniors | v Beith Juniors | 1-4 |
| Stoneyburn | v Maryhill | 1-1 |
| Maryhill | v Stoneyburn | 1-0 |
| Lochgelly Albert | v Johnstone Burgh | 0-2 |
| Arthurlie | v Broxburn Athletic | 2-1 |
| Girvan F.C. | v Penicuik Athletic | 0-3 |
| Edinburgh United | v Scone Thistle | 3-0 |
| Bonnyrigg Rose Athletic | v Maud | 4-1 |
| Steelend Victoria | v Lossiemouth United | 3-0 |
| Dunipace | v Livingston United | 0-0 |
| Livingston United | v Dunipace | 2-1 |
| Armadale Thistle | v Hall Russell United | 2-1 |
| Royal Albert | v Montrose Roselea | 2-4 |
| Shettleston | v Cruden Bay | 4-1 |
| Pumpherston | v Whitehills | 3-2 |
| Glenrothes Juniors | v Benburb | 1-1 |
| Benburb | v Glenrothes Juniors | 4-2 |

## ROUND 3

| | | |
|---|---|---|
| Deveronside | v Rutherglen Glencairn | 0-6 |
| Kirriemuir Thistle | v Kilsyth Rangers | 1-4 |
| Camelon Juniors | v Thorniewood United | 3-3 |
| Thorniewood United | v Camelon Juniors | 2-3 |
| Cumbernauld United | v Forfar West End | 0-0 |
| Forfar West End | v Cumbernauld United | 1-4 |
| St. Anthony's | v Irvine Meadow X1 F.C. | 1-4 |
| St. Andrew's United | v Jeanfield Swifts | 0-3 |
| Newtongrange Star | v Auchinleck Talbot | 0-1 |
| Musselburgh Athletic | v Bellshill Athletic | 4-0 |
| Yoker Athletic | v Forth Wanderers | 2-1 |
| Hermes | v Bo'ness United | 1-2 |
| Dyce | v Lochee United | 1-6 |
| Linlithgow Rose | v Fauldhouse United | 3-1 |
| Pumpherston | v Inverness City | 4-3 |
| Culter | v Edinburgh United | 7-2 |
| Ashfield | v Ardeer Thistle | 0-1 |
| Dundee Violet | v Livingston United | 5-0 |
| Dundonald Bluebell | v Oakley United | 2-1 |
| Cumnock Juniors | v Islavale | 6-0 |
| Bonnyrigg Rose Athletic | v Petershill | 3-6 |
| Beith Juniors | v Sauchie Juniors | 2-1 |
| Montrose Roselea | v Maryhill | 3-1 |
| Shettleston | v Tayport | 3-1 |
| Armadale Thistle | v Kirkintilloch Rob Roy | 2-5 |
| Blackburn United | v Blairgowrie Juniors | 3-2 |
| Rosyth Recreation | v Brechin Victoria | 4-0 |
| Benburb | v Saltcoats Victoria | 4-2 |
| Greenock Juniors | v Shotts Bon Accord | 2-4 |
| Johnstone Burgh | v Buchanhaven Hearts | 7-1 |
| Glenafton Athletic | v Pollok | 0-1 |
| Steelend Victoria | v Arthurlie | 1-6 |
| Kinnoull | v East Kilbride Thistle | 4-0 |
| Kelty Hearts | v Penicuik Athletic | 2-1 |

## ROUND 4

| | | |
|---|---|---|
| Culter | v Cumnock Juniors | 4-5 |
| Montrose Roselea | v Jeanfield Swifts | 1-1 |
| Jeanfield Swifts | v Montrose Roselea | 5-0 |
| Irvine Meadow X1 F.C. | v Shettleston | 2-2 |
| Shettleston | v Irvine Meadow X1 F.C. | 0-1 |
| Yoker Athletic | v Camelon Juniors | 0-2 |
| Auchinleck Talbot | v Petershill | 7-0 |
| Arthurlie | v Linlithgow Rose | 2-4 |
| Musselburgh Athletic | v Pumpherston | 3-3 |
| Pumpherston | v Musselburgh Athletic | 3-0 |
| Kelty Hearts | v Cumbernauld United | 2-0 |
| Pollok | v Beith Juniors | 3-2 |
| Lochee United | v Ardeer Thistle | 1-0 |
| Johnstone Burgh | v Dundonald Bluebell | 0-2 |
| Kirkintilloch Rob Roy | v Rosyth Recreation | 5-0 |
| Kinnoull | v Kilsyth Rangers | 0-0 |
| Kilsyth Rangers | v Kinnoull | 4-1 |
| Blackburn United | v Rutherglen Glencairn | 0-1 |
| Dundee Violet | v Bo'ness United | 1-1 |
| Bo'ness United | v Dundee Voilet | 4-1 |
| Shotts Bon Accord | v Benburb | 2-1 |

## ROUND 5

| | | |
|---|---|---|
| Lochee United | v Auchinleck Talbot | 1-3 |
| Pollok | v Shotts Bon Accord | 0-1 |
| Irvine Meadow X1 F.C. | v Cumnock Juniors | 0-1 |
| Linlithgow Rose | v Jeanfield Swifts | 3-1 |
| Dundonald Bluebell | v Camelon Juniors | 0-3 |
| Kirkintilloch Rob Roy | v Bo'ness United | 2-3 |
| Kelty Hearts | v Kilsyth Rangers | 2-0 |
| Rutherglen Glencairn | v Pumpherston | 3-2 |

### Quarter Finals

| | | |
|---|---|---|
| Rutherglen Glencairn | v Camelon Juniors | 3-1 |
| Cumnock Juniors | v Shotts Bon Accord | 3-5 |
| Linlithgow Rose | v Bo'ness United | 4-1 |
| Kelty Hearts | v Auchinleck Talbot | 0-4 |

### Semi Finals

| | | |
|---|---|---|
| Auchinleck Talbot | v Rutherglen Glencairn | 2-1 |
| Linlithgow Rose | v Shotts Bon Accord | 4-2 |

## FINAL

| | | |
|---|---|---|
| Auchinleck Talbot | v Linlithgow Rose | 1-0 |

# WELSH TABLES 2012-13

## WELSH PREMIER

| | | P | W | D | L | F | A | Pts |
|---|---|---|---|---|---|---|---|---|
| 1 | The New Saints | 32 | 24 | 4 | 4 | 86 | 22 | 76 |
| 2 | Airbus UK Broughton | 32 | 17 | 3 | 12 | 76 | 42 | 54 |
| 3 | Bangor City | 32 | 14 | 9 | 9 | 64 | 52 | 51 |
| 4 | Port Talbot Town | 32 | 13 | 8 | 11 | 51 | 52 | 47 |
| 5 | Prestatyn Town | 32 | 11 | 7 | 14 | 62 | 79 | 40 |
| 6 | Carmarthen Town AFC | 32 | 10 | 7 | 15 | 36 | 50 | 37 |
| 7 | Bala Town FC | 32 | 17 | 5 | 10 | 62 | 41 | 56 |
| 8 | Gap Connah's Quay (-1pt) | 32 | 12 | 5 | 15 | 62 | 69 | 40 |
| 9 | Newtown AFC | 32 | 10 | 7 | 15 | 44 | 54 | 37 |
| 10 | Aberystwyth Town | 32 | 9 | 10 | 13 | 40 | 59 | 37 |
| 11 | Llanelli AFC | 32 | 10 | 6 | 16 | 41 | 69 | 36 |
| 12 | Afan Lido | 32 | 8 | 3 | 22 | 43 | 79 | 27 |

The table splits after each team has played each other twice. Each team then meet twice more, top six to determine the Champions, bottom six the relegation.

## CYMRU ALLIANCE

| | | P | W | D | L | F | A | Pts |
|---|---|---|---|---|---|---|---|---|
| 1 | Rhyl | 30 | 24 | 6 | 0 | 100 | 24 | 78 |
| 2 | Cefn Druids | 30 | 22 | 3 | 5 | 79 | 32 | 69 |
| 3 | Conwy Borough | 30 | 18 | 7 | 5 | 57 | 37 | 61 |
| 4 | Caersws | 30 | 18 | 3 | 9 | 90 | 42 | 57 |
| 5 | Buckley Town | 30 | 13 | 10 | 7 | 60 | 35 | 49 |
| 6 | Flint Town United | 30 | 14 | 6 | 10 | 61 | 51 | 48 |
| 7 | Holyhead Hotspur | 30 | 13 | 4 | 13 | 51 | 55 | 43 |
| 8 | Guilsfield | 30 | 12 | 6 | 12 | 61 | 54 | 42 |
| 9 | Porthmadog | 30 | 11 | 5 | 14 | 48 | 52 | 38 |
| 10 | Penrhyncoch | 30 | 9 | 7 | 14 | 50 | 63 | 34 |
| 11 | Rhayader Town | 30 | 9 | 6 | 15 | 44 | 66 | 33 |
| 12 | Llandudno | 30 | 8 | 8 | 14 | 36 | 59 | 32 |
| 13 | Penycae | 30 | 7 | 5 | 18 | 49 | 84 | 26 |
| 14 | Rhydymwyn | 30 | 6 | 8 | 16 | 49 | 96 | 26 |
| 15 | Llanrhaeadr YM | 30 | 4 | 7 | 19 | 29 | 87 | 19 |
| 16 | Ruthin Town | 30 | 3 | 7 | 20 | 47 | 74 | 16 |

## WELSH LEAGUE

### Division One

| | | P | W | D | L | F | A | Pts |
|---|---|---|---|---|---|---|---|---|
| 1 | West End | 28 | 18 | 4 | 6 | 64 | 29 | 58 |
| 2 | Cambrian & Clydach | 28 | 17 | 5 | 6 | 56 | 26 | 56 |
| 3 | Taffs Well | 28 | 14 | 7 | 7 | 57 | 39 | 49 |
| 4 | Haverfordwest County | 28 | 13 | 8 | 7 | 63 | 35 | 47 |
| 5 | Aberdare Town | 28 | 13 | 8 | 7 | 45 | 35 | 47 |
| 6 | AFC Porth | 28 | 13 | 7 | 8 | 39 | 34 | 46 |
| 7 | Monmouth Town (-3pts) | 28 | 13 | 6 | 9 | 54 | 43 | 42 |
| 8 | Bryntirion Athletic | 28 | 10 | 9 | 9 | 38 | 40 | 39 |
| 9 | Ton Pentre | 28 | 9 | 9 | 10 | 39 | 39 | 36 |
| 10 | Pontardawe Town | 28 | 10 | 5 | 13 | 34 | 39 | 35 |
| 11 | Goytre United | 28 | 10 | 4 | 14 | 33 | 51 | 34 |
| 12 | Cwmbran Celtic | 28 | 9 | 5 | 14 | 41 | 52 | 32 |
| 13 | Bridgend Town | 28 | 8 | 7 | 13 | 28 | 51 | 31 |
| 14 | Tata Steel | 28 | 5 | 6 | 17 | 28 | 61 | 21 |
| 15 | Caerleon | 28 | 1 | 4 | 23 | 18 | 63 | 7 |

Barry Town withdrew - record expunged.

## Division Two

| | | P | W | D | L | F | A | Pts |
|---|---|---|---|---|---|---|---|---|
| 1 | Goytre | 30 | 23 | 3 | 4 | 78 | 32 | 72 |
| 2 | Aberbargoed Buds | 30 | 15 | 10 | 5 | 49 | 33 | 55 |
| 3 | Caerau (Ely) | 30 | 14 | 10 | 6 | 66 | 37 | 52 |
| 4 | Undy Athletic | 30 | 15 | 6 | 9 | 60 | 35 | 51 |
| 5 | Caerau | 30 | 14 | 8 | 8 | 70 | 52 | 50 |
| 6 | Ammanford | 30 | 13 | 7 | 10 | 54 | 49 | 46 |
| 7 | Garden Village | 30 | 13 | 6 | 11 | 42 | 44 | 45 |
| 8 | Briton Ferry Llansawel | 30 | 13 | 5 | 12 | 71 | 57 | 44 |
| 9 | Penrhiwceiber Rangers | 30 | 12 | 7 | 11 | 61 | 58 | 43 |
| 10 | Caldicot Town | 30 | 11 | 10 | 9 | 51 | 54 | 43 |
| 11 | Croesyceiliog | 30 | 10 | 10 | 10 | 65 | 64 | 40 |
| 12 | Newport YMCA | 30 | 12 | 4 | 14 | 42 | 45 | 40 |
| 13 | Dinas Powys | 30 | 9 | 12 | 9 | 63 | 43 | 39 |
| 14 | Ely Rangers | 30 | 6 | 7 | 17 | 55 | 77 | 25 |
| 15 | Cardiff Corinthians | 30 | 3 | 7 | 20 | 33 | 81 | 16 |
| 16 | Cwmaman Institute | 30 | 0 | 2 | 28 | 21 | 120 | 2 |

## Division Three

| | | P | W | D | L | F | A | Pts |
|---|---|---|---|---|---|---|---|---|
| 1 | Cardiff Met University | 30 | 23 | 3 | 4 | 98 | 41 | 72 |
| 2 | AFC Llwydcoed | 30 | 19 | 3 | 8 | 74 | 51 | 60 |
| 3 | Chepstow Town | 30 | 19 | 2 | 9 | 81 | 49 | 59 |
| 4 | Pontypridd Town | 30 | 17 | 8 | 5 | 54 | 30 | 59 |
| 5 | Risca United | 30 | 14 | 11 | 5 | 56 | 29 | 53 |
| 6 | Llantwit Major | 30 | 15 | 5 | 10 | 62 | 43 | 50 |
| 7 | Llanwern | 30 | 13 | 5 | 12 | 54 | 58 | 44 |
| 8 | Newport Civil Service | 30 | 10 | 9 | 11 | 60 | 64 | 39 |
| 9 | Bridgend Street | 30 | 11 | 5 | 14 | 53 | 56 | 38 |
| 10 | Abertillery Bluebirds | 30 | 9 | 8 | 13 | 44 | 56 | 35 |
| 11 | Treowen Stars | 30 | 9 | 6 | 15 | 32 | 56 | 33 |
| 12 | Cardiff Grange Harlequins | 30 | 9 | 5 | 16 | 43 | 57 | 32 |
| 13 | Tredegar Town | 30 | 9 | 3 | 18 | 44 | 61 | 30 |
| 14 | Newcastle Emlyn | 30 | 8 | 2 | 20 | 37 | 86 | 26 |
| 15 | Treharris Ath Western | 30 | 6 | 7 | 17 | 50 | 68 | 25 |
| 16 | Bettws | 30 | 6 | 4 | 20 | 42 | 79 | 22 |

## WELSH ALLIANCE

### Division One

| | | P | W | D | L | F | A | Pts |
|---|---|---|---|---|---|---|---|---|
| 1 | Caernarfon Town | 28 | 21 | 3 | 4 | 91 | 30 | 66 |
| 2 | Denbigh Town | 28 | 20 | 4 | 4 | 89 | 39 | 64 |
| 3 | Holywell Town | 28 | 18 | 7 | 3 | 98 | 38 | 61 |
| 4 | Barmouth & Dyffryn Utd | 28 | 14 | 5 | 9 | 60 | 59 | 47 |
| 5 | Llanrug Utd | 28 | 14 | 4 | 10 | 70 | 43 | 46 |
| 6 | Llanberis | 28 | 13 | 5 | 10 | 65 | 51 | 44 |
| 7 | Llanrwst Utd | 28 | 10 | 8 | 10 | 55 | 42 | 38 |
| 8 | Gwalchmai | 28 | 11 | 5 | 12 | 53 | 55 | 38 |
| 9 | Glantraeth | 28 | 11 | 2 | 15 | 57 | 59 | 35 |
| 10 | Pwllheli | 28 | 10 | 5 | 13 | 45 | 66 | 35 |
| 11 | Glan Conwy | 28 | 8 | 8 | 12 | 45 | 58 | 32 |
| 12 | Bodedern Ath | 28 | 9 | 2 | 17 | 40 | 60 | 29 |
| 13 | Nefyn Utd | 28 | 8 | 4 | 16 | 40 | 81 | 28 |
| 14 | Llandudno Junction | 28 | 8 | 2 | 18 | 42 | 69 | 26 |
| 15 | Llangefni Town | 28 | 2 | 2 | 24 | 18 | 118 | 8 |

## WELSH ALLIANCE

### Division Two

| | P | W | D | L | F | A | Pts |
|---|---|---|---|---|---|---|---|
| 1 Llandyrnog Utd | 24 | 18 | 4 | 2 | 66 | 29 | 58 |
| 2 Llanfairpwll | 24 | 18 | 3 | 3 | 66 | 26 | 57 |
| 3 Penrhyndeudraeth | 24 | 15 | 3 | 6 | 73 | 32 | 48 |
| 4 Kinmel Bay (-3pts) | 24 | 15 | 4 | 5 | 48 | 32 | 46 |
| 5 Meliden | 24 | 13 | 3 | 8 | 73 | 38 | 42 |
| 6 Greenfield | 24 | 11 | 4 | 9 | 75 | 55 | 37 |
| 7 Penmaenmawr Phoenix | 24 | 10 | 4 | 10 | 47 | 50 | 34 |
| 8 Halkyn Utd | 24 | 8 | 6 | 10 | 45 | 48 | 30 |
| 9 Blaenau Ffestiniog | 24 | 7 | 4 | 13 | 48 | 79 | 25 |
| 10 Gaerwen | 24 | 4 | 4 | 16 | 38 | 65 | 16 |
| 11 Connahs Quay Town (-9pts) | 24 | 6 | 5 | 13 | 38 | 75 | 14 |
| 12 Amlwch Town | 24 | 3 | 5 | 16 | 21 | 67 | 14 |
| 13 Nantlle Vale | 24 | 2 | 3 | 19 | 39 | 81 | 9 |

## CLYWD LEAGUE

### Premier Division

| | P | W | D | L | F | A | Pts |
|---|---|---|---|---|---|---|---|
| 1 St Asaph | 16 | 14 | 2 | 0 | 65 | 24 | 44 |
| 2 Rhuddlan Town | 16 | 10 | 3 | 3 | 53 | 35 | 33 |
| 3 Prestatyn Rovers | 16 | 9 | 4 | 3 | 53 | 36 | 31 |
| 4 Mochdre Sports | 16 | 8 | 2 | 6 | 44 | 37 | 26 |
| 5 Llansannan | 16 | 6 | 3 | 7 | 34 | 37 | 21 |
| 6 Rhyl Athletic | 16 | 5 | 2 | 9 | 34 | 44 | 17 |
| 7 Old Colwyn | 16 | 4 | 2 | 10 | 37 | 55 | 14 |
| 8 Rhos United | 16 | 3 | 2 | 11 | 30 | 52 | 11 |
| 9 Betws-Yn-Rhos | 16 | 1 | 4 | 11 | 27 | 57 | 7 |

### Division One

| | P | W | D | L | F | A | Pts |
|---|---|---|---|---|---|---|---|
| 1 Machno United | 16 | 11 | 4 | 1 | 66 | 23 | 37 |
| 2 Cerrigydrudion | 16 | 11 | 3 | 2 | 47 | 26 | 36 |
| 3 Llannefydd | 16 | 9 | 3 | 4 | 53 | 26 | 30 |
| 4 Bro Cernyw | 16 | 8 | 4 | 4 | 39 | 33 | 28 |
| 5 Llandudno United | 16 | 7 | 5 | 4 | 53 | 29 | 26 |
| 6 Y Glannau | 16 | 6 | 4 | 6 | 33 | 42 | 22 |
| 7 F.C. Tudno | 16 | 3 | 5 | 8 | 31 | 51 | 14 |
| 8 Rhyl Hearts | 16 | 1 | 1 | 14 | 25 | 63 | 4 |
| 9 Betws-Y-Coed | 16 | 1 | 1 | 14 | 20 | 74 | 4 |

## GWENT COUNTY LEAGUE

### Division One

| | P | W | D | L | F | A | Pts |
|---|---|---|---|---|---|---|---|
| 1 Lliswerry | 28 | 22 | 2 | 4 | 63 | 27 | 68 |
| 2 Pill | 28 | 19 | 4 | 5 | 83 | 43 | 61 |
| 3 Govilon | 28 | 19 | 3 | 6 | 79 | 53 | 60 |
| 4 AC Pontymister | 28 | 15 | 5 | 8 | 62 | 48 | 50 |
| 5 Fairfield United | 28 | 13 | 5 | 10 | 59 | 39 | 44 |
| 6 Albion Rovers | 28 | 13 | 5 | 10 | 62 | 62 | 44 |
| 7 Panteg | 28 | 11 | 8 | 9 | 76 | 59 | 41 |
| 8 Abercarn United | 28 | 11 | 6 | 11 | 60 | 63 | 39 |
| 9 Coed Eva Athletic | 28 | 12 | 2 | 14 | 60 | 66 | 38 |
| 10 Abertillery Excelsiors | 28 | 9 | 4 | 15 | 47 | 62 | 31 |
| 11 Blaenavon Blues | 28 | 6 | 9 | 13 | 52 | 66 | 27 |
| 12 Clydach Wasps | 28 | 7 | 4 | 17 | 35 | 65 | 25 |
| 13 Cwmbran Town | 28 | 6 | 6 | 16 | 50 | 66 | 24 |
| 14 P.I.L.C.S. | 28 | 5 | 7 | 16 | 47 | 71 | 22 |
| 15 Pentwynmawr Athletic | 28 | 5 | 4 | 19 | 47 | 92 | 19 |

Fleur-De-Lys Welfare withdrew.

## GWENT COUNTY LEAGUE

### Division Two

| | P | W | D | L | F | A | Pts |
|---|---|---|---|---|---|---|---|
| 1 Newport Corinthians | 28 | 22 | 2 | 4 | 108 | 42 | 68 |
| 2 Trethomas Bluebirds | 28 | 20 | 7 | 1 | 105 | 36 | 67 |
| 3 Blackrock Rovers | 28 | 17 | 7 | 4 | 72 | 33 | 58 |
| 4 Cwmffrwdoer Sports | 28 | 16 | 5 | 7 | 84 | 57 | 53 |
| 5 Tredegar Athletic | 28 | 17 | 0 | 11 | 87 | 53 | 51 |
| 6 Malpas United | 28 | 15 | 4 | 9 | 88 | 74 | 49 |
| 7 Spencer Youth & Boys | 28 | 14 | 4 | 10 | 72 | 62 | 46 |
| 8 Cromwell | 28 | 13 | 6 | 9 | 90 | 64 | 45 |
| 9 Rockfield Rovers | 28 | 9 | 7 | 12 | 56 | 70 | 34 |
| 10 Mardy | 28 | 7 | 6 | 15 | 55 | 82 | 27 |
| 11 Lucas Cwmbran | 28 | 6 | 5 | 17 | 58 | 87 | 23 |
| 12 RTB Ebbw Vale | 28 | 7 | 2 | 19 | 45 | 89 | 23 |
| 13 Cefn Forest | 28 | 6 | 3 | 19 | 63 | 107 | 21 |
| 14 Llanhilleth Athletic | 28 | 6 | 3 | 19 | 38 | 106 | 21 |
| 15 Rogerstone | 28 | 4 | 1 | 23 | 40 | 99 | 13 |

### Division Three

| | P | W | D | L | F | A | Pts |
|---|---|---|---|---|---|---|---|
| 1 Ynysddu Crusaders | 28 | 22 | 1 | 5 | 102 | 44 | 67 |
| 2 New Inn | 28 | 18 | 6 | 4 | 105 | 40 | 60 |
| 3 Marshfield | 28 | 19 | 1 | 8 | 101 | 52 | 58 |
| 4 Abergavenny Thursdays | 28 | 18 | 4 | 6 | 69 | 41 | 58 |
| 5 Neuadd Wen | 28 | 15 | 6 | 7 | 93 | 53 | 51 |
| 6 Rhymney | 28 | 15 | 6 | 7 | 63 | 41 | 51 |
| 7 Ponthir | 28 | 11 | 5 | 12 | 81 | 58 | 38 |
| 8 Tranch | 28 | 11 | 5 | 12 | 95 | 92 | 38 |
| 9 Sebastopol | 28 | 12 | 1 | 15 | 65 | 83 | 37 |
| 10 Trinant | 28 | 11 | 2 | 15 | 72 | 94 | 35 |
| 11 Thornwell Red & White | 28 | 10 | 3 | 15 | 53 | 83 | 33 |
| 12 Whiteheads (-3pts) | 28 | 9 | 2 | 17 | 66 | 85 | 26 |
| 13 Caldicot Castle | 28 | 8 | 2 | 18 | 43 | 91 | 26 |
| 14 Race | 28 | 4 | 2 | 22 | 36 | 109 | 14 |
| 15 Pontypool Town | 28 | 3 | 2 | 23 | 49 | 127 | 11 |

## GWYNEDD LEAGUE

| | P | W | D | L | F | A | Pts |
|---|---|---|---|---|---|---|---|
| 1 Trearddur Bay United | 22 | 20 | 2 | 0 | 79 | 24 | 62 |
| 2 CPD Waunfawr | 22 | 13 | 5 | 4 | 63 | 37 | 44 |
| 3 CPD Llanerchymedd | 22 | 13 | 3 | 6 | 59 | 35 | 42 |
| 4 Beaumaris Town | 22 | 12 | 3 | 7 | 67 | 42 | 39 |
| 5 CPD Bro Goronwy | 22 | 11 | 3 | 8 | 69 | 53 | 36 |
| 6 CPD Bethel | 22 | 10 | 3 | 9 | 58 | 40 | 33 |
| 7 CPD Llanllyfni | 22 | 8 | 3 | 11 | 56 | 66 | 27 |
| 8 Holyhead Hotspur | 22 | 7 | 5 | 10 | 37 | 45 | 26 |
| 9 Bangor University (-6pts) | 22 | 9 | 4 | 9 | 51 | 49 | 25 |
| 10 CPD Llanystumdwy | 22 | 6 | 2 | 14 | 49 | 59 | 20 |
| 11 Llanfairfechan Town (-3pts) | 22 | 4 | 0 | 18 | 38 | 105 | 9 |
| 12 CPD Bontnewydd | 22 | 1 | 3 | 18 | 23 | 94 | 6 |

Holyhead Town withdrew.

# MID WALES LEAGUE

## Division One

| | | P | W | D | L | F | A | Pts |
|---|---|---|---|---|---|---|---|---|
| 1 | Llanidloes Town | 30 | 26 | 2 | 2 | 132 | 31 | 80 |
| 2 | Montgomery | 30 | 22 | 4 | 4 | 106 | 27 | 70 |
| 3 | Builth Wells | 30 | 17 | 6 | 7 | 78 | 53 | 57 |
| 4 | Tywyn Bryncrug | 30 | 18 | 2 | 10 | 91 | 50 | 56 |
| 5 | Four Crosses | 30 | 17 | 3 | 10 | 82 | 64 | 54 |
| 6 | Waterloo | 30 | 16 | 4 | 10 | 81 | 60 | 52 |
| 7 | Berriew | 30 | 14 | 7 | 9 | 64 | 41 | 49 |
| 8 | Aberaeron | 30 | 15 | 3 | 12 | 63 | 47 | 48 |
| 9 | Bow Street | 30 | 11 | 8 | 11 | 78 | 70 | 41 |
| 10 | Aberystwyth Uni | 30 | 12 | 4 | 14 | 65 | 61 | 40 |
| 11 | Llansantffraid Village | 30 | 10 | 5 | 15 | 66 | 71 | 35 |
| 12 | Carno | 30 | 11 | 2 | 17 | 46 | 57 | 35 |
| 13 | Welshpool | 30 | 9 | 2 | 19 | 51 | 79 | 29 |
| 14 | Dyffryn Banw | 30 | 7 | 0 | 23 | 33 | 101 | 21 |
| 15 | Newbridge | 30 | 6 | 3 | 21 | 39 | 151 | 21 |
| 16 | Dolgellau | 30 | 1 | 1 | 28 | 22 | 134 | 4 |

## Division Two

| | | P | W | D | L | F | A | Pts |
|---|---|---|---|---|---|---|---|---|
| 1 | Llanfair Utd | 24 | 21 | 2 | 1 | 92 | 21 | 65 |
| 2 | Llandrindod Wells | 24 | 16 | 2 | 6 | 70 | 31 | 50 |
| 3 | Rhosgoch | 24 | 13 | 6 | 5 | 68 | 37 | 45 |
| 4 | Kerry | 24 | 14 | 1 | 9 | 43 | 43 | 43 |
| 5 | Presteigne | 24 | 12 | 5 | 7 | 67 | 59 | 41 |
| 6 | Knighton | 24 | 11 | 4 | 9 | 56 | 45 | 37 |
| 7 | Machynlleth | 24 | 11 | 4 | 9 | 66 | 60 | 37 |
| 8 | Hay St Marys | 24 | 9 | 6 | 9 | 67 | 64 | 33 |
| 9 | Llanfyllin Town | 24 | 7 | 5 | 12 | 48 | 62 | 26 |
| 10 | Talgarth | 24 | 5 | 5 | 14 | 36 | 62 | 20 |
| 11 | Abermule | 24 | 6 | 2 | 16 | 38 | 71 | 20 |
| 12 | Bont | 24 | 4 | 2 | 18 | 34 | 79 | 14 |
| 13 | Aberdyfi | 24 | 4 | 2 | 18 | 44 | 95 | 14 |

# SOUTH WALES AMATEUR LEAGUE

## Division One

| | | P | W | D | L | F | A | Pts |
|---|---|---|---|---|---|---|---|---|
| 1 | Rhoose | 30 | 22 | 2 | 6 | 103 | 40 | 68 |
| 2 | Treforest | 30 | 21 | 4 | 5 | 93 | 37 | 67 |
| 3 | Ton & Gelli BC | 30 | 18 | 3 | 9 | 85 | 41 | 57 |
| 4 | Trefelin BGC | 30 | 15 | 6 | 9 | 70 | 59 | 51 |
| 5 | Llantwit Fardre AFC | 30 | 14 | 6 | 10 | 61 | 49 | 48 |
| 6 | STM Sports AFC | 30 | 15 | 3 | 12 | 89 | 79 | 48 |
| 7 | Baglan Dragons | 30 | 15 | 5 | 10 | 70 | 48 | 47 |
| 8 | Trelewis Welfare | 30 | 13 | 7 | 10 | 55 | 59 | 46 |
| 9 | Splott Albion | 30 | 13 | 5 | 12 | 59 | 62 | 44 |
| 10 | Pontyclun | 30 | 11 | 9 | 10 | 64 | 51 | 42 |
| 11 | Caerau Link | 29 | 13 | 3 | 13 | 69 | 64 | 42 |
| 12 | Aber Valley YMCA | 30 | 12 | 2 | 16 | 54 | 75 | 38 |
| 13 | Cardiff Draconians | 30 | 10 | 2 | 18 | 60 | 73 | 32 |
| 14 | Perthcelyn United | 30 | 5 | 6 | 19 | 60 | 106 | 18 |
| 15 | Carnetown BGC | 29 | 3 | 5 | 21 | 32 | 97 | 14 |
| 16 | Kenfig Hill | 30 | 4 | 2 | 24 | 39 | 123 | 14 |

## Division Two

| | | P | W | D | L | F | A | Pts |
|---|---|---|---|---|---|---|---|---|
| 1 | Merthyr Saints | 28 | 21 | 3 | 4 | 94 | 43 | 66 |
| 2 | Clwb Cymric | 28 | 20 | 4 | 4 | 84 | 29 | 64 |
| 3 | Cardiff Hibernian | 28 | 19 | 3 | 6 | 69 | 42 | 60 |
| 4 | Pencoed Athletic | 28 | 18 | 4 | 6 | 89 | 38 | 58 |
| 5 | Llangynwyd Rangers | 28 | 18 | 3 | 7 | 78 | 32 | 57 |
| 6 | Aberfan SDC | 28 | 14 | 5 | 9 | 45 | 40 | 47 |
| 7 | Blaenrhondda | 28 | 11 | 5 | 12 | 62 | 49 | 38 |
| 8 | Hirwaun Welfare/Mackworth | 28 | 10 | 5 | 13 | 58 | 70 | 35 |
| 9 | AFC Bargoed | 28 | 10 | 4 | 14 | 63 | 67 | 34 |
| 10 | Brynna AFC | 28 | 9 | 4 | 15 | 46 | 70 | 31 |
| 11 | Rhydyfelin AFC | 28 | 9 | 4 | 15 | 41 | 68 | 31 |
| 12 | Graig AFC | 28 | 7 | 7 | 14 | 57 | 94 | 28 |
| 13 | Llanharry AFC | 28 | 7 | 2 | 19 | 40 | 69 | 23 |
| 14 | Ferndale BGC | 28 | 6 | 4 | 18 | 44 | 69 | 22 |
| 15 | FC Abercwmboi | 28 | 2 | 1 | 25 | 27 | 117 | 7 |

# SOUTH WALES SENIOR LEAGUE

## Division One

| | | P | W | D | L | F | A | Pts |
|---|---|---|---|---|---|---|---|---|
| 1 | Sully Sports | 30 | 23 | 4 | 3 | 97 | 29 | 73 |
| 2 | CWM Welfare AFC | 30 | 19 | 6 | 5 | 76 | 39 | 63 |
| 3 | Grange Albion | 30 | 17 | 4 | 9 | 66 | 42 | 55 |
| 4 | Lewistown FC | 30 | 14 | 8 | 8 | 71 | 52 | 50 |
| 5 | AFC Butetown | 30 | 14 | 8 | 8 | 66 | 53 | 49 |
| 6 | Ynyshir Albions FC | 30 | 15 | 3 | 12 | 61 | 56 | 48 |
| 7 | Brecon Corriers FC | 30 | 14 | 3 | 13 | 60 | 53 | 45 |
| 8 | Penydarren BGC | 30 | 12 | 7 | 11 | 52 | 50 | 43 |
| 9 | Porthcawl Town Athletic | 30 | 12 | 7 | 11 | 59 | 56 | 42 |
| 10 | Cwmbach Royal Stars SC | 30 | 12 | 5 | 13 | 58 | 63 | 41 |
| 11 | Fochriw AFC | 30 | 12 | 3 | 15 | 50 | 71 | 38 |
| 12 | Cogan Coronation AFC | 30 | 10 | 6 | 14 | 64 | 62 | 36 |
| 13 | Tonypandy Albion | 30 | 10 | 5 | 15 | 60 | 77 | 35 |
| 14 | St Josephs | 30 | 9 | 4 | 17 | 44 | 69 | 31 |
| 15 | Pentwyn Dynamos | 30 | 5 | 1 | 24 | 39 | 101 | 16 |
| 16 | Llanrumney United | 30 | 3 | 4 | 23 | 32 | 83 | 15 |

## SOUTH WALES SENIOR

| Division Two | P | W | D | L | F | A | Pts |
|---|---|---|---|---|---|---|---|
| 1 Cornelly United | 26 | 21 | 3 | 2 | 86 | 27 | 66 |
| 2 Pontlottyn AFC | 26 | 18 | 4 | 4 | 77 | 31 | 58 |
| 3 Fairwater | 26 | 17 | 5 | 4 | 99 | 38 | 56 |
| 4 Penrhiwfer AFC | 26 | 16 | 4 | 6 | 73 | 41 | 51 |
| 5 St Albans AFC | 26 | 13 | 4 | 9 | 65 | 53 | 43 |
| 6 Cadoxton Barry | 26 | 12 | 5 | 9 | 69 | 64 | 41 |
| 7 AFC Whitchurch | 26 | 11 | 5 | 10 | 55 | 44 | 38 |
| 8 Tonyreffail BGC | 26 | 9 | 4 | 13 | 34 | 53 | 31 |
| 9 Max United | 26 | 8 | 5 | 13 | 54 | 100 | 29 |
| 10 Garw SGBC | 26 | 6 | 8 | 12 | 41 | 71 | 26 |
| 11 Tongwynlais AFC | 26 | 6 | 6 | 14 | 43 | 64 | 24 |
| 12 Stanleytown | 26 | 4 | 4 | 18 | 31 | 68 | 16 |
| 13 Penrhiwceiber Cons Athletic | 26 | 3 | 7 | 16 | 35 | 77 | 16 |
| 14 Llwynypia BGC | 26 | 3 | 6 | 17 | 43 | 74 | 15 |

## CEREDIGION LEAGUE

| Division One | P | W | D | L | F | A | Pts |
|---|---|---|---|---|---|---|---|
| 1 New Quay | 20 | 18 | 1 | 1 | 78 | 17 | 55 |
| 2 Lampeter | 20 | 16 | 0 | 4 | 76 | 36 | 48 |
| 3 St Dogmaels | 20 | 15 | 0 | 5 | 90 | 26 | 45 |
| 4 NCE Reserves (-3pts) | 20 | 14 | 2 | 4 | 58 | 21 | 41 |
| 5 Crannog | 20 | 10 | 2 | 8 | 45 | 44 | 32 |
| 6 Bargod | 20 | 7 | 5 | 8 | 27 | 47 | 26 |
| 7 Llanybydder | 20 | 7 | 0 | 13 | 32 | 59 | 21 |
| 8 Maesglas | 20 | 4 | 4 | 12 | 25 | 42 | 16 |
| 9 Aberaeron Reserves | 20 | 3 | 5 | 12 | 32 | 70 | 14 |
| 10 Felinfach | 20 | 3 | 2 | 15 | 23 | 80 | 11 |
| 11 Llanboidy | 20 | 2 | 1 | 17 | 25 | 69 | 7 |

Pencader withdrew - record expunged.

| Division Two | P | W | D | L | F | A | Pts |
|---|---|---|---|---|---|---|---|
| 1 Cardigan | 22 | 19 | 1 | 2 | 102 | 19 | 58 |
| 2 Aberporth | 22 | 15 | 3 | 4 | 65 | 25 | 48 |
| 3 Llandysul | 22 | 15 | 0 | 7 | 69 | 42 | 45 |
| 4 Dewi Stars | 22 | 13 | 3 | 6 | 58 | 37 | 42 |
| 5 Saron | 22 | 12 | 2 | 8 | 69 | 42 | 38 |
| 6 St Dogmaels Reserves | 22 | 10 | 3 | 9 | 43 | 50 | 33 |
| 7 New Quay Reserves | 22 | 8 | 2 | 12 | 45 | 58 | 26 |
| 8 Llanybydder Reserves | 22 | 8 | 1 | 13 | 41 | 61 | 25 |
| 9 Ffostrasol | 22 | 6 | 2 | 14 | 37 | 66 | 20 |
| 10 Cilgerran *-3pts) | 22 | 6 | 1 | 15 | 31 | 72 | 16 |
| 11 Bargod Reserves | 22 | 5 | 1 | 16 | 34 | 78 | 16 |
| 12 SDUC (-3pts) | 22 | 5 | 1 | 16 | 25 | 69 | 13 |

Maesglas Reserves withdrew - record expunged.

## MID WALES (SOUTH) LEAGUE

| | P | W | D | L | F | A | Pts |
|---|---|---|---|---|---|---|---|
| 1 Rhayader Reserves | 28 | 20 | 4 | 4 | 75 | 27 | 64 |
| 2 Penybont | 28 | 20 | 3 | 5 | 93 | 38 | 63 |
| 3 Builth Wells Reserves | 28 | 18 | 7 | 3 | 100 | 34 | 61 |
| 4 Bronllys | 27 | 16 | 5 | 6 | 64 | 53 | 53 |
| 5 Llanidloes Reserves | 28 | 15 | 6 | 7 | 89 | 31 | 48 |
| 6 Knighton Reserves | 28 | 15 | 4 | 9 | 67 | 63 | 46 |
| 7 Newcastle | 28 | 12 | 4 | 12 | 57 | 45 | 40 |
| 8 Presteigne Reserves | 28 | 12 | 4 | 12 | 51 | 63 | 40 |
| 9 Brecon | 28 | 12 | 3 | 13 | 56 | 54 | 39 |
| 10 Bucknell | 28 | 9 | 7 | 12 | 56 | 63 | 28 |
| 11 Radnor Valley | 28 | 8 | 4 | 16 | 46 | 71 | 28 |
| 12 Talgarth Reserves | 28 | 6 | 5 | 17 | 30 | 102 | 23 |
| 13 Llandrindod Reserves | 28 | 5 | 6 | 17 | 44 | 68 | 21 |
| 14 Sennybridge | 27 | 3 | 10 | 14 | 33 | 61 | 19 |
| 15 St Harmon | 28 | 0 | 4 | 24 | 23 | 111 | 4 |

## NEATH & DISTRICT LEAGUE

| Premier Division | P | W | D | L | F | A | Pts |
|---|---|---|---|---|---|---|---|
| 1 Ystradgynlais AFC(A) | 22 | 18 | 3 | 1 | 79 | 18 | 57 |
| 2 Cwmamman Utd(A) | 22 | 16 | 3 | 3 | 85 | 31 | 51 |
| 3 Giants Grave (A) | 22 | 14 | 5 | 3 | 85 | 30 | 47 |
| 4 Seven Sisters FC (A) | 22 | 15 | 2 | 5 | 64 | 33 | 47 |
| 5 Bryn Rovers (A) | 22 | 10 | 3 | 9 | 57 | 56 | 33 |
| 6 Park Travellers (A) | 22 | 10 | 3 | 9 | 77 | 67 | 31 |
| 7 Sunnybank WMC (A) | 22 | 9 | 2 | 11 | 42 | 48 | 29 |
| 8 Ynysymeudwy Ath (A) | 22 | 9 | 2 | 11 | 44 | 54 | 29 |
| 9 FC Clydach (A) | 22 | 8 | 1 | 13 | 38 | 63 | 25 |
| 10 Resolven (A) | 22 | 6 | 0 | 16 | 54 | 88 | 18 |
| 11 Cilfrew Rovers (A) | 22 | 3 | 2 | 17 | 31 | 81 | 9 |
| 12 Coelbren Ath | 22 | 1 | 0 | 21 | 31 | 118 | 3 |

| Division One | P | W | D | L | F | A | Pts |
|---|---|---|---|---|---|---|---|
| 1 Briton Ferry FC(A) | 16 | 15 | 0 | 1 | 75 | 19 | 45 |
| 2 Ynysygerwen (A) | 16 | 11 | 2 | 3 | 56 | 24 | 35 |
| 3 Glynneath Town (A) | 16 | 10 | 3 | 3 | 49 | 34 | 33 |
| 4 Cambrian FC(A) | 16 | 9 | 0 | 7 | 44 | 40 | 27 |
| 5 Cwm Wanderers (A) | 16 | 8 | 0 | 8 | 43 | 37 | 24 |
| 6 Pontardawe Town | 16 | 7 | 3 | 6 | 34 | 33 | 24 |
| 7 Clydach Sports (A) | 16 | 3 | 2 | 11 | 25 | 56 | 11 |
| 8 AFC Pontardawe (A) | 16 | 1 | 3 | 12 | 30 | 56 | 6 |
| 9 Rhos FC (A) | 16 | 1 | 1 | 14 | 24 | 81 | 4 |

| Division Two | P | W | D | L | F | A | Pts |
|---|---|---|---|---|---|---|---|
| 1 Onllwyn | 16 | 13 | 1 | 2 | 55 | 14 | 40 |
| 2 FC Cimla | 16 | 12 | 3 | 1 | 88 | 27 | 39 |
| 3 FC Nedd | 16 | 8 | 2 | 6 | 60 | 28 | 26 |
| 4 Harp Rovers (A) | 16 | 7 | 3 | 6 | 50 | 35 | 24 |
| 5 Bryncoch FC (A) | 16 | 6 | 6 | 4 | 50 | 36 | 24 |
| 6 Tonna FC(A) | 16 | 5 | 3 | 8 | 38 | 39 | 18 |
| 7 Godregraig Ath (A) | 16 | 5 | 2 | 9 | 34 | 69 | 17 |
| 8 I.N.C.O Vale FC(A) | 16 | 3 | 3 | 10 | 32 | 65 | 12 |
| 9 Borough (A) | 16 | 1 | 1 | 14 | 16 | 110 | 4 |

## NEWPORT & DISTRICT LEAGUE

### Premier X Division

| | P | W | D | L | F | A | Pts |
|---|---|---|---|---|---|---|---|
| 1 Pontnewydd Utd | 18 | 14 | 2 | 2 | 65 | 25 | 44 |
| 2 Machen FC | 18 | 13 | 4 | 1 | 70 | 27 | 43 |
| 3 FC Boilermakers | 18 | 12 | 3 | 3 | 65 | 31 | 39 |
| 4 West of St Julians | 18 | 10 | 5 | 3 | 56 | 28 | 35 |
| 5 Cwmcarn Athletic | 18 | 8 | 2 | 8 | 40 | 38 | 26 |
| 6 Villa Dino C/Ch | 18 | 7 | 1 | 10 | 43 | 56 | 22 |
| 7 Docks Cons | 18 | 6 | 1 | 11 | 35 | 57 | 19 |
| 8 Graig-Y-Rhacca | 18 | 4 | 3 | 11 | 44 | 47 | 15 |
| 9 Newport Eagles | 18 | 3 | 2 | 13 | 46 | 65 | 11 |
| 10 Athletico Cwmbran | 18 | 1 | 1 | 16 | 20 | 110 | 4 |

Llanyrafon FC, Bettws Socialdad, Oakfield Inn and K-2 AFC all withdrawn.

### Premier Y

| | P | W | D | L | F | A | pts |
|---|---|---|---|---|---|---|---|
| 1 AC Pontymister | 24 | 20 | 4 | 0 | 106 | 23 | 64 |
| 2 Pill AFC | 24 | 19 | 2 | 3 | 106 | 40 | 59 |
| 3 Albion Rovers | 24 | 18 | 2 | 4 | 92 | 40 | 56 |
| 4 Lliswerry | 24 | 13 | 3 | 8 | 76 | 59 | 42 |
| 5 Coed Eva Ath | 24 | 10 | 4 | 10 | 67 | 57 | 34 |
| 6 Spencer Boys Club | 24 | 10 | 3 | 11 | 59 | 69 | 33 |
| 7 Cromwell Youth | 24 | 9 | 4 | 11 | 72 | 91 | 31 |
| 8 Trethomas Bluebirds | 24 | 9 | 0 | 15 | 50 | 72 | 27 |
| 9 Marshfield | 24 | 6 | 5 | 13 | 43 | 65 | 23 |
| 10 Npt Corinthians | 24 | 6 | 5 | 13 | 43 | 71 | 23 |
| 11 Cwmbran Town | 24 | 6 | 5 | 13 | 60 | 93 | 23 |
| 12 Lucas Cwmbran | 24 | 5 | 1 | 18 | 41 | 86 | 16 |
| 13 Cwmbran Celtic | 24 | 4 | 4 | 16 | 43 | 92 | 16 |

Malpas United withdrawn.

### Division One

| | P | W | D | L | F | A | pts |
|---|---|---|---|---|---|---|---|
| 1 Pioneer FC | 22 | 17 | 3 | 2 | 98 | 32 | 54 |
| 2 Pill AFC | 22 | 16 | 0 | 6 | 89 | 28 | 48 |
| 3 Rogerstone | 22 | 14 | 1 | 7 | 72 | 50 | 43 |
| 4 AC Pontymister | 22 | 12 | 2 | 8 | 69 | 43 | 38 |
| 5 K-2 AFC | 22 | 11 | 3 | 8 | 46 | 62 | 36 |
| 6 Lliswerry | 22 | 9 | 6 | 7 | 51 | 46 | 33 |
| 7 Ponthir | 22 | 10 | 2 | 10 | 60 | 65 | 32 |
| 8 Albion Rovers | 22 | 10 | 2 | 10 | 54 | 65 | 32 |
| 9 Shaftesbury Youth | 22 | 8 | 5 | 9 | 58 | 75 | 29 |
| 10 Villa Dino C/Ch | 22 | 5 | 1 | 16 | 48 | 88 | 16 |
| 11 Caerleon Town | 22 | 3 | 3 | 16 | 48 | 97 | 12 |
| 12 Crosskeys | 22 | 2 | 2 | 18 | 30 | 72 | 8 |

Maesglas United withdrawn.

### Division Two

| | P | W | D | L | F | A | pts |
|---|---|---|---|---|---|---|---|
| 1 Infusion Sports Bar | 20 | 18 | 1 | 1 | 137 | 27 | 55 |
| 2 Docks Cons | 20 | 16 | 2 | 2 | 123 | 37 | 50 |
| 3 Cwmcarn Athletic | 20 | 11 | 3 | 6 | 55 | 44 | 36 |
| 4 Pontnewydd Utd | 20 | 11 | 3 | 6 | 64 | 66 | 36 |
| 5 FC Rileys | 20 | 9 | 2 | 9 | 67 | 58 | 29 |
| 6 Racing Club Npt | 20 | 8 | 4 | 8 | 67 | 66 | 28 |
| 7 Risca Athletic | 20 | 7 | 1 | 12 | 48 | 67 | 22 |
| 8 Albion Rovers | 20 | 6 | 3 | 11 | 46 | 81 | 21 |
| 9 Machen FC | 20 | 6 | 0 | 14 | 55 | 89 | 18 |
| 10 Caerleon Town | 20 | 3 | 3 | 14 | 45 | 95 | 12 |
| 11 Cromwell Youth | 20 | 3 | 2 | 15 | 39 | 116 | 11 |

Lucas Cwmbran and Bettws Socialdad both withdrawn.

### Division Three

| | P | W | D | L | F | A | pts |
|---|---|---|---|---|---|---|---|
| 1 Racing Club | 24 | 20 | 1 | 3 | 96 | 37 | 61 |
| 2 AC Pontymister | 24 | 19 | 3 | 2 | 75 | 31 | 60 |
| 3 Spencer Boys | 24 | 16 | 3 | 5 | 111 | 45 | 51 |
| 4 Pill AFC | 24 | 10 | 2 | 12 | 60 | 59 | 32 |
| 5 Riverside Rovers | 24 | 9 | 2 | 13 | 65 | 77 | 29 |
| 6 Coed Eva | 24 | 8 | 2 | 14 | 49 | 68 | 26 |
| 7 Ponthir | 24 | 7 | 1 | 16 | 52 | 93 | 22 |
| 8 Newport Eagles | 24 | 7 | 0 | 17 | 57 | 102 | 21 |
| 9 Rogerstone | 24 | 5 | 0 | 19 | 45 | 98 | 15 |

Llanyrafon FC withdrawn.

## PEMBROKESHIRE LEAGUE

### Division One

| | P | W | D | L | F | A | Pts |
|---|---|---|---|---|---|---|---|
| 1 Hakin United | 24 | 18 | 4 | 2 | 91 | 26 | 58 |
| 2 Johnston | 24 | 16 | 6 | 2 | 63 | 24 | 54 |
| 3 Goodwick United | 24 | 15 | 4 | 5 | 75 | 42 | 49 |
| 4 Merlins Bridge | 24 | 12 | 6 | 6 | 68 | 41 | 42 |
| 5 Narberth | 24 | 12 | 5 | 7 | 52 | 35 | 41 |
| 6 Tenby | 24 | 10 | 4 | 10 | 61 | 57 | 34 |
| 7 Monkton Swifts | 24 | 10 | 3 | 11 | 52 | 68 | 32 |
| 8 Saundersfoot Sports | 24 | 9 | 5 | 10 | 45 | 52 | 31 |
| 9 Pennar Robins | 24 | 8 | 3 | 13 | 52 | 59 | 27 |
| 10 Neyland | 24 | 6 | 7 | 11 | 38 | 55 | 25 |
| 11 St Ishmaels | 24 | 6 | 6 | 12 | 45 | 71 | 24 |
| 12 Hundleton | 24 | 4 | 1 | 19 | 32 | 82 | 13 |
| 13 Solva | 24 | 3 | 0 | 21 | 27 | 89 | 8 |

### Division Two

| | P | W | D | L | F | A | Pts |
|---|---|---|---|---|---|---|---|
| 1 West Dragons | 26 | 19 | 5 | 2 | 106 | 31 | 62 |
| 2 St Clears | 26 | 19 | 2 | 5 | 71 | 35 | 59 |
| 3 Herbrandston | 26 | 16 | 6 | 4 | 86 | 40 | 54 |
| 4 Milford Athletic | 26 | 14 | 6 | 6 | 68 | 41 | 48 |
| 5 Angle | 26 | 13 | 5 | 8 | 68 | 42 | 44 |
| 6 Clarbeston Road | 26 | 13 | 6 | 7 | 84 | 59 | 44 |
| 7 Milford United | 26 | 12 | 5 | 9 | 58 | 58 | 41 |
| 8 Prendergast Villa | 26 | 9 | 6 | 11 | 42 | 47 | 33 |
| 9 Kilgetty | 26 | 9 | 4 | 13 | 62 | 89 | 31 |
| 10 Carew | 26 | 6 | 5 | 15 | 44 | 77 | 23 |
| 11 Goodwick United II | 26 | 7 | 3 | 16 | 43 | 77 | 21 |
| 12 Pennar Robins II | 26 | 6 | 2 | 18 | 47 | 83 | 19 |
| 13 Letterston | 26 | 5 | 3 | 18 | 29 | 70 | 17 |
| 14 Lamphey | 26 | 4 | 2 | 20 | 52 | 111 | 12 |

## PEMBROKESHIRE LEAGUE

### WELSH NATIONAL LEAGUE (WREXHAM) AREA

### Division Three

| | | P | W | D | L | F | A | Pts |
|---|---|---|---|---|---|---|---|---|
| 1 | Fishguard Sports | 26 | 19 | 4 | 3 | 83 | 41 | 61 |
| 2 | Johnston II | 26 | 14 | 4 | 8 | 77 | 50 | 46 |
| 3 | Broad Haven | 26 | 14 | 3 | 9 | 93 | 57 | 45 |
| 4 | Narberth II | 26 | 14 | 3 | 9 | 82 | 63 | 45 |
| 5 | Cosheston Cougars | 26 | 14 | 3 | 9 | 68 | 58 | 45 |
| 6 | Lawrenny | 26 | 12 | 6 | 8 | 68 | 55 | 42 |
| 7 | Hakin United II | 26 | 12 | 4 | 10 | 68 | 56 | 40 |
| 8 | Tenby II | 26 | 15 | 3 | 8 | 86 | 68 | 39 |
| 9 | Haverfordwest Cricket Club | 26 | 11 | 5 | 10 | 65 | 58 | 38 |
| 10 | Camrose | 26 | 8 | 3 | 15 | 75 | 79 | 27 |
| 11 | Hubberston | 26 | 9 | 0 | 17 | 64 | 90 | 27 |
| 12 | Manorbier United | 26 | 9 | 3 | 14 | 54 | 64 | 26 |
| 13 | Merlins Bridge II | 26 | 7 | 3 | 16 | 58 | 84 | 21 |
| 14 | Pembroke Boro | 26 | 2 | 0 | 24 | 28 | 146 | 6 |

### Division Four

| | | P | W | D | L | F | A | Pts |
|---|---|---|---|---|---|---|---|---|
| 1 | Clarbeston Road II | 26 | 20 | 3 | 3 | 97 | 42 | 63 |
| 2 | Pennar Robins III | 26 | 17 | 4 | 5 | 92 | 45 | 55 |
| 3 | St Ishmaels II | 26 | 17 | 2 | 7 | 92 | 32 | 53 |
| 4 | Milford United II | 26 | 15 | 4 | 7 | 81 | 51 | 49 |
| 5 | Monkton Swifts II | 26 | 13 | 3 | 10 | 83 | 73 | 39 |
| 6 | Hundleton II | 26 | 11 | 1 | 14 | 76 | 82 | 34 |
| 7 | Neyland II | 26 | 10 | 4 | 12 | 60 | 81 | 34 |
| 8 | Milford Athletic II | 26 | 9 | 4 | 13 | 63 | 79 | 31 |
| 9 | Saundersfoot Sports II | 26 | 9 | 3 | 14 | 72 | 75 | 30 |
| 10 | Carew II | 26 | 9 | 2 | 15 | 44 | 70 | 29 |
| 11 | Pendine | 26 | 9 | 1 | 16 | 64 | 97 | 28 |
| 12 | Prendergast Villa II | 26 | 8 | 3 | 15 | 57 | 69 | 27 |
| 13 | St Florence | 26 | 9 | 1 | 16 | 58 | 90 | 25 |
| 14 | Herbrandston II | 26 | 8 | 1 | 17 | 65 | 118 | 25 |

### Division Five

| | | P | W | D | L | F | A | Pts |
|---|---|---|---|---|---|---|---|---|
| 1 | West Dragons II | 26 | 20 | 2 | 4 | 112 | 37 | 62 |
| 2 | St Clears II | 26 | 20 | 2 | 4 | 89 | 40 | 62 |
| 3 | Haverfordwest Cricket Club II | 26 | 18 | 1 | 7 | 86 | 54 | 55 |
| 4 | Fishguard Sports II | 26 | 16 | 3 | 7 | 66 | 40 | 51 |
| 5 | Solva II | 26 | 14 | 6 | 6 | 91 | 50 | 45 |
| 6 | Llangwm AFC | 26 | 13 | 3 | 10 | 102 | 49 | 42 |
| 7 | Cosheston Cougars II | 26 | 11 | 3 | 12 | 68 | 70 | 36 |
| 8 | Lawrenny II | 26 | 11 | 2 | 13 | 58 | 56 | 35 |
| 9 | Camrose II | 26 | 10 | 2 | 14 | 58 | 70 | 32 |
| 10 | Letterston II | 26 | 8 | 4 | 14 | 45 | 85 | 26 |
| 11 | Manorbier United II | 26 | 7 | 3 | 16 | 63 | 89 | 24 |
| 12 | Kilgetty II | 26 | 7 | 3 | 16 | 43 | 81 | 21 |
| 13 | Broad Haven II | 26 | 5 | 2 | 19 | 41 | 95 | 17 |
| 14 | Pembroke Boro II | 26 | 4 | 0 | 22 | 41 | 147 | 12 |

### Premier

| | | P | W | D | L | F | A | Pts |
|---|---|---|---|---|---|---|---|---|
| 1 | Chirk AAA | 28 | 18 | 7 | 3 | 84 | 38 | 61 |
| 2 | Mold Alex | 28 | 16 | 6 | 6 | 71 | 37 | 54 |
| 3 | Hawarden Rangers | 28 | 14 | 6 | 8 | 71 | 33 | 48 |
| 4 | Gresford Athletic | 28 | 14 | 6 | 8 | 57 | 46 | 48 |
| 5 | Brymbo | 28 | 12 | 8 | 8 | 58 | 41 | 44 |
| 6 | Llangollen Town | 28 | 13 | 5 | 10 | 67 | 58 | 44 |
| 7 | Penyffordd | 28 | 12 | 4 | 12 | 66 | 57 | 40 |
| 8 | Coedpoeth United | 28 | 10 | 8 | 10 | 55 | 54 | 38 |
| 9 | Saltney Town | 28 | 10 | 7 | 11 | 66 | 60 | 37 |
| 10 | Overton | 28 | 10 | 7 | 11 | 51 | 49 | 37 |
| 11 | Corwen | 28 | 9 | 8 | 11 | 48 | 46 | 35 |
| 12 | Rhos Aelwyd | 28 | 9 | 6 | 13 | 55 | 60 | 33 |
| 13 | Brickfield Rangers | 28 | 8 | 3 | 17 | 40 | 79 | 27 |
| 14 | Llay Welfare | 28 | 5 | 6 | 17 | 40 | 82 | 21 |
| 15 | Venture  (-3pts) | 28 | 5 | 3 | 20 | 39 | 128 | 15 |

### Division One

| | | P | W | D | L | F | A | Pts |
|---|---|---|---|---|---|---|---|---|
| 1 | Borras Park Albion | 24 | 21 | 1 | 2 | 156 | 25 | 64 |
| 2 | FC Nomads of CQ | 24 | 20 | 2 | 2 | 122 | 29 | 62 |
| 3 | Llanuwchllyn | 24 | 16 | 6 | 2 | 106 | 26 | 54 |
| 4 | Castell AC | 24 | 14 | 5 | 5 | 68 | 55 | 47 |
| 5 | New Brighton | 24 | 14 | 2 | 8 | 77 | 54 | 44 |
| 6 | Acrefair Youth (-3pts) | 24 | 12 | 4 | 8 | 77 | 65 | 31 |
| 7 | Argoed United | 24 | 9 | 3 | 12 | 44 | 59 | 30 |
| 8 | Penley | 24 | 9 | 3 | 12 | 50 | 83 | 30 |
| 9 | Lex X1 | 24 | 6 | 4 | 14 | 34 | 95 | 22 |
| 10 | Johnstown Youth (-3pts) | 24 | 6 | 2 | 16 | 47 | 93 | 17 |
| 11 | Garden Village | 24 | 4 | 3 | 17 | 32 | 78 | 15 |
| 12 | Mold Juniors | 24 | 2 | 8 | 14 | 32 | 87 | 14 |
| 13 | Glyn Ceiriog (-6pts) | 24 | 0 | 3 | 21 | 31 | 127 | -3 |

## WELSH CUP

### FIRST QUALIFYING ROUND

| | | |
|---|---|---|
| FC Halifax Town | v Ossett Town | 1-0 |
| Johnstown Youth | v Llanuwchllyn | 0-6 |
| Knighton Town | v Gaerwen | 4-1 |
| Lex XI | v Machynlleth | 3-1 |
| Llandyrnog United | v Bodedern Athletic | 3-4 |
| Llanfairpwll | v Dyffryn Nantlle Vale | 3-1 |
| Llanfyllin Town | v Bethel | 2-6 |
| Llanllyfni | v Castell Alun Colts | 4-3 |
| Llanystumdwy | v Caerwys | 0-2 |
| Montgomery Town | v Blaenau Amateur | 7-1 |
| Pen Y Ffordd | v Penmaenmawr Phoenix | 1-0 |
| Penrhyndeudraeth FC | v Acton Village | Home W/Over |
| Presteigne St. Andrews | v Kerry | 4-1 |
| Trearddur Bay United | v Penley | Home W/Over |
| AFC Llwydcoed | v Cwmbran Town | 8-2 |
| Cardiff Hibernian | v Aber Valley YMCA | 0-1 |
| Cardiff Metropolitan | v Splott Albion | 1-2 |

# WELSH LEAGUES

| | | |
|---|---|---|
| Carnetown | v Aberfan | 2-5 |
| Ely Valley FC | v Kenfig Hill | 3-5 |
| Fleur de Lys Welfare | v Bridgend Street | 1-2 |
| Garw | v Llantwit Major FC | 0-2 |
| Llanharry | v Treforest | 0-5 |
| Llanwern | v Tonyrefail Welfare | 3-1 |
| Merthyr Saints | v Cwmamman United | 0-2 |
| Nelson Cavaliers | v Pontyclun | 1-3 |
| Newcastle Emlyn | v Chepstow Town FC | 1-3 |
| Newport Civil Service | v Cardiff Grange Harlequins | 3-4 |
| Penrhiwceiber Constitutional Ath | v Abertillery Bluebirds | 1-9 |
| Perthcelyn United | v Tredegar Athletic | 4-0 |
| Pontypridd Town | v Graig y Rhacca | 5-0 |
| Porthcawl Town Athletic | v Brecon Corinthians FC | 1-2 |
| Rhydyfelin | v Llantwit Fardre | 1-4 |
| STM Sports | v Ton & Gelli | 0-4 |
| Tredegar Town | v Llandrindod Wells | 5-1 |
| Trefelin | v Risca United | 2-3 |
| Treharris Athletic Western | v Baglan Dragons | 3-2 |
| Treowen Stars | v Trethomas Bluebirds | 5-1 |

## SECOND QUALIFYING ROUND

| | | |
|---|---|---|
| Berriew | v Caernarfon Town | 3-2 |
| Bethel | v Llanrug United | 1-2 |
| Bethesda Athletic | v Corwen | 0-3 |
| Bodedern Athletic | v Lex XI | 4-2 |
| Brickfield Rangers FC | v Dolgellau Athletic Amateur | 3-1 |
| Brymbo | v Caerwys | 6-0 |
| Coedpoeth United | v Trearddur Bay United | 3-2 |
| Connahs Quay Town | v Gwalchmai | 0-7 |
| FC Cefn | v Greenfield | Away W/over |
| FC Nomads of Connah's Quay | v Llanidloes Town | 1-4 |
| Gresford Athletic | v Denbigh Town | 0-7 |
| Holywell Town | v Llanfairpwll | 3-0 |
| Knighton Town | v Four Crosses | 2-4 |
| Llanberis | v Pen Y Ffordd | 1-0 |
| Llandudno Junction | v Llangollen Town | 3-0 |
| Llangefni Town | v Waterloo Rovers | 0-4 |
| Llanllyfni | v Barmouth & Dyffryn United | 2-1 |
| Llanrwst United | v Pwllheli | 1-3 |
| Llansantffraid Village | v Bow Street FC | 1-0 |
| Llanuwchllyn | v Nefyn United | 2-0 |
| Montgomery Town | v Chirk AAA | 6-2 |
| Penrhyndeudraeth FC | v Halkyn United | 2-3 |
| Presteigne St. Andrews | v Glantraeth | 3-2 |
| Rhos Aelwyd | v Glan Conwy | 0-4 |
| Tywyn Bryncrug | v Mold Alexandra | 0-3 |
| Venture Community | v Overton Recreational | 2-0 |
| Welshpool Town | v Carno | 1-2 |
| Aberbargoed Buds | v Perthcelyn United | 3-0 |
| Ammanford | v Kenfig Hill | 5-1 |
| Bettws | v Pontyclun | 2-2 |
| Brecon Corinthians FC | v Aberaeron | 4-1 |
| Bridgend Street | v Aberfan | 1-0 |
| Briton Ferry Llansawel | v Pontypridd Town | 1-3 |
| Builth Wells | v AFC Llwydcoed | 0-4 |
| Caldicot Town | v Treforest | 1-2 |
| Cardiff Corinthians | v Caerau | 0-5 |
| Cardiff Grange Harlequins | v Treharris Athletic Western | 3-0 |
| Chepstow Town FC | v Ton & Gelli | 2-1 |
| Croesyceiliog | v Treowen Stars | 4-0 |
| Cwmaman Institute | v Newbridge on Wye | 4-6 |
| Garden Village | v Ely Rangers | 1-4 |
| Goytre (Gwent) | v Abertillery Bluebirds | 3-0 |

| | | |
|---|---|---|
| Llantwit Fardre | v Aber Valley YMCA | 1-0 |
| Llantwit Major FC | v Caerau Ely | 1-2 |
| Penrhiwceiber Rangers | v Dinas Powys | 1-3 |
| Risca United | v Newport YMCA | 2-1 |
| Splott Albion | v Cwmamman United | 2-6 |
| Tredegar Town | v Llanwern | 1-2 |

## ROUND 1

| | | |
|---|---|---|
| Brickfield Rangers FC | v Pwllheli | 2-5 |
| Brymbo | v Penycae | 1-1, 3-0p |
| Cefn Druids | v Llanberis | 7-1 |
| Coedpoeth United | v Caersws | 1-2 |
| Corwen | v Ruthin Town | 2-1 aet |
| CPD Porthmadog | v Llandudno | 2-3 |
| Flint Town United | v Guilsfield Athletic | 3-2 |
| Four Crosses | v Llanrug United | 1-2 |
| Gwalchmai | v Carno | 4-1 |
| Halkyn United | v Llanidloes Town | 1-6 |
| Holyhead Hotspurs | v Llansantffraid Village | 6-2 |
| Holywell Town | v Denbigh Town | 3-1 |
| Llandudno Junction | v Mold Alexandra | 4-2 |
| Llanllyfni | v Greenfield | 0-4 |
| Llanrhaeadr Ym Mochant | v Glan Conwy | 2-1 aet |
| Llanuwchllyn | v Buckley Town | 3-6 aet |
| Rhyl | v Bodedern Athletic | 7-0 |
| Venture Community | v Montgomery Town | 2-5 aet |
| Waterloo Rovers | v Rhydymwyn | 5-1 |
| Caernarfon Town | v Conwy Borough FC | 0-0, 3-4p |
| Aberbargoed Buds | v Treforest | 2-1 |
| AFC Porth | v Monmouth Town | 0-0, 5-6p |
| Ammanford | v Chepstow Town FC | 1-2 |
| Brecon Corinthians FC | v Haverfordwest County | 2-5 |
| Caerau | v Llantwit Fardre | 8-0 |
| Caerleon | v Barry Town | 2-5 |
| Cardiff Grange Harlequins | v Llanwern | 4-3 |
| Croesyceiliog | v Caerau Ely | 3-7 |
| Cwmamman United | v Newbridge on Wye | 1-5 |
| Cwmbran Celtic | v Cambrian & Clydach Vale | 0-1 |
| Dinas Powys | v Ton Pentre | 1-3 |
| Ely Rangers | v Bryntirion Athletic | 3-1 |
| Goytre (Gwent) | v AFC Llwydcoed | 3-0 |
| Goytre United | v Pontyclun | 6-0 |
| Pontypridd Town | v Aberdare Town | 0-0, 0-3p |
| Presteigne St. Andrews | v Penrhyncoch | 0-2 |
| Rhayader Town | v Risca United | 2-0 |
| Tata Steel | v Bridgend Street | 7-4 |
| West End | v Taffs Well | 4-0 |
| Bridgend Town | v Pontardawe Town | 0-1 |

## ROUND 2

| | | |
|---|---|---|
| Brymbo | v Cefn Druids | 1-3 |
| Conwy Borough FC | v Buckley Town | 1-1, 4-3p |
| Corwen | v Gwalchmai | 1-2 aet |
| Flint Town United | v Greenfield | 3-0 |
| Holywell Town | v Llandudno | 5-3 aet |
| Llanidloes Town | v Caersws | 3-2 |
| Llanrhaeadr Ym Mochant | v Llanrug United | 2-3 |
| Montgomery Town | v Llandudno Junction | 1-3 |
| Waterloo Rovers | v Rhyl | 0-5 |
| Holyhead Hotspur | v Pwllheli | 5-2 |
| Caerau | v Goytre (Gwent) | 1-3 |
| Goytre United | v Caerau Ely | 2-4 |
| Pontardawe Town | v Ton Pentre | 2-0 |
| Aberdare Town | v Tata Steel | 2-1 |

## WELSH CUP - Round 2 continued...

| | | |
|---|---|---|
| Cambrian & Clydach Vale | v Haverfordwest County | 0-1 |
| Chepstow Town FC | v Cardiff Grange Harlequins | 4-1 |
| Ely Rangers | v Aberbargoed Buds | 6-1 |
| Newbridge on Wye | v Monmouth Town | 1-5 |
| Penrhyncoch | v Barry Town | 1-2 |
| West End | v Rhayader Town | 2-0 |

### ROUND 3

| | | |
|---|---|---|
| Aberystwyth Town | v Rhyl | 2-5 |
| Afan Lido | v Prestatyn Town | 3-4 |
| Airbus UK Broughton | v Port Talbot Town | 3-0 |
| Bangor City | v Aberdare Town | 4-1 |
| Barry Town | v Ely Rangers | 3-1 |
| Flint Town United | v Llanidloes Town | 1-0 |
| Gap Connahs Quay | v Llanelli | 4-2 |
| Gwalchmai | v Chepstow Town FC | 0-2 |
| Holyhead Hotspur | v Carmarthen Town | 1-2 |
| Holywell Town | v Caerau Ely | 0-2 |
| Llandudno Junction | v Haverfordwest County | 2-3 |
| Llanrug United | v West End | 0-5 |
| Monmouth Town | v Bala Town | 2-3 |
| Newtown | v Cefn Druids | 2-0 |
| Pontardawe Town | v Goytre (Gwent) | 2-0 |
| The New Saints | v Conwy Borough FC | 3-1 aet |

### ROUND 4

| | | |
|---|---|---|
| Newtown | v Airbus UK Broughton | 1-1, 4-5p |
| The New Saints | v Rhyl | 5-1 |
| Flint Town United | v Caerau Ely | 3-1 |
| Barry Town | v Pontardawe Town | 2-1 |
| Carmarthen Town | v Bala Town | 3-2 aet |
| Chepstow Town FC | v Haverfordwest County | 3-4 |
| Gap Connahs Quay | v Bangor City | 0-2 |
| Prestatyn Town | v West End | 2-0 |

### QUARTER FINALS

| | | |
|---|---|---|
| Bangor City | v Airbus UK Broughton | 1-0 |
| Carmarthen Town | v Prestatyn Town | 2-3 aet |
| Flint Town United | v Barry Town | 0-2 |
| Haverfordwest County | v The New Saints | 0-1 |

### SEMI FINALS

| | | |
|---|---|---|
| Bangor City | v The New Saints | 1-0 |
| Barry Town | v Prestatyn Town | 1 Feb 2013 |

**FINAL** (Played @ Racecourse Ground Wrexham - 06/05/2013)

| | | |
|---|---|---|
| Prestatyn Town | v Bangor City | 3-1 aet |

## WELSH TROPHY

### ROUND 1

| | | |
|---|---|---|
| Acton Village | v Borras Park Rangers | Away W/Over |
| Llanllyfni | v Bethel | 0-10 |
| Llanystumdwy | v St Asaph City FC | 2-1 |
| Mostyn Dragons FC | v Caerwys | 2-5 |
| Rhos United FC | v Flint Mountain FC | 4-3 |
| Talysarn Celts FC | v Trearddur Bay United | 4-2 |
| West Shore FC | v Beaumaris Town FC | 0-10 |
| Blaenrhondda | v Garw | 8-1 |
| Cowbridge Town FC | v Kingsbridge Colts FC | 4-3 |
| Merthyr Candac | v Creigiau | 1-7 |
| Pencoed Athletic Amateur FC | v Cathays Tennants | 4-0 |
| Penrhiwceiber Constitutional Ath | v Cefn Fforest | 2-8 |
| Stanley Town FC | v Graig y Rhacca | 4-2 |
| Tredegar Athletic | v S P Construction | 4-2 |
| AFC Bargoed | v Baili Glas | 5-3 aet |

### ROUND 2

| | | |
|---|---|---|
| Bow Street FC | v Llanidloes Town | 1-0 |
| Carno | v Llandrindod Wells | 1-2 |
| Knighton Town | v Tywyn Bryncrug | 0-2 |
| Llanfair United | v Welshpool Town | H-W |
| Machynlleth | v Berriew | 6-1 |
| Montgomery Town | v Four Crosses | 3-2 |
| Pontrhydfendigaid | v Presteigne St. Andrews | 3-5 |
| Connahs Quay Town | v Gwalchmai | 0-9 |
| New Brighton Villa | v Nefyn United | 2-3 |
| Rhos United FC | v Llandyrnog United | 0-3 |
| Amlwch Town | v Llanystumdwy | 3-0 |
| Borras Park Albion | v Llanuwchllyn | 4-2 |
| Borras Park Rangers FC | v Penley | 1-6 |
| Brickfield Rangers FC | v FC Nomads of Connah's Quay | 4-4 |
| *Nomads won on penalties* | | |
| Caernarfon Town | v Llanfyllin Town | HW |
| Caerwys | v Johnstown Youth | 2-4aet |
| Castell Alun Colts | v Bodedern Athletic | 0-3 |
| Denbigh Town | v Caernarfon Wanderers | HW |
| Dyffryn Nantlle Vale | v Chirk AAA | 1-5 |
| FC Cefn | v Argoed United | AW |
| Glantraeth | v Holywell Town | 0-4 |
| Greenfield | v Kinmel Bay Sports | 6-2 |
| Gresford Athletic | v Corwen | 1-0 |
| Hawarden Rangers | v Halkyn United | 2-1 |
| Lex XI | v Overton Recreational | 1-2 |
| Llanberis | v Rhos Aelwyd | 4-3 |
| Llandudno Junction | v Gaerwen | 3-1 aet |
| Llangollen Town | v Bethel | 5-1 |
| Llanrwst United | v Coedpoeth United | 3-2 |
| Meliden | v Beaumaris Town FC | 4-2 |
| Mold Alexandra | v Llanfairpwll | 1-1, 1-3p |
| Penmaenmawr Phoenix | v Brymbo | 1-2 |
| Penrhyndeudraeth FC | v Pen Y Ffordd | 5-6 aet |
| Talysarn Celts FC | v Pwllheli | 4-5 |
| Venture Community | v Glan Conwy | 2-6 |
| Aberbargoed Buds | v CRC Rangers | 9-0 |
| Abercanaid FC | v Penlan FC | 2-6 |
| Abertillery Excelsiors | v Cefn Fforest | 5-5, 4-1p |
| AFC Bargoed | v Pentwynmawr Athletic | 4-5 aet |
| Albion Rovers FC | v Tredegar Athletic | 3-1 aet |
| Baglan Dragons | v Abercarn United | 4-2 |
| Blaenavon Blues | v Pencoed Athletic Amateur FC | 3-1 aet |

# WELSH LEAGUES

| | | |
|---|---|---|
| Blaenrhondda | v Race | 5-0 |
| Bonymaen Colts | v Fleur de Lys Welfare | 6-7 |
| Bryn Rovers | v Porthcawl Town Athletic | 1-0 |
| Caldicot Town | v Perthcelyn United | 1-2 |
| Carnetown | v Cowbridge Town FC | 1-5 |
| Dafen Welfare | v Ely Valley FC | 7-0 |
| Kenfig Hill | v Swansea Dockers | 5-3 aet |
| Kilvey Fords FC | v Margam Youth Centre | 4-0 |
| Llanharry | v Cardiff Hibernian | 3-2 |
| Maltsters Sports | v Llangynwydd Rangers | 3-5 |
| Nelson Cavaliers | v Morriston Olympic FC | 2-4 |
| Newcastle Emlyn | v STM Sports | 1-2 aet |
| Ragged School | v AFC Whitchurch | 2-0 |
| Rhydyfelin | v Creigiau | 0-2 |
| Stanley Town FC | v Aber Valley YMCA | 4-6 |
| Sully Sports | v Clydach Wasps | 2-1 |
| Talgarth Town | v Cwm & Llantwit Welfare FC | 0-3 |
| Ton & Gelli | v Lewistown FC | 11-0 |
| Tongwynlais | v Gors | HW |
| Trelewis Welfare | v Treorchy Athletic FC | 3-1 |
| Treowen Stars | v Cwmfelin Press | 2-0 |

## ROUND 3

| | | |
|---|---|---|
| Gwalchmai | v Bodedern Athletic | 2-1 |
| Borras Park Albion | v Presteigne St. Andrews | 5-3 |
| Bow Street FC | v Glan Conwy | 0-1 |
| Caernarfon Town | v Meliden | 2-1 |
| Chirk AAA | v Johnstown Youth | 7-0 |
| Denbigh Town | v Tywyn Bryncrug | 3-2 |
| FC Nomads of Connah's Quay | v Gresford Athletic | 2-1 |
| Greenfield | v Pwllheli | 2-3 |
| Llanberis | v Argoed United | 5-1 |
| Llandudno Junction | v Holywell Town | 1-3 |
| Llanfairpwll | v Llanfair United | 1-2 |
| Llangollen Town | v Nefyn United | 4-0 |
| Llanrug United | v Brymbo | 1-2 |
| Llanrwst United | v Pen Y Ffordd | 3-1 |
| Machynlleth | v Amlwch Town | 3-1 |
| Montgomery Town | v Llandrindod Wells | 5-2 |
| Overton Recreational | v Llandyrnog United | 2-2, 9-8p |
| Penley | v Hawarden Rangers | 1-3 |
| Aber Valley YMCA | v Ragged School | 3-5 |
| Baglan Dragons | v Llanharry | 1-6 |
| Bryn Rovers | v Blaenavon Blues | 2-3 |
| Cwm & Llantwit Welfare FC | v Blaenrhondda | 7-1 |
| Fleur de Lys Welfare | v Aberbargoed Buds | AW |
| Kilvey Fords FC | v Cowbridge Town FC | 5-1 |
| Llangynwydd Rangers | v Ton & Gelli | 1-4 |
| Penlan FC | v Pentwynmawr Athletic | 4-2 |
| Perthcelyn United | v Dafen Welfare | 1-4 |
| STM Sports | v Morriston Olympic FC | 4-4, 4-2p |
| Sully Sports | v Kenfig Hill | 5-2 |
| Tongwynlais | v Creigiau | 1-2 aet |
| Trelewis Welfare | v Albion Rovers FC | 1-3 aet |
| Treowen Stars | v Abertillery Excelsiors | 5-3 |

| | | |
|---|---|---|
| Round 4 | | |
| Borras Park Albion | v Pwllheli | 1-0 |
| Denbigh Town | v Montgomery Town | 4-2 |
| Glan Conwy | v Llangollen Town | 4-3 |
| Holywell Town | v Chirk AAA | 4-2 |
| Llanfair United | v Llanberis | 2-3 |
| Llanrwst United | v Brymbo | 2-4 |
| Machynlleth | v Hawarden Rangers | 5-4 |
| Overton Recreational | v FC Nomads of Connah's Quay | 0-1 |
| Caernarfon Town | v Gwalchmai | 2-0 |
| Aberbargoed Buds | v STM Sports | 4-4, 8-9p |
| Blaenavon Blues | v Dafen Welfare | 0-2 |
| Creigiau | v Treowen Stars | 0-2 |
| Llanharry | v Cwm & Llantwit Welfare FC | 0-2 |
| Penlan FC | v Ragged School | 3-4 aet |
| Sully Sports | v Kilvey Fords FC | 2-3 |
| Ton & Gelli | v Albion Rovers FC | 3-1 |

## ROUND 5

| | | |
|---|---|---|
| Holywell Town | v Brymbo | 1-0 |
| FC Nomads of Connah's Quay | v Borras Park Albion | 1-3 |
| Glan Conwy | v Denbigh Town | 3-2 aet |
| Llanberis | v Caernarfon Town | 0-2 |
| Cwm & Llantwit Welfare FC | v Machynlleth | 4-2 |
| Ragged School | v Kilvey Fords FC | 0-2 |
| STM Sports | v Dafen Welfare | 2-3 |
| Ton & Gelli | v Treowen Stars | 1-2 |

## QUARTER FINALS

| | | |
|---|---|---|
| Caernarfon Town | v Glan Conwy | 1-0 |
| Cwm & Llantwit Welfare FC | v Holywell Town | 2-6 |
| Kilvey Fords FC | v Dafen Welfare | 4-1 |
| Treowen Stars | v Borras Park Albion | 3-1 aet |

## SEMI FINALS

| | | |
|---|---|---|
| Holywell Town | v Caernarfon Town | 1-3 |
| Kilvey Fords FC | v Treowen Stars | 1-0 |

**FINAL** (Played @ Latham Park, Newtown - 13/04/2013)

| | | |
|---|---|---|
| Kilvey Ford FC | v Caernarfon Town | 0-6 |

the
# FOOTBALL
# ASSOCIATION
# COMPETITIONS

# ENGLAND C

## RESULTS
2012-13

| No. | Date | Comp | H/A | Opponents | Att: | Result | Goalscorers |
|-----|------|------|-----|-----------|------|--------|-------------|
| 1 | Sept 12 | ICT GA | A | Belgium | | W 2-1 | Spencer 14 (pen), Gray 76 |
| 2 | Feb 2 | ICT KO | H | Turkey | 3,212 | L 0-1 | |
| 3 | Jun 6 | F | A | Bermuda | | W 6-1 | Sarcevic, M Jackson (pen), Norwood (3), Gray |

ICT - International Challenge Trophy (Group A). F - Friendly

## THE PLAYERS

| NAME | | CLUB | 2012-13 CAPS | 12-13 GOALS | TOTAL CAPS | TOTAL GOALS |
|------|--|------|------|-------|------|-------|
| Acheampong | Anthony | Welling United | 1 | 0 | 1 | 0 |
| Ainge | Simon | Guiseley | 2 | 0 | 3 | 0 |
| Beautyman | Harry | Sutton United | 1 | 0 | 1 | 0 |
| Bradley | Danny | Alfreton Town | 1 | 0 | 1 | 0 |
| Brogan | Stephen | Stalybridge Celtic | 1 | 0 | 2 | 0 |
| Clucas | Sam | Hereford United | 1 | 0 | 1 | 0 |
| Cook | Andy | Grimsby Town | 1 | 0 | 1 | 0 |
| Davis | Kenny | Braintree Town | 1 | 0 | 4 | 0 |
| Demetriou | Mickey | Kidderminster Harriers | 1 | 0 | 1 | 0 |
| Edwards | Preston | Ebbsfleet United | 3 | 0 | 5 | 0 |
| Forbes | Kieron | Forest Green Rovers | 2 | 0 | 4 | 0 |
| Franks | Fraiser | Welling United | 1 | 0 | 1 | 0 |
| Gillies | Josh | Gateshead | 2 | 0 | 2 | 0 |
| Gray | Andre | Luton Town | 3 | 2 | 4 | 2 |
| Hunt | Johnny | Wrexham | 1 | 0 | 1 | 0 |
| Jackson | Marlon | Hereford United | 1 | 1 | 1 | 1 |
| Jackson | Ryan | Macclesfield Town | 2 | 0 | 2 | 0 |
| Jarvis | Rossie | Luton Town | 0 | 0 | 3 | 0 |
| Jolley | Christian | Newport County | 1 | 0 | 1 | 0 |
| Meikle | Lindon | Mansfield Town | 2 | 0 | 4 | 0 |
| Mott | Sam | Welling United | 0 | 0 | 0 | 0 |
| Norwood | James | Forest Green Rovers | 1 | 3 | 1 | 3 |
| Ormson | Ian | Stockport County | 0 | 0 | 0 | 0 |
| Oshodi | Edward | Forest Green Rovers | 2 | 0 | 3 | 0 |
| Sarcevic | Antoni | Chester | 1 | 1 | 1 | 1 |
| Spencer | Scott | Hyde | 2 | 1 | 3 | 1 |
| Stokes | Chris | Forest Green Rovers | 1 | 0 | 1 | 0 |
| Taylor | Greg | Luton Town | 1 | 0 | 1 | 0 |
| Thomas | Aswad | Grimsby Town | 2 | 0 | 2 | 0 |
| Turley | Jamie | Forest Green | 2 | 0 | 4 | 0 |
| Vincent | James | Kidderminster Harriers | 1 | 0 | 2 | 0 |
| Walker | Mitchell | Dover Athletic | 1 | 0 | 1 | 0 |
| Watkins | Adam | Luton Town | 1 | 0 | 3 | 1 |
| Wedgbury | Sam | Macclesfield Town | 1 | 0 | 1 | 0 |
| Wilson | Josh | Vauxhall Motors | 1 | 0 | 2 | 0 |
| **CLUBS REPRESENTATIVE TOTALS** | | | | | | |
| Forest Green Rovers | 5 | | | | | |
| Luton Town | 3 | | | | | |
| Grimsby Town | 2 | | | | | |
| Hereford United | 2 | | | | | |
| Kidderminster Harriers | 2 | | | | | |
| Macclesfield Town | 2 | | | | | |
| Welling United | 2 | | | | | |
| Alfreton Town | 1 | | | | | |
| Braintree Town | 1 | | | | | |
| Chester | 1 | | | | | |
| Dover Athletic | 1 | | | | | |
| Ebbsfleet United | 1 | | | | | |
| Gateshead | 1 | | | | | |
| Guiseley | 1 | | | | | |
| Hyde | 1 | | | | | |
| Mansfield Town | 1 | | | | | |
| Newport County | 1 | | | | | |
| Stalybridge Celtic | 1 | | | | | |
| Sutton United | 1 | | | | | |
| Vauxhall Motors | 1 | | | | | |
| Wrexham | 1 | | | | | |

## ENGLAND'S RESULTS 1979 - 2013

**BARBADOS**
| | | |
|---|---|---|
| 02.06.08 | Bridgetown | 2 - 0 |

**BELGIUM**
| | | |
|---|---|---|
| 11.02.03 | KV Ostend | 1 - 3 |
| 04.11.03 | Darlington | 2 - 2 |
| 15.11.05 | FC Racing Jets | 2 - 0 |
| 19.05.09 | Oxford United | 0 - 1 |
| 09.02.11 | Luton Town | 1 - 0 |
| 12.09.12 | Gemeentalijk Sportstadion | 2 - 1 |

**BERMUDA**
| | | |
|---|---|---|
| 04.06.13 | Hamilton | 6 - 1 |

**BOSNIA & HERZEGOVINA**
| | | |
|---|---|---|
| 16.09.08 | Grbavia Stadium | 2 - 6 |

**ESTONIA**
| | | |
|---|---|---|
| 12.10.10 | | 1 - 0 |

**FINLAND UNDER-21**
| | | |
|---|---|---|
| 14.04.93 | Woking | 1 - 3 |
| 30.05.94 | Aanekoski | 0 - 2 |
| 01.06.07 | FC Hakka | 1 - 0 |
| 15.11.07 | Helsinki | 2 - 0 |

**GIBRALTAR**
| | | |
|---|---|---|
| 27.04.82 | Gibraltar | 3 - 2 |
| 31.05.95 | Gibraltar | 3 - 2 |
| 21.05.08 | Colwyn Bay | 1 - 0 |
| 15.11.11 | Gibraltar | 1 - 3 |

**GRENADA**
| | | |
|---|---|---|
| 31.05.08 | St. George's | 1 - 1 |

**HOLLAND**
| | | |
|---|---|---|
| 03.06.79 | Stafford | 1 - 0 |
| 07.06.80 | Zeist | 2 - 1 |
| 09.06.81 | Lucca | 2 - 0 |
| 03.06.82 | Aberdeen | 1 - 0 |
| 02.06.83 | Scarborough | 6 - 0 |
| 05.06.84 | Palma | 3 - 3 |
| 13.06.85 | Vleuten | 3 - 0 |
| 20.05.87 | Kirkaldy | 4 - 0 |
| 11.04.95 | Aalsmeer | 0 - 0 |
| 02.04.96 | Irthlingborough | 3 - 1 |
| 18.04.97 | Appingedam | 0 - 0 |
| 13.03.98 | Crawley | 2 - 1 |
| 30.03.99 | Genemuiden | 1 - 1 |
| 21.03.00 | Northwich | 1 - 0 |
| 22.03.01 | Wihemina FC | 3 - 0 |
| 24.04.02 | Yeovil Town | 1 - 0 |
| 25.03.03 | BV Sparta 25 | 0 - 0 |
| 16.02.05 | Woking | 3 - 0 |
| 29.11.06 | Burton Albion | 4 - 1 |

**HUNGARY**
| | | |
|---|---|---|
| 15.09.09 | Szekesfehervar | 1 - 1 |

**IRAQ**
| | | |
|---|---|---|
| 27.05.04 | Macclesfield | 1 - 5 |

**IRISH PREMIER LEAGUE XI**
| | | |
|---|---|---|
| 13.02.07 | Glenavon FC | 1 - 3 |

**ITALY**
| | | |
|---|---|---|
| 03.06.80 | Zeist | 2 - 0 |
| 13.06.81 | Montecatini | 1 - 1 |
| 01.06.82 | Aberdeen | 0 - 0 |
| 31.05.83 | Scarborough | 2 - 0 |
| 09.06.84 | Reggio Emilia | 0 - 1 |
| 11.06.85 | Houten | 2 - 2 |
| 18.05.87 | Dunfermline | 1 - 2 |
| 29.01.89 | La Spezia | 1 - 1 |
| 25.02.90 | Solerno | 0 - 2 |
| 05.03.91 | Kettering | 0 - 0 |
| 01.03.99 | Hayes | 4 - 1 |
| 01.03.00 | Padova | 1 - 1 |
| 20.11.02 | AC Cremonese | 3 - 2 |
| 11.02.04 | Shrewsbury | 1 - 4 |
| 10.11.04 | US Ivrea FC | 1 - 0 |
| 15.02.06 | Cambridge United | 3 - 1 |
| 12.11.08 | Benevento | 2 - 2 |
| 28.02.12 | Fleetwood Town | 1 - 1 |

**MALTA UNDER-21**
| | | |
|---|---|---|
| 17.02.09 | Malta | 4 - 0 |

**NORWAY UNDER-21**
| | | |
|---|---|---|
| 01.06.94 | Slemmestad | 1 - 2 |

**POLAND**
| | | |
|---|---|---|
| 17.11.09 | Gradiszk Wielpolski | 2 - 1 |

**PORTUGAL**
| | | |
|---|---|---|
| 19.05.11 | Sixfields Stadium | 0 - 1 |

**REPUBLIC OF IRELAND**
| | | |
|---|---|---|
| 24.05.86 | Kidderminster | 2 - 1 |
| 26.05.86 | Nuneaton | 2 - 1 |
| 25.05.90 | Dublin | 2 - 1 |
| 27.05.90 | Cork | 3 - 0 |
| 27.02.96 | Kidderminster | 4 - 0 |
| 25.02.97 | Dublin | 0 - 2 |
| 16.05.02 | Boston | 1 - 2 |
| 20.05.03 | Merthyr Tydfil | 4 - 3 |
| 18.05.04 | Deverondale | 2 - 3 |
| 24.05.05 | Cork | 1 - 0 |
| 23.05.06 | Eastbourne Boro' | 2 - 0 |
| 22.05.07 | Clachnacuddin | 5 - 0 |
| 26.05.10 | Waterford United | 2 - 1 |

**RUSSIA**
| | | |
|---|---|---|
| 05.06.12 | Russia | 0 - 4 |

**SCOTLAND**
| | | |
|---|---|---|
| 31.05.79 | Stafford | 5 - 1 |
| 05.06.80 | Zeist | 2 - 4 |
| 11.06.81 | Empoli | 0 - 0 |
| 05.06.82 | Aberdeen | 1 - 1 |
| 04.06.83 | Scarborough | 2 - 1 |
| 07.06.84 | Modena | 2 - 0 |
| 15.06.85 | Harderwijk | 1 - 3 |
| 23.05.87 | Dunfermline | 2 - 1 |
| 18.05.02 | Kettering | 2 - 0 |
| 24.05.03 | Carmarthen Town | 0 - 0 |
| 23.05.04 | Deverondale | 3 - 1 |
| 28.05.05 | Cork | 3 - 2 |
| 27.05.06 | Eastbourne Boro' | 2 - 0 |
| 25.05.07 | Ross County | 3 - 0 |
| 22.05.08 | Colwyn Bay | 1 - 0 |

**TURKEY**
| | | |
|---|---|---|
| 05.02.13 | Dartford FC | 0 - 1 |

**USA**
| | | |
|---|---|---|
| 20.03.02 | Stevenage Boro. | 2 - 1 |
| 09.06.04 | Charleston USA | 0 - 0 |

**WALES**
| | | |
|---|---|---|
| 27.03.84 | Newtown | 1 - 2 |
| 26.03.85 | Telford | 1 - 0 |
| 18.03.86 | Merthyr Tydfil | 1 - 3 |
| 17.03.87 | Gloucester | 2 - 2 |
| 15.03.88 | Rhyl | 2 - 0 |
| 21.03.89 | Kidderminster | 2 - 0 |
| 06.03.90 | Merthyr Tydfil | 0 - 0 |
| 17.05.91 | Stafford | 1 - 2 |
| 03.03.92 | Aberystwyth | 1 - 0 |
| 02.03.93 | Cheltenham | 2 - 1 |
| 22.02.94 | Bangor | 2 - 1 |
| 28.02.95 | Yeovil Town | 1 - 0 |
| 23.05.99 | St Albans | 2 - 1 |
| 16.05.00 | Llanelli | 1 - 1 |
| 13.02.01 | Rushden & Dia. | 0 - 0 |
| 14.05.02 | Boston | 1 - 1 |
| 22.05.03 | Merthyr Tydfil | 2 - 0 |
| 20.05.04 | Keith FC | 0 - 2 |
| 26.05.05 | Cork | 1 - 0 |
| 25.05.06 | Eastbourne Boro' | 1 - 1 |
| 27.05.07 | Clachnacuddin | 3 - 0 |
| 21.02.08 | Exeter City | 2 - 1 |
| 24.05.08 | Rhyl | 3 - 0 |
| 15.09.10 | Newtown FC | 2 - 2 |

### RESULTS SUMMARY 1979 - 2013

| | P | W | D | L | F | A |
|---|---|---|---|---|---|---|
| Barbados | 1 | 1 | 0 | 0 | 2 | 0 |
| Belgium | 6 | 3 | 1 | 2 | 8 | 7 |
| Bermuda | 1 | 1 | 0 | 0 | 6 | 1 |
| Bosnia & Herzegovina | 1 | 0 | 0 | 1 | 2 | 6 |
| Finland Under-21 | 4 | 2 | 0 | 2 | 4 | 5 |
| Estonia | 1 | 1 | 0 | 0 | 1 | 0 |
| Grenada | 1 | 0 | 1 | 0 | 1 | 1 |
| Gibraltar | 4 | 3 | 0 | 1 | 8 | 7 |
| Holland | 19 | 14 | 5 | 0 | 40 | 8 |
| Hungary | 1 | 0 | 1 | 0 | 1 | 1 |
| Iraq | 1 | 0 | 0 | 1 | 1 | 5 |
| Irish Premier League XI | 1 | 0 | 0 | 1 | 1 | 3 |
| Italy | 18 | 5 | 8 | 4 | 24 | 22 |
| Malta | 1 | 1 | 0 | 0 | 4 | 0 |
| Norway Under-21 | 1 | 0 | 0 | 1 | 1 | 2 |
| Poland | 1 | 1 | 0 | 0 | 2 | 1 |
| Portugal | 1 | 0 | 0 | 1 | 0 | 1 |
| Republic of Ireland | 13 | 10 | 0 | 3 | 30 | 11 |
| Russia | 1 | 0 | 0 | 1 | 0 | 4 |
| Scotland | 15 | 10 | 3 | 2 | 30 | 15 |
| Turkey | 1 | 0 | 0 | 1 | 0 | 1 |
| USA | 2 | 1 | 1 | 0 | 2 | 1 |
| Wales | 24 | 13 | 7 | 4 | 34 | 20 |
| **TOTALS** | **119** | **66** | **27** | **25** | **202** | **122** |

# GOALSCORERS 1979 - 2013

**13 GOALS...**
Carter, Mark

**7 GOALS...**
Cole, Mitchell

**6 GOALS...**
Ashford, Noel

**5 GOALS...**
Davison, Jon
Williams, Colin

**4 GOALS...**
Culpin, Paul
D'Sane, Roscoe
Johnson, Jeff
Mackhail-Smith, Craig

**3 GOALS...**
Adamson, David
Guinan, Steve
Grayson,Neil
Hatch, Liam
Kirk, Jackson
Morison, Steve
Morrison, Michael
Norwood, James
Opponents
Watkins, Dale

**2 GOALS...**
Alford, Carl
Barnes-Homer, Matthew
Barrett, Keith
Bishop, Andrew
Burgess, Andrew
Casey, Kim
Cordice, Neil
Elding, Anthony
Gray, Andre
Hayles, Barry
Hill, Kenny
Howell, David
Mutrie, Les
Patmore, Warren
Richards, Justin
Seddon, Gareth
Southam, Glen
Watson, John
Weatherstone, Simon
Whitbread, Barry

**1 GOAL...**
Agana, Tony
Anderson, Dale
Ashton, John
Benson, Paul
Blackburn, Chris
Boardman, Jon
Bolton, Jimmy
Boyd, George
Bradshaw, Mark
Briscoe, Louis
Brown, Paul
Browne, Corey
Carey-Bertram, Daniel
Carr, Michael
Cavell, Paul
Charles, Lee
Charley, Ken
Charnock, Kieran
Constable, James
Crittenden, Nick
Davies, Paul
Day, Matt
Densmore, Shaun
Drummond, Stewart
Fleming, Andrew
Furlong, Paul
Grant, John
Harrad, Shaun
Hine, Mark
Holroyd, Chris
Humphreys, Delwyn
Howells, Jake
Jackson, Marlon
Jennings, Connor
Kennedy, John
Kerr, Scott

Kimmins,Ged
King, Simon
Leworthy, David
McDougald, Junior
McFadzean, Kyle
Mayes, Bobby
Moore, Neil
Moore, Luke
Newton, Sean
O'Keefe, Eamon
Oli, Dennis
Penn, Russell
Pitcher, Geoff
Porter, Max
Ricketts, Sam
Robbins, Terry
Robinson, Mark
Roddis,Nick
Rodgers, Luke
Rodman, Alex
Rogers, Paul
Ryan, Tim
Sarcevic, Antoni
Sellars, Neil
Shaw, John
Sheldon, Gareth
Simpson, Josh
Sinclair, Dean
Smith, Ian
Smith, Ossie
Spencer, Scott
Stansfield, Adam
Stephens, Mickey
Stott, Steve
Taylor, Steve
Thurgood, Stuart
Tubbs, Matthew
Venables, David
Watkins, Adam
Way, Darren
Webb, Paul
Wilcox, Russ

## MANAGERS 1979 - 2013

| | | P | W | D | L | F | A | *Win% |
|---|---|---|---|---|---|---|---|---|
| 1979 | Howard Wilkinson | 2 | 2 | 0 | 0 | 6 | 1 | - |
| 1980 - 1984 | Keith Wright | 17 | 9 | 5 | 3 | 30 | 16 | 53 |
| 1985 - 1988 | Kevin Verity | 12 | 7 | 2 | 3 | 23 | 15 | 58 |
| 1989 - 1996 | Tony Jennings | 19 | 10 | 4 | 5 | 27 | 18 | 53 |
| 1997 | Ron Reid | 2 | 0 | 1 | 1 | 0 | 2 | - |
| 1998 - 2002 | John Owens | 14 | 8 | 5 | 1 | 22 | 10 | 57 |
| 2002 - | Paul Fairclough | 53 | 30 | 10 | 13 | 94 | 58 | 57 |

*Calculated for those who managed for 10 games or more.

Mansfield Town got the tie of the Cup when they played host to Premiership side Liverpool. Photos: Peter Barnes

THE FA CUP 2012-13

Rushden & Higham score from the penalty spot to score a consolation goal during their Extra-Preliminary round 1-3 defeat by visitors Bugbrooke St Michaels. Photo: Gordon Whittington.

## EXTRA PRELIMINARY ROUND

One of the oldest and most famous football competitions in the world actually kicked off on Friday 11th August, when four ties were played and provided a draw and three home wins causing the very early departure of Calne Town, Cogenhoe United and Sandhurst Town from the competition

In fact, once the replays had been decided, over 200 clubs had actually lost interest in the FA Cup by the middle of August last season. This must be a disappointing start to the football season, especially for those returning from holiday only to find their clubs already out of the FA Cup!

A pairing that might have sparked a few memories was Aylesbury United v Enfield 1893, two clubs recovering well from financial problems, whose older supporters would remember previous exciting FA Cup runs. A tie in the North West which may have had southern supporters puzzled was AFC Blackpool v AFC Liverpool which finished as a 6-3 victory for the away side. The 'thrillers of the round' must have been Guisborough Town's 5-4 away victory at Northallerton and Pilkington XXX who beat Atherstone by the same score. While clubs who must have realized they weren't quite ready for the season to start, included Whitehaven who lost 0-6 at home to Shildon, Rothwell Corinthians who were beaten 7-1 at Ely City and Horsham YMCA who crashed out 0-8 at Raynes Park Vale.

Clubs are still proud to be accepted into The FA Challenge Cup, but starting this early really tests their pre season training and a little luck is needed to stay in the competition long enough to settle into the season.

Shane Saunders, Hailsham Town (hidden), heads a goal against Greenwich Borough in the Extra-Preliminary Round. Photo: Roger Turner.

# EXTRA PRELIMINARY ROUND
## SATURDAY 11 AUGUST 2012 - WINNING CLUBS TO RECEIVE £100

| # | Home | Away | Score | Att |
|---|------|------|-------|-----|
| 1 | Dunston UTS v | Armthorpe Welfare | 2-1 | 175 |
| 2 | Liversedge v | West Auckland Town | 2-4 | 237 |
| 3 | Crook Town v | Penrith | 2-1 | 102 |
| 4 | Thackley v | Hebburn Town | 1-3 | 99 |
| 5 | Jarrow Roofing Boldon CA v | Pickering Town | 1-1 | 38 |
|  | Pickering Town v | Jarrow Roofing Boldon CA (14/8) | 2-4 | 152 |
| 6 | Newton Aycliffe v | Holker OBs | 1-1 | 136 |
|  | Holker OBs v | Newton Aycliffe (14/8) | 3-0 | 101 |
| 7 | Tadcaster Albion v | Consett | 1-1 | 123 |
|  | Consett v | Tadcaster Albion (14/8) | 2-3aet | 140 |
| 8 | Ashington v | Sunderland RCA | 1-1 | 230 |
|  | Sunderland RCA v | Ashington (14/8) | 1-2 | 133 |
| 9 | Chester-Le-Street Town v | Billingham Town | 0-0 | 76 |
|  | Billingham Town v | Chester-Le-Street Town (14/8) | 1-0 | 88 |
| 10 | South Shields v | Darlington RA | 0-0 | 106 |
|  | Darlington RA v | South Shields (14/8) | 5-6 | 107 |
| 11 | Northallerton Town v | Guisborough Town | 4-5 | 118 |
| 12 | Billingham Synthonia v | Celtic Nation | 0-1 | 153 |
| 13 | Marske United v | Stokesley SC | 1-0 | 160 |
| 14 | North Shields v | Birtley Town | 1-1 | 146 |
|  | Birtley Town v | North Shields (14/8) | 2-0 | 174 |
| 15 | Durham City v | Newcastle Benfield | 2-1 | 102 |
| 16 | Washington v | Esh Winning | 1-3 | 64 |
| 17 | Tow Law Town v | Bishop Auckland | 0-2 | 136 |
| 18 | Eccleshill United v | Glasshoughton Welfare | 4-2 | 28 |
| 19 | Spennymoor Town v | Scarborough Athletic | 1-0 | 365 |
| 20 | Bedlington Terriers v | Morpeth Town | 2-1 | 101 |
| 21 | Pontefract Collieries v | Norton & Stockton Ancients | 2-2 | 88 |
|  | Norton & Stockton Ancients v | Pontefract Collieries (15/8) | 5-2aet | 73 |
| 22 | Silsden v | Brighouse Town | 2-3 | 123 |
| 23 | Whitehaven v | Shildon | 0-6 | 84 |
| 24 | West Allotment Celtic v | Selby Town | 2-1 | 85 |
| 25 | Bridlington Town v | Whitley Bay | 1-2 | 206 |
| 26 | Daisy Hill v | Formby | 0-5 | 60 |
| 27 | AFC Blackpool v | AFC Liverpool | 3-6 | 92 |
| 28 | Dinnington Town v | Atherton Collieries | 0-2 | 102 |
| 29 | Irlam v | Hallam | 5-3 | 102 |
| 30 | Bootle v | Alsager Town | 4-1 | 111 |
| 31 | Maine Road v | Squires Gate | 3-0 | 85 |
| 32 | Atherton LR v | Rossington Main | 4-2 | 38 |
| 33 | St Helens Town v | Abbey Hey | 1-5 | 62 |
| 34 | Padiham v | Wigan Robin Park | 1-0 | 135 |
| 35 | Hemsworth MW v | Runcorn Linnets | 1-1 | 197 |
|  | Runcorn Linnets v | Hemsworth MW (14/8) | 2-2aet | 281 |
|  | (Hemsworth MW won 4-3 on kicks from the penalty mark) | | | |
| 36 | Colne v | Congleton Town | 0-0 | 66 |
|  | Congleton Town v | Colne (14/8) | 5-2 | 111 |
| 37 | Stockport Sports v | Ashton Athletic | 0-0 | 53 |
|  | (at Mossley FC) | | | |
|  | Ashton Athletic v | Stockport Sports (14/8) | 2-1 | 70 |
| 38 | Cheadle Town v | Maltby Main | 1-1 | 52 |
|  | Maltby Main v | Cheadle Town (15/8) | 1-0 | 92 |
| 39 | Parkgate v | Runcorn Town | 2-3 | 94 |
| 40 | AFC Emley v | Chadderton (12/8) | 0-2 | 152 |
| 41 | Staveley MW v | Hall Road Rangers | 2-1 | 102 |
| 42 | Nostell MW v | Winsford United | 0-1 | 54 |
| 43 | Barton Town OBs v | Barnoldswick Town | 2-0 | 80 |
| 44 | Winterton Rangers v | Bacup Borough | 0-3 | 49 |
|  | (at Selby Town FC) | | | |
| 45 | Shepshed Dynamo v | Heanor Town | 0-3 | 162 |
| 46 | Long Eaton United v | Dunkirk | 0-1 | 150 |
| 47 | Blackstones v | Barrow Town | 5-1 | 71 |
| 48 | Spalding United v | Blaby & Whetstone Athletic | 1-2 | |
| 49 | Arnold Town v | Holbeach United | 0-2 | 105 |
| 50 | Shirebrook Town v | Kirby Muxloe | 0-1 | 82 |
| 51 | Boston Town v | Quorn | 0-2 | 106 |
| 52 | Glossop North End v | Louth Town | 0-0 | 192 |
|  | Louth Town v | Glossop North End (15/8) | 1-2aet | 123 |
| 53 | Retford United v | Bardon Hill Sports | 2-1 | 100 |
| 54 | Oadby Town v | Anstey Nomads | 3-1 | 175 |
| 55 | Holbrook Sports v | Deeping Rangers | 3-1 | |
| 56 | Thurnby Nirvana v | Lincoln Moorlands Railway | 4-2 | 47 |
| 57 | St Andrews v | Borrowash Victoria | 1-2 | 86 |
| 58 | Sleaford Town v | Holwell Sports | 2-0 | 113 |
| 59 | Teversal v | Loughborough University | 1-2 | 74 |
| 60 | Causeway United v | Continental Star (12/8) | 1-1 | 94 |
|  | (at Boldmere St Michaels FC) | | | |
|  | Continental Star v | Causeway United (15/8) | 3-0 | 71 |
| 61 | Norton United v | Alvechurch | 2-2 | 94 |
|  | Alvechurch v | Norton United (14/8) | 1-2 | 80 |
| 62 | Highgate United v | Wellington | 1-1 | 53 |
|  | Wellington v | Highgate United (14/8) | 3-3aet | 64 |
|  | (Wellington won 7-6 on kicks from the penalty mark) | | | |
| 63 | Coleshill Town v | AFC Wulfrunians | 1-1 | 53 |
|  | AFC Wulfrunians v | Coleshill Town (14/8) | 3-2aet | |
| 64 | Bloxwich United v | Studley | 2-3 | 51 |
| 65 | Brocton v | Bewdley Town | 2-2 | 71 |
|  | Bewdley Town v | Brocton (14/8) | 1-0 | 51 |
| 66 | Dudley Sports v | Heath Hayes | 2-2 | 62 |
|  | Heath Hayes v | Dudley Sports (14/8) | 2-1aet | 85 |
| 67 | Boldmere St Michaels v | Bridgnorth Town | 1-3 | 53 |
| 68 | Pilkington XXX v | Atherstone Town | 5-4 | 95 |
| 69 | Stone Dominoes v | Rocester | 0-3 | 70 |
| 70 | Dudley Town v | Southam United | 4-1 | 77 |
| 71 | Eccleshall v | Stourport Swifts | 0-1 | 68 |
| 72 | Lye Town v | Bartley Green (10/8) | 2-2 | 145 |
|  | Bartley Green v | Lye Town (14/8) | 1-2 | |
| 73 | Cradley Town v | Shifnal Town | 3-0 | 56 |
| 74 | Tipton Town v | Wolverhampton Casuals | 0-1 | 84 |
| 75 | Ellesmere Rangers v | Coventry Sphinx | 0-4 | 51 |
| 76 | Gornal Athletic v | Malvern Town | 4-0 | 60 |
| 77 | Earlswood Town v | Nuneaton Griff | 3-3 | 50 |
|  | Nuneaton Griff v | Earlswood Town (15/8) | 3-1 | 71 |
| 78 | Shawbury United v | Westfields | 2-4 | 57 |
| 79 | Pegasus Juniors v | Long Buckby | 2-1 | 74 |
| 80 | Tividale v | Stratford Town | 5-2 | 117 |
| 81 | Willenhall Town v | Sporting Khalsa | 1-1 | 72 |
|  | Sporting Khalsa v | Willenhall Town (14/8) | 3-2 | 71 |
| 82 | Godmanchester Rovers v | Thetford Town | 2-1 | 106 |
| 83 | Irchester United v | Huntingdon Town (12/8) | 0-1 | 67 |
| 84 | Ely City v | Rothwell Corinthians | 7-1 | 87 |
| 85 | Peterborough Northern Star v | Wellingborough Whitworths | 5-1 | 110 |
| 86 | Dereham Town v | Stewarts & Lloyds Corby | 3-1 | 108 |
| 87 | Rushden & Higham United v | Bugbrooke St Michaels | 1-3 | 62 |
| 88 | Fakenham Town v | St Ives Town | 0-1 | 151 |
| 89 | Thrapston Town v | Cogenhoe United (10/8) | 2-1 | 125 |
| 90 | Wellingborough Town v | March Town United | 2-1 | 94 |
| 91 | Wisbech Town v | Desborough Town | 1-1 | 80 |
|  | Desborough Town v | Wisbech Town (14/8) | 2-5 | 120 |
| 92 | Northampton Spencer v | Yaxley | 1-1 | 80 |
|  | Yaxley v | Northampton Spencer (14/8) | 3-1 | 71 |
| 93 | Brantham Athletic v | Mildenhall Town | 1-0 | 53 |
| 94 | Wivenhoe Town v | Haverhill Rovers | 1-1 | 115 |
|  | Haverhill Rovers v | Wivenhoe Town (14/8) | 2-0 | 75 |
| 95 | FC Clacton v | Halstead Town | 1-3 | 126 |
| 96 | Felixstowe & Walton United v | Team Bury | 3-1 | 99 |
| 97 | Walsham Le Willows v | Burnham Ramblers | 1-3 | 72 |
| 98 | Barkingside v | Great Yarmouth Town | 1-1 | 186 |
|  | Great Yarmouth Town v | Barkingside (14/8) | 3-0 | 57 |
|  | (at Kirkley & Pakefield FC) | | | |
| 99 | Kirkley & Pakefield v | Sawbridgeworth Town | 1-1 | 70 |
|  | Sawbridgeworth Town v | Kirkley & Pakefield (14/8) | 3-7 | 70 |

Carl Brown of Bishop's Cleeve is trying to evade the attentions of Ascot defender Joe Yeates during a Preliminary Round match that had to be abandoned on 81 minutes with the score at 2-2, due to rain!
Photos: Jonathan Holloway.

(Below) More Preliminary Round action, here we see Sittingbourne defenders clear a corner against Burnham.
Photo: Alan Coomes.

# EXTRA PRELIMINARY ROUND
## SATURDAY 11 AUGUST 2012 - WINNING CLUBS TO RECEIVE £1000

| No | Home | v | Away | Score | Att |
|---|---|---|---|---|---|
| 100 | Stansted | v | Norwich United | 1-2 | 53 |
| | (at Norwich United FC) | | | | |
| 101 | Gorleston | v | Stanway Rovers | 3-1 | 85 |
| 102 | Takeley | v | Newmarket Town | 2-1 | 151 |
| 103 | London APSA | v | Long Melford | 3-1 | 30 |
| | (at Aveley FC) | | | | |
| 104 | Basildon United | v | Diss Town | 1-0 | 51 |
| 105 | Debenham LC | v | Whitton United | 0-2 | 90 |
| 106 | Southend Manor | v | Hullbridge Sports | 1-0 | 84 |
| 107 | Woodbridge Town | v | Great Wakering Rovers | 1-2 | 88 |
| 108 | Bowers & Pitsea | v | Eton Manor | 1-3 | 52 |
| 109 | Ipswich Wanderers | v | Hadleigh United | 0-3 | 97 |
| 110 | AFC Dunstable | v | Ampthill Town | 4-1 | 83 |
| 111 | Hanworth Villa | v | Bethnal Green United | 2-2 | 98 |
| | Bethnal Green United | v | Hanworth Villa (14/8) | 1-5 | 115 |
| | (at Hanworth Villa FC) | | | | |
| 112 | Hoddesdon Town | v | Berkhamsted | 1-1 | 57 |
| | (at Waltham Abbey FC) | | | | |
| | Berkhamsted | v | Hoddesdon Town (14/8) | 2-1 | 102 |
| 113 | Wodson Park | v | Colney Heath | 0-4 | 87 |
| 114 | Bedfont Sports | v | Tring Athletic | 0-1 | 65 |
| 115 | Haringey Borough | v | AFC Kempston Rovers | 1-3 | 57 |
| 116 | Staines Lammas | v | Barking | 4-4 | 42 |
| | Barking | v | Staines Lamas (14/8) | 0-1 | 56 |
| 117 | Wembley | v | Langford | 3-2 | 654 |
| 118 | Biggleswade United | v | Cranfield United | 2-0 | 42 |
| 119 | Broxbourne Borough V&E | v | Dunstable Town | | |
| | (walkover for Dunstable Town – Broxbourne Borough V&E removed) | | | | |
| 120 | Hadley | v | Hertford Town | 2-0 | 60 |
| 121 | Hanwell Town | v | Haringey & Waltham Development | 1-3 | 71 |
| 122 | Harefield United | v | Hillingdon Borough | 3-1 | 141 |
| 123 | Crawley Green | v | Stotfold | 1-2 | 65 |
| 124 | London Colney | v | Hatfield Town | 3-0 | 65 |
| 125 | Kings Langley | v | St Margaretsbury | 1-1 | 72 |
| | St Margaretsbury | v | Kings Langley (14/8) | 3-2 | 60 |
| 126 | Aylesbury United | v | Enfield 1893 | 4-0 | 136 |
| 127 | London Lions | v | Clapton | 4-0 | 70 |
| | (at Hemel Hempstead Town FC) | | | | |
| 128 | Sporting Bengal United | v | Cockfosters | 1-3 | 78 |
| | (at Cockfosters FC) | | | | |
| 129 | Oxhey Jets | v | Leverstock Green | 5-2 | 80 |
| 130 | Ardley United | v | Holyport | 4-2 | 46 |
| 131 | Kidlington | v | Shrivenham | 2-2 | 59 |
| | Shrivenham | v | Kidlington (15/8) | 6-3 | 75 |
| 132 | Cove | v | Slimbridge | 2-0 | 55 |
| 133 | Reading Town | v | Newport Pagnell Town | 1-6 | 71 |
| 134 | Hartley Wintney | v | Holmer Green | 2-1 | |
| 135 | Old Woodstock Town | v | Wantage Town | 1-4 | 135 |
| 136 | Bracknell Town | v | Binfield | 2-1 | 374 |
| 137 | Ascot United | v | Sandhurst Town (10/8) | 6-1 | 231 |
| 138 | Thame United | v | Newbury | 1-0 | 65 |
| 139 | Witney Town | v | Marlow | 1-1 | 142 |
| | Marlow | v | Witney Town (14/8) | 4-3 | 131 |
| 140 | Wokingham & Emmbrook | v | Camberley Town (12/8) | 0-2 | 140 141 |
| | Abingdon Town | v | Fairford Town | 1-0 | 47 |
| 142 | Flackwell Heath | v | Windsor | 0-1 | 86 |
| 143 | Erith Town | v | Ringmer | 2-4 | 37 |
| 144 | Littlehampton Town | v | Molesey (12/8) | 4-0 | 141 |
| 145 | Tunbridge Wells | v | Beckenham Town | 1-4 | 137 |
| 146 | Peacehaven & Telscombe | v | Banstead Athletic | 2-1 | 80 |
| 147 | Chessington & Hook United | v | Warlingham | 2-2 | |
| | Warlingham | v | Chessington & Hook (15/8) | 2-3 | 82 |
| 148 | Cobham | v | South Park (12/8) | 1-1 | 125 |
| | South Park | v | Cobham (15/8) | 3-0 | |
| 149 | Pagham | v | Sevenoaks Town | 2-1 | |

| No | Home | v | Away | Score | Att |
|---|---|---|---|---|---|
| 150 | Arundel | v | Epsom & Ewell | 1-2 | 79 |
| 151 | Lordswood | v | Erith & Belvedere | 3-2 | 110 |
| 152 | Dorking | v | VCD Athletic | 3-4 | 54 |
| 153 | Redhill | v | Whyteleafe | 1-0 | 140 |
| 154 | Deal Town | v | Ashford United | 1-2 | 166 |
| 155 | Lingfield | v | AFC Uckfield | 4-2 | 59 |
| | (at Whyteleafe FC) | | | | |
| 156 | Hailsham Town | v | Greenwich Borough | 2-4 | 40 |
| 157 | Fisher | v | East Preston | 1-1 | 71 |
| | East Preston | v | Fisher (14/8) | 1-0 | 79 |
| 158 | Mole Valley SCR | v | Badshot Lea | 1-1 | 63 |
| | Badshot Lea | v | Mole Valley SCR (14/8) | 4-1 | 60 |
| 159 | Horley Town | v | Holmesdale | 5-1 | 63 |
| 160 | Lancing | v | Selsey | 6-1 | 89 |
| 161 | Egham Town | v | Westfield | 4-0 | 56 |
| 162 | Chichester City | v | Crowborough Athletic | 2-5 | 53 |
| 163 | Shoreham | v | Colliers Wood United | 2-2 | 71 |
| | Colliers Wood United | v | Shoreham (15/8) | 4-1 | 71 |
| 164 | St Francis Rangers | v | Rye United (12/8) | 0-1 | 110 |
| 165 | Corinthian | v | Croydon | 3-2 | 55 |
| 166 | Hassocks | v | Sidley United | 0-1 | 80 |
| 167 | Raynes Park Vale | v | Horsham YMCA | 8-0 | 79 |
| 168 | Bitton | v | Bristol Manor Farm | 3-1 | 97 |
| 169 | Bemerton Heath Harlequins | v | Hamworthy United | 1-2 | 52 |
| 170 | Winterbourne United | v | Moneyfields | 1-2 | 55 |
| 171 | Hallen | v | Fawley | 4-0 | 58 |
| 172 | Farnham Town | v | Alresford Town | 0-3 | 60 |
| 173 | Highworth Town | v | Corsham Town (12/8) | 3-1 | 72 |
| 174 | GE Hamble | v | Whitchurch United (12/8) | 2-0 | 87 |
| 175 | Almondsbury UWE | v | Petersfield Town | 1-1 | 43 |
| | Petersfield Town | v | Almondsbury UWE (14/8) | 2-3aet | 63 |
| 176 | East Cowes VA | v | Verwood Town | 3-2 | 137 |
| 177 | Downton | v | Ash United | 4-1 | 56 |
| 178 | Hayling United | v | Fareham Town | 0-3 | 95 |
| | (at Fareham Town FC) | | | | |
| 179 | Wootton Bassett Town | v | Calne Town (10/8) | 4-2 | 248 |
| 180 | Horndean | v | Brockenhurst | 2-1 | 40 |
| 181 | Fleet Spurs | v | Totton & Eling | 2-3 | 60 |
| | (at Totton & Eling FC) | | | | |
| 182 | Alton Town | v | Bradford Town | 3-0 | 66 |
| 183 | Ringwood Town | v | Cadbury Heath | 1-5 | 61 |
| 184 | Longwell Green Sports | v | Melksham Town | 0-0 | 59 |
| | Melksham Town | v | Longwell Green Sports (13/8) | 3-1 | 115 |
| 185 | Christchurch | v | Cowes Sports (12/8) | 5-0 | 91 |
| 186 | Romsey Town | v | Lymington Town | 4-0 | 50 |
| 187 | New Milton Town | v | Newport (IW) | 0-2 | 40 |
| 188 | Blackfield & Langley | v | AFC Portchester | 6-1 | 40 |
| 189 | Bournemouth | v | Pewsey Vale | 0-1 | 57 |
| 190 | Plymouth Parkway | v | Welton Rovers | 3-1 | 104 |
| 191 | Gillingham Town | v | Tavistock | 5-0 | 124 |
| 192 | Bodmin Town | v | Brislington | 3-1 | 92 |
| 193 | Bishop Sutton | v | Radstock Town | 3-2 | 51 |
| 194 | Street | v | Hengrove Athletic | 1-3 | |
| 195 | Chard Town | v | Ilfracombe Town | 1-0 | 102 |
| 196 | Wells City | v | Barnstaple Town | 3-2 | 65 |
| 197 | Larkhall Athletic | v | Willand Rovers | 2-1 | 75 |
| 198 | Odd Down | v | Saltash United | 3-1 | 61 |
| 199 | Buckland Athletic | v | Bridport | 2-1 | 144 |
| 200 | Sherborne Town | v | Elmore | 3-1 | 97 |

# PRELIMINARY ROUND

The draw for the preliminary round is made on a regional basis so a number of attractive local derbies gave supporters an exciting start to the season. However, as some players may be playing their first game of the  season and may not be fully fit there are sometimes some one sided ties.

| Malden & Tiptree | 9 | London APSA | 1 |
|---|---|---|---|
| Bishop Auckland | 7 | Esh Winning | 1 |
| North Leigh | 6 | Thame United | 0 |
| Needham Market | 6 | Gorleston | 2 |
| Newpor Pagnell | 6 | Ardley United | 2 |

And the best away victories were:

| Great Yarmouth Town | 1 | Witham Town | 8 |
|---|---|---|---|
| Stotfold | 3 | Colney Heath | 10 |
| Halstead Town | 0 | Brentwood Town | 6 |
| Holbrook Sports | 1 | Belper Town | 6 |

This was a chance missed for Tilbury in their comfortable Preliminary Round win over Brantham Athletic. Photo: Gordon Whittington.

First Qualifying Round action between Bridgnorth Town 3 v 1 Rushall Olympic.

Here Bridgnorth's Anwar Olugbon has a shot blocked by a Rushall defender at Crown Meadow.

Photo: Jonathan Holloway.

# PRELIMINARY ROUND
## SATURDAY 25 AUGUST 2012 - WINNERS RECEIVE £1,750

| No | Home | v | Away | Score | Att |
|---|---|---|---|---|---|
| 1 | Harrogate Railway Athletic | v | South Shields | 1-1 | 72 |
| | South Shields | v | Harrogate Railway Athletic (28/8) | 1-0 | 83 |
| 2 | Birtley Town | v | West Auckland Town | 1-4 | 135 |
| 3 | Jarrow Roofing Boldon CA | v | Farsley | 2-3 | 39 |
| 4 | Shildon | v | Guisborough Town | 1-1 | 120 |
| | Guisborough Town | v | Shildon (29/8) | 0-6 | 140 |
| 5 | Bishop Auckland | v | Esh Winning | 7-1 | 94 |
| 6 | Ossett Town | v | Goole | 1-0 | 113 |
| 7 | Garforth Town | v | Wakefield | 1-0 | 71 |
| 8 | Tadcaster Albion | v | Norton & Stockton Ancients | 3-0 | 96 |
| 9 | Brighouse Town | v | Eccleshill United | 1-2 | 49 |
| 10 | Hebburn Town | v | Ossett Albion | 1-3 | 109 |
| 11 | Celtic Nation | v | Dunston UTS | 2-1 | 102 |
| | (tie awarded to Dunston UTS – Celtic Nation removed) | | | | |
| 12 | Crook Town | v | Holker Old Boys | 4-4 | 98 |
| | Holker Old Boys | v | Crook Town (28/8) | 3-1 | 140 |
| 13 | Marske United | v | Ashington | 1-4 | 189 |
| 14 | Spennymoor Town | v | West Allotment Celtic | 3-0 | 201 |
| 15 | Whitley Bay | v | Bedlington Terriers | 0-3 | 329 |
| 16 | Durham City | v | Billingham Town | 2-1 | 100 |
| 17 | Staveley MW | v | Bamber Bridge | 3-3 | 121 |
| | Bamber Bridge | v | Staveley MW (28/8) | 5-2 | |
| 18 | Chadderton | v | Maltby Main | 0-1 | 37 |
| 19 | Ashton Athletic | v | Lancaster City | 2-2 | 79 |
| | Lancaster City | v | Ashton Athletic (28/8) | 4-1 | 134 |
| 20 | Padiham | v | Burscough (27/8) | 0-0 | 170 |
| | Burscough | v | Padiham (5/9) | 2-1aet | 139 |
| 21 | Mossley | v | Bootle | 0-3 | 132 |
| 22 | Maine Road | v | Bacup Borough | 2-1 | 68 |
| 23 | Barton Town OBs | v | Cammell Laird | 1-2 | 94 |
| 24 | Atherton Collieries | v | Congleton Town | 2-1 | 81 |
| 25 | Ramsbottom United | v | Brigg Town (27/8) | 3-0 | 203 |
| 26 | Winsford United | v | Trafford | 0-2 | 116 |
| 27 | AFC Liverpool | v | Prescot Cables | 0-1 | 361 |
| 28 | Irlam | v | Runcorn Town | 3-5 | 75 |
| 29 | Atherton LR | v | Warrington Town | 0-3 | 58 |
| 30 | Formby | v | Skelmersdale United | 1-3 | |
| 31 | Northwich Victoria | v | Curzon Ashton (26/8) | 0-0 | 156 |
| | Curzon Ashton | v | Northwich Victoria (28/8) | 2-2aet | 175 |
| | (Curzon Ashton won 4-2 on kicks from the penalty mark) | | | | |
| 32 | Sheffield | v | Abbey Hey (4/9) | 1-2 | 198 |
| 33 | Clitheroe | v | Radcliffe Borough | 2-2 | 160 |
| | Radcliffe Borough | v | Clitheroe (28/8) | 0-1 | 117 |
| 34 | Salford City | v | Hemsworth MW | 5-1 | 102 |
| 35 | Loughborough Dynamo | v | Glossop North End | 3-0 | 110 |
| 36 | Lincoln United | v | Thurnby Nirvana | 1-2 | 72 |
| 37 | New Mills | v | Mickleover Sports (27/8) | 2-2 | 117 |
| | Mickleover Sports | v | New Mills (4/9) | 1-1aet | 12 |
| 38 | Holbrook Sports | v | Belper Town | 1-6 | 204 |
| 39 | Coalville Town | v | Loughborough University | 5-3 | 140 |
| 40 | Stamford | v | Borrowash Victoria | 1-0 | 110 |
| 41 | Kirby Muxloe | v | Holbeach United | 0-2 | 60 |
| 42 | Blaby & Whetsone Athletic | v | Heanor Town | 2-1 | 88 |
| 43 | Carlton Town | v | Oadby Town | 3-2 | 81 |
| 44 | Hucknall Town | v | Retford United | 0-1 | 173 |
| 45 | Sleaford Town | v | Rainworth MW | 1-2 | 97 |
| 46 | Blackstones | v | Gresley | 1-3 | 72 |
| 47 | Quorn | v | Dunkirk | 2-1 | 74 |
| 48 | Chasetown | v | Rocester | 2-1 | 235 |
| 49 | Cradley Town | v | Norton United | 4-4 | 27 |
| | Norton United | v | Cradley Town (28/8) | 5-0 | 66 |
| 50 | Studley | v | Rugby Town | 1-4 | 113 |
| 51 | Halesowen Town | v | Dudley Town | 1-2 | 295 |
| 52 | Gornal Athletic | v | Coventry Sphinx | 6-0 | 60 |
| 53 | Leek Town | v | Evesham United | 2-1 | 177 |
| 54 | Market Drayton Town | v | Newcastle Town | 2-1 | 92 |
| 55 | Heath Hayes | v | Tividale | 3-4 | 70 |
| 56 | Sporting Khalsa | v | Nuneaton Griff | 1-1 | 50 |
| | Nuneaton Griff | v | Sporting Khalsa (29/8) | 5-1 | 106 |
| 57 | AFC Wulfrunians | v | Kidsgrove Athletic | 1-0 | 90 |
| 58 | Stourport Swifts | v | Continental Star | 1-1 | 67 |
| | Continental Star | v | Stourport Swifts (29/8) | 1-3 | 62 |
| 59 | Wellington | v | Bewdley Town | 3-5 | 59 |
| 60 | Lye Town | v | Bridgnorth Town (24/8) | 0-1 | 128 |
| 61 | Westfields | v | Romulus | 2-1 | 82 |
| 62 | Sutton Coldfield Town | v | Pegasus Juniors | 2-1 | 70 |
| 63 | Wolverhampton Casuals | v | Pilkington XXX | 2-0 | 65 |
| 64 | Godmanchester Rovers | v | Daventry Town | 3-4 | 90 |
| 65 | Peterborough Northern Star | v | Thrapston Town | 3-1 | 72 |
| 66 | Bugbrooke St Michaels | v | Ely City | 2-2 | 47 |
| | Ely City | v | Bugbrooke St Michaels (28/8) | 1-3 | 107 |
| 67 | Huntingdon Town | v | St Ives Town | 3-2 | 301 |
| 68 | Dereham Town | v | Woodford United (28/8) | 3-0 | 102 |
| | (25/8 tie abandoned after 23 mins due to waterlogged pitch, 2-0) | | | | |
| 69 | Wisbech Town | v | Yaxley | 3-0 | 286 |
| 70 | Wellingborough Town | v | King's Lynn Town | 1-3 | 220 |
| 71 | Soham Town Rangers | v | Burnham Ramblers | 5-1 | 117 |
| 72 | Great Yarmouth Town | v | Witham Town | 1-8 | 66 |
| 73 | Grays Athletic | v | Takeley | 1-0 | 145 |
| 74 | Tilbury | v | Brantham Athletic | 5-1 | 69 |
| 75 | AFC Sudbury | v | Ilford | 5-0 | 181 |
| 76 | Kirkley & Pakefield | v | Southend Manor | 0-2 | 65 |
| 77 | Harlow Town | v | Hadleigh United | 1-2 | 131 |
| 78 | Halstead Town | v | Brentwood Town | 0-6 | |
| 79 | Needham Market | v | Gorleston | 6-2 | 213 |
| 80 | Eton Manor | v | Norwich United | 0-2 | 39 |
| 81 | Felixstowe & Walton United | v | Heybridge Swifts | 1-1 | 82 |
| | Heybridge Swifts | v | Felixstowe & Walton United (28/8) | 4-0 | 117 |
| 82 | Whitton United | v | Aveley | 0-3 | 47 |
| 83 | Basildon United | v | Haverhill Rovers | 1-0 | 48 |

Beckenham's Alex Wilks clears from Billy Crook of the Met Police in the First Qualifying Round. Photo: Alan Coomes.

(Below) More First Qualifying Round action - Chitty (Frome) makes a fine save from Horan (Larkhall). Photo: Keith Clayton.

(Left) Stokoe (Bashley) prepares to shoot at Ashmore in the Gosport goal, however, his shot hits the crossbar (Right). Photos: Keith Clayton.

# PRELIMINARY ROUND
## SATURDAY 25 AUGUST 2012 - WINNERS RECEIVE £1,750

| No | Home | | Away | Score | |
|---|---|---|---|---|---|
| 84 | Maldon & Tiptree | v | London APSA | 9-1 | |
| 85 | Wroxham | v | Great Wakering Rovers | 2-0 | 103 |
| 86 | St Margaretsbury | v | Leighton Town | 0-0 | 53 |
| | Leighton Town | v | St Margaretsbury (28/8) | 2-3 | 104 |
| 87 | London Colney | v | Harefield United | 1-2 | 57 |
| 88 | Haringey & Waltham Dev. | v | Waltham Abbey | 1-2 | 24 |
| 89 | Biggleswade United | v | Ware | 0-1 | 48 |
| 90 | Ashford Town (Middx) | v | Tring Athletic | 2-2 | 75 |
| | Tring Athletic | v | Ashford Town (Middx) (28/8) | 0-2 | 117 |
| 91 | AFC Kempston Rovers | v | Cockfosters | 2-0 | 65 |
| 92 | London Lions | v | Oxhey Jets | 3-1 | 50 |
| | (at Hemel Hempstead Town FC) | | | | |
| 93 | Berkhamsted | v | Hadley | 3-1 | 84 |
| 94 | Cheshunt | v | Potters Bar Town | 2-2 | 123 |
| | Potters Bar Town | v | Cheshunt (28/8) | 3-1 | 172 |
| 95 | Aylesbury United | v | Northwood | 2-5 | 118 |
| 96 | Hanworth Villa | v | Royston Town | 1-2 | 86 |
| 97 | Colney Heath | v | Stotfold | 1-1 | 57 |
| | Stotfold | v | Colney Heath (28/8) | 3-7 | 60 |
| 98 | Staines Lammas | v | Barton Rovers (24/8) | 0-2 | |
| 99 | AFC Dunstable | v | Redbridge | 5-0 | 42 |
| 100 | Biggleswade Town | v | AFC Hayes | 3-0 | 99 |
| 101 | Uxbridge | v | Wembley (26/8) | 2-2 | 754 |
| | Wembley | v | Uxbridge (29/8) | 0-5 | 317 |
| 102 | Romford | v | Waltham Forest (24/8) | 1-4 | |
| 103 | North Greenford United | v | Dunstable Town | 2-4 | 56 |
| 104 | Bishop's Cleeve | v | Ascot United (4/9) | 2-1 | 88 |
| 105 | Cinderford Town | v | Abingdon Town | 5-0 | 96 |
| 106 | Didcot Town | v | Abingdon United | 2-1 | 142 |
| 107 | Camberley Town | v | Chalfont St Peter | 0-5 | 65 |
| 108 | Hungerford Town | v | Beaconsfield SYCOB | 5-2 | 55 |
| 109 | Aylesbury | v | Windsor | 0-2 | 150 |
| 110 | Wantage Town | v | Hartley Wintney | 4-1 | 46 |
| 111 | Newport Pagnell Town | v | Ardley United | 6-2 | 140 |
| 112 | Fleet Town | v | Marlow | 0-2 | 76 |
| 113 | North Leigh | v | Thame United | 6-0 | 75 |
| 114 | Cirencester Town | v | Merthyr Town | 0-1 | 108 |
| 115 | Cove | v | Thatcham Town | 2-5 | 54 |
| 116 | Bracknell Town | v | Shrivenham | 2-0 | 136 |
| 117 | Lordswood | v | Pagham | 0-0 | |
| | Pagham | v | Lordswood (28/8) | 1-1aet | |
| | (Pagham won 4-2 on kicks from the penalty mark) | | | | |
| 118 | Chertsey Town | v | Beckenham Town | 1-4 | 112 |
| 119 | Horley Town | v | Leatherhead | 1-1 | 104 |
| | Leatherhead | v | Horley Town (29/8) | 3-0 | 141 |
| 120 | Lancing | v | South Park | 0-1 | 99 |
| 121 | Epsom & Ewell | v | Three Bridges (26/8) | 2-1 | 120 |
| 122 | Badshot Lea | v | Egham Town (26/8) | 2-1 | 58 |
| 123 | Chipstead | v | Crowborough Athletic | 5-2 | 63 |
| 124 | Sittingbourne | v | Burnham | 2-1 | 112 |
| 125 | Faversham Town | v | Ringmer | 3-0 | 110 |
| 126 | Chatham Town | v | Peacehaven & Telscombe | 2-1 | 113 |
| 127 | Crawley Down Gatwick | v | Tooting & Mitcham United | 1-3 | 153 |
| 128 | Slough Town | v | Corinthian | 4-2 | 154 |
| 129 | Horsham | v | Raynes Park Vale | 2-2 | 186 |
| | Raynes Park Vale | v | Horsham (28/8) | 1-3 | 138 |
| 130 | Merstham | v | Walton & Hersham | 1-5 | 95 |
| 131 | VCD Athletic | v | Whitstable Town | 2-1 | 75 |
| 132 | Burgess Hill Town | v | Littlehampton Town | 0-3 | 241 |
| 133 | Redhill | v | Corinthian Casuals | 3-0 | 121 |
| 134 | Godalming Town | v | Ramsgate | 5-2 | 142 |
| 135 | Herne Bay | v | Folkestone Invicta | 1-3 | 314 |
| 136 | Dulwich Hamlet | v | Hythe Town | 1-0 | 210 |
| 137 | Maidstone United | v | Colliers Wood United | 4-1 | 938 |
| 138 | Guildford City | v | East Preston | 5-3 | 86 |
| 139 | Eastbourne Town | v | Chessington & Hook Utd | 2-0 | 110 |
| 140 | Walton Casuals | v | Thamesmead Town (28/8) | 1-2 | 53 |
| | (25/8 tie abandoned after 45 mins due to waterlogged pitch, 0-2) | | | | |
| 141 | Ashford United | v | Lingfield | 1-3 | 235 |
| 142 | Worthing | v | Rye United | 5-1 | 217 |
| 143 | Greenwich Borough | v | Sidley United | 2-2 | 48 |
| | Sidley United | v | Greenwich Borough (29/8) | 0-1 | 74 |
| | (at Hailsham Town) | | | | |
| 144 | Christchurch | v | Alresford Town (24/8) | 2-1 | 78 |
| 145 | Highworth Town | v | Shortwood United (26/8) | 1-0 | 102 |
| 146 | Blackfield & Langley | v | Downton | 1-0 | 77 |
| 147 | Mangotsfield United | v | Bitton | 2-0 | 175 |
| 148 | Yate Town | v | Poole Town | 5-0 | 128 |
| 149 | GE Hamble | v | Totton & Eling (24/8) | 0-1 | 59 |
| 150 | Pewsey Vale | v | Melksham Town | 2-3 | 98 |
| 151 | Moneyfields | v | Newport (IW) | 0-1 | 72 |
| 152 | Sholing | v | East Cowes VA (24/8) | 4-0 | 96 |
| 153 | Cadbury Heath | v | Almondsbury UWE | 2-3 | 79 |
| 154 | Hallen | v | Swindon Supermarine | 1-4 | 70 |
| 155 | Horndean | v | Romsey Town | 2-0 | 53 |
| 156 | Wootton Bassett Town | v | Hamworthy United (24/8) | 1-0 | 99 |
| 157 | Wimborne Town | v | Fareham Town | 0-1 | 190 |
| 158 | Winchester City | v | Alton Town | 3-0 | 80 |
| 159 | Gillingham Town | v | Bishop Sutton | 3-3 | 107 |
| | Bishop Sutton | v | Gillingham Town (28/8) | 2-3 | 85 |
| 160 | Wells City | v | Bodmin Town | 0-4 | 85 |
| 161 | Clevedon Town | v | Tiverton Town | 2-0 | 96 |
| 162 | Buckland Athletic | v | Hengrove Athletic | 5-0 | 146 |
| 163 | Sherborne Town | v | Odd Down | 2-0 | 78 |
| 164 | Larkhall Athletic | v | Bridgwater Town | 3-2 | 90 |
| 165 | Paulton Rovers | v | Taunton Town | 1-1 | 123 |
| | Taunton Town | v | Paulton Rovers (28/8) | 3-2 | 154 |
| 166 | Chard Town | v | Plymouth Parkway | 1-4 | 91 |

## FIRST QUALIFYING ROUND

Clubs from Steps Three and Four were all involved in this round which was still based on regional draws.

North Leigh from the Southern League Division One South West were certainly enjoying their FA Cup football, scoring six in a second consecutive cup tie with Wantage Town being the unlucky opponents this time.

Some clubs with fine FA Cup traditions found themselves competing in the early rounds included Bishop Auckland, Marine, Kingstonian and Maidstone United, all of whom won away from home. Most ties were keenly contested, thirty replays were needed, but a few one sided games produced spectacular goalscoring such as:

| | | | |
|---|---|---|---|
| Curzon Ashton | 8 | Maltby Main | 1 |
| Cambridge City | 7 | Huntingdon Town | 0 |
| North Leigh | 6 | Wantage Town | 1 |
| Aveley | 6 | Hadleigh United | 1 |
| Blshops Cleeve | 6 | Bracknell | 0 |

and Metropolitan Police produced an outstanding 7-1 away victory at Beckenham Town with Jonte Smith scoring five!

(Above) George Jones of Greenwich Borough blocks this effort from Leigh Bremner of Cray Wanderers in the First Qualifying Round.
Photo: Alan Coomes
(Left) More action from the Gosport v Bashley tie - here we see Molyneaux (Gosport) put the ball past Middleton and Prodomo in the Bashley goal to open the scoring.
Photo: Keith Clayton

# FIRST QUALIFYING ROUND
## SATURDAY 9 SEPTEMBER 2012 - WINNERS RECEIVE £3,000

| # | Home | | Away | Score | Att |
|---|---|---|---|---|---|
| 1 | Spennymoor Town | v | South Shields | 2-0 | 268 |
| 2 | Tadcaster Albion | v | Holker OBs | 3-0 | 111 |
| 3 | Durham City | v | Shildon | 1-3 | 214 |
| 4 | Farsley | v | Ossett Albion | 1-1 | 196 |
| | Ossett Albion | v | Farsley (11/9) | 1-0 | 146 |
| 5 | Ossett Town | v | Whitby Town | 1-1 | 75 |
| | Whitby Town | v | Ossett Town (12/9) | 1-0 | 179 |
| 6 | Bedlington Terriers | v | Bishop Auckland | 0-1 | 206 |
| 7 | Dunston UTS | v | Kendal Town | 3-3 | 212 |
| | Kendal Town | v | Dunston UTS (11/9) | 4-2aet | 159 |
| 8 | Ashington | v | West Auckland Town | 2-3 | 277 |
| 9 | Eccleshill United | v | North Ferriby United | 0-2 | 99 |
| 10 | Blyth Spartans | v | Garforth Town | 1-0 | 401 |
| 11 | Abbey Hey | v | Atherton Collieries | 2-1 | 72 |
| 12 | Warrington Town | v | Maine Road | 1-0 | 224 |
| 13 | Burscough | v | Witton Albion | 2-4 | 217 |
| 14 | Worksop Town | v | Frickley Athletic (7/9) | 0-2 | 274 |
| 15 | Skelmersdale United | v | Clitheroe | 1-0 | |
| 16 | Lancaster City | v | Salford City | 0-4 | 178 |
| 17 | Chorley | v | Nantwich Town | 2-0 | 633 |
| 18 | Bootle | v | Bamber Bridge | 1-2 | 206 |
| 19 | Prescot Cables | v | Ashton United | 1-3 | 167 |
| 20 | Stocksbridge Park Steels | v | Marine | 0-3 | 159 |
| 21 | FC United of Manchester | v | Cammell Laird (9/9) | 5-0 | 1024 |
| 22 | Runcorn Town | v | Trafford | 0-4 | 100 |
| 23 | Curzon Ashton | v | Maltby Main | 8-1 | 135 |
| 24 | AFC Fylde | v | Ramsbottom United | 3-1 | 302 |
| 25 | Retford United | v | New Mills | 2-2 | |
| 26 | Matlock Town | v | Belper Town | 2-2 | 460 |
| | Belper Town | v | Matlock Town (11/9) | 3-0 | 341 |
| 27 | Holbeach United | v | Stamford | 1-2 | 307 |
| 28 | Eastwood Town | v | Blaby & Whetstone Athletic | 1-1 | |
| | Blaby & Whetstone | v | Eastwood Town (12/9) | 1-3 | 254 |
| 29 | Quorn | v | Buxton | 1-2 | 165 |
| 30 | Thurnby Nirvana | v | Gresley | 2-2 | 135 |
| | Gresley | v | Thurnby Nirvana (11/9) | 4-1 | 203 |
| 31 | Loughborough Dynamo | v | Grantham Town | 2-2 | 175 |
| | Grantham Town | v | Loughborough Dynamo (11/9) | 3-1 | 200 |
| 32 | Rainworth MW | v | Carlton Town | 2-2 | 124 |
| | Carlton Town | v | Rainworth MW (12/9) | 3-1 | 63 |
| 33 | Coalville Town | v | Ilkeston | 0-1 | 322 |
| 34 | Dudley Town | v | Nuneaton Griff | 0-1 | 119 |
| 35 | Rugby Town | v | Bedworth United | 1-1 | 237 |
| | Bedworth United | v | Rugby Town (11/9) | 1-0aet | 215 |
| 36 | Chasetown | v | Market Drayton Town | 1-1 | 290 |
| | Market Drayton Town | v | Chasetown (11/9) | 1-2aet | 120 |
| 37 | Redditch United | v | Hednesford Town | 0-3 | 276 |
| 38 | Norton United | v | Westfields | 2-5 | 51 |
| 39 | Barwell | v | AFC Wulfrunians | 3-0 | 125 |
| 40 | Bridgnorth Town | v | Rushall Olympic | 3-1 | 149 |
| 41 | Leamington | v | Stourbridge | 2-2 | 601 |
| | Stourbridge | v | Leamington (11/9) | 1-2 | 440 |
| 42 | Sutton Coldfield Town | v | Gornal Athletic | 0-3 | 80 |
| 43 | Stourport Swifts | v | Stafford Rangers | 1-1 | 171 |
| | Stafford Rangers | v | Stourport Swifts (11/9) | 2-1aet | 309 |
| 44 | Wolverhampton Casuals | v | Tividale | 1-1 | 112 |
| | Tividale | v | Wolverhampton Casuals (11/9) | 4-2 | 101 |
| 45 | Leek Town | v | Bewdley Town | 5-1 | 251 |
| 46 | Cambridge City | v | Huntingdon Town | 7-0 | 240 |
| 47 | Daventry Town | v | King's Lynn Town | 1-1 | 180 |
| | King's Lynn Town | v | Daventry Town (11/9) | 2-3aet | 387 |
| 48 | St Neots Town | v | Peterborough Northern Star | 5-0 | 342 |
| 49 | Wisbech Town | v | Kettering Town | 0-0 | 527 |
| | Kettering Town | v | Wisbech Town (11/9) | 3-0 | |
| 50 | Bugbrooke St Michaels | v | Dereham Town | 1-4 | 80 |
| 51 | Tilbury | v | Lowestoft Town | 0-2 | 134 |
| 52 | Heybridge Swifts | v | AFC Sudbury | 4-1 | 203 |
| 53 | Soham Town Rangers | v | Maldon & Tiptree | 0-2 | 132 |
| 54 | Basildon United | v | Thurrock | 0-3 | 50 |
| 55 | Bury Town | v | Canvey Island | 3-0 | 375 |
| 56 | Wroxham | v | Brentwood Town | 0-5 | 178 |
| 57 | Leiston | v | Southend Manor | 5-1 | 153 |
| 58 | Concord Rangers | v | Needham Market | 1-0 | 132 |
| 59 | East Thurrock United | v | Witham Town | 2-0 | 155 |
| 60 | Grays Athletic | v | Norwich United | 2-1 | 157 |
| 61 | Aveley | v | Hadleigh United | 6-1 | 74 |
| 62 | Dunstable Town | v | Ashford Town (Middx) | 2-2 | 82 |
| | Ashford Town (Middx) | v | Dunstable Town (11/9) | 3-0aet | 116 |
| 63 | AFC Kempston Rovers | v | Hampton & Richmond Borough | 0-3 | 130 |
| 64 | Chesham United | v | Northwood | 0-1 | 252 |
| 65 | Enfield Town | v | St Margaretsbury | 2-0 | 346 |
| 66 | Harrow Borough | v | St Albans City | 1-3 | 219 |
| 67 | London Lions | v | AFC Dunstable (9/9) | 2-4 | 120 |
| | (at Hemel Hempstead Town FC) | | | | |
| 68 | Hemel Hempstead Town | v | Waltham Forest | 2-5 | 248 |
| 69 | Waltham Abbey | v | Bedford Town | 1-0 | |
| 70 | Hendon | v | Potters Bar Town | 1-1 | 119 |
| | Potters Bar Town | v | Hendon (11/9) | 0-3 | 139 |
| 71 | Uxbridge | v | Berkhamsted | 3-4 | 190 |
| 72 | Ware | v | Hitchin Town | 0-5 | 181 |
| 73 | Barton Rovers | v | Arlesey Town | 0-1 | 152 |
| 74 | Colney Heath | v | Harefield United | 1-2 | 70 |
| 75 | Wingate & Finchley | v | Royston Town | 1-1 | |
| | Royston Town | v | Wingate & Finchley (11/9) | 2-3aet | 155 |
| 76 | Wealdstone | v | Biggleswade Town | 2-0 | 302 |
| 77 | Bishop's Cleeve | v | Bracknell Town | 6-0 | 105 |
| 78 | Chalfont St Peter | v | Newport Pagnell Town | 3-2 | |
| 79 | Windsor | v | Didcot Town | 0-1 | 232 |
| 80 | Cinderford Town | v | Merthyr Town | 1-1 | 221 |
| | Merthyr Town | v | Cinderford Town (11/9) | 3-0 | 306 |
| 81 | Hungerford Town | v | Banbury United | 1-1 | 104 |
| | Banbury United | v | Hungerford Town (11/9) | 0-2 | 145 |
| 82 | North Leigh | v | Wantage Town | 6-1 | 92 |
| 83 | Marlow | v | Thatcham Town | 1-3 | 121 |
| 84 | Littlehampton Town | v | Eastbourne Town | 0-1 | 174 |
| 85 | VCD Athletic | v | Horsham | 0-1 | 126 |
| 86 | Slough Town | v | Lingfield | 4-1 | 194 |
| 87 | Faversham Town | v | Margate | 2-2 | 409 |
| | Margate | v | Faversham Town (11/9) | 3-0 | 248 |
| 88 | Bognor Regis Town | v | Epsom & Ewell | 4-0 | 368 |
| 89 | Badshot Lea | v | Folkestone Invicta | 3-2 | 98 |
| 90 | Godalming Town | v | Dulwich Hamlet (9/9) | 2-2 | 311 |
| | Dulwich Hamlet | v | Godalming Town (11/9) | 2-2aet | 157 |
| | (Dulwich Hamlet won 3-1 on kicks from the penalty mark) | | | | |
| 91 | Leatherhead | v | Tooting & Mitcham United | 3-1 | 183 |
| 92 | Greenwich Borough | v | Cray Wanderers (9/9) | 0-1 | 141 |
| 93 | Redhill | v | Lewes | 1-3 | 200 |
| 94 | Beckenham Town | v | Metropolitan Police | 1-7 | 48 |
| 95 | South Park | v | Walton & Hersham | 1-1 | 103 |
| | Walton & Hersham | v | South Park (11/9) | 0-1 | 90 |
| 96 | Chipstead | v | Maidstone United | 0-4 | 189 |
| 97 | Pagham | v | Carshalton Athletic | 0-0 | 140 |
| | Carshalton Athletic | v | Pagham (11/9) | 3-0 | 151 |
| 98 | Guildford City | v | Kingstonian | 0-3 | 295 |
| 99 | Whitehawk | v | Sittingbourne | 5-0 | 136 |
| 100 | Thamesmead Town | v | Worthing | 2-0 | 58 |
| 101 | Hastings United | v | Chatham Town | 3-1 | 338 |
| 102 | Fareham Town | v | Christchurch | 2-1 | 130 |
| 103 | Newport (IW) | v | Horndean | 2-0 | 149 |
| 104 | Chippenham Town | v | Mangotsfield United | 3-1 | 303 |
| 105 | Blackfield & Langley | v | Almondsbury UWE | 4-0 | 45 |
| 106 | Totton & Eling | v | Weymouth | 2-2 | 430 |
| | Weymouth | v | Totton & Eling (11/9) | 3-0 | 356 |
| 107 | Winchester City | v | Yate Town | 1-2 | 71 |
| 108 | Swindon Supermarine | v | AFC Totton | 0-6 | 131 |
| 109 | Wootton Bassett Town | v | Highworth Town (7/9) | 3-1 | 299 |
| 110 | Sholing | v | Melksham Town | 4-0 | 104 |
| 111 | Bashley | v | Gosport Borough | 1-1 | 205 |
| | Gosport Borough | v | Bashley (11/9) | 3-2aet | 182 |
| 112 | Plymouth Parkway | v | Buckland Athletic | 1-1 | 202 |
| | Buckland Athletic | v | Plymouth Parkway (11/9) | 5-1 | 209 |
| 113 | Gillingham Town | v | Taunton Town | 0-0 | 219 |
| | Taunton Town | v | Gillingham Town (11/9) | 1-3 | 222 |
| 114 | Bideford | v | Bodmin Town | 2-2 | 220 |
| | Bodmin Town | v | Bideford (12/9) | 2-3aet | 189 |
| 115 | Larkhall Athletic | v | Frome Town | 0-0 | 185 |
| | Frome Town | v | Larkhall Athletic (12/9) | 4-0 | 204 |
| 116 | Clevedon Town | v | Sherborne Town | 5-0 | 157 |

## SECOND QUALIFYING ROUND

The Conference North and South clubs are welcomed into the draw and the smaller clubs hope it's their turn for some giant killing.

Gresley will have been pleased with a 3-2 home victory over Stafford Rangers, as would Badshot Leigh who beat Leiston 4-2 and North Leigh with their third home tie and third victory, this time by the only goal of the game against Havant & Waterlooville.

Less big scores were recorded in this round as the competition becomes tougher, but exciting ties were enjoyed at:

| | | | |
|---|---|---|---|
| Trafford | 5 | Spennymoor Town | 3 |
| Whitby Town | 4 | Droylsden | 3 |
| Eastwood Town | 3 | Histon | 5 |
| Carlton Town | 4 | New Mills | 3 |
| Hinckley United | 5 | Tividale | 3 |

Clubs such as North Leigh, Blackfield & Langley, Dereham Town, Tadcaster Albion and South Park were looking forward to the draw for the Third Qualifying Round with great excitement.

An easy take for Enfield Town 'keeper Noel Imber, however, the visitors, Bishop's Stortford, went on to record a comfortable 4-0 win to take them through to the Third Qualifying Round. Photo: Gordon Whittington.

Thamesmead goalkeeper, Rob Budd, punches clear from Mark Willy (5) and Tyrone Sterling of Cray Wanderers during this Second Qualifying Round match. Photo: Alan Coomes.

# SECOND QUALIFYING ROUND
## SATURDAY 22 SEPTEMBER 2012 - WINNERS RECEIVE £4,500

| Home | | Away | Score | Att |
|---|---|---|---|---|
| Bishop Auckland | v | AFC Fylde | 1-2 | 298 |
| FC Halifax Town | v | Abbey Hey | 6-0 | 936 |
| Curzon Ashton | v | Bradford (Park Avenue) | 1-3 | 237 |
| Blyth Spartans | v | Workington | 1-1 | 502 |
| Workington | v | Blyth Spartans (1/10) | 1-0 | 219 |
| Shildon | v | Altrincham | 0-3 | 280 |
| Ashton United | v | Marine | 0-2 | 193 |
| Salford City | v | FC United of Manchester | 2-3 | 1298 |
| Trafford | v | Spennymoor Town | 5-3 | 311 |
| Stalybridge Celtic | v | Vauxhall Motors | 1-0 | 420 |
| Bamber Bridge | v | Guiseley | 0-1 | 249 |
| Kendal Town | v | Witton Albion | 4-2 | 277 |
| Colwyn Bay | v | Warrington Town | 3-2 | 249 |
| Gainsborough Trinity | v | Chester | 1-1 | 756 |
| Chester | v | Gainsborough Trinity (2/10) | 2-1aet | 1492 |
| Tadcaster Albion | v | Skelmersdale United | 4-1 | 183 |
| Whitby Town | v | Droylsden | 4-3 | 202 |
| North Ferriby United | v | Ossett Albion | 1-2 | 236 |
| West Auckland Town | v | Harrogate Town | 2-2 | 194 |
| Harrogate Town | v | West Auckland Town (2/10) | 5-1 | 171 |
| Chorley | v | Frickley Athletic | 1-3 | 642 |
| Gornal Athletic | v | Worcester City | 0-4 | 400 |
| Boston United | v | Kettering Town | 1-0 | 901 |
| Solihull Moors | v | Westfields | 1-1 | 124 |
| Westfields | v | Solihull Moors (25/9) | 1-2 | 153 |
| Hinckley United | v | Tividale | 5-3 | 239 |
| Cambridge City | v | Grantham Town | 3-1 | 379 |
| Eastwood Town | v | Histon | 3-5 | 159 |
| Nuneaton Griff | v | Hednesford Town | 2-3 | 298 |
| Gresley | v | Stafford Rangers | 3-2 | 414 |
| Carlton Town | v | New Mills | 4-3 | 78 |
| Brackley Town | v | Daventry Town | 4-0 | 332 |
| Dereham Town | v | Chasetown | 2-1 | 243 |
| Ilkeston | v | Belper Town | 2-2 | 519 |
| Belper Town | v | Ilkeston (25/9) | 1-5 | 320 |
| Stamford | v | Buxton | 1-3 | 201 32 |
| Leek Town | v | Bridgnorth Town | 3-0 | 356 |
| Barwell | v | Bedworth United | 3-2 | 304 |
| Corby Town | v | Leamington | 3-2 | 516 |
| Northwood | v | AFC Dunstable | 1-1 | 111 |
| AFC Dunstable | v | Northwood (26/9) | 0-3 | 109 |
| Wealdstone | v | Lowestoft Town | 1-2 | 413 |
| Ashford Town (Middx) | v | St Albans City | 2-6 | 176 |
| Hayes & Yeading United | v | Heybridge Swifts (23/9) | 3-2 | 139 |
| Carshalton Athletic | v | Chalfont St Peter | 0-1 | 185 |
| 40 Hendon | v | Lewes | 3-0 | 166 |
| 41 St Neots Town | v | Boreham Wood | 1-2 | 432 |
| 42 Chelmsford City | v | Leatherhead | 2-1 | 519 |
| 43 Dover Athletic | v | Tonbridge Angels | 2-1 | 625 |
| 44 Brentwood Town | v | Maldon & Tiptree | 1-1 | 136 |
| Maldon & Tiptree | v | Brentwood Town (25/9) | 1-1aet | 106 |
| (Brentwood Town won 9-8 on kicks from the penalty mark) | | | | |
| 45 Badshot Lea | v | Leiston | 4-2 | 98 |
| 46 Aveley | v | Margate | 1-4 | 131 |
| 47 Waltham Abbey | v | Eastbourne Borough | 2-4 | 223 |
| 48 Billericay Town | v | AFC Hornchurch | 3-1 | 509 |
| 49 Concord Rangers | v | Welling United | 1-1 | 235 |
| Welling United | v | Concord Rangers (26/9) | 2-1 | 287 |
| 50 Enfield Town | v | Bishop's Stortford | 1-4 | 460 |
| 51 Cray Wanderers | v | Thamesmead Town | 3-1 | 92 |
| 52 Waltham Forest | v | Hampton & Richmond Borough | 0-1 | 89 |
| 53 Whitehawk | v | Hitchin Town | 1-1 | 144 |
| Hitchin Town | v | Whitehawk (24/9) | 5-0 | 185 |
| 54 South Park | v | Harefield United | 0-0 | 171 |
| Harefield Town | v | South Park (25/9) | 1-4 | 135 |
| 55 Arlesey Town | v | Dulwich Hamlet | 1-0 | 156 |
| 56 Staines Town | v | Hastings United | 2-3 | 289 |
| 57 Berkhamsted | v | Metropolitan Police | 0-3 | 204 |
| 58 Slough Town | v | Eastbourne Town (23/9) | 5-1 | 182 |
| 59 Bury Town | v | Wingate & Finchley | 2-1 | 366 |
| 60 Horsham | v | Thurrock | 1-2 | 221 |
| 61 Sutton United | v | Bromley | 0-1 | 511 |
| 62 Grays Athletic | v | Maidstone United | 0-5 | 345 |
| 63 Kingstonian | v | East Thurrock United | 2-3 | 306 |
| 64 Bishop's Cleeve | v | Chippenham Town | 1-2 | 187 |
| 65 Truro City | v | AFC Totton | 2-3 | 424 |
| 66 Dorchester Town | v | Wootton Bassett Town | 4-0 | 406 |
| 67 Buckland Athletic | v | Bath City | 1-2 | 367 |
| 68 Gloucester City | v | Thatcham Town | 2-1 | 231 |
| 69 Gillingham Town | v | Sholing | 1-3 | 227 |
| 70 North Leigh | v | Havant & Waterlooville | 1-0 | 194 |
| 71 Basingstoke Town | v | Weymouth | 3-1 | 324 |
| 72 Merthyr Town | v | Hungerford Town | 0-0 | 513 |
| Hungerford Town | v | Merthyr Town (24/9) | 1-1aet | 115 |
| (Merthyr Town won 5-4 on kicks from the penalty mark) | | | | |
| 73 Frome Town | v | Weston Super Mare | 0-2 | 256 |
| 74 Didcot Town | v | Clevedon Town (21/9) | 3-1 | 190 |
| 75 Newport (IW) | v | Salisbury City | 0-3 | 559 |
| 76 Gosport Borough | v | Bideford | 2-0 | 232 |
| 77 Fareham Town | v | Blackfield & Langley | 0-2 | 224 |
| 78 Farnborough | v | Eastleigh | 1-2 | 444 |
| 79 Maidenhead United | v | Bognor Regis Town | 4-2 | 316 |
| 80 Yate Town | v | Oxford City | 2-1 | 179 |

## THIRD QUALIFYING ROUND

Just one more round before The Conference Premier clubs enter the fray and then one more before the First Round Proper. There's all to play for and more headlines to make.

The luck of the draw deserted North Leigh, who made the short journey to Yate Town but lost by the odd goal in three. Tadcaster Town lost 0-2 at home to traditional cup fighters Boston United while Dereham Town drew at home to Metropolitan Police before losing the replay.

However, headlines were grabbed by Blackfield & Langley from The Wessex League who won 2-1 at nearby Sholing and South Park from The Combined Counties also made made progress with a 2-1 home victory over Brentwood Town.

High scoring cup ties were also enjoyed:

| | | | |
|---|---|---|---|
| Arlesey Town | 4 | Brackley Town | 3 |
| Harrogate Town | 3 | Frickley Athletic | 2 |
| Ilkeston | 4 | Gresley | 2 |
| Replay | | | |
| Billericay Town | 2 | Cambridge CIty | 4 |

One more round before Football League clubs enter the draw and 32 non-league teams will be involved.

Action from the Fourth Qualifying Round tie between Alfreton and Gateshead.
Photo: Bill Wheatcroft.

## FOURTH QUALIFYING ROUND

The quality of the Conference Premier Division was clear for everyone to see, as just two clubs, Newport County and Hyde, lost to lower level teams. Yate Town, a Southern League Division One South West club drew 3-3 with Newport at home and won in Wales, while Harrogate Town drew at Hyde and won the replay 1-0 after extra time.

Strong challenges came in some thrilling cup ties:-

| | | | |
|---|---|---|---|
| Braintree Town | 3 | Lowestoft Town | 2 |
| Stockport County | 5 | Stalybridge Celtic | 3 |
| Woking | 0 | Ebbsfleet United | 1 |
| Workington | 1 | Mansfield Town | 2 |

Two of the smallest challengers Blackfield & Langley and South Park had no luck in the draw. They were faced by possibly stronger opposition in Hastings United and Met Police who both won 3-0.

Fourteen Conference Clubs and eighteen others waited for one of the most exciting cup draws of the season. The supporters of Slough Town and Yate Town certainly enjoyed 'cup fever' !

## THIRD QUALIFYING ROUND
### SATURDAY 6 OCTOBER 2012 - WINNERS RECEIVE £7,500

| # | Home | v | Away | Score | Att |
|---|------|---|------|-------|-----|
| 1 | Ilkeston | v | Gresley | 4-2 | 621 |
| 2 | Chester | v | FC Halifax Town | 1-1 | 2613 |
| | FC Halifax | v | Chester (9/10) | 3-1 | 1541 |
| 3 | Hednesford Town | v | Buxton | 2-2 | 498 |
| | Buxton | v | Hednesford Town (10/10) | 2-1aet | 302 |
| 4 | AFC Fylde | v | Solihull Moors | 4-1 | 278 |
| 5 | Carlton Town | v | Bradford (Park Avenue) | 1-3 | 151 |
| 6 | Colwyn Bay | v | Guiseley | 1-1 | 318 |
| | Guiseley | v | Colwyn Bay (9/10) | 3-1 | 360 |
| 7 | Stalybridge Celtic | v | Whitby Town | 3-1 | 372 |
| 8 | Barwell | v | Workington | 1-1 | 217 |
| | Workington | v | Barwell (9/10) | 2-0 | 385 |
| 9 | Hinckley United | v | Ossett Albion | 2-2 | 270 |
| | Ossett Albion | v | Hinckley United (9/10) | 1-0 | 222 |
| 10 | FC United Of Manchester | v | Kendal Town (7/10) | 3-1 | 1186 |
| 11 | Leek Town | v | Altrincham | 0-2 | 962 |
| 12 | Trafford | v | Marine | 1-3 | 515 |
| 13 | Harrogate Town | v | Frickley Athletic | 3-2 | 349 |
| 14 | Tadcaster Albion | v | Boston United | 0-2 | 368 |
| 15 | Hastings United | v | Hitchin Town | 2-2 | 459 |
| | Hitchin Town | v | Hastings United (8/10) | 1-2 | 289 |
| 16 | Histon | v | Corby Town | 1-1 | 330 |
| | Corby Town | v | Histon (10/10) | 2-1 | 510 |
| 17 | Cambridge City | v | Billericay Town | 1-1 | 394 |
| | Billericay Town | v | Cambridge City (9/10) | 2-4 | 364 |
| 18 | Margate | v | Slough Town | 0-1 | 410 |
| 19 | Dereham Town | v | Metropolitan Police | 1-1 | 328 |
| | Metropolitan Police | v | Dereham Town (10/10) | 2-0 | 191 |
| 20 | South Park | v | Brentwood Town | 3-1 | 255 |
| 21 | Chalfont St Peter | v | Bishop's Stortford | 1-1 | 241 |
| | Bishop's Stortford | v | Chalfont St Peter (9/10) | 3-1 | 268 |
| 22 | Cray Wanderers | v | Chelmsford City | 1-2 | 350 |
| 23 | Dover Athletic | v | Bromley | 1-2 | 715 |
| 24 | Northwood | v | Boreham Wood | 0-4 | 225 |
| 25 | East Thurrock United | v | Maidstone United | 3-0 | |
| 26 | Bury Town | v | Hampton & Richmond Borough | 4-0 | 405 |
| 27 | St Albans City | v | Lowestoft Town | 0-1 | 306 |
| 28 | Eastbourne Borough | v | Hendon | 2-2 | 493 |
| | Hendon | v | Eastbourne Borough (9/10) | 2-1aet | 190 |
| 29 | Arlesey Town | v | Brackley Town | 4-3 | 227 |
| 30 | Welling United | v | Thurrock | 1-1 | 402 |
| | Thurrock | v | Welling United (9/10) | 1-3 | 176 |
| 31 | Weston Super Mare | v | Worcester City | 1-1 | 556 |
| | Worcester City | v | Weston Super Mare (8/10) | 1-0 | 1013 |
| 32 | Dorchester Town | v | Basingstoke Town | 1-0 | 466 |
| 33 | Yate Town | v | North Leigh | 2-1 | 191 |
| 34 | Gloucester City | v | Eastleigh (7/10) | 1-0 | 432 |
| 35 | Chippenham Town | v | Badshot Lea | 3-1 | 367 |
| 36 | Didcot Town | v | Maidenhead United | 1-0 | 301 |
| 37 | AFC Totton | v | Merthyr Town | 3-2 | 539 |
| 38 | Bath City | v | Gosport Borough | 1-1 | 586 |
| | Gosport Borough | v | Bath City (9/10) | 3-1 | 342 |
| 39 | Sholing | v | Blackfield & Langley | 1-3 | 165 |
| 40 | Hayes & Yeading United | v | Salisbury City | 2-1 | 345 |

## FOURTH QUALIFYING ROUND
### SATURDAY 20 OCTOBER 2012 - WINNERS RECEIVE £12,500

| # | Home | v | Away | Score | Att |
|---|------|---|------|-------|-----|
| 1 | Alfreton Town | v | Gateshead | 2-0 | 338 |
| 2 | Hyde | v | Harrogate Town | 1-1 | 393 |
| | Harrogate Town | v | Hyde (31/10) | 1-0 | 247 |
| | (at Harrogate Railway Athletic FC) | | | | |
| 3 | FC United of Manchester | v | Hereford United | 0-2 | 2212 |
| 4 | Barrow | v | Tamworth | 2-0 | 1104 |
| 5 | Guiseley | v | Buxton | 2-0 | 847 |
| 6 | Grimsby Town | v | Kidderminster Harriers | 2-4 | 2092 |
| 7 | Bradford Park Avenue | v | Ossett Albion | 4-1 | 477 |
| 8 | Wrexham | v | Southport | 2-0 | 1911 |
| 9 | AFC Fylde | v | Ilkeston | 1-1 | 482 |
| | Ilkeston | v | AFC Fylde (22/10) | 0-1 | 696 |
| 10 | Boston United | v | Altrincham | 1-3 | 1200 |
| 11 | Lincoln City | v | FC Halifax Town | 0-0 | 1940 |
| | FC Halifax Town | v | Lincoln City (23/10) | 0-2 | 1418 |
| 12 | Macclesfield Town | v | Marine | 3-1 | 1189 |
| 13 | Workington | v | Mansfield Town | 1-2 | 701 |
| 14 | Stockport County | v | Stalybridge Celtic | 5-3 | 2123 |
| 15 | AFC Telford United | v | Nuneaton Town | 2-2 | 1251 |
| | Nuneaton Town | v | AFC Telford United (23/10) | 1-0aet | 616 |
| 16 | South Park | v | Metropolitan Police | 0-3 | 643 |
| 17 | Didcot Town | v | Arlesey Town | 0-1 | 414 |
| 18 | Forest Green Rovers | v | Dartford | 1-1 | 891 |
| | Dartford | v | Forest Green Rovers (23/10) | 1-4 | 804 |
| 19 | Yate Town | v | Newport County | 3-3 | 1190 |
| | Newport County | v | Yate Town (23/10) | 1-3aet | 1463 |
| 20 | Slough Town | v | Gosport Borough (21/10) | 0-0 | 523 |
| | Gosport Borough | v | Slough Town (23/10) | 1-2 | 635 |
| 21 | Hastings United | v | Blackfield & Langley | 3-0 | 800 |
| 22 | Bromley | v | Worcester City | 1-0 | 610 |
| 23 | Chelmsford City | v | East Thurrock United | 2-2 | 902 |
| | East Thurrock United | v | Chelmsford City (23/10) | 4-4aet | 595 |
| | (Chelmsford City won 5-3 on kicks from the penalty mark) | | | | |
| 24 | Hayes & Yeading United | v | Boreham Wood (21/10) | 2-3 | 312 |
| 25 | AFC Totton | v | Cambridge City | 2-3 | 674 |
| 26 | Welling United | v | Bishop's Stortford | 1-3 | 544 |
| 27 | Braintree Town | v | Lowestoft Town | 3-2 | 634 |
| 28 | Dorchester Town | v | Bury Town | 3-1 | 555 |
| 29 | Cambridge United | v | Luton Town | 0-2 | 2321 |
| 30 | Gloucester City | v | Chippenham Town | 1-0 | 675 |
| 31 | Corby Town | v | Hendon | 1-2 | 692 |
| 32 | Woking | v | Ebbsfleet United | 0-1 | 1272 |

FAC 3Q: Eastbourne Borough's Chris Shephard (left) scores in the last minute to earn a draw.

FAC 4Q: Zac Attwood (10) scores for Hastings v Blackfield & Langley. Photos: Roger Turner.

FAC 3Q: Goal mouth action between Ilkeston and Gresley.
Photo: Bill Wheatcroft.

FAC 4Q: Midfield action between Alfreton and Gateshead. Photo: Bill Wheatcroft.

FAC 1Q: Pip Hurdley of Bridgnorth Town seen here in poscession during their giant-killing win over Rushall Olympic. Photo: Jonathan Holloway.

FAC 4Q: A wasted free-kick for the hosts Welling United as the ball drifts past the far post in their 1-3 defeat by Bishop's Stortford. Photo: Gordon Whittington.

FAC P: Matt Crabb, Eastbourne Town No.11, fires a shot at the Chessington & Hooks goal. Photo: Roger Turner.

Shane Blackett's shot evades Brackley 'keeper, Billy Turley, to put Arlesey 4-1 up, they hung on to win 4-3!
Photo: Gordon Whittington.

## FIRST ROUND PROPER

The thirty-two non-league clubs in the draw were made up of 14 Conference Premier, 6 Conference North, 4 Conference South, 3 Isthmian Premier, 2 Southern League Premier and one each from The Northern Premier and the two Southern League Divisions One.

Television payments, improved gate money and national publicity were all possibilities for these clubs. What was the best outcome? A home tie or a visit to glamourous opponents?

AFC Fylde, Boreham Wood, Forest Green Rovers and Kidderminster Harriers all lost at home to League opposition in front of good attendances but Chelmsford City and Hereford United thrilled their fans with 3-1 defeats of Colchester United and Shrewsbury Town respectively.

Yate Town travelled up the M5 to Cheltenham, Arlesey Town visited more attractive opposition in Coventry City and Bromley visited Fleetwood Town but all three non-league clubs conceded three goals and lost. Ebbsfleet United did score twice at Carlisle United but conceded four.

Slough Town took Mansfield Town to a replay and penalties before their wonderful cup run came to an end and Cambridge City drew at home to Milton Keynes but conceded six in the replay.There was a sad story at Metropolitan Police where their star goalscorer Jonte Smith couldn't play in their tie at home to Crawley, as he was in fact on loan from the Sussex club!

Impressive away performances were produced by Alfreton Town who won 4-2 at high flying Wrexham, Harrogate Town who won 1-0 at Torquay United and Macclesfield Town who achieved a superb 2-0 victory at a very confident Swindon Town.

Luton Town and Barrow beat Nuneaton Town and Guiseley respectively after replays, but three more non-league successes were achieved by Lincoln City who won their replay, 3-2 in a thriller at Walsall. While Oxford United won 2-0 at Barnet and Dorchester Town had a 1-0 success against another West country club Plymouth Argyle.

## SECOND ROUND PROPER

The draw in this round proved to be unique as four of the seven ties paired non-league clubs against each other and Chelmsford City travelled to Crawley Town who were only in their first Football League season.

So, with Hereford United losing a replay against Cheltenham Town, Leyton Orient beating Alfreton Town 4-2 and Crawley beating Cheltenham Town, it was left to the results of the four all non-league ties to decide who would be representing their level of the game, when the games elite were welcomed to the competition in the Third Round.

The favourites in three ties produced winning performances, so LutonTown, Mansfield Town and Macclesfield Town eventually eliminated Barrow after a replay, although the weather prevented their game being decided until the end of December.

The fourth tie brought two real outsiders together with Harrogate Town's home advantage expected to be the difference. However, after two tough 1-1 draws and extra time, it was Hastings United that won after a penalty shoot out and qualified for a trip to Middlesbrough.

## THIRD ROUND PROPER

Mansfield Town were recipients of the best draw with a visit from Liverpool and did well to keep the score to 1-2, while Hastings United had nothing to lose with a long trip to Middlesbrough but went down 1-4. Both matches provided a financial boost, so, along with the round by round payments from The Football Association, the cup runs had been a great success.

Home ties were enjoyed by Luton Town, who recorded a famous 1-0 win over Wolverhampton Wanderers, with a goal just after half time from Alex Lawless in front of 9,638 fans and Macclesfield Town, who beat Championship high flyers Cardiff City with two goals in the last five minutes from Matthew Barnes-Homer. The drama was accentuated by the fact the winner was from the penalty spot.

Two clubs, both recent Football League members in their own right, would be representing non-league football in the Fourth Round and once again giving extra glamour to the Fourth Round draw.

## FOURTH & FIFTH ROUND PROPER

Two 1-0 score lines for our clubs, but although Macclesfield were just beaten by a penalty from Premier Division Wigan Athletic, the consequent success of their North Western neighbours in the FA Cup, made that result considerably more impressive.

To visit a Premier Division club in the FA Cup is the dream of every non-league team but once you have been given the tie, no one really gives you a chance of progressing in the competition. So when Luton Town's Scott Rendell scored with just ten minutes to go, the 4,000 traveling fans must have really suffered as the minutes ticket away. The final whistle signaled a first ever defeat for a Premier League club by a non-league club and the first time a top level club had lost since First Division Coventry City had been beaten by Sutton United in 1989.

The Norwich City club took their disappointment in a sporting fashion and Luton Town moved on to be drawn against Millwall who,wisely learnt form Luton's fine form at Norwich, and took no chances. An exciting cup run had come to an end, but everyone involved with 'The Hatters' will remember 'that great cup run when we were a non-league club'.

Its interesting to note that Macclesfield Town and Luton Town's excellent cup runs were halted by Wigan Athletic and Millwall who were to meet in the Semi-Final!

# FIRST ROUND PROPER
### SATURDAY 3 NOVEMBER 2012 - WINNERS RECEIVE £18,000

| | | | | | |
|---|---|---|---|---|---|
| 1 | Kidderminster Harriers | v | Oldham Athletic | 0-2 | 2888 |
| 2 | Boreham Wood | v | Brentford | 0-2 | 1495 |
| 3 | Chelmsford City | v | Colchester United | 3-1 | 3016 |
| 4 | Metropolitan Police | v | Crawley Town | 1-2 | 1435 |
| 5 | Luton Town | v | Nuneaton Town | 1-1 | 3089 |
| | Nuneaton Town | v | Luton Town (13/11) | 0-2 | 1596 |
| 6 | Portsmouth | v | Notts County | 0-2 | 7560 |
| 7 | Bishop's Stortford | v | Hastings United | 1-2 | 1212 |
| 8 | Fleetwood Town | v | Bromley | 3-0 | 1696 |
| 9 | Forest Green Rovers | v | Port Vale | 2-3 | |
| 10 | Torquay United | v | Harrogate Town | 0-1 | 1817 |
| 11 | AFC Bournemouth | v | Dagenham & Redbridge | 4-0 | 5827 |
| 12 | Morecambe | v | Rochdale | 1-1 | 1839 |
| | Rochdale | v | Morecambe (13/11) | 0-1 | 1675 |
| 13 | Swindon Town | v | Macclesfield Town | 0-2 | 6403 |
| 14 | Cambridge City | v | Milton Keynes Dons (2/11) | 0-0 | 1564 |
| | Milton Keynes Dons | v | Cambridge City (13/11) | 6-1 | 4126 |
| 15 | Cheltenham Town | v | Yate Town | 3-0 | 3055 |
| 16 | Dorchester Town | v | Plymouth Argyle (4/11) | 1-0 | 3196 |
| 17 | Coventry City | v | Arlesey Town | 3-0 | 6594 |
| 18 | York City | v | AFC Wimbledon | 1-1 | 2752 |
| | AFC Wimbledon | v | York City (12/11) | 4-3aet | 1954 |
| 19 | Bury | v | Exeter City | 1-0 | 1821 |
| 20 | Chesterfield | v | Hartlepool United | 6-1 | 3083 |
| 21 | Doncaster Rovers | v | Bradford Park Avenue | 3-1 | 4062 |
| 22 | Gillingham | v | Scunthorpe United | 4-0 | 4070 |
| 23 | Aldershot Town | v | Hendon | 2-1 | 1822 |
| 24 | Lincoln City | v | Walsall | 1-1 | 2032 |
| | Walsall | v | Lincoln City (13/11) | 2-3aet | 1762 |
| 25 | Wrexham | v | Alfreton Town | 2-4 | 2409 |
| 26 | Southend United | v | Stockport County | 3-0 | 3084 |
| 27 | Crewe Alexandra | v | Wycombe Wanderers | 4-1 | 2417 |
| 28 | Bristol Rovers | v | Sheffield United | 1-2 | 4712 |
| 29 | Hereford United | v | Shrewsbury Town | 3-1 | 3251 |
| 30 | Mansfield Town | v | Slough Town | 0-0 | 1686 |
| | Slough Town | v | Mansfield Town (13/11) | 1-1aet | 1593 |
| | (Mansfield Town won 4-1 on kicks from the penalty mark) | | | | |
| 31 | Barnet | v | Oxford United | 0-2 | 2346 |
| 32 | Rotherham United | v | Stevenage | 3-2 | 4324 |
| 33 | AFC Fylde | v | Accrington Stanley | 1-4 | 1213 |
| 34 | Gloucester City | v | Leyton Orient (14/11) | 0-2 | 1381 |
| 35 | Burton Albion | v | Altrincham (4/11) | 3-3 | 1989 |
| | Altrincham | v | Burton Albion (15/11) | 0-2 | 2428 |
| 36 | Guiseley | v | Barrow | 2-2 | 1604 |
| | Barrow | v | Guiseley (13/11) | 1-0 | 1402 |
| 37 | Northampton Town | v | Bradford City | 1-1 | 2512 |
| | Bradford City | v | Northampton Town (13/11) | 3-3aet | 2951 |
| | (Bradford City won 4-2 on kicks from the penalty mark) | | | | |
| 38 | Preston North End | v | Yeovil Town | 3-0 | 4757 |
| 39 | Braintree Town | v | Tranmere Rovers (13/11) | 0-3 | 1503 |
| 40 | Carlisle United | v | Ebbsfleet United | 4-2 | 2373 |

# SECOND ROUND PROPER
### SATURDAY 1 DECEMBER 2012 - WINNERS RECEIVE £27,000

| | | | | | |
|---|---|---|---|---|---|
| 1 | Preston North End | v | Gillingham | 2-0 | 5271 |
| 2 | Bury | v | Southend United | 1-1 | 2391 |
| | Southend United | v | Bury (11/12) | 1-1aet | 3043 |
| | (Southend United won 3-2 on kicks from the penalty mark) | | | | |
| 3 | Sheffield United | v | Port Vale | 2-1 | 10215 |
| 4 | Carlisle United | v | AFC Bournemouth | 1-3 | 2980 |
| 5 | Crewe Alexandra | v | Burton Albion | 0-1 | 3065 |
| 6 | Bradford City | v | Brentford (30/11) | 1-1 | 3620 |
| | Brentford | v | Bradford City (18/12) | 4-2aet | 2643 |
| 7 | Luton Town | v | Dorchester Town | 3-1 | 3287 |
| 8 | Alfreton Town | v | Leyton Orient (2/12) | 2-4 | 1104 |
| 9 | Oldham Athletic | v | Doncaster Rovers | 3-1 | 2783 |
| 10 | Tranmere Rovers | v | Chesterfield | 2-1 | 3781 |
| 11 | Rotherham United | v | Notts County | 1-1 | 7903 |
| | Notts County | v | Rotherham United (18/12) | 0-3 | 2990 |
| 12 | Cheltenham Town | v | Hereford United (3/12) | 1-1 | 5070 |
| | Hereford United | v | Cheltenham Town (11/12) | 1-2aet | 5026 |
| 13 | Barrow | v | Macclesfield Town (18/12) | 1-1 | 1592 |
| | Macclesfield Town | v | Barrow (29/12) | 4-1 | 1554 |
| 14 | Accrington Stanley | v | Oxford United | 3-3 | 1195 |
| | Oxford United | v | Accrington Stanley (18/12) | 2-0 | 2566 |
| 15 | Lincoln City | v | Mansfield Town | 3-3 | 4127 |
| | Mansfield Town | v | Lincoln City (12/12) | 2-1 | 5304 |
| 16 | Harrogate Town | v | Hastings United | 1-1 | 2986 |
| | Hastings United | v | Harrogate Town (13/12) | 1-1aet | 4028 |
| | (Hastings United won 5-4 on kicks from the penalty mark) | | | | |
| 17 | Coventry City | v | Morecambe | 2-1 | 6339 |
| 18 | Milton Keynes Dons | v | AFC Wimbledon (2/12) | 2-1 | 16459 |
| 19 | Crawley Town | v | Chelmsford City | 3-0 | 3012 |
| 20 | Fleetwood Town | v | Aldershot Town | 2-3 | 1757 |

# THIRD ROUND PROPER
### SATURDAY 5 JANUARY 2013 - WINNERS RECEIVE £67,000

| | | | | | |
|---|---|---|---|---|---|
| 1 | Crystal Palace | v | Stoke City | 0-0 | 13693 |
| | Stoke City | v | Crystal Palace (15/1) | 4-1 | 11617 |
| 2 | Brighton & Hove Albion | v | Newcastle United | 2-0 | 21740 |
| 3 | Tottenham Hotspur | v | Coventry City | 3-0 | 35766 |
| 4 | WIGAN ATHLETIC | v | AFC Bournemouth | 1-1 | 8199 |
| | AFC Bournemouth | v | Wigan (15/1) | 0-1 | 8890 |
| 5 | Fulham | v | Blackpool | 1-1 | 14473 |
| | Blackpool | v | Fulham (15/1) | 1-2aet | 8706 |
| 6 | Aston Villa | v | Ipswich Town | 2-1 | 24854 |
| 7 | Charlton Athletic | v | Huddersfield Town | 0-1 | 6657 |
| 8 | Macclesfield Town | v | Cardiff City | 2-1 | 3165 |
| 9 | Barnsley | v | Burnley | 1-0 | 5091 |
| 10 | MANCHESTER CITY | v | Watford | 3-0 | 46821 |
| 11 | Swansea City | v | Arsenal (6/1) | 2-2 | 18648 |
| | Arsenal | v | Swansea City (16/1) | 1-0 | 58359 |
| 12 | Leicester City | v | Burton Albion | 2-0 | 14463 |
| 13 | Millwall | v | Preston North End | 1-0 | 5364 |
| 14 | Cheltenham Town | v | Everton (7/1) | 1-5 | 6891 |
| 15 | Derby County | v | Tranmere Rovers | 5-0 | 11740 |
| 16 | Crawley Town | v | Reading | 1-3 | 5880 |
| 17 | Aldershot Town | v | Rotherham United | 3-1 | 2992 |
| 18 | Middlesbrough | v | Hastings United | 4-1 | 12579 |
| 19 | Oxford United | v | Sheffield United | 0-3 | 7079 |
| 20 | Southampton | v | Chelsea | 1-5 | 27813 |
| 21 | Queens Park Rangers | v | West Bromwich Albion | 1-1 | 8984 |
| | West Bromwich Albion | v | Queens Park Rangers (15/1) | 0-1 | 11184 |
| 22 | Peterborough United | v | Norwich City | 0-3 | 13198 |
| 23 | Mansfield Town | v | Liverpool (6/1) | 1-2 | 7574 |
| 24 | Bolton Wanderers | v | Sunderland | 2-2 | 12204 |
| | Sunderland | v | Bolton Wanderers (15/1) | 0-2 | 17505 |
| 25 | Nottingham Forest | v | Oldham Athletic | 2-3 | 11293 |
| 26 | West Ham United | v | Manchester United | 2-2 | 32922 |
| | Manchester United | v | West Ham United (16/1) | 1-0 | 71081 |
| 27 | Hull City | v | Leyton Orient | 1-1 | 8565 |
| | Leyton Orient | v | Hull City (15/1) | 1-2aet | 3601 |
| 28 | Blackburn Rovers | v | Bristol City | 2-0 | 5504 |
| 29 | Leeds United | v | Birmingham City | 1-1 | 11447 |
| | Birmingham City | v | Leeds United (15/1) | 1-2 | 8962 |
| 30 | Southend United | v | Brentford | 2-2 | 5540 |
| | Brentford | v | Southend United (15/1) | 2-1 | 6526 |
| 31 | Luton Town | v | Wolverhampton Wanderers | 1-0 | 9638 |
| 32 | Sheffield Wednesday | v | Milton Keynes Dons | 0-0 | 11462 |
| | Milton Keynes Dons | v | Sheffield Wednesday (15/1) | 2-0 | 6782 |

FAC 1P: Leyton Orient skipper, Clarke, goes in to block the attempted clearance by Gloucester City's Harris. Photo: Keith Clayton.

Saturday 26th January 2013

| MACCLESFIELD TOWN | | WIGAN ATHLETIC | |
|---|---|---|---|
| 40 | Joe Anyon | 1 | Joel Robles |
| 2 | Ryan Jackson | 11 | Angelo Henriquez |
| 5 | Nat Brown (c) | 14 | Jordi Gomez |
| 7 | Jack Mackreth | 15 | Callum McManaman |
| 8 | Keiran Murtagh | 18 | Roger Espinoza |
| 9 | Matthew Barnes-Homer | 20 | Fraser Fyvie |
| 17 | Sam Wedgbury | 23 | Ronnie Stam |
| 19 | John Paul Kissock | 25 | Roman Golobart |
| 20 | Waide Fairhurst | 27 | Jordan Mustoe |
| 22 | Craig Braham-Barrett | 29 | Nouha Dicko |
| 30 | Thierry Audel | 31 | Maynor Figueroa (c) |
| 10 | Amari Morgan-Smith | 6 | David Jones |
| 11 | Peter Winn | 10 | Shaun Maloney |
| 13 | Andrew Mills | 16 | James McArthur |
| 14 | Tony Diagne | 24 | Adrian Lopez |
| 18 | Charlie Henry | 26 | Ali Al Habsi |
| 23 | Dean McDonald | 28 | Danny Redmond |
| 31 | Carl Martin | 44 | Edu Campabadal |

Referee
R East

Asst Referee (Red/Yellow)       Asst Referee (Yellow)
R West                          A Halliday

Reserve Official

McGregor's Office Supplies

FAC 4P: Macclesfield Town full back, Ryan Jackson, gets his toe to the ball ahead of Wigan Athletic's Callum McManaman. Photo: Peter Barnes.

FAC 2P: Alfreton's No.21 fires in a shot before the Leyton Orient defender can get in a block. Photo: Bill Wheatcroft.

FAC 5P: Luton Town striker Andre Gray challanges Millwall's Shane Lowery for the ball. Photo: Peter Barnes.

# FOURTH ROUND PROPER
## SATURDAY 26 JANUARY 2013 - WINNERS RECEIVE £90,000

| 1 | Norwich City | v | Luton Town | 0-1 | 26521 |
|---|---|---|---|---|---|
| 2 | Oldham Athletic | v | Liverpool (27/1) | 3-2 | 10295 |
| 3 | Macclesfield Town | v | WIGAN ATHLETIC | 0-1 | 5849 |
| 4 | Derby County | v | Blackburn Rovers | 0-3 | 14013 |
| 5 | Hull City | v | Barnsley | 0-1 | 9932 |
| 6 | Middlesbrough | v | Aldershot Town | 2-1 | 12684 |
| 7 | Millwall | v | Aston Villa (25/1) | 2-1 | 15007 |
| 8 | Leeds United | v | Tottenham Hotspur (27/1) | 2-1 | 29943 |
| 9 | Brighton & Hove Albion | v | Arsenal | 2-3 | 27113 |

| 10 | Stoke City | v | MANCHESTER CITY | 0-1 | 19814 |
|---|---|---|---|---|---|
| 11 | Manchester United | v | Fulham | 4-1 | 72596 |
| 12 | Brentford | v | Chelsea (27/1) | 2-2 | 12146 |
|  | Chelsea | v | Brentford (17/2) | 4-0 |  |
| 13 | Reading | v | Sheffield United | 4-0 | 14715 |
| 14 | Huddersfield Town | v | Leicester City | 1-1 | 11945 |
|  | Leicester City | v | Huddersfield Town (12/2) | 1-2 | 14517 |
| 15 | Queens Park Rangers | v | Milton Keynes Dons | 2-4 | 17081 |
| 16 | Bolton Wanderers | v | Everton | 1-2 | 18760 |

# FIFTH ROUND PROPER
## SATURDAY 16 FEBRUARY 2013 - WINNERS RECEIVE £180,000

| 1 | Huddersfield Town | v | WIGAN ATHLETIC (17/2) | 1-4 | 12117 |
|---|---|---|---|---|---|
| 2 | Milton Keynes Dons | v | Barnsley | 1-3 | 14475 |
| 3 | Oldham Athletic | v | Everton | 2-2 | 9473 |
|  | Everton | v | Oldham Athletic (26/2) | 3-1 | 32688 |
| 4 | Luton Town | v | Millwall | 0-3 | 9768 |

| 5 | Arsenal | v | Blackburn Rovers | 0-1 | 60070 |
|---|---|---|---|---|---|
| 6 | MANCHESTER CITY | v | Leeds United (17/2) | 4-0 | 46849 |
| 7 | Manchester United | v | Reading (18/2) | 2-1 | 75213 |
| 8 | Middlesbrough | v | Chelsea (27/2) | 0-2 | 27856 |

# SIXTH ROUND PROPER
## SATURDAY 9 MARCH 2013 - WINNERS RECEIVE £360,000

| 1 | Everton | v | WIGAN ATHLETIC | 0-3 | 35068 |
|---|---|---|---|---|---|
| 2 | MANCHESTER CITY | v | Barnsley | 5-0 | 46728 |
| 3 | Manchester United | v | Chelsea (10/3) | 2-2 | 75196 |

|  | Chelsea | v | Manchester United (1/4) | 1-0 | 40704 |
|---|---|---|---|---|---|
| 4 | Millwall | v | Blackburn Rovers (10/3) | 0-0 | 14885 |
|  | Blackburn Rovers | v | Millwall (13/3) | 0-1 | 8635 |

# SEMI FINALS
## WINNERS RECEIVE £900,000        RUNNERS-UP £450,000

SATURDAY 13 APRIL 2013 - at Wembley Stadium

| 2 | Millwall | v | WIGAN ATHLETIC | 0-2 | 62336 |
|---|---|---|---|---|---|

SUNDAY 14 APRIL 2013 - at Wembley Stadium

| 1 | Chelsea | v | MANCHESTER CITY | 0-1 | 85621 |
|---|---|---|---|---|---|

# THE FINAL
## SATURDAY 5 MAY 2012 - at Wembley Stadium    WINNERS RECEIVE £1.8m    RUNNERS-UP £900,000

| MANCHESTER CITY | 0 | 1 | WIGAN ATHLETIC | 86254 |
|---|---|---|---|---|

FAC 2P: Alfreton's 'keeper tips an Orient shot on to the bar during their 2-4 defeat. Photo: Bill Wheatcroft.

For some, a once in a career chance to play one of the biggest teams in Football. Photo: Bill Wheatcroft.

Mansfield's Matt Green puts Uruguayan international Sebastian Coates under pressure. Photo: Peter Barnes

Suarez shaping up to take on the Mansfield defence. Photo: Bill Wheatcroft.

Mansfield defender, John Dempster, guides the ball back to Alan Marriott with Louis Suarez bearing down on him. Photo: Peter Barnes.

**Mansfield Town FC**

Mansfield Town
versus
Liverpool
FA Cup with Budweiser Third Round
Sunday 06 January 2013, 4pm

| Mansfield Town | | | Liverpool |
|---|---|---|---|
| Alan Marriott | 1 | 1 | Brad Jones |
| John Thompson | 5 | 15 | Daniel Sturridge |
| John Dempster | 4 | 16 | Sebastian Coates |
| Lindon Meikle | 7 | 19 | Stewart Downing |
| Matt Green | 10 | 21 | Lucas Leiva |
| Louis Briscoe | 11 | 23 | Jamie Carragher © |
| Anthony Howell | 13 | 24 | Joe Allen |
| Chris Clements | 14 | 30 | Suarez |
| Lee Beevers | 17 | 35 | Jonjo Shelvey |
| Adam Murray © | 21 | 37 | Andre Wisdom |
| Exodus Geohaghon | 33 | 49 | Jack Robinson |

**Substitutes**

| | | | Luis Suarez |
|---|---|---|---|
| Ritchie Sutton | 2 | 6 | Jordan Henderson |
| Jake Speight | 8 | 14 | Raheem Sterling |
| Nick Wright | 12 | 33 | Conor Coady |
| Matt Rhead | 16 | 35 | Martin Skrtel |
| Ben Hutchinson | 25 | 37 | Jon Flanagan |
| Lee Stevenson | 26 | 38 | Peter Gulacsi |
| Colin Daniel | 31 | 42 | |

Manager: Paul Cox        Manager: Brendan Rodgers

Referee: Andre Marriner (Birmingham)
Assistants: Mike Mullarkey & Sean Lodger
Fourth Official: Michael Jones

Mansfield put the Liverpool defence under pressure
Photo: Bill Wheatcroft

WEMBLEY

Wrexham lift the 2012-13 FA Trophy. Photos: Peter Barnes

CLUBS
278

THE FA TROPHY

2012-13

Ian Holmes' penalty sets the hosts, Rainworth MW, on their way to a first ever Trophy win at the expense of Leighton Town. Photos: Gordon Whittington.

Guildford City's Dan Moody scores from the penalty spot, whilst below Cirencester register a goal themselves, however, it was the former who progressed to the 1st Qualifying round courtesy of a 3-2 win. Photo: Peter Barnes.

# PRELIMINARY ROUND
## SATURDAY 15 SEPTEMBER 2012 - WINNERS RECEIVE £2,300

| | | | | | | | | | | |
|---|---|---|---|---|---|---|---|---|---|---|
| 1 | New Mills | v | Ossett Albion | 1-0 | 144 | 30 | Folkestone Invicta | v | Merstham | 0-0 | 173 |
| 2 | Lancaster City | v | Wakefield | 1-2 | 119 | | Merstham | v | Folkestone Invicta (18/9) | 2-0 | 95 |
| 3 | Northwich Victoria | v | Clitheroe | 1-1 | 65 | 31 | Northwood | v | Leatherhead | 0-4 | 108 |
| | Clitheroe | v | Northwich Victoria (18/9) | 0-3 | 151 | 32 | Needham Market | v | Maidstone United | 2-4 | 290 |
| 4 | Harrogate Railway Athletic | v | Bamber Bridge | 2-1 | 62 | 33 | Heybridge Swifts | v | Worthing | 4-1 | 95 |
| 5 | Warrington Town | v | Leek Town | 1-2 | 172 | 34 | Cheshunt | v | Waltham Forest | 1-3 | 65 |
| 6 | Farsley | v | Radcliffe Borough | 1-1 | 138 | 35 | Sittingbourne | v | Horsham | 4-0 | 155 |
| | Radcliffe Borough | v | Farsley (18/9) | 1-0 | 74 | 36 | Chipstead | v | Waltham Abbey | 0-1 | 51 |
| 7 | Brigg Town | v | Ramsbottom United | 0-1 | 105 | 37 | Walton Casuals | v | Ashford Town (Middx) | 1-5 | 69 |
| 8 | Garforth Town | v | Burscough | 1-2 | 70 | 38 | Chertsey Town | v | Tilbury | 4-1 | 116 |
| 9 | Trafford | v | Sheffield | 2-0 | 143 | 39 | Faversham Town | v | AFC Sudbury | 1-0 | 137 |
| 10 | Goole | v | Curzon Ashton | 1-1 | 135 | 40 | Herne Bay | v | Chatham Town | 0-2 | 258 |
| | Curzon Ashton | v | Goole (17/9) | 3-3aet | 126 | 41 | Crawley Down Gatwick | v | Witham Town | 2-1 | 67 |
| | (Curzon Ashton won 4-3 on kicks from the penalty mark) | | | | | 42 | North Greenford United | v | Tooting & Mitcham United | 1-3 | 67 |
| 11 | Skelmersdale United | v | Salford City | 4-2 | 133 | 43 | Clevedon Town | v | Wimborne Town | 2-2 | 112 |
| 12 | Loughborough Dynamo | v | Belper Town | 3-4 | 110 | | Wimborne Town | v | Clevedon Town (18/9) | 3-0 | 94 |
| 13 | Carlton Town | v | Newcastle Town | 0-2 | 46 | 44 | Merthyr Town | v | Fleet Town | 1-1 | 303 |
| 14 | Sutton Coldfield Town | v | Gresley | 0-1 | 110 | | Fleet Town | v | Merthyr Town (18/9) | 0-4 | 95 |
| 15 | Stamford | v | Evesham United | 1-0 | 152 | 45 | Winchester City | v | Sholing | 1-2 | 62 |
| 16 | Mickleover Sports | v | Romulus | 0-3 | 131 | 46 | Thatcham Town | v | Tiverton Town | 0-1 | 86 |
| 17 | Rainworth MW | v | Leighton Town | 3-0 | 86 | 47 | Godalming Town | v | North Leigh | 0-1 | 158 |
| 18 | Biggleswade Town | v | Halesowen Town | 2-2 | 100 | 48 | Abingdon United | v | Bridgwater Town | 2-4 | 63 |
| | Halesowen Town | v | Biggleswade Town (18/9) | 4-1 | 115 | 49 | Slough Town | v | Hungerford Town (16/9) | 2-1 | 228 |
| 19 | Hucknall Town | v | Market Drayton Town | 2-1 | 95 | 50 | Cirencester Town | v | Guildford City | 2-3 | 78 |
| 20 | Kidsgrove Athletic | v | Daventry Town | 4-1 | 117 | 51 | Didcot Town | v | Paulton Rovers | 0-0 | 115 |
| 21 | Brentwood Town | v | Harlow Town | 0-0 | 137 | | Paulton Rovers | v | Didcot Town (18/9) | 2-3 | |
| | Harlow Town | v | Brentwood Town (18/9) | 0-4 | 93 | 52 | Beaconsfield SYCOB | v | Poole Town | 0-0 | 108 |
| 22 | Grays Athletic | v | Aylesbury | 2-1 | 113 | | Poole Town | v | Beaconsfield SYCOB (18/9) | 3-1 | 202 |
| 23 | Walton & Hersham | v | Maldon & Tiptree | 3-2 | 75 | 53 | Swindon Supermarine | v | Yate Town | 0-0 | 104 |
| 24 | Hythe Town | v | Ware | 4-0 | 165 | | Yate Town | v | Swindon Supermarine (18/9) | 0-3 | 81 |
| 25 | Thamesmead Town | v | Burgess Hill Town | 1-1 | 28 | 54 | Mangotsfield United | v | Shortwood United | 0-0 | 116 |
| | Burgess Hill Town | v | Thamesmead Town (18/9) | 0-2 | 81 | | Shortwood United | v | Mangotsfield United (18/9) 0-0aet | | |
| 26 | Royston Town | v | Aveley | 5-1 | 136 | | (Shortwood United won 5-4 on kicks from the penalty mark) | | | | |
| 27 | Wroxham | v | AFC Hayes | 3-1 | 82 | | | | | | |
| 28 | Corinthian Casuals | v | Potters Bar Town | 1-2 | 59 | | | | | | |
| 29 | Romford | v | Dulwich Hamlet | 3-1 | 97 | | | | | | |

## PRELIMINARY ROUND

As The FA Challenge Trophy Final had been moved forward to the 24th March last season, it wasn't surprising that the competitions' Preliminary Round kicked off a month earlier than usual. At least all the clubs featuring in the early round had been training together for a couple of months, but among the junior clubs, some might be featuring in the FA Trophy for the first time and would not be expecting to stay in the competition for very long.

Burscough had won The FA Trophy at Villa Park in 2003 and many clubs had enjoyed good memories of exciting FA Vase or FA Amateur Cup runs, possibly with Wembley experiences, but this competition might prove just that bit more competitive.

The old version of Northwich Victoria had featured in three finals, winning in 1984 and Leek Town had also competed in an FA Trophy Final at Wembley. Maidstone United had sampled life in the Conference and the Football League, so some experienced clubs might well be leaving the competition in the very first round, but of course they would then be able to concentrate on their league position!

Chris Breach, Lewes, has a shot at the Lowestoft Town goal in the 1st Qualifying Round. Photo: Roger Turner.

(Below) Ed Adjei of St. Neots Town takes on the Chasetown defence in their 2-3 FA Trophy defeat. Photo: Jonathan Holloway.

Graham Purdy gives Walton & Hersham the lead, however, Brentwood Town come back to win 2-1 in the 1st Qualifying Round. Photo: Gordon Whittington.

(Right) More action from the Chasetown v St Neots match, here we see Gary Hay of Chasetown pounce early in the game to score his team's first goal. Photo: Jonathan Holloway.

# FIRST QUALIFYING ROUND
## SATURDAY 29 SEPTEMBER 2012 - WINNERS RECEIVE £2,550

| No | Home | | Away | Score | Att |
|---|---|---|---|---|---|
| 1 | Witton Albion | v | Blyth Spartans | 4-1 | 313 |
| 2 | AFC Fylde | v | Marine | 1-0 | 317 |
| 3 | Cammell Laird | v | Kendal Town | 1-1 | 58 |
|  | Kendal Town | v | Cammell Laird (9/10) | 0-2 | 116 |
| 4 | Ramsbottom United | v | Northwich Victoria | 4-2 | 227 |
| 5 | Leek Town | v | Radcliffe Borough | 2-1 | 281 |
| 6 | Frickley Athletic | v | North Ferriby United | 1-4 | 146 |
| 7 | Burscough | v | Wakefield | 3-2 | 129 |
| 8 | FC United Of Manchester | v | Mossley | 3-3 | 871 |
|  | Mossley | v | FC United of Manchester (2/10) | 1-3 | 405 |
| 9 | Chorley | v | Whitby Town | 1-3 | 338 |
| 10 | Prescot Cables | v | Skelmersdale United | 0-3 | |
| 11 | Harrogate Railway Athletic | v | Trafford | 2-4 | 89 |
| 12 | Lincoln United | v | Buxton | 0-4 | |
| 13 | Curzon Ashton | v | Worksop Town | 2-3 | 164 |
| 14 | Ossett Town | v | Ashton United | 1-0 | 88 |
| 15 | New Mills | v | Stocksbridge Park Steels | 3-2 | 155 |
| 16 | Stourbridge | v | Ilkeston | 0-1 | 349 |
| 17 | Grantham Town | v | Bedford Town | 0-2 | 271 |
| 18 | King's Lynn Town | v | Barwell | 1-0 | 466 |
| 19 | Halesowen Town | v | Gresley | 3-0 | 262 |
| 20 | Romulus | v | Rainworth MW | 2-0 | 44 |
| 21 | Hednesford Town | v | Bedworth United | 3-1 | 307 |
| 22 | Hucknall Town | v | Newcastle Town | 2-1 | 175 |
| 23 | Rushall Olympic | v | Woodford United | 3-0 | |
| 24 | Nantwich Town | v | Redditch United | 2-1 | 247 |
| 25 | Barton Rovers | v | Coalville Town | 0-5 | 87 |
| 26 | Stamford | v | Kidsgrove Athletic | 3-1 | 153 |
| 27 | Eastwood Town | v | Matlock Town | 1-2 | |
| 28 | Chasetown | v | St Neots Town | 3-2 | 244 |
| 29 | Rugby Town | v | Stafford Rangers | 1-1 | 206 |
|  | Stafford Rangers | v | Rugby Town (2/10) | 1-0aet | 232 |
| 30 | Belper Town | v | Leamington | 2-2 | 228 |
|  | Leamington | v | Belper Town (2/10) | 2-2aet | 226 |
|  | (Belper Town won 4-3 on kicks from the penalty mark) | | | | |
| 31 | Soham Town Rangers | v | Tooting & Mitcham United | 2-0 | 156 |
| 32 | Enfield Town | v | Cambridge City | 4-1 | 281 |
| 33 | Crawley Down Gatwick | v | Three Bridges | 1-2 | 182 |
| 34 | Lewes | v | Lowestoft Town (30/9) | 1-0 | 407 |
| 35 | Canvey Island | v | Wroxham | 0-0 | 261 |
|  | Wroxham | v | Canvey Island (2/10) | 1-2aet | 155 |
| 36 | Chatham Town | v | Merstham | 2-4 | 129 |
| 37 | Faversham Town | v | Leatherhead | 0-2 | 146 |
| 38 | Ramsgate | v | Waltham Forest | 4-0 | 127 |
| 39 | Whitstable Town | v | Harrow Borough | 2-0 | 161 |
| 40 | Wealdstone | v | Chertsey Town | 3-1 | 254 |
| 41 | East Thurrock United | v | Hastings United | 4-0 | 143 |
| 42 | Kettering Town | v | Concord Rangers | 0-3 | 213 |
| 43 | Burnham | v | Waltham Abbey | 4-3 | 103 |
| 44 | Thamesmead Town | v | Cray Wanderers | 0-1 | 40 |
| 45 | Grays Athletic | v | Ashford Town (Middx) | 1-1 | 122 |
|  | Ashford Town (Middx) | v | Grays Athletic (2/10) | 1-2 | 86 |
| 46 | Wingate & Finchley | v | Potters Bar Town | 2-1 | 91 |
| 47 | Margate | v | Maidstone United | 1-2 | 475 |
| 48 | Kingstonian | v | Eastbourne Town (30/9) | 2-1 | 279 |
| 49 | Romford | v | Thurrock | 1-3 | 139 |
| 50 | Uxbridge | v | Royston Town | 2-2 | 85 |
|  | Royston Town | v | Uxbridge (2/10) | 1-3 | 114 |
| 51 | Bury Town | v | Whitehawk | 0-0 | 301 |
|  | Whitehawk | v | Bury Town (2/10) | 1-0 | 50 |
| 52 | Redbridge | v | Metropolitan Police | 0-5 | 55 |
| 53 | Carshalton Athletic | v | Heybridge Swifts | 3-0 | 172 |
| 54 | St Albans City | v | Arlesey Town | 1-2 | 335 |
| 55 | Walton & Hersham | v | Brentwood Town | 1-2 | 79 |
| 56 | Bognor Regis Town | v | Ilford | 4-1 | 321 |
| 57 | Hampton & Richmond B. | v | Hythe Town | 1-1 | 202 |
|  | Hythe Town | v | Hampton & Richmond B (2/10) | 0-4 | 151 |
| 58 | Hitchin Town | v | Sittingbourne | 3-1 | 198 |
| 59 | Leiston | v | Hendon | 2-1 | 186 |
| 60 | Banbury United | v | Wimborne Town | 1-1 | |
|  | Wimborne Town | v | Banbury United (2/10) | 3-3aet | 99 |
|  | (Wimborne Town won 6-5 on kicks from the penalty mark) | | | | |
| 61 | Didcot Town | v | Cinderford Town | 3-1 | 118 |
| 62 | Chippenham Town | v | Swindon Supermarine | 4-0 | 280 |
| 63 | Shortwood United | v | Guildford City | 4-0 | 121 |
| 64 | Bridgwater Town | v | Hemel Hempstead Town | 2-2 | 113 |
|  | Hemel Hempstead Town | v | Bridgwater Town (2/10) | 1-3 | 93 |
| 65 | Weymouth | v | Tiverton Town | 3-0 | 402 |
| 66 | AFC Totton | v | Bideford | 2-0 | 288 |
| 67 | Merthyr Town | v | Chalfont St Peter | 1-0 | |
| 68 | Bishop's Cleeve | v | Chesham United | 1-2 | 96 |
| 69 | Slough Town | v | Gosport Borough | 0-4 | 190 |
| 70 | Poole Town | v | Bashley | 1-1 | 351 |
|  | Bashley | v | Poole Town (2/10) | 0-4 | 171 |
| 71 | Frome Town | v | Taunton Town | 0-1 | 151 |
| 72 | North Leigh | v | Sholing | 2-2 | 64 |
|  | Sholing | v | North Leigh (10/10) | 4-3 | 35 |

## FIRST QUALIFYING ROUND

Although the clubs from Steps 1 and 2 were exempt, some much fancied cup fighters such as Blyth Spartans, Marine, Northwich Victoria and Kettering left the competition at the very first attempt.

The modern trend that tends to belittle the national knock out competitions will never take away the enjoyment of visiting new grounds, possibly claiming a scalp of a more senior club and obviously the chance of qualifying to play at Wembley.

With the Final being played in March, all the rounds were pushed forward in the fixture list but the clubs who produced the best early results were:

| | | | |
|---|---|---|---|
| Home | Enfield Town | 4-1 | Cambridge City |
|  | East Thurrock United | 4-0 | Hastings United |
| Away | Frickley Athletic | 1-4 | North Ferriby United |
|  | Kettering | 0-3 | Concord Rangers |
| Replay | Hemel Hempstead Town | 1-3 | Bridgwater |

With five goals being scored away from home by Coalville Town and Metropolitan Police at Barton Rovers and Redbridge respectively.

Of the eleven replays only three were won by home clubs. Included in these ties was possibly the most exiting pairing - Mossley held FC United to a thrilling 3-3 draw at Bury in front of 861 but then lost the home replay 1-3.

## SECOND QUALIFYING ROUND

This was the last Round before the three Conference divisions entered the fray but some of the round's successful clubs certainly had memories of Wembley to inspire them:

| | | |
|---|---|---|
| Merstham | 2-6 | Wealdstone |
| Whitby Town | 4-2 | Ilkeston |
| Witton Albion | 2-3 | Skelmersdale United |
| Stafford Rangers | 3-0 | Ramsbottom United |

Substantial victories that must have brought great satisfaction to the winners were:

| | | |
|---|---|---|
| Kings Lynn Town | 6-1 | Carshalton Athletic |
| New Mills | 5-1 | Coalville Town |
| Wimborne Town | 1-5 | Merthyr Town |

While these surprise victories were possibly the results of the round:

| | | |
|---|---|---|
| Weymouth | 1-2 | Shortwood United |
| Lewes | 0-3 | Brentwood Town |

Particularly appreciated local derby victories were achieved by Rushall Olympic who won 3-1 at Chasetown and AFC Totton's 3-2 success at home against Gosport Borough.

A thrilling couple of games were provided by East Thurrock who beat Thurrock 4-3 after a 1-1 draw and hat tricks were achieved by Simon Thomas for Chesham United and Danny Quinn of Stafford Rangers.

Zac Burke completes his hat-trick to give Hitchen Town a 3-0 2nd Qualifying Round replay win over Wingate & Finchley. Photo: Gordon Whittington.

Shortwood midfielder Jake Parrott fires in a fierce shot against Methyr Town in the 3rd Qualifying Round. Photo: Peter Barnes.

## THIRD QUALIFYING ROUND

The Blue Square North and South clubs entered the competition in this round and it was Guiseley who proved their class most emphatically in a 7-0 victory over Whitby Town with James Walshaw scoring three.

The best attendances were:

| | | | | |
|---|---|---|---|---|
| Maidstone United | 3-2 | Whitehawk | 1,571 |
| Chester | 2-2 | Worksop Town | 1,410 |
| Worcester City | 0-3 | Altrincham | 785 |
| Dove Athletic | 2-4 | Chelmsford City | 720 |
| Bognor Regis Town | 1-4 | Havant & Waterlooville | 702 |
| Boston United | 3-1 | Colwyn Bay | 694 |
| King's Lynn Town | 3-0 | Eastbourne Borough | 661 |

Probably the most exciting tie of the round was Bath City's 4-4 draw at Leatherhead with City winning the replay. In fact there were not many shocks in the competition although it was good to see King's Lynn Town, Maidstone United and Merthyr Town underlining their determination to get back to their previous levels.

# SECOND QUALIFYING ROUND
## SATURDAY 27 OCTOBER 2012 - WINNERS RECEIVE £3,250

| No | Home | | Away | Score | Att |
|----|------|---|------|-------|-----|
| 1 | Matlock Town | v | Leek Town | 0-0 | 264 |
| | Leek Town | v | Matlock Town (31/10) | 1-3 | 145 |
| | (at Belper Town FC) | | | | |
| 2 | Witton Albion | v | Skelmersdale United | 2-3 | 346 |
| 3 | Romulus | v | Hucknall Town | 1-0 | 49 |
| 4 | Burscough | v | Ossett Town | 0-1 | 140 |
| 5 | Belper Town | v | Cammell Laird | 0-2 | 203 |
| 6 | AFC Fylde | v | Nantwich Town | 0-0 | 261 |
| | Nantwich Town | v | AFC Fylde (30/10) | 2-2aet | 181 |
| | (AFC Fylde won 3-1 on kicks from the penalty mark) | | | | |
| 7 | Buxton | v | North Ferriby United | 2-1 | 215 |
| 8 | Chasetown | v | Rushall Olympic | 1-3 | 286 |
| 9 | Trafford | v | Hednesford Town | 0-2 | 188 |
| 10 | New Mills | v | Coalville Town | 5-2 | 203 |
| 11 | Stafford Rangers | v | Ramsbottom United | 3-0 | 341 |
| 12 | Stamford | v | FC United Of Manchester | 2-1 | 749 |
| 13 | Whitby Town | v | Ilkeston | 4-2 | 272 |
| 14 | Halesowen Town | v | Worksop Town | 0-1 | 265 |
| 15 | Soham Town Rangers | v | Ramsgate | 1-2 | 131 |
| 16 | Cray Wanderers | v | Arlesey Town (28/10) | 0-0 | 96 |
| | Arlesey Town | v | Cray Wanderers (30/10) | 2-3aet | 100 |
| 17 | Kingstonian | v | Burnham (28/10) | 2-1 | 261 |
| 18 | Leiston | v | Metropolitan Police | 1-1 | 153 |
| | Metropolitan Police | v | Leiston (30/10) | 3-4 | 66 |
| 19 | Uxbridge | v | Canvey Island | 3-3 | 152 |
| | Canvey Island | v | Uxbridge (30/10) | 4-2 | 176 |
| 20 | Whitstable Town | v | Leatherhead | 0-1 | 222 |
| 21 | Merstham | v | Wealdstone | 2-6 | 245 |
| 22 | Wingate & Finchley | v | Hitchin Town | 2-2 | 101 |
| | Hitchin Town | v | Wingate & Finchley (29/10) | 3-0 | 171 |
| 23 | East Thurrock United | v | Thurrock | 1-1 | |
| | Thurrock | v | East Thurrock United (30/10) | 4-3aet | 145 |
| 24 | Hampton & Richmond B. | v | Three Bridges | 1-0 | 229 |
| 25 | Bedford Town | v | Maidstone United | 2-3 | 402 |
| 26 | Concord Rangers | v | Enfield Town | 0-2 | 148 |
| 27 | King's Lynn Town | v | Carshalton Athletic | 6-1 | 497 |
| 28 | Whitehawk | v | Grays Athletic | 1-1 | 140 |
| | Grays Athletic | v | Whitehawk (30/10) | 0-1 | 121 |
| 29 | Brentwood Town | v | Lewes | 3-3 | 118 |
| | Lewes | v | Brentwood Town (30/10) | 0-3 | 335 |
| 30 | Bognor Regis Town | v | Bridgwater Town | 3-0 | 313 |
| 31 | Poole Town | v | Didcot Town | 1-1 | 257 |
| | Didcot Town | v | Pool Town (30/10) | 2-0 | 141 |
| 32 | Chesham United | v | Taunton Town | 5-1 | 214 |
| 33 | Wimborne Town | v | Merthyr Town | 1-5 | 230 |
| 34 | AFC Totton | v | Gosport Borough | 3-2 | 349 |
| 35 | Chippenham Town | v | Sholing | 1-2 | 237 |
| 36 | Weymouth | v | Shortwood United | 1-2 | 366 |

# THIRD QUALIFYING ROUND
## SATURDAY 10 NOVEMBER 2012 - WINNERS RECEIVE £4,000

| No | Home | | Away | Score | Att |
|----|------|---|------|-------|-----|
| 1 | Matlock Town | v | Stalybridge Celtic | 2-1 | 402 |
| 2 | Guiseley | v | Whitby Town | 7-0 | 506 |
| 3 | Cammell Laird | v | FC Halifax Town | 0-1 | 301 |
| 4 | Gainsborough Trinity | v | Hinckley United | 1-1 | 357 |
| | Hinckley United | v | Gainsborough Trinity (13/11) | 1-4 | 181 |
| 5 | Worcester City | v | Altrincham | 0-3 | 785 |
| 6 | Vauxhall Motors | v | Harrogate Town | 1-3 | 131 |
| 7 | Stamford | v | Buxton | 0-2 | 239 |
| 8 | Chester | v | Worksop Town | 2-2 | 1410 |
| | Worksop Town | v | Chester (14/11) | 2-0 | 457 |
| 9 | Skelmersdale United | v | New Mills | 3-1 | 187 |
| 10 | Stafford Rangers | v | Bradford Park Avenue | 3-1 | 419 |
| 11 | Solihull Moors | v | AFC Fylde | 2-1 | 155 |
| 12 | Droylsden | v | Rushall Olympic | 1-2 | 211 |
| 13 | Romulus | v | Hednesford Town (11/11) | 1-2 | 224 |
| 14 | Boston United | v | Colwyn Bay | 3-1 | 694 |
| 15 | Ossett Town | v | Workington | 2-1 | 158 |
| 16 | Thurrock | v | Brackley Town | 0-2 | 99 |
| 17 | King's Lynn Town | v | Eastbourne Borough | 3-0 | 661 |
| 18 | Histon | v | Boreham Wood | 1-2 | 177 |
| 19 | Cray Wanderers | v | Welling United (11/11) | 0-1 | 262 |
| 20 | Sutton United | v | Ramsgate | 2-0 | 281 |
| 21 | Canvey Island | v | Chesham United | 1-1 | 275 |
| | Chesham United | v | Canvey Island (13/11) | 2-1 | 241 |
| 22 | Bromley | v | Staines Town | 1-1 | 309 |
| | Staines Town | v | Bromley (13/11) | 0-2 | 191 |
| 23 | Kingstonian | v | Brentwood Town | 2-2 | 291 |
| | Brentwood Town | v | Kingstonian (13/11) | 1-4 | 117 |
| 24 | Maidstone United | v | Whitehawk | 3-2 | 1571 |
| 25 | AFC Hornchurch | v | Bishop's Stortford | 2-3 | 271 |
| 26 | Wealdstone | v | Corby Town | 1-1 | 405 |
| | Corby Town | v | Wealdstone (14/11) | 3-2 | 280 |
| 27 | Tonbridge Angels | v | Hitchin Town | 2-1 | 513 |
| 28 | Billericay Town | v | Enfield Town | 3-2 | 417 |
| 29 | Chelmsford City | v | Dover Athletic | 1-1 | 570 |
| | Dover Athletic | v | Chelmsford City (13/11) | 2-4aet | 418 |
| 30 | Leiston | v | Hampton & Richmond Borough | 1-1 | 201 |
| | Hampton & Richmond B. | v | Leiston (13/11) | 3-2 | 190 |
| 31 | Gloucester City | v | Maidenhead United (11/11) | 0-1 | 242 |
| 32 | Sholing | v | Oxford City | 0-1 | 68 |
| 33 | AFC Totton | v | Basingstoke Town | 3-0 | 368 |
| 34 | Didcot Town | v | Dorchester Town | 1-2 | 179 |
| 35 | Eastleigh | v | Hayes & Yeading United | 1-4 | 241 |
| 36 | Farnborough | v | Truro City | 3-2 | 326 |
| 37 | Leatherhead | v | Bath City | 4-4 | 287 |
| | Bath City | v | Leatherhead (13/11) | 2-0 | 341 |
| 38 | Shortwood United | v | Merthyr Town | 1-1 | 130 |
| | Merthyr Town | v | Shortwood United (13/11) | 2-1 | 193 |
| 39 | Bognor Regis Town | v | Havant & Waterlooville | 1-4 | 702 |
| 40 | Salisbury City | v | Weston Super Mare | 3-0 | 510 |

## FIRST ROUND PROPER

Everyone joins in and we will soon be able to tell which senior clubs are taking the competition seriously by their team selections. Last season York City reached Wembley, won The Trophy and won promotion back into the League and proved the winning habit is important for all competitions.
Not many surprises in this round but certainly some emphatic home victories:

|             |     |                  |
|-------------|-----|------------------|
| Woking      | 7-0 | Farnborough      |
| Stockport County | 6-0 | Ossett Town |
| Wrexham     | 5-0 | Rushall Olympic  |

Hat tricks were recorded by Gareth Seddon (FC Halifax Town), Connor Jennings (Stockport County), Andy Morrell ( Wrexham) and Marcus Kelly (Tamworth)
A spectacular game was enjoyed at Halifax where the home side beat Altrincham 5-2 and good victories were claimed by Kings Lynn at Worksop Town, Skelmersdale United who beat Boston United at home after a 1-1 away draw and Maidstone United who beat high flying Salisbury City 2-0
The best attendances of the Round were:-

|                  |   |                |      |
|------------------|---|----------------|------|
| Stockport County | v | Ossett Town    | 1679 |
| Mansfield Town   | v | Matlock Town   | 1615 |
| Grimsby Town     | v | Buxton         | 1369 |
| Maidstone United | v | Salisbury City | 1365 |
| Wrexham          | v | Rushall Olympic| 1085 |

Good to see Maidstone United attracting such good support alongside the more recent ex FootballLeague clubs.

## SECOND ROUND PROPER

This was the round in which the serious challengers for a Wembley place were beginning to show their colours. Gateshead won away to Cambridge United while Kidderminster Harriers lost at Bromley.
King's Lynn won 3-1 at home to AFC Telford United but Grimsby Town and Dartford won convincingly against Havant & Waterlooville and Tonbridge Angels.
Gainsborough Trinity, enjoying a good season, produced a fine away victory at high flying Forest Green Rovers and two more Premier Division clubs lost at home - Hereford United 0-3 to Chelmsford City and Woking 0-1 to Welling United. Even Wrexham had to recover after going a goal behind twice against Solihull Moors.
There were no hat tricks in this round but it was good to see Matlock Town attracting 829 for their tie against Luton Town and Kings Lynn supported by a crowd of 955. The last sixteen clubs were made up of half from The Blue Blue Square Premier and half from the lower divisions!
**Conference Premier:** Barrow, Dartford, Gateshead, Grimsby Town, Luton Town, Southport, Tamworth and Wrexham.
**Conference South:** Bromley, Chelmsford City Sutton United and Welling United
**Conference North:** FC Halifax Town and Gainsborough Trinity
**Northern Premier Lg. Division One South:** King's Lynn
**Northern Premier Lg. Division One South:** Skelmersdale United

## THIRD ROUND PROPER

Six of the Conference Premier clubs were paired with opposition from lower levels and just two clashed. Barrow beat Gateshead 3-2 who had been drawn at home but had to play the tie at Barrow. Five of the other six Premier clubs won their ties with Kings Lynn losing at home to Southport and Skelmersdale United at home to Luton Town.
Attendances were growing with the two outsiders involved in the best attendances and the Kent local 'derby' also attracting a good crowd to see six goals and hat- trick from Dartford's Dominic Green.

|                 |   |                    |       |
|-----------------|---|--------------------|-------|
| Luton Town      | v | Skelmersdale United| 2,479 |
| King's Lynn     | v | Southport          | 1,498 |
| Dartford        | v | Bromley            | 1,305 |
| FC Halifax Town | v | Chelmsford City    | 1,137 |
| Welling United  | v | Grimsby Town       | 1,037 |

## QUARTER FINALS AND SEMI-FINALS

The weather created a very disjointed round and it was only Wrexham who claimed their semi-final place on the original allocated date and they stormed to a fine 3-1 victory at Southport.
Grimsby enjoyed a splendid 3-0 victory over Luton Town and FC Halifax Town took Barrow to a replay but lost by the odd goal in five. The other 'outsider' Gainsborough Trinity, capped a splendid season by reaching the semi-finals with a 2-0 home victory over Barrow but would the draw for the semi-finals keep the two top of the table Conference challengers apart?
In the Semi-Finals the two favourites did avoid each other and they made their quality show with comprehensive home wins. The following week neither Barrow nor Gainsborough Trinity lost their home ties, in fact 'Trinity' showed their undoubted quality and fighting spirit with a second leg victory against Wrexham, but the final would be between two well supported clubs Grimsby Town and Wrexham who certainly deserved their day at Wembley.

# FIRST ROUND PROPER
## SATURDAY 24 NOVEMBER 2012 - WINNERS RECEIVE £5,000

| # | Home | v | Away | Score | Att |
|---|------|---|------|-------|-----|
| 1 | Alfreton Town | v | Kidderminster Harriers | 1-3 | 361 |
| 2 | Hednesford Town | v | Solihull Moors | 1-2 | 355 |
| 3 | Gainsborough Trinity | v | Harrogate Town | 2-0 | 386 |
| 4 | WREXHAM | v | Rushall Olympic | 5-0 | 1035 |
| 5 | Tamworth | v | Lincoln City | 3-1 | 726 |
| 6 | Boston United | v | Skelmersdale United | 1-1 | 710 |
| | Skelmersdale United | v | Boston United (27/11) | 2-1 | 295 |
| 7 | FC Halifax Town | v | Altrincham | 5-2 | 885 |
| 8 | Mansfield Town | v | Matlock Town | 1-1 | 1615 |
| | Matlock Town | v | Mansfield Town (27/11) | 2-1 | 758 |
| 9 | Stafford Rangers | v | Southport | 0-4 | 531 |
| 10 | Guiseley | v | Brackley Town | 3-1 | 523 |
| 11 | Worksop Town | v | King's Lynn Town | 0-1 | 488 |
| 12 | AFC Telford United | v | Nuneaton Town | 1-0 | 737 |
| 13 | Gateshead | v | Macclesfield Town (23/11) | 2-0 | 312 |
| 14 | Hyde | v | Barrow | 1-1 | 438 |
| | Barrow | v | Hyde (27/11) | 1-0 | 728 |
| 15 | Stockport County | v | Ossett Town | 6-0 | 1679 |
| 16 | GRIMSBY TOWN | v | Buxton | 0-0 | 1369 |
| | Buxton | v | GRIMSBY TOWN (28/11) | 0-1 | 444 |
| 17 | Woking | v | Farnborough | 7-0 | 979 |
| 18 | Oxford City | v | Bishop's Stortford (4/12) | 1-0 | 134 |
| 19 | Kingstonian | v | Dartford | 0-4 | 508 |
| 20 | Welling United | v | Newport County | 2-0 | 441 |
| 21 | Ebbsfleet United | v | Hereford United | 0-1 | 651 |
| 22 | Dorchester Town | v | Luton Town (27/11) | 2-2 | 688 |
| | Luton Town | v | Dorchester Town (4/12) | 3-1 | 897 |
| 23 | Braintree Town | v | Havant & Waterlooville (4/12) | 1-2 | 192 |
| 24 | Chesham United | v | Bath City | 2-1 | 301 |
| 25 | Corby Town | v | Hayes & Yeading United | 3-2 | 322 |
| 26 | Bromley | v | Boreham Wood | 1-1 | 242 |
| | Boreham Wood | v | Bromley (26/11) | 0-2 | 188 |
| 27 | Billericay Town | v | Cambridge United | 0-3 | 536 |
| 28 | Merthyr Town | v | Tonbridge Angels | 1-2 | 229 |
| 29 | Maidenhead United | v | Sutton United (4/12) | 0-1 | 217 |
| 30 | Forest Green Rovers | v | AFC Totton | 2-1 | 523 |
| 31 | Maidstone United | v | Salisbury City | 2-0 | 1365 |
| 32 | Hampton & Richmond B. | v | Chelmsford City | 1-1 | 241 |
| | Chelmsford City | v | Hampton&Richmond B (10/12) | 3-2 | 301 |

# SECOND ROUND PROPER
## SATURDAY 15 DECEMBER 2012 - WINNERS RECEIVE £6,000

| # | Home | v | Away | Score | Att |
|---|------|---|------|-------|-----|
| 1 | Dartford | v | Tonbridge Angels | 3-0 | 926 |
| 2 | Stockport County | v | Southport | 1-1 | 1328 |
| | Southport | v | Stockport County (18/12) | 3-1 | 540 |
| 3 | Sutton United | v | Oxford City | 1-0 | 347 |
| 4 | King's Lynn Town | v | AFC Telford United | 3-1 | 955 |
| 5 | Bromley | v | Kidderminster Harriers | 1-0 | 432 |
| 6 | Forest Green Rovers | v | Gainsborough Trinity | 1-2 | 496 |
| 7 | Tamworth | v | Corby Town | 1-1 | 683 |
| | Corby Town | v | Tamworth (19/12) | 2-4 | 300 |
| 8 | Cambridge United | v | Gateshead | 0-1 | 1019 |
| 9 | Woking | v | Welling United | 0-1 | 826 |
| 10 | WREXHAM | v | Solihull Moors | 3-2 | 1111 |
| 11 | Chesham United | v | Barrow | 1-5 | 470 |
| 12 | FC Halifax Town | v | Maidstone United (18/12) | 2-1 | 747 |
| 13 | Hereford United | v | Chelmsford City | 0-3 | 1124 |
| 14 | GRIMSBY TOWN | v | Havant & Waterlooville | 4-0 | 1215 |
| 15 | Skelmersdale United | v | Guiseley | 2-0 | 310 |
| 16 | Matlock Town | v | Luton Town | 1-2 | 829 |

# THIRD ROUND PROPER
## SATURDAY 12 JANUARY 2013 - WINNERS RECEIVE £7,000

| # | Home | v | Away | Score | Att |
|---|------|---|------|-------|-----|
| 1 | King's Lynn Town | v | Southport | 0-2 | 1498 |
| 2 | Sutton United | v | WREXHAM | 0-5 | 775 |
| 3 | Dartford | v | Bromley | 4-2 | 1305 |
| 4 | Welling United | v | GRIMSBY TOWN | 1-2 | 1037 |
| 5 | FC Halifax Town | v | Chelmsford City | 3-0 | 1137 |
| 6 | Gateshead | v | Barrow (29/1) | 2-3 | 728 |
| 7 | Gainsborough Trinity | v | Tamworth | 2-1 | 750 |
| 8 | Luton Town | v | Skelmersdale United | 2-0 | 2479 |

# FOURTH ROUND PROPER
## SATURDAY 26 JANUARY 2013 - WINNERS RECEIVE £8,000

| # | Home | v | Away | Score | Att |
|---|------|---|------|-------|-----|
| 1 | FC Halifax Town | v | Dartford (30/1) | 1-1 | 921 |
| | Dartford | v | FC Halifax Town (6/2) | 3-2 | 805 |
| 2 | Southport | v | WREXHAM | 1-3 | 1473 |
| 3 | Gainsborough Trinity | v | Barrow (5/2) | 2-0 | 785 |
| 4 | GRIMSBY TOWN | v | Luton Town (29/1) | 3-0 | 2791 |

# SEMI FINALS
## WINNERS RECEIVE £16,000

**1ST LEG – SATURDAY 16 FEBRUARY 2013**

| # | Home | v | Away | Score | Att |
|---|------|---|------|-------|-----|
| 1 | WREXHAM | v | Gainsborough Trinity | 3-1 | 3409 |
| 2 | GRIMSBY TOWN | v | Dartford | 3-0 | 3573 |

**2ND LEG – SATURDAY 23 FEBRUARY 2013**

| # | Home | v | Away | Score | Att |
|---|------|---|------|-------|-----|
| 1 | Gainsborough Trinity | v | WREXHAM | 2-1 | 2307 |
| 2 | Dartford | v | GRIMSBY TOWN | 0-0 | 2153 |

(Left) Hythe Town
shields the ball fr
of Hampton and
their 1st Qualifyir
Photo: Alan Coor

(Right) 'Tigers' Tom Webb and 'Magpies'
Michael Pook in an ariel battle for the ball
during their 3rd Qualifying Round match.
Photo: Peter Barnes.

More 3rd Qualifying Round action, this time Gloucester City's Webb battles with Maidenhead's Joe Crook.

Gainsborogh Trinity's centre-half, Luke Waterfall sets up a goal for Darryn Stamp on 72 minutes against Forest Green Rovers in the 2nd Round Proper. Whilst below Forest Green's full back Chris Stokes scores with a header seven minutes later.
Photos: Peter Barnes.

# The Final...

## GRIMSBY TOWN     1
*(Cook 71)*

## WREXHAM     1
*(Thornton 82 [pen])*
*(Wrexham won 4-1 on kicks from the penalty mark after extra time)*

**Wembley Stadium**     **Att: 35,226**

| GRIMSBY TOWN | WREXHAM |
|---|---|
| Sam Hatton | Chris Maxwell |
| Aswad Thomas | Stephen Wright |
| Shaun Pearson | Martin Riley |
| Ian Miller | Jay Harris |
| Joe Colbeck | Danny Wright |
| Craig Disley | Brett Ormerod |
| Frankie Artus | (Robert Ogleby 77 min) |
| Andy Cook | Andy Morrell |
| James McKeown | (Adrian Cieslewicz 61 min) |
| Ross Hannah | Dean Keates |
| (Andi Thanoj 55 min) | Johnny Hunt |
| Marcus Marshall | Chris Westwood, |
| (Richard Brodie 87 min) | Kevin Thornton |
|  | (Joe Clarke 89 min) |
| **Subs not used** | **Subs not used** |
| Jamie Devitt | Andy Coughlin (gk) |
| Bradley Wood | Glen Little |
| Lenell John-Lewis. |  |

Referee Jonathan Moss
Assisted by Darren England and Harry Lennard.
Fourth official – James Adcock.

I believe this to be the first time supporters have been permitted to occupy the whole circuit of the lower tier of the Stadium for memory tells me they have been previously restricted to the two lower tiers with the Royal Box as the divider. Consequently numbers meant that the far side was left empty, producing an eery silence there. Not so this time and the atmosphere all the better for it. Wrexham appeared to have a slight edge in supporter numbers but there was good natured enthusiasm from all sides, thankfully the norm for non-league fixtures. To reach Wembley is the ultimate for smaller clubs and an occasion to be relished for seldom does it come.

Trivialities often being my forte I can never help but count the number of Stadium staff forking the ground pre match and again at half time. 13 this time on both occasions. Was this to prove an ill omen? Intriguing too were the different coloured coats of the staff overseeing the spectators - yellow, orange and blue jacketed personnel but presumably above them all in ranking are those who wear suits. They strut authoritatively across the turf at full time and stand as if daring anyone to vacate the stands and make for the grass. How would they have reacted to the crazy streaker who greeted Grimsby's score? Maybe they could have revealed their purpose. What on earth is it? Intriguing.

Winning on penalties never gives the same feeling of absolute satisfaction as managing to clinch victory within live playing time, be it 90 or 120 minutes. In the record books, and in after match celebrations, of course that is forgotten but at the time it leaves you with the same tinge of guilt as when you win on the toss of a coin. In other words luck has played a significant part in your triumph. However, any Wrexham sensations of guilt could more easily be washed away on reflecting that over the 120 minutes theirs had been the team mainly in the ascendancy in terms of attacks and missed chances, therefore their ultimate victory was justified and earned.

To be honest, at half time with the match goalless, there was a deal of surmise about extra time and penalties as there had been few moments of excitement in that first 45 minutes. A foul by Mariners' skipper Craig Disley, for which he was booked, provoked a short lived hostile gathering of would be combatants. Wrexham's Jay Harris whistled a shot just over James McKeown's bar after 20 minutes. These were the only significant moments of a lacklustre first half. Even the crowd's singing was not sustained, and as the second period began spectators delayed reappearing. Were supporters disillusioned or had service been slow?

Despite the best efforts of Wrexham's Stephen Wright, Andy Cook scores to put Grimsby ahead.
Photo: Alan Coomes.

Thankfully the pace and the excitement picked up. A long kick from keeper Chris Maxwell sent player manager Andy Morrell clear. Alas his hesitation allowed McKeown to regain his feet to block Morrell's first and second efforts. Brett Ormerod headed a good chance over as Wrexham continued to threaten. There were more goal attempts in the first third of the second half than there had been in the whole first 45 minutes. Grimsby's best effort came from Andy Cook although offside would have denied a score. At the other end Danny Wright skilfully brought down namesake Stephen's pass but failed to make clean contact as he shot. And so to the opening goal in the 71st minute.

James McKeown, Grimsby Town's 'keeper, punches clear a Wrexham attack. Photo: Roger Turner.

Joe Colbeck raced away down the right and there was Cook, unmarked. He sidefooted low against the keeper and then firmly drove home the rebound to put Grimsby ahead.

Wrexham substitute Adrian Cieslewicz engineered a shooting chance but McKeown got down to grab his effort at the second attempt. With 8 minutes to go Dean Keates was brought down in the area and Kevin Thornton equalised from the spot. This was Wrexham's first goal of the season in their encounters with Grimsby. And so to extra time. Grimsby's Richard Brodie, whose constant warming up and silent pleading to his managers at last paid dividends, was introduced with 3 minutes of normal time left. He

Thornton equalises from the spot. Photo: Keith Clayton.

seemed out of sorts though and was lucky to escape sanction for attempting to con his way to a free kick as extra time opened.

Extra time was most noticeable for Grimsby's hero, McKeown, and the opposition's Cieslewicz. The keeper produced a stunning save to stop a 30 yard volley from Cieslewicz and then denied the same player twice as the lively winger threatened to break Grimsby resistance. Finally McKeown, with the help of a goal post, frustrated Robert Ogleby, and so to penalties.

With the Wrexham fans at his back McKeown was beaten from the spot in turn by Cieslewicz, Danny Wright, Chris Westwood and finally Johnny Hunt, only Colbeck hitting the net for a dejected Grimsby. The Trophy was thus carried off to the principality for the very first time.

*Arthur Evans*

Kevin Thornton's equaliser from behind the goal.
Photo: Gordon Whittington.

(Below) Wrexham's Ogleby gets in a well timed challenge on grimsby's Thomas.
Photo: Keith Clayton.

Grimby's 'keeper James McKeown and Frankie Artus combine to keep out Chris Westwood. Photo: Alan Coomes.

Fantastic acton shot sees Grimsby's 'keeper pleased to see this Wrexham effort hit the post. Photo: Peter Barnes.

# PAST FINALS

**1970  MACCLESFIELD TOWN** 2 (Lyons, B Fidler)   **TELFORD UNITED** 0                     Att: 28,000
*Northern Premier League*                  *Southern League*
Macclesfield: Cooke, Sievwright, Bennett, Beaumont, Collins, Roberts, Lyons, B Fidler,Young, Corfield, D Fidler.
Telford: Irvine, Harris, Croft, Flowers, Coton, Ray,Fudge, Hart, Bentley, Murray, Jagger.                    Ref: K Walker

**1971  TELFORD UTD** 3 (Owen, Bentley, Fudge)   **HILLINGDON BORO.** 2 (Reeve, Bishop)     Att: 29,500
*Southern League*                      *Southern League*
Telford: Irvine, Harris, Croft, Ray, Coton, Carr, Fudge, Owen, Bentley, Jagger ,Murray.
Hillingdon B.: Lowe, Batt, Langley, Higginson, Newcombe, Moore, Fairchild,Bishop, Reeve, Carter, Knox.       Ref: D Smith

**1972  STAFFORD RANGERS** 3 (Williams 2, Cullerton)   **BARNET** 0                        Att: 24,000
*Northern Premier League*                   *Southern League*
Stafford R.: Aleksic, Chadwick, Clayton, Sargeant, Aston, Machin, Cullerton, Chapman,Williams, Bayley, Jones.
Barnet: McClelland, Lye, Jenkins, Ward, Embrey, King, Powell, Ferry, Flatt, Easton, Plume .               Ref: P Partridge

**1973  SCARBOROUGH** 2 (Leask, Thompson)     **WIGAN ATHLETIC** 1 (Rogers) aet          Att:23,000
*Northern Premier League*                  *Northern Premier League*
Scarborough: Garrow, Appleton, Shoulder, Dunn, Siddle, Fagan, Donoghue, Franks,Leask (Barmby), Thompson, Hewitt.
Wigan: Reeves, Morris, Sutherland, Taylor,Jackson, Gillibrand, Clements, Oats (McCunnell), Rogers, King, Worswick.   Ref: H Hackney

**1974  MORECAMBE** 2 (Richmond, Sutton)      **DARTFORD** 1 (Cunningham)                 Att: 19,000
*Northern Premier League*                  *Southern League*
Morecambe: Coates, Pearson, Bennett, Sutton, Street, Baldwin, Done, Webber,Roberts (Galley), Kershaw, Richmond.
Dartford: Morton, Read, Payne, Carr, Burns,Binks, Light, Glozier, Robinson (Hearne), Cunningham, Halleday.      Ref: B Homewood

**1975(1) MATLOCK TOWN** 4 (Oxley, Dawson, T Fenoughty, N Fenoughty)   **SCARBOROUGH** 0    Att: 21,000
*Northern Premier League*                  *Northern Premier League*
Matlock: Fell, McKay, Smith, Stuart, Dawson, Swan, Oxley, N Fenoughty, Scott, T Fenoughty, M Fenoughty.
Scarborough: Williams, Hewitt, Rettitt, Dunn, Marshall, Todd, Houghton, Woodall, Davidson, Barnby, Aveyard.      Ref: K Styles

**1976  SCARBOROUGH** 3 (Woodall, Abbey, Marshall(p))   **STAFFORD R.** 2 (Jones 2) aet   Att: 21,000
*Northern Premier League*                  *Northern Premier League*
Scarborough: Barnard, Jackson, Marshall, H Dunn, Ayre (Donoghue), HA Dunn, Dale,Barmby, Woodall, Abbey, Hilley.
Stafford: Arnold, Ritchie, Richards, Sargeant,Seddon, Morris, Chapman, Lowe, Jones, Hutchinson, Chadwick.       Ref: R Challis

**1977  SCARBOROUGH** 2 (Dunn(p), Abbey)      **DAGENHAM** 1 (Harris)                     Att: 21,500
*Northern Premier League*                  *Isthmian League*
Scarborough: Chapman, Smith, Marshall (Barmby), Dunn, Ayre, Deere, Aveyard,Donoghue, Woodall, Abbey, Dunn.
Dagenham: Hutley, Wellman, P Currie, Dunwell,Moore, W Currie, Harkins, Saul, Fox, Harris, Holder.            Ref: G Courtney

**1978  ALTRINCHAM** 3 (King, Johnson, Rogers)   **LEATHERHEAD** 1 (Cook)                  Att: 20,000
*Northern Premier League*                  *Isthmian League*
Altrincham: Eales, Allan, Crossley, Bailey, Owens, King, Morris, Heathcote,Johnson, Rogers, Davidson (Flaherty).
Leatherhead: Swannell, Cooper, Eaton, Davies,Reid, Malley, Cook, Salkeld, Baker, Boyle (Bailey).             Ref: A Grey

**1979  STAFFORD RANGERS** 2 (A Wood 2)       **KETTERING TOWN** 0                        Att: 32,000
*Northern Premier League*                  *Southern League*
Stafford: Arnold, F Wood, Willis, Sargeant, Seddon, Ritchie, Secker, Chapman, A Wood, Cullerton, Chadwick (Jones).
Kettering: Lane, Ashby, Lee, Eastell, Dixey,Suddards, Flannagan, Kellock, Phipps, Clayton, Evans (Hughes).     Ref: D Richardson

**1980(2) DAGENHAM** 2 (Duck, Maycock)        **MOSSLEY** 1 (Smith)                       Att: 26,000
*Isthmian League*                      *Northern Premier League*
Dagenham: Huttley, Wellman, Scales, Dunwell, Moore, Durrell, Maycock, Horan,Duck, Kidd, Jones (Holder).
Mossley: Fitton, Brown, Vaughan, Gorman, Salter, Polliot, Smith, Moore, Skeete, O'Connor, Keelan (Wilson).    Ref: K Baker

**1981(3) BISHOP'S STORTFORD** 1 (Sullivan)    **SUTTON UNITED** 0                        Att: 22,578
*Isthmian League*                      *Isthmian League*
Bishop's Stortford: Moore, Blackman, Brame, Smith (Worrell), Bradford, Abery, Sullivan,Knapman, Radford, Simmonds, Mitchell.
Sutton Utd.: Collyer, Rogers, Green, J Rains,T Rains, Stephens (Sunnucks), Waldon, Pritchard, Cornwell, Parsons, Dennis.   Ref: J Worrall

**1982  ENFIELD** 1 (Taylor)                  **ALTRINCHAM** 0                            Att: 18,678
*Alliance Premier League*                  *Alliance Premier League*
Enfield: Jacobs, Barrett, Tone, Jennings, Waite, Ironton, Ashford, Taylor,Holmes, Oliver (Flint), King.         Ref: B Stevens
Altrincham: Connaughton, Crossley, Davison, Bailey, Cuddy, King (Whitbread), Allan, Heathcote, Johnson, Rogers, Howard.

**Notes:**

1       The only occasion three members of the same family played in the same FA Trophy Final team.
2       The first of the Amateurs from the Isthmian League to win the FA Trophy.
3       Goalkeeper Terry Moore had also won an Amateur Cup Winners Medal with Bishop's Stortford in 1974.
        All games played at Wembley (old & new) unless stated.

# THE FA TROPHY

**1983  TELFORD UTD** 2 (Mather 2)      **NORTHWICH VICTORIA** 1 (Bennett)      **Att: 22,071**
*Alliance Premier League*      *Alliance Premier League*
Telford: Charlton, Lewis, Turner, Mayman (Joseph), Walker, Easton, Barnett,Williams, Mather, Hogan, Alcock.
Northwich: Ryan, Fretwell, Murphy, Jones, Forshaw, Ward, Anderson, Abel (Bennett), Reid, Chesters, Wilson.      Ref: B Hill

**1984  NORTHWICH VICTORIA** 1 (Chester)      **BANGOR CITY** 1 (Whelan)      **Att: 14,200**
Replay **NORTHWICH VICTORIA** 2 (Chesters(p), Anderson) BANGOR CITY 1 (Lunn)      Att: 5,805 (at Stoke)
*Alliance Premier League*      *Alliance Premier League*
Northwich: Ryan, Fretwell, Dean, Jones, Forshaw (Power 65), Bennett, Anderson,Abel, Reid, Chesters, Wilson.      Ref: J Martin
Bangor: Letheren, Cavanagh, Gray, Whelan, Banks,Lunn, Urqhart, Morris, Carter, Howat, Sutcliffe (Westwood 105) . Same in replay.

**1985  WEALDSTONE** 2 (Graham, Holmes)      **BOSTON UNITED** 1 (Cook)      **Att: 20,775**
*Alliance Premier League*      *Alliance Premier League*
Wealdstone: Iles, Perkins, Bowgett, Byatt, Davies, Greenaway, Holmes, Wainwright,Donnellan, Graham (N Cordice 89), A Cordice.
Boston: Blackwell, Casey, Ladd,Creane, O'Brien, Thommson, Laverick (Mallender 78), Simpsom, Gilbert, Lee, Cook.      Ref: J Bray

**1986  ALTRINCHAM** 1 (Farrelly)      **RUNCORN** 0      **Att: 15,700**
*Gola League*      *Gola League*
Altrincham: Wealands, Gardner, Densmore, Johnson, Farrelly, Conning, Cuddy,Davison, Reid, Ellis, Anderson. Sub: Newton.
Runcorn: McBride, Lee, Roberts,Jones, Fraser, Smith, S Crompton (A Crompton), Imrie, Carter, Mather, Carrodus.      Ref: A Ward

**1987  KIDDERMINSTER HARRIERS** 0      **BURTON ALBION** 0      **Att: 23,617**
Replay **KIDDERMINSTER HARRIERS** 2 (Davies 2)      BURTON ALBION 1 (Groves)      Att: 15,685 (at West Brom)
*Conference*      *Southern League*
Kidderminster: Arnold, Barton, Boxall, Brazier (sub Hazlewood in rep), Collins (sub Pearson 90 at Wembley), Woodall, McKenzie, O'Dowd, Tuohy, Casey, Davies. sub:Jones.
Burton: New, Essex, Kamara, Vaughan, Simms, Groves, Bancroft, Land, Dorsett, Redfern, (sub Wood in replay), Gauden.
Sub: Patterson.      Ref: D Shaw

**1988  ENFIELD** 0      **TELFORD UNITED** 0      **Att: 20,161**
Replay **ENFIELD** 3 (Furlong 2, Howell)      TELFORD UNITED 2 (Biggins, Norris(p))      Att: 6,912 (at W Brom)
*Conference*      *Conference*
Enfield: Pape, Cottington, Howell, Keen (sub Edmonds in rep), Sparrow (sub Hayzleden at Wembley), Lewis (sub Edmonds at Wembley), Harding, Cooper, King,Furlong, Francis.
Telford: Charlton, McGinty, Storton, Nelson, Wiggins, Mayman (sub Cunningham in rep (sub Hancock)), Sankey, Joseph, Stringer (sub Griffiths at Wembley, Griffiths in replay), Biggins, Norris.      Ref: L Dilkes

**1989  TELFORD UNITED** 1 (Crawley)      **MACCLESFIELD TOWN** 0      **Att: 18,102**
*Conference*      *Conference*
Telford: Charlton, Lee, Brindley, Hancock, Wiggins, Mayman, Grainger, Joseph, Nelson, Lloyd, Stringer. Subs: Crawley, Griffiths.
Macclesfield: Zelem, Roberts, Tobin, Edwards, Hardman, Askey, Lake, Hanton, Imrie, Burr, Timmons. Subs: Devonshire, Kendall.

**1990  BARROW** 3 (Gordon 2, Cowperthwaite)      **LEEK TOWN** 0      **Att: 19,011**
*Conference*      *Northern Premier League*
Barrow: McDonnell, Higgins, Chilton, Skivington, Gordon, Proctor, Doherty (Burgess), Farrell (Gilmore), Cowperthwaite, Lowe, Ferris.
Leek: Simpson, Elsby (Smith), Pearce, McMullen, Clowes, Coleman (Russell),Mellor, Somerville, Sutton, Millington, Norris      Ref: T Simpson

**1991  WYCOMBE W.** 2 (Scott, West)      **KIDDERMINSTER HARRIERS** 1 (Hadley)      **Att: 34,842**
*Conference*      *Conference*
Wycombe: Granville, Crossley, Cash, Kerr, Creaser, Carroll, Ryan, Stapleton,West, Scott, Guppy (Hutchinson).      Ref: J Watson
Kidderminster: Jones, Kurila, McGrath, Weir, Barnett, Forsyth, Joseph (Wilcox), Howell (Whitehouse), Hadley, Lilwall, Humphries

**1992  COLCHESTER UTD\*** 3 (Masters, Smith, McGavin)      **WITTON ALBION** 1 (Lutkevitch)      **Att: 27,806**
*Conference*      *Conference*
Colchester: Barrett, Donald, Roberts, Knsella, English, Martin, Cook, Masters,McDonough (Bennett 65), McGavin, Smith.      Ref: K P Barratt
Witton: Mason, Halliday, Coathup, McNeilis, Jim Connor, Anderson, Thomas, Rose, Alford, Grimshaw (Joe Connor), Lutkevitch (McCluskie)

**1993  WYCOMBE W\*.** 4 (Cousins, Kerr, Thompson, Carroll) RUNCORN 1 (Shaughnessy)      **Att: 32,968**
*Conference*      *Conference*
Wycombe: Hyde, Cousins, Cooper, Kerr, Crossley, Thompson (Hayrettin 65),Carroll, Ryan, Hutchinson, Scott, Guppy. Sub: Casey.
Runcorn: Williams, Bates, Robertson, Hill, Harold (Connor 62), Anderson, Brady (Parker 72), Brown, Shaughnessy, McKenna, Brabin

**1994  WOKING** 2 (D Brown, Hay)      **RUNCORN** 1 (Shaw (pen))      **Att: 15,818**
*Conference*      *Conference*
Woking: Batty, Tucker, L Wye, Berry, Brown, Clement, Brown (Rattray 32), Fielder, Steele, Hay (Puckett 46), Walker.      Ref: Paul Durkin
Runcorn: Williams, Bates, Robertson, Shaw, Lee, Anderson, Thomas, Connor, McInerney (Hill 71), McKenna, Brabin. Sub: Parker

**1995  WOKING** 2 (Steele, Fielder)      **KIDDERMINSTER HARRIERS** 1 aet (Davies)      **Att: 17,815**
*Conference*      *Conference*
Woking: Batty, Tucker, L Wye, Fielder, Brown, Crumplin (Rattray 42), S Wye, Ellis, Steele, Hay (Newberry 112), Walker. (Sub: Read(gk)
Kidderminster: Rose, Hodson, Bancroft, Webb, Brindley (Cartwright 94), Forsyth, Deakin, Yates, Humphreys (Hughes 105), Davies, Purdie. Sub: Dearlove (gk)      Ref: D J Gallagher

**1996  MACCLESFIELD TOWN** 3 (Payne, OG, Hemmings)  **NORTHWICH VICTORIA 1 (Williams)**    Att: 8,672
*Conference*                                            *Conference*
Macclesfield:  Price, Edey, Gardiner, Payne, Howarth(C), Sorvel, Lyons, Wood (Hulme 83), Coates, Power, Hemmings (Cavell 88).
Northwich: Greygoose, Ward, Duffy, Burgess (Simpson 87), Abel (Steele), Walters, Williams, Butler (C), Cooke, Humphries, Vicary.
Ref: M Reed

**1997  WOKING** 1 (Hay 112)                     **DAGENHAM & REDBRIDGE 0**           Att: 24,376
*Conference*                                            *Isthmian League*
Woking: Batty, Brown, Howard, Foster, Taylor, S Wye, Thompson (sub Jones 115), Ellis, Steele (L Wye 108), Walker, Jackson (Hay 77).
Dagenham: Gothard, Culverhouse, Connor, Creaser, Jacques (sub Double 75), Davidson, Pratt (Naylor 81), Parratt, Broom, Rogers,
Stimson (John 65).                                                                           Ref: J Winter

**1998  CHELTENHAM TOWN** 1 (Eaton 74)            **SOUTHPORT 0**                      Att: 26,387
*Conference*                                            *Conference*
Cheltenham: Book, Duff, Freeman, Banks, Victory, Knight (Smith 78), Howells, Bloomer, Walker (sub Milton 78), Eaton, Watkins. Sub:
Wright.
Southport: Stewart, Horner, Futcher, Ryan, Farley, Kielty, Butler, Gamble, Formby (sub Whittaker 80), Thompson (sub Bollard 88),
Ross. Sub: Mitten.                                                                           Ref: G S Willard

**1999  KINGSTONIAN** 1 (Mustafa 49)             **FOREST GREEN ROVERS 0**           Att: 20,037
*Conference*                                            *Conference*
Kingstonian: Farrelly, Mustafa, Luckett, Crossley, Stewart, Harris, Patterson, Pitcher, Rattray, Leworthy (Francis 87), Akuamoah. Subs
not used): John, Corbett, Brown, Tranter
Forest Green Rovers: Shuttlewood, Hedges, Forbes, Bailey (Smart 76), Kilgour, Wigg (Cook 58), Honor (Winter 58), Drysdale,
McGregor, Mehew, Sykes. Subs (not used): Perrin, Coupe                                       Ref: A B Wilkie

**2000  KINGSTONIAN** 3 (Akuamoah 40, 69, Simba 75)  **KETTERING TOWN** 2 (Vowden 55, Norman 64p)  Att: 20,034
*Conference*                                            *Conference*
Kingstonian: Farelly, Mustafa, Luckett, Crossley, Stewart (Saunders 77), Harris, Kadi (Leworthy 83), Pitcher, Green (Basford 86),
Smiba, Akuamoah. Subs (not used): Hurst, Allan
Kettering Town: Sollit, McNamara, Adams, Perkins, Vowden, Norman (Duik 76), Fisher, Brown, Shutt, Watkins (Hudson 46), Setchell
Hopkins 81). Subs (not used): Ridgway, Wilson                                                Ref: S W Dunn

**2001  CANVEY ISLAND** 1 (Chenery)              **FOREST GREEN ROVERS 0**           Att: 10,007
*Isthmian League*                                       *Conference*                         at Villa Park
Forest Green Rovers: Perrin, Cousins, Lockwood, Foster, Clark, Burns, Daley, Drysdale (Bennett 46), Foster (Hunt 75), Meecham,
Slater. Subs (not used): Hedges, Prince, Ghent
Canvey Island: Harrison, Duffy, Chenery, Bodley, Ward, Tilson, Stimson (Tanner 83), Gregory, Vaughan (Jones 76), Parmenter. Subs
not used): Bennett, Miller, Thompson.                                                        Ref: A G Wiley

**2002  YEOVIL TOWN** 2 (Alford, Stansfield)      **STEVENAGE BOROUGH 0**             Att: 18,809
*Conference*                                            *Conference*                         at Villa Park
Yeovil Town: Weale, Lockwood, Tonkin, Skiverton, Pluck (White 51), Way, Stansfield, Johnson, Alford (Giles 86), Crittenden (Lindegaard
83), McIndoe. Subs (not used): O'Brien, Sheffield
Stevenage Borough: Wilkerson, Hamsher, Goodliffe, Trott, Fraser, Fisher, Wormull (Stirling 71), Evers (Williams 56), Jackson, Sigere
Campbell 74), Clarke. Subs (not used): Campbell, Greygoose                                    Ref: N S Barry

**2003  BURSCOUGH** 2 (Martindale 25, 55)         **TAMWORTH** 1 (Cooper 78)          Att: 14,265
*Northern Premier*                                      *Southern Premier*                   at Villa Park
Burscough: Taylor, Teale, Taylor, Macauley (White 77), Lawless, Bowen, Wright, Norman, Martindale (McHale 80), Byrne (Bluck 84),
Burns. Subs (not used): McGuire (g/k) Molyneux.
Tamworth: Acton, Warner, Follett, Robinson, Walsh, Cooper, Colley, Evans (Turner 64), Rickards (Hatton 88), McGorry,
Sale (Hallam 54). Subs (not used): Grocutt, Barnes (g/k).                                     Ref: U D Rennie

**2004  HEDNESFORD TOWN** 3 (Maguire 28, Hines 53, Brindley 87)  **CANVEY ISLAND** 2 (Boylan 46, Brindley 48 og)  Att: 6,635
*Southern Premier*                                      *Isthmian Premier Champions*         at Villa Park
Hednesford Town: Young, Simkin, Hines, King, Brindley, Ryder (Barrow 59), Palmer, Anthrobus, Danks (Piearce 78), Maguire,
Charie (Evans 55). Subs (not used): Evans (g/k) McGhee.
Canvey Island: Potter, Kennedy, Duffy, Chenery, Cowan, Gooden (Dobinson 89), Minton, Gregory (McDougald 80), Boylan,
Midgley (Berquez 73), Ward. Subs (not used): Theobald, Harrison (g/k).
Ref: M L Dean

**2005  GRAYS ATHLETIC** 1 (Martin 65) Pens: 6    **HUCKNALL TOWN** 1 (Ricketts 75) Pens: 5   Att: 8,116
*Conference South*                                      *Conference North*                   at Villa Park
Grays Athletic: Bayes, Brennan, Nutter, Stuart, Matthews, Thurgood, Oli (Powell 80), Hopper (Carthy 120), Battersby (sub West 61),
Martin, Cole. Subs (not used): Emberson, Bruce..
Hucknall Town: Smith, Asher, Barrick (Plummer 30), Hunter, Timons, Cooke, Smith (Ward 120), Palmer (Heathcote 94), Ricketts,
Bacon, Todd. Subs (not used): Winder, Lindley.                                               Ref: P Dowd

**2006  GRAYS ATHLETIC** 2 (Oli, Poole)           **WOKING 0**                         Att: 13,997
*Conference*                                            *Conference*                         at Upton Park
Grays Athletic: Bayes, Sambrook, Nutter, Stuart, Hanson, Kightly (Williamson 90), Thurgood, Martin, Poole, Oli, McLean.
Subs (not used): Eyre (g/k), Hooper, Olayinka, Mawer.
Woking: Jalal, Jackson, MacDonald, Nethercott (Watson 60), Hutchinson, Murray, Smith (Cockerill 60), Evans (Blackman 85),
Ferguson, McAllister, Justin Richards. Subs (not used): Davis (g/k), El-Salahi.
Ref: Howard Webb (Sheffield)

# THE FA TROPHY

**2007** **STEVENAGE BOROUGH** 3 (Cole, Dobson, Morrison) **KIDDERMINSTER HARRIERS** 2 (Constable 2) **Att: 53,262**
*Conference*                                                                        *Conference*                                              **(New Trophy record)**
Stevenage Borough: Julian, Fuller, Nutter, Oliver, Gaia, Miller, Cole, Morrison, Guppy (Dobson 63), Henry, Beard.
Subs not used: Potter, Slabber, Nurse, McMahon.
Kidderminster Harriers: Bevan, Kenna, Hurren, Creighton, Whitehead, Blackwood, Russell, Penn, Smikle (Reynolds 90),
Christie (White 75) , Constable.
Subs not used: Taylor, Sedgemore, McGrath.                                                       Ref: Chris Foy (Merseyside)

**2008** **EBBSFLEET UNITED** 1 (McPhee) **TORQUAY UNITED** 0 **Att: 40,186**
*Blue Square Premier*                                                              *Blue Square Premier*
Ebbsfleet United: Cronin, Hawkins, McCarthy, Smith, Opinel, McPhee, Barrett, Bostwick, Long (MacDonald 84), Moore, Akinde.
Subs not used: Eribenne, Purcell, Ricketts, Mott.
Torquay United: Rice, Mansell, Todd, Woods, Nicholson, D'Sane (Benyon 66), Hargreaves, Adams, Zebroski, Sills (Hill 88),
Phillips (Stevens 46). Subs not used: Hockley and Robertson.                          Ref: Martin Atkinson (West Riding)

**2009** **STEVENAGE BOROUGH** 2 (Morison, Boylan) **YORK CITY** 0 **Att: 27,102**
*Blue Square Premier*                                                              *Blue Square Premier*
Stevenage Borough: Day, Henry, Bostwick, Roberts, Wilson, Mills, Murphy, Drury, Vincenti (Anaclet 86), Boylan, Morison.
Subs not used: Bayes, Albrighton, Maamria and Willock.
York City:Ingham, Purkiss, McGurk, Parslow, Pejic, Mackin, Greaves(McWilliams 74), Rusk (Russell 80), Brodie, McBreen (Sodje 60),
Boyes. Subs not used – Mimms and Robinson.                                              Referee: Michael Jones.

**2010** **BARROW** 2 (McEvilly 79, Walker 117) **STEVENAGE BOROUGH** 1 (Drury 10) **Att: 21,223**
*Blue Square Premier*                                                              *Blue Square Premier*
Barrow: Stuart Tomlinson, Simon Spender, Paul Jones, Phil Bolland, Paul Edwards, Simon Wiles (sub Carlos Logan 63rd min),
Robin Hulbert, Andy Bond, Paul Rutherford (sub Mark Boyd 109th min), Jason Walker, Gregg Blundell (sub Lee McEvilly 73rd min).
Subs not used – Tim Deasy and Mike Pearson.
Stevenage Borough: Chris Day (sub Ashley Bayes 90th min), Ronnie Henry, Jon Ashton, Mark Roberts,  Scott Laird,
Joel Byrom (sub Lawrie Wilson 58th min), David Bridges, Michael Bostwick, Andy Drury, Chris Beardsley (sub Charlie Griffin 64th min),
Yemi Odubade. Subs not used – Stacey Long and Peter Vincenti.
**Man of the match** - Paul Rutherford.                                                          Referee Lee Probert.

**2011** **DARLINGTON** 1 (Senior 120) **MANSFIELD TOWN** 0 **Att: 24,668**
*Blue Square Premier*                                                              *Blue Square Premier*
Darlington: Sam Russell, Paul Arnison, Ian Miller, Liam Hatch, Aaron Brown, Jamie  Chandler, Chris Moore, Marc Bridge-Wilkinson (sub
Paul Terry 100th min), Gary Smith (sub Arman Verma 38th min), John Campbell (sub Chris Senior 75th min), Tommy Wright.
*Subs not used* – Danzelle St Louis-Hamilton (gk) and Phil Gray.
Mansfield Town: Alan Marriott, Gary Silk, Stephen Foster, Tom Naylor, Dan Spence, Louis Briscoe, Tyrone Thompson, Kyle Nix, Adam
Smith (sub Ashley Cain 95th min), Adam Murray (sub Danny Mitchley 108th min), Paul Connor
*Subs not used* – Paul Stonehouse and Neil Collett (gk)
**Man of the match** - Jamie Chandler.                                                           Referee Stuart Atwell

**2012** **YORK CITY** 2 (Blair 61, Oyebanjo 68) **NEWPORT COUNTY** 0 **Att: 19,844**
*Blue Square Premier*                                                              *Blue Square Premier*
York City: Michael Ingham, Jon Challinor, Chris Smith, Daniel Parslow, Ben Gibson, Matty Blair, Lanre Oyebanjo, Patrick McLaughlan
(sub Jamal Fyfield 82nd min), James Meredith, Ashley Chambers (Adriano Moke (89th min), Jason Walker (Jamie Reed 90th min).
Subs not used – Paul Musselwhite (g/k), Michael Potts.
Newport County: Glyn Thompson, David Pipe, Ismail Yakubu, Gary Warren, Andrew Hughes, Sam Foley, Lee Evans, Nat Jarvis (sub
Jake Harris 68th min), Max Porter (sub Darryl Knights 79th min), Romone Rose (sub Elliott Buchanan 68th min), Lee Minshull.
Subs not used – Matthew Swan (g/k), Paul Rodgers.
**Man of the match** - Lanre Oyebanjo.                                                           Referee Anthony Taylor

Wrexham player/manager, Andy Morrell, is thwarted by Grimsby's James McKeown. Photo: Peter Barnes.

The FA Carlsberg Vase Final
2013 Winners

Spennymoor Town celebrate their FA Vase win over Tunbridge Wells.
Photo: Roger Turner.

CLUBS
543

THE FA VASE 2012–13

# FIRST QUALIFYING ROUND

Over 150 clubs were knocked out of the The FA Vase competition in the first week of September, which left a great many supporters bereft of a national cup to liven up their football season.

Famous names to leave the competition at this stage included, Crook Town and North Shields from The North East and Epsom & Ewell and Redhill from Surrey.

*Incredible high scoring thrillers were provided:-*

| | | | |
|---|---|---|---|
| Holwell Sports | 5 | Kirby Muxloe | 6 |
| Worthing United | 5 | Horsham YMCA | 5 |
| Jattow Roofing | 7 | Brandon United | 4 |

*and also some one sided victories:-*

| | | | |
|---|---|---|---|
| Holbrook Sports | 7 | Birstall United | 2 |
| GE Hamble | 6 | Wootton Basssett | 0 |
| Fareham Town | 6 | Amesbury Town | 0 |

'Outsiders' have a history of success in the FA Vase, so all over the country clubs who have quietly built a fresh and stronger squad are looking forward to the possibility of surprising a few 'favourites' in the rounds ahead.

# SECOND QUALIFYING ROUND

Once again another 150 clubs will be leaving the FA Vase which underlines the popularity of the competition and how success brings great credit to the successful clubs.

Those with Wembley Vase memories who survived the qualifying rounds included:-

Bishop Auckland, Bedlington Terriers, Deal Town, Diss Town, Guisborough Town and St Helens Town.

One club that was experiencing Vase football for the very first time was Guernsey FC who were drawn at home to Farnham Town and celebrated with a 2-0 victory. Bringing the best players on the island into one club to represent the island, had been disappointing for Guernsey's well established senior clubs who have lost their best players. However, the new club had won the Combined Counties Division in 2011-2012 and gained promotion to the Premier Division and their development was causing great excitement in the Channel Islands.

# FIRST ROUND PROPER

With over 300 clubs already knocked out of the competition, another 100 would join them after the FIrst Round Proper where the draw was still made on a regional basis. However, the stronger clubs with serious ambitions would be showing their quality and impressive results were achieved by:-

| | | | |
|---|---|---|---|
| Bridlington Town | 1 | Spennymoor Town | 5 |
| St Helens Town | 2 | Parkgate | 4 |
| Whyteleafe | 2 | Guernsey | 3 |
| Bodmin Town | 3 | Brislington | 2 |
| Replay | | | |
| Erith & Belvedere | 3 | VCD Athletic | 2 |

Large victories cannot be ignored but there's always the doubt abut the quality of clubs on the wrong end of a big defeat:-

| | | | |
|---|---|---|---|
| Swaffham Town | 0 | Desborough Town | 6 |
| Sandhust Town | 1 | Wantage Town | 8 |
| Moneyfields | 6 | Hallen | 0 |

With the FA Vase well under way, clubs who have survived three rounds are beginning to wonder whether it could be their year.

# SECOND ROUND

Saturday afternoons in November begin to create a winter football atmosphere and the national knock out cup very rarely fails to catch the fans' imagination. Some of the regular favourites live up to their reputations and the North East once again appeared to be providing a wide selection of strong and confident Vase prospects.

Quality non-league footballers in the North East have always appeared happier to play for a club in their area rather than join clubs in the Northern Premier League or encourage their local teams to join the non-league pyramid. Consequently the top half of the Northern League are all possible Vase finalists, and the only consolation for the rest of the country's Vase challengers is the fact that in the early regional draws sees many of the quality sides knocking each other out of the competition.

For example, in this round, Consett, Esh Winning, Jarrow Roofing, West Auckland, Newcastle Benfield and Sunderland RCA are all knocked out by reasonably near neighbours.

An interesting result in Kent was achieved by Tunbridge Wells who beat a confident Wantage Town, who had won 8-1 away in the previous round. Other special results brought attention to Bodmin Town who crushed Odd Down 5-1, an amazing 9-2 victory for Croydon at home to Newbury and Guernsey who travelled to Kent to take on a confident Erith Town and win 3-2. Another South West prospect was emerging in St Blazey who won 4-1 at Sherborne Town.

All regions of the country now had some clear favourites and there were only 64 clubs remaining in the competition.

# THIRD ROUND

This round was crippled by horrendous weather but the draw was more of a straight north and south split so th eclubs were not expected to travel to far. However, the North East 'power' was still evident, Spennymoor Town hosted Bilingham Synthonia and Whitley Bay, Shildon and Ashington were all drawn at home to Causeway United, Parkgate and AFC Rushden & Diamonds respectively and all four qualified for the last sixteen!

Surprises at this stage were mainly found in the South, where the clubs threatening in the FA Vase may not have appeared to be outstanding in their respective leagues. For example, Enfield 1893 (Essex Senior League), Ampthill (Spartan South Midlands), Ascot United (Hellenic League), Brantham Athletic and Hadleigh United (Eastern Counties League), Tunbridge Wells (Kent League), Bitton and Larkhall Athletic (Western League) and Bemerton Heath Harlequins (Wessex League).

Could one of these 'outsiders' emerge from the bad weather and actually take on the experienced 'favourites' from the North East. The next round would include an open draw with clubs possibly traveling the length or breadth of the country.

FAV 5P: This superb strike from Gary King gave Spalding an early lead but visitors Guernsey, came back to win 2-1. Photo: Gordon Whittington.

## FOURTH ROUND

Once again the Round was badly affected by the weather with only seven of the sixteen playing on the original date for the Fourth Round. The open draw certainly produced some fascinating ties, the most dramatic of which was provided by Guernsey's 6-5 victory at Rye United. If the Channel Islands were getting good publicity then The Isle of Wight could also claim a last sixteen club in Newport, who beat Brighouse 2-1.
Some Northern Clubs did manage to complete their ties on the original Fourth Round date. Shildon went all the way to Bitton and won 2-0, but Ashington travelled even further to Bodmin and lost by the odd goal in five, while Whitley Bay lost by the only goal at Brantham.
Two ties took two weeks to complete and eventually Walsall Wood beat Hanworth Villa and Tunbidge Wells eliminated Dunston UTS.

## FIFTH ROUND

A good geographical balance in this round eventually saw Ascot United (Hellenic League ) beat Newport IoW (Wessex League) after a replay and Walsall Wood ( Midland Combination won after extra time at Runcorn (North West Counties).
The Guernsey 'fairytale' continued with yet another away victory, this time at Spalding United (Eastern Counties). Spennymoor and Shildon two of the strongest Northern challengers both scored four, with Spennymoor at home to Bemerton Heath Harlequins and Shildon away at Brantham.
It was noticeable how many away victories there had been in the competition and four more were provided by Hadleigh United, 2-1 at Ampthill, Gornall Athletic,1-0 at Bodmin Town, Tonbridge Wells 4-3 at Larkhall Athletic and Walsall Wood 2-1 at Runcorn!

## SIXTH ROUND - THE QUARTER FINALS

What an excellent cross section of non-league football from North East to the Channel Islands. The North Eastern clubs were certainly amongst the favourites, but the odds against any of the others would have been very high as the excitement surged throughout the clubs created by their unexpected Vase runs.
Ascot Town's draw at Shildon was a terrific result but as the competition had underlined, away teams often succeed and Shildon won the replay. Top North Eastern club Spennymoor, relishing life as 'Town' after many years as 'United', won convincingly against Gornal Athletic, while Guernsey, the last Combined

Counties representative, who were playing away again, battled for a no score draw with Walsall Wood before qualifying for the Semi-Finals with a 3-1 replay victory in Guernsey in front of 2,597.
In the fourth tie, Tunbridge Wells, a long serving Kent League club with a very humble record, found themselves at home in the last four of a massive national knockout competition - and won with a solid performance that earned them a famous 2-0 victory. A thousand fans witnessed the club's great day and realized that 'The Wells' were just one round from Wembley.

## SEMI-FINALS

The two Northern favourites avoided each other in the draw and it looked like a second consecutive all North East Vase Final for Wembley.
A wonderful 4,290 attended Guernsey's home first leg but, sadly for the locals, the scoreline underlined the reason why Spennymoor Town were favourites to win the competition outright and they certainly appeared to have built a tie winning lead.
After one goal each at half time, a superb second period produced two more goals and a substantial 3-1 lead to take home with them.
The second semi-final produced a shock result in the first leg, played in Kent in front of 1,754. Tunbridge Wells, very much the least favoured of the four semi-finalists, built a magnificent 2-0 lead and the second meeting was expected to be a thriller in the North East the following week.
As it turned out, Spennymoor produced the expected professional performance to confirm their Wembley place with a 1-0 victory and a 4-1 overall success.
Guernsey had given the competition great headlines, exciting matches and had built a fine reputation for themselves on and off the field. There will be more to come from Channel Islanders in an exciting football future.
Tunbridge Wells' second leg in Shildon produced a wonderful Vase tie and but after two early goals, the home side appeared to have done hard work of drawing level after 23 minutes and surely they had plenty of time to win the tie.
Sure enough, a third goal in the 63 minute may well have relaxed all the home supporters, but nine minutes later a goal for the visitors brought the overall scoreline to 3-3 and then nerve wracking extra time.
There would have been good odds against a Tunbridge winner but centre half Perry Spackman headed home a corner in 112th minute and produced a fairy tale ending to the Tunbridge Wells FA Vase journey to Wembley.
Spennymoor Town will be red hot favourites for the Final, but presumably that will suit the pure amateur club from Kent, whose players, committee and supporters will have had a wonderful five weeks looking forward to their little club gracing one of the most famous football stadiums in the world.
This is what the FA Challenge Vase is all about and it is very special!

(Left & Above) FAV 1Q: Action from the Buckland Athletic v Portishead Town (dark shorts) which the hosts won 5-1. Photo: Peter Barnes.

(Left) FAV 1Q: Dominic Heaume climbs high to head Guernsey's second goal against Crowborough Athletic. Photo: Roger Turner.

FAV 1Q: A goal-line clearance by the visitors denies Thame United this time, however Thame won 3-2 to knock Clanfield out. Photo: Gordon Whittington.

FAV 1Q: Cranfield's Sam Evans and Bush Hill Rangers' Calvin Ecobichon-Gray challenge for the ball. Photo: Alan Coomes.

# FIRST QUALIFYING ROUND
## SATURDAY 1 SEPTEMBER 2012 - WINNERS RECEIVE £500

| No | Home | | Away | Score | Att |
|---|---|---|---|---|---|
| 1 | Esh Winning | v | Tadcaster Albion | 3-2 | 61 |
| 2 | Guisborough Town | v | Crook Town | 2-1 | 101 |
| 3 | Darlington Railway Athletic | v | Eccleshill United | 2-1aet | 57 |
| 4 | Billingham Town | v | Pickering Town | 1-3 | 107 |
| 5 | Thornaby | v | Stokesley SC | 0-3 | 51 |
| 6 | Seaham Red Star | v | Willington | 1-2 | 67 |
| 7 | Celtic Nation | v | Birtley Town | 4-0 | 48 |
| 8 | Marske United | v | Morpeth Town | 2-2aet | 143 |
| | Morpeth Town | v | Marske United (5/9) | 1-1aet | 85 |
| | (Morpeth Town won 4-3 on kicks from the penalty mark) | | | | |
| 9 | West Allotment Celtic | v | Thackley | 1-5 | 78 |
| 10 | Holker Old Boys | v | Hebburn Town | 1-2 | 25 |
| 11 | Liversedge | v | North Shields | 2-1aet | 78 |
| 12 | Jarrow Roofing Boldon CA | v | Brandon United | 7-4aet | 30 |
| 13 | Tow Law Town | v | Penrith (5/9) | 0-1 | 50 |
| 14 | Consett | v | Alnwick Town | 5-0 | 97 |
| 15 | Hemsworth MW | v | Nostell MW | 1-3 | 96 |
| 16 | Atherton Collieries | v | Ashton Town | 2-4 | 59 |
| 17 | Rochdale Town | v | Dinnington Town | 1-0 | 43 |
| 18 | Worksop Parramore | v | Glasshoughton Welfare (31/8) | 1-2 | 85 |
| 19 | Wigan Robin Park | v | Oldham Boro | 2-1 | 21 |
| 20 | Bottesford Town | v | Hallam | 2-0 | 51 |
| 21 | Winsford United | v | Abbey Hey | 2-1 | 86 |
| 22 | West Didsbury & Chorlton | v | Cheadle Town | 1-3 | 79 |
| 23 | AFC Liverpool | v | Bacup Borough | 0-0aet | 111 |
| | Bacup Borough | v | AFC Liverpool (5/9) | 0-1 | |
| 24 | Worsbrough Bridge Athletic | v | Parkgate | 0-1 | 75 |
| 25 | Formby | v | Padiham | 5-1 | 56 |
| 26 | Atherton LR | v | Kinsley Boys+ | 1-4 | 58 |
| 27 | Northwich Villa | v | Daisy Hill | 0-1 | 21 |
| 28 | Ashton Athletic | v | Runcorn Linnets | 0-2 | 109 |
| 29 | Glossop North End | v | Barton Town Old Boys | 2-1 | 150 |
| 30 | Nelson | v | Appleby Frodingham | 3-2 | 30 |
| 31 | St Helens Town | v | Westella & Willerby | | |
| | (walkover for St Helens Town – Westella & Willerby withdrawn) | | | | |
| 32 | Irlam | v | Maltby Main | 2-3 | 55 |
| 33 | Congleton Town | v | Rossington Main | 3-0 | 118 |
| 34 | Pinxton | v | Ollerton Town | 4-3 | 96 |
| 35 | Boston Town | v | Loughborough University | 4-3 | 57 |
| 36 | Ibstock United | v | Stapenhill | 3-2 | 46 |
| 37 | Grimsby Borough | v | St Andrews | 0-1 | 45 |
| 38 | Bardon Hill Sports | v | Dunkirk | 1-2 | 35 |
| 39 | Arnold Town | v | Thurnby Nirvana | 5-3 | 60 |
| 40 | Teversal | v | Radcliffe Olympic | 4-2 | 59 |
| 41 | Holwell Sports | v | Kirby Muxloe | 5-6aet | 43 |
| 42 | Holbrook Sports | v | Birstall United | 7-2 | 37 |
| 43 | Long Eaton United | v | Lincoln Moorlands Railway | 3-0 | 52 |
| 44 | Harborough Town | v | Barrow Town | 3-1 | 60 |
| 45 | Glapwell | v | Radford | 0-1 | 54 |
| 46 | Malvern Town | v | Bromyard Town | 3-5aet | 70 |
| 47 | AFC Wombourne United | v | Shifnal Town | 0-3 | 26 |
| 48 | Pilkington XXX | v | Wellington | 2-1 | 46 |
| 49 | Pegasus Juniors | v | Coventry Copsewood | 4-3 | 28 |
| 50 | Earlswood Town | v | Alvechurch | 2-5aet | 80 |
| 51 | Pelsall Villa | v | AFC Wulfrunians | 0-4 | 37 |
| 52 | Dudley Town | v | Causeway United | 2-4aet | 79 |
| 53 | Heath Hayes | v | Boldmere St Michaels | 0-3 | 45 |
| 54 | Sporting Khalsa | v | Rocester | 1-2 | 45 |
| 55 | Tipton Town | v | Bolehall Swifts | 2-1aet | 79 |
| 56 | Coleshill Town | v | Stafford Town | 2-3 | 22 |
| 57 | Cradley Town | v | Studley | 4-1 | 39 |
| 58 | Continental Star | v | Ellesmere Rangers (2/9) | 2-2aet | 50 |
| | Ellesmere Rangers | v | Continental Star (5/9) | 3-4 | 48 |
| 59 | Willenhall Town | v | Lye Town (31/8) | 0-3 | 52 |
| 60 | Wednesfield | v | Bridgnorth Town | 0-3 | 60 |
| 61 | Atherstone Town | v | Gornal Athletic | 2-5 | 131 |
| 62 | Cadbury Athletic | v | Wolverhampton SC | | |
| | (walkover for Wolverhampton SC – Cadbury Athletic withdrawn) | | | | |
| 63 | Pershore Town | v | Wolverhampton Casuals | 3-0 | 40 |
| 64 | Brocton | v | Shawbury United | 2-3 | 58 |
| 65 | Highgate United | v | Warstones Wanderers | 3-2aet | 31 |
| 66 | Stone Dominoes | v | Bilston Town | 0-2 | 37 |
| 67 | Bloxwich United | v | Dudley Sports | 4-1 | 41 |
| 68 | Cambridge Regional College | v | Fakenham Town | 0-1 | 58 |
| 69 | March Town United | v | Thrapston Town | 1-2 | 73 |
| 70 | Huntingdon Town | v | Desborough Town | 1-5 | 42 |
| 71 | Godmanchester Rovers | v | Rothwell Corinthians | 2-1 | |
| 72 | Wellingborough Town | v | Bugbrooke St Michaels | 0-3 | 112 |
| 73 | Cornard United | v | Haverhill Rovers | 0-11 | 45 |
| 74 | Harold Hill | v | Walsham Le Willows (2/9) | 0-3 | 100 |
| 75 | Ipswich Wanderers | v | Eton Manor | 2-0 | 47 |
| 76 | Stowmarket Town | v | Stansted | 0-2 | 54 |
| 77 | Long Melford | v | Bowers & Pitsea | 3-2 | 56 |
| 78 | Great Yarmouth Town | v | Gorleston | 1-4 | 164 |
| 79 | Newmarket Town | v | Mildenhall Town | 3-2aet | 116 |
| 80 | Halstead Town | v | Basildon United | 2-0 | |
| 81 | Stanway Rovers | v | Debenham LC | 3-1 | 47 |
| 82 | Felixstowe & Walton United | v | Kirkley & Pakefield | 2-1 | 61 |
| 83 | Broxbourne Borough V&E | v | Feltham | | |
| | (walkover for Feltham – Broxbourne Borough V&E removed) | | | | |
| 84 | Welwyn Garden City | v | London Lions | 0-3 | 37 |
| 85 | AFC Kempston Rovers | v | Stotfold | 3-2 | 54 |
| 86 | Barking | v | Barkingside | 3-1aet | 61 |
| 87 | Haringey & Waltham Dev. | v | St Margaretsbury (31/8) | 2-2aet | 62 |
| | St Margraretsbury | v | Haringey&Waltham Dev(4/9) | 2-0 | 35 |
| 88 | Haringey Borough | v | Staines Lammas | 3-1 | 33 |
| 89 | Kings Langley | v | Biggleswade United | 1-3 | 50 |
| 90 | Sawbridgeworth Town | v | London APSA | 1-0 | 40 |
| 91 | Kentish Town | v | Langford | 0-1 | 14 |
| 92 | FC Romania | v | Tring Athletic | 3-1 | 20 |
| 93 | Bedfont Sports | v | Leverstock Green | 4-1 | 76 |
| 94 | Bush Hill Rangers | v | Cranfield United (2/9) | 2-2aet | 40 |
| | Cranfield United | v | Bush Hill Rangers (4/9) | 4-1 | 35 |
| 95 | Codicote | v | Wodson Park | 1-0 | 26 |
| 96 | Harefield United | v | Colney Heath | 0-5 | |
| 97 | Ascot United | v | Slimbridge | 1-0 | 49 |
| 98 | Henley Town | v | Amersham Town | 0-5 | 39 |
| 99 | Cheltenham Saracens | v | Abingdon Town | 5-1 | 28 |
| 100 | Hartley Wintney | v | Shrivenham | 0-3 | 86 |
| 101 | Thame United | v | Clanfield 85 | 3-2 | 52 |
| 102 | Westfield | v | Holmesdale | 2-3 | 41 |
| 103 | Shoreham | v | Ringmer | 1-7 | 61 |
| 104 | Worthing United | v | Horsham YMCA | 5-5aet | 38 |
| | Horsham YMCA | v | Worthing United (4/9) | 4-0 | 70 |
| 105 | Ash United | v | Knaphill | 2-1 | 54 |
| 106 | Mole Valley SCR | v | Sidley United | 2-0 | 37 |
| 107 | Crowborough Athletic | v | Guernsey | 2-3 | 251 |
| 108 | Canterbury City | v | Greenwich Borough (2/9) | 5-1 | 73 |
| 109 | AFC Croydon Athletic | v | Southwick | 3-1aet | 67 |
| 110 | Beckenham Town | v | Corinthian | 3-2 | 71 |
| 111 | Warlingham | v | Lordswood | 0-3 | 47 |
| 112 | Epsom Athletic | v | Camberley Town | 3-4 | 29 |
| 113 | Colliers Wood United | v | Badshot Lea | 3-1 | 37 |
| 114 | Steyning Town | v | Pagham | 2-3 | 67 |
| 115 | Dorking Wanderers | v | Eastbourne United | 1-0aet | 50 |
| 116 | Dorking | v | Peacehaven & Telscombe | 2-4 | |

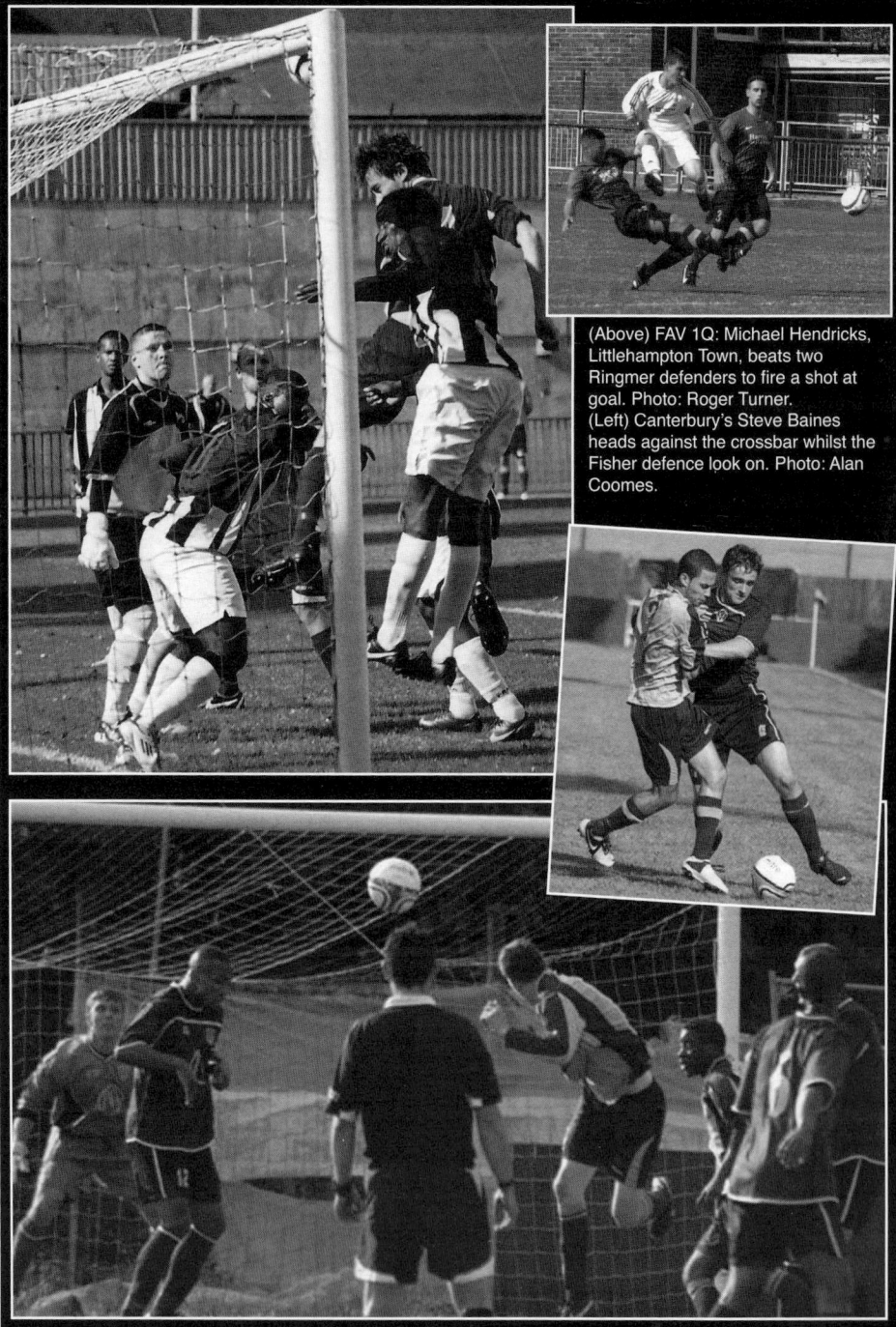

(Above) FAV 1Q: Michael Hendricks, Littlehampton Town, beats two Ringmer defenders to fire a shot at goal. Photo: Roger Turner.
(Left) Canterbury's Steve Baines heads against the crossbar whilst the Fisher defence look on. Photo: Alan Coomes.

(Above & inset) FAV 2Q: Action from the Radford v Long Eaton United tie which the visitors won 2-0. Photo: Bill Wheatcroft.

# FIRST QUALIFYING ROUND
## SATURDAY 1 SEPTEMBER 2012 - WINNERS RECEIVE £500

| No | Home | | Away | Score | |
|---|---|---|---|---|---|
| 117 | Frimley Green | v | Selsey | 4-0 | 43 |
| 118 | Hailsham Town | v | Arundel | 1-3aet | 74 |
| 119 | Farnham Town | v | Kent Football United | 3-2 | 20 |
| 120 | St Francis Rangers | v | Epsom & Ewell | 2-1 | 82 |
| 121 | Newhaven | v | Littlehampton Town | 1-4 | 108 |
| 122 | Saltdean United | v | Banstead Athletic | 1-7 | 41 |
| 123 | Redhill | v | Horley Town | 1-3aet | 79 |
| 124 | Cray Valley (PM) | v | Lingfield | 1-2 | 58 |
| 125 | Cobham | v | Oakwood (2/9) | 3-2aet | |
| 126 | AFC Uckfield | v | Molesey | 2-1aet | 55 |
| 127 | East Grinstead Town | v | Raynes Park Vale | 4-4aet | |
| | Raynes Park Vale | v | East Grinstead Town (4/9) | 2-1 | 56 |
| 128 | Blackfield & Langley | v | Pewsey Vale | 4-1 | 35 |
| 129 | Verwood Town | v | Hayling United | 2-2aet | 55 |
| | Hayling United | v | Verwood Town (4/9) | 3-0 | 49 |
| 130 | Almondsbury UWE | v | Bristol Academy | 1-2aet | 33 |
| 131 | Melksham Town | v | East Cowes Victoria Athletic | 3-0 | 98 |
| 132 | Totton & Eling | v | Petersfield Town | 1-3 | |
| 133 | GE Hamble | v | Wootton Bassett Town | 6-0 | 41 |
| 134 | Highworth Town | v | Calne Town | 1-1aet | 70 |
| | Calne Town | v | Highworth Town (5/9) | 4-2aet | 52 |
| 135 | Downton | v | Oldland Abbotonians | 5-3aet | 52 |
| 136 | Swanage Town & Herston | v | Andover New Street | 3-0 | 68 |
| 137 | AFC Portchester | v | Hythe & Dibden | 4-1 | 68 |
| 138 | Team Solent | v | Whitchurch United | 0-2 | 49 |
| 139 | Shrewton United | v | Cadbury Heath | 0-4 | 46 |
| 140 | Cowes Sports | v | Brockenhurst | 3-0 | 63 |
| 141 | Fleet Spurs | v | Devizes Town | 4-1 | 20 |
| 142 | Warminster Town | v | Ringwood Town | 2-0 | 109 |
| 143 | Laverstock & Ford | v | Roman Glass St George | 0-1 | 44 |
| 144 | New Milton Town | v | Tadley Calleva | 1-0 | 43 |
| 145 | Fareham Town | v | Amesbury Town | 6-0 | 75 |
| 146 | Corsham Town | v | Longwell Green Sports | 1-2 | 87 |
| 147 | Plymouth Parkway | v | Gillingham Town | 1-2 | 119 |
| 148 | Ilfracombe Town | v | Brislington | 0-1 | 47 |
| 149 | Keynsham Town | v | Sherborne Town | 1-2 | 53 |
| 150 | Tavistock | v | Bridport | 0-2 | 50 |
| 151 | Radstock Town | v | Shepton Mallet | 2-1 | 73 |
| 152 | St Blazey | v | Wadebridge Town | 4-1 | 71 |
| 153 | Elmore | v | Exmouth Town | 0-2 | 53 |
| 154 | Buckland Athletic | v | Portishead Town | 5-1 | 73 |
| 155 | Chard Town | v | Odd Down | 0-1 | 84 |
| 156 | Crediton United | v | Bishop Sutton | 0-2 | 43 |

# SECOND QUALIFYING ROUND
## SATURDAY 15 SEPTEMBER 2012 - WINNERS RECEIVE £700

| No | Home | | Away | Score | |
|---|---|---|---|---|---|
| 1 | Shildon | v | Liversedge | 3-2 | 100 |
| 2 | Esh Winning | v | Albion Sports | 4-2 | |
| 3 | Silsden | v | Northallerton Town | 2-3 | 91 |
| 4 | Chester-Le-Street Town | v | Norton & Stockton Ancients | 1-2aet | 61 |
| 5 | Morpeth Town | v | Whitehaven | 2-0 | 79 |
| 6 | Willington | v | Newton Aycliffe | 0-1 | 152 |
| 7 | Ryton & Crawcrook Albion | v | Bishop Auckland | 0-2 | 76 |
| 8 | Stokesley SC | v | Guisborough Town | 0-5 | 83 |
| 9 | Penrith | v | Horden CW | 6-0 | 80 |
| 10 | Pickering Town | v | Team Northumbria | 3-1 | 137 |
| 11 | Thackley | v | Celtic Nation | 2-0 | 63 |
| 12 | Washington | v | Jarrow Roofing Boldon CA | 0-2 | 54 |
| 13 | Yorkshire Amateur | v | South Shields | 0-2 | 28 |
| 14 | Bedlington Terriers | v | Darlington Railway Athletic | 7-0 | 105 |
| 15 | Consett | v | Hebburn Town | 1-0 | 103 |
| 16 | Kinsley Boys | v | Rochdale Town | 0-3 | 43 |
| 17 | Glossop North End | v | Winsford United | 1-1aet | 183 |
| | Winsford United | v | Glossop North End (18/9) | 4-1 | 89 |
| 18 | Pontefract Collieries | v | Cheadle Town | 1-3 | 78 |
| 19 | Ashton Town | v | Parkgate | 0-2 | 29 |
| 20 | Nostell MW | v | AFC Blackpool | 2-1 | 42 |
| 21 | Alsager Town | v | Runcorn Linnets | 0-1 | 136 |
| 22 | Maine Road | v | Glasshoughton Welfare | 4-0 | 55 |
| 23 | Selby Town | v | Formby | 1-5 | 90 |
| 24 | Maltby Main | v | AFC Emley | 0-1aet | 47 |
| 25 | Askern Villa | v | AFC Liverpool | 1-3 | 72 |
| 26 | Hall Road Rangers | v | Chadderton | 2-1 | 68 |
| 27 | Daisy Hill | v | St Helens Town | 0-5 | 39 |
| 28 | Colne | v | Bottesford Town | 1-2 | 68 |
| 29 | Congleton Town | v | Winterton Rangers | 3-0 | 126 |
| 30 | Nelson | v | Wigan Robin Park | 2-3 | 29 |
| 31 | Armthorpe Welfare | v | Squires Gate | 3-1 | 68 |
| 32 | Harborough Town | v | Boston Town | 0-2 | 107 |
| 33 | Heanor Town | v | Arnold Town | 4-2 | 147 |
| 34 | Greenwood Meadows | v | Teversal | 3-2 | 30 |
| 35 | Blackstones | v | Holbrook Sports | 1-3 | 70 |
| 36 | Pinxton | v | Heather St Johns | 1-2 | 84 |
| 37 | Ellistown | v | Shirebrook Town | 0-3 | 57 |
| 38 | Blidworth Welfare | v | Ibstock United | 1-2 | 37 |
| | (at Ibstock United FC) (tie awarded to Blidworth Welfare – Ibstock United removed) | | | | |
| 39 | Radford | v | Long Eaton United | 0-2 | 56 |
| 40 | Anstey Nomads | v | Sutton Town | 1-2 | 103 |
| 41 | Gedling MW | v | Kirby Muxloe | 2-3 | 76 |
| 42 | Lutterworth Athletic | v | Spalding United | 0-2 | 80 |
| 43 | South Normanton Athletic | v | Graham St Prims | 0-4 | 52 |
| 44 | Louth Town | v | Dunkirk | 1-3 | 100 |
| 45 | Blaby & Whetstone Athletic | v | Sleaford Town | 0-1 | 54 |
| 46 | Borrowash Victoria | v | St Andrews | 3-0 | 44 |
| 47 | Basford United | v | Holbeach United | 1-0 | 83 |
| 48 | Leek CSOB | v | Bewdley Town | 0-3 | 46 |
| 49 | Stafford Town | v | Tipton Town | 0-3 | 66 |
| 50 | Bartley Green | v | Pilkington XXX | 4-2 | 30 |
| 51 | Nuneaton Griff | v | Gornal Athletic | 0-2 | 50 |
| 52 | Bridgnorth Town | v | Racing Club Warwick | 5-1 | 75 |
| 53 | Pershore Town | v | AFC Wulfrunians | 2-5 | 42 |
| 54 | Bustleholme | v | Bilston Town | 0-4 | 61 |
| 55 | Bloxwich United | v | Shifnal Town | 1-3 | 42 |
| 56 | Pegasus Juniors | v | Wolverhampton SC | 3-0 | 48 |
| 57 | Alvechurch | v | Walsall Wood | 2-3 | 91 |
| 58 | Causeway United | v | Highgate United | 3-2aet | 59 |
| 59 | Lye Town | v | Cradley Town | 4-2 | 91 |
| 60 | Rocester | v | Castle Vale JKS | 4-0 | 83 |
| 61 | Southam United | v | Continental Star (14/9) | 4-3 | 129 |
| 62 | Shawbury United | v | Bromyard Town | 8-3 | 46 |
| 63 | Stratford Town | v | Eccleshall | 1-3 | 136 |
| 64 | Boldmere St Michaels | v | Black Country Rangers | 0-4 | 25 |

FAV 1P: Andy Atkin, Rye United (right) has his powerful header saved by Horley Town's 'keeper. Whilst below the same 'keeper has no chance as Rye's Sam Adams scores from the penalty spot. Photos: Roger Turner.

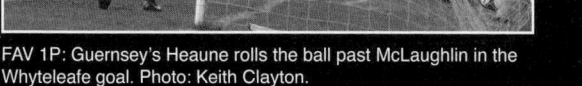

FAV 1P: Guernsey's Heaune rolls the ball past McLaughlin in the Whyteleafe goal. Photo: Keith Clayton.

(Above) FAV 1P: Black Country Rangers striker, Liam Hughes, powers past Westfields defender, Dene Whittal-Williams to score his and his sides second goal in their 4-1 away win. Photo: Jonathan Holloway.

FAV 1P: Action from the Cheltenham Saracens v Ardley United match which Ardley won 2-1. Photo: Peter Barnes.

# SECOND QUALIFYING ROUND
## SATURDAY 15 SEPTEMBER 2012 - WINNERS RECEIVE £700

| | | | | |
|---|---|---|---|---|
| 65 | Rushden & Higham United v | Eynesbury Rovers | 0-3 | 49 |
| 66 | Cambridge University Press v | Thrapston Town | 3-0 | 62 |
| 67 | Stewarts & Lloyds Corby v | Raunds Town | 3-1 | 21 |
| 68 | Swaffham Town v | Wellingborough Whitworths | 2-1 | 63 |
| 69 | AFC Rushden & Diamonds v | Fakenham Town | 4-1 | 607 |
| 70 | Thetford Town v | Godmanchester Rovers | 0-3 | 60 |
| 71 | Bugbrooke St Michaels v | Yaxley | 1-2 | 45 |
| 72 | Downham Town v | Northampton Spencer | 0-2 | 62 |
| 73 | Dereham Town v | Cogenhoe United | 2-1 | 110 |
| 74 | Desborough Town v | Irchester United | 2-0 | 62 |
| 75 | Wivenhoe Town v | Hullbridge Sports | 1-1aet | |
| | Hullbridge Sports v | Wivenhoe Town (18/9) | 2-0 | 51 |
| 76 | Walsham Le Willows v | Stansted | 5-0 | 58 |
| 77 | Whitton United v | FC Clacton | 3-2aet | 64 |
| 78 | Norwich United v | Haverhill Sports Association | 0-1 | 32 |
| | (at Fakenham Town FC) | | | |
| 79 | Haverhill Rovers v | Saffron Walden Town | 4-2 | 250 |
| 80 | Gorleston v | Newmarket Town | 2-0 | 92 |
| 81 | Woodbridge Town v | Long Melford | 2-3 | 63 |
| 82 | Diss Town v | Halstead Town | 3-1 | 96 |
| 83 | Team Bury v | Brightlingsea Regent (14/9) | 2-3aet | 58 |
| 84 | Stanway Rovers v | Hadleigh United | 1-4 | 80 |
| 85 | Felixstowe & Walton United v | Ipswich Wanderers | 0-1 | 92 |
| 86 | Hoddesdon Town v | FC Romania | 7-0 | 46 |
| 87 | Feltham v | Hanwell Town | 2-6 | 53 |
| 88 | Hillingdon Borough v | Clapton | 1-2 | 25 |
| 89 | Potton United v | Hatfield Town | 1-2 | 58 |
| 90 | Biggleswade United v | Colney Heath | 1-3 | 48 |
| 91 | Haringey Borough v | Hadley | 0-4 | 34 |
| 92 | Hertford Town v | Crawley Green | 2-2aet | 123 |
| | Crawley Green v | Hertford Town (19/9) | 2-3 | 43 |
| 93 | St Margaretsbury v | London Lions | 0-3 | 35 |
| 94 | Cranfield United v | Berkhamsted | 1-2 | 40 |
| 95 | Barking v | London Tigers | 1-0 | 39 |
| 96 | Sawbridgeworth Town v | Sporting Bengal United | 4-5aet | 36 |
| 97 | Oxhey Jets v | Bedfont Sports | 5-2 | 50 |
| 98 | Wembley v | London Colney | 4-1 | 69 |
| 99 | Cockfosters v | AFC Kempston Rovers | 3-2 | 60 |
| 100 | Codicote v | Langford | 2-0aet | 33 |
| 101 | Holyport v | Winslow United | 3-0 | 52 |
| 102 | Fairford Town v | Hook Norton | 3-3aet | 34 |
| | Hook Norton v | Fairford Town (18/9) | 0-3 | 41 |
| 103 | Amersham Town v | Carterton | 4-2 | 46 |
| 104 | Kidlington v | Bracknell Town | 3-2 | 51 |
| 105 | Holmer Green v | Witney Town | 0-6 | 54 |
| 106 | Sandhurst Town v | Milton United | 6-1 | 40 |
| 107 | Newbury v | Lydney Town | 6-0 | 44 |
| 108 | Highmoor Ibis v | Wokingham & Emmbrook | 1-3aet | 52 |
| 109 | Cove v | Wantage Town | 1-6 | 33 |
| 110 | Shrivenham v | Cheltenham Saracens | 0-4 | 52 |
| 111 | Chinnor v | Ascot United | 0-1 | 271 |
| 112 | Thame United v | Buckingham Athletic | 3-2 | 80 |
| 113 | Fisher v | Canterbury City | 1-2 | 85 |
| 114 | Pagham v | Chichester City | 3-1 | 83 |
| 115 | Mole Valley SCR v | Frimley Green (14/9) | 0-1 | 76 |
| 116 | Peacehaven & Telscombe v | AFC Uckfield | 5-2 | 95 |
| 117 | Beckenham Town v | Wick | 3-0 | 58 |
| 118 | Ash United v | Banstead Athletic | 4-1 | 41 |
| 119 | Lingfield v | Dorking Wanderers | 3-2 | 45 |
| 120 | Cobham v | AFC Croydon Athletic | 0-1 | 30 |
| 121 | Ringmer v | Littlehampton Town | 1-2aet | 61 |
| 122 | Horley Town v | Seaford Town | 4-1 | 73 |
| 123 | Camberley Town v | Colliers Wood United | 1-4 | 36 |
| 124 | Arundel v | Deal Town | 1-2 | 57 |
| 125 | Horsham YMCA v | Holmesdale | 4-2 | 57 |
| 126 | East Preston v | Croydon | 0-1 | 48 |
| 127 | St Francis Rangers v | Ashford United | 2-0 | 83 |
| 128 | Guernsey v | Farnham Town | 2-0 | 1026 |
| 129 | Sevenoaks Town v | Chessington & Hook United | 3-2aet | 38 |
| 130 | Lordswood v | Raynes Park Vale | 2-1 | 61 |
| 131 | Whitchurch United v | Bristol Academy | 3-3aet | |
| | Bristol Academy won 4-2 on kicks from the penalty mark | | | |
| 132 | Fleet Spurs v | Calne Town | 0-3 | 15 |
| 133 | Bradford Town v | Downton | 1-2 | 68 |
| 134 | Hayling United v | AFC Portchester | 5-2 | 29 |
| 135 | Blackfield & Langley v | Bristol Manor Farm | 3-2 | 58 |
| 136 | Longwell Green Sports v | Cowes Sports | 2-0 | 53 |
| 137 | Horndean v | Melksham Town | 4-3 | 45 |
| 138 | Westbury United v | Romsey Town | 4-1 | 54 |
| 139 | New Milton Town v | Lymington Town | 3-1 | 50 |
| 140 | United Services Portsmouth v | Swanage Town & Herston | 0-3 | 23 |
| 141 | Hamworthy United v | Fawley | 1-5 | 73 |
| 142 | Cadbury Heath v | Roman Glass St George | 2-1 | 67 |
| 143 | Winterbourne United v | GE Hamble | 0-3 | 48 |
| 144 | Fareham Town v | Alton Town | 3-6 | 97 |
| 145 | Warminster Town v | Petersfield Town | 0-4 | 120 |
| 146 | Newport (IW) v | Alresford Town | 2-1aet | 136 |
| 147 | Odd Down v | Cullompton Rangers | 8-1 | 32 |
| 148 | Barnstaple Town v | Wellington | 2-1aet | 79 |
| 149 | Brislington v | Hengrove Athletic | 1-0 | 72 |
| 150 | Spenny City v | Exmouth Town | 0-1 | 54 |
| 151 | Bovey Tracey v | Welton Rovers | 3-0 | 46 |
| 152 | St Blazey v | Bishop Sutton | 3-1 | 76 |
| 153 | AFC St Austell v | Ashton & Backwell United | 1-0aet | 90 |
| 154 | Buckland Athletic v | Porthleven | 7-1 | 89 |
| 155 | Minehead v | Bodmin Town | 0-4 | 84 |
| 156 | Bridport v | Sherborne Town | 0-3 | 145 |
| 157 | Street v | Gillingham Town | 5-0 | 74 |
| 158 | Radstock Town v | Saltash United | 1-2aet | 64 |

# FIRST ROUND PROPER
## SATURDAY 13 OCTOBER 2012 - WINNERS RECEIVE £900

| # | Home | | Away | Score | Ref |
|---|---|---|---|---|---|
| 1 | Sunderland RCA | v | Bishop Auckland | 1-0 | 147 |
| 2 | Newton Aycliffe | v | Esh Winning | 1-2 | 141 |
| 3 | Bridlington Town | v | SPENNYMOOR TOWN | 1-5 | 332 |
| 4 | Thackley | v | Scarborough Athletic | 3-2 | 202 |
| 5 | South Shields | v | Shildon (24/10) | 2-3 | |
| 6 | Jarrow Roofing Boldon CA | v | Norton & Stockton Ancients (23/10) | 1-0 | 42 |
| 7 | Morpeth Town | v | Guisborough Town | 1-0aet | 128 |
| 8 | Pickering Town | v | Durham City | 4-1 | 159 |
| 9 | Penrith | v | Bedlington Terriers | 1-2 | 145 |
| 10 | Northallerton Town | v | Consett | 1-1aet | 154 |
| | Consett | v | Northallerton Town (16/10) | 3-2 | 89 |
| 11 | Barnoldswick Town | v | Maine Road (23/10) | 4-2 | 164 |
| | (13/10 - tie abandoned after 12 minutes due to injury to player, 0-0) | | | | |
| 12 | Runcorn Linnets | v | Winsford United | 1-3 | 315 |
| 13 | Bootle | v | Stockport Sports | 3-2 | 151 |
| 14 | Hall Road Rangers | v | Brighouse Town | 2-5 | 50 |
| 15 | Bottesford Town | v | Rochdale Town | 2-1 | 71 |
| 16 | St Helens Town | v | Parkgate | 2-4aet | 45 |
| 17 | Nostell MW | v | Formby | 1-2 | 43 |
| 18 | AFC Liverpool | v | Armthorpe Welfare | 1-3 | 152 |
| 19 | AFC Emley | v | Congleton Town | 1-0 | 151 |
| 20 | Cheadle Town | v | Wigan Robin Park | 1-3 | 62 |
| 21 | Shepshed Dynamo | v | Blidworth Welfare | 2-0 | 104 |
| 22 | Shirebrook Town | v | Heanor Town | 1-1aet | 153 |
| | Heanor Town | v | Shirebrook Town (17/10) | 2-4 | 138 |
| 23 | Deeping Rangers | v | Quorn | 2-1 | 99 |
| 24 | Spalding United | v | Retford United | 3-2 | 147 |
| 25 | Dunkirk | v | Boston Town | 1-2 | 62 |
| 26 | Graham St Prims | v | Holbrook Sports | 2-3 | 100 |
| 27 | Heather St Johns | v | Long Eaton United | 0-1 | 75 |
| 28 | Kirby Muxloe | v | Basford United | 1-4 | 64 |
| 29 | Sutton Town | v | Sleaford Town | 3-1 | 85 |
| 30 | Greenwood Meadows | v | Borrowash Victoria | 3-3aet | 57 |
| | Borrowash Victoria | v | Greenwood Meadows (16/10) | 5-2aet | 58 |
| | (at Graham St Prims FC) | | | | |
| 31 | Coventry Sphinx | v | Bilston Town | 5-4aet | 101 |
| 32 | AFC Wulfrunians | v | Tipton Town | 3-0 | 129 |
| 33 | Westfields | v | Black Country Rangers | 1-4 | 65 |
| 34 | Causeway United | v | Stourport Swifts (14/10) | 2-0 | 126 |
| 35 | Rocester | v | Bewdley Town | 4-0 | 117 |
| 36 | Lye Town | v | Gornal Athletic | 1-3 | 162 |
| 37 | Bridgnorth Town | v | Shifnal Town | 3-1aet | 117 |
| 38 | Walsall Wood | v | Eccleshall | 2-0 | 64 |
| 39 | Pegasus Juniors | v | Southam United | 1-2 | 42 |
| 40 | Bartley Green | v | Shawbury United | 0-5 | |
| 41 | Long Buckby | v | Northampton Spencer | 2-2aet | 64 |
| | Northampton Spencer | v | Long Buckby (16/10) | 1-0 | 78 |
| 42 | Yaxley | v | AFC Rushden & Diamonds | 1-2 | 250 |
| 43 | Godmanchester Rovers | v | Cambridge University Press | 1-3aet | 160 |
| 44 | Ely City | v | Eynesbury Rovers | 2-0 | 81 |
| 45 | Swaffham Town | v | Desborough Town | 0-6 | 105 |
| 46 | Dereham Town | v | Stewarts & Lloyds Corby | 4-1 | 157 |
| 47 | Whitton United | v | Brightlingsea Regent | 0-1 | 64 |
| 48 | Hullbridge Sports | v | Diss Town | 0-2 | 56 |
| 49 | Hadleigh United | v | Walsham Le Willows | 1-1aet | 124 |
| | Walsham Le Willows | v | Hadleigh United (17/10) | 0-2aet | 118 |
| 50 | Long Melford | v | Brantham Athletic | 0-8 | 14 |
| 51 | Haverhill Sports Association | v | Ipswich Wanderers (14/10) | 3-2 | 145 |
| 52 | Takeley | v | Great Wakering Rovers | 3-2aet | 81 |
| 53 | Burnham Ramblers | v | Gorleston | 3-1 | 72 |
| 54 | Haverhill Rovers | v | Southend Manor | 0-2 | 110 |
| 55 | Colney Heath | v | Sporting Bengal United | 3-2 | 50 |
| 56 | London Lions | v | Codicote (14/10) | 2-1aet | 27 |
| | (at Hemel Hempstead Town FC) | | | | |
| 57 | Oxhey Jets | v | Hanwell Town | 1-1aet | 56 |
| | Hanwell Town | v | Oxhey Jets (16/10) | 0-1 | 56 |
| 58 | AFC Dunstable | v | Hatfield Town | 1-3 | 44 |
| 59 | Hadley | v | Berkhamsted (14/10) | 4-4aet | 62 |
| | Berkhamsted | v | Hadley (16/10) | 2-0 | 80 |
| 60 | Clapton | v | Cockfosters | 0-3 | 84 |
| 61 | Barking | v | Dunstable Town | 0-3 | 80 |
| 62 | Hanworth Villa | v | Wembley | 2-0 | 83 |
| 63 | Hoddesdon Town | v | Hertford Town | 3-5 | 144 |
| 64 | Witney Town | v | Ascot United | 0-2 | 79 |
| 65 | Wokingham & Emmbrook | v | Marlow (14/10) | 0-1aet | 202 |
| 66 | Thame United | v | Fairford Town | 3-2 | 213 |
| 67 | Aylesbury United | v | Kidlington (14/10) | 0-2 | 59 |
| 68 | Sandhurst Town | v | Wantage Town | 1-8 | 32 |
| 69 | Amersham Town | v | Flackwell Heath | 4-3aet | 67 |
| 70 | Cheltenham Saracens | v | Ardley United | 1-2 | 46 |
| 71 | Oxford City Nomads | v | Windsor (14/10) | 2-1 | 50 |
| 72 | Holyport | v | Newbury | 1-4 | 50 |
| 73 | Pagham | v | Horsham YMCA | 2-2aet | 84 |
| | Horsham YMCA | v | Pagham (17/10) | 1-0 | 82 |
| 74 | VCD Athletic | v | Erith & Belvedere | 0-0aet | 101 |
| | Erith & Belvedere | v | VCD Athletic (16/10) | 3-2 | 68 |
| 75 | Sevenoaks Town | v | Ash United | 2-4 | 54 |
| 76 | Littlehampton Town | v | Beckenham Town | 2-1 | 141 |
| 77 | Erith Town | v | AFC Croydon Athletic | 3-2 | 37 |
| 78 | Egham Town | v | Lordswood | 2-3 | 48 |
| 79 | Lingfield | v | Colliers Wood United | 1-2 | 50 |
| 80 | Lancing | v | Peacehaven & Telscombe | 0-5 | 156 |
| 81 | St Francis Rangers | v | Croydon | 0-2 | 73 |
| 82 | Rye United | v | Horley Town | 3-2 | 89 |
| 83 | Whyteleafe | v | Guernsey | 2-3 | 252 |
| 84 | Deal Town | v | Hassocks | 2-0 | 162 |
| 85 | Frimley Green | v | Canterbury City | 2-1aet | 74 |
| 86 | Christchurch | v | Horndean | 1-3aet | 65 |
| 87 | Longwell Green Sports | v | Calne Town | 2-0 | 97 |
| 88 | Moneyfields | v | Hallen | 6-0 | 70 |
| 89 | Fawley | v | Bemerton Heath Harlequins | 1-2 | 51 |
| 90 | GE Hamble | v | Bristol Academy | 3-1 | 57 |
| 91 | Cadbury Heath | v | Hayling United | 3-2 | 92 |
| 92 | Blackfield & Langley | v | Westbury United | 5-1 | 74 |
| 93 | Swanage Town & Herston | v | Newport (IW) | 0-2 | 203 |
| 94 | New Milton Town | v | Alton Town | 2-1 | 52 |
| 95 | Downton | v | Petersfield Town | 2-1 | 99 |
| 96 | Saltash United | v | Buckland Athletic | 0-1 | 125 |
| 97 | AFC St Austell | v | Bovey Tracey | 4-3 | 132 |
| 98 | St Blazey | v | Barnstaple Town | 2-1 | 83 |
| 99 | Street | v | Odd Down | 0-1 | 76 |
| 100 | Exmouth Town | v | Sherborne Town | 1-2 | 190 |
| 101 | Bodmin Town | v | Brislington | 3-2 | 74 |

# SECOND ROUND PROPER
## SATURDAY 17 NOVEMBER 2012 - WINNERS RECEIVE £1,200

| | | | | | | | | | |
|---|---|---|---|---|---|---|---|---|---|
| AFC Emley | v | Bottesford Town | 3-2 | 118 | 34 | Berkhamsted | v | Southend Manor | 1-2 | 103 |
| Bedlington Terriers | v | Wigan Robin Park | 1-2 | 116 | 35 | Haverhill Sports Association | v | Dereham Town | 2-1 | 140 |
| Pickering Town | v | Billingham Synthonia | 2-3 | 202 | 36 | Takeley | v | Hertford Town | 0-1 | 143 |
| Dunston UTS | v | West Auckland Town | 5-0 | 375 | 37 | St Ives Town | v | Wisbech Town | 2-2aet | 483 |
| Ashington | v | Sunderland RCA | 2-1 | 175 | | Wisbech Town | v | St Ives Town (20/11) | 2-1 | 446 |
| Staveley MW | v | Brighouse Town | 1-3aet | 130 | 38 | Newport Pagnell Town | v | Enfield 1893 | 1-2 | 159 |
| Barnoldswick Town | v | Armthorpe Welfare | 5-2 | 172 | 39 | Burnham Ramblers | v | Bethnal Green United | 1-2 | 56 |
| Consett | v | Shildon | 2-3 | 201 | 40 | Brantham Athletic | v | Cambridge University Press | 3-2 | 60 |
| Winsford United | v | Morpeth Town | 1-0 | 128 | 41 | **TUNBRIDGE WELLS** | v | Wantage Town | 2-0 | 159 |
| Whitley Bay | v | Jarrow Roofing Boldon CA | 2-1 | 352 | 42 | Amersham Town | v | Rye United | 1-0 | 78 |
| Runcorn Town | v | Formby | 2-1 | | | (tie awarded to Rye United – Amersham Town removed) | | | | |
| **SPENNYMOOR TOWN** | v | Newcastle Benfield | 5-1 | 271 | 43 | Marlow | v | Kidlington | 2-4 | 107 |
| Parkgate | v | Esh Winning | 4-2 | 106 | 44 | Ascot United | v | Reading Town | 3-0 | 86 |
| Bootle | v | Thackley (20/11) | 1-3 | 56 | 45 | Croydon | v | Newbury | 9-2 | 65 |
| (at Thackley FC) | | | | | 46 | Oxford City Nomads | v | Peacehaven & Telscombe | 0-3 | |
| Sutton Town | v | Tividale | 2-1 | 85 | 47 | Deal Town | v | Binfield | 2-5 | 162 |
| Bridgnorth Town | v | Boston Town | 2-3 | 101 | 48 | Ash United | v | South Park | 0-2 | 52 |
| AFC Rushden & Diamonds | v | Basford United | 5-3 | 558 | 49 | Erith & Belvedere | v | Frimley Green (18/11) | 5-1 | 85 |
| Oadby Town | v | Spalding United | 2-3 | 203 | 50 | Littlehampton Town | v | Hanworth Villa | 1-1aet | 188 |
| Shirebrook Town | v | Walsall Wood | 3-3aet | 149 | | Hanworth Villa | v | Littlehampton Town (4/12) | 2-1 | |
| Walsall Wood | v | Shirebrook Town (20/11) | 3-0 | 136 | 51 | Horsham YMCA | v | Ardley United | 0-1 | 80 |
| Southam United | v | Long Eaton United (4/12) | 0-1 | 62 | 52 | Thame United | v | Lordswood | 2-3 | 168 |
| (at Coventry Sphinx FC) | | | | | 53 | Erith Town | v | Guernsey | 3-4aet | 123 |
| AFC Wulfrunians | v | Shawbury United | 5-3aet | 120 | 54 | Colliers Wood United | v | Old Woodstock Town | | |
| Causeway United | v | Desborough Town | 2-1 | 70 | | (walkover for Colliers Wood United – Old Woodstock Town removed) | | | | |
| Shepshed Dynamo | v | Rocester | 1-3 | 130 | 55 | Horndean | v | Willand Rovers | 4-3aet | 60 |
| Black Country Rangers | v | Holbrook Sports | 2-3 | 59 | 56 | Buckland Athletic | v | Downton | 2-5 | 108 |
| Coventry Sphinx | v | Gornal Athletic | 1-8 | | 57 | Sherborne Town | v | St Blazey | 1-4 | 157 |
| Deeping Rangers | v | Norton United | 0-1 | 106 | 58 | Newport (IW) | v | Cadbury Heath | 1-0 | 201 |
| Borrowash Victoria | v | Northampton Spencer | 1-0 | 116 | 59 | AFC St Austell | v | Bemerton Heath Harlequins | 2-3 | 142 |
| Ampthill Town | v | Diss Town | 1-0 | 138 | 60 | Larkhall Athletic | v | Longwell Green Sports | 0-0aet | 110 |
| London Lions | v | Brightlingsea Regent (18/11) | 2-3 | 48 | | Longwell Green Sports | v | Larkhall Athletic (1/12) | 1-2 | 82 |
| (at Hemel Hempstead Town FC) | | | | | 61 | Bodmin Town | v | Odd Down | 5-1 | 64 |
| Colney Heath | v | Hadleigh United | 1-2 | 79 | 62 | Blackfield & Langley | v | Bournemouth | 1-0 | 57 |
| Oxhey Jets | v | Cockfosters | 4-0 | 67 | 63 | Moneyfields | v | GE Hamble | 0-1 | 60 |
| Peterborough Northern Star | v | Dunstable Town | 1-3 | 72 | 64 | New Milton Town | v | Bitton | 1-2 | 77 |
| Hatfield Town | v | Ely City | 3-7 | 56 | | | | | | |

FAV 2P: Gareth Tucker, Wantage Town's goalkeeper, cut out a Tunbridge Wells attack. Photo: Roger Turner.

FAV 2P: Andrew Claydon, Ely City, nets the first of his hat-trick in his side's 7-3 win over Hatfield Town. Photo: Gordon Whittington.

(Below) FAV 3P: Ampthill's Michael McKenzie is on his knees and Hertford's 'keeper is airborne to save the former's header Photo: Gordon Whittington

(Below) FAV 4P: Gornal Athletic (light shirts) are on the attack against Wisbech. Photo: Jonathan Holloway.

FAV SF1: Jon Pilbeam scores from the penalty spot against Shildon. Photo: Roger Turner

FAV 4P: Paul Lyon's spot kick gets him on the scoresheet in Ampthill's comfortable 3-0 win over Enfield. Photo: Gordon Whittington.

# THIRD ROUND PROPER
## SATURDAY 8 DECEMBER 2012 - WINNERS RECEIVE £1,500

| # | Home | | Away | Score | Att |
|---|---|---|---|---|---|
| 1 | Shildon | v | Parkgate (15/12) | 3-1 | 157 |
| 2 | Thackley | v | Wisbech Town | 2-4 | 162 |
| 3 | Ashington | v | AFC Rushden & Diamonds | 2-1 | 444 |
| 4 | Rocester | v | Long Eaton Utd | 2-1 | 147 |
| 5 | Walsall Wood | v | Wigan Robin Park | 4-1 | 176 |
| | (at Sutton Coldfield Town FC) | | | | |
| 6 | Brighouse Town | v | Holbrook Sports | 4-1 | 97 |
| 7 | AFC Wulfrunians | v | Borrowash Victoria | 2-3aet | 121 |
| 8 | Winsford United | v | Runcorn Town | 1-3 | 129 |
| 9 | Whitley Bay | v | Causeway United | 6-0 | 382 |
| 10 | SPENNYMOOR TOWN | v | Billingham Synthonia (15/12) | 2-0 | 201 |
| 11 | Norton United | v | Dunston UTS | 0-2 | 147 |
| 12 | Sutton Town | v | Spalding United (15/12) | 1-5 | 99 |
| 13 | Barnoldswick Town | v | AFC Emley | 1-3 | 202 |
| 14 | Gornal Atheltic | v | Boston Town | 1-0 | 70 |
| 15 | Brightlingsea Regent | v | Brantham Athletic | 2-3 | 226 |
| 16 | Lordswood | v | Southend Manor | 3-0 | 220 |
| 17 | Rye United | v | South Park (18/12) | 1-0 | 119 |
| 18 | Guernsey | v | Erith & Belvedere (9/12) | 4-0 | 1005 |
| 19 | Croydon | v | Hanworth Villa | 0-2 | 68 |
| 20 | Haverhill Sports Association | v | Peacehaven & Telscombe | 3-4 | 109 |
| 21 | Enfield 1893 | v | Dunstable Town | 1-0 | 85 |
| 22 | Hadleigh United | v | Oxhey Jets | 2-0 | 103 |
| 23 | Binfield | v | TUNBRIDGE WELLS | 1-2 | 212 |
| 24 | Bethnal Green United | v | Ely City (15/12) | 1-3 | 44 |
| 25 | Ampthill Town | v | Hertford Town | 1-0 | 118 |
| 26 | Colliers Wood United | v | Ascot United | 2-3 | 70 |
| 27 | Larkhall Athletic | v | Kidlington | 3-2 | 93 |
| 28 | St Blazey | v | Bitton | 0-3 | 102 |
| 29 | GE Hamble | v | Blackfield & Langley | 0-2 | 81 |
| 30 | Bodmin Town | v | Downton | 2-0 | 98 |
| 31 | Ardley United | v | Newport (IW) | 1-4 | 71 |
| 32 | Horndean | v | Bemerton Heath Harlequins | 0-5 | 80 |

# FOURTH ROUND PROPER
## SATURDAY 19 JANUARY 2013 - WINNERS RECEIVE £2,000

| # | Home | | Away | Score | Att |
|---|---|---|---|---|---|
| 1 | Gornal Athletic | v | Wisbech Town (2/2) | 4-2aet | 260 |
| 2 | Bodmin Town | v | Ashington (26/1) | 3-2 | 325 |
| 3 | AFC Emley | v | Hadleigh United (2/2) | 0-1 | 305 |
| 4 | TUNBRIDGE WELLS | v | Dunston UTS (9/2) | 1-0 | 508 |
| 5 | Rye United | v | Guernsey (26/1) | 5-6aet | 276 |
| 6 | Bitton | v | Shildon (26/1) | 0-2 | 264 |
| 7 | Larkhall Athletic | v | Peacehaven & Telscombe (26/1) | 2-1 | 155 |
| 8 | Brantham Athletic | v | Whitley Bay (26/1) | 1-0aet | 422 |
| 9 | Newport (IW) | v | Brighouse Town (26/1) | 2-1 | 446 |
| 10 | Bemerton Heath Harlequins | v | Blackfield & Langley (26/1) | 3-2 | 155 |
| 11 | Ampthill Town | v | Enfield 1893 (2/2) | 3-0 | 148 |
| 12 | Ely City | v | Spalding United (29/1) | 1-2 | 212 |
| 13 | SPENNYMOOR TOWN | v | Lordswood (2/2) | 3-1 | 468 |
| 14 | Rocester | v | Runcorn Town (2/2) | 1-2 | 218 |
| 15 | Borrowash Victoria | v | Ascot United (2/2) | 0-3 | 157 |
| 16 | Walsall Wood | v | Hanworth Villa (16/2) | 3-2 | 210 |
| | (at Hanworth Villa FC) | | | | |

# FIFTH ROUND PROPER
## SATURDAY 9 FEBRUARY 2013 - WINNERS RECEIVE £2,500

| # | Home | | Away | Score | Att |
|---|---|---|---|---|---|
| 1 | SPENNYMOOR TOWN | v | Bemerton Heath Harlequins | 4-2 | 398 |
| 2 | Newport (IW) | v | Ascot United (16/2) | 2-2aet | 474 |
| | (at Ascot United FC) | | | | |
| | Ascot United | v | Newport (IW) (19/2) | 2-1 | 359 |
| 3 | Spalding United | v | Guernsey | 1-3 | 392 |
| 4 | Brantham Athletic | v | Shildon | 1-4 | 302 |
| 5 | Ampthill Town | v | Hadleigh United | 1-2 | 182 |
| 6 | Runcorn Town | v | Walsall Wood (23/2) | 1-2aet | 233 |
| 7 | Larkhall Athletic | v | TUNBRIDGE WELLS (23/2) | 3-4aet | 280 |
| 8 | Bodmin Town | v | Gornal Athletic | 0-1 | 355 |

# SIXTH ROUND PROPER
## SATURDAY 2 MARCH 2013 - WINNERS RECEIVE £3,500

| # | Home | | Away | Score | Att |
|---|---|---|---|---|---|
| 1 | Walsall Wood | v | Guernsey | 0-0aet | 656 |
| | Guernsey | v | Walsall Wood (9/3) | 3-1 | 2597 |
| 2 | Shildon | v | Ascot United | 1-1aet | 448 |
| | Ascot United | v | Shildon (9/3) | 1-4 | 780 |
| 3 | SPENNYMOOR TOWN | v | Gornal Athletic | 3-1 | 684 |
| 4 | TUNBRIDGE WELLS | v | Hadleigh United | 2-0 | 1180 |

# SEMI FINALS
## WINNERS RECEIVE £5,000

| 1ST LEG – SATURDAY 23 MARCH 2013 | | | | | |
|---|---|---|---|---|---|
| 1 | Guernsey | v | Spennymoor Town | 1-3 | 4290 |
| 2 | Tunbridge Wells | v | Shildon | 2-0 | 1754 |

| 2ND LEG – SATURDAY 30 March 2013 | | | | | |
|---|---|---|---|---|---|
| 1 | SPENNYMOOR TOWN | v | Guernsey (5.30) | 1-0 | 1638 |
| 2 | Shildon | v | TUNBRIDGE WELLS | 3-2aet | 901 |

# The Final...

## SPENNYMOOR TOWN 2
(Cogdon 18, Graydon 80)
## TUNBRIDGE WELLS 1
(Stanford 78)

### Wembley Stadium        Att: 16,751

| SPENNYMOOR TOWN | TUNBRIDGE WELLS |
|---|---|
| Robert Dean | Chris Oladogba |
| Kallum Griffiths | Jason Bourne |
| Leon Ryan | Scott Whibley |
| Chris Mason | Perry Spackman |
| Stephen Capper | Lewis Mingle |
| Keith Graydon | Jon Pilbeam |
| Lewis Dodds | (Richard Sinden 85 min) |
| Wayne Phillips | Andy McMath |
| (Anthony Peacock 64 min) | Joe Fuller |
| Joe Walton | (Tom Davey 58 min) |
| (Andrew Stephenson 73 min) | Andy Irvine |
| Mark Davison | Carl Connell |
| (Michael Rae 76 min) | (Jack Harris 58 min) |
| Gavin Congdon | Josh Stanford |
| | |
| **Subs not used** | **Subs not used** |
| David Knight (gk) | Michael Czanner (gk) |
| Steven Richardson | Andy Boyle |

Referee Michael Naylor (Sheffield & Hallamshire).
Assisted by Ian Hussin and Dan Robathan.
Four official - Stephen Martin.

Photo: Eric Marsh.

Most regular, annual spectators of both Trophy and Vase finals would agree that the Vase usually provides the greater entertainment. The play seems more spontaneous, the players more adventurous and less primarily concentrated on defence. Coupled with this in general the players are based in the communities they represent and thus closer to their supporters in everyday life. Very much to the credit of the Kent Leaguers, and I suspect unusually, none of their players is paid.

There was again much to enjoy in the 2013 final which witnessed yet another victory for a Northern League team, a fifth successive triumph for that competition. There could be no arguments about it either: the winning team, thrice recent winner of the domestic league, was deservedly the victor. Someone surmised at the final whistle that Spennymoor had just toyed with Tunbridge Wells, citing the immediate response to the Wells' equaliser by going ahead again. I would not subscribe to that view. There was a gap in the performance of the two teams but not by any stretch of the imagination a gulf.

It was however the Kent representatives who pressed first when Josh Stanford burst through, evading three tacklers before Robert Dean parried and then scrambled away his fierce shot. Mainly though it was Tunbridge who were under pressure, Chris Mason and the physically strong Perry Spackman much to the fore in repelling Spennymoor attacks. Neat interchanging of passes by Keith Graydon, eventually man of the match, and Joe Walton carved an opportunity for Gavin Cogdon, scorer of eleven goals already en route to Wembley, who required no second invitation to head powerfully past keeper Chris Oladogba. Cogdon, cupping his ears to accentuate the silence of the Wells fans, and somersaulting in celebration, made certain he would be the target of Kent booing for the rest of the match. He was not to blame though for the "We pay your benefits" chant which is too often heard at such regional competitions from those who have regrettably thoughtlessly swallowed the stereotype image portrayed by elements of the popular press.

As the half closed it was Spennymoor threatening to double their lead, Cogdon again to the fore, abetted well by Mark Davison, with both provided materially by Wayne Phillips' penetrating crosses. Tunbridge Wells had really only tested Dean once in the whole forty five minutes and were fortunate to be going in with only a deficit of one.

This they all but cleared with their first attack of the second half when skipper Jason Bourne (yes, he's heard all the banter associated with his name)

Spennymoor's Mark Davison fires a shot past Perry Spackman.
Photo: Alan Coomes

troubled Dean with a deep cross which the keeper first dropped before falling on it at the foot of the post just as Andy Irvine threatened to force it home. That was just a false alarm though as Spennymoor continued to dominate, being noticeably much slicker in passing and organised when defending. Cogdon almost got a second, Oladogba just managing to parry over before falling to his left to deny Davison and then fractionally beating Cogdon to a through ball on the edge of the penalty area. An unusual sight these days was an indirect free kick for handling a back pass in the area but Oladogba was untroubled by Graydon's shot soaring way over.

Wells' spirits were raised when Spackman nearly hooked in Stanford's free kick and then headed close from Andy McMath's corner. Then, with twelve minutes

Spennymoor's Kallum Griffiths and Tunbridge's Josh Standford challenge for the ball. Photo: Peter Barnes.

to go, they were justifiably elated. A weak punch out by Dean fell to Stanford near the penalty spot. He required no second invitation to volley home. All square. How the Wells fans crowed. Unfortunately only two minutes later they were silenced. Their defence cleared only to Graydon whose scorcher from eighteen yards found the net before anyone could move. His energetic performance throughout the ninety minutes made him a worthy scorer.

The Tunbridge defence get up highest to clear the ball to safety. Photo: Eric Marsh.

The Kent Leaguers tried their hardest to hit back in the remaining minutes. A free kick from Tom Davey, Jon Pilbeam's foray down the right and McMath's corner threatened only minimally. At one end of the stadium noise from the reds' supporters subsided, although they outnumbered Spennymoor fans by roughly two to one. Contrastingly the black and white end raised its decibel count. And so the Vase was carried northwards yet again. That was some consolation for regular Spennymoor skipper Darren Moore who had to sit out the team's biggest day having broken an ankle only a week before the final.

There still remains a major question – when will this northern domination end?

Joe Fuller gets to the ball in front of Tunbridge's Josh Stanford.
Photo: Alan Coomes.

Gavin Cogdon bares down on the Tunbridge goal. Photo: Eric Marsh.

John Pilbeam, Tunbridge Wells, takes on several Spennymoor Town players. Photo: Roger Turner

Tunbridge's 'keeper, Chris Oladogba, saves at the feet of Spennymoor forward Gavin Cogdon. Photo: Peter Barnes.

# PAST FINALS

**1975 HODDESDON TOWN** 2 *(South Midlands)*     **EPSOM & EWELL** 1 *(Surrey Senior)*     **Att: 9,500**
Sedgwick 2     Wales     Ref: Mr R Toseland
Hoddesdon: Galvin, Green, Hickey, Maybury, Stevenson, Wilson, Bishop, Picking, Sedgwick, Nathan, Schofield
Epsom & Ewell: Page, Bennett, Webb, Wales, Worby, Jones, O'Connell, Walker, Tuite, Eales, Lee

**1976 BILLERICAY TOWN** 1 *(Essex Senior)*     **STAMFORD** 0 (aet) *(United Counties)*     **Att: 11,848**
Aslett     Ref: Mr A Robinson
Billericay: Griffiths, Payne, Foreman, Pullin, Bone, Coughlan, Geddes, Aslett, Clayden, Scott, Smith
Stamford: Johnson, Kwiatowski, Marchant, Crawford, Downs, Hird, Barnes, Walpole, Smith, Russell, Broadbent

**1977 BILLERICAY TOWN** 1 *(Essex Senior)*     **SHEFFIELD** 1 (aet) *(Yorkshire)*     **Att: 14,000**
Clayden     Coughlan og     Ref: Mr J Worrall
Billericay: Griffiths, Payne, Bone, Coughlan, Pullin, Scott, Wakefield, Aslett, Clayden,Woodhouse, McQueen. Sub: Whettell
Sheffield: Wing, Gilbody, Lodge, Hardisty, Watts, Skelton, Kay, Travis, Pugh, Thornhill,Haynes. Sub: Strutt
Replay **BILLERICAY TOWN** 2     **SHEFFIELD** 1     **Att: 3,482**
Aslett, Woodhouse     Thornhill     at Nottingham Forest
Billericay: Griffiths, Payne, Pullin, Whettell, Bone, McQueen, Woodhouse, Aslett, Clayden, Scott, Wakefield
Sheffield: Wing, Gilbody, Lodge, Strutt, Watts, Skelton, Kay, Travis, Pugh, Thornhill, Haynes

**1978 NEWCASTLE BLUE STAR** 2 *(Wearside)*     **BARTON ROVERS** 1 *(South Midlands)*     **Att: 16,858**
Dunn, Crumplin     Smith     Ref: Mr T Morris
Newcastle: Halbert, Feenan, Thompson, Davidson, S Dixon, Beynon, Storey, P Dixon, Crumplin, Callaghan, Dunn. Sub: Diamond
Barton Rovers: Blackwell, Stephens, Crossley, Evans, Harris, Dollimore, Dunn, Harnaman, Fossey, Turner, Smith. Sub: Cox

**1979 BILLERICAY TOWN** 4 *(Athenian)*     **ALMONDSBURY GREENWAY** 1 *(Glos. Co)*     **Att: 17,500**
Young 3, Clayden     Price     Ref: Mr C Steel
Billericay: Norris, Blackaller, Bingham, Whettell, Bone, Reeves, Pullin, Scott, Clayden,Young, Groom. Sub: Carrigan
Almondsbury: Hamilton, Bowers, Scarrett, Sulllivan, Tudor, Wookey, Bowers, Shehean, Kerr, Butt, Price. Sub: Kilbaine

**1980 STAMFORD** 2 *(United Counties)*     **GUISBOROUGH TOWN** 0 *(Northern Alliance)*     **Att: 11,500**
Alexander, McGowan     Ref: Neil Midgeley
Stamford: Johnson, Kwiatkowski, Ladd, McGowan, Bliszczak I, Mackin, Broadhurst, Hall,Czarnecki, Potter, Alexander. Sub: Bliszczak S
Guisborough: Cutter, Scott, Thornton, Angus, Maltby, Percy, Skelton, Coleman, McElvaney,Sills, Dilworth. Sub: Harrison

**1981 WHICKHAM** 3 *(Wearside)*     **WILLENHALL** 2 (aet) *(West Midlands)*     **Att: 12,000**
Scott, Williamson, Peck og     Smith, Stringer     Ref: Mr R Lewis
Whickham: Thompson, Scott, Knox, Williamson, Cook, Ward, Carroll, Diamond, Cawthra,Robertson, Turnbull. Sub: Alton
Willenhall: Newton, White, Darris, Woodall, Heath, Fox, Peck, Price, Matthews, Smith,Stringer. Sub: Trevor

**1982 FOREST GREEN ROVERS** 3 *(Hellenic)*     **RAINWORTH M.W** 0 *(Notts Alliance)*     **Att: 12,500**
Leitch 2, Norman     Ref: Mr K Walmsey
Forest Green: Moss, Norman, Day, Turner, Higgins, Jenkins, Guest, Burns, Millard, Leitch, Doughty. Sub: Dangerfield
Rainworth M.W: Watson, Hallam, Hodgson, Slater, Sterland, Oliver, Knowles, Raine, Radzi, Reah, Comerford. Sub: Robinson

**1983 V.S. RUGBY** 1 *(West Midlands)*     **HALESOWEN TOWN** 0 *(West Midlands)*     **Att: 13,700**
Crawley     Ref: Mr B Daniels
V'S Rugby: Burton, McGinty, Harrison, Preston, Knox, Evans, ingram, Setchell, Owen,Beecham, Crawley. Sub: Haskins
Halesowen Town: Coldicott, Penn, Edmonds, Lacey, Randall, Shilvock, Hazelwood, Moss, Woodhouse,P Joinson, L Joinson. Sub: Smith

**1984 STANSTED** 3 *(Essex Senior)*     **STAMFORD** 2 *(United Counties)*     **Att: 8,125**
Holt, Gillard, Reading     Waddicore, Allen     Ref: Mr T Bune
Stanstead: Coe, Williams, Hilton, Simpson, Cooper, Reading, Callanan, Holt, Reevs,Doyle, Gillard. Sub: Williams
Stamford: Parslow, Smitheringate, Blades, McIlwain, Lyon, Mackin, Genovese, Waddicore,Allen, Robson, Beech. Sub: Chapman

**1985 HALESOWEN TOWN** 3 *(West Midlands)*     **FLEETWOOD TOWN** 1 *(N W Counties)*     **Att: 16,715**
L Joinson 2, Moss     Moran     Ref: Mr C Downey
Halesowen: Coldicott, Penn, Sherwood, Warner, Randle, Heath, Hazlewood, Moss (Smith),Woodhouse, P Joinson, L Joinson
Fleetwood Town: Dobson, Moran, Hadgraft, Strachan, Robinson, Milligan, Hall, Trainor, Taylor(Whitehouse), Cain, Kennerley

**1986 HALESOWEN TOWN** 3 *(West Midlands)*     **SOUTHALL** 0 *(Isthmian 2 South)*     **Att: 18,340**
Moss 2, L Joinson     Ref: Mr D Scott
Halesowen: Pemberton, Moore, Lacey, Randle (Rhodes), Sherwood, Heath, Penn, Woodhouse, PJoinson, L Joinson, Moss
Southall: Mackenzie, James, McGovern, Croad, Holland, Powell (Richmond), Pierre,Richardson, Sweales, Ferdinand, Rowe

# THE FA VASE

**1987  ST. HELENS** 3 *(N W Counties)*       **WARRINGTON TOWN** 2 *(N W Counties)*       **Att: 4,254**
Layhe 2, Rigby                               Reid, Cook                                     **Ref: Mr T Mills**
St Helens: Johnson, Benson, Lowe, Bendon, Wilson, McComb, Collins (Gledhill), O'Neill,Cummins, Lay, Rigby. Sub: Deakin
Warrington: O'Brien. Copeland, Hunter, Gratton, Whalley, Reid, Brownville (Woodyer), Cook,Kinsey, Looker (Hill), Hughes

**1988  COLNE DYNAMOES** 1 *(N W Counties)*       **EMLEY** 0 *(Northern Counties East)*       **Att: 15,000**
Anderson                                                                                        **Ref: Mr A Seville**
Colne Dynamoes: Mason, McFafyen, Westwell, Bentley, Dunn, Roscoe, Rodaway, Whitehead (Burke),Diamond, Anderson, Wood (Coates)
Emley: Dennis, Fielding, Mellor, Codd, Hirst (Burrows), Gartland (Cook), Carmody,Green, Bramald, Devine, Francis

**1989  TAMWORTH** 1 *(West Midlands)*       **SUDBURY TOWN** 1 (aet)  *(Eastern)*       **Att: 26,487**
Devaney                                      Hubbick                                     **Ref: Mr C Downey**
Tamworth: Bedford, Lockett, Atkins, Cartwright, McCormack, Myers, Finn, Devaney, Moores,Gordon, Stanton. Subs: Rathbone, Heaton
Sudbury Town: Garnham, Henry, G Barker, Boyland, Thorpe, Klug, D Barker, Barton, Oldfield,Smith, Hubbick. Subs: Money, Hunt
**Replay TAMWORTH** 3                        **SUDBURY TOWN** 0                           **Att: 11,201**
Stanton 2, Moores                                                                        **at Peterborough**
Tamworth: Bedford, Lockett, Atkins, Cartwright, Finn, Myers, George, Devaney, Moores,Gordon, Stanton. Sub: Heaton
Sudbury Town: Garnham, Henry, G Barker, Boyland, Thorpe, Klug, D Barker, Barton, Oldfield,Smith, Hubbick. Subs: Money, Hunt

**1990  YEADING** 0 *(Isthmian 2 South)*       **BRIDLINGTON TOWN** 0 (aet)  *(N Co East)*       **Att: 7,932**
                                                                                               **Ref: Mr R Groves**
Yeading: Mackenzie, Wickens, Turner, Whiskey (McCarthy), Croad, Denton, Matthews, James(Charles), Sweates, Impey, Cordery
Bridlington: Taylor, Pugh, Freeman, McNeill, Warburton, Brentano, Wilkes (Hall), Noteman,Gauden, Whiteman, Brattan (Brown)
**Replay YEADING** 1                         **BRIDLINGTON TOWN** 0                      **Att: 5,000**
Sweales                                                                                  **at Leeds Utd FC**
Yeading: Mackenzie, Wickens, Turner, Whiskey, Croad (McCarthy), Schwartz, Matthews,James, Sweates, Impey (Welsh), Cordery
Bridlington: Taylor, Pugh, Freeman, McNeill, Warburton, Brentano, Wilkes (Brown), Noteman,Gauden (Downing), Whiteman, Brattan

**1991  GRESLEY ROVERS** 4 *(West Midlands)*       **GUISELEY** 4  (aet)  *(Northern Co East)*       **Att: 11,314**
Rathbone, Smith 2, Stokes                          Tennison 2, Walling, A Roberts                   **Ref: Mr C Trussell**
Gresley: Aston, Barry, Elliott (Adcock), Denby, Land, Astley, Stokes, K Smith, Acklam,Rathbone, Lovell (Weston)
Guiseley: Maxted, Bottomley, Hogarth, Tetley, Morgan, McKenzie, Atkinson (Annan),Tennison, Walling, A Roberts, B Roberts
**Replay GUISELEY** 3                        **GRESLEY ROVERS** 1                        **Att: 7,585**
Tennison, Walling, Atkinson                  Astley                                      **at Bramall Lane**
Guiseley: Maxted, Annan, Hogarth, Tetley, Morgan, McKenzie (Bottomley), Atkinson,Tennison (Noteman), Walling, A Roberts, B Roberts
Gresley: Aston, Barry, Elliott, Denby, Land, Astley, Stokes (Weston), K Smith, Acklam, Rathbone, Lovell (Adcock)

**1992  WIMBORNE TOWN** 5 *(Wessex)*       **GUISELEY** 3 *(Northern Premier Div 1)*       **Att: 10,772**
Richardson, Sturgess 2, Killick 2          Noteman 2, Colville                            **Ref: Mr M J Bodenham**
Wimborne: Leonard, Langdown, Wilkins, Beacham, Allan, Taplin, Ames, Richardson, Bridle,Killick, Sturgess (Lovell), Lynn
Guiseley: Maxted, Atkinson, Hogarth, Tetley (Wilson), Morgan, Brockie, A Roberts,Tennison, Noteman (Colville), Annan, W Roberts

**1993  BRIDLINGTON TOWN** 1 *(NPL Div 1)*       **TIVERTON TOWN** 0 *(Western)*       **Att: 9,061**
Radford                                                                                  **Ref: Mr R A Hart**
Bridlington: Taylor, Brentano, McKenzie, Harvey, Bottomley, Woodcock, Grocock, A Roberts, Jones, Radford (Tyrell), Parkinson. Sub: Swailes
Tiverton Town: Nott, J Smith, N Saunders, M Saunders, Short (Scott), Steele, Annunziata, KSmith, Everett, Daly, Hynds (Rogers)

**1994  DISS TOWN** 2 *(Eastern)*       **TAUNTON TOWN** 1 *(Western)*       **Att: 13,450**
Gibbs (p), Mendham                      Fowler                                **Ref: Mr K. Morton**
Diss Town: Woodcock, Carter, Wolsey (Musgrave), Casey (Bugg), Hartle, Smith, Barth, Mendham, Miles, Warne, Gibbs
Taunton Town: Maloy, Morris, Walsh, Ewens, Graddon, Palfrey, West (Hendry), Fowler, Durham, Perrett (Ward), Jarvis

**1995  ARLESEY TOWN** 2 *(South Midlands)*       **OXFORD CITY** 1 *(Ryman 2)*       **Att: 13,670**
Palma, Gyalog                                     S Fontaine                            **Ref: Mr G S Willard**
Arlesey: Young, Cardines, Bambrick, Palma (Ward), Hull, Gonsalves, Gyalog, Cox, Kane,O'Keefe, Marshall (Nicholls). Sub: Dodwell
Oxford: Fleet, Brown (Fisher), Hume, Shepherd, Muttock, Hamilton (Kemp), Thomas, Spittle, Sherwood, S Fontaine, C Fontaine. Sub: Torres

**1996  BRIGG TOWN** 3 *(N Co East)*       **CLITHEROE** 0 *(N W Counties)*       **Att: 7,340**
Stead 2, Roach                                                                     **Ref: Mr S J Lodge**
Brigg: Gawthorpe, Thompson, Rogers, Greaves (Clay), Buckley (Mail), Elston, C Stead, McLean, N Stead (McNally), Flounders, Roach
Clitheroe: Nash, Lampkin, Rowbotham (Otley), Baron, Westwell, Rovine, Butcher, Taylor (Smith), Grimshaw, Darbyshire, Hill (Dunn)

**1997  WHITBY TOWN** 3 *(Northern)*       **NORTH FERRIBY UTD.** 0 *(N Co East)*       **Att: 11,098**
Williams, Logan, Toman                                                                  **Ref: Graham Poll**
North Ferriby: Sharp, Deacey, Smith, Brentano, Walmsley, M Smith, Harrison (Horne), Phillips (Milner), France (Newman), Flounders, Tennison
Whitby Town: Campbell, Williams, Logan, Goodchild, Pearson, Cook, Goodrick (Borthwick), Hodgson, Robinson, Toman (Pyle), Pitman (Hall)

**1998 TIVERTON TOWN 1** *(Western)*      **TOW LAW TOWN 0** *(Northern Division 1)*     **Att: 13,139**
Varley        **Ref: M A Riley**
Tiverton: Edwards, Felton, Saunders, Tatterton, Smith J, Conning, Nancekivell (Rogers), Smith K (Varley), Everett, Daly, Leonard (Waters)
Tow Law: Dawson, Pickering, Darwent, Bailey, Hague, Moan, Johnson, Nelson, Suddick, Laidler (Bennett), Robinson.

**1999 TIVERTON TOWN 1** *(Western)*      **BEDLINGTON TERRIERS 0** *(Northern)*     **Att: 13, 878**
Rogers 88        **Ref: W. C. Burns**
Bedlington Terriers: O'Connor, Bowes, Pike, Boon (Renforth), Melrose, Teasdale, Cross, Middleton (Ludlow), Gibb, Milner, Bond. Subs: Pearson, Cameron, Gowans
Tiverton Town: Edwards, Fallon, Saunders, Tatterton, Tallon, Conning (Rogers), Nancekivell (Pears), Varley, Everett, Daly, Leonard. Subs: Tucker, Hynds, Grimshaw

**2000 DEAL TOWN 1** *(Kent)*      **CHIPPENHAM TOWN 0** *(Western)*     **Att: 20,000**
Graham 87        **Ref: E. K. Wolstenholme**
Deal Town: Tucker, Kempster, Best, Ash, Martin, Seager, Monteith, Graham, Lovell, Marshall, Ribbens. Subs: Roberts, Warden, Turner
Chippenham Town: Jones, James, Andrews, Murphy, Burns, Woods, Brown, Charity, Tweddle, Collier, Godley. Subs: Tiley, Cutler

**2001 TAUNTON TOWN 2** *(Western)*      **BERKHAMPSTED TOWN 1** *(Isthmian 2)*     **(at Villa Park) Att: 8,439**
Fields 41, Laight 45      Lowe 71        **Ref: E. K. Wolstenholme**
Taunton Town: Draper, Down, Chapman, West, Hawkings, Kelly, Fields (Groves), Laight, Cann (Tallon), Bastow, Lynch (Hapgood). Subs: Ayres, Parker
Berkhampsted Town: O'Connor, Mullins, Lowe, Aldridge, Coleman, Brockett, Yates, Adebowale, Richardson, Smith, Nightingale. Subs: Ringsell, Hall, Knight, Franklin, Osborne

**2002 WHITLEY BAY 1** *(Northern)*      **TIPTREE UNITED 0** *(Eastern)*     **(at Villa Park) Att: 4742**
Chandler 97        **Ref: A Kaye**
Whitley Bay: Caffrey, Sunderland, Walmsley, Dixon (Neil), Anderson, Locker, Middleton, Bowes (Carr), Chandler, Walton, Fenwick (Cuggy). Subs: Cook, Livermore
Tiptree United: Haygreen, Battell, Wall, Houghton, Fish, Streetley (Gillespie), Wareham (Snow), Daly, Barefield, Aransibia (Parnell), Brady. Subs: Powell, Ford.

**2003 BRIGG TOWN 2** *(Northern Co.East)*      **A.F.C SUDBURY 1** *(Eastern Counties)*     **(at Upton Park) Att: 6,634**
Housham 2, Carter 68      Raynor 30        **Ref: M Fletcher**
Brigg Town:- Steer, Raspin, Rowland, Thompson, Blanchard, Stones, Stead (Thompson 41), Housham, Borman (Drayton 87), Roach, Carter. Subs (not used) Nevis, Gawthorpe.
AFC Sudbury:- Greygoose, Head (Norfolk 63), Spearing, Tracey, Bishop, Anderson (Owen 73), Rayner, Gardiner (Banya 79), Bennett, Claydon, Betson. Subs (not used) Taylor, Hyde.

**2004 WINCHESTER CITY 2** *(Wessex)*      **A.F.C SUDBURY 0** *(Eastern Counties)*     **(at St Andrews) Att: 5,080**
Forbes 19, Smith 73 (pen)        **Ref: P Crossley**
Winchester City:- Arthur, Dyke (Tate 83), Bicknell, Redwood, Goss, Blake, Webber, Green, Mancey, Forbes (Rogers 70), Smith (Green 90). Subs (not used) - Lang and Rastall.
AFC Sudbury:- Greygoose, Head, Wardley, Girling, Tracey, Norfolk, Owen (Banya 62), Hyde (Calver 57), Bennett, Claydon, Betson (Francis 73n). Subs (not used) - Rayner, Nower.

**2005 DIDCOT TOWN 3** *(Hellenic)*      **A.F.C SUDBURY 2** *(Eastern Counties)* (at White Hart Lane)    **Att: 8,662**
Beavon (2), Wardley (og)      Wardley, Calver (pen)        **Ref: R Beeeby**
Didcot Town:- Webb, Goodall, Heapy, Campbell, Green, Parrott, Hannigan, Ward, Concannon (Jones 88), Beavon (Bianchini 90), Powell. Subs (not used) – Cooper, Allen, Spurrett.
AFC Sudbury:- Greygoose, Girling, Wardley, Bennett, Hyde (Hayes 78), Owen (Norfolk 65), Claydon (Banya 59), Head, Calver, Betson, Jerry Rayner. Subs (not used) – Howlett, Nower.

**2006 NANTWICH TOWN 3** *(NWC 1)*      **HILLINGDON BOROUGH 1** *(Spartan S.Mids P.)* (at St Andrews)    **Att: 3,286**
Kinsey (2), Scheuber      Nelson
Nantwich Town:- Hackney, A.Taylor, T.Taylor, Smith, Davis, Donnelly, Beasley, Scheuber (Parkinson 69), Kinsey (Marrow 69), Blake (Scarlett 86) and Griggs. Subs (not used): O'Connor and Read.
Hillingdon Borough:- Brown, Rundell (Fenton 80),Kidson, Phillips, Croft, Lawrence, Duncan (Nelson 46), Tilbury, Hibbs, Wharton (Lyons 38). Subs (not used): O'Grady, White.

**2007 TRURO 3** *(Western Division 1)*      **AFC TOTTON 1** *(Wessex Division 1)*    **Att: 27,754 (New Vase record)**
Wills (2), Broad      Potter        **Ref: P Joslin**
AFC Totton: Brunnschweiler, Reacord, Troon (Stevens 60), Potter (Gregory 82), Bottomley, Austen, Roden, Gosney, Hamodu (Goss 89), Osman, Byres. Subs not used: Zammit, McCormack.
Truro City: Stevenson, Ash, Power, Smith, Martin (Pope 84), Broad, Wills, Gosling, Yetton, Watkins, Walker (Ludlam 90). Subs not used: Butcher, Routledge, Reski.

# THE FA VASE

**2008**   **KIRKHAM & WESHAM** 2 *(North West Co. Div.2)*    LOWESTOFT TOWN 1 *(Eastern Co. Premier)*    **Att: 19,537**
Walwyn (2)      Thompson (og)      **Ref: A D'Urso**
Kirkham and Wesham: Summerfield, Jackson (Walwyn 79), Keefe (Allen 55), Thompson, Shaw, Eastwood, Clark, Blackwell, Wane,
Paterson (Sheppard 90), Smith. Subs not used: Moffat and Abbott
Lowestoft Town: Reynolds, Poppy, Potter, Woodrow, Saunders, Plaskett (McGee 79), Godbold, Darren Cockrill (Dale Cockrill 46), Stock, Hough,
King (Hunn 55). Subs not used: McKenna and Rix.

**2009**   **WHITLEY BAY** 2 *(Northern Division One)*    GLOSSOP NORTH END 0 *(North West Co. Prem)* Att: 12,212
Kerr, Chow      **Ref: K Friend**
Whitley Bay: Burke, Taylor, Picton, McFarlane (Fawcett 60), Coulson, Ryan, Moore, Robson, Kerr, Chow (Robinson 73), Johnston (Bell 60).
Subs not used: McLean and Reay.
Glossop North End: Cooper, Young, Kay, Lugsden, Yates, Gorton, Bailey (Hind 57), Morris, Allen (Balfe 65), Hamilton (Bailey 72), Hodges.
Subs not used: Whelan and Parker.

**2010**   **WHITLEY BAY** 6 *(Northern Division One)*    WROXHAM 1 *(Eastern Counties Premier Division)*    **Att: 8,920**
Chow 21(sec), Easthaugh 16 (og), Kerr, Johnston,    Cook 12      **Ref: A Taylor**
Robinson, Gillies
Whitley Bay: Terry Burke, Craig McFarlane, Callum Anderson, Richard Hodgson, (sub Lee Picton 69th min), Darren Timmons, Leon Ryan,
Adam Johnston (sub Joshua Gillies 77th min), Damon Robson, Lee Kerr, Paul Chow (sub Phillip Bell 61st min), Paul Robinson.
Subs not used – Tom Kindley and Chris Reid.
Wroxham: Scott Howie, Gavin Pauling (sub Ross Durrant 57th min), Shaun Howes, Graham Challen, Martin McNeil (sub Josh Carus 46th min), Andy
Easthaugh (sub Owen Paynter 69th min), Steve Spriggs, Gavin Lemmon, Paul Cook, Danny White, Gary Gilmore.
Subs not used – Danny Self and Gareth Simpson.

**2011**   **WHITLEY BAY** 3 *(Northern Division One)*    COALVILLE TOWN 2 *(Midland Alliance)*    **Att: 8,778**
Chow 28, 90, Kerr 61      Moore 58, Goodby 80      **Ref: S Mathieson**
Whitley Bay: Terry Burke, Craig McFarlane (sub Steve Gibson 90th min), Callum Anderson, Darren Timmons, Gareth Williams (sub David Coulson 68th
min), Damon Robson, Lee Kerr, Paul Chow, Paul Robinson, David Pounder (sub Brian Smith 68th min), Gary Ormston.
Subs not used – Kyle Hayes (gk) and Brian Rowe. Coalville Town: Sean Bowles, Ashley Brown (sub Matthew Gardner 88th min), Cameron Stuart, Adam
Goodby, Zach Costello, Lee Miveld,
Callum Woodward, Anthony Carney (sub Craig Attwood 90th min), Ryan Robbins (sub Ashley Wells 66th min), Matt Moore, Jerome Murdock.
Subs not used – Richard Williams (gk) and James Dodd.

**2012**   **DUNSTON UTS** 2 *(Northern League Div.1)*    WEST AUCKLAND TOWN 0 *(Northern League Div.1)*    **Att: 5,126**
Bulford 32, 79      **Ref: R East**
Dunston UTS: Liam Connell, Ben Cattenach, Terry Galbraith, Michael Robson, Chris Swailes, Kane Young, Steven Shaw, Michael Dixon,
Stephen Goddard (sub Sreven Preen 84th min), Andrew Bulford (sub Danny Craggs 88th min), Lee McAndrew.
*Subs not used* – Andrew Clark (g/k), Ian Herron, Jack Burns.
West Auckland Town: Mark Bell, Neil Pattinson, Andrew Green, Jonny Gibson, John Parker, Mark Stephenson (sub Daniel Hindmarsh 76th min),
Stuart Banks, Mark Hudson, Mattie Moffatt, Michael Rae, Adam Nicholls (sub Martin Young 60th min).
*Subs not used* – Daryll Hall, Ross Preston, Matthew Coad.

*All Finals at Wembley unless otherwise stated.*

FAV 6P:
Striker Ahmet
Bilgimer chips
the ball over the
Guernsey keeper
Chris Tardif, but
sees it cleared of
the line. Walsall
Wood drew 0-0.

Photo:
Jonathan
Holloway.

## PRELIMINARY ROUND

| # | Home | | Away | Score | |
|---|------|---|------|-------|---|
| 1 | Pickering Town | v | Gateshead (3/9) | 1-5 | 39 |
| 2 | Nantwich Town | v | Runcorn Linnets (6/9) | 3-9 | 93 |
| 3 | Altrincham | v | Macclesfield Town (11/9) | 1-2 | 230 |
| 4 | Marine | v | Stalybridge Celtic (5/9) | 2-4 | 115 |
| 5 | Salford City | v | Vauxhall Motors (6/9) | 2-3 | 52 |
| 6 | Ashton Town | v | Southport (5/9) | 1-0 | 40 |
| 7 | North Ferriby United | v | Hall Road Rangers (5/9) | 1-2 | 90 |
| 8 | Grimsby Town | v | Pontefract Collieries (5/9) | 9-1 | 50 |
| 9 | Harrogate Town | v | Ossett Albion (5/9) | 5-2 | 90 |
| | (at Ossett Albion FC) | | | | |
| 10 | Lutterworth Athletic | v | Lincoln City (3/9) | 0-9 | 40 |
| 11 | Glossop North End | v | Mansfield Town (5/9) | 0-3 | 95 |
| 12 | Spalding United | v | Oadby Town (5/9) | 0-10 | 50 |
| 13 | Buxton | v | Ibstock United (5/9) | 2-1 | 49 |
| 14 | Retford United | v | Holwell Sports (5/9) | 1-2 | 88 |
| 15 | Teversal | v | Blaby & Whetstone Athletic (5/9) | 2-4 | 49 |
| 16 | Boldmere St Michaels | v | Coventry Copsewood | | |
| | (walkover for Boldmere St Michaels – Coventry Copsewood withdrawn) | | | | |
| 17 | Stratford Town | v | Newcastle Town (6/9) | 2-3 | 86 |
| 18 | Walsall Wood | v | Lye Town (5/9) | 2-1 | 48 |
| 19 | Earlswood Town | v | Solihull Moors (6/9) | 1-2 | 28 |
| 20 | Hednesford Town | v | Hereford United (5/9) | 1-2 | 54 |
| 21 | Cradley Town | v | Atherstone Town (5/9) | 2-4 | 29 |
| 22 | Highgate United | v | Chasetown (5/9) | 1-4 | 40 |
| 23 | Halesowen Town | v | Rugby Town (5/9) | 2-5 | 32 |
| 24 | Nuneaton Griff | v | Racing Club Warwick (5/9) | 4-0 | 68 |
| 25 | Eccleshall | v | Gornal Athletic (5/9) | 1-4 | 48 |
| 26 | Pegasus Juniors | v | Stone Dominoes (5/9) | 4-0 | 36 |
| 27 | Stowmarket Town | v | Cambridge United (5/9) | 0-13 | 55 |
| 28 | Needham Market | v | Fakenham Town (5/9) | 5-1 | 85 |
| 29 | Bury Town | v | Swaffham Town (3/9) | 9-0 | 66 |
| 30 | Cornard United | v | Norwich United (6/9) | 3-0 | 30 |
| 31 | AFC Kempston Rovers | v | AFC Dunstable (5/9) | 2-1 | 59 |
| 32 | Bedford Town | v | Stewarts & Lloyds Corby (5/9) | 2-1aet | 44 |
| 33 | Peterborough Northern Star | v | Rushden & Higham United (6/9) | 3-1 | 50 |
| 34 | Southend Manor | v | Kings Langley (5/9) | 4-1 | 50 |
| 35 | Halstead Town | v | Hoddesdon Town (5/9) | 1-3 | 35 |
| 36 | Wivenhoe Town | v | Heybridge Swifts (3/9) | 0-3 | 42 |
| 37 | Ilford | v | Canvey Island | | |
| | (walkover for Canvey Island – Ilford withdrawn) | | | | |
| 38 | Concord Rangers | v | Redbridge (5/9) | 2-5 | 71 |
| 39 | Burnham Ramblers | v | Berkhamsted | | |
| | (walkover for Berkhamsted – Burnham Ramblers withdrawn) | | | | |
| 40 | Thurrock | v | Witham Town (10/9) | 1-0 | 95 |
| 41 | Oxhey Jets | v | Hullbridge Sports (5/9) | 7-0 | 37 |
| 42 | Cheshunt | v | Barking (5/9) | 0-0aet | 75 |
| | (Cheshunt won 6-5 on kicks from the penalty mark) | | | | |
| 43 | East Thurrock United | v | Billericay Town (5/9) | 0-2 | 104 |
| 44 | Hitchin Town | v | Tilbury (5/9) | 2-4 | 54 |
| 45 | St Albans City | v | Romford (5/9) | 4-2 | 79 |
| 46 | Sawbridgeworth Town | v | Leverstock Green (5/9) | 4-1aet | 49 |
| 47 | Colney Heath | v | FC Clacton (5/9) | 2-1 | 34 |
| 48 | Chelmsford City | v | Waltham Abbey (10/9) | 3-0 | 66 |
| 49 | Bowers & Pitsea | v | Boreham Wood (6/9) | 1-6 | 40 |
| 50 | Potters Bar Town | v | St Margaretsbury (7/9) | 2-0 | 51 |
| 51 | Bishop's Stortford | v | Ware (5/9) | 2-0 | 64 |
| 52 | AFC Hornchurch | v | Brentwood Town (6/9) | 0-6 | 97 |
| 53 | Clapton | v | Stansted | | |
| | (walkover for Clapton – Stansted withdrawn) | | | | |
| 54 | Hatfield Town | v | Royston Town (6/9) | 0-5 | |
| 55 | Hampton & Richmond Borough | v | Uxbridge (5/9) | 1-4aet | 64 |
| 56 | Hanworth Villa | v | North Greenford United (6/9) | 3-1 | 20 |
| 57 | Northwood | v | Harefield United (6/9) | 1-1aet | 50 |
| | (Northwood won 8-7 on kicks from the penalty mark) | | | | |
| 58 | Wingate & Finchley | v | Bedfont Sports (4/9) | 12-1 | 52 |
| 59 | Tonbridge Angels | v | South Park (3/9) | 1-2 | 47 |
| 60 | Maidstone United | v | Redhill (5/9) | 13-0 | |
| 61 | Thamesmead Town | v | Margate (6/9) | 2-2aet | 35 |
| | (Thamesmead Town won 6-5 on kicks from the penalty mark) | | | | |
| 62 | Sevenoaks Town | v | Dover Athletic (4/9) | 4-3aet | 46 |
| 63 | Erith & Belvedere | v | Saltdean United (5/9) | 2-0 | 107 |
| 64 | Dartford | v | Welling United (7/9) | 1-2 | |
| 65 | Dulwich Hamlet | v | Metropolitan Police (5/9) | 6-0 | 78 |
| 66 | Tooting & Mitcham United | v | Ramsgate (5/9) | 1-0 | 68 |
| 67 | Colliers Wood United | v | St Francis Rangers (6/9) | 3-1 | 30 |
| 68 | Faversham Town | v | Bromley (3/9) | 5-2 | 52 |
| 69 | Westfield | v | Erith Town (5/9) | 0-3 | 44 |
| 70 | Eastbourne Borough | v | Sittingbourne (6/9) | 2-1 | 110 |
| 71 | Hastings United | v | Sutton United (3/9) | 1-5 | 94 |
| 72 | Horley Town | v | Folkestone Invicta (5/9) | 2-5 | 36 |
| 73 | Ebbsfleet United | v | Fisher (5/9) | 6-7aet | 88 |
| 74 | Corinthian | v | Chipstead (6/9) | 2-1 | 52 |
| 75 | Molesey | v | Three Bridges (5/9) | 2-1 | 32 |
| 76 | Carshalton Athletic | v | Lewes (3/9) | 5-4 | 57 |
| 77 | Ashford United | v | Cray Wanderers (5/9) | 0-4 | 30 |
| 78 | Eastbourne Town | v | VCD Athletic (3/9) | 2-6 | 60 |
| 79 | Kingstonian | v | Crowborough Athletic (3/9) | 1-7 | 53 |
| | (at Banstead Athletic FC) | | | | |
| 80 | Shoreham | v | Leatherhead (6/9) | 0-6 | 31 |
| 81 | Godalming Town | v | Walton & Hersham (3/9) | 3-1 | 71 |
| 82 | Farnham Town | v | Lancing (5/9) | 5-2 | 20 |
| 83 | Horsham | v | Burgess Hill Town (6/9) | 1-4 | 50 |
| | (at Three Bridges FC) | | | | |
| 84 | Dorking | v | Crawley Down Gatwick (5/9) | 2-1 | 61 |
| 85 | Aylesbury | v | Binfield (6/9) | 5-2aet | |
| 86 | Cove | v | Oxford City (3/9) | 3-11 | |
| 87 | Witney Town | v | Newport Pagnell Town | | |
| | (walkover for Newport Pagnell Town – Witney Town withdrawn) | | | | |
| 88 | Farnborough | v | Hartley Wintney (5/9) | 2-1 | 72 |
| 89 | Chesham United | v | Windsor (6/9) | 0-1 | 53 |
| 90 | Maidenhead United | v | Fleet Spurs (5/9) | 2-0 | |
| 91 | Burnham | v | Ascot United (5/9) | 4-7aet | 60 |
| 92 | Marlow | v | Banbury United (5/9) | 1-3 | 45 |
| 93 | Flackwell Heath | v | Thatcham Town (6/9) | 2-5 | 36 |
| 94 | Reading Town | v | Sandhurst Town (4/9) | 8-0 | 38 |
| 95 | North Leigh | v | Didcot Town (6/9) | 2-4 | 38 |
| 96 | Fleet Town | v | Thame United (6/9) | 1-1aet | 46 |
| | (Thame United won 3-0 on kicks from the penalty mark) | | | | |
| 97 | Bournemouth | v | AFC Portchester (5/9) | 2-1 | 57 |
| 98 | Chippenham Town | v | Gillingham Town (3/9) | 1-0 | 43 |
| 99 | Salisbury City | v | Moneyfields (10/9) | 5-0 | 56 |
| 100 | Sholing | v | Dorchester Town (6/9) | 2-0 | 55 |
| 101 | Elmore | v | Tiverton Town (6/9) | 0-3 | |
| | (at Tiverton Town FC) | | | | |
| 102 | Chard Town | v | Taunton Town (4/9) | 3-0 | |
| 103 | Weston Super Mare | v | Gloucester City (6/9) | 4-1 | 75 |
| 104 | Frome Town | v | Odd Down (6/9) | 1-5 | 52 |
| 105 | Bristol Academy | v | Bishop Sutton (5/9) | 1-0 | 35 |
| 106 | Cirencester Town | v | Hengrove Athletic (5/9) | 3-2 | 63 |
| 107 | Barnstaple Town | v | Paulton Rovers | | |
| | (walkover for Paulton Rovers – Barnstaple Town withdrawn) | | | | |
| 108 | Forest Green Rovers | v | Bishop's Cleeve (5/9) | 3-1 | 106 |
| 109 | Cheltenham Saracens | v | Bath City (3/9) | 1-2 | 30 |
| 110 | Lydney Town | v | Mangotsfield United (5/9) | 1-2 | 72 |
| 111 | Radstock Town | v | Bristol Manor Farm (4/9) | 1-3 | 42 |
| 112 | Larkhall Athletic | v | Wells City (3/9) | 2-3aet | 41 |

# THE FA YOUTH CUP

## FIRST ROUND QUALIFYING

| No | Home | | Away | Score | |
|---|---|---|---|---|---|
| 1 | Chester-Le-Street Town | v | Bedlington Terriers (19/9) | 0-1aet | 63 |
| 2 | Gateshead | v | Ryton & Crawcrook Albion (19/9) | 8-1 | 137 |
| 3 | Newton Aycliffe | v | Whitley Bay (19/9) | 4-1 | 56 |
| 4 | Birtley Town | v | Scarborough Athletic (18/9) | 3-0 | 66 |
| 5 | Bootle | v | Macclesfield Town (19/9) | 1-4aet | 111 |
| 6 | Prescot Cables | v | Curzon Ashton (17/9) | 0-1 | 90 |
| 7 | Stockport Sports | v | Vauxhall Motors | | |
| | (walkover for Vauxhall Motors – Stockport Sports withdrawn) | | | | |
| 8 | Skelmersdale United | v | AFC Blackpool (19/9) | 0-1 | 92 |
| 9 | AFC Fylde | v | Padiham (17/9) | 0-3 | 55 |
| 10 | Warrington Town | v | Wrexham (19/9) | 2-4 | 142 |
| 11 | Lancaster City | v | Stalybridge Celtic (1/10) | 2-0 | 41 |
| 12 | Ashton Town | v | Ashton Athletic (20/9) | 1-3 | 114 |
| 13 | Runcorn Linnets | v | Northwich Victoria (19/9) | 3-1 | 120 |
| 14 | Burscough | v | Chester (19/9) | 1-2 | 71 |
| 15 | Goole | v | Grimsby Town (18/9) | 0-4 | |
| 16 | Liversedge | v | Thackley (18/9) | 1-3 | 45 |
| 17 | Staveley MW | v | Bottesford Town (17/9) | 2-4 | 59 |
| 18 | Silsden | v | Stocksbridge Park Steels (19/9) | 2-1 | 43 |
| 19 | Worksop Town | v | FC Halifax Town (20/9) | 2-4 | 56 |
| | (at Shirebrook Town FC) | | | | |
| 20 | Sheffield | v | Yorkshire Amateur (19/9) | 1-2 | 43 |
| 21 | Farsley | v | Harrogate Town (17/9) | 1-6 | 75 |
| 22 | Dinnington Town | v | Brighouse Town | | |
| | (walkover for Brighouse Town – Dinnington Town withdrawn) | | | | |
| 23 | Hall Road Rangers | v | Kinsley Boys (18/9) | 4-1 | 55 |
| 24 | Guiseley | v | Hallam (11/9) | 5-3 | 90 |
| 25 | Lincoln United | v | Boston United (19/9) | 0-6 | 89 |
| 26 | Blaby & Whetstone Athletic | v | Lincoln City (19/9) | 1-6 | 30 |
| 27 | Arnold Town | v | Buxton (17/9) | 2-2aet | |
| | (Buxton won 4-2 on kicks from the penalty mark) | | | | |
| 28 | New Mills | v | Holwell Sports (19/9) | 2-0 | 75 |
| 29 | Dunkirk | v | Oadby Town (19/9) | 2-1 | 40 |
| 30 | Mansfield Town | v | Gresley (21/9) | 6-0 | 163 |
| 31 | St Andrews | v | Matlock Town (19/9) | 0-1 | 36 |
| 32 | Ilkeston | v | Hinckley United (19/9) | 1-0 | 85 |
| 33 | Redditch United | v | Newcastle Town (19/9) | 0-1 | 19 |
| 34 | Southam United | v | Kidderminster Harriers (17/9) | 1-6 | 109 |
| 35 | Rugby Town | v | Ellesmere Rangers (20/9) | 2-0 | 50 |
| 36 | Stourbridge | v | Nuneaton Griff (19/9) | 4-2 | 64 |
| 37 | Gornal Athletic | v | Coleshill Town (20/9) | 0-9 | |
| 38 | Chasetown | v | Malvern Town (19/9) | 6-0 | 60 |
| 39 | Coventry Sphinx | v | Walsall Wood (20/9) | 1-5 | 65 |
| 40 | Solihull Moors | v | Pegasus Juniors (19/9) | 1-3 | 51 |
| 41 | Boldmere St Michaels | v | Atherstone Town (17/9) | 0-2 | 45 |
| 42 | Romulus | v | Hereford United (18/9) | 0-6 | 32 |
| 43 | Ipswich Wanderers | v | Needham Market (19/9) | 2-3 | 100 |
| 44 | Lowestoft Town | v | Walsham Le Willows (19/9) | 2-1 | 52 |
| 45 | Wroxham | v | Cornard United (17/9) | 4-1 | 86 |
| 46 | Newmarket Town | v | AFC Sudbury (19/9) | 2-3 | 45 |
| 47 | Brantham Athletic | v | Haverhill Rovers (19/9) | 0-4 | 33 |
| 48 | Diss Town | v | Woodbridge Town (20/9) | 1-7 | 77 |
| 49 | Hadleigh United | v | Bury Town (19/9) | 1-12 | 44 |
| 50 | Histon | v | Felixstowe & Walton Utd (17/9) | 7-1 | 72 |
| 51 | Cambridge United | v | Dereham Town (19/9) | 3-0 | 68 |
| 52 | Leiston | v | Soham Town Rangers (19/9) | 1-3 | 40 |
| 53 | Daventry Town | v | Bedford Town (19/9) | 1-5 | |
| 54 | Rothwell Corinthians | v | Wellingborough Whitworths (17/9) | 5-2 | 35 |
| 55 | St Ives Town | v | Barton Rovers (20/9) | 3-3aet | 53 |
| | (Barton Rovers won 4-2 on kicks from the penalty mark) | | | | |
| 56 | Thrapston Town | v | St Neots Town (20/9) | 1-10 | 26 |
| 57 | Yaxley | v | Corby Town (20/9) | 4-3 | 40 |
| 58 | Stotfold | v | Woodford United (20/9) | 2-0 | 44 |
| 59 | Cogenhoe United | v | Peterborough Northern Star (20/9) | 0-3 | 43 |
| 60 | Langford | v | Brackley Town (20/9) | 2-0 | 46 |
| 61 | AFC Kempston Rovers | v | Luton Town (18/9) | 0-4 | |
| 62 | Kettering Town | v | Leighton Town (20/9) | 1-1aet | 41 |
| | (Leighton Town won 3-1 on kicks from the penalty mark) | | | | |
| 63 | Southend Manor | v | Grays Athletic (18/9) | 3-2aet | |
| 64 | Hemel Hempstead Town | v | Redbridge (20/9) | 2-3 | 71 |
| 65 | Canvey Island | v | Royston Town (19/9) | 4-0 | 72 |
| 66 | Oxhey Jets | v | Billericay Town (20/9) | 1-1aet | 60 |
| | (Billericay Town won 6-5 on kicks from the penalty mark) | | | | |
| 67 | Berkhamsted | v | Sawbridgeworth Town (18/9) | 5-2 | 50 |
| 68 | Tilbury | v | Boreham Wood (18/9) | 0-6 | 74 |
| 69 | Brentwood Town | v | Stanway Rovers (18/9) | 6-0 | 35 |
| 70 | Bishop's Stortford | v | Heybridge Swifts (19/9) | 5-2 | 65 |
| 71 | Chelmsford City | v | Hoddesdon Town (19/9) | 0-1 | 74 |
| 72 | Clapton | v | Colney Heath (19/9) | 4-4aet | 19 |
| | (Colney Heath won 5-3 on kicks from the penalty mark) | | | | |
| 73 | Thurrock | v | Potters Bar Town (19/9) | 2-1 | 104 |
| 74 | Cheshunt | v | St Albans City (19/9) | 3-1 | 113 |
| 75 | Hanwell Town | v | Wealdstone (17/9) | 0-4 | 49 |
| 76 | Staines Town | v | Cockfosters (17/9) | 3-0 | 33 |
| 77 | Hayes & Yeading United | v | Ashford Town (Middx) (17/9) | 0-1 | 56 |
| | (at AFC Hayes) | | | | |
| 78 | Uxbridge | v | Wingate & Finchley (19/9) | 2-1 | 88 |
| 79 | Northwood | v | Hanworth Villa (20/9) | 4-0 | 51 |
| 80 | Enfield 1893 | v | Enfield Town (20/9) | 2-1 | 59 |
| 81 | South Park | v | Lordswood (20/9) | 4-3 | 54 |
| 82 | Lingfield | v | Erith & Belvedere (20/9) | 5-4 | 61 |
| 83 | Sevenoaks Town | v | Crowborough Athletic (18/9) | 2-0 | 111 |
| 84 | Tooting & Mitcham United | v | Faversham Town (17/9) | 1-3 | 46 |
| 85 | Welling United | v | Sutton United (18/9) | 3-3aet | 84 |
| | (Welling United won 5-4 on kicks from the penalty mark) | | | | |
| 86 | Erith Town | v | Corinthian (17/9) | 2-3 | 64 |
| 87 | Cray Wanderers | v | Whitstable Town (20/9) | 1-0 | |
| | (at Whitstable Town FC) | | | | |
| 88 | Carshalton Athletic | v | Thamesmead Town (17/9) | 6-0 | 28 |
| 89 | Fisher | v | Maidstone United (17/9) | 2-4 | 84 |
| 90 | VCD Athletic | v | Folkestone Invicta (20/9) | 10-0 | 68 |
| 91 | Dulwich Hamlet | v | Molesey (19/9) | 6-1 | 48 |
| 92 | Colliers Wood United | v | Eastbourne Borough (20/9) | 4-1 | 60 |
| 93 | Worthing | v | Chichester City (17/9) | 3-1 | 70 |
| 94 | Camberley Town | v | Leatherhead (20/9) | 1-0 | 65 |
| 95 | Pagham | v | Burgess Hill Town (20/9) | 1-8 | 72 |
| 96 | Woking | v | Dorking (18/9) | 7-0 | 71 |
| 97 | Horsham YMCA | v | Farnham Town | | |
| | (walkover for Farnham Town – Horsham YMCA withdrawn) | | | | |
| 98 | Godalming Town | v | Cobham (17/9) | 0-3 | 67 |
| 99 | Bognor Regis Town | v | Whyteleafe (19/9) | 5-4 | 176 |
| 100 | Guildford City | v | Arundel (19/9) | 0-1 | 36 |
| 101 | Shrivenham | v | Oxford City (18/9) | 3-4 | 68 |
| 102 | Alton Town | v | Ardley United (1/10) | 6-4aet | |
| | (17/9, tie abandoned after 56 mins due to serious injury to player, 1-0) | | | | |
| 103 | Thatcham Town | v | Farnborough (19/9) | 2-5 | |
| 104 | Basingstoke Town | v | Reading Town (19/9) | 2-1aet | 123 |
| 105 | Didcot Town | v | Chalfont St Peter (20/9) | 11-0 | 53 |
| 106 | Banbury United | v | Kidlington (19/9) | 2-1 | 32 |
| 107 | Bracknell Town | v | Newport Pagnell Town (19/9) | 2-5 | |
| 108 | Windsor | v | Thame United (19/9) | 6-0 | 47 |
| 109 | Aylesbury | v | Ascot United (20/9) | 3-1aet | 64 |
| 110 | Slough Town | v | Maidenhead United (18/9) | 0-6 | |
| 111 | Petersfield Town | v | Eastleigh (20/9) | 1-7 | 63 |
| 112 | Poole Town | v | Bournemouth (20/9) | 3-0 | 71 |
| 113 | Ringwood Town | v | Sholing | | |
| | (walkover for Sholing – Ringwood Town withdrawn) | | | | |
| 114 | AFC Totton | v | Hamworthy United (20/9) | 10-2 | 94 |
| 115 | Havant & Waterlooville | v | Salisbury City (19/9) | 4-2 | 69 |
| 116 | Chippenham Town | v | Sherborne Town (19/9) | 2-1 | 45 |
| 117 | Christchurch | v | Wimborne Town (19/9) | 5-3 | 109 |
| 118 | Weymouth | v | Bemerton Heath Harlequins (18/9) | 1-4 | 71 |
| 119 | Yate Town | v | Chard Town (19/9) | 0-7 | 42 |
| 120 | Bridgwater Town | v | Merthyr Town (16/9) | 1-2 | 59 |
| 121 | Bath City | v | Odd Down (18/9) | 3-0 | 134 |
| 122 | Brislington | v | Mangotsfield United (18/9) | 1-2 | 19 |
| 123 | Bristol Manor Farm | v | Bitton (19/9) | 3-2 | 46 |
| 124 | Forest Green Rovers | v | Newport County (18/9) | 3-1 | 112 |
| 125 | Almondsbury UWE | v | Weston Super Mare (19/9) | 2-5 | |
| 126 | Bristol Academy | v | Wells City (17/9) | 2-0 | 45 |
| 127 | Tiverton Town | v | Paulton Rovers (18/9) | 7-0 | 33 |
| 128 | Ashton & Backwell United | v | Cirencester Town (27/9) | 0-4 | 56 |
| | (at Clevedon Town FC) | | | | |

## SECOND ROUND QUALIFYING

| | Home | | Away | Score | Att |
|---|---|---|---|---|---|
| 1 | Bedlington Terriers | v | Birtley Town (3/10) | 1-0 | 57 |
| 2 | Gateshead | v | Newton Aycliffe (2/10) | 5-2 | |
| 3 | Vauxhall Motors | v | Curzon Ashton (4/10) | 3-2 | 84 |
| 4 | Runcorn Linnets | v | Lancaster City (9/10) | 0-0aet | 141 |
| | (Runcorn Linnets won 5-4 on kicks from the penalty mark) | | | | |
| 5 | Macclesfield Town | v | Wrexham (3/10) | 1-4 | 102 |
| 6 | Padiham | v | AFC Blackpool (4/10) | 2-3 | 62 |
| 7 | Chester | v | Ashton Athletic (4/10) | 5-2aet | 121 |
| 8 | Bottesford Town | v | Thackley | 5-1 | 67 |
| 9 | Hall Road Rangers | v | Harrogate Town | 2-0 | 68 |
| 10 | Grimsby Town | v | Yorkshire Amateur (3/10) | 6-0 | |
| 11 | FC Halifax Town | v | Silsden (3/10) | 0-0aet | 53 |
| | (FC Halifax Town won 7-6 on kicks from the penalty mark - at Brighouse Town FC) | | | | |
| 12 | Guiseley | v | Brighouse Town (27/9) | 0-2 | 98 |
| 13 | Buxton | v | Matlock Town (9/10) | 1-2 | 79 |
| 14 | Boston United | v | Dunkirk (3/10) | 2-3 | 174 |
| 15 | New Mills | v | Ilkeston (10/10) | 1-5 | 93 |
| 16 | Lincoln City | v | Mansfield Town (2/10) | 8-1 | |
| 17 | Rugby Town | v | Kidderminster Harriers (3/10) | 0-2 | 70 |
| 18 | Atherstone Town | v | Walsall Wood (4/10) | 3-0 | 50 |
| 19 | Newcastle Town | v | Chasetown (4/10) | 0-4 | 89 |
| 20 | Coleshill Town | v | Stourbridge (3/10) | 0-1 | 52 |
| 21 | Hereford United | v | Pegasus Juniors (1/10) | 3-1 | |
| 22 | Wroxham | v | Lowestoft Town (1/10) | 6-0 | 65 |
| 23 | Cambridge United | v | Bury Town (3/10) | 1-3 | 116 |
| 24 | Needham Market | v | Woodbridge Town (3/10) | 4-2 | 135 |
| 25 | Haverhill Rovers | v | AFC Sudbury (1/10) | 0-3 | 52 |
| 26 | Soham Town Rangers | v | Histon (1/10) | 0-7 | 122 |
| 27 | Barton Rovers | v | Rothwell Corinthians | 7-2 | |
| 28 | Luton Town | v | Peterborough Northern Star (3/10) | 6-0 | 119 |
| 29 | Bedford Town | v | Stotfold (3/10) | 1-2aet | 52 |
| 30 | Yaxley | v | St Neots Town (4/10) | 3-2 | 65 |
| 31 | Leighton Town | v | Langford (1/10) | 1-3 | 61 |
| 32 | Hoddesdon Town | v | Colney Heath (3/10) | 4-2aet | 45 |
| 33 | Cheshunt | v | Berkhamsted (3/10) | 2-0 | 80 |
| 34 | Thurrock | v | Boreham Wood (3/10) | 0-2 | 75 |
| 35 | Southend Manor | v | Billericay Town (2/10) | 1-4 | 55 |
| 36 | Canvey Island | v | Redbridge (3/10) | 3-2 | 101 |
| 37 | Brentwood Town | v | Bishop's Stortford (4/10) | 2-0 | 50 |
| 38 | Staines Town | v | Uxbridge (1/10) | 4-2 | |
| 39 | Wealdstone | v | Enfield 1893 (1/10) | 0-2 | 55 |
| 40 | Northwood | v | Ashford Town (Middx) (4/10) | 0-1 | 52 |
| 41 | Maidstone United | v | VCD Athletic (2/10) | 2-3 | 133 |
| 42 | Colliers Wood United | v | Welling United (4/10) | 2-6 | 40 |
| 43 | Dulwich Hamlet | v | Corinthian (3/10) | 5-3aet | 71 |
| 44 | South Park | v | Faversham Town (4/10) | 4-4aet | |
| | (Faversham Town won 5-4 on kicks from the penalty mark) | | | | |
| 45 | Sevenoaks Town | v | Lingfield (2/10) | 4-1 | 47 |
| 46 | Cray Wanderers | v | Carshalton Athletic (1/10) | 0-4 | 41 |
| | (at Carshalton Athletic FC) | | | | |
| 47 | Burgess Hill Town | v | Bognor Regis Town (1/10) | 2-7 | 41 |
| 48 | Worthing | v | Farnham Town (1/10) | 3-0 | 52 |
| 49 | Woking | v | Arundel (4/10) | 3-0 | 51 |
| 50 | Camberley Town | v | Cobham (1/10) | 4-1 | 50 |
| 51 | Farnborough | v | Alton Town (10/10) | 3-2aet | 81 |
| 52 | Aylesbury | v | Newport Pagnell Town (4/10) | 4-2 | 72 |
| 53 | Oxford City | v | Banbury United (1/10) | 4-1 | |
| 54 | Didcot Town | v | Basingstoke Town (4/10) | 6-0 | 76 |
| 55 | Maidenhead United | v | Windsor (3/10) | 4-0 | 30 |
| 56 | Sholing | v | Christchurch (4/10) | 2-0 | 74 |
| 57 | Eastleigh | v | Havant & Waterlooville (3/10) | 4-4aet | |
| | (Havant & Waterlooville won 4-3 on kicks from the penalty mark) | | | | |
| 58 | AFC Totton | v | Bemerton Heath Harlequins (2/10) | 4-2 | 86 |
| 59 | Poole Town | v | Chippenham Town (3/10) | 0-3 | 67 |
| 60 | Bath City | v | Merthyr Town (3/10) | 2-0 | 59 |
| 61 | Tiverton Town | v | Weston Super Mare (2/10) | 3-0 | 48 |
| 62 | Chard Town | v | Forest Green Rovers (2/10) | 1-3 | |
| 63 | Bristol Manor Farm | v | Mangotsfield United (3/10) | 1-6 | 44 |
| 64 | Cirencester Town | v | Bristol Academy (3/10) | 4-0 | 36 |

## THIRD ROUND QUALIFYING

| | Home | | Away | Score | Att |
|---|---|---|---|---|---|
| 1 | FC Halifax Town | v | Bedlington Terriers (22/10) | 1-0 | 45 |
| | (at Brighouse Town FC) | | | | |
| 2 | Runcorn Linnets | v | Chester (18/10) | 0-3 | 168 |
| 3 | Gateshead | v | Wrexham (24/10) | 3-1 | 130 |
| 4 | Vauxhall Motors | v | Grimsby Town (18/10) | 0-4 | 114 |
| 5 | AFC Blackpool | v | Bottesford Town (16/10) | 0-4 | 31 |
| 6 | Brighouse Town | v | Hall Road Rangers (18/10) | 4-1 | 77 |
| 7 | Dunkirk | v | Yaxley (17/10) | 5-0 | 51 |
| 8 | Matlock Town | v | Kidderminster Harriers (18/10) | 0-4 | 110 |
| 9 | Hereford United | v | Atherstone Town (16/10) | 3-0 | |
| 10 | Chasetown | v | Stourbridge (17/10) | 1-2 | 62 |
| 11 | Ilkeston | v | Lincoln City (17/10) | 1-4 | 107 |
| 12 | Cheshunt | v | Histon (17/10) | 0-2 | |
| 13 | Luton Town | v | Barton Rovers (17/10) | 3-1 | 226 |
| 14 | Brentwood Town | v | AFC Sudbury (16/10) | 2-0 | 30 |
| 15 | Hoddesdon Town | v | Langford (17/10) | 1-0 | 14 |
| 16 | Wroxham | v | Needham Market (18/10) | 2-0 | 93 |
| 17 | Stotfold | v | Billericay Town (17/10) | 2-1 | 60 |
| 18 | Enfield 1893 | v | Bury Town (18/10) | 0-1 | 54 |
| 19 | Staines Town | v | Ashford Town (Middx) (15/10) | 3-1 | 124 |
| 20 | Canvey Island | v | Boreham Wood (17/10) | 2-1 | 101 |
| 21 | Farnborough | v | VCD Athletic (17/10) | 4-3aet | 79 |
| 22 | Faversham Town | v | Bognor Regis Town (15/10) | 4-2 | 88 |
| 23 | Welling United | v | Sevenoaks Town (23/10) | 2-3aet | 92 |
| 24 | Dulwich Hamlet | v | Camberley Town (18/10) | 0-2 | 83 |
| 25 | Carshalton Athletic | v | Worthing (16/10) | 4-2 | 64 |
| 26 | Aylesbury | v | Woking (18/10) | 0-2 | 66 |
| 27 | Mangotsfield United | v | Oxford City (24/10) | 3-2 | 65 |
| 28 | Sholing | v | Chippenham Town (18/10) | 2-0 | 49 |
| 29 | Didcot Town | v | Havant & Waterlooville (18/10) | 3-0 | 101 |
| 30 | Maidenhead United | v | Forest Green Rovers (15/10) | 2-1aet | 82 |
| 31 | AFC Totton | v | Bath City (16/10) | 2-1 | 151 |
| 32 | Cirencester Town | v | Tiverton Town (24/10) | 7-1 | 79 |

## FIRST ROUND PROPER

| | Home | | Away | Score | Att |
|---|---|---|---|---|---|
| 1 | Gateshead | v | Preston North End (31/10) | 1-1aet | 133 |
| | (Gateshead won 4-1 on kicks from the penalty mark) | | | | |
| 2 | Chester | v | York City (31/10) | 0-3 | 163 |
| 3 | Doncaster Rovers | v | Morecambe (31/10) | 1-0 | 208 |
| 4 | Oldham Athletic | v | Accrington Stanley (26/10) | 2-0 | 200 |
| 5 | Bottesford Town | v | Brighouse Town (30/10) | 1-0 | 110 |
| 6 | Tranmere Rovers | v | Bury (30/10) | 0-2 | 241 |
| 7 | FC Halifax Town | v | Scunthorpe United (31/10) | 1-4 | 52 |
| | (at Brighouse Town FC) | | | | |
| 8 | Crewe Alexandra | v | Carlisle United (31/10) | 2-1aet | 370 |
| 9 | Rochdale | v | Rotherham United (16/10) | 2-1 | 251 |
| 10 | Bradford City | v | Grimsby Town (24/10) | 2-0 | 187 |
| 11 | Hartlepool United | v | Fleetwood Town (24/10) | 1-1aet | 100 |
| | (Hartlepool United won 5-3 on kicks from the penalty mark) | | | | |
| 12 | Hereford United | v | Milton Keynes Dons (30/10) | 0-5 | |
| 13 | Lincoln City | v | Notts County (24/10) | 3-2 | 197 |
| 14 | Stevenage | v | Luton Town (30/10) | 3-0 | 478 |
| 15 | Coventry City | v | Shrewsbury Town (24/10) | 4-3 | 396 |
| 16 | Chesterfield | v | Northampton Town (24/10) | 0-3 | 150 |
| 17 | Port Vale | v | Walsall (24/10) | 1-0 | 173 |
| 18 | Burton Albion | v | Kidderminster Harriers (30/10) | 2-1 | 125 |
| 19 | Dunkirk | v | Stourbridge (30/10) | 1-4 | 91 |
| 20 | Bury Town | v | Histon (31/10) | 1-4 | 125 |
| 21 | Colchester United | v | Camberley Town (2/11) | 13-1 | 186 |
| 22 | Carshalton Athletic | v | Woking (29/10) | 1-3 | 121 |
| 23 | AFC Wimbledon | v | Farnborough (31/10) | 2-0 | 220 |
| 24 | Portsmouth | v | Southend United (26/10) | 2-1 | |
| 25 | Hoddesdon Town | v | Canvey Island (31/10) | 0-3 | 109 |
| 26 | Brentford | v | Barnet (17/10) | 5-1 | 248 |
| 27 | Faversham Town | v | Sevenoaks Town (1/11) | 4-2 | 114 |
| 28 | Staines Town | v | Wroxham (7/11) | 4-2 | 81 |
| 29 | Brentwood Town | v | Gillingham (31/10) | 1-2 | 160 |
| 30 | Crawley Town | v | Dagenham & Redbridge (30/10) | 3-2aet | |
| 31 | Stotfold | v | Leyton Orient (8/11) | 1-7 | 192 |
| 32 | Bristol Rovers | v | Torquay United (31/10) | 2-1 | |
| 33 | Oxford United | v | Yeovil Town (31/10) | 4-2 | |
| | (at Thame United FC) | | | | |
| 34 | AFC Bournemouth | v | AFC Totton (30/10) | 1-1aet | 506 |
| | (AFC Totton won 11-10 on kicks from the penalty mark) | | | | |
| 35 | Didcot Town | v | Aldershot Town (1/11) | 0-6 | 224 |
| 36 | Plymouth Argyle | v | Exeter City (24/10) | 3-0 | 748 |
| 37 | Cirencester Town | v | Mangotsfield United (1/11) | 5-2 | 57 |
| 38 | Swindon Town | v | Sholing (31/10) | 6-1 | 190 |
| 39 | Cheltenham Town | v | Maidenhead United (30/10) | 8-0 | 170 |

Bye - Sheffield United

## SECOND ROUND PROPER

| 1 | Stourbridge | v | Bradford City (14/11) | 2-2aet | 437 |
|---|---|---|---|---|---|
| | (Bradford City won 5-3 on kicks from the penalty mark) | | | | |
| 2 | Oldham Athletic | v | Coventry City (21/11) | 0-2 | 183 |
| 3 | Milton Keynes Dons | v | Stevenage (17/11) | 2-6 | 315 |
| 4 | Crewe Alexandra | v | Scunthorpe United (13/11) | 5-3 | 584 |
| 5 | Burton Albion | v | Bottesford Town (8/11) | 5-0 | 246 |
| 6 | Rochdale | v | Sheffield United (14/11) | 2-1 | 260 |
| 7 | Lincoln City | v | Hartlepool United (14/11) | 1-3 | |
| 8 | Doncaster Rovers | v | Gateshead (7/11) | 1-2 | 203 |
| 9 | Bury | v | Port Vale (13/11) | 1-2 | 262 |
| 10 | Northampton Town | v | York City (14/11) | 5-0 | 241 |
| 11 | Swindon Town | v | Cirencester Town (13/11) | 6-1 | 527 |
| 12 | Crawley Town | v | Histon (13/11) | 2-4 | |
| 13 | Leyton Orient | v | Aldershot Town (15/11) | 2-3 | 445 |
| 14 | Portsmouth | v | Woking (13/11) | 2-1 | 561 |
| 15 | AFC Wimbledon | v | Cheltenham Town (22/11) | 2-5aet | 272 |
| 16 | Brentford | v | Brentwood Town (7/11) | 3-2 | 255 |
| 17 | Colchester United | v | Faversham Town (10/11) | 8-1 | 187 |
| 18 | AFC Totton | v | Canvey Island (15/11) | 1-2 | 303 |
| 19 | Bristol Rovers | v | Staines Town (14/11) | 3-0 | 178 |
| 20 | Oxford United | v | Plymouth Argyle (14/11) | 3-2 | 214 |
| | (at Didcot Town FC) | | | | |

## THIRD ROUND PROPER

| 1 | Stevenage | v | Wigan Athletic (1/12) | 2-1 | 342 |
|---|---|---|---|---|---|
| 2 | Arsenal | v | Newcastle United (27/11) | 3-0 | 420 |
| | (at Barnet FC) | | | | |
| 3 | Manchester United | v | Burnley (7/12) | 3-4aet | 3146 |
| 4 | Coventry City | v | Bristol Rovers (15/12) | 0-1 | |
| | (at Nuneaton Town FC) | | | | |
| 5 | Hull City | v | Swansea City (19/12) | 3-2aet | 143 |
| | (at North Ferriby United FC) | | | | |
| 6 | Birmingham City | v | West Bromwich Albion (1012) 3-1 | | 494 |
| | (at Solihull Moors FC) | | | | |
| 7 | Swindon Town | v | Liverpool (4/12) | 0-5 | 1533 |
| 8 | Fulham | v | Middlesbrough (15/12) | 6-4aet | 112 |
| | (at Motspur Park) | | | | |
| 9 | Oxford United | v | Barnsley (15/1) | 1-3 | 247 |
| | (tie reversed - at Barnsley FC) | | | | |
| 10 | Cheltenham Town | v | Tottenham Hotspur (18/12) | 0-1 | 771 |
| 11 | Crystal Palace | v | Port Vale (14/12) | 0-2 | 537 |
| 12 | Burton Albion | v | Sheffield Wednesday (3/12) | 2-1 | 332 |
| 13 | Northampton Town | v | Canvey Island (12/12) | 2-1 | 185 |
| 14 | Brentford | v | Reading (12/12) | 1-5 | 346 |
| 15 | Derby County | v | Gateshead (11/12) | 4-0 | 385 |
| 16 | NORWICH CITY | v | Queens Park Rangers (5/12) | 1-0 | 209 |
| 17 | Rochdale | v | Crewe Alexandra (18/12) | 3-2aet | 205 |
| 18 | Millwall | v | Blackpool (4/12) | 4-3 | 296 |
| 19 | Colchester United | v | CHELSEA (1/12) | 2-3 | 1043 |
| 20 | Southampton | v | Everton (10/12) | 0-2 | 524 |
| 21 | Wolverhampton Wanderers | v | Charlton Athletic (12/12) | 0-1 | 306 |
| 22 | Brighton & Hove Albion | v | Stoke City (11/12) | 0-4 | 651 |
| 23 | Hartlepool United | v | Huddersfield Town (11/12) | 0-3 | 180 |
| 24 | Aldershot Town | v | West Ham United (10/12) | 1-3 | |
| 25 | Peterborough United | v | Aston Villa (8/1) | 4-0 | 879 |
| 26 | Bolton Wanderers | v | Portsmouth (10/12) | 2-1 | 573 |
| 27 | Blackburn Rovers | v | Leicester City (11/12) | 1-3 | 349 |
| 28 | Bradford City | v | Histon (10/1) | 2-2aet | 150 |
| | (Histon won 4-2 on kicks from the penalty mark) | | | | |
| 29 | Watford | v | Leeds United (28/11) | 0-4 | 535 |
| 30 | Manchester City | v | Sunderland (12/12) | 3-1 | 382 |
| | (at Stockport County FC) | | | | |
| 31 | Bristol City | v | Ipswich Town (4/12) | 0-1 | 235 |
| 32 | Nottingham Forest | v | Cardiff City (12/12) | 2-1 | 432 |

## FOURTH ROUND PROPER

| 1 | Port Vale | v | Everton (7/2) | 2-3aet | 525 |
|---|---|---|---|---|---|
| 2 | NORWICH CITY | v | Millwall (31/1) | 2-1 | 277 |
| 3 | Barnsley | v | Stevenage (1/2) | 4-3 | 412 |
| 4 | Reading | v | Bolton Wanderers (16/1) | 0-2 | 495 |
| 5 | Derby County | v | Ipswich Town (23/1) | 3-2 | 436 |
| 6 | West Ham United | v | Tottenham Hotspur (22/1) | 2-5 | 1189 |
| 7 | Stoke City | v | Huddersfield Town (16/1) | 2-3aet | |
| 8 | Arsenal | v | Fulham (29/1) | 2-1aet | 414 |
| 9 | Manchester City | v | Burnley (10/1) | 2-0 | 2570 |
| 10 | Histon | v | Liverpool (13/2) | 0-4 | 1596 |
| 11 | Charlton Athletic | v | CHELSEA (16/1) | 2-3aet | 1452 |
| 12 | Northampton Town | v | Hull City (30/1) | 0-1 | 514 |
| 13 | Birmingham City | v | Bristol Rovers (31/1) | 1-0 | 240 |
| 14 | Leicester City | v | Peterborough United (23/1) | 4-1 | 758 |
| 15 | Leeds United | v | Burton Albion (16/1) | 6-1 | 489 |
| 16 | Nottingham Forest | v | Rochdale (16/1) | 2-1 | 369 |

## FIFTH ROUND PROPER

| 1 | CHELSEA | v | Barnsley (15/2) | 3-0 | 402 |
|---|---|---|---|---|---|
| 2 | Hull City | v | Leicester City (27/2) | 3-1aet | 271 |
| 3 | Derby County | v | Manchester City (26/2) | 2-0 | 1256 |
| 4 | Nottingham Forest | v | Huddersfield Town (5/2) | 3-2 | 546 |
| 5 | NORWICH CITY | v | Birmingham City (26/2) | 2-1aet | 384 |
| 6 | Tottenham Hotspur | v | Bolton Wanderers (15/2) | 4-8 | 1382 |
| 7 | Arsenal | v | Everton | 2-4 | 726 |
| 8 | Liverpool | v | Leeds United (28/2) | 3-1 | |

## SIXTH ROUND PROPER

| 1 | Hull City | v | Liverpool (12/3) | 0-3 | 1636 |
|---|---|---|---|---|---|
| 2 | Everton | v | NORWICH CITY (5/4) | 2-4 | 1093 |
| 3 | Nottingham Forest | v | Bolton Wanderers (27/2) | 3-2aet | 901 |
| 4 | Derby County | v | CHELSEA (8/3) | 1-2 | 4188 |

## SEMI FINALS 1ST LEG

| 1 | Liverpool | v | CHELSEA | 0-2 | 3527 |
|---|---|---|---|---|---|
| 2 | Nottingham Forest | v | NORWICH CITY (10/4) | 0-1 | 2078 |

## SEMI FINALS 2ND LEG

| 1 | CHELSEA | v | Liverpool | 2-1 | 4130 |
|---|---|---|---|---|---|
| 2 | NORWICH CITY | v | Nottingham Forest | 0-1aet | 9690 |

## THE FINAL 1ST LEG

| NORWICH CITY | v | CHELSEA | 1-0 | 21595 |
|---|---|---|---|---|

## THE FINAL 2ND LEG

| CHELSEA | v | NORWICH CITY | 2-3 | 17626 |
|---|---|---|---|---|

## PREVIOUS TEN FINALS

| | | | | Aggregate Score |
|---|---|---|---|---|
| 2012 | Chelsea | v | Blackburn Rovers | 4-1 |
| 2011 | Manchester Utd | v | Sheffield United | 4-1 |
| 2010 | Chelsea | v | Aston Villa | 3-2 |
| 2009 | Arsenal | v | Liverpool | 6-2 |
| 2008 | Manchester City | v | Chelsea | 4-1 |
| 2007 | Liverpool | v | Manchester Utd | 2-2* 4-3p |
| 2006 | Liverpool | v | Manchester City | 3-2 |
| 2005 | Ipswich Town | v | Southampton | 3-2 |
| 2004 | Middlesbrough | v | Aston Villa | 4-0 |
| 2003 | Manchester Utd | v | Middlesbrough | 3-1 |

## FIRST ROUND

| | | | | |
|---|---|---|---|---|
| 1 | Leicestershire & Rutland | v | Birmingham (6/10) | 4-2 |
| 2 | Sheffield & Hallamshire | v | Nottinghamshire (10/10) | 3-2 |
| 3 | North Riding | v | Cumberland (6/10) | 2-2 |
| | (Cumberland won 4-3 on kicks from the penalty mark) | | | |
| 4 | Northumberland | v | Westmorland (13/10) | 7-1 |
| 5 | Shropshire | v | Cheshire (6/10) | 2-4 |
| 6 | Worcestershire | v | BEDFORDSHIRE (13/10) | 0-4 |
| 7 | Devon | v | Norfolk (6/10) | 0-5 |
| 8 | Suffolk | v | Gloucestershire (6/10) | 7-2 |
| 9 | Guernsey | v | Oxfordshire (13/10) | 1-4 |
| 10 | Kent | v | Cornwall (13/10) | 3-1 |
| 11 | Sussex | v | Middlesex (14/10) | 2-2aet |
| | (Sussex won 5-4 on kicks from the penalty mark) | | | |
| 12 | Cambridgeshire | v | Jersey (23/9) | 4-0 |

## SECOND ROUND

| | | | | |
|---|---|---|---|---|
| 1 | East Riding | v | Lincolnshire (3/11) | 2-4 |
| 2 | MANCHESTER | v | Sheffield & Hallamshire (20/10) | 4-1 |
| 3 | Leicestershire & Rutland | v | Cheshire (3/11) | 2-1 |
| 4 | Liverpool | v | Lancashire (17/11) | 3-2aet |
| | (at Liverpool Soccer Centre) | | | |
| 5 | Northumberland | v | Durham (10/11) | 5-5aet |
| | (Northumberland won 5-3 on kicks from the penalty mark) | | | |
| 6 | West Riding | v | Cumberland (3/11) | 4-1 |
| 7 | Isle of Man | v | Staffordshire (10/11) | 1-4 |
| 8 | BEDFORDSHIRE | v | Northamptonshire (5/11) | 5-1 |
| 9 | Berks & Bucks | v | Wiltshire (3/11) | 1-3 |
| 10 | Essex | v | Oxfordshire (10/11) | 4-1 |
| 11 | Hertfordshire | v | Dorset (3/11) | 6-3 |
| 12 | Kent | v | Amateur Football Alliance (3/11) | 0-1 |
| 13 | Norfolk | v | Suffolk (10/11) | 4-1 |
| 14 | London | v | Cambridgeshire (3/11) | 5-2 |
| 15 | Herefordshire | v | Huntingdonshire (10/11) | 5-2 |
| 16 | Somerset | v | Sussex (3/11) | 3-5aet |

## THIRD ROUND

| | | | | |
|---|---|---|---|---|
| 1 | London | v | West Riding (8/12) | 0-4 |
| 2 | Hertfordshire | v | Staffordshire (16/12) | 1-2 |
| 3 | BEDFORDSHIRE | v | Herefordshire (9/12) | 7-1 |
| 4 | Norfolk | v | Amateur Football Alliance (15/12) | 5-0 |
| 5 | Lincolnshire | v | MANCHESTER (5/1) | 0-3 |
| 6 | Essex | v | Wiltshire (15/12) | 1-2 |
| 7 | Sussex | v | Liverpool (8/12) | 0-3 |
| 8 | Leicestershire & Rutland | v | Northumberland (12/1) | 5-0 |

## FOURTH ROUND

| | | | | |
|---|---|---|---|---|
| 1 | Wiltshire | v | Staffordshire (12/1) | 2-1 |
| 2 | Norfolk | v | BEDFORDSHIRE (2/3) | 2-3aet |
| 3 | Leicestershire & Rutland | v | Liverpool (9/2) | 1-2 |
| 4 | West Riding | v | MANCHESTER (9/2) | 1-2aet |

## SEMI FINALS

| | | | | |
|---|---|---|---|---|
| 1 | Wiltshire | v | BEDFORDSHIRE (30/3) | 1-3 |
| | (tie reversed – at The 61 FC (Luton)) | | | |
| 2 | Liverpool | v | MANCHESTER (23/2) | 0-1 |

## THE FINAL

SATURDAY 20 APRIL 2013

| | | | |
|---|---|---|---|
| MANCHESTER | V | BEDFORDSHIRE | 4-4aet 558 |

(Bedfordshire won 4-2 on kicks from the penalty mark)

## PREVIOUS TEN FINALS

| | | | |
|---|---|---|---|
| 2012 | Essex FA | v West Riding FA | 4-2 aet |
| 2011 | Norfolk FA | v Staffordshire FA | 4-2 |
| 2010 | Kent FA | v Sheffield & Hallamshire | 1-0 |
| 2009 | Birmingham FA | v Kent FA | 2-1 |
| 2008 | Suffolk FA | v Cambridgeshire FA | 2-1 |
| 2007 | West Riding FA | v Suffolk FA | 1-1 aet, 4-3p |
| 2006 | Bedfordshire FA | v Durham FA | 3-2 |
| 2005 | Suffolk FA | v Hampshire FA | 2-1 |
| 2004 | Durham FA | v North Riding FA | 4-0 |
| 2003 | Northumberland FA | v Liverpool FA | 1-0 |

# PRELIMINARY ROUND

| | | | | |
|---|---|---|---|---|
| 1 | FC Labour | v | Sportsmans | 0-6 |
| 2 | JOB | v | Queens Park | 4-3 |
| 3 | Alder | v | Lobster | 2-0 |
| 4 | FC Houghton Centre | v | AC Sportsman | 2-4aet |
| 5 | Enfield Rangers | v | London Maccabi Lions | 2-1 |

# FIRST ROUND

| | | | | |
|---|---|---|---|---|
| 1 | Humbledon Plains Farm Nissan v | | Witton Park Rose & Crown | 10-2 |
| 2 | Kelloe WMC | v | Stockton Rosegale N&SA | 3-1 |
| 3 | RCA Grangetown Florists | v | Sportsmans | 2-1 |
| 4 | Herrington CW | v | South Bank (2006) | 2-4 |
| 5 | Hartlepool Rovers Quoit | v | Burradon & New Fordley | 0-1 |
| 6 | Newton Aycliffe WMC | v | Winlaton Commercial | 3-1aet |
| 7 | Coxhoe WMC | v | Cleator Moor | 2-1 |
| 8 | Club Victoria Athletic | v | Northallerton Police | 0-9 |
| 9 | Dawdon Colliery Welfare | v | Hartlepool Athletic Rovers | 4-1 |
| 10 | Thornton United | v | Hessle Rangers | 4-0 |
| 11 | Kirkdale | v | Nicosia | 2-4 |
| 12 | Garston | v | Alder | 2-3 |
| 13 | Mariners | v | HT Sports | 0-1 |
| 14 | St John Fisher OB | v | Oak Tree Pub | 3-0 |
| 15 | Home & Bargain | v | Larkspur | 3-0 |
| 16 | Suttonfields | v | BRNESC | 4-0 |
| 17 | Pineapple | v | Poulton Royal | 1-1aet |
| | (Poulton Royal won 7-6 on kicks from the penalty mark) | | | |
| 18 | Eden Vale | v | St Sebastians | 5-7aet |
| | (tie awarded to Eden Vale – St Sebastians removed) | | | |
| 19 | West Bowling | v | Thirly | 1-1aet |
| | (Thirly won 5-4 on kicks from the penalty mark) | | | |
| 20 | Bolton Woods | v | Drum | 2-1 |
| 21 | Salisbury Athletic | v | St Johns | 3-2 |
| 22 | Chapeltown Fforde Grene v | | JOB | 0-2 |
| 23 | Paddock | v | AFC Blackburn Leisure | 7-0 |
| 24 | Derby Lane Gym | v | OYSTER MARTYRS | 0-7 |
| 25 | Liverpool North | v | Allerton | |
| | (walkover for Allerton – Liverpool North withdrawn) | | | |
| 26 | Bilsthorpe Celtic | v | Premier Sports | 4-1aet |
| 27 | RHP Sports & Social | v | Birstall Stamford | 4-2aet |
| 28 | Whitwick Compass | v | Sileby Athletic | 4-1 |
| 29 | Plough Barfly's | v | Loughborough Saints | |
| | (walkover for Loughborough Saints – Plough Barfly's withdrawn) | | | |
| 30 | Magnet Tavern | v | T8's | 2-5 |
| 31 | Clumber | v | Sparta Moshdock | 3-2aet |
| 32 | Wymeswold | v | Pattesons | 3-2aet |
| 33 | Travellers | v | Sporting Khalsa (Sunday) | 3-6aet |
| 34 | Seven Allstars | v | Pelsall Bush 2012 | |
| | (walkover for Seven Allstars – Pelsall Bush 2012 withdrawn) | | | |
| 35 | Advance Couriers | v | Albion | 2-0 |
| 36 | Duke Of Rutland | v | Hundred Acre | 2-4 |
| 37 | Punchbowl | v | Bartley Green Sunday | 2-1 |
| 38 | AC Sportsman | v | Co-op Sports | 4-3 |
| 39 | Britannia United | v | Highfield Social Club (28/10) | 6-0 |
| 40 | Cube Old Boys | v | AC Cadoza | 0-2 |
| 41 | Crawley Green (Sunday) | v | Club Lewsey | 1-5aet |
| 42 | Wycombe Town | v | Stanbridge & Tilsworth | |
| | (walkover for Stanbridge & Tilsworth – Wycombe Town withdrawn) | | | |
| 43 | Upshire | v | Torrun United (28/10) | 6-1 |
| 44 | New Salamis | v | Manor House | 1-2 |
| 45 | Windmill (Yarmouth) | v | Enfield Rangers (28/10) | 5-0 |
| 46 | Sungate | v | El Sol (28/10) | 0-1 |
| 47 | Bedfont Sunday | v | Broadfields United | 5-2 |
| 48 | Comets Sports Club | v | North Wembley | 5-1 |
| 49 | Dee Road Rangers | v | Hammer (28/10) | 0-2 |
| 50 | Gadeside Rangers | v | Rayners Lane (Sunday) | 3-5 |
| 51 | NLO | v | CB Hounslow United (Sunday) | 1-3 |

| | | | | |
|---|---|---|---|---|
| 52 | AFC Donsville | v | Belstone (Sunday) | 3-3aet |
| | (Belstone won 5-4 on kicks from the penalty mark) | | | |
| 53 | Rosehill Athletic | v | Marquis Rangers | |
| | (walkover for Marquis Rangers – Rosehill Athletic withdrawn) | | | |
| 54 | FC Camberley | v | Putney Town | 5-2 |
| 55 | Lambeth All Stars | v | Artois United | 5-0 |
| 56 | Worthing Park Vale | v | BARNES ALBION (28/10) | 0-2 |
| 57 | AFC Kumazi Strikers | v | Ajax LA | 2-0 |
| 58 | Knighton Arms | v | Windmill | 4-0aet |
| 59 | The Railway Inn | v | Cutters Friday | 7-3 |
| 60 | All Saints | v | Queens Park (Hampshire) | 2-0 |
| 61 | Sporting Bristol | v | Kings Tamerton CA (28/10) | 5-1 |
| 62 | Navy Inn | v | Lebeqs Tavern Courage | 1-6 |

# SECOND ROUND

| | | | | |
|---|---|---|---|---|
| 1 | OYSTER MARTYRS | v | St John Fisher OB (2/12) | 5-0 |
| 2 | Home & Bargain | v | Dawdon Colliery Welfare (2/12) | 3-0 |
| 3 | Thirly | v | Burradon & New Fordley | 1-3 |
| 4 | Hetton Lyons Cricket Club v | | JOB (16/12) | 5-0 |
| 5 | South Bank (2006) | v | Bolton Woods (16/12) | 8-2 |
| 6 | RCA Grangetown Florists | v | Eden Vale | 3-0 |
| 7 | Suttonfields | v | Alder (2/12) | 1-4 |
| 8 | Coxhoe WMC | v | HT Sports (9/12) | 0-5 |
| 9 | Poulton Royal | v | Northallerton Police (2/12) | 0-3 |
| 10 | Canada | v | Kelloe WMC (9/12) | 2-3 |
| 11 | Humbledon Plains Farm Nissan v | | Newton Aycliffe WMC (9/12) | 2-0 |
| 12 | Salisbury Athletic | v | Nicosia (9/12) | 4-1 |
| 13 | Allerton | v | Paddock (2/12) | 2-3 |
| 14 | Loughborough Saints | v | Wymeswold (2/12) | 1-0 |
| 15 | Clumber | v | Hundred Acre (2/12) | 1-4 |
| 16 | Sporting Khalsa (Sunday) | v | Bilsthorpe Celtic (2/12) | 3-2aet |
| 17 | Thornton United | v | Punchbowl (9/12) | 3-7 |
| 18 | RHP Sports & Social | v | Whitwick Compass (2/12) | 1-0 |
| 19 | Advance Couriers | v | T8's | 1-2aet |
| 20 | Stanbridge & Tilsworth | v | Britannia United (9/12) | 3-4aet |
| 21 | Club Lewsey | v | AC Sportsman (2/12) | 2-0 |
| 22 | AC Cadoza | v | Seven Allstars (2/12) | 2-1 |
| 23 | Comets Sports Club | v | Windmill (Yarmouth) (2/12) | 3-2 |
| 24 | Bedfont Sunday | v | Manor House (2/12) | 4-1 |
| 25 | El Sol | v | Upshire (16/12) | 0-1 |
| 26 | FC Camberley | v | AFC Kumazi Strikers (2/12) | 0-5 |
| 27 | BARNES ALBION | v | Knighton Arms (2/12) | 3-1 |
| 28 | CB Hounslow United (Sunday) v | | Hammer | 3-1 |
| 29 | Marquis Rangers | v | Lambeth All Stars (2/12) | 2-4aet |
| 30 | Rayners Lane (Sunday) | v | Belstone (Sunday) (9/12) | 4-1 |
| 31 | Lebeqs Tavern Courage | v | The Railway Inn (2/12) | 4-3aet |
| 32 | Sporting Bristol | v | All Saints (9/12) | 4-0 |

# THIRD ROUND

| | | | | | |
|---|---|---|---|---|---|
| 1 | Alder | v | Humbledon Plains Farm Nissan | 5-2aet | |
| 2 | OYSTER MARTYRS | v | Burradon & New Fordley (6/1) | 3-1 | |
| 3 | Kelloe WMC | v | South Bank (2006) (23/12) | 3-3aet | |
| | (South Bank won 5-4 on kicks from the penalty mark) | | | | |
| 4 | T8's | v | RCA Grangetown Florists (13/1) | 0-1 | |
| 5 | Allerton | v | Home & Bargain (6/1) | 5-3aet | |
| 6 | Hetton Lyons CC | v | Northallerton Police (6/1) | 3-0 | |
| 7 | HT Sports | v | Salisbury Athletic | 3-1 | |
| 8 | Punchbowl | v | Britannia United | 4-1 | |
| 9 | Hundred Acre | v | Comets Sports Club | 2-3aet | |
| 10 | Sporting Khalsa (Sunday) | v | AC Cadoza | 6-3 | |
| 11 | RHP S&S | v | Club Lewsey | 2-5 | |
| 12 | Upshire | v | CB Hounslow Utd (Sunday) (13/1) | 2-0 | |
| 13 | Bedfont Sunday | v | Loughborough Saints | 4-2 | |
| 14 | AFC Kumazi Strikers | v | BARNES ALBION | 2-5aet | |
| 15 | Rayners Lane (Sunday) | v | Lambeth All Stars | 2-0 | |
| 16 | Lebeqs Tavern Courage | v | Sporting Bristol | 2-0 | |

## FOURTH ROUND

| 1 | HT Sports | v | RCA Grangetown Florists (3/2)2-0 | |
| 2 | Hetton Lyons CC | v | Allerton (3/2) | 3-2 |
| 3 | South Bank (2006) | v | Punchbowl (3/2) | 3-0 |
| 4 | **OYSTER MARTYRS** | v | Alder (3/2) | 4-3 |
| 5 | Upshire | v | Rayners Lane (Sunday) (3/2) 2-1 | |
| 6 | **BARNES ALBION** | v | Bedfont Sunday (17/2) | 0-0aet |

(Barnes Albion won 7-6 on kicks from the penalty mark)

| 7 | Club Lewsey | v | Lebeqs Tavern Courage (3/2) 3-4 | |
| 8 | Sporting Khalsa (Sunday) | v | Comets Sports Club (27/1) | 2-3 |

## FIFTH ROUND

| 1 | Lebeqs Tavern Courage | v | Oyster Martyrs | 2-3 |
| 2 | Barnes Albion | v | Hetton Lyons CC (24/2) | 2-1 |
| 3 | Upshire | v | Comets SC | 3-2 |
| 4 | South Bank (2006) | v | HT Sports | 1-3aet |

## SEMI FINALS

| 1 | HT Sports | v | **OYSTER MARTYRS** | 2-3 | 350 |
| | (at Guiseley FC) | | | | |
| 2 | **BARNES ALBION** | v | Upshire (24/3) | 4-3aet | 252 |
| | (at Staines Town FC) | | | | |

## THE FINAL

SUNDAY 21 APRIL 2013

| BARNES ALBION | V | OYSTER MARTYRS | 3-4 | 392 |

AT BURTON ALBION FC

# UEFA REGIONS' CUP

## SECOND QUALIFYING ROUND

### GROUP 6

| Leinster & Munster | v | **JERSEY** | 1-2 |

**JERSEY TEAM:**
James Styles
Jay Reid (Aaron Parkinson 85 min)
Christopher Andrews
Craig Russell (Joseph Murphy 90)
Luke Watson (C)
James Scott
Jack McKenna
Luke Campbell
Jack Cannon (Goal 53)
Ben Gallichan
Jamie Savory (Goal 54 - Ross Crick 70)
Non-Playing Subs: Craig Fletcher (Gk), Russell Le Feuvre.

| **JERSEY** | v | **Eastern Region** | 1-2 |

**JERSEY TEAM:**
James Styles
Jay Reid
Christopher Andrews (Charlie Petulla 85)
Craig Russell (Goal 64)
Luke Watson (C)
James Scott
Jack McKenna (Stuart Andre 46)
Luke Campbell
Jack Cannon
Ben Gallichan
Jamie Savory (Joseph Murphy 70)
Non-Playing Subs: Craig Fletcher (Gk), Aaron Parkinson, Ross Crick,
Russell Le Feuvre.

| **JERSEY** | v | **San Marino** | 1-0 |

**JERSEY TEAM:**
Craig Fletcher
Aaron Parkinson
Luke Watson (C) (Goal 70)
James Scott
Charlie Petulla (Craig Russell 46)
Luke Campbell
Jack Cannon
Ben Gallichan
Joseph Murphy
Russell Le Feuvre (Jamie Savory 71)
Stuart Andre
Non-Playing Subs: James Styles (Gk)

### FINAL GROUP 6 TABLE

| | | | | | | | | |
|---|---|---|---|---|---|---|---|---|
| Eastern Region | 3 | 2 | 0 | 1 | 3 | 3 | 0 | 6 |
| **JERSEY** | 3 | 2 | 0 | 1 | 4 | 3 | 1 | 6 |
| Leinster & Munster | 3 | 1 | 1 | 1 | 3 | 2 | 1 | 4 |
| San Marino | 3 | 0 | 1 | 2 | 0 | 2 | -2 | 1 |

Eastern Region qualify for UEFA Regions' Cup Finals

Other Results

| San Marino | v | Eatern Region | 0-1 |
| San Marino | v | Leinster & Munster | 0-0 |
| Eastern Region | v | Leinster & Munster | 0-2 |

### GROUP 3

| Württemberg | v | West Central Scotland | 6-1 |
| West Central Scotland | v | East Region | 2-4 |
| West Central Scotland | v | Zlin | 2-6 |

## FIRST QUALIFYING ROUND

| | | | | |
|---|---|---|---|---|
| 1 | Chester-Le-Street Town | v | York City | 6-1 |
| 2 | Crown Newlaithes | v | Jarrow Ladies | 1-5 |
| | (at Creighton RUFC, Carlisle) | | | |
| 3 | Consett | v | Peterlee St Francis | 1-12 |
| 4 | Forest Hall Women's | v | Durham Wildcats | 0-10 |
| 5 | Redcar Athletic | v | Kendal Town | 3-3aet |
| | (Kendal Town won 3-2 on kicks from the penalty mark) | | | |
| 6 | Workington Reds | v | Whitley Bay | 0-5 |
| | (at Workington FC) | | | |
| 7 | Lowick United | v | Norton & Stockton Ancients | 3-5 |
| 8 | North Shields | v | Birtley Town | 5-2 |
| 9 | Whickham Fellside | v | California | 5-0 |
| 10 | Keighley Oaks | v | Steel City Wanderers | 0-2 |
| 11 | Appleby Frodingham | v | Rothwell | 0-12 |
| 12 | Barnsley | v | Kirklees | 3-0 |
| 13 | Bradford Park Avenue | v | Brighouse | 5-1 |
| 14 | Handsworth | v | Guiseley AFC Ladies | 0-3 |
| 15 | Wetherby Athletic | v | Ossett Albion | 1-4 |
| 16 | Accrington Girls & Ladies | v | Tranmere Rovers | 3-5 |
| 17 | Crewe Alexandra | v | Irlam | 3-1 |
| 18 | Warrington Town | v | Blackpool Ladies | 1-11 |
| 19 | Padiham | v | Preston North End | 2-3 |
| 20 | Middleton Athletic | v | City of Manchester | 3-5 |
| 21 | Morecambe | v | Blackpool Wren Rovers | 4-1 |
| 22 | Long Eaton United | v | Nettleham | 1-2 |
| 23 | Sandiacre Town | v | Retford United | 4-2 |
| 24 | Oadby & Wigston Dynamo | v | Dronfield Town | 2-1aet |
| 25 | West Bridgford | v | Mansfield Town | 1-6 |
| 26 | Ruddington Village | v | Rise Park | 3-4 |
| 27 | Arnold Town | v | Lutterworth Athletic | 2-6 |
| 28 | Birmingham & West Mids Police | v | AFC Telford United Ladies | 7-1 |
| 29 | Cottage Farm Rangers | v | Coventry Sphinx | 0-9 |
| 30 | Coventry Ladies Development | v | Walsall | 2-3 |
| 31 | Pegasus Juniors | v | Malvern Town | 2-1 |
| 32 | Bradwell Belles | v | FC Reedswood Ladies | 0-8 |
| 33 | Allscott | v | Lightwood | 2-1 |
| 34 | TNS | v | Bilbrook | 4-1 |
| 35 | Lichfield Diamonds | v | Crusaders | 0-2 |
| 36 | Lye Town | v | Kenilworth Town KH | 1-7 |
| 37 | Shenstone | v | Ellistown | 1-2 |
| 38 | Peterborough Sports Parkway | v | Raunds Town | 10-0 |
| 39 | AFC Trinity | v | Gt Shelford | 6-5 |
| 40 | Roade | v | Outwell Swifts | |
| | (walkover for Roade – Outwell Swifts withdrawn) | | | |
| 41 | Netherton United | v | Stewarts & Lloyds Corby | 3-1 |
| 42 | Huntingdon Town | v | Brackley Sports | 4-3 |
| 43 | AFC Sudbury Ladies | v | Colchester Town | 5-2 |
| 44 | Chelmsford City | v | Fakenham Town | |
| | (walkover for Chelmsford City – Fakenham Town withdrawn) | | | |
| 45 | Hutton | v | Haverhill Rovers | 2-3 |
| 46 | Hockering | v | Wymondham Town | 1-3 |
| 47 | West Billericay | v | Assandun Vikings | 5-0 |
| 48 | Hethersett Athletic | v | Lowestoft Town | 4-2 |
| 49 | Leighton United Vixens | v | Leverstock Green | 2-1 |
| 50 | Barking | v | Stevenage Borough | 4-2 |
| 51 | Standon & Puckeridge | v | Sandy | 4-1 |
| 52 | MSA | v | Sawbridgeworth Town | 3-1 |
| 53 | Kikk United | v | Haringey Borough | 3-1 |

| | | | | |
|---|---|---|---|---|
| 54 | Royston Town | v | St Albans City | 0-1 |
| 55 | Old Actonians | v | Launton | 1-3 |
| 56 | Maidenhead United | v | Banbury United | 5-1 |
| 57 | Tring Athletic | v | City Belles | 2-4aet |
| 58 | Headington | v | Denham United | 0-5 |
| 59 | Oxford City | v | Ascot United | 5-0 |
| 60 | Reading | v | Colne Valley | 1-2 |
| 61 | Marlow | v | Bracknell Town | 4-6 |
| 62 | Hemel Hempstead Town | v | Newbury | 6-3 |
| 63 | Abbey Rangers | v | Meridian | 2-1aet |
| 64 | Rusthall | v | Maidstone United Rascals | 1-4 |
| 65 | Ashford Girls | v | South Park | 4-1 |
| 66 | AFC Wimbledon Ladies | v | East Preston | |
| | (walkover for AFC Wimbledon Ladies – East Preston removed) | | | |
| 67 | Ramsgate | v | Crawley Wasps | 2-5 |
| 68 | Milford & Witley | v | Eastbourne | 0-6 |
| 69 | Eastbourne Town | v | Claygate Royals | 8-1 |
| 70 | Parkwood Rangers | v | Anchorians | 3-3aet |
| | (Parkwood won 5-4 on kicks from the penalty mark) | | | |
| 71 | Haywards Heath Town | v | London Corinthians | 3-4 |
| 72 | Long Lane | v | Bexhill United | 3-2 |
| 73 | Prince of Wales | v | Knaphill | 2-3aet |
| 74 | Regents Park Rangers | v | Battersea Ironsides | 2-2aet |
| | (Battersea Ironsides won 7-6 on kicks from the penalty mark) | | | |
| 75 | Victoire | v | Maidstone Town | |
| | (walkover for Maidstone Town – Victoire withdrawn) | | | |
| 76 | Dartford YMCA | v | Westfield | 1-4 |
| 77 | Rottingdean Village | v | New Forest | 3-1 |
| 78 | Weymouth | v | Aldershot Town | 3-3aet |
| | (Aldershot Town won 3-2 on kicks from the penalty mark) | | | |
| 79 | Parley | v | Shanklin | 1-5 |
| 80 | Fleet Town | v | Poole Town | 0-5 |
| 81 | Swindon Spitfires | v | Gosport Borough | 2-1 |
| 82 | Wootton Bassett Town | v | Southampton Women's | 2-6 |
| 83 | Andover New Street | v | Christchurch | 3-1 |
| 84 | Cheltenham Civil Service | v | Brislington | 0-6 |
| 85 | Quedgeley Wanderers | v | Bristol Ladies Union | 2-7 |
| 86 | St Nicholas | v | Launceston | 3-2 |
| 87 | Forest Of Dean | v | Heavitree Social | 1-0 |
| 88 | Larkhall Athletic | v | Bude Town | 5-1 |
| 89 | Ilminster Town | v | Street | 6-0 |
| 90 | Pen Mill | v | Bitton | 3-5 |
| 91 | Falmouth Town | v | Cheltenham Town | 8-2 |
| 92 | Downend Flyers | v | AEK Boco | 9-1 |
| 93 | Bridgwater Town | v | Stoke Lane | 3-4 |

## SECOND QUALIFYING ROUND

| | | | | |
|---|---|---|---|---|
| 1 | Jarrow Ladies | v | Whitley Bay | 2-1 |
| 2 | Peterlee St Francis | v | Whickham Fellside | 7-1 |
| 3 | Kendal Town | v | Chester-Le-Street Town | 1-5 |
| 4 | Abbeytown | v | North Shields | 3-1 |
| 5 | Prudhoe Town | v | Penrith | 2-5 |
| 6 | Norton & Stockton Ancients | v | Durham Wildcats | 2-8 |
| 7 | Guiseley AFC Ladies | v | Barnsley | 1-3 |
| 8 | Ossett Albion | v | Hull City | 2-6 |
| 9 | Steel City Wanderers | v | Bradford Park Avenue | 6-2 |
| 10 | Rothwell | v | Westella & Willerby | 4-2 |
| 11 | City of Manchester | v | Blackpool Ladies (21/10) | 1-2 |
| 12 | Morecambe | v | Birkenhead | 7-0 |

| | | | | |
|---|---|---|---|---|
| 13 | Tranmere Rovers | v | Preston North End | 3-0 |
| 14 | Crewe Alexandra | v | Chester City | 1-0 |
| 15 | Rise Park | v | Nettleham | 2-1 |
| 16 | Mansfield Town | v | Oadby & Wigston Dynamo | 4-1 |
| 17 | Sandiacre Town | v | Lutterworth Athletic | 3-4 |
| 18 | Pegasus Juniors | v | Ellistown | 1-3 |
| 19 | Kenilworth Town KH | v | TNS | 1-4 |
| 20 | FC Reedswood Ladies | v | Crusaders | 6-2 |
| 21 | Walsall | v | Coventry Sphinx | 2-3 |
| 22 | Birmingham & West Mids Police | v | Allscott | 2-1 |
| 23 | Huntingdon Town | v | Roade | 2-5 |
| 24 | Peterborough Northern Star | v | Hampton | 7-3 |
| 25 | Peterborough Sports Parkway | v | Netherton United | 10-1 |
| 26 | AFC Trinity | v | Moulton | 6-2 |
| 27 | West Billericay | v | Haverhill Rovers | 4-0 |
| 28 | Hethersett Athletic | v | Billericay Town | 0-2 |
| 29 | AFC Sudbury Ladies | v | Wymondham Town | 3-1 |
| 30 | Chelmsford City | v | C&K Basildon | 2-3 |
| 31 | Kikk United | v | Leighton United Vixens | 9-3 |
| 32 | MSA | v | Standon & Puckeridge | 3-1 |
| 33 | Barking | v | St Albans City | 6-1 |
| 34 | Oxford City | v | City Belles | 3-0 |
| 35 | Colne Valley | v | Bracknell Town | 4-1 |
| 36 | Launton | v | Denham United | 0-4 |
| 37 | Maidenhead United | v | Hemel Hempstead Town | 4-1 |
| 38 | Panthers | v | Long Lane | 4-2 |
| 39 | Ashford Girls | v | Battersea Ironsides | 3-5 |
| 40 | London Corinthians | v | Maidstone United Rascals | 14-0 |
| 41 | Maidstone Town | v | Rottingdean Village | 9-1 |
| 42 | Knaphill | v | Eastbourne Town | 1-4 |
| 43 | Eastbourne | v | Westfield | 0-7 |
| 44 | AFC Wimbledon Ladies | v | Abbey Rangers | 6-0 |
| 45 | Parkwood Rangers | v | Crawley Wasps | 2-1 |
| 46 | Southampton Women's | v | Aldershot Town | 0-3 |
| 47 | Swindon Spitfires | v | Poole Town | 3-4aet |
| 48 | Shanklin | v | Andover New Street | 2-0 |
| 49 | Forest Of Dean | v | Stoke Lane | 3-1 |
| 50 | Downend Flyers | v | Bitton | 4-2 |
| 51 | Larkhall Athletic | v | Falmouth Town | 5-1 |
| 52 | St Nicholas | v | Bristol Ladies Union | 1-3 |
| 53 | Brislington | v | Ilminster Town | 4-2 |

## THIRD QUALIFYING ROUND

| | | | | |
|---|---|---|---|---|
| 1 | Steel City Wanderers | v | Blackpool Ladies | 0-2 |
| 2 | Abbeytown | v | Leeds City Vixens | 0-4 |
| 3 | Sheffield United Community | v | Jarrow Ladies | 1-0 |
| 4 | Chorley | v | Rotherham United | 4-1 |
| 5 | Middlesbrough | v | Curzon Ashton | 6-4 |
| 6 | Cheadle Heath Nomads | v | Huddersfield Town | 0-4 |
| 7 | Peterlee St Francis | v | Hull City | 1-0 |
| | (tie awarded to Peterlee St Francis – Hull City failed to fulfil the fixture) | | | |
| 8 | Durham Wildcats | v | Wakefield Ladies | 10-0 |
| 9 | Mossley Hill | v | South Durham & Cestria | 2-1 |
| 10 | Chester-Le-Street Town | v | Stockport County | 1-7 |
| 11 | Bradford City | v | Rothwell | 4-0 |
| 12 | Crewe Alexandra | v | Tranmere Rovers | 3-1 |
| 13 | Penrith | v | Morecambe | 2-6 |
| 14 | Barnsley | v | Liverpool Feds | 1-2 |
| 15 | Ellistown | v | Stoke City | 0-4 |

| | | | | |
|---|---|---|---|---|
| 16 | Rise Park | v | Coventry Sphinx | 2-1 |
| 17 | Loughborough Foxes | v | Daventry Town | 5-0 |
| 18 | Loughborough Students | v | Copsewood Coventry | 0-3 |
| 19 | Lutterworth Athletic | v | Mansfield Town | 4-1 |
| 20 | Leicester City | v | FC Reedswood Ladies | 4-3 |
| 21 | Radcliffe Olympic | v | TNS | 2-0 |
| 22 | Leamington Lions | v | MK Dons | 0-3 |
| 23 | Leafield Athletic | v | Birmingham & West Midlands Police | 5-4 |
| 24 | MSA | v | AFC Trinity | 2-1aet |
| 25 | Billericay Town | v | Brentwood Town | 2-4 |
| 26 | Arlesey Town | v | Peterborough Northern Star | 2-0 |
| 27 | Norwich City | v | Luton Town Ladies | 2-4 |
| 28 | Cambridge Women's | v | Kikk United (18/11) | 3-1 |
| | (at Ely City FC) | | | |
| 29 | Peterborough Sports Parkway | v | C&K Basildon | 3-4aet |
| 30 | Chesham United | v | Roade | 15-0 |
| 31 | Barking | v | Enfield Town | 0-4 |
| 32 | Oxford City | v | Ipswich Town | 0-7 |
| 33 | AFC Sudbury Ladies | v | West Billericay | 5-1 |
| 34 | AFC Wimbledon Ladies | v | Aldershot Town | 1-0 |
| 35 | London Corinthians | v | Panthers | 7-1 |
| 36 | Oxford United | v | Battersea Ironsides | 5-0 |
| 37 | Eastbourne Town | v | Southampton Saints | 0-1 |
| 38 | Maidenhead United | v | Colne Valley | 2-3 |
| 39 | Chichester City | v | Denham United | 1-0 |
| 40 | Maidstone Town | v | University of Portsmouth | 1-3 |
| 41 | Westfield | v | Ebbsfleet United | 3-2 |
| 42 | Crystal Palace | v | Parkwood Rangers | 1-4 |
| 43 | Shanklin | v | Brislington | 1-3 |
| 44 | Forest of Dean | v | Exeter City | 3-9 |
| 45 | Forest Green Rovers | v | Downend Flyers | 7-3 |
| 46 | Plymouth Argyle | v | Keynsham Town Development | 4-2 |
| 47 | Poole Town | v | Swindon Town | 1-9 |
| 48 | Larkhall Athletic | v | Bristol Ladies Union | 2-0 |
| 49 | Gloucester City | v | Keynsham Town | 0-5 |
| | Bye - Newquay | | | |

## FIRST ROUND

| | | | | |
|---|---|---|---|---|
| 1 | Chorley | v | Morecambe | 2-4 |
| 2 | Leeds City Vixens | v | Huddersfield Town (16/12) | 3-3aet |
| | (Huddersfield Town won 5-4 on kicks from the penalty mark) | | | |
| 3 | Bradford City | v | Stockport County | 3-1 |
| 4 | Middlesbrough | v | Peterlee St Francis | 5-2 |
| 5 | Durham Wildcats | v | Blackpool Ladies | 4-0 |
| 6 | Sheffield United Community | v | Mossley Hill | 2-1 |
| 7 | Liverpool Feds | v | Crewe Alexandra | 1-0 |
| 8 | Loughborough Foxes | v | Leicester City | 1-0 |
| 9 | Stoke City | v | Leafield Athletic | 2-3 |
| 10 | MK Dons | v | Luton Town Ladies | 2-1 |
| 11 | Rise Park | v | Copsewood Coventry | 1-3 |
| 12 | Radcliffe Olympic | v | Lutterworth Athletic | 6-1 |
| 13 | Arlesey Town | v | C&K Basildon | 1-3 |
| 14 | AFC Sudbury Ladies | v | London Corinthians | 0-5 |
| 15 | Cambridge Women's | v | Brentwood Town | 4-0 |
| 16 | Enfield Town | v | Chesham United | 1-3 |
| 17 | Parkwood Rangers | v | Colne Valley | 1-4 |
| 18 | Ipswich Town | v | AFC Wimbledon | 5-1 |
| 19 | Westfield | v | MSA | 2-1 |
| 20 | Forest Green Rovers | v | Plymouth Argyle | 2-3aet |

| 21 | Southampton Saints | v | Larkhall Athletic | 0-2aet |
| 22 | Keynsham Town | v | University of Portsmouth | 8-0 |
| 23 | Chichester City | v | Swindon Town | 1-4 |
| 24 | Oxford United | v | Newquay | 2-1 |
| 25 | Exeter City | v | Brislington | 7-0 |

## SECOND ROUND

| 1 | Middlesbrough | v | Huddersfield Town | 4-1 |
| 2 | Leicester City | v | Preston North End | 0-2 |
| 3 | Newcastle United | v | Radcliffe Olympic | 2-0 |
| 4 | Sheffield United Community | v | Durham Wildcats | 4-2 |
| 5 | Nottingham Forest | v | Bradford City (3/2) | 6-3 |
| 6 | Sheffield FC Ladies | v | Blackburn Rovers | 2-1 |
| 7 | Loughborough Foxes | v | Derby County | 0-2 |
| 8 | Morecambe | v | Liverpool Feds | 6-3 |
| 9 | Millwall Lionesses | v | Wolverhampton Wanderers | 3-1 |
| 10 | Gillingham | v | MK Dons | 6-1 |
| 11 | London Corinthians | v | West Ham United | 0-3 |
| 12 | Leafield Athletic | v | C&K Basildon | 6-0 |
| 13 | Ipswich Town | v | Cambridge Women's | 1-0 |
| 14 | Chesham United | v | Queens Park Rangers | 1-2aet |
| 15 | Colchester United | v | Sporting Club Albion | 1-5 |
| 16 | Tottenham Hotspur | v | Copsewood Coventry | 2-0 |
| 17 | Westfield | v | Brighton & Hove Albion | 2-9 |
| 18 | Oxford United | v | Keynsham Town | 6-1 |
| 19 | Lewes | v | Reading FC Women | 1-2 |
| 20 | Exeter City | v | Swindon Town | 2-3 |
| 21 | Colne Valley | v | Yeovil Town | 0-8 |
| 22 | Larkhall Athletic | v | Plymouth Argyle | 0-2 |

## THIRD ROUND

| 1 | Middlesbrough | v | Sunderland | 1-6 |
| 2 | Charlton Athletic | v | Oxford United | 1-2 |
| 3 | Newcastle United | v | Plymouth Argyle | 2-1 |
| 4 | Coventry City | v | Morecambe | 2-1 |
| 5 | Tottenham Hotspur | v | Cardiff City | 0-4 |
| 6 | Reading FC Women | v | Brighton & Hove Albion | 4-2 |
| 7 | Portsmouth | v | Queens Park Rangers | 5-0 |
| 8 | Ipswich Town | v | Aston Villa | 0-2 |
| 9 | Barnet FC Ladies | v | Yeovil Town | 0-3 |
| 10 | Leafield Athletic | v | Sporting Club Albion | 2-3 |
| 11 | Preston North End | v | Millwall Lionesses | 3-2 |
| 12 | Swindon Town | v | Gillingham | 0-1aet |
| 13 | Leeds United | v | West Ham United | 3-2 |
| 14 | Manchester City | v | Sheffield FC Ladies | 3-2 |
| 15 | Derby County | v | Watford | 0-4 |
| 16 | Sheffield United Community | v | Nottingham Forest (17/2) | 1-5 |

## FOURTH ROUND

| 1 | Yeovil Town | v | Portsmouth | 3-0 |
| 2 | Gillingham | v | Nottingham Forest | 2-3 |
| 3 | Coventry City | v | Manchester City | 0-1 |
| 4 | Watford | v | Leeds United | 0-2 |
| 5 | Cardiff City | v | Reading FC Women | 2-1aet |
| 6 | Oxford United | v | Newcastle United | 2-1 |
| 7 | Sporting Club Albion | v | Sunderland | 1-2 |
| 8 | Aston Villa | v | Preston North End | 3-0 |

## FIFTH ROUND

| 1 | Sunderland | v | Manchester City | 4-0 |
| 2 | Aston Villa | v | Liverpool | 0-5 |
| 3 | Doncaster Rovers Belles | v | Bristol Academy | 0-2 |
| 4 | Cardiff City | v | Birmingham City | 1-3 |
| 5 | Nottingham Forest | v | Arsenal (31/3) | 0-7 |
| 6 | Oxford United | v | Everton (30/3) | 0-7 |
| 7 | Lincoln | v | Chelsea | 1-0 |
| 8 | Leeds United | v | Yeovil Town | 4-0 |

## SIXTH ROUND

| 1 | Arsenal | v | Birmingham City | 6-0 | 520 |
| | (at Bishop's Stortford FC) | | | | |
| 2 | Bristol Academy | v | Everton | 3-2 | |
| | (at Stoke Gifford Stadium, Bristol) | | | | |
| 3 | Sunderland | v | Liverpool | 1-2 | |
| 4 | Lincoln | v | Leeds United | 4-0 | |

## SEMI FINALS

| 1 | Bristol Academy | v | Lincoln | 2-0 | 900 |
| | (at Bristol City FC) | | | | |
| 2 | Liverpool | v | Arsenal (26/4) | 1-2 | 2008 |
| | (at Anfield, Liverpool FC) | | | | |

## THE FINAL

SUNDAY 26 MAY 2012

ARSENAL    v    BRISTOL ACADEMY    3-0

AT DONCASTER ROVERS FC

# THE FA NATIONAL FUTSAL LEAGUE

## NATIONAL LEAGUES

### NORTH

| | P | W | D | L | F | A | GD | Pts |
|---|---|---|---|---|---|---|---|---|
| 1 Sheffield Futsal Club | 14 | 12 | 1 | 1 | 109 | 37 | 72 | 37 |
| 2 Manchester Futsal Club | 14 | 10 | 3 | 1 | 108 | 38 | 70 | 33 |
| 3 Middlesbrough Futsal Club | 14 | 8 | 1 | 5 | 88 | 56 | 32 | 25 |
| 4 CYDC Leeds Futsal Club | 14 | 8 | 1 | 5 | 70 | 42 | 28 | 25 |
| 5 Liverpool Futsal Club | 14 | 7 | 0 | 7 | 92 | 78 | 14 | 21 |
| 6 Leeds & Wakefield Futsal Club | 14 | 6 | 0 | 8 | 90 | 131 | -41 | 18 |
| 7 Hull Futsal Club | 14 | 2 | 0 | 12 | 44 | 134 | -90 | 6 |
| 8 F.S Derby Willows | 14 | 0 | 0 | 14 | 47 | 132 | -85 | 0 |

### MIDLANDS

| | P | W | D | L | F | A | GD | Pts |
|---|---|---|---|---|---|---|---|---|
| 1 Team Bath Futsal Club | 14 | 12 | 1 | 1 | 107 | 42 | 65 | 37 |
| 2 Oxford City Lions Futsal Team | 14 | 11 | 2 | 1 | 143 | 41 | 102 | 35 |
| 3 Loughborough Student Futsal Club | 14 | 8 | 2 | 4 | 107 | 62 | 45 | 26 |
| 4 Birmingham Futsal Club | 14 | 7 | 2 | 5 | 71 | 59 | 12 | 23 |
| 5 Birmingham Tigers Futsal Club | 14 | 3 | 2 | 9 | 55 | 93 | -38 | 11 |
| 6 Hereford Futsal Club | 14 | 3 | 2 | 9 | 40 | 90 | -50 | 11 |
| 7 Gloucester Futsal Revolution | 14 | 3 | 2 | 9 | 48 | 129 | -81 | 11 |
| 8 Cardiff City FC Futsal | 14 | 2 | 1 | 11 | 36 | 91 | -55 | 7 |

### SOUTH

| | P | W | D | L | F | A | GD | Pts |
|---|---|---|---|---|---|---|---|---|
| 1 Helvecia Futsal Club | 14 | 12 | 1 | 1 | 96 | 27 | 69 | 37 |
| 2 Baku United FC | 14 | 9 | 2 | 3 | 83 | 42 | 41 | 29 |
| 3 London United Futsal Club | 14 | 8 | 3 | 3 | 70 | 39 | 31 | 27 |
| 4 FC Baltic United | 14 | 8 | 2 | 4 | 72 | 50 | 22 | 26 |
| 5 Kaunas FC | 14 | 6 | 0 | 8 | 58 | 73 | -15 | 18 |
| 6 Genesis Futsal Club | 14 | 4 | 2 | 8 | 66 | 88 | -22 | 14 |
| 7 West London Futsal | 14 | 1 | 2 | 11 | 40 | 83 | -43 | 5 |
| 8 Kickers Futsal | 14 | 1 | 2 | 11 | 27 | 110 | -83 | 5 |

## SUPER LEAGUE

### GROUP A

| | P | W | D | L | F | A | GD | Pts |
|---|---|---|---|---|---|---|---|---|
| 1 Sheffield Futsal Club | 4 | 2 | 0 | 2 | 17 | 11 | 6 | 6 |
| 2 Oxford City Lions Futsal Team | 4 | 2 | 0 | 2 | 19 | 17 | 2 | 6 |
| 3 FC Baltic United | 4 | 2 | 0 | 2 | 20 | 28 | -8 | 6 |

### GROUP B

| | P | W | D | L | F | A | GD | Pts |
|---|---|---|---|---|---|---|---|---|
| 1 Helvecia Futsal Club | 4 | 3 | 1 | 0 | 20 | 10 | 10 | 10 |
| 2 Manchester Futsal Club | 4 | 2 | 0 | 2 | 24 | 16 | 8 | 6 |
| 3 Birmingham Futsal Club | 4 | 0 | 1 | 3 | 10 | 28 | -18 | 1 |

### GROUP C

| | P | W | D | L | F | A | GD | Pts |
|---|---|---|---|---|---|---|---|---|
| 1 London United Futsal Club | 4 | 3 | 0 | 1 | 19 | 10 | 9 | 9 |
| 2 Middlesbrough Futsal Club | 4 | 2 | 1 | 1 | 17 | 17 | 0 | 7 |
| 3 Team Bath Futsal Club | 4 | 0 | 1 | 3 | 13 | 22 | -9 | 1 |

### GROUP D

| | P | W | D | L | F | A | GD | Pts |
|---|---|---|---|---|---|---|---|---|
| 1 Baku United FC | 4 | 3 | 1 | 0 | 39 | 6 | 33 | 10 |
| 2 Loughborough Student Futsal Club | 4 | 2 | 1 | 1 | 24 | 20 | 4 | 7 |
| 3 CYDC Leeds Futsal Club | 4 | 0 | 0 | 4 | 9 | 46 | -37 | 0 |

### GRAND FINAL

Baku United claimed their first FA National Futsal League title beating five time champions Helvecia 3-1 on penalties having finished 3-3 after extra time. Baku beat Sheffield FC in their semi-final whilst Helvecia reached their sixth consecutive final at the expence of London United.

# ENGLAND FUTSAL RESULTS 2012-13

| Date | Opponent | H/A | Competition | Result | |
|---|---|---|---|---|---|
| Dec 6 | Denmark | A | Friendly | W | 3-2 |
| Dec 7 | Norway | A | Friendly | D | 1-1 |
| 2013 | | | | | |
| Jan 6 | Malta | A | Friendly | W | 2-0 |
| Jan 7 | Greece | A | Friendly | L | 0-3 |
| Jan 9 | Georgia | A | Friendly | D | 2-2 |
| Jan 25 | Lithuania | A | European Championship 2013 - Preliminary Qual. | W | 4-3 |
| Jan 26 | Cyprus | H | European Championship 2013 - Preliminary Qual. | W | 2-1 |
| Feb 8 | Turkey | H | Friendly | L | 2-5 |
| Feb 9 | Turkey | H | Friendly | L | 0-2 |
| Mar 17 | Wales | H | Friendly | W | 1-0 |
| Mar 27 | Ukraine | A | European Championship 2013 - Main Round | L | 0-7 |
| Mar 28 | Turkey | A | European Championship 2013 - Main Round | L | 3-4 |
| Mar 30 | Slovenia | H | European Championship 2013 - Main Round | L | 2-5 |
| June 6 | USA | H | Friendly | L | 1-2 |

# Click Back in Time!

Over 36 years of publishing the Non-League Club Directory has filled a room full of information and photographs covering the game we know and love.

What we intend, over time, is to create a website that shares with you everything we have accumulated, which we hope will bring back some fond memories of season's gone by.

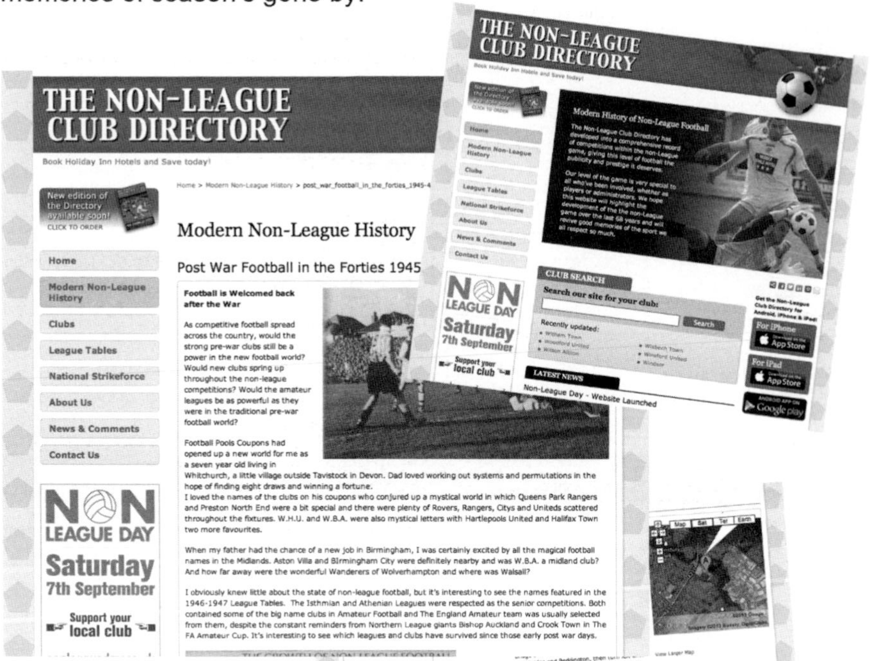

A unique look back at how the game has evolved since the 1940s will also make for interesting reading, including league tables from season's gone by.

Log on to **www.non-leagueclubdirectory.co.uk** today and see how many faces from teams gone by you recognise

# COUNTY FOOTBALL ASSOCIATION CONTACTS

**AMATEUR FOOTBALL ALLIANCE**
CEO: Mike Brown
Address: Unit 3, 7 Wenlock Road, London, N1 7SL
Tel: 020 8733 2613 Fax: 020 7250 1338
Website: www.amateur-fa.com
Email: info@amateur-fa.com
Chairman: David Dunn

**ARMY FA**
Secretary: Major Billy Thomson
Address: Ministry of Defence (ASCB), Clayton Barracks,
Thornhill Road, Aldershot, Hampshire, GU11 2BG
Tel: 01252 348 571/4 Fax: 01252 348 630/b
Website: www.armyfa.com
Email: info@armyfa.com
Chairman: Major Gen. M.D. Wood CBE

**BEDFORDSHIRE FA**
CEO: Peter Brown
Address: Century House, Skimpot Road, Dunstable,
Bedfordshire, LU5 4JU
Tel: 01582 565 111 Fax: 01582 565 222/b
Website: www.bedfordshirefa.com
Email: info@bedfordshirefa.com
Chairman: Richard Robinson

**BERKS & BUCKS FA**
CEO: Brian Moore
Address: 15a London Street, Faringdon, Oxon, SN7 7HD
Tel: 01367 242 099 Fax: 01367 242 158
Website: www.berks-bucksfa.com
Email: info@berks-bucksfa.com
Chairman: Jim Atkins

**BIRMINGHAM FA**
CEO: Mike Pennick
Address: Ray Hall Lane, Great Barr, Birmingham, B43 6JF
Tel: 0121 357 4278 Fax: 0121 358 1661
Website: www.birminghamfa.com
Email: info@birminghamfa.com
Chairman: Roger Wood

**CAMBRIDGESHIRE FA**
Chief Executive: Chris Pringle
Address: Bridge Road, Impington, Cambridgeshire, CB24 9PH
Tel: 01223 209 025 Fax: 01223 209 030
Website: www.cambridgeshirefa.com
Email: info@cambridgeshirefa.com
Chairman: Bill Coad

**CHESHIRE FA**
CEO: Ms Maureen Dunford
Address: Hartford House, Hartford Moss Recreation Centre,
Northwich, Cheshire, CW8 4BG
Tel: 01606 871 166 Fax: 01606 871 292
Website: www.cheshirefa.com
Email: info@cheshirefa.com
Chairman: Eddie Crabtree

**CORNWALL FA**
CEO: Dawn Aberdeen
Address: Kernow House, 15 Callywith Gate, Launceston
Road, Bodmin, Cornwall, PL31 2RQ
Tel: 01208 269010 Fax: 01208 892665
Website: www.cornwallfa.com
Email: secretary@cornwallfa.com
Chairman: Geoff Lee

**CUMBERLAND FA**
CEO: Geoff Turrell
Address: 17 Oxford Street, Workington, Cumbria, CA14 2AL
Tel: 01900 872 310 Fax: 01900 616 470
Website: www.cumberlandfa.com
Email: secretary@cumberlandfa.com
Chairman: Fred Conway

**DERBYSHIRE FA**
CEO: Dawn Heron
Address: Units 8-9 Stadium Business Ct, Millenium Way, Pride
Park, Derby, DE24 8HZ
Tel: 01332 361 422 Fax: 01332 360 130
Website: www.derbyshirefa.com
Email: info@derbyshirefa.com
Chairman: Dave Heron

**DEVON FA**
CEO: Paul Morrison
Address: Coach Road, Newton Abbot, Devon, TQ12 1EJ
Tel: 01626 332 077
Fax: 01626 336 814/b
Website: www.devonfa.com
Email: info@devonfa.com
Chairman: Dennis Smith

**DORSET FA**
CEO: Sue Hough
Address: County Ground, Blanford Close, Hamworthy, Poole,
BH15 4BF
Tel: 01202 682 375
Fax: 01202 666 577
Website: www.dorsetfa.com
Email: footballoperations@dorsetfa.com
Chairman: Douglas Smurthwaite

**DURHAM FA**
CEO: John Topping
Address: Chester le Street Riverside South, Chester le Street,
Co. Durham, DH3 3SJ
Tel: 01913 872 929
Website: www.durhamfa.com
Email: info@durhamfa.com
Chairman: Frank Pattison

**EAST RIDING FA**
CEO: Adam Lowthorpe
Address: Roy West Centre, 220 Inglemire Lane, Hull, HU6 7TS
Tel: 01482 221 158 Fax: 01482 221 169
Website: www.eastridingfa.com
Email: info@eastridingfa.com
Chairman: John Suddards

**ENGLISH SCHOOLS FA**
Secretary: John Read
Address: 4 Parker Court, Staffordshire Technology Park,
Stafford, ST18 0WP
Tel: 01785 785 970 Fax: 01785 785 971
Website: www.esfa.co.uk
Email: info@schoolsfa.com
Chairman: Phil Harding

**ESSEX FA**
CEO: Phil Sammons
Address: The County Office, Springfield Lyons Approach,
Springfield, Chelmsford, Essex, CM2 5EY
Tel: 01245 465 271 Fax: 01245 393 089
Website: www.essexfa.com
Email: info@essexfa.com
Chairman: Eddie Rhymes

**GLOUCESTERSHIRE FA**
CEO: David Neale
Address: Oaklands Park, Almondsbury, Bristol, BS32 4AG
Tel: 01454 615 888 Fax: 01454 618 088
Website: www.gloucestershirefa.com
Email: info@gloucestershirefa.com
Chairman: Roger Burden

**GUERNSEY FA**
County Secretary: Gary Robert
Address: GFA Headquarters, Corbet Field, Grand Fort Road,
St Sampsons, Guernsey, GY2 4FG
Tel: 01481 200 443 Fax: 01481 200 451
Website: www.guernseyfa.com
Email: info@guernseyfa.com

**HAMPSHIRE FA**
CEO: Neil Cassar
Address: Winklebury Football Complex, Winklebury Way,
Basingstoke, RG23 8BF
Tel: 01256 853 000 Fax: 01256 357 973
Website: www.hampshirefa.com
Email: info@hampshirefa.com
Chairman: John Ward

**HEREFORDSHIRE FA**
CEO: Jim Lambert
Address: County Ground Offices, Widemarsh Common,
Hereford, HR4 9NA
Tel: 01432 342 179 Fax: 01432 279 265
Website: www.herefordshirefa.com
Email: val.lambert@herefordshirefa.com
Chairman: Bill Shorten

**HERTFORDSHIRE FA**
CEO: Nick Perchard
Address: County Ground, Baldock road, Letchworth,
Hertfordshire, SG6 2EN
Tel: 01462 677 622 Fax: 01462 677 624
Website: www.hertfordshirefa.com
Email: secretary@hertfordshirefa.com
Chairman: Gary Norman

**HUNTINGDONSHIRE FA**
Secretary: Mark Frost
Address: Cromwell Chambers, 8 St Johns Street, Huntingdon,
Cambridgshire, PE29 3DD
Tel: 01480 414 422 Fax: 01480 447489
Website: www.huntsfa.com
Email: info@huntsfa.com
Chairman: Maurice Armstrong

**ISLE OF MAN FA**
CEO: Frank Stennet
Address: PO Box 53, The Bowl, Douglas, Isle of Man, IM2
1AD
Tel: 01624 615 576 Fax: 01624 615 578
Website: www.isleofmanfa.com
Email: ann.garrett@isleofmanfa.com
Chairman: Tony Jones

**JERSEY FA**
CEO: Dave Brookland
Address: Springfield Stadium, St Helier, Jersey, JE2 4LF
Tel: 01534 730 433 Fax: 01534 500 029
Website: www.jerseyfa.com
Email: paul.creeden@jerseyfa.com
Chairman: Ricky Weir

**KENT FA**
CEO: Paul Dolan
Address: Invicta House, Cobdown Park, London Road, Ditton,
Nr Aylesford, Kent, ME20 6DQ.
Tel: Governance 01622 791850, Development 01622 792140
Fax: 01622 790658
Website: www.kentfa.com
Email: info@kentfa.com
Chairman: Barry Bright

**LANCASHIRE FA**
CEO: David Burgess
Address: The County Ground, Thurston Road, Leyland,
Preston, PR25 2LF
Tel: 01772 624 000 Fax: 01772 624 700
Website: www.lancashirefa.com
Email: secretary@lancashirefa.com
Chairman: Brett Warburton

**LEICESTERSHIRE & RUTLAND FA**
Football Operations Manager: Matt Edkins
Address: Holmes Park, Dog & Gun Lane, Whetstone,
Leicestershire, LE8 6FA
Tel: 01162 867 828 Fax: 01162 864 858
Website: www.leicestershirefa.com
Email: info@leicestershirefa.com
Chairman: David Jamieson

**LINCOLNSHIRE FA**
Secretary: John Griffin
Address: Deepdale Enterprise Park, Deepdale Lane,
Nettleham, Lincoln, LN2 2LL
Tel: 01522 524 917 Fax: 01522 528 859
Website: www.lincolnshirefa.com
Email: secretary@lincolnshirefa.com
Chairman: Grahame Lyner

**LIVERPOOL FA**
CEO: David Pugh
Address: Liverpool Soccer Centre, Walton Hall Park, Walton
Hall Avenue, Liverpool, L4 9XP
Tel: 01515 234 488 Fax: 01515 234 477
Website: www.liverpoolfa.com
Email: info@liverpoolfa.com
Chairman: C Welsh

**LONDON FA**
CEO: David Fowkes
Address: 11 Hurlington Business Park, Sulivan Road, Fulham,
London, SW6 3DU
Tel: 020 7610 8360 Fax: 020 7610 8370
Website: www.londonfa.com
Email: info@londonfa.com
Chairman: Tony Sharples

**MANCHESTER FA**
CEO: Colin Bridgford
Address: Manchester BT Academy, Silchester Drive,
Manchester, M40 8NT
Tel: 01616 047 620 Fax: 01616 047 622
Website: www.manchesterfa.com
Email: info@manchesterfa.com
Chairman: Frank Hannah

**MIDDLESEX FA**
CEO: Peter Clayton
Address: 39 Roxborough Road, Harrow, Middlesex, HA1 1NS
Tel: 020 8515 1919 Fax: 020 8515 1910
Website: www.middlesexfa.com
Email: info@middlesexfa.com
Chairman: Jim Taylor

**NORFOLK FA**
CEO: Shaun Turner
Address: 11 Meridian Way, Thorpe St Andrew, Norwich, NR7
0TA
Tel: 01603 704 050 Fax: 01603 704 059
Website: www.norfolkfa.com
Email: info@norfolkfa.com
Chairman: Michael Banham

**NORTHAMPTONSHIRE FA**
CEO: Kevin Shoemake
Address: 9 Duncan Close, Red House Square, Moulton Park,
Northampton, NN3 6WL
Tel: 01604 670 741 Fax: 01604 670 742
Website: www.northamptonshirefa.com
Email: N/A
Chairman: Bob Cotter

**NORTH RIDING FA**
CEO: Tom Radigan
Address: Broughton Road, Stokesley, Middlesborough, TS9
5NY
Tel: 01642 717 770 Fax: 01642 717 776
Website: www.northridingfa.com
Email: info@northridingfa.com
Chairman: Len Scott

**NORTHUMBERLAND FA**
CEO: Rowland Maughan
Address: Whitley Park, Whitley Road, Newcastle upon Tyne,
NE12 9FA
Tel: 01912 700 700 Fax: 01912 700 700
Website: www.northumberlandfa.com
Email: rowland.maughan@northumberlandfa.com
Chairman: Alan Wright

## NOTTINGHAMSHIRE FA
CEO: Elaine Oram
Address: Unit 6b, Chetwynd Business Park, Chilwell,
Nottinghamshire, NG9 6RZ
Tel: 0115 983 7400 Fax: 0115 946 1977
Website: www.nottinghamshirefa.com
Email: info@nottinghamshirefa.com
Chairman: Malcolm Fox

## OXFORDSHIRE FA
CEO: Ian Mason
Address: Unit 3, Witan Park, Avenue 2, Station Lane, Witney,
Oxfordshire, OX28 4FH
Tel: 01993 894400 Fax: 01993 772 191
Website: www.oxfordshirefa.com
Email: Ian.Mason@oxfordshirefa.com
Chairman: Terry Williams

## RAF FA
Secretary: Vince Williams
Address: RAF FA, RAF Brize Norton, Carterton, Oxfordshire,
OX18 3LX
Tel: 01993 895 559 Fax: 01993 897 752
Website: www.raffootball.co.uk
Email: info@royalairforcefa.com
Chairman: Group Captain Mike Neville BSc (RAF)

## ROYAL NAVY FA
CEO: Lt Cdr Steve Vasey
Address: HMS Temeraire, Burnaby Road, Portsmouth,
Hampshire, PO1 2HB
Tel: 02392 722 671 Fax: 02932 724 923
Website: www.royalnavyfa.com
Email: secretary@navyfa.com
Chairman: Capt Rupert Wallace

## SHEFFIELD & HALLAMSHIRE FA
CEO: James Hope-Gill
Address: Clegg House, 69 Cornish Place, Cornish Street,
Shalesmoor, Sheffield, S6 3AF
Tel: 01142 414 999 Fax: 01142 414 990
Website: www.sheffieldfa.com
Email: info@sheffieldfa.com
Chairman: Brian Jones

## SHROPSHIRE FA
CEO: David Rowe
Address: The New Stadium, Oteley Road, Shrewsbury,
Shropshire, SY2 6ST
Tel: 01743 362 769 Fax: 01743 270 494
Website: www.shropshirefa.com
Email: secretary@shropshirefa.com
Chairman: Tom Farmer

## SOMERSET FA
CEO: Jon Pike
Address: Charles Lewin House, Unit 10 Landmark House,
Wirral Business Park, Glastonbury, BA6 9FR
Tel: 01458 832359 Fax: 01458 835588
Website: www.somersetfa.com
Email: info@somersetfa.com
Chairman: Alan Hobbs

## STAFFORDSHIRE FA
CEO: Brian Adshead
Address: Dyson Court, Staffordshire Technology Park,
Beaconside, Stafford, ST18 0LQ
Tel: 01785 256 994 Fax: 01785 279 837
Website: www.staffordshirefa.com
Email: secretary@staffordshirefa.com
Chairman: David Ramsbottom

## SUFFOLK FA
CEO: Phil Knight
Address: The Buntings, Cedars Park, Stowmarket, Suffolk,
IP14 5GZ
Tel: 01449 616 606 Fax: 01449 616 607
Website: www.suffolkfa.com
Email: info@suffolkfa.com
Chairman: Mick Pearce

## SURREY FA
CEO: Ray Ward
Address: Connaught House, 36 Bridge Street, Leatherhead,
Surrey, KT22 8BZ
Tel: 01372 373 543 Fax: 01372 361 310
Website: www.surreyfa.com
Email: info@surreyfa.com
Chairman: Les Pharo

## SUSSEX FA
CEO: Ken Benham
Address: SCFA Headquarters, Culver Road, Lancing, West
Sussex, BN15 9AX
Tel: 01903 753 547 Fax: 01903 761 608
Website: www.sussexfa.com
Email: info@sussexfa.com
Chairman: Peter Bentley

## WESTMORLAND FA
CEO: Peter Ducksbury
Address: 35/37 Appleby Road, Kendal, LA9 6ET
Tel: 01539 730 946 Fax: 01539 740 567
Website: www.westmorlandfa.com
Email: info@westmorlandfa.com
Chairman: Gary Aplin

## WEST RIDING FA
CEO: Roy Carter
Address: Fleet Lane, Woodlesford, Leeds, LS26 8NX
Tel: 01132 821 222 Fax: 01132 821 525
Website: www.wrcfa.com
Email: info@wrcfa.com
Chairman: Peter Marsden

## WILTSHIRE FA
Secretary: Michael Benson
Address: Units 2/3 Dorcan Business Village, Murdock Road,
Dorcan, Swindon, SN3 5HY
Tel: 01793 486 047 Fax: 01793 692 699
Website: www.wiltshirefa.com
Email: mike.benson@wiltshirefa.com
Chairman: Richard Gardiner

## WORCESTERSHIRE FA
CEO: Mervyn Leggett
Address: Craftsman House, De Salis Drive, Hampton Lovett
Industrial Estate, Droitwich, Worcestershire, WR9 0QE
Tel: 01905 827 137
Fax: 01905 798 963
Website: www.worcestershirefa.com
Email: info@worcestershirefa.com
Chairman: Roy Northall

# COUNTY & MISCELLANEOUS CUPS

## A.F.A. Senior Cup
Quarter finals

| | | |
|---|---|---|
| Old Minchendenians | v Old Owens | 2 - 1 aet |
| West Wickham | v Alexandra Park | 2 - 2, 5-4p |
| Bealonians | v Old Meadonians | 0 - 3 |
| Old Salesians | v Honourable Artillery Company | 2 - 1 |

Semi-finals

| | | |
|---|---|---|
| West Wickham | v Old Salesians | 1 - 2 aet |
| Old Minchendenians | v Old Meadonians | 2 - 0 |

Final

| | | |
|---|---|---|
| Old Salesians | v Old Minchendenians | 0 - 3 |

## Aldershot Senior Invitation Challenge Cup
Quarter Finals

| | | |
|---|---|---|
| Chertsey Town | v Farnborough | 4-1 |
| Old Farnboronians | v Ash United | 0-1 |
| Fleet Spurs | v Eversley & California | 1-0 |
| Badshot Lea | v Cove | 1-3 |

Semi Finals

| | | |
|---|---|---|
| Ash United | v Fleet Spurs | 3-3 |

*abandoned at 90 mins: waterlogged pitch*

| | | |
|---|---|---|
| Cove | v Chertsey Town | 4-0 |
| Fleet Spurs | v Ash United | 3-1 aet |

Final

| | | |
|---|---|---|
| Fleet Spurs | v Cove | 0-3 |

## Army FA Challenge Cup
Quarter Finals

| | | |
|---|---|---|
| 3 RSME Regt | v 1 Royal Welsh | 2-0 |
| 23 Engr Regt | v 1 Welsh Gds | 6-1 |
| BA (G) Major | v 22 Sig Regt | 0-4 |
| 11 Trg Bn REME | v 9 Regt AAC | 1-0 |

Semi Finals

| | | |
|---|---|---|
| 3 RSME Regt | v 23 Engr Regt | 2-1 |
| 22 Sig Regt | v 11 Trg Bn REME | 1-0 aet |

Final

| | | |
|---|---|---|
| 3 RSME Regt | v 22 Sig Regt | 1-4 |

## Army FA Minor Units Cup
2MI Signal Regiment beat A Sqn 1 RTR in the final.

## Arthur Dunn Cup
Quarter Finals

| | | |
|---|---|---|
| Old Brentwoods | v Old Carthusians | 2-3 |
| Old Bradfieldians | v Old Wykehamists | 2-6 |
| Old King's (Wimbledon) | v Old Marlburians | 1-2 |
| Old Harrovians | v Old Foresters | 2-1 |

Semi-Finals

| | | |
|---|---|---|
| Old Wykehamists | v Old Harrovians | 4-0 |
| Old Marlburians | v Old Carthusians | 0-5 |

Final

| | | |
|---|---|---|
| Old Carthusians | v Old Wykehamists | 4-0 |

## Baisingstoke Senior Cup
Final

| | | |
|---|---|---|
| Hungerford Town | v Fleet Town | 3-1 |

## Bedfordshire Senior Challenge Cup
Quarter Finals

| | | |
|---|---|---|
| Stotfold | v AFC Dunstable | 2-3 |
| Barton Rovers | v Arlesey Town | 0-0, 5-4p |
| Bedford Town | v Ampthill Town | 2-0 |
| Dunstable Town | v Biggleswade Town | 0-3 |

Semi Finals

| | | |
|---|---|---|
| AFC Dunstable | v Barton Rovers | 3-2 |
| Biggleswade Town | v Bedford Town | 3-1 |

Final

| | | |
|---|---|---|
| AFC Dunstable | v Biggleswade Town | 0-3 |

## Bedfordshire Senior Trophy
Quarter Finals

| | | |
|---|---|---|
| Potton United | v Langford | 4-2 |
| Ickwell & Old Warden | v Bedford | 0-8 |
| Caldecote | v AFC Kempston T & B.C. | 4-3 |
| The 61 FC | v Renhold United | 0-2 |

Semi Finals

| | | |
|---|---|---|
| Potton United | v Renhold United | 1-0 |
| Caldecote | v Bedford | 0-4 |

Final

| | | |
|---|---|---|
| Potton United | v Bedford | 0-1 |

## Berks & Bucks Senior Cup
Quarter Finals

| | | |
|---|---|---|
| Aylesbury | v MIlton Keynes Dons | 0-4 |
| Maidenhead United | v Slough Town | 4-1 |
| Chesham United AFC | v Chalfont St Peter | 4-2 |
| Beaconsfield SYCOB | v Burnham | 2-0 |

Semi Finals

| | | |
|---|---|---|
| Beaconsfield SYCOB | v Milton Keynes Dons | 3-0 |
| Chesham United AFC | v Maidenhead United | 1-0 |

Final

| | | |
|---|---|---|
| Beaconsfield SYCOB | v Chesham United AFC | 2-0 |

## Berks & Bucks Senior Trophy
Quarter Finals

| | | |
|---|---|---|
| Flackwell Heath | v Wokingham & Ennbrook | 2-1 |
| Aylesbury United | v Shrivenham | 4-0 |
| Ascot United | v Holyport | 1-0 |
| Binfield | v Windsor | 0-2 |

Semi Finals

| | | |
|---|---|---|
| Ascot United | v Aylesbury United | 0-2 |
| Windsor | v Flackwell Heath | 2-3 |

Final

| | | |
|---|---|---|
| Flackwell Heath | v Aylesbury United | AW |

2MI Signal Regiment celebrate their Cup success. Photo: Eric Marsh

Hungerford Town stalwart, Ron Tarry, proudly holds the Basingstoke Senior Cup. Photo: Eric Marsh.

Bedfordshire Senior trophy winners Bedford FC. Photo: Gordon Whttington.

## Birmingham Senior Cup

Quarter Finals

| | | | |
|---|---|---|---|
| Coventry Sphinx | v | Banbury United | 5-1 |
| Hednesford Town | v | Alvechurch | 5-3 |
| Sutton Coldfield Town | v | Walsall | 3-2 |
| Stourbridge | v | Birmingham City | 3-1 |

Semi Finals

| | | | |
|---|---|---|---|
| Sutton Coldfield Town | v | Stourbridge | 5-4 aet |
| Coventry Sphinx | v | Hednesford Town | 2-3 |

Final

| | | | |
|---|---|---|---|
| Hednesford Town | v | Sutton Coldfield Town | 4-1 |

## Cambridgeshire Professional Cup

Final

| | | | |
|---|---|---|---|
| Histon | v | Cambridge City | 2-1 |

## Cambridgeshire Invitation Cup

Round 1

| | | | |
|---|---|---|---|
| CRC | v | Great Shelford | 0-3 |
| March Town United | v | Lakenheath | 1-0 |
| Wisbech Town | v | Linton Granta | 4-1 |
| Cambridge University Press | v | Over Sports | 3-0 |

Byes for: Cambridge City, Ely City, Histon, Soham Town Rangers
Cambridge Invitation Cup Continued...

Quarter Finals

| | | | |
|---|---|---|---|
| Cambridge City | v | Great Shelford | 6-1 |
| March Town United | v | Wisbech Town | 1-5 |
| Ely City | v | Histon | 1-1, 4-3p |
| Soham Town Rangers | v | Cambridge University Press | 1-2 |

Semi-Finals

| | | | |
|---|---|---|---|
| Cambridge City | v | Wisbech Town | 3-2 |
| Ely City | v | Cambridge University Press | 2-0 |

Final

| | | | |
|---|---|---|---|
| Cambridge City | v | Ely City | 0-3 |

## Channel Islands - Muratti Vase

Semi Finals

| | | | |
|---|---|---|---|
| Alderney | v | Jersey | 2-9 |

Final

| | | | |
|---|---|---|---|
| Guernsey | v | Jersey | 2-1 |

## Cheshire Senior Cup

Quarter Finals

| | | | |
|---|---|---|---|
| Vauxhall Motors | v | Northwich Victoria | 0-4 |
| Chester | v | Tranmere Rovers | 1-0 aet |
| Stalybridge Celtic | v | Runcorn Linnets | 2-1 |
| Congleton Town | v | Witton Ablion | 1-2 |

Semi Finals

| | | | |
|---|---|---|---|
| Chester | v | Witton Ablion | 3-0 |
| Stalybridge Celtic | v | Northwich Victoria | 3-0 |

Final

| | | | |
|---|---|---|---|
| Chester | v | Stalybridge Celtic | 2-1 |

## Cornwall Senior Cup

Quarter Finals

| | | | |
|---|---|---|---|
| Torpoint Athletic | v | Penryn Athletic | 1-2 |
| Liskeard Athletic | v | Helston Athletic | 3-5 aet |
| Dobwells | v | Bodmin Town | 0-3 |
| St Dennis | v | Newquay | 3-4 |

Semi Finals

| | | | |
|---|---|---|---|
| Bodmin Town | v | Penryn Athletic | 3-2 |
| Newquay | v | Helston Athletic | 2-3 aet |

Final

| | | | |
|---|---|---|---|
| Helston Athletic | v | Bodmin Town | 0-0 |
| Helston Athletic | v | Bodmin Town | 3-4 aet |

## Cumberland Senior Cup

Quarter Finals

| | | | |
|---|---|---|---|
| Mirehouse AFC | v | Kirkoswald | 2-0 |
| Whitehaven AFC | v | Silloth | 3-0 |
| Penrith AFC | v | Workington Red Star | 5-2 |
| Carlsile United | v | Carlisle City | 1-0 |

Semi-Finals

| | | | |
|---|---|---|---|
| Carlisle United | v | Penrith AFC | 3-1 |
| Mirehouse AFC | v | Whitehaven AFC | 3-4 |

Final

| | | | |
|---|---|---|---|
| Carlisle United | v | Whitehaven AFC | 8-1 |

## Derbyshire Senior Challenge Cup

Final

| | | | |
|---|---|---|---|
| Matlock Town | v | Ilkeston | 1-2 |

## Devon St Lukes Cup

Quarter Finals

| | | | |
|---|---|---|---|
| Tiverton Town | v | Exeter City | 1-4 |
| Buckland Athletic | v | Torquay United | 1-3 |
| Witheridge | v | Plymouth Argyle | 2-7 |
| Plymouth Parkway | v | Bideford | 1-2 |

Semi Finals

| | | | |
|---|---|---|---|
| Plymouth Argyle | v | Exeter City | 1-0 |
| Torquay United | v | Bideford | 3-0 |

Final

| | | | |
|---|---|---|---|
| Torquay United | v | Plymouth Argyle | 1-4 |

## Devon Premier Cup

Quarter Finals

| | | | |
|---|---|---|---|
| Alphington | v | University of Exeter | 1-1, 3-4p |
| Stoke Gabriel | v | Teignmouth | 5-1 |
| Exmouth Town | v | Exwick Villa | 2-0 |
| Buckland Athletic Reserves | v | St Martins | 3-2 |

Semi Finals

| | | | |
|---|---|---|---|
| University of Exeter | v | Buckland Athletic Reserves | 0-1 |
| Exmouth Town | v | Stoke Gabriel | 2-0 |

Final

| | | | |
|---|---|---|---|
| Exmouth Town | v | Buckland Athletic Reserves | 2-1 |

# Devon Senior Cup

Quarter Finals

| | | | |
|---|---|---|---|
| Bow Amateur Athletic | v | Windmill | 2-2, 2-4p |
| Buckfastleigh Rangers | v | Topsham Town Reserves | 1-2 |
| Tiverton Town (Reserves) | v | Bovey Tracey Reserves | 4-1 |
| Newton Poppleford | v | Honiton Town | 4-7 aet |

Semi Finals

| | | | |
|---|---|---|---|
| Honiton Town | v | Tiverton Town Reserves | 1-4 |
| Topsham Town | v | Windmill | 1-2 |

Final

| | | | |
|---|---|---|---|
| Windmill | v | Tiverton Town Reserves | 0-3 |

# Dorset Senior Cup

Quarter Finals

| | | | |
|---|---|---|---|
| Gillingham Town | v | Sherborne Town | 6-1 |
| Wimborne Town | v | Dorchester Town | 3-2 |
| Poole Town | v | Bridport | 4-1 |
| Weymouth | v | Portland United | 3-1 |

Semi Finals

| | | | |
|---|---|---|---|
| Poole Town | v | Gillingham Town | 4-1 |
| Weymouth | v | Wimborne Town | 0-1 |

Final

| | | | |
|---|---|---|---|
| Poole Town | v | Wimborne Town | 4-1 |

# Durham Senior Challenge Cup

Quarter Finals

| | | | |
|---|---|---|---|
| Durham City | v | Gateshead | 1-3 |
| Shildon AFC | v | Seaham Red Star | 7-0 |
| Bishop Auckland | v | Norton & Stockton Ancients | 2-1 |
| Spennymoor Town | v | Billingham Synthonia | 4-0 |

Semi-Finals

| | | | |
|---|---|---|---|
| Gateshead | v | Bishop Auckland | 1-2 |
| *Played at Bishop Auckland* | | | |
| Spennymoor Town | v | Shildon AFC | 0-3 |

Final

| | | | |
|---|---|---|---|
| Bishop Auckland | v | Spennymoor Town | 2-1 |

# East Riding Senior Cup

Quarter Finals

| | | | |
|---|---|---|---|
| Reckitts AFC | v | Pockington Town | 3-0 |
| Crown | v | Hull City | 1-8 |
| Beverley Town | v | Bridlington Town | 0-2 |
| North Ferriby United | v | Hessle Rangers | 6-0 |

Semi Finals

| | | | |
|---|---|---|---|
| North Ferriby United | v | Bridlington Town | 3-1 |
| Hull City | v | Reckitts AFC | 2-3 aet |

Final

| | | | |
|---|---|---|---|
| Reckitts AFC | v | North Ferriby United | 1-2 |

# Essex Senior Cup

Quarter Finals

| | | | |
|---|---|---|---|
| AFC Hornchurch | v | Colchester United | 4-3 |
| Barking | v | Grays Athletic | 1-2 |
| Concord Rangers | v | Chelmsford City | 3-3, 6-5p |
| Waltham Abbey | v | Southend United | 2-1 |
| (at Great Wakering Rovers FC) | v | | |

Semi Finals

| | | | |
|---|---|---|---|
| Concord Rangers | v | Grays Athletic | 0-2 |
| Waltham Abbey | v | AFC Hornchurch | 2-3 |

Final

| | | | |
|---|---|---|---|
| AFC Hornchurch | v | Grays Athletic | 2-1 |

# Gloucestershire Senior Challenge Cup

Quarter Finals

| | | | |
|---|---|---|---|
| Cirencester Town | v | Cheltenham Town Reserves | 1-1, 3-4p |
| Forest Green Rovers | v | Cinderford Town | 2-2, 6-7p |
| Bristol Rovers Reserves | v | Yate Town | 4-0 |
| Bishops Cleeve | v | Mangotsfield United | 0-5 |

Semi Finals

| | | | |
|---|---|---|---|
| Bristol Rovers Reserves | v | Cinderford Town | 0-1 |
| Mangotsfield United | v | Cheltenham Town Reserves | 2-1 |

Final

| | | | |
|---|---|---|---|
| Mangotsfield United | v | Cinderford Town | 4-0 |

# Hampshire Senior Cup

Quarter Finals

| | | | |
|---|---|---|---|
| Folland Sports | v | Alresford Town | 0-1 |
| Havant & Waterlooville | v | Sholing | 1-3 |
| AFC Bournemouth | v | Eastleigh | 2-2, 4-3p |
| AFC Totton | v | Gosport Borough | 3-1 |

Semi Finals

| | | | |
|---|---|---|---|
| Alresford Town | v | Sholing | 2-1 aet |
| AFC Bournemouth | v | AFC Totton | 1-1, 4-2p |

Final

| | | | |
|---|---|---|---|
| AFC Bournemouth | v | Alresford Town | 2-3 |

# Herefordshire Challenge Cup

Quarter Finals

| | | | |
|---|---|---|---|
| Bromyard Town | v | Westfields | 0-5 |
| Ledbury Town | v | Fownhope | 5-1 |
| Bartestree | v | Leominster Town | 4-1 |
| Pegasus Juniors | v | Sinkum | 2-0 |

Semi Finals

| | | | |
|---|---|---|---|
| Pegasus Juniors | v | Westfields | 0-1 |
| Bartestree | v | Ledbury Town | 1-3 |

Final

| | | | |
|---|---|---|---|
| Ledbury Town | v | Westfields | 2-3 |

## Herts Senior Challenge Cup

Quarter Finals

| | | | |
|---|---|---|---|
| Colney Heath | v | Royston Town | 0-2 |
| St Margaretsbury | v | Potters Bar Town | 1-6 |
| Bishop's Stortford | v | Ware | 3-0 |
| St Albans City | v | Hemel Hempstead Town | 2-3 |

Semi Finals

| | | | |
|---|---|---|---|
| Hemel Hempstead Town | v | Bishop's Stortford | 2-1 |
| Potters Bar Town | v | Royston Town | 3-2 aet |

Final

| | | | |
|---|---|---|---|
| Hemel Hempstead Town | v | Potters Bar Town | 2-0 |

## Hertfordshire Senior Centenary Trophy

Quarter Finals

| | | | |
|---|---|---|---|
| Hoddesdon Town | v | Chipperfield Corinthians | 3-0 |
| Met. Police Bushey | v | FC Broxbourne Borough | 1-3 |
| Welwyn Garden City | v | Baldock Town | 0-4 |
| Kings Langley | v | Codicote | 1-3 |

Semi Finals

| | | | |
|---|---|---|---|
| FC Broxbourne Borough | v | Codicote | 2-0 |
| Hoddesdon Town | v | Baldock Town | 0-1 |

Final

| | | | |
|---|---|---|---|
| FC Broxbourne Borough | v | Baldock Town | 1-1, 3-5p |

## Huntingdonshire Senior Cup

Final

| | | | |
|---|---|---|---|
| Huntingdon Town | v | St Neots Town | 0-0, 2-4p |

## Isle of Man FA Cup

Quarter Finals

| | | | |
|---|---|---|---|
| Peel | v | Ramsey | 6-2 |
| Castletown | v | St Georges | 0-16 |
| Laxey | v | Douglas & District | 5-0 |
| St Marys | v | Pulrose United | 9-1 |

SEMI-FINALS

| | | | |
|---|---|---|---|
| Peel | v | St Georges | 1-3 |
| Laxey | v | St Marys | 0-4 |

FINAL

| | | | |
|---|---|---|---|
| St Georges | v | St Marys | 1-2 |

## Kent Senior Cup

Quarter Finals

| | | | |
|---|---|---|---|
| Herne Bay | v | Charlton Athletic | 0-3 |
| Margate | v | Ebbsfleet United | 2-4 |
| Thamesmead Town | v | Ramsgate | 3-0 |
| Tonbridge Angels | v | Bromley | 5-1 |

Semi Finals

| | | | |
|---|---|---|---|
| Thamesmead Town | v | Charlton Athletic | 2-3 aet |
| Ebbsfleet United | v | Tonbridge Angels | 1-2 |

Final

| | | | |
|---|---|---|---|
| Charlton Athletic | v | Tonbridge Angels | 7-1 |

## Kent Senior Trophy

Quarter Finals

| | | | |
|---|---|---|---|
| Erith Town | v | Deal Town | 2-3 aet |
| Woodstock Sports | v | Lordswood | 1-2 |
| Tunbridge Wells | v | Canterbury City | 3-1 |
| Fisher | v | Erith & Belvedere | 0-2 |

Baldock Town celebrate their Herts Senior Centenary Trophy success. Photo: Gordon Whittington.

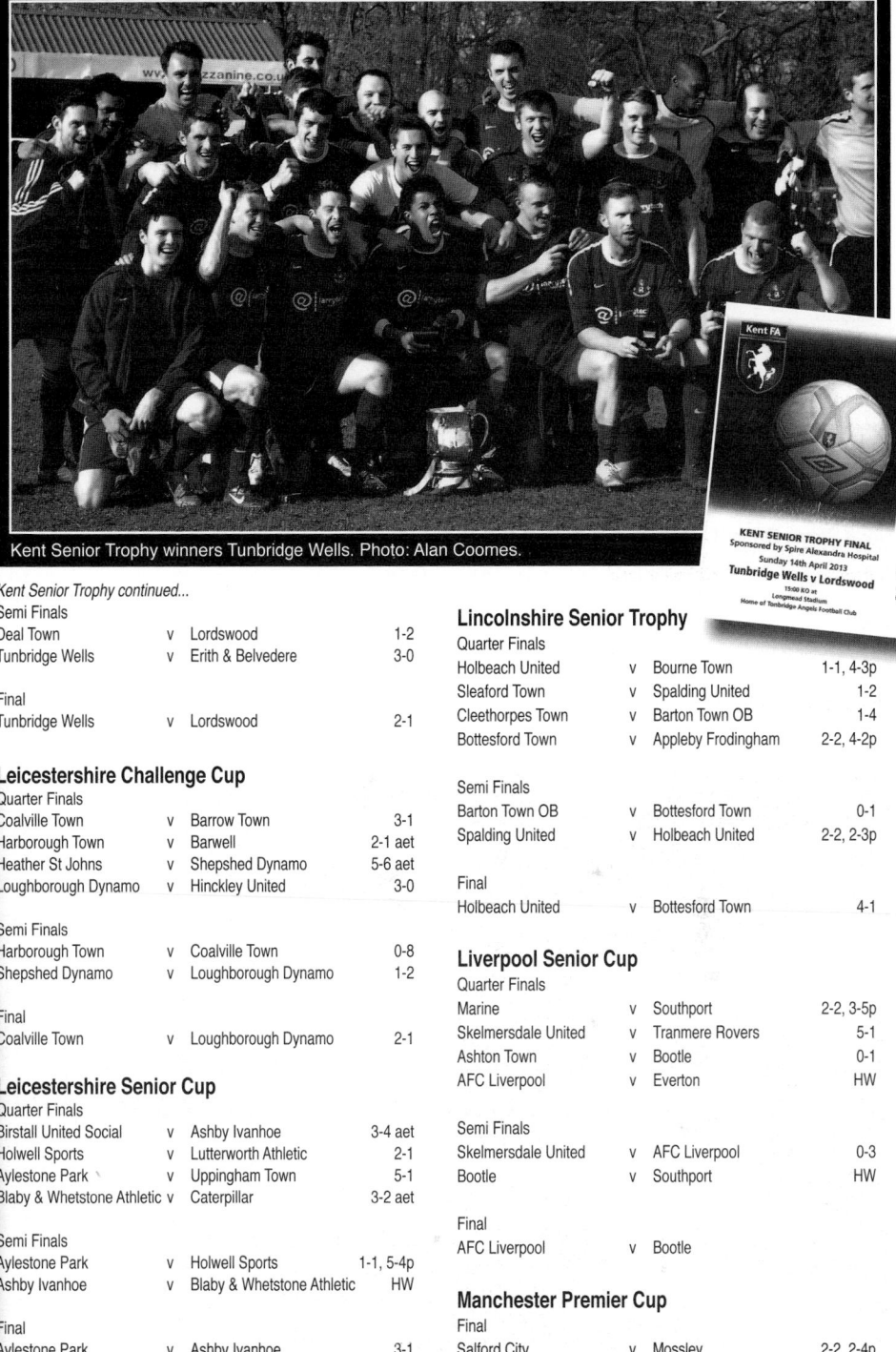

Kent Senior Trophy winners Tunbridge Wells. Photo: Alan Coomes.

KENT FA

OFFICIAL PROGRAMME

£1.50

KENT SENIOR TROPHY FINAL
Sponsored by Spire Alexandra Hospital
Sunday 14th April 2013
**Tunbridge Wells v Lordswood**
13:00 KO at
Longmead Stadium
Home of Tunbridge Angels Football Club

*Kent Senior Trophy continued...*

**Semi Finals**

| | | | |
|---|---|---|---|
| Deal Town | v | Lordswood | 1-2 |
| Tunbridge Wells | v | Erith & Belvedere | 3-0 |

**Final**

| | | | |
|---|---|---|---|
| Tunbridge Wells | v | Lordswood | 2-1 |

## Leicestershire Challenge Cup

**Quarter Finals**

| | | | |
|---|---|---|---|
| Coalville Town | v | Barrow Town | 3-1 |
| Harborough Town | v | Barwell | 2-1 aet |
| Heather St Johns | v | Shepshed Dynamo | 5-6 aet |
| Loughborough Dynamo | v | Hinckley United | 3-0 |

**Semi Finals**

| | | | |
|---|---|---|---|
| Harborough Town | v | Coalville Town | 0-8 |
| Shepshed Dynamo | v | Loughborough Dynamo | 1-2 |

**Final**

| | | | |
|---|---|---|---|
| Coalville Town | v | Loughborough Dynamo | 2-1 |

## Leicestershire Senior Cup

**Quarter Finals**

| | | | |
|---|---|---|---|
| Birstall United Social | v | Ashby Ivanhoe | 3-4 aet |
| Holwell Sports | v | Lutterworth Athletic | 2-1 |
| Aylestone Park | v | Uppingham Town | 5-1 |
| Blaby & Whetstone Athletic | v | Caterpillar | 3-2 aet |

**Semi Finals**

| | | | |
|---|---|---|---|
| Aylestone Park | v | Holwell Sports | 1-1, 5-4p |
| Ashby Ivanhoe | v | Blaby & Whetstone Athletic | HW |

**Final**

| | | | |
|---|---|---|---|
| Aylestone Park | v | Ashby Ivanhoe | 3-1 |

## Lincolnshire Senior Trophy

**Quarter Finals**

| | | | |
|---|---|---|---|
| Holbeach United | v | Bourne Town | 1-1, 4-3p |
| Sleaford Town | v | Spalding United | 1-2 |
| Cleethorpes Town | v | Barton Town OB | 1-4 |
| Bottesford Town | v | Appleby Frodingham | 2-2, 4-2p |

**Semi Finals**

| | | | |
|---|---|---|---|
| Barton Town OB | v | Bottesford Town | 0-1 |
| Spalding United | v | Holbeach United | 2-2, 2-3p |

**Final**

| | | | |
|---|---|---|---|
| Holbeach United | v | Bottesford Town | 4-1 |

## Liverpool Senior Cup

**Quarter Finals**

| | | | |
|---|---|---|---|
| Marine | v | Southport | 2-2, 3-5p |
| Skelmersdale United | v | Tranmere Rovers | 5-1 |
| Ashton Town | v | Bootle | 0-1 |
| AFC Liverpool | v | Everton | HW |

**Semi Finals**

| | | | |
|---|---|---|---|
| Skelmersdale United | v | AFC Liverpool | 0-3 |
| Bootle | v | Southport | HW |

**Final**

| | | | |
|---|---|---|---|
| AFC Liverpool | v | Bootle | |

## Manchester Premier Cup

**Final**

| | | | |
|---|---|---|---|
| Salford City | v | Mossley | 2-2, 2-4p |

## Middlesex Senior Cup
Quarter Finals

| | | | |
|---|---|---|---|
| Uxbridge | v | Hayes & Yeading United | 3-5 |
| Ashford Town (Middx) | v | North Greenford United | 1-0 |
| Staines Town | v | Harefield United | 2-2, 7-6p |
| Northwood | v | Hampton & Richmond Borough | 3-0 |

Semi Finals

| | | | |
|---|---|---|---|
| Ashford Town (Middx) | v | Northwood | 0-0, 5-4p |
| Staines Town | v | Hayes & Yeading United | 3-2 |

Final

| | | | |
|---|---|---|---|
| Staines Town | v | Ashford Town (Middx) | 2-0 |

## Norfolk Senior Cup
Quarter Finals

| | | | |
|---|---|---|---|
| Wroxham | v | Gorleston | 3-2 |
| Norwich City | v | King's Lynn Town | 6-3 |
| Reepham Town | v | Spixworth | 0-1 |
| Diss Town | v | Cromer Town | 0-0 |
| Cromer Town | v | Diss Town | 2-1 aet |

Semi Finals

| | | | |
|---|---|---|---|
| Spixworth | v | Wroxham | 0-3 |
| Cromer Town | v | Norwich City | 0-4 |

Final

| | | | |
|---|---|---|---|
| Norwich City | v | Wroxham | 2-0 |

## North Riding Senior Cup
Quarter Finals

| | | | |
|---|---|---|---|
| Middlesbrough | v | Marske United | 1-2 |
| Guisborough Town | v | Redcar Athletic | 4-1 |
| Grangetown Boys Club | v | Pickering Town Community | 0-2 |
| York City | v | Northallerton Town | 3-0 |

Semi-Finals

| | | | |
|---|---|---|---|
| Marske United | v | York City | 2-0 |
| Pickering Town Community | v | Guisborough Town | 1-1, 4-2p |

Final

| | | | |
|---|---|---|---|
| Pickering Town Community | v | Marske United | 3-0 |

## Northants Hillier Senior Cup
Quarter Finals

| | | | |
|---|---|---|---|
| Kettering Town | v | Wellingborough Town | 3-0 |
| Daventry Town | v | Woodford United | 3-0 |
| Long Buckby AFC | v | Corby Town | 1-2 |
| Desborough Town | v | Cogenhoe United | 4-3 |

Semi-Finals

| | | | |
|---|---|---|---|
| Desborough Town | v | Corby Town | 1-4 |
| Daventry Town | v | Kettering Town | 3-0 |

Final

| | | | |
|---|---|---|---|
| Corby Town | v | Daventry Town | 3-1 |

## Northants Junior Cup
Final

| | | | |
|---|---|---|---|
| Cogenhoe United Reserves | v | Rushden & Higham United | 0-2 |

## Northumberland Senior Cup
Quarter Finals

| | | | |
|---|---|---|---|
| Blyth Spartans | v | Whitley Bay | 0-0 |
| Whitley Bay | v | Blyth Spartans | 2-0 |
| Bedlington Terriers | v | Newcastle United Reserves | 3-2 |
| Morpeth Town | v | Ashington | 3-6 |
| West Allotment Celtic | v | North Shields | 1-6 |

Semi Finals

| | | | |
|---|---|---|---|
| North Shields | v | Ashington | 0-2 |
| Whitley Bay | v | Bedlington Terriers | 4-3 |

Final

| | | | |
|---|---|---|---|
| Whitley Bay | v | Ashington | 0-3 |

Northants Junior Cup winners Rushden & Higham United. Photo: Gordon Whittington.

# Nottinghamshire Senior Cup

Quarter Finals

| | | | |
|---|---|---|---|
| Linby Colliery Welfare | v | Clifton All Whites | 1-3 |
| Greenwood Meadows | v | Sutton Town AFC | 0-1 |
| Dunkirk | v | Rainworth Miners Welfare | 2-3 |
| Bulwell | v | Carlton Town | 1-2 |

Semi Finals

| | | | |
|---|---|---|---|
| Carlton Town | v | Clifton All Whites | 4-0 |
| Sutton Town AFC | v | Rainworth Miners Welfare | 2-0 |

Final

| | | | |
|---|---|---|---|
| Sutton Town AFC | v | Carlton Town | 2-5 |

# Oxfordshire Senior Cup

Final

| | | | |
|---|---|---|---|
| Oxford United | v | Oxford City | 4-2 aet |

# RAF Cup

Quarter Finals

| | | | |
|---|---|---|---|
| RAF Benson | v | RAF Cosford | 0-2 |
| RAF Brampton/Wyton | v | RAF Coningsby | 2-4 |
| RAF Leeming | v | RAF Halton | 4-1 |
| RAF Lossiemouth | v | RAF Marham | 2-1 |

Semi Finals

| | | | |
|---|---|---|---|
| RAF Lossiemouth | v | RAF Cosford | 2-1 |
| RAF Leeming | v | RAF Coningsby | 0-1 |

Final

| | | | |
|---|---|---|---|
| RAF Lossiemouth | v | RAF Coningsby | 0-2 |

# RAF PLATE

Quarter Finals

| | | | |
|---|---|---|---|
| RAF Linton-On-Ouse | v | RAF Wittering | 2-1 |
| RAF Cranwell | v | RAF Shawbury aet | 3-1 aet |
| DMRC Headley Court | v | DISC Chicksands | 1-1 aet, 2-3p |
| RAF Brize Norton | v | RAF Boulmer | 7-0 |

Semi-Finals

| | | | |
|---|---|---|---|
| RAF Brize Norton | v | RAF Cranwell | 5-0 |
| DISC Chicksands | v | RAF Linton-On-Ouse | 0-1 |

Final

| | | | |
|---|---|---|---|
| RAF Brize Norton | v | RAF Linton-On-Ouse | 4-0 |

# Royal Navy Cup

Quarter Finals

| | | | |
|---|---|---|---|
| CTCRM | v | HMS Seahawk | 5-2 |
| 30 Commando RM | v | HMS Raleigh | 0-1 |
| FPG RM / 43 Cdo | v | HM Naval Base Portsmouth | 12-5 |
| HMS Collingwood | v | HMS Sultan | 5-5 aet, 4-3p |

Semi Finals

| | | | |
|---|---|---|---|
| CTCRM | v | HMS Raleigh | 0-2 |
| FPG RM / 43 Cdo | v | HMS Collingwood | 3-3 aet, 4-3p |

Final

| | | | |
|---|---|---|---|
| HMS Raleigh | v | FPG RM / 43 Cdo | 0-0 aet, 5-6p |

# Sheffield & Hallamshire Senior Challenge Cup

Quarter Finals

| | | | |
|---|---|---|---|
| Rossington Main | v | Staveley Miners Welfare | 0-2 |
| Worsbrough Bridge Athletic | v | Sheffield | 2-2, 1-3p |
| AFC Emley | v | Stocksbridge Park Steels | 1-2 |
| Frickley Athleitc | v | Athersley Recreation | 3-1 |

Semi Finals

| | | | |
|---|---|---|---|
| Stocksbridge Park Steels | v | Frickley Athletic | 1-3 |
| Sheffield | v | Staveley Miners Welfare | 4-2 |

Final

| | | | |
|---|---|---|---|
| Sheffield | v | Frickley Athletic | 3-4 |

# Shropshire Challenge Cup

Quarter Finals

| | | | |
|---|---|---|---|
| Newport Town | v | Wem Town | 2-3 |
| Hanwood United | v | Wellington Amateurs | 1-2 |
| Shawbury United | v | Allscott AFC | 7-2 |
| Church Stretton Town | v | Haughmond | 0-3 |

Semi-finals

| | | | |
|---|---|---|---|
| Shawbury United | v | Wem Town | 3-1 |
| Haughmond | v | Wellington Amateurs | 2-3 |

Final

| | | | |
|---|---|---|---|
| Wellington Amateurs | v | Shawbury United | 0-2 |

# Somerset Premier Cup

Quarter Finals

| | | | |
|---|---|---|---|
| Bishop Sutton | v | Bridgwater Town 1984 | 2-3 |
| Bath City | v | Odd Down | 2-0 |
| Paulton Rovers | v | Larkhall Athletic | 3-1 |
| Taunton Town | v | Frome Town | 5-2 |

Semi Finals

| | | | |
|---|---|---|---|
| Paulton Rovers | v | Bath City | 3-2 |
| Bridgwater Town 1984 | v | Taunton Town | 3-2 |

Final

| | | | |
|---|---|---|---|
| Paulton Rovers | v | Bridgwater Town 1984 | 3-1 |

# Somerset Senior Cup

Quarter Finals

| | | | |
|---|---|---|---|
| Stockwood Green | v | Middlezoy Rovers | 1-1, 3-4p |
| Wincaton Town | v | Langford Rovers 2000 | 5-3 |
| Brislington Reserves | v | Portishead Town Reserves | 3-0 |
| Nailsea Town | v | Clevedon United | 0-4 |

Semi Finals

| | | | |
|---|---|---|---|
| Middlezoy Rovers | v | Wincanton Town | 1-7 |
| Brislington Reserves | v | Clevedon United | 2-1 |

Final

| | | | |
|---|---|---|---|
| Brislington Reserves | v | Wincanton Town | 0-1 |

## Staffordshire Senior Cup

Quarter Finals

| Hednesford Town | v | Stafford Rangers | 3-0 |
|---|---|---|---|
| Chasetown | v | Heath Hayes | 2-1 |
| Rushall Olympic | v | Kidsgrove Athletic | 4-1 |
| Norton United | v | Port Vale | 1-2 aet |

Semi Finals

| Chasetown | v | Rushall Olympic | 1-3 |
|---|---|---|---|
| Hednesford Town | v | Port Vale | 3-2 |

Final

| Hednesford Town | v | Rushall Olympic | 5-1 |
|---|---|---|---|

## Suffolk Premier Cup

Quarter Finals

| Hadleigh United | v | Lowestoft Town | 1-3 |
|---|---|---|---|
| Leiston | v | Woodbridge | 1-0 |
| Felixstowe & Walton United | v | Ipswich Town | AW |
| Bury Town | v | Kirkley & Pakefield | 2-0 |

Semi-Finals

| Ipswich Town | v | Lowestoft Town | 0-1 |
|---|---|---|---|
| Leiston | v | Bury Town | 1-2 |

Final

| Bury Town | v | Lowestoft Town | 2-0 |
|---|---|---|---|

## Suffolk Senior Cup

Quarter Finals

| Corton | v | Mewmarket Town | 1-1, 5-3p |
|---|---|---|---|
| Ipswich Wanderers | v | Beccles Town | 3-1 |
| Long Melford | v | Crane Sports | 1-2 |
| Whitton United | v | Ipswich Valley Rangers | 4-3 |

Semi Finals

| Ipswich Wanderers | v | Crane Sports | 4-0 |
|---|---|---|---|
| Corton | v | Whitton United | 0-2 |

Final

| Whitton United | v | Ipswich Wanderers | 1-1, 2-3p |
|---|---|---|---|

## Surrey Premier Cup

Quarter Finals

| Staines Lammas | v | Raynes Park Vale | 3-1 |
|---|---|---|---|
| Mole Valley SCR | v | Farleigh Rovers | 4-1 |
| Westfield | v | Warlingham | 3-0 |
| Old Wilsonians | v | Walton Casuals Reserves | 1-2 aet |

Semi-Finals

| Mole Valley SCR | v | Walton Casuals Reserves | 2-5 aet |
|---|---|---|---|
| Westfield | v | Staines Lammas | HW |

Final

| Walton Casuals Reserves | v | Westfield | 2-1 |
|---|---|---|---|

## Surrey Saturday Senior Cup

Quarter Finals

| Chipstead | v | AFC Wimbledon | 1-2 |
|---|---|---|---|
| Metropolitan Police | v | Leatherhead | 4-2 |
| Godalming Town | v | Woking | 1-1, 2-0p |
| Sutton United | v | Molesey | 6-2 |

Semi-Finals

| Godalming Town | v | Metropolitan Police | 2-1 |
|---|---|---|---|
| Sutton United | v | AFC Wimbledon | 5-2 |

Final

| Godalming Town | v | Sutton United | 1-0 |
|---|---|---|---|

## Sussex Senior Challenge Cup

Quarter Finals

| Eastbourne Town | v | East Preston | 1-2 aet |
|---|---|---|---|
| Brighton & Hove Albion | v | Three Bridges | 2-0 |
| Bognor Regis Town | v | Eastbourne Borough | 3-1 |
| Hastings United | v | Crawley Town | 3-0 |

Semi-Finals

| Bognor Regis Town | v | Hastings United | 2-1 |
|---|---|---|---|
| Brighton & Hove Albion | v | East Preston | 3-2 |

Final

| Brighton & Hove Albion | v | Bognor Regis Town | 4-0 |
|---|---|---|---|

## West Riding County Cup

Quarter Finals

| Harrogate Town | v | Guiseley AFC | 0-5 |
|---|---|---|---|
| Harrogate Railway Athletic | v | Tadcaster Albion | 3-2 |
| Albion Sports | v | FC Halifax Town | 0-2 |
| Ossett Town | v | Knaresborough Town | 2-1 aet |

Semi-Finals

| FC Halifax Town | v | Ossett Town | 1-0 |
|---|---|---|---|
| Guiseley AFC | v | Harrogate Railway Athletic | 5-0 |

Final

| FC Halifax Town | v | Guiseley AFC | 1-0 |
|---|---|---|---|

## Westmorland Senior Cup

Quarter Finals

| Lunesdale United | v | Appleby | 2-3 aet |
|---|---|---|---|
| Kendal County | v | Ambleside United | 3-0 |
| Corinthians | v | Kendal United | 1-2 |
| Keswick | v | Wetheriggs United | 3-0 |

Semi-Finals

| Kendal United | v | Kendal County | 1-3 |
|---|---|---|---|
| Keswick | v | Appleby | 5-3 |

Final

| Keswick | v | Kendal County | 1-2 |
|---|---|---|---|

## Wiltshire Senior Cup

Quarter Finals

| Corsham Town | v | Downton | 0-2 |
|---|---|---|---|
| Westbury United | v | Bemerton Heath Harlequins | 0-3 |
| Melksham Town | v | Bradford Town | HW |
| Shrewton United | v | Cricklade Town | 2-3 aet |

Semi Finals

| Cricklade Town | v | Downton | 2-5 aet |
|---|---|---|---|
| Bemerton Heath Harlequins | v | Melksham Town | 2-2, 3-4p |

Final

| Melksham Town | v | Downton | 2-0 aet |
|---|---|---|---|

# Worcestershire Senior Cup

Quarter Final

| | | | |
|---|---|---|---|
| Redditch United | v | Worcester City | 3-1 |

Semi Finals

| | | | |
|---|---|---|---|
| Kidderminster Harriers | v | Redditch United | 1-2 |
| Stourbridge | v | Evesham United | 3-0 |

Final

| | | | |
|---|---|---|---|
| Redditch United | v | Stourbridge | 0-0, 3-4p |

# Worcestershire Senior Urn

Quarter Finals

| | | | |
|---|---|---|---|
| Bewdley Town | v | Alvechurch | 0-3 |
| Pershore Town 88 | v | Dudley Sports | 1-0 |
| Malvern Town | v | Bromsgrove Sporting | 1-4 |
| Studley | v | Lye Town | 3-0 |

Semi Finals

| | | | |
|---|---|---|---|
| Alvechurch | v | Studley | 2-1 |
| Bromsgrove Sporting | v | Pershore Town 88 | 1-1, 3-4p |

Final

| | | | |
|---|---|---|---|
| Alvechurch | v | Pershore Town 88 | 1-1, 4-3p |

(Above) Bognor Regis Town line-up before their Sussex Senior Cup final against Brighton & Hove Albion. Whilst right, Bognor's Terry Dodd keeps Brighton's Chimdi Akubuine at arms length as he shapes up to cross the ball.
Photos: Roger Turner.

# ENGLISH SCHOOLS' FOOTBALL ASSOCIATION

4, Parker Court, Staffordshire Technology Park, Beaconside, Stafford ST 18 0WP

Tel: 01785 785970; website: www.esfa.co.uk

Chief Executive: John Read (john.read@schoolsfa.com)

Competitions Manager: Darren Alcock (Darren.alcock@schoolsfa.com)

Non-League Directory Contributor: Mike Simmonds (m.simmonds31@btinternet.com)

(0115 9313299)

**Photos: RWT Photogrpahy**

Website: www.rwt.photography.co.uk

## THE INTERNATIONAL SEASON

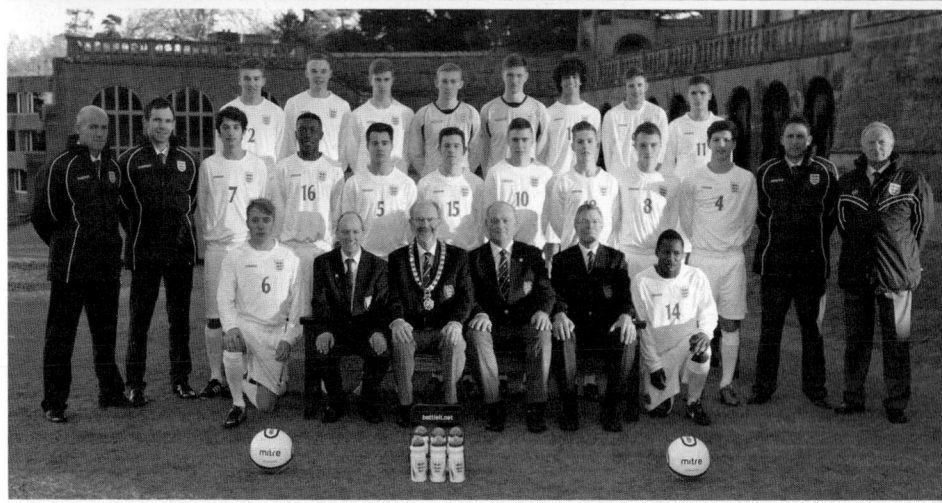

Back: Curtis Gayler Kieran Morris Conor McCormack Mikey Pearce Tom Gowans James Fergany Jack Owen Luke Donaldson
Middle: Andy Blight (Assistant Manager) Michael Johnston (GK Coach) Steve Wilderspin (Sports Therapist) Arthur Tabor (Team Doctor)
Ryan Fergany Shaquille Hippolyte-Patrick Lewis Binns Michael Smith Rhys Turner Nicholas Haughton Robert Gilroy Gani Nuredini
Front: Ross Bailey Andy Buckingham (Team Manager) Neil Pont (ESFA Chairman) John Read (CEO) Nigel Brown (Chair Selectors) Ruhandulca Ombeni

## SAFIB UNDER 18 INTERNATIONAL SHIELD 2013

|  | P | W | D | L | F | A | Pts |
|---|---|---|---|---|---|---|---|
| Northern Ireland | 4 | 1 | 1 | 0 | 7 | 3 | 10 |
| Republic of Ireland | 4 | 2 | 1 | 1 | 5 | 4 | 7 |
| Wales | 4 | 2 | 0 | 2 | 7 | 5 | 6 |
| England | 4 | 1 | 2 | 1 | 7 | 8 | 5 |
| Scotland | 4 | 0 | 0 | 4 | 2 | 9 | 0 |

### ENGLAND RESULTS

| | | |
|---|---|---|
| v. Wales (Lincoln City F.C.) | L | 1-4 |
| v. Northern Ireland (Plymouth Argyle F.C.) | D | 1-1 |
| v. Scotland (St johnstone F.C.) | W | 3-1 |
| v. Republic of Ireland (Cork City F.C.) | D | 2-2 |
| v. New Zealand (AFC Wulfrunians) | D | 1-1 |

Goalscorers: Rob Gilroy (2), Rhys Turner (2), Shaquille Hippolyte-Patrick (2), Jack Odam (1), Luke Donaldson (1).

## E.S.F.A. GIRLS' UNDER 15 INTERNATIONAL SQUAD

The E.S.F.A. fielded a girls' international squad for only the second d time when they took part in the 5 national Bob Docherty Cup. which was held this year in Belfast. The winners of a very close competition were Scotland with England although losing only one game, finishing third. Final standings were:

| | | | | | | | | |
|---|---|---|---|---|---|---|---|---|
| Scotland | 4 | - 1 | - 3 | - 0 | - 7 | - 2 | - 6 | |
| Eire | 4 | - 1 | - 3 | - 0 | - 7 | - 3 | - 6 | |
| England | 4 | - 1 | - 2 | - 1 | - 4 | - 4 | - 5 | |
| Wales | 4 | - 1 | - 1 | - 2 | - 4 | - 7 | - 4 | |
| N. Ireland | 4 | - 1 | - 1 | - 2 | - 2 | - 8 | - 4 | |

In addition, England played Scotland twice, losing 3-1 at St. George's Park, Burton in a friendly game and then, in the match for the Lloyds TSB Cup in Glasgow, went down 5-0.

Under 15 Squad: Back Row: Andy Norwood (GK Coach), Sarah Steadman (Manager) Charlotte Steggles, Jessica Lewandowski, Keeley Wilkinson, Chloe Beattie, Jordan Littleboy, Miranda Hall (Assistant Manager), Dave Burns (Physio).Middle Row: Ellie Bohannan, Kelly Snook, Natasha Fenton, Megan Taylor, Amber Tullett, Hollie Gibson. Front Row: Tori Adlam, Laura Hooper, Zoe Tynan, Millie Elson, Georgia Stanway, Lucy Shepherd.

# ENGLISH SCHOOLS' F.A NATIONAL COMPETITIONS

The major feature of the last ten years of the English Schools' F.A. has been the great increase in the number of national competitions. 23 national competitions were played last season compared with less than half that number which were featured in the Non-League Directory ten years ago.

Apart from the four Primary competitions, the finals of which were played on the excellent facilities of the Watford Training ground and the two Under 12 indoor competitions, the remainder of the National Finals were played with six F.A. Premier Clubs providing their facilities and clubs as far apart geographically as Accrington Stanley and Exeter City playing host to a Cup Final. This, of course, gave nearly 550 students the chance of playing on a League club ground, something which the vast majority will remember for the rest of their lives. In addition, the E.S.F.A. has developed links with the Royal School for the Deaf and has organised a number of competitions in partnership with them while Futsal has been introduced to the programme

Broadening the base of the E.S.F.A. is the major aim in extending the number of competitions which are organised. This has certainly been successful as some figures illustrate. The Under 11 Boys' 7-a-side last season attracted over 3000 entries from Primary and Junior sides while 1687 girls' teams participated in the parallel competition. At Secondary level, the largest entry was at Under 16 Individual Schools' Level with over 1000 entries for the boys' Cup and 556 for the girls' competition. Entries for the other competitions varied between 1100 and 600 and when one considers the myriad events organised by County and Local Associations, it can be seen that schools' football is still flourishing.

Most of last season's finals were well contested although it was disappointing that the Association's oldest competition, the Under 15 Inter-Association Trophy which began in the 1904-05 season was a one-sided affair. Congratulations, nevertheless, go to Liverpool who went further ahead in the list of national winners. Two of the most exciting finals were in the Under 15 Boys' Cup and the Girls' Under 16 County Championship; in the former, Harefield Academy, whose Under 16 team also won the National title, opened the scoring only for Lancaster of Leicester to draw level before half-time. Harefield raced into a 3-1 lead soon after the break but the Leicester school forced extra time before Jordan Bholo netted the winner for Harefield

In the Under 16 Girls' inter-county final, Grace Teah gave Leicestershire and Rutland and Jesse Hickey added a second just after the break. Wiltshire then mounted a great fight-back thanks to goals from Abby Picton and Niamh Rawlins before Jesse Hickey scored the winner in added time. Another game to go to extra time was the Under 13 Girls Final and it need penalties before Thomas Telford just pipped Maiden Erlegh.

## PRIMARY (UNDER 11)

**SMALL SCHOOLS SOCCER SEVENS**
Saturday 1st May. University College, London (Watford F.C. Training Ground)
Winners: LANCING COLLEGE PREPARATORY SCHOOL (Brighton, Hove and Portslade SFA)
Runners-up : ST. AIDANS RC PRIMARY SCHOOL (Huyton SFA)

**UNDER 11 INTER-ASSOCIATION 7-A-SIDE TROPHY**
Saturday, May 1st : University College, London (Watford F.C. Training Ground)
Winners : LIVERPOOL SFA
Runners-up : SOUTH BIRMINGHAM PSFA

**UNDER 11 BOYS 7-A-SIDE CUP**
Saturday, May 1st : University College, London (Watford F.C. Training Ground)
Winners : FOLVILLE JUNIOR SCHOOL (Leicester SFA)
Runners-up : STANFORD LE HOPE PRIMARY SCHOOL (Thurrock SFA)

**UNDER 11 GIRLS 7-A-SIDE CUP**
Saturday, May 1st : University College, London (Watford F.C. Training Ground)
Joint Winners : NEWBOTTLE PRIMARY SCHOOL (Lambton and Hetton SFA) and
THOMAS JOYFFE PRIMARY SCHOOL (South Warwickshire SFA)

## SECONDARY INDIVIDUAL SCHOOLS (11-18)
## GIRLS

**UNDER 12 GIRLS INDOOR 5-A-SIDE CUP FINAL**
Monday, March 1st : Power League Soccerdome, Derby
PRIORY SCHOOL (Shrewsbury and District SFA) **2**
QUEENS SCHOOL (Watford and District SFA) **1**

**UNDER 13 GIRLS NATIONAL FINAL**
Saturday, May 1st : Pirelli Stadium, Burton Albion F.C.
THOMAS TELFORD SCHOOL (Telford and Wrekin SFA) **1** (Courtney Owen)
MAIDEN ERLEIGH SCHOOL (Reading SFA) **1** (Laura Harris-Steers)
Thomas Telford won 4-3 on penalties.

**UNDER 15 GIRLS NATIONAL FINAL**
Wednesday, May 12th : St. James' Park, Exeter City F.C.
ST, JULIE'S SCHOOL ((Liverpool SFA) **3** (Shannon Beckwith 3)
HABERDASHERS' ASKE KNIGHTS SCHOOL (Blackheath SFA) **1** (Vyan Simpson)

**UNDER 16 GIRLS NATIONAL CUP FINAL**
Wednesday, May 5th ; The Hawthorns, West Bromwich Albion F.C.)
WILLIAM FARR SCHOOL (Lincoln and Gainsborough SFA) **2** (Martha Harris, Caitlyn Lynch)
THOMAS TELFORD SCHOOL (Telford and Wrekin SFA) **0**

**UNDER 18 GIRLS (SCHOOLS) TROPHY FINAL**
Monday, March 29th : Madejski Stadium, Reading F.C.
BALBY CARR SCHOOL (Doncaster SFA) **6** (Jenny Knibbs 3, Lauren Rodway, Becky Kendall, Beth Smith)
JOHN MADEJSKI SCHOOL (Reading SFA) **2** (Danielle Puddifoot, Francesca Kirby)

PHOTO 2738  Determined action from Balby Carr School and John Madejski School (Horizontal
stripes) in the Under 18 Girls Trophy Final

**UNDER 18 GIRLS (COLLEGES) TROPHY FINAL**
Wednesday, March 17th : Fraser Eagle Stadium, Accrington Stanley F.C.
ACCRINGTON AND ROSSENDALE COLLEGE (Hyndburn and Ribble SFA) **1** (Jayde Clegg)
FILTON COLLEGE (Glucestershire SFA) **4** (Connie Short, Gabby Bird, Nadine Grogan, Daisy Allen)

## BOYS
**UNDER 12 BOYS INDOOR 5-A-SIDE CUP FINAL**
Monday, March 1st : Power League Soccerdome, Derby
TRINITY SCHOOL (Carlisle SFA) **3**
KIBWORTH SCHOOL (South Leicestershire SFA)**1**

**UNDER 12 E.S.F.A. BOYS CUP FINAL(SPONSORED BY DANONE NATIONS UK)**
Monday, May 17th  : Stamford Bridge, Chelsea F.C.)
WHITGIFT SCHOOL (Croydon SFA) **1** (Andre Coker)
ST. CUTHBERT'S SCHOOL (Rochdale SFA) **0**

**UNDER 13 BOYS CUP FINAL**
Tuesday, May 18th : Goodison Park, Everton F.C.
ARCHBISHOP BECK SCHOOL (Liverpool SFA) **1** (Brian Ellison)
GRANGE SCHOOL (Bristol and South Gloucestershire SFA) **0**

## UNDER 14 BOYS CUP : FINAL (SPONSORED BY THE F.A. PREMIER LEAGUE)
Thursday, May 6th : Craven Cottage, Fulham F.C.
THOMAS TELFORD SCHOOL (Telford and Wrekin SFA) **2** (Chaquille Buchanan, Ben Carter)
QUEEN'S SCHOOL (Watford SFA) **0**

## UNDER 15 BOYS CUP FINAL
Monday, May 24th : Ashton Gate, Bristol City F.C.
HAREFIELD ACADEMY (Hillingdon SFA) **4** (Bernard Mensah 2, Afolabi Obafemi, Jordan Bholo)
LANCASTER SCHOOL (Leicester SFA) **3** (Jamaal Quailey, Sam Rogers, Elliot Francis)
(after extra time)

## UNDER 16 BOYS CUP FINAL
Tuesday, May 11th : Boundary Park, Oldham F.C.
HAREFIELD ACADEMY (Hillingdon SFA) **4** (Michael Kalu, Frankie Sutherland, Trey Horne, Mani O'Sullivan)
MANCHESTER GRAMMAR SCHOOL (Manchester SFA) **1**

## UNDER 18 BOYS (SCHOOLS) TROPHY FINAL
Tuesday, May 18th : Goodison Park, Everton F.C.
BARKING ABBEY SCHOOL (Barking and Dagenham SFA) **3** (Joe Bricknell, Michael Thalassitis, Glenn O'Hanlon)
ST. MARGARET'S SCHOOL (Liverpool SFA) **0**

## UNDER 18 BOYS (COLLEGES) TROPHY FINAL
Wednesday, March 17th : Christie Park, Morecambe F.C.
HARTPURY COLLEGE (West Glucestershire SFA) **2** (Callum Preece, Jack Wood)
GATESHEAD COLLEGE (Gateshead SFA) **1** (Lee Dial)

## BOYS INTER-DISTRICT COMPETITIONS

## E.S.F.A UNDER 13 INTER-ASSOCIATION TROPHY FINAL
Friday, May 14th : Reebok Stadium, Bolton Wanderers F.C.
WARRINGTON SCHOOLS' F.A. **1** (George Cooper)
BARNET SCHOOLS' F.A. **0**

PHOTO IMG 5441x Warrington Schools' at the Reebok Stadium after their victory in the Final

## E.S.F.A UNDER 15 INTER-ASSOCIATION TROPHY FINAL
Tuesday, May 11th : Anfield, Liverpool F.C.
LIVERPOOL SCHOOLS' F.A. **8**
(Ryan Cox 5, Joel Kerwin, Kellen Daly)
CAMBRIDGE AND DISTRICT SCHOOLS' F.A. **0**

## INTER-COUNTY COMPETITIONS (BOYS AND GIRLS)

## E.S.F.A UNDER 16 BOYS COUNTY CHAMPIONSHIP : FINAL
Wednesday, May 12th : Hillsborough, Sheffield Wednesday F.C.
GREATER MANCHESTER COUNTY SCHOOLS' F.A. **5** (Jay Mehmet 3, Kyle Riley, Godwin Abadaki)
SUFFOLK COUNTY SCHOOLS' F.A. **1** (Charlie King)

## E.S.F.A. UNDER 16 GIRLS COUNTY CHAMPIONSHIP : FINAL
Thursday, March 18th : Sincil Bank, Lincoln City F.C.
LEICESTERHIRE AND RUTLAND COUNTY SFA **3** (Grace Teah, Jess Hickey 2)
WILTSHIRE COUNTY SCHOOLS' F.A. **2** (Abby Picton, Niamh Rawlins)

PHOTO IMG 6032 Leicester and Rutland in jubilant mood

## E.S.F.A. UNDER 18 BOYS COUNTY CHAMPIONSHIP : FINAL
Wednesday, May 5th : Bramall Lane, Sheffield United F.C.
GWENT COUNTY SCHOOLS' F.A. **2** (Jamie Davies, Josh Brown)
DURHAM COUNTY SCHOOLS' F.A. **0**

# ENGLISH SCHOOLS' F.A COMPETITIONS

The English Schools' F.A. staged 39 national competions last season and this number will increase next season to 41. These are in addition to the many competitions organised at County and Local Associations levels every season which indicate the vast amout of football played by schools in membership with the E.S.F.A.

## U11 Inter Association Trophy - Sponsored By Danone Nations UK
Saturday 11 May 2013 - The Hive, Barnet FC Training Ground
Wirral PSFA        0      Kingston Upon Hull PSFA      1

## U11 Small Schools Soccer Sevens - Sponsored By Danone Nations UK
Saturday 11 May 2013- The Hive, Barnet FC Training Ground
Esh CE Primary School    0    Rickling C of E Primary School  2
(Durham City PSFA)    (Uttlesford PSFA)

## U11 Schools Cup for School Teams - Sponsored By Danone Nations UK
Saturday 11 May 2013 - The Hive, Barnet FC Training Ground
Edmund Waller Primary School 2    Elmbridge Junior School    1
(Lewisham PSFA)    (Gloucester PSFA)

## U11 Girls Cup - Sponsored By Danone Nations UK
Saturday 11 May 2013 - The Hive, Barnet FC Training Ground
Waverton Primary School   3    Elloughton Primary School    1
(Chester SFA)    (East Riding SFA)

## U12 Boys Indoor 5-A-Side Cup Final - Sponsored By Munich Trophies
Saturday 2 March 2013 - Powerleague, Derby
Alameda Middle School    0    William Howard School    1
(Bedford & District SFA)    (Carlisle SFA)

## U12 Girls Indoor 5-A-Side Cup Final - Sponsored By Munich Trophies
Saturday 2 March 2013 - Powerleague, Derby
Thomas Telford School    1 (AET)  Broadstone Middle School    1 (AET)
    4 (PENS)  5 (PENS)
(Telford & Wrekin SFA)    (Poole & East Dorset SFA)

## U12 Boys Schools Cup Final -Sponsored By Danone Nations UK
Saturday 11 May 2013 - The Hive, Barnet FC Training Ground
Cardinal Heenan Sports College    3    Emerson Park Academy    0
(Liverpool SFA)    (Havering SFA)

## U12 Boys Schools Cup for B Teams Final - Wednesday 15 May 2013 - Bramall Lane, Sheffield United FC
Harefield Academy    1    Thomas Telford School    0
(Hillingdon SFA)    (Telford & Wrekin SFA)

## U13 Boys Schools Cup Final - Monday 20 May 2013 - The Proact Stadium, Chesterfield FC
Northampton School for Boys  4 (AET)  Walkwood CE Middle School   3 (AET)
(Northampton SFA)    (Redditch SFA)

## U13 Girls Schools Cup Final - Monday 20 May 2013 - The Proact Stadium, Chesterfield FC
Didcot Girls' School  3    Thomas Estley Community College    2
(Vale of White Horse SFA)    (South Leicestershire SFA)

## U13 Boys Small Schools Cup Final - Wednesday 1 May 2013 - The Banks's Stadium, Walsall FC
Clitheroe Royal Grammar School    1    Great Cornard Middle School  0
(Hyndburn & Ribble Valley SFA)    (West Suffolk SFA)

## U13 Inter Association Trophy Final - Wednesday 8 May 2013 - Edgar Street, Hereford United FC
West Cornwall SFA    2    Liverpool SFA    0

## U14 Boys Inter County Trophy Final - Friday 17 May 2013 - The King Power Stadium, Leicester City FC
Essex CSFA    1    Merseyside CSFA    2

## U14 Girls Inter County Trophy Final - Tuesday 7 May 2013 - Hillsborough, Sheffield Wednesday FC
Kent CSFA    1    Lancashire CSFA    2

## U14 Boys Schools Cup Final - Sponsored By Premier League
Tuesday 7 May 2013 - Hillsborough, Sheffield United FC
St Leonards RC Comp School  2    St Ignatius College   1
(Chester Le Street & Washington SFA)    (Enfield SFA)

**U14 Boys Small Schools Cup Final -** Friday 3 May 2013 - The Banks's Stadium, Walsall FC
Ibstock Place School      1      Seaton Burn Community College    3
(Richmond SFA)           (North Tyneside SFA)

**U15 Inter Association Trophy Final -** Friday 17 May 2013 - The King Power Stadium, Leicester City FC
Bradford Metro SFA      3      Brent SFA 0

**U15 Boys Schools Cup Final -** Wednesday 15 May 2013 -Pride Park, Derby County FC
Winterbourne International Academy    0    Blessed Trinity RC College    5
(Bristol & South Gloucestershire SFA)        (Burnley SFA)

**U15 Girls Schools Cup Final -** Wednesday 15 May 2013 -Pride Park, Derby County FC
Queens' School      5      Laurence Jackson School    0
(Watford & District SFA)        (Redcar & Cleveland SFA)

**U16 Boys Inter County Trophy Final -** Saturday 27 April 2013 - The Ricoh Arena, Coventry City FC
Lancashire CSFA      2 (AET)    Greater Manchester CSFA    2 (AET)
        5 (PENS) 3 (PENS)

**U16 Inter County Girls Trophy Final -** Saturday 27 April 2013 - The Ricoh Arena, Coventry City FC
Essex CSFA      2      Lancashire CSFA    1

**U16 Boys Schools Cup Final -** Monday 18 March 2013 - Pirelli Stadium, Burton Albion FC
Chelmer Valley High School    0    Thomas Telford School    3
(Chelmsford & Mid Essex SFA)        (Telford & Wrekin) SFA)

**U16 Girls Schools Cup Final -** Monday 18 March 2013 - Pirelli Stadium, Burton Albion FC
Laurence Jackson School    2    Maiden Erlegh School    3
(Redcar & Cleveland SFA)        (East Berkshire SFA)

**U18 Boys Inter County Trophy Final -** Wednesday 20 March 2013 - Stadium:MK, Milton Keynes Dons FC
Cleveland CSFA      0 (AET)    Sussex CSFA    1 (AET)

**U18 Girls Schools Trophy Final -** Wednesday 24 April 2013 - The Keepmoat Stadium, Doncaster Rovers FC
Balby Carr Community Sports Coll    2    Thurstable School    0
(Doncaster SFA)        (Colchester & North East Essex SFA)

**U18 Boys Schools Trophy Final -** Tuesday 30 April 2013 - The Molineux, Wolverhampton Wanderers FC
Thomas Telford      4    Haberdashers' Aske's Knights Acad    3
(Telford & Wrekin SFA)        (Bromley SFA)

**U18 Boys Colleges Trophy Final -** Tuesday 12 March 2013 - Highbury Stadium, Fleetwood Town FC
Stanmore College      5    Hopwood Hall College    3
(Harrow SFA)        (Rochdale Metro SFA)

**U18 Girls Colleges Trophy Final -** Friday 15 March 2013 - The Moss Rose Stadium, Mansfield Town FC
South Gloucs & Stroud College 0    Gateshead College  3
(Bristol & South Gloucestershire SFA)        (Gateshead SFA)

**ESFA / NDCSA Senior Boys 5-a-side Cup -** Tuesday 5 February 2013 - Powerleague, Derby
Hamilton Lodge School "A"    0    Oak Lodge School  1

**ESFA / NDCSA Junior Boys 5-a-side Cup -** Tuesday 5 February 2013 - Powerleague, Derby
Derby School "A"    0    Heathlands School  1

**ESFA / NDCSA Girls 5-a-side Cup -** Tuesday 5 February 2013 - Powerleague, Derby
Braidwood "A" School    1    Derby "A" School  0

# CLUB INDEX

# CLUB INDEX

# CLUB INDEX

# CLUB INDEX

# CLUB INDEX

# CLUB INDEX

# CLUB INDEX

# CLUB INDEX

# CLUB INDEX

# CLUB INDEX

# CLUB INDEX

# CLUB INDEX

# CLUB INDEX